GV 867 **Turkin, Hy.**
.T8

The official encyclopedia of baseball, by Hy Turkin and S. C. Thompson. [1st]– ed. New York, Barnes [1951–

v. illus., ports., diagrs. 26 cm.

First ed. called Jubilee edition.
Some vols. issued in revised editions.
Supplements accompany some volumes.

1. Baseball. I. Thompson, Sherley Clark, 1897– joint author. II. Title.

GV867.T8 796.35703 63–9369

The OFFICIAL ENCYCLOPEDIA of BASEBALL

3rd REVISED EDITION

The OFFICIAL ENCYCLOPEDIA of BASEBALL

3rd REVISED EDITION

by

Hy TURKIN and S. C. THOMPSON

NEW YORK: A. S. BARNES AND COMPANY, INC.
LONDON AND TORONTO: THOMAS YOSELOFF LTD.

Library of Congress Catalog Card Number: 63-9369

Printed in the United States of America

PREFACE

It took an earthquake to start this book.

One evening in September, 1944, Hy Turkin felt his chair shake and saw his living-room pictures sway. To an abstemious sportswriter the deduction was simple: an earthly tremor. So he phoned his paper, the *New York Daily News*. His report was included in a Page Two story of the major earthquake that had rocked the Atlantic seaboard.

Next morning, S. C. Thompson read the account, complete with name and address. Discovering therefrom that Turkin lived only about a fungo-hit from his home, Thompson decided to go around the corner and introduce himself to his sports-minded neighbor. "I'd like you to visit my house sometime, Hy, and look over my baseball collection. I know you'll find it interesting."

Interesting? It proved to be overwhelming. His profession as a musician in Broadway shows provided "Tommy" with spare time and money. These he parlayed with an unquenchable thirst for big league data to amass one of the most exhaustive files in baseball history.

Almost 20 years had gone into the collection of this statistical "diamond" treasure. But it took less than 20 minutes to fully appreciate the immensity of his compilation. Thus began a paired project dedicated to presenting sports fans the most complete baseball compendium ever attempted. Thompson, in several years at his sideline job as statistician in the Al Munro Elias Baseball Bureau, had perfected his technique of collecting and collating data. Turkin burrowed through musty ledgers in Health Departments of distant cities, and interviewed the ever-thinning legion of 19th century heroes of the game, seeking vital data of the more obscure players of bygone years.

The entire project was slanted toward publication in baseball's Jubilee Year, 1951.

This all-time register offered the fascinating challenge of a private-detective job. Every clue had to be tracked down. For instance, a yellowed newspaper in the public library, dated 1892, carried an agate line about a certain rookie being signed by a National League team after pitching three shutouts for the University of Maryland. Needed—full name, birthplace and birthdate of this player. Next step—a wire sent to the registrar of the college.

Came the reply: "No school record for such a name. However, it might interest you to know that before 1895 it was not necessary for a boy to be enrolled at this college in order to play for its baseball team!"

A better source proved to be the obituary columns. It's boring and slightly ghoulish to snoop through death notices in the newspapers 365 days a year, but any item involving an old ballplayer was quickly followed up by a letter to the Board of Health in the city where the player died, enclosing a dollar for a photostatic copy of the death certificate. The return document bore the authentic full name, age and birthplace. It also invariably revealed the man to be one to four years older than his "baseball age." The latter is a stock-in-trade fib every player uses to attract pro scouts in the beginning and to shield time's true toll from managers toward the end of an active career.

So some leads died. But others, which literally led to the graveyard, brought rewards of vital information. Thompson trekked to four cemeteries in Philadelphia to copy data directly off the tombstones of former major leaguers.

Turkin visited the Indian reservation burial grounds of Chief Sockalexis and learned the famous outfielder's true birthdate from a plaque placed there by the Penobscot tribe.

The project continued to grow, with years of interviewing baseball officials and players...of searching through private collections...of comparing notes with assorted amateur statisticians...of chasing all over the country for original box scores that would help reconstruct season averages of the very first professional league, the National Association 1871-75, all of whose official records were destroyed in a fire...of bringing compass and steel tape to ballparks to plot the playing area and measure the height of every fence...of pumping league publicity directors...of writing and rewriting and editing.

To pour such oceans of effort into a job, long before any sign of financial backing or official endorsement, proves it was a labor of love. Writing baseball history is never as much fun as playing it, watching it or even reading it. The authors will therefore be ever grateful for encouragement early and late, from such experts as Ernest J. Lanigan, Frank G. Marcellus, Thomas P. Shea, Lee Allen, Phil Redelheim and Harry Simmons who made possible The Jubilee Edition.

Fifty thousand copies of the Jubilee Edition were sold and it was obvious that a new edition would have to be placed in print before too long. Work started on the Revised Edition directly after the Jubilee Edition was issued, and five years later, in 1956, the First Revised Edition, greatly expanded, was published.

It was expected that another five years would be permitted to pass before issuing still another revised work. But the face of baseball was altered with the shifts of two franchises to the West Coast; the major league audience was now spread from border to border, and the ever-increasing televising of games created additional interest and new fans. As a result work on a Second Revised Edition was speeded and many more facts had to be added, re-checked and verified for the ever-growing All-Time Register of Players and Managers. Many had to be called to help, and among them were George S. Hipp of Indianapolis, Indiana, Robert McConnell of Wilmington, Delaware, Joseph M. Overfield of Buffalo, New York, Ralph E. Lin Weber of Toledo, Ohio, Robert A. Styer of Seattle, Washington, and Clarence Blasco of Kirkwood, Missouri. Their contributions were enormous in helping this Third Revised Edition arrive on schedule.

CONTENTS

INTRODUCTION

It doesn't seem possible that it was fourteen years ago, (February 5, 1949, to be exact) that the Major League Executive Council, of which I was a member, voted to recognize the book written by Hy Turkin and S. C. Thompson as the Official Encyclopedia of Baseball.

Since the publication of that book, called the Jubilee Edition, two revisions have been published. And now the publishers have seen fit to bring out this, the third revised edition.

A great deal has happened in baseball in the period since this book first came into being. The Major Leagues have expanded, records have been broken, great stars have come and gone, the Hall of Fame has welcomed more immortals, and chapters have been added to the great history of our game.

Baseball is fortunate that all these happenings have been chronicled and put into this edition of the Official Encyclopedia of Baseball.

We are fortunate, too, that two diligent men have done the tremendous research that was necessary to establish the base for this book. Since Mr. Turkin's untimely death in 1955, Mr. Thompson has continued the task of digging out the countless facts that go into a book of this nature. To him, and his late partner, all of us in the game are most grateful.

I am sure that any baseball fan will find not only the answers to a great many questions in this book, but also a great deal of pleasure. I know I will.

Ford C. Frick
Commissioner of Baseball

The OFFICIAL ENCYCLOPEDIA of BASEBALL

3rd REVISED EDITION

I EVOLUTION OF BASEBALL

HISTORICAL ORIGIN

Just when, where, and by whom baseball was introduced in its most primitive form has made historians dig as far back as the early days of civilization to supply some evidence of the origin of a game which is now perhaps one of the most highly-specialized of all team skills.

No matter the amount of scientific probing into its earlier beginnings the game has been placed in various birthplaces . . . France . . . England . . . the United States, and some have even drawn strong hints that the first bat-and-ball activity can be traced to the era of the caveman. Then there is that school of diamond thought which insists all evolution should be traced from 1884, many years after the first recorded activity, since that is the year overhand pitching was first introduced. Others are just as certain that a form of the game which bears some facsimile to the present-day sport was in vogue many centuries ago.

However, most of the unbiased probers have come to accept the version unearthed by Robert William Henderson in his book, *Ball, Bat and Bishop* (Rockport Press, 1947). Henderson, as the librarian of the Racquet and Tennis Club of New York, had an abiding interest in bat-and-ball games. Also, his role as supervisory chief of the main reading room in the New York Public Library and his 35 years of research on game origins come through this volume as clear-cut, complete and convincing.

Quoting eminent anthropologists, Henderson repeatedly proves that all modern ball games are derived from religious rites of ancient times, with fertility (of crops or people) as the main theme. He places the first recorded "batting contest" in Egypt some 5,000 years ago.

Stick-wielding worshippers of the Egyptian god of agriculture, Osiris, would place his image on a cart and try to rush it into the Temple of Papremis. An army of priests, also wielding wooden clubs, would line up just outside the Temple and try to fight them back. Though many heads were split in this annual affair, it was only mock combat and more of a traditional drama around crop-planting time.

As for games with a ball, these sprang up not as natural amusement but also as an offshoot of rituals. Egyptian king-gods and high priests used a ball as the central symbol of Springtime ceremonies. Authorities disagree as to whether the ball represented the sun (which is the source of life) or the mummified head of Osiris (symbol of growth and fertility). But in either case it is an object of potency, and so ball-tossing "games" or "rituals" became common among women. Archeologists have found pictures of semi-nude women playing ball, carved into the tomb of Beni Hasan, which was built before 2,000 BC.

Ancient Greeks and Romans played ball. The Romans built "ball rooms" in their bath houses. But in these cultures ball-playing was strictly for conditioning, much as the medicine ball is used in our modern gymnasium. The ball games that climaxed religious rites spread from the Egyptians to the Arabs and finally into southern Europe by way of the invading Moors.

Noticing how tremendously popular were the pagan fertility rites, the Christian church decided to adopt it in their Easter ceremony. Islamic customs had reached southwestern France, and records show that early in the

12th century, in the high church of Vienna, the Archbishop would pass a ball back and forth with clerics lined up for the processional. After the services, the Archbishop threw the ball among the assembled people, who followed the Moorish custom of splitting into "teams."

The popular custom spread throughout France and Spain. Even the Cathedral of Rheims wound up Easter services with a ball game. Contending teams developed two different styles of propelling the ball: either they kicked it (leading eventually to modern soccer and football) or they swatted it with a stick (leading to games like lacrosse, golf and... eventually... baseball!). The French called these early mass games "la soule."

When the ball-playing phase of the medieval Easter festival crossed the English Channel, the British soon developed a variation nearer the modern game of baseball, called stoolball. It first was played in a churchyard, with a pitcher trying to throw the ball against an upturned stool and an opponent trying to punch or bat the ball away before it reached the "home" stool.

The game soon spread over the countryside. Milkmaids added a second stool, then a third, fourth and more "bases" to be circled after striking the ball. When players added the rule that a runner could be put out by being hit with a thrown ball, this led into the more familiar British youngsters' game of rounders... the French game of "poison ball"... and our own "Massachusetts game" of baseball in the 1800's. In rounders, the stools were replaced by wooden posts driven into the ground. These posts or "bases" were sometimes called "goals," so that researcher Henderson found 18th Century references to "goal ball" and "base ball" in Britain.

AMERICAN DEVELOPMENT

English immigrants brought the game of rounders to these shores. When there weren't enough boys to make up two full teams, they would play variations so commonly known to sandlot youngsters of today: One Old Cat, Two Old Cat, etc. In One Old Cat, only one base is used, and the game requires only three players: pitcher, catcher and batter. More men, more bases, higher "Old Cats."

Sometimes called rounders, other times baseball, a game closely resembling our present national pastime was played in the United States long before its supposed invention by Doubleday in 1839. Dr. Oliver Wendell Holmes told of playing baseball while at Harvard in 1829. Henderson's scholarly volume mentions other similar evidence.

Helping prove his contention that the American game of baseball is derived directly from the British game of rounders, Henderson reveals that the first U.S. book to deal with baseball was Robin Carver's *Book of Sports*, printed in 1834 in Boston. In the preface, Carver admits being "indebted" to a London book published six years earlier, *The Boy's Own Book*. The latter explains in detail the game of rounders, including a lettered diagram for placing the posts (bases) in the shape of a diamond.

Carver's book copies the rules for rounders almost verbatim—yet the Bostonian calls this game "base, or goal ball." Carver's book is notable in another respect: it printed the first American picture of the game.

Baseball was still a waddling infant with uncertain step when a bewhiskered surveyor named Alexander J. Cartwright put it on a solid footing in 1845. For several years, he had been playing the game with fellow New Yorkers of high social standing. Tired of haphazard games, he proposed a regular organization and proceeded to sign enough men to make a formal ball club, the first in history.

Cartwright headed a committee to frame a standard set of rules. Drawing heavily upon the popular Carver's *Book of Sports* and exercising excellent judgment in using the best phases of play in the community, Cartwright proposed a list of rules which was adopted September 23, 1845. Much of that original code still is in force today. Here are some of the more interesting provisions (with the authors' comments appended in parentheses):

(1) Bases shall be from home to second, and first to third, 42 paces equidistant. (Remember, a pace is three feet, making that home-to-second distance 126 feet as compared with the present 127 feet, 3⅜ inches. Also, the infield was made square, not an elongated diamond.)

(2) The game is to consist of 21 counts or aces, but at the conclusion an equal number of hands must be played. (An ace meant a run, hand was an out.)

(3) The ball must be pitched, not thrown for the bat. (This meant underhand pitching only.)

(4) A ball knocked outside the range of first or third base is foul.

(5) Three balls being struck at and missed, and the last one caught is a hand out; if not caught is considered fair and the striker bound to run.

(6) A ball being struck or tipped, and caught either flying or on the first bound, is a hand out.

(7) A player running the bases shall be out if the ball is in the hands of an adversary on the base and the runner is touched by it before he makes his base; it being understood, however, that in no instance is a ball to be thrown at him. (This put it out of the rounders class.)

(8) A player running, who shall prevent an adversary from catching or getting the ball before making his base, is a hand out.

(9) Three hands out, all out.

(10) No ace or base can be made on a foul strike.

(11) But one base allowed when the ball bounds out of the field when struck.

Since the Knickerbockers were about to lose their playing field, in midtown Manhattan, a committee went looking for a new site. They took the ferry across the Hudson River and ended their hunt at the Elysian Fields, Hoboken, New Jersey. That was the home field for the elegant Knickerbockers the next year when they accepted a challenge from a group called the New York Nine.

Though all teams in those days were amateur, this first recorded match in history was for the side bet of a dinner per player. On this ill-starred afternoon of June 19, 1846, the Knickerbockers suffered just about the worst defeat in their 37-year career—23 to 1 in four innings. One of the New York players named Davis was fined six cents for swearing at the umpire, who was Cartwright himself.

Though the Knickerbockers didn't play a match game again for five years, their rules were universally adopted by many other clubs which sprang up in this period. The Elysian Fields drew clubs like the Gothams, Eagles, Empires and Mutuals. The Baltics played in Harlem, the Unions in the Bronx and the Atlantic, Excelsior, Putnam and Eckford clubs in Brooklyn.

In Philadelphia, an organization named the Olympic Club antedated the Knickerbockers, but played town ball from 1833 on and didn't switch to baseball until 1860. In New England, teams still "soaked" the runner with the ball, but the game grew rapidly there after the Olympic Club of Boston became the first to organize in that area.

By May of 1857 there were so many clubs in the field that the Knickerbockers begrudgingly called a convention in New York. They accomplished little beyond fixing the rules for the coming season: the complete Knickerbocker set, with the one important exception that nine innings, not 21 runs, constituted a game.

Three delegates from each of 25 different clubs flocked to the next convention, March 10, 1858. This time they formed the game's first league, the

Here is where it all began, the Elysian Fields in Hoboken, N. J., on June 19, 1846 where the first game under the Cartwright rules was played. No admission was charged to see the New York team rout the Knickerbockers, 23-1.

National Association of Base Ball Players. Their rules gained nationwide prestige, and the game was on its way to becoming the national pastime, though still amateur.

In its first season of operation, the new league capitalized on the natural Brooklyn-New York rivalry by staging a series of All-Star Games between teams from those cities. Because of the cost of fixing up the Fashion Race Course on Long Island for the opening game on July 20, 1858, an admission fee of 50 cents was charged. This is the first time fans were ever asked to pay at the gate. For the record, a crowd of 1,500 saw New York beat Brooklyn, 22 to 18.

The year 1860 saw the first tour by an organized baseball club. The Excelsiors of Brooklyn visited central and western New York and thumped all opposition. Later they traveled to Philadelphia and Baltimore to beat picked teams. The triumphal tour was heralded throughout the sports world, and more and more baseball teams began springing up all over the country.

Baseball suffered a sharp readjustment from 1861-65. In those years of Civil War, the number of clubs in and around New York City dwindled from 62 to 28. The championship went to the Atlantic Club of Brooklyn in 1861, 1864-65, but the Eckfords of New York finished first in 1862 and repeated with an unbeaten slate in 1863.

While the grade of league ball deteriorated during the war, the game's gospel was spread so effectively through intermingling of the troops from far-separated states that valuable groundwork was laid for post-war expansion. In Army camps and prison stockades, soldiers from both sides were teaching and learning this popular game.

POST-CIVIL WAR HIGHLIGHTS

Veterans coming home from the Civil War found baseball changed in one important aspect—an 1864 rule abolished the "out" for a fair hit caught on one bounce. There were even bigger surprises in store, for the game was headed for a record post-war boom, just as it was to flourish immediately after later wars.

The league's annual convention in 1866 drew representatives from more than 100 clubs. The next year the number rose to 237, including over 100 from states as far west as Ohio, Wisconsin, Illinois and Indiana.

Increasing interest in the midwest built up a natural rivalry between sections of the country. However, since all clubs were supposedly 100 per cent amateur at this time, no one could afford an extended trip till a group of government clerks and college students representing the Nationals of Washington, D. C., started out in July, 1867 for a 3,000-mile tour of the west. The club bore all its own expenses. Since the Nationals did not share in any of the gate receipts, the trip cost $5,000.

Washington won every game of that memorable trip but one—losing to the Forest City Club of Rockford, Illinois. Pitching for the winners that day was a 17-year-old boy named A. G. Spalding, who had learned the game from an invalided Civil War veteran in his home town.

Spalding, who later became a great player, famous clubowner and successful sporting goods dealer, also figured in the first eastern trip taken by an amateur western team. Early in 1870, a group of businessmen in Rockford pooled $7,000 to underwrite their home town heroes' junket. The trip was highly successful, including Spalding victories over the Atlantics and Nationals.

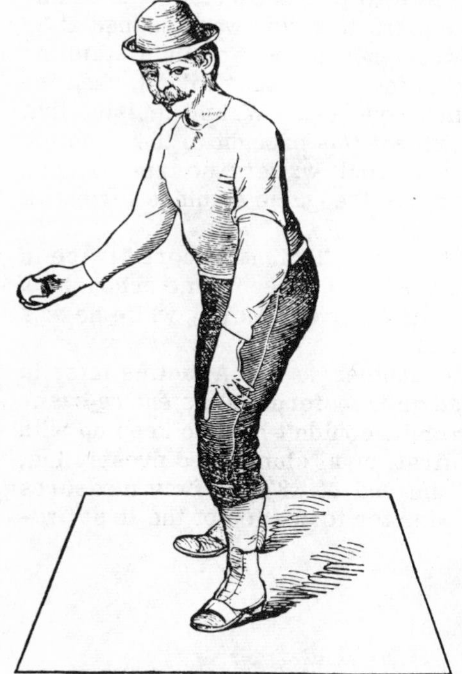

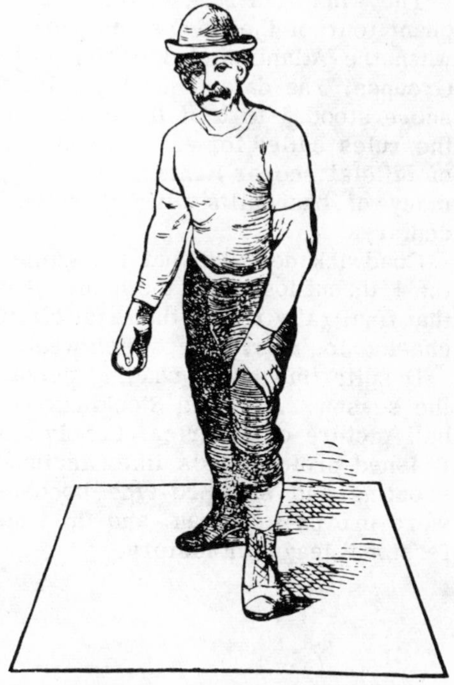

Pitching deliveries—improper and legal—under the game's earliest rules. A pitch (left) was illegal if delivered from above the hip line. A legal delivery was made with an underhand toss to the plate.

Though baseball was booming, its lone league was steadily waning. Heavy betting surrounded each game, and soon some players were blatantly "throwing" games in return for bribes. The league was powerless ... or at least it didn't choose to use any disciplinary powers it had.

By the late 1860's, amateurism was a sham. Star players either were being paid sub rosa or with semipro inducements like sinecure jobs with local merchants. Al Reach, who like Spalding later became a wealthy sporting goods manufacturer and publisher of the annual baseball guide, was the first admittedly pro player, drawing a regular salary from the Philadelphia club in 1864.

The straw that really broke the amateur association's back was Cincinnati's determination to organize an out-and-out pro club in 1869. Harry Wright, captain and center fielder, drew $1,200, and lured his brother George, a brilliant shortstop, from the Unions club by paying him $1,400. Pitcher Asa Brainard drew $1,100 and third baseman Fred Waterman an even thousand. The rest got $800 each: Doug Allison, C; Charles Gould, 1B; Charles Sweazy, 2B; Andy Leonard, LF; Cal McVey, RF, and Dick Hurley, substitute. That made a total payroll of $9,500.

Playing every prominent club between California and Massachusetts, the legendary Red Stockings never lost a game all season. They won 65 and drew one—when the Haymakers of Troy, New York, pulled their team off the field in the sixth inning because of an argument over a foul tip with the score 17 to 17. The club traveled 11,877 miles and played before 200,000 people, and upon their triumphal return "home" (Gould was the only actual Cincinnatian) were greeted by club president Aaron Champion who exulted at the victory banquet, "I'd rather be president of the Cincinnati Reds than of the United States!"

The winning streak carried over into the next season, including a triumphant tour of the deep south. However, the historic string was snapped at 92 when the Atlantics of Brooklyn pulled the tremendous upset on the Capitoline Grounds. The date: June 14, 1870. The Atlantics were ready to quit when the score stood 5 to 5 at the end of nine innings, but Harry Wright insisted that the rules called for extra innings. The argument was brought to the attention of official scorer Henry Chadwick, pioneer baseball writer who later framed many of baseball's official rules and edited the game's guides for half a century.

Chadwick decreed that the game should go on. Cincinnati scored twice in the 11th, but lost when the home team came back with three. Some accounts of that final rally report that a fan climbed on outfielder Cal McVey while he was chasing Joe Start's fly, which went for a triple.

Despite this heartbreaking defeat ... and another to the Atlantics later in the season ... the Red Stockings succeeded in transforming the entire baseball picture of America. Purely amateur clubs couldn't hope to keep up with finished professionals like Cincinnati. At first, rival clubs tried proselyting, scouting and semipro-type bonuses. By the end of 1870 halfway measures were proven too weak, and the time was ripe for formation of the first professional league in history.

II MAJOR LEAGUE HISTORY

NATIONAL ASSOCIATION

The diamond success of the Cincinnati Red Stockings spurred other cities in the midwest to seek the same national publicity which a baseball team had brought to the Rhineland.

"Why can't we attain similar status?" was the cry of civic leaders through the west and the east. Cincinnati had showed them how a successful baseball team can bring fame to a metropolis, and civic pride more than profit provided the impetus toward the formation of baseball's first professional league.

If smart business operators had taken time to examine the financial ledgers of the Cincinnati Baseball Club of the day they would have shied away from such a speculative venture. The Red Stockings, although the most artistic success of their time, were a profound financial failure even if their statements were marked in black ink.

Baseball's No. 1 attraction, which had awakened a spirit of sport among promoters in other cities, showed a net profit of ONE DOLLAR AND THIRTY-NINE CENTS the preceding year, scarcely a sum to excite industrial giants to get on the baseball bandwagon.

The figures were not deceiving. The Red Stocking gate receipts amounted to $29,726.26; salaries and expenses in maintaining the club totalled $29,724.87. Net profit: $1.39. Yet Harry Wright's red-hued heroes had reaped so much glory for the Rhineland City that almost all the other leading clubs were turning professional, too.

With the amateur National Association withering away from sheer impotence, Father Chadwick campaigned in his *New York Clipper* columns for formation of a professional group. Al Wright echoed this in his *Philadelphia Mercury*. Another powerful advocate was Nick Young, secretary of the Washington club, who was later to become secretary of the National Association and president of the National League.

Ten club delegates held a preliminary parley on March 4, 1871. Two weeks later, on St. Patrick's Day, they met again in Collier's Cafe, on New York's Broadway and 13th Street. There, in a smoky gaslit hallroom adjoining the Cafe (saloon), pro baseball suffered its real birth pangs, for that meeting established the National Association of Professional Base-Ball Players.

After electing James N. Kerns of Troy, New York, as president, they drew up a set of championship rules, but no fixed schedule. Every club was to play each of the others a best three-out-of-five series, and the team with the best record at the end of the season was entitled to fly the championship streamer (also called the "whip pennant") at its ballpark for a year. The entry fee was fixed at $10 per club.

Brooklyn's Eckfords thought the organization too loosely knit to survive. They wouldn't risk the $10 fee for a chance to be recognized as champions of the United States. So the NAPBBP (generally shortened to NA) started the season with the remaining nine clubs represented at that meeting: Athletics, of Philadelphia; Bostons, of Boston; White Stockings, of Chicago; Haymakers, of Troy; Olympics, of Washington; Forest City, of Rockford, Illinois; Kekiongas, of Fort Wayne, Indiana; Mutuals, of New York, and Forest City, of Cleveland.

When the Kekionga franchise wilted in August, the Eckfords belatedly decided that professional league baseball was here to stay, so they paid their $10 and replaced Kekionga. But a special post-season convention nullified their games because of the late entry, and they were stricken from the league standings.

It is ironic that the Kekionga club, the only one not to weather the season, won the opening game by 2 to 0. Not only was this noteworthy as the first pro league game of record, but it was also the lowest-scoring game in the first four years of the league. Here are the highlights of that historic inaugural:

The Kekiongas won the toss and sent Forest City to bat. Bobby Mathews threw the first pitch, a ball. James (Deacon) White was the first batter and he led off with the first major league hit, a double. Gene Kimball followed with a fly to second, but when White took too long a lead, Tom Carey pulled an unassisted double play.

There were several other "famous firsts" in that game. In the second inning, Art Allison struck out. However, Jim Lennon missed the third strike, and Allison reached base safely. Lennon atoned for his error in the home half of the inning by scoring the first run, which also proved to be the winning run. He doubled and came in on Joe McDermott's single. Kekionga had the game clinched by the ninth, but was ready to take its last batting turn anyway when a sudden rainfall caused umpire Boake to call a halt.

FOREST CITY (Cleveland) at KEKIONGA (Fort Wayne)

May 4, 1871

CLEVELAND	AB	R	H	O	A
J. White, c	4	0	3	9	0
Kimball, 2b	4	0	0	3	4
Pabor, cf	4	0	0	0	0
Allison, rf	4	0	1	2	0
E. White, lf	3	0	0	1	0
Pratt, p	3	0	0	1	0
Sutton, 3b	3	0	1	0	0
Carleton, 1b	3	0	0	6	0
Bass, ss	3	0	0	2	3
Totals	31	0	5	24	7

FORT WAYNE	AB	R	H	O	A
Williams, rf	4	0	0	4	0
Mathews, p	4	0	0	1	0
Foran, 3b	3	0	1	2	0
Goldsmith, 2b	3	0	0	3	1
Lennon, c	3	1	1	9	1
Carey, ss	3	0	0	3	1
Mincher, lf	3	0	0	2	0
McDermott, cf	3	0	1	0	1
Kelly, 1b	3	1	1	3	0
Totals	29	2	4	27	4

Cleveland	000	000	000	---	0
Fort Wayne	010	010	00x	---	2

(Called, in 9th: rain)

First base by errors—Cleveland 4, Fort Wayne 0. Two base hits—J. White, Lennon. Double play—Carey (unassisted). Walks, by—Mathews 1, Pratt 1. Strikeouts, by—Mathews 6. Passed balls—J. White 2, Lennon 1. Umpire—J. L. Boake. Time—2 hours.

Chicago quickly displaced Kekionga as league leader by winning its first seven straight games. Unbeaten, the White Stockings invaded New York on June 5 to meet the Mutuals, owned by the notorious political potentate, Boss Tweed. Despite the 50-cent admission fee, a record 6,000 crowd jammed the stands, and 3,000 others watched from beyond the fences, perched on neighboring roofs or wagons. Pushcart owners charged 10 cents for standing room on their vehicles.

The Mutuals brought great joy to Gotham fans by beating Chicago, 8 to 5. The New Yorkers continued on a winning streak of their own that soon put them in first place. Incidentally, though at first they refused to share their gate receipts, the Mutuals finally agreed to grant the visiting club one-third of the gross.

New York fortunes sagged in July. George Zettlein proceeded to pitch Chicago back into the league lead. However, the most destructive cow of all time, Mrs. O'Leary's bovine villain, ruined more than a good part of the city of Chicago by kicking over that fateful kerosene lamp in a barn on October 8. Rockford players entering the city that day saw the colossal blaze that seared the lakefront grounds as well as millions of dollars of other property. No ballpark . . . no game . . . and, as it turned out, no pennant.

The demoralized White Stockings had to play their remaining games on the road, where they lost the last three straight and the flag. In the game that decided the championship, October 30, Chicago was "home team" at the Union Grounds, Brooklyn, where the Athletics took a 4-1 decision behind the fine efforts of the league's ace pitcher, ex-cricketeer Dick McBride, and the batting champion, Long Levi Meyerle (.403).

Still, it took a post-season decision by the NA's championship committee to determine the whip-pennant winner. Two games which the Athletics had lost to Rockford were declared forfeited to the Philadelphia team because Rockford had used an ineligible player, W. Scott Hastings.

Boston's failure to finish on top, due to an untimely series of player injuries, upset the experts of the day. The Beaneaters had taken over more than the Red Stocking nickname of the old invincible Cincinnati club. They had the four key players: the Wright brothers, McVey and Gould. They also bore the same "professional" stamp of competence as their famed predecessors. There was less gambling and swearing and fighting in Boston games than anywhere else in the circuit, so Harry Wright's team was respected.

Even more brilliant an organizer and leader than a player, bewhiskered Harry Wright bolstered his Red Stocking nucleus in Boston by proselyting A. G. Spalding, destined to become the NA's greatest pitcher, Ross Barnes and Fred Cone from the 1870 Rockfords.

In 1872, it was decided to name a player as NA president. The honor went to Bob Ferguson, famed captain-third baseman of Brooklyn's Atlantics. Chicago, not sufficiently recovered from the big fire, dropped out of pro ball for two years. Rockford quit, and its best player, Adrian Constantine (Cap) Anson, switched to the Athletics to continue a big league career that lasted 27 years, an all-time record.

Four new clubs swelled the NA to 11 teams in '72. A vital new rule allowed pitchers to use snap and jerk deliveries, though still restricted to underhand serves, thereby opening the door to curve ball pitching. Spalding never threw a curve in his life. The rugged Westerner relied on control and change of pace, and these proved enough to carry Boston to four straight pennants, by steadily wider margins, from 1872-75. Boston added two more diamond immortals to its rolls in '73, Deacon White and James (Orator) O'Rourke.

The monotony of Boston triumphs (one local paper gloated that Boston Conquers All with this headline in Latin: "BOSTON OMNIA VINCIT") was only a minor factor in the demise of the NA. Gamblers infested the ranks sc badly that the public was fast losing confidence in pro games.

Open pool-selling on the day's results used to take place right in the park. As much as $20,000 would be bet on a game, with the expected consequence of widespread bribery and open intimidation of umpires and players. Toughs who had come to the park mainly to bet would pour profanity at a player whose error or strikeout hurt the club they were backing. Compounded with this were growing evils such as liquor-selling on the premises, contract-jumping and player desertions.

Boston, scourge of the first league, took NA titles from 1872 through '75. Standing (l. to r.): McVey, Spalding, White, Barnes. Seated: O'Rourke, Leonard, George Wright, Harry Wright, Hall, Schaefer, Beals.

Small wonder the NA proved a pushover for the logical reform wave leading to the formation of the National League in 1876.

NATIONAL LEAGUE

When William A. Hulbert of Chicago died in 1882, the National League passed a resolution "that to him alone is due the credit of having founded the National League, and to his able leadership, sound judgment and impartial management is the success of the league chiefly due."

True enough. Yet if Hulbert had been able to hear his eulogy, the walrus-mustached pioneer would have insisted that A. G. Spalding be credited with an "assist" in the founding of baseball's first indestructible league.

The Hulbert-Spalding saga goes back to 1875. Early that year, owners of the weak Chicago franchise offered the club presidency to Hulbert, a successful businessman who was a die-hard rooter for the die-easy White Stockings team of his home city. He asked for a few weeks to consider the offer.

The next time the champion Bostons came to Chicago, Hulbert visited their star pitcher, Spalding himself, and told how thousands of Chicago fans were wild for a winning team but couldn't get one because of constant player piracy on the part of Eastern clubs, which dominated professional baseball. He emphasized the other growing evils in the sport, including gambling, and Spalding nodded sympathetically. Finally Hulbert spoke of his own proffered job and urged in earnest tones:

"Spalding, you've no business playing in Boston. You're a Western boy and you belong right here. If you come to Chicago to play and manage next season, I'll accept the presidency of this club, and we'll give those fellows a fight for their lives."

Promise of a handsome contract dispelled any remaining doubt in Spalding's mind. Shaking hands to seal the deal, he promised to bring Chicago a real contender for 1876. In June of 1875, Hulbert visited Boston, where Spalding helped him sign teammates Ross Barnes, Cal McVey and Deacon Jim White. Then they went to Philadelphia, where they secretly signed Cap Anson and Ezra Sutton, who had been recruited earlier by Spalding. Sutton later backed out because of pressure from the Athletics' fans and officials.

Every effort was made to keep the signings a secret till the end of the season, since a man contracting in midseason to play with a different club the next year was subject to automatic expulsion by the NA . . . though this threat was rarely invoked. Chicagoans were bursting with too much pride and joy to keep the coup quiet for more than a few weeks. When the entire story came to light in a Chicago newspaper, tremors were felt throughout the league.

Bostonians felt bitter over the defection of their Big Four. Boys followed them on the street, hooting, "Oh, you seceders! Your White Stockings will get dirty." With the country still feeling the scourge of post-Civil War reconstruction, the term "seceder" was still as vile an epithet as a New Englander could summon.

Stung by criticism, the Big Four leaned over backward to prove their integrity. Spalding led the league's pitchers, Barnes paced the batters. Boston never lost a game all year on home grounds. Their season's won-lost of 71-8 meant a winning percentage of .899, which never has been matched in major league history.

Worried over rumors of his expulsion at the next NA convention, Spalding visited Hulbert's home at the end of the season. Chicago's enterprising president reassured him, "Why, they can't expel you. They wouldn't dare. In the eyes of the public, you six players are stronger than the whole Association."

Hulbert put Spalding further at ease by vowing that regardless of any action by the Association, the newly signed players would be paid for the entire 1876

Charley Comiskey, St. Louis leader of AA days; first owner of the Chicago (AL) White Sox.

John Montgomery Ward, brilliant all-around performer; he won 84 games in 1879 and '80.

Hoss Radbourn, Providence pitching great of the 80s.

Pop Anson, NA pioneer; he played the longest, 27 years.

season. Then the wavy-haired, silver-tongued executive became engrossed in deep thought. Suddenly he jumped up and said, "Spalding, I have a new scheme. Let us anticipate the Eastern cusses and organize a new association before their March meeting. Then we'll see who'll do the expelling!"

They held daily conferences thereafter. In one of these, Hulbert suggested, "Let us get away from the old, wornout title, 'National Association of Base Ball Players,' and call it 'The National League of Professional Base Ball Clubs.'" His idea here was to organize reform on a responsible business basis of clubs rather than depend on a flabby federation of players.

When they had determined most of the principles of their projected league, Hulbert and Spalding had Judge Orrick C. Bishop of St. Louis draw up a formal constitution. The jurist also framed a standard form of player's contract designed to end the evil of "revolving" (jumping).

In January of 1876, Hulbert summoned officials of the Cincinnati, St. Louis and Louisville clubs to a secret meeting in Louisville. The downtrodden Westerners gave Hulbert an enthusiastic vote of confidence. Most important, they assigned power of attorney to him and Charles A. Fowles of St. Louis in dealing with Eastern clubs.

Hulbert and Fowles sent a circular letter to the remaining NA teams, asking for a conference "on matters of interest to the game at large, with special reference to reformation of existing abuses." Time: 12 noon, Wednesday, February 2, 1876. Place: Hulbert's suite in the Grand Central Hotel, Broadway at Third Street, New York City.

Impelled by curiosity, caution and common sense, the Eastern club presidents all came—G. W. Thompson of Philadelphia, N. T. Appolonio of Boston, M. G. Bulkeley of Hartford and W. H. Cammeyer of the New York Mutuals. According to Spalding's historical volume, *America's National Game,* Hulbert locked the door of his room, put the key in his pocket, turned to the puzzled magnates and said, "Gentlemen, you have no occasion for uneasiness. I locked the door simply to prevent any intrusions from without... and incidentally to make it impossible for any of you to leave until I have finished what I have to say. I promise not to take more than an hour."

In that historic hour, Hulbert expertly outlined all the evils that were demoralizing the players and fans. He proved that the NA was either unable or unwilling to correct the abuses. He climaxed his remarks by producing a copy of the model constitution for a new National League. Chicago's spellbinder won their support on the spot, and the NL was born right then and there.

One of the first steps taken by the new league was to raise the franchise fee from $10 to $100. To insure sizeable gate receipts, so that payrolls could be met, membership was limited to cities of at least 75,000 population. Bookmaking and liquor selling were banned on league ball-grounds. Players found guilty of betting or taking bribes were to be expelled from professional baseball.

When it came to election of officers, Hulbert diplomatically appeased the uneasy Easterners by plumping for "one of their own" for the presidency of the league, Hartford's esteemed Morgan G. Bulkeley. Backed unanimously, Bulkeley accepted. Never more than a league figurehead, he quit a year later to pursue a political career that saw him elected Mayor of Hartford, Governor of Connecticut and U. S. Senator. Hulbert succeeded Bulkeley and ruled the league with an iron hand until his death in 1882.

For that inaugural season of 1876, the NL decided on five home games and five road games round-robin style between the charter member clubs—New York, Boston, Hartford, Philadelphia, Chicago, St. Louis, Cincinnati and Louisville. They played three times a week, making 70 games for each team.

Admission was pegged at 50 cents, though tickets were sold for a dime after the third inning had been played.

With rain delaying the other openers, the first game in NL history was played at Philadelphia on Saturday, April 22, 1876. Boston won by a score of 6 to 5. Jim (Orator) O'Rourke of the winners made the first hit, and teammate Tom McGinley the first run, while Ezra Sutton, who had changed his mind about jumping to Chicago with Spalding, committed the first error. The full box score follows:

BOSTON (6)	AB	R	H	PO	A	E
G. Wright, ss	4	2	1	2	2	0
Leonard, 2b	4	0	2	0	4	1
O'Rourke, cf	5	1	2	0	0	0
Murnane, 1b	6	1	2	8	0	0
Schafer, 3b	5	1	1	1	0	1
McGinley, c	5	1	0	8	0	3
Manning, rf	4	0	0	4	0	0
Parks, lf	4	0	0	3	0	1
Borden, p	3	0	0	1	1	1
Totals	40	6	8	27	7	7

PHILADELPHIA (5)	AB	R	H	PO	A	E
Force, ss	5	0	1	0	4	1
Eggler, cf	5	0	0	4	1	1
Fisler, 1b	5	1	3	13	0	1
Meyerle, 2b	5	1	1	3	2	0
Sutton, 3b	5	0	0	1	0	2
Coons, c	4	2	2	1	2	3
Hall, lf	4	0	2	1	0	0
Fouser, rf	4	0	0	3	1	1
Knight, p	4	1	1	1	3	2
Totals	41	5	10	27	13	11

Boston	012	010	002	---	6
Philadelphia	010	003	001	---	5

Earned runs—Boston 1, Philadelphia 2. Total bases on hits—Boston 9, Philadelphia 12. First base on errors—Boston 6, Philadelphia 3. Left on bases—Boston 7, Philadelphia 9. Double plays—Eggler-Coons, Force-Fouser-Fisler. Umpire—Mr. William McLean. Time—2:05. Attendance—3,000.

Joseph Borden, under the pseudonym of "Josephs," not only won that historic opener, but also pitched the league's first no-hit game against Cincinnati a month later. For almost 75 years, this no-hitter went unrecognized before baseball historian Lee Allen finally discovered that the two "hits" charged against Borden really were only bases on balls.

As the season rolled on, gambling and drinking were markedly reduced, though not wiped out completely. Hulbert's dream of conquest came true in that very first year as his beloved Chicagos, bolstered by Boston's Big Four and Cap Anson, romped off with the pennant. However, Hulbert's brainchild league was threatened in midseason when the Philadelphia and New York clubs, fearing they would lose money on long road trips, refused to play their return games in the West.

Boasting the bulk of the NL's population, the Philadelphia and New York franchises announced, "The league needs us more than we need them." They were counting on the old practice of the NA, which condoned such offenses. But when Hulbert ascended to the league presidency at the December, 1876, meetings, he saw to it that both clubs were expelled.

There was further trial-by-fire the next year, but Hulbert had the courage and conviction to guide the league according to its avowed principles. Cincinnati, disheartened by a last-place finish in 1876, failed to pay its dues the next year. Though the league was already reduced to six members, Hulbert insisted Cincinnati be dropped, too. This season of 1877 also saw a prearranged league schedule, another Hulbert innovation, instead of the old plan whereby it was left to club secretaries to arrange series with other league teams.

With Spalding retiring from the mound in 1877, Tommy Bond of Boston became the hotshot pitcher of the season, leading his club to the pennant. But the Beaneaters' return to glory was vitiated by the game's worst scandal of the 19th century. Embarking on a road trip late in the season with the pennant

They started it all, William A. Hulbert and Ban Johnson. Through their efforts, the National and American Leagues were organized. Hulbert was the NL's second president; Johnson was the first in the AL.

practically clinched, Louisville proceeded to lose games with such regularity that the club's vice-president, Charles E. Chase, initiated an investigation.

Struck by the great number of telegrams received daily by Louisville's substitute player, Al Nichols, Chase asked him for a written authorization to open all his wires, since he was one of the players suspected of dealing with gamblers. Nichols refused.

"Your refusal is an admission of guilt," Chase insisted. "That means you're barred for life."

"All right, then," muttered Nichols. "Open them."

Damning, damaging evidence was brought to light. Several of the Grays players had been taking bribes from Eastern gamblers, telegraphing the code word "sash" for games that they agreed to throw. Faced with the wires, George Hall and Jim Devlin confessed, implicating Nichols and Bill Craver. Devlin had been the team's star pitcher. Outfielder Hall was the team captain and the league's first home run king, with five for the 1876 season.

Chase suspended the four players for life. Though Devlin was a personal friend of his, league president Hulbert sustained the decision, and none of the four ever played professional baseball again. Devlin visited every annual league meeting thereafter, humbly repenting and begging for reinstatement. It never was granted. Ironically, he ended his days enforcing law and order as a member of the Philadelphia city police force.

Though expulsion of the crooked players insured the league of a stronger footing in the country's estimation, it caused several immediate headaches. Bereft of its star players, Louisville dropped out of the league. So did St. Louis, which had secretly negotiated for the ill-fated four to join them the following season... until the gambling scandal broke. Hartford couldn't draw at home, and had to give up the ghost.

Cincinnati was reinstated for 1878. Indianapolis, Milwaukee and Providence were rounded up by Hulbert, to make the NL a six-club circuit again. Indianapolis and Milwaukee had to quit after one season, but the Providence team prospered for eight years, never finishing worse than third. These were the halcyon days in Rhode Island, which toasted the Wright brothers, George and Harry, and the immortal pitcher, Charles Radbourn.

The 1879 season was distinguished for several reasons. It saw the institution of the reserve rule by the Boston club's thrifty president, Arthur H. Soden, allowing each club exclusive bargaining rights with a designated five of its players for the following season. The number of reserve players rapidly increased, finally reaching the 100 per cent figure under which all professional sports operate in America today.

In 1879, too, Hulbert expanded the NL to eight teams. This is the number of clubs it has fielded until 1962; except for the turbulent 90's when the collapse of two rival leagues caused the league to expand to an even dozen clubs.

From 1880-82, Cap Anson's Chicago White Stockings ran roughshod over the league. Featuring such colorful stars as King Kelly, Silver Flint, Ed Williamson and Larry Corcoran, the flamboyant Westerners rang up three straight pennants. Club president Hulbert and secretary Spalding decked the team out in expensive uniforms, put them up at the best hotels and had the White Stockings ride to the ballpark in open barouches drawn by white horses.

The NL faced a series of crises in 1882. Hulbert died of heart failure that April. Soden presided over the league strictly as a fill-in. It was not until December that a capable successor was found in Abraham G. Mills, former Civil War soldier and brilliant lawyer who had played and served as club president for the old Washington Olympics. Also, that year, Dick Higham

Baseball pioneers were Henry Chadwick (left), who designed the rules changes in the 19th century, and Branch Rickey, who created the game's 'farm' system which supplied an endless stream of minor league players to the majors.

became the first (and last) umpire convicted of collusion with gamblers, and was instantly fired.

But the sharpest threat of all came from a newly-founded major league, the American Association, which charged only half the NL's admission fee and played Sunday ball (which was expressly forbidden in the NL constitution). The popular AA ran franchises in large cities which had dropped out of the NL for one reason or another. And it weathered player piracy by the senior circuit. The NL monopoly of professional baseball was at an end.

Mills set to work realistically. Rather than embark on a suicidal war with the AA, the new NL president formulated a live-and-let-live National Agreement. Under this historic document, all organized major and minor leagues agreed to honor existing player contracts. The AA and NL clubs were each allowed to bind 14 players via reserve clause. Blacklists of dishonest players were to be mutually recognized.

With interleague peace came prosperity in 1883. Attendances boomed. Gearing his league for full-blown competition with the AA, Mills made two small fading franchises, Troy and Worcester, transfer their players to the great cities of New York and Philadelphia. He also adopted the AA's plan of hiring a staff of league umpires, free from all club control, and paying them on a yearly basis. To bolster the league further, he reinstated 15 players who had been suspended for minor offenses.

A scant year later, war thundered across baseball's plains again. St. Louis realtor Henry V. Lucas organized the Union Association in 1884 specifically to fight the "outrageous" reserve rule. His UA stole players wholesale from the AA and NL, though the latter circuits pitched into a secret cash pool to pay bonuses to would-be jumpers from their leagues.

Soon after Charlie Sweeney of Providence NL had struck out 19 batters in one game for a new record, the star-struck UA plucked him with a heavily-moneyed hand. That left poor Providence with only one able-bodied pitcher, Radbourn . . . who happened to be under temporary suspension for insubordination. Manager Frank Bancroft raised the ban. The 30-year-old right-hander proceeded to earn his nickname of Old Hoss by pitching the last 38 consecutive games. Radbourn won 60 games that season, the last 18 in a row, against only 12 defeats. He not only clinched the pennant but added a World Series fillip with three straight victories to sweep the interleague playoffs.

With three major leagues and 34 clubs operating in 1884, there simply were not enough cash customers to go around. The UA sank in a sea of red ink. NL president Mills, who had temporized with the AA, felt no mercy toward the insurgent UA.

Over Mills' bitter objection, UA founder Lucas was admitted into the NL as head of a new St. Louis franchise in 1885. When the league over-rode his decision to blacklist the contract-jumping players, welcoming them back instead upon payment of a fine, Mills resigned in protest. Nick Young, a conciliatory Washingtonian who had served as league secretary continuously since 1876, was elevated to the presidency, and he held the post for 18 years.

Now owner and president of the Chicago NL club, Spalding exulted in two more league pennants, 1885-86. But when his team blew the winner-take-all World Series to the underdog St. Louis Browns in '86, he angrily sold his league batting champion, King Kelly, to Boston for the record price of $10,000. The next year he shipped Kelly's batterymate, pitcher John Clarkson, to the same team for the same fabulous fee. Having won five times in seven years, Chicago now entered an era of NL pennant drought that lasted 20 years . . . so the lucrative sales turned out to be poor deals indeed.

Another major player deal of that period involved the end of Buffalo's franchise in the NL. Detroit bought Buffalo's "Big Four" of Dan Brouthers, Deacon White (who had been a member of the original "Big Four" in Boston a decade earlier), Hardy Richardson and Jack Rowe for $8,500, and entered the league in 1886. These four sluggers made Detroit a strong contender the first year, world champions the next.

Stovepipe-hatted Jim Mutrie lorded it when his Giants brought New York the flag in 1888 and '89, abetted by the fearless backstopping of Buck Ewing, the blazing pitching of Tim Keefe and the classic shortstopping of John Montgomery Ward. However, around this time the lesser-clarioned classification rule came to life... a veritable bombshell that exploded into another three-league war in 1890.

John T. Brush, president of the Indianapolis club, fathered the classification rule, designed to clamp a ceiling on ever-growing player salaries. Players were to be graded according to ability from class A to E, corresponding salaries to range from $2,500 down to $1,500.

This unjust and unworkable harness was slipped over the players at a time when John Montgomery Ward, leader of their benevolent organization (called the Brotherhood), was out of the country on a world tour with Spalding's squads. As brilliant a lawyer as he was a shortstop, Ward approached the magnates upon his return to protest, but was brushed off with the statement, "There is nothing to discuss." It was too late to organize any resistance for the 1889 season, but the next year Ward obtained financial backing for a Players' League, which drew most of the best players from the AA and NL.

The 1890 season was disastrous for all. Aggregate deficit for the three leagues ran close to a million dollars. Brooklyn was represented in all three leagues, but was proudest of its NL team which won the 1890 pennant.

Though they outdrew their rivals, the PL had to surrender at the close of 1890. But this peaceful settlement quickly touched off a disastrous battle destined to doom the AA, as the surviving leagues squabbled over the player spoils.

Somehow, the Athletics AA team forgot to include their PL jumpers, Louis Bierbauer and Harry Stovey, on their reserve list. Bierbauer (father of musical comedy star Elsie Janis) was claimed by Pittsburgh NL, and irate Philadelphians shouted "Pirates! ". a nickname that stuck to Pittsburgh. Boston NL claimed Stovey, former home-run and base-stealing king. When the board of arbitration deprived the A's of both their straying stars, the entire junior circuit angrily rebelled by withdrawing from the National Agreement.

The cold war between the former friendly enemies lasted just one year. The AA began to raid the NL's players in the fall of 1891 . . . but the senior league meanwhile maneuvered a series of deals that brought over four of the best franchises from the AA. That spelled finis for the AA.

From 1892-1900, the NL reigned alone. It listed a dozen clubs, shrinking to eight in the depression following the Spanish-American War. During the Gay Nineties, Frank Selee managed five pennant winners and Ned Hanlon the other five. Selee's star in Boston was Charles (Kid) Nichols, who notched at least 20 victories in each of his first 10 seasons. Hanlon led the boisterous, brainy Baltimore Orioles to 1894-95-96 flags, thanks to the brillance of Wee Willie Keeler, John McGraw, Hughie Jennings, et al. Hanlon switched to Brooklyn in '99 and brought along most of his Oriole prodigies, a combination that rang up two quick pennants.

But the new century brought new woes to the NL. The public now was ready for a second major league. Not so the NL. It fought the inevitable trend with its worst weapon: smugness. Far worse, the league was wracked internally by a secret plot to reorganize baseball's entire structure on a syndicate

Smallest but mightiest New York Giant was John McGraw, a fiery third baseman, a crafty manager. He created an early Polo Grounds dynasty.

basis. Behind all this was Andrew Freedman, subway contractor who owned the New York franchise.

First of the vital challenges which the NL bungled developed when a zealous ex-sportswriter named Ban Johnson came to the league meeting, hat in hand, to discuss Eastern franchises for his soundly-organized American League in 1901. Instead of hearing his proposition, the NL sneaked an adjournment and left Johnson standing foolishly in the foyer.

This spelled "war," and Ban waged it brilliantly. First, he pulled out of the National Agreement with the NL. Then he raided the haughty enemy's ranks with devastating sweeps. Star players of the NL were practically "sitting ducks" for Johnson the hunter, since the old league was still operating under a player salary limit of $2,400. Of 182 AL players that first season, 111 came directly from the NL, including Cy Young, Nap Lajoie, Jimmy Collins and Clark Griffith.

In the summer of 1901, the NL made its next mistake. To patch up its riddled ranks it abrogated the National Agreement and thereby made all minor leaguers fair game. New suggestions of truce with the AL were immediately squashed by the Freedman faction.

Prior to the league's winter meetings of 1901, Freedman gathered his fellow conspirators from the Cincinnati, Boston and St. Louis clubs. At a parley on his estate at Red Bank, New Jersey, they worked out a master plan to syndicate the league, issuing preferred stock to the league "trust" and common stock among the clubs, with Freedman's henchmen to get the lion's share.

With the four remaining clubs solidly opposed to syndicate baseball, the matter came to a showdown at the annual meeting in December. Freedman's group wanted Nick Young as league president again. The opposition put up Spalding, by now a million-dollar sporting goods dealer, who still bore tremendous prestige as a constant crusader for the sport. Twenty-five times they balloted. Twenty-five times the vote was 4 to 4.

When the Freedman clique finally left the room, Spalding was elected "Unanimously." Spalding seized league papers and records, but had to resign the following March when a New York court granted a permanent injunction against him. Instead of a league president, the circuit was ruled by a three-man "compromise board" the rest of the season.

In April of that tumultuous 1902 campaign, the Pennsylvania Supreme Court granted an injunction against Lajoie, who had jumped from Philadelphia NL to the A's, and ordered his return to the NL club. Johnson's antidote was to switch Lajoie to Cleveland and keep him out of the state of Pennsylvania. It was a hollow victory for the NL.

Three months later, the new league suffered a real jolt when John McGraw deserted Baltimore to manage the Giants under Freedman's banner. It was to be Freedman's last triumph. He sold out his baseball holdings at the year's end to John T. Brush, opening the avenue to NL settlement on a sensible candidate for president, young Harry C. Pulliam.

When Pulliam initiated truce talks with the AL early in 1903, Brush sought to employ the injunction weapon his predecessor had used successfully against Spalding. Brush bristled at the AL for moving the Baltimore franchise, which wilted after McGraw's flight, to New York, not far from his Polo Grounds. However, Brush was persuaded to drop the court action, and by August full-scale peace reigned with the signing of a new National Agreement. The AL-NL olive branch became a tangible reality that fall when their teams tangled in the first modern World Series.

On the field of battle, a bowlegged "Flying Dutchman" called Honus Wagner performed daily miracles at shortstop and wielded a murderous bat to bring Pittsburgh pennants in 1901-02-03. Christy Mathewson's pitching genius featured Giant victories the next two years. But the Cubs dominated the NL for the rest of that dead-ball decade. The Tinker-Evers-Chance combination

Tinker (left) to Evers (right) to Chance, the fabulous trio which carried the Chicago Cubs to early 20th century glory in the National League. All three were simultaneously placed in the Hall of Fame.

came out on top in 1906-07-08 and '10, with a 104-games-won second-place team to show for that one-year gap.

Chicago's 1906 array set an all-time mark by winning 116 games. But the '08 team roused its fandom most. That was the year Chicago, New York and Pittsburgh all came down the stretch neck-and-neck. In the last Cub visit to New York, the last game of the series was tied with two out in the ninth, with Moose McCormick on third and Fred Merkle on first, when Al Bridwell lashed a clean hit to center. McCormick scampered in with the "winning" run, and the joyous crowd swarmed on the field. But...

The big "but" centered around the actions of Merkle, then a 19-year-old substitute first baseman. Noticing Bridwell's drive landing safely, and McCormick scampering home with ease, Merkle veered away on his run toward second and headed for the clubhouse in centerfield instead.

The throw from the outfield landed near third base, and amid the confusion of people streaming on the field, Giant coach Joe McGinnity grabbed the ball and threw it into the stands. Floyd Kroh, Cub pitcher not in the game, retrieved it, and second baseman Johnny Evers was credited with putting out Merkle for the inning-ending force out at second base. As umpire Hank O'Day was led off the field by police, he kept shouting, "The man is out. The game has got to go on." By now there were too many people on the field to resume play, so O'Day called the game on account of darkness.

At first the game went into the books as a Giant victory. If this result had remained, the New Yorkers would have won the flag by a full game from Chicago and Pittsburgh. However, after considerable official delay, the league board of directors ordered the game replayed. On October 8, one day after the scheduled close of the season, the teams tangled at the Polo Grounds. Heroic Matty, who had won 37 games that season for the Giants, lost this crucial one to his lifelong rival, Mordecai (Three-Fingered) Brown, 4 to 2.

The modern era of offensive baseball unfolded when the leagues sanctioned the use of a cork-center ball in 1911. The AL placed 35 hitters in the .300 circle that season. Over in the NL, Frank (Wildfire) Schulte of the Cubs broke all home-run records with a total of 21. Apparently a master of offense as well as defense, McGraw led the Giants to successive pennants in 1911-12-13; but the Little Napoleon met his Waterloo in the World Series each of those years.

Assassination of an archduke in far off Serbia touched off a world war in 1914. Baseball faced virtual assassination around the same time, as the newly-formed Federal League sued to have the entire structure of organized ball invalidated by the courts. Time proved a valuable ally for the old leagues. The lawsuit languished. On the field, the inexperienced Feds failed to find the gold mine they had envisioned. With the world situation steadily worsening in 1916, FL ring-leaders surrendered to generous settlement terms by the NL and AL...ending the last major league "war" after over-all losses totalling perhaps $10,000,000.

In the two troubled years of FL activity, the NL sprang two of the most surprising winners of all. Boston's "Miracle Team" rose from last place on July 19, 1914, to a breathtaking pennant finish and a sweep of the World Series. The next year, Philadelphia took its first NL championship as Grover Alexander notched 31 victories.

Congress declared war just before the baseball season opened in 1917. Catcher Hank Gowdy of the Braves was the first to enlist, but the bulk of hundreds of major leaguers who joined the armed forces did not leave until the following season. McGraw won another pennant with his Giants in '17.

Baseball had tougher going in 1918. Army drafting claimed many star players. "Work or fight" was the national slogan, with orders from Washington curtailing the season to Labor Day.

The post-war boom took most magnates by surprise. Attendance records were set in many parks in 1919. The World Series drew almost a quarter of a million dollars more than the previous all-time high, the half-million dollar Series of 1912. Amidst such prosperity, baseball suffered a near-fatal blow upon the revelation that the infamous Chicago "Black Sox" had thrown the 1919 Series to Cincinnati.

Between its sturdy new Commissioner, Judge Landis, and its astounding new home-run hero , Babe Ruth, baseball recaptured public confidence and enthusiasm. The game headed for unprecedented prosperity. Sunday baseball was legalized in New York in 1920, and the Gotham crowds were rewarded with topnotch teams in both leagues. Quite a bit more portly, but not a mite mellower than in his firebreathing Oriole days, McGraw rose to the apex of his managerial career by conquering all NL rivals with his Giants of 1921-22-23-24, the longest unbroken reign in league history.

McGraw now had 10 flags in 21 years. He never won another. But a bright new dynasty was about to dawn: nine flags in the next 21 years for the St. Louis Cardinals. Guiding genius behind this plethora of pennants was Branch Rickey, who had a versatile background as country schoolmaster, college football coach, lawyer, big league catcher, major league scout, manager in both major leagues, etc. Rickey finally found his perfect niche in baseball as a general manager.

Joining the impoverished Cards in 1919, Rickey hit upon a brilliant scheme. It was the only way his team could become a contender in a league where rich clubs like McGraw's Giants regularly paid outlandish prices for star players of rival teams. "Let's grow our own talent," Rickey told St. Louis clubowner Sam Breadon. "We can round up promising young prospects and develop them on our own minor league clubs."

It was simple enough to find minor clubs as a framework for a "farm system." The critical test was to discover enough diamond nuggets in-the-rough. Rickey himself had a matchless gift for evaluating the baseball potential of even the most callow teen-ager... "putting a dollar sign on a muscle," his admirers termed it. But he couldn't transmit such talent to his scouts, so he told them this rule-of-thumb to use on a prospect: "Can he run? Can he throw? Can he hit?"

In 1926, the first of a long string of home-grown Cardinal champions hit the headlines. Player-manager Rogers Hornsby spurred them on to trample seven league rivals, and they went on to whip the vaunted Yankees in the Series. It was the beginning of a familiar pattern of St. Louis pennants—Bill McKechnie's Cards of '28; Gabby Street's crew of 1930 and '31; Frankie Frisch's Gashouse Gang of 1934; Billy Southworth's lean-and-hungry kids from '42 through '44, and Eddie Dyer, the slow-speaking and quick-thinking Texan, led the Redbirds to a tight victory over the slam-bang Red Sox in 1946.

Rickey was gone from St. Louis when the Cards registered pennants in 1943 and 1946, but those title teams were still mainly his farm products. When he switched to Brooklyn in 1943, the Dodgers already were blessed with a widespread farm system established by one of the many Rickey proteges in major league front offices, Larry MacPhail. Flatbush farmhands fashioned two more flags under Rickey, 1947 and 1949.

In between Card pennant winners, the NL turned up other worthy titlists. Big Poison and Little Poison, those deadly-hitting Waner brothers, brought Pittsburgh home in front in 1927. Two years later, a former minor league

It's World Series time, and here's part of stylishly-attired crowd which attended 1905 classic between Athletics and Giants. Derby hats and milady's best bonnet add to the festive atmosphere.

infielder named Joe McCarthy managed the Cubs for the first of his nine big league pennants.

Replacing Rogers Hornsby as Cub manager on August 2, 1932, first baseman Charlie Grimm drove his team to the top in the two remaining months. That depression year also saw probably the greatest manager of all time, John McGraw, retire in ill health. The sulphuric-tongued, trigger-brained taskmaster's last official move was typically brilliant. Passing over more popular candidates, he hand-picked as successor his coldly efficient first baseman, Bill Terry, who proceeded to win the world championship in his first full season at the helm, 1933. Terry and the Giants repeated as pennant winners in 1936-37.

Terry's pacemakers of 1934 were overtaken on the last day of the race by the fantastic Gashouse Gang of St. Louis. This was the most colorful club since the old Orioles. They had Pepper Martin, who used his chest to slide on or to stop hard-hit grounders; Dizzy Dean, 30-game winner who outdid his lurid boasts; fun-loving Rip Collins on first base; Lippy Durocher, literally a howling success at shortstop, and similar characters. But manager Frankie Frisch, still the old "Fordham Flash" at second base, could match any of his charges for verve, nerve and deeds of derring-do. These were worthy world champions.

A month after the 1934 World Series, John A. Heydler retired as league president after 18 years of distinguished service in that post. He was followed by Ford C. Frick, former Hoosier schoolmaster, front-line baseball writer and radio sportscaster, who had joined the league as service bureau director the preceding year. Frick's blend of tact, intelligence and devotion to the game earned him continuous re-election, and eventually the post as commissioner.

The same 1934 meetings that elected Frick also voted to allow Leland Stanford (Larry) MacPhail to institute night baseball in his Cincinnati ballpark, and the first game was played on May 24, 1935 when the Reds beat the Phillies, 4 to 1. It proved an instant success. Chicago took the pennant in 1935, and also won in 1938, but increasing night ball revenue enabled general manager MacPhail to plow funds into a farm system that developed pennant winners at Cincinnati in 1939-40.

Redhaired MacPhail was goné from the Reds by the time his farm talent matured into title winners. The boldly imaginative "Barnum" went to work reviving the arid Dodger franchise, and by 1941 he had fashioned a flag for Flatbush. However, Larry suffered his bitterest disappointment just before entering war service in the Fall of 1942, for his star-studded Dodgers frittered away a 10 1/2-game lead in August to the Cardinal youngsters. St. Louis repeated as rulers the next two years, which saw hundreds of big leaguers doff playing flannels to don military uniforms.

Baseball weathered World War II, despite severe travel restrictions, thanks to a heartening "green light" letter from President Franklin D. Roosevelt, who lauded the game's contribution to the nation's morale.

Bolstered by the effective pitching of Hank Borowy, a $100,000 waiver "cast-off" from the Yankees, the Cubs captured the 1945 pennant. That year was also notable for the signing of Jackie Robinson, first Negro in modern pro baseball, by the Dodgers' farm club of Montreal.

Baseball's new Commissioner, former U. S. Senator Albert B. (Happy) Chandler, was hardly in office a year when the Mexican League raided the major rosters heavily in the spring of 1946. Chandler warned all contract jumpers that they would be banned from organized baseball for five years, but dozens of them ignored the warning to scoop up the free-flowing pesos south of the border.

Despite the loss of its star pitcher, Max Lanier, and two others who went along on the "Mexican hayride," St. Louis spurted in the last week and finished

Judge Kenesaw Mountain Landis signs contract which makes him baseball's first commissioner. Club owners gathered at the historic scene are (l. to r.) Phil Ball, Browns; Barney Dreyfuss, Pirates; Connie Mack, Athletics; Clark Griffith, Senators; Jacob Ruppert, Yankees; Frank Navin, Tigers; Sam Breadon, Cardinals; Charles Ebbets, Dodgers; James C. Dunn, Indians; Charles Stoneham, Giants; Garry Herrmann, Reds; Harry Frazee, Red Sox; William Veeck, Cubs; Bob Quinn, Braves.

the season in a tie with Brooklyn, the first deadlock in league history. The Cards swept the two-game playoff and went on to greater glory by outhustling the heavily-favored Red Sox in the Series.

Between the Mexican League threat and a near-successful attempt at player unionization by a Boston lawyer named Bob Murphy, the perturbed clubowners made many important concessions in 1946. The players organized a permanent committee, which had no trouble gaining beneficent terms like a $5,000 salary minimum; pension fund to be bolstered by club payments; limitation of salary cuts to 25 per cent in one season and a shortened spring training season.

Brooklyn's "Peck's Bad Boy," Leo Durocher, climaxed a series of run-ins with baseball's top brass by popping off during the spring training exhibition season of 1947 against his former boss, Yankee general manager MacPhail. Commissioner Chandler clamped down with a year's suspension for the Dodger manager. Called out of semi-retirement to lead the Flock, Burt Shotton succeeded in winning the flag, thanks to the spark of a flock of Rickey farm products, notably Jackie Robinson, who won the base-stealing title in his rookie season.

Billy Southworth skillfully piloted a collection of oldsters in Boston uniform to first place in 1948. The next year, with Shotton replacing Durocher in mid-season, Brooklyn won another flag, bolstered by batting-king Robinson. The game was jolted early in 1949 when stranded Mexican Leaguers brought lawsuits for being blacklisted by pro baseball. Commissioner Chandler wisely declared a general amnesty in June of that year, and later made an out-of-court settlement with the last challenger of the legality of the reserve clause, Danny Gardella.

Bonuses boomed in post-war years. Half a dozen prospects collected more than $50,000 each to sign with pro teams. One of the heaviest investors in this costly market was a young Delaware millionaire, Bob Carpenter, who owned the lowly Phillies. The policy paid off. Fashioned mainly by general manager Herb Pennock, who unfortunately died of a heart attack before his handiwork blossomed into Philadelphia's first pennant in 35 years, the Phillie Whiz Kids won all the NL marbles in 1950. It took a 10th-inning homer on the last day of the season by Dick Sisler, son of the first base immortal, to bring the Phils the decision over Brooklyn's fast finishers. Serving as chief Dodger scout at the time, George Sisler sat in the stands on that final day and watched his son's homer kayo the pennant hopes of the club he was working for.

The league lost a president when Frick was named Commissioner of Baseball, replacing Chandler who resigned July 15, 1951 when he learned his contract wouldn't be renewed. Frick was handed a three-year pact at $65,000 a year and brought in his manager of the service bureau, Charley Segar, to serve as secretary-treasurer.

Warren C. Giles, head of the Cincinnati Reds, was elected to Frick's vacant post and Dave Grote, who handled the publicity of the Rhinelanders, was appointed manager of the service bureau.

Perhaps the most historic dash toward a pennant since the run of Boston's Miracle Braves in 1914, occurred in 1951 when the New York Giants, after being 13½ games behind Brooklyn in mid-August, finally caught the Dodgers, but only after the two clubs finished the season in a dead tie upon conclusion of the regular playing schedule. The stage was now set for the second league playoff in five years.

The Giants, after winning the first of the best-of-three-game playoff series, 3 to 1, lost the second clash 10 to 0. What followed provided perhaps the most dramatic climax recorded in the league's history.

Leading 4 to 1 entering the ninth inning of the final clash, the Dodgers needed but three outs to win the pennant. But they were to get only one. With one run in and runners on second and third base for the Giants, Dodger manager Chuck Dressen replaced starting pitcher Don Newcombe with Ralph Branca. Bobby Thomson was at the plate, and he represented the winning run. After Branca threw one strike, Thomson swung on the next pitch and lofted it into the left field stands for a home run, a 5-4 Giant victory and the league flag.

The Dodgers were winners in 1952 and '53, the latter year a notable one since it marked the first franchise shift in 53 years.

The shift was made March 18, 1953 when the Perini brothers, Lou and Charles, announced the transfer of their Boston Braves to Milwaukee. Sagging attendance figures and apathy on the part of the fans to adequately support the Braves were the reasons given by the Perinis for the switch.

Milwaukee proved a gold lode. In the first 13 home dates at the beer capital the Braves drew a total of 302,667, more than had flocked through the portals of Braves' Field for all of their 1952 home dates. A season attendance mark of 1,826,397 was a new league standard.

Milwaukee continued to prosper in 1954 when 2,131,388 paid to watch the third place Braves. The financial success of the Braves started baseball owners thinking of new diamond horizons, where television could be controlled in an intelligent manner and people would pay to see their heroes in the flesh instead of watching them from their own living room.

The Giants were 1954 champions, sweeping Cleveland in the Series, and the Dodgers bounced back to win in 1955 and '56. In both these seasons the Milwaukee attendance continued above the two million mark and these high figures evidently began to start a couple of clubowners wondering just how they could also increase their own gate receipts. Brooklyn president Walter O'Malley made a significant move in '56 when he took his Brooklyn team to Jersey City, New Jersey where the Dodgers played seven "home" games, one with each league rival. This started the speculation that the Dodgers would soon depart from Brooklyn permanently.

The Dodgers again played seven games in Jersey City in 1957, the year Milwaukee drew a record attendance of 2,215,404—the fourth straight season the Braves topped the two-million mark. On the field, the Braves rewarded their faithful with their first pennant, climaxed by a World Series victory over the Yankees.

The most historic events of the year—in fact in the history of baseball—were the announcements, first by the New York Giants, then by the Brooklyn Dodgers, that their teams were leaving the vast metropolitan New York area for the West Coast. On August 19, Horace Stoneham, president of the Giants, announced that his club would leave New York at the end of the season and move to San Francisco. Brooklyn's O'Malley made it official on October 8 when he stated the Dodgers would be transferred to Los Angeles. Both owners cited old parks and limited parking facilities as main reasons for the shifts, but the unlimited possibilities of pay-television and the opportunity to acquire vast real estate properties were other vital factors in the move to the West.

Milwaukee repeated as pennant winners in 1958, the year the league took on a coast-to-coast "new look." The Dodgers, who were unable to get immediate approval for construction of a new stadium in the Chavez Ravine area of Los Angeles, played their games in the vast Los Angeles Memorial Coliseum, a field constructed specifically for football, and drew 1,845,556 fans. The Giants moved into much-smaller Seals' Stadium, where they attracted 1,272,625 fans.

These attendance figures represented an increase over the previous season when both teams were located in the East. However the Dodgers became involved in legal battles and delays over the construction of their new playing area; the Giants had little trouble in obtaining permission to start construction on a new park which was scheduled to be ready for the 1960 season.

Los Angeles set a new single-day league attendance mark on April 18 when 78,672 fans saw the Dodgers play the Giants in the first major league game ever to be played on the Pacific Coast.

A proposed third major league, headed by Branch Rickey and Congressional hearings into the laws governing organized baseball, overshadowed the events on the playing field to a considerable extent in 1959. When Congress failed to pass the Kefauver bill and the game's status remained unchanged Rickey's embryo Continental League was dealt a body blow from which it never recovered. The successful move to the West Coast by the Dodgers and Giants created a demand for expansion which was discussed in great detail by both leagues without reaching an agreement.

On the playing field the Dodgers, participating in their third play-off, defeated the Braves and went on to win the World Championship from the White Sox in a Series that shattered the former attendance mark of 86,288 set at Cleveland in 1948. Playing in the huge Los Angeles Coliseum the Dodgers bettered that record in all three home games. The first game drew 92,394 fans, the second was witnessed by 92,650 while the third game saw the largest crowd in World Series history—92,796—a record topped only by the Campanella benefit exhibition against the Yankees which drew 93,103, largest turnout in Major League history.

Definite expansion plans for both major leagues after the demise of Branch Rickey's proposed Continental League marked 1960 as a year of dramatic development. First, the National, then the American edged into the lead in the expansion race with President Cronin's American League finally emerging as the winner by voting to expand to ten clubs in 1961, while the more conservative National decided to withhold their plans until 1962.

On the field the swash-buckling Pirates landed Pittsburgh it's first pennant since 1927. Their specialty was coming from behind to win games apparently hopelessly lost. They won 23 games during the season in their final turn at bat—12 of these after two were out. Warren Spahn of the Braves won 21 games. It was the eleventh time in his major league career in which he has won 20 or more games per season. Established as preseason favorites, the Giants folded completely after the sudden discharge of Skipper Bill Rigney on June 18th. The Cubs tried a novel but unsuccessful move when Manager Charlie Grimm and radio announcer Lou Boudreau switched jobs. Boudreau, however, had no more success than "Jolly Chollie" and the club finished a bad seventh, just one game ahead of the perpetual cellar-dwelling Phillies.

The underdog Reds surprised all of the experts by winning the 1961 flag despite the presence of some slightly "shopworn" players. In the race all of the way, they finished four games ahead of the favored Los Angeles Dodgers. It was the first Cincinnati pennant since 1940. On August 16th their double header with the Dodgers at the Coliseum in Los Angeles set a National League record for double headers when 72,140 fans witnessed the twin bill. The Pirates, winners in 1960, collapsed completely and finished a poor 6th. Phil Wrigley's innovation of installing a staff of coaches rather than a single manager failed miserably to improve the Cubs who finished a poor 7th just ahead of the perennial cellar-dwellers, the Phils, who rounded out their 4th consecutive year trailing the pack. Starting on July 23rd, they lost 28 out of 29 games setting a 20th century record of 23 losses in a row.

The 1962 National League season was marked by the Senior Circuit's expansion into a ten-club league, the first time the league has had more than the conventional 8 clubs since 1899. The clubs were poorly balanced and the result, while tense with the Giants, Dodgers and Reds fighting for the pennant, was just another season for the rest of the league. The Giants and Dodgers had to go into a play-off as they finished in a dead heat at the end of the regular season, the Giants winning two of the three play-off games. The Dodgers opened the season in their magnificent new Chavez Ravine Stadium. Maury Wills of the Dodgers was the toast of the league when he stole 104 bases, surpassing the immortal Ty Cobb's 1915 record of 96. Stan (The Man) Musial added a few more records to his already bulging collection when he passed Honus Wagner for the most total hits in National League history and moved past Tris Speaker in the all-time hit total where he is surpassed only by the great Ty Cobb. On the debit side of the ledger was the extremely poor showing of the New York Mets under Casey Stengel who set a new record for losses in a single season by dropping 120 decisions while the floundering Cubs lost 100 games for the first time in their National League history.

AMERICAN LEAGUE

The groundwork for the formation of the American League actually was started nine years before its official beginning in 1901. Byron (Ban) Johnson, a minister's son, and Charles Albert Comiskey, player-manager of the Cincinnati team in the unwieldy National League, began their dreams of secession and a new diamond empire in the beer parlors of the Rhineland, as early as 1892.

The 27-year-old Johnson, who conducted a no-holds barred baseball column for the *Cincinnati Gazette*, held no particular affection for John T. Brush, clubowner of the local nine. But, for Comiskey, Johnson had nothing but admiration. Brush, a clothing magnate, was the target of some of Ban's choicest and most sulphuric adjectives, and was severely criticized for what Johnson claimed were "stingy tactics" which he said were harming the local franchise.

Comiskey, recognizing in Johnson an alert and imaginative mind who envisioned greater horizons for baseball, soon convinced clubowners anxious to reform the old Western Association that Ban was their man to head the league. Johnson, who went to the league's convention as a reporter, returned as its new president, mainly because Commy was so lavish in his praise of the sports writer.

Comiskey himself left Cincinnati at the close of the 1894 season to take a managerial post with Sioux City, where he started on a club-owning career which was to make him one of the game's most powerful and influential figures.

Johnson tackled his new assignment in typical fashion, hard-hitting and hard-working, and his eyes were cocked continuously at major-league status. He was especially alert for defections in the NL ranks and kept his ears close to the ground for rumblings of discontent.

Ban made his initial move in 1896, after Connie Mack had been fired as Pittsburgh pilot for making caustic comments against the second-guessing of a critical front office. Ban snapped up Mack for his league, offering the lean catcher-manager a bonus which consisted of part-interest in the Milwaukee club. Three years later, a series of bold and shrewd moves by Ban convinced him that his dreams of an American League were not too far removed from reality.

When the NL dropped four of its dozen clubs after the 1899 season, Johnson persuaded Charles Somers, Great Lakes shipping tycoon, to take over the vacated Cleveland franchise. Somers "steered" the league in its roughest period, over the next two years. Ban also set up a club in Buffalo. It took Commy's engineering, though, before Jim Hart, owner of the Chicago NL team, allowed Comiskey to switch his St. Paul team to Chicago's South Side. Hart never thought fans would tolerate the stockyard smells to see a ball game in that rundown district of town.

At this point, prestige-wise Johnson announced that his circuit was changing its name from the Western to the American League. Commy's team won the 1900 pennant after a prosperous season for the league in general. Johnson was now ready for the master stroke. Using as a pretext the rumored re-organization of the old American Association as a direct threat against his league, Ban sought NL permission to expand into Baltimore, Washington and Philadelphia. Unable to obtain even the courtesy of an audience with the haughty Nationals, Johnson launched open warfare.

First, Ban scrapped the National Agreement, so that all players became fair game in the eyes of rival leagues. He forestalled an AA-inspired plan to move into Boston by sending Connie Mack to the Hub to lease a plot for a ballpark (using Somers' bankroll). Somers, who had loaned Comiskey money to build a park in Chicago, also had a financial finger in the Philadelphia club, as well as his own titular Cleveland franchise.

The AL's expansion to the East proved popular, and the dissension-ridden rival league lost customers. Johnson's full-fledged major league began official operations on Wednesday, April 24, 1901. Other teams were rained out that day, but there was a gala inaugural in Chicago, which was destined to win the flag with Clark Griffith as manager and Comiskey now in the front office. The first American League box score:

CLEVELAND (2)	AB	R	H	PO	A	E
Pickering, rf	4	0	1	0	0	0
McCarthy, lf	4	0	2	4	0	0
Genins, cf	4	0	0	1	0	0
LaChance, 1b	4	1	1	13	0	1
Bradley, 3b	4	0	0	2	5	0
Beck, 2b	2	0	2	0	4	0
Hallman, ss	3	1	0	1	3	1
Wood, c	4	0	1	2	2	0
Hoffer, p	4	0	0	1	0	0
Totals	33	2	7	24	14	2

CHICAGO (8)	AB	R	H	PO	A	E
Hoy, cf	5	0	1	3	0	0
Jones, rf	2	2	1	4	0	0
Mertes, lf	3	2	1	4	0	0
Shugart, ss	2	2	0	4	4	0
Isbell, 1b	3	1	1	8	0	0
Hartman, 3b	4	0	1	0	5	1
Brain, 2b	4	0	0	1	3	0
Sullivan, c	4	1	2	2	0	0
Patterson, p	4	0	0	1	1	0
Totals	31	8	7	27	13	1

Cleveland	000	100	100	---	2
Chicago	250	000	10x	---	8

Left on base—Chicago 5, Cleveland 3. Two base hit—Beck. Double plays—Shugart-Isbell, Hoffer-Hallman-LaChance. Struck out—by Hoffer 1. Bases on balls—off Patterson 2, Hoffer 6. Umpire—Connolly. Time--1:30. Attendance—14,500.

Johnson's platform of "clean baseball and more 25-cent seats" drew increasing patronage. Star players kept streaming toward the better-paying AL. Ban backed his umpires religiously, even though it brought him head-on against such personal friends as Clark Griffith. Griff took the censure in good grace. Not so John McGraw, who couldn't shed his "Old Orioles" stripe. In midseason of 1902, irascible McGraw sold out his Baltimore holdings and jumped back to the NL. Johnson's answer was to move the Baltimore franchise to New York for 1903—despite politicians' threats to run city streets through his ballpark—and the AL finally had an eight-club alignment.

Connie Mack's A's were hard hit by an injunction that cost them the services of Nap Lajoie and other NL "jumpers." But an erratic southpaw named Rube Waddell came in from the Coast to strong-arm Mack's team to the 1902 pennant.

By now, the NL knew it had had enough. At a peace meeting in January of 1903, the old circuit tried the old stratagem that worked against the AA—

offering to absorb the stronger teams of the rival circuit. Johnson and his fellow delegates snapped out of their seats, reached for their hats and stomped out of the conference. Four days later, there was a different tone at the interleague meeting. The NL asked only that Johnson promise not to invade Pittsburgh. Ban nodded. They shook hands, signed a preliminary agreement that established the dual-major league principle and finally set up a joint committee to settle ownership of disputed players.

Cy Young, still a 28-game winner at the age of 36, led Boston to the 1903 pennant. Teammate Bill Dinneen, who won 21, beat the Pirates three times in the ensuing World Series.

Hairbreadth finishes featured AL races the next few years. Of these, none brought greater satisfaction to Johnson than the 1906 campaign. Ban exulted along with his crony, Commy, whose Chicago "Hitless Wonders" put together 19 straight victories at one stage to finish on top of the heap. Then they deflated the mighty Cubs in baseball's first intracity World Series.

From 1907-09, it was all Detroit. Hughie Jennings managed this triumphant Tiger pack. As one of the "Old Orioles," Hughie was used to blood-and-thunder aggressiveness on the field. But he had to admit none of his former teammates could approach the fierce, flaming will-to-win of his young outfielder, a tight-lipped Georgian named Ty Cobb. A basepath terror and batting wonder, Cobb captured the hitting crown all three of these pennant-winning seasons . . . and nine times afterward. His lifetime average over 24 years was a stratospheric .367, just one of the dozens of records still held by the "Georgia Peach."

Connie Mack's A's ruled the roost for four of the first five years after the cork ball came into use. Boasting the "Hundred thousand dollar infield" of McInnis-Collins-Barry-Baker, and the iron-armed pitching trio of Bender-Plank-Coombs, the White Elephants trumpeted triumphantly in 1910-11, 1913-14.

Boston's Red Sox, with a famed outfield trio of Speaker-Hooper-Lewis, also bagged four flags around that time: 1912, 1915-16, 1918. Comiskey's club in Chicago won the other pair of pennants in the second decade of this century. League overlord Johnson chortled as his clubs of this period posted four Series successes over the Giants of McGraw, his despised enemy ever since the 1902 desertion of Baltimore.

The Damon-Pythias bond between Johnson and Comiskey was strained when the AL chief suspended a White Sox outfielder for three days. Returning from a fishing trip that week, Ban sent Commy his best catch. Back came a bitter wire: "Do you think I can play that fish in left field?" The rift widened into an angry feud when Commy's infamous "Black Sox" were exposed for throwing the 1919 World Series.

Tris Speaker and his world champion Clevelands of 1920 were overshadowed by the eruption of the Sox scandal. Along came Babe Ruth, to fire the imagination with his wondrous homers, and Judge K. M. Landis, to restore faith in the game, and baseball was back on the glory road of sportsdom's Golden Era.

Ruth already had gained fame as a Red Sox pitching star and a part-time outfielder who could practically knock the cover off the ball. But his light shone brightest after his sale to the Yankees, who had never won a pennant. Babe helped dispel the title famine by whacking the unbelievable total of 59 homers in 1921. His howitzer at the plate enabled New York to stay on top in 1922 and 1923. In the latter year, his team moved from the National League's Polo Grounds into its own million dollar ballpark, Yankee Stadium, which was suitably tagged "The House that Ruth Built."

After 17 seasons with a trailing team, old faithful Walter Johnson, greatest pitcher in AL history, broke into two World Series when his Senators won in 1924-25. Manager Bucky Harris was the "Boy Wonder' at the helm each time.

The next phase of league history featured the "Murderers' Row" Yankee champions of 1926-27-28. Beer baron Col. Jacob Ruppert made a fetish of success, and the Yankee owner had the right men to insure it—richly experienced Edward G. Barrow as general manager, clever little Miller Huggins as field pilot and Babe Ruth backboning a lineup of "window breakers" like Lou Gehrig, Bob Meusel, Tony Lazzeri, et al. Babe hit 60 homers in 1927, the all-time record.

Even as these awe-inspiring Yanks enjoyed the spotlight, other real titans were bowing out in the wings. Ty Cobb and Tris Speaker closed their active careers after spending the 1928 season side by side in the A's outfield. Walter Johnson and Ban Johnson quit in 1927, the former after winning more than 400 games and the latter after broken-heartedly losing his long vendetta against the all-powerful Commissioner.

Ban Johnson's successor as AL president was Cleveland's chief executive, Ernest S. Barnard. Johnson and Barnard both died suddenly in 1931, as did Comiskey. Gentlemanly Will Harridge rose to the presidency after 20 years in the league office as secretary.

Coincident with the cataclysmic Wall Street crash of 1929 was Connie Mack's return to baseball prosperity. Buoyant as ever in his late 60's, the league's managerial dean paraded to three straight pennants from 1929-31. Four of his aces came from Jack Dunn's Baltimore club, which had spawned Babe Ruth earlier. Dunn received upwards of $150,000 for Lefty Grove, George Earnshaw, Max Bishop and Joe Boley. Mack's fame finally transcended baseball's halls, and he received the Bok Award in 1929 for distinguished service to the city of Philadelphia.

An NL managerial castoff, Joe McCarthy, came to the Yankees to restore the regal sway of the Bronx Bombers. Holdovers from the Huggins regime helped him nail the flag in 1932. A frustrated runnerup each of the next three years, McCarthy finally hit his stride in 1936 for seven pennants in the next eight seasons and four straight world championships.

The renewed dynasty started in the rookie season of Joe DiMaggio, a fisherman's son grown into a graceful outfielder second only to Ruth in New York annals. It continued unabated as the farm chain, master-minded by Barrow and George Weiss, developed a string of summa cum laude graduates—Joe Gordon, Charlie Keller, Spud Chandler, Phil Rizzuto, Hank Borowy, et al. These youngsters were balanced with ageless veterans of topnotch caliber, like Lefty Gomez, Bill Dickey, Red Ruffing and Frank Crosetti. Tommy Henrich was a free-agent bargain at $20,000 in 1937.

Detroit's slow but slugging club of 1940 interrupted the Yank pennant monopoly. Cries of "Break up the Yankees" were often raised, but it took the tail end of World War II to do it. After the Yankees won in 1941, '42 and '43 the lowly Browns, under Luke Sewell, won their only AL title in 1944. Detroit, with slim Hal Newhouser and bespectacled Dizzy Trout as the 1-2 mound punch, won in 1945. The next year was the payoff for long-suffering Tom Yawkey, who had poured millions into the Red Sox for more than a decade before finally realizing a pennant. It was powered by batting king Ted Williams, baseball's most feared slugger since Babe Ruth.

With diamond dynamo Larry MacPhail operating as one-third owner of the Yanks in 1947, world championship days were back in the Bronx. Larry brought Bucky Harris back from the managerial boneyard to guide this club.

Cleveland interrupted a new Yankee era of domination in 1948, beating Boston in the league's first post-season playoff after the Indians and the Red Sox had concluded the regular season with identical records. Lou Boudreau, manager-shortstop, paced the Tribe down the stretch with his great hitting and fielding, and it was his momentum which enabled Cleveland to down Boston in an unprecedented one-game, sudden-death playoff battle in the Hub's Fenway Park.

The Yankees resumed their old position at the top of the heap for the next five years (1949-53), Casey Stengel leading a new group of Bombers to five straight world championships, a new record in the annals of the game. This was the same Stengel who had been found deficient as a manager of the Boston and Brooklyn entries of the NL.

It was Cleveland again which temporarily halted the fantastic Yankee pennant pushes. Al Lopez, who once played for Stengel in the NL, whipped his teacher in 1954. The Indians rolled up an impressive total of 111 victories—an all-time AL season high—but were humiliated in the Series when they dropped four straight to the New York Giants. It was the first AL post-season defeat in eight years.

During the Indians' drive they established another record, this for attendance for a single day when 84,587 stormed Municipal Stadium on September 12 to see the Tribe belt the Yankees in a doubleheader.

The Korean conflict, during the '50s, claimed several players who previously had served in the forces during World War II. Ted Williams, who held a reserve commission in the Marine Air Corps, was recalled to active duty soon after the start of the '52 year, not to return until the '53 campaign was well under way.

Perhaps the most startling developments of the early '50s were the franchise shifts which left St. Louis and Philadelphia bereft of AL representation for the first time since Ban Johnson organized the loop.

The St. Louis Browns were transferred to Baltimore on September 29, 1953 for a total reported to be $2,475,000. The Philadelphia Athletics were to go one year later, being bought by Arnold Johnson and associates for the sum of approximately three and one half million dollars. Both clubs drew well in their initial season, the Orioles pulling 1,060,910 through the gates in '54 and the Athletics, despite a sixth-place finish, attracting 1,393,054 in '55.

It was the same old AL story as the 1950s drew to a close—too much Yankee dominance. The greatest baseball dynasty ever created won pennants from 1955 through '58, but only got an even break in Series competition, losing the '55 and '57 sets to Brooklyn and Milwaukee. For manager Stengel it made nine pennants in 10 years.

Ted Williams remained the game's most provocative personality, and in 1956 created some sort of history by getting stung with a record-equaling fine of $5,000. The Boston thumper was penalized this amount by his club when he spat in the direction of the stands after the fans in his home park booed him for desultory play.

Although the Yankees had the vast Metropolitan area to themselves in 1958 their attendance dropped some 68,000 over their 1957 total. Many theories were advanced for this fall-off, but there was no doubt that the day and night televising of games was beginning to take its toll of the attendance.

Will Harridge, president of the AL since 1931, startled the mid-winter league 1958 meeting when he announced his retirement. He gave no reasons for his decision but many believed that Harridge was bowing out due to the many problems baseball would be forced to face in the next few years. Talk of a third league, a demand by the players for 20 per cent of all gate, concession and television monies and constant discussion on the problems of television and how it should be regulated were some of the factors which, many believed, decided to make the 72-year-old Harridge announce his retirement. Joe Cronin, former star shortstop and manager of Boston and Washington,

Hall-of-Famer, and general manager of the Red Sox, was named as his successor.

Picked to win their fifth straight pennant in 1959 the Yankees suddenly found themselves in the unfamiliar surroundings of the cellar where they landed on May 20th. From there they waged an up-hill battle but they were never able to regain their former prestige winding up in third place, 15 games behind the pennant-winning White Sox. Early Wynn of the White Sox was the biggest winner in the majors with 22 victories. Meanwhile the magnates were experiencing "growing pains." Expansion fever was at a high pitch due to the threat of Branch Rickey's Continental League. Suddenly the American League voted to study the request of Minneapolis-St. Paul for a spot in the junior circuit. Cronin's loop proposed expansion to nine clubs for each league by taking a franchise in Minneapolis-St. Paul and granting the National a club in New York. The National rejected this plan claiming they were "not interested" in expansion at the time.

With the Continental League on the ropes due to the pigeon-holing of the Kefauver bill in 1960, the American League once more discussed expansion and decided to go into action as soon as the National advised them of similar word. Meeting in Chicago on July 18th the National League cast a solid vote in favor of the move. When the senior circuit voted to add Houston and New York to the loop in 1962 the American League broke all speed records by boosting their league to 10 clubs. They authorized Calvin Griffith of the Washington club to make his move to Minneapolis-St. Paul, approved a new franchise for Washington to a syndicate headed by General Elwood Quesada, head of the FAA, and awarded a Los Angeles franchise to a group led by cowboy singer Gene Autry and TV tycoon Bob Reynolds. Starting from scratch it was a herculean task to field two brand new major league clubs in less than four months and the result was the wildest talent scramble in major league history.

The year also witnessed the dissolution of the game's most successful managerial team when both General Manager George Weiss and Manager Casey Stengel, of the New York Yankees, were relieved of their posts. This pair had guided the Yanks to ten pennants and three World Championships in the last twelve years. Another unusual managerial shift occurred in 1960 when Jimmie Dykes of the Tigers and Joe Gordon of the Indians switched jobs. The American League launched the 1961 season with the first 10-club league in its history and also embarked on a marathon 162-games schedule. The new clubs, Minneapolis and Los Angeles, had rough going finishing 7th and 8th respectively. The Yankees, as usual, topheavy favorites did not disappoint their followers and repeated for their 12th pennant in 15 years. Under a new manager, Ralph Houk who assumed the helm after the departure of Casey Stengel, they did not lose their stride and not only copped the flag but continued on to take the Reds four games to one in the World Series. The big guns were Roger Maris who topped the famous Bambino's Home Run record by clouting 61, Mickey Mantle who was right behind him with 54 and pitcher Ed Ford who copped 24 decisions while losing only 4. In winning the pennant on his first try, manager Houk joined the select list of freshman managers, namely Bucky Harris and Eddie Dyer. The Tigers under Bob Scheffing proved to be the surprise club of the year, setting the pace for the first half of the season. Unfortunately the Tigers lacked the pitching depth necessary to stay in front but they were topped only by the Yanks in batting. Norm Cash won the batting crown with an average of .361 while Al Kaline and Rocky Colavito helped the cause with Kaline hitting .324 and Rocky clubbing 45 homers. The newly-born Angels surprised their followers by winning a respectable 70 victories.

It was the old, old story again in 1962 when the Yanks won their 10th flag in the past 12 years. However, they faced unexpected opposition from the two new clubs, the Minnesota Twins and the Los Angeles Angels who finished second and third respectively and gave the Yanks a run for their money, in fact, the Yanks could not find the magic wand until the final two weeks of the season when the Twins and Angels ran out of gas. General manager Fred Haney, the man of the hour in the Angel's set-up made some astounding deals which kept the club in the running until the very end. It was the most surprising club in the history of the game. Early Wynn was one of the tragic figures of the campaign. Trying hard for his 300th victory, he missed on several occasions and had to be satisfied with 299 lifetime wins, one short of the magic 300. Freshman Bo Belinsky, Earl Wilson and Bill Monbouquette of the Bosox and Jack Kralick of the Minnesota Twins all pitched no-hit games while 20-game winners included Dick Donovan, Ralph Terry, Ray Herbert and Camilo Pascual.

AMERICAN ASSOCIATION

In the earlier years of the National League many of the mid-western cities were envious of the financial inroads the league had made, especially in hinterland towns which were not of major league status. Touring Easterners from the NL drew heavy gates in exhibitions played in Western areas, and the West soon started to sound out several cities as prospective entries in a new major circuit.

H. D. (Denny) Knight of Pittsburgh and Justus Thorner of Cincinnati rounded up a half dozen clubs and went into the field in 1882, avowed rivals of the NL. The newly-founded American Association was now in business.

With prideful, suspicious Soden acting as NL president, Eastern reception was openly hostile, extending to bold player raids and the coining of a favorite epithet. "Beer and Whiskey League," they termed the AA, deriding the fact that financial backers of the new circuit mainly derived their income from alcohol.

On the other side of the fence, name-calling consisted of tagging the NL the "rich man's league." To court the "plain workingmen" clientele, the AA slashed the admission price to half its rival's 50-cent standard, featured Sunday baseball (then expressly forbidden in the NL under threat of expulsion) and dispensed beer in the stands.

Cincinnati won the first AA flag behind the pitching of bespectacled Will White. The novelty of good baseball in fertile cities, bringing a host of new Western heroes into the diamond limelight, resulted in a prosperous inaugural season. The AA added two more franchises for 1883. Thanks to newly-elected president A. G. Mills, the NL wisely made peace with its lusty young rival, and under the National Agreement they operated as dual major leagues.

The most fabulous figure in AA history was not any of its new playing heroes, but a bulbous-nosed German immigrant named Chris Von der Ahe. Owner of a pleasure resort in the St. Louis suburbs, the hearty and generous "sport" became interested in baseball as a means of attracting customers to his place. But he was smart enough to know how ignorant he was of the game's intricacies, so Chris relied on the judgment of Alfred H. Spink, a zealous baseball writer and guiding spirit of the game in early St. Louis days.

Another colorful character who helped develop the Browns was Ted Sullivan, railroad concessionaire who sponsored a powerful team in Dubuque, Iowa. Ted brought the newly-formed Browns his best men, including first baseman Charlie Comiskey. St. Louis finished a close second to the pennant-winning Athletics in 1883, slumped in '84, and the next year, with Commy at the helm, started a streak of four straight pennants.

Though Al Spink, who founded *The Sporting News* soon afterward, and Comiskey, who revolutionized first base play, were the guiding geniuses behind the Browns' dynasty, expansive Von der Ahe swaggered under such sustained success and unabashedly proclaimed himself "the smartest feller in baseball." On the contrary, Chris' petulant orders to dispose of several important players after his crushing World Series loss to Detroit in 1887 proved costly. Commy repeated the flag in '88, but was nipped in quest of a fifth straight pennant by a Brooklyn team that had bought the standout players who incurred the displeasure of the St. Louis baron.

War with the Players' League in 1890 crippled the AA. Unable to meet budgets on a 25-cent-admission plank, several key clubs deserted to the NL. A year later, the AA withdrew from the National Agreement. . . only to lose the "cold war" when more clubowners secretly capitulated to the NL.

Despite its inglorious finish, the AA played a valuable role in baseball history. It pioneered reforms which the NL eventually adopted, like league control of umpires, Sunday baseball and the percentage system of determining pennant winners. Healthy competition also forced the NL to draft a National Agreement that served as a basis for present-day pacts guiding major and minor league operations.

UNION ASSOCIATION

Insisting that the reserve rule "reserves all that is good for the owners, leaving the remainder for the players," St. Louis millionaire Henry V. Lucas embarked on a one-man crusade to end the players' "bondage." He organized the Union Association as a third major league in 1884. George Wright, given the concession of manufacturing the official ball for the circuit, agreed to run the Boston franchise. Thorner came in with his Cincinnati club after the AA founder thought he had received short shrift in his circuit.

Widely-traveled Ted Sullivan was dispatched to round up players willing to ignore the reserve clause binding them to the AA or NL. Before the season started, the Unions had about 50 of these. But most of the recruits suddenly repented and stayed with their old clubs. As owner of the St. Louis Maroons franchise, Lucas was able to ante up extra bonus money to keep his reserve-clause jumpers in line, so the UA's "angel" wound up with an overpowering pennant-winner that won its first 20 games and quickly killed interest in the "race." Only five clubs finished the season, though a dozen participated.

Unwilling to draw any distinction between breaking a current contract or the holdover clause, both the AA and NL raided UA ranks in the early months, and kidnapped many players who had drawn heavy advances in salary. On July 1, the UA declared open warfare and started to induce the stars of rival leagues to jump in mid-season, too.

The three-way war was too costly all around. Weaker clubs in the UA folded in profusion. Only in St. Louis, where Lucas unstintingly gave his fans the best in players and accommodations—including dozens of caged canaries strewn about the stands—was there any sustained prosperity.

When the UA expired at the end of the season, Lucas opportunistically snapped up the Cleveland NL franchise (which he had helped ruin by mid-season player raids) for $2,500. As part of his price for peace, Lucas insisted on moving into the NL. He transferred his Cleveland holding to St. Louis, paid Von der Ahe $5,000 for territorial privileges and ungraciously absented himself from the UA's dissolution meeting in order to concentrate on his new NL interest.

PLAYERS' LEAGUE

The one-year stand of the Players' League (1890) was actually a movement motivated by players who were members of the National Brotherhood of Professional Players. This was a benevolent organization which used dues of five dollars a month from its members to aid its sick and needy.

After the 1885 season, the NL and AA magnates set a ceiling on players' salaries and forbade any cash advances during the off-season. John Montgomery Ward, later a successful attorney, served as the Brotherhood's spokesman in protesting the salary scale of $2,000. Although the salary limit never was enforced, though kept on the books, additional grievances were fought successfully by the Brotherhood which demanded, and received, official recognition in 1887.

While Ward was away on a world tour, the magnates instituted the unfair Classification System of scaling players' salaries. Upon his return, the brilliant Giant shortstop couldn't even get an audience with the NL. Declaring lack of good faith on the part of the league, the Brotherhood published a Declaration of Independence on November 4, 1889, and lined up financial support for a Players' League in 1890.

Players in the new circuit signed three-year contracts at their 1889 figure, which could be raised at the discretion of the club, but not slashed. Even more interesting, the PL abandoned the reserve rule by allowing players to switch clubs at will at the close of the season. However, the latter plan never got a trial, since the league lived only one year.

The secession movement was popular. Four out of five NL regulars jumped to the PL. Though forced to operate with makeshift lineups, the NL magnates boldly took on the insurgents by scheduling and re-scheduling games in order to conflict with PL contests in the same city. In New York, only a wall separated games played simultaneously by the rival leagues.

Spalding, appointed head of a "war committee" of the NL, offered King Kelly a $10,000 bribe plus a three-year League contract "at any figure you want to write in" to skip back. But the colorful "King Kel" couldn't go back on his Brotherhood mates and turned down the offer. Kelly went on to pilot the PL pennant-winners in Boston.

Rainy weather in the late stages of the race hurt PL attendances, and inexperienced magnates quickly lost heart at the reverses. A few sold out to eager NL rivals, and the Brotherhood collapsed. All contract-jumpers were restored to their original clubs without penalty.

FEDERAL LEAGUE

Unlike the Union Association and Players' League, which became third major leagues principally on "reform" platforms, the Federal League moved into the baseball picture strictly in the spirit of a capital investment. When coal magnate James A. Gilmore became president of the FL in September, 1913, it was still a sectional minor league operating in the Midwest.

Gilmore had the gift of gab, and soon sold a group of businessmen on the wisdom of backing a third major league. Glib Jim painted a rosy financial picture, dipping heavily into the figures of the "Half million dollar World Series" of 1912, which netted each of the competing clubs almost $150,000.

As a clincher, he accented the advertising value of owning a ball club which daily made nation-wide headlines.

The spellbinder convinced the Ward baking brothers, who took the Brooklyn franchise; Charles Weeghman, who owned a chain of Chicago restaurants; Harry Sinclair, oil tycoon who took the Newark Club; Phil Ball, St. Louis ice king; Otto Stifel, wealthy brewer, and others.

Gilmore then went to work on the players. His first conquest was Joe Tinker of Cub fame, who was hired to manage the Chicago Whales. Other established stars followed. Even though they didn't fall for the greenback bait, such standouts as Ty Cobb and Tris Speaker had their salaries doubled to keep them from joining the "outlaw league."

Eight new ballparks were built within three months, including the Chicago plant that is now known as Wrigley Field. Indianapolis nosed out Chicago in a close race in 1914, while Chicago shaded St. Louis by one percentage point the next year. Only the imminence of American entry into the World War persuaded the FL magnates to listen to peace feelers from the AL and NL.

The price of peace came high. First, the Feds insisted that their rivals assume the $385,000 worth of FL player contracts. Weeghman was permitted to buy the Cubs and Ball the Browns. Payments spread over five to 20 years were to reimburse the Ward interests, Sinclair and Pittsburgh backers. Of the many Fed players sold back to the majors, the highest price went for Benny Kauff, the "Ty Cobb of the Feds," whom the Giants snapped up for $35,000.

The settlement made no provision for the Baltimore club, which thereupon instituted an anti-trust suit against organized baseball that went all the way to the U. S. Supreme Court before Chief Justice Holmes finally ruled in 1922 the sport was not "interstate commerce."

CLUB STANDINGS YEAR-BY-YEAR

CLUB STANDINGS YEAR-BY-YEAR
F indicates where club finished at end of season. x indicates did not finish season. t indicates finished in a tie for this position. p indicates playoff used to break tie at end of scheduled season.

1871—NATIONAL ASSOCIATION

CLUB	F	W	L	PCT	MGR
ATH	1	22	7	.759	Hayhurst
CHI	2	20	9	.690	Foley
BOS	3	22	10	.688	Wright
OLY	4	16	15	.516	Young
HAY	5	15	15	500	Pike Craver
MUT	6	16	18	.471	Ferguson
CLE	7	10	19	.345	Pabor
KEK	8x	7	21	.250	Deane Lennon
ROK	9	6	20	.231	Waldo

1872—NATIONAL ASSOCIATION

CLUB	F	W	L	PCT	MGR
BOS	1	38	8	.826	Wright
ATH	2	31	15	.674	Hayhurst
L BAL	3	35	19	.648	Henderson
MUT	4	35	21	.625	Pearce
HAY	5x	15	10	.600	Wood
CLE	6x	6	15	.286	Hastings
ATL	7	9	28	.243	Ferguson
OLY	8x	2	7	.222	Young
MAN	9x	5	19	.208	Putnam
ECK	10	3	26	.103	Clinton Wood
NAT	11x	0	11	.000	Miller

1873—NATIONAL ASSOCIATION

CLUB	F	W	L	PCT	MGR
BOS	1	43	16	.729	Wright
PHI	2	36	16	.692	Young, G.
L BAL	3	34	22	.607	Henderson
ATH	4	28	23	.549	Hayhurst
MUT	5	29	25	.537	Cammeyer
ATL	6	17	37	.315	Ferguson
NAT	7	8	31	.205	Young, N.
RES	8x	2	21	.087	Benjamin
MAR	9x	0	6	.000	Smith

1874—NATIONAL ASSOCIATION

CLUB	F	W	L	PCT	MGR
BOS	1	52	18	.743	Wright
MUT	2	42	23	.646	Higham
ATH	3	33	22	.600	Hayhurst
PHI	4	29	29	.500	Craver
CHI	5	28	31	.475	Young, N.
ATL	6	23	32	.418	Ferguson
HAR	7	15	38	.283	Pike
L BAL	8	9	38	.191	Henderson

1875—NATIONAL ASSOCIATION

CLUB	F	W	L	PCT	MGR
BOS	1	71	8	.899	Wright
ATH	2	53	20	.726	Hayhurst
HAR	3	54	28	.659	Ferguson
ST.L	4	37	28	.569	Graffen
PHI	5	37	31	.544	Young, G
MUT	6	31	38	.449	Hicks
CHI	7	30	37	.448	Wood
RS	8x	4	15	.211	Sweazy
NAT	9x	5	23	.179	Childs
N H	10	7	40	.149	Gould
CEN	11x	2	12	.143	Craver
WES	12x	1	12	.077	Trimble
ATL	13	2	42	.045	Pabor

1876—NATIONAL LEAGUE

CLUB	F	W	L	PCT	MGR
CHI	1	52	14	.788	Spalding
St. L	2	45	19	.703	Graffen
HAR	3	47	21	.691	Ferguson
BOS	4	39	31	.557	Wright, W.
LOU	5	30	36	.455	Fulmer
MUT	6	21	35	.375	Cammeyer
ATH	7	14	45	.237	Wright, A.
CIN	8	9	56	.135	Gould

1877—NATIONAL LEAGUE

CLUB	F	W	L	PCT	MGR
BOS	1	42	18	.700	Wright
LOU	2	35	25	.583	Chapman
HAR	3	31	27	.534	Ferguson
ST.L	4	28	32	.467	Lucas McManus
CHI	5	26	33	.441	Spalding
CIN	6	15	42	.263	Pike Addy

1878—NATIONAL LEAGUE

CLUB	F	W	L	PCT	MGR
BOS	1	41	19	.683	Wright
CIN	2	37	23	.617	McVey
PRO	3	33	27	.550	Ware
CHI	4	30	30	.500	Ferguson
IND	5	24	36	.400	Clapp
MIL	6	15	45	.250	Chapman

1879—NATIONAL LEAGUE

CLUB	F	W	L	PCT	MGR
PRO	1	55	23	.705	Wright, G.
BOS	2	49	29	.628	Wright, W.
BUF	3t	44	32	.579	McGunnigle
CHI	3t	44	32	.579	Anson
CIN	5	38	36	.514	White, J. L. McVey
SYR	6x	15	27	.357	Smith
CLE	7	24	53	.312	McCormick
TRO	8	19	56	.253	Ferguson

1880—NATIONAL LEAGUE

CLUB	F	W	L	PCT	MGR
CHI	1	67	17	.798	Anson
PRO	2	52	32	.619	Bullock
CLE	3	47	37	.559	McCormick
TRO	4	41	42	.494	Ferguson
WOR	5	40	43	.482	Bancroft Brown
BOS	6	40	44	.476	Wright, W
BUF	7	24	58	.293	McGunningle Crane
CIN	8	21	59	.263	Clapp

1881—NATIONAL LEAGUE

CLUB	F	W	L	PCT	MGR
CHI	1	56	28	.667	Anson
PRO	2	47	37	.559	Bullock Morrow
BUF	3	45	38	.542	O'Rourke
DET	4	41	43	.488	Bancroft
TRO	5	39	45	.464	Ferguson
BOS	6	38	45	.458	Wright, W
CLE	7	36	48	.429	McCormick
WOR	8	32	50	.390	Brown

1882—NATIONAL LEAGUE

CLUB	F	W	L	PCT	MGR
CHI	1	55	29	.655	Anson
PRO	2	52	32	.619	Wright, W
BOS	3t	45	39	.536	Morrill
BUF	3t	45	39	.536	O'Rourke
CLE	5	42	40	.512	Evans
DET	6	42	41	.506	Bancroft
TRO	7	35	48	.422	Ferguson
WOR	8	18	66	.214	Brown Bond Chapman

1882—AMERICAN ASSOCIATION

CLUB	F	W	L	PCT	MGR
CIN	1	54	26	.675	Fulmer
ECL	2	44	35	.557	Dyler Reccius Maskrey
ATH	3	40	35	.533	Sharsig Mason
ALL	4	39	39	.500	Pratt
ST.L	5	36	43	.456	Cuthbert Sullivan
BAL	6	19	54	.260	Myers

1883—NATIONAL LEAGUE

CLUB	F	W	L	PCT	MGR
BOS	1	63	35	.643	Burdock Morrill
CHI	2	59	39	.602	Anson
PRO	3	58	40	.592	Wright, W
CLE	4	55	42	.567	Bancroft
BUF	5	52	45	.536	O'Rourke
N Y	6	46	50	.479	Clapp
DET	7	40	58	.408	Chapman
PHI	8	17	81	.173	Ferguson

1883—AMERICAN ASSOCIATION

CLUB	F	W	L	PCT	MGR
ATH	1	66	32	.673	Knight Mason Sharsig
St. L	2	65	33	.663	Sullivan Comiskey
CIN	3	62	36	.633	Snyder
MET	4	54	42	.563	Mutrie
ECL	5	52	45	.536	Reccius Maskrey Gerhardt
COL	6	32	65	.330	Phillips
ALL	7	30	68	.306	Pratt Butler Battin
BAL	8	28	68	.292	Barnie

1884—NATIONAL LEAGUE

CLUB	F	W	L	PCT	MGR
PRO	1	84	28	.750	Bancroft
BOS	2	73	38	.658	Morrill
BUF	3	64	47	.577	O'Rourke
CHI	4t	62	50	.554	Anson
N Y	4t	62	50	.554	Price
PHI	6	39	73	.348	Wright, W
CLE	7	35	77	.313	Hackett
DET	8	28	84	.250	Chapman

1884—AMERICAN ASSOCIATION

CLUB	F	W	L	PCT	MGR
MET	1	75	32	.701	Mutrie
COL	2	69	39	.639	Schmelz
ECL	3	68	40	.630	Gerhardt Walsh
St. L	4	67	40	.626	Williams Von der Ahe
CIN	5	68	41	.624	Snyder White
BAL	6	63	43	.594	Barnie
ATH	7	61	46	.570	Mason Sharsig
TOL	8	46	58	.442	Morton
BRO	9	40	64	.385	Taylor
VIR	10	12	30	.286	Moses
ALL	11	30	78	.278	Battin Creamer Ferguson McKnight Phillips
IND	12	29	78	.271	Gifford Watkins
NAT	13x	12	51	.190	Hollingshead

1884—UNION ASSOCIATION

CLUB	F	W	L	PCT	MGR
St. L	1	91	16	.850	Sullivan
					Dunlap
MIL	2x	8	3	.727	McKee
CIN	3	68	35	.660	O'Leary
					Crane
BAL	4	56	48	.538	Levis
					Henderson
BOS	5	58	51	.532	Murnane
					Furniss
					Morse
CHI	6x	33	35	.485	Hengle
NAT	7	47	66	.416	Scanlon
PIT	8x	7	10	.412	Battin
					Ellick
KEY	9x	21	46	.313	Malone
					Pratt
St. P	10	2	6	.250	Thompson
ALT	11x	6	19	.240	Curtis
K C	12	14	63	.182	Sullivan
WIL	13x	2	15	.118	Simmons

1885—NATIONAL LEAGUE

CLUB	F	W	L	PCT	MGR
CHI	1	87	25	.776	Anson
N Y	2	85	27	.758	Mutrie
PHI	3	56	54	.509	Wright, W
PRO	4	53	57	.481	Bancroft
BOS	5	46	66	.410	Morrill
DET	6	41	67	.379	Morton
					Watkins
BUF	7	38	74	.339	Chapman
					Hughson
					Galvin
St. L	8	36	72	.333	Dunlap
					Fine
					Lucas

1885—AMERICAN ASSOCIATION

CLUB	F	W	L	PCT	MGR
St. L	1	79	33	.705	Comiskey
CIN	2	63	49	.563	Caylor
ALL	3	56	55	.505	Phillips
ATH	4	55	57	.491	Knight
					Mason
					Sharsig
BRO	5t	53	59	.473	Doyle
					Hackett
					Byrne
ECL	5t	53	59	.473	Hart
MET	7	44	64	.407	Gifford
BAL	8	41	68	.376	Barnie

1886—NATIONAL LEAGUE

CLUB	F	W	L	PCT	MGR
CHI	1	90	34	.725	Anson
DET	2	87	36	.707	Watkins
N Y	3	75	44	.630	Mutrie
PHI	4	71	43	.622	Wright, W
BOS	5	56	61	.478	Morrill
St. L	6	43	79	.352	Schmelz
K C	7	30	91	.247	Rowe
WAS	8	28	92	.233	Scanlon
					Gaffney

1886—AMERICAN ASSOCIATION

CLUB	F	W	L	PCT	MGR
ST.L	1	93	46	.669	Comiskey
ALL	2	80	57	.584	Phillips
BRO	3	76	61	.555	Byrne
ECL	4	66	70	.485	Hart
CIN	5	65	72	.471	Caylor
ATH	6	63	73	.467	Simmons
					Mason
					Sharsig
MET	7	53	82	.393	Gifford
					Ferguson
BAL	8	48	83	.366	Barnie

1887—NATIONAL LEAGUE

CLUB	F	W	L	PCT	MGR
DET	1	79	45	.637	Watkins
PHI	2	75	48	.610	Wright, W
CHI	3	71	50	.587	Anson
N Y	4	68	55	.553	Mutrie
BOS	5	61	60	.504	Morrill
PIT	6	55	69	.444	Phillips
WAS	7	46	76	.377	Gaffney
					Dennis
IND	8	37	89	.294	Fogel
					Burnham
					Thomas

1887—AMERICAN ASSOCIATION

CLUB	F	W	L	PCT	MGR
ST.L	1	95	40	.704	Comiskey
CIN	2	81	54	.600	Schmelz
BAL	3	77	58	.570	Barnie
ECL	4	76	60	.559	Kelly
ATH	5	64	69	.481	Bancroft
					Mason
					Sharsig
BRO	6	60	74	.448	Byrne
MET	7	44	89	.331	Ferguson
					Caylor
					Orr
CLE	8	39	92	.298	Williams

1888—NATIONAL LEAGUE

CLUB	F	W	L	PCT	MGR
N Y	1	84	47	.641	Mutrie
CHI	2	77	58	.578	Anson
PHI	3	69	61	.531	Wright, W
BOS	4	70	64	.522	Morrill
DET	5	68	63	.519	Watkins
					Leadley
PIT	6	66	68	.493	Phillips
IND	7	50	85	.370	Spence
WAS	8	48	86	.358	Hewitt
					Sullivan
					Whitney

1888—AMERICAN ASSOCIATION

CLUB	F	W	L	PCT	MGR
ST.L	1	92	43	.681	Comiskey
BRO	2	88	52	.629	McGunnigle
ATH	3	81	52	.609	Sharsig
CIN	4	80	54	.597	Schmelz
BAL	5	57	80	.416	Barnie
CLE	6	50	82	.378	Williams
					Loftus
ECL	7	48	87	.360	Kerins
					Davidson
K C	8	43	89	.326	Rowe
					Barkley
					Watkins

1889—NATIONAL LEAGUE

CLUB	F	W	L	PCT	MGR
N Y	1	83	43	.659	Mutrie
BOS	2	83	45	.648	Hart
CHI	3	67	65	.508	Anson
PHI	4	63	64	.496	Wright, W
PIT	5	61	71	.462	Phillips
					Dunlap
					Hanlon
CLE	6	61	72	.459	Loftus
IND	7	59	75	.440	Bancroft
					Glasscock
WAS	8	41	83	.331	Morrill
					Irwin

1889—AMERICAN ASSOCIATION

CLUB	F	W	L	PCT	MGR
BRO	1	93	44	.679	McGunnigle
ST.L	2	90	45	.667	Comiskey
ATH	3	75	58	.564	Sharsig
CIN	4	76	63	.547	Schmelz
BAL	5	70	65	.519	Barnie
COL	6	60	78	.435	Buckenberger

(Continued)

1889-American Association (Cont.)

CLUB	F	W	L	PCT	MGR
K C	7	55	82	.401	Watkins
					Manning
ECL	8	27	111	.195	Davidson
					Brown
					Means
					McKinney
					Shannon
					Wolf
					Chapman

1890—NATIONAL LEAGUE

CLUB	F	W	L	PCT	MGR
BRO	1	86	43	.667	McGunnigle
CHI	2	83	53	.610	Anson
PHI	3	78	53	.595	Wright, W
CIN	4	78	55	.586	Loftus
BOS	5	76	57	.571	Selee
N Y	6	63	68	.481	Mutrie
CLE	7	44	88	.333	Schmelz
					Leadley
PIT	8	23	114	.168	Hecker

1890—AMERICAN ASSOCIATION

CLUB	F	W	L	PCT	MGR
ECL	1	88	44	.667	Chapman
COL	2	79	55	.590	Buckenberger
					Sullivan
					Schmelz
ST.L	3	78	58	.574	McCarthy
					Roseman
					Campau
TOL	4	68	64	.515	Morton
ROC	5	63	63	.500	Powers
BAL	6	15	19	.441	Barnie
SYR	7	55	72	.433	Fessenden
					Frazer
ATH	8	54	78	.409	Sharsig
BRO	9x	26	73	.263	Kennedy

1890—PLAYERS' LEAGUE

CLUB	F	W	L	PCT	MGR
BOS	1	81	48	.628	Kelly
BRO	2	76	56	.576	Ward
N Y	3	74	57	.565	Ewing
CHI	4	75	62	.547	Comiskey
PHI	5	68	63	.519	Hilt
					Fogarty
					Buffinton
PIT	6	60	68	.469	Hanlon
CLE	7	55	75	.423	Faatz
					Larkin
					Tebeau
BUF	8	36	96	.273	Rowe

1891—NATIONAL LEAGUE

CLUB	F	W	L	PCT	MGR
BOS	1	87	51	.630	Selee
CHI	2	82	53	.607	Anson
N Y	3	71	61	.538	Mutrie
PHI	4	68	69	.496	Wright, W
CLE	5	65	74	.468	Leadley
					Tebeau
BRO	6	61	76	.445	Ward
CIN	7	56	81	.409	Loftus
PIT	8	55	80	.407	Hanlon
					McGunnigle

1891—AMERICAN ASSOCIATION

CLUB	F	W	L	PCT	MGR
BOS	1	93	42	.689	Irwin
ST.L	2	86	52	.623	Comiskey
MIL	3	21	15	.583	Cushman
BAL	4	71	64	.526	Barnie
					Van Haltren
ATH	5	73	66	.525	Sharsig
					Wood
					Barnie
COL	6	61	76	.445	Schmelz
CIN	7x	43	57	.430	Kelly
ECL	8	55	84	.396	Chapman
WAS	9	44	91	.326	Trott
					Snyder
					Shannon
					Griffin

1892—NATIONAL LEAGUE

CLUB	F	W	L	PCT	MGR
BOS	1	102	48	.680	Selee
CLE	2	93	56	.624	Tebeau
BRO	3	95	59	.617	Ward
PHI	4	87	66	.569	Wright, W
CIN	5	82	68	.547	Comiskey
PIT	6	80	73	.523	Burns
					Buckenberger
CHI	7	70	76	.479	Anson
N Y	8	71	80	.470	Powers
LOU	9	63	89	.414	Pfeffer
					Chapman
WAS	10	58	93	.384	Barnie
					Irwin
					Richardson
					Wagner
ST.L	11	56	94	.373	Von der Ahe
BAL	12	46	101	.313	Van Haltren
					Waltz
					Hanlon

1893—NATIONAL LEAGUE

CLUB	F	W	L	PCT	MGR
BOS	1	86	44	.662	Selee
PIT	2	81	48	.628	Buckenberger
CLE	3	73	55	.570	Tebeau
PHI	4	72	57	.558	Wright, W
N Y	5	68	64	.515	Ward
BRO	6t	65	63	.508	Foutz
CIN	6t	65	63	.508	Comiskey
BAL	8	60	70	.462	Hanlon
CHI	9	57	71	.445	Anson
ST.L	10	57	75	.432	Watkins
LOU	11	50	75	.400	Barnie
WAS	12	40	89	.310	Wagner
					O'Rourke

1894—NATIONAL LEAGUE

CLUB	F	W	L	PCT	MGR
BAL	1	89	39	.695	Hanlon
N Y	2	88	44	.667	Ward
BOS	3	83	49	.629	Selee
PHI	4	71	56	.559	Irwin
BRO	5	70	61	.534	Foutz
CLE	6	68	61	.527	Tebeau
PIT	7	65	65	.500	Buckenberger
					Mack
CHI	8	57	75	.432	Anson
ST.L	9	56	76	.424	Miller
CIN	10	54	75	.419	Comiskey
WAS	11	45	87	.341	Schmelz
LOU	12	36	94	.277	Barnie

1895—NATIONAL LEAGUE

CLUB	F	W	L	PCT	MGR
BAL	1	87	43	.669	Hanlon
CLE	2	84	46	.646	Tebeau
PHI	3	78	53	.595	Irwin
CHI	4	72	58	.554	Anson
BOS	5t	71	60	.542	Selee
BRO	5t	71	60	.542	Foutz
PIT	7	71	61	.538	Mack
CIN	8	66	64	.508	Ewing
N Y	9	66	65	.504	Davis
					Doyle
					Watkins
WAS	10	43	85	.336	Schmelz
ST.L	11	39	92	.298	Buckenberger
					Quinn
					Phelan
					Von der Ahe
LOU	12	35	96	.267	McCloskey

1896—NATIONAL LEAGUE

CLUB	F	W	L	PCT	MGR
BAL	1	90	39	.698	Hanlon
CLE	2	80	48	.625	Tebeau
CIN	3	77	50	.606	Ewing
BOS	4	74	57	.565	Selee
CHI	5	71	57	.555	Anson
PIT	6	66	63	.512	Mack
N Y	7	64	67	.489	Irwin
					Joyce

(Continued)

1896-National League (Cont.)

CLUB	F	W	L	PCT	MGR
PHI	8	62	68	.477	Nash
BRO	9t	58	73	.443	Foutz
WAS	9t	58	73	.443	Schmelz
ST.L	11	40	90	.306	Diddlebock
					Latham
					Conner
					Dowd
LOU	12	38	93	.290	McCloskey
					McGunnigle

1897—NATIONAL LEAGUE

CLUB	F	W	L	PCT	MGR
BOS	1	93	39	.705	Selee
BAL	2	90	40	.693	Hanlon
N Y	3	83	48	.634	Joyce
CIN	4	76	56	.576	Ewing
CLE	5	69	62	.527	Tebeau
BRO	6t	61	71	.462	Barnie
WAS	6t	61	71	.462	Schmelz
					Brown
PIT	8	60	71	.458	Donovan
CHI	9	59	73	.447	Anson
PHI	10	55	77	.417	Stallings
LOU	11	52	78	.400	Rogers
					Clarke
ST.L	12	29	102	.221	Dowd
					Nicol
					Hallman
					Von der Ahe

1898—NATIONAL LEAGUE

CLUB	F	W	L	PCT	MGR
BOS	1	102	47	.685	Selee
BAL	2	96	53	.644	Hanlon
CIN	3	92	60	.605	Ewing
CHI	4	85	65	.567	Burns
CLE	5	81	68	.544	Tebeau
PHI	6	78	71	.523	Stallings
					Shettsline
N Y	7	77	73	.513	Joyce
					Anson
PIT	8	72	76	.486	Watkins
LOU	9	70	81	.464	Clarke
BRO	10	54	91	.372	Barnie
					Griffin
					Ebbets
WAS	11	51	101	.336	Brown
					Doyle
					McGuire
					Irwin
ST.L	12	39	111	.260	Hurst

1899—NATIONAL LEAGUE

CLUB	F	W	L	PCT	MGR
BRO	1	88	42	.677	Hanlon
BOS	2	95	57	.625	Selee
PHI	3	94	58	.618	Shettsline
BAL	4	84	58	.592	McGraw
ST.L	5	83	66	.557	Tebeau
CIN	6	83	67	.553	Ewing
PIT	7	76	73	.510	Watkins
					Donovan
CHI	8	75	73	.507	Burns
LOU	9	75	77	.493	Clarke
N Y	10	60	86	.411	Day
					Hoey
WAS	11	53	95	.358	Irwin
CLE	12	20	134	.129	Cross
					Quinn

1900—NATIONAL LEAGUE

CLUB	F	W	L	PCT	MGR
BRO	1	82	54	.603	Hanlon
PIT	2	79	60	.568	Clarke
PHI	3	75	63	.543	Shettsline
BOS	4	66	72	.478	Selee
CHI	5t	65	75	.464	Loftus
ST.L	5t	65	75	.464	Tebeau
					Heilbroner
CIN	7	62	77	.446	Allen
N Y	8	60	78	.435	Ewing
					Davis

1901—NATIONAL LEAGUE

CLUB	F	W	L	PCT	MGR
PIT	1	90	49	.647	Clarke
PHI	2	83	57	.593	Shettsline'
BRO	3	79	57	.581	Hanlon
ST.L	4	76	64	.543	Donovan
BOS	5	69	69	.500	Selee
CHI	6	53	86	.381	Loftus
N Y	7	52	85	.380	Davis
CIN	8	52	87	.374	McPhee

1901—AMERICAN LEAGUE

CLUB	F	W	L	PCT	MGR
CHI	1	83	53	.610	Griffith
BOS	2	79	57	.581	Collins
DET	3	74	61	.548	Stallings
PHI	4	74	62	.544	Mack
BAL	5	68	65	.511	McGraw
WAS	6	61	72	.459	Manning
CLE	7	54	82	.397	McAleer
MIL	8	48	89	.350	Duffy

1902—NATIONAL LEAGUE

CLUB	F	W	L	PCT	MGR
PIT	1	103	36	.741	Clarke
BRO	2	75	63	.543	Hanlon
BOS	3	73	64	.533	Buckenberger
CIN	4	70	70	.500	McPhee
					Bancroft
					Kelley
CHI	5	68	69	.496	Selee
ST.L	6	56	78	.418	Donovan
PHI	7	56	81	.409	Shettsline
N Y	8	48	88	.353	Fogel
					Smith
					McGraw

1902—AMERICAN LEAGUE

CLUB	F	W	L	PCT	MGR
PHI	1	83	53	.610	Mack
ST.L	2	78	58	.574	McAleer
BOS	3	77	60	.562	Collins
CHI	4	74	60	.552	Griffith
CLE	5	69	67	.507	Armour
WAS	6	61	75	.449	Loftus
DET	7	52	83	.385	Dwyer
BAL	8	50	88	.362	McGraw
					Robinson

1903—NATIONAL LEAGUE

CLUB	F	W	L	PCT	MGR
PIT	1	91	49	.650	Clarke
N Y	2	84	55	.604	McGraw
CHI	3	82	56	.594	Selee
CIN	4	74	65	.532	Kelley
BRO	5	70	66	.515	Hanlon
BOS	6	58	80	.420	Buckenberger
PHI	7	49	86	.363	Zimmer
ST.L	8	43	94	.314	Donovan

1903—AMERICAN LEAGUE

CLUB	F	W	L	PCT	MGR
BOS	1	91	47	.659	Collins
PHI	2	75	60	.556	Mack
CLE	3	77	63	.550	Armour
N Y	4	72	62	.537	Griffith
DET	5	65	71	.478	Barrow
ST.L	6	65	74	.468	McAleer
CHI	7	60	77	.438	Callahan
WAS	8	43	94	.314	Loftus

1904—NATIONAL LEAGUE

CLUB	F	W	L	PCT	MGR
N Y	1	106	47	.693	McGraw
CHI	2	93	60	.608	Selee
CIN	3	88	65	.575	Kelley
PIT	4	87	66	.569	Clarke
ST.L	5	75	79	.487	Nichols
BRO	6	56	97	.366	Hanlon
BOS	7	55	98	.360	Buckenberger
PHI	8	52	100	.342	Duffy

1904—AMERICAN LEAGUE

CLUB	F	W	L	PCT	MGR
BOS	1	95	59	.617	Collins
N Y	2	92	59	.609	Griffith
CHI	3	89	65	.578	Callahan
					Jones
CLE	4	86	65	.570	Armour
PHI	5	81	70	.536	Mack
ST.L	6	65	87	.428	McAleer
DET	7	62	90	.408	Barrow
					Lowe
WAS	8	38	113	.251	Kittredge
					Donovan

1905—NATIONAL LEAGUE

CLUB	F	W	L	PCT	MGR
N Y	1	105	48	.686	McGraw
PIT	2	96	57	.627	Clarke
CHI	3	92	61	.601	Selee
					Chance
PHI	4	83	69	.546	Duffy
CIN	5	79	74	.516	Kelley
ST.L	6	58	96	.377	Nichols
					Burke
					Robison
BOS	7	51	103	.331	Tenney
BRO	8	48	104	.316	Hanlon

1905—AMERICAN LEAGUE

CLUB	F	W	L	PCT	MGR
PHI	1	92	56	.621	Mack
CHI	2	92	60	.605	Jones
DET	3	79	74	.516	Armour
BOS	4	78	74	.513	Collins
CLE	5	76	78	.494	Lajoie
N Y	6	71	78	.477	Griffith
WAS	7	64	87	.421	Stahl
ST.L	8	54	99	.354	McAleer

1906—NATIONAL LEAGUE

CLUB	F	W	L	PCT	MGR
CHI	1	116	36	.763	Chance
N Y	2	96	56	.632	McGraw
PIT	3	93	60	.608	Clarke
PHI	4	71	82	.464	Duffy
BRO	5	66	86	.434	Donovan
CIN	6	64	87	.424	Hanlon
ST.L	7	52	98	.347	McCloskey
BOS	8	49	102	.324	Tenney

1906—AMERICAN LEAGUE

CLUB	F	W	L	PCT	MGR
CHI	1	93	58	.616	Jones
N Y	2	90	61	.596	Griffith
CLE	3	89	64	.582	Lajoie
PHI	4	78	67	.538	Mack
ST.L	5	76	73	.510	McAleer
DET	6	71	78	.477	Armour
WAS	7	55	95	.367	Stahl, G.
BOS	8	49	105	.318	Collins
					Stahl, C.

1907—NATIONAL LEAGUE

CLUB	F	W	L	PCT	MGR
CHI	1	107	45	.704	Chance
PIT	2	91	63	.591	Clarke
PHI	3	83	64	.566	Murray
N Y	4	82	71	.536	McGraw
BRO	5	65	83	.439	Donovan
CIN	6	66	87	.431	Hanlon
BOS	7	58	90	.392	Tenney
ST.L	8	52	101	.340	McCloskey

1907—AMERICAN LEAGUE

CLUB	F	W	L	PCT	MGR
DET	1	92	58	.613	Jennings
PHI	2	88	57	.607	Mack
CHI	3	87	64	.576	Jones
CLE	4	85	67	.559	Lajoie
N Y	5	70	78	.473	Griffith

(Continued)

1907-American League (Cont.)

CLUB	F	W	L	PCT	MGR
ST.L	6	69	83	.454	McAleer
BOS	7	59	90	.396	Young
					Huff
					Unglaub
					McGuire
WAS	8	49	102	.325	Cantillon

1908—NATIONAL LEAGUE

CLUB	F	W	L	PCT	MGR
CHI	1	99	55	.643	Chance
N Y	2t	98	56	.636	McGraw
PIT	2t	98	56	.636	Clarke
PHI	4	83	71	.539	Murray
CIN	5	73	81	.474	Ganzel
BOS	6	63	91	.409	Kelley
BRO	7	53	101	.344	Donovan
ST.L	8	49	105	.318	McCloskey

1908—AMERICAN LEAGUE

CLUB	F	W	L	PCT	MGR
DET	1	90	63	.588	Jennings
CLE	2	90	64	.584	Lajoie
CHI	3	88	64	.579	Jones
ST.L	4	83	69	.546	McAleer
BOS	5	75	79	.487	McGuire
					Lake
PHI	6	68	85	.444	Mack
WAS	7	67	85	.441	Cantillon
N Y	8	51	103	.331	Griffith
					Elberfeld

1909—NATIONAL LEAGUE

CLUB	F	W	L	PCT	MGR
PIT	1	110	42	.724	Clarke
CHI	2	104	49	.680	Chance
N Y	3	92	61	.601	McGraw
CIN	4	77	76	.504	Griffith
PHI	5	74	79	.484	Murray
BRO	6	55	98	.359	Lumley
ST.L	7	54	98	.355	Bresnahan
BOS	8	45	108	.294	Bowernam
					Smith

1909—AMERICAN LEAGUE

CLUB	F	W	L	PCT	MGR
DET	1	98	54	.645	Jennings
PHI	2	95	58	.621	Mack
BOS	3	88	63	.583	Lake
CHI	4	78	74	.513	Sullivan
N Y	5	74	77	.490	Stallings
CLE	6	71	82	.464	Lajoie
					McGuire
ST.L	7	61	89	.407	McAleer
					O'Connor
WAS	8	42	110	.276	Cantillon

1910—NATIONAL LEAGUE

CLUB	F	W	L	PCT	MGR
CHI	1	104	50	.676	Chance
N Y	2	91	63	.591	McGraw
PIT	3	86	67	.562	Clarke
PHI	4	78	75	.510	Dooin
CIN	5	75	79	.487	Griffith
BRO	6	64	90	.416	Dahlen
ST.L	7	63	90	.412	Bresnahan
BOS	8	53	100	.346	Lake

1910—AMERICAN LEAGUE

CLUB	F	W	L	PCT	MGR
PHI	1	102	48	.680	Mack
N Y	2	88	63	.583	Stallings
					Chase
DET	3	86	68	.558	Jennings
BOS	4	81	72	.529	Donovan
CLE	5	71	81	.467	McGuire
CHI	6	68	85	.444	Duffy
WAS	7	66	85	.437	McAleer
ST.L	8	47	107	.305	O'Connor

1911—NATIONAL LEAGUE

CLUB	F	W	L	PCT	MGR
N Y	1	99	54	.647	McGraw
CHI	2	92	62	.597	Chance
PIT	3	85	69	.552	Clarke
PHI	4	79	73	.520	Dooin
ST.L	5	75	74	.503	Bresnahan
CIN	6	70	83	.458	Griffith
BRO	7	64	86	.427	Dahlen
BOS	8	44	107	.291	Tenney

1911—AMERICAN LEAGUE

CLUB	F	W	L	PCT	MGR
PHI	1	101	50	.669	Mack
DET	2	89	65	.578	Jennings
CLE	3	80	73	.523	McGuire
					Stovall
CHI	4	77	74	.5099	Duffy
BOS	5	78	75	.5098	Donovan
N Y	6	76	76	.500	Chase
WAS	7	64	90	.416	McAleer
ST.L	8	45	107	.296	Wallace

1912—NATIONAL LEAGUE

CLUB	F	W	L	PCT	MGR
N Y	1	103	48	.682	McGraw
PIT	2	93	58	.616	Clarke
CHI	3	91	59	.607	Chance
CIN	4	75	78	.490	O'Day
PHI	5	73	79	.480	Dooin
ST.L	6	63	90	.412	Bresnahan
BRO	7	58	95	.379	Dahlen
BOS	8	52	101	.340	Kling

1912—AMERICAN LEAGUE

CLUB	F	W	L	PCT	MGR
BOS	1	105	47	.691	Stahl
WAS	2	91	61	.599	Griffith
PHI	3	90	62	.592	Mack
CHI	4	78	76	.506	Callahan
CLE	5	75	78	.490	Davis
					Birmingham
DET	6	69	84	.451	Jennings
ST.L	7	53	101	.344	Wallace
					Stovall
N Y	8	50	102	.329	Wolverton

1913—NATIONAL LEAGUE

CLUB	F	W	L	PCT	MGR
N Y	1	101	51	.664	McGraw
PHI	2	88	63	.583	Dooin
CHI	3	88	65	.575	Evers
PIT	4	78	71	.523	Clarke
BOS	5	69	82	.457	Stallings
BRO	6	65	84	.436	Dahlen
CIN	7	64	89	.418	Tinker
ST.L	8	51	99	.340	Huggins

1913—AMERICAN LEAGUE

CLUB	F	W	L	PCT	MGR
PHI	1	96	57	.627	Mack
WAS	2	90	64	.584	Griffith
CLE	3	86	66	.566	Birmingham
BOS	4	79	71	.527	Stahl
					Carrigan
CHI	5	78	74	.513	Callahan
DET	6	66	87	.431	Jennings
N Y	7	57	94	.377	Chance
ST.L	8	57	96	.373	Stovall
					Austin
					Rickey

1914—NATIONAL LEAGUE

CLUB	F	W	L	PCT	MGR
BOS	1	94	59	.614	Stallings
N Y	2	84	70	.545	McGraw
ST.L	3	81	72	.529	Huggins
CHI	4	78	76	.506	O'Day
BRO	5	75	79	.487	Robinson
PHI	6	74	80	.481	Dooin
PIT	7	69	85	.448	Clarke
CIN	8	60	94	.390	Herzog

1914—AMERICAN LEAGUE

CLUB	F	W	L	PCT	MGR
PHI	1	99	53	.651	Mack
BOS	2	91	62	.595	Carrigan
WAS	3	81	73	.526	Griffith
DET	4	80	73	.523	Jennings
ST.L	5	71	82	.464	Rickey
CHI	6t	70	84	.455	Callahan
N Y	6t	70	84	.455	Chance, Peckinpaugh
CLE	8	51	102	.333	Birmingham

1914—FEDERAL LEAGUE

CLUB	F	W	L	PCT	MGR
IND	1	88	65	.575	Phillips
CHI	2	87	67	.565	Tinker
BAL	3	84	69	.549	Knabe
BUF	4	80	71	.530	Schlafly
BRO	5	77	77	.500	Bradley
K C	6	69	84	.451	Stovall
PIT	7	64	88	.421	Gessler, Oakes
ST.L	8	61	89	.407	Brown, Jones

1915—NATIONAL LEAGUE

CLUB	F	W	L	PCT	MGR
PHI	1	90	62	.592	Moran
BOS	2	83	69	.546	Stallings
BRO	3	80	72	.527	Robinson
CHI	4	73	80	.477	Bresnahan
PIT	5	73	81	.474	Clarke
ST.L	6	72	81	.471	Huggins
CIN	7	71	83	.461	Herzog
N Y	8	69	83	.454	McGraw

1915—AMERICAN LEAGUE

CLUB	F	W	L	PCT	MGR
BOS	1	101	50	.669	Carrigan
DET	2	100	54	.649	Jennings
CHI	3	93	61	.604	Rowland
WAS	4	85	68	.556	Griffith
N Y	5	69	83	.454	Donovan
ST.L	6	63	91	.409	Rickey
CLE	7	57	95	.375	Birmingham, Fohl
PHI	8	43	109	.283	Mack

1915—FEDERAL LEAGUE

CLUB	F	W	L	PCT	MGR
CHI	1	86	66	.566	Tinker
ST.L	2	87	67	.565	Jones
PIT	3	86	67	.562	Oakes
K C	4	81	72	.533	Stovall
NEW	5	80	72	.526	Phillips, McKechnie
BUF	6	74	78	.487	Schlafly, Blair, Lord
BRO	7	70	82	.461	Magee, Ganzel
BAL	8	47	107	.305	Knabe

1916—NATIONAL LEAGUE

CLUB	F	W	L	PCT	MGR
BRO	1	94	60	.610	Robinson
PHI	2	91	62	.595	Moran
BOS	3	89	63	.586	Stallings
N Y	4	86	66	.566	McGraw
CHI	5	67	86	.438	Tinker
PIT	6	65	89	.422	Callahan
CIN	7t	60	93	.392	Herzog, Wingo, Mathewson
ST.L	7t	60	93	.392	Huggins

1916—AMERICAN LEAGUE

CLUB	F	W	L	PCT	MGR
BOS	1	91	63	.591	Carrigan
CHI	2	89	65	.578	Rowland
DET	3	87	67	.565	Jennings
N Y	4	80	74	.519	Donovan
ST.L	5	79	75	.513	Jones
CLE	6	77	77	.500	Fohl
WAS	7	76	77	.497	Griffith
PHI	8	36	117	.235	Mack

1917—NATIONAL LEAGUE

CLUB	F	W	L	PCT	MGR
N Y	1	98	56	.636	McGraw
PHI	2	87	65	.572	Moran
ST.L	3	82	70	.539	Huggins
CIN	4	78	76	.506	Mathewson
CHI	5	74	80	.481	Mitchell
BOS	6	72	81	.471	Stallings
BRO	7	70	81	.464	Robinson
PIT	8	51	103	.331	Callahan, Wagner, Bezdek

1917—AMERICAN LEAGUE

CLUB	F	W	L	PCT	MGR
CHI	1	100	54	.649	Rowland
BOS	2	90	62	.592	Barry
CLE	3	88	66	.571	Fohl
DET	4	78	75	.510	Jennings
WAS	5	74	79	.484	Griffith
N Y	6	71	82	.464	Donovan
ST.L	7	57	97	.370	Jones
PHI	8	55	98	.359	Mack

1918—NATIONAL LEAGUE

CLUB	F	W	L	PCT	MGR
CHI	1	84	45	.651	Mitchell
N Y	2	71	53	.573	McGraw
CIN	3	68	60	.531	Mathewson, Groh
PIT	4	65	60	.520	Bezdek
BRO	5	57	69	.452	Robinson
PHI	6	55	68	.447	Moran
BOS	7	53	71	.427	Stallings
ST.L	8	51	78	.395	Hendricks

1918—AMERICAN LEAGUE

CLUB	F	W	L	PCT	MGR
BOS	1	75	51	.595	Barrow
CLE	2	73	54	.575	Fohl
WAS	3	72	56	.563	Griffith
N Y	4	60	63	.488	Huggins
ST.L	5	58	64	.475	Jones, Austin, Burke
CHI	6	57	67	.460	Rowland
DET	7	55	71	.437	Jennings
PHI	8	52	76	.402	Mack

1919—NATIONAL LEAGUE

CLUB	F	W	L	PCT	MGR
CIN	1	96	44	.686	Moran
N Y	2	87	53	.621	McGraw
CHI	3	75	65	.536	Mitchell
PIT	4	71	68	.511	Bezdek
BRO	5	69	71	.493	Robinson
BOS	6	57	82	.410	Stallings
ST.L	7	54	83	.394	Rickey
PHI	8	47	90	.343	Coombs, Cravath

1919—AMERICAN LEAGUE

CLUB	F	W	L	PCT	MGR
CHI	1	88	52	.629	Gleason
CLE	2	84	55	.604	Fohl, Speaker
N Y	3	80	59	.576	Huggins
DET	4	80	60	.571	Jennings
ST.L	5	67	72	.4820	Burke
BOS	6	66	71	.4817	Barrow
WAS	7	56	84	.400	Griffith
PHI	8	36	104	.257	Mack

1920—NATIONAL LEAGUE

CLUB	F	W	L	PCT	MGR
BRO	1	93	61	.604	Robinson
N Y	2	86	68	.558	McGraw
CIN	3	82	71	.536	Moran
PIT	4	79	75	.513	Gibson
CHI	5t	75	79	.487	Mitchell
ST.L	5t	75	79	.487	Rickey
BOS	7	62	90	.408	Stallings
PHI	8	62	91	.405	Cravath

1920—AMERICAN LEAGUE

CLUB	F	W	L	PCT	MGR
CLE	1	98	56	.636	Speaker
CHI	2	96	58	.623	Gleason
N Y	3	95	59	.617	Huggins
ST.L	4	76	77	.497	Burke
BOS	5	72	81	.471	Barrow
WAS	6	68	84	.447	Griffith
DET	7	61	93	.396	Jennings
PHI	8	48	106	.312	Mack

1921—NATIONAL LEAGUE

CLUB	F	W	L	PCT	MGR
N Y	1	94	59	.614	McGraw
PIT	2	90	63	.588	Gibson
ST.L	3	87	66	.569	Rickey
BOS	4	79	74	.516	Mitchell
BRO	5	77	75	.507	Robinson
CIN	6	70	83	.458	Moran
CHI	7	64	89	.418	Evers, Killefer
PHI	8	51	103	.331	Donovan, Wilhelm

1921—AMERICAN LEAGUE

CLUB	F	W	L	PCT	MGR
N Y	1	98	55	.641	Huggins
CLE	2	94	60	.610	Speaker
ST.L	3	81	73	.526	Fohl
WAS	4	80	73	.523	McBride
BOS	5	75	79	.487	Duffy
DET	6	71	82	.464	Cobb
CHI	7	62	92	.403	Gleason
PHI	8	53	100	.346	Mack

1922—NATIONAL LEAGUE

CLUB	F	W	L	PCT	MGR
N Y	1	93	61	.604	McGraw
CIN	2	86	68	.558	Moran
PIT	3t	85	69	.552	Gibson, McKechnie
ST.L	3t	85	69	.552	Rickey
CHI	5	80	74	.520	Killefer
BRO	6	76	78	.494	Robinson
PHI	7	57	96	.373	Wilhelm
BOS	8	53	100	.346	Mitchell

1922—AMERICAN LEAGUE

CLUB	F	W	L	PCT	MGR
N Y	1	94	60	.610	Huggins
ST.L	2	93	61	.604	Fohl
DET	3	79	75	.513	Cobb
CLE	4	78	76	.507	Speaker
CHI	5	77	77	.500	Gleason
WAS	6	69	85	.448	Milan
PHI	7	65	89	.422	Mack
BOS	8	61	93	.396	Duffy

1923—NATIONAL LEAGUE

CLUB	F	W	L	PCT	MGR
N Y	1	95	58	.621	McGraw
CIN	2	91	63	.591	Moran
PIT	3	87	67	.565	McKechnie
CHI	4	83	71	.539	Killefer
ST.L	5	79	74	.516	Rickey
BRO	6	76	78	.494	Robinson
BOS	7	54	100	.351	Mitchell
PHI	8	50	104	.325	Fletcher

1923—AMERICAN LEAGUE

CLUB	F	W	L	PCT	MGR
N Y	1	98	54	.645	Huggins
DET	2	83	71	.539	Cobb
CLE	3	82	71	.536	Speaker
WAS	4	75	78	.490	Bush
ST.L	5	74	78	.487	Fohl Austin
PHI	6	69	83	.454	Mack
CHI	7	69	85	.448	Gleason
BOS	8	61	91	.401	Chance

1924—NATIONAL LEAGUE

CLUB	F	W	L	PCT	MGR
N Y	1	93	60	.608	McGraw
BRO	2	92	62	.597	Robinson
PIT	3	90	63	.588	McKechnie
CIN	4	83	70	.542	Hendricks
CHI	5	81	72	.530	Killefer
ST.L	6	65	89	.422	Rickey
PHI	7	55	96	.364	Fletcher
BOS	8	53	100	.346	Bancroft

1924—AMERICAN LEAGUE

CLUB	F	W	L	PCT	MGR
WAS	1	92	62	.597	Harris
N Y	2	89	63	.586	Huggins
DET	3	86	68	.558	Cobb
ST.L	4	74	78	.487	Sisler
PHI	5	71	81	.467	Mack
CLE	6	67	86	.438	Speaker
BOS	7	67	87	.435	Fohl
CHI	8	66	87	.431	Evers

1925—NATIONAL LEAGUE

CLUB	F	W	L	PCT	MGR
PIT	1	95	58	.621	McKechnie
N Y	2	86	66	.566	McGraw
CIN	3	80	73	.523	Hendricks
ST.L	4	77	76	.503	Rickey Hornsby
BOS	5	70	83	.458	Bancroft
BRO	6t	68	85	.444	Robinson
PHI	6t	68	85	.444	Fletcher
CHI	8	68	86	.442	Killefer Maranville Gibson

1925—AMERICAN LEAGUE

CLUB	F	W	L	PCT	MGR
WAS	1	96	55	.636	Harris
PHI	2	88	64	.579	Mack
ST.L	3	82	71	.536	Sisler
DET	4	81	73	.526	Cobb
CHI	5	79	75	.513	Collins
CLE	6	70	84	.455	Speaker
N Y	7	69	85	.448	Huggins
BOS	8	47	105	.309	Fohl

1926—NATIONAL LEAGUE

CLUB	F	W	L	PCT	MGR
ST.L	1	89	65	.578	Hornsby
CIN	2	87	67	.565	Hendricks
PIT	3	84	69	.549	McKechnie
CHI	4	82	72	.532	McCarthy
N Y	5	74	77	.490	McGraw
BRO	6	71	82	.464	Robinson
BOS	7	66	86	.434	Bancroft
PHI	8	58	93	.384	Fletcher

1926—AMERICAN LEAGUE

CLUB	F	W	L	PCT	MGR
N Y	1	91	63	.591	Huggins
CLE	2	88	66	.571	Speaker
PHI	3	83	67	.553	Mack
WAS	4	81	69	.540	Harris
CHI	5	81	72	.529	Collins
DET	6	79	75	.513	Cobb
ST.L	7	62	92	.403	Sisler
BOS	8	46	107	.301	Fohl

1927—NATIONAL LEAGUE

CLUB	F	W	L	PCT	MGR
PIT	1	94	60	.610	Bush
ST.L	2	92	61	.601	O'Farrell
N Y	3	92	62	.597	McGraw
CHI	4	85	68	.556	McCarthy
CIN	5	75	78	.490	Hendricks
BRO	6	65	88	.425	Robinson
BOS	7	60	94	.390	Bancroft
PHI	8	51	103	.331	McInnis

1927—AMERICAN LEAGUE

CLUB	F	W	L	PCT	MGR
N Y	1	110	44	.714	Huggins
PHI	2	91	63	.591	Mack
WAS	3	85	69	.552	Harris
DET	4	82	71	.536	Moriarty
CHI	5	70	83	.458	Schalk
CLE	6	66	87	.431	McCallister
ST.L	7	59	94	.386	Howley
BOS	8	51	103	.331	Carrigan

1928—NATIONAL LEAGUE

CLUB	F	W	L	PCT	MGR
ST.L	1	95	59	.617	McKechnie
N Y	2	93	61	.604	McGraw
CHI	3	91	63	.591	McCarthy
PIT	4	85	67	.559	Bush
CIN	5	78	74	.513	Hendricks
BRO	6	77	76	.503	Robinson
BOS	7	50	103	.327	Slattery Hornsby
PHI	8	43	109	.283	Shotton

1928—AMERICAN LEAGUE

CLUB	F	W	L	PCT	MGR
N Y	1	101	53	.656	Huggins
PHI	2	98	55	.641	Mack
ST.L	3	82	72	.532	Howley
WAS	4	75	79	.487	Harris
CHI	5	72	82	.468	Schalk Blackburne
DET	6	68	86	.442	Moriarty
CLE	7	62	92	.403	Peckinpaugh
BOS	8	57	96	.373	Carrigan

1929—NATIONAL LEAGUE

CLUB	F	W	L	PCT	MGR
CHI	1	98	54	.645	McCarthy
PIT	2	88	65	.575	Bush Ens
N Y	3	84	67	.556	McGraw
ST.L	4	78	74	.513	McKechnie Southworth
PHI	5	71	82	.464	Shotton
BRO	6	70	83	.458	Robinson
CIN	7	66	88	.429	Hendricks
BOS	8	56	98	.364	Fuchs Evers

1929—AMERICAN LEAGUE

CLUB	F	W	L	PCT	MGR
PHI	1	104	46	.693	Mack
N Y	2	88	66	.571	Huggins Fletcher
CLE	3	81	71	.533	Peckinpaugh
ST.L	4	79	73	.520	Howley
WAS	5	71	81	.467	Johnson
DET	6	70	84	.455	Harris
CHI	7	59	93	.388	Blackburne
BOS	8	58	96	.377	Carrigan

1930—NATIONAL LEAGUE

CLUB	F	W	L	PCT	MGR
ST.L	1	92	62	.597	Street
CHI	2	90	64	.584	McCarthy Hornsby
N Y	3	87	67	.565	McGraw
BRO	4	86	68	.558	Robinson
PIT	5	80	74	.519	Ens
BOS	6	70	84	.455	McKechnie
CIN	7	59	95	.383	Howley
PHI	8	52	102	.338	Shotton

1930—AMERICAN LEAGUE

CLUB	F	W	L	PCT	MGR
PHI	1	102	52	.662	Mack
WAS	2	94	60	.610	Johnson
N Y	3	86	68	.558	Shawkey
CLE	4	81	73	.526	Peckinpaugh
DET	5	75	79	.487	Harris
ST.L	6	64	90	.416	Killefer
CHI	7	62	92	.403	Bush
BOS	8	52	102	.338	Wagner

1931—NATIONAL LEAGUE

CLUB	F	W	L	PCT	MGR
ST.L	1	101	53	.656	Street
N Y	2	87	65	.572	McGraw
CHI	3	84	70	.545	Hornsby
BRO	4	79	73	.520	Robinson
PIT	5	75	79	.487	Ens
PHI	6	66	88	.429	Shotton
BOS	7	64	90	.416	McKechnie
CIN	8	58	96	.377	Howley

1931—AMERICAN LEAGUE

CLUB	F	W	L	PCT	MGR
PHI	1	107	45	.704	Mack
N Y	2	94	59	.614	McCarthy
WAS	3	92	62	.597	Johnson
CLE	4	78	76	.506	Peckinpaugh
ST.L	5	63	91	.409	Killefer
BOS	6	62	90	.408	Collins
DET	7	61	93	.396	Harris
CHI	8	56	97	.366	Bush

1932—NATIONAL LEAGUE

CLUB	F	W	L	PCT	MGR
CHI	1	90	64	.584	Hornsby Grimm
PIT	2	86	68	.558	Gibson
BRO	3	81	73	.526	Carey
PHI	4	78	76	.506	Shotton
BOS	5	77	77	.500	McKechnie
N Y	6t	72	82	.468	McGraw Terry
ST.L	6t	72	82	.468	Street
CIN	8	60	94	.390	Howley

1932—AMERICAN LEAGUE

CLUB	F	W	L	PCT	MGR
N Y	1	107	47	.695	McCarthy
PHI	2	94	60	.610	Mack
WAS	3	93	61	.604	Johnson
CLE	4	87	65	.572	Peckinpaugh
DET	5	76	75	.503	Harris
ST.L	6	63	91	.409	Killefer
CHI	7	49	102	.325	Fonseca
BOS	8	43	111	.279	Collins McManus

1933—NATIONAL LEAGUE

CLUB	F	W	L	PCT	MGR
N Y	1	91	61	.599	Terry
PIT	2	87	67	.565	Gibson
CHI	3	86	68	.558	Grimm
BOS	4	83	71	.539	McKechnie
ST.L	5	82	71	.536	Street Frisch
BRO	6	65	88	.425	Carey
PHI	7	60	92	.395	Shotton
CIN	8	58	94	.382	Bush

1933—AMERICAN LEAGUE

CLUB	F	W	L	PCT	MGR
WAS	1	99	53	.651	Cronin
N Y	2	91	59	.607	McCarthy
PHI	3	79	72	.523	Mack
CLE	4	75	76	.497	Peckinpaugh Johnson
DET	5	75	79	.487	Harris Baker

(Continued)

1933-American League (Cont.)

CHI	6	67	83	.447	Fonseca
BOS	7	63	86	.423	McManus
ST.L	8	55	96	.364	Killefer
					Sothoron
					Hornsby

1934—NATIONAL LEAGUE

CLUB	F	W	L	PCT	MGR
ST.L	1	95	58	.621	Frisch
N Y	2	93	60	.608	Terry
CHI	3	86	65	.570	Grimm
BOS	4	78	73	.517	McKechnie
PIT	5	74	76	.493	Gibson
					Traynor
BRO	6	71	81	.467	Stengel
PHI	7	56	93	.376	Wilson
CIN	8	52	99	.344	O'Farrell
					Shotton
					Dressen

1934—AMERICAN LEAGUE

CLUB	F	W	L	PCT	MGR
DET	1	101	53	.656	Cochrane
N Y	2	94	60	.610	McCarthy
CLE	3	85	69	.552	Johnson
BOS	4	76	76	.500	Harris
PHI	5	68	82	.453	Mack
ST.L	6	67	85	.441	Hornsby
WAS	7	66	86	.434	Cronin
CHI	8	53	99	.349	Fonseca
					Dykes

1935—NATIONAL LEAGUE

CLUB	F	W	L	PCT	MGR
CHI	1	100	54	.649	Grimm
ST.L	2	96	58	.623	Frisch
N Y	3	91	62	.595	Terry
PIT	4	86	67	.562	Traynor
BRO	5	70	83	.458	Stengel
CIN	6	68	85	.444	Dressen
PHI	7	64	89	.418	Wilson
BOS	8	38	115	.248	McKechnie

1935—AMERICAN LEAGUE

CLUB	F	W	L	PCT	MGR
DET	1	93	58	.616	Cochrane
N Y	2	89	60	.597	McCarthy
CLE	3	82	71	.536	Johnson
					O'Neill
BOS	4	78	75	.510	Cronin
CHI	5	74	78	.487	Dykes
WAS	6	67	86	.438	Harris
ST.L	7	65	87	.428	Hornsby
PHI	8	58	91	.389	Mack

1936—NATIONAL LEAGUE

CLUB	F	W	L	PCT	MGR
N Y	1	92	62	.597	Terry
CHI	2t	87	67	.565	Grimm
ST.L	2t	87	67	.565	Frisch
PIT	4	84	70	.545	Traynor
CIN	5	74	80	.481	Dressen
BOS	6	71	83	.461	McKechnie
BRO	7	67	87	.435	Stengel
PHI	8	54	100	.351	Wilson

1936—AMERICAN LEAGUE

CLUB	F	W	L	PCT	MGR
N Y	1	102	51	.667	McCarthy
DET	2	83	71	.539	Cochrane
CHI	3	81	70	.5364	Dykes
WAS	4	82	71	.5359	Harris
CLE	5	80	74	.519	O'Neill
BOS	6	74	80	.481	Cronin
ST.L	7	57	95	.375	Hornsby
PHI	8	53	100	.346	Mack

1937—NATIONAL LEAGUE

CLUB	F	W	L	PCT	MGR
N Y	1	95	57	.625	Terry
CHI	2	93	61	.604	Grimm
PIT	3	86	68	.558	Traynor
ST.L	4	81	73	.526	Frisch
BOS	5	79	73	.520	McKechnie
BRO	6	62	91	.405	Grimes
PHI	7	61	92	.399	Wilson
CIN	8	56	98	.364	Dressen
					Wallace

1937—AMERICAN LEAGUE

CLUB	F	W	L	PCT	MGR
N Y	1	102	52	.662	McCarthy
DET	2	89	65	.578	Cochrane
CHI	3	86	68	.558	Dykes
CLE	4	83	71	.539	O'Neill
BOS	5	80	72	.526	Cronin
WAS	6	73	80	.477	Harris
PHI	7	54	97	.358	Mack
ST.L	8	46	108	.299	Hornsby
					Bottomley

1938—NATIONAL LEAGUE

CLUB	F	W	L	PCT	MGR
CHI	1	89	63	.586	Grimm
					Hartnett
PIT	2	86	64	.573	Traynor
N Y	3	83	67	.553	Terry
CIN	4	82	68	.547	McKechnie
BOS	5	77	75	.507	Stengel
ST.L	6	71	80	.470	Frisch
					Gonzales
BRO	7	69	80	.463	Grimes
PHI	8	45	105	.300	Wilson
					Lobert

1938—AMERICAN LEAGUE

CLUB	F	W	L	PCT	MGR
N Y	1	99	53	.651	McCarthy
BOS	2	88	61	.591	Cronin
CLE	3	86	66	.566	Vitt
DET	4	84	70	.545	Cochrane
					Baker
WAS	5	75	76	.497	Harris
CHI	6	65	83	.439	Dykes
ST.L	7	55	97	.362	Street
					Melillo
PHI	8	53	99	.349	Mack

1939—NATIONAL LEAGUE

CLUB	F	W	L	PCT	MGR
CIN	1	97	57	.630	McKechnie
ST.L	2	92	61	.601	Blades
BRO	3	84	69	.549	Durocher
CHI	4	84	70	.545	Hartnett
N Y	5	77	74	.510	Terry
PIT	6	68	85	.444	Traynor
BOS	7	63	88	.417	Stengel
PHI	8	45	106	.298	Prothro

1939—AMERICAN LEAGUE

CLUB	F	W	L	PCT	MGR
N Y	1	106	45	.702	McCarthy
BOS	2	89	62	.589	Cronin
CLE	3	87	67	.565	Vitt
CHI	4	85	69	.552	Dykes
DET	5	81	73	.526	Baker
WAS	6	65	87	.428	Harris
PHI	7	55	97	.362	Mack
ST.L	8	43	111	.279	Haney

1940—NATIONAL LEAGUE

CLUB	F	W	L	PCT	MGR
CIN	1	100	53	.654	McKechnie
BRO	2	88	65	.575	Durocher
ST.L	3	84	69	.549	Blades
					Gonzales
					Southworth

(Continued)

1940-National League (Cont.)

PIT	4	78	76	.506	Frisch
CHI	5	75	79	.487	Hartnett
N Y	6	72	80	.474	Terry
BOS	7	65	87	.428	Stengel
PHI	8	50	103	.327	Prothro

1940—AMERICAN LEAGUE

CLUB	F	W	L	PCT	MGR
DET	1	90	64	.584	Baker
CLE	2	89	65	.578	Vitt
N Y	3	88	66	.571	McCarthy
BOS	4t	82	72	.532	Cronin
CHI	4t	82	72	.532	Dykes
ST.L	6	67	87	.435	Haney
WAS	7	64	90	.416	Harris
PHI	8	54	100	.351	Mack

1941—NATIONAL LEAGUE

CLUB	F	W	L	PCT	MGR
BRO	1	100	54	.649	Durocher
ST.L	2	97	56	.634	Southworth
CIN	3	88	66	.571	McKechnie
PIT	4	81	73	.526	Frisch
N Y	5	74	79	.484	Terry
CHI	6	70	84	.455	Wilson
BOS	7	62	92	.403	Stengel
PHI	8	43	111	.279	Prothro

1941—AMERICAN LEAGUE

CLUB	F	W	L	PCT	MGR
N Y	1	101	53	.656	McCarthy
BOS	2	84	70	.545	Cronin
CHI	3	77	77	.500	Dykes
CLE	4t	75	79	.487	Peckinpaugh
DET	4t	75	79	.487	Baker
ST.L	6t	70	84	.455	Haney
					Sewell
WAS	6t	70	84	.455	Harris
PHI	8	64	90	.416	Mack

1942—NATIONAL LEAGUE

CLUB	F	W	L	PCT	MGR
ST.L	1	106	48	.688	Southworth
BRO	2	104	50	.675	Durocher
N Y	3	85	67	.559	Ott
CIN	4	76	76	.500	McKechnie
PIT	5	66	81	.449	Frisch
CHI	6	68	86	.442	Wilson
BOS	7	59	89	.399	Stengel
PHI	8	42	109	.278	Lobert

1942—AMERICAN LEAGUE

CLUB	F	W	L	PCT	MGR
N Y	1	103	51	.669	McCarthy
BOS	2	93	59	.612	Cronin
ST.L	3	82	69	.543	Sewell
CLE	4	75	79	.487	Boudreau
DET	5	73	81	.474	Baker
CHI	6	66	82	.446	Dykes
WAS	7	62	89	.411	Harris
PHI	8	55	99	.357	Mack

1943—NATIONAL LEAGUE

CLUB	F	W	L	PCT	MGR
ST.L	1	105	49	.682	Southworth
CIN	2	87	67	.565	McKechnie
BRO	3	81	72	.529	Durocher
PIT	4	80	74	.519	Frisch
CHI	5	74	79	.484	Wilson
BOS	6	68	85	.444	Stengel
PHI	7	64	90	.416	Harris
					Fitzsimmons
N Y	8	55	98	.359	Ott

1943—AMERICAN LEAGUE

CLUB	F	W	L	PCT	MGR
N Y	1	98	56	.636	McCarthy
WAS	2	84	69	.549	Bluege
CLE	3	82	71	.536	Boudreau
CHI	4	82	72	.532	Dykes
DET	5	78	76	.506	O'Neill
ST.L	6	72	80	.474	Sewell
BOS	7	68	84	.447	Cronin
PHI	8	49	105	.318	Mack

1944—NATIONAL LEAGUE

CLUB	F	W	L	PCT	MGR
ST.L	1	105	49	.682	Southworth
PIT	2	90	63	.588	Frisch
CIN	3	89	65	.578	McKechnie
CHI	4	75	79	.487	Wilson Johnson Grimm
N Y	5	67	87	.435	Ott
BOS	6	65	89	.422	Coleman
BRO	7	63	91	.409	Durocher
PHI	8	61	92	.399	Fitzsimmons

1944—AMERICAN LEAGUE

CLUB	F	W	L	PCT	MGR
ST.L	1	89	65	.578	Sewell
DET	2	88	66	.571	O'Neill
N Y	3	83	71	.539	McCarthy
BOS	4	77	77	.500	Cronin
CLE	5t	72	82	.468	Boudreau
PHI	5t	72	82	.468	Mack
CHI	7	71	83	.461	Dykes
WAS	8	64	90	.416	Bluege

1945—NATIONAL LEAGUE

CLUB	F	W	L	PCT	MGR
CHI	1	98	56	.636	Grimm
ST.L	2	95	59	.617	Southworth
BRO	3	87	67	.565	Durocher
PIT	4	82	72	.532	Frisch
N Y	5	78	74	.513	Ott
BOS	6	67	85	.441	Coleman Bissonette
CIN	7	61	93	.396	McKechnie
PHI	8	46	108	.299	Fitzsimmons Chapman

1945—AMERICAN LEAGUE

CLUB	F	W	L	PCT	MGR
DET	1	88	65	.575	O'Neill
WAS	2	87	67	.565	Bluege
ST.L	3	81	70	.536	Sewell
N Y	4	81	71	.533	McCarthy
CLE	5	73	72	.503	Boudreau
CHI	6	71	78	.477	Dykes
BOS	7	71	83	.461	Cronin
PHI	8	52	98	.347	Mack

1946—NATIONAL LEAGUE

CLUB	F	W	L	PCT	MGR
ST.L	1p	98	58	.628	Dyer
BRO	2p	96	60	.615	Durocher
CHI	3	82	71	.536	Grimm
BOS	4	81	72	.529	Southworth
PHI	5	69	85	.448	Chapman
CIN	6	67	87	.435	McKechnie Gowdy
PIT	7	63	91	.409	Frisch Davis
N Y	8	61	93	.396	Ott

1946—AMERICAN LEAGUE

CLUB	F	W	L	PCT	MGR
BOS	1	104	50	.675	Cronin
DET	2	92	62	.597	O'Neill
N Y	3	87	67	.565	McCarthy Dickey Neun
WAS	4	76	78	.494	Bluege

(Continued)

1946-American League (Cont.)

CLUB	F	W	L	PCT	MGR
CHI	5	74	80	.481	Dykes Lyons
CLE	6	68	86	.442	Boudreau
ST.L	7	66	88	.429	Sewell Taylor
PHI	8	49	105	.318	Mack

1947—NATIONAL LEAGUE

CLUB	F	W	L	PCT	MGR
BRO	1	94	60	.610	Sukeforth Shotton
ST.L	2	89	65	.578	Dyer
BOS	3	86	68	.558	Southworth
N Y	4	81	73	.526	Ott
CIN	5	73	81	.474	Neun
CHI	6	69	85	.448	Grimm
PHI	7t	62	92	.403	Chapman
PIT	7t	62	92	.403	Herman Burwell

1947—AMERICAN LEAGUE

CLUB	F	W	L	PCT	MGR
N Y	1	97	57	.630	Harris
DET	2	85	69	.552	O'Neill
BOS	3	83	71	.539	Cronin
CLE	4	80	74	.519	Boudreau
PHI	5	78	76	.506	Mack
CHI	6	70	84	.455	Lyons
WAS	7	64	90	.416	Bluege
ST.L	8	59	95	.383	Ruel

1948—NATIONAL LEAGUE

CLUB	F	W	L	PCT	MGR
BOS	1	91	62	.595	Southworth
ST.L	2	85	69	.552	Dyer
BRO	3	84	70	.545	Durocher Shotton
PIT	4	83	71	.539	Meyer
N Y	5	78	76	.506	Ott Durocher
PHI	6	66	88	.429	Chapman Cooke Sawyer
CIN	7	64	89	.418	Neun Walters
CHI	8	64	90	.416	Grimm

1948—AMERICAN LEAGUE

CLUB	F	W	L	PCT	MGR
CLE	1p	97	58	.626	Boudreau
BOS	2p	96	59	.619	McCarthy
N Y	3	94	60	.610	Harris
PHI	4	84	70	.545	Mack
DET	5	78	76	.506	O'Neill
ST.L	6	59	94	.386	Taylor
WAS	7	56	97	.366	Kuhel
CHI	8	51	101	.336	Lyons

1949—NATIONAL LEAGUE

CLUB	F	W	L	PCT	MGR
BRO	1	97	57	.630	Shotton
ST.L	2	96	58	.623	Dyer
PHI	3	81	73	.526	Sawyer
BOS	4	75	79	.487	Southworth Cooney
N Y	5	73	81	.474	Durocher
PIT	6	71	83	.461	Meyer
CIN	7	62	92	.403	Walters Sewell
CHI	8	61	93	.396	Grimm Frisch

1949—AMERICAN LEAGUE

CLUB	F	W	L	PCT	MGR
N Y	1	97	57	.630	Stengel
BOS	2	96	58	.623	McCarthy
CLE	3	89	65	.578	Boudreau
DET	4	87	67	.565	Rolfe
PHI	5	81	73	.526	Mack
CHI	6	63	91	.409	Onslow
ST.L	7	53	101	.344	Taylor
WAS	8	50	104	.324	Kuhel

1950—NATIONAL LEAGUE

CLUB	F	W	L	PCT	MGR
PHI	1	91	63	.591	Sawyer
BRO	2	89	65	.578	Shotton
N Y	3	86	68	.558	Durocher
BOS	4	83	71	.539	Southworth
ST.L	5	78	75	.510	Dyer
CIN	6	66	87	.431	Sewell
CHI	7	64	89	.418	Frisch
PIT	8	57	96	.373	Meyer

1950—AMERICAN LEAGUE

CLUB	F	W	L	PCT	MGR
N Y	1	98	56	.636	Stengel
DET	2	95	59	.617	Rolfe
BOS	3	94	60	.610	McCarthy O'Neill
CLE	4	92	62	.597	Boudreau
WAS	5	67	87	.435	Harris
CHI	6	60	94	.390	Onslow Corriden
ST.L	7	58	96	.377	Taylor
PHI	8	52	102	.338	Mack

1951—NATIONAL LEAGUE

CLUB	F	W	L	PCT	MGR
N Y	1p	98	59	.624	Durocher
BRO	2p	97	60	.618	Dressen
ST.L	3	81	73	.526	Marion
BOS	4	76	78	.494	Southworth Holmes
PHI	5	73	81	.474	Sawyer
CIN	6	68	86	.442	Sewell
PIT	7	64	90	.416	Meyer
CHI	8	62	92	.403	Frisch Cavarretta

1951—AMERICAN LEAGUE

CLUB	F	W	L	PCT	MGR
N Y	1	98	56	.636	Stengel
CLE	2	93	61	.604	Lopez
BOS	3	87	67	.565	O'Neill
CHI	4	81	73	.526	Richards
DET	5	73	81	.474	Rolfe
PHI	6	70	84	.455	Dykes
WAS	7	62	92	.403	Harris
ST.L	8	52	102	.338	Taylor

1952—NATIONAL LEAGUE

CLUB	F	W	L	PCT	MGR
BRO	1	96	57	.627	Dressen
N Y	2	92	62	.597	Durocher
ST.L	3	88	66	.571	Stanky
PHI	4	87	67	.565	Sawyer O'Neill
CHI	5	77	77	.500	Cavarretta
CIN	6	69	85	.448	Sewell Hornsby
BOS	7	64	89	.418	Holmes Grimm
PIT	8	42	112	.273	Meyer

1952—AMERICAN LEAGUE

CLUB	F	W	L	PCT	MGR
N Y	1	95	59	.617	Stengel
CLE	2	93	61	.604	Lopez
CHI	3	81	73	.526	Richards
PHI	4	79	75	.513	Dykes
WAS	5	78	76	.506	Harris
BOS	6	76	78	.494	Boudreau
ST.L	7	64	90	.416	Hornsby Marion
DET	8	50	104	.325	Rolfe Hutchinson

1953—NATIONAL LEAGUE

CLUB	F	W	L	PCT	MGR
BRO	1	105	49	.682	Dressen
MIL	2	92	62	.597	Grimm
PHI	3t	83	71	.539	O'Neill
ST.L	3t	83	71	.539	Stanky
N Y	5	70	84	.455	Durocher
CIN	6	68	86	.442	Hornsby Mills
CHI	7	65	89	.422	Cavarretta
PIT	8	50	104	.325	Haney

1953—AMERICAN LEAGUE

CLUB	F	W	L	PCT	MGR
N Y	1	99	52	.656	Stengel
CLE	2	92	62	.597	Lopez
CHI	3	89	65	.578	Richards
BOS	4	84	69	.549	Boudreau
WAS	5	76	76	.500	Harris
DET	6	60	94	.390	Hutchinson
PHI	7	59	95	.383	Dykes
ST.L	8	54	100	.351	Marion

1954—NATIONAL LEAGUE

CLUB	F	W	L	PCT	MGR
N Y	1	97	57	.630	Durocher
BRO	2	92	62	.597	Alston
MIL	3	89	65	.578	Grimm
PHI	4	75	79	.487	O'Neill Moore
CIN	5	74	80	.481	Tebbetts
ST.L	6	72	82	.468	Stanky
CHI	7	64	90	.416	Hack
PIT	8	53	101	.344	Haney

1954—AMERICAN LEAGUE

CLUB	F	W	L	PCT	MGR
CLE	1	111	43	.721	Lopez
N Y	2	103	51	.669	Stengel
CHI	3	94	60	.610	Richards Marion
BOS	4	69	85	.448	Boudreau
DET	5	68	86	.442	Hutchinson
WAS	6	66	88	.429	Harris
BAL	7	54	100	.351	Dykes
PHI	8	51	103	.331	Joost

1955—NATIONAL LEAGUE

CLUB	F	W	L	PCT	MGR
BRO	1	98	55	.641	Alston
MIL	2	85	69	.552	Grimm
N Y	3	80	74	.519	Durocher
PHI	4	77	77	.500	Smith
CIN	5	75	79	.487	Tebbetts
CHI	6	72	81	.471	Hack
St.L	7	68	86	.442	Stanky Walker
PIT	8	60	94	.390	Haney

1955—AMERICAN LEAGUE

CLUB	F	W	L	PCT	MGR
N Y	1	96	58	.623	Stengel
CLE	2	93	61	.604	Lopez
CHI	3	91	63	.591	Marion
BOS	4	84	70	.545	Higgins
DET	5	79	75	.513	Harris
K C	6	63	91	.409	Boudreau
BAL	7	57	97	.370	Richards
WAS	8	53	101	.344	Dressen

1956—NATIONAL LEAGUE

CLUB	F	W	L	PCT	MGR
BRO	1	93	61	.604	Alston
MIL	2	92	62	.597	Grimm Haney
CIN	3	91	63	.591	Tebbetts
ST.L	4	76	78	.494	Hutchinson
PHI	5	71	83	.461	Smith
N Y	6	67	87	.435	Rigney
PIT	7	66	88	.429	Bragan
CHI	8	60	94	.390	Hack

1956—AMERICAN LEAGUE

CLUB	F	W	L	PCT	MGR
N Y	1	97	57	.630	Stengel
CLE	2	88	66	.571	Lopez
CHI	3	85	69	.552	Marion
BOS	4	84	70	.545	Higgins
DET	5	82	72	.532	Harris
BAL	6	69	85	.448	Richards
WAS	7	59	95	.383	Dressen
K C	8	52	102	.338	Boudreau

1957—NATIONAL LEAGUE

CLUB	F	W	L	PCT	MGR
MIL	1	95	59	.617	Haney
ST.L	2	87	67	.565	Hutchinson
BRO	3	84	70	.545	Alston
CIN	4	80	74	.519	Tebbetts
PHI	5	77	77	.500	Smith
N Y	6	69	85	.448	Rigney
CHI t	7t	62	92	.403	Scheffing
PIT t	7t	62	92	.403	Bragan Murtaugh

1957—AMERICAN LEAGUE

CLUB	F	W	L	PCT	MGR
N Y	1	98	56	.636	Stengel
CHI	2	90	64	.584	Lopez
BOS	3	82	72	.532	Higgins
DET	4	78	76	.506	Tighe
BAL	5	76	76	.500	Richards
CLE	6	76	77	.497	Farrell
K C	7	59	94	.386	Boudreau Craft
WAS	8	55	99	.357	Dressen Lavagetto

1958—NATIONAL LEAGUE

CLUB	F	W	L	PCT	MGR
MIL	1	92	62	.597	Haney
PIT	2	84	70	.545	Murtaugh
SF	3	80	74	.519	Rigney
CIN	4	76	78	.494	Tebbetts Dykes
ST.L	5t	72	82	.468	Hutchinson Hack
CHI	5t	72	82	.468	Scheffing
LA	7	71	83	.461	Alston
PHI	8	69	85	.448	Smith Sawyer

1958—AMERICAN LEAGUE

CLUB	F	W	L	PCT	MGR
N Y	1	92	62	.597	Stengel
CHI	2	82	72	.532	Lopez
BOS	3	79	75	.513	Higgins
CLE	4	77	76	.503	Bragan Gordon
DET	5	77	77	.500	Tighe Norman
BAL	6	74	79	.484	Richards
K C	7	73	81	.474	Craft
WASH	8	61	93	.396	Lavagetto

1959—NATIONAL LEAGUE

CLUB	F	W	L	PCT	MGR
LA	1p	88	68	.564	Alston
MIL	2p	86	70	.551	Haney
SF	3	83	71	.539	Rigney
PIT	4	78	76	.506	Murtaugh
CHI	5t	74	80	.481	Scheffing
CIN	5t	74	80	.481	Smith Hutchinson
ST.L	7	71	83	.461	Hemus
PHI	8	64	90	.416	Sawyer

1959—AMERICAN LEAGUE

CLUB	F	W	L	PCT	MGR
CHI	1	94	60	.610	Lopez
CLE	2	89	65	.578	Gordon
NY	3	79	75	.513	Stengel
DET	4	76	78	.494	Norman Dykes
BOS	5	75	79	.487	Higgins York Jurges
BAL	6	74	80	.481	Richards
KC	7	66	88	.429	Craft
WAS	8	63	91	.409	Lavagetto

1960—NATIONAL LEAGUE

CLUB	F	W	L	PCT	MGR
PIT	1	95	59	.617	Murtaugh
MIL	2	88	66	.571	Dressen
ST.L	3	86	68	.558	Hemus
LA	4	82	72	.532	Alston
SF	5	79	75	.513	Rigney Sheehan
CIN	6	67	87	.435	Hutchinson
CHI	7	60	94	.390	Grimm Boudreau
PHI	8	59	95	.383	Sawyer Mauch

1960—AMERICAN LEAGUE

CLUB	F	W	L	PCT	MGR
NY	1	97	57	.630	Stengel
BAL	2	89	65	.578	Richards
CHI	3	87	67	.565	Lopez Gordon
CLE	4	76	78	.494	White Dykes
WAS	5	73	81	.474	Lavagetto Dykes
DET	6	71	83	.461	Hitchcock Gordon
BOS	7	65	89	.422	Jurges Higgins
KC	8	58	96	.377	Elliott

1961—NATIONAL LEAGUE

CLUB	F	W	L	PCT	MGR
CIN	1	93	61	.604	Hutchinson
LA	2	89	65	.578	Alston
SF	3	85	69	.552	Dark
MIL	4	83	71	.539	Dressen Tebbetts
ST.L	5	80	74	.519	Hemus Keane
PIT	6	75	79	.497	Murtaugh Himsl
CHI	7	64	90	.416	Craft Tappe Klein
PHI	8	47	107	.305	Mauch

1961—AMERICAN LEAGUE

CLUB	F	W	L	PCT	MGR
NY	1	109	53	.673	Houk
DET	2	101	61	.623	Scheffing
BAL	3	95	67	.586	Richards Harris
CHI	4	86	76	.531	Lopez
CLE	5	78	83	.484	Dykes Harder
BOS	6	76	86	.469	Higgins
MIN	7	70	90	.438	Lavagetto Mele
LA	8	70	91	.435	Rigney
KC	9t	61	100	.379	Gordon Bauer
WAS	9t	61	100	.379	Vernon

1962—NATIONAL LEAGUE

CLUB	F	W	L	PCT	MGR
SF	1	103	62	.624	Dark
LA	2	102	63	.618	Alston
CIN	3	98	64	.605	Hutchinson
PIT	4	93	68	.578	Murtaugh
MIL	5	86	76	.531	Tebbetts
ST.L	6	84	78	.519	Keane
PHI	7	81	80	.503	Mauch
HOU	8	64	96	.400	Craft
CHI	9	59	103	.364	Grimm Walker Adams Holt Tappe Martin Himsl Klein Collins Metro
NY	10	40	120	.250	Stengel

1962—AMERICAN LEAGUE

CLUB	F	W	L	PCT	MGR
NY	1	96	66	.593	Houk
MIN	2	91	71	.562	Mele
LA	3	86	76	.531	Rigney
DET	4	85	76	.528	Scheffing
CHI	5	85	77	.525	Lopez
CLE	6	80	82	.494	McGaha
BAL	7	77	85	.475	Hitchcock
BOS	8	76	84	.475	Higgins
KC	9	72	90	.444	Bauer
WAS	10	60	101	.373	Vernon

EVOLUTION OF MAJOR LEAGUE CITIES
(alphabetically)

A total of 38 cities, since the formation of the National Association in 1871, the first major league, have held major league franchises. More than one team, through the years, has represented its city in the major leagues. The following list reveals the number of leagues and teams in each city through the history of the majors.

The letters in parenthesis indicate the league. (n) National Association; (N) National League; (a) American Association; (U) Union Association; (p) Players League; (A) American League; (F) Federal League.

ALTOONA: (U) 1884.

BALTIMORE: (n) 1872-74, listed as Lord Baltimore in club standings; also had second club in league in 1873, listed as Marylands in club standings; (a) 1882-91; (U) 1884; (N) 1892-99; (A) 1901-02. 1954 to date; (F) 1914-15.

BOSTON: (n) 1871-75; (N) 1876-1952; (U) 1884; (p) 1890; (a) 1891; (A) 1901 to date.

BROOKLYN: (n) 1872-75, listed as Atlantics in club standings; also had second club in league in 1872, listed as Eckfords in club standings; (a) 1884-90; (p) 1890; (N) 1890-1957; (F) 1914-15.

BUFFALO: (N) 1879-85; (p) 1890; (F) 1914-15.

CHICAGO: (n) 1871, 1874-75; (N) 1876 to date; (U) 1884; (p) 1890; (A) 1901 to date; (F) 1914-15.

CINCINNATI: (N) 1876-80, 1890 to date; (a) 1882-89, 1891; (U) 1884.

CLEVELAND: (n) 1871-72; (N) 1879-84, 1889-99; (a) 1887-88; (p) 1890; (A) 1901 to date.

COLUMBUS: (a) 1883-84, 1889-91.

DETROIT: (N) 1881-88; (A) 1901 to date.

ELIZABETH: (n) 1873, listed as Resolutes in club standings.

FT. WAYNE: (n) 1871, listed as Kekiongas in club standings.

HARTFORD: (n) 1874-75; (N) 1876-77.

HOUSTON: (n) 1962 to date.

INDIANAPOLIS: (N) 1878, 1887-89; (a) 1884; (F) 1914.

KANSAS CITY: (U) 1884; (N) 1886; (a) 1888-89; (F) 1914-15; (A) 1955 to date.

KEOKUK: (n) 1875, listed as Westerns in club standings.

LOS ANGELES: (N) 1958 to date. (A) 1961 to date.

LOUISVILLE: (N) 1876-77; 1892-99; (a) 1882-91, listed as Eclipse in club standings.

MIDDLETOWN: (n) 1872, listed as Mansfields in club standings.

MILWAUKEE: (N) 1878, 1953 to date; (U) 1884; (a) 1891; (A) 1901.

MINNESOTA: (A) 1961 to date (Minneapolis-St. Paul).

NEWARK: (F) 1915.

NEW HAVEN: (n) 1875.

NEW YORK: (n) 1871-75, listed as Mutuals in club standings; (N) 1876, listed as Mutuals in club standings; 1883-1957, 1962 to date;
(a) 1883-87, listed as Metropolitans in club standings; (p) 1890; (A) 1903 to date.

PHILADELPHIA: (n) 1871-75, listed as Athletics in club standings; also had second club in league, 1873-75; also had third club in league in 1875, listed as Centennials in club standings; (N) 1876, listed as Athletics in club standings; 1883 to date; (a) 1882-91, listed as Athletics in club standings; (U) 1884, listed as Keystone in club standings; (p) 1890; (A) 1901-54.

PITTSBURGH: (a) 1882-86, listed as Allegheny in club standings; (U) 1884; (N) 1887 to date; (p) 1890; (F) 1914-15.

PROVIDENCE: (N) 1878-85.

RICHMOND: (a) 1884, listed as Virginia in club standings.

ROCKFORD: (n) 1871.

ROCHESTER: (a) 1890.

ST. LOUIS: (n) 1875, listed as Red Stockings in club standings; also had second club in league; (N) 1876-77, 1885-86, 1892 to date; (a) 1882-91; (U) 1884; (A) 1902-53; (F) 1914-15

ST. PAUL: (U) 1884.

SAN FRANCISCO: (N) 1958 to date.

SYRACUSE: (N) 1879; (a) 1890.

TOLEDO: (a) 1884, 1890.

TROY: (n) 1871-72, listed as Haymakers in club standings; (N) 1879-82.

WASHINGTON: (n) 1871, listed as Olympics in club standings; in 1872 had two clubs in league, listed as Olympics and Nationals in club standings; 1873, 1875, listed as Nationals in club standings; (a) 1884, listed as Nationals in club standings; 1891; (U) 1884, listed as Nationals in club standings; (N) 1886-89; 1892-99; (A) 1901 to date.

WILMINGTON: (U) 1884.

WORCESTER: (N) 1880-82.

BALL PARKS

American League

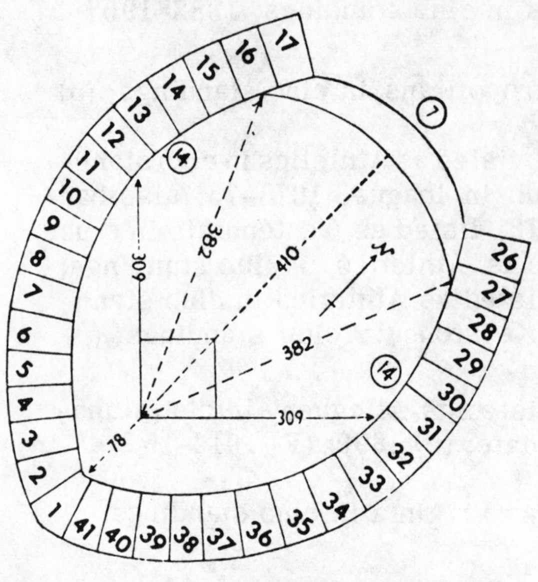

MEMORIAL STADIUM

MEMORIAL STADIUM
Home of:
Baltimore Orioles AL since 1954.
Location:
33rd St.
Ellerslie Ave.
36th St.
Ednor Rd.
Seating capacity:
47,778
Record crowd:
46,796
vs. New York (2)
May 16, 1954.
Season record gate:
1,060,910 in 1954.

(Numbers inside circles indicate height of fences in feet)

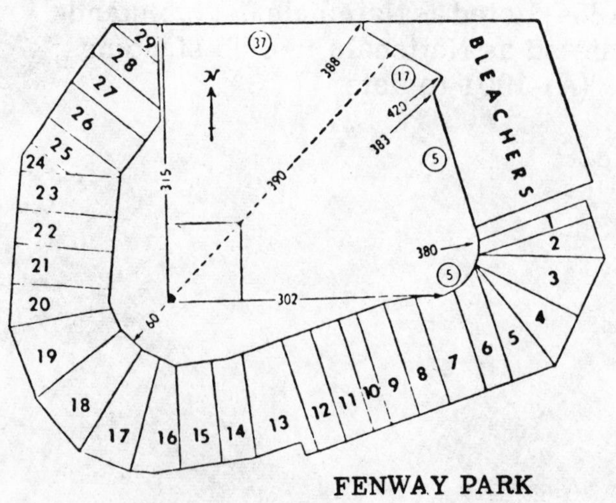

FENWAY PARK

FENWAY PARK
Home of:
Boston Red Sox AL since 1912.
Location:
Van Ness St.
Jersey St.
Lansdowne St.
Ipswich St.
Seating capacity:
34,819
Record crowd:
41,766
vs. New York (2)
Aug. 12, 1934.
Season record gate:
1,596,650 in 1949.

COMISKEY PARK

Home of:
Chicago White Sox AL since 1910.
Location:
W. 35th St.
S. Shields Ave.
W. 34th Pl.
S. Wentworth Ave.
Seating capacity:
46,550.
Record crowd:
54,215 vs. New York (2) July 19, 1953.
Season record gate:
1,328,234 in 1951.

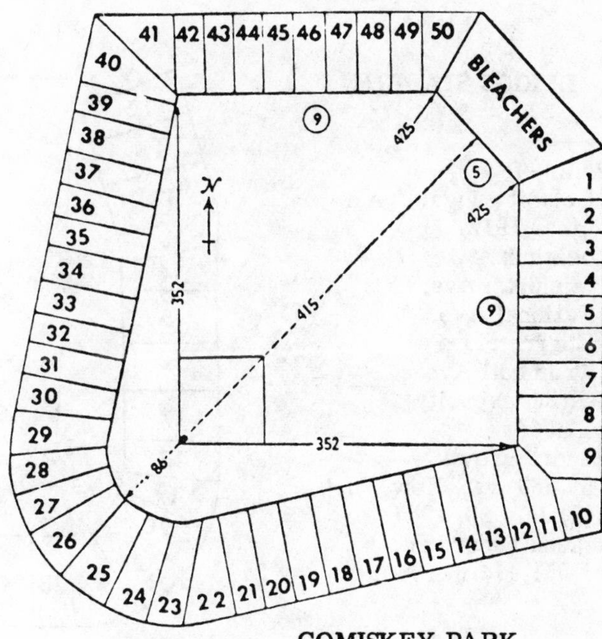

COMISKEY PARK

(Numbers inside circles indicate height of fences in feet)

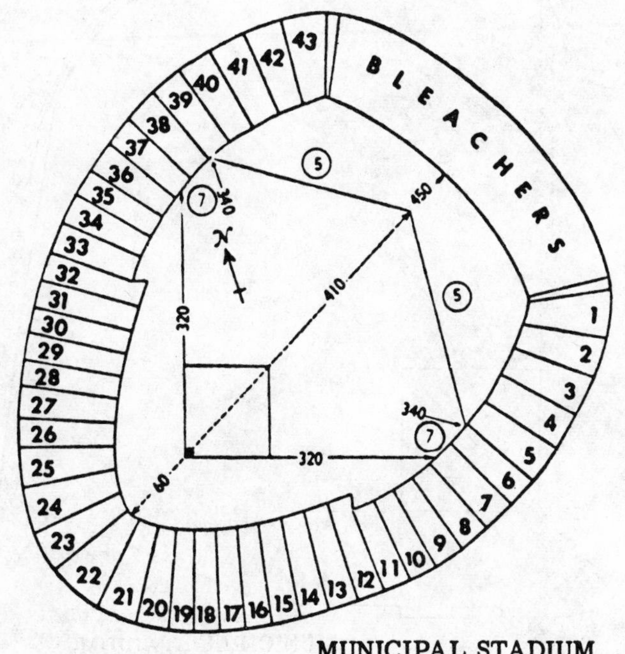

MUNICIPAL STADIUM

MUNICIPAL STADIUM

Home of:
Cleveland Indians AL since 1932.
Location:
W. 3rd St.
Lake Erie
Lake Shore Dr.
Seating capacity:
73,811.
Record crowd:
84,587 vs. New York (2) Sept. 12, 1954.
Season record gate:
2,620,627 in 1948.

BRIGGS STADIUM

Home of:
Detroit Tigers AL since 1912.
Location:
Michigan Ave.
National Ave.
Cherry St.
Trumbull Ave.
Seating capacity:
52,904.
Record crowd:
58,369 vs. New York (2) July 20, 1947.
Season record gate:
1,951,474 in 1950.

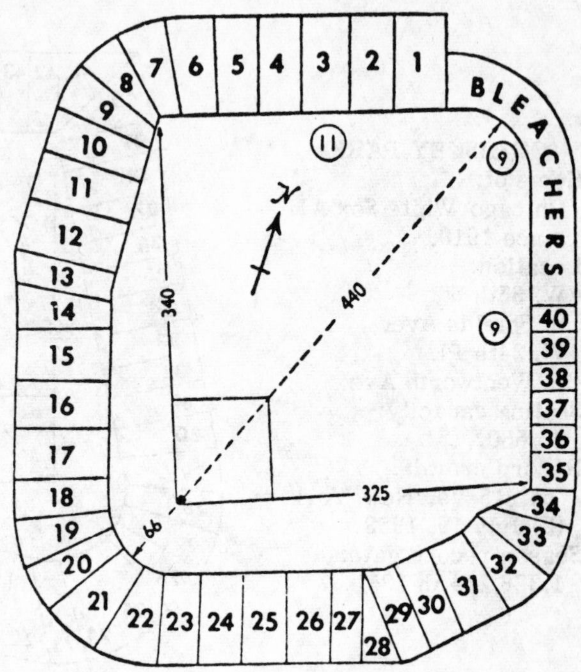

BRIGGS STADIUM

(Numbers inside circles indicate height of fences in feet)

MUNICIPAL STADIUM

Home of:
Kansas City Athletics AL since 1955.

Location:
Brooklyn Ave.
22nd St.
Woodland Ave.
21st St.

Seating capacity:
32,561.

Record crowd:
53,147 vs New York Aug. 18, 1962

Season record gate:
1,393,054 in 1955.

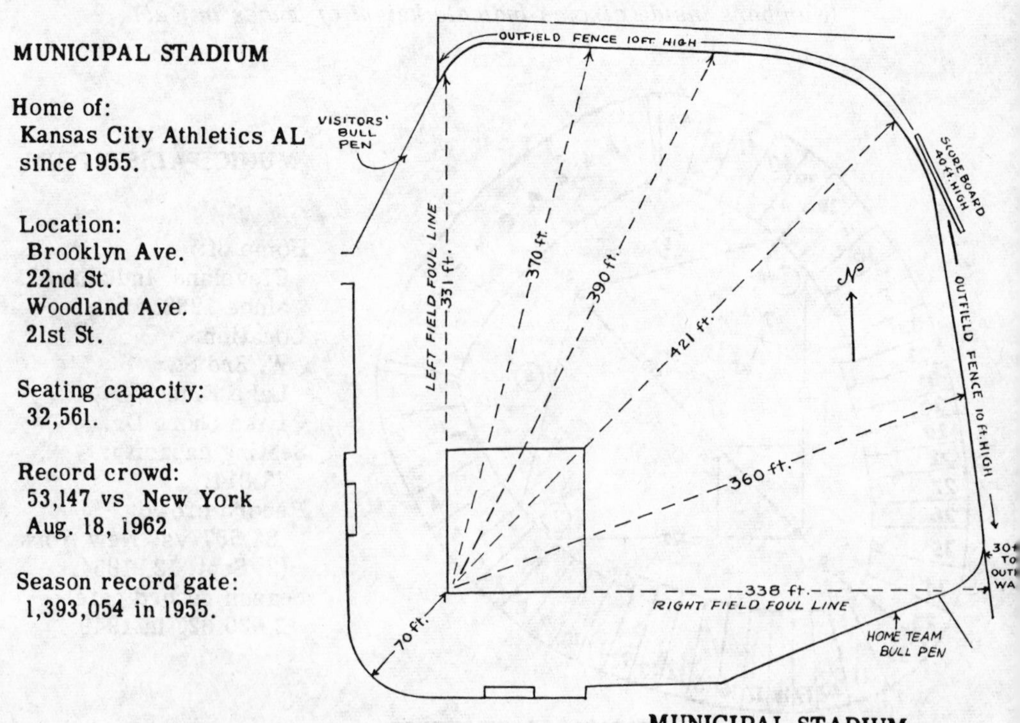

MUNICIPAL STADIUM

DODGER STADIUM

Home of:
Los Angeles Angels AL
since 1962.

Location:
Chavez Ravine
(no street boundaries).

Seating capacity:
56,000.

Record crowd:
53,591 vs. New York
July 13, 1962.

Season record gate:
1,144,063 in 1962.

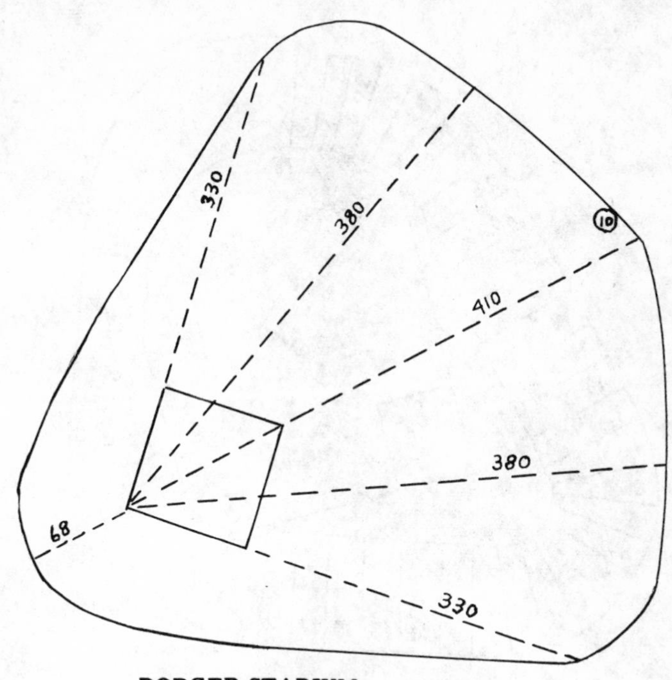

DODGER STADIUM

METROPOLITAN STADIUM

METROPOLITAN STADIUM

Home of:
Minnesota Twins AL
since 1961.

Location:
Cedar Ave.
Highway 494
24th Ave.
83rd St.
Bloomington, Minn.

Seating capacity:
39,525.

Record crowd:
41,536 vs. New York
Aug. 15, 1962.

Season record gate:
1,433,116 in 1962.

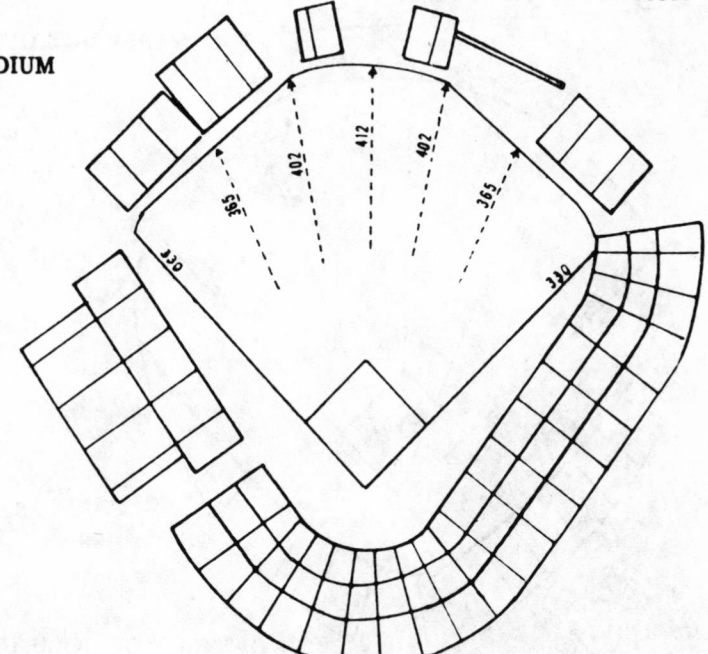

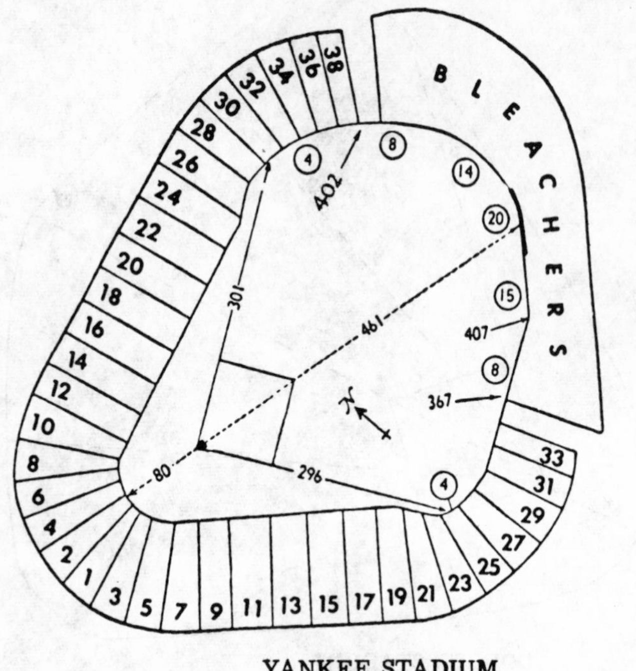

YANKEE STADIUM

YANKEE STADIUM
Home of:
New York Yankees AL since 1923.
Location:
E. 157th St.
Ruppert Pl.
E. 161st St.
River Ave.
Seating capacity:
70,000.
Record crowd:
81,841
vs. Boston (2)
May 30, 1938.
Season record gate:
2,373,901 in 1948.

(Numbers inside circles indicate height of fences in feet)

DISTRICT OF COLUMBIA STADIUM

Home of:
Washington Senators AL since 1962.

Location:
22nd St.
East Capitol St.

Seating capacity:
45,000.

Record crowd:
48,147 vs. New York
Aug 1, 1962.

Season record gate:
729,775 in 1962.

DISTRICT OF COLUMBIA STADIUM

National League

WRIGLEY FIELD
Home of:
Chicago Cubs NL
since 1916.
Location:
Waveland Ave.
Sheffield Ave.
Addison St.
Clark St.
Seating capacity:
36,755.
Record crowd:
46,965
vs. Pittsburgh (2)
May 31, 1948.
Record season gate:
1,485,166 in 1929.

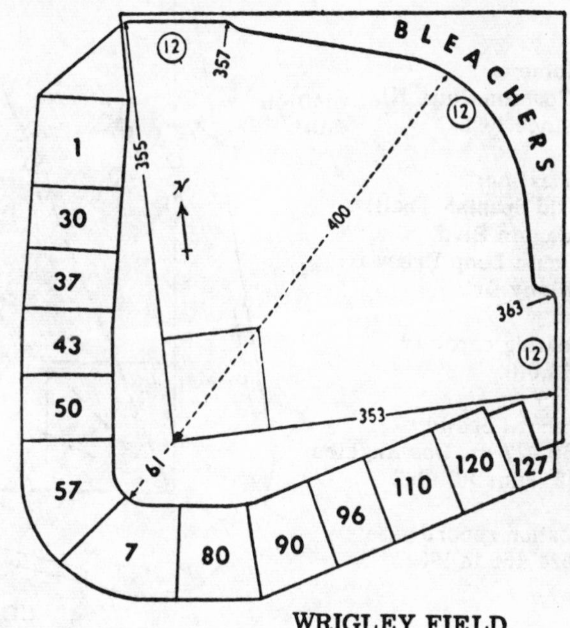

WRIGLEY FIELD

(Numbers inside circles indicate height of fences in feet)

CROSLEY FIELD
Home of:
Cincinnati Reds NL
since 1912.
Location:
Findlay St.
York St.
Western Ave.
Seating capacity:
30,328.
Record crowd:
36,961
vs. Pittsburgh (2)
April 27, 1947.
Season record gate:
1,125,928 in 1956.

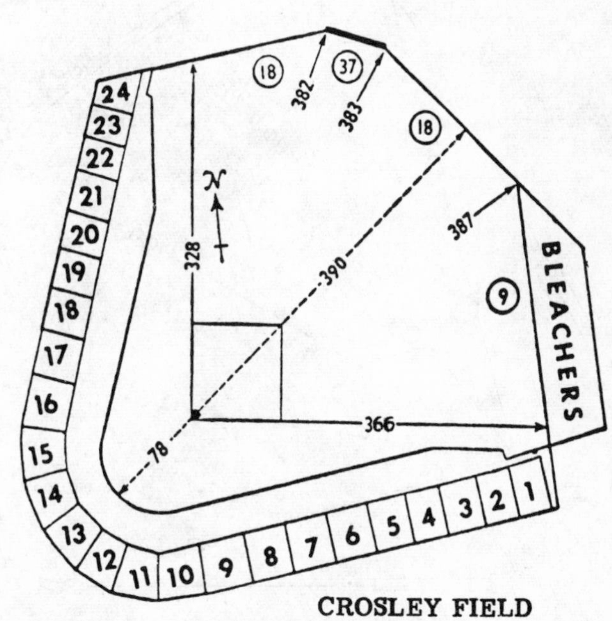

CROSLEY FIELD

COLT STADIUM

Home of:
Houston Colts NL
since 1962.

Location:
Old Spanish Trail.
Fannin Blvd.
South Loop Freeway.
Kirby Drive.

Seating capacity:
33,010.

Record crowd:
30,027 vs. Los Angeles
(2) June 10, 1962.

Season record gate:
924,456 in 1962.

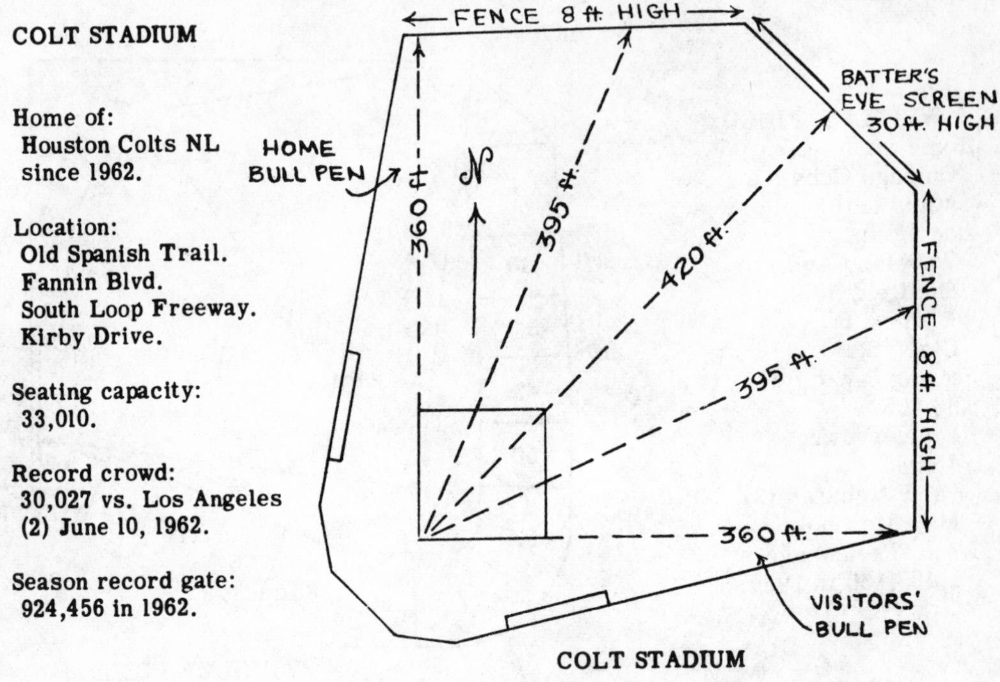

COLT STADIUM

DODGER STADIUM

Home of:
Los Angeles Dodgers NL
since 1962.

Location:
Chavez Ravine
(no street boundaries).

Seating capacity:
56,000.

Record crowd:
54,418 vs. San Francisco
Sept. 3, 1962.

Season record gate:
2,755,184 in 1962.

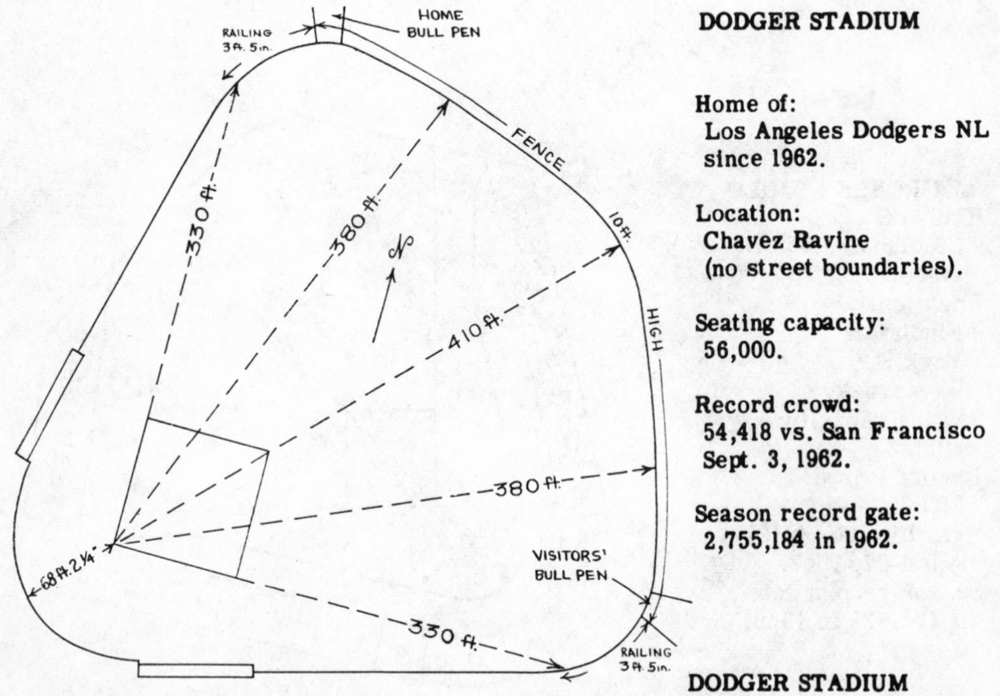

DODGER STADIUM

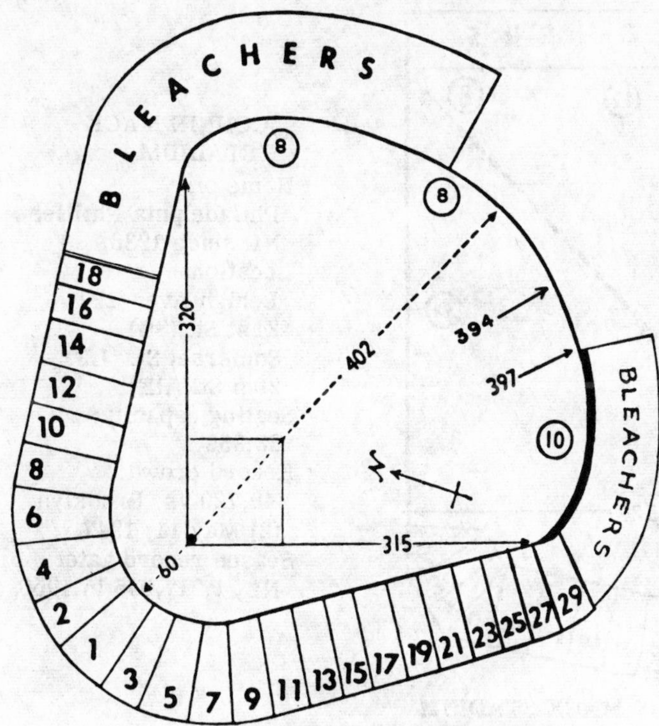

MILWAUKEE COUNTY STADIUM

MILWAUKEE COUNTY STADIUM

Home of:
Milwaukee Braves NL since 1953.

Location:
Mitchell Blvd. Rd.
Story Pkway Rd.
South 44th St.

Seating capacity:
43,827.

Record crowd:
47,604.
vs. Cincinnati (2)
Sept. 3, 1956.

Season record gate:
2,215,404 in 1957.

POLO GROUNDS

Home of:
New York Mets NL
since 1962.
(New York Giants 1891-1957)

Location:
Eighth Ave.
157th St.
159th St.

Seating capacity:
55,000.

Record crowd:
60,747 vs. Brooklyn
(2) May 31, 1937.

Season record gate:
1,600,793 in 1947.

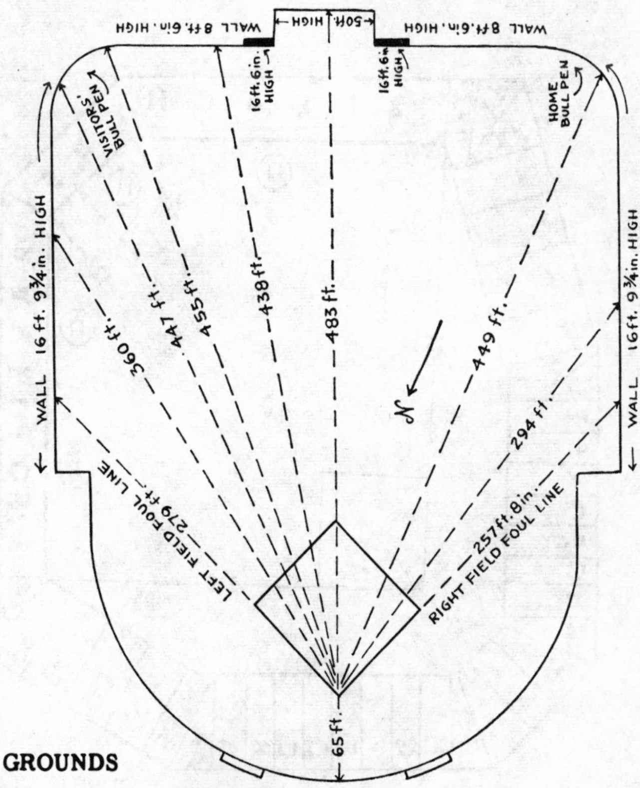

POLO GROUNDS

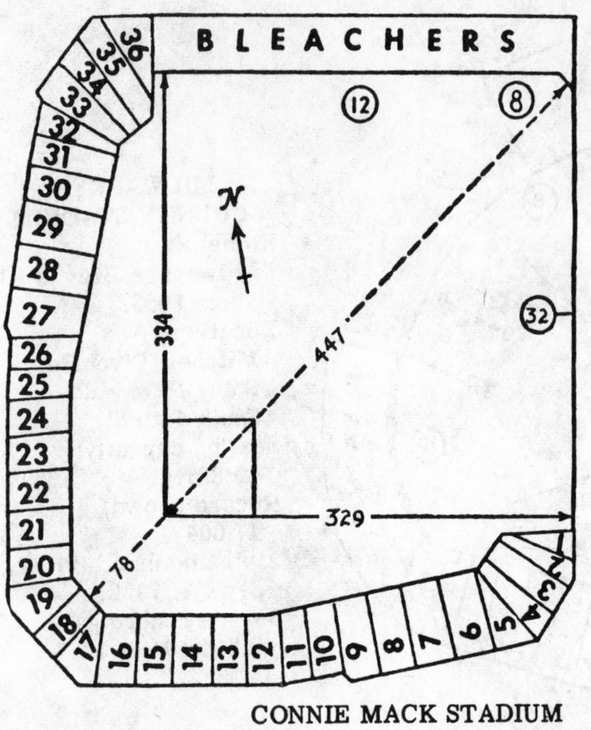

CONNIE MACK STADIUM

CONNIE MACK STADIUM

Home of:
Philadelphia Phillies
NL since 1938.

Location:
Lehigh Ave. (1B)
21 st St. (3B)
Somerset St. (LF)
20th St. (RF)

Seating capacity:
33,359

Record crowd:
40,720 vs. Brooklyn
(2) May 11, 1947.

Season record gate:
NL, 1,217,035 in 1950.

(Numbers inside circles indicate height of fences in feet)

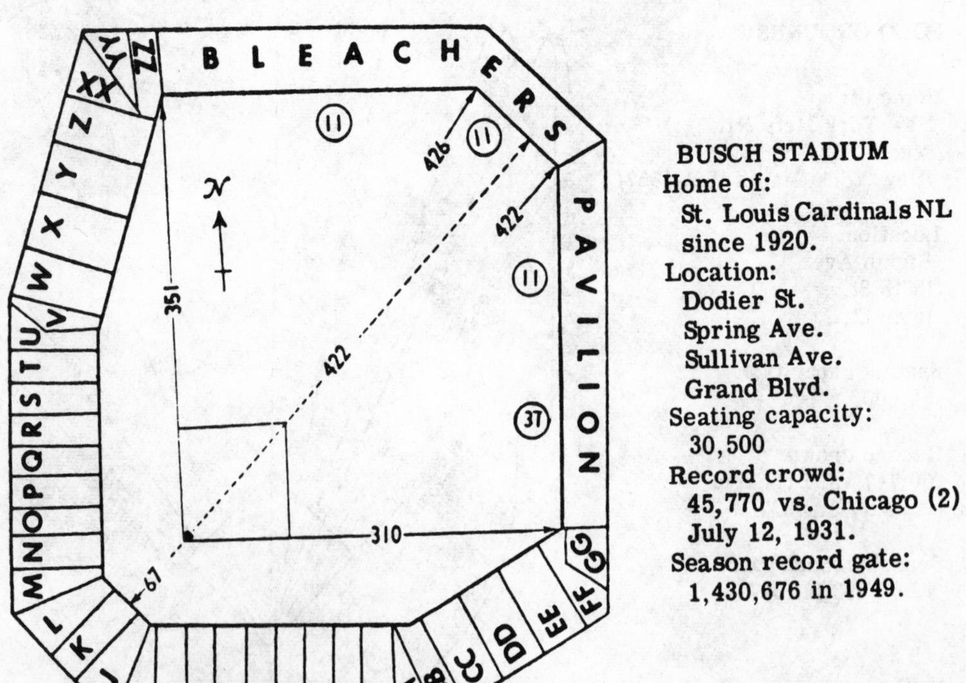

BUSCH STADIUM

Home of:
St. Louis Cardinals NL
since 1920.

Location:
Dodier St.
Spring Ave.
Sullivan Ave.
Grand Blvd.

Seating capacity:
30,500

Record crowd:
45,770 vs. Chicago (2)
July 12, 1931.

Season record gate:
1,430,676 in 1949.

BUSCH STADIUM

FORBES FIELD
Home of:
Pittsburgh Pirates NL since 1909.
Location:
Boquet St.
Sennott St.
Schenley Park
Seating capacity:
35,000
Record crowd:
44,932
vs. Brooklyn
Sept. 23, 1956.
Season record gate:
1,517,021 in 1948.

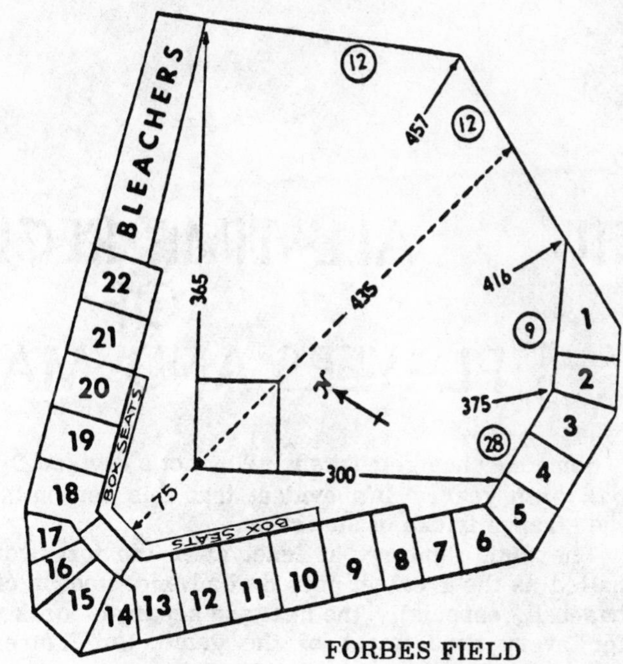

FORBES FIELD

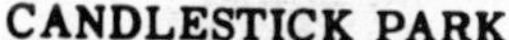

CANDLESTICK PARK

Home of:
San Francisco Giants NL since 1961.

Location:
San Francisco Freeway at Bayshore.

Seating Capacity:
42,500.

Record crowd:
41,735 vs. Los Angeles

Season record gate:
1,795,356 in 1961.

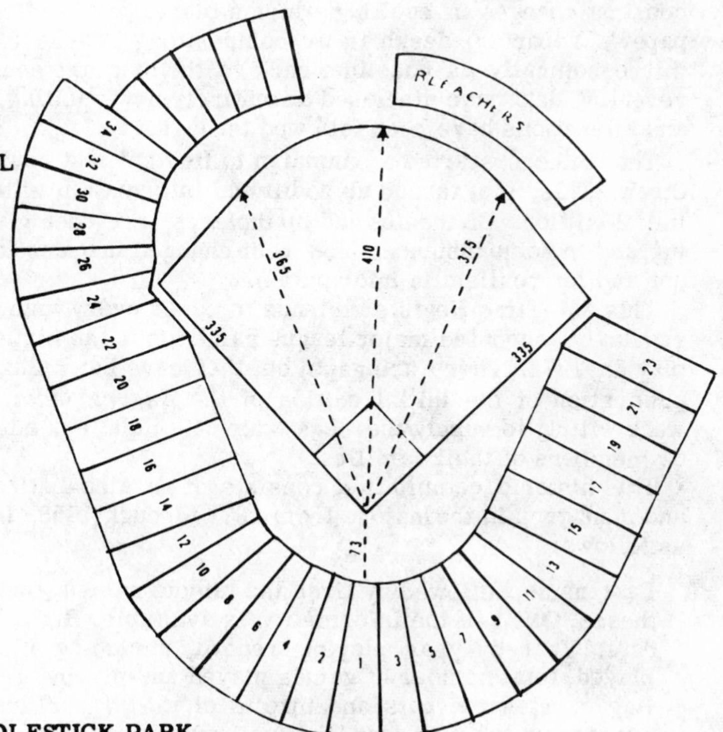

CANDLESTICK PARK

III ALL-TIME REGISTER OF PLAYERS AND MANAGERS

Someone once remarked: "Why not a revised *Official Encyclopedia of Baseball* each year?" It's evident that this person is not on speaking terms with the strange tricks of statistics.

The 20th Century, at least after the fuzz wore off just a trifle, has been hailed as the greatest period of advancement in civilization. And so it is with baseball, especially the neat and accurate bookkeeping systems now in effect for every department of the game. But figures constantly will crop up as fabrications, misprints in old newspapers and stretches of imagination which have been handed down from so-called authorities.

This All-Time Register, since first compiled for publication in 1951, has changed considerably in character. Original research revealed names which, after further probing between the first edition and this spanking new Third Revised Edition, were only phantoms in some cases, names which were listed incorrectly in a major league boxscore. Another point of aggravation was the constant changes in spelling which a player would effect, or was it the newspaper's reporter, deskman or compositor? These too have been traced, as microscopically as possible, back to the original source and in many cases revealing data have disclosed an entirely new spelling. So these corrections and alterations have been followed through.

The authors started a campaign to find out just how each player batted and threw. This, too, turned up additional information which was incorrect in the initial edition. Birthdates and birthplaces have been given a further researching, and in some instances have been changed in order to meet with the current demand for realism in information.

This All-Time Register intends to cover every man who ever appeared in a regularly scheduled major league game since the birth of professional league play in 1871. There are gaps, but they have been plugged considerably since publication of the initial edition of the *Encyclopedia,* many by readers who were willing to supply the pegs which fitted holes; others by former players or members of their families.

This historic compilation consists of an alphabetical listing of all players and managers in the majors from 1871 through 1958. Information is arranged as follows:

> Last name, followed by first and middle names, then nickname in parentheses, ONLY if the information is available. Birthplace, birthdate, death date. Year-by-year playing record, including club, league, positions played, total number of games played and playing performance. The last line carries the bats and throws of the player and his lifetime batting average or his won-lost lifetime total if a pitcher, or both.

KEY TO ABBREVIATIONS

Teams:

ALL(Allegheny); ALT(Altoona); ATH(Athletics); ATL(Atlantics); BAL(Baltimore); BOS(Boston); BRO(Brooklyn); BUF(Buffalo); CEN(Centennials); CHI (Chicago); CIN(Cincinnati); CLE(Cleveland); COL(Columbus); DET(Detroit); ECK(Eckford); ECL(Eclipse); HAR(Hartford); HOU(Houston); IND(Indianapolis); KC(Kansas City); KEK(Kekiongas); KEO(Keokuk); KEY(Keystone); LA (Los Angeles); LB (Lord Baltimore); LOU(Louisville); MAN(Mansfield); MAR (Maryland); MET (Metropolitans); MIL(Milwaukee); MINN(Minnesota); MUT (Mutuals); NAT(Nationals); NEW (Newark); NH (New Haven); NY (New York); OLY(Olympics); PHI(Philadelphia); PIT(Pittsburgh); PRO(Providence); RES(Resolutes); RIC(Richmond); ROC (Rochester); ROK(Rockford); RS(Red Stockings); St. L (St. Louis); SF(San Francisco); SYR(Syracuse); TOL(Toledo); TRO(Troy); VIR(Virginia); WAS (Washington); WIL(Wilmington); WOR(Worcester).

LEAGUES

n—National Association
N—National League
a—American Association
U—Union Association
p—Players League
A—American League
F—Federal League

POSITIONS

1—First base
2—Second base
S—Shortstop
3—Third base
O—Outfield
C—Catcher
P—Pitcher
H—pinch hitter
M—Manager

NR—No record available

BL—bats left
BR—bats right
BB—bats both

TL—throws left
TR– throws right

ALL-TIME REGISTER

AARON, HENRY LOUIS

b.Feb.5,1934 Mobile,Ala.

Yr	Cl	Lea	Pos	G	Rec
1954	Mil	N	O	122	.280
1955	Mil	N	2-O	153	.314
1956	Mil	N	O	153	.328
1957	Mil	N	O	151	.322
1958	Mil	N	O	153	.326
1959	Mil	N	3-O	154	.355
1960	Mil	N	2-O	153	.292
1961	Mil	N	3-O	155	.327
1962	Mil	N	1-O	156	.323
		BRTR		1350	.320

AARON, TOMMIE LEE

b.Aug.5,1939 Mobile,Ala.

Yr	Cl	Lea	Pos	G	Rec
1962	Mil	N	1-2-3-O	141	.231
		BRTR			

ABADIE, JOHN

b.1854 Philadelphia,Pa.

Yr	Cl	Lea	Pos	G	Rec
1875	Cen	n	1	11	NR
1875	Atl	n	1	1	.250
				12	NR

ABBATICCHIO, EDWARD JAMES (Batty)

b.Apr.15,1877 Latrobe,Pa.
d.Jan.6,1957

Yr	Cl	Lea	Pos	G	Rec
1897	Phi	N	2	3	.300
1898	Phi	N	3	20	.262
1903	Bos	N	2-S	133	.227
1904	Bos	N	S	154	.256
1905	Bos	N	S	153	.279
1907	Pit	N	2	147	.262
1908	Pit	N	2	144	.250
1909	Pit	N	S	23	.230
1910	Pit	N	S	1	.000
1910	Bos	N	S	47	.247
		BRTR		825	.255

ABBEY, BERT WOOD

b.Nov.29,1869 Essex,Vt.
d.June 11,1962

Yr	Cl	Lea	Pos	G	Rec
1892	Was	N	P	21	6-15
1893	Chi	N	P	8	3-5
1894	Chi	N	P	11	2-7
1895	Chi	N	P	2	0-1
1895	Bro	N	P	8	4-3
1896	Bro	N	P	19	8-8
		BRTR		69	23-39

ABBEY, CHARLES S.

b.1867 Omaha,Neb.

Yr	Cl	Lea	Pos	G	Rec
1893	Was	N	O	31	.277
1894	Was	N	O	129	.318
1895	Was	N	O	133	.275
1896	Was	N	O	75	.255
1897	Was	N	O	78	.264
				446	.283

ABBOTT, FREDERICK H.

(Real name Frederick H. Vandemann)
b.Oct.22,1874 Versailles,O.
d.June 11,1935

Yr	Cl	Lea	Pos	G	Rec
1903	Cle	A	C	76	.271
1904	Cle	A	C	42	.168
1905	Phi	N	C	39	.195
		BRTR		157	.226

ABBOTT, LEANDER FRANKLIN (Big Dan)

b.Mar.16,1862 Weston,O.
d.Feb.13,1930

Yr	Cl	Lea	Pos	G	Rec
1890	Tol	a	P	3	1-2
		TR			

ABBOTT, ODY CLEON (Odd)

b.Sept.5,1888 Pittsburgh,Pa.
d.Apr.13,1933

Yr	Cl	Lea	Pos	G	Rec
1910	St.L	N	O	21	.186

ABER, ALBERT JULIUS (Lefty)

b.July 31,1927 Cleveland,O.

Yr	Cl	Lea	Pos	G	Rec
1950	Cle	A	P	1	1-0
1953	Cle	A	P	6	1-1
1953	Det	A	P	17	4-3
1954	Det	A	P	32	5-11
1955	Det	A	P	39	6-3
1956	Det	A	P	42	4-4
1957	Det	A	P	28	3-3
1957	KC	A	P	3	0-0
		BLTL		168	24-25

ABERCROMBIE, DAVID

b.Baltimore,Md.
d.Sept.2,1916

Yr	Cl	Lea	Pos	G	Rec
1871	Tro	n	S	1	.000

ABERNATHIE, WILLIAM EDWARD

b.Jan.30,1930 Torrance,Cal.

Yr	Cl	Lea	Pos	G	Rec
1952	Cle	A	P	1	0-0
		BRTR			

ABERNATHY, TALMADGE LAFAYETTE (Ted)

b.Oct.30,1921 Bynum,N.C.

Yr	Cl	Lea	Pos	G	Rec
1942	Phi	A	P	1	0-0
1943	Phi	A	P	5	0-3
1944	Phi	A	P	1	0-0
		BRTL		7	0-3

ABERNATHY, THEODORE WADE

b.Mar.6,1933 Stanley,N.C.

Yr	Cl	Lea	Pos	G	Rec
1955	Was	A	P	40	5-9
1956	Was	A	P	5	1-3
1957	Was	A	P	26	2-10
1960	Was	A	P	2	0-0
		BRTR		73	8-22

ABERNATHY, VIRGIL WOODROW(Woody)

b.Feb.1,1915 Forest City,N.C.

Yr	Cl	Lea	Pos	G	Rec
1946	NY	N	P	15	1-1
1947	NY	N	P	1	0-0
		BLTL		16	1-1

ABERSON, CLIFFORD ALEXANDER

b.Aug.28,1921 Chicago,Ill.

Yr	Cl	Lea	Pos	G	Rec
1947	Chi	N	O	47	.279
1948	Chi	N	O	12	.188
1949	Chi	N	O	4	.000
		BRTR		63	.251

ABLES, HARRY TERRELL (Hans)

b.Oct.4,1884 Terrell,Tex.
d.Feb.8,1951

(Continued)

Yr	Cl	Lea	Pos	G	Rec
1905	St.L	A	P	6	0-3
1909	Cle	A	P	6	1-1
1911	NY	A	P	3	0-1
		BRTL		15	1-5

ABRAMS, CALVIN ROSS

b.Mar.2,1924 Philadelphia,Pa.

Yr	Cl	Lea	Pos	G	Rec
1949	Bro	N	O	8	.083
1950	Bro	N	O	38	.205
1951	Bro	N	O	67	.280
1952	Bro	N	O	10	.200
1952	Cin	N	O	71	.278
1953	Pit	N	O	119	.286
1954	Pit	N	O	17	.143
1954	Bal	A	O	115	.293
1955	Bal	A	1-O	118	.243
1956	Chi	A	O	4	.333
		BLTL		567	.269

ABRAMS, GEORGE ALLEN

b.Nov.9,1899 Seattle,Wash.

Yr	Cl	Lea	Pos	G	Rec
1923	Cin	N	P	3	0-0
		BRTR			

ABREU, JOSEPH LAWRENCE

b.May 24,1916 Oakland, Cal.

Yr	Cl	Lea	Pos	G	Rec
1942	Cin	N	2-3	9	.214
		BRTR			

ABSTEIN, WILLIAM HENRY (Big Bill)

b.Feb.2,1885 St.Louis,Mo.
d.Apr.8,1940

Yr	Cl	Lea	Pos	G	Rec
1906	Pit	N	O	8	.200
1909	Pit	N	1	135	.260
1910	St.L	A	1	25	.149
		BRTR		168	.242

ACKER, THOMAS JAMES

b.Mar.7,1930 Paterson,N.J.

Yr	Cl	Lea	Pos	G	Rec
1956	Cin	N	P	29	4-3
1957	Cin	N	P	49	10-5
1958	Cin	N	P	38	4-3
1959	Cin	N	P	37	1-2
		BRTR		153	19-13

ACOSTA, BALMADERO MERITO

b.May 19,1896 Havana,Cuba

Yr	Cl	Lea	Pos	G	Rec
1913	Was	A	O	12	.250
1914	Was	A	O	38	.257
1915	Was	A	O	72	.209
1916	Was	A	O	5	.125
1918	Was	A	O	3	.000
1918	Phi	A	O	49	.302
		BLTL		179	.252

ACOSTA, JOSE

b.Mar.4,1894 Havana,Cuba

Yr	Cl	Lea	Pos	G	Rec
1920	Was	A	P	17	5-4
1921	Was	A	P	33	5-4
1922	Chi	A	P	5	0-2
		BBTR		55	10-10

ADAIR, JAMES AUDREY (Choppy)

b.Jan.25,1908 Waxahachie,Tex.

Yr	Cl	Lea	Pos	G	Rec
1931	Chi	N	S	18	.276
		BRTR			

ADAIR, KENNETH JERRY
b.Dec.17,1936 Tulsa,Okla.

Yr	Cl	Lea	Pos	G	Rec
1958	Bal	A	2-S	11	.105
1959	Bal	A	2-S	12	.314
1960	Bal	A	2	3	.200
1961	Bal	A	2-S-3	133	.264
1962	Bal	A	2-S-3	139	.284
		BRTR		298	.274

ADAMS, ACE TOWNSEND
b.Mar.2,1914 Willows,Cal.

Yr	Cl	Lea	Pos	G	Rec
1941	NY	N	P	38	4-1
1942	NY	N	P	61	7-4
1943	NY	N	P	70	11-7
1944	NY	N	P	65	8-11
1945	NY	N	P	65	11-9
1946	NY	N	P	3	0-1
		BRTR		302	41-33

ADAMS, CHARLES BENJAMIN(Babe)
b.May 18,1883 Tipton,Ind.

Yr	Cl	Lea	Pos	G	Rec
1906	St.L	N	P	1	0-1
1907	Pit	N	P	4	2-2
1909	Pit	N	P	25	12-3
1910	Pit	N	P	34	18-9
1911	Pit	N	P	40	22-12
1912	Pit	N	P	28	11-8
1913	Pit	N	P	43	21-10
1914	Pit	N	P	40	13-16
1915	Pit	N	P	40	14-14
1916	Pit	N	P	16	2-9
1918	Pit	N	P	3	1-1
1919	Pit	N	P	34	17-10
1920	Pit	N	P	35	17-13
1921	Pit	N	P	25	14-5
1922	Pit	N	P	27	8-11
1923	Pit	N	P	26	13-7
1924	Pit	N	P	9	3-1
1925	Pit	N	P	33	6-5
1926	Pit	N	P	19	2-3
		BLTR		482	196-140

ADAMS, CHARLES DWIGHT
(Red)
b.Oct.7,1921 Parlier,Cal.

Yr	Cl	Lea	Pos	G	Rec
1946	Chi	N	P	8	0-1
		BRTR			

ADAMS, DANIEL LESLIE
b.June 19,1889 St.Louis,Mo.

Yr	Cl	Lea	Pos	G	Rec
1914	KC	F	P	26	4-9
1915	KC	F	P	11	0-2
		BRTR		37	4-11

ADAMS, EARL JOHN
(Sparky)
b.Aug.26,1897 Newtown,Pa.

Yr	Cl	Lea	Pos	G	Rec
1922	Chi	N	2	11	.250
1923	Chi	N	S-O	95	.289
1924	Chi	N	2-S	117	.280
1925	Chi	N	2-S	149	.287
1926	Chi	N	2-3	154	.309
1927	Chi	N	2-S-3	146	.292
1928	Pit	N	2-S	135	.276
1929	Pit	N	2-S-3	74	.260
1930	St.L	N	2-3	137	.314
1931	St.L	N	3	143	.293
1932	St.L	N	3	31	.276
1933	St.L	N	S-3	8	.167
1933	Cin	N	S-3	137	.262
1934	Cin	N	2-3	87	.252
		BRTR		1424	.286

ADAMS, ELVIN CLARK
(Buster)
b.June 24,1916 Trinidad,Col.

Yr	Cl	Lea	Pos	G	Rec
1939	St.L	N	H	2	.000
1943	St.L	N	O	8	.091

(Continued)

Yr	Cl	Lea	Pos	G	Rec
1943	Phi	N	O	111	.256
1944	Phi	N	O	151	.283
1945	Phi	N	O	14	.232
1945	St.L	N	O	140	.292
1946	St.L	N	O	81	.185
1947	Phi	N	O	69	.247
		BRTR		576	.266

ADAMS, GEORGE
b.Syracuse,N.Y.

Yr	Cl	Lea	Pos	G	Rec
1879	Syr	N	1-O	4	.214

ADAMS, HERBERT LOREN
b.Apr.14,1928 Oak Park, Ill.

Yr	Cl	Lea	Pos	G	Rec
1948	Chi	A	O	5	.273
1949	Chi	A	O	56	.293
1950	Chi	A	O	34	.203
		BLTL		95	.261

ADAMS, JAMES IRWIN
(Willie)
b.Sept.27,1890 Clearfield,Pa.
d.June 18,1937

Yr	Cl	Lea	Pos	G	Rec
1912	St.L	A	P	13	2-3
1913	St.L	A	P	4	0-1
1914	Pit	F	P	15	1-1
1918	Phi	A	P	32	5-12
1919	Phi	A	P	1	0-0
		BRTR		65	8-17

ADAMS, JAMES J.
b. St.Louis,Mo.

Yr	Cl	Lea	Pos	G	Rec
1890	St.L	a	C	1	.250

ADAMS, JOHN BERTRAM
b.June 21,1891 Wharton,Tex.
d.June 24,1940

Yr	Cl	Lea	Pos	G	Rec
1910	Cle	A	C	5	.230
1911	Cle	A	C	2	.250
1912	Cle	A	C	20	.204
1915	Phi	N	C	24	.111
1916	Phi	N	C	11	.231
1917	Phi	N	C	43	.206
1918	Phi	N	C	84	.176
1919	Phi	N	C-1	78	.233
		BRTR		267	.202

ADAMS, JOSEPH EDWARD
b.Oct.28,1877 Cowden,Ill.
d.Oct.8,1952

Yr	Cl	Lea	Pos	G	Rec
1902	St.L	N	P	1	0-0
	TL				

ADAMS, KARL TUTWEILER
(Rebel)
b.Aug.11,1891 Columbus,Ga.

Yr	Cl	Lea	Pos	G	Rec
1914	Cin	N	P	4	0-0
1915	Chi	N	P	26	1-9
		BRTR		30	1-9

ADAMS, RICHARD LEROY
b.Apr.8,1920 Tuolumne,Cal.

Yr	Cl	Lea	Pos	G	Rec
1947	Phi	A	1-O	37	.202
		BRTL			

ADAMS, RICK ALEXANDER
b.Dec.23,1879 Paris,Tex.
d.Mar.10,1955

Yr	Cl	Lea	Pos	G	Rec
1905	Was	A	P	8	2-6
		BLTL			

ADAMS, ROBERT
b.Jan.20,1910 Birmingham,Ala.

Yr	Cl	Lea	Pos	G	Rec
1931	Phi	N	P	1	0-1
1932	Phi	N	P	4	0-0
		BRTR		5	0-1

ADAMS, ROBERT DALE
b.Jan.21, 1899 Bedford,Ind.
d.Sept.6,1944

Yr	Cl	Lea	Pos	G	Rec
1925	Bos	A	P	2	0-0
		BRTR			

ADAMS, ROBERT HENRY
b.Dec.14,1921 Tuolumne,Cal.

(Continued)

Yr	Cl	Lea	Pos	G	Rec
1946	Cin	N	2-3-O	94	.244
1947	Cin	N	2	81	.272
1948	Cin	N	2-3	87	.298
1949	Cin	N	2-3	107	.253
1950	Cin	N	2-3	115	.282
1951	Cin	N	2-3-O	125	.266
1952	Cin	N	3	154	.283
1953	Cin	N	3	150	.275
1954	Cin	N	2-3	110	.269
1955	Cin	N	2-3	64	.273
1955	Chi	A	2-3	28	.095
1956	Bal	A	2-3	41	.225
1957	Chi	N	2-3	60	.251
1958	Chi	N	1-2-3	62	.281
1959	Chi	N	1	3	.000
		BRTR		1281	.269

ADAMS, SPENCER DEWEY
b.June 21,1897 Layton,Utah

Yr	Cl	Lea	Pos	G	Rec
1923	Pit	N	2-S	25	.250
1925	Was	A	2-S-3	39	.272
1926	NY	A	2	28	.120
1927	St.L	A	2-3	88	.266
		BLTR		180	.256

ADCOCK, JOSEPH WILBUR
b.Oct.30,1927 Coushatta,La.

Yr	Cl	Lea	Pos	G	Rec
1950	Cin	N	1-O	102	.293
1951	Cin	N	O	113	.243
1952	Cin	N	1-O	117	.278
1953	Mil	N	1	157	.285
1954	Mil	N	1	133	.308
1955	Mil	N	1	84	.264
1956	Mil	N	1	137	.291
1957	Mil	N	1	65	.287
1958	Mil	N	1-O	105	.275
1959	Mil	N	1-O	115	.292
1960	Mil	N	1	138	.298
1961	Mil	N	1	152	.285
1962	Mil	N	1	121	.248
		BRTR		1539	.282

ADDIS, ROBERT GORDON
b.Nov.6,1925 Mineral,O.

Yr	Cl	Lea	Pos	G	Rec
1950	Bos	N	O	16	.250
1951	Bos	N	O	85	.276
1952	Chi	N	O	93	.295
1953	Chi	N	O	10	.167
1953	Pit	N	H	4	.000
		BLTR		208	.281

ADDY, ROBERT EDWARD
(Magnet)
b.1838 Rochester,N.Y.
d.Apr.10,1910

Yr	Cl	Lea	Pos	G	Rec
1871	Rok	n	2-S	24	NR
1873	Phi	n	2	10	NR
1873	Bos	n	O	31	NR
1874	Har	n	2-S-3	50	NR
1875	Phi	n	2-O	69	.263
1876	Chi	N	O	33	.272
1877	Cin	N	M-O	57	.278
		BLTL		274	NR

ADERHOLT, MORRIS WOODROW
b.Sept.13,1916 Mt.Olive,N.C.
d.Mar.18,1955

Yr	Cl	Lea	Pos	G	Rec
1939	Was	A	2	7	.200
1940	Was	A	2	1	.000
1941	Was	A	2-3	11	.143
1944	Bro	N	O	17	.271
1945	Bro	N	O	39	.217
1945	Bos	N	2-O	31	.333
		BLTR		106	.267

ADKINS, GRADY EMMETT
(Butcher Boy)
b.June 29,1897 Little Rock,Ark.

Yr	Cl	Lea	Pos	G	Rec
1928	Chi	A	P	39	10-16
1929	Chi	A	P	37	2-11
		BRTR		76	12-27

ADKINS, JOHN DEWEY
b.May 11,1918 Norcatur,Kan.

Yr	Cl	Lea	Pos	G	Rec
1942	Was	A	P	1	0-0
1943	Was	A	P	7	0-0
1949	Chi	N	P	30	2-4
	BRTR			38	2-4

ADKINS, MERLE THERON (Doc)
b.Aug.5,1872 Troy,Wis.
d.Feb.21,1934

Yr	Cl	Lea	Pos	G	Rec
1902	Bos	A	P	4	1-1
1903	NY	A	P	2	0-1
	TR			6	1-2

ADKINS, RICHARD EARL
b.Mar.3,1920 Electra,Tex.
d.Sept.1955

Yr	Cl	Lea	Pos	G	Rec
1942	Phi	A	S	3	.143
	BRTR				

ADKINSON, HENRY MAGEE
b.Sept.1,1874 Chicago,Ill.
d.May 1,1923

Yr	Cl	Lea	Pos	G	Rec
1895	St.L	N	O	1	.400

AGEE, THOMAS LEE
b.Aug.9,1942 Magnolia,Ala.

Yr	Cl	Lea	Pos	G	Rec
1962	Cle	A	O	5	.214
	BRTR				

AGGANIS, HARRY (Greek)
b.Apr.30,1930 Lynn,Mass.
d.June 27,1955

Yr	Cl	Lea	Pos	G	Rec
1954	Bos	A	1	132	.251
1955	Bos	A	1	25	.313
	BLTL			157	.261

AGLER, JOSEPH ABRAM
b.June 12,1889 Beach City,O.

Yr	Cl	Lea	Pos	G	Rec
1912	Was	A	1	2	.000
1914	Buf	F	1-O	135	.272
1915	Buf	F	1	25	.178
1915	Bal	F	1-2	70	.214
	BLTL			232	.246

AGNEW, SAMUEL LESTER (Slam)
b.Apr.12,1889 Farmington,Mo.
d.July 19,1951

Yr	Cl	Lea	Pos	G	Rec
1913	St.L	A	C	104	.208
1914	St.L	A	C	113	.212
1915	St.L	A	C	104	.203
1916	Bos	A	C	40	.209
1917	Bos	A	C	85	.208
1918	Bos	A	C	72	.166
1919	Was	A	C	42	.235
	BRTR			560	.204

AGUIRRE, HENRY JOHN
b.Jan.31,1932 Azusa,Cal.

Yr	Cl	Lea	Pos	G	Rec
1955	Cle	A	P	4	2-0
1956	Cle	A	P	16	3-5
1957	Cle	A	P	10	1-1
1958	Det	A	P	44	3-4
1959	Det	A	P	3	0-0
1960	Det	A	P	37	5-3
1961	Det	A	P	45	4-4
1962	Det	A	P	42	16-8
	BRTL			201	34-25

AHEARN, CHARLES
b. Troy,N.Y.

Yr	Cl	Lea	Pos	G	Rec
1880	Tro	N	C	1	.250

AINSMITH, EDWARD WILBUR (Dorf)
b.Feb.21,1887 Cambridge,Mass.

Yr	Cl	Lea	Pos	G	Rec
1910	Was	A	C	33	.192
1911	Was	A	C	61	.222
1912	Was	A	C	60	.226
1913	Was	A	C	77	.210
1914	Was	A	C	58	.225
1915	Was	A	C	47	.200
1916	Was	A	C	51	.170

(Continued)

Yr	Cl	Lea	Pos	G	Rec
1917	Was	A	C	125	.191
1918	Was	A	C	96	.212
1919	Det	A	C	114	.272
1920	Det	A	C	69	.231
1921	Det	A	C	35	.276
1921	St.L	N	C	27	.290
1922	St.L	N	C	119	.293
1923	St.L	N	C	82	.213
1923	Bro	N	C	2	.200
1924	NY	N	C	10	.600
	BRTR			1066	.232

AITCHISON, RALEIGH LEONIDAS
b.Dec.5,1887 Tyndall,S.D.
d.Sept.26,1958

Yr	Cl	Lea	Pos	G	Rec
1911	Bro	N	P	1	0-1
1914	Bro	N	P	26	12-7
1915	Bro	N	P	7	0-4
	BRTL			34	12-12

AITON, GEORGE WILSON
b.Dec. 29,1890 Kingman,Kan.

Yr	Cl	Lea	Pos	G	Rec
1912	St.L	A	O	10	.235
	BBTR				

AKE, JOHN L.
b.1863 Altoona,Pa.
d.May 11,1887

Yr	Cl	Lea	Pos	G	Rec
1884	Bal	a	S-3-O	13	.208

AKERS, ALBERT EARL
b.Nov.1,1887 Shelbyville, Ind.

Yr	Cl	Lea	Pos	G	Rec
1912	Was	A	P	5	0-0
	BRTR				

AKERS, WILLIAM (Bump)
b.Dec.25,1904 Chattanooga,Tenn.
d.Apr.13,1962

Yr	Cl	Lea	Pos	G	Rec
1929	Det	A	S	24	.265
1930	Det	A	S-3	85	.278
1931	Det	A	S	29	.197
1932	Bos	N	3	36	.258
	BRTR			174	.261

ALBANESE, JOSEPH PETER
b.June 26,1933 New York,N.Y.

Yr	Cl	Lea	Pos	G	Rec
1958	Was	A	P	6	0-0
	BRTR				

ALBERTS, AUGUST P.
b.1861 Reading,Pa.
d.May 8,1912

Yr	Cl	Lea	Pos	G	Rec
1884	Pit	a	S	2	.200
1884	Was	U	S	4	.250
1888	Cle	a	S-3	101	.192
1891	Mil	a	3	12	.100
	BRTR			119	.186

ALBERTS, FREDERICK JOSEPH (Cy)
b.Jan.14,1882 Grand Rapids,Mich.
d.Aug.27,1917

Yr	Cl	Lea	Pos	G	Rec
1910	St.L	N	P	4	1-2

ALBERTS, JAMES
(Played under name of Alvin James Dolan)

ALBOSTA, EDWARD JOHN (Rube)
b.Oct.27,1918 Saginaw,Mich.

Yr	Cl	Lea	Pos	G	Rec
1941	Bro	N	P	2	0-2
1946	Pit	N	P	17	0-6
	BRTR			19	0-8

ALBRECHT, EDWARD ARTHUR
b.Feb.28,1929 St.Louis Co.,Mo.

Yr	Cl	Lea	Pos	G	Rec
1949	St.L	A	P	1	1-0
1950	St.L	A	P	2	0-1
	BRTR			3	1-1

ALBRIGHT, JOHN HAROLD
b.June 30,1921 St.Petersburg,Fla.

Yr	Cl	Lea	Pos	G	Rec
1947	Phi	N	S	41	.232
	BRTR				

ALCOCK, JOHN FORBES (Scotty)
b.Nov.29,1889 Wooster,O.

Yr	Cl	Lea	Pos	G	Rec
1914	Chi	A	3	54	.173
	BRTR				

ALDERSON, DALE LEONARD
b.Mar.9,1918 Belden,Neb.

Yr	Cl	Lea	Pos	G	Rec
1943	Chi	N	P	4	0-1
1944	Chi	N	P	12	0-0
	BRTR			16	0-1

ALDRIDGE, VICTOR EDDINGTON
b.Oct.25,1893 Indian Springs,Ind.

Yr	Cl	Lea	Pos	G	Rec
1917	Chi	N	P	30	6-6
1918	Chi	N	P	3	0-1
1922	Chi	N	P	36	16-15
1923	Chi	N	P	30	16-9
1924	Chi	N	P	32	15-12
1925	Pit	N	P	30	15-7
1926	Pit	N	P	30	10-13
1927	Pit	N	P	35	15-10
1928	NY	N	P	22	4-7
	BRTR			248	97-80

ALENO, CHARLES (Chuck)
b.Feb.19,1918 St.Louis,Mo.

Yr	Cl	Lea	Pos	G	Rec
1941	Cin	N	1-3	54	.243
1942	Cin	N	2-3	7	.143
1943	Cin	N	O	7	.300
1944	Cin	N	1-S-3	50	.165
	BRTR			118	.209

ALEXANDER, DAVID DALE (Moose)
b.Apr.26,1903 Greeneville,Tenn.

Yr	Cl	Lea	Pos	G	Rec
1929	Det	A	1	155	.343
1930	Det	A	1	154	.326
1931	Det	A	1	135	.325
1932	Det	A	1	23	.250
1932	Bos	A	1	101	.372
1933	Bos	A	1	94	.281
	BRTR			662	.331

ALEXANDER, GROVER CLEVELAND (Pete)
b.Feb.26,1887 St.Paul,Neb.
d.Nov.4,1950

Yr	Cl	Lea	Pos	G	Rec
1911	Phi	N	P	48	28-13
1912	Phi	N	P	46	19-17
1913	Phi	N	P	47	22-8
1914	Phi	N	P	48	27-15
1915	Phi	N	P	49	31-10
1916	Phi	N	P	49	33-12
1917	Phi	N	P	47	30-13
1918	Chi	N	P	3	2-1
1919	Chi	N	P	30	16-11
1920	Chi	N	P	46	27-14
1921	Chi	N	P	31	15-13
1922	Chi	N	P	33	16-13
1923	Chi	N	P	39	22-12
1924	Chi	N	P	21	12-5
1925	Chi	N	P	32	15-11
1926	Chi	N	P	7	3-3
1926	St.L	N	P	23	9-7
1927	St.L	N	P	37	21-10
1928	St.L	N	P	34	16-9
1929	St.L	N	P	22	9-8
1930	Phi	N	P	9	0-3
	BRTR			701	373-208

ALEXANDER, HUGH
b.July 10,1917 Buffalo,Mo.

Yr	Cl	Lea	Pos	G	Rec
1937	Cle	A	O	7	.091
	BRTR				

ALEXANDER, ROBERT SOMERVILLE
b.Aug.7,1922 Vancouver,B.C.,Canada

Yr	Cl	Lea	Pos	G	Rec
1955	Bal	A	P	4	1-0
1957	Cle	A	P	5	0-1
	BRTR			9	1-1

ALEXANDER, WALTER E.
b.Mar.5,1891 Atlanta,Ga.

Yr	Cl	Lea	Pos	G	Rec
1912	St.L	A	C	37	.175
1913	St.L	A	C	42	.141
1915	St.L	A	C	1	.000
1915	NY	A	C	25	.250
1916	NY	A	C	36	.256
1917	NY	A	C	20	.137
	BRTR			161	.189

ALEXANDER, WILLIAM HENRY
(Nin)
b.Nov,24,1858 Pana,Ill.
d.Dec.22,1933

Yr	Cl	Lea	Pos	G	Rec
1884	KC	U	C-S-O	19	.127
1884	St.L	a	C-O	1	.000
				20	.119

ALLEN, ARTEMUS WARD
(Nick)
b.Sept.14,1889 Udall,Kan.
d.Oct.16,1939

Yr	Cl	Lea	Pos	G	Rec
1914	Buf	F	C	31	.235
1915	Buf	F	C	83	.205
1916	Chi	N	C	5	.063
1918	Cin	N	C	37	.260
1919	Cin	N	C	15	.320
1920	Cin	N	C	43	.271
	BRTR			214	.231

ALLEN, BERNARD KEITH
b.Apr.16,1939 E.Liverpool,O.

Yr	Cl	Lea	Pos	G	Rec
1962	Min	A	2	159	.269
	BLTR				

ALLEN, CYRUS ALBAN
(Dick)
b.1855 Girard,Pa.
d.Apr.21,1915

Yr	Cl	Lea	Pos	G	Rec
1879	Syr	N	3-O	11	.184
1879	Cle	N	3-O	16	.117
				27	.165

ALLEN, ETHAN NATHAN
b.Jan.1,1904 Cincinnati,O.

Yr	Cl	Lea	Pos	G	Rec
1926	Cin	N	O	18	.308
1927	Cin	N	O	111	.295
1928	Cin	N	O	129	.305
1929	Cin	N	O	143	.292
1930	Cin	N	O	21	.271
1930	NY	N	O	76	.307
1931	NY	N	O	94	.329
1932	NY	N	O	54	.175
1933	St.L	N	O	91	.241
1934	Phi	N	O	145	.330
1935	Phi	N	O	156	.307
1936	Phi	N	O	30	.296
1936	Chi	N	O	91	.295
1937	St.L	A	O	103	.316
1938	St.L	A	O	19	.303
	BRTR			1281	.300

ALLEN, FLETCHER MANSON
(Sled)
b.Aug.23,1886 West Plains,Mo.
d.Oct.16,1959

Yr	Cl	Lea	Pos	G	Rec
1910	St.L	A	C	14	.095
	TR				

ALLEN, FRANK LEON
b.Aug.26,1888 Newbern,Ala.
d.July 30,1933

Yr	Cl	Lea	Pos	G	Rec
1912	Bro	N	P	20	3-9
1913	Bro	N	P	34	4-18
1914	Bro	N	P	37	8-14
1914	Pit	F	P	1	1-0
1915	Pit	F	P	38	23-13
1916	Bos	N	P	19	8-2
1917	Bos	N	P	29	3-11
	BRTL			178	50-67

ALLEN, HEZEKIAH (Ham)
b. Norwalk,Conn.

Yr	Cl	Lea	Pos	G	Rec
1872	Man	n	S-O	14	NR
1884	Phi	N	C	1	.667
				15	NR

ALLEN, HORACE TANNER
(Pug)
b.June 11,1899 DeLand,Fla.

Yr	Cl	Lea	Pos	G	Rec
1919	Bro	N	O	4	.000
	BLTR				

ALLEN, JESSE HALL
b.May 1,1868 Columbiana,O.
d.Apr.16,1946

Yr	Cl	Lea	Pos	G	Rec
1893	Cle	N	C	1	.000
	BRTR				

ALLEN, JOHN MARSHALL
b.Oct.27,1890 Berkeley Springs,W.Va.

Yr	Cl	Lea	Pos	G	Rec
1914	Bal	F	P	1	0-0
	BRTR				

ALLEN, JOHN THOMAS
b.Sept.30,1905 Lenoir,N.C.
d.Mar.29,1959

Yr	Cl	Lea	Pos	G	Rec
1932	NY	A	P	33	17-4
1933	NY	A	P	25	15-7
1934	NY	A	P	13	5-2
1935	NY	A	P	23	13-6
1936	Cle	A	P	37	20-10
1937	Cle	A	P	24	15-1
1938	Cle	A	P	30	14-8
1939	Cle	A	P	34	9-7
1940	Cle	A	P	32	9-8
1941	St.L	A	P	20	2-5
1941	Bro	N	P	11	3-0
1942	Bro	N	P	27	10-6
1943	Bro	N	P	17	5-1
1943	NY	N	P	15	1-3
1944	NY	N	P	24	4-7
	BRTR			365	142-75

ALLEN, MYRON S.
b.Mar.22,1854 Rondout,N.Y.
d.Mar.8,1924

Yr	Cl	Lea	Pos	G	Rec
1883	NY	N	P	1	0-1
1887	Cle	a	O	117	.330
1888	KC	a	O	37	.215
				155	{0-1 .304

ALLEN, ROBERT
b.1896

Yr	Cl	Lea	Pos	G	Rec
1919	Phi	A	O	11	.094
	BRTR				

ALLEN, ROBERT EARL
b.July 2,1914 Smithville,Tenn.

Yr	Cl	Lea	Pos	G	Rec
1937	Phi	N	P	3	0-1
	BRTR				

ALLEN, ROBERT GILMAN
b.July 10,1867 Marion,O.
d.May 14,1943

Yr	Cl	Lea	Pos	G	Rec
1890	Phi	N	S	133	.225
1891	Phi	N	S	117	.227
1892	Phi	N	S	148	.229
1893	Phi	N	S	123	.283
1894	Phi	N	S	40	.253
1897	Bos	N	S	33	.309
1900	Cin	N	M-S	5	.175
	BRTR			599	.246

ALLEN, ROBERT GRAY
b.Oct.23,1937 Tatum,Tex.

Yr	Cl	Lea	Pos	G	Rec
1961	Cle	A	P	48	3-2
1962	Cle	A	P	30	1-1
	BLTL			78	4-3

ALLIE, GAIR ROOSEVELT
b.Oct.28,1931 Statesville,N.C.

Yr	Cl	Lea	Pos	G	Rec
1954	Pit	N	S-3	121	.199
	BRTR				

ALLISON, ANDREW K.
b.1848 New York,N.Y.

Yr	Cl	Lea	Pos	G	Rec
1872	Eck	n	1-O	21	NR

ALLISON, ARTHUR ALGERNON
b.Jan.29,1849 Philadelphia,Pa.
d.Feb.25,1916

Yr	Cl	Lea	Pos	G	Rec
1871	Cle	n	O	29	NR
1872	Cle	n	O	18	NR
1873	Res	n	C-1-O	22	NR
1875	Nat	n	C-1-O	25	NR
1875	Har	n	2-O	35	NR
1876	Lou	N	1-O	31	.205
				160	NR

ALLISON, DOUGLASS L.
(Dona)
b.1846 Philadelphia,Pa.
d.Dec.19,1916

Yr	Cl	Lea	Pos	G	Rec
1871	Oly	n	C	27	NR
1872	Tro	n	C-S	23	NR
1872	Eck	n	C	16	NR
1873	Res	n	C-O	17	NR
1873	Mut	n	C	11	NR
1874	Mut	n	C-O	65	NR
1875	Har	n	C-1	60	NR
1876	Har	N	C	43	.256
1877	Har	N	C	29	.148
1878	Pro	N	C	18	.267
1879	Pro	N	C	1	.000
1883	Bal	a	C	1	.500
	BRTR			311	NR

ALLISON, MACK PENDLETON
b.Jan.23,1887 Owensboro,Ky.

Yr	Cl	Lea	Pos	G	Rec
1911	St.L	A	P	3	2-1
1912	St.L	A	P	27	6-17
1913	St.L	A	P	11	1-2
	BRTR			41	9-20

ALLISON, MILO HENRY
b.Oct.16,1890 Elk Rapids,Mich.
d.June 18,1957

Yr	Cl	Lea	Pos	G	Rec
1913	Chi	N	O	2	.333
1914	Chi	N	O	1	1.000
1916	Cle	A	O	14	.263
1917	Cle	A	O	32	.143
	BLTR			49	.213

ALLISON, WILLIAM

Yr	Cl	Lea	Pos	G	Rec
1872	Eck	n	2-O	3	NR

ALLISON, WILLIAM ANDREW
b.Sept.18,1848 Philadelphia,Pa.
d.June 12,1923

Yr	Cl	Lea	Pos	G	Rec
1872	Eck	n	1-O	21	NR

ALLISON, WILLIAM ROBERT
b.July 11,1934 Raytown,Mo.

Yr	Cl	Lea	Pos	G	Rec
1958	Was	A	O	11	.200
1959	Was	A	O	150	.261
1960	Was	A	1-O	144	.251
1961	Min	A	1-O	159	.245
1962	Min	A	O	149	.266
	BRTR			613	.255

ALMADA, MELO BALDOMERO
(Mel)
b.Feb.7,1914 Hwatabampo,Sonora, Mexico

Yr	Cl	Lea	Pos	G	Rec
1933	Bos	A	O	14	.341
1934	Bos	A	O	23	.233
1935	Bos	A	1-O	151	.290
1936	Bos	A	O	96	.253
1937	Bos	A	O	32	.236
1937	Was	A	O	100	.309
1938	Was	A	O	47	.244
1938	St.L	A	O	102	.342
1939	St.L	A	O	42	.239
1939	Bro	N	O	39	.214
	BLTL			646	.284

ALMEIDA, RAFAEL D.
(Mike)
b.July 30,1887 Havana,Cuba

Yr	Cl	Lea	Pos	G	Rec
1911	Cin	N	3	29	.313
1912	Cin	N	3	16	.220

(Continued)

Yr	Cl	Lea	Pos	G	Rec
1913	Cin	N	3	50	.262
		BRTR		95	.270

ALOMA, LUIS BARBA
(Witto)
b.July 23,1923 Havana,Cuba

Yr	Cl	Lea	Pos	G	Rec
1950	Chi	A	P	42	7-2
1951	Chi	A	P	25	6-0
1952	Chi	A	P	25	3-1
1953	Chi	A	P	24	2-0
		BRTR		116	18-3

ALOU, FELIPE ROJAS
b.May 12,1935 Ciudad Trujillo,D.R.

Yr	Cl	Lea	Pos	G	Rec
1958	SF	N	O	75	.253
1959	SF	N	O	95	.275
1960	SF	N	O	106	.264
1961	SF	N	O	132	.289
1962	SF	N	O	154	.316
		BRTR		562	.287

ALOU, MATEO ROJAS
b.Dec.20,1938 Haina,D.R.

Yr	Cl	Lea	Pos	G	Rec
1960	SF	N	O	4	.333
1961	SF	N	O	81	.310
1962	SF	N	O	78	.292
		BLTL		163	.302

ALPERMAN, CHARLES AUGUSTUS
(Whitey)
b.Nov.10,1879 Etna,Pa.
d.Dec.25,1942

Yr	Cl	Lea	Pos	G	Rec
1906	Bro	N	2-S	127	.252
1907	Bro	N	2	138	.233
1908	Bro	N	2	57	.197
1909	Bro	N	2	108	.248
		BRTR		430	.237

ALSTON, THOMAS EDISON
b.Jan.31,1931 Greensboro,N.C.

Yr	Cl	Lea	Pos	G	Rec
1954	St.L	N	1	66	.246
1955	St.L	N	1	13	.125
1956	St.L	N	1	3	.000
1957	St.L	N	1	9	.294
		BLTR		91	.244

ALSTON, WALTER EMMONS
(Smokey)
b.Dec.1,1911 Venice,O.

Yr	Cl	Lea	Pos	G	Rec
1936	St.L	N	1	1	.000
		BRTR			

Non-playing manager Bro (N) 1954-57 and LA (N) 1958-1962

ALTEN, ERNEST MATTHIAS
(Lefty)
b.Dec.1,1894 Avon,O.

Yr	Cl	Lea	Pos	G	Rec
1920	Det	A	P	14	0-1
		BRTL			

ALTENBURG, JESSE HOWARD
b.Jan.2,1895 Ashley,Mich.

Yr	Cl	Lea	Pos	G	Rec
1916	Pit	N	O	8	.429
1917	Pit	N	O	11	.176
		BLTR		19	.290

ALTIZER, DAVID TILDEN
(Filipino)
b.Nov.6,1876 Peoria,Ill.

Yr	Cl	Lea	Pos	G	Rec
1906	Was	A	S	115	.256
1907	Was	A	1-S-O	147	.269
1908	Was	A	O	66	.218
1908	Cle	A	S-O	30	.227
1909	Chi	A	1-O	116	.233
1910	Cin	N	S	3	.600
1911	Cin	N	S	26	.227
		BLTR		503	.250

ALTMAN, GEORGE LEE
b.Mar.20,1934 Goldsboro,N.C.

Yr	Cl	Lea	Pos	G	Rec
1959	Chi	N	O	135	.245
1960	Chi	N	1-O	119	.266
1961	Chi	N	1-O	138	.303
1962	Chi	N	1-O	147	.318
		BLTR		539	.287

ALTOBELLI, JOSEPH
b.May 26,1932 Detroit,Mich.

Yr	Cl	Lea	Pos	G	Rec
1955	Cle	A	1	42	.200
1957	Cle	A	1-O	83	.207
1961	Min	A	1-O	41	.221
		BLTL		166	.210

ALTROCK, NICHOLAS (Nick)
b.Sept.15,1876 Cincinnati,O.

Yr	Cl	Lea	Pos	G	Rec
1898	Lou	N	P	11	3-4
1902	Bos	A	P	3	1-2
1903	Bos	A	P	3	0-3
1903	Chi	A	P	11	4-2
1904	Chi	A	P	38	21-13
1905	Chi	A	P	41	21-10
1906	Chi	A	P	38	20-13
1907	Chi	A	P	30	8-12
1908	Chi	A	P	23	3-7
1909	Chi	A	P	5	1-4
1909	Was	A	P-O	12	1-3 .053
1912	Was	A	P	1	0-0
1913	Was	A	P	4	0-0
1914	Was	A	P	1	0-0
1S15	Was	A	P	1	0-0
1918	Was	A	P	6	1-2
1919	Was	A	P	1	0-0
1924	Was	A	P	1	0-0
1929	Was	A	O	1	1.000
1931	Was	A	H	1	.000
1933	Was	A	H	1	.000
		BLTL		233	84-75 .178

ALUSIK, GEORGE JOSEPH
b.Feb.11,1935 Elizabeth,N.J.

Yr	Cl	Lea	Pos	G	Rec
1958	Det	A	O	2	.000
1961	Det	A	O	15	.143
1962	Det	A	H	2	.000
1962	KC	A	1-O	90	.273
		BRTR		109	.260

ALVAREZ, OSWALDO GONZALES
b.Oct.19,1933 Bolondron,Cuba

Yr	Cl	Lea	Pos	G	Rec
1958	Was	A	2-S-3	87	.209
1959	Det	A	H	8	.500
		BRTR		95	.212

ALBAREZ, ROGELIO HERNANDEZ
b.Apr.18,1938 Pinar Del Rio,Cuba

Yr	Cl	Lea	Pos	G	Rec
1960	Cin	N	1	3	.111
1962	Cin	N	1	14	.214
		BRTR		17	.189

ALVIS, ROY MAXWELL
b.Feb.2,1938 Jasper, Tex.

Yr	Cl	Lea	Pos	G	Rec
1962	Cle	A	3	12	.216
		BRTR			

ALVORD, WILLIAM C.
(Uncle Bill)
b. St.Louis,Mo.

Yr	Cl	Lea	Pos	G	Rec
1885	St.L	N	3	2	.000
1889	KC	a	3	50	.221
1890	Tol	a	3	120	.283
1891	Cle	N	3	13	.282
1891	Was	a	3	81	.235
1893	Cle	N	3	3	.250
				269	.256

AMALFITANO, JOHN JOSEPH
b.Jan.23,1934 San Pedro,Cal.

Yr	Cl	Lea	Pos	G	Rec
1954	NY	N	2-3	9	.000
1955	NY	N	S-3	36	.227
1960	SF	N	2-S-3-O	106	.277
1961	SF	N	2-3	109	.255

(Continued)

Yr	Cl	Lea	Pos	G	Rec
1962	Hou	N	2-3	117	.237
		BRTR		377	.254

AMARO, RUBEN MORA
b.Jan.6,1936 Vera Cruz,Mexico

Yr	Cl	Lea	Pos	G	Rec
1958	St.L	N	2-S	40	.224
1960	Phi	N	S	92	.231
1961	Phi	N	1-2-S	135	.257
1962	Phi	N	1-S-3	79	.243
		BRTR		346	.244

AMBLER, WAYNE HARPER
b.Nov.8,1915 Abington,Pa.

Yr	Cl	Lea	Pos	G	Rec
1937	Phi	A	2	56	.216
1938	Phi	A	S	120	.234
1939	Phi	A	2-S	95	.211
		BRTR		271	.224

AMES, LEON KESSLING
(Red)
b.Aug.2,1882 Warren,O.
d.Oct.8,1936

Yr	Cl	Lea	Pos	G	Rec
1903	NY	N	P	2	2-0
1904	NY	N	P	16	4-6
1905	NY	N	P	34	19-7
1906	NY	N	P	31	12-10
1907	NY	N	P	39	10-12
1908	NY	N	P	18	7-4
1909	NY	N	P	34	15-10
1910	NY	N	P	33	12-11
1911	NY	N	P	34	11-10
1912	NY	N	P	33	11-5
1913	NY	N	P	8	2-1
1913	Cin	N	P	31	11-13
1914	Cin	N	P	47	15-23
1915	Cin	N	P	17	2-4
1915	St.L	N	P	15	9-3
1916	St.L	N	P	45	11-16
1917	St.L	N	P	43	15-10
1918	St.L	N	P	27	9-14
1919	St.L	N	P	23	3-5
1919	Phi	N	P	3	0-2
		BLTR		533	180-166

AMOLE, MORRIS GEORGE
(Doc)
b.July 5,1878 Coatesville,Pa.
d.Mar.7,1912

Yr	Cl	Lea	Pos	G	Rec
1897	Bal	N	P	10	4-4
1898	Was	N	P	7	0-6
				17	4-10

AMOR, VICENTE ALVAREZ
b.Aug.9,1932 Havana,Cuba

Yr	Cl	Lea	Pos	G	Rec
1955	Chi	N	P	4	0-1
1957	Cin	N	P	9	1-2
		BRTR		13	1-3

AMOROS, EDMUNDO ISASI
(Sandy)
b.Jan.30,1932 Matanzas,Cuba

Yr	Cl	Lea	Pos	G	Rec
1952	Bro	N	O	20	.250
1954	Bro	N	O	79	.274
1955	Bro	N	O	119	.247
1956	Bro	N	O	114	.260
1957	Bro	N	O	106	.277
1959	LA	N	H	5	.200
1960	LA	N	O	9	.143
1960	Det	A	O	65	.149
		BLTL		517	.255

ANCKER, WALTER
b.Apr.10.1894 New York,N.Y.
d.Feb.13,1954

Yr	Cl	Lea	Pos	G	Rec
1915	Phi	A	P	4	0-1
		BRTR			

ANDERSON, ALFRED WALTON
b.Jan.28,1915 Gainesville,Ga.

Yr	Cl	Lea	Pos	G	Rec
1941	Pit	N	S	70	.215
1942	Pit	N	S	54	.271
1946	Pit	N	H	2	.000
		BRTR		126	.238

Yr Cl Lea Pos G Rec

ANDERSON, ANDY HOLM
b.Nov.13,1922 Bremerton,Wash.
1948 St.L A 1-2-S 51 .276
1949 St.L A 2-S-3 71 .125
BRTR 122 .184

ANDERSON, ARNOLD REVOLA
(Red)
b.June 19,1914 Lawton,Ia.
1937 Was A P 2 0-1
1940 Was A P 2 1-1
1941 Was A P 32 4-6
BRTR 36 5-8

ANDERSON, DAVID S.
(Varney)
b.Oct.10,1868 Chester,Pa.
d.Mar.22,1897
1889 Ind N P 1 0-1
1889 Phi N P 3 0-2
1890 Phi N P 6 1-2
1890 Pit N P 13 2-11
1894 Was N P 2 0-2
1895 Was N P 26 9-16
1896 Was N P 2 0-1
53 12-35

ANDERSON, EDWARD JOHN (Goat)
b.Jan.13,1880 Cleveland,O.
d.Mar.15,1923
1907 Pit N O 121 .206
TR

ANDERSON, FERRELL JACK
b.Jan.9,1918 Maple City,Kan.
1946 Bro N C 79 .256
1953 St.L N C 18 .286
BRTR 97 .261

ANDERSON,GEORGE JENDRUS (Andy)
b.Sept. 26,1889 Chicago,Ill.
d.May 28,1962
1914 Bro F O 97 .310
1915 Bro F O 134 .259
1918 St.L N O 35 .295
BLTR 266 .282

ANDERSON, GEORGE LEE
b.Feb.22,1934 Bridgewater,S.Dak.
1959 Phi N 2 152 .218
BRTR

ANDERSON, HAROLD
b.Feb.10,1904 St.Louis,Mo.
1932 Chi A O 9 .250
BRTR

ANDERSON, HARRY WALTER
b.Sept.10,1931 North East,Md.
1957 Phi N O 118 .268
1958 Phi N 1-O 140 .301
1959 Phi N O 142 .240
1960 Phi N 1-O 38 .247
1960 Cin N 1-O 42 .167
1961 Cin N H 4 .250
BLTR 484 .264

ANDERSON, JOHN CHARLES
b.Nov.23,1932 St. Paul,Minn.
1958 Phi N P 5 0-0
1960 Bal A P 4 0-0
1962 St.L N P 5 0-0
1962 Hou N P 10 0-0
BRTR 24 0-0

ANDERSON, JOHN FREDERICK
(Fred)
b.Dec.11,1885 Calahan,N.C.
d.Nov.8,1957
1909 Bos A P 1 0-0
1913 Bos A P 10 0-6
1914 Buf F P 36 13-15
1915 Buf F P 33 19-13
1916 NY N P 38 9-13
1917 NY N P 38 8-8
1918 NY N P 18 4-2
BRTR 174 53-57

ANDERSON, JOHN JOSEPH
(Honest John)
b.Dec.14,1873 Sasbourg,Norway
d.July 23,1949
1894 Bro N O 16 .301
1895 Bro N O 103 .296
1896 Bro N 1-O 104 .314
1897 Bro N O 116 .332
1898 Bro N O 6 .158
1898 Was N O 108 .305
1898 Bro N 1-O 19 .275
1899 Bro N 1-O 112 .274
1901 Mil A 1 138 .339
1902 St.L A 1-O 126 .284
1903 St.L A 1 139 .285
1904 NY A 1-O 143 .281
1905 NY A O 25 .212
1905 Was A O 100 .295
1906 Was A O 151 .271
1907 Was A 1-O 87 .288
1908 Chi A O 123 .262
BRTR 1616 .293

ANDERSON, NORMAN CRAIG
b.July 1,1938 Washington,D.C.
1961 St.L N P 25 4-3
1962 NY N P 50 3-17
BRTR 75 7-20

ANDERSON, ROBERT CARL
b.Sept.29,1935 E. Chicago,Ind.
1957 Chi N P 8 0-1
1958 Chi N P 17 3-3
1959 Chi N P 37 12-13
1960 Chi N P 39 9-11
1961 Chi N P 57 7-10
1962 Chi N P 57 2-7
BRTR 215 33-45

ANDERSON, WALTER CARL
(Lefty)
b.Sept.25,1897 Grand Rapids,Mich.
1917 Phi A P 14 0-0
1919 Phi A P 3 1-1
BLTL 17 1-1

ANDERSON, WINGO CHARLIE
b.Aug.13,1886 Alvarado,Tex.
d.Dec.19,1950
1910 Cin N P 7 0-0

ANDERSON, WILLIAM
1889 Lou a P 1 0-1

ANDERSON, WILLIAM EDWARD
(Lefty)
b.Dec.3,1896 Boston,Mass.
1925 Bos N P 2 0-0
BRTL

ANDRE, JOHN EDWARD
b.Jan.3,1925 Brockton,Mass.
1955 Chi N P 22 0-1
BLTR

ANDRES, ERNEST HENRY
(Junie)
b.Jan.11,1918 Jeffersonville,Ind.
1946 Bos A 3 15 .098
BRTR

ANDREWS, ELBERT DEVORE
b.Dec.11,1902 Greenwood,S.C.
1925 Phi A P 6 0-0
BLTR

ANDREWS, GEORGE EDWARD
(Ed)
b.Apr.5,1859 Painesville,O.
d.Aug.12,1934
1884 Phi N 2 108 .221
1885 Phi N 2-O 103 .266
1886 Phi N O 106 .249
1887 Phi N O 103 .354
1888 Phi N O 123 .238
1889 Phi N 2-O 10 .282
1889 Ind N O 40 .306
1890 Bro p O 95 .258
1891 Cin a O 83 .210
BRTR 771 .263

ANDREWS, HERBERT CARL
(Hub)
b.Aug.31,1922 Burbank,Okla.
1947 NY N P 7 0-0
1948 NY N P 1 0-0
BRTR 8 0-0

ANDREWS, IVY PAUL
(Poison)
b.May 6,1907 Dora,Ala.
1931 NY A P 7 2-0
1932 NY A P 4 2-1
1932 Bos A P 27 8-6
1933 Bos A P 36 7-13
1934 St.L A P 43 4-11
1935 St.L A P 50 13-7
1936 St.L A P 36 7-12
1937 Cle A P 20 3-4
1937 NY A P 11 3-2
1938 NY A P 19 1-3
BRTR 253 50-59

ANDREWS, JAMES P.
b.June 6,1859 Shelburne Falls,Mass.
1890 Chi N O 53 .188

ANDREWS, NATHAN HARDY
b.Sept.30,1913 Pembroke,N.C.
1937 St.L N P 4 0-0
1939 St.L N P 11 1-2
1940 Cle A P 6 0-1
1941 Cle A P 2 0-0
1943 Bos N P 36 14-20
1944 Bos N P 37 16-15
1945 Bos N P 22 7-12
1946 Cin N P 7 2-4
1946 NY N P 3 1-0
BBTR 128 41-54

ANDREWS, STANLEY JOSEPH
(Polo)
(Real name Stanley Joseph Andruskewicz)
b.Apr.17,1917 Lynn,Mass.
1939 Bos N C 13 .231
1940 Bos N C 19 .182
1944 Bro N C 4 .125
1945 Bro N C 21 .163
1945 Phi N C 13 .333
BRTR 70 .215

ANDREWS, WILLIAM WALTER
b.Sept.18,1859 Philadelphia,Pa.
d.Jan.20,1940
1884 Lou a 1 15 .185
1885 Pro N 3 1 .000
1888 Lou a 1 27 .202
43 .191

ANDRUS, FREDERICK HOTHAM
b.Aug.23,1850 Washington,Mich.
1876 Chi N O 8 .306
1884 Chi N P 1 0-0
BRTR 9 { 0-0 / .286 }

ANDRUS, WILLIAM MORGAN
(Andy)
b.July 25,1907 Beaumont,Tex.
1931 Was A 3 3 .000
1937 Phi N 3 3 .000
BRTR 6 .000

ANDRUSKEWICZ, STANLEY JOSEPH
(Played under name of Stanley Joseph Andrews)

ANGLEY, THOMAS SAMUEL
b.Oct.2,1904 Baltimore,Md.
d.Oct.26,1952

Yr	Cl	Lea	Pos	G	Rec
1929	Chi	N	C	5	.250

BLTR

ANKENMAN, FREDERICK NORMAN
(Pat)
b.Dec.23,1912 Houston,Tex.

Yr	Cl	Lea	Pos	G	Rec
1936	St.L	N	S	1	.000
1943	Bro	N	S	1	.500
1944	Bro	N	2-S	13	.250
	BRTR			15	.241

ANNIS, WILLIAM PERLEY
b.May 24,1857 Stoneham,Mass.

Yr	Cl	Lea	Pos	G	Rec
1884	Bos	N	O	26	.184

ANSON, ADRIAN CONSTANTINE
(Cap)
b.Apr.11,1851 Marshalltown,Ia.
d.Apr.14,1922

Yr	Cl	Lea	Pos	G	Rec
1871	Rok	n	C-2-3	24	NR
1872	Ath	n	3	47	NR
1873	Ath	n	C-1-2-3-O	50	NR
1874	Ath	n	1-S-3-O	54	NR
1875	Ath	n	C-1-3-O	69	.318
1876	Chi	N	3	66	.343
1877	Chi	N	C-3	59	.337
1878	Chi	N	2-O	59	.336
1879	Chi	N	M-1	49	.407
1880	Chi	N	M-1-2-S-3	84	.338
1881	Chi	N	M-C-1-S	84	.399
1882	Chi	N	M-C-1	82	.362
1883	Chi	N	M-P-C-1	98	0-0 / .307
1884	Chi	N	M-P-C-1-S	111	0-0 / .337
1885	Chi	N	M-C-1	112	.310
1886	Chi	N	M-1	125	.371
1887	Chi	N	M-1	122	.421
1888	Chi	N	M-1	134	.343
1889	Chi	N	M-1	134	.341
1890	Chi	N	M-1	139	.311
1891	Chi	N	M-1	136	.294
1892	Chi	N	M-1	147	.274
1893	Chi	N	M-1	101	.322
1894	Chi	N	M-1	83	.394
1895	Chi	N	M-1	122	.338
1896	Chi	N	M-1	106	.335
1897	Chi	N	M-1	112	.302
	BRTR			2509	0-0 / NR

Non-playing manager NY (N) 1898

ANTOLICK, JOSEPH
b.Sept.13,1916 Hokendauqua,Pa.

Yr	Cl	Lea	Pos	G	Rec
1944	Phi	N	C	4	.333

BRTR

ANTONELLI, JOHN AUGUST
b.Apr.12,1930 Rochester,N.Y.

Yr	Cl	Lea	Pos	G	Rec
1948	Bos	N	P	4	0-0
1949	Bos	N	P	22	3-7
1950	Bos	N	P	20	2-3
1953	Mil	N	P	31	12-12
1954	NY	N	P	39	21-7
1955	NY	N	P	38	14-16
1956	NY	N	P	49	20-13
1957	NY	N	P	47	12-18
1958	SF	N	P	47	16-13
1959	SF	N	P	43	19-10
1960	SF	N	P	42	6-7
1961	Cle	A	P	12	0-4
1961	Mil	N	P	9	1-0
	BLTL			403	126-110

ANTONELLI, JOHN LAWRENCE
b.July 15,1915 Memphis,Tenn.

Yr	Cl	Lea	Pos	G	Rec
1944	St.L	N	1-2-3	8	.190
1945	St.L	N	3	2	.000
1945	Phi	N	1-2-S-3	125	.256
	BRTR			135	.252

ANTONELLO, WILLIAM JAMES
b.May 19,1927 Brooklyn,N.Y.

Yr	Cl	Lea	Pos	G	Rec
1953	Bro	N	O	40	.163

BRTR

APARICIO, LUIS ERNESTO
b.Apr.29,1934 Maracaibo,Venezuela

Yr	Cl	Lea	Pos	G	Rec
1956	Chi	A	S	152	.266
1957	Chi	A	S	143	.257
1958	Chi	A	S	145	.266
1959	Chi	A	S	152	.257
1960	Chi	A	S	153	.277
1961	Chi	A	S	156	.272
1962	Chi	A	S	153	.241
	BRTR			1054	.262

APPLEGATE, FREDERICK ROMAINE
b.May 9,1879 Williamsport,Pa.

Yr	Cl	Lea	Pos	G	Rec
1904	Phi	A	P	3	1-2

BRTR

APPLETON, EDWARD SAM
(Whitey)
b.Feb.29,1892 Arlington,Tex.
d.Jan.27,1932

Yr	Cl	Lea	Pos	G	Rec
1915	Bro	N	P	34	4-10
1916	Bro	N	P	14	1-2
	BRTR			48	5-12

APPLETON, PETER WILLIAM
(Jake)
(Played 1927-33 under the name of Peter Wm. Jablonowski, rest of career under the name of Peter Wm. Appleton, after changing name legally.)
b.May 20,1904 Terryville,Conn.

Yr	Cl	Lea	Pos	G	Rec
1927	Cin	N	P	6	2-1
1928	Cin	N	P-O	32	3-4 / .323
1930	Cle	A	P	39	8-7
1931	Cle	A	P	30	4-4
1932	Cle	A	P	4	0-0
1932	Bos	A	P	11	0-3
1933	NY	A	P	1	0-0
1936	Was	A	P	38	14-9
1937	Was	A	P	35	8-15
1938	Was	A	P	43	7-9
1939	Was	A	P	40	5-10
1940	Chi	A	P	25	4-0
1941	Chi	A	P	13	0-3
1942	Chi	A	P	4	0-0
1942	St.L	A	P	14	1-1
1945	St.L	A	P	2	0-0
1945	Was	A	P	6	1-0
	BRTR			343	57-66 / .233

APPLING, LUCIUS BENJAMIN
(Luke)
b.Apr.2,1908 High Point,N.C.

Yr	Cl	Lea	Pos	G	Rec
1930	Chi	A	S	6	.308
1931	Chi	A	S	96	.232
1932	Chi	A	2-S-3	139	.274
1933	Chi	A	S	151	.322
1934	Chi	A	S	118	.303
1935	Chi	A	S	153	.307
1936	Chi	A	S	138	.388
1937	Chi	A	S	154	.317
1938	Chi	A	S	81	.303
1939	Chi	A	S	148	.314
1940	Chi	A	S	150	.348
1941	Chi	A	S	154	.314
1942	Chi	A	S	142	.262
1943	Chi	A	S	155	.328
1945	Chi	A	S	18	.362
1946	Chi	A	S	149	.309
1947	Chi	A	S-3	139	.306
1948	Chi	A	S-3	139	.314
1949	Chi	A	S	142	.301
1950	Chi	A	1-2-S	50	.234
	BRTR			2422	.310

ARAGON, ANGEL VALDES JR.
(Jack)
b.Nov.20,1915 Havana,Cuba

Yr	Cl	Lea	Pos	G	Rec
1941	NY	N	H	1	.000

BRTR

ARAGON, ANGEL VALDES SR.
(Pete)
b.Aug.2,1893 Havana,Cuba
d.Jan.24,1952

Yr	Cl	Lea	Pos	G	Rec
1914	NY	A	O	6	.142
1916	NY	A	3-O	12	.208
1917	NY	A	S-3-O	14	.067
	BRTR			32	.123

ARCHDEACON, MAURICE JOHN
(Flash)
b.Dec.14,1897 St.Louis,Mo.
d.Sept.5,1954

Yr	Cl	Lea	Pos	G	Rec
1923	Chi	A	O	22	.402
1924	Chi	A	O	95	.319
1925	Chi	A	O	10	.111
	BLTL			127	.333

ARCHER, FREDERICK MARVIN
(Lefty)
b.Mar.7,1912 Johnson City,Tenn.

Yr	Cl	Lea	Pos	G	Rec
1936	Phi	A	P	6	2-3
1937	Phi	A	P	1	0-0
	BLTL			7	2-3

ARCHER, JAMES PATRICK
b.May 13,1883 Dublin,Ireland
d.Mar.29,1958

Yr	Cl	Lea	Pos	G	Rec
1904	Pit	N	C	7	.157
1907	Det	A	C	18	.119
1909	Chi	N	C	80	.230
1910	Chi	N	C-1	89	.259
1911	Chi	N	C	112	.252
1912	Chi	N	C	120	.283
1913	Chi	N	C	111	.266
1914	Chi	N	C	79	.258
1915	Chi	N	C	97	.243
1916	Chi	N	C	77	.220
1917	Chi	N	C	2	.000
1918	Pit	N	C-1	24	.155
1918	Bro	N	C	9	.273
1918	Cin	N	C-1-O	9	.269
	BRTR			834	.250

ARCHER, JAMES WILLIAM
b.May25,1933 Wytheville,Va.

Yr	Cl	Lea	Pos	G	Rec
1961	KC	A	P	39	9-15
1962	KC	A	P	18	0-1
	BRTL			.57	9-16

ARCHIE, GEORGE ALBERT
b.Apr.27,1914 Nashville,Tenn.

Yr	Cl	Lea	Pos	G	Rec
1938	Det	A	H	3	.000
1941	Was	A	1-3	105	.269
1941	St.L	A	1	9	.379
1946	St.L	A	1	4	.182
	BRTR			121	.273

ARDELL, DANIEL MIERS
b.May 27,1941 Seattle,Wash.

Yr	Cl	Lea	Pos	G	Rec
1961	LA	A	1	7	.250

BLTL

ARDIZOLA, RINALDO JOSEPH
(Rugger)
b.Nov.20,1919 Novara,Italy

Yr	Cl	Lea	Pos	G	Rec
1947	NY	A	P	1	0-0

BRTR

ARDNER, JOSEPH A.
(Old Hoss)
b.Feb.29,1858 Mt.Vernon,O.
d.Sept.15,1935

Yr	Cl	Lea	Pos	G	Rec
1884	Cle	N	2-3	26	.174
1890	Cle	N	2	84	.223
	BRTR			110	.212

ARELLANES, FRANK JULIAN
b.Jan.28,1882 Santa Cruz,Cal.
d.Dec.13,1918

Yr	Cl	Lea	Pos	G	Rec
1908	Bos	A	P	12	4-3
1909	Bos	A	P	46	16-12

Yr Cl Lea Pos G Rec

(Continued)
1910 Bos A P 18 4-7
BRTR 76 24-22

ARFT, HENRY IRVEN
(Bow Wow)
b.Jan.28,1922 Manchester,Mo.
1948 St.L A 1 69 .238
1949 St.L A H 6 .200
1950 St.L A 1 98 .268
1951 St.L A 1 112 .261
1952 St.L A 1 15 .143
BLTL 300 .253

ARIAS, RODOLFO MARTINEZ
b.June 6,1932 Camaguey,Cuba
1959 Chi A P 34 2-0
BLTL

ARLETT, RUSSELL LORIS
(Buzz)
b.Jan.3,1899 Oakland,Cal.
1931 Phi N 1-O 121 .313
BBTR

ARMBRUST, ORVILLE MARTIN
b.Mar.2,1910 Gurdon,Ark.
1934 Was A P 3 1-0
BRTR

ARMBRUSTER, CHARLES A.
b.1882 Cincinnati,O.
1905 Bos A C 35 .198
1906 Bos A C 72 .144
1907 Bos A C 23 .100
1907 Chi A C 1 .000
TR 131 .149

ARMBRUSTER, HERMAN (Buster)
b.Mar.20,1882 Cincinnati,O.
d.Dec.10,1953
1906 Phi A O 91 .238
BLTL

ARMOUR, WILLIAM R.
b.Sept.3,1869 Homestead,Pa.
d.Dec.2,1922
Non-playing manager Cle (A) 1902-04 and Det (A) 1905-06.

ARMSTRONG, GEORGE NOBLE
(Dodo)
b.June 3,1925 Orange,N.J.
1946 Phi A C 8 .167
BRTR

ARMSTRONG, HOWARD EDWARD
b.Dec.2,1889 Geauga Co.,O.
d.Mar.8,1926
1911 Phi A P 1 0-1
TR

ARMSTRONG, SAMUEL
b.Ft. Wayne, Ind.
1871 Kek n O 13 NR

ARNDT, HARRY A.
b.Feb.12,1879 South Bend,Ind.
d.Mar.25,1921
1902 Det A 1-O 10 .135
1902 Bal A 2-S-3-O 67 .257
1905 St.L N 2 111 .243
1906 St.L N 3 67 .270
1907 St.L N 1 9 .130
264 .248

ARNOLD, WILLIS S.
(Billy)
b.Mar.2,1851 Middletown,Conn.
d.Jan.17,1899
1872 Man n M-O 2 NR

ARNOVICH, MORRIS (Snooker)
b.Nov.16,1910 Superior,Wis.
d.July 20,1959
1936 Phi N O 13 .313
1937 Phi N O 117 .290
1938 Phi N O 139 .275
1939 Phi N O 134 .324
1940 Phi N O 39 .199

Yr Cl Lea Pos G Rec

(Continued)
1940 Cin N O 62 .284
1941 NY N O 85 .280
1946 NY N O 1 .000
BRTR 590 .287

ARNTZEN, ORIE EDGAR
(Old Folks)
b.Oct.18,1909 Beverly,Ill.
1943 Phi A P 32 4-13
BRTR

ARRIGO, GERALD WILLIAM
b.June 12,1941 Chicago,Ill.
1961 Min A P 7 0-1
1962 Min A P 1 0-0
BLTL 8 0-1

ARROYO, LUIS ENRIQUE
b.Feb.18,1928 Penuelas,P.R.
1955 St.L N P 35 11-8
1956 Pit N P 18 3-3
1957 Pit N P 56 3-11
1959 Cin N P 10 1-0
1960 NY A P 29 5-1
1961 NY A P 65 15-5
1962 NY A P 27 1-3
BLTL 240 39-31

ARUNDEL, HARVEY
b.1857 Philadelphia,Pa.
d.Mar.25,1904
1875 Atl n O 1 .000
1882 Pit a P-S 14 {4-10 .192}
1884 Pro' N P 1 1-0
16 {5-10 .183}

ARUNDEL, JOHN THOMAS
(Tug)
b.June 30,1862 Auburn,N.Y.
d.Sept.5,1912
1882 Ath a C-O 1 .000
1884 Tol a C 14 .087
1887 Ind N C 43 .236
1888 Was N C 16 .196
74 .199

ASBELL, JAMES MARION
(Big Train)
b.June 22,1914 Dallas,Tex.
1938 Chi N O 17 .182
BRTR

ASBJORNSON, ROBERT ANTHONY
b.June 19,1909 Concord,Mass.
1928 Bos A C 6 .187
1929 Bos A C 17 .103
1931 Cin N C 45 .305
1932 Cin N C 29 .172
BRTR 97 .235

ASCHENBACH, CHARLES S.
(Played under name of Raymond Charles)

ASH, KENNETH LOWTHER
b.Sept.16,1901 Anmoore,W.Va.
1925 Chi A P 2 0-0
1928 Cin N P 9 3-3
1929 Cin N P-O 30 {1-5 .143}
1930 Cin N P 17 2-0
BRTR 58 {6-8 .133}

ASHBURN, RICHIE (Whitey)
b.Mar.19,1927 Tilden,Neb.
1948 Phi N O 117 .333
1949 Phi N O 154 .284
1950 Phi N O 151 .303
1951 Phi N O 154 .344
1952 Phi N O 154 .282
1953 Phi N O 156 .330

Yr Cl Lea Pos G Rec

(Continued)
1954 Phi N O 153 .313
1955 Phi N O 140 .338
1956 Phi N O 154 .303
1957 Phi N O 156 .297
1958 Phi N O 152 .350
1959 Phi N O 153 .266
1960 Chi N O 151 .291
1961 Chi N O 109 .257
1962 NY N 2-O 135 .306
BLTR 2189 .308

ASMUSSEN, THOMAS WILLIAM
b.Sept.26,1878 Chicago,Ill.
1907 Bos N C 2 .000
TR

ASPROMONTE, KENNETH JOSEPH
b.Sept.22,1931 Brooklyn,N.Y.
1957 Bos A 2 24 .269
1958 Bos A 2 6 .125
1958 Was A 2-S-3 92 .225
1959 Was A 1-2-S-O 70 .244
1960 Was A H 4 .000
1960 Cle A 2-3 117 .290
1961 LA A 2 66 .223
1961 Cle A 2 22 .229
1962 Cle A 2-3-O 20 .143
1962 Mil N 2-3 34 .291
BRTR 455 .251

ASPROMONTE, ROBERT THOMAS
b.June 19,1938 Brooklyn,N.Y.
1956 Bro N H 1 .000
1960 LA N S-3 21 .182
1961 LA N 2-S-3 47 .241
1962 Hou N 2-S-3 149 .266
BRTR 218 .256

ASTROTH, JOSEPH HENRY
b.Sept.1,1922 E.Alton,Ill.
1945 Phi A C 10 .059
1946 Phi A C 4 .143
1949 Phi A C 55 .243
1950 Phi A C 39 .327
1951 Phi A C 64 .246
1952 Phi A C 104 .249
1953 Phi A C 82 .296
1954 Phi A C 77 .221
1955 KC A C 101 .252
1956 KC A C 8 .077
BRTR 544 .254

ATHERTON, CHARLES MORGAN HERBERT (Prexy)
b.Oct.1873 New Brunswick,N.J.
d.Dec.19,1935
1899 Was N 3 63 .240

ATKINS, FRANK MONTGOMERY
(Tommy)
b.Dec.9,1887 Pancau,Neb.
d.May 7,1956
1909 Phi A P 1 0-0
1910 Phi A P 15 3-2
BLTL 16 3-2

ATKINS, JAMES CURTIS
b.Mar.10,1921 Birmingham,Ala.
1950 Bos A P 1 0-0
1952 Bos A P 3 0-1
BLTR 4 0-1

ATKINSON, EDWARD
b. Baltimore,Md.
1873 Nat n O 2 .000

ATKINSON, HUBERT B.
b.June 2,1906 Chicago,Ill.
1927 Was A H 1 .000

ATKISSON, ALBERT W.
b.Mar.9,1861 Clinton,Ill.
d.June 17,1952

Yr	Cl	Lea	Pos	G	Rec
1884	Ath	a	P	22	11-11
1884	Chi	U	P-O	12	5-7 .278
1884	Pit	U	P-O	9	2-6 .121
1884	Bal	U	P	8	3-5
1886	Ath	a	P	43	25-17
1887	Ath	a	P	16	5-9
				110	51-55 .183

ATTREAU, RICHARD GILBERT
b.Apr.8,1899 Chicago,Ill.

Yr	Cl	Lea	Pos	G	Rec
1926	Phi	N	1	17	.230
1927	Phi	N	1	44	.205
	BLTL			61	.215

ATWELL, MAURICE DAILEY
(Toby)
b.Mar.8,1924 Leesburg,Va.

Yr	Cl	Lea	Pos	G	Rec
1952	Chi	N	C	107	.290
1953	Chi	N	C	24	.230
1953	Pit	N	C	53	.245
1954	Pit	N	C	96	.289
1955	Pit	N	C	71	.213
1956	Pit	N	C	12	.111
1956	Mil	N	C	15	.167
	BLTR			378	.260

ATWOOD, WILLIAM FRANKLIN
b.Sept.11,1912 Rome,Ga.

Yr	Cl	Lea	Pos	G	Rec
1936	Phi	N	C	71	.302
1937	Phi	N	C	87	.244
1938	Phi	N	C	102	.196
1939	Phi	N	C	4	.000
1940	Phi	N	C	78	.192
	BRTR			342	.229

ATZ, JACOB HENRY
b.July 1,1879 Washigton,D.C.
d.May 22,1945

Yr	Cl	Lea	Pos	G	Rec
1902	Was	A	2	3	.100
1907	Chi	A	3	4	.125
1908	Chi	A	2	83	.194
1909	Chi	A	2	119	.236
	BRTR			209	.218

AUBREY, HARVEY HERBERT
b.July 5,1880 St.Joseph,Mo.

Yr	Cl	Lea	Pos	G	Rec
1903	Bos	N	S	94	.212
	TR				

AUKER, ELDON LEROY
(Submarine)
b.Sept.21,1910 Norcatur,Kan.

Yr	Cl	Lea	Pos	G	Rec
1933	Det	A	P	15	3-3
1934	Det	A	P	43	15-7
1935	Det	A	P	36	18-7
1936	Det	A	P	35	13-16
1937	Det	A	P	43	17-9
1938	Det	A	P	27	11-10
1939	Bos	A	P	31	9-10
1940	St.L	A	P	38	16-11
1941	St.L	A	P	37	14-15
1942	St.L	A	P	51	14-13
	BRTR			356	130-101

AULDS, LEYCESTER DOYLE
b.Dec.21,1920 Farmerville,La.

Yr	Cl	Lea	Pos	G	Rec
1947	Bos	A	C	3	.250
	BRTR				

AUSTIN, HENRY C.
b. Brooklyn,N.Y.
d.Sept.3,1895

Yr	Cl	Lea	Pos	G	Rec
1873	Res	n	O	22	NR

AUSTIN, JAMES PHILIP
(Pepper)
b.Dec.8,1879 Swansea,Wales

Yr	Cl	Lea	Pos	G	Rec
1909	NY	A	S-3	136	.231
1910	NY	A	3	133	.218
1911	St.L	A	3	148	.261
1912	St.L	A	3	149	.252
1913	St.L	A	M-3	142	.273
1914	St.L	A	3	130	.238
1915	St.L	A	3	141	.266
1916	St.L	A	3	129	.207
1917	St.L	A	3	127	.239
1918	St.L	A	M-S-3	110	.264
1919	St.L	A	3	106	.237
1920	St.L	A	3	83	.271
1921	St.L	A	S	27	.273
1922	St.L	A	3	15	.290
1923	St.L	A	M-H	1	.000
1925	St.L	A	3	1	.000
1926	St.L	A	3	1	.500
1929	St.L	A	3	1	.000
	BBTR			1580	.247

AUTRY, MARTIN GORDON
b.Mar.5,1903 Martindale,Tex.
d.Jan.26,1950

Yr	Cl	Lea	Pos	G	Rec
1924	NY	A	C	2	.000
1926	Cle	A	C	3	.143
1927	Cle	A	C	16	.255
1928	Cle	A	C	22	.300
1929	Chi	A	C	43	.208
1930	Chi	A	C	34	.253
	BRTR			120	.245

AUTRY, WILLIAM A.
(Chick)
b.Jan.2,1885 Decatur,Tenn.

Yr	Cl	Lea	Pos	G	Rec
1907	Cin	N	O	7	.200
1909	Cin	N	1	9	.182
1909	Bos	N	1	61	.196
	BLTL			77	.199

AVERILL, EARL DOUGLAS
b.Sept.9,1931 Cleveland,O.

Yr	Cl	Lea	Pos	G	Rec
1956	Cle	A	C	42	.237
1958	Cle	A	3	17	.182
1959	Chi	N	C-2-3-O	74	.237
1960	Chi	N	C-3-O	52	.235
1960	Chi	A	C	10	.214
1961	LA	A	C-2-O	115	.266
1962	LA	A	C-O	92	.219
	BRTR			402	.240

AVERILL, HOWARD EARL
(Rock)
b.May 21,1902 Snohomish,Wash.

Yr	Cl	Lea	Pos	G	Rec
1929	Cle	A	O	152	.330
1930	Cle	A	O	139	.339
1931	Cle	A	O	155	.333
1932	Cle	A	O	153	.314
1933	Cle	A	O	151	.301
1934	Cle	A	O	154	.313
1935	Cle	A	O	140	.288
1936	Cle	A	O	152	.378
1937	Cle	A	O	156	.299
1938	Cle	A	O	134	.330
1939	Cle	A	O	24	.273
1939	Det	A	O	87	.262
1940	Det	A	O	64	.280
1941	Bos	N	O	8	.118
	BLTR			1669	.316

AVILA, ROBERTO FRANCISCO GONZALEZ
b.June 7,1926 Vera Cruz,Mexico

Yr	Cl	Lea	Pos	G	Rec
1949	Cle	A	2	31	.214
1950	Cle	A	2-S	80	.299
1951	Cle	A	2	141	.305
1952	Cle	A	2	150	.300
1953	Cle	A	2	141	.286
1954	Cle	A	2-S	143	.341
1955	Cle	A	2	141	.272
1956	Cle	A	2	138	.224
1957	Cle	A	2-3	129	.268
1958	Cle	A	2-3	113	.253
1959	Bal	A	2-3-O	20	.170
1959	Bos	A	2	22	.244
1959	Mil	N	2	51	.238
	BRTR			1300	.281

AVREA, JAMES EPHERIUM
(Jay)
b.July 6,1923 Alvarado,Tex.

Yr	Cl	Lea	Pos	G	Rec
1950	Cin	N	P	2	0-0
	BRTR				

AYDELOTTE, JACOB S.
b. Marion,Ind.

Yr	Cl	Lea	Pos	G	Rec
1884	Ind	a	P-O	12	5-7 .114
1886	Ath	a	P	2	0-2
				14	5-9 .098

AYERS, WILLIAM OSCAR
b.Aug.27,1918 Newnan,Ga.

Yr	Cl	Lea	Pos	G	Rec
1947	NY	N	P	13	0-3
	BRTR				

AYERS, YANCEY WYATT
(Doc)
b.Apr.21,1891 Hillsville,Va.

Yr	Cl	Lea	Pos	G	Rec
1913	Was	A	P	4	2-1
1914	Was	A	P	45	12-16
1915	Was	A	P	40	15-9
1916	Was	A	P	43	5-9
1917	Was	A	P	40	11-10
1918	Was	A	P	40	10-12
1919	Was	A	P	12	2-6
1919	Det	A	P	23	4-3
1920	Det	A	P	46	7-14
1921	Det	A	P	2	0-0
	BRTR			295	68-80

AYLWARD, RICHARD JOHN
(Dandy)
b.June 4,1925 Baltimore,Md.

Yr	Cl	Lea	Pos	G	Rec
1953	Cle	A	C	4	.000
	BRTR				

AZCUE, JOSE JOAQUIN
b.Aug.18,1939 Cienfuegos,Cuba

Yr	Cl	Lea	Pos	G	Rec
1960	Cin	N	C	14	.097
1962	KC	A	C	72	.229
	BRTR			86	.213

BABB, CHARLES AMOS
b.Feb.20,1873 Portland,Ore.
d.Mar.20,1954

Yr	Cl	Lea	Pos	G	Rec
1903	N Y	N	S	121	.248
1904	Bro	N	S	151	.265
1905	Bro	N	1-S	74	.187
	BBTR			346	.243

BABE, LOREN ROLLAND
b.Jan.11,1928 Pisgah,Ia.

Yr	Cl	Lea	Pos	G	Rec
1952	N Y	A	3	12	.095
1953	N Y	A	3	5	.333
1953	Phi	A	S-3	103	.224
	BLTR			120	.223

BABICH, JOHN CHARLES
b.May 14,1913 Albion,Cal.

Yr	Cl	Lea	Pos	G	Rec
1934	Bro	N	P	25	7-11
1935	Bro	N	P	37	7-14
1936	Bos	N	P	3	0-0
1940	Phi	A	P	31	14-13
1941	Phi	A	P	16	2-7
	BRTR			112	30-45

BABINGTON, CHARLES PERCY
b.May 4,1895 Cranston,R.I.
d. Mar.22,1957

Yr	Cl	Lea	Pos	G	Rec
1915	N Y	N	O	28	.242
	BRTR				

BACKMAN, LESTER JOHN
b.Mar.20,1888 Cleves, O.

Yr	Cl	Lea	Pos	G	Rec
1909	St.L	N	P	21	3-11
1910	St.L	N	P	26	6-7
	TR			47	9-18

BACON, ELMER

Yr	Cl	Lea	Pos	G	Rec
1917	Phi	A	P	4	0-0

BACZEWSKI, FREDERICK JOHN
b.May 15,1926 St.Paul,Minn.

Yr	Cl	Lea	Pos	G	Rec
1953	Chi	N	P	9	0-0
1953	Cin	N	P	24	11-4
1954	Cin	N	P	29	6-6
1955	Cin	N	P	1	0-0
	BLTL			63	17-10

BADER, ARTHUR HERMAN
b.Sept.21,1886 St.Louis,Mo.

Yr	Cl	Lea	Pos	G	Rec
1904	St.L	A	O	2	.000
		BRTR			

BADER, LOREN VERNE (King)
b.Apr.27,1888 Astoria,Ill.

Yr	Cl	Lea	Pos	G	Rec
1912	NY	N	P	2	2-0
1917	Bos	A	P	15	2-0
1918	Bos	A	P	5	1-3
	BLTR			22	5-3

BADGRO, MORRIS HIRAM (Red)
b.Dec.1,1902 Orilla,Wash.

Yr	Cl	Lea	Pos	G	Rec
1929	St.L	A	O	54	.284
1930	St.L	A	O	89	.239
	BLTR			143	.257

BAECHT, EDWARD JOSEPH
b.May 15,1907 Paden.Okla.
d.Aug.15,1957

Yr	Cl	Lea	Pos	G	Rec
1926	Phi	N	P	28	2-0
1927	Phi	N	P	1	0-1
1928	Phi	N	P	9	1-1
1931	Chi	N	P	22	2-4
1932	Chi	N	P	1	0-0
1937	St.L	A	P	3	0-0
	BRTR			64	5-6

BAERWALD, RUDOLPH FRED
(Played under name of John Bell)

BAGBY, JAMES CHARLES JR.
b.Sept.8,1916 Cleveland,O.

Yr	Cl	Lea	Pos	G	Rec
1938	Bos	A	P	45	15-11
1939	Bos	A	P	21	5-5
1940	Bos	A	P-O	44	10-16 .203
1941	Cle	A	P	35	9-15
1942	Cle	A	P	39	17-9
1943	Cle	A	P-S	41	17-14 .268
1944	Cle	A	P	14	4-5
1945	Cle	A	P	25	8-11
1946	Bos	A	P	21	7-6
1947	Pit	N	P	37	5-4
	BRTR			322	97-96 .226

BAGBY, JAMES CHARLES JACOB SR. (Sarge)
b.Oct.5,1887 Barnett,Ga.
d.July 28,1954

Yr	Cl	Lea	Pos	G	Rec
1912	Cin	N	P	5	2-0
1916	Cle	A	P	51	16-15
1917	Cle	A	P	49	23-13
1918	Cle	A	P	47	17-16
1919	Cle	A	P	37	17-11
1920	Cle	A	P	49	31-12
1921	Cle	A	P	41	14-12
1922	Cle	A	P	25	4-5
1923	Pit	N	P	21	3-2
	BBTR			325	127-86

BAGWELL, WILLIAM MALLORY (Big Bill)
b.Feb.24,1897 Choudrant,La.

Yr	Cl	Lea	Pos	G	Rec
1923	Bos	N	O	56	.290
1925	Phi	A	O	36	.300
	BLTL			92	.294

BAHR, EDSON GARFIELD
b.June 26,1920 Rouceau,Sask.,Canada

Yr	Cl	Lea	Pos	G	Rec
1946	Pit	N	P	29	8-6
1947	Pit	N	P	21	3-5
	BRTR			50	11-11

BAHRET, FRANK J.

Yr	Cl	Lea	Pos	G	Rec
1884	Bal	U	O	1	.000
1884	Ind	a	C-O	5	.071
				6	.056

BAICHLEY, GROVER
b.Jan.7,1890 Toledo,Ill.
d.June 30,1956

Yr	Cl	Lea	Pos	G	Rec
1914	St.L	A	P	4	0-0
	BRTR				

BAILEY, ABRAHAM LINCOLN (Sweetbreads)
b.Feb.12,1895 Joliet,Ill.
d.Sept.27,1939

Yr	Cl	Lea	Pos	G	Rec
1919	Chi	N	P	21	3-5
1920	Chi	N	P	21	1-2
1921	Chi	N	P	3	0-0
1921	Bro	N	P	7	0-0
	BRTR			52	4-7

BAILEY, ARTHUR EUGENE (Gene)
b.Nov.25,1895 Pearsall,Tex.

Yr	Cl	Lea	Pos	G	Rec
1917	Phi	A	O	5	.083
1919	Bos	N	O	4	.333
1920	Bos	N	O	13	.083
1920	Bos	A	O	46	.230
1923	Bro	N	1-O	127	.265
1924	Bro	N	O	18	.239
	BRTR			213	.247

BAILEY, FREDERICK MIDDLETON (Penny)
b.Aug.16,1895 Mt.Hope,W.Va.

Yr	Cl	Lea	Pos	G	Rec
1916	Bos	N	O	6	.100
1917	Bos	N	O	50	.191
1918	Bos	N	O	9	.250
	BLTL			65	.185

BAILEY, HARRY LOUIS
b.Nov.19,1884 Shawnee,O.

Yr	Cl	Lea	Pos	G	Rec
1911	N Y	A	O	5	.111
	BLTR				

BAILEY, HARVEY FRANCIS
b.Nov.24,1876 Adrian,Mich.
d.July 11,1922

Yr	Cl	Lea	Pos	G	Rec
1899	Bos	N	P	12	6-4
1900	Bos	N	P	4	0-1
	TL			16	6-5

BAILEY, JAMES HOPKINS
b.Dec.16,1934 Strawberry Plains,Tenn.

Yr	Cl	Lea	Pos	G	Rec
1959	Cin	N	P	3	0-1
	BBTL				

BAILEY, LONAS EDGAR (Ed)
b.Apr.15,1931 Strawberry Plains, Tenn.

Yr	Cl	Lea	Pos	G	Rec
1953	Cin	N	C	2	.375
1954	Cin	N	C	73	.197
1955	Cin	N	C	21	.205
1956	Cin	N	C	118	.300
1957	Cin	N	C	122	.261
1958	Cin	N	C	112	.250
1959	Cin	N	C	121	.264
1960	Cin	N	C	133	.261
1961	Cin	N	C	12	.302
1961	SF	N	C-O	107	.238
1962	SF	N	C	96	.232
	BBTR			917	.256

BAILEY, LEMUEL (King)
b.Cincinnati,O.
d.June 2,1952

Yr	Cl	Lea	Pos	G	Rec
1895	Cin	N	P	1	1-0
	BLTL				

BAILEY, ROBERT SHERWOOD
b.Oct.13,1942 Long Beach,Cal.

Yr	Cl	Lea	Pos	G	Rec
1962	Pit	N	3	14	.167
	BRTR				

BAILEY, WILLIAM F.
b.Apr.12,1889 Ft.Smith,Ark.
d.Nov.2,1926

Yr	Cl	Lea	Pos	G	Rec
1907	St.L	A	P	6	4-1
1908	St.L	A	P	22	3-5
1909	St.L	A	P	38	9-11
1910	St.L	A	P	34	3-18
1911	St.L	A	P	5	0-4
1912	St.L	A	P	3	0-0
1914	Bal	F	P	19	7-9
1915	Bal	F	P	30	4-15
1915	Chi	F	P	11	6-5
1918	Det	A	P	8	1-2
1921	St.L	N	P	19	2-5
1922	St.L	N	P	12	0-2
	BLTL			207	39-77

BAIN, HERBERT LOREN
b.July 4,1922 Staples,Minn.

Yr	Cl	Lea	Pos	G	Rec
1945	N Y	N	P	3	0-0
	BRTR				

BAIRD, ALBERT WELLS
b.June 2,1895 Cleburne,Tex.

Yr	Cl	Lea	Pos	G	Rec
1917	N Y	N	2	10	.292
1919	N Y	N	2-S-3	38	.241
	BRTR			48	.251

BAIRD, HOWARD DOUGLASS (Doug)
b.Sept.27,1891 St.Charles,Mo.

Yr	Cl	Lea	Pos	G	Rec
1915	Pit	N	3-O	145	.219
1916	Pit	N	2-3-O	128	.216
1917	Pit	N	3	43	.259
1917	St.L	N	3	104	.253
1918	St.L	N	3-O	82	.247
1919	Phi	N	3	66	.260
1919	St.L	N	2-3-O	16	.260
1919	Bro	N	3	20	.167
1920	Bro	N	H	6	.333
1920	N Y	N	3	7	.125
	BRTR			617	.234

BAIRD, ROBERT ALLEN
b.Jan.16,1940 Knoxville,Tenn.

Yr	Cl	Lea	Pos	G	Rec
1962	Was	A	P	3	0-1

BAKELY, EDWARD (Enoch)
b.Apr.17,1864 Blackwood,N.J.
d.Feb.17,1915

Yr	Cl	Lea	Pos	G	Rec
1883	Ath	a	P-O	9	5-4 .139
1884	Key	U	P-1-O	43	14-24 .134
1884	Wil	U	P	2	0-2
1884	K C	U	P-O	6	2-2 .167
1888	Cle	a	P	60	25-33
1889	Cle	N	P	34	12-22
1890	Cle	p	P	44	13-26
1891	Was	a	P	12	2-10
1891	Bal	a	P	13	4-2
	BRTR			223	77-125 .154

BAKER, ALBERT JONES
b.Feb.28,1906 Batesville, Miss.

Yr	Cl	Lea	Pos	G	Rec
1938	Bos	A	P	3	0-0
	BRTR				

BAKER, CHARLES
b.Hudson,Mass.

Yr	Cl	Lea	Pos	G	Rec
1884	Pit	U	O	3	.083
1884	Chi	U	2-S-O	11	.167
				14	.148

BAKER, CHARLES (Smiling Bock)
b.July 17,1878 Troy,N.Y.

Yr	Cl	Lea	Pos	G	Rec
1901	Cle	A	P	1	0-1
1901	Phi	A	P	1	0-1
				2	0-2

BAKER, DELMER DAVID
b.May 3,1892 Sherwood,Ore.

Yr	Cl	Lea	Pos	G	Rec
1914	Det	A	C	43	.214
1915	Det	A	C	68	.246
1916	Det	A	C	61	.153
		BRTR		172	.209

Non-playing manager Det (A) 1933, 1938-42.

BAKER, ERNEST G.
b.Aug.8,1875 Three Rivers,Mich.
d.Oct.25.1945

Yr	Cl	Lea	Pos	G	Rec
1905	Cin	N	P	1	0-0

BAKER, EUGENE WALTER
b.June 15,1925 Davenport,Ia.

Yr	Cl	Lea	Pos	G	Rec
1953	Chi	N	2	7	.227
1954	Chi	N	2	135	.275
1955	Chi	N	2	154	.268
1956	Chi	N	2	140	.258
1957	Chi	N	3	12	.250
1957	Pit	N	2-S-3	111	.266
1958	Pit	N	2-3	29	.250
1960	Pit	N	2-3	33	.243
1961	Pit	N	3	9	.100
		BRTR		630	.265

BAKER, FLOYD WILSON
b.Oct.10,1918 Luray,Va.

Yr	Cl	Lea	Pos	G	Rec
1943	St.L	A	S-3	22	.174
1944	St.L	A	2-S	44	.175
1945	Chi	A	2-3	82	.250
1946	Chi	A	3	9	.250
1947	Chi	A	2-3	105	.264
1948	Chi	A	2-S-3	104	.215
1949	Chi	A	2-S-3	125	.260
1950	Chi	A	2-3-O	83	.317
1951	Chi	A	2-S-3	82	.263
1952	Was	A	2-S-3	79	.262
1953	Was	A	3	9	.000
1953	Bos	A	2-3	81	.273
1954	Bos	A	2-3	21	.200
1954	Phi	N	2-3	23	.227
1955	Phi	N	3	5	.000
		BLTR		874	.251

BAKER, GEORGE F.
b.1859 St.Louis,Mo.

Yr	Cl	Lea	Pos	G	Rec
1883	Bal	a	C-S	6	.227
1884	St.L	U	C	64	.171
1885	St.L	N	C-2-3-O	39	.122
1886	K C	N	C	1	.250
				110	.159

BAKER, HOWARD FRANCIS
b.Mar.1,1888 Bridgeport,Conn.

Yr	Cl	Lea	Pos	G	Rec
1912	Cle	A	3	11	.167
1914	Chi	A	3	15	.277
1915	Chi	A	H	2	.000
1915	N Y	N	3	1	.000
		BRTR		29	.220

BAKER, JESSE
(Real Name Jesse Silverman)

Yr	Cl	Lea	Pos	G	Rec
1919	Was	A	S	1	.000
		BRTR			

BAKER, JESSE ORMAND
b.June 3,1888 Steilacoom,Wash.

Yr	Cl	Lea	Pos	G	Rec
1911	Chi	A	P	22	2-7
		BLTL			

BAKER, JOHN FRANKLIN
(Home Run)
b.Mar.13,1886 Trappe,Md.

Yr	Cl	Lea	Pos	G	Rec
1908	Phi	A	3	9	.290
1909	Phi	A	3	148	.305
1910	Phi	A	3	146	.283
1911	Phi	A	3	148	.334
1912	Phi	A	3	149	.347
1913	Phi	A	3	149	.336
1914	Phi	A	3	150	.319
1916	N Y	A	3	100	.269
1917	N Y	A	3	146	.282
1918	N Y	A	3	126	.306
1919	N Y	A	3	141	.293

(Continued)

Yr	Cl	Lea	Pos	G	Rec
1921	N Y	A	3	94	.294
1922	N Y	A	3	69	.277
		BLTR		1575	.307

BAKER, KIRTLY
b.June 24,1869 Aurora,Ind.
d.Apr.15,1927

Yr	Cl	Lea	Pos	G	Rec
1890	Pit	N	P	23	2-19
1893	Bal	N	P	19	3-10
1894	Bal	N	P	2	0-0
1898	Was	N	P	6	1-3
1899	Was	N	P	12	1-8
				62	7-40

BAKER, NEAL VERNON
b.Apr.30,1904 LaPorte,Tex

Yr	Cl	Lea	Pos	G	Rec
1927	Phi	A	P	5	0-0
		BRTR			

BAKER, NORMAN LESLIE
b.Oct.14,1862 Philadelphia,Pa.

Yr	Cl	Lea	Pos	G	Rec
1883	Pit	a	P-O	4	0-2 / .000
1885	Lou	a	P	25	13-12
1890	Bal	a	P	2	1-1
				31	14-15 / .143

BAKER, PHILIP
b.Sept.19,1856 Philadelphia, Pa.
d.June 4,1940

Yr	Cl	Lea	Pos	G	Rec
1883	Bal	a	C-S-O	27	.280
1884	Was	U	C-1	83	.282
1886	Was	N	1-O	81	.221
				191	.257

BAKER, THOMAS CALVIN
(Rattlesnake)
b.June 11,1915 Victoria,Tex.

Yr	Cl	Lea	Pos	G	Rec
1935	Bro	N	P	11	1-0
1936	Bro	N	P	37	1-8
1937	Bro	N	P	7	0-1
1937	N Y	N	P	13	1-0
1938	N Y	N	P	2	0-0
		BBTR		70	3-9

BAKER, TRACY LEE
b.1891 Pendleton, Ore.

Yr	Cl	Lea	Pos	G	Rec
1911	Bos	A	1	1	.000
		BRTR			

BAKER, WILLIAM PRESLEY
b.Feb.22,1911 Paw Creek,N.C.

Yr	Cl	Lea	Pos	G	Rec
1940	Cin	N	C	27	.217
1941	Cin	N	C	2	.000
1941	Pit	N	C	35	.224
1942	Pit	N	C	18	.118
1943	Pit	N	C	63	.273
1946	Pit	N	C-1	53	.239
1948	St.L	N	C	45	.294
1949	St.L	N	C	20	.133
		BRTR		263	.253

BALAS, MITCHELL FRANCIS (Mike)
(Real Name Mitchell Francis Balaski)
b.May 17,1910 Lowell,Mass.

Yr	Cl	Lea	Pos	G	Rec
1938	Bos	N	P	1	0-0
		BRTR			

BALASKI, MITCHELL FRANCIS
(Played under name of Mitchell Francis Balas)

BALCENA, ROBERT RUDOLPH
b.Aug.1,1928 San Pedro,Cal.

Yr	Cl	Lea	Pos	G	Rec
1956	Cin	N	O	7	.000
		BRTL			

BALDSCHUN, JACK EDWARD
b.Oct.16,1936 Greenville,O.

Yr	Cl	Lea	Pos	G	Rec
1961	Phi	N	P	65	5-3
1962	Phi	N	P	67	12-7
		BRTR		132	17-10

BALDWIN, CHARLES BUSTED
(Lady)
b.Apr.10,1859 Ormel,N.Y.

(Continued)
d.Mar.7,1937

Yr	Cl	Lea	Pos	G	Rec
1884	Mil	U	P-O	7	1-1 / .214
1885	Det	N	P-O	31	11-9 / .241
1886	Det	N	P	57	42-13
1887	Det	N	P	24	13-10
1888	Det	N	P	6	3-3
1890	Bro	N	P	2	1-0
1890	Buf	p	P	7	2-5
		BLTL		134	73-41 / .226

BALDWIN, CLARENCE GEOGHAN (Kid)
b.Nov.1,1864 Newport,Ky.
d.July 12,1897

Yr	Cl	Lea	Pos	G	Rec
1884	KC	U	C-2-3-O	49	.202
1884	Chi	U	C	1	1.000
1885	Cin	a	P-C-2-3-O	26	0-0 / .147
1886	Cin	a	C-O	86	.238
1887	Cin	a	C-O	96	.262
1888	Cin	a	C-1-O	66	.220
1889	Cin	a	C-1-3-O	60	.248
1890	Cin	N	C	21	.153
1890	Ath	a	C	24	.239
		BRTR		429	0-0 / .227

BALDWIN, FRANK DEWITT
b.Dec.25,1928 Califon,N.J.

Yr	Cl	Lea	Pos	G	Rec
1953	Cin	N	C	16	.100
		BRTR			

BALDWIN, HENRY CLAY
b.June 13,1894 Philadelphia,Pa.

Yr	Cl	Lea	Pos	G	Rec
1927	Phi	N	S-3	6	.313
		BRTR			

BALDWIN, HOWARD EDWARD
(Harry)
b.June 30,1900 Baltimore,Md.
d.Jan.23,1958

Yr	Cl	Lea	Pos	G	Rec
1924	N Y	N	P	11	3-1
1925	N Y	N	P	1	0-0
		BRTR		12	3-1

BALDWIN, MARCUS ELMORE
(Fido)
b.Oct.29,1865 Pittsburgh,Pa.
d.Nov.10,1929

Yr	Cl	Lea	Pos	G	Rec
1887	Chi	N	P	40	19-17
1888	Chi	N	P	30	13-15
1889	Col	a	P	64	26-34
1890	Chi	p	P	58	32-21
1891	Pit	N	P	54	20-28
1892	Pit	N	P	57	25-27
1893	Pit	N	P	5	1-1
1893	N Y	N	P	35	12-19
		BRTR		343	148-162

BALDWIN, O. F.
b.Youngstown,O.

Yr	Cl	Lea	Pos	G	Rec
1908	St.L	N	P	4	1-3

BALENTI, MICHAEL RICHARD
b.July 3,1889 Darlington,Okla.
d.Aug.4,1955

Yr	Cl	Lea	Pos	G	Rec
1911	Cin	N	S	7	.250
1913	St.L	A	S	70	.181
		BRTR		77	.183

BALL, ARTHUR
b.1874 Chicago, Ill.
d.Dec.26,1915

Yr	Cl	Lea	Pos	G	Rec
1894	St.L	N	2	1	.333
•1898	Bal	N	3	25	.175
		TR		26	.181

BALL, JAMES CHANDLER
b.1885 Harford Co.,Md.

Yr	Cl	Lea	Pos	G	Rec
1907	Bos	N	C	11	.150
1908	Bos	N	C	6	.133
		TR		17	.145

BALL, NEAL
b.Apr.22,1881 Grand Haven,Mich.
d.Oct.15,1957

Yr	Cl	Lea	Pos	G	Rec
1907	N Y	A	S	15	.205
1908	N Y	A	S	132	.247
1909	N Y	A	S	8	.214
1909	Cle	A	S	96	.255
1910	Cle	A	S	53	.210
1911	Cle	A	2-3	116	.296
1912	Cle	A	2	38	.233
1912	Bos	A	2	17	.182
1913	Bos	A	2	21	.172
	BRTR			496	.251

BALLAS, SIMON D (Sim)
b.1862 England
d.Jan.14,1908

Yr	Cl	Lea	Pos	G	Rec
1884	Tol	a	C-O	13	.067

(Formerly listed as BULLIS, SAMUEL)

BALLENGER, PELHAM ASHBY
b.Feb.6,1896 Gilreath Mill,S.C.
d.Dec.8,1948

Yr	Cl	Lea	Pos	G	Rec
1928	Was	A	2-3	3	.111
	BRTR				

BALLOU, NOBLE WINFRED (Win)
b.Nov.30,1897 Williamsburg,Ky.
d.Jan.30,1963

Yr	Cl	Lea	Pos	G	Rec
1925	Was	A	P	10	1-1
1926	St.L	A	P	43	10-10
1927	St.L	A	P	21	5-6
1929	Bro	N	P	25	2-3
	BRTL			99	18-20

BALSAMO, ANTHONY FRED
b.Nov.21,1937 Brooklyn,N.Y.

Yr	Cl	Lea	Pos	G	Rec
1962	Chi	N	P	18	0-1
	BRTR				

BAMBERGER, GEORGE IRVIN
b.Aug.1,1925 Staten Island,N.Y.

Yr	Cl	Lea	Pos	G	Rec
1951	N Y	N	P	2	0-0
1952	N Y	N	P	6	0-0
1959	Bal	A	P	3	0-0
	BRTR			11	0-0

BAMBERGER, HAROLD EARL (Dutch)
b.Oct.29,1924 Lebanon,Pa.

Yr	Cl	Lea	Pos	G	Rec
1948	N Y	N	O	7	.083
	BLTR				

BANCROFT, DAVID JAMES (Beauty)
b.Apr.20,1892 Sioux City,Ia.

Yr	Cl	Lea	Pos	G	Rec
1915	Phi	N	S	153	.254
1916	Phi	N	S	142	.212
1917	Phi	N	S	127	.243
1918	Phi	N	S	125	.265
1919	Phi	N	S	92	.272
1920	Phi	N	S	42	.276
1920	N Y	N	S	108	.308
1921	N Y	N	S	153	.319
1922	N Y	N	S	156	.321
1923	N Y	N	2-S	107	.304
1924	Bos	N	M-S	79	.279
1925	Bos	N	M-S	128	.319
1926	Bos	N	M-S	127	.311
1927	Bos	N	M-S	111	.243
1928	Bro	N	S	149	.247
1929	Bro	N	S	104	.277
1930	N Y	N	S	10	.059
	BBTR			1913	.279

BANCROFT, FRANK CARTER
b.May 9,1846 Lancaster,Mass.
d.Mar.31,1921
Non-playing manager Wor (N) 1880, Det (N) 1881-82 Cle (N) 1883, Pro (N) 1884-85, Ath (a) 1887, Ind (N) 1889 and Cin (N) 1902.

BANKHEAD, DANIEL ROBERT
b.May 3,1921 Empire,Ala.

Yr	Cl	Lea	Pos	G	Rec
1947	Bro	N	P	6	0-0
1950	Bro	N	P	41	9-4
1951	Bro	N	P	15	0-1
	BRTR			62	9-5

BANKS, ERNEST
b.Jan.31,1931 Dallas,Tex.

Yr	Cl	Lea	Pos	G	Rec
1953	Chi	N	S	10	.314
1954	Chi	N	S	154	.275
1955	Chi	N	S	154	.295
1956	Chi	N	S	139	.297
1957	Chi	N	S-3	156	.285
1958	Chi	N	S	154	.313
1959	Chi	N	S	155	.304
1960	Chi	N	S	156	.271
1961	Chi	N	1-S-O	138	.278
1962	Chi	N	1-3	154	.269
	BRTR			1370	.288

BANKS, GEORGE EDWARD
b.Sept.24,1938 Pacolet Mills,S.C.

Yr	Cl	Lea	Pos	G	Rec
1962	Min	A	3-O	63	.252
	BRTR				

BANKS, WILLIAM J.
(Real name William J. Yerrick)
b.1873 Danville,Pa.

Yr	Cl	Lea	Pos	G	Rec
1895	Bos	N	P	1	1-0
1896	Bos	N	P	4	0-3
				5	1-3

BANKSTON, WILBORN EVERETT
b.May 25,1893 Barnesville,Ga.

Yr	Cl	Lea	Pos	G	Rec
1915	Phi	A	O	11	.142
	BLTR				

BANNING, JAMES M.
b.St.Paul, Minn.

Yr	Cl	Lea	Pos	G	Rec
1888	Was	N	C	1	.000
1889	Was	N	C	2	.000
	BLTR			3	.000

BANNOCK, ...

Yr	Cl	Lea	Pos	G	Rec
1871	Chi	n	3	3	NR
1875	Chi	n	3	2	.000
				5	NR

BANNON, JAMES H. (Foxy)
b.May 5,1871 Amesbury,Mass.
d.Mar.24,1948

Yr	Cl	Lea	Pos	G	Rec
1893	St.L	N	P-O	23	{ 0-1 / .363
1894	Bos	N	O	127	.336
1895	Bos	N	O	121	.339
1896	Bos	N	O	87	.256
	BR			358	{ 0-1 / .320

BANNON, THOMAS EDWARD (Ward Six)
b.May 8,1869 Amesbury,Mass.
d.Jan.26,1950

Yr	Cl	Lea	Pos	G	Rec
1895	N Y	N	1-O	37	.266
1896	N Y	N	O	2	.143
				39	.267

BANTA, JOHN KAY
b.June 24,1925 Hudson,Kan.

Yr	Cl	Lea	Pos	G	Rec
1947	Bro	N	P	3	0-1
1948	Bro	N	P	2	0-1
1949	Bro	N	P	48	10-6
1950	Bro	N	P	16	4-4
	BLTR			69	14-12

BARBARE, WALTER LAWRENCE (Dinty)
b.Aug.11,1891 Greenville,S.C.

Yr	Cl	Lea	Pos	G	Rec
1914	Cle	A	S	15	.308
1915	Cle	A	3	77	.191
1916	Cle	A	3	13	.229
1918	Bos	A	3	13	.172
1919	Pit	N	2-3	85	.273
1920	Pit	N	S	57	.274
1921	Bos	N	S	134	.302
1922	Bos	N	1-2-3	106	.231
	BRTR			500	.260

BARBARY, DONALD ODELL (Red)
b.June 20,1920 Simpsonville,S.C.

Yr	Cl	Lea	Pos	G	Rec
1943	Was	A	H	1	.000
	BRTR				

BARBEAU, WILLIAM JOSEPH (Jap)
b.June 10,1884 New York,N.Y.

Yr	Cl	Lea	Pos	G	Rec
1905	Cle	A	3	12	.237
1906	Cle	A	3	42	.194
1909	Pit	N	3	85	.220
1909	St.L	N	3	44	.251
1910	St.L	N	2-3-O	7	.227
	BRTR			190	.224

BARBEE, DAVID MONROE
b.May 7,1905 Greensboro,N.C.

Yr	Cl	Lea	Pos	G	Rec
1926	Phi	A	O	19	.170
1932	Pit	N	O	97	.257
	BRTR			116	.246

BARBER, CHARLES D.
b.1854 Martinsburg,Pa.
d.Nov.23,1910

Yr	Cl	Lea	Pos	G	Rec
1884	Cin	U	2	48	.190
	BRTR				

BARBER, SAMUEL TURNER
b.July 9,1894 St.Louis,Mo.

Yr	Cl	Lea	Pos	G	Rec
1915	Was	A	O	20	.302
1916	Was	A	O	15	.212
1917	Chi	N	O	7	.214
1918	Chi	N	1-O	55	.236
1919	Chi	N	O	76	.313
1920	Chi	N	1-O	94	.265
1921	Chi	N	O	127	.314
1922	Chi	N	1-O	84	.309
1923	Bro	N	O	13	.217
	BLTR			491	.289

BARBER, STEPHEN DAVID
b.Feb.22,1939 Takoma Park,Md.

Yr	Cl	Lea	Pos	G	Rec
1960	Bal	A	P	36	10-7
1961	Bal	A	P	37	18-12
1962	Bal	A	P	28	9-6
	BLTL			101	37-25

BARBERICH, FRANK
b.Feb.3,1882 Astoria,N.Y.

Yr	Cl	Lea	Pos	G	Rec
1907	Bos	N	P	2	1-0
1910	Bos	A	P	2	0-0
	BRTR			4	1-0

BARCLAY, CURTIS CORDELL
b.Aug.22,1931 Chicago,Ill.

Yr	Cl	Lea	Pos	G	Rec
1957	NY	N	P	37	9-9
1958	SF	N	P	6	1-0
1959	SF	N	P	1	0-0
	BRTR			44	10-9

BARCLAY, GEORGE OLIVER (Deerfoot)
b.May 16,1875 Millville,Pa.
d.Apr.2,1909

Yr	Cl	Lea	Pos	G	Rec
1902	St.L	N	O	137	.301
1903	St.L	N	O	107	.248
1904	St.L	N	O	103	.200
1904	Bos	N	O	24	.226
1905	Bos	N	O	28	.176
				399	.249

BARFOOT, CLYDE RAYMOND (Foots)
b.July 8,1891 Richmond,Va.

Yr	Cl	Lea	Pos	G	Rec
1922	St.L	N	P	42	4-5
1923	St.L	N	P	37	3-3
1926	Det	A	P	11	1-2
	BRTR			90	8-10

BARGER, EROS BOLLIVAR (Cy)
b.May 18,1885 Jamestown,Ky.

Yr	Cl	Lea	Pos	G	Rec
1906	N Y	A	P	2	0-0
1907	N Y	A	P	1	0-0
1910	Bro	N	P	35	15-15
1911	Bro	N	P	42	11-15
1912	Bro	N	P	17	1-9
1914	Pit	F	P	33	10-16
1915	Pit	F	P	28	9-8
	BLTR			158	46-63

Yr Cl Lea Pos G Rec

BARKER, ALFRED
b.Jan.18,1839 Rockford,Ill.
d.Sept.15,1912
1871 Rok n O 1 NR

BARKER, RAYMOND HERRELL
b.Mar.12,1936 Martinsburg,W.Va.
1960 Bal A O 5 .000
BLTR

BARKLEY, JOHN DUNCAN (Red)
b.Sept.19,1914 Childress,Tex
1937 St.L A 2 31 .267
1939 Bos N S-3 12 .000
1943 Bro N S 20 .314
BRTR 63 .264

BARKLEY, SAMUEL WILSON
b.May 19,1859 Wheeling,W.Va.
d.Apr.20,1912
1884 Tol a 2 104 .300
1885 St.L a 1-2 96 .179
1886 Pit a 2 122 .269
1887 Pit N 1-2 90 .286
1888 K C a M-2 116 .220
1889 K C a 2 45 .277
TR 573 .279

BARLOW, THOMAS H.
1872 Atl n C-S 36 NR
1873 Atl n C 23 NR
1873 Mut n C 1 NR
1873 Atl n C 31 NR
1874 Har n S 32 NR
1875 N H n S 1 NR
1875 Atl n 2 1 .000
125 NR

BARMES, BRUCE RAYMOND
(Squeaky)
b.Oct.23,1929 Vincennes,Ind.
1953 Was A O 5 .200
BLTR

BARNA, HERBERT PAUL (Babe)
b.Mar.2,1915 Clarksburg,W.Va.
1937 Phi A H 14 .389
1938 Phi A O 9 .133
1941 N Y N O 10 .214
1942 N Y N O 104 .257
1943 N Y N O 40 .204
1943 Bos A O 30 .170
BLTR 207 .232

BARNABE, CHARLES EDWARD
b.June 12,1900 Russell Gulch,Col.
1927 Chi A P 18 0-5
1928 Chi A P 11 0-2
BLTL 29 0-7

BARNES, EMILE DURING (Red)
b.Dec.25,1904 Suggsville,Ala.
d.July 3,1959
1927 Was A O 3 .364
1928 Was A O 114 .305
1929 Was A O 72 .200
1930 Was A O 12 .167
1930 Chi A O 85 .248
BLTR 286 .269

BARNES, EVERETT DUANE (Eppie)
b.Dec.1,1900 Ossining,N.Y.
1923 Pit N 1 2 .500
1924 Pit N 1 2 .000
BLTL 4 .143

BARNES, FRANK
b.Aug.26,1928 Greenville,Miss.
1957 St.L N P 4 0-1
1958 St.L N P 13 1-1
1960 St.L N P 4 0-1
BRTR 21 1-3

BARNES, FRANK SAMUEL (Lefty)
b.Jan.9,1901 Dallas,Tex
1929 Det A P 4 0-1
(Continued)
1930 N Y A P 3 0-1
BLTL 7 0-2

BARNES, JESSE LAWRENCE
b.Aug.26,1892 Guthrie,Okla.
d.Sept.9,1961
1915 Bos N P 9 3-0
1916 Bos N P 33 6-14
1917 Bos N P 53 13-21
1918 N Y N P 9 6-1
1919 N Y N P 46 25-9
1920 N Y N P 45 20-15
1921 N Y N P 42 15-9
1922 N Y N P 37 13-8
1923 N Y N P 12 3-1
1923 Bos N P 31 10-14
1924 Bos N P 37 15-20
1925 Bos N P 32 11-16
1926 Bro N P 31 10-11
1927 Bro N P 18 2-10
BLTR 435 152-149

BARNES, JOHN FRANCIS (Honey)
b.Jan.31,1900 Fulton,N.Y.
1926 N Y A C 1 .000
BLTR

BARNES, JUNE SHOAF (Lefty)
b.June 14,1911 Churchland,N.C.
1934 Cin N P 2 0-0
BLTL

BARNES, ROBERT AVERY (Lefty)
b.Jan.6,1902 Washburn,Ill.
1924 Chi A P 2 0-0
BLTL

BARNES, ROSCOE CONKLING
(Ross)
b.May 8,1850 Mt.Morris,N.Y.
d.Feb.8,1915
1871 Bos n 2-S 33 .374
1872 Bos n 2 44 .404
1873 Bos n 2-3 60 .406
1874 Bos n 2 52 .353
1875 Bos n 2-O 78 .372
1876 Chi N 2 66 .404
1877 Chi N 2 22 .272
1879 Cin N 2-S 76 .256
1881 Bos N 2-S 69 .271
BRTR 500 .350

BARNES, SAMUEL THOMAS
b.Dec.18,1899 Jackson,Ala.
1921 Det A 2 7 .182
BLTR

BARNES, VIRGIL JENNINGS
(Zeke)
b.Mar.5,1897 Circleville,Kan.
d.July 24,1958
1919 N Y N P 1 0-0
1920 N Y N P 1 0-1
1922 N Y N P 22 1-0
1923 N Y N P 22 2-3
1924 N Y N P 35 16-10
1925 N Y N P 32 15-11
1926 N Y N P 31 8-13
1927 N Y N P 35 14-11
1928 N Y N P 10 3-3
1928 Bos N P 16 2-7
BRTR 205 61-59

BARNES, WILLIAM H.
b.Indianapolis,Ind.
1884 St.P U O 8 .161

BARNEY, EDMOND J.
b.Jan.23,1890 Amery,Wis.
1915 N Y A O 11 191
1915 Pit N O 32 .273
1916 Pit N O 45 .197
BLTR 88 .224

BARNEY, REX EDWARD
b.Dec.19,1924 Omaha,Neb.
(Continued)
1943 Bro N P 9 2-2
1946 Bro N P 16 2-5
1947 Bro N P 28 5-2
1948 Bro N P 44 15-13
1949 Bro N P 38 9-8
1950 Bro N P 20 2-1
BRTR 155 35-31

BARNHART, CLYDE LEE (Pooch)
b.Dec.29,1895 Buck Valley,Pa.
1920 Pit N 3 12 .326
1921 Pit N 3 124 .258
1922 Pit N 3-O 75 .330
1923 Pit N O 114 .324
1924 Pit N O 102 .276
1925 Pit N O 142 .325
1926 Pit N O 76 .192
1927 Pit N O 108 .319
1928 Pit N O 61 .296
BRTR 814 .295

BARNHART, EDGAR VERNON
(Barney)
b.Sept.16,1904 Columbia,Mo.
1924 St.L A P 1 0-0
BLTR

BARNHART, LESLIE EARL
(Barney)
b.Feb.23,1905 Hoxie,Kan.
1928 Cle A P 2 0-1
1930 Cle A P 1 1-0
BRTR 3 1-1

BARNHART, VICTOR DEE
b.Sept.1,1922 Hagerstown,Md.
1944 Pit N S 1 .500
1945 Pit N S-3 71 .269
1946 Pit N H 2 .000
BRTR 74 .270

BARNICLE, GEORGE BERNARD
(Barney)
b.Aug.26,1917 Fitchburg,Mass.
1939 Bos N P 6 2-2
1940 Bos N P 13 1-0
1941 Bos N P 1 0-1
BRTR 20 3-3

BARNIE, WILLIAM S.
b.Jan.26,1853 New York,N.Y.
d.July15,1900
1874 Har n C-S-O 44 NR
1875 Wes n C-O 10 NR
1875 Mut n C-O 10 NR
1883 Bal a M-C-S-O 17 .200
81 NR
Non-playing manager Bal (a) 1884-91, Ath (a) 1891, Was (N) 1892, Lou (N) 1893-94 and Bro (N) 1897-98.

BARONE, RICHARD ANTHONY
b.Oct.13,1932 San Jose, Cal.
1960 Pit N S 3 .000
BRTR

BARR, HYDER EDWARD (Scotty)
b.Oct.6,1886 Bristol,Tenn.
d.Dec.2,1934
1908 Phi A 2 19 .143
1909 Phi A O 22 .079
BRTR 41 .112

BARR, ROBERT ALEXANDER
b.Mar.12,1909 Newton,Mass.
1935 Bro N P 2 0-0
BRTR

BARR, ROBERT M.
b.1856 Washington,D.C.
d.Nov.14,1893
1883 Pit a P-1-O 28 { 6-18 .230
1884 Was a P-1-O 39 { 9-24 .152
1884 Ind a P-O 18 { 3-11 .188

(Continued)

Yr	Cl	Lea	Pos	G	Rec
1886	Was	N	P	22	4-18
1890	Roc	a	P	57	28-25
1891	N Y	N	P	5	0-3
				169	50-99 .204

BARRAGAN, FACUNDO ANTHONY
b.June 20,1932 Sacramento,Cal.

Yr	Cl	Lea	Pos	G	Rec
1961	Chi	N	C	10	.214
1962	Chi	N	C	58	.201
	BRTR			68	.204

BARRETT, CHARLES HENRY (Red)
b.Feb.14,1915 Santa Barbara,Cal.

Yr	Cl	Lea	Pos	G	Rec
1937	Cin	N	P	1	0-0
1938	Cin	N	P	6	2-0
1939	Cin	N	P	2	0-0
1940	Cin	N	P	3	1-0
1943	Bos	N	P	38	12-18
1944	Bos	N	P	42	9-16
1945	Bos	N	P	9	2-3
1945	St.L	N	P	36	21-9
1946	St.L	N	P	23	3-2
1947	Bos	N	P	36	11-12
1948	Bos	N	P	34	7-8
1949	Bos	N	P	23	1-1
	BRTR			253	69-69

BARRETT, FRANCIS JOSEPH
b.July 1,1913 Ft.Lauderdale,Fla.

Yr	Cl	Lea	Pos	G	Rec
1939	St.L	N	P	1	0-1
1944	Bos	A	P	38	8-7
1945	Bos	A	P	37	4-3
1946	Bos	N	P	23	2-4
1950	Pit	N	P	5	1-2
	BRTR			104	15-17

BARRETT, JAMES ERIGENA
b.Mar.28,1875 Athol,Mass.
d.Oct.24,1921

Yr	Cl	Lea	Pos	G	Rec
1899	Cin	N	O	26	.374
1900	Cin	N	O	138	.316
1901	Det	A	O	136	.294
1902	Det	A	O	136	.304
1903	Det	A	O	136	.315
1904	Det	A	O	162	.264
1905	Det	A	O	18	.254
1906	Cin	N	O	5	.000
1907	Bos	A	O	106	.243
1908	Bos	A	O	3	.125
	BLTR			866	.291

BARRETT, JOHN JOSEPH
b.Dec.18,1915 Lowell,Mass.

Yr	Cl	Lea	Pos	G	Rec
1942	Pit	N	O	111	.247
1943	Pit	N	O	130	.231
1944	Pit	N	O	149	.269
1945	Pit	N	O	142	.256
1946	Pit	N	O	32	.169
1946	Bos	N	O	24	.233
	BLTL			588	.251

BARRETT, MARTIN
b.Central Falls,R.I.

Yr	Cl	Lea	Pos	G	Rec
1884	Bos	N	C	3	.000

BARRETT, RICHARD OLIVER
(Played in (A) under name of Richard Oliver and in (N) under name of Richard Oliver Barrett, and under real name of Tracy Souter Barrett.)

BARRETT, ROBERT SCHLEY
(Jumbo)
b.Jan.27,1901 Atlanta,Ga.

Yr	Cl	Lea	Pos	G	Rec
1923	Chi	N	H	3	.333
1924	Chi	N	1-2-3	54	.241
1925	Chi	N	2-3	14	.313
1925	Bro	N	H	1	.000
1927	Bro	N	3	99	.259
1929	Bos	A	3	68	.270
	BRTR			239	.260

BARRETT, TRACY SOUTER
(Kewpie)
(Also played under names of Richard Oliver, 1933, and Richard Oliver Barrett, 1934-43.
b.Sept.28,1906 Montoursville,Pa.

Yr	Cl	Lea	Pos	G	Rec
1933	Phi	A	P	15	4-4
1934	Bos	N	P	15	1-3
1943	Chi	N	P	15	0-4
1943	Phi	N	P	23	10-9
1944	Phi	N	P	37	12-18
1945	Phi	N	P	36	8-20
	BRTR			141	35-58

BARRETT, WILLIAM
b.Washington,D.C.

Yr	Cl	Lea	Pos	G	Rec
1871	Kek	n	C	1	NR
1872	Oly	n	C	1	.000
1872	Atl	n	O	7	NR
1873	Bal	n	O	1	NR
				10	NR

BARRETT, WILLIAM JOSEPH
(Whispering Bill)
b.May 28,1900 Cambridge,Mass.
d.Jan.26,1951

Yr	Cl	Lea	Pos	G	Rec
1921	Phi	A	P	14	1-0
1923	Chi	A	O	44	.271
1924	Chi	A	S-O	119	.271
1925	Chi	A	2-S-3-O	81	.363
1926	Chi	A	O	111	.307
1927	Chi	A	O	147	.286
1928	Chi	A	2-O	76	.277
1929	Chi	A	O	3	.000
1929	Bos	A	O	111	.270
1930	Bos	A	O	6	.176
1930	Was	A	H	6	.000
	BRTR			718	1-0 .288

BARRON, DAVID IRENUS (Red)
b.June 21,1900 Clarksville,Ga.

Yr	Cl	Lea	Pos	G	Rec
1929	Bos	N	O	10	.190
	BRTR				

BARRON, FRANK JOHN
b.July 31,1890 Brooklyn,N.Y.

Yr	Cl	Lea	Pos	G	Rec
1914	Was	A	P	1	0-0
	BLTL				

BARROW, EDWARD GRANT
(Cousin Ed)
b.May 10,1868 Springfield,Ill.
d.Dec.15,1953
Non-playing manager Det (A) 1903-04 and Bos (A) 1918-20.

BARROWS, FRANK LEWIS
b.Boston,Mass.
d.Sept.24,1901

Yr	Cl	Lea	Pos	G	Rec
1871	Bos	n	2-O	20	NR
1874	Bal	n	O	16	NR
				36	NR

BARROWS, ROLAND (Cuke)
b.Oct.20,1883 Raymond,Me.
d.Feb.10,1955

Yr	Cl	Lea	Pos	G	Rec
1909	Chi	A	O	4	.150
1910	Chi	A	O	6	.200
1911	Chi	A	O	13	.195
1912	Chi	A	O	8	.231
	BLTR			31	.190

BARRY, EDWARD (Jumbo)
b.Freeport,Ind.

Yr	Cl	Lea	Pos	G	Rec
1905	Bos	A	P	7	1-2
1906	Bos	A	P	3	0-3
1907	Bos	A	P	2	0-1
	TL			12	1-6

BARRY, HARDIN
b.Mar.26,1891 Susanville,Cal.

Yr	Cl	Lea	Pos	G	Rec
1912	Phi	A	P	3	0-0
	BRTR				

BARRY, JOHN C. (Shad)
b.Sept.28,1876 Newburgh,N.Y.
d.Nov.27,1936

Yr	Cl	Lea	Pos	G	Rec
1899	Was	N	O	75	.303
1900	Bos	N	2-S-O	66	.261
1901	Bos	N	O	11	.179
1901	Phi	N	3-O	63	.245
1902	Phi	N	1-O	138	.302
1903	Phi	N	1-O	138	.276
1904	Phi	N	O	33	.205
1904	Chi	N	1-O	72	.262
1905	Chi	N	1	26	.212
1905	Cin	N	1	126	.324
1906	Cin	N	1-O	73	.287
1906	St.L	N	1-O	62	.249
1907	St.L	N	O	81	.248
1908	St.L	N	O	71	.228
1908	NY	N	O	31	.149
	BRTR			1066	.270

BARRY, JOHN JOSEPH
b.Apr.26,1887 Meriden,Conn.
d.Apr.23,1961

Yr	Cl	Lea	Pos	G	Rec
1908	Phi	A	2	40	.222
1909	Phi	A	S	124	.215
1910	Phi	A	S	145	.259
1911	Phi	A	S	127	.265
1912	Phi	A	S	139	.261
1913	Phi	A	S	135	.275
1914	Phi	A	S	140	.242
1915	Phi	A	S	54	.218
1915	Bos	A	2	78	.265
1916	Bos	A	2	94	.203
1917	Bos	A	M-2	116	.214
1919	Bos	A	2	31	.241
	BRTR			1223	.243

BARRY, THOMAS ARTHUR
b.Apr.10,1879 St.Louis,Mo.
d.June 4,1946

Yr	Cl	Lea	Pos	G	Rec
1904	Phi	N	P	1	0-1

BARTELL, RICHARD WILLIAM
(Rowdy Dick)
b.Nov.22,1907 Chicago,Ill.

Yr	Cl	Lea	Pos	G	Rec
1927	Pit	N	S	1	.000
1928	Pit	N	2-S	72	.305
1929	Pit	N	2-S	143	.302
1930	Pit	N	S	129	.320
1931	Phi	N	S	135	.289
1932	Phi	N	S	154	.308
1933	Phi	N	S	152	.271
1934	Phi	N	S	146	.310
1935	NY	N	S	137	.262
1936	NY	N	S	145	.298
1937	NY	N	S	128	.306
1938	NY	N	S	127	.262
1939	Chi	N	S	105	.238
1940	Det	A	S	139	.233
1941	Det	A	S	5	.167
1941	NY	N	S-3	104	.303
1942	NY	N	S-3	90	.244
1943	NY	N	S-3	99	.270
1946	NY	N	2-3	5	.000
	BRTR			2016	.284

BARTHELSON, ROBERT EDWARD
b.July 15,1924 New Haven,Conn.

Yr	Cl	Lea	Pos	G	Rec
1944	NY	N	P	7	1-1
	BRTR				

BARTHOLD, JOHN FRANCIS
b.Apr.14,1882 Philadelphia,Pa.
d.Nov.4,1946

Yr	Cl	Lea	Pos	G	Rec
1904	Phi	A	P	4	0-1
	BBTR				

BARTHOLOMEW, LESTER JUSTIN
b.Apr.4,1905 Madison,Wis.

Yr	Cl	Lea	Pos	G	Rec
1928	Pit	N	P	6	0-0
1932	Chi	A	P	3	0-0
	BRTL			9	0-0

BARTIROME, ANTHONY JOSEPH
b.May 9,1932 Pittsburgh,Pa.

Yr	Cl	Lea	Pos	G	Rec
1952	Pit	N	1	124	.220
	BLTL				

BARTLEY, BOYD OWEN
b.Feb.11,1921 Chicago,Ill.

Yr	Cl	Lea	Pos	G	Rec
1943	Bro	N	S	9	.048
	BRTR				

BARTLEY, WILLIAM JACKSON
b.Jan.8,1885 Cincinnati,O.

Yr	Cl	Lea	Pos	G	Rec
1903	NY	N	P	1	0-0
1906	Phi	A	P	3	0-0
1907	Phi	A	P	15	0-0
			BRTR	19	0-0

BARTLING, IRVING HENRY
b.June 27,1916 Bay City,Mich.

Yr	Cl	Lea	Pos	G	Rec
1938	Phi	A	S	14	.174
			BRTR		

BARTON, CARROLL R. (Buck)
b.1893 Washington,D.C.

Yr	Cl	Lea	Pos	G	Rec
1914	Was	A	P	1	0-0

BARTON, HARRY LAMB
b.Jan.20,1875 Chester,Pa.
d.Jan.25,1955

Yr	Cl	Lea	Pos	G	Rec
1905	Phi	A	C	18	.167
			BBTR		

BARTON, VINCENT DAVID
b.Feb.1,1908 Edmonton,Alta.,Canada

Yr	Cl	Lea	Pos	G	Rec
1931	Chi	N	O	66	.238
1932	Chi	N	O	36	.224
			BLTR	102	.233

BARTOSCH, DAVID ROBERT
b.Mar.24,1917 St.Louis,Mo.

Yr	Cl	Lea	Pos	G	Rec
1945	St.L	N	O	24	.255
			BRTR		

BARTSON, CHARLES FRANKLIN
b.Mar.13,1865 Peoria,Ill.
d.June 9,1936

Yr	Cl	Lea	Pos	G	Rec
1890	Chi	p	P	26	9-14

BASGALL, ROMANUS (Monty)
b.Feb.8,1922 Pfeifer,Kan.

Yr	Cl	Lea	Pos	G	Rec
1948	Pit	N	2	38	.216
1949	Pit	N	2-3	107	.218
1951	Pit	N	2	55	.209
			BRTR	200	.215

BASHANG, ALBERT
b.Aug.22,1888 Cincinnati,O.

Yr	Cl	Lea	Pos	G	Rec
1912	Det	A	O	6	.167
1918	Bro	N	O	2	.200
			BBTR	8	.174

BASHORE, WALTER FRANKLIN
b.Oct.6,1909 Harrisburg,Pa.

Yr	Cl	Lea	Pos	G	Rec
1936	Phi	N	O	10	.200
			BRTR		

BASINSKI, EDWIN FRANK (Bazooka)
b.Nov.4,1922 Buffalo,N.Y.

Yr	Cl	Lea	Pos	G	Rec
1944	Bro	N	2-S	39	.257
1945	Bro	N	2-S	108	.262
1947	Pit	N	2	56	.199
			BRTR	203	.244

BASKETTE, JAMES BLAINE (Big Jim)
b.Dec.10,1887 Athens,Tenn.
d.July 30,1942

Yr	Cl	Lea	Pos	G	Rec
1911	Cle	A	P	4	1-2
1912	Cle	A	P	19	8-4
1913	Cle	A	P	2	0-0
			BRTR	25	9-6

BASS, JOHN E.
b.1850 Baltimore,Md.

Yr	Cl	Lea	Pos	G	Rec
1871	Cle	n	3	23	NR
1872	Atl	n	O	1	NR
1877	Har	N	O	1	.250
				25	NR

BASS, RICHARD WILLIAM
b.July 7,1906 Rogersville,Tenn.

Yr	Cl	Lea	Pos	G	Rec
1939	Was	A	P	1	0-1
			BRTR		

BASS, NORMAN DELANEY
b.Jan.21,1939 Laurel,Miss.

Yr	Cl	Lea	Pos	G	Rec
1961	KC	A	P	41	11-11
1962	KC	A	P	22	2-6
			BRTR	63	13-17

BASS, WILLIAM C. (Doc)
b.Cincinnati,O.

Yr	Cl	Lea	Pos	G	Rec
1918	Bos	N	O	1	1.000

BASSETT, CHARLES EDWIN
b.Feb.9,1863 Lincoln,R.I.
d.May 28,1942

Yr	Cl	Lea	Pos	G	Rec
1884	Pro	N	2-S-3-O	21	.144
1885	Pro	N	2-S-3	81	.143
1886	KC	N	S	90	.260
1887	Ind	N	2	119	.270
1888	Ind	N	2	128	.241
1889	Ind	N	2	126	.253
1890	NY	N	2	100	.239
1891	NY	N	3	130	.266
1892	NY	N	2-3	34	.185
1892	Lou	N	2-3	78	.213
			TR	907	.237

BASSLER, JOHN LANDIS
b.June 3,1895 Lancaster,Pa.

Yr	Cl	Lea	Pos	G	Rec
1913	Cle	A	C	1	.000
1914	Cle	A	C	43	.182
1921	Det	A	C	119	.307
1922	Det	A	C	121	.323
1923	Det	A	C	135	.298
1924	Det	A	C	124	.346
1925	Det	A	C	121	.279
1926	Det	A	C	66	.305
1927	Det	A	C	81	.285
			BLTR	811	.304

BASTIAN, CHARLES J.
b.July 4,1860 Philadelphia,Pa.
d.Jan.18,1932

Yr	Cl	Lea	Pos	G	Rec
1884	Wil	U	P-2-S	17	{ 0-0 / .200
1884	KC	U	2	11	.255
1885	Phi	N	S	104	.167
1886	Phi	N	2	104	.217
1887	Phi	N	2-S	60	.275
1888	Phi	N	2	80	.192
1889	Chi	N	S	46	.135
1890	Chi	p	2-S	80	.186
1891	Cin	a	2	1	.000
1891	Phi	N	S	1	.000
			BRTR	504	{ 0-0 / .198

BATCH, EMIL HENRY (Heinie)
b.Jan.21,1880 Brooklyn,N.Y.

Yr	Cl	Lea	Pos	G	Rec
1904	Bro	N	3	28	.255
1905	Bro	N	3	145	.252
1906	Bro	N	O	52	.256
1907	Bro	N	O	106	.247
			BRTR	331	.251

BATCHELDER, JOSEPH EDMUND
b.July 11,1898 Wenham,Mass.

Yr	Cl	Lea	Pos	G	Rec
1923	Bos	N	P	4	1-0
1924	Bos	N	P	3	0-0
1925	Bos	N	P	4	0-0
			BRTL	11	1-0

BATES, BUSH

Yr	Cl	Lea	Pos	G	Rec
1889	KC	a	P	1	0-1

BATES, CHARLES WILLIAM
b.Sept.17,1905 Philadelphia,Pa.

Yr	Cl	Lea	Pos	G	Rec
1927	Phi	A	O	9	.237
			BRTR		

BATES, FRANK CHARLES
b.Chattanooga,Tenn.

Yr	Cl	Lea	Pos	G	Rec
1898	Cle	N	P	4	2-1
1899	St.L	N	P	4	0-0

(Continued)

Yr	Cl	Lea	Pos	G	Rec
1899	Cle	N	P	20	1-19
				28	3-20

BATES, HUBERT EDGAR (Bud)
b.Mar.16,1913 Los Angeles,Cal.

Yr	Cl	Lea	Pos	G	Rec
1939	Phi	N	O	15	.259
			BRTR		

BATES, JOHN WILLIAM
b.Aug.21,1882 Steubenville,O.
d.Feb.10,1949

Yr	Cl	Lea	Pos	G	Rec
1906	Bos	N	O	140	.252
1907	Bos	N	O	119	.260
1908	Bos	N	O	117	.258
1909	Bos	N	O	60	.288
1909	Phi	N	O	73	.293
1910	Phi	N	O	131	.305
1911	Cin	N	O	147	.292
1912	Cin	N	O	81	.289
1913	Cin	N	O	131	.278
1914	Cin	N	O	58	.252
1914	Chi	N	O	9	.125
1914	Bal	F	O	59	.307
			BLTL	1125	.278

BATES, RAYMOND
b.Dec. 12,1892 Paterson,N.J.

Yr	Cl	Lea	Pos	G	Rec
1913	Cle	A	3	20	.167
1917	Phi	A	3	127	.237
			BRTR	147	.233

BATSCH, WILLIAM McKINLEY
b.May 18,1892 Mingo Junction,O.

Yr	Cl	Lea	Pos	G	Rec
1916	Pit	N	H	1	.000
			BRTR		

BATTAM, LAWRENCE
b.May 1,1878 Brooklyn,N.Y.
d.Jan.27,1938

Yr	Cl	Lea	Pos	G	Rec
1895	NY	N	3	2	.250

BATTEN, GEORGE BURNETT
b.Oct.7,1891 Haddonfield,N.J.

Yr	Cl	Lea	Pos	G	Rec
1912	NY	A	2	1	.000
			TR		

BATTEY, EARL JESSE
b.Jan.5,1935 Los Angeles,Cal.

Yr	Cl	Lea	Pos	G	Rec
1955	Chi	A	C	5	.286
1956	Chi	A	C	4	.250
1957	Chi	A	C	48	.174
1958	Chi	A	C	68	.226
1959	Chi	A	C	26	.219
1960	Was	A	C	137	.270
1961	Min	A	C	133	.302
1962	Min	A	C	148	.280
			BRTR	569	.269

BATTIN, JOSEPH V.
b.Nov.11,1851 Philadelphia,Pa.
d.Dec.11,1937

Yr	Cl	Lea	Pos	G	Rec
1871	Cle	n	O	1	NR
1873	Ath	n	O	1	NR
1874	Ath	n	2-S-O	51	NR
1875	St.L	n	2-3	63	.263
1876	St.L	N	3	64	.294
1877	St.L	N	P-2-3-O	57	{ 0-0 / .199
1882	Pit	a	3	28	.207
1883	Pit	a	M-P-3	96	{ 0-0 / .202
1884	Pit	a	M-3	43	.178
1884	Pit	U	M-3	18	.197
1884	Bal	U	2-3	17	.086
1890	Syr	a	3	29	.194
			BRTR	468	{ 0-0 / NR

BATTLE, JAMES MILTON
b.Mar.26,1904 Celeste, Tex

Yr	Cl	Lea	Pos	G	Rec
1927	Chi	A	S-3	6	.375
			BRTR		

BATTS, MATTHEW DANIEL
b.Oct.16,1921 San Antonio,Tex.

Yr	Cl	Lea	Pos	G	Rec
1947	Bos	A	C	7	.500
1948	Bos	A	C	46	.314
1949	Bos	A	C	60	.242
1950	Bos	A	C	75	.273
1951	Bos	A	C	11	.138
1951	St.L	A	C	79	.302

(Continued)

Yr	Cl	Lea	Pos	G	Rec
1952	Det	A	C	56	.237
1953	Det	A	C	116	.278
1954	Det	A	C	12	.286
1954	Chi	A	C	55	.228
1955	Cin	N	C	26	.254
1956	Cin	N	H	3	.000
	BRTR			546	.269

BAUCKER, JOHN (Stud)
b.Philadelphia, Pa.

Yr	Cl	Lea	Pos	G	Rec
1875	NH	n	C-2-S-3	19	NR

BAUER, HENRY ALBERT
b.July 31,1922 E.St.Louis,Ill.

Yr	Cl	Lea	Pos	G	Rec
1948	NY	A	O	19	.180
1949	NY	A	O	103	.272
1950	NY	A	O	113	.320
1951	NY	A	O	118	.296
1952	NY	A	O	141	.293
1953	NY	A	O	133	.304
1954	NY	A	O	114	.294
1955	NY	A	C-O	139	.278
1956	NY	A	O	147	.241
1957	NY	A	O	137	.259
1958	NY	A	O	128	.268
1959	NY	A	O	114	.238
1960	KC	A	O	95	.275
1961	KC	A	M-O	43	.264
	BRTR			1544	.277

Non-playing Manager KC (A)1962

BAUER, LOUIS W.
b.Philadelphia,Pa.

Yr	Cl	Lea	Pos	G	Rec
1918	Phi	A	P	1	0-0

BAUERS, ALBERT J.
b.1850 Columbus,O.

Yr	Cl	Lea	Pos	G	Rec
1884	Col	a	P	3	1-2
1886	St.L	N	P	4	0-4
	TL			7	1-6

BAUERS, RUSSELL LEE
b.May 10,1915 Townsend,Wis.

Yr	Cl	Lea	Pos	G	Rec
1936	Pit	N	P	1	0-0
1937	Pit	N	P	34	13-6
1938	Pit	N	P	40	13-14
1939	Pit	N	P	15	2-4
1940	Pit	N	P	15	0-2
1941	Pit	N	P	8	1-3
1946	Chi	N	P	15	2-1
1950	St.L	A	P	1	0-0
	BLTR			129	31-30

BAUMANN, CHARLES JOHN (Paddy)
b.Dec.20,1885 Indianapolis,Ind.

Yr	Cl	Lea	Pos	G	Rec
1911	Det	A	2	26	.256
1912	Det	A	3-O	13	.262
1913	Det	A	2	49	.298
1914	Det	A	2	3	.000
1915	NY	A	2-3	76	.292
1916	NY	A	3-O	79	.287
1917	NY	A	2	49	.218
	BRTR			295	.268

BAUMANN, FRANK MATTHEW
b.July 1,1933 St. Louis,Mo.

Yr	Cl	Lea	Pos	G	Rec
1955	Bos	A	P	7	2-1
1956	Bos	A	P	7	2-1
1957	Bos	A	P	4	1-0
1958	Bos	A	P	10	2-2
1959	Bos	A	P	26	6-4
1960	Chi	A	P	47	13-6
1961	Chi	A	P	55	10-13
1962	Chi	A	P	40	7-6
	BLTL			196	43-33

BAUMER, JAMES SLOAN
b.Jan.29,1931 Tulsa,Okla.

Yr	Cl	Lea	Pos	G	Rec
1949	Chi	A	S	8	.400
1961	Cin	N	2	10	.125
	BRTR			18	.206

BAUMGARDNER, GEORGE WASHINGTON
b.July 22,1891 Barboursville, W. Va.

Yr	Cl	Lea	Pos	G	Rec
1912	St.L	A	P	28	11-14
1913	St.L	A	P	32	10-19
1914	St.L	A	P	38	14-13
1915	St.L	A	P	7	0-2
1916	St.L	A	P	4	1-0
	BLTR			109	36-48

BAUMGARTNER, HARRY E.
b.Oct.8,1892 S.Pittsburg Tenn.
d.Dec.3,1930

Yr	Cl	Lea	Pos	G	Rec
1920	Det	A	P	9	0-1
	BL				

BAUMGARTNER, JOHN EDWARD
b.May 29,1931 Birmingham,Ala.

Yr	Cl	Lea	Pos	G	Rec
1953	Det	A	3	7	.185
	BRTR				

BAUMGARTNER, STANWOOD FULTON
b.Dec.14,1894 Houston,Tex
d.Oct.4,1955

Yr	Cl	Lea	Pos	G	Rec
1914	Phi	N	P	15	2-2
1915	Phi	N	P	16	0-2
1916	Phi	N	P	1	0-0
1921	Phi	N	P	31	3-6
1922	Phi	N	P	6	1-1
1924	Phi	A	P	36	13-6
1925	Phi	A	P	37	6-3
1926	Phi	A	P	10	1-1
	BLTL			152	26-21

BAUMHOLTZ, FRANK CONRAD
b.Oct.7,1919 Midvale,O.

Yr	Cl	Lea	Pos	G	Rec
1947	Cin	N	O	151	.283
1948	Cin	N	O	128	.296
1949	Cin	N	O	27	.235
1949	Chi	N	O	58	.226
1951	Chi	N	O	146	.284
1952	Chi	N	O	103	.325
1953	Chi	N	O	133	.306
1954	Chi	N	O	90	.297
1955	Chi	N	O	105	.289
1956	Phi	N	O	76	.270
1957	Phi	N	H	2	.000
	BLTL			1019	.293

BAUSEWINE, GEORGE
b.Mar.22,1869 Philadelphia, Pa.
d.July 29,1947

Yr	Cl	Lea	Pos	G	Rec
1889	Ath	a	P	7	1-4

BAUTA, EDUARDO GALVEZ
b.Jan.6,1935 Fla.Central Cespedes,Cuba

Yr	Cl	Lea	Pos	G	Rec
1960	St.L	N	P	9	0-0
1961	St.L	N	P	13	2-0
1962	St.L	N	P	20	1-0
	BRTR			42	3-0

BAXES, DIMITRIOS S.
b.July 5,1928 San Francisco,Cal.

Yr	Cl	Lea	Pos	G	Rec
1959	LA	N	3	11	.303
1959	Cle	A	2-3	77	.239
	BRTR			88	.246

BAXES, MICHAEL
b.Dec.18,1930 San Francisco,Cal.

Yr	Cl	Lea	Pos	G	Rec
1956	KC	A	2-S	73	.226
1958	KC	A	2-S	73	.212
	BRTR			146	.217

BAXTER, JOHN
b.Spokane,Wash.

Yr	Cl	Lea	Pos	G	Rec
1907	St.L	N	1	6	.190

BAY, HARRY ELBERT (Deerfoot)
b.Jan.17,1878 Pontiac,Ill.
d.Mar.20,1952

Yr	Cl	Lea	Pos	G	Rec
1901	Cin	N	O	34	.205
1902	Cin	N	O	6	.375

(Continued)

Yr	Cl	Lea	Pos	G	Rec
1902	Cle	A	O	108	.287
1903	Cle	A	O	141	.310
1904	Cle	A	O	132	.260
1905	Cle	A	O	143	.298
1906	Cle	A	O	68	.275
1907	Cle	A	O	34	.179
1908	Cle	A	H	2	.000
	BLTL			668	.280

BAYER, CHRISTOPHER A. (Burley)
b.Dec.19,1875 Louisville,Ky.
d.May 30,1933

Yr	Cl	Lea	Pos	G	Rec
1899	Lou	N	S	1	.000

BAYLESS, HARRY OWEN (Dick)
b.Sept.6,1883 Joplin,Mo.
d.Dec.16,1920

Yr	Cl	Lea	Pos	G	Rec
1908	Cin	N	O	19	.225

BAYNE, WILLIAM LEAR (Beverly)
b.Apr.18,1899 Pittsburgh,Pa.

Yr	Cl	Lea	Pos	G	Rec
1919	St.L	A	P	2	1-1
1920	St.L	A	P	18	5-6
1921	St.L	A	P	47	11-5
1922	St.L	A	P	26	4-5
1923	St.L	A	P	19	2-2
1924	St.L	A	P	22	1-3
1928	Cle	A	P	37	2-5
1929	Bos	A	P	27	5-5
1930	Bos	A	P	1	0-0
	BLTL			199	31-32

BEACH, JACKSON
b.Alexandria,Va.

Yr	Cl	Lea	Pos	G	Rec
1884	Was	a	O	8	.094

BEALL, JOHN WOOLF
b.Mar.12,1882 Beltsville,Md.
d.June 14,1926

Yr	Cl	Lea	Pos	G	Rec
1913	Cle	A	H	6	.167
1913	Chi	A	O	17	.267
1915	Cin	N	O	10	.232
1916	Cin	N	O	6	.333
1918	St.L	N	O	19	.224
	BLTR			58	.257

BEALL, WALTER ESAU
b.July 29,1899 Washington,D.C.
d.Jan.28,1959

Yr	Cl	Lea	Pos	G	Rec
1924	NY	A	P	4	2-0
1925	NY	A	P	8	0-1
1926	NY	A	P	20	2-4
1927	NY	A	P	1	0-0
1929	Was	A	P	3	1-0
	BRTR			36	5-5

BEALS, THOMAS L.
(Played in 1871 and 1873 under name of W. Thomas)
d.Nov.9,1911

Yr	Cl	Lea	Pos	G	Rec
1871	Oly	n	2-O	10	.194
1872	Oly	n	2-S-O	9	NR
1873	Nat	n	C-2-O	37	NR
1874	Bos	n	1-2-O	19	.204
1875	Bos	n	2-O	35	.293
1880	Chi	N	2-O	13	.149
				123	NR

BEAM, ALEXANDER RODGER
b.Nov.21,1870 Johnstown,Pa.
d.Apr.17,1938

Yr	Cl	Lea	Pos	G	Rec
1889	Pit	N	P	2	1-1

BEAM, ERNEST
b.1867 Mansfield,O.

Yr	Cl	Lea	Pos	G	Rec
1895	Phi	N	P	9	0-2

BEAMON, CHARLES ALONZO
b.Dec.25,1934 Oakland,Cal.

Yr	Cl	Lea	Pos	G	Rec
1956	Bal	A	P	2	2-0
1957	Bal	A	P	4	0-0
1958	Bal	A	P	22	1-3
	BRTR			28	3-3

BEAN, BELVEDERE BENTON
(Bill)
b.Apr.23,1906 Mullin,Tex.

Yr	Cl	Lea	Pos	G	Rec
1930	Cle	A	P	23	3-3
1931	Cle	A	P	4	0-1
1933	Cle	A	P	27	1-2
1934	Cle	A	P	21	5-1
1935	Cle	A	P	1	0-0
1935	Was	A	P	10	2-0
	BRTR			86	11-7

BEAN, JOSEPH WILLIAM
b.Mar.18,1874 Boston,Mass.
d.Feb.15,1961

Yr	Cl	Lea	Pos	G	Rec
1902	NY	N	S	50	.235
	TR				

BEARD, CRAMER THEODORE
(Ted)
b.Jan.7,1921 Woodsboro,Md.

Yr	Cl	Lea	Pos	G	Rec
1948	Pit	N	O	25	.198
1949	Pit	N	O	14	.083
1950	Pit	N	O	61	.232
1951	Pit	N	O	22	.188
1952	Pit	N	O	15	.182
1957	Chi	A	O	38	.205
1958	Chi	A	O	19	.091
	BLTL			194	.198

BEARD, OLIVER PERRY
b.May 2,1862 Lexington,Ky.
d.May 28,1929

Yr	Cl	Lea	Pos	G	Rec
1889	Cin	a	S	141	.293
1890	Cin	N	S	122	.268
1891	Lou	a	2	68	.247
	BRTR			331	.273

BEARD, RALPH WM.
b.Feb.11,1929 Cincinnati,O.

Yr	Cl	Lea	Pos	G	Rec
1954	St.L	N	P	13	0-4
	BRTR				

BEARDEN, HENRY EUGENE
(Gene)
b.Sept.5,1920 Lexa,Ark.

Yr	Cl	Lea	Pos	G	Rec
1947	Cle	A	P	1	0-0
1948	Cle	A	P	37	20-7
1949	Cle	A	P	32	8-8
1950	Cle	A	P	14	1-3
1950	Was	A	P-1	14	3-5 .227
1951	Was	A	P	1	0-0
1951	Det	A	P	37	3-4
1952	St.L	A	P	45	7-8
1953	Chi	A	P	31	3-3
	BLTL			212	45-38 .236

BEARMAN, CHARLES S.
b.1848 Hoboken,N.J.
d.1879

Yr	Cl	Lea	Pos	G	Rec
1871	Kek	n	1	1	.000

BEATIN, EBENEZER AMBROSE
b.Aug.10,1866 Baltimore,Md.
d.May 9,1925

Yr	Cl	Lea	Pos	G	Rec
1887	Det	N	P	2	1-1
1888	Det	N	P	16	5-7
1889	Cle	N	P	37	20-14
1890	Cle	N	P	53	22-31
1891	Cle	N	P	5	1-4
	BRTR			113	49-57

BEATLE, DAVID
b.1861 New York,N.Y.

Yr	Cl	Lea	Pos	G	Rec
1884	Det	N	C-O	1	.000

BEATTY, DESMOND (Desperate)
b.1894 New York,N.Y.

Yr	Cl	Lea	Pos	G	Rec
1914	NY	N	3	1	.000
	BRTR				

BEAUMONT, CLARENCE HOWETH
(Ginger)
b.July 23,1876 Rochester,Wis.
d.Apr.10,1956

Yr	Cl	Lea	Pos	G	Rec
1899	Pit	N	O	104	.350

(Continued)

Yr	Cl	Lea	Pos	G	Rec
1900	Pit	N	O	138	.282
1901	Pit	N	O	132	.328
1902	Pit	N	O	131	.357
1903	Pit	N	O	141	.341
1904	Pit	N	O	153	.301
1905	Pit	N	O	97	.328
1906	Pit	N	O	78	.265
1907	Bos	N	O	149	.322
1908	Bos	N	O	121	.267
1909	Bos	N	O	111	.263
1910	Chi	N	O	56	.267
	BLTR			1411	.311

BEAZLEY, JOHN ANDREW (Nig)
b.May 25,1919 Nashville,Tenn.

Yr	Cl	Lea	Pos	G	Rec
1941	St.L	N	P	1	1-0
1942	St.L	N	P	43	21-6
1946	St.L	N	P	19	7-5
1947	Bos	N	P	9	2-0
1948	Bos	N	P	3	0-1
1949	Bos	N	P	1	0-0
	BRTR			76	31-12

BECANNON, JAMES MELVILLE
(Buck)
b.Aug.22,1859 New York,N.Y.
d.Nov.5,1923

Yr	Cl	Lea	Pos	G	Rec
1884	Met	a	P	1	1-0
1885	Met	a	P	10	2-8
1887	NY	N	3	1	.000
				12	3-8 .238

BECHTEL, GEORGE A.
b.1848 Philadelphia,Pa.

Yr	Cl	Lea	Pos	G	Rec
1871	Ath	n	P-3-O	21	1-2 .360
1872	Mut	n	1-O	51	NR
1873	Phi	n	P-O	52	1-2 NR
1874	Phi	n	P-O	31	1-3 NR
1875	Cen	n	P	14	2-12
1875	Ath	n	P-O	34	3-1 NR
1876	Lou	N	O	14	.182
1876	Mut	N	O	2	.273
				219	8-20 NR

BECK, CLYDE EUGENE
b.Jan.6,1902 El Monte,Cal.

Yr	Cl	Lea	Pos	G	Rec
1926	Chi	N	2	30	.198
1927	Chi	N	2-3	147	.258
1928	Chi	N	S-3	131	.257
1929	Chi	N	S-3	54	.211
1930	Chi	N	2-S	83	.213
1931	Cin	N	S-3	53	.154
	BRTR			498	.232

BECK, ERWIN THOMAS (Dutch)
b.Juiy 19,1878 Toledo,O.
d.Dec.22,1916

Yr	Cl	Lea	Pos	G	Rec
1899	Bro	N	S	7	.158
1901	Cle	A	2	135	.283
1902	Cin	N	1-2-O	43	.305
1902	Det	A	1-O	41	.304
	BRTR			226	.298

BECK, FRANK J.
b.1862 Poughkeepsie,N.Y.

Yr	Cl	Lea	Pos	G	Rec
1884	Pit	a	P	3	0-3
1884	Bal	U	P-O	6	0-2 .208
	TR			9	0-5 .257

BECK, FREDERICK THOMAS
b.Nov.17,1887 Havana,Ill.
d.Mar.12,1962

Yr	Cl	Lea	Pos	G	Rec
1909	Bos	N	1-O	88	.198
1910	Bos	N	1-O	153	.275
1911	Cin	N	O	41	.184
1911	Phi	N	O	64	.281
1914	Chi	F	1	158	.279
1915	Chi	F	1	121	.219

(Continued)

Yr	Cl	Lea	Pos	G	Rec
	BLTL			625	.251

BECK, GEORGE F.
b.1889 Moline,Ill.

Yr	Cl	Lea	Pos	G	Rec
1914	Cle	A	P	1	0-0
	BRTR				

BECK, WALTER WILLIAM
(Boom-Boom)
b.Oct.16,1904 Decatur,Ill.

Yr	Cl	Lea	Pos	G	Rec
1924	St.L	A	P	1	0-0
1927	St.L	A	P	3	1-0
1928	St.L	A	P	16	2-3
1933	Bro	N	P	43	12-20
1934	Bro	N	P	22	2-6
1939	Phi	N	P	34	7-14
1940	Phi	N	P	29	4-9
1941	Phi	N	P	34	1-9
1942	Phi	N	P	27	0-1
1943	Phi	N	P	4	0-0
1944	Det	A	P	28	1-2
1945	Cin	N	P	11	2-4
1945	Pit	N	P	14	6-1
	BRTR			266	38-69

BECK, ZINN BERTRAM
b.Sept.30,1889 Steubenville,O.

Yr	Cl	Lea	Pos	G	Rec
1913	St.L	N	3	10	.218
1914	St.L	N	S-3	137	.232
1915	St.L	N	3	70	.233
1916	St.L	N	3	62	.223
1918	NY	A	1	11	.000
	BRTR			290	.227

BECKENDORF, HENRY WARD
(Heinie)
b.June 15,1884 New York,N.Y.
d.Sept.15,1949

Yr	Cl	Lea	Pos	G	Rec
1909	Det	A	C	15	.259
1910	Det	A	C	3	.429
1910	Was	A	C	37	.146
	BRTR			55	.182

BECKER, BEALS
b.July 5,1886 El Dorado,Kan.
d.Aug.16,1943

Yr	Cl	Lea	Pos	G	Rec
1908	Pit	N	O	17	.154
1908	Bos	N	O	43	.275
1909	Bos	N	O	152	.245
1910	NY	N	O	46	.286
1911	NY	N	O	55	.262
1912	NY	N	O	125	.264
1913	Cin	N	O	30	.296
1913	Phi	N	O	88	.324
1914	Phi	N	O	138	.325
1915	Phi	N	O	112	.246
	BLTL			806	.276

BECKER, CHARLES S. (Buck)
b.1890 Washington,D.C.
d.July 30,1928

Yr	Cl	Lea	Pos	G	Rec
1911	Was	A	P	11	3-5
1912	Was	A	P	4	0-0
	BLTL			15	3-5

BECKER, HEINZ REINHARD
(Dutch)
b.Aug.26,1915 Berlin,Germany

Yr	Cl	Lea	Pos	G	Rec
1943	Chi	N	1	24	.145
1945	Chi	N	1	67	.286
1946	Chi	N	H	9	.286
1946	Cle	A	1	50	.299
1947	Cle	A	H	2	.000
	BBTR			152	.263

BECKER, JOSEPH EDWARD
b.June 25,1909 St.Louis,Mo.

Yr	Cl	Lea	Pos	G	Rec
1936	Cle	A	C	22	.180
1937	Cle	A	C	18	.333
	BRTR			40	.241

BECKER, MARTIN HENRY
b.Dec.25,1889 Tiffin,O.
d.Sept.25,1957

Yr	Cl	Lea	Pos	G	Rec
1915	NY	N	O	17	.250
	BBTL				

Yr Cl Lea Pos G Rec

BECKER, ROBERT CHARLES
b.Aug.15,1875 Syracuse,N.Y.
d.Oct.11,1951
1897 Phi N P 5 0-2
1898 Phi N P 1 0-0
6 0-2

BECKLEY, JACOB PETER
(Eagle Eye)
b.Aug.4,1867 Hannibal,Mo.
d.June 25,1918
1888 Pit N 1 71 .342
1889 Pit N 1 123 .300
1890 Pit p 1 121 .325
1891 Pit N 1 129 .291
1892 Pit N 1 152 .250
1893 Pit N 1 131 .324
1894 Pit N 1 132 .344
1895 Pit N 1 131 .324
1896 Pit N 1 54 .244
1896 NY N 1 45 .297
1897 NY N 1 18 .268
1897 Cin N 1 96 .336
1898 Cin N 1 116 .299
1899 Cin N 1 135 .333
1900 Cin N 1 138 .343
1901 Cin N 1 140 .300
1902 Cin N P-1 129 {0-1 .331
1903 Cin N 1 119 .327
1904 St.L N 1 142 .325
1905 St.L N 1 134 .286
1906 St.L N 1 85 .247
1907 St.L N 1 32 .209
BLTL 2373 {0-1 .309

BECKMAN, JAMES JOSEPH
b.Mar.1,1907 Cincinnati,O.
1927 Cin N P 4 0-1
1928 Cin N P 6 0-1
BRTR 10 0-2

BECKMAN, WILLIAM ALOYSIUS
b.Dec.8,1907 Clayton,Mo.
1939 Phi A P 27 7-11
1940 Phi A P 34 8-4
1941 Phi A P 22 5-9
1942 Phi A P 5 0-1
1942 St.L N P 2 1-0
BRTR 90 21-25

BECQUER, JULIO VELLEGAS
b.Dec.20,1932 Havana,Cuba
1955 Was A 1 10 .214
1957 Was A 1 105 .226
1958 Was A 1-O 86 .238
1959 Was A 1 108 .268
1960 Was A P-1 110 {0-0 .252
1961 LA A 1 11 .000
1961 Min A P-1-O 57 {0-0 .238
BLTL 487 {0-0 .244

BEDELL, HOWARD WILLIAM
b.Sept.29,1935 Clearfield,Pa.
1962 Mil N O 58 .196
BLTR

BEDFORD, JAMES ELDRED
b.Mar.26,1902 Hudson,N.Y.
1925 Cle A 2 2 .000
TR

BEDGOOD, PHILIP BURDETTE
b.Mar.8,1899 Harrison,Ga.
d.Nov.8,1927
1922 Cle A P 1 1-0
1923 Cle A P 9 0-2
BRTR 10 1-2

BEDIENT, HUGH CARPENTER
b.Oct.23,1889 Gerry,N.Y.
1912 Bos A P 34 20-10
1913 Bos A P 38 15-14
1914 Bos A P 36 8-12
1915 Buf F P 44 16-18
BRTR 152 59-54

Yr Cl Lea Pos G Rec

BEDNAR, ANDREW F.
b.Aug.16,1909 Streator,Ill.
d.Nov.25,1937
1930 Pit N P 2 0-0
1931 Pit N P 3 0-0
BRTR 5 0-0

BEEBE, FREDERICK LEONARD
b.Dec.31,1880 Lincoln,Neb.
d.Oct.30,1957
1906 Chi N P 14 6-1
1906 St.L N P 20 9-9
1907 St.L N P 31 7-19
1908 St.L N P 29 5-13
1909 St.L N P 44 15-21
1910 Cin N P 35 12-14
1911 Phi N P 9 3-3
1916 Cle A P 21 5-3
BRTR 203 62-83

BEECHER, EDWARD
b.July 2,1859 Guilford,Conn.
1887 Pit N O 40 .272
1889 Was N O 41 .296
1890 Buf p P-O 126 {0-1 .357
1891 Was a O 56 .233
1891 Ath a O 16 .205
BL 279 {0-1 .299

BEECHER, LEROY
b.May 10,1884 Swanton,O.
d.Oct.11,1952
1907 NY N P 2 0-2
1908 NY N P 2 0-0
BLTR 4 0-2

BEELER, JOSEPH SAM
(Jodie)
b.Nov.26,1921 Dallas,Tex.
1944 Cin N 2-3 3 .000
BRTR

BEERS, CLARENCE SCOTT
b.Dec.9,1918 El Dorado,Kan.
1948 St.L N P 1 0-0
BRTR

BEGGS, JOSEPH STANLEY
(Fireman)
b.Nov.4,1913 Rankin,Pa.
1938 NY A P 14 3-2
1940 Cin N P 37 12-3
1941 Cin N P 37 4-3
1942 Cin N P 38 6-5
1943 Cin N P 39 7-6
1944 Cin N P 1 1-0
1946 Cin N P 28 12-10
1947 Cin N P 11 0-3
1947 NY N P 32 3-3
1948 NY N P 1 0-0
BRTR 238 48-35

BEGLEY, EDWARD N.
b.1863 New York,N.Y.
1884 NY N P-O 32 {12-18 .181
1885 Met a P-O 15 {4-9 .173
47 {16-27 .179

BEGLEY, EUGENE I.
b.1863 Brooklyn,N.Y.
1886 NY N C 3 .111

BEGLEY, JAMES LAWRENCE (Imp)
b.Sept.19,1903 San Francisco,Cal.
1924 Cin N 2 2 .200
BRTR

Yr Cl Lea Pos G Rec

BEHAN, CHARLES FREDERICK
(Pete)
b.Dec.11,1887 Dallas City,Pa.
d.Jan.21,1957
1921 Phi N P 2 0-1
1922 Phi N P 7 4-2
1923 Phi N P 34 3-12
BRTR 43 7-15

BEHEL, STEPHEN
ARNOLD DOUGLAS
b.Rockford,Ill.
1884 Mil U O 9 .222
1886 Met a O 59 .208
68 .211

BEHRMAN, HENRY BERNARD
b.June 27,1921 Brooklyn,N.Y.
1946 Bro N P 47 11-5
1947 Bro N P 40 5-3
1947 Pit N P 10 0-2
1948 Bro N P 34 5-4
1949 NY N P 43 3-3
BRTR 174 24-17

BEJMA, ALOYSIUS FRANK (Ollie)
b.Sept.12,1907 South Bend,Ind.
1934 St.L A 2-S-3-O 95 .271
1935 St.L A 2-S-3 64 .192
1936 St.L A 2 67 .259
1939 Chi A 2 90 .251
BRTR 316 .245

BELANGIO, PROSPER ALBERT
(Played under name of
Prosby Albert Blanche)

BELARDI, CARROLL WAYNE
b.Sept.5,1930 St. Helena,Cal.
1950 Bro N 1 10 .000
1951 Bro N H 3 .333
1953 Bro N 1 69 .239
1954 Bro N H 11 .222
1954 Det A 1 88 .232
1955 Det A H 3 .000
1956 Det A 1-O 79 .279
BLTL 263 .242

BELDEN, IRA A.
b.Apr.16,1874 Cleveland,O.
d.July 15,1916
1897 Cle N O 8 .250

BELINSKY, ROBERT
b.Nov.7,1936 New York,N.Y.
1962 LA A P 34 10-11
BLTL

BELL, CHARLES C.
b.Aug.12,1868 Cincinnati,O.
d.Feb.7,1937
1889 KC a P 1 1-0
1891 Lou a P 11 3-8
1891 Cin a P 4 1-0
16 5-8

BELL, DAVID RUSSELL (Gus)
b.Nov.15,1928 Louisville,Ky.
1950 Pit N O 111 .282
1951 Pit N O 149 .278
1952 Pit N O 131 .250
1953 Cin N O 151 .300
1954 Cin N O 153 .299
1955 Cin N O 154 .308
1956 Cin N O 150 .292
1957 Cin N O 121 .292
1958 Cin N O 112 .252
1959 Cin N O 148 .293
1960 Cin N O 143 .262
1961 Cin N O 103 .255
1962 NY N O 30 .149
1962 Mil N O 79 .285
BLTR 1735 .282

Yr	Cl	Lea	Pos	G	Rec

BELL, FERN LEE (Danny)
b.Jan.21,1913 Ada,Okla.

Yr	Cl	Lea	Pos	G	Rec
1939	Pit	N	O	83	.286
1940	Pit	N	H	6	.000
	BRTR			89	.283

BELL, FRANK GUSTAV
b.1863 Cincinnati,O.
d.Apr.14,1891

Yr	Cl	Lea	Pos	G	Rec
1885	Bro	a	C-3-O	10	.167

BELL, GARY
b.Nov.17,1936 San Antonio,Tex.

Yr	Cl	Lea	Pos	G	Rec
1958	Cle	A	P	33	12-10
1959	Cle	A	P	44	16-11
1960	Cle	A	P	30	9-10
1961	Cle	A	P	34	12-16
1962	Cle	A	P	57	10-9
	BRTR			198	59-56

BELL, GEORGE GLENN (Farmer)
b.Nov.2,1874 Greenwood,N.Y.
d.Dec.25,1941

Yr	Cl	Lea	Pos	G	Rec
1907	Bro	N	P	35	8-16
1908	Bro	N	P	29	4-15
1909	Bro	N	P	33	16-15
1910	Bro	N	P	44	10-27
1911	Bro	N	P	19	5-6
	BRTR			160	43-79

BELL, HERMAN S. (Hi)
b.July 16,1895 Louisville,Ky.
d.June 7,1949

Yr	Cl	Lea	Pos	G	Rec
1924	St.L	N	P	28	3-8
1926	St.L	N	P	27	6-6
1927	St.L	N	P	25	1-3
1929	St.L	N	P	7	0-2
1930	St.L	N	P	39	4-3
1932	NY	N	P	35	8-4
1933	NY	N	P	38	6-5
1934	NY	N	P	22	4-3
	BRTR			221	32-34

BELL, JOHN
(Real name Rudolph Fred Baerwald)
b.Jan.1,1881 Wausau,Wis.
d.July 28,1955

Yr	Cl	Lea	Pos	G	Rec
1907	NY	A	O	17	.212
	BRTR				

BELL, LESTER ROWLAND
b.Dec.14,1901 Harrisburg,Pa.

Yr	Cl	Lea	Pos	G	Rec
1923	St.L	N	S	15	.373
1924	St.L	N	S	17	.246
1925	St.L	N	S-3	153	.285
1926	St.L	N	3	155	.325
1927	St.L	N	S-3	115	.259
1928	Bos	N	3	153	.277
1929	Bos	N	3	139	.298
1930	Chi	N	3	74	.278
1931	Chi	N	3	75	.282
	BRTR			896	.290

BELL, RALPH A. (Lefty)
b.1889

Yr	Cl	Lea	Pos	G	Rec
1912	Chi	A	P	2	0-0
	BLTL				

BELL, ROY CHESTER (Beau)
b.Aug.20,1907 Bellville,Tex.

Yr	Cl	Lea	Pos	G	Rec
1935	St.L	A	1-3-O	76	.250
1936	St.L	A	1-O	155	.344
1937	St.L	A	1-O	156	.340
1938	St.L	A	O	147	.262
1939	St.L	A	O	11	.219
1939	Det	A	O	54	.239
1940	Cle	A	1-O	120	.279
1941	Cle	A	1-O	48	.192
	BRTR			767	.297

BELL, WILLIAM SAMUEL
b.Oct.24,1933 Goldsboro,N.C.

Yr	Cl	Lea	Pos	G	Rec
1952	Pit	N	P	4	0-1
1955	Pit	N	P	1	0-0
	BRTR			5	0-1

BELLA, JOHN
b.Aug.23,1932 Greenwich,Conn.

Yr	Cl	Lea	Pos	G	Rec
1957	NY	A	O	5	.100
1959	KC	A	1-O	47	.207
	BRTL			52	.196

BELLAN, ESTEBAN ENRIQUE
b.1850 Cuba
d.Aug.8,1932

Yr	Cl	Lea	Pos	G	Rec
1871	Tro	n	S-3	29	.213
1872	Tro	n	S-3-O	23	NR
1873	Mut	n	3	7	NR
				59	NR

BELLMAN, JOHN CHARLES
b.Louisville,Ky.

Yr	Cl	Lea	Pos	G	Rec
1889	St.L	a	C	1	.500

BEMIS, HARRY PARKER
b.Feb.1,1874 Farmington,N.H.
d.May 23,1947

Yr	Cl	Lea	Pos	G	Rec
1902	Cle	A	C-2-O	93	.311
1903	Cle	A	C	93	.258
1904	Cle	A	C	95	.225
1905	Cle	A	C	69	.292
1906	Cle	A	C	93	.274
1907	Cle	A	C	65	.250
1908	Cle	A	C	91	.224
1909	Cle	A	C	42	.187
1910	Cle	A	C	61	.215
	BRTR			702	.254

BENDER, CHARLES ALBERT
(Chief)
b.May 5,1883 Brainerd,Minn.
d.May 22,1954

Yr	Cl	Lea	Pos	G	Rec
1903	Phi	A	P	43	17-15
1904	Phi	A	P	29	7-14
1905	Phi	A	P	35	15-10
1906	Phi	A	P	44	15-10
1907	Phi	A	P	45	16-8
1908	Phi	A	P	20	8-9
1909	Phi	A	P	40	18-8
1910	Phi	A	P	36	23-5
1911	Phi	A	P	32	17-5
1912	Phi	A	P	26	13-8
1913	Phi	A	P	36	19-9
1914	Phi	A	P	24	17-3
1915	Bal	F	P	23	4-16
1916	Phi	N	P	28	7-7
1917	Phi	N	P	20	8-2
1925	Chi	A	P	1	0-0
	BRTR			482	204-129

BENEDICT, ARTHUR M.
b.Mar.31,1862 Cornwall,Ill.

Yr	Cl	Lea	Pos	G	Rec
1883	Phi•	N	2	3	.267

BENES, JOSEPH ANTHONY
(Bananas)
b.Jan.8,1901 Long Island City,N.Y.

Yr	Cl	Lea	Pos	G	Rec
1931	St.L	N	2-S-3	10	.167
	BRTR				

BENGE, RAYMOND ADELPHIA
(Cal)
b.Apr.22,1902 Jacksonville,Tex

Yr	Cl	Lea	Pos	G	Rec
1925	Cle	A	P	2	1-0
1926	Cle	A	P	8	1-0
1928	Phi	N	P	42	8-18
1929	Phi	N	P	43	11-15
1930	Phi	N	P	38	11-15
1931	Phi	N	P	38	14-18
1932	Phi	N	P	41	13-12
1933	Bro	N	P	37	10-17
1934	Bro	N	P	36	14-12
1935	Bro	N	P	23	9-9
1936	Bos	N	P	21	7-9
1936	Phi	N	P	15	1-4
1938	Cin	N	P	9	1-1
	BRTR			353	101-130

BENGOUGH, BERNARD OLIVER
(Benny)
b.July 27,1898 Niagara Falls,N.Y.

Yr	Cl	Lea	Pos	G	Rec
1923	NY	A	C	19	.132
1924	NY	A	C	11	.312
1925	NY	A	C	95	.258
1926	NY	A	C	36	.381
1927	NY	A	C	31	.247
1928	NY	A	C	58	.267
1929	NY	A	C	23	.194
1930	NY	A	C	44	.235
1931	St.L	A	C	40	.250
1932	St.L	A	C	54	.252
	BRTR			411	.255

BENJAMIN, ALFRED STANLEY
(Stan)
b.May 20,1914 Framingham,Mass.

Yr	Cl	Lea	Pos	G	Rec
1939	Phi	N	3-O	12	.140
1940	Phi	N	O	8	.222
1941	Phi	N	1-2-3-O	129	.235
1942	Phi	N	1-O	78	.224
1945	Cle	A	O	14	.333
	BRTR			241	.229

BENJAMIN, JOHN W.
b.1837 Elizabeth,N.J.
d.Nov.14,1895
Non-playing manager Res (n) 1873

BENN, HENRY OMER
b.Jan.25,1890 Viola,Wis.

Yr	Cl	Lea	Pos	G	Rec
1914	Cle	A	P	1	0-0
	BRTR				

BENNERS, ISAAC B.
b.Philadelphia,Pa.

Yr	Cl	Lea	Pos	G	Rec
1884	Bro	a	O	49	.209
1884	Wil	U	O	6	.045
				55	.191

BENNETT, CHARLES WESLEY
b.Nov.21,1854 New Castle,Pa.
d.Feb.24,1927

Yr	Cl	Lea	Pos	G	Rec
1878	Mil	N	C-O	48	.246
1880	Wor	N	C-O	50	.223
1881	Det	N	C-O	76	.301
1882	Det	N	C-1-2-3	80	.304
1883	Det	N	C-2-O	89	.301
1884	Det	N	C-1-2-S-O	88	.264
1885	Det	N	C-3-O	91	.269
1886	Det	N	C	69	.242
1887	Det	N	C	46	.363
1888	Det	N	C	72	.263
1889	Bos	N	C	80	.230
1890	Bos	N	C	85	.213
1891	Bos	N	C	74	.215
1892	Bos	N	C	32	.201
1893	Bos	N	C	58	.218
	BRTR			1038	.262

BENNETT, DENNIS JOHN
b.Oct.4,1939 Oakland,Cal.

Yr	Cl	Lea	Pos	G	Rec
1962	Phi	N	P	31	9-9
	BLTL				

BENNETT, FRANCIS ALLEN
b.Oct.27,1905 Mardela Springs,Md.

Yr	Cl	Lea	Pos	G	Rec
1927	Bos	A	P	4	0-1
1928	Bos	A	P	1	0-0
	BRTR			5	0-1

BENNETT HERSCHEL EMMETT
b.Sept.21,1896 Springfield,Mo.

Yr	Cl	Lea	Pos	G	Rec
1923	St.L	A	O	5	.000
1924	St.L	A	O	41	.330
1925	St.L	A	O	93	.279
1926	St.L	A	O	80	.266
1927	St.L	A	O	93	.266
	BLTR			312	.276

BENNETT, JAMES FRED (Red)
b.Mar.15,1902 Atkins,Ark.
d.May 12,1957

Yr	Cl	Lea	Pos	G	Rec
1928	St.L	A	O	7	.250
1931	Pit	N	O	32	.281
	BRTR			39	.278

BENNETT, JOSEPH HARLEY
(Bugs)
(Also played under name of Joseph Bennett Morris)
b.Apr.19,1892 Weir City,Kan.
d.Nov.21,1957

Yr	Cl	Lea	Pos	G	Rec
1918	St.L	A	P	4	0-2
1921	Chi	A	P	4	0-4
1921	St.L	A	P	1	0-0
	BRTR			9	0-6

BENNETT, JOSEPH R.

Yr	Cl	Lea	Pos	G	Rec
1923	Phi	N	3	1	.000
	BRTR				

BENNETT, JUSTIN TITUS (Pug)
b.Feb.20,1874 Ponca,Neb.
d.Sept.12,1935

Yr	Cl	Lea	Pos	G	Rec
1906	St.L	N	2	153	.262
1907	St.L	N	2	86	.222
	TR			239	.248

BENSON, ALLEN WILBERT
b.July12,1908 Hurley,S.Dak.

Yr	Cl	Lea	Pos	G	Rec
1934	Was	A	P	2	0-1
	BRTR				

BENSON, VERNON ADAIR
b.Sept.19,1924 Granite Quarry, N.C

Yr	Cl	Lea	Pos	G	Rec
1943	Phi	A	H	2	.000
1946	Phi	A	O	7	.000
1951	St.L	N	3-O	13	.261
1952	St.L	N	3	20	.191
1953	St.L	N	H	13	.000
	BLTR			55	.202

BENTLEY, CYRUS G.
b.Waterbury,Conn.

Yr	Cl	Lea	Pos	G	Rec
1872	Man	n	P-O	18	1-13 / NR

BENTLEY, JOHN NEEDLES
b.Mar.8,1895 Sandy Springs,Md.

Yr	Cl	Lea	Pos	G	Rec
1913	Was	A	P	3	0-0
1914	Was	A	P	23	5-7
1915	Was	A	P	4	0-2
1916	Was	A	P	2	0-0
1923	NY	N	P	52	13-8
1924	NY	N	P	46	16-5
1925	NY	N	P-1-O	64	11-9 / .303
1926	Phi	N	P-1	75	0-2 / .258
1926	NY	N	P	3	0-0
1927	NY	N	P	8	0-0
	BLTL			280	45-33 / .291

BENTON, JOHN ALTON (Al)
b.Mar.18,1911 Noble,Okla.

Yr	Cl	Lea	Pos	G	Rec
1934	Phi	A	P	32	7-9
1935	Phi	A	P	27	3-4
1938	Det	A	P	19	5-3
1939	Det	A	P	37	6-8
1940	Det	A	P	42	6-10
1941	Det	A	P	38	15-6
1942	Det	A	P	35	7-13
1945	Det	A	P	31	13-8
1946	Det	A	P	28	11-7
1947	Det	A	P	36	6-7
1948	Det	A	P	30	2-2
1949	Cle	A	P	40	9-6
1950	Cle	A	P	36	4-2
1952	Bos	A	P	24	4-3
	BRTR			455	98-88

BENTON, JOHN CLEVELAND
(Rube)
b.June 27,1890 Clinton,N.C.
d.Dec.12,1937

Yr	Cl	Lea	Pos	G	Rec
1910	Cin	N	P	12	0-1
1911	Cin	N	P	6	3-3
1912	Cin	N	P	50	18-20
1913	Cin	N	P	23	11-7
1914	Cin	N	P	41	16-18
1915	Cin	N	P	34	6-13
1915	Pit	N	P	1	0-0
1915	NY	N	P	10	3-5
1916	NY	N	P	38	16-8
1917	NY	N	P	35	15-9
1918	NY	N	P	3	1-2
1919	NY	N	P	35	17-11
1920	NY	N	P	33	9-16
1921	NY	N	P	18	5-2
1923	Cin	N	P	33	14-10
1924	Cin	N	P	32	7-9
1925	Cin	N	P	33	9-10
	BLTL			437	150-144

BENTON, LAWRENCE JAMES
b.Nov.20,1897 Cincinnati,O.
d.Apr.3,1953

Yr	Cl	Lea	Pos	G	Rec
1923	Bos	N	P	35	5-9
1924	Bos	N	P	30	5-7
1925	Bos	N	P	32	14-7
1926	Bos	N	P	45	14-14
1927	Bos	N	P	11	4-2
1927	NY	N	P	31	13-5
1928	NY	N	P	42	25-9
1929	NY	N	P	41	11-17
1930	NY	N	P	8	1-3
1930	Cin	N	P	35	7-12
1931	Cin	N	P	38	10-15
1932	Cin	N	P	35	6-13
1933	Cin	N	P	34	10-11
1934	Cin	N	P	16	0-1
1935	Bos	N	P	29	2-3
	BRTR			462	127-128

BENTON, SIDNEY WRIGHT
b.Aug.4,1895 Buckner,Ark.

Yr	Cl	Lea	Pos	G	Rec
1922	St.L	N	P	1	0-0
	BRTR				

BENTON, STANLEY W. (Rabbit)
b.Sept.29,1901 Lexington,Ky.

Yr	Cl	Lea	Pos	G	Rec
1922	Phi	N	2	6	.211
	BRTR				

BENZ, JOSEPH LOUIS (Blitzen)
b.Jan21,1886 New Alsace,Ind.
d.Apr.23,1957

Yr	Cl	Lea	Pos	G	Rec
1911	Chi	A	P	12	3-2
1912	Chi	A	P	38	13-17
1913	Chi	A	P	28	7-10
1914	Chi	A	P	44	14-19
1915	Chi	A	P	39	15-11
1916	Chi	A	P	28	9-5
1917	Chi	A	P	19	7-3
1918	Chi	A	P	29	7-8
1919	Chi	A	P	1	0-0
	BRTR			238	75-75

BERARDINO, JOHN (Bernie)
b.May 1,1917 Los Angeles,Cal.

Yr	Cl	Lea	Pos	G	Rec
1939	St.L	A	2	126	.256
1940	St.L	A	2-S-3	142	.258
1941	St.L	A	S-3	128	.271
1942	St.L	A	1-2-S-3	29	.284
1946	St.L	A	2	144	.265
1947	St.L	A	2	90	.261
1948	Cle	A	1-2-S-3	66	.190
1949	Cle	A	2-S-3	49	.191
1950	Cle	A	2-3	4	.400
1950	Pit	N	2-3	40	.206
1951	St.L	A	1-2-3-O	39	.227
1952	Cle	A	1-2-S-3	35	.094
1952	Pit	N	2	19	.143
	BRTR			911	.249

BERBERET, LOUIS JOSEPH
b.Nov.20,1929 Long Beach,Cal.

Yr	Cl	Lea	Pos	G	Rec
1954	NY	A	C	5	.400
1955	NY	A	C	2	.400
1956	Was	A	C	95	.261
1957	Was	A	C	99	.261
1958	Was	A	C	5	.167
1958	Bos	A	C	57	.210
1959	Det	A	C	100	.216
1960	Det	A	C	85	.194
	BLTR			448	.230

BERG, MORRIS (Moe)
b.Mar.2,1902 New York,N.Y.

Yr	Cl	Lea	Pos	G	Rec
1923	Bro	N	2-S	49	.186
1926	Chi	A	S	41	.221
1927	Chi	A	C-2	35	.247
1928	Chi	A	C	76	.246
1929	Chi	A	C	107	.287
1930	Chi	A	C	20	.115
1931	Cle	A	C	10	.077
1932	Was	A	C	75	.236
1933	Was	A	C	40	.185
1934	Was	A	C	33	.244
1934	Cle	A	C	29	.258
1935	Bos	A	C	38	.286
1936	Bos	A	C	39	.240
1937	Bos	A	C	47	.255
1938	Bos	A	C	10	.333
1939	Bos	A	C	14	.273
	BRTR			663	.243

BERGAMO, AUGUST SAMUEL
b.Feb.14,1918 Detroit,Mich.

Yr	Cl	Lea	Pos	G	Rec
1944	St.L	N	1-O	80	.286
1945	St.L	N	1-O	94	.316
	BLTL			174	.305

BERGEN, MARTIN
b.Oct.25,1871 N. Brookfield,Mass.
d.Jan.19,1900

Yr	Cl	Lea	Pos	G	Rec
1896	Bos	N	C	62	.267
1897	Bos	N	C	83	.247
1898	Bos	N	C	120	.289
1899	Bos	N	C	71	.257
	TR			336	.268

BERGEN, WILLIAM ALOYSIUS
b.June 13,1873 N.Brookfield,Mass.
d.Dec.19,1943

Yr	Cl	Lea	Pos	G	Rec
1901	Cin	N	C	82	.172
1902	Cin	N	C	89	.181
1903	Cin	N	C	58	.227
1904	Bro	N	C	94	.182
1905	Bro	N	C	76	.190
1906	Bro	N	C	103	.161
1907	Bro	N	C	51	.159
1908	Bro	N	C	99	.175
1909	Bro	N	C	112	.139
1910	Bro	N	C	89	.161
1911	Bro	N	C	84	.132
	BRTR			937	.170

BERGER, CHARLES (Heinie)
b.Jan.7,1882 LaSalle,Ill.
d.Feb.10,1954

Yr	Cl	Lea	Pos	G	Rec
1907	Cle	A	P	14	3-3
1908	Cle	A	P	29	13-8
1909	Cle	A	P	34	13-14
1910	Cle	A	P	13	3-4
	TR			90	32-29

BERGER, CLARENCE E.
b.July 10,1894 Brooklyn,N.Y.

Yr	Cl	Lea	Pos	G	Rec
1914	Pit	N	O	5	.083
	BLTR				

BERGER, JOHN HENNE
b.Aug.28,1902 Philadelphia,Pa.

Yr	Cl	Lea	Pos	G	Rec
1922	Phi	A	C	2	1.000
1927	Was	A	C	9	.267
	BRTR			11	.353

BERGER, JOHN HENRY (Tun)
b.1867 Pittsburgh,Pa.
d.June 11,1907

Yr	Cl	Lea	Pos	G	Rec
1890	Pit	N	C-S-O	104	.266
1891	Pit	N	C-2	37	.240
1892	Was	N	S	25	.142
				166	.241

BERGER, JOSEPH AUGUST (Fats)
b.Dec.20,1886 St.Louis,Mo.
d.Mar.6,1956

Yr	Cl	Lea	Pos	G	Rec
1913	Chi	A	2	77	.215
1914	Chi	A	S	47	.155
BRTR				124	.191

BERGER, LOUIS WILLIAM (Boze)
b.May 12,1910 Baltimore,Md.

Yr	Cl	Lea	Pos	G	Rec
1932	Cle	A	S	1	.000
1935	Cle	A	1-2-S-3	124	.258
1936	Cle	A	1-2-S-3	28	.173
1937	Chi	A	3	52	.238
1938	Chi	A	2-S	118	.217
1939	Bos	A	S	20	.300
BRTR				343	.236

BERGER, WALTER ANTONE
b.Oct.10,1905 Chicago,Ill.

Yr	Cl	Lea	Pos	G	Rec
1930	Bos	N	O	151	.310
1931	Bos	N	O	156	.323
1932	Bos	N	1-O	145	.307
1933	Bos	N	O	137	.313
1934	Bos	N	O	150	.298
1935	Bos	N	O	150	.295
1936	Bos	N	O	138	.288
1937	Bos	N	O	30	.274
1937	NY	N	O	59	.291
1938	NY	N	O	16	.188
1938	Cin	N	O	99	.307
1939	Cin	N	O	97	.258
1940	Cin	N	H	2	.000
1940	Phi	N	1-O	20	.317
BRTR				1350	.300

BERGH, JOHN BAPTIST
b.Oct.8,1857 Boston,Mass.
d.Apr.16,1883

Yr	Cl	Lea	Pos	G	Rec
1876	Ath	N	C	1	.000
1880	Bos	N	C	11	.167
				12	.152

BERGHAMMER, MARTIN ANDREW
b.Jan.18,1886 Pittsburgh,Pa.
d.Dec.21,1957

Yr	Cl	Lea	Pos	G	Rec
1911	Chi	A	2	2	.000
1913	Cin	N	S	74	.218
1914	Cin	N	S	77	.223
1915	Pit	F	S	132	.238
BLTR				285	.230

BERGMAN, ALFRED HENRY (Dutch)
b.Sept.27,1890 Peru,Ind.

Yr	Cl	Lea	Pos	G	Rec
1916	Cle	A	2	7	.214
BRTR					

BERKELBACH, FRANK P.
b.Philadelphia,Pa.

Yr	Cl	Lea	Pos	G	Rec
1884	Cin	a	O	6	.231

BERKENSTOCK, NATHAN
b.1833 Pa.
d.Feb.23,1900

Yr	Cl	Lea	Pos	G	Rec
1871	Ath	n	O	1	.000

BERLY, JOHN CHALMERS
b.May 24,1903 Natchitoches,La.

Yr	Cl	Lea	Pos	G	Rec
1924	St.L	N	P	4	0-0
1931	NY	N	P	27	7-8
1932	Phi	N	P	21	1-2
1933	Phi	N	P	13	2-3
BRTR				65	10-13

BERMAN, ROBERT LEON
b.Jan.24,1899 New York,N.Y.

Yr	Cl	Lea	Pos	G	Rec
1918	Was	A	C	2	.000
BRTR					

BERNARD, CURTIS HENRY
b.Feb.18,1879 Parkersburg,W.Va.

Yr	Cl	Lea	Pos	G	Rec
1900	NY	N	O	19	.243
1901	NY	N	O	19	.192
TR				38	.217

BERNARD, JOSEPH

Yr	Cl	Lea	Pos	G	Rec
1909	St.L	N	P	1	0-0

BERNHARD, WILLIAM HENRY (Strawberry Bill)
b.Mar.15,1871 Clarence,N.Y.
d.Mar.30,1949

Yr	Cl	Lea	Pos	G	Rec
1899	Phi	N	P	17	6-5
1900	Phi	N	P	28	14-11
1901	Phi	A	P	31	17-11
1902	Phi	A	P	1	1-0
1902	Cle	A	P	27	17-6
1903	Cle	A	P	20	14-5
1904	Cle	A	P	38	21-13
1905	Cle	A	P	22	6-14
1906	Cle	A	P	31	16-15
1907	Cle	A	P	8	0-1
BBTR				223	112-81

BERNHARDT, WALTER JACOB
b.May 20,1893 Roulette,Pa.
d.July 26,1958

Yr	Cl	Lea	Pos	G	Rec
1918	NY	A	P	1	0-0
BRTR					

BERNIER, CARLOS RODRIGUEZ
b.Jan.28,1929 Juana Diaz,Porto Rico

Yr	Cl	Lea	Pos	G	Rec
1953	Pit	N	O	105	.213
BRTR					

BERO, JOHN GEORGE
b.Dec.22,1923 Gary,W.Va.

Yr	Cl	Lea	Pos	G	Rec
1948	Det	A	2	4	.000
1951	St.L	A	2-S	61	.213
BLTR				65	.201

BERRA, LAWRENCE PETER (Yogi)
b.May 12,1925 St.Louis,Mo.

Yr	Cl	Lea	Pos	G	Rec
1946	NY	A	C	7	.364
1947	NY	A	C-O	83	.280
1948	NY	A	C-O	125	.305
1949	NY	A	C	116	.277
1950	NY	A	C	151	.322
1951	NY	A	C	141	.294
1952	NY	A	C	142	.273
1953	NY	A	C	137	.296
1954	NY	A	C-3	151	.307
1955	NY	A	C	147	.272
1956	NY	A	C-O	140	.298
1957	NY	A	C-O	134	.251
1958	NY	A	C-1-O	122	.266
1959	NY	A	C-O	131	.284
1960	NY	A	C-O	120	.276
1961	NY	A	C-O	119	.271
1962	NY	A	C-O	86	.224
BLTR				2052	.284

BERRENS, JOSEPH

Yr	Cl	Lea	Pos	G	Rec
1912	Chi	A	O	2	.250

BERRES, RAYMOND FREDERICK
b.Aug.21,1908 Kenosha,Wis.

Yr	Cl	Lea	Pos	G	Rec
1934	Bro	N	C	39	.215
1936	Bro	N	C	105	.240
1937	Pit	N	C	2	.167
1938	Pit	N	C	40	.230
1939	Pit	N	C	81	.229
1940	Pit	N	C	21	.188
1940	Bos	N	C	85	.192
1941	Bos	N	C	120	.201
1942	NY	N	C	12	.188
1943	NY	N	C	20	.143
1944	NY	N	C	16	.471
1945	NY	N	C	20	.167
BRTR				561	.216

BERRY, ALLEN KENNETH
b.May 10,1941 Kansas City,Mo.

Yr	Cl	Lea	Pos	G	Rec
1962	Chi	A	O	3	.333
BRTR					

BERRY, CHARLES FRANCIS
b.Oct.18,1902 Phillipsburg,N.J.

Yr	Cl	Lea	Pos	G	Rec
1925	Phi	A	C	10	.214
1928	Bos	A	C	80	.260
1929	Bos	A	C	77	.242
1930	Bos	A	C	88	.289
1931	Bos	A	C	111	.283
1932	Bos	A	C	10	.188
1932	Chi	A	C	72	.305
1933	Chi	A	C	86	.255
1934	Phi	A	C	99	.268
1935	Phi	A	C	62	.253
1936	Phi	A	C	13	.059
1938	Phi	A	C	1	.000
BRTR				709	.267

BERRY, CHARLES JOSEPH
b.Sept.6,1860 Elizabeth,N.J.
d.Feb.16,1940

Yr	Cl	Lea	Pos	G	Rec
1884	Alt	U	2	7	.269
1884	KC	U	2-3-O	29	.267
1884	Chi	U	2	5	.118
1884	Pit	U	2	2	.100
BRTR				43	.243

BERRY, CLAUDE ELZY (Admiral)
b.Feb.14,1880 Losantville,Ind.

Yr	Cl	Lea	Pos	G	Rec
1904	Chi	A	C	3	.000
1906	Phi	A	C	10	.226
1907	Phi	A	C	8	.291
1914	Pit	F	C	124	.243
1915	Pit	F	C	99	.192
BRTR				244	.224

BERRY, CORNELIUS JOHN (Neil)
b.Jan.11,1922 Kalamazoo,Mich.

Yr	Cl	Lea	Pos	G	Rec
1948	Det	A	2-S	87	.266
1949	Det	A	2-S	109	.237
1950	Det	A	2-S-3	38	.256
1951	Det	A	2-S-3	67	.229
1952	Det	A	S-3	73	.228
1953	St.L	A	2-S-3	57	.283
1953	Chi	A	2	5	.125
1954	Bal	A	S	5	.111
BRTR				441	.244

BERRY, JONAS ARTHUR (Jittery Joe)
b.Dec,16,1904 Huntsville,Ark.
d.Sept.27.1958

Yr	Cl	Lea	Pos	G	Rec
1942	Chi	N	P	2	0-0
1944	Phi	A	P	53	10-8
1945	Phi	A	P	52	8-7
1946	Phi	A	P	5	0-1
1946	Cle	A	P	21	3-6
BLTR				133	21-22

BERRY, JOSEPH HOWARD JR. (Nig)
b.Dec.31,1896 Philadelphia,Pa.

Yr	Cl	Lea	Pos	G	Rec
1921	NY	N	2	9	.333
1922	NY	N	H	6	.000
BBTR				15	.333

BERRY, JOSEPH HOWARD SR. (Hodge)
b.Sept.10,1872 Wheeling,W.Va.
d.Mar.13,1961

Yr	Cl	Lea	Pos	G	Rec
1902	Phi	N	C	1	.250
TR					

BERRY, THOMAS HANEY
b.Dec.31,1842 Chester,Pa.
d.June 6,1915

Yr	Cl	Lea	Pos	G	Rec
1871	Ath	n	O	1	.250

BERTE, HARRY
b.May 10,1872 Covington,Ky.

Yr	Cl	Lea	Pos	G	Rec
1903	St.L	N	2-S	4	.357
TR					

BERTHRONG, HARRY W.
b.Dec.31,1843 Munford,N.Y.
d.Apr.28,1928

Yr	Cl	Lea	Pos	G	Rec
1871	Oly	n	2-3-O	17	.244

BERTELL, RICHARD GEORGE
b.Nov.21,1935 Oak Park,Ill.

Yr	Cl	Lea	Pos	G	Rec
1960	Chi	N	C	5	.133
1961	Chi	N	C	92	.273
1962	Chi	N	C	77	.302
	BRTR			174	.282

BERTOIA, RENO PETER
b.Jan.8,1935 St.Vito,Udine,Italy

Yr	Cl	Lea	Pos	G	Rec
1953	Det	A	2	1	.000
1954	Det	A	2-S-3	54	.162
1955	Det	A	S-3	38	.206
1956	Det	A	2-3	22	.182
1957	Det	A	2-S-3	97	.275
1958	Det	A	S-3-O	86	.233
1959	Was	A	2-S-3	90	.237
1960	Was	A	2-3	121	.265
1961	Min	A	3	35	.212
1961	KC	A	2-3	39	.242
1961	Det	A	2-S-3	24	.217
1962	Det	A	2-S-3	5	.000
	BRTR			412	.244

BERTRAND, ROMAN MATHIAS
(Lefty)
b.Feb.28,1909 Cobden,Minn.

Yr	Cl	Lea	Pos	G	Rec
1936	Phi	N	P	1	0-0
	BRTL				

BESANA, FREDERICK CYRIL
b.Apr.5,1931 Lincoln,Cal.

Yr	Cl	Lea	Pos	G	Rec
1956	Bal	A	P	7	1-0
	BRTL				

BESCHER, ROBERT HENRY
b.Feb.25,1884 London,O.
d.Nov.29,1942

Yr	Cl	Lea	Pos	G	Rec
1908	Cin	N	O	32	.272
1909	Cin	N	O	117	.240
1910	Cin	N	O	150	.250
1911	Cin	N	O	153	.275
1912	Cin	N	O	145	.281
1913	Cin	N	O	141	.258
1914	NY	N	O	135	.270
1915	St.L	N	O	130	.263
1916	St.L	N	O	151	.235
1917	St.L	N	O	42	.155
1918	Cle	A	O	25	.333
	BLTL			1221	.258

BESSE, HERMAN
b.Aug.16,1915 St. Louis,Mo.

Yr	Cl	Lea	Pos	G	Rec
1940	Phi	A	P	17	0-3
1941	Phi	A	P	6	2-0
1942	Phi	A	P	34	2-9
1943	Phi	A	P	7	1-1
1946	Phi	A	P	7	0-2
	BLTL			71	5-15

BESSENT, FRED DONALD
b.Mar.13,1931 Jacksonville,Fla.

Yr	Cl	Lea	Pos	G	Rec
1955	Bro	N	P	24	8-1
1956	Bro	N	P	38	4-3
1957	Bro	N	P	27	1-3
1958	LA	N	P	19	1-0
	BRTR			108	14-7

BESTICK, ...

Yr	Cl	Lea	Pos	G	Rec
1872	Eck	n	C	2	NR

BETCHER, FRANKLIN LYLE
(Real name Franklin Lyle Bettger)
b.Feb.15,1888 Philadelphia,Pa.

Yr	Cl	Lea	Pos	G	Rec
1910	St.L	N	S	27	.202
	BBTR				

BETTENCOURT, LAWRENCE JOSEPH
b.Sept.22,1907 Newark,Cal.

Yr	Cl	Lea	Pos	G	Rec
1928	St.L	A	3	67	.283
1931	St.L	A	O	74	.257
1932	St.L	A	3-O	27	.133
	BRTR			168	.258

BETTGER, FRANKLIN LYLE
(Played under name of
Franklin Lyle Betcher)

BETTS, HAROLD M.
b.1888 St.Louis,Mo.

Yr	Cl	Lea	Pos	G	Rec
1903	St.L	N	P	1	0-1
1913	Cin	N	P	1	0-0
	BRTR			2	0-1

BETTS, WALTER MARTIN
(Huck)
b.Feb.18,1897 Millsboro,Del.

Yr	Cl	Lea	Pos	G	Rec
1920	Phi	N	P	27	1-1
1921	Phi	N	P	32	3-7
1922	Phi	N	P	7	1-0
1923	Phi	N	P	20	2-4
1924	Phi	N	P	38	7-10
1925	Phi	N	P	37	4-5
1932	Bos	N	P	31	13-11
1933	Bos	N	P	35	11-11
1934	Bos	N	P	40	17-10
1935	Bos	N	P	44	2-9
	BRTR			311	61-68

BETZEL, CHRISTIAN FREDERICK ALBERT JOHN HENRY DAVID
(Bruno)
b.Dec.6,1894 Celina,O.

Yr	Cl	Lea	Pos	G	Rec
1914	St.L	N	2-3	7	.000
1915	St.L	N	3	117	.251
1916	St.L	N	2-3	142	.233
1917	St.L	N	2-O	106	.217
1918	St.L	N	2-3-O	76	.222
	BRTR			448	.231

BEVAN, JOSEPH HAROLD
b.Nov.15,1930 New Orleans,La.

Yr	Cl	Lea	Pos	G	Rec
1952	Bos	A	3	1	.000
1952	Phi	A	3	8	.353
1955	KC	A	3	3	.000
1961	Cin	N	H	3	.333
	BRTR			15	.292

BEVANS, E.P.
b.1848 N.Y.

Yr	Cl	Lea	Pos	G	Rec
1871	Tro	n	2	3	.333
1872	Atl	n	2-S-O	10	NR
	TR			13	NR

BEVENS, FLOYD CLIFFORD (Bill)
b.Oct.20,1916 Hubbard,Ore.

Yr	Cl	Lea	Pos	G	Rec
1944	NY	A	P	8	4-1
1945	NY	A	P	29	13-9
1946	NY	A	P	31	16-13
1947	NY	A	P	28	7-13
	BRTR			96	40-36

BEVIL, LOUIS EUGENE
(Real name
Louis Eugene Bevilacqua)
b.Nov.27,1921 Dixon,Ill.

Yr	Cl	Lea	Pos	G	Rec
1942	Was	A	P	4	0-1
	BBTR				

BEVILACQUA, LOUIS EUGENE
(Played under name of
Louis Eugene Bevil)

BEVILLE, CHARLES E (Candy)

Yr	Cl	Lea	Pos	G	Rec
1901	Bos	A	P	3	0-2

BEVILLE, HENRY MONTE
b.Feb.24,1875 Dublin,Ind.
d.Jan.24,1955

Yr	Cl	Lea	Pos	G	Rec
1903	NY	A	C	82	.194
1904	NY	A	C-1	9	.273
1904	Det	A	C	53	.225
	BLTR			144	.210

BEZDEK, HUGO FRANK
b.Apr.1,1884 Prague,Czechoslovakia
d.Sept.19,1952
Non-playing manager Pit (N) 1917-19

BIASATTI, HENRY ARCADO
b.Jan.14,1925 Beano,Italy

Yr	Cl	Lea	Pos	G	Rec
1949	Phi	A	1	21	.083
	BLTL				

BICKFORD, VERNON EDGELL
b.Aug.17,1920 Hellier,Ky.
d.May 6,1960

Yr	Cl	Lea	Pos	G	Rec
1948	Bos	N	P	33	11-5
1949	Bos	N	P	37	16-11
1950	Bos	N	P	40	19-14
1951	Bos	N	P	25	11-9
1952	Bos	N	P	26	7-12
1953	Mil	N	P	20	2-5
1954	Bal	A	P	1	0-1
	BRTR			182	66-57

BICKHAM, DANIEL DENISON
b.Oct.31,1864 Dayton,O.
d.Mar.3,1951

Yr	Cl	Lea	Pos	G	Rec
1886	Cin	a	P	1	1-0

BICKNELL, CHARLES (Bud)
b.July 27,1928 Plainfield,N.J.

Yr	Cl	Lea	Pos	G	Rec
1948	Phi	N	P	17	0-1
1949	Phi	N	P	13	0-0
	BRTR			30	0-1

BIELASKI, OSCAR
b.Mar.21,1847 Washington,D.C.
d.Nov.9,1911

Yr	Cl	Lea	Pos	G	Rec
1872	Nat	n	O	9	NR
1873	Nat	n	O	38	NR
1874	Bal	n	1-2-O	25	NR
1875	Chi	n	O	52	NR
1876	Chi	N	O	31	.206
	BRTR			155	NR

BIEMILLER, HARRY LEE
b.Oct.9,1898 Baltimore,Md.

Yr	Cl	Lea	Pos	G	Rec
1920	Was	A	P	5	1-0
1925	Cin	N	P	23	0-1
	BRTR			28	1-1

BIERBAUER, LOUIS W.
b.Sept.28,1865 Erie,Pa.
d.Feb.1,1926

Yr	Cl	Lea	Pos	G	Rec
1886	Ath	a	2	137	.244
1887	Ath	a	2	126	.302
1888	Ath	a	2	134	.279
1889	Ath	a	2	130	.313
1890	Bro	p	2	132	.319
1891	Pit	N	2	117	.202
1892	Pit	N	2	153	.240
1893	Pit	N	2	128	.298
1894	Pit	N	2	131	.301
1895	Pit	N	2	119	.255
1896	Pit	N	2	57	.277
1897	St.L	N	2	12	.217
1898	St.L	N	2	4	.000
	BRTR			1380	.275

BIGBEE, CARSON LEE (Skeeter)
b.Mar.31,1895 Waterloo,Ore.

Yr	Cl	Lea	Pos	G	Rec
1916	Pit	N	2-O	43	.250
1917	Pit	N	2-O	133	.239
1918	Pit	N	O	92	.255
1919	Pit	N	O	125	.276
1920	Pit	N	O	137	.280
1921	Pit	N	O	147	.323
1922	Pit	N	O	150	.350
1923	Pit	N	O	123	.299
1924	Pit	N	O	89	.262
1925	Pit	N	O	66	.238
1926	Pit	N	O	42	.221
	BLTR			1147	.287

BIGBEE, LYLE RANDOLPH (Al)
b.Aug.22,1893 Sweet Home,Ore.
d.Aug.5,1942

Yr	Cl	Lea	Pos	G	Rec
1920	Phi	A	P	37	0-3
1921	Pit	N	P	5	0-0
	BLTR			42	0-3

BIGELOW, ELLIOT ALLARDICE (Babe)
b.Oct.13,1898 Tarpon Springs,Fla.
d.Aug.10,1933

Yr	Cl	Lea	Pos	G	Rec
1929	Bos	A	O	100	.285
	BLTL				

BIGGS, CHARLES ORVAL
b.Sept.15,1906 French Lick,Ind.
d.May 24,1954

Yr	Cl	Lea	Pos	G	Rec
1932	Chi	A	P	6	1-1
	BRTR				

BIGLER, IVAN EDWARD
b.Dec.13,1894 Bradford,O.

Yr	Cl	Lea	Pos	G	Rec
1917	St.L	A	1	1	.000
	BRTR				

BIGNAL, GEORGE WILLIAM
b.July 18,1858 Taunton,Mass.
d.Jan.16,1925

Yr	Cl	Lea	Pos	G	Rec
1884	Mil	U	C	4	.222

BILBREY, JAMES MELVIN
b.Apr.20,1924 Monterey,Tenn.

Yr	Cl	Lea	Pos	G	Rec
1949	St.L	A	P	1	0-0
	BRTR				

BILDILLI, EMIL (Hill Billy)
b.Sept.16,1914 Diamond,Ind.
d.Sept.16,1946

Yr	Cl	Lea	Pos	G	Rec
1937	St.L	A	P	4	0-1
1938	St.L	A	P	5	1-2
1939	St.L	A	P	2	1-1
1940	St.L	A	P	29	2-4
1941	St.L	A	P	2	0-0
	BRTL			42	4-8

BILKO, STEPHEN THOMAS
b.Nov.13,1928 Nanticoke,Pa.

Yr	Cl	Lea	Pos	G	Rec
1949	St.L	N	1	6	.294
1950	St.L	N	1	10	.182
1951	St.L	N	1	21	.222
1952	St.L	N	1	20	.264
1953	St.L	N	1	154	.251
1954	St.L	N	1	8	.143
1954	Chi	N	1	47	.239
1958	Cin	N	1	31	.264
1958	LA	N	1	47	.208
1960	Det	A	1	78	.207
1961	LA	A	1-O	114	.279
1962	LA	A	1	64	.287
	BRTR			600	.249

BILLIARD, HARRY P.
b.Nov.21,1885 Wooster,O.
d.June 3,1923

Yr	Cl	Lea	Pos	G	Rec
1908	NY	A	P	6	0-0
1914	Ind	F	P	24	8-7
1915	New	F	P	14	0-1
	BRTR			44	8-8

BILLINGS, HASKELL CLARK
b.Sept.27,1907 New York,N.Y.

Yr	Cl	Lea	Pos	G	Rec
1927	Det	A	P	10	5-4
1928	Det	A	P	21	5-10
1929	Det	A	P	8	0-1
	BRTR			39	10-15

BILLINGS, JOHN AUGUSTUS (Josh)
b.Nov.30,1891 Grantville,Kan.

Yr	Cl	Lea	Pos	G	Rec
1913	Cle	A	C	1	.000
1914	Cle	A	C	10	.250
1915	Cle	A	C	7	.266
1916	Cle	A	C	22	.160
1917	Cle	A	C	66	.178
1918	Cle	A	C	2	.333
1919	St.L	A	C	38	.198
1920	St.L	A	C	66	.278
1921	St.L	A	C	20	.217
1922	St.L	A	C	5	.429
1923	St.L	A	C	4	.000
	BRTR			241	.217

BINKOWSKI, GEORGE EUGENE (Played under name of BINKS, GEORGE EUGENE)
b.July 11,1916 Chicago,Ill.

Yr	Cl	Lea	Pos	G	Rec
1944	Was	A	O	5	.250
1945	Was	A	1-O	145	.278
1946	Was	A	O	65	.194
1947	Phi	A	1-O	104	.258
1948	Phi	A	O	17	.098
1948	St.L	A	1-O	15	.217
	BLTL			351	.254

BIRAS, STEPHEN ALEXANDER
b.Feb.26,1922 E. St. Louis,Ill.

Yr	Cl	Lea	Pos	G	Rec
1944	Cle	A	2	2	1.000
	BRTR				

BIRCHALL, A. JUDSON (Jud)
b.1858 Philadelphia,Pa.
d.Dec.22,1887

Yr	Cl	Lea	Pos	G	Rec
1882	Ath	a	2-O	75	.263
1883	Ath	a	O	95	.230
1884	Ath	a	O	53	.262
				223	.256

BIRD, FRANK (Dodo)
b.Mar.19,1869 Spencer,Mass.
d.May 20,1958

Yr	Cl	Lea	Pos	G	Rec
1892	St.L	N	C	17	.196
	BRTR				

BIRD, GEORGE R.
b.June 23,1850 Stillman Valley,Ill.
d.Nov.9,1940

Yr	Cl	Lea	Pos	G	Rec
1871	Rok	n	O	25	NR

BIRD, JAMES EDWIN (Red)
b.Apr.25,1895 Stephenville,Tex.

Yr	Cl	Lea	Pos	G	Rec
1921	Was	A	P	1	0-0
	BLTL				

BIRDSALL, DAVID SOLOMON
b.July 16,1839 New York,N.Y.
d.Jan.30,1896

Yr	Cl	Lea	Pos	G	Rec
1871	Bos	n	C-O	31	NR
1872	Bos	n	C-O	15	.179
1873	Bos	n	O	3	NR
	BRTR			49	NR

BIRKOFER, RALPH JOSEPH (Lefty)
b.Nov.5,1909 Cincinnati,O

Yr	Cl	Lea	Pos	G	Rec
1933	Pit	N	P	9	4-2
1934	Pit	N	P	41	11-12
1935	Pit	N	P	38	9-7
1936	Pit	N	P	34	7-5
1937	Bro	N	P	12	0-2
	BLTL			134	31-28

BIRMINGHAM, JOSEPH LEO (Dode)
b.Aug.6,1884 Elmira,N.Y.
d.Apr.24,1946

Yr	Cl	Lea	Pos	G	Rec
1906	Cle	A	O	10	.275
1907	Cle	A	O	136	.235
1908	Cle	A	O	122	.213
1909	Cle	A	O	100	.289
1910	Cle	A	O	104	.229
1911	Cle	A	3-O	125	.304
1912	Cle	A	M-O	107	.255
1913	Cle	A	M-O	47	.282
1914	Cle	A	M-O	19	.128
	BRTR			770	.253

Non-playing manager Cle (A) 1915

BIRRER, WERNER JOSEPH
b.July 4,1928 Buffalo,N.Y.

Yr	Cl	Lea	Pos	G	Rec
1955	Det	A	P	36	4-3
1956	Bal	A	P	4	0-0
1958	LA	N	P	16	0-0
	BRTR			56	4-3

BISCAN, FRANK STEPHEN (Porky)
b.Mar.13,1920 Mt.Olive, Ill.
d.May 22,1959

Yr	Cl	Lea	Pos	G	Rec
1942	St.L	A	P	11	0-1
1946	St.L	A	P	16	1-1
1948	St.L	A	P	47	6-7
	BLTL			74	7-9

BISCHOFF, JOHN GEORGE (Smiley)
b.Oct.28,1897 Granite City,Ill.

Yr	Cl	Lea	Pos	G	Rec
1925	Chi	A	C	7	.091
1925	Bos	A	C	41	.278
1926	Bos	A	C	59	.260
	BRTR			107	.262

BISHOP, CHARLES TULLER
b.Jan.1,1924 Atlanta,Ga.

Yr	Cl	Lea	Pos	G	Rec
1952	Phi	A	P	6	2-2
1953	Phi	A	P	40	3-14
1954	Phi	A	P	22	4-6
1955	KC	A	P	4	1-0
	BRTR			72	10-22

BISHOP, FRANK
b.Chicago,Ill.

Yr	Cl	Lea	Pos	G	Rec
1884	Chi	U	S-3	4	.200

BISHOP, JAMES MORTON
b.Jan.22,1898 Montgomery City,Mo.

Yr	Cl	Lea	Pos	G	Rec
1923	Phi	N	P	15	0-3
1924	Phi	N	P	7	0-1
	BRTR			22	0-4

BISHOP, LLOYD CLIFTON
b.Apr.25,1890 Conway Springs,Kan.

Yr	Cl	Lea	Pos	G	Rec
1914	Cle	A	P	3	0-1
	BRTR				

BISHOP, MAX FREDERICK (Tilly)
b.Sept.5,1899 Waynesboro,Pa.
d.Feb.24,1962

Yr	Cl	Lea	Pos	G	Rec
1924	Phi	A	2	91	.255
1925	Phi	A	2	105	.280
1926	Phi	A	2	122	.265
1927	Phi	A	2	117	.277
1928	Phi	A	2	126	.316
1929	Phi	A	2	129	.232
1930	Phi	A	2	130	.252
1931	Phi	A	2	130	.294
1932	Phi	A	2	114	.254
1933	Phi	A	2	117	.294
1934	Bos	A	1-2	97	.261
1935	Bos	A	1-2-S	60	.230
	BLTR			1338	.271

BISHOP, WILLIAM H. (Lefty)
b.Oct.22,1900 Clearfield,Pa.

Yr	Cl	Lea	Pos	G	Rec
1921	Phi	A	P	2	0-0
	BLTL				

BISHOP, WILLIAM R.
b.Dec.27,1869 Adamsburg,Pa.
d.Dec.15,1932

Yr	Cl	Lea	Pos	G	Rec
1886	Pit	a	P	2	0-1
1887	Pit	N	P	4	0-4
1889	Chi	N	P	2	0-0
				8	0-5

BISLAND, RIVINGTON MARTIN
b.Feb.17,1890 New York,N.Y.

Yr	Cl	Lea	Pos	G	Rec
1912	Pit	N	H	1	.000
1913	St.L	A	S	12	.136
1914	Cle	A	S	18	.105
	BRTR			31	.117

BISSONETTE, ADELPHIA LOUIS (Del)
b.Sept.6,1899 Winthrop,Me.

Yr	Cl	Lea	Pos	G	Rec
1928	Bro	N	1	155	.320
1929	Bro	N	1	116	.281
1930	Bro	N	1	146	.336
1931	Bro	N	1	152	.290
1933	Bro	N	1	35	.246
	BLTL			604	.305

Non-playing manager Bos (N) 1945

BITHORN, HIRAM GABRIEL
b.Mar.18,1916 Santurce,Puerto Rico.
d.Jan.1,1952

Yr	Cl	Lea	Pos	G	Rec
1942	Chi	N	P	38	9-14
1943	Chi	N	P	39	18-12
1946	Chi	N	P	26	6-5
1947	Chi	A	P	2	1-0
			BRTR	105	34-31

BITTMAN, HENRY (Red)
b.Cincinnati,O.

Yr	Cl	Lea	Pos	G	Rec
1889	KC	a	2	4	.286

BIVIN, JAMES NATHANIEL
b.Dec.11,1909 Jackson,Miss.

Yr	Cl	Lea	Pos	G	Rec
1935	Phi	N	P	47	2-9
			BRTR		

BLACK, DAVID
b.Apr.19,1892 Chicago,Ill.
d.Oct.27,1936

Yr	Cl	Lea	Pos	G	Rec
1914	Chi	F	P	9	1-0
1915	Chi	F	P	21	3-2
1915	Bal	F	P	12	4-8
1923	Bos	A	P	2	0-0
			TR	44	8-10

BLACK, DONALD PAUL
b.July 20,1916 Salix,Ia.
d.Apr.21,1959

Yr	Cl	Lea	Pos	G	Rec
1943	Phi	A	P	33	6-16
1944	Phi	A	P	29	10-12
1945	Phi	A	P	26	5-11
1946	Cle	A	P	18	1-2
1947	Cle	A	P	30	10-12
1948	Cle	A	P	18	2-2
			BRTR	154	34-55

BLACK, JOHN B.
(Real name John Falcnor Haddow)
b.Feb.23,1890 Covington,Ky.

Yr	Cl	Lea	Pos	G	Rec
1911	St.L	A	1	54	.150
			BRTR		

BLACK, JOHN WILLIAM (Jiggy)
b.Aug.12,1899 Philadelphia,Pa.

Yr	Cl	Lea	Pos	G	Rec
1924	Chi	A	2	6	.200
			BLTR		

BLACK, JOSEPH
b.Feb.8,1924 Plainfield,N.J.

Yr	Cl	Lea	Pos	G	Rec
1952	Bro	N	P	57	15-4
1953	Bro	N	P	34	6-3
1954	Bro	N	P	5	0-0
1955	Bro	N	P	6	1-0
1955	Cin	N	P	32	5-2
1956	Cin	N	P	34	3-2
1957	Was	A	P	7	0-1
			BRTR	175	30-12

BLACK, ROBERT BENJAMIN
b.Dec.10,1864 Cincinnati,O.
d.Mar.21,1933

Yr	Cl	Lea	Pos	G	Rec
1884	KC	U	P-2-S-O	38	{3-9 .245}

BLACK, WILLIAM CARROLL
b.July 9,1932 University City,Mo.

Yr	Cl	Lea	Pos	G	Rec
1952	Det	A	P	2	0-1
1955	Det	A	P	3	1-1
1956	Det	A	P	5	1-1
			BRTR	10	2-3

BLACKABY, ETHAN ALLAN
b.July 24,1940 Cincinnati,O.

Yr	Cl	Lea	Pos	G	Rec
1962	Mil	N	O	6	.154
			BLTL		

BLACKBURN, FOSTER EDWIN
b.Jan.6,1895 Chicago,Ill.

Yr	Cl	Lea	Pos	G	Rec
1915	KC	F	P	7	0-1
1921	Chi	A	P	1	0-0
				8	0-1

BLACKBURN, GEORGE W.
(Smiling George)
b.Sept.21,1871 Ozark,Mo.

Yr	Cl	Lea	Pos	G	Rec
1897	Bal	N	P	5	2-2

BLACKBURN, JAMES RAY
b.June 19,1924 Warsaw,Ky.

Yr	Cl	Lea	Pos	G	Rec
1948	Cin	N	P	16	0-2
1951	Cin	N	P	2	0-0
			BRTR	18	0-2

BLACKBURN, RONALD HAMILTON
b.Apr.23,1935 Mt.Airy,N.C.

Yr	Cl	Lea	Pos	G	Rec
1958	Pit	N	P	38	2-1
1959	Pit	N	P	26	1-1
			BRTR	64	3-2

BLACKBURN, EARL STUART
b.Nov.1,1892 Leesville,O.

Yr	Cl	Lea	Pos	G	Rec
1912	Pit	N	C	1	.000
1912	Cin	N	C	1	.000
1913	Cin	N	C	17	.259
1915	Bos	N	C	3	.167
1916	Bos	N	C	47	.273
1917	Chi	N	C	2	.000
			BRTR	71	.262

BLACKBURNE, RUSSELL AUBREY
(Lena)
b.Oct.23,1886 Clifton Heights,Pa.

Yr	Cl	Lea	Pos	G	Rec
1910	Chi	A	S	75	.174
1912	Chi	A	S	5	.000
1914	Chi	A	2	144	.222
1915	Chi	A	3	96	.216
1918	Cin	N	S	125	.228
1919	Bos	N	1-2-S-3	31	.272
1919	Phi	N	1-3	72	.197
1927	Chi	A	H	1	1.000
1929	Chi	A	M-P	1	0-0
			BRTR	550	{0-0 .214}

Non-playing manager Chi (A) 1928

BLACKERBY, GEORGE FRANCIS
b.Nov.10,1906 Oklahoma City,Okla.

Yr	Cl	Lea	Pos	G	Rec
1928	Chi	A	O	30	.253
			BRTR		

BLACKSTONE, ROBERT J.
(Played under name of
Robert J. Blakiston)

BLACKWELL, EWELL (Whip)
b.Oct.23,1922 Fresno,Cal.

Yr	Cl	Lea	Pos	G	Rec
1942	Cin	N	P	2	0-0
1946	Cin	N	P	33	9-13
1947	Cin	N	P	33	22-8
1948	Cin	N	P	22	7-9
1949	Cin	N	P	29	5-5
1950	Cin	N	P	40	17-15
1951	Cin	N	P	39	16-15
1952	Cin	N	P	23	3-12
1952	NY	A	P	5	1-0
1953	NY	A	P	8	2-0
1955	KC	A	P	2	0-1
			BRTR	236	82-78

BLACKWELL, FREDERICK WILLIAM
b.Sept.7,1895 Bowling Green,Ky.

Yr	Cl	Lea	Pos	G	Rec
1917	Pit	N	C	3	.200
1918	Pit	N	C	8	.153
1919	Pit	N	C	24	.215
			BLTR	35	.205

BLADES, FRANCIS RAYMOND (Ray)
b.Aug.6,1897 Mt. Vernon,Ill.

Yr	Cl	Lea	Pos	G	Rec
1922	St.L	N	S-3-O	37	.300
1923	St.L	N	3-O	98	.246
1924	St.L	N	2-3-O	131	.311
1925	St.L	N	3-O	122	.342
1926	St.L	N	O	107	.305
1927	St.L	N	O	61	.317
1928	St.L	N	O	51	.235
1930	St.L	N	O	45	.396
1931	St.L	N	O	35	.284
1932	St.L	N	O	80	.229
			BRTR	767	.301

Non-playing manager St.L (N) 1939-40

BLAEHOLDER, GEORGE FRANKLIN
b.Jan.26,1904 Orange,Cal.
d.Dec.29,1947

Yr	Cl	Lea	Pos	G	Rec
1925	St.L	A	P	2	0-0
1927	St.L	A	P	1	0-1
1928	St.L	A	P	38	10-15
1929	St.L	A	P	42	14-15
1930	St.L	A	P	37	11-13
1931	St.L	A	P	35	11-15
1932	St.L	A	P	42	14-14
1933	St.L	A	P	38	15-19
1934	St.L	A	P	39	14-18
1935	St.L	A	P	6	1-1
1935	Phi	A	P	23	6-10
1936	Cle	A	P	35	8-4
			BRTR	338	104-125

BLAEMIRE, RAE BERTRAM
b.Feb.8,1914 Gary,Ind.

Yr	Cl	Lea	Pos	G	Rec
1941	NY	N	C	2	.400
			BRTR		

BLAIR, CLARENCE VICK (Footsie)
b.July 13,1903 Texarkana,Tex.

Yr	Cl	Lea	Pos	G	Rec
1929	Chi	N	1-2-3	26	.319
1930	Chi	N	2-3	134	.273
1931	Chi	N	1-2	86	.258
			BLTR	246	.273

BLAIR, LOUIS NATHAN (Buddy)
b.Sept.15,1914 Columbia,Miss.

Yr	Cl	Lea	Pos	G	Rec
1942	Phi	A	3	137	.279
			BLTR		

BLAIR, WALTER ALLAN (Heavy)
b.Oct.13,1883 Arnot,Pa.
d.Aug.20,1948

Yr	Cl	Lea	Pos	G	Rec
1907	NY	A	C	7	.173
1908	NY	A	C	76	.190
1909	NY	A	C	42	.209
1910	NY	A	C	6	.227
1911	NY	A	C	85	.194
1914	Buf	F	C	127	.239
1915	Buf	F	M-C	98	.224
			BRTR	441	.215

BLAIR, WILLIAM ELLSWORTH
b.1862 Pittsburgh,Pa.
d.Feb.22,1890

Yr	Cl	Lea	Pos	G	Rec
1888	Ath	a	P	5	1-4
			TL		

BLAISDELL, HOWARD CARLETON
(Dick)
b.June 18,1862 Bradford,Mass.
d.Aug.20,1886

Yr	Cl	Lea	Pos	G	Rec
1884	KC	U	P-O	4	{0-3 .295}

BLAKE, EDWARD JAMES
b.Dec.23,1925 Granite City,Ill.

Yr	Cl	Lea	Pos	G	Rec
1951	Cin	N	P	3	0-0
1952	Cin	N	P	2	0-0
1953	Cin	N	P	1	0-0
1957	KC	A	P	2	0-0
			BRTR	8	0-0

BLAKE, HENRY C.
b.June 16,1874 Portsmouth,O.
d.Oct.14,1919

Yr	Cl	Lea	Pos	G	Rec
1894	Cle	N	O	73	.286
1895	Cle	N	O	83	.280
1896	Cle	N	O	102	.242
1897	Cle	N	O	31	.256
1898	Cle	N	O	137	.245
1899	St.L	N	O	94	.238
				520	.257

BLAKE, JOHN FREDERICK (Sheriff)
b.Sept.17,1899 Ansted,W.Va.

Yr	Cl	Lea	Pos	G	Rec
1920	Pit	N	P	6	0-0
1924	Chi	N	P	29	6-6
1925	Chi	N	P	36	10-18
1926	Chi	N	P	39	11-12
1927	Chi	N	P	32	13-14
1928	Chi	N	P	35	17-11
1929	Chi	N	P	38	14-13
1930	Chi	N	P	36	10-14
1931	Chi	N	P	16	0-4
1931	Phi	N	P	14	4-5
1937	St.L	A	P	15	2-2
1937	St.L	N	P	14	0-3
	BBTR			310	87-102

BLAKELY, LINCOLN HOWARD (Bink)
b.Feb.12,1913 Oakland,Cal.

Yr	Cl	Lea	Pos	G	Rec
1934	Cin	N	O	34	.225
	BRTR				

BLAKISTON, ROBERT J.
(Real name Robert J. Blackstone)
b.Oct.2,1855 San Frncisco,Cal.
d.Dec.25,1918

Yr	Cl	Lea	Pos	G	Rec
1882	Ath	a	2-3-O	72	.242
1883	Ath	a	1-3-O	40	.249
1884	Ath	a	1-2-S-3-O	33	.266
1884	Ind	a	1-O	6	.200
				151	.248

BLANCHARD, JOHN EDWIN
b.Feb.26,1933 Minneapolis,Minn.

Yr	Cl	Lea	Pos	G	Rec
1955	NY	A	C	1	.000
1959	NY	A	C-1-O	49	.169
1960	NY	A	C	53	.242
1961	NY	A	C-O	93	.305
1962	NY	A	C-1-O	93	.232
	BLTR			289	.254

BLANCHE, PROSBY ALBERT
(Real name Prosper Belangio)
b.Sept.21,1909 Somerville,Mass.

Yr	Cl	Lea	Pos	G	Rec
1935	Bos	N	P	6	0-0
1936	Bos	N	P	11	0-1
	BRTR			17	0-1

BLANDING, FRED JAMES (Fritz)
b.Feb.8,1888 Redlands,Cal.
d.July 16,1950

Yr	Cl	Lea	Pos	G	Rec
1910	Cle	A	P	6	2-2
1911	Cle	A	P	30	7-11
1912	Cle	A	P	36	18-14
1913	Cle	A	P	39	15-10
1914	Cle	A	P	27	3-9
	BRTR			138	45-46

BLANK, ...

Yr	Cl	Lea	Pos	G	Rec
1909	St.L	N	C	1	.000

BLANK, FREDERICK AUGUST
b.June 18,1874 DeSoto,Mo.
d.Feb.5,1936

Yr	Cl	Lea	Pos	G	Rec
1894	Cin	N	P	1	0-1
	BLTL				

BLANKENSHIP, CLIFFORD DOUGLAS
b.Apr.10,1880 Columbus,Ga.
d.Apr.26,1956

Yr	Cl	Lea	Pos	G	Rec
1905	Cin	N	1	15	.196
1907	Was	A	C	37	.225
1909	Was	A	C	39	.250
	BRTR			91	.225

BLANKENSHIP, HOMER (Si)
b.Aug.4,1902 Bonham,Tex

Yr	Cl	Lea	Pos	G	Rec
1922	Chi	A	P	4	0-0
1923	Chi	A	P	4	1-1
1928	Pit	N	P	5	0-2
	BRTR			13	1-3

BLANKENSHIP, THEODORE
b.May 10,1901 Bonham,Tex.
d.Jan.14,1945

Yr	Cl	Lea	Pos	G	Rec
1922	Chi	A	P	24	8-10
1923	Chi	A	P	44	9-14
1924	Chi	A	P	25	7-6
1925	Chi	A	P	40	17-8
1926	Chi	A	P	29	13-10
1927	Chi	A	P	38	12-17
1928	Chi	A	P	27	9-11
1929	Chi	A	P	8	0-2
1930	Chi	A	P	7	2-1
	BRTR			242	77-79

BLANTON, DARRELL ELIJAH (Cy)
b.Mar.3,1909 Waurika,Okla.
d.Sept.13,1945

Yr	Cl	Lea	Pos	G	Rec
1934	Pit	N	P	1	0-1
1935	Pit	N	P	35	18-13
1936	Pit	N	P	44	13-15
1937	Pit	N	P	36	14-12
1938	Pit	N	P	29	11-7
1939	Pit	N	P	10	2-3
1940	Phi	N	P	13	4-3
1941	Phi	N	P	28	6-13
1942	Phi	N	P	6	0-4
	BLTR			202	68-71

BLASINGAME, DONALD LEE
b.Mar.16,1932 Corinth,Miss.

Yr	Cl	Lea	Pos	G	Rec
1955	St.L	N	2-S	5	.375
1956	St.L	N	2-S-3	150	.261
1957	St.L	N	2	154	.271
1958	St.L	N	2	143	.274
1959	St.L	N	2	150	.289
1960	SF	N	2	136	.235
1961	SF	N	2	3	.000
1961	Cin	N	2	123	.222
1962	Cin	N	2	141	.281
	BLTR			1005	.264

BLATNIK, JOHN LOUIS
b.Mar.10,1921 Bridgeport,O.

Yr	Cl	Lea	Pos	G	Rec
1948	Phi	N	O	121	.260
1949	Phi	N	O	6	.125
1950	Phi	N	O	4	.250
1950	St.L	N	O	7	.150
	BRTR			138	.253

BLATTNER, ROBERT GARNETT (Buddy)
b.Feb.8,1920 St.Louis,Mo.

Yr	Cl	Lea	Pos	G	Rec
1942	St.L	N	2-S	19	.043
1946	NY	N	1-2	126	.255
1947	NY	N	2-3	55	.261
1948	NY	N	2	8	.200
1949	Phi	N	2-S-3	64	.247
	BRTR			272	.247

BLAUVELT, HENRY R.
b.Rochester,N.Y.

Yr	Cl	Lea	Pos	G	Rec
1890	Roc	a	P	2	0-1

BLAYLOCK, GARY NELSON
b.Oct.11,1931 Clarkton,Mo.

Yr	Cl	Lea	Pos	G	Rec
1959	St.L	N	P	31	4-5
1959	NY	A	P	15	0-1
	BRTR			46	4-6

BLAYLOCK, MARVIN EDWARD
b.Sept.30,1929 Fort Smith,Ark.

Yr	Cl	Lea	Pos	G	Rec
1950	NY	N	H	1	.000
1955	Phi	N	1-O	113	.208
1956	Phi	N	1-O	136	.254
1957	Phi	N	1-O	37	.154
	BLTL			287	.235

BLAYLOCK, ROBERT EDWARD
b.June 28,1935 Chattanooga,Okla.

Yr	Cl	Lea	Pos	G	Rec
1956	St.L	N	P	14	1-6
1959	St.L	N	P	3	0-1
	BRTR			17	1-7

BLEMKER, RAYMOND
b.Aug.9,1937 Huntingburg,Ind.

Yr	Cl	Lea	Pos	G	Rec
1960	KC	A	P	1	0-0
	BRTL				

BLETHEN, CLARENCE WALDO (Climax)
b.July 11,1893 Dover-Foxcroft,Me.

Yr	Cl	Lea	Pos	G	Rec
1923	Bos	A	P	5	0-0
1929	Bro	N	P	2	0-0
	BLTR			7	0-0

BLEWETT, ROBERT LAWRENCE
b.June28,1877 Fond du Lac,Wis.
d.Mar.17,1958

Yr	Cl	Lea	Pos	G	Rec
1902	NY	N	P	5	0-2
	BLTL				

BLIGH, EDWIN FORREST (Ned)
b.June 30,1864 Brooklyn,N.Y.
d.Apr.18,1892

Yr	Cl	Lea	Pos	G	Rec
1886	Bal	a	C	3	.000
1888	Cin	a	C-O	3	.000
1889	Col	a	C	27	.126
1890	Col	a	C	8	.214
1890	Lou	a	C	24	.154
	BRTR			65	.151

BLISS, F. E.
b.Milwaukee,Wis.

Yr	Cl	Lea	Pos	G	Rec
1878	Mil	N	3-O	2	.125

BLISS, ELMER WARD
b.Mar.9,1875 Penfield,Pa.

Yr	Cl	Lea	Pos	G	Rec
1903	NY	A	P	1	1-0
1904	NY	A	P	1	0-0
	BLTR			2	1-0

BLISS, JOHN J.
b.Jan.9,1883 Vancouver,Wash.

Yr	Cl	Lea	Pos	G	Rec
1908	St.L	N	C	43	.213
1909	St.L	N	C	32	.221
1910	St.L	N	C	16	.063
1911	St.L	N	C	85	.229
1912	St.L	N	C	49	.246
	BRTR			225	.219

BLOCHOWICZ, JAMES JOHN
(Played under name of James John Block)

BLOCK, JAMES JOHN (Bruno)
(Real name James John Blochowicz)
b.Mar.14,1885 Wisconsin Rapids,Wis.
d.Aug.6,1937

Yr	Cl	Lea	Pos	G	Rec
1907	Was	A	C	24	.140
1910	Chi	A	C	55	.210
1911	Chi	A	C	39	.304
1912	Chi	A	C	46	.257
1914	Chi	F	C	45	.212
	BRTR			209	.234

BLOCK, SEYMOUR (Cy)
b.May 4,1922 Brooklyn,N.Y.

Yr	Cl	Lea	Pos	G	Rec
1942	Chi	N	2-3	9	.364
1945	Chi	N	2-3	2	.143
1946	Chi	N	3	6	.231
	BRTR			17	.302

BLOGG, WESLEY C.
b.Norfolk,Va.

Yr	Cl	Lea	Pos	G	Rec
1883	Pit	a	C-1-O	9	.147

BLONG, JOSEPH MYLES
b.Sept.17,1853 St.Louis,Mo.
d.Sept.17,1892

Yr	Cl	Lea	Pos	G	Rec
1875	RS	n	P-O	16	3-10 NR
1876	St.L	N	O	62	.233
1877	St.L	N	P-2-O	58	10-9 .216
	BRTR			136	13-19 NR

BLOODWORTH, JAMES HENRY

b.July 26,1917 Tallahassee,Fla.

Yr	Cl	Lea	Pos	G	Rec
1937	Was	A	2	15	.220
1939	Was	A	2	83	.289
1940	Was	A	1-2-3	119	.245
1941	Was	A	2-S-3	142	.245
1942	Det	A	2-S	137	.242
1943	Det	A	2	129	.241
1946	Det	A	2	76	.245
1947	Pit	N	2	88	.250
1949	Cin	N	1-2-3	134	.261
1950	Cin	N	2	4	.214
1950	Phi	N	1-2-3	54	.229
1951	Phi	N	1-2	21	.143
	BRTR			1002	.248

BLOTT, JOHN LEONARD

b.Aug.24,1902 Girard,O.

Yr	Cl	Lea	Pos	G	Rec
1924	Cin	N	C	2	.000
	BRTR				

BLUE, BERT W.

b.Pine Bluff,Ark.

Yr	Cl	Lea	Pos	G	Rec
1908	St.L	A	C	11	.375
1908	Phi	A	C	6	.167
	TR			17	.286

BLUE, LUZERNE ATWELL

b.Mar.5,1897 Washington,D.C.

d.July 28,1958

Yr	Cl	Lea	Pos	G	Rec
1921	Det	A	1	153	.308
1922	Det	A	1	145	.300
1923	Det	A	1	129	.284
1924	Det	A	1	108	.311
1925	Det	A	1	150	.307
1926	Det	A	1	128	.287
1927	Det	A	1	112	.260
1928	St.L	A	1	154	.281
1929	St.L	A	1	151	.293
1930	St.L	A	1	117	.235
1931	Chi	A	1	155	.304
1932	Chi	A	1	112	.249
1933	Bro	N	1	1	.000
	BBTL			1615	.287

BLUEGE, OSWALD LOUIS

b.Oct.24,1900 Chicago,Ill.

Yr	Cl	Lea	Pos	G	Rec
1922	Was	A	3	19	.197
1923	Was	A	3	109	.245
1924	Was	A	3	117	.281
1925	Was	A	S-3	145	.287
1926	Was	A	3	139	.271
1927	Was	A	3	146	.274
1928	Was	A	3	146	.297
1929	Was	A	2-S-3	64	.295
1930	Was	A	3	134	.290
1931	Was	A	3	152	.272
1932	Was	A	3	149	.258
1933	Was	A	3	140	.261
1934	Was	A	S-3-O	99	.246
1935	Was	A	2-S-3	100	.263
1936	Was	A	2-S-3	90	.288
1937	Was	A	S	42	.283
1938	Was	A	2-S	58	.261
1939	Was	A	1	18	.153
	BRTR			1867	.272

Non-playing manager Was (A) 1943-47

BLUEGE, OTTO ADAM (Squeaky)

b.July 20,1910 Chicago,Ill.

Yr	Cl	Lea	Pos	G	Rec
1932	Cin	N	H	1	.000
1933	Cin	N	2-S-3	108	.213
	BRTR			109	.213

BLUEJACKET, JAMES

b.July 8,1887 Adair,Okla.

d.Mar.26,1947

Yr	Cl	Lea	Pos	G	Rec
1914	Bro	F	P	17	4-4
1915	Bro	F	P	24	10-11
1916	Cin	N	P	3	0-1
	BRTR			44	14-16

BLUHM, HARVEY FRED (Red)

b.June 27,1894 Cleveland,O.

d.May 7,1952

Yr	Cl	Lea	Pos	G	Rec
1918	Bos	A	H	1	.000
	BRTR				

BLUME, CLINTON WILLIS

b.Oct.17,1900 Brooklyn,N.Y.

Yr	Cl	Lea	Pos	G	Rec
1922	NY	N	P	1	1-0
1923	NY	N	P	12	2-0
	BRTR			13	3-0

BLYZKA, MICHAEL JOHN

b.Dec.25,1928 Hamtramck,Mich.

Yr	Cl	Lea	Pos	G	Rec
1953	St.L	A	P	33	2-6
1954	Bal	A	P	37	1-5
	BRTR			70	3-11

BOAK, CHESTER ROBERT

b.June 19,1935 New Castle,Pa.

Yr	Cl	Lea	Pos	G	Rec
1960	KC	A	2	5	.154
1961	Was	A	2	5	.000
	BRTR			10	.100

BOARDMAN, CHARLES LOUIS

b.Apr.27,1893 Seneca Falls,N.Y.

Yr	Cl	Lea	Pos	G	Rec
1913	Phi	A	P	2	0-2
1914	Phi	A	P	2	0-0
1915	St.L	N	P	3	1-0
	BLTL			7	1-2

BOARDMAN, FREDERICK

Yr	Cl	Lea	Pos	G	Rec
1874	Bal	n	O	1	NR

BOCEK, MILTON FRANCIS

b.July 16,1912 Chicago,Ill.

Yr	Cl	Lea	Pos	G	Rec
1933	Chi	A	O	11	.364
1934	Chi	A	O	19	.211
	BRTR			30	.267

BOCKMAN, JOSEPH EDWARD (Eddie)

b.July 26,1920 Santa Ana,Cal.

Yr	Cl	Lea	Pos	G	Rec
1946	NY	A	3	4	.083
1947	Cle	A	2-S-3	46	.258
1948	Pit	N	2-3	70	.239
1949	Pit	N	2-3	79	.223
	BRTR			199	.230

BODIE, FRANK L. (Ping)

(Real name Francesco Stephano Pezzolo)

b.Oct.8,1887 San Francisco,Cal.

d.Dec.17,1961

Yr	Cl	Lea	Pos	G	Rec
1911	Chi	A	2-O	145	.288
1912	Chi	A	O	137	.294
1913	Chi	A	O	127	.265
1914	Chi	A	O	107	.229
1917	Phi	A	O	148	.291
1918	NY	A	O	91	.256
1919	NY	A	O	134	.278
1920	NY	A	O	129	.295
1921	NY	A	O	31	.172
	BRTR			1049	.276

BOECKEL, NORMAN D. (Tony)

b.Aug.25,1894 Los Angeles,Cal.

d.Feb.16,1924

Yr	Cl	Lea	Pos	G	Rec
1917	Pit	N	3	64	.265
1919	Pit	N	3	45	.250
1919	Bos	N	3	95	.249
1920	Bos	N	3	153	.268
1921	Bos	N	3	153	.313
1922	Bos	N	3	119	.289
1923	Bos	N	S-3	148	.298
	BRTR			777	.282

BOEHLER, GEORGE HENRY

b.Jan.2,1892 Lawrenceburg,Ind.

d.June 23,1958

Yr	Cl	Lea	Pos	G	Rec
1912	Det	A	P	4	1-2
1913	Det	A	P	1	0-1
1914	Det	A	P	13	2-3
1915	Det	A	P	9	1-1
1916	Det	A	P	5	1-1
1920	St.L	A	P	3	0-1
1921	St.L	A	P	1	0-0
1923	Pit	N	P	10	1-3

(Continued)

Yr	Cl	Lea	Pos	G	Rec
1926	Bro	N	P	11	1-0
	BRTR			57	7-12

BOEHLING, JOHN JOSEPH

b.Mar.20,1892 Richmond,Va.

d.Sept.8,1941

Yr	Cl	Lea	Pos	G	Rec
1912	Was	A	P	3	0-0
1913	Was	A	P	34	17-7
1914	Was	A	P	27	12-8
1915	Was	A	P	41	13-13
1916	Was	A	P	28	9-10
1916	Cle	A	P	11	2-4
1917	Cle	A	P	14	1-6
1920	Cle	A	P	3	0-1
	BLTL			161	54-49

BOERNER, LAURENCE HYER

b.Jan.21,1905 Staunton,Va.

Yr	Cl	Lea	Pos	G	Rec
1932	Bos	A	P	21	0-4
	BRTR				

BOGART, JOHN RENZIE (Big John)

b.Sept.21,1901 Bloomsburg,Pa.

Yr	Cl	Lea	Pos	G	Rec
1920	Det	A	P	4	2-1
	BRTR				

BOGGS, RAYMOND JOSEPH (Lefty)

b.Dec.12,1904 Reamsville,Kan.

Yr	Cl	Lea	Pos	G	Rec
1928	Bos	N	P	4	0-0
	BLTL				

BOHEN, LEO J. (Pat)

b.Oct. 20, 1891 Napa,Cal.

d.Apr.9,1942

Yr	Cl	Lea	Pos	G	Rec
1913	Phi	A	P	1	0-1
1914	Pit	N	P	1	0-0
	BRTR			2	0-1

BOHN. CHARLES

b.1857 Cleveland,O.

d.Aug.1,1903

Yr	Cl	Lea	Pos	G	Rec
1882	Lou	a	P-O	4	1-1 / .154

BOHNE, SAMUEL ARTHUR

(Real name Samuel Arthur Cohen)

b.Oct.22,1896 San Francisco,Cal.

Yr	Cl	Lea	Pos	G	Rec
1916	St.L	N	S	14	.237
1921	Cin	N	2-3	153	.285
1922	Cin	N	2-S	112	.274
1923	Cin	N	1-2-S-3	139	.252
1924	Cin	N	2-S-3	100	.255
1925	Cin	N	1-2-S-3-O	73	.257
1926	Cin	N	2	25	.204
1926	Bro	N	S-3	47	.200
	BRTR			663	.261

BOKELMANN, RICHARD WERNER

b.Oct.26,1926 Arlington Heights,Ill.

Yr	Cl	Lea	Pos	G	Rec
1951	St.L	N	P	20	3-3
1952	St.L	N	P	11	0-1
1953	St.L	N	P	3	0-0
	BRTR			34	3-4

BOKEN, ROBERT ANTHONY

b.Feb.23,1908 Maryville,Ill.

Yr	Cl	Lea	Pos	G	Rec
1933	Was	A	2-S-3	55	.278
1934	Was	A	2	11	.222
1934	Chi	A	2-S	81	.236
	BRTR			147	.247

BOKINA, JOSEPH

b.Apr.7,1910 Northampton,Mass.

Yr	Cl	Lea	Pos	G	Rec
1936	Was	A	P	5	0-2
	BRTR				

BOLAND, ...

Yr	Cl	Lea	Pos	G	Rec
1875	Atl	n	O	1	NR

BOLAND, BERNARD ANTHONY

b.Jan.21,1892 Rochester,N.Y.

Yr	Cl	Lea	Pos	G	Rec
1915	Det	A	P	47	13-6
1916	Det	A	P	49	10-3
1917	Det	A	P	45	16-11

(Continued)

Yr	Cl	Lea	Pos	G	Rec
1918	Det	A	P	29	14-10
1919	Det	A	P	35	14-16
1920	Det	A	P	4	0-2
1921	St.L	A	P	7	1-4
	BRTR			216	68-52

BOLAND, EDWARD JOHN
b.Apr.18,1912 Long Island City,N.Y.

Yr	Cl	Lea	Pos	G	Rec
1934	Phi	N	O	8	.300
1935	Phi	N	O	30	.213
1944	Was	A	O	19	.271
	BLTL			57	.257

BOLD, CHARLES D. (Dutch)
b.Oct.27,1894 Paris,Me.

Yr	Cl	Lea	Pos	G	Rec
1914	St.L	A	1	2	.000
	BRTR				

BOLDEN, WILLIAM HORACE (Big Bill)
b.May 9,1894 Dandridge,Tenn.

Yr	Cl	Lea	Pos	G	Rec
1919	St.L	N	P	3	0-1
	BRTR				

BOLEN, STEWART O'NEAL
b.Oct.12,1902 Jackson,Ala.

Yr	Cl	Lea	Pos	G	Rec
1926	St.L	A	P	5	0-0
1927	St.L	A	P	3	0-1
1931	Phi	N	P	28	3-12
1932	Phi	N	P	5	0-0
	BLTL			41	3-13

BOLEY, JOHN PETER (Joe)
(Real name John Peter Bolinsky)
b.July 26,1898 Mahanoy City,Pa.
d.Dec.30,1962

Yr	Cl	Lea	Pos	G	Rec
1927	Phi	A	S	118	.311
1928	Phi	A	S	132	.264
1929	Phi	A	S	91	.251
1930	Phi	A	S	121	.276
1931	Phi	A	S	67	.228
1932	Phi	A	S	10	.206
1932	Cle	A	S	1	.250
	BRTR			540	.269

BOLES, CARL THEODORE
b.Oct.31,1934 Center Point,Ark.

Yr	Cl	Lea	Pos	G	Rec
1962	SF	N	O	19	.375
	BRTR				

BOLGER, JAMES CYRIL (Dutch)
b.Feb.23,1932 Cincinnati,O.

Yr	Cl	Lea	Pos	G	Rec
1950	Cin	N	O	2	.000
1951	Cin	N	H	2	.000
1954	Cin	N	O	5	.333
1955	Chi	N	O	64	.206
1957	Chi	N	3-O	112	.275
1958	Chi	N	O	84	.225
1959	Cle	A	H	8	.000
1959	Phi	N	O	35	.083
	BRTR			312	.229

BOLIN, BOBBY DONALD
b.Jan.29,1939 Smyrna, S.Car.

Yr	Cl	Lea	Pos	G	Rec
1961	SF	N	P	37	2-2
1962	SF	N	P	41	7-3
	BRTR			78	9-5

BOLINSKY, JOHN PETER
(Played under name of John Peter Boley)

BOLLING, FRANK ELMORE
b.Nov.16,1931 Mobile,Ala.

Yr	Cl	Lea	Pos	G	Rec
1954	Det	A	2	117	.236
1956	Det	A	2	102	.281
1957	Det	A	2	146	.259
1958	Det	A	2	154	.269
1959	Det	A	2	127	.266
1960	Det	A	2	139	.254
1961	Mil	N	2	148	.262
1962	Mil	N	2	122	.271
	BRTR			1055	.262

BOLLING, JOHN EDWARD
b.Feb.20,1918 Mobile,Ala.

Yr	Cl	Lea	Pos	G	Rec
1939	Phi	N	1	69	.289
1944	Bro	N	1	56	.351
	BLTL			125	.313

BOLLING, MILTON JOSEPH
b.Aug.9,1930 Mississippi City,Miss.

Yr	Cl	Lea	Pos	G	Rec
1952	Bos	A	S	11	.222
1953	Bos	A	S	109	.263
1954	Bos	A	S-3	113	.249
1955	Bos	A	S	6	.200
1956	Bos	A	2-S-3	45	.212
1957	Bos	A	H	1	.000
1957	Was	A	2-S-3	91	.227
1958	Det	A	2-S-3	24	.194
	BRTR			400	.241

BOLLWEG, DONALD RAYMOND
b.Feb.12,1921 Wheaton,Ill.

Yr	Cl	Lea	Pos	G	Rec
1950	St.L	N	1	4	.182
1951	St.L	N	1	6	.111
1953	NY	A	1-O	70	.297
1954	Phi	A	1	103	.224
1955	KC	A	1	12	.111
	BLTL			195	.243

BOLTON, CECIL GLENN
b.Feb.13,1904 Booneville,Miss.

Yr	Cl	Lea	Pos	G	Rec
1928	Cle	A	1	4	.154
	BLTR				

BOLTON, WILLIAM CLIFTON (Cliff)
b.Apr.10,1907 Greensboro,N.C.

Yr	Cl	Lea	Pos	G	Rec
1931	Was	A	C	23	.255
1933	Was	A	C-O	33	.410
1934	Was	A	C	42	.270
1935	Was	A	C	110	.304
1936	Was	A	C	86	.291
1937	Det	A	C	27	.263
1941	Was	A	C	14	.000
	BLTR			335	.291

BOND, THOMAS H.
b.Apr.2,1856 New York,N.Y.
d.Jan.24,1941

Yr	Cl	Lea	Pos	G	Rec
1874	Atl	n	P	55	23-31
1875	Har	n	P-1-2-O	71	19-16 NR
1876	Har	N	P	45	32-13
1877	Bos	N	P-O	61	40-17 .228
1878	Bos	N	P	59	40-19
1879	Bos	N	P	65	42-19
1880	Bos	N	P-1-O	74	26-29 .216
1881	Bos	N	P	3	0-3
1882	Wor	N	M-P-O	8	0-0 .125
1884	Bos	U	P-3-O	36	12-9 .291
1884	Ind	a	P-O	7	0-5 .136
	BRTR			484	234-161 NR

BOND, WALTER FRANKLIN
b.Oct.10,1937 Denmark,Tenn.

Yr	Cl	Lea	Pos	G	Rec
1960	Cle	A	O	40	.221
1961	Cle	A	O	38	.173
1962	Cle	A	O	12	.380
	BLTR			90	.245

BONE, GEORGE DRUMMOND
b.Aug.27,1874 New Haven,Conn.
d.May 28,1918

Yr	Cl	Lea	Pos	G	Rec
1901	Mil	A	S	12	.292
	TR				

BONETTI, JULIO JAMES PAUL
b.July 4,1912 San Francisco,Cal.
d.June 18,1952

Yr	Cl	Lea	Pos	G	Rec
1937	St.L	A	P	28	4-11
1938	St.L	A	P	17	2-3
1940	Chi	N	P	1	0-0
	BRTR			46	6-14

BONEY, HENRY TATE (Haney)
b.Oct.28,1905 Wallace,N.C.

Yr	Cl	Lea	Pos	G	Rec
1927	NY	N	P	3	0-0
	BRTR				

BONGIOVANNI, ANTHONY THOMAS (Nino)
b.Dec.21,1913 New Orleans,La.

Yr	Cl	Lea	Pos	G	Rec
1938	Cin	N	O	2	.286
1939	Cin	N	O	66	.258
	BLTL			68	.259

BONHAM, ERNEST EDWARD (Tiny)
b.Aug.16,1913 Ione,Cal.
d.Sept.15,1949

Yr	Cl	Lea	Pos	G	Rec
1940	NY	A	P	12	9-3
1941	NY	A	P	23	9-6
1942	NY	A	P	28	21-5
1943	NY	A	P	28	15-8
1944	NY	A	P	26	12-9
1945	NY	A	P	23	8-11
1946	NY	A	P	18	5-8
1947	Pit	N	P	33	11-8
1948	Pit	N	P	22	6-10
1949	Pit	N	P	18	7-4
	BRTR			231	103-72

BONIKOWSKI, JOSEPH PETER
b.Jan.16,1941 Philadelphia,Pa.

Yr	Cl	Lea	Pos	G	Rec
1962	Min	A	P	30	5-7
	BRTR				

BONIN, ERNEST LUTHER (Bonnie)
b.Jan.13,1888 Green Hill,Ind.

Yr	Cl	Lea	Pos	G	Rec
1913	St.L	A	H	1	.000
1914	Buf	F	O	21	.173
	BLTR			22	.171

BONNER, FRANK J.
b.Aug.20,1869 Lowell,Mass.
d.Dec.31,1905

Yr	Cl	Lea	Pos	G	Rec
1894	Bal	N	2	27	.301
1895	Bal	N	3	11	.295
1895	St.L	N	S	14	.132
1896	Bro	N	2	7	.185
1899	Was	N	2	85	.276
1902	Cle	A	2	34	.278
1902	Phi	A	2	11	.182
1903	Bos	N	2-S	46	.220
	TR			235	.254

BONNESS, WILLIAM JOHN
b.Dec.15,1923 Cleveland,O.

Yr	Cl	Lea	Pos	G	Rec
1944	Cle	A	P	2	0-1
	BRTL				

BONO, ADLAI WENDELL (Gus)
b.Aug.29,1895 Doe Run,Mo.
d.Dec.3,1948

Yr	Cl	Lea	Pos	G	Rec
1920	Was	A	P	4	0-2
	BRTR				

BONURA, HENRY JOHN (Zeke)
b.Sept.20,1908 New Orleans,La.

Yr	Cl	Lea	Pos	G	Rec
1934	Chi	A	1	127	.302
1935	Chi	A	1	138	.295
1936	Chi	A	1	148	.330
1937	Chi	A	1	116	.345
1938	Was	A	1	137	.289
1939	NY	N	1	123	.321
1940	Was	A	1	79	.273
1940	Chi	N	1	49	.264
	BRTR			917	.307

BOOE, EVERETT LITTLE
b.Sept.28,1891 Meekville,N.C.

Yr	Cl	Lea	Pos	G	Rec
1913	Pit	N	O	29	.200
1914	Ind	F	O	19	.233
1914	Buf	F	O	73	.220
	BLTR			121	.217

BOOL, ALBERT J.
b.Aug.24,1897 Lincoln,Neb.

Yr	Cl	Lea	Pos	G	Rec
1928	Was	A	C	2	.143
1930	Pit	N	C	78	.259
1931	Bos	N	C	49	.188
	BRTR			129	.237

BOOLES, SEABRON JAMES
b.July 14,1880 Bernice,La.
d.Mar.16,1955

Yr	Cl	Lea	Pos	G	Rec
1909	Cle	A	P	4	0-1
	BLTL				

BOONE, GEORGE M.
b.Louisville,Ky.

Yr	Cl	Lea	Pos	G	Rec
1891	Lou	a	P	4	1-0

BOONE, ISAAC MORGAN
b.Feb.17,1897 Samantha,Ala.
d.Aug.1,1958

Yr	Cl	Lea	Pos	G	Rec
1922	NY	N	O	2	.500
1923	Bos	A	O	5	.267
1924	Bos	A	O	128	.333
1925	Bos	A	O	133	.330
1927	Chi	A	O	29	.226
1930	Bro	N	O	40	.297
1931	Bro	N	H	6	.200
1932	Bro	N	O	13	.143
	BLTR			356	.319

BOONE, JAMES ALBERT (Dan)
b.Jan.19,1898 Samantha,Ala.

Yr	Cl	Lea	Pos	G	Rec
1919	Phi	A	P	3	0-1
1921	Det	A	P	1	0-0
1922	Cle	A	P	11	4-6
1923	Cle	A	P	27	4-6
	BRTR			42	8-13

BOONE, LUTE JOSEPH (Luke)
b.May 6,1890 Pittsburgh,Pa.

Yr	Cl	Lea	Pos	G	Rec
1913	NY	A	S	6	.250
1914	NY	A	2	106	.222
1915	NY	A	2	130	.204
1916	NY	A	3	46	.185
1918	Pit	N	2-S	27	.198
	BRTR			315	.208

BOONE, RAYMOND OTIS (Ike)
b.July 27,1923 San Diego,Cal.

Yr	Cl	Lea	Pos	G	Rec
1948	Cle	A	S	6	.400
1949	Cle	A	S	86	.252
1950	Cle	A	S	109	.301
1951	Cle	A	S	151	.233
1952	Cle	A	2-S-3	103	.263
1953	Cle	A	S	34	.241
1953	Det	A	S-3	101	.312
1954	Det	A	S-3	148	.295
1955	Det	A	3	135	.284
1956	Det	A	3	131	.308
1957	Det	A	1-3	129	.273
1958	Det	A	1	39	.237
1958	Chi	A	1	77	.244
1959	Chi	A	1	9	.238
1959	KC	A	1-3	61	.273
1959	Mil	N	1	13	.200
1960	Mil	N	1	7	.250
1960	Bos	A	1	34	.205
	BRTR			1373	.275

BOOTH, AMOS SMITH (Darling)
b.Sept.4,1852 Cincinnati,O.
d.July 1,1921

Yr	Cl	Lea	Pos	G	Rec
1876	Cin	N	P-C-S-3	63	0-1 / .253
1877	Cin	N	P-C-2-S-3-O	43	1-7 / .170
1880	Cin	N	O	1	.000
1882	Bal	a	3	1	.000
1882	Lou	a	2	1	.000
	BRTR			109	1-8 / .219

BOOTH, EDGAR H.

Yr	Cl	Lea	Pos	G	Rec
1872	Man	n	2-O	19	NR
1872	Atl	n	2-O	14	NR
1873	Res	n	2-O	18	NR
1873	Atl	n	O	13	NR
1874	Atl	n	O	44	NR
1875	Mut	n	2-O	68	NR
1876	Mut	N	O	57	.213
				233	NR

BOOZER, JOHN MORGAN
b.July 6,1939 Columbia,S.C.

Yr	Cl	Lea	Pos	G	Rec
1962	Phi	N	P	9	0-0
	BRTR				

BORCHERS, GEORGE B.
b.Apr.18,1869 Sacramento,Cal.

Yr	Cl	Lea	Pos	G	Rec
1888	Chi	N	P	10	4-5
1895	Lou	N	P	1	0-1
				11	4-6

BORDAGARAY, STANLEY GEORGE (Frenchy)
b.Jan.3,1912 Coalinga,Cal.

Yr	Cl	Lea	Pos	G	Rec
1934	Chi	A	O	29	.322
1935	Bro	N	O	120	.282
1936	Bro	N	2-O	125	.315
1937	St.L	N	3-O	96	.293
1938	St.L	N	O	81	.282
1939	Cin	N	2-O	63	.197
1941	NY	A	O	36	.260
1942	Bro	N	O	48	.241
1943	Bro	N	3-O	89	.302
1944	Bro	N	3-O	130	.281
1945	Bro	N	3-O	113	.256
	BRTR			930	.283

BORDEN, JOSEPH EMLEY
(Also played under name of Joseph Emley Josephs)
b.May 9,1854 Jacobstown,N.J.
d.Oct.14,1929

Yr	Cl	Lea	Pos	G	Rec
	(Joseph E. Josephs)				
1875	Phi	n	P	7	2-4 / NR
	(Joseph E. Borden)				
1876	Bos	N	P-O	32	12-12 / .202
	BRTR			39	14-16 / NR

BORDETZKI, ANTONIO
(Played under name of Anthony Vincent Brief)

BORKOWSKI, ROBERT VILARIAN
b.Jan.27,1927 Dayton,O.

Yr	Cl	Lea	Pos	G	Rec
1950	Chi	N	1-O	85	.273
1951	Chi	N	O	58	.157
1952	Cin	N	1-O	126	.252
1953	Cin	N	1-O	94	.269
1954	Cin	N	1-O	73	.265
1955	Cin	N	1-O	25	.167
1955	Bro	N	O	9	.105
	BRTR			470	.251

BORLAND, THOMAS BRUCE
b.Feb.14,1933 El Dorado,Kans.

Yr	Cl	Lea	Pos	G	Rec
1960	Bos	A	P	26	0-4
1961	Bos	A	P	1	0-0
	BLTL			27	0-4

BOROM, EDWARD JONES (Red)
b.Oct.30,1915 Spartanburg,S.C.

Yr	Cl	Lea	Pos	G	Rec
1944	Det	A	2	7	.071
1945	Det	A	2-S-3	55	.269
	BLTR			62	.250

BOROS, STEVEN A.
b.Sept.3,1936 Flint,Mich.

Yr	Cl	Lea	Pos	G	Rec
1957	Det	A	S-3	24	.146
1958	Det	A	2	6	.000
1961	Det	A	3	116	.270
1962	Det	A	2-3	116	.228
	BRTR			262	.244

BOROWY, HENRY LUDWIG
b.May 12,1916 Bloomfield,N.J.

Yr	Cl	Lea	Pos	G	Rec
1942	NY	A	P	25	15-4
1943	NY	A	P	29	14-9
1944	NY	A	P	35	17-12
1945	NY	A	P	18	10-5
1945	Chi	N	P	15	11-2
1946	Chi	N	P	33	12-10

(Continued)

Yr	Cl	Lea	Pos	G	Rec
1947	Chi	N	P	41	8-12
1948	Chi	N	P	39	5-10
1949	Phi	N	P	28	12-12
1950	Phi	N	P	3	0-0
1950	Pit	N	P	11	1-3
1950	Det	A	P	13	1-1
1951	Det	A	P	26	2-2
	BRTR			316	108-72

BORTON, WILLIAM BAKER (Babe)
b.July 14,1884 Marion,Ill.

Yr	Cl	Lea	Pos	G	Rec
1912	Chi	A	1	31	.371
1913	Chi	A	1	28	.275
1913	NY	A	1	33	.121
1915	St.L	F	1	159	.289
1916	St.L	A	1	66	.225
	BLTL			317	.271

BOSS, ELMER HARLEY (Lefty)
b.Nov.19,1908 Hodge,La.

Yr	Cl	Lea	Pos	G	Rec
1928	Was	A	1	12	.250
1929	Was	A	1	28	.273
1930	Was	A	1	3	.000
1933	Cle	A	1	112	.269
	BLTL			155	.268

BOSSER, MELVIN EDWARD
b.Feb.8,1920 Johnstown,Pa.

Yr	Cl	Lea	Pos	G	Rec
1945	Cin	N	P	7	2-0
	BRTR				

BOSTICK, HENRY LANDERS
(Real name Henry Landers Lifsit)
b.Jan.12,1895 Boston,Mass.

Yr	Cl	Lea	Pos	G	Rec
1915	Phi	A	3	2	.000
	BRTR				

BOSWELL, ANDREW COTTRELL
b.Sept.5,1874 New Gretna,N.J.
d.Feb.3,1936

Yr	Cl	Lea	Pos	G	Rec
1895	NY	N	P	5	2-2
1895	Was	N	P-1	7	1-3 / .231
				12	3-5 / .200

BOTTARINI, JOHN CHARLES
b.Sept.14,1911 Crockett,Cal.

Yr	Cl	Lea	Pos	G	Rec
1937	Chi	N	C	26	.275
	BRTR				

BOTTOMLEY, JAMES LEROY (Sunny Jim)
b.Apr.23,1900 Oglesby,Ill.
d.Dec.11,1959

Yr	Cl	Lea	Pos	G	Rec
1922	St.L	N	1	37	.325
1923	St.L	N	1	134	.371
1924	St.L	N	1-2	137	.316
1925	St.L	N	1	153	.367
1926	St.L	N	1	154	.299
1927	St.L	N	1	152	.303
1928	St.L	N	1	149	.325
1929	St.L	N	1	146	.314
1930	St.L	N	1	131	.304
1931	St.L	N	1	108	.348
1932	St.L	N	1	91	.296
1933	Cin	N	1	145	.250
1934	Cin	N	1	142	.284
1935	Cin	N	1	107	.258
1936	St.L	A	1	140	.298
1937	St.L	A	M-1	65	.239
	BLTL			1991	.309

BOTZ, ROBERT ALLEN
b.Apr.28,1935 Milwaukee,Wis.

Yr	Cl	Lea	Pos	G	Rec
1962	LA	A	P	35	2-1
	BRTR				

BOUCHEE, EDWARD FRANCIS
b.Mar.7,1933 Livingston,Mont.

Yr	Cl	Lea	Pos	G	Rec
1956	Phi	N	1	9	.273
1957	Phi	N	1	154	.293
1958	Phi	N	1	89	.257
1959	Phi	N	1	136	.285
1960	Phi	N	1	22	.262
1960	Chi	N	1	98	.237
1961	Chi	N	1	112	.248

(Continued)

Yr	Cl	Lea	Pos	G	Rec
1962	NY	N	1	50	.161
	BLTL			670	.252

BOUCHER, ALEXANDER FRANCIS
b.Dec.10,1881 Franklin,Mass.

Yr	Cl	Lea	Pos	G	Rec
1914	St.L	F	3	147	.232
	BRTR				

BOUCHER, MEDRIC T.
b.1889

Yr	Cl	Lea	Pos	G	Rec
1914	Bal	F	C	14	.235
1914	Pit	F	C	1	.000
	BRTR			15	.235

BOUDREAU, LOUIS
b.July 17,1917 Harvey,Ill.

Yr	Cl	Lea	Pos	G	Rec
1938	Cle	A	3	1	.000
1939	Cle	A	S	53	.258
1940	Cle	A	S	155	.295
1941	Cle	A	S	148	.257
1942	Cle	A	M-S	147	.283
1943	Cle	A	M-C-S	152	.286
1944	Cle	A	M-C-S	150	.327
1945	Cle	A	M-S	97	.306
1946	Cle	A	M-S	140	.293
1947	Cle	A	M-S	150	.307
1948	Cle	A	M-C-S	152	.355
1949	Cle	A	M-1-2-S-3	134	.284
1950	Cle	A	M-1-2-S-3	81	.269
1951	Bos	A	1-S-3	82	.267
1952	Bos	A	M-S-3	4	.000
	BRTR			1646	.295

Non-playing manager Bos (A) 1953-54, KC (A) 1955-57, Chi (N) 1960

BOULDIN, CARL EDWARD
b.Sept.17,1939 Germantown,Ky.

Yr	Cl	Lea	Pos	G	Rec
1961	Was	A	P	2	0-1
1962	Was	A	P	7	1-2
	BLTR			9	1-3

BOULTES, JAKE JOHN
b.Aug.6,1884 St.Louis,Mo.
d.Dec.24,1955

Yr	Cl	Lea	Pos	G	Rec
1907	Bos	N	P	29	5-9
1908	Bos	N	P	17	3-5
1909	Bos	N	P	1	0-0
	TR			47	8-14

BOUTHILLIER, ARTHUR E.
(Played under name of Arthur E. Butler)

BOUTON, JAMES ALAN
b.Mar.8,1939 Newark,N.J.

Yr	Cl	Lea	Pos	G	Rec
1962	NY	A	P	38	7-7
	BRTR				

BOWCOCK, BENJAMIN F.
b.Oct.28,1879 Fall River,Mass.

Yr	Cl	Lea	Pos	G	Rec
1903	St.L	A	2	14	.300
	TR				

BOWDEN, DAVID TIMON (Tim)
b.Aug.15,1891 McDonough,Ga.
d.Oct.25,1949

Yr	Cl	Lea	Pos	G	Rec
1914	St.L	A	O	6	.285
	BLTR				

BOWEN, EMMONS JOSEPH (Chick)
b.July 26,1897 New Haven,Conn.
d.Aug.9,1948

Yr	Cl	Lea	Pos	G	Rec
1919	NY	N	O	3	.200
	BRTR				

BOWEN, SUTHERLAND M. (Cy)
b.Feb.17,1874 Kingston,Ind.

Yr	Cl	Lea	Pos	G	Rec
1896	NY	N	P	2	0-1

BOWERMAN, FRANK EUGENE (Mike)
b.Dec.5,1868 Romeo,Mich.
d.Nov.30,1948

Yr	Cl	Lea	Pos	G	Rec
1895	Bal	N	C	1	.000

(Continued)

Yr	Cl	Lea	Pos	G	Rec
1896	Bal	N	C	4	.125
1897	Bal	N	C	33	.323
1898	Bal	N	C	5	.438
1898	Pit	N	C	62	.278
1899	Pit	N	C-1	107	.269
1900	NY	N	C	73	.256
1901	NY	N	C	52	.217
1902	NY	N	C-1	99	.253
1903	NY	N	C	59	.276
1904	NY	N	C	90	.232
1905	NY	N	C-1	90	.269
1906	NY	N	C-1	87	.228
1907	NY	N	C-1	90	.260
1908	Bos	N	C	74	.228
1909	Bos	N	M-C	27	.212
	BRTR			953	.255

BOWERS, GROVER BILL
b.Mar.25,1923 Parkin,Ark.

Yr	Cl	Lea	Pos	G	Rec
1949	Chi	A	O	26	.192
	BLTR				

BOWERS, STEWART COLE
b.Feb.26,1915 New Freedom,Pa.

Yr	Cl	Lea	Pos	G	Rec
1935	Bos	A	P	11	2-1
1936	Bos	A	P	6	0-0
1937	Bos	A	P	1	0-0
	BRTR			18	2-1

BOWES, FRANK C.
b.1865 Bath,N.Y.
d.Jan.21,1895

Yr	Cl	Lea	Pos	G	Rec
1890	Bro	a	C	62	.207
	TR				

BOWLER, GRANT TIERNEY
b.Oct.24,1907 Denver,Col.

Yr	Cl	Lea	Pos	G	Rec
1931	Chi	A	P	13	0-1
1932	Chi	A	P	4	0-0
	BRTR			17	0-1

BOWLES, CHARLES JAMES
b.Mar.15,1918 Norwood,Mass.

Yr	Cl	Lea	Pos	G	Rec
1943	Phi	A	P	3	1-1
1945	Phi	A	P	13	0-3
	BRTR			16	1-4

BOWLES, EMMETT JEROME
b.Aug.2,1898 Wanette,Okla.
d.Sept.3,1959

Yr	Cl	Lea	Pos	G	Rec
1922	Chi	A	P	1	0-0

BOWMAN, ALVAH EDSON (Abe)
b.Jan.25,1893 Greenup,Ill.

Yr	Cl	Lea	Pos	G	Rec
1914	Cle	A	P	20	2-7
1915	Cle	A	P	2	0-1
	BRTR			22	2-8

BOWMAN, ELMARI WILHELM
b.Mar.19,1900 Proctor,Vt.

Yr	Cl	Lea	Pos	G	Rec
1920	Was	A	H	2	.000
	BRTR				

BOWMAN, ERNEST FERRELL
b.July 28,1937 Johnson City,Tenn.

Yr	Cl	Lea	Pos	G	Rec
1961	SF	N	2-S-3	38	.211
1962	SF	N	2-S-3-O	46	.190
	BRTR			84	.200

BOWMAN, JOSEPH EMIL
b.June 17,1910 Argentine,Kan.

Yr	Cl	Lea	Pos	G	Rec
1932	Phi	A	P	7	0-1
1934	NY	N	P	31	5-4
1935	Phi	N	P-O	49	7-10 .194
1936	Phi	N	P	44	9-20
1937	Pit	N	P	35	8-8
1938	Pit	N	P	18	3-4
1939	Pit	N	P	70	10-14
1940	Pit	N	P	57	9-10
1941	Pit	N	P	22	3-2
1944	Bos	A	P	59	12-8

(Continued)

Yr	Cl	Lea	Pos	G	Rec
1945	Bos	A	P	9	0-2
1945	Cin	N	P	29	11-13
	BLTR			430	77-96 .221

BOWMAN, ROBERT JAMES
b.Oct.3,1914 Keystone,W.Va.

Yr	Cl	Lea	Pos	G	Rec
1939	St.L	N	P	51	13-5
1940	St.L	N	P	28	7-5
1941	NY	N	P	29	6-7
1942	Chi	N	P	1	0-0
	BRTR			109	26-17

BOWMAN, ROBERT LEROY
b.May 10,1931 Willits,Cal.

Yr	Cl	Lea	Pos	G	Rec
1955	Phi	N	O	3	.000
1956	Phi	N	O	6	.188
1957	Phi	N	O	99	.266
1958	Phi	N	O	91	.288
1959	Phi	N	P-O	57	0-1 .127
	BRTR			256	0-1 .249

BOWMAN, ROGER CLINTON
b.Aug.18,1927 Amsterdam,N.Y.

Yr	Cl	Lea	Pos	G	Rec
1949	NY	N	P	2	0-0
1951	NY	N	P	9	2-4
1952	NY	N	P	2	0-0
1953	Pit	N	P	30	0-4
1955	Pit	N	P	7	0-3
	BRTL			50	2-11

BOWMAN, SUMNER SALLADE
b.Feb.9,1867 Millersburg,Pa.
d.Jan.11,1954

Yr	Cl	Lea	Pos	G	Rec
1890	Phi	N	P	4	1-0
1890	Pit	N	P	10	2-7
1891	Ath	a	P-O	14	2-5 .215
	TL			28	5-12 .258

BOWMAN, WILLIAM G.
b.Chicago,Ill.

Yr	Cl	Lea	Pos	G	Rec
1891	Chi	N	C	15	.088

BOWSER, JAMES H. (Red)
b.Greensburg,Pa.

Yr	Cl	Lea	Pos	G	Rec
1910	Chi	A	O	1	.000

BOWSFIELD, EDWARD OLIVER
b.Jan.10,1936 Vernon,B.C.,Canada

Yr	Cl	Lea	Pos	G	Rec
1958	Bos	A	P	17	4-2
1959	Bos	A	P	5	0-1
1960	Bos	A	P	17	1-2
1960	Cle	A	P	11	3-4
1961	LA	A	P	46	11-8
1962	LA	A	P	44	9-8
	BRTL			140	28-25

BOYD, FRANK C. (Jake)
b.Norfolk,Va.

Yr	Cl	Lea	Pos	G	Rec
1894	Was	N	P	6	0-3
1895	Was	N	P-O	46	1-7 .284
1896	Was	N	P	4	1-2
	TL			56	2-12 .257

BOYD, FRANK JOHN
b.Apr.2,1868 West Middletown,Pa.
d.Dec.17,1937

Yr	Cl	Lea	Pos	G	Rec
1893	Cle	N	C	1	.200

BOYD, RAYMOND C.
b.Feb.11,1887 Hortonville,Ind.
d.Feb.11,1920

Yr	Cl	Lea	Pos	G	Rec
1910	St.L	A	P	3	0-2
1911	Cin	N	P	7	3-3
	BRTR			10	3-5

BOYD, ROBERT RICHARD
b.Oct.1,1926 Potts Camp,Miss.

Yr	Cl	Lea	Pos	G	Rec
1951	Chi	A	1	12	.167
1953	Chi	A	1-O	55	.297
1954	Chi	A	1-O	29	.179
1956	Bal	A	1-O	70	.311
1957	Bal	A	1-O	141	.318
1958	Bal	A	1	125	.309
1959	Bal	A	1	128	.265
1960	Bal	A	1	71	.317
1961	KC	A	1	26	.229
1961	Mil	N	1	36	.244
			BLTL	693	.293

BOYD, WILLIAM J.

Yr	Cl	Lea	Pos	G	Rec
1872	Mut	n	S-3-O	36	NR
1873	Atl	n	3-O	48	NR
1874	Har	n	3-O	26	NR
1875	Atl	n	1-2-3-O	36	NR
				146	NR

BOYER, CLETIS LEROY
b.Feb.8,1937 Cossville,Mo.

Yr	Cl	Lea	Pos	G	Rec
1955	KC	A	2-S-3	47	.241
1956	KC	A	2-3	67	.217
1957	KC	A	2-3	10	.000
1959	NY	A	S-3	47	.175
1960	NY	A	S-3	124	.242
1961	NY	A	S-3-O	148	.224
1962	NY	A	3	158	.272
			BRTR	601	.240

BOYER, CLOYD VICTOR (Junior)
b.Sept.1,1927 Liberty,Mo.

Yr	Cl	Lea	Pos	G	Rec
1949	St.L	N	P	4	0-0
1950	St.L	N	P	36	7-7
1951	St.L	N	P	19	2-5
1952	St.L	N	P	24	6-6
1955	KC	A	P	30	5-5
			BRTR	113	20-23

BOYER, KENTON LLOYD
b.May 20,1931 Liberty,Mo.

Yr	Cl	Lea	Pos	G	Rec
1955	St.L	N	S-3	147	.264
1956	St.L	N	3	150	.306
1957	St.L	N	3-O	142	.265
1958	St.L	N	S-3-O	150	.307
1959	St.L	N	S-3	149	.309
1960	St.L	N	3	151	.304
1961	St.L	N	3	153	.329
1962	St.L	N	3	160	.291
			BRTR	1202	.298

BOYLE, EDWARD J.
b.May 8,1874 Cincinnati,O.
d.Feb.9,1941

Yr	Cl	Lea	Pos	G	Rec
1896	Lou	N	C	3	.111
1896	Pit	N	C	2	.000
				5	.071

BOYLE, HENRY J. (Handsome)
b.Sept.20,1860 Philadelphia,Pa.

Yr	Cl	Lea	Pos	G	Rec
1884	St.L	U	P-O	49	16-2 .260
1885	St.L	N	P-2-O	72	15-25 .201
1886	St.L	N	P	30	9-15
1887	Ind	N	P	41	13-24
1888	Ind	N	P	37	15-22
1889	Ind	N	P	44	20-23
			TR	273	88-111 .224

BOYLE, JAMES JOHN
b.Jan.19.1904 Cincinnati,O.
d.Dec.24,1958

Yr	Cl	Lea	Pos	G	Rec
1926	NY	N	C	1	.000

BRTR

BOYLE, JOHN ANTHONY
(Honest John)
b.Mar.22,1866 Cincinnati,O.

(Continued)
d.Jan.7,1913

Yr	Cl	Lea	Pos	G	Rec
1886	Cin	a	C	1	.250
1887	St.L	a	C	88	.240
1888	St.L	a	C	71	.245
1889	St.L	a	C	99	.250
1890	Chi	p	C-S-3	100	.257
1891	St.L	a	C-S	120	.280
1892	NY	N	C-1	116	.201
1893	Phi	N	1	117	.305
1894	Phi	N	1	116	.291
1895	Phi	N	1	133	.254
1896	Phi	N	C	39	.288
1897	Phi	N	C-1	73	.259
1898	Phi	N	C-1	6	.091
			BRTR	1079	.259

BOYLE, JOHN BELLEW
b.July 9,1889 Morris,Ill.

Yr	Cl	Lea	Pos	G	Rec
1912	Phi	N	S-3	15	.280

BLTR

BOYLE, RALPH FRANCIS (Buzz)
b.Feb.9,1910 Cincinnati,O.

Yr	Cl	Lea	Pos	G	Rec
1929	Bos	N	O	17	.263
1930	Bos	N	O	1	.000
1933	Bro	N	O	93	.299
1934	Bro	N	O	128	.305
1935	Bro	N	O	127	.272
			BLTL	366	.293

BOYLES, HARRY (Stretch)
b.Nov.29,1912 Granite City,Ill.

Yr	Cl	Lea	Pos	G	Rec
1938	Chi	A	P	9	0-4
1939	Chi	A	P	2	0-0
			BRTR	11	0-4

BRACK, GILBERT HERMAN (Gibby)
b.Mar.29,1912 Chicago,Ill.
d.Jan.20,1960

Yr	Cl	Lea	Pos	G	Rec
1937	Bro	N	O	112	.274
1938	Bro	N	O	40	.214
1938	Phi	N	O	72	.287
1939	Phi	N	1-O	91	.289
			BRTR	315	.279

BRACKEN, JOHN JAMES
b.Apr.14,1881 Cleveland,O.
d.July 16,1954

Yr	Cl	Lea	Pos	G	Rec
1901	Cle	A	P	12	4-8

BRTR

BRACKINRIDGE, JOHN CALHOUN
b.Dec.24,1880 Harrisburg,Pa.
d.Mar.20,1953

Yr	Cl	Lea	Pos	G	Rec
1904	Phi	N	P	7	0-2

BRADFORD, HENRY VICTOR (Vic)
b.Mar.5,1916 Brownsville,Tenn.

Yr	Cl	Lea	Pos	G	Rec
1943	NY	N	O	6	.200

BRTR

BRADFORD, WILLIAM D.
b.Aug.28,1924 Choctaw,Ark.

Yr	Cl	Lea	Pos	G	Rec
1956	KC	A	P	1	0-0

BRTR

BRADLEY, FREDERICK LANGDON
b.July 31,1920 Parsons,Kan.

Yr	Cl	Lea	Pos	G	Rec
1948	Chi	A	P	8	0-0
1949	Chi	A	P	1	0-0
			BRTR	9	0-0

BRADLEY, GEORGE H. (Foghorn)
b.1853 Milford,Mass.
d.Apr.3,1900

Yr	Cl	Lea	Pos	G	Rec
1876	Bos	N	P	22	11-9

BRTR

BRADLEY, GEORGE WASHINGTON (Grin)
b.July 13,1852 Reading,Pa.
d.Oct.2,1931

Yr	Cl	Lea	Pos	G	Rec
1875	St.L	n	P-3	58	31-25 .228
1876	St.L	N	P	64	45-19
1877	Chi	N	P-1-3-O	55	19-23 .243
1879	Tro	N	P	61	13-40

(Continued)

Yr	Cl	Lea	Pos	G	Rec
1880	Pro	N	P-1-3-O	78	12-9 .226
1831	Det	N	S	1	.000
1881	Cle	N	P-S-3-O	61	3-4 .252
1882	Cle	N	P-1-3-O	29	7-10 .183
1883	Cle	N	S	4	.313
1883	Ath	a	P-1-3-O	77	17-7 .238
1884	Cin	U	P-S	52	21-13 .202
1886	Ath	a	S	13	.149
1888	Bal	a	S	1	.000
			BRTR	554	168-150 .229

BRADLEY, GEORGE WASHINGTON
b.Apr.1,1918 Greenwood,Ark.

Yr	Cl	Lea	Pos	G	Rec
1946	St.L	A	O	4	.167

BRTR

BRADLEY, HERBERT THEODORE
b.Jan.3,1904 Agenda,Kan.
d.Oct.16,1959

Yr	Cl	Lea	Pos	G	Rec
1927	Bos	A	P	6	1-1
1928	Bos	A	P	15	0-3
1929	Bos	A	P	3	0-0
			BRTR	24	1-4

BRADLEY, HUGH FREDERICK
(Carus)
b.May23,1885 Grafton,Mass.
d.Jan.26,1949

Yr	Cl	Lea	Pos	G	Rec
1910	Bos	A	1	32	.169
1911	Bos	A	1	12	.300
1912	Bos	A	1	40	.190
1914	Pit	F	1	118	.302
1915	Pit	F	1	26	.288
1915	Bro	F	1	37	.246
1915	New	F	1	12	.094
			BRTR	277	.257

BRADLEY, J. NICHOLAS (Nick)
b.Altoona,Pa.
d.Jan.16,1889

Yr	Cl	Lea	Pos	G	Rec
1884	Was	U	O	1	.000

BRADLEY, JOHN THOMAS
b.Sept.20,1893 Denver,Col.

Yr	Cl	Lea	Pos	G	Rec
1916	Cle	A	C	2	.667

BRTR

BRADLEY, WILLIAM JOSEPH
b.Feb.13,1878 Cleveland,O.
d.Mar.11,1954

Yr	Cl	Lea	Pos	G	Rec
1899	Chi	N	3	35	.307
1900	Chi	N	1-3	120	.288
1901	Cle	A	3	133	.296
1902	Cle	A	3	136	.341
1903	Cle	A	3	137	.315
1904	Cle	A	3	154	.300
1905	Cle	A	3	145	.268
1906	Cle	A	3	82	.275
1907	Cle	A	3	139	.223
1908	Cle	A	S-3	148	.243
1909	Cle	A	3	95	.186
1910	Cle	A	3	61	.196
1914	Bro	F	M-H	7	.500
1915	KC	F	3	66	.192
			BRTR	1458	.272

BRADSHAW, DALLAS CARL
(Rabbit)
b.Nov.23,1895 Herrin,Ill.
d.Dec.11,1939

Yr	Cl	Lea	Pos	G	Rec
1917	Phi	A	2	2	.000

BLTR

BRADSHAW, GEORGE THOMAS
b.Sept.12,1924 Salisbury,N.C.

Yr	Cl	Lea	Pos	G	Rec
1952	Was	A	C	10	.217

BRTR

BRADSHAW, JOE SIAH
b.Aug.17,1897 Dyersburg,Tenn.

Yr	Cl	Lea	Pos	G	Rec
1929	Bro	N	P	2	0-0

BRTR

BRADY, CLIFFORD FRANCIS
b.Mar.6,1897 St.Louis,Mo.

Yr	Cl	Lea	Pos	G	Rec
1920	Bos	A	2	53	.228
	BRTR				

BRADY, CORNELIUS JOSEPH (Neal)
b.Mar.4,1897 Covington,Ky.
d.June 19,1947

Yr	Cl	Lea	Pos	G	Rec
1915	NY	A	P	2	0-0
1917	NY	A	P	2	1-0
1925	Cin	N	P	20	1-3
	BRTR			24	2-3

BRADY, FREDERICK
(Played under name of William Lorenz Kopf)

BRADY, JAMES JOSEPH
b.Mar.2,1936 Jersey City,N.J.

Yr	Cl	Lea	Pos	G	Rec
1956	Det	A	P	6	0-0
	BLTL				

BRADY, JAMES WARD (King)
b.May 28,1881 Monroeville,N.Y.
d.Aug.21,1947

Yr	Cl	Lea	Pos	G	Rec
1905	Phi	N	P	2	1-1
1906	Pit	N	P	3	1-1
1907	Pit	N	P	1	0-0
1908	Bos	A	P	1	1-0
1912	Bos	N	P	1	0-0
	BLTR			8	3-2

BRADY, ROBERT JAY
b.Nov.8,1922 Lewistown,Pa.

Yr	Cl	Lea	Pos	G	Rec
1946	Bos	N	C	3	.200
1947	Bos	N	H	1	.000
	BLTR			4	.167

BRADY, STEPHEN A.
b.July 14,1851 Worcester,Mass.
d.Nov.2,1917

Yr	Cl	Lea	Pos	G	Rec
1874	Har	n	3-O	25	NR
1875	Nat	n	1-2-O	18	NR
1875	Chi	n	O	1	NR
1883	Met	a	1-O	97	.280
1884	Met	a	O	112	.269
1885	Met	a	O	108	.296
1886	Met	a	O	123	.234
				484	NR

BRADY, THOMAS
b.Hartford,Conn.

Yr	Cl	Lea	Pos	G	Rec
1875	Har	n	O	1	.000

BRADY, WILLIAM A. (King)
b.1888
d.Apr.12,1917

Yr	Cl	Lea	Pos	G	Rec
1912	Bos	N	P	1	0-0
	TR				

BRAGAN, ROBERT RANDALL (Nig)
b.Oct.30,1918 Birmingham,Ala.

Yr	Cl	Lea	Pos	G	Rec
1940	Phi	N	S-3	132	.222
1941	Phi	N	2-S-3	154	.251
1942	Phi	N	C-2-S-3	109	.218
1943	Bro	N	C-3	74	.264
1944	Bro	N	C-2-S-3	94	.267
1947	Bro	N	C	25	.194
1948	Bro	N	C	9	.167
	BRTR			597	.240

Non-playing manager Pit (N) 1956-57 and Cle (A) 1958

BRAGGINS, RICHARD REALF
b.Dec.25,1879 Mercer,Pa.

Yr	Cl	Lea	Pos	G	Rec
1901	Cle	A	P	4	1-2
	BRTR				

BRAIN, DAVID L.
b.1877 Ashley,Ill.

Yr	Cl	Lea	Pos	G	Rec
1901	Chi	A	2	5	.350
1903	St.L	N	S-3	118	.231
1904	St.L	N	S-3-O	125	.266
1905	St.L	N	S-3	41	.228

(Continued)

Yr	Cl	Lea	Pos	G	Rec
1905	Pit	N	S-3	82	.257
1906	Bos	N	3	139	.250
1907	Bos	N	3	133	.279
1908	Cin	N	O	16	.109
1908	NY	N	O	9	.076
	BRTR			668	.254

BRAINARD, ASA (Count)
b.1841 Albany,N.Y.
d.Dec.10,1888

Yr	Cl	Lea	Pos	G	Rec
1871	Oly	n	P	30	13-15
1872	Oly	n	P	9	2-7
1872	Man	n	P-2	6	0-2 NR
1873	Bal	n	P-O	15	5-7 NR
1874	Bal	n	P-2-O	46	5-23 NR
	TR			106	25-54 NR

BRAINARD, FREDERICK
b.Jan.17,1892 Champaign,Ill.
d.Apr.17,1959

Yr	Cl	Lea	Pos	G	Rec
1914	NY	N	2	2	.500
1915	NY	N	1-3	91	.201
1916	NY	N	3	2	.000
	BRTR			95	.202

BRAITHWOOD, ALBERT
b.1892 Fayette City,Pa.

Yr	Cl	Lea	Pos	G	Rec
1915	Pit	F	P	1	0-0

BRAME, ERVIN BECKHAM
b.Oct.12,1901 LaFayette,Ky.
d.Nov.22,1949

Yr	Cl	Lea	Pos	G	Rec
1928	Pit	N	P	35	7-4
1929	Pit	N	P	59	16-11
1930	Pit	N	P	50	17-8
1931	Pit	N	P	48	9-13
1932	Pit	N	P	26	3-1
	BLTR			218	52-37

BRAMHALL, ARTHUR WASHINGTON
b.Feb.22,1910 Chicago,Ill.

Yr	Cl	Lea	Pos	G	Rec
1935	Phi	N	S-3	2	.000
	BRTR				

BRANCA, RALPH THEODORE JOSEPH (Hawk)
b.Jan.6,1926 Mt.Vernon,N.Y.

Yr	Cl	Lea	Pos	G	Rec
1944	Bro	N	P	21	0-2
1945	Bro	N	P	16	5-6
1946	Bro	N	P	24	3-1
1947	Bro	N	P	43	21-12
1948	Bro	N	P	36	14-9
1949	Bro	N	P	34	13-5
1950	Bro	N	P	43	7-9
1951	Bro	N	P	42	13-12
1952	Bro	N	P	16	4-2
1953	Bro	N	P	7	0-0
1953	Det	A	P	17	4-7
1954	Det	A	P	17	3-3
1954	NY	A	P	5	1-0
1956	Bro	N	P	1	0-0
	BRTR			322	88-68

BRANCATO, ALBERT (Bronk)
b.May 29,1919 Philadelphia,Pa.

Yr	Cl	Lea	Pos	G	Rec
1939	Phi	A	3	21	.206
1940	Phi	A	S-3	107	.191
1941	Phi	A	S-3	144	.234
1945	Phi	A	S	10	.118
	BRTR			282	.214

BRANCH, HARVEY ALFRED
b.Feb.8,1939 Memphis,Tenn.

Yr	Cl	Lea	Pos	G	Rec
1962	St.L	N	P	1	0-1
	BRTL				

BRANCH, NORMAN DOWNS (Red)
b.Mar.22,1916 Spokane,Wash.

Yr	Cl	Lea	Pos	G	Rec
1941	NY	A	P	27	5-1
1942	NY	A	P	10	0-1
	BRTR			37	5-2

BRANDOM, CHESTER MILTON (Chick)
b.Mar.31,1887 Oklahoma City,Okla.
d.Oct.7,1958

Yr	Cl	Lea	Pos	G	Rec
1908	Pit	N	P	3	1-0
1909	Pit	N	P	13	1-0
1915	New	F	P	16	1-1
	TR			32	3-1

BRANDT, EDWARD ARTHUR (Big Ed)
b.Feb.17,1905 Spokane,Wash.
d.Nov.1,1944

Yr	Cl	Lea	Pos	G	Rec
1928	Bos	N	P	39	9-21
1929	Bos	N	P	29	8-13
1930	Bos	N	P	41	4-11
1931	Bos	N	P	34	18-11
1932	Bos	N	P	35	16-16
1933	Bos	N	P	47	18-14
1934	Bos	N	P	48	16-14
1935	Bos	N	P	31	5-19
1936	Bro	N	P	43	11-13
1937	Pit	N	P	33	11-10
1938	Pit	N	P	24	5-4
	BLTL			404	121-146

BRANDT, JOHN GEORGE
b.Apr.28,1934 Omaha,Neb.

Yr	Cl	Lea	Pos	G	Rec
1956	St.L	N	O	27	.286
1956	NY	N	O	98	.299
1958	SF	N	O	18	.250
1959	SF	N	1-2-3-O	137	.270
1960	Bal	A	1-3-O	145	.254
1961	Bal	A	3-O	139	.297
1962	Bal	A	3-O	143	.255
	BRTR			707	.273

BRANDT, WILLIAM GEORGE
b.Mar.21,1918 Aurora,Ind.

Yr	Cl	Lea	Pos	G	Rec
1941	Pit	N	P	2	0-1
1942	Pit	N	P	3	1-1
1943	Pit	N	P	29	4-1
	BRTR			34	5-3

BRANNAN, OTIS OWEN
b.Mar.13,1902 Greenbrier,Ark.

Yr	Cl	Lea	Pos	G	Rec
1928	St.L	A	2	135	.244
1929	St.L	A	2	23	.294
	BRTR			158	.249

BRANOM, EDGAR DUDLEY (Dud)
b.Nov.30,1897 Sulphur Springs,Tex

Yr	Cl	Lea	Pos	G	Rec
1927	Phi	A	1	30	.234
	BLTL				

BRANSFIELD, WILLIAM EDWARD (Kitty)
b.Jan.7,1875 Worcester,Mass.
d.May 1,1947

Yr	Cl	Lea	Pos	G	Rec
1898	Bos	N	C	5	.222
1901	Pit	N	1	139	.274
1902	Pit	N	1	100	.308
1903	Pit	N	1	127	.265
1904	Pit	N	1	139	.223
1905	Phi	N	1	151	.259
1906	Phi	N	1	139	.275
1907	Phi	N	1	92	.233
1908	Phi	N	1	143	.304
1909	Phi	N	1	138	.292
1910	Phi	N	1	110	.239
1911	Phi	N	1	23	.256
1911	Chi	N	1	3	.400
	BRTR			1309	.270

BRASHEAR, ROBERT NORMAN (Kitty)
b.Aug.12,1878 Mansfield,O.
d.Dec.23,1934

Yr	Cl	Lea	Pos	G	Rec
1902	St.L	N	1-2-S-O	106	.284

BRASHEAR, ROY PARKS
b.Jan.3,1874 Ashtabula,O.
d.Apr.20,1951

Yr	Cl	Lea	Pos	G	Rec
1899	Lou	N	P	3	1-0
1903	Phi	N	2	20	.227
			TR	23	1-0 .231

BRATCHER, JOSEPH WARLICK
b.July 22,1900 Grand Saline,Tex.

Yr	Cl	Lea	Pos	G	Rec
1924	St.L	N	O	4	.000

BLTR

BRATCHI, FREDERICK OSCAR
b.Jan.16,1892 Alliance,O

Yr	Cl	Lea	Pos	G	Rec
1921	Chi	A	O	16	.286
1926	Bos	A	O	72	.275
1927	Bos	A	H	1	.000
			BRTR	89	.276

BRAXTON, EDGAR GARLAND
b.June 10,1900 Snow Camp,N.C.

Yr	Cl	Lea	Pos	G	Rec
1921	Bos	N	P	17	1-3
1922	Bos	N	P	25	1-2
1925	NY	A	P	3	1-1
1926	NY	A	P	37	5-1
1927	Was	A	P	58	10-9
1928	Was	A	P	38	13-11
1929	Was	A	P	37	12-10
1930	Was	A	P	15	3-2
1930	Chi	A	P	19	4-10
1931	Chi	A	P	17	0-3
1931	St.L	A	P	11	0-0
1933	St.L	A	P	5	0-1
			BBTL	282	50-53

BRAY, CLARENCE WILBUR (Buster)
b.Apr.1,1913 Birmingham,Ala.

Yr	Cl	Lea	Pos	G	Rec
1941	Bos	N	O	4	.091

BLTL

BRAZILL, FRANK LEO
b.Aug.11,1899 Spangler,Pa.

Yr	Cl	Lea	Pos	G	Rec
1921	Phi	A	1	66	.271
1922	Phi	A	3	6	.077
			BLTR	72	.258

BRAZLE, ALPHA EUGENE (Cotton)
b.Oct.19,1914 Loyal,Okla.

Yr	Cl	Lea	Pos	G	Rec
1943	St.L	N	P	13	8-2
1946	St.L	N	P	37	11-10
1947	St.L	N	P	44	14-8
1948	St.L	N	P	45	10-6
1949	St.L	N	P	39	14-8
1950	St.L	N	P	47	11-9
1951	St.L	N	P	56	6-5
1952	St.L	N	P	46	12-5
1953	St.L	N	P	60	6-7
1954	St.L	N	P	58	5-4
			BLTL	445	97-64

BRECHEEN, HARRY DAVID (TheCat)
b.Oct.14,1914 Broken Bow,Okla.

Yr	Cl	Lea	Pos	G	Rec
1940	St.L	N	P	3	0-0
1943	St.L	N	P	29	9-6
1944	St.L	N	P	31	16-5
1945	St.L	N	P	24	15-4
1946	St.L	N	P	37	15-15
1947	St.L	N	P	29	16-11
1948	St.L	N	P	33	20-7
1949	St.L	N	P	32	14-11
1950	St.L	N	P	27	8-11
1951	St.L	N	P	24	8-4
1952	St.L	N	P	25	7-5
1953	St.L	A	P	27	5-13
			BLTL	321	133-92

BRECKINRIDGE, WILLIAM ROBERTSON
b.Oct.27,1906 Tulsa,Okla.

Yr	Cl	Lea	Pos	G	Rec
1929	Phi	A	P	3	0-0

BRTR

BREEDING, MARVIN EUGENE
b.Mar.8,1934 Decatur,Ala.

Yr	Cl	Lea	Pos	G	Rec
1960	Bal	A	2	152	.267
1961	Bal	A	2	90	.209
1962	Bal	A	2-S-3	95	.246
			BRTR	337	.248

BREITENSTEIN, ALONZO
b.Nov.9,1857 Utica,N.Y.
d.June 19,1932

Yr	Cl	Lea	Pos	G	Rec
1883	Phi	N	P	1	0-1

BREITENSTEIN, THEODORE P.
b.June 1,1869 St.Louis,Mo.
d.May 3,1935

Yr	Cl	Lea	Pos	G	Rec
1891	St.L	a	P	5	0-1
1892	St.L	N	P	38	14-20
1893	St.L	N	P	41	19-20
1894	St.L	N	P	53	27-25
1895	St.L	N	P	66	18-30
1896	St.L	N	P	48	17-26
1897	Cin	N	P	39	23-12
1898	Cin	N	P	39	21-14
1899	Cin	N	P	33	14-10
1900	Cin	N	P	33	10-10
1901	St.L	N	P	3	0-3
			BLTL	398	163-171

BREMER, HERBERT T. FREDERICK
b.Oct.25,1913 Chicago,Ill.

Yr	Cl	Lea	Pos	G	Rec
1937	St.L	N	C	11	.212
1938	St.L	N	C	50	.219
1939	St.L	N	C	9	.111
			BRTR	70	.212

BRENEGAN, SELMAR G.
b.Sept.2,1891 Galesville,Wis.
d.Apr.20,1956

Yr	Cl	Lea	Pos	G	Rec
1914	Pit	N	C	1	.000

BLTR

BRENNAN, ADDISON FOSTER (Ad)
b.July 18,1887 LaHarpe,Kan.
d.Jan.7,1962

Yr	Cl	Lea	Pos	G	Rec
1910	Phi	N	P	21	2-0
1911	Phi	N	P	5	3-1
1912	Phi	N	P	27	11-9
1913	Phi	N	P	40	14-12
1914	Chi	F	P	15	5-5
1915	Chi	F	P	16	3-9
1918	Was	A	P	2	0-0
1918	Cle	A	P	1	0-0
			BLTL	127	38-36

BRENNAN, JAMES A.
b.1862 St.Louis,Mo.
d.Oct.18,1904

Yr	Cl	Lea	Pos	G	Rec
1884	St.L	U	C-O	45	.210
1885	St.L	N	3-O	3	.100
1888	KC	a	C	34	.174
1889	Ath	a	C	31	.214
1890	Cle	p	C-3	59	.251
				172	.217

BRENNAN, JAMES DONALD (Don)
b.Dec.2,1903 Augusta,Me.
d.Apr.26,1953

Yr	Cl	Lea	Pos	G	Rec
1933	NY	A	P	18	5-1
1934	Cin	N	P	28	4-3
1935	Cin	N	P	38	5-5
1936	Cin	N	P	41	5-2
1937	Cin	N	P	10	1-1
1937	NY	N	P	6	1-0
			BRTR	141	21-12

BRENNER, DELBERT HENRY (Bert)
b.July 18,1887 Minneapolis,Minn.

Yr	Cl	Lea	Pos	G	Rec
1912	Cle	A	P	2	1-0

BRTR

BRENTON, LYNN DAVIS (Buck)
b.Oct.7,1893 Peoria,Ill.

Yr	Cl	Lea	Pos	G	Rec
1913	Cle	A	P	1	0-0
1915	Cle	A	P	11	2-3
1920	Cin	N	P	5	2-1
1921	Cin	N	P	17	1-8
			BRTR	34	5-12

BRENZEL, WILLIAM RICHARD
b.Mar.3,1910 Oakland,Cal.

Yr	Cl	Lea	Pos	G	Rec
1932	Pit	N	C	9	.042
1934	Cle	A	C	15	.216
1935	Cle	A	C	52	.218
			BRTR	76	.198

BRESNAHAN, ROGER PATRICK (Duke)
b.June 14,1880 Tralee,Ireland
d.Dec.4,1944

Yr	Cl	Lea	Pos	G	Rec
1897	Was	N	P	7	4-1
1900	Chi	N	C	1	.000
1901	Bal	A	P-C	86	0-0 .262
1902	Bal	A	C-3-O	66	.273
1902	NY	N	C-1-S-3-O	50	.292
1903	NY	N	O	111	.350
1904	NY	N	O	107	.284
1905	NY	N	C	95	.302
1906	NY	N	C-O	124	.281
1907	NY	N	C	104	.253
1908	NY	N	C	139	.283
1909	St.L	N	M-C	69	.244
1910	St.L	N	M-C	78	.278
1911	St.L	N	M-C	78	.278
1912	St.L	N	M-C	48	.333
1913	Chi	N	C	69	.228
1914	Chi	N	C	101	.278
1915	Chi	N	M-C	77	.204
			BRTR	1410	4-1 .279

BRESSLER, RAYMOND BLOOM (Rube)
b.Oct.23,1894 Brookville,Pa.

Yr	Cl	Lea	Pos	G	Rec
1914	Phi	A	P	26	10-4
1915	Phi	A	P	33	4-17
1916	Phi	A	P	4	0-3
1917	Cin	N	P	3	0-0
1918	Cin	N	P-O	23	8-5 .274
1919	Cin	N	P-O	61	2-4 .206
1920	Cin	N	P-1	21	2-0 .267
1921	Cin	N	O	109	.307
1922	Cin	N	1-O	52	.264
1923	Cin	N	1-O	54	.277
1924	Cin	N	1-O	115	.347
1925	Cin	N	1-O	97	.348
1926	Cin	N	1-O	86	.357
1927	Cin	N	O	124	.291
1928	Bro	N	O	145	.295
1929	Bro	N	O	136	.318
1930	Bro	N	O	109	.299
1931	Bro	N	O	67	.281
1932	Phi	N	O	27	.229
1932	St.L	N	O	10	.158
			BRTL	1302	26-33 .302

BRESSOUD, EDWARD FRANCIS
b.May 2,1932 Los Angeles,Cal.

Yr	Cl	Lea	Pos	G	Rec
1956	NY	N	S	49	.227
1957	NY	N	S-3	49	.268
1958	SF	N	2-S-3	66	.263
1959	SF	N	1-2-S-	104	.251
1960	SF	N	S	116	.225
1961	SF	N	2-S-3	59	.211
1962	Bos	A	S	153	.277
			BRTR	596	.251

BRETON, JAMES FREDERICK
b.July 15,1891 Chicago,Ill.

Yr	Cl	Lea	Pos	G	Rec
1913	Chi	A	2-3	12	.173
1914	Chi	A	3	81	.212
1915	Chi	A	3	16	.139
	BRTR			109	.202

BRETT, HERBERT JAMES (Duke)
b.May23,1900 Lawrenceville,Va.

Yr	Cl	Lea	Pos	G	Rec
1924	Chi	N	P	1	0-0
1925	Chi	N	P	10	1-1
	BRTR			11	1-1

BREUER, MARVIN HOWARD
(Baby Face)
b.Apr.29,1914 Rolla,Mo.

Yr	Cl	Lea	Pos	G	Rec
1939	NY	A	P	1	0-0
1940	NY	A	P	27	8-9
1941	NY	A	P	26	9-7
1942	NY	A	P	27	8-9
1943	NY	A	P	5	0-1
	BRTR			86	25-26

BREWER, JAMES THOMAS
b.Nov.17,1937 Merced,Cal.

Yr	Cl	Lea	Pos	G	Rec
1960	Chi	N	P	6	0-3
1961	Chi	N	P	36	1-7
1962	Chi	N	P	6	0-1
	BLTL			48	1-11

BREWER, JOHN HERNDON (Buddy)
b.July 21,1919 Long Beach,Cal.

Yr	Cl	Lea	Pos	G	Rec
1944	NY	N	P	14	1-4
1945	NY	N	P	28	8-6
1946	NY	N	P	1	0-0
	BRTR			43	9-10

BREWER, THOMAS AUSTIN
b.Sept.3,1931 Cheraw,S.C.

Yr	Cl	Lea	Pos	G	Rec
1954	Bos	A	P	37	10-9
1955	Bos	A	P	33	11-10
1956	Bos	A	P	38	19-9
1957	Bos	A	P	45	16-13
1958	Bos	A	P	42	12-12
1959	Bos	A	P	47	10-12
1960	Bos	A	P	45	10-15
1961	Bos	A	P	18	3-2
	BRTR			305	91-82

BREWSTER, CHARLES LAWRENCE
b.Dec.17,1916 Marthaville,La.

Yr	Cl	Lea	Pos	G	Rec
1943	Cin	N	2-S	7	.125
1943	Phi	N	S	49	.220
1944	Chi	N	S	10	.250
1946	Cle	A	S	3	.000
	BRTR			69	.221

BRICE, ALAN HEALEY
b.Oct.1,1937 New York,N.Y.

Yr	Cl	Lea	Pos	G	Rec
1961	Chi	A	P	3	0-1
	BRTR				

BRICKELL, GEORGE FREDERICK
b.Nov.9,1906 Saffordville,Kan.
d.Apr.8,1961

Yr	Cl	Lea	Pos	G	Rec
1926	Pit	N	O	24	.345
1927	Pit	N	O	32	.286
1928	Pit	N	O	81	.322
1929	Pit	N	O	60	.314
1930	Pit	N	O	68	.297
1930	Phi	N	O	53	.246
1931	Phi	N	O	130	.253
1932	Phi	N	O	45	.333
1933	Phi	N	O	8	.308
	BLTR			501	.281

BRICKELL, FRITZ DARRELL
b.Mar.19,1935 Wichita,Kan.

Yr	Cl	Lea	Pos	G	Rec
1958	NY	A	2	2	.000
1959	NY	A	2-S	18	.256
1961	LA	A	S	21	.122
	BRTR			41	.182

BRICKLEY, GEORGE VINCENT
b.July19,1894 Everett,Mass.
d.Feb.23,1947

Yr	Cl	Lea	Pos	G	Rec
1913	Phi	A	O	5	.166
	BRTR				

BRICKNER, RALPH HAROLD
b.May 2,1926 Cincinnati,O.

Yr	Cl	Lea	Pos	G	Rec
1952	Bos	A	P	14	3-1
	BRTR				

BRIDEWESER,
JAMES EHRENFELD
b.Feb.13,1927 Lancaster,O.

Yr	Cl	Lea	Pos	G	Rec
1951	NY	A	S	2	.375
1952	NY	A	2-S-3	42	.263
1953	NY	A	S	7	1.000
1954	Bal	A	2-S	73	.265
1955	Chi	A	2-S-3	34	.207
1956	Chi	A	S	10	.182
1956	Det	A	2-S-3	70	.218
1957	Bal	A	2-S-3	91	.268
	BRTR			329	.252

BRIDGES, EVERETT LAMAR
(Rocky)
b.Aug.7,1927 Refugio,Tex.

Yr	Cl	Lea	Pos	G	Rec
1951	Bro	N	2-S-3	63	.254
1952	Bro	N	2-S-3	51	.196
1953	Cin	N	2-S-3	122	.227
1954	Cin	N	2-S-3	53	.231
1955	Cin	N	2-S-3	95	.286
1956	Cin	N	2-S-3-O	71	.211
1957	Cin	N	2-S-3	5	.000
1957	Was	A	2-S-3	120	.228
1958	Was	A	2-S-3	116	.263
1959	Det	A	2-S	116	.268
1960	Det	A	S-3	10	.200
1960	Cle	A	S-3	10	.333
1960	St.L	N	2	3	.000
1961	LA	A	2-S-3	84	.240
	BRTR			919	.247

BRIDGES, MARSHALL
b.June 2,1931 Jackson,Miss.

Yr	Cl	Lea	Pos	G	Rec
1959	St.L	N	P	27	6-3
1960	St.L	N	P	20	2-2
1960	Cin	N	P	14	4-0
1961	Cin	N	P	13	0-1
1962	NY	A	P	52	8-4
	BBTL			126	20-10

BRIDGES, THOMAS JEFFERSON DAVIS
b.Dec.28,1906 Gordonsville,Tenn.

Yr	Cl	Lea	Pos	G	Rec
1930	Det	A	P	8	3-2
1931	Det	A	P	35	8-16
1932	Det	A	P	34	14-12
1933	Det	A	P	33	14-12
1934	Det	A	P	36	22-11
1935	Det	A	P	36	21-10
1936	Det	A	P	39	23-11
1937	Det	A	P	34	15-12
1938	Det	A	P	25	13-9
1939	Det	A	P	29	17-7
1940	Det	A	P	29	12-9
1941	Det	A	P	25	9-12
1942	Det	A	P	23	9-7
1943	Det	A	P	25	12-7
1945	Det	A	P	4	1-0
1946	Det	A	P	9	1-1
	BRTR			424	194-138

BRIDWELL, ALBERT HENRY
b.Jan.4,1884 Friendship,O.

Yr	Cl	Lea	Pos	G	Rec
1905	Cin	N	3-O	74	.252
1906	Bos	N	S	120	.227
1907	Bos	N	S	140	.218
1908	NY	N	S	147	.285
1909	NY	N	S	145	.294
1910	NY	N	S	141	.276
1911	NY	N	S	76	.270
1911	Bos	N	S	51	.291
1912	Bos	N	S	31	.236
1913	Chi	N	S	136	.240
1914	St.L	F	S	117	.234
1915	St.L	F	2-3	63	.226
	BLTR			1241	.255

BRIEF, ANTHONY VINCENT (Bunny)
(Real name Antonio Bordetzki)
b.July 3,1892 Big Rapids,Mich.
d.Feb.10,1963

Yr	Cl	Lea	Pos	G	Rec
1912	St.L	A	1-O	15	.310
1913	St.L	A	1	84	.217
1915	Chi	A	1	48	.214
1917	Pit	N	1	36	.217
	BRTR			183	.223

BRIGGS, CHARLES R.

Yr	Cl	Lea	Pos	G	Rec
1884	Chi	U	2-O	50	.171

BRIGGS, GRANT
b.Philadelphia,Pa.

Yr	Cl	Lea	Pos	G	Rec
1890	Syr	a	C	86	.179
1891	Lou	a	C	1	.250
1892	St.L	N	C-O	23	.070
1895	Lou	N	C	1	.000
				111	.163

BRIGGS, HERBERT T. (Buttons)
b.Feb.18,1876 Glenville,O.
d.Feb.18,1911

Yr	Cl	Lea	Pos	G	Rec
1896	Chi	N	P	22	12-8
1897	Chi	N	P	22	5-17
1898	Chi	N	P	5	1-4
1904	Chi	N	P	34	19-11
1905	Chi	N	P	20	9-10
	BRTR			103	46-50

BRIGGS, JOHN TIFT
b.Jan.24,1934 Natoma,Cal.

Yr	Cl	Lea	Pos	G	Rec
1956	Chi	N	P	3	0-0
1957	Chi	N	P	3	0-1
1958	Chi	N	P	20	5-5
1959	Cle	A	P	4	0-1
1960	Cle	A	P	21	4-2
1960	KC	A	P	8	0-2
	BRTR			59	9-11

BRIGHT, HARRY JAMES
b.Sept.22,1929 Kansas City,Mo.

Yr	Cl	Lea	Pos	G	Rec
1958	Pit	N	3	15	.250
1959	Pit	N	2-3-O	40	.250
1960	Pit	N	H	4	.000
1961	Was	A	C-2-3	72	.240
1962	Was	A	C-1-3	113	.273
	BRTR			244	.260

BRILL, JOHN
b.Astoria,N.Y.

Yr	Cl	Lea	Pos	G	Rec
1884	Det	N	P-O	13	2-10 .130

BRILLHEART, JAMES BENSON
b.Sept.28,1903 Dublin,Va.

Yr	Cl	Lea	Pos	G	Rec
1922	Was	A	P	31	4-6
1923	Was	A	P	12	0-1
1927	Chi	N	P	32	4-2
1931	Bos	A	P	11	0-0
	BRTL			86	8-9

BRINKER, WILLIAM HUTCHINSON
(Dode)
b.Aug.30,1883 Warrensburg,Mo.

Yr	Cl	Lea	Pos	G	Rec
1912	Phi	N	3-O	9	.222
	BBTR				

BRINKMAN, EDWIN ALBERT
b.Dec.8,1941 Cincinnati,O.

Yr	Cl	Lea	Pos	G	Rec
1961	Was	A	3	4	.091
1962	Was	A	2-S-3	54	.165
	BRTR			58	.160

BRINKOPF, LEON CLARENCE
b.Oct.20,1926 Cape Girardeau,Mo.

Yr	Cl	Lea	Pos	G	Rec
1952	Chi	N	S	9	.182
	BRTR				

BRIODY, CHARLES F. (Alderman)
b.Aug.13,1858 Lansingburg,N.Y.

Yr	Cl	Lea	Pos	G	Rec
1880	Tro	N	C	1	.000
1882	Cle	N	C	52	.263
1883	Cle	N	C-1-2-3	39	.232
1884	Cle	N	C-O	43	.169
1884	Cin	U	C	23	.326
1885	St.L	N	C-2-3	61	.195
1886	KC	N	C	55	.237
1887	Det	N	C	32	.277
1888	KC	a	C	13	.208
				319	.234

BRISSIE, LELAND VICTOR (Lou)
b.June 5,1924 Anderson,S.C.

Yr	Cl	Lea	Pos	G	Rec
1947	Phi	A	P	1	0-1
1948	Phi	A	P	39	14-10
1949	Phi	A	P	34	16-11
1950	Phi	A	P	46	7-19
1951	Phi	A	P	2	0-2
1951	Cle	A	P	54	4-3
1952	Cle	A	P	42	3-2
1953	Cle	A	P	16	0-0
		BLTL		234	44-48

BRISTOW, GEORGE
b.1871 Pawpaw,Ill.

Yr	Cl	Lea	Pos	G	Rec
1899	Cle	N	O	3	.125

BRITT, JAMES E.

Yr	Cl	Lea	Pos	G	Rec
1872	Atl	n	P	36	9-27
1873	Atl	n	P	23	9-14
1873	Mut	n	P	1	0-1
1873	Atl	n	P	53	16-36
				113	34-78

BRITTAIN, AUGUST SCHUSTER
b.Nov.29,1912 Wilmington,N.C.

Yr	Cl	Lea	Pos	G	Rec
1937	Cin	N	C	3	.167
		BRTR			

BRITTIN, JOHN ALBERT
b.Mar.4,1926 Athens,Ill.

Yr	Cl	Lea	Pos	G	Rec
1950	Phi	N	P	3	0-0
1951	Phi	N	P	3	0-0
		BRTR		6	0-0

BRITTON, STEPHEN GILBERT (Gil)
b.Sept.21,1891 Parsons,Kan.

Yr	Cl	Lea	Pos	G	Rec
1913	Pit	N	S	3	.000
		BRTR			

BROACA, JOHN JOSEPH
b.Oct.3,1909 Lawrence,Mass.

Yr	Cl	Lea	Pos	G	Rec
1934	NY	A	P	26	12-9
1935	NY	A	P	29	15-7
1936	NY	A	P	37	12-7
1937	NY	A	P	7	1-4
1939	Cle	A	P	22	4-2
		BRTR		121	44-29

BROCK, JOHN ROY
b.Oct.19,1896 Hamilton,Ill.
d.Oct.27 1951

Yr	Cl	Lea	Pos	G	Rec
1917	St.L	N	C	7	.400
1918	St.L	N	C-O	27	..212
		BRTR		34	.263

BROCK, LOUIS CLARK
b.June 8,1936 El Dorado,Ark.

Yr	Cl	Lea	Pos	G	Rec
1961	Chi	N	O	4	.091
1962	Chi	N	O	123	.263
		BLTL		127	.258

BROCKETT, LOUIS ALBERT (King)
b.July 23,1880 Carmi,Ill.
d.Sept.19,1960

Yr	Cl	Lea	Pos	G	Rec
1907	NY	A	P	10	1-3
1909	NY	A	P	26	10-8
1911	NY	A	P	19	2-4
		TR		55	13-15

BRODERICK, MATTHEW T.
b.Dec.2,1876 Lattimer Mines,Pa.
d.Feb.22,1941

Yr	Cl	Lea	Pos	G	Rec
1903	Bro	N	2	2	.000
		TR			

BRODIE, WALTER SCOTT (Steve)
b.Sept.11,1868 Roanoke,Va.
d.Oct.29,1933

Yr	Cl	Lea	Pos	G	Rec
1890	Bos	N	O	132	.295
1891	Bos	N	O	134	.266
1892	St.L	N	2-O	154	.256
1893	St.L	N	O	107	.336
1893	Bal	N	O	25	.372
1894	Bal	N	O	129	.369
1895	Bal	N	O	130	.365
1896	Bal	N	O	132	.294
1897	Pit	N	O	100	.298
1898	Pit	N	O	42	.274
1898	Bal	N	O	23	.286
1899	Bal	N	O	138	.309
1901	Bal	A	O	84	.310
1902	NY	N	O	109	.281
		BL		1439	.308

BRODOWSKI, RICHARD STANLEY
b.July 26,1932 Bayonne,N.J.

Yr	Cl	Lea	Pos	G	Rec
1952	Bos	A	P	20	5-5
1955	Bos	A	P	16	1-0
1956	Was	A	P	7	0-3
1957	Was	A	P	6	0-1
1958	Cle	A	P	5	1-0
1959	Cle	A	P	18	2-2
		BRTR		72	9-11

BROGLIO, ERNEST GILBERT
b.Aug.27,1935 Berkeley,Cal.

Yr	Cl	Lea	Pos	G	Rec
1959	St.L	N	P	35	7-12
1960	St.L	N	P	52	21-9
1961	St.L	N	P	29	9-12
1962	St.L	N	P	34	12-9
		BRTR		150	49-42

BRONDELL, KENNETH LEROY
b.Oct.17,1921 Bradshaw,Neb.

Yr	Cl	Lea	Pos	G	Rec
1944	NY	N	P	8	0-1
		BRTR			

BRONKIE, HERMAN CHARLES (Dutch)
b.Mar.31,1885 S. Manchester,Conn

Yr	Cl	Lea	Pos	G	Rec
1910	Cle	A	S-3	5	.181
1911	Cle	A	3	2	.167
1912	Cle	A	3	6	.000
1914	Chi	N	3	1	1.000
1918	St.L	N	3	18	.221
1919	St.L	A	2-3	67	.255
1922	St.L	A	3	23	.281
		BRTR		122	.240

BRONSTAD, JAMES WARREN
b.June 22,1936 Ft.Worth,Tex.

Yr	Cl	Lea	Pos	G	Rec
1959	NY	A	P	16	0-3
		BRTR			

BROOKS, F. HARRY
b.Philadelphia,Pa.

Yr	Cl	Lea	Pos	G	Rec
1886	Met	a	P	1	0-1

BROOKS, JOHNATHAN JOSEPH (Mandy)
(Real name Johnathan Joseph Brozek)
b.Aug.18,1898 Milwaukee,Wis.

Yr	Cl	Lea	Pos	G	Rec
1925	Chi	N	O	90	.281
1926	Chi	N	O	26	.188
		BRTR		116	.270

BROSKIE, SIGMUND THEODORE (Chops)
b.Mar.23,1911 Iselin,Pa.

Yr	Cl	Lea	Pos	G	Rec
1940	Bos	N	C	11	.273
		BRTR			

BROSNAN, JAMES PATRICK
b.Oct.24,1929 Cincinnati,O.

Yr	Cl	Lea	Pos	G	Rec
1954	Chi	N	P	18	1-0
1956	Chi	N	P	30	5-9
1957	Chi	N	P	41	5-5
1958	Chi	N	P	8	3-4
1958	St.L	N	P	33	8-4
1959	St.L	N	P	20	1-3
1959	Cin	N	P	26	8-3
1960	Cin	N	P	57	7-2
1961	Cin	N	P	53	10-4
1962	Cin	N	P	48	4-4
		BRTR		334	52-38

BROTTEM, ANTON CHRISTIAN (Tony)
b.Apr.30,1892 Halstad,Minn.
d.Aug.5,1929

Yr	Cl	Lea	Pos	G	Rec
1916	St.L	N	C-O	26	.182
1918	St.L	N	1	2	.000
1921	Was	A	C	4	.147
1921	Pit	N	C	30	.242
		BRTR		62	.218

BROUGHTON, CECIL CALVERT (Cal)
b.Dec.28,1860 Magnolia,Wis.
d.Mar.15,1939

Yr	Cl	Lea	Pos	G	Rec
1883	Cle	N	C	4	.167
1883	Bal	a	C-O	9	.188
1884	Mil	U	C-O	11	.308
1885	St.L	a	C	3	.083
1885	Met	a	C	12	.356
1888	Det	N	C	1	.000
		BRTR		40	.257

BROUTHERS, ARTHUR H.
b.Nov.25,1882 Montgomery,Ala.

Yr	Cl	Lea	Pos	G	Rec
1906	Phi	A	3	36	.208
		TR			

BROUTHERS, DENNIS (Big Dan)
b.May 8,1858 Sylvan Lake,N.Y.
d.Aug.2,1932

Yr	Cl	Lea	Pos	G	Rec
1879	Tro	N	P-1	39	0-2 / .273
1880	Tro	N	1	3	.154
1881	Buf	N	1-O	65	.318
1882	Buf	N	1	84	.367
1883	Buf	N	P-1-3	97	0-0 / .371
1884	Buf	N	1-3	90	.325
1885	Buf	N	1	98	.358
1886	Det	N	1	121	.370
1887	Det	N	1	122	.419
1888	Det	N	1	129	.306
1889	Bos	N	1	126	.373
1890	Bos	p	1	123	.345
1891	Bos	a	1	130	.352
1892	Bro	N	1	152	.335
1893	Bro	N	1	75	.348
1894	Bal	N	1	123	.344
1895	Bal	N	1	5	.261
1895	Lou	N	1	24	.296
1896	Phi	N	1	57	.330
1904	NY	N	1	2	.000
		BLTL		1665	0-2 / .348

BROVIA, JOSEPH JOHN
b.Feb.18,1922 Davenport,Cal.

Yr	Cl	Lea	Pos	G	Rec
1955	Cin	N	H	21	.111
		BLTR			

BROWER, FRANK WILLARD (Turkeyfoot)
b.Mar.26.1893 Gainesville.Va.
d.Nov.20,1960

Yr	Cl	Lea	Pos	G	Rec
1920	Was	A	O	36	.311
1921	Was	A	O	83	.261
1922	Was	A	O	139	.293
1923	Cle	A	1	126	.285
1924	Cle	A	P-1-O	66	0-0 / .280
		BLTR		450	0-0 / .286

BROWER, LOUIS LESTER
b.July 1,1900 Cleveland,O.

Yr	Cl	Lea	Pos	G	Rec
1931	Det	A	S	21	.161
	BRTR				

BROWN, ALTON LEO
b.Apr.16,1928 Norfolk,Va.

Yr	Cl	Lea	Pos	G	Rec
1951	Was	A	P	7	0-0
	BRTR				

BROWN, CARROLL WILLIAM
(Boardwalk)
b.Feb.20,1887 Woodbury,N.J.

Yr	Cl	Lea	Pos	G	Rec
1911	Phi	A	P	2	0-1
1912	Phi	A	P	30	13-11
1913	Phi	A	P	38	18-11
1914	Phi	A	P	15	1-6
1914	NY	A	P	19	5-5
1915	NY	A	P	21	3-5
	BRTR			125	40-39

BROWN, CHARLES E.
b.1878 Baltimore,Md.

Yr	Cl	Lea	Pos	G	Rec
1897	Cle	N	P	4	1-3
	TL				

BROWN, CHARLES EDWARD
(Buster)
b.Aug.31,1881 Boone,Ia.
d.Feb.9,1914

Yr	Cl	Lea	Pos	G	Rec
1905	St.L	N	P	23	8-11
1906	St.L	N	P	32	8-16
1907	St.L	N	P	9	2-7
1907	Phi	N	P	21	8-5
1908	Phi	N	P	4	0-0
1909	Phi	N	P	7	0-0
1909	Bos	N	P	18	4-8
1910	Bos	N	P	46	9-23
1911	Bos	N	P	42	8-18
1912	Bos	N	P	31	4-15
1913	Bos	N	P	2	0-0
	BRTR			235	51-103

BROWN, CHARLES ROY (Curly)
b.Dec.9,1888 Spring Hill,Kan.

Yr	Cl	Lea	Pos	G	Rec
1911	St.L	A	P	3	0-2
1912	St.L	A	P	13	1-3
1913	St.L	A	P	2	1-1
1915	Cin	N	P	9	0-2
	BLTL			27	2-8

BROWN, CLINTON HAROLD
b.July 8,1903 Guy's Mills,Pa.
d.Dec.31,1955

Yr	Cl	Lea	Pos	G	Rec
1928	Cle	A	P	2	0-1
1929	Cle	A	P	3	0-2
1930	Cle	A	P	35	11-13
1931	Cle	A	P	39	11-15
1932	Cle	A	P	39	15-12
1933	Cle	A	P	34	11-12
1934	Cle	A	P	17	4-3
1935	Cle	A	P	23	4-3
1936	Chi	A	P	38	6-2
1937	Chi	A	P	53	7-7
1938	Chi	A	P	8	1-3
1939	Chi	A	P	61	11-10
1940	Chi	A	P	37	4-6
1941	Cle	A	P	41	3-3
1942	Cle	A	P	7	1-1
	BLTR			437	89-93

BROWN, DELOS HIGHT
b.Sept.9,1892 Centralia,Ill.

Yr	Cl	Lea	Pos	G	Rec
1914	Chi	A	H	1	.000
	BRTR				

BROWN, DRUMMOND N.
b.1885 Taft,Cal.

Yr	Cl	Lea	Pos	G	Rec
1913	Bos	N	C	15	.324
1914	KC	F	C	30	.207
1915	KC	F	C	77	.239
	BRTR			122	.242

BROWN, EDWARD P.
b.Chicago,Ill.

Yr	Cl	Lea	Pos	G	Rec
1882	St.L	a	P-2-O	17	0-0 .177
1884	Tol	a	3	42	.174
	TR			59	0-0 .175

BROWN, EDWARD WILLIAM
b.July 17,1892 Milligan,Neb.
d.Sept.10,1956

Yr	Cl	Lea	Pos	G	Rec
1920	NY	N	O	3	.125
1921	NY	N	O	70	.281
1924	Bro	N	O	114	.308
1925	Bro	N	O	153	.306
1926	Bos	N	O	153	.328
1927	Bos	N	O	155	.306
1928	Bos	N	O	142	.268
	BRTR			790	.303

BROWN, ELMER YOUNG (Shook)
b.Aug.25,1883 Southport,Ind.
d.Jan.23,1955

Yr	Cl	Lea	Pos	G	Rec
1911	St.L	A	P	5	2-1
1912	St.L	A	P	21	4-8
1913	Bro	N	P	3	0-0
1914	Bro	N	P	11	1-2
1915	Bro	N	P	1	0-0
	BLTR			41	7-11

BROWN, FRED HERBERT
b.Apr.12,1879 Ossipee,N.H.
d.Feb.3,1955

Yr	Cl	Lea	Pos	G	Rec
1901	Bos	N	O	7	.125
1902	Bos	N	O	1	.000
	BRTR			8	.111

BROWN, FREEMAN
b.Jan.31,1845 Hubbardstown,Mass.
d.Dec.27,1916
Non-playing manager Wor (N) 1880-82

BROWN, HECTOR HAROLD (Skinny)
b.Dec.11,1924 Greensboro,N.C.

Yr	Cl	Lea	Pos	G	Rec
1951	Chi	A	P	4	0-0
1952	Chi	A	P	51	2-3
1953	Bos	A	P	30	11-6
1954	Bos	A	P	40	1-8
1955	Bos	A	P	2	1-0
1955	Bal	A	P	25	0-4
1956	Bal	A	P	42	9-7
1957	Bal	A	P	30	7-8
1958	Bal	A	P-3	21	7-5 .148
1959	Bal	A	P	31	11-9
1960	Bal	A	P	30	12-5
1961	Bal	A	P	27	10-6
1962	Bal	A	P	22	6-4
1962	NY	A	P	2	0-1
	BRTR			357	77-66

BROWN, JAMES DONALDSON
(Moose)
b.Mar.31,1897 Laurel,Ind.

Yr	Cl	Lea	Pos	G	Rec
1915	St.L	N	O	1	.500
1916	Phi	A	O	14	.233
	BRTR			15	.244

BROWN, JAMES ROBERSON
b.Apr.25,1912 Jamesville,N.C.

Yr	Cl	Lea	Pos	G	Rec
1937	St.L	N	2-S	138	.276
1938	St.L	N	2-S-3	108	.301
1939	St.L	N	2-S	147	.298
1940	St.L	N	2-S-3	107	.280
1941	St.L	N	2-3	132	.306
1942	St.L	N	2-S-3	145	.256
1943	St.L	N	2-S-3	34	.182
1946	Pit	N	2-S-3	79	.241
	BBTR			890	.279

BROWN, JAMES W. 21
b.Lock Haven,Pa.

Yr	Cl	Lea	Pos	G	Rec
1884	Alt	U	P-O	22	2-9 .239
1884	NY	N	P	1	0-1
1884	St.P	U	P-1-O	6	1-3 .313
1886	Ath	a	P	1	0-1
				29	3-14 .237

BROWN, JOHN J. (Ad)
b.Trenton,N.J.

Yr	Cl	Lea	Pos	G	Rec
1897	Bro	N	P	2	0-2

BROWN, JOHN LINDSAY (Red)
b.July 22,1913 Mason,Tex.

Yr	Cl	Lea	Pos	G	Rec
1937	Bro	N	S	48	.270
	BRTR				

BROWN, JOSEPH E.
b.Apr.4,1859 Warren,Pa.
d.June 28,1888

Yr	Cl	Lea	Pos	G	Rec
1884	Chi	N	P-C-1-O	15	3-2 .220
1885	Bal	a	P-2	5	0-4 .158
				20	3-6 .205

BROWN, JOSEPH HENRY
b.July 3,1901 Little Rock,Ark.

Yr	Cl	Lea	Pos	G	Rec
1927	Chi	A	P	1	0-0
	BRTR				

BROWN, LEWIS J. (Blower)
b.Feb.1,1858 Leominster,Mass.
d.Jan.16,1889

Yr	Cl	Lea	Pos	G	Rec
1876	Bos	N	C	45	.207
1877	Bos	N	C-1	58	.253
1878	Pro	N	P-C-1-O	57	0-0 .315
1879	Pro	N	C-O	51	.262
1879	Chi	N	1	6	.273
1881	Det	N	1	27	.243
1881	Pro	N	1-O	18	.228
1883	Bos	N	1	14	.236
1883	Lou	a	C-1	14	.197
1884	Bos	U	P-C-1-O	84	1-0 .236
	BRTR			374	1-0 .252

BROWN, LLOYD ANDREW
b.Dec.25,1904 Beeville,Tex.

Yr	Cl	Lea	Pos	G	Rec
1925	Bro	N	P	17	0-3
1928	Was	A	P	27	4-4
1929	Was	A	P	40	8-7
1930	Was	A	P	38	16-12
1931	Was	A	P	42	15-14
1932	Was	A	P	46	15-12
1933	St.L	A	P	8	1-6
1933	Bos	A	P	33	8-11
1934	Cle	A	P	38	5-10
1935	Cle	A	P	42	8-7
1936	Cle	A	P	24	8-10
1937	Cle	A	P	31	2-6
1940	Phi	N	P	18	1-3
	BLTL			404	91-105

BROWN, MACE STANLEY
b.May 21,1909 North English,Ia.

Yr	Cl	Lea	Pos	G	Rec
1935	Pit	N	P	18	4-1
1936	Pit	N	P	47	10-11
1937	Pit	N	P	50	7-2
1938	Pit	N	P	51	15-9
1939	Pit	N	P	47	9-13
1940	Pit	N	P	48	10-9
1941	Pit	N	P	1	0-0
1941	Bro	N	P	24	3-2
1942	Bos	A	P	34	9-3
1943	Bos	A	P	49	6-6
1946	Bos	A	P	18	3-1
	BRTR			387	76-57

BROWN, MORDECAI PETER CENTENNIAL (Three Finger)
b.Oct.19,1876 Nyesville,Ind.
d.Feb.14,1948

Yr	Cl	Lea	Pos	G	Rec
1903	St.L	N	P	26	9-13
1904	Chi	N	P	27	15-9
1905	Chi	N	P	30	17-9
1906	Chi	N	P	36	26-6
1907	Chi	N	P	35	20-6
1908	Chi	N	P	44	29-9
1909	Chi	N	P	50	27-9
1910	Chi	N	P	46	25-14
1911	Chi	N	P	53	21-11
1912	Chi	N	P	16	5-6
1913	Cin	N	P	39	11-12
1914	St.L	F	M-P	26	11-5
1914	Bro	F	P	6	3-6
1915	Chi	F	P	35	17-8
1916	Chi	N	P	12	2-3
		BBTR		481	238-126

BROWN, MYRL L.
b.Oct.10,1897 Waynesboro,Pa.

Yr	Cl	Lea	Pos	G	Rec
1922	Pit	N	P	7	3-1
		BRTR			

BROWN, NORMAN
b.Feb.1,1919 Evergreen,N.C.

Yr	Cl	Lea	Pos	G	Rec
1943	Phi	A	P	1	0-0
1946	Phi	A	P	4	0-1
		BBTR		5	0-1

BROWN, OLIVER S.

Yr	Cl	Lea	Pos	G	Rec
1872	Atl	n	O	4	NR
1874	Bal	n	S	1	.000
1875	Atl	n	1-O	3	.000
				8	NR

BROWN, PAUL DWAYNE
b.June18,1941 Ft.Smith,Ark.

Yr	Cl	Lea	Pos	G	Rec
1961	Phi	N	P	5	0-1
1962	Phi	N	P	23	0-6
		BRTR		28	0-7

BROWN, PAUL PERCIVAL (Ray)
b.Jan.30,1889 Chicago,Ill.

Yr	Cl	Lea	Pos	G	Rec
1909	Chi	N	P	1	1-0

BROWN, RICHARD ERNEST
b.Jan.17,1935 Shinnston,W.Va.

Yr	Cl	Lea	Pos	G	Rec
1957	Cle	A	C	34	.263
1958	Cle	A	C	68	.237
1959	Cle	A	C	48	.220
1960	Chi	A	C	16	.163
1961	Det	A	C	93	.266
1962	Det	A	C	134	.241
		BRTR		393	.244

BROWN, RICHARD P. (Stub)
b.Aug.3,1870 Baltimore,Md.
d.Mar.11,1948

Yr	Cl	Lea	Pos	G	Rec
1893	Bal	N	P	11	0-0
1894	Bal	N	P	9	4-2
1897	Cin	N	P	2	0-2
		TL		22	4-4

BROWN, ROBERT M.
Non-playing manager Lou (a) 1889

BROWN, ROBERT M.
b.1891

Yr	Cl	Lea	Pos	G	Rec
1914	Buf	F	P	15	0-0
		BRTR			

BROWN, ROBERT MURRAY
b.Apr.1,1911 Ashmont,Mass.

Yr	Cl	Lea	Pos	G	Rec
1930	Bos	N	P	3	0-0
1931	Bos	N	P	3	0-1
1932	Bos	N	P	35	14-7
1933	Bos	N	P	6	0-0
1934	Bos	N	P	16	1-3
1935	Bos	N	P	16	1-8
1936	Bos	N	P	2	0-2
		BRTR		81	16-21

BROWN, ROBERT WILLIAM (Doc)
b.Oct.25,1924 Seattle,Wash.

Yr	Cl	Lea	Pos	G	Rec
1946	NY	A	S-3	7	.333
1947	NY	A	S-3-O	69	.300
1948	NY	A	2-S-3-O	113	.300
1949	NY	A	3-O	104	.283
1950	NY	A	3	95	.267
1951	NY	A	3	103	.268
1952	NY	A	3	29	.247
1954	NY	A	3	28	.217
		BLTR		548	.279

BROWN, SAMUEL WAKEFIELD
b.May 21,1878 Webster,Pa.
d.Nov.8,1931

Yr	Cl	Lea	Pos	G	Rec
1906	Bos	N	C	65	.208
1907	Bos	N	C	66	.190
		BRTR		131	.199

BROWN, THOMAS MICHAEL (Buckshot)
b.Dec.6,1927 Brooklyn,N.Y.

Yr	Cl	Lea	Pos	G	Rec
1944	Bro	N	S	46	.164
1945	Bro	N	S-O	57	.245
1947	Bro	N	S-3-O	15	.235
1948	Bro	N	1-3	54	.241
1949	Bro	N	O	41	.303
1950	Bro	N	O	48	.291
1951	Bro	N	O	11	.160
1951	Phi	N	1-2-3-O	78	.219
1952	Phi	N	1-O	18	.160
1952	Chi	N	1-2-S	61	.320
1953	Chi	N	S-O	65	.196
		BRTR		494	.241

BROWN, THOMAS T.
b.Sept.21,1860 Liverpool,England
d.Oct.27,1927

Yr	Cl	Lea	Pos	G	Rec
1882	Bal	a	P-O	46	0-0 .293
1883	Col	a	P-S-O	97	0-2 .276
1884	Col	a	P-O	107	1-1 .275
1885	Pit	a	O	108	.304
1886	Pit	a	O	114	.280
1887	Pit	N	O	46	.284
1887	Ind	N	O	36	.223
1888	Bos	N	O	107	.247
1889	Bos	N	O	88	.232
1890	Bos	p	O	127	.277
1891	Bos	a	O	137	.323
1892	Lou	N	O	153	.232
1893	Lou	N	O	121	.253
1894	Lou	N	O	130	.251
1895	St.L	N	O	87	.226
1895	Was	N	O	31	.227
1896	Was	N	O	113	.299
1897	Was	N	M-O	116	.287
1898	Was	N	M-O	15	.164
		BLTR		1779	1-3 .269

BROWN, WALTER GEORGE (Jumbo)
b.Apr.30,1907 Greene,R.I.

Yr	Cl	Lea	Pos	G	Rec
1925	Chi	N	P	2	0-0
1927	Cle	A	P	8	0-2
1928	Cle	A	P	5	0-1
1932	NY	A	P	19	5-2
1933	NY	A	P	21	7-5
1935	NY	A	P	20	6-5
1936	NY	A	P	20	1-4
1937	Cin	N	P	4	1-0
1937	NY	N	P	4	1-0
1938	NY	N	P	43	5-3
1939	NY	N	P	31	4-0
1940	NY	N	P	41	2-4
1941	NY	N	P	31	1-5
		BRTR		249	33-31

BROWN, WALTER IRVING
b.Apr.23,1915 Jamestown,N.Y.

Yr	Cl	Lea	Pos	G	Rec
1947	St.L	A	P	19	1-0
		BRTR			

BROWN, WILLARD
b.1866 SanFrancisco,Cal.
d.Dec.20,1897

Yr	Cl	Lea	Pos	G	Rec
1887	NY	N	C	47	.261
1888	NY	N	C	17	.271
1889	NY	N	C	33	.259
1890	NY	p	C-1	59	.274
1891	Phi	N	1	112	.242
1893	Bal	N	1	7	.129
1893	Lou	N	1	111	.320
1894	Lou	N	1	13	.192
1894	St.L	N	1	117	.257
		BRTR		416	.268

BROWN, WILLARD JESSE
b.June 26,1921 Shreveport,La.

Yr	Cl	Lea	Pos	G	Rec
1947	St.L	A	O	21	.179
		BRTR			

BROWN, WILLIAM V.
b.1885 Mexia,Tex.

Yr	Cl	Lea	Pos	G	Rec
1912	St.L	A	O	9	.200
		BLTR			

BROWNE, PRENTICE ALMONT
b.Mar.21,1929 Peekskill,N.Y.

Yr	Cl	Lea	Pos	G	Rec
1962	Hou	N	1	65	.210
		BLTL			

BROWNE, GEORGE E.
b.Nov.20,1876 Washington,D.C.
d.Dec.9,1920

Yr	Cl	Lea	Pos	G	Rec
1901	Phi	N	O	8	.192
1902	Phi	N	O	68	.237
1902	NY	N	O	55	.348
1903	NY	N	O	141	.313
1904	NY	N	O	149	.283
1905	NY	N	O	127	.293
1906	NY	N	O	121	.264
1907	NY	N	O	121	.260
1908	Bos	N	O	138	.228
1909	Chi	N	O	12	.200
1909	Was	A	O	103	.272
1910	Was	A	O	7	.182
1910	Chi	A	O	30	.241
1911	Bro	N	O	7	.333
1912	Phi	N	H	6	.200
		BLTR		1093	.274

BROWNE, JAMES WILLIAM EARL (Snitz)
b.Mar.5,1911 Louisville,Ky.

Yr	Cl	Lea	Pos	G	Rec
1935	Pit	N	1	9	.250
1936	Pit	N	1-O	8	.304
1937	Phi	N	1-O	105	.292
1938	Phi	N	1	21	.257
		BLTL		143	.283

BROWNING, CALVIN DUANE
b.Mar.16,1938 Burns Flat,Okla.

Yr	Cl	Lea	Pos	G	Rec
1960	St.L	N	P	1	0-0
		BLTL			

BROWNING, FRANK (Dutch)
b.Oct.29,1882 Falmouth,Ky.
d.May 20,1948

Yr	Cl	Lea	Pos	G	Rec
1910	Det	A	P	11	2-2
		BRTR			

BROWNING, LOUIS ROGER (Pete)
b.July 17,1861 Louisville,Ky.
d.Sept.10,1905

Yr	Cl	Lea	Pos	G	Rec
1882	Lou	a	2-S-3	69	.382
1883	Lou	a	1-2-S-3-O	83	.349
1884	Lou	a	P-1-3-O	105	0-1 .341
1885	Lou	a	O	113	.367
1886	Lou	a	O	112	.339
1887	Lou	a	O	134	.471
1888	Lou	a	O	99	.313
1889	Lou	a	O	83	.253
1890	Cle	p	O	118	.391
1891	Pit	N	O	50	.287
1891	Cin	N	O	51	.362
1892	Lou	N	O	21	.260

Yr	Cl	Lea	Pos	G	Rec
(Continued)					
1892	Cin	N	O	81	.300
1893	Lou	N	O	57	.371
1894	St.L	N	O	2	.143
1894	Bro	N	O	1	1.000
	BRTR			1179	0-1 .355

BROZEK, JONATHAN JOSEPH
(Played under name of
Jonathan Joseph Brooks)

BRUBAKER, WILBUR LEE (Bill)
b.Nov.7,1910 Cleveland,O.

Yr	Cl	Lea	Pos	G	Rec
1932	Pit	N	3	7	.417
1933	Pit	N	3	2	.000
1934	Pit	N	3	3	.333
1935	Pit	N	3	6	.000
1936	Pit	N	3	145	.289
1937	Pit	N	3	120	.254
1938	Pit	N	3	45	.295
1939	Pit	N	2-3	100	.232
1940	Pit	N	1-S-3	38	.192
1943	Bos	N	1-3	13	.421
	BRTR			479	.264

BRUCE, LOUIS
b.Jan.16,1877 Franklin Co.,N.Y.

Yr	Cl	Lea	Pos	G	Rec
1904	Phi	A	P-O	30	0-0 277
	BLTR				

BRUCE, ROBERT JAMES
b.May 16,1934 Detroit,Mich.

Yr	Cl	Lea	Pos	G	Rec
1959	Det	A	P	2	0-1
1960	Det	A	P	34	4-7
1961	Det	A	P	14	1-2
1962	Hou	N	P	32	10-9
	BRTR			82	15-19

BRUCKBAUER, FREDERICK JOHN
b.May 27,1938 New Ulm,Minn.

Yr	Cl	Lea	Pos	G	Rec
1961	Min	A	P	1	0-0
	BRTR				

BRUCKER, EARLE FRANCIS SR.
b.May 6,1901 Albany,N.Y.

Yr	Cl	Lea	Pos	G	Rec
1937	Phi	A	C	102	.259
1938	Phi	A	C	53	.374
1939	Phi	A	C	62	.291
1940	Phi	A	C	23	.196
1943	Phi	A	H	1	.000
	BRTR			241	.290

BRUCKMILLER, ANDREW
b.Jan.1,1882 Pittsburgh,Pa.

Yr	Cl	Lea	Pos	G	Rec
1905	Det	A	P	1	0-0
	BRTR				

BRUGGY, FRANK LEO
b.May 4,1891 Elizabeth.N.J.
d.Apr.5,1959

Yr	Cl	Lea	Pos	G	Rec
1921	Phi	N	C	96	.310
1922	Phi	A	C	53	.279
1923	Phi	A	C	54	.210
1924	Phi	A	C	50	.265
1925	Cin	N	C	6	.214
	BRTR			259	.277

BRUNER, JACK RAYMOND
b.July 1,1924 Waterloo,Ia.

Yr	Cl	Lea	Pos	G	Rec
1949	Chi	A	P	4	1-2
1950	Chi	A	P	9	0-0
1950	St.L	A	P	13	1-2
	BLTL			26	2-4

BRUNER, WALTER ROY
b.Feb.10,1918 Louisville,Ky.

Yr	Cl	Lea	Pos	G	Rec
1939	Phi	N	P	4	0-4
1940	Phi	N	P	2	0-0
1941	Phi	N	P	13	0-3
	BRTR			19	0-7

BRUNET, GEORGE STUART
b.June 8,1935 Houghton,Mich.

Yr	Cl	Lea	Pos	G	Rec
1956	KC	A	P	6	0-0
1957	KC	A	P	4	0-2
(Continued)					
1959	KC	A	P	2	0-0
1960	KC	A	P	3	0-2
1960	Mil	N	P	17	2-0
1961	Mil	N	P	5	0-0
1962	Hou	N	P	17	2-4
	BRTL			54	4-8

BRUSH, ROBERT

Yr	Cl	Lea	Pos	G	Rec
1907	Bos	N	1	2	.000

BRUTON, WILLIAM HARON
b.Dec.22,1929 Panola,Ala.

Yr	Cl	Lea	Pos	G	Rec
1953	Mil	N	O	151	.250
1954	Mil	N	O	142	.284
1955	Mil	N	O	149	.275
1956	Mil	N	O	147	.272
1957	Mil	N	O	79	.278
1958	Mil	N	O	100	.280
1959	Mil	N	O	133	.289
1960	Mil	N	O	151	.286
1961	Det	A	O	160	.257
1962	Det	A	O	147	.278
	BLTR			1359	.274

BRUYETTE, EDWARD
b.Aurora,Ill.

Yr	Cl	Lea	Pos	G	Rec
1901	Mil	A	O	28	.180
	TR				

BRYAN, BILLY RONALD
b.Dec.4,1938 Morgan,Ga.

Yr	Cl	Lea	Pos	G	Rec
1961	KC	A	C	9	.158
1962	KC	A	C	25	.149
	BLTR			34	.151

BRYANT, ...

Yr	Cl	Lea	Pos	G	Rec
1885	Det	N	2	1	.000

BRYANT, CLAIBORNE HENRY
(Clay)
b.Nov.16,1911 Lynchburg,Va.

Yr	Cl	Lea	Pos	G	Rec
1935	Chi	N	P	12	1-2
1936	Chi	N	P	32	1-2
1937	Chi	N	P	47	9-3
1938	Chi	N	P	50	19-11
1939	Chi	N	P	28	2-1
1940	Chi	N	P	16	0-1
	BRTR			185	32-20

BRYNAN, CHARLES R.
b.Philadelphia,Pa.

Yr	Cl	Lea	Pos	G	Rec
1888	Chi	N	P	3	2-1
1891	Bos	N	P	1	0-0
	BRTR			4	2-1

BUBSER, HAROLD FRED
b.Sept.28,1895 Chicago,Ill.

Yr	Cl	Lea	Pos	G	Rec
1922	Chi	A	H	3	.000
	BRTR				

BUCHA, JOHN GEORGE
b.Jan.22,1925 Allentown,Pa.

Yr	Cl	Lea	Pos	G	Rec
1948	St.L	N	C	2	.000
1950	St.L	N	C	22	.139
1953	Det	A	C	60	.222
	BRTR			84	.205

BUCHANAN, JAMES F.
b.July 11,1878 Smyth Co.,Va.

Yr	Cl	Lea	Pos	G	Rec
1905	St.L	A	P	22	7-9

BUCHEK, GERALD PETER
b.May 9,1942 St.Louis,Mo.

Yr	Cl	Lea	Pos	G	Rec
1961	St.L	N	S	31	.133
	BRTR				

BUCHER, JAMES QUINTER
b.Mar.24,1912 Manassas,Va.

Yr	Cl	Lea	Pos	G	Rec
1934	Bro	N	2	47	.226
1935	Bro	N	2-3-O	123	.302
1936	Bro	N	2-3-O	110	.251
1937	Bro	N	2-3	125	.253
(Continued)					
1938	St.L	N	2	17	.228
1944	Bos	A	2-3	80	.274
1945	Bos	A	2-3	52	.225
	BLTR			554	.265

BUCKENBERGER, ALBERT C.
b.Jan.31,1861 Detroit,Mich.
d.July 1,1917
Non-playing manager Col (a) 1889-90, Pit (N) 1892-94, St.L (N) 1895 and Bos (N) 1902-04

BUCKEYE, GARLAND MAIERS (Gob)
b.Oct.16,1897 Heron Lake,Minn.

Yr	Cl	Lea	Pos	G	Rec
1918	Was	A	P	1	0-0
1925	Cle	A	P	30	13-8
1926	Cle	A	P	32	6-9
1927	Cle	A	P	35	10-17
1928	Cle	A	P	9	1-5
1928	NY	N	P	1	0-0
	BBTL			108	30-39

BUCKINGHAM, EDWARD TAYLOR
b.May 12,1874 Bridgeport,Conn.
d.July 30,1942

Yr	Cl	Lea	Pos	G	Rec
1895	Was	N	P	1	0-1

BUCKLES, JESSE ROBERT (Jim)
b.May 20,1890 Lordsburg,Cal.

Yr	Cl	Lea	Pos	G	Rec
1916	NY	A	P	2	0-0
	BLTL				

BUCKLEY, JOHN EDWARD
b.Mar.20,1870 Marlboro,Mass.
d.May 4,1942

Yr	Cl	Lea	Pos	G	Rec
1890	Buf	p	P	4	1-3

BUCKLEY, RICHARD D.
b.Sept.21,1858 Troy,N.Y.
d.Dec.12,1929

Yr	Cl	Lea	Pos	G	Rec
1888	Ind	N	C-3	71	.273
1889	Ind	N	C	65	.258
1890	NY	N	C	70	.255
1891	NY	N	C	67	.211
1892	St.L	N	C	106	.220
1893	St.L	N	C	7	.057
1894	St.L	N	C	28	.169
1894	Phi	N	C	39	.302
1895	Phi	N	C	29	.255
	TR			482	.243

BUDD, ...

Yr	Cl	Lea	Pos	G	Rec
1890	Cle	p	O	1	.000

BUDDIN, DONALD THOMAS
b.May 5,1934 Turbeville,S.C.

Yr	Cl	Lea	Pos	G	Rec
1956	Bos	A	S	114	.239
1958	Bos	A	S	136	.237
1959	Bos	A	S	151	.241
1960	Bos	A	S	124	.245
1961	Bos	A	S	115	.263
1962	Hou	N	S-3	40	.163
1962	Det	A	2-S-3	31	.229
	BRTR			711	.241

BUDNICK, MICHAEL JOE
b.Sept.15,1919 Astoria,Ore.

Yr	Cl	Lea	Pos	G	Rec
1946	NY	N	P	35	2-3
1947	NY	N	P	7	0-0
	BRTR			42	2-3

BUELOW, CHARLES JOHN
b.Jan.12,1877 Dubuque,Ia.
d.May 4,1951

Yr	Cl	Lea	Pos	G	Rec
1901	NY	N	3	19	.112
	BRTR				

BUELOW, FREDERICK WILLIAM
(Fritz)
b.Feb.13,1876 Berlin,Germany
d.Dec.27,1933

Yr	Cl	Lea	Pos	G	Rec
1899	St.L	N	C	7	.285
1900	St.L	N	C	7	.235
1901	Det	A	C	69	.229
1902	Det	A	C-1	64	.223
1903	Det	A	C	90	.222
1904	Det	A	C	42	.115

Yr Cl Lea Pos G Rec

(Continued)
1904 Cle A C 42 .180
1905 Cle A C 74 .174
1906 Cle A C 34 .163
1907 St.L A C 26 .147
BRTR 455 .182

BUES, ARTHUR FREDERICK
b.Mar.3,1888 Milwaukee,Wis.
d.Nov.7,1954
1913 Bos N 3 2 .000
1914 Chi N 2-3 14 .227
BRTR 16 .222

BUFFINTON, CHARLES G.
b.June 14,1861 Fall River,Mass.
d.Sept.23,1907
1882 Bos N P-1-O 15 2-3 .250
1883 Bos N P-1-O 86 24-13 .237
1884 Bos N P-1-O 84 40-14 .263
1885 Bos N P-1-O 82 23-27 .239
1886 Bos N P-1 44 7-10 .289
1887 Phi N P-O 66 21-17 .296
1888 Phi N P 44 28-15
1889 Phi N P 43 26-17
1890 Phi p M-P 41 19-13
1891 Bos a P 56 27-9
1892 Bal N P 13 5-8
BRTR 574 222-146 .253

BUHL, ROBERT RAY
b.Aug.12,1928 Saginaw,Mich.
1953 Mil N P 30 13-8
1954 Mil N P 31 2-7
1955 Mil N P 38 13-11
1956 Mil N P 38 18-8
1957 Mil N P 34 18-7
1958 Mil N P 11 5-2
1959 Mil N P 31 15-9
1960 Mil N P 36 16-9
1961 Mil N P 32 9-10
1962 Mil N P 1 0-1
1962 Chi N P 34 12-13
BRTR 316 121-85

BUKER, CYRIL OWEN
b.Feb.5,1919 Greenwood,Wis.
1945 Bro N P 42 7-2
BLTR

BUKER, HARRY L. (Happy)
1884 Det N S-O 30 .136

BULLARD, GEORGE DONALD
b.Oct.24,1928 Lynn,Mass.
1954 Det A S 4 .000
BRTR

BULLOCK, JAMES LEONARD
b.Jan.13,1845 Bristol,R.I.
d.Aug.12,1912
Non-playing manager Pro (N) 1880-81

BULLOCK, MALTON JOSEPH
b.Oct.12,1914 Biloxi,Miss.
1936 Phi A P 12 0-2
BLTL

BUNCE, JOSHUA
b.Brooklyn,N.Y.
1877 Har N O 1 .000

BUNNING, JAMES PAUL
b.Oct.23,1931 Covington,Ky.
1955 Det A P 15 3-5
1956 Det A P 15 5-1
1957 Det A P 45 20-8
1958 Det A P 36 14-12
1959 Det A P 40 17-13
1960 Det A P 38 11-14

Yr Cl Lea Pos G Rec

(Continued)
1961 Det A P 38 17-11
1962 Det A P 43 19-10
BRTR 270 106-74

BURBRINK, NELSON EDWARD
b.Dec.28,1921 Cincinnati,O.
1955 St.L N C 58 .276
BRTR

BURCH, ALBERT WILLIAM
b.Oct.7,1883 Albany,N.Y.
d.Oct.5,1926
1906 St.L N O 91 .266
1907 St.L N O 48 .227
1907 Bro N O 36 .292
1908 Bro N O 116 .243
1909 Bro N O 152 .271
1910 Bro N O 83 .236
1911 Bro N O 46 .228
BLTR 572 .254

BURCH, EARNEST W.
b.1858 DeKalb Co.,Ill.
1884 Cle N O 31 .201
1886 Bro a O 114 .253
1887 Bro a O 48 .400
BL 193 .285

BURCHELL, FREDERICK DUFF
b.July 14,1879 Perth Amboy,N.J.
d.Nov.20,1951
1903 Phi N P 6 0-3
1907 Bos A P 2 0-1
1908 Bos A P 32 10-8
1909 Bos A P 10 3-3
BLTL 50 13-15

BURDA, EDWARD ROBERT
b.July 16,1938 St.Louis,Mo.
1962 St.L N O 8 0-0
BLTL

BURDETTE, FREDDIE THOMASON
b.Sept.15,1936 Moultrie,Ga.
1962 Chi N P 8 0-0
BRTR

BURDETTE, SELVA LEWIS (Lew)
b.Nov.22,1926 Nitre,W.Va.
1950 NY A P 2 0-0
1951 Bos N P 3 0-0
1952 Bos N P 45 6-11
1953 Mil N P 46 15-5
1954 Mil N P 39 15-14
1955 Mil N P 45 13-8
1956 Mil N P 45 19-10
1957 Mil N P 41 17-9
1958 Mil N P 47 20-10
1959 Mil N P 52 21-15
1960 Mil N P 46 19-13
1961 Mil N P 42 18-11
1962 Mil N P 39 10-9
BRTR 492 173-115

BURDICK, WILLIAM B.
b.1862 Janesville,Wis.
1888 Ind N P 31 10-10
1889 Ind N P 9 0-3
BRTR 40 10-13

BURDOCK, JOHN JOSEPH (Black Jack)
b.1851 Brooklyn,N.Y.
d.Nov.28,1931
1872 Atl n C-2-S 36 NR
1873 Atl n C-2 55 NR
1874 Mut n 3 61 NR
1875 Har n 2-3 74 NR
1876 Har N 2 69 .248
1877 Har N 2-3 58 .260
1878 Bos N 2 60 .260
1879 Bos N 2 84 .240

Yr Cl Lea Pos G Rec

(Continued)
1880 Bos N 2 84 .256
1881 Bos N 2-S 73 .237
1882 Bos N 2 82 .239
1883 Bos N M-2 96 .330
1884 Bos N 2 84 .267
1885 Bos N 2 45 .142
1886 Bos N 2 59 .217
1887 Bos N 2 64 .305
1888 Bos N 2 21 .202
1888 Bro a 2 69 .125
1891 Bro N 2 3 .083
BRTR 1177 NR

BURG, JOSEPH PETER (Pete)
b.1886 Chicago,Ill.
1910 Bos N S-3 13 .348
TR

BURGESS, FORREST HARRILL (Smokey)
b.Feb.6,1927 Caroleen,N.C.
1949 Chi N C 46 .268
1951 Chi N C 94 .251
1952 Phi N C 110 .296
1953 Phi N C 102 .292
1954 Phi N C 108 .368
1955 Phi N C 7 .190
1955 Cin N C 116 .306
1956 Cin N C 90 .275
1957 Cin N C 90 .283
1958 Cin N C 99 .283
1959 Pit N C 114 .297
1960 Pit N C 110 .294
1961 Pit N C 100 .303
1962 Pit N C 103 .328
BLTR 1289 .300

BURGESS, THOMAS ROLAND
b.Sept.1,1927 London,Ont.,Canada
1954 St.L N O 17 .048
1962 LA A 1-O 87 .196
BLTL 104 .177

BURGO, WILLIAM ROSS
b.Nov.5,1922 Johnstown,Pa.
1943 Phi A O 17 .371
1944 Phi A O 27 .239
BRTR 44 .297

BURICH, WILLIAM MAX
b.May 29,1918 Calumet,Mich.
1942 Phi N S-3 25 .288
1946 Phi N 3 2 .000
BRTR 27 .284

BURK, CHARLES SANFORD (Sandy)
b.Apr.22,1887 Columbus,O.
d.Oct.11,1934
1910 Bro N P 4 0-3
1911 Bro N P 13 1-3
1912 Bro N P 2 0-0
1912 St.L N P 12 1-3
1913 St.L N P 19 0-2
1915 Pit F P 2 0-0
BRTR 52 2-11

BURK, MACK EDWIN
b.Apr.21,1935 Nacogdoches,Tex.
1956 Phi N C 15 1.000
1958 Phi N H 1 .000
BRTR 16 .500

BURKAM, ...
1915 St.L A H 1 .000

BURKART, ELMER ROBERT (Swede)
b.Feb.1,1917 Philadelphia,Pa.
1936 Phi N P 2 0-0
1937 Phi N P 7 0-0
1938 Phi N P 2 0-1
1939 Phi N P 5 1-0
BRTR 16 1-1

BURKE, DANIEL F.
b.Oct.25,1868 S.Abington,Mass.
d.Mar.20,1933

Yr	Cl	Lea	Pos	G	Rec
1890	Roc	a	O	30	.286
1890	Syr	a	C	9	.000
1892	Bos	N	C	1	.000
				40	.204

BURKE, EDWARD D.
b.Oct.6,1866 Northumberland,Pa.
d.Nov.26,1907

Yr	Cl	Lea	Pos	G	Rec
1890	Phi	N	O	100	.280
1890	Pit	N	O	32	.225
1891	Mil	a	O	34	.224
1892	Cin	N	2-O	14	.139
1892	NY	N	2-O	83	.266
1893	NY	N	O	135	.289
1894	NY	N	O	138	.299
1895	NY	N	O	39	.256
1895	Cin	N	O	56	.279
1896	Cin	N	O	122	.342
1897	Cin	N	O	94	.269
BRTR				847	.284

BURKE, FRANK ALOYSIUS
b.Feb.16,1880 Carbon Co.,Pa.
d.Sept.17,1946

Yr	Cl	Lea	Pos	G	Rec
1906	NY	N	O	8	.222
1907	Bos	N	O	36	.178
TR				44	.181

BURKE, JAMES TIMOTHY (Sunset)
b.Oct.12,1874 St.Louis,Mo.
d.Mar.26,1942

Yr	Cl	Lea	Pos	G	Rec
1898	Cle	N	3	13	.111
1901	Mil	A	S-3	64	.207
1901	Chi	A	3	41	.248
1901	Pit	N	3	34	.211
1902	Pit	N	2-S-3-O	55	.296
1903	St.L	N	2-3	113	.285
1904	St.L	N	3	118	.227
1905	St.L	N	M-3	122	.225
BRTR				560	.243

Non-playing manager St.L (A) 1918-20

BURKE, JOHN PATRICK
b.Jan.27,1877 Hazleton,Pa.
d.Aug.4,1950

Yr	Cl	Lea	Pos	G	Rec
1899	St.L	N	2	2	.333
1902	NY	N	P-O	4	0-1 .153
				6	0-1 .211

BURKE, JOSEPH M.
b.Cincinnati,O.
d.Dec.29,1896

Yr	Cl	Lea	Pos	G	Rec
1890	St.L	a	3	2	.571
1891	Cin	a	2	1	.250
				3	.455

BURKE, LEO PATRICK
b.May 6,1934 Hagerstown,Md.

Yr	Cl	Lea	Pos	G	Rec
1958	Bal	A	3-O	7	455
1959	Bal	A	2-3	5	.200
1961	LA	A	H	6	.000
1962	LA	A	S-3-O	19	.266
				37	.267

BURKE, LESLIE KINGDON (Buck)
b.Dec.18,1902 Lynn,Mass.

Yr	Cl	Lea	Pos	G	Rec
1923	Det	A	2-3	9	.090
1924	Det	A	2	72	.253
1925	Det	A	2	77	.289
1926	Det	A	2	38	.227
BLTR				196	.258

BURKE, MICHAEL E.
b.Cincinnati,O.
d.June 6,1889

Yr	Cl	Lea	Pos	G	Rec
1879	Cin	N	S-3-O	29	.222
BRTR					

BURKE, PATRICK EDWARD
b.May 13,1902 St.Louis,Mo.

Yr	Cl	Lea	Pos	G	Rec
1924	St.L	A	3	1	.000
BRTR					

BURKE, ROBERT JAMES
b.Jan.23,1907 Joliet,Ill.

Yr	Cl	Lea	Pos	G	Rec
1927	Was	A	P	36	3-2
1928	Was	A	P	26	2-4
1929	Was	A	P	37	6-8
1930	Was	A	P	24	3-4
1931	Was	A	P	30	8-3
1932	Was	A	P	23	3-6
1933	Was	A	P	25	4-3
1934	Was	A	P	41	8-8
1935	Was	A	P	16	1-8
1937	Phi	N	P	2	0-0
BLTL				260	38-46

BURKE, WALTER R.
b.California
d.Mar.3,1911

Yr	Cl	Lea	Pos	G	Rec
1882	Buf	N	P-O	1	0-1 .000
1883	Buf	N	P-O	1	0-0 .200
1884	Bos	U	P-O	45	19-15 .212
1887	Det	N	P	2	0-1
				49	19-17 .209

BURKE, WILLIAM IGNATIUS
b.July 11,1889 Clinton,Mass.

Yr	Cl	Lea	Pos	G	Rec
1910	Bos	N	P	20	1-0
1911	Bos	N	P	2	0-1
BLTL				22	1-1

BURKETT, JESSE CAIL (Crab)
b.Dec.4,1868 Wheeling, W.Va.
d.May 27,1953

Yr	Cl	Lea	Pos	G	Rec
1890	NY	N	P-O	101	3-11 .309
1891	Cle	N	O	40	.271
1892	Cle	N	O	145	.277
1893	Cle	N	O	124	.372
1894	Cle	N	O	124	.357
1895	Cle	N	O	132	.423
1896	Cle	N	O	133	.410
1897	Cle	N	O	128	.383
1898	Cle	N	O	148	.345
1899	St.L	N	O	138	.402
1900	St.L	N	O	142	.360
1901	St.L	N	O	142	.382
1902	St.L	A	P-S-3-O	137	0-1 .306
1903	St.L	A	O	133	.296
1904	St.L	A	O	147	.273
1905	Bos	A	O	149	.257
BLTL				2063	3-12 .342

BURKHART, WILLIAM KENNETH (Ken)
b.Nov.18,1916 Knoxville,Tenn.

Yr	Cl	Lea	Pos	G	Rec
1945	St.L	N	P	42	18-8
1946	St.L	N	P	25	6-3
1947	St.L	N	P	34	3-6
1948	St.L	N	P	21	0-0
1948	Cin	N	P	16	0-3
1949	Cin	N	P	11	0-0
BRTR				149	27-20

BURNETT, HERCULES H.
b.Aug.13,1869 Louisville,Ky.

Yr	Cl	Lea	Pos	G	Rec
1888	Lou	a	O	1	.000
1895	Lou	N	O	5	.411
				6	.333

BURNETT, JOHN HENDERSON
b.Nov.1,1906 Bartow,Fla.
d.Aug.12.1959

Yr	Cl	Lea	Pos	G	Rec
1927	Cle	A	2	17	.000
1928	Cle	A	S	3	.500
1929	Cle	A	S	19	.152
1930	Cle	A	S-3	54	.312
1931	Cle	A	2-S-3	111	.300
1932	Cle	A	2-S	129	.297
1933	Cle	A	2-S-3	83	.272
1934	Cle	A	S-3-O	72	.293
1935	St.L	A	2-S-3	70	.223
BLTR				558	.283

BURNETT, JOHN P.

Yr	Cl	Lea	Pos	G	Rec
1907	St.L	N	O	59	.238

BURNETTE, WALLACE HARPER
b.June 20,1929 Blairs,Va.

Yr	Cl	Lea	Pos	G	Rec
1956	KC	A	P	18	6-8
1957	KC	A	P	38	7-11
1958	KC	A	P	12	1-1
BRTR				68	14-20

BURNHAM, GEORGE WALTER (Watch)
b.May 20,1860 Albion,Mich.
d.Nov.18,1902
Non-playing manager Ind (N) 1887

BURNS, DENNIS
b.May 24,1899 Tiff City,Mo.

Yr	Cl	Lea	Pos	G	Rec
1923	Phi	A	P	3	2-1
1924	Phi	A	P	37	6-8
BRTR				40	8-9

BURNS, EDWARD JAMES
b.Oct.31,1887 San Francisco,Cal.
d.June 1,1942

Yr	Cl	Lea	Pos	G	Rec
1912	St.L	N	C	1	.000
1913	Phi	N	C	17	.200
1914	Phi	N	C	70	.259
1915	Phi	N	C	67	.241
1916	Phi	N	C	78	.233
1917	Phi	N	C	20	.204
1918	Phi	N	C	68	.207
BRTR				321	.229

BURNS, GEORGE HENRY (Tioga)
b.Jan.31,1893 Niles,O.

Yr	Cl	Lea	Pos	G	Rec
1914	Det	A	1	137	.291
1915	Det	A	1	105	.253
1916	Det	A	1	135	.286
1917	Det	A	1	119	.226
1918	Phi	A	1	130	.352
1919	Phi	A	1-O	126	.296
1920	Phi	A	1	21	.259
1920	Cle	A	1	45	.242
1921	Cle	A	1-O	84	.361
1922	Bos	A	1	147	.306
1923	Bos	A	1	146	.328
1924	Cle	A	1	129	.310
1925	Cle	A	1	127	.336
1926	Cle	A	1	151	.358
1927	Cle	A	1	140	.319
1928	Cle	A	1	82	.249
1928	NY	A	1	4	.500
1929	NY	A	1	9	.000
1929	Phi	A	1	29	.265
BRTR				1866	.307

BURNS, GEORGE JOSEPH
b.Nov.24,1889 Utica,N.Y.

Yr	Cl	Lea	Pos	G	Rec
1911	NY	N	O	6	.059
1912	NY	N	O	29	.294
1913	NY	N	O	150	.286
1914	NY	N	O	154	.303
1915	NY	N	O	155	.272
1916	NY	N	O	155	.279
1917	NY	N	O	152	.302
1918	NY	N	O	119	.290
1919	NY	N	O	139	.303
1920	NY	N	O	154	.287
1921	NY	N	O	149	.299
1922	Cin	N	O	156	.285
1923	Cin	N	O	154	.274
1924	Cin	N	O	93	.256
1925	Phi	N	O	88	.292
BRTR				1853	.287

BURNS, JAMES (Farmer)
b.Ashtabula,O.

Yr	Cl	Lea	Pos	G	Rec
1901	St.L	N	P	1	0-0
TR					

BURNS, JAMES M.
b.Quincy,Ill.

Yr	Cl	Lea	Pos	G	Rec
1888	KC	a	O	15	.273
1889	KC	a	O	133	.303
1891	Was	a	O	20	.313
				168	.303

BURNS, JOHN IRVING (Slug)
b.Aug.31,1907 Cambridge,Mass.

Yr	Cl	Lea	Pos	G	Rec
1930	St.L	A	1	8	.300
1931	St.L	A	1	144	.260
1932	St.L	A	1	150	.305
1933	St.L	A	1	144	.288
1934	St.L	A	1	154	.257
1935	St.L	A	1	143	.286
1936	St.L	A	1	9	.214
1936	Det	A	1	138	.283
	BLTL			890	.280

BURNS, JOHN JOSEPH
b.May 13,1877
d.June 24,1957

Yr	Cl	Lea	Pos	G	Rec
1903	Det	A	2	10	.256
1904	Det	A	2	4	.125
	BRTR			14	.211

BURNS, JOSEPH FRANCIS
b.Mar.26,1889 Ipswich,Mass.

Yr	Cl	Lea	Pos	G	Rec
1910	Cin	N	H	1	1.000
1913	Det	A	O	4	.309
	BLTL			5	.357

BURNS, JOSEPH FRANCIS
b.Feb.25,1900 Trenton,N.J.

Yr	Cl	Lea	Pos	G	Rec
1924	Chi	A	C	8	.105
		BRTR			

BURNS, JOSEPH JAMES
b.June 17,1916 Bryn Mawr,Pa.

Yr	Cl	Lea	Pos	G	Rec
1943	Bos	N	3-O	52	.208
1944	Phi	A	2-3	28	.240
1945	Phi	A	1-3-O	31	.256
	BRTR			111	.230

BURNS, PATRICK

Yr	Cl	Lea	Pos	G	Rec
1884	Bal	a	1	6	.154
1884	Bal	U	1	1	.500
				7	.200

BURNS, RICHARD SIMON
b.Dec.26,1863 Holyoke,Mass.
d.Nov.11,1890

Yr	Cl	Lea	Pos	G	Rec
1883	Det	N	P-O	36	2-12 .192
1884	Cin	U	P-O	68	25-16 .315
1885	St.L	N	P-O	14	0-0 .218
	BL			120	27-28 .271

BURNS, THOMAS EVERETT
b.Mar.30,1857 Honesdale,Pa.
d.Mar.19,1902

Yr	Cl	Lea	Pos	G	Rec
1880	Chi	N	P-C-S-3	82	0-0 .309
1881	Chi	N	2-S-3	84	.277
1882	Chi	N	2-S	84	.247
1883	Chi	N	2-S-O	97	.293
1884	Chi	N	S-3	82	.245
1885	Chi	N	2-S	111	.271
1886	Chi	N	3	111	.276
1887	Chi	N	3	115	.317
1888	Chi	N	3	134	.238
1889	Chi	N	3	136	.257
1890	Chi	N	3	139	.277
1891	Chi	N	3	57	.231
1892	Pit	N	M-3-O	12	.210
				1244	0-0 .271

BURNS, THOMAS P. (Oyster)
b.Sept.6,1862 Philadelphia,Pa.
d.Nov.16,1928

Yr	Cl	Lea	Pos	G	Rec
1884	Wil	U	S	2	.143
1884	Bal	a	P-2-3-O	36	0-0 .304
1885	Bal	a	P-2-S-O	76	7-4 .229
1887	Bal	a	S-3	140	.401
1888	Bal	a	S-O	77	.308
1888	Bro	a	2-S-O	52	.286
1889	Bro	a	O	132	.316
1890	Bro	N	O	119	.284
1891	Bro	N	O	122	.281
1892	Bro	N	O	139	.310
1893	Bro	N	O	107	.279
1894	Bro	N	O	126	.358
1895	Bro	N	O	17	.192
1895	NY	N	O	33	.298
	BRTR			1178	7-4 .310

BURNS, WILLIAM
b.Hagerstown,Md.

Yr	Cl	Lea	Pos	G	Rec
1902	Bal	A	H	1	1.000

BURNS, WILLIAM THOMAS
(Sleepy Bill)
b.Jan.29,1880 San Saba,Tex.
d.June 6,1953

Yr	Cl	Lea	Pos	G	Rec
1908	Was	A	P	23	6-11
1909	Was	A	P	6	2-0
1909	Chi	A	P	20	7-13
1910	Chi	A	P	1	0-0
1910	Cin	N	P	31	8-13
1911	Cin	N	P	6	0-0
1911	Phi	N	P	21	3-7
1912	Det	A	P	6	1-4
	BBTL			114	27-48

BURNSIDE, PETER WILLITS
b.July 2,1930 Evanston,Ill.

Yr	Cl	Lea	Pos	G	Rec
1955	NY	N	P	2	1-0
1957	NY	N	P	10	1-4
1958	SF	N	P	6	0-0
1959	Det	A	P	30	1-3
1960	Det	A	P	31	7-7
1961	Was	A	P	33	4-9
1962	Was	A	P	40	5-11
	BRTL			152	19-34

BURPO, GEORGE HARVIE
b.Oct.7,1922 Jenkins,Ky.

Yr	Cl	Lea	Pos	G	Rec
1946	Cin	N	P	2	0-0
		BRTL			

BURR, ALEXANDER THOMSON
b.Nov.1,1893 Chicago,Ill.
d.Nov.1,1918

Yr	Cl	Lea	Pos	G	Rec
1914	NY	A	O	1	.000
		BRTR			

BURRIGHT, LAWRENCE ALLEN
b.July 10,1937 Roseville,Ill.

Yr	Cl	Lea	Pos	G	Rec
1962	LA	N	2-S	115	.205
		BRTR			

BURRILL, FRANK ANDREW
(Buster)
b.Dec.22,1867 E.Weymouth,Mass.
d.May 8,1962

Yr	Cl	Lea	Pos	G	Rec
1891	NY	N	C	15	.075
1895	Bro	N	C	10	.160
1896	Bro	N	C	58	.307
1897	Bro	N	C	31	.238
	BRTR			114	.243

BURRILL, HARRY J.
b.1866 E. Weymouth,Mass.
d.Dec.11,1914

Yr	Cl	Lea	Pos	G	Rec
1891	St.L	a	P	9	3-2

BURRIS, ALVA BURTON
b.Jan.28,1874 Warwick,Md.
d.Mar.24,1938

Yr	Cl	Lea	Pos	G	Rec
1894	Phi	N	P	1	0-0

BURRIS, PAUL ROBERT
b.July 21,1923 Hickory,N.C.

Yr	Cl	Lea	Pos	G	Rec
1948	Bos	N	C	2	.500
1950	Bos	N	C	10	.174
1952	Bos	N	C	55	.220
1953	Mil	N	C	2	.000
	BRTR			69	.219

BURROUGHS, HENRY F.
b.1845 Detroit,Mich.

Yr	Cl	Lea	Pos	G	Rec
1871	Oly	n	3-O	12	.174
1872	Oly	n	O	2	NR
				14	NR

BURROWS, JOHN
b.Oct.30,1913 Winnfield,La.

Yr	Cl	Lea	Pos	G	Rec
1943	Phi	A	P	4	0-1
1943	Chi	N	P	23	0-2
1944	Chi	N	P	3	0-0
	BRTL			30	0-3

BURRUS, MAURICE LENNON
(Dick)
b.Jan.29,1898 Hatteras,N.C.

Yr	Cl	Lea	Pos	G	Rec
1919	Phi	A	1	70	.258
1920	Phi	A	1	71	.185
1925	Bos	N	1	152	.340
1926	Bos	N	1	131	.270
1927	Bos	N	1	72	.318
1928	Bos	N	1	64	.270
	BLTL			560	.291

BURT, FRANK J.
b.Camden,N.J.

Yr	Cl	Lea	Pos	G	Rec
1882	Bal	a	O	10	.108

BURTON, ELLIS NARRINGTON
b.Aug.12,1936 Los Angeles,Cal.

Yr	Cl	Lea	Pos	G	Rec
1958	St.L	N	O	8	233
1960	St.L	N	O	29	.214
	BBTR			37	.224

BURTSCHY, EDWARD FRANK (Moe)
b.Apr.18,1922 Cincinnati,O.

Yr	Cl	Lea	Pos	G	Rec
1950	Phi	A	P	9	0-1
1951	Phi	A	P	7	0-0
1954	Phi	A	P	46	5-4
1955	KC	A	P	7	2-0
1956	KC	A	P	21	3-1
	BRTR			90	10-6

BURWELL, RICHARD MATTHEW
b.Jan.23,1940 Alton,Ill.

Yr	Cl	Lea	Pos	G	Rec
1960	Chi	N	P	3	0-0
1961	Chi	N	P	2	0-0
	BRTR			5	0-0

BURWELL, WILLIAM EDWIN
b.May 27,1895 Jarbalo,Kan.

Yr	Cl	Lea	Pos	G	Rec
1920	St.L	A	P	35	6-4
1921	St.L	A	P	33	2-4
1928	Pit	N	P	4	1-0
	BLTR			72	9-8

Non-playing manager Pit (N) 1947

BUSBY, JAMES FRANKLIN
b.Jan.8,1927 Kenedy,Tex.

Yr	Cl	Lea	Pos	G	Rec
1950	Chi	A	O	18	.208
1951	Chi	A	O	143	.283
1952	Chi	A	O	16	.128
1952	Was	A	O	129	.244
1953	Was	A	O	150	.312
1954	Was	A	O	155	.298
1955	Was	A	O	47	.230
1955	Chi	A	O	99	.243
1956	Cle	A	O	135	.235
1957	Cle	A	O	30	.189
1957	Bal	A	O	86	.250
1958	Bal	A	3-O	113	.237

(Continued)

Yr	Cl	Lea	Pos	G	Rec
1959	Bos	A	O	61	.225
1960	Bos	A	O	1	.000
1960	Bal	A	O	79	.258
1961	Bal	A	O	75	.258
1962	Hou	N	C-O	15	.182
	BRTR			1352	.263

BUSBY, PAUL MILLER (Red)
b.Aug.25,1918 Waynesboro,Miss.

Yr	Cl	Lea	Pos	G	Rec
1941	Phi	N	O	10	.313
1943	Phi	N	O	26	.250
	BLTR			36	.268

BUSCH, EDGAR JOHN
b.Nov.6,1917 Lebanon,Ill.

Yr	Cl	Lea	Pos	G	Rec
1943	Phi	A	S	4	.294
1944	Phi	A	2-S-3	140	.271
1945	Phi	A	1-2-S-3	126	.250
	BRTR			270	.262

BUSH, GUY TERRELL
b.Aug.23,1905 Aberdeen,Miss.

Yr	Cl	Lea	Pos	G	Rec
1923	Chi	N	P	1	0-0
1924	Chi	N	P	16	2-5
1925	Chi	N	P	42	6-13
1926	Chi	N	P	35	13-9
1927	Chi	N	P	36	10-10
1928	Chi	N	P	42	15-6
1929	Chi	N	P	50	18-7
1930	Chi	N	P	46	15-10
1931	Chi	N	P	39	16-8
1932	Chi	N	P	40	19-11
1933	Chi	N	P	41	20-12
1934	Chi	N	P	41	18-10
1935	Pit	N	P	41	11-11
1936	Pit	N	P	16	1-3
1936	Bos	N	P	15	4-5
1937	Bos	N	P	33	8-15
1938	St.L	N	P	6	0-1
1945	Cin	N	P	4	0-0
	BRTR			544	176-136

BUSH, LESLIE AMBROSE
(Bullet Joe)
b.Nov.27,1892 Brainerd,Minn.

Yr	Cl	Lea	Pos	G	Rec
1912	Phi	A	P	1	0-0
1913	Phi	A	P	33	13-7
1914	Phi	A	P	35	16-12
1915	Phi	A	P	25	5-15
1916	Phi	A	P	41	15-22
1917	Phi	A	P	37	11-17
1918	Bos	A	P	36	15-15
1919	Bos	A	P	5	0-0
1920	Bos	A	P	45	15-15
1921	Bos	A	P	51	16-9
1922	NY	A	P	39	26-7
1923	NY	A	P	38	19-15
1924	NY	A	P	60	17-16
1925	St.L	A	P-O	57	14-14 .254
1926	Was	A	P	17	1-8
1926	Pit	N	P	28	6-6
1927	Pit	N	P	10	1-2
1927	NY	N	P	3	1-1
1928	Phi	A	P	15	2-1
	BRTR			576	193-182 .242

BUSH, OWEN JOSEPH (Donie)
b.Oct.8,1868 Indianapolis,Ind.

Yr	Cl	Lea	Pos	G	Rec
1908	Det	A	S	20	.294
1909	Det	A	S	157	.273
1910	Det	A	S	142	.262
1911	Det	A	S	150	.232
1912	Det	A	S	144	.231
1913	Det	A	S	152	.251
1914	Det	A	S	157	.252
1915	Det	A	S	155	.228
1916	Det	A	S	145	.225
1917	Det	A	S	147	.281
1918	Det	A	S	128	.234
1919	Det	A	S	129	.244
1920	Det	A	S	141	.263
1921	Det	A	2-S	104	.279
1921	Was	A	S	23	.238

(Continued)

Yr	Cl	Lea	Pos	G	Rec
1922	Was	A	3	41	.238
1923	Was	A	M-2-3	10	.409
	BBTR			1945	.250

Non-playing manager Pit (N) 1927-29, Chi (A) 1930-31, and Cin (N) 1933

BUSHELMAN, JOHN FRANCIS
b.Aug.29,1885 Cincinnati,O.
d.Oct.26,1955

Yr	Cl	Lea	Pos	G	Rec
1909	Cin	N	P	1	0-1
1911	Bos	A	P	3	0-1
1912	Bos	A	P	3	1-0
	BRTR			7	1-2

BUSHEY, FRANCIS CLYDE
b.Aug.1,1906 Wheaton,Kan.

Yr	Cl	Lea	Pos	G	Rec
1927	Bos	A	P	1	0-0
1930	Bos	A	P	11	0-1
	BRTR			12	0-1

BUSHONG, ALBERT JOHN (Doc)
b.Sept.15,1856 Philadelphia,Pa.
d.Aug.19,1908

Yr	Cl	Lea	Pos	G	Rec
1875	Atl	n	C	1	.600
1876	Ath	N	C	5	.048
1880	Wor	N	C-O	37	.163
1881	Wor	N	C	75	.229
1882	Wor	N	C	69	.152
1883	Cle	N	C	61	.172
1884	Cle	N	C	60	.231
1885	St.L	a	C	85	.265
1886	St.L	a	C	107	.229
1887	St.L	a	C	53	.295
1888	Bro	a	C	69	.220
1889	Bro	a	C	25	.163
1890	Bro	N	C	16	.234
	BRTR			663	.219

BUSKEY, JOSEPH HENRY
b.Dec.18,1902 Cumberland,Md.
d.Apr.11,1949

Yr	Cl	Lea	Pos	G	Rec
1926	Phi	N	S	5	.000
	BRTR				

BUTCHER, ALBERT MAXWELL
(Max)
b.Sept.21,1910 Holden,W.Va.
d.Sept.15,1957

Yr	Cl	Lea	Pos	G	Rec
1936	Bro	N	P	42	6-6
1937	Bro	N	P	40	11-15
1938	Bro	N	P	25	5-4
1938	Phi	N	P	12	4-8
1939	Phi	N	P	19	2-13
1939	Pit	N	P	14	4-4
1940	Pit	N	P	36	8-9
1941	Pit	N	P	33	17-12
1942	Pit	N	P	24	5-8
1943	Pit	N	P	33	10-8
1944	Pit	N	P	36	13-11
1945	Pit	N	P	28	10-8
	BRTR			342	95-106

BUTCHER, HENRY C.
b.July 12,1887 Chicago,Ill.

Yr	Cl	Lea	Pos	G	Rec
1911	Cle	A	O	38	.240
1912	Cle	A	O	24	.195
	BRTR			62	.223

BUTKA, EDWARD LUKE
b.Jan.7,1919 Canonsburg,Pa.

Yr	Cl	Lea	Pos	G	Rec
1943	Was	A	1	3	.333
1944	Was	A	1	15	.195
	BRTR			18	.220

BUTLAND, WILBURN RUE (Bill)
b.Mar.22,1918 Terre Haute,Ind.

Yr	Cl	Lea	Pos	G	Rec
1940	Bos	A	P	3	1-2
1942	Bos	A	P	23	7-1
1946	Bos	A	P	5	1-0
1947	Bos	A	P	1	0-0
	BRTL			32	9-3

BUTLER, ARTHUR E.
(Real name Arthur E. Bouthillier)
b.Dec.19,1887 Fall River,Mass.

Yr	Cl	Lea	Pos	G	Rec
1911	Bos	N	3	19	.176

(Continued)

Yr	Cl	Lea	Pos	G	Rec
1912	Pit	N	2	43	.273
1913	Pit	N	2-S	82	.280
1914	St.L	N	S	86	.201
1915	St.L	N	S	130	.254
1916	St.L	N	O	86	.209
	BRTR			446	.241

BUTLER, CECIL DEAN
b.Oct.23,1937 Dallas,Ga.

Yr	Cl	Lea	Pos	G	Rec
1962	Mil	N	P	9	2-0
	BRTR				

BUTLER, CHARLES THOMAS
b.May 12,1906 Green Cove Springs,Fla

Yr	Cl	Lea	Pos	G	Rec
1933	Phi	N	P	1	0-0
	BRTL				

BUTLER, FRANK DEAN
(Goldbrick)
b.July 18,1860 Savannah,Ga.
d.July 10,1945

Yr	Cl	Lea	Pos	G	Rec
1895	NY	N	O	5	.272
	BLTL				

BUTLER, FRANK E. (Kid)
b.1862 Boston,Mass.
d.Apr.9,1921

Yr	Cl	Lea	Pos	G	Rec
1884	Bos	U	O	70	.160

BUTLER, ISAAC B.
b.Aug.22,1873 Montcalm Co.,Mich.

Yr	Cl	Lea	Pos	G	Rec
1902	Bal	A	P-O	18	2-11 .115
	TR				

BUTLER, JOHN ALBERT
b.July 26,1879 S.Boston,Mass.

Yr	Cl	Lea	Pos	G	Rec
1904	St.L	N	C	12	.167
1906	Bro	N	C	1	.000
1907	Bro	N	C	29	.127
	BRTR			42	.127

BUTLER, JOHN STEPHEN
(Trolley Line)
b.Mar.20,1894 Eureka,Kan.

Yr	Cl	Lea	Pos	G	Rec
1926	Bro	N	S-3	147	.269
1927	Bro	N	S-3	149	.238
1928	Chi	N	3	62	.270
1929	St.L	N	S-3	17	.164
	BRTR			375	.252

BUTLER, ORMOND H.
b.Baltimore,Md.
Non-playing manager Pit (a) 1883

BUTLER, RICHARD H.
b.Brooklyn,N.Y.

Yr	Cl	Lea	Pos	G	Rec
1897	Lou	N	C	10	.184
1899	Was	N	C	12	.263
				22	.224

BUTLER, WILLIS EVERETT (Kid)
b.Aug.9,1887 Franklin,Pa.

Yr	Cl	Lea	Pos	G	Rec
1907	St.L	A	3	20	.220
	BRTR				

BUTLER, W. J.
b.1861 New Orleans,La.

Yr	Cl	Lea	Pos	G	Rec
1884	Ind	a	O	9	.206

BUTTERS, THOMAS ARDEN
b.Apr.8,1938 Delaware,O.

Yr	Cl	Lea	Pos	G	Rec
1962	Pit	N	P	4	0-0
	BRTR				

BUTTERY, FRANK
b.Norwalk,Conn.

Yr	Cl	Lea	Pos	G	Rec
1872	Man	n	P-3-O	13	1-2 NR

BUXTON, RALPH STANLEY
b.June 7,1914 Weyburn,Sask.,Canada

Yr	Cl	Lea	Pos	G	Rec
1938	Phi	A	P	5	0-1
1949	NY	A	P	14	0-1
	BRTR			19	0-2

BUZAS, JOSEPH JOHN
b.Oct.2,1919 Alpha,N.J.

Yr	Cl	Lea	Pos	G	Rec
1945	NY	A	S	30	.262
	BRTR				

BUZHARDT, JOHN WILLIAM
b.Aug.17,1936 Newberry,S.C.

Yr	Cl	Lea	Pos	G	Rec
1958	Chi	N	P	6	3-0
1959	Chi	N	P	31	4-5
1960	Phi	N	P	32	5-16
1961	Phi	N	P	41	6-18
1962	Chi	A	P	28	8-12
	BRTR			138	26-51

BYERLY, ELDRED WILLIAM (Bud)
b.Oct.26,1920 Webster Groves,Mo.

Yr	Cl	Lea	Pos	G	Rec
1943	St.L	N	P	2	1-0
1944	St.L	N	P	9	2-2
1945	St.L	N	P	33	4-5
1950	Cin	N	P	4	0-1
1951	Cin	N	P	41	2-1
1952	Cin	N	P	12	0-1
1956	Was	A	P	25	2-4
1957	Was	A	P	47	6-6
1958	Was	A	P	17	2-0
1958	Bos	A	P	18	1-2
1959	SF	N	P	11	1-0
1960	SF	N	P	19	1-0
	BRTR			238	22-22

BYERS, JOHN WILLIAM (Big Bill)
b.Baltimore,Md.

Yr	Cl	Lea	Pos	G	Rec
1904	St.L	N	C	17	.217
	TR				

BYRD, HARRY GLADWIN
b.Feb.3,1925 Darlington,S.C.

Yr	Cl	Lea	Pos	G	Rec
1950	Phi	A	P	6	0-0
1952	Phi	A	P	37	15-15
1953	Phi	A	P	40	11-20
1954	NY	A	P	25	9-7
1955	Bal	A	P	14	3-2
1955	Chi	A	P	25	4-6
1956	Chi	A	P	3	0-1
1957	Det	A	P	37	4-3
	BRTR			187	46-54

BYRD, SAMUEL DEWEY
b.Oct.15,1907 Bremen,Ga.

Yr	Cl	Lea	Pos	G	Rec
1929	NY	A	O	62	.312
1930	NY	A	O	92	.284
1931	NY	A	O	115	.270
1932	NY	A	O	104	.297
1933	NY	A	O	85	.280
1934	NY	A	O	106	.246
1935	Cin	N	O	121	.262
1936	Cin	N	O	59	.248
	BRTR			744	.274

BYRNE, CHARLES H.
b.Sept.1843 New York,N.Y.
d.Jan.4,1898
Non-playing manager Bro (A) 1885-87

BYRNE, GERALD WILFRED
b.Feb.2,1907 Parnell,Mich.
d.Aug.11,1955

Yr	Cl	Lea	Pos	G	Rec
1929	Chi	A	P	3	0-1
	BRTR				

BYRNE, JOHN K.
(Played under name of John K. O'Brien)

BYRNE, ROBERT MATHEW
b.Dec.31,1885 St.Louis,Mo.

Yr	Cl	Lea	Pos	G	Rec
1907	St.L	N	3	149	.256
1908	St.L	N	3	126	.191
1909	St.L	N	3	105	.214
1909	Pit	N	3	46	.256

(Continued)

Yr	Cl	Lea	Pos	G	Rec
1910	Pit	N	3	148	.296
1911	Pit	N	3	152	.259
1912	Pit	N	3	130	.288
1913	Pit	N	3	113	.270
1913	Phi	N	3	19	.224
1914	Phi	N	2-3	126	.272
1915	Phi	N	3	105	.209
1916	Phi	N	3	48	.234
1917	Phi	N	3	13	.357
1917	Chi	A	2	1	.000
	BRTR			1281	.253

BYRNE, THOMAS JOSEPH
b.Dec.31,1919 Baltimore,Md.

Yr	Cl	Lea	Pos	G	Rec
1943	NY	A	P	13	2-1
1946	NY	A	P	14	0-1
1947	NY	A	P	4	0-0
1948	NY	A	P	31	8-5
1949	NY	A	P	35	15-7
1950	NY	A	P	34	15-9
1951	NY	A	P	9	2-1
1951	St.L	A	P	34	4-10
1952	St.L	A	P	40	7-14
1953	Chi	A	P	18	2-0
1953	Was	A	P	14	0-5
1954	NY	A	P	7	3-2
1955	NY	A	P	45	16-5
1956	NY	A	P	44	7-3
1957	NY	A	P	35	4-6
	BLTL			377	85-69

BYRNES, JAMES JOSEPH
b.Jan.5,1880 San Francisco,Cal.
d.July 31,1941

Yr	Cl	Lea	Pos	G	Rec
1906	Phi	A	C	10	.167
	BRTR				

BYRNES, MILTON JOHN (Skippy)
b.Nov.15,1916 St.Louis,Mo.

Yr	Cl	Lea	Pos	G	Rec
1943	St.L	A	O	129	.280
1944	St.L	A	O	128	.295
1945	St.L	A	1-O	133	.249
	BLTL			390	.274

CABALLERO, RALPH JOSEPH
(Putsy)
b.Nov. 5,1927 New Orleans,La.

Yr	Cl	Lea	Pos	G	Rec
1944	Phi	N	3	4	.000
1945	Phi	N	3	9	.000
1947	Phi	N	2-3	2	.143
1948	Phi	N	2-3	113	.245
1949	Phi	N	2-S	29	.279
1950	Phi	N	2-S-3	46	.167
1951	Phi	N	2-S-3	84	.186
1952	Phi	N	2-S-3	35	.238
	BRTR			322	.228

CABRERA, ALFREDO A.
b.1883 Canary Islands

Yr	Cl	Lea	Pos	G	Rec
1913	St.L	N	S	1	.000
	TR				

CADORE, LEON JOSEPH
(Caddy)
b.Nov.20,1891 Chicago,Ill.
d.Mar.16,1958

Yr	Cl	Lea	Pos	G	Rec
1915	Bro	N	P	7	0-2
1916	Bro	N	P	1	0-0
1917	Bro	N	P	37	13-13
1918	Bro	N	P	2	1-0
1919	Bro	N	P	37	14-12
1920	Bro	N	P	35	15-14
1921	Bro	N	P	35	13-14
1922	Bro	N	P	29	8-15
1923	Bro	N	P	9	4-1
1923	Chi	A	P	1	0-1
1924	NY	N	P	2	0-0
	BRTR			195	68-72

CADY, CHARLES B.
b.Chicago,Ill.

Yr	Cl	Lea	Pos	G	Rec
1883	Cle	N	P-O	3	0-1 .000

(Continued)

Yr	Cl	Lea	Pos	G	Rec
1884	Chi	U	P-O	6	2-0 .095
1884	KC	U	2	1	.000
				10	2-1 .056

CADY, FORREST LEROY
(Hick)
b.Jan.26,1886 Bishop Hill,Ill.
d.Mar.3,1946

Yr	Cl	Lea	Pos	G	Rec
1912	Bos	A	C	47	.259
1913	Bos	A	C	39	.242
1914	Bos	A	C	61	.258
1915	Bos	A	C	78	.278
1916	Bos	A	C	78	.191
1917	Bos	A	C	17	.152
1919	Phi	N	C	34	.214
	BRTR			354	.239

CAFEGO, THOMAS
b.Aug.21,1911 Whipple,W.Va.
d.Oct.29,1961

Yr	Cl	Lea	Pos	G	Rec
1937	St.L	A	O	4	.000
	BLTR				

CAFFIE, JOSEPH CLIFFORD
b.Feb.14,1931 Ramer,Ala.

Yr	Cl	Lea	Pos	G	Rec
1956	Cle	A	O	12	.342
1957	Cle	A	O	32	.270
	BLTR			44	.291

CAFFYN, BENJAMIN THOMAS
b.Feb.10,1880 Peoria,Ill.
d.Nov.22,1942

Yr	Cl	Lea	Pos	G	Rec
1906	Cle	A	O	30	.194

CAHILL, JOHN FRANCIS
b.Philadelphia,Pa.
d.Nov.1,1901

Yr	Cl	Lea	Pos	G	Rec
1884	Col	a	P-O	59	1-0 .210
1886	St.L	N	O	125	.198
1887	Ind	N	O	68	.231
	BR			252	1-0 .211

CAHILL, THOMAS H.
b.Oct.1868 Fall River,Mass.
d.Dec.25,1894

Yr	Cl	Lea	Pos	G	Rec
1891	Lou	a	P-C-S	119	0-0 .263

CAIN, MERRITT PATRICK
(Sugar)
b.Apr.5,1908 Macon,Ga.

Yr	Cl	Lea	Pos	G	Rec
1932	Phi	A	P	10	3-4
1933	Phi	A	P	39	13-12
1934	Phi	A	P	36	9-17
1935	Phi	A	P	6	0-5
1935	St.L	A	P	31	9-8
1936	St.L	A	P	4	1-1
1936	Chi	A	P	31	14-10
1937	Chi	A	P	18	4-2
1938	Chi	A	P	5	0-1
	BLTR			180	53-60

CAIN, ROBERT MAX
b.Oct.16,1924 Longford,Kan.

Yr	Cl	Lea	Pos	G	Rec
1949	Chi	A	P	6	0-0
1950	Chi	A	P	35	9-12
1951	Chi	A	P	4	1-2
1951	Det	A	P	35	11-10
1952	St.L	A	P	35	12-10
1953	St.L	A	P	34	4-10
1954	Chi	A	H	1*	.000
	BLTL			150	37-44 .196

CAITHAMER, GEORGE THEODORE
(Sidel)
b.July 22,1910 Chicago,Ill.
d.June 1,1954

Yr	Cl	Lea	Pos	G	Rec
1934	Chi	A	C	5	.316
	BRTR				

CALDERONE, SAMUEL FRANCIS

b.Feb.6,1926 Beverly,N.J.

Yr	Cl	Lea	Pos	G	Rec
1950	NY	N	C	34	.299
1953	NY	N	C	35	.222
1954	Mil	N	C	22	.379
			BRTR	91	.291

CALDWELL, BRUCE

b.Feb.8,1906 Ashton,R.I.

d.Feb.15,1959

Yr	Cl	Lea	Pos	G	Rec
1928	Cle	A	O	18	.222
1932	Bro	N	1	7	.091
			BRTR	25	.184

CALDWELL, CHARLES WILLIAM

b.Aug.2,1901 Bristol,Va.

d.Nov.1,1957

Yr	Cl	Lea	Pos	G	Rec
1925	NY	A	P	3	0-0
			BRTR		

CALDWELL, EARL WELTON
(Teach)

b.Apr.9,1905 Sparks,Tex.

Yr	Cl	Lea	Pos	G	Rec
1928	Phi	N	P	5	1-4
1935	St.L	A	P	6	3-2
1936	St.L	A	P	41	7-16
1937	St.L	A	P	9	0-0
1945	Chi	A	P	27	6-7
1946	Chi	A	P	39	13-4
1947	Chi	A	P	40	1-4
1948	Chi	A	P	25	1-5
1948	Bos	A	P	8	1-1
			BRTR	200	33-43

CALDWELL, RALPH GRANT

b.Jan.18,1884 Philadelphia,Pa.

Yr	Cl	Lea	Pos	G	Rec
1904	Phi	N	P	6	3-3
1905	Phi	N	P	7	1-1
			BLTL	13	4-4

CALDWELL, RAYMOND BENJAMIN
(Rube)

b.Apr.26,1888 Corydon,Pa.

Yr	Cl	Lea	Pos	G	Rec
1910	NY	A	P	6	1-0
1911	NY	A	P	59	14-14
1912	NY	A	P	39	8-16
1913	NY	A	P	51	9-8
1914	NY	A	P	58	17-9
1915	NY	A	P	72	19-16
1916	NY	A	P	45	5-12
1917	NY	A	P	63	13-16
1918	NY	A	P-O	65	9-8 .291
1919	Bos	A	P	31	5-4
1919	Cle	A	P	8	7-1
1920	Cle	A	P	41	20-10
1921	Cle	A	P	37	6-6
			BLTR	575	133-120 .248

CALHOUN, JOHN CHARLES

b.Dec.14,1879

d.Feb.27,1947

Yr	Cl	Lea	Pos	G	Rec
1902	St.L	N	1-3-O	17	.156
			BRTR		

CALHOUN, WILLIAM DAVITTE
(Mary)

b.June 23,1890 Cartersville,Ga.

d.Feb.11,1955

Yr	Cl	Lea	Pos	G	Rec
1913	Bos	N	1	6	.076
			BLTL		

CALIGIURI, FREDERICK JOHN

b.Oct.22,1918 W.Hickory,Pa.

Yr	Cl	Lea	Pos	G	Rec
1941	Phi	A	P	5	2-2
1942	Phi	A	P	13	0-3
			BRTR	18	2-5

CALIHAN, WILLIAM T.

b.1869 Oswego,N.Y.

d.Dec.20,1917

Yr	Cl	Lea	Pos	G	Rec
1890	Roc	a	P	48	18-13
1891	Ath	a	P	16	5-7
				64	23-20

CALLAGHAN, MARTIN FRANCIS

b.June 9,1901 Norwood,Mass.

Yr	Cl	Lea	Pos	G	Rec
1922	Chi	N	O	74	.257
1923	Chi	N	O	61	.225
1928	Cin	N	O	81	.290
1930	Cin	N	O	79	.276
			BLTL	295	.270

CALLAHAN, DAVID JOSEPH

b.July 20,1888 Ottawa,Ill.

Yr	Cl	Lea	Pos	G	Rec
1910	Cle	A	O	13	.181
1911	Cle	A	O	6	.250
			BLTR	19	.194

CALLAHAN, EDWARD J.

b.Boston,Mass.

Yr	Cl	Lea	Pos	G	Rec
1884	St.L	U	O	1	.000
1884	KC	U	S	1	.250
1884	Bos	U	O	4	.357
				6	.286

CALLAHAN, JAMES J.

b.Marlboro,Mass.

Yr	Cl	Lea	Pos	G	Rec
1902	NY	N	O	1	.000

CALLAHAN, JAMES JOSEPH

b.Mar,18,1874 Fitchburg,Mass.

d.Oct.4,1934

Yr	Cl	Lea	Pos	G	Rec
1894	Phi	N	P	9	2-3
1897	Chi	N	P-2-S-O	90	13-10 .308
1898	Chi	N	P	42	20-11
1899	Chi	N	P	45	21-12
1900	Chi	N	P	33	12-16
1901	Chi	A	P	45	15-7
1902	Chi	A	P-S-O	68	16-14 .239
1903	Chi	A	M-P-3	118	1-2 .290
1904	Chi	A	M-2-O	132	.263
1905	Chi	A	O	96	.272
1911	Chi	A	O	120	.281
1912	Chi	A	M-O	111	.272
1913	Chi	A	M-O	6	.222
			BRTR	915	100-75 .275

Non-playing manager Chi (A) 1914 and Pit (N) 1916-17

CALLAHAN, JAMES W.

b.Moberly,Mo.

Yr	Cl	Lea	Pos	G	Rec
1898	St.L	N	P	2	0-2

CALLAHAN, JOSEPH THOMAS

b.Oct.8,1916 E.Boston,Mass.

d.May 24,1949

Yr	Cl	Lea	Pos	G	Rec
1939	Bos	N	P	4	1-0
1940	Bos	N	P	6	0-2
			BRTR	10	1-2

CALLAHAN, LEO DAVID

b.Aug.9,1890 Boston,Mass.

Yr	Cl	Lea	Pos	G	Rec
1913	Bro	N	O	33	.171
1913	Phi	N	O	81	.230
			BLTL	114	.221

CALLAHAN, PATRICK J.

b.New York,N.Y.

Yr	Cl	Lea	Pos	G	Rec
1884	Ind	a	3	61	.263

CALLAHAN, RAY JAMES
(Pat)

b.Aug.29,1891 Ashland,Wis.

Yr	Cl	Lea	Pos	G	Rec
1915	Cin	N	P	3	0-0
			BLTL		

CALLAHAN, WESLEY LEROY

b.July 3,1888

d.Sept.13,1953

Yr	Cl	Lea	Pos	G	Rec
1913	St.L	N	S	7	.285
			TR		

CALLAWAY, FRANK BURNETT

(Continued)

b.Feb.26,1898 Knoxville,Tenn.

Yr	Cl	Lea	Pos	G	Rec
1921	Phi	A	S	14	.240
1922	Phi	A	2	29	.270
			BRTR	43	.255

CALLISON, JOHN WESLEY

b.Mar.12,1939 Qualls,Okla.

Yr	Cl	Lea	Pos	G	Rec
1958	Chi	A	O	18	.297
1959	Chi	A	O	49	.173
1960	Phi	N	O	99	.260
1961	Phi	N	O	138	.266
1962	Phi	N	O	157	.300
			BLTR	461	.273

CALVERT, LEO PAUL EMILE

b.Oct.6,1917 Montreal,Que.,Canada

Yr	Cl	Lea	Pos	G	Rec
1942	Cle	A	P	1	0-0
1943	Cle	A	P	5	0-0
1944	Cle	A	P	35	1-3
1945	Cle	A	P	1	0-0
1949	Was	A	P	35	6-17
1950	Det	A	P	32	2-2
1951	Det	A	P	1	0-0
			BRTR	110	9-22

CALVO, JACINTO
(Jack)

b.June11,1894 Havana,Cuba

Yr	Cl	Lea	Pos	G	Rec
1913	Was	A	O	16	.242
1920	Was	A	O	17	.043
			BLTL	33	.161

CAMELLI, HENRY RICHARD

b.Dec.12,1915 Gloucester,Mass.

Yr	Cl	Lea	Pos	G	Rec
1943	Pit	N	C	1	.000
1944	Pit	N	C	63	.296
1945	Pit	N	C	1	.000
1946	Pit	N	C	42	.208
1947	Bos	N	C	52	.193
			BRTR	159	.229

CAMERON, JOHN WILLIAM

b.1885 Boston,Mass.

Yr	Cl	Lea	Pos	G	Rec
1906	Bos		P-O	18	0-0 .180

CAMILLI, ADOLPH LOUIS
(Dolf)

b.Apr.23,1907 San Francisco,Cal.

Yr	Cl	Lea	Pos	G	Rec
1933	Chi	N	1	16	.224
1934	Chi	N	1	32	.275
1934	Phi	N	1	102	.212
1935	Phi	N	1	156	.261
1936	Phi	N	1	151	.315
1937	Phi	N	1	131	.339
1938	Bro	N	1	146	.251
1939	Bro	N	1	157	.290
1940	Bro	N	1	142	.287
1941	Bro	N	1	149	.285
1942	Bro	N	1	150	.252
1943	Bro	N	1	95	.247
1945	Bos	A	1	63	.212
			BLTL	1490	.277

CAMILLI, DOUGLAS JOSEPH

b.Sept.22,1936 Philadelphia,Pa.

Yr	Cl	Lea	Pos	G	Rec
1960	LA	N	C	6	.333
1961	LA	N	C	13	.133
1962	LA	N	C	45	.284
			BRTR	64	.261

CAMMEYER, WILLIAM HENRY

b.Mar.20,1821

d.Sept.4,1898

Non-playing manager Mut (n) 1873 and Mut (N) 1876

CAMNITZ, R. HARRY

b.Oct.26,1884 Hustonville,Ky.

d.Jan.6,1951

Yr	Cl	Lea	Pos	G	Rec
1909	Pit	N	P	1	0-0
1911	St.L	N	P	2	1-0
			BRTR	3	1-0

CAMNITZ, SAMUEL HOWARD
(Howie)
b.Aug.22,1881 Covington,Ky.
d.Mar.2,1960

Yr	Cl	Lea	Pos	G	Rec
1904	Pit	N	P	10	1-2
1906	Pit	N	P	2	1-0
1907	Pit	N	P	31	13-8
1908	Pit	N	P	38	16-9
1909	Pit	N	P	41	25-6
1910	Pit	N	P	38	12-13
1911	Pit	N	P	40	20-15
1912	Pit	N	P	41	22-12
1913	Pit	N	P	36	6-17
1913	Phi	N	P	9	3-3
1914	Pit	F	P	36	14-19
1915	Pit	F	P	4	0-0
	BRTR			326	133-104

CAMP, HOWARD LEE
(Red)
b.July 1,1894 Mumford,Ala.
d.May 8,1950

Yr	Cl	Lea	Pos	G	Rec
1917	NY	A	O	5	.286
	BLTR				

CAMP, LLEWELLYN ROBERT
b.Feb.22,1868 Columbus,O
d.Oct.1,1948

Yr	Cl	Lea	Pos	G	Rec
1892	St.L	N	3	43	.204
1893	Chi	N	3	38	.268
1894	Chi	N	2	8	.156
	TR			89	.229

CAMP, WINFIELD SCOTT
(Kid)
b.1870 Columbus,O
d.Mar.2,1895

Yr	Cl	Lea	Pos	G	Rec
1892	Pit	N	P	4	0-2
1894	Chi	N	P	3	0-1
				7	0-3

CAMPANELLA, ROY
b.Nov.19,1921 Philadelphia,Pa.

Yr	Cl	Lea	Pos	G	Rec
1948	Bro	N	C	83	.258
1949	Bro	N	C	130	.287
1950	Bro	N	C	126	.281
1951	Bro	N	C	143	.325
1952	Bro	N	C	128	.269
1953	Bro	N	C	144	.312
1954	Bro	N	C	111	.207
1955	Bro	N	C	123	.318
1956	Bro	N	C	124	.219
1957	Bro	N	C	103	.242
	BRTR			1215	.276

CAMPANIS, ALEXANDER SEBASTIAN
b.Nov.2,1916 Cos,Dodecanese Islands

Yr	Cl	Lea	Pos	G	Rec
1943	Bro	N	2	7	.100
	BBTR				

CAMPAU, CHARLES C.
(Count)
b.Oct.17,1863 Detroit,Mich.
d.Apr.3,1938

Yr	Cl	Lea	Pos	G	Rec
1888	Det	N	O	70	.203
1890	St.L	a	M-O	74	.274
1894	Was	N	O	2	.142
				146	.245

CAMPBELL, ARCHER STEWART
b.Oct.20,1903 Maplewood,N.J.

Yr	Cl	Lea	Pos	G	Rec
1928	NY	A	P	13	0-1
1929	Was	A	P	4	0-1
1930	Cin	N	P	23	2-4
	BRTR			40	2-6

CAMPBELL, ARTHUR VINCENT
(Vin)
b.Jan.30,1888 St.Louis,Mo.

Yr	Cl	Lea	Pos	G	Rec
1908	Chi	N	O	1	.000
1910	Pit	N	O	74	.326
1911	Pit	N	O	21	.312
1912	Bos	N	O	145	.296
1914	Ind	F	O	133	.315
1915	New	F	O	127	.314
	BLTR			501	.310

CAMPBELL, BRUCE DOUGLAS
b.Oct.20,1909 Chicago,Ill.

Yr	Cl	Lea	Pos	G	Rec
1930	Chi	A	O	5	.500
1931	Chi	A	O	4	.412
1932	Chi	A	O	7	.222
1932	St.L	A	O	139	.285
1933	St.L	A	O	148	.277
1934	St.L	A	O	138	.279
1935	Cle	A	O	80	.325
1936	Cle	A	O	76	.372
1937	Cle	A	O	134	.301
1938	Cle	A	O	133	.290
1939	Cle	A	O	130	.287
1940	Det	A	O	103	.283
1941	Det	A	O	141	.275
1942	Was	A	O	122	.278
	BLTR			1360	.290

CAMPBELL, CLARENCE
(Soup)
b.Mar.7,1917 Sparta,Va.

Yr	Cl	Lea	Pos	G	Rec
1940	Cle	A	O	35	.226
1941	Cle	A	O	104	.250
	BLTR			139	.246

CAMPBELL, HUGH
d.1881

Yr	Cl	Lea	Pos	G	Rec
1873	Res	n	P-2-O	19	2-15 NR

CAMPBELL, JAMES ROBERT
b.June 24,1937 Palo Alto,Cal.

Yr	Cl	Lea	Pos	G	Rec
1962	Hou	N	C	27	.221
	BRTR				

CAMPBELL, JOHN MILLARD
b.Sept.13,1907 Washington,D.C.

Yr	Cl	Lea	Pos	G	Rec
1933	Was	A	P	1	0-0
	BRTR				

CAMPBELL, MARC THADDEUS
b.Nov.29,1884 Punxsutawney,Pa.
d.Feb.13,1946

Yr	Cl	Lea	Pos	G	Rec
1907	Pit	N	S	2	.250
	BLTR				

CAMPBELL, MICHAEL
b.New Jersey

Yr	Cl	Lea	Pos	G	Rec
1873	Res	n	1-S-O	20	NR

CAMPBELL, PAUL McLAUGHLIN
b.Sept.1,1917 Paw Creek,N.C.

Yr	Cl	Lea	Pos	G	Rec
1941	Bos	A	H	1	.000
1942	Bos	A	O	26	.067
1946	Bos	A	1	28	.115
1948	Det	A	1	59	.265
1949	Det	A	1	87	.278
1950	Det	A	H	3	.000
	BLTL			204	.255

CAMPBELL, SAMUEL
b.Philadelphia,Pa.

Yr	Cl	Lea	Pos	G	Rec
1890	Ath	a	2	2	.000

CAMPBELL, WILLIAM GILTHORPE
(Gilly)
b.Feb.13,1907 KansasCity,Kan.

Yr	Cl	Lea	Pos	G	Rec
1933	Chi	N	C	46	281
1935	Cin	N	C-1-O	88	.257
1936	Cin	N	C-1	89	.268
1937	Cin	N	C	18	.275
1938	Bro	N	C	54	.246
	BLTR			295	.263

CAMPBELL, WILLIAM JAMES
b.Nov.5,1873 Pittsburgh,Pa.
d.Oct.7,1957

Yr	Cl	Lea	Pos	G	Rec
1905	St.L	N	P	2	1-1
1907	Cin	N	P	3	2-0
1908	Cin	N	P	35	12-13
1909	Cin	N	P	30	7-11
	BLTL			70	22-25

CAMPFIELD, WILLIAM HOLTON
(Sal)
b.Feb.19,1868 Meadville,Pa.
d.May 16,1952

Yr	Cl	Lea	Pos	G	Rec
1896	NY	N	P	6	0-1

CAMPOS, FRANCISCO JOSE LOPEZ
(Frank)
b.May 11,1925 Havana,Cuba.

Yr	Cl	Lea	Pos	G	Rec
1951	Was	A	O	8	.423
1952	Was	A	O	53	.259
1953	Was	A	H	10	.111
	BLTL			71	.279

CANAVAN, HUGH EDWARD
b.May 13,1897 Worcester,Mass.

Yr	Cl	Lea	Pos	G	Rec
1918	Bos	N	P	16	0-4
	BLTL				

CANAVAN, JAMES E.
b.Nov.26,1866 NewBedford,Mass.
d.May 27,1949

Yr	Cl	Lea	Pos	G	Rec
1891	Cin	a	S	91	.253
1891	Mil	a	2-S	34	.268
1892	Chi	N	2	118	.166
1893	Cin	N	O	118	.238
1894	Cin	N	O	100	.293
1897	Bro	N	2	63	.222
	BRTR			524	.231

CANDINI, MARIO CAIN
b.Aug.3,1917 Manteca,Cal.

Yr	Cl	Lea	Pos	G	Rec
1943	Was	A	P	28	11-7
1944	Was	A	P	28	6-7
1946	Was	A	P	9	2-0
1947	Was	A	P	38	3-4
1948	Was	A	P	35	2-3
1949	Was	A	P	3	0-0
1950	Phi	N	P	18	1-0
1951	Phi	N	P	15	1-0
	BRTR			174	26-21

CANNELL, WIRT VIRGIN
(Rip)
b.Jan.23,1880 Naples,Me.
d.Aug.26,1948

Yr	Cl	Lea	Pos	G	Rec
1904	Bos	N	O	93	.234
1905	Bos	N	O	154	.247
	BLTR			247	.242

CANNIZZARO, CHRISTOPHER JOHN
b.May 3,1938 Oakland,Cal.

Yr	Cl	Lea	Pos	G	Rec
1960	St.L	N	C	7	.222
1961	St.L	N	C	6	.500
1962	NY	N	C-O	59	.241
	BRTR			72	.243

CANTILLON, JOE
(Pongo)
b.Aug.19,1861 Janesville,Wis.
d.Jan.31,1930
Non-playing manager Was (A) 1907-09

CANTRELL, GUY DEWEY
(Gunner)
b.Apr.9,1904 Clarita,Okla.

Yr	Cl	Lea	Pos	G	Rec
1925	Bro	N	P	14	1-0
1927	Bro	N	P	6	0-0
1927	Phi	A	P	2	0-2
1930	Det	A	P	16	1-5
	BRTR			38	2-7

CANTWELL, BENJAMIN CALDWELL
b.Apr.13,1902 Milan,Tenn.
d.Dec.4,1962

Yr	Cl	Lea	Pos	G	Rec
1927	NY	N	P	5	1-1
1928	NY	N	P	7	1-0
1928	Bos	N	P	22	3-3
1929	Bos	N	P	27	4-13
1930	Bos	N	P	34	9-15
1931	Bos	N	P	40	7-9
1932	Bos	N	P	37	13-11
1933	Bos	N	P	49	20-10
1934	Bos	N	P	29	5-11
1935	Bos	N	P	41	4-25
1936	Bos	N	P	35	9-9
1937	NY	N	P	1	0-1
1937	Bro	N	P	13	0-0
	BRTR			340	76-108

CANTWELL, MICHAEL JOSEPH
b.Jan.15,1896 Washington,D.C.
d.Jan.9,1953

Yr	Cl	Lea	Pos	G	Rec
1916	NY	A	P	1	0-0
1919	Phi	N	P	5	1-3
1920	Phi	N	P	5	0-3
			BLTL	11	1-6

CANTWELL, THOMAS ALOYSIUS
b.Dec.23,1888 Washington,D.C.

Yr	Cl	Lea	Pos	G	Rec
1909	Cin	N	P	6	1-0
1910	Cin	N	P	2	0-0
			BLTR	8	1-0

CANTZ, BARTHOLOMEW L.
b.Jan.29,1860 Philadelphia,Pa.
d.Feb.12,1943

Yr	Cl	Lea	Pos	G	Rec
1888	Bal	a	C	37	.165
1889	Bal	a	C	21	.158
1890	Ath	a	C	5	.096
				63	.157

CAPRI, PATRICK NICHOLAS
b.Nov.7,1918 New York,N.Y.

Yr	Cl	Lea	Pos	G	Rec
1944	Bos	N	2	7	.000
			BRTR		

CAPRON, RALPH E.
b.Mar.11,1893 Minneapolis,Minn.

Yr	Cl	Lea	Pos	G	Rec
1912	Pit	N	O	1	.000
1913	Phi	N	O	5	.000
			BLTR	6	.000

CARAWAY, CECIL PATRICK
(Pat)
b.Sept.26,1906 Gordon,Tex

Yr	Cl	Lea	Pos	G	Rec
1930	Chi	A	P	38	10-10
1931	Chi	A	P	52	10-24
1932	Chi	A	P	19	2-6
			BLTL	109	22-40

CARBINE, JOHN C.
b.1852 Chicago,Ill.

Yr	Cl	Lea	Pos	G	Rec
1875	Wes	n	1	10	NR
1876	Lou	N	1	6	.150
				16	NR

CARDEN, JOHN BRUTON
b.May 19,1922 Killeen,Tex.
d.Feb.8,1949

Yr	Cl	Lea	Pos	G	Rec
1946	NY	N	P	1	0-0
			BRTR		

CARDENAS, LEONARDO ALFONSO LAZARO
b.Dec.17,1938 Matanzas,Cuba.

Yr	Cl	Lea	Pos	G	Rec
1960	Cin	N	S	48	.232
1961	Cin	N	S	74	.308
1962	Cin	N	S	153	.294
			BRTR	275	.287

CARDONI, ARMAND JOSEPH
(Big Ben)
b.Aug.21,1921 Jessup,Pa.

Yr	Cl	Lea	Pos	G	Rec
1943	Bos	N	P	11	0-0
1944	Bos	N	P	29	0-6
1945	Bos	N	P	3	0-0
			BRTR	43	0-6

CARDWELL, DONALD EUGENE
b.Dec.7,1935 Winston-Salem,N.C.

Yr	Cl	Lea	Pos	G	Rec
1957	Phi	N	P	30	4-8
1958	Phi	N	P	16	3-6

(Continued)

Yr	Cl	Lea	Pos	G	Rec
1959	Phi	N	P	26	9-10
1960	Phi	N	P	5	1-2
1960	Chi	N	P	33	8-14
1961	Chi	N	P	40	15-14
1962	Chi	N	P	41	7-16
			BRTR	191	47-70

CAREY, ANDREW ARTHUR
(Real Name Andrew Arthur Nordstrom)
b.Oct.18,1931 Oakland,Cal.

Yr	Cl	Lea	Pos	G	Rec
1952	NY	A	S-3	16	.150
1953	NY	A	2-S-3	51	.321
1954	NY	A	3	122	.302
1955	NY	A	3	135	.257
1956	NY	A	3	132	.237
1957	NY	A	3	85	.255
1958	NY	A	3	102	.286
1959	NY	A	3	41	.257
1960	NY	A	3-O	4	.333
1960	KC	A	3	102	.233
1961	KC	A	3	39	.244
1961	Chi	A	3	56	.266
1962	LA	N	3	53	.234
			BRTR	938	.260

CAREY, GEORGE C.
(Scoops)
b.Dec.4,1870 E.Liverpool,O
d.Dec.17,1916

Yr	Cl	Lea	Pos	G	Rec
1895	Bal	N	1	123	.271
1898	Lou	N	1	8	.187
1902	Was	A	1	120	.316
1903	Was	A	1	48	.198
			BRTR	299	.275

CAREY, MAX GEORGE
(Real Name Maximilian Carnarius)
b.Jan.11,1890 Terre Haute,Ind.

Yr	Cl	Lea	Pos	G	Rec
1910	Pit	N	O	2	.500
1911	Pit	N	O	122	.258
1912	Pit	N	O	150	.302
1913	Pit	N	O	154	.277
1914	Pit	N	O	156	.243
1915	Pit	N	O	140	.254
1916	Pit	N	O	154	.264
1917	Pit	N	O	155	.296
1918	Pit	N	O	126	.274
1919	Pit	N	O	66	.307
1920	Pit	N	O	130	.289
1921	Pit	N	O	140	.309
1922	Pit	N	O	155	.329
1923	Pit	N	O	153	.308
1924	Pit	N	O	149	.297
1925	Pit	N	O	133	.343
1926	Pit	N	O	86	.222
1926	Bro	N	O	27	.260
1927	Bro	N	O	144	.266
1928	Bro	N	O	108	.247
1929	Bro	N	O	19	.304
			BBTR	2469	.285

Non-playing manager Bro (N), 1932-33

CAREY, THOMAS FRANCIS ALOYSIUS
(Scoops)
b.Oct.11,1908 Hoboken,N.J.

Yr	Cl	Lea	Pos	G	Rec
1935	St.L	A	2	76	.291
1936	St.L	A	2	134	.273
1937	St.L	A	2-S	130	.275
1939	Bos	A	2-S	54	.242
1940	Bos	A	2-S-3	43	.323
1941	Bos	A	2-S	24	.200
1942	Bos	A	2	1	1.000
1946	Bos	A	2	3	.200
			BRTR	465	.275

CAREY, THOMAS JOHN
(Real Name J. J. Norton)
b.1849 Brooklyn,N.Y.
d.Feb.13,1899

Yr	Cl	Lea	Pos	G	Rec
1871	Kek	n	2	19	NR
1872	Bal	n	1-2-S-3-O	41	.293
1873	Bal	n	2-S-3	55	NR
1874	Mut	n	2-S	64	NR
1875	Har	n	S	85	NR
1876	Har	N	S	68	.301
1877	Har	N	S	60	.255
1878	Pro	N	S	59	.251

(Continued)

Yr	Cl	Lea	Pos	G	Rec
1879	Cle	N	S	80	.238
			TR	531	NR

CARGO, ROBERT J.
(Chic)
b.1871 Pittsburgh,Pa.
d.Apr.27,1904

Yr	Cl	Lea	Pos	G	Rec
1892	Pit	N	S	2	.200
			BRTR		

CARISCH, FREDERICK BEHLMER
b.Nov.14,1881 FountainCity,Wis.

Yr	Cl	Lea	Pos	G	Rec
1903	Pit	N	C	5	.352
1904	Pit	N	C-1	36	.248
1905	Pit	N	C	30	.206
1906	Pit	N	C	4	.083
1912	Cle	A	C	24	.275
1913	Cle	A	C	81	.216
1914	Cle	A	C	40	.216
1923	Det	A	C	2	.000
			BRTR	222	.228

CARL, FREDERICK E.
b.1858 Baltimore,Md.
d.July 30,1897

Yr	Cl	Lea	Pos	G	Rec
1889	Lou	a	2-O	25	.202

CARL, LEWIS
b.Baltimore,Md.

Yr	Cl	Lea	Pos	G	Rec
1874	Bal	n	C	1	.000

CARLETON, JAMES
b.1849 N.Y.

Yr	Cl	Lea	Pos	G	Rec
1871	Cle	n	1	29	NR
1872	Cle	n	1	7	NR
				36	NR

CARLETON, JAMES OTTO
(Tex)
b.Aug.19,1906 Comanche,Tex

Yr	Cl	Lea	Pos	G	Rec
1932	St.L	N	P	44	10-13
1933	St.L	N	P	46	17-11
1934	St.L	N	P	41	16-11
1935	Chi	N	P	31	11-8
1936	Chi	N	P	35	14-10
1937	Chi	N	P	34	16-8
1938	Chi	N	P	33	10-9
1940	Bro	N	P	34	6-6
			BBTR	298	100-76

CARLIN, JAMES ARTHUR
b.Feb.23,1918 Wylam,Ala.

Yr	Cl	Lea	Pos	G	Rec
1941	Phi	N	3-O	16	.143
			BRTR		

CARLISLE, WALTER G.
(Rosy)
b.July 6,1883 Yeadon,England
d.May 27,1945

Yr	Cl	Lea	Pos	G	Rec
1908	Bos	A	O	3	.100

CARLOCK, JOHN H.

Yr	Cl	Lea	Pos	G	Rec
1912	Cle	A	H	1	.000

CARLSEN, DONALD HERBERT
b.Oct.15,1926 Chicago,Ill.

Yr	Cl	Lea	Pos	G	Rec
1948	Chi	N	P	1	0-0
1951	Pit	N	P	7	2-3
1952	Pit	N	P	5	0-1
			BRTR	13	2-4

CARLSON, HAROLD GUST
b.May 17,1894 Rockford,Ill.
d.May 28,1930

Yr	Cl	Lea	Pos	G	Rec
1917	Pit	N	P	34	7-11
1918	Pit	N	P	3	0-1
1919	Pit	N	P	22	8-10
1920	Pit	N	P	39	14-13
1921	Pit	N	P	31	4-8
1922	Pit	N	P	39	9-12
1923	Pit	N	P	4	0-0
1924	Phi	N	P	39	8-17

(Continued)

Yr	Cl	Lea	Pos	G	Rec
1925	Phi	N	P	38	13-14
1926	Phi	N	P	38	17-12
1927	Phi	N	P	12	4-5
1927	Chi	N	P	27	12-8
1928	Chi	N	P	20	3-2
1929	Chi	N	P	31	11-5
1930	Chi	N	P	8	4-2
	BRTR			385	114-120

CARLSON, JOSEPH MARTIN NAPOLEON
(Played under name of Joseph Martin Napoleon Munson)

CARLSON, LEON ALTON
b.Feb.17,1897 Jamestown,N.Y.
d.Sept.15,1961

Yr	Cl	Lea	Pos	G	Rec
1920	Was	A	P	3	0-0
	BRTR				

CARLSTROM, ALBIN OSCAR
(Swede)
b.Oct.26,1890 Elizabeth,N.J.
d.Apr.23,1935

Yr	Cl	Lea	Pos	G	Rec
1911	Bos	A	S	2	.167
	BRTR				

CARLYLE, HIRAM CLEO
b.Sept.7,1903 Fairburn,Ga.

Yr	Cl	Lea	Pos	G	Rec
1927	Bos	A	O	95	.234
	BLTR				

CARLYLE, ROY EDWARD
(Dizzy)
b.Dec.10,1900 Buford,Ga.
d.Nov.22,1956

Yr	Cl	Lea	Pos	G	Rec
1925	Was	A	O	1	.000
1925	Bos	A	O	93	.326
1926	Bos	A	O	45	.285
1926	NY	A	O	35	.385
	BLTR			174	.318

CARMEL, LEON JAMES
b.Apr.23,1937 New York,N.Y.

Yr	Cl	Lea	Pos	G	Rec
1959	St.L	N	O	10	.130
1960	St.L	N	1-O	4	.000
	BLTL			14	.115

CARMEN, GEORGE W.
b.Doylestown,Pa.

Yr	Cl	Lea	Pos	G	Rec
1890	Ath	a	S	25	.151

CARMICHAEL, CHESTER RALPH
b.Sept.9,1888 Eaton,Ind.
d.Aug.23,1960

Yr	Cl	Lea	Pos	G	Rec
1909	Cin	N	P	2	0-0
	BRTR				

CARNARIUS, MAXIMILIAN
(Played under name of Max George Carey)

CARNETT, EDWIN ELLIOTT
(Lefty)
b.Oct.21,1916 Springfield,Mo.

Yr	Cl	Lea	Pos	G	Rec
1941	Bos	N	P	2	0-0
1944	Chi	A	P-1-O	126	0-0 / .276
1945	Cle	A	P-O	30	0-0 / .219
	BLTL			158	0-0 / .268

CARNEY, JOHN JOSEPH
b.Nov.10,1867 Salem,Mass.
d.Oct.19,1925

Yr	Cl	Lea	Pos	G	Rec
1889	Was	N	1-O	69	.230
1890	Buf	p	1	28	.262
1890	Cle	p	O	25	.344
1891	Cin	a	1	91	.276
1891	Mil	a	1	30	.291
	BRTR			243	.270

CARNEY, PATRICK JOSEPH
(Doc)
b.Aug.7,1876 Holyoke,Mass.
d.Jan.9,1953

Yr	Cl	Lea	Pos	G	Rec
1901	Bos	N	O	13	.302
1902	Bos	N	P-O	137	0-1 / .266
1903	Bos	N	P-O	102	4-4 / .240
1904	Bos	N	P-O	76	0-2 / .204
	BLTL			328	4-7 / .245

CARNEY, WILLIAM J.
b.1878 St.Paul,Minn.

Yr	Cl	Lea	Pos	G	Rec
1904	Chi	N	O	2	.000

CARPENTER, LEWIS EMMETT
b.Aug.16,1915 Woodstock,Ga.

Yr	Cl	Lea	Pos	G	Rec
1943	Was	A	P	4	0-0
	BRTR				

CARPENTER, PAUL CALVIN
b.Aug.12,1894 Granville,O

Yr	Cl	Lea	Pos	G	Rec
1916	Pit	N	P	5	0-0
	BRTR				

CARPENTER, ROBERT LOUIS
b.Dec.12,1917 Chicago,Ill.

Yr	Cl	Lea	Pos	G	Rec
1940	NY	N	P	5	2-0
1941	NY	N	P	29	11-6
1942	NY	N	P	28	11-10
1946	NY	N	P	12	1-3
1947	NY	N	P	2	0-0
1947	Chi	N	P	4	0-1
	BRTR			80	25-20

CARPENTER, WARREN WILLIAM
(Hick)
b.Aug.16,1855 Grafton,Mass.
d.Apr.18,1937

Yr	Cl	Lea	Pos	G	Rec
1879	Syr	N	1-3-O	63	.201
1880	Cin	N	1-3	76	.243
1881	Wor	N	3	82	.209
1882	Cin	a	3	80	.354
1883	Cin	a	3	94	.308
1884	Cin	a	3-O	109	.265
1885	Cin	a	3	112	.291
1886	Cin	a	3	111	.221
1887	Cin	a	3	127	.269
1888	Cin	a	3	135	.269
1889	Cin	a	1-3	123	.257
1892	St.L	N	3	1	.333
	BRTL			1113	.264

CARR, CHARLES CARBITT
b.Dec.27,1876 Coatesville,Pa.
d.Nov.26,1932

Yr	Cl	Lea	Pos	G	Rec
1898	Was	N	1	20	.197
1901	Phi	A	1	2	.125
1903	Det	A	1	135	.282
1904	Det	A	1	91	.270
1904	Cle	A	1	32	.223
1905	Cle	A	1	89	.235
1906	Cin	N	1	22	.191
1914	Ind	F	1	115	.292
	BRTR			506	.251

CARR, LEWIS SMITH
b.Aug.15,1872 Union Springs,N.Y.
d.June 15,1954

Yr	Cl	Lea	Pos	G	Rec
1901	Pit	N	S	9	.233
	TR				

CARRASQUEL, ALEJANDRO ALEXANDER APARICIO
(Alex)
b.July 24,1912 Caracas,Venezuela

Yr	Cl	Lea	Pos	G	Rec
1939	Was	A	P	40	5-9
1940	Was	A	P	28	6-2
1941	Was	A	P	35	6-2
1942	Was	A	P	35	7-7

(Continued)

Yr	Cl	Lea	Pos	G	Rec
1943	Was	A	P	39	11-7
1944	was	A	P	43	8-7
1945	Was	A	P	35	7-5
1949	Chi	A	P	3	0-0
	BRTR			258	50-39

CARRASQUEL, ALFONSO COLON
(Chico)
b.Jan.23,1928 Caracas,Venezuela.

Yr	Cl	Lea	Pos	G	Rec
1950	Chi	A	S	141	.282
1951	Chi	A	S	147	.264
1952	Chi	A	S	100	.248
1953	Chi	A	S	149	.279
1954	Chi	A	S	155	.255
1955	Chi	A	S	145	.256
1956	Cle	A	S-3	141	.243
1957	Cle	A	S	125	.276
1958	Cle	A	S-3	49	.256
1958	KC	A	S-3	59	.213
1959	Bal	A	1-2-S-3	114	.223
	BRTR			1325	.258

CARREON, CAMILO GARCIA
b.Aug.6,1937 Colton,Cal.

Yr	Cl	Lea	Pos	G	Rec
1959	Chi	A	C	1	.000
1960	Chi	A	C	8	.235
1961	Chi	A	C	78	.271
1962	Chi	A	C	106	.256
	BRTR			193	.261

CARRICK, WILLIAM MARTIN
(Doughnut Bill)
b.Sept.5,1873 Erie,Pa.
d.Mar.7,1932

Yr	Cl	Lea	Pos	G	Rec
1898	NY	N	P	5	3-1
1899	NY	N	P	44	16-25
1900	NY	N	P	42	19-21
1901	Was	A	P	42	15-22
1902	Was	A	P-O	33	12-17 / .187
	TR			166	65-86 / .161

CARRIGAN, WILLIAM FRANCIS
(Rough)
b.Oct.22,1883 Lewiston,Me.

Yr	Cl	Lea	Pos	G	Rec
1906	Bos	A	C	37	.211
1908	Bos	A	C	57	.235
1909	Bos	A	C	94	.296
1910	Bos	A	C	114	.249
1911	Bos	A	C	72	.289
1912	Bos	A	C	87	.263
1913	Bos	A	M-C	85	.242
1914	Bos	A	M-C	81	.253
1915	Bos	A	M-C	46	.200
1916	Bos	A	M-C	33	.270
	BRTR			706	.257

Non-playing manager Bos (A) 1927-29

CARROLL, DORSEY LEE
(Dixie)
b.May 9,1892 Paducah,Ky.

Yr	Cl	Lea	Pos	G	Rec
1919	Bos	N	O	15	.265
	BLTR				

CARROLL, E.
(Chick)
b.Chicago,Ill.

Yr	Cl	Lea	Pos	G	Rec
1884	Was	U	O	4	.200

CARROLL, EDGAR FLEISCHER
b.July 27,1907 Baltimore,Md.

Yr	Cl	Lea	Pos	G	Rec
1929	Bos	A	P	24	1-0
	BRTR				

CARROLL, FREDERICK HERBERT
b.July 2,1864 Sacramento,Cal.
d.Nov.7,1904

Yr	Cl	Lea	Pos	G	Rec
1884	Col	a	C-O	69	.283
1885	Pit	a	C	69	.263
1886	Pit	a	C-1	122	.292
1887	Pit	N	C-1-O	101	.380
1888	Pit	N	C-O	96	.243

(Continued)

Yr	Cl	Lea	Pos	G	Rec
1889	Pit	N	C-O	90	.330
1890	Pit	p	C-O	111	.302
1891	Pit	N	O	87	.228
			BRTR	745	.295

CARROLL, JOHN E.
(Scrappy)
b.Aug.15,1863 Buffalo,N.Y.
d.Nov.14,1942

Yr	Cl	Lea	Pos	G	Rec
1884	St.P	U	3-O	9	.083
1885	Buf	N	2-O	12	.056
1887	Cle	a	O	57	.252
1892	Chi	N	3	1	.000
				79	.206

CARROLL, OWEN THOMAS
(Ownie)
b.Nov.11,1902 Kearny,N.J.

Yr	Cl	Lea	Pos	G	Rec
1925	Det	A	P-O	11	2-2 .375
1927	Det	A	P	37	10-6
1928	Det	A	P	43	16-12
1929	Det	A	P	37	9-17
1930	Det	A	P	6	0-5
1930	NY	A	P	11	0-1
1930	Cin	N	P	3	0-1
1931	Cin	N	P	30	3-9
1932	Cin	N	P	35	10-19
1933	Bro	N	P	34	13-15
1934	Bro	N	P	28	1-3
			BRTR	275	64-90 .200

CARROLL, PATRICK
b.Philadelphia,Pa.

Yr	Cl	Lea	Pos	G	Rec
1884	Alt	U	C-O	11	.255
1884	Key	U	C	5	.158
				16	.229

CARROLL, RALPH ARTHUR
(Doc)
b.Dec.28,1891 Worcester,Mass.

Yr	Cl	Lea	Pos	G	Rec
1916	Phi	A	C	10	.091
			BRTR		

CARROLL, RICHARD T.
b.July 21,1884 Cleveland,O.
d.Nov.22,1945

Yr	Cl	Lea	Pos	G	Rec
1909	NY	A	P	2	0-0

CARROLL, SAMUEL
(Cliff)
b.Oct.18,1859 Clay Grove,Ia
d.June 29,1923

Yr	Cl	Lea	Pos	G	Rec
1882	Pro	N	O	10	.121
1883	Pro	N	O	58	.264
1884	Pro	N	O	112	.261
1885	Pro	N	O	104	.232
1886	Was	N	O	111	.228
1887	Was	N	O	101	.276
1888	Pit	N	O	7	.107
1890	Chi	N	O	136	.285
1891	Chi	N	O	130	.255
1892	St.L	N	O	100	.273
1893	Bos	N	O	120	.234
			BB	989	.256

CARROLL, THOMAS EDWARD
b.Sept.17,1936 Jamaica,N.Y.

Yr	Cl	Lea	Pos	G	Rec
1955	NY	A	S	14	.333
1956	NY	A	S-3	36	.353
1959	KC	A	S-3	14	.143
			BRTR	64	.300

CARRUTHERS, CHARLES PRESTON (Pres)
b.Sept.8,1890 Philadelphia,Pa.

Yr	Cl	Lea	Pos	G	Rec
1913	Phi	A	2	5	.235
1914	Phi	A	2	4	.200
			BRTR	9	.219

CARSEY, WILFRED
(Kid)
b.Oct.22,1870 New York,N.Y.

Yr	Cl	Lea	Pos	G	Rec
1891	Was	a	P	59	14-33
1892	Phi	N	P	35	19-16
1893	Phi	N	P	36	22-12

(Continued)

Yr	Cl	Lea	Pos	G	Rec
1894	Phi	N	P	32	16-14
1895	Phi	N	P	41	24-17
1896	Phi	N	P	24	11-13
1897	Phi	N	P	6	4-2
1897	St.L	N	P	13	1-7
1898	St.L	N	P	33	1-12
1899	Cle	N	P	9	1-8
1899	Was	N	P	7	1-2
1899	NY	N	S-3	5	.333
1901	Bro	N	P	2	1-0
			BRTR	302	115-136 .212

CARSON, ALEXANDER JAMES
(Soldier)
b.New York,N.Y.

Yr	Cl	Lea	Pos	G	Rec
1910	Chi	N	P	2	0-0
			TR		

CARSON, WALTER LLOYD
(Kit)
b.Nov.15,1912 Colton,Cal.

Yr	Cl	Lea	Pos	G	Rec
1934	Cle	A	O	5	.278
1935	Cle	A	O	16	.227
			BLTL	21	.250

CARSWELL, FRANK WILLIS
(Tex)
b.Nov.6,1919 Palestine,Tex

Yr	Cl	Lea	Pos	G	Rec
1953	Det	A	O	16	.267
			BRTR		

CARTER, ARNOLD LEE
b.Mar.14,1920 Rainelle,W.Va.

Yr	Cl	Lea	Pos	G	Rec
1944	Cin	N	P	37	11-7
1945	Cin	N	P	19	2-4
			BLTL	56	13-11

CARTER, CONRAD POWELL
(Nick)
b.May 19,1879 Oatlands,Va.
d.Nov.23,1961

Yr	Cl	Lea	Pos	G	Rec
1908	Phi	A	P	17	2-5
			TR		

CARTER, JOHN HOWARD
(Howie)
b.Oct.13,1904 New York,N.Y.

Yr	Cl	Lea	Pos	G	Rec
1926	Cin	N	2-S	5	.000
			BBTR		

CARTER, OTIS LEONARD
(Blackie)
b.Sept.30,1902 Langley,S.C.

Yr	Cl	Lea	Pos	G	Rec
1925	NY	N	O	1	.000
1926	NY	N	O	5	.235
			BRTR	6	.190

CARTER, PAUL WARREN
(Nick)
b.May 1,1894 Lake Park,Ga.

Yr	Cl	Lea	Pos	G	Rec
1914	Cle	A	P	5	1-3
1915	Cle	A	P	12	1-2
1916	Chi	N	P	8	2-2
1917	Chi	N	P	23	5-8
1918	Chi	N	P	21	3-2
1919	Chi	N	P	29	5-4
1920	Chi	N	P	31	3-6
			BLTR	129	20-27

CARTER, SOLOMON MOBLEY
b.Dec.23,1908 Picayune,Miss.

Yr	Cl	Lea	Pos	G	Rec
1931	Phi	A	P	2	0-0
			BRTR		

CARTWRIGHT, EDWARD H.
(Jumbo)
b.Oct.6,1859 Johnstown,Pa.

Yr	Cl	Lea	Pos	G	Rec
1890	St.L	a	1	75	.281
1894	Was	N	1	132	.292
1895	Was	N	1	121	.327
1896	Was	N	1	131	.274
1897	Was	N	1	33	.250
			BR	492	.292

CARUTHERS, ROBERT LEE
(Parisian Bob)
b.Jan.5,1864 Memphis,Tenn.
d.Aug.5,1911

Yr	Cl	Lea	Pos	G	Rec
1884	St.L	a	P-O	23	7-2 .253
1885	St.L	a	P	60	40-13
1886	St.L	a	P-O	86	30-14 .342
1887	St.L	a	P-O	98	29-9 .459
1888	Bro	a	P-O	94	29-15 .230
1889	Bro	a	P	57	40-12
1890	Bro	N	P-O	71	22-11 .265
1891	Bro	N	P	47	17-17
1892	St.L	N	P-O	142	2-8 .277
1893	Chi	N	P	1	0-0
1893	Cin	N	O	13	.286
			BLTR	692	216-101 .301

CARY, SCOTT RUSSELL
(Red)
b.Apr.11,1923 Kendallville,Ind.

Yr	Cl	Lea	Pos	G	Rec
1947	Was	A	P	23	3-1
			BLTL		

CASALE, JERRY JOSEPH
b.Sept.27,1933 Brooklyn,N.Y.

Yr	Cl	Lea	Pos	G	Rec
1958	Bos	A	P	2	0-0
1959	Bos	A	P	31	13-8
1960	Bos	A	P	29	2-9
1961	LA	A	P	13	1-5
1961	Det	A	P	3	0-0
1962	Det	A	P	18	1-2
			BRTR	96	17-24

CASCARELLA, JOSEPH THOMAS
b.June 28,1907 Philadelphia,Pa.

Yr	Cl	Lea	Pos	G	Rec
1934	Phi	A	P	42	12-15
1935	Phi	A	P	9	1-6
1935	Bos	A	P	6	0-3
1936	Bos	A	P	10	0-2
1936	Was	A	P	22	9-8
1937	Was	A	P	10	0-5
1937	Cin	N	P	11	1-2
1938	Cin	N	P	33	4-7
			BRTR	143	27-48

CASE, CHARLES E.
b.1880 Cincinnati,O
d.Jan.30,1918

Yr	Cl	Lea	Pos	G	Rec
1901	Cin	N	P	3	1-2
1904	Pit	N	P	18	10-5
1905	Pit	N	P	31	12-10
1906	Pit	N	P	2	1-1
			BRTR	54	24-18

CASE, GEORGE WASHINGTON
b.Nov.11,1915 Trenton,N.J.

Yr	Cl	Lea	Pos	G	Rec
1937	Was	A	O	22	.289
1938	Was	A	O	107	.305
1939	Was	A	O	128	.302
1940	Was	A	O	154	.293
1941	Was	A	O	153	.271
1942	Was	A	O	125	.320
1943	Was	A	O	141	.294
1944	Was	A	O	119	.249
1945	Was	A	O	123	.294
1946	Cle	A	O	118	.225
1947	Was	A	O	36	.150
			BRTR	1226	.282

CASEY, DANIEL MAURICE
b.Oct.2,1865 Binghamton,N.Y.
d.Feb.8,1943

Yr	Cl	Lea	Pos	G	Rec
1884	Wil	U	P	2	1-1
1885	Det	N	P	12	4-8
1886	Phi	N	P	44	25-19
1887	Phi	N	P	44	28-13
1888	Phi	N	P	33	14-19
1889	Phi	N	P	18	8-10
1890	Syr	a	P	48	20-22
			BRTL	201	100-92

CASEY, DENNIS PATRICK
b.Mar.30,1858 Binghamton,N.Y.
d.Jan.19,1909

Yr	Cl	Lea	Pos	G	Rec
1882	Det	N	2-3	9	.231
1884	Wil	U	O	2	.167
1884	Bal	a	O	38	.274
1885	Bal	a	O	64	.282
1887	NY	N	2	1	.000
	BLTR			114	.272

CASEY, HUGH THOMAS
b.Oct.14,1913 Atlanta,Ga.
d.July 3,1951

Yr	Cl	Lea	Pos	G	Rec
1935	Chi	N	P	13	0-0
1939	Bro	N	P	40	15-10
1940	Bro	N	P	45	11-8
1941	Bro	N	P	45	14-11
1942	Bro	N	P	50	6-3
1946	Bro	N	P	46	11-5
1947	Bro	N	P	46	10-4
1948	Bro	N	P	22	3-0
1949	Pit	N	P	33	4-1
1949	NY	A	P	4	1-0
	BRTR			344	75-42

CASEY, JAMES PETER
(Doc)
b.Mar.15,1871 Lawrence,Mass.
d.Dec.30,1936

Yr	Cl	Lea	Pos	G	Rec
1898	Was	N	3	28	.270
1899	Was	N	3	9	.118
1899	Bro	N	3	136	.267
1900	Bro	N	3	1	.333
1901	Det	A	3	131	.280
1902	Det	A	3	132	.275
1903	Chi	N	3	112	.290
1904	Chi	N	3	136	.268
1905	Chi	N	3	142	.232
1906	Bro	N	3	149	.233
1907	Bro	N	3	138	.231
	BLTR			1114	.253

CASEY, JOSEPH FELIX
b.Aug.15,1887 Boston,Mass.

Yr	Cl	Lea	Pos	G	Rec
1909	Det	A	C	3	.200
1910	Det	A	C	23	.194
1911	Det	A	C	15	.152
1918	Was	A	C	8	.235
	BRTR			49	.188

CASEY, WILLIAM B.
b.St.Louis,Mo.

Yr	Cl	Lea	Pos	G	Rec
1887	Ath	a	P	1	0-0

CASH, NORMAN DALTON
b.Nov.10,1934 Justiceburg,Tex.

Yr	Cl	Lea	Pos	G	Rec
1958	Chi	A	O	13	.250
1959	Chi	A	1	58	.240
1960	Det	A	1-O	121	.286
1961	Det	A	1	159	.361
1962	Det	A	1-O	148	.243
	BLTL			499	.295

CASHION, JAY CARL
b.June 6,1891 Mecklenburg,N.C.
d.Nov.17,1935

Yr	Cl	Lea	Pos	G	Rec
1911	Was	A	P	21	2-3
1912	Was	A	P	42	11-6
1913	Was	A	P-O	9	1-2 .294
1914	Was	A	P	2	0-1
	BLTR			74	14-12 .247

CASKIN, EDWARD JAMES
b.Dec.30,1851 Danvers,Mass.

Yr	Cl	Lea	Pos	G	Rec
1879	Tro	N	C-S	67	.259
1880	Tro	N	C-S	82	.231
1881	Tro	N	S	62	.226
1883	NY	N	2-S	93	.238
1884	NY	N	C-S	97	.232
1885	St.L	N	C-S-3	70	.179
1886	NY	N	S	1	.500
				472	.230

CASSADY, HARRY D.
b.July 20,1880 Belleflower,Ill.

Yr	Cl	Lea	Pos	G	Rec
1904	Pit	N	O	11	.214
1905	Was	A	O	10	.128
				21	.181

CASSIAN, EDWIN
b.Connecticut

Yr	Cl	Lea	Pos	G	Rec
1891	Phi	N	P	6	1-3
1891	Was	a	P	7	0-0
				13	1-3

CASSIDY, JOHN P.
b.1855 Brooklyn,N.Y.
d.July 3,1891

Yr	Cl	Lea	Pos	G	Rec
1875	Atl	a	P-1-2-O	40	1-24 NR
1875	NH	n	1	6	NR
1876	Har	N	O	12	.271
1877	Har	N	P-O	60	1-1 .378
1878	Chi	N	O	60	.261
1879	Tro	N	1-O	8	.176
1880	Tro	N	2-O	83	.253
1881	Tro	N	O	84	.219
1882	Tro	N	3-O	28	.176
1883	Pro	N	1-2-O	89	.237
1884	Bro	a	O	106	.263
1885	Bro	a	O	54	.211
	TL			630	2-25 NR

CASSIDY, JOSEPH PHILLIP
b.Feb.8,1883 Chester,Pa.
d.Mar.25,1906

Yr	Cl	Lea	Pos	G	Rec
1904	Was	A	S-3-O	152	.234
1905	Was	A	S	151	.215
	BRTR			303	.225

CASSIDY, PETER FRANCIS
b.Apr.8,1873 Wilmington,Del.
d.July 9,1929

Yr	Cl	Lea	Pos	G	Rec
1896	Lou	N	1	48	.221
1899	Bro	N	S-3	6	.150
1899	Was	N	1	45	.315
	BRTR			99	.261

CASSINI, JACK DEMPSEY
(Gabby)
b.Oct.26,1920 Dearborn,Mich.

Yr	Cl	Lea	Pos	G	Rec
1949	Pit	N	H	8	.000
	BRTR				

CASTER, GEORGE JASPER
(Ug)
b.Aug.4,1907 Colton,Cal.
d.Dec.19,1955

Yr	Cl	Lea	Pos	G	Rec
1934	Phi	A	P	5	3-2
1935	Phi	A	P	26	1-4
1937	Phi	A	P	37	12-19
1938	Phi	A	P	42	16-20
1939	Phi	A	P	28	9-9
1940	Phi	A	P	36	4-19
1941	St.L	A	P	32	3-7
1942	St.L	A	P	39	8-2
1943	St.L	A	P	35	6-8
1944	St.L	A	P	42	6-6
1945	St.L	A	P	10	1-2
1945	Det	A	P	22	5-1
1946	Det	A	P	26	2-1
	BRTR			380	76-100

CASTIGLIA, JAMES VINCENT
b.Sept.30,1918 Passaic,N.J.

Yr	Cl	Lea	Pos	G	Rec
1942	Phi	A	C	16	.389
	BBTR				

CASTIGLIONE, PETER PAUL
b.Feb.13,1921 Greenwich,Conn.

Yr	Cl	Lea	Pos	G	Rec
1947	Pit	N	S	13	.280
1948	Pit	N	S	4	.000
1949	Pit	N	S-3-O	118	.268
1950	Pit	N	1-2-S-3	94	.255
1951	Pit	N	S-3	132	.261
1952	Pit	N	1-3-O	67	.266
1953	Pit	N	3	45	.208

(Continued)

Yr	Cl	Lea	Pos	G	Rec
1953	St.L	N	2-S-3	67	.173
1954	St.L	N	3	5	.000
	BRTR			545	.255

CASTINO, VINCENT CHARLES
b.Oct.11,1918 Willisville,Ill.

Yr	Cl	Lea	Pos	G	Rec
1943	Chi	A	C	33	.228
1944	Chi	A	C	29	.231
1945	Chi	A	C	26	.216
	BRTR			88	.227

CASTLE, JOHN FRANCIS
b.June 1,1883 Honey Brook,Pa.
d.Apr.15,1929

Yr	Cl	Lea	Pos	G	Rec
1910	Phi	N	O	2	.250

CASTLEMAN, CLYDELL
(Slick)
b.Sept.8,1914 Donelson,Tenn.

Yr	Cl	Lea	Pos	G	Rec
1934	NY	N	P	7	1-0
1935	NY	N	P	29	15-6
1936	NY	N	P	30	4-7
1937	NY	N	P	23	11-6
1938	NY	N	P	22	4-5
1939	NY	N	P	12	1-2
	BRTR			123	36-26

CASTLEMAN, FOSTER EPHRAIM
b.Jan.1,1931 Nashville,Tenn.

Yr	Cl	Lea	Pos	G	Rec
1954	NY	N	3	13	.250
1955	NY	N	2-3	15	.214
1956	NY	N	2-S-3	124	.226
1957	NY	N	2-S-3	18	.162
1958	Bal	A	2-S-3-O	98	.170
	BRTR			268	.205

CASTLETON, ROY J. C.
b.1886 Salt Lake City,Utah

Yr	Cl	Lea	Pos	G	Rec
1907	NY	A	P	3	1-1
1909	Cin	N	P	4	1-1
1910	Cin	N	P	4	1-2
	BRTL			11	3-4

CASTNER, PAUL HENRY
(Lefty)
b.Feb.16,1897 St.Paul,Minn.

Yr	Cl	Lea	Pos	G	Rec
1923	Chi	A	P	6	0-0
	BLTL				

CASTRO, LOUIS M.
(Jud)
b.1877 Colombia,South America

Yr	Cl	Lea	Pos	G	Rec
1902	Phi	A	2-S-3-O	41	.248
	TR				

CATES, ELI ELDO
b.Jan.26,1877 Greensfork,Ind.

Yr	Cl	Lea	Pos	G	Rec
1908	Was	A	P	40	4-8
	TR				

CATHER, THEODORE P.
b.May 20,1889 Chester,Pa.
d.Apr.9,1945

Yr	Cl	Lea	Pos	G	Rec
1912	St.L	N	O	5	.421
1913	St.L	N	P-1-O	67	0-0 .213
1914	St.L	N	O	39	.273
1914	Bos	N	O	50	.296
1915	Bos	N	O	40	.206
	BRTR			201	0-0 .252

CATHEY, HARDIN
(Abner)
b.July 6,1919 Burns,Tenn.

Yr	Cl	Lea	Pos	G	Rec
1942	Was	A	P	12	1-1
	BRTR				

CATON, JAMES HOWARD
(Buster)
b.July 16,1896 Zanesville,O.
d.Jan.8,1948

Yr	Cl	Lea	Pos	G	Rec
1917	Pit	N	S	14	.211
1918	Pit	N	S	80	.234
1919	Pit	N	S-3-O	39	.176
1920	Pit	N	S	98	.236
	BRTR			231	.226

CATTANACH, JOHN L.
b.May 10,1863 Providence,R.I.
d.Nov.10,1926

Yr	Cl	Lea	Pos	G	Rec
1884	Pro	N	P-O	1	0-1 .000
1884	St.L	U	P	2	1-1
				3	1-2 .000

CATTERSON, THOMAS HENRY
b.Aug.25,1884 Arctic,R.I.
d.Feb.5,1920

Yr	Cl	Lea	Pos	G	Rec
1908	Bro	N	O	18	.191
1909	Bro	N	O	9	.222
	BL			27	.200

CAULFIELD, JOHN JOSEPH
(Jake)
b.Nov.23,1919 San Francisco,Cal.

Yr	Cl	Lea	Pos	G	Rec
1946	Phi	A	S-3	44	.277
	BRTR				

CAUSEY, CECIL ALGERNON
(Red)
b.Aug.11,1893 Seville,Fla.

Yr	Cl	Lea	Pos	G	Rec
1918	NY	N	P	29	11-6
1919	NY	N	P	21	9-3
1919	Bos	N	P	10	4-5
1920	Phi	N	P	44	7-14
1921	Phi	N	P	8	3-3
1921	NY	N	P	9	1-1
1922	NY	N	P	25	4-3
	BLTR			146	39-35

CAUSEY, JAMES WAYNE
b.Dec.26,1936 Monroe,La.

Yr	Cl	Lea	Pos	G	Rec
1955	Bal	A	2-S-3	68	.194
1956	Bal	A	2-3	53	.170
1957	Bal	A	2-3	14	.200
1961	KC	A	2-S-3	104	.276
1962	KC	A	2-S-3	117	.252
	BLTR			356	.240

CAVANAUGH, PATRICK JOHN
b.1900 Reading,Pa.

Yr	Cl	Lea	Pos	G	Rec
1919	Phi	N	3	1	.000

CAVARRETTA, PHILIP JOSEPH
b.July 19,1916 Chicago,Ill.

Yr	Cl	Lea	Pos	G	Rec
1934	Chi	N	1	7	.381
1935	Chi	N	1	146	.275
1936	Chi	N	1	124	.273
1937	Chi	N	1-O	106	.286
1938	Chi	N	1-O	92	.239
1939	Chi	N	1	22	.273
1940	Chi	N	1	65	.280
1941	Chi	N	1-O	107	.286
1942	Chi	N	1-O	136	.270
1943	Chi	N	1-O	143	.291
1944	Chi	N	1-O	152	.321
1945	Chi	N	1-O	132	.355
1946	Chi	N	1-O	139	.294
1947	Chi	N	1-O	127	.314
1948	Chi	N	1-O	111	.279
1949	Chi	N	1-O	105	.294
1950	Chi	N	1-O	82	.273
1951	Chi	N	M-1	89	.311
1952	Chi	N	M-1	41	.238
1953	Chi	N	M-H	27	.286
1954	Chi	A	1-O	71	.316
1955	Chi	A	1	6	.000
	BLTL			2030	.293

CAVENEY, JAMES CHRISTOPHER
(Ike)
b.Dec.10,1896 San Francisco,Cal.
d.July 6,1949

Yr	Cl	Lea	Pos	G	Rec
1922	Cin	N	S	118	.238
1923	Cin	N	S	138	.277
1924	Cin	N	2-S	95	.273
1925	Cin	N	S	115	.249
	BRTR			466	.260

CAVET, TILLAR H.
(Pug)
b.Dec.26,1889 McGregor,Tex.

Yr	Cl	Lea	Pos	G	Rec
1911	Det	A	P	1	0-0
1914	Det	A	P	29	7-7
1915	Det	A	P	17	4-3
	TL			47	11-10

CAYLOR, OLIVER PERRY
b.Dec.14,1849 Dayton,O
d.Oct.19,1897
Non-playing manager Cin (a) 1885-86 and Met (a) 1887

CECCARELLI, ARTHUR EDWARD
b.Apr.2,1930 New Haven,Conn.

Yr	Cl	Lea	Pos	G	Rec
1955	KC	A	P	31	4-7
1956	KC	A	P	3	0-1
1957	Bal	A	P	20	0-5
1959	Chi	N	P	18	5-5
1960	Chi	N	P	7	0-0
	BRTL			79	9-18

CECIL, REX ROLSTON
b.Oct.8,1916 Lindsay,Okla.

Yr	Cl	Lea	Pos	G	Rec
1944	Bos	A	P	11	4-5
1945	Bos	A	P	7	2-5
	BLTR			18	6-10

CENTER, MARVIN EARL
(Pete)
b.Apr.22,1914 Hazel Green,Ky.

Yr	Cl	Lea	Pos	G	Rec
1942	Cle	A	P	1	0-0
1943	Cle	A	P	24	1-2
1945	Cle	A	P	31	6-3
1946	Cle	A	P	21	0-2
	BRTR			77	7-7

CEPEDA, ORLANDO MANUEL
b.Sept.17,1937 Ponce,Porto Rico

Yr	Cl	Lea	Pos	G	Rec
1958	SF	N	1	148	.312
1959	SF	N	1-3-O	151	.317
1960	SF	N	1-O	151	.297
1961	SF	N	1-O	152	.311
1962	SF	N	1-O	162	.306
	BRTR			764	.309

CERMAK, EDWARD
b.July 23,1881 Cleveland,O.
d.Nov.22,1911

Yr	Cl	Lea	Pos	G	Rec
1901	Cle	A	O	1	.000

CERV, ROBERT HENRY
b.May 5,1926 Weston,Neb.

Yr	Cl	Lea	Pos	G	Rec
1951	NY	A	O	12	.214
1952	NY	A	O	36	.241
1953	NY	A	H	8	.000
1954	NY	A	O	56	.260
1955	NY	A	O	55	.341
1956	NY	A	O	54	.304
1957	KC	A	O	124	.272
1958	KC	A	O	141	.305
1959	KC	A	O	125	.285
1960	KC	A	O	23	.256
1960	NY	A	1-O	87	.250
1961	LA	A	O	18	.158
1961	NY	A	1-O	58	.271
1962	NY	A	O	14	.118
1962	Hou	N	O	19	.226
	BRTR			829	.276

CHACON, ELIO RODRIGUEZ
b.Oct.26,1936 Caracas, Venezuela

Yr	Cl	Lea	Pos	G	Rec
1960	Cin	N	2-O	49	.181
(Continued)					
1961	Cin	N	2-O	61	.265
1962	NY	N	2-S-3	118	.236
	BRTR			228	.232

CHADBOURNE, CHESTER JAMES
b.Oct.26,1884 Parkman,Me.
d.June 23,1943

Yr	Cl	Lea	Pos	G	Rec
1906	Bos	A	2	11	.302
1907	Bos	A	O	10	.289
1914	KC	F	O	147	.278
1915	KC	F	O	152	.224
1918	Bos	N	O	27	.260
	BLTR			347	.255

CHADRAUN, WILLIAM
(Played under name of William Chouneau)

CHAGNON, LEON WILBUR
(Shag)
b.Sept.28,1903 Pittsfield,N.H.
d.July 30,1953

Yr	Cl	Lea	Pos	G	Rec
1929	Pit	N	P	1	0-0
1930	Pit	N	P	18	0-3
1932	Pit	N	P	30	9-6
1933	Pit	N	P	39	6-4
1934	Pit	N	P	33	4-1
1935	NY	N	P	14	0-2
	BRTR			135	19-16

CHAKALES, ROBERT EDWARD
(Chick)
b.Aug.10,1927 Asheville,N.C.

Yr	Cl	Lea	Pos	G	Rec
1951	Cle	A	P	17	3-4
1952	Cle	A	P	5	1-2
1953	Cle	A	P	7	0-2
1954	Cle	A	P	3	2-0
1954	Bal	A	P	38	3-7
1955	Chi	A	P	7	0-0
1955	Was	A	P	29	2-3
1956	Was	A	P	43	4-4
1957	Was	A	P	4	0-1
1957	Bos	A	P	18	0-2
	BRTR			171	15-25

CHALMERS, GEORGE W.
(Dut)
b.June 7,1888 Aberdeen,Scotland
d.Aug.5,1960

Yr	Cl	Lea	Pos	G	Rec
1910	Phi	N	P	4	1-1
1911	Phi	N	P	38	13-10
1912	Phi	N	P	12	3-4
1913	Phi	N	P	26	3-10
1914	Phi	N	P	3	0-3
1915	Phi	N	P	26	8-9
1916	Phi	N	P	12	1-4
	BRTR			121	29-41

CHAMBERLAIN, ELTON P.
(Iceberg)
b.Nov.5,1867 Warsaw,N.Y.
d.Sept.24,1929

Yr	Cl	Lea	Pos	G	Rec
1886	Lou	a	P-O	6	0-3 .150
1887	Lou	a	P	37	18-16
1888	Lou	a	P	26	9-8
1888	St.L	a	P-O	20	11-2 .080
1889	St.L	a	P	53	35-15
1890	St.L	a	P	5	2-3
1890	Col	a	P	28	13-7
1891	Ath	a	P	54	21-22
1892	Cin	N	P	44	19-23
1893	Cin	N	P	27	14-9
1894	Cin	N	P	20	9-11
1896	Cle	N	P	2	0-1
	BRTR			322	151-120 .195

CHAMBERLAIN, WILLIAM VINCENT
b.Apr.21,1909 Stoughton,Mass.

Yr	Cl	Lea	Pos	G	Rec
1932	Chi	A	P	12	0-5
	BRTL				

CHAMBERLIN, JOSEPH JEREMIAH
b.May 10,1910 San Francisco,Cal.

Yr	Cl	Lea	Pos	G	Rec
1934	Chi	A	S-3	43	241
	BRTR				

CHAMBERS, CLIFFORD DAY (Lefty)
b.Jan.10,1922 Portland,Ore.

Yr	Cl	Lea	Pos	G	Rec
1948	Chi	N	P	29	2-9
1949	Pit	N	P	34	13-7
1950	Pit	N	P	37	12-15
1951	Pit	N	P	10	3-6
1951	St.L	N	P	21	11-6
1952	St.L	N	P	26	4-4
1953	St.L	N	P	32	3-6
	BLTL			189	48-53

CHAMBERS, JOHN MONROE
b.Sept.10,1911 Copper Hill,Tenn.

Yr	Cl	Lea	Pos	G	Rec
1937	St.L	N	P	2	0-0
	BLTR				

CHAMBERS, ROME J.
b.Kernersville,N.C.

Yr	Cl	Lea	Pos	G	Rec
1900	Bos	N	P	1	0-0
	BLTL				

CHAMBERS, WILLIAM CHRISTOPHER
b.Sept.13,1889 Cameron, W.Va.
d.Mar.27,1962

Yr	Cl	Lea	Pos	G	Rec
1910	St.L	N	P	1	0-0

CHANCE, FRANK LEROY (Husk)
b.Sept.9,1877 Fresno,Cal.
d.Sept.14,1924

Yr	Cl	Lea	Pos	G	Rec
1898	Chi	N	C-O	42	.288
1899	Chi	N	C	57	.289
1900	Chi	N	C	48	.304
1901	Chi	N	O	63	.289
1902	Chi	N	C-I-O	67	.284
1903	Chi	N	1	123	.327
1904	Chi	N	1	124	.310
1905	Chi	N	M-1	115	.316
1906	Chi	N	M-1	136	.319
1907	Chi	N	M-1	109	.293
1908	Chi	N	M-1	126	.272
1909	Chi	N	M-1	92	.271
1910	Chi	N	M-1	87	.298
1911	Chi	N	M-1	29	.239
1912	Chi	N	M-1	2	.200
1913	NY	A	M-1	11	.208
1914	NY	A	M-1	1	.000
	BRTR			1232	.297

Non-playing manager Bos (A) 1923

CHANCE, WILMER DEAN
b.June 1,1941 Wayne,O.

Yr	Cl	Lea	Pos	G	Rec
1961	LA	A	P	5	0-2
1962	LA	A	P	50	14-10
	BRTR			55	14-12

CHANDLER, EDWARD OLIVER
b.Feb.6,1922 Pinson,Ala.

Yr	Cl	Lea	Pos	G	Rec
1947	Bro	N	P	15	0-1
	BRTR				

CHANDLER, SPURGEON FERDINAND (Spud)
b.Sept.12,1909 Commerce,Ga.

Yr	Cl	Lea	Pos	G	Rec
1937	NY	A	P	12	7-4
1938	NY	A	P	23	14-5
1939	NY	A	P	11	3-0
1940	NY	A	P	27	8-7
1941	NY	A	P	28	10-4
1942	NY	A	P	24	16-5
1943	NY	A	P	30	20-4
1944	NY	A	P	1	0-0
1945	NY	A	P	4	2-1
1946	NY	A	P	34	20-8
1947	NY	A	P	17	9-5
	BRTR			211	109-43

CHANEY, ESTY CLEON
b.Jan.29,1891 Hadley,Pa.

Yr	Cl	Lea	Pos	G	Rec
1913	Bos	A	P	1	0-0
1914	Bro	F	P	1	0-0
	BRTR			2	0-0

CHANNELL, LESTER CLARK (Dude)
b.Mar.3,1886 Crestline,O.
d.May 7,1954

Yr	Cl	Lea	Pos	G	Rec
1910	NY	A	O	6	.263
1914	NY	A	O	1	1.000
	BLTL			7	.300

CHAPLIN, BERT E.
b.1896 Pelzer,S.C.

Yr	Cl	Lea	Pos	G	Rec
1920	Bos	A	C	4	.250
1921	Bos	A	C	3	.000
1922	Bos	A	C	28	.189
	BLTR			35	.182

CHAPLIN, JAMES BAILEY (Tiny)
b.July 13,1905 Los Angeles,Cal.
d.Mar.25,1939

Yr	Cl	Lea	Pos	G	Rec
1928	NY	N	P	12	0-2
1930	NY	N	P	19	2-6
1931	NY	N	P	16	3-0
1936	Bos	N	P	40	10-15
	BRTR			87	15-23

CHAPMAN, CALVIN LOUIS
b.Dec.20,1912 Courtland,Miss.

Yr	Cl	Lea	Pos	G	Rec
1935	Cin	N	2-S	15	.340
1936	Cin	N	2-O	96	.247
	BLTR			111	.265

CHAPMAN, EDWIN VOLNEY
b.Nov.28,1905 Courtland,Miss.

Yr	Cl	Lea	Pos	G	Rec
1933	Was	A	P	6	0-0
	BRTR				

CHAPMAN, FREDERICK JAMES
b.Nov.25,1870 Little Cooley,Pa.
d.Dec.14,1957

Yr	Cl	Lea	Pos	G	Rec
1887	Ath	a	P	1	1-0

CHAPMAN, FREDERICK WILLIAM
b.July 17,1916 Liberty,S.C.

Yr	Cl	Lea	Pos	G	Rec
1939	Phi	A	S	15	.286
1940	Phi	A	S	26	.159
1941	Phi	A	2-S-3	35	.159
	BRTR			76	.193

CHAPMAN, GLENN JUSTICE (Pete)
b.Jan.21,1908 Cambridge City,Ind.

Yr	Cl	Lea	Pos	G	Rec
1934	Bro	N	2-O	67	.280
	BRTR				

CHAPMAN, HARRY E.
b.Oct.26,1887 Severance,Kan.
d.Oct.21,1918

Yr	Cl	Lea	Pos	G	Rec
1912	Chi	N	C	1	.250
1913	Cin	N	C	2	.500
1914	St.L	F	C	59	.209
1915	St.L	F	C	62	.198
1916	St.L	A	C	18	.097
	BRTR			142	.195

CHAPMAN, JOHN CURTIS
b.May 8,1843 Brooklyn,N.Y.
d.June 10,1916

Yr	Cl	Lea	Pos	G	Rec
1874	Atl	n	1-O	53	NR
1875	St.L	n	O	41	.246
1876	Lou	N	O	17	.235
	TR			111	NR

Non-playing manager Lou (N) 1877, Mil (N) 1878, Wor (N) 1882, Det (N) 1883-84, Buf (N) 1885, Lou (a) 1889-91 and Lou (N) 1892

CHAPMAN, JOHN JOSEPH
b.Oct.15,1901 Centralia,Pa.
d.Nov.3,1953

Yr	Cl	Lea	Pos	G	Rec
1924	Phi	A	S	19	.282
	BRTR				

CHAPMAN, RAYMOND JOHNSON
b.Jan.15,1891 McHenry,Ky.
d.Aug.17,1920

Yr	Cl	Lea	Pos	G	Rec
1912	Cle	A	S	31	.312
1913	Cle	A	S	146	.254
1914	Cle	A	2-S	106	.275
1915	Cle	A	S	154	.270
1916	Cle	A	2-S-3	109	.231
1917	Cle	A	S	156	.302
1918	Cle	A	S	128	.267
1919	Cle	A	S	115	.300
1920	Cle	A	S	111	.303
	BRTR			1056	.278

CHAPMAN, SAMUEL BLAKE
b.Apr.11,1916 Tiburon,Cal.

Yr	Cl	Lea	Pos	G	Rec
1938	Phi	A	O	114	.259
1939	Phi	A	1-O	140	.269
1940	Phi	A	O	134	.276
1941	Phi	A	O	143	.322
1945	Phi	A	O	9	.200
1946	Phi	A	O	146	.261
1947	Phi	A	O	149	.252
1948	Phi	A	O	123	.258
1949	Phi	A	O	154	.278
1950	Phi	A	O	144	.251
1951	Phi	A	O	18	.169
1951	Cle	A	1-O	94	.228
	BRTR			1368	.266

CHAPMAN, WILLIAM BENJAMIN (Ben)
b.Dec.25,1908 Nashville,Tenn.

Yr	Cl	Lea	Pos	G	Rec
1930	NY	A	2-3	138	.316
1931	NY	A	2-O	149	.315
1932	NY	A	O	150	.299
1933	NY	A	O	147	.312
1934	NY	A	O	149	.308
1935	NY	A	O	140	.289
1936	NY	A	O	36	.266
1936	Was	A	O	97	.332
1937	Was	A	O	35	.262
1937	Bos	A	O	113	.307
1938	Bos	A	O	127	.340
1939	Cle	A	O	149	.290
1940	Cle	A	O	143	.286
1941	Was	A	O	28	.255
1941	Chi	A	O	57	.226
1944	Bro	N	P	20	5-3
1945	Bro	N	P	13	3-3
1945	Phi	N	M-P-3-O	24	0-0 / .314
1946	Phi	N	M-P	1	0-0 / .000
	BRTR			1716	8-6 / .302

Non-playing manager Phi (N) 1947-48

CHAPPELL, LAWRENCE A.
b.Feb.19,1891 Jerseyville,Ill.
d.Nov.9,1918

Yr	Cl	Lea	Pos	G	Rec
1913	Chi	A	O	60	.229
1914	Chi	A	O	21	.231
1915	Chi	A	H	1	.000
1916	Cle	A	O	3	.000
1916	Bos	N	O	20	.226
1917	Bos	N	O	3	.000
	BLTR			108	.225

CHAPPELLE, WILLIAM HOGAN (Big Bill)
b.Mar.22,1884 Waterloo,N.Y.
d.Dec.31,1944

Yr	Cl	Lea	Pos	G	Rec
1908	Bos	N	P	13	2-4
1909	Bos	N	P	5	1-1
1909	Cin	N	P	1	0-0
1914	Bro	F	P	15	4-2
	BRTR			34	7-7

CHARLES, EDWIN DOUGLAS
b.Apr.29,1933 Daytona Beach,Fla.

Yr	Cl	Lea	Pos	G	Rec
1962	KC	A	2-3	147	.288

BRTR

CHARLES, RAYMOND
(Chappy)
(Real Name Charles S. Aschenbach)
b.1883 Phillipsburg,N.J.

Yr	Cl	Lea	Pos	G	Rec
1908	St.L	N	2-S-3	119	.205
1909	St.L	N	2-S	99	.236
1909	Cin	N	2-S	13	.256
1910	Cin	N	S	4	.133
		BRTR		235	.219

CHARTAK, MICHAEL GEORGE
b.Apr.28,1917 Brooklyn,N.Y.

Yr	Cl	Lea	Pos	G	Rec
1940	NY	A	O	11	.133
1942	NY	A	O	5	.000
1942	Was	A	O	24	.217
1942	St.L	A	O	73	.249
1943	St.L	A	1-O	108	.256
1944	St.L	A	1-O	35	.236
		BLTL		256	.243

CHASE, HAROLD HOMER
(Prince Hal)
b.Feb.13,1883 Los Gatos,Cal.
d.May 18,1947

Yr	Cl	Lea	Pos	G	Rec
1905	NY	A	1	126	.249
1906	NY	A	1	151	.323
1907	NY	A	1	125	.287
1908	NY	A	1	106	.257
1909	NY	A	1	118	.283
1910	NY	A	M-1	130	.290
1911	NY	A	M-1	133	.315
1912	NY	A	1	131	.274
1913	NY	A	1-2-O	39	.228
1913	Chi	A	1	102	.281
1914	Chi	A	1	58	.267
1914	Buf	F	1	75	.354
1915	Buf	F	1	145	.284
1916	Cin	N	1-2-O	142	.339
1917	Cin	N	1	152	.277
1918	Cin	N	1-O	74	.301
1919	NY	N	1	110	.284
		BRTL		1917	.291

CHASE, KENDALL FAY
(Lefty)
b.Oct.6,1913 Oneonta,N.Y.

Yr	Cl	Lea	Pos	G	Rec
1936	Was	A	P	1	0-0
1937	Was	A	P	14	4-3
1938	Was	A	P	32	9-10
1939	Was	A	P	32	10-19
1940	Was	A	P	35	15-17
1941	Was	A	P	33	6-18
1942	Bos	A	P	13	5-1
1943	Bos	A	P	7	0-4
1943	NY	N	P	23	4-12
		BLTL		190	53-84

CHATHAM, CHARLES L.
(Buster)
b.Dec.25,1901 West,Tex.

Yr	Cl	Lea	Pos	G	Rec
1930	Bos	N	S-3	112	.267
1931	Bos	N	S-3	17	.227
		BRTR		129	.263

CHATTERTON, JAMES M.
b.Oct.14,1864 Brooklyn,N.Y.
d.Dec.18,1944

Yr	Cl	Lea	Pos	G	Rec
1884	KC	U	P-1-O	4	{ 0-1 .125

CHECH, CHARLES WILLIAM
b.Apr.27,1879 Madison,Wis.
d.Jan.31,1938

Yr	Cl	Lea	Pos	G	Rec
1905	Cin	N	P	39	13-13
1906	Cin	N	P	11	1-4
1908	Cle	A	P	27	11-7
1909	Bos	A	P	17	7-6
		BRTR		94	32-30

CHEEK, HARRY G.
b.Kansas City,Mo.

Yr	Cl	Lea	Pos	G	Rec
1910	Phi	N	C	2	.500

TR

CHEEVES, VIRGIL EARL
(Chief)
b.Feb.12,1901 Oklahoma City,Okla.

Yr	Cl	Lea	Pos	G	Rec
1920	Chi	N	P	5	0-0
1921	Chi	N	P	37	11-12
1922	Chi	N	P	39	12-11
1923	Chi	N	P	19	3-4
1924	Cle	A	P	8	0-0
1927	NY	N	P	3	0-0
		BRTR		111	26-27

CHELINI, ITALO VINCENT
(Chilly)
b.Oct.10,1914 San Francisco,Cal.

Yr	Cl	Lea	Pos	G	Rec
1935	Chi	A	P	2	0-0
1936	Chi	A	P	18	4-3
1937	Chi	A	P	4	0-1
		BLTL		24	4-4

CHENEY, LAWRENCE RUSSELL
b.May 2,1886 Belleville,Kan.

Yr	Cl	Lea	Pos	G	Rec
1911	Chi	N	P	3	1-0
1912	Chi	N	P	42	26-10
1913	Chi	N	P	56	21-14
1914	Chi	N	P	50	20-18
1915	Chi	N	P	25	8-9
1915	Bro	N	P	5	0-2
1916	Bro	N	P	41	18-12
1917	Bro	N	P	35	8-12
1918	Bro	N	P	33	11-13
1919	Bro	N	P	9	1-3
1919	Bos	N	P	8	0-2
1919	Phi	N	P	9	2-5
		BRTR		316	116-100

CHENEY, THOMAS EDGAR
b.Oct.14,1934 Morgan,Ga.

Yr	Cl	Lea	Pos	G	Rec
1957	St.L	N	P	4	0-1
1959	St.L	N	P	11	0-1
1960	Pit	N	P	11	2-2
1961	Pit	N	P	1	0-0
1961	Was	A	P	13	1-3
1962	Was	A	P	37	7-9
		BRTR		77	10-16

CHERVINKO, PAUL
b.July 28,1910 Trauger,Pa.

Yr	Cl	Lea	Pos	G	Rec
1937	Bro	N	C	30	.146
1938	Bro	N	C	12	.148
		BRTR		42	.147

CHESBRO, JOHN DWIGHT
(Happy Jack)
b.June 5,1874 N.Adams,Mass.
d.Nov.6,1931

Yr	Cl	Lea	Pos	G	Rec
1899	Pit	N	P	19	6-9
1900	Pit	N	P	29	15-13
1901	Pit	N	P	33	21-9
1902	Pit	N	P	34	27-6
1903	NY	A	P	40	21-15
1904	NY	A	P	55	41-13
1905	NY	A	P	41	20-13
1906	NY	A	P	48	24-16
1907	NY	A	P	29	9-10
1908	NY	A	P	44	14-20
1909	NY	A	P	8	0-3
1909	Bos	A	P	2	0-2
		BRTR		382	198-129

CHESLEY, HARRY STEPHEN
(Played under name of Harry Stephen Child)

CHESNES, ROBERT VINCENT
b.May 6,1921 Oakland,Cal.

Yr	Cl	Lea	Pos	G	Rec
1948	Pit	N	P	39	14-6
1949	Pit	N	P	42	7-13
1950	Pit	N	P	9	3-3
		BBTR		90	24-22

CHETKOVICH, MITCHELL
b.July 21,1918 Fairpoint,O

Yr	Cl	Lea	Pos	G	Rec
1945	Phi	N	P	4	0-0

BRTR

CHILD, HARRY STEPHEN
(Real name Harry Stephen Chesley)
b.May 23,1906 Baltimore,Md.

Yr	Cl	Lea	Pos	G	Rec
1930	Was	A	P	5	0-0

BLTR

CHILDERS, ...
b.St. Louis,Mo.

Yr	Cl	Lea	Pos	G	Rec
1895	Lou	N	P	1	0-0

CHILDS, A. F.
Non-playing manager Nat (n) 1875

CHILDS, CLARENCE ALGERNON
(Cupid)
b.Aug.14,1868 Calvert Co.,Md.
d.Nov.8,1912

Yr	Cl	Lea	Pos	G	Rec
1888	Phi	N	2	2	.000
1890	Syr	a	2	136	.344
1891	Cle	N	2	141	.295
1892	Cle	N	2	144	.335
1893	Cle	N	2	122	.332
1894	Cle	N	2	117	.365
1895	Cle	N	2	120	.312
1896	Cle	N	2	132	.348
1897	Cle	N	2	114	.336
1898	Cle	N	2	109	.289
1899	St.L	N	2	125	.266
1900	Chi	N	2	138	.243
1901	Chi	N	2	63	.257
		BLTR		1463	.313

CHILDS, PETER PIENE
b.Nov.15,1871 Philadelphia,Pa.
d.Feb.15,1922

Yr	Cl	Lea	Pos	G	Rec
1901	St.L	N	2	8	.609
1901	Chi	N	2	60	.221
1902	Phi	N	2	120	.192
		TR		188	.217

CHILES, PEARCE NUGET
(What's The Use)
b.May 28,1867 Deepwater,Mo.

Yr	Cl	Lea	Pos	G	Rec
1899	Phi	N	1-O	81	.329
1900	Phi	N	1-O	28	.220
				109	.301

CHIOZZA, DINO JOSEPH
b.Oct.17,1916 New Orleans,La.

Yr	Cl	Lea	Pos	G	Rec
1935	Phi	N	S	2	.000

BLTR

CHIOZZA, LOUIS PEO
b.May 17,1910 Tallulah,La.

Yr	Cl	Lea	Pos	G	Rec
1934	Phi	N	2-3-O	134	.304
1935	Phi	N	2-3	124	.284
1936	Phi	N	2-3-O	144	.297
1937	NY	N	3-O	117	.232
1938	NY	N	2-O	57	.235
1939	NY	N	3	40	.268
		BLTR		616	.277

CHIPMAN, ROBERT HOWARD
b.Oct.11,1918 Brooklyn,N.Y.

Yr	Cl	Lea	Pos	G	Rec
1941	Bro	N	P	1	1-0
1942	Bro	N	P	2	0-0
1943	Bro	N	P	1	0-0
1944	Bro	N	P	11	3-1
1944	Chi	N	P	26	9-9
1945	Chi	N	P	25	4-5
1946	Chi	N	P	34	6-5
1947	Chi	N	P	33	7-6
1948	Chi	N	P	34	2-1
1949	Chi	N	P	38	7-8
1950	Bos	N	P	27	7-7
1951	Bos	N	P	33	4-3
1952	Bos	N	P	29	1-1
		BLTL		294	51-46

CHIPPLE, WALTER JOHN
(Real Name Walter John Chlipala)
b.Sept.26,1919 Utica,N.Y.

Yr	Cl	Lea	Pos	G	Rec
1945	Was	A	O	18	.136

BRTR

Yr Cl Lea Pos G Rec

CHITI, HARRY
b.Nov.16,1932 Kincaid,Ill.
1950 Chi N C 3 .333
1951 Chi N C 9 .355
1952 Chi N C 32 .274
1955 Chi N C 113 .231
1956 Chi N C 72 .212
1958 KC A C 103 .268
1959 KC A C 55 .272
1960 KC A C 58 .221
1960 Det A C 37 .163
1961 Det A C 5 .083
1962 NY N C 15 .195
BRTR 502 .238

CHITTUM, NELSON BOYD
b.Mar.25,1933 Harrisonburg,Va.
1958 St.L N P 13 0-1
1959 Bos A P 21 3-0
1960 Bos A P 6 0-0
BRTR 40 3-1

CHLIPALA, WALTER JOHN
(Played under name of Walter John Chipple)

CHOATE, DONALD LEON
b.July2,1938 Potosi,Mo.
1960 SF N P 4 0-0
BRTR

CHOUINARD, FELIX GEORGE
b.1888 Chicago,Ill.
1910 Chi A O 24 .195
1911 Chi A 2-O 14 .157
1914 Pit F O 5 .440
1914 Bro F O 15 .366
1914 Bal F O 26 .217
1915 Bro F O 4 .500
BLTR 88 .244

CHOUNEAU, WILLIAM
(Chief)
(Real name William Chadraun)
b.Sept.2,1889 Cloquet,Minn.
d.Sept.17,1948
1910 Chi A P 1 0-0
TR

CHOZEN, HARRY KENNETH
b.Sept.27,1915 Winnebago,Minn.
1937 Cin N C 1 .250
BRTR

CHRISLEY, BARBRA O'NEIL
b.Dec.16,1932 Calhoun Falls,S.C.
1957 Was A O 26 .157
1958 Was A 3-O 105 .215
1959 Det A O 65 .132
1960 Det A 1-O 96 .255
1961 Mil N H 10 .222
BLTR 202 .210

CHRISTENBURY, LLOYD REID
b.Oct.19,1894 Mecklenburg Co., N.C.
d.Dec.13,1944
1919 Bos N O 7 .290
1920 Bos N 2-S-O 65 .208
1921 Bos N 2 62 .352
1922 Bos N 2-3-O 71 .250
BLTR 205 .271

CHRISTENSEN, WALTER NIELS
(Seacap)
b.Oct.24,1899 San Francisco,Cal.
1926 Cin N O 114 .350
1927 Cin N O 57 .254
BLTL 171 .315

CHRISTMAN, H. B.
b.Dayton,O
1888 KC a C 1 .250

Yr Cl Lea Pos G Rec

CHRISTMAN, MARQUETTE JOSEPH
(Mark)
b.Oct.21,1913 Maplewood,Mo.
1938 Det A S-3 95 .248
1939 Det A S 6 .250
1939 St.L A S 79 .216
1943 St.L A 1-2-S-3 98 .271
1944 St.L A 1-3 148 .271
1945 St.L A 3 78 .277
1946 St.L A S-3 128 .258
1947 Was A 2-S 110 .223
1948 Was A 2-S-3 120 .259
1949 Was A 1-2-S-3 49 .214
BRTR 911 .253

CHRISTOPHER, JOSEPH O'NEAL
b.Dec.13,1935 Frederiksted,Virgin Is.
1959 Pit N O 15 .000
1960 Pit N O 50 .232
1961 Pit N O 76 .263
1962 NY N O 119 .244
BRTR 260 .244

CHRISTOPHER, LOYD EUGENE
b.Dec.31,1919 Point Richmond,Cal.
1945 Bos A O 8 .286
1945 Chi N O 1 .000
1947 Chi A O 7 .217
BRTR 16 .243

CHRISTOPHER, RUSSELL ORMAND
b.Sept.12,1907 Point Richmond,Cal.
d.Dec.5,1954
1942 Phi A P 30 4-13
1943 Phi A P 24 5-8
1944 Phi A P 35 14-14
1945 Phi A P 34 13-13
1946 Phi A P 30 5-7
1947 Phi A P 44 10-7
1948 Cle A P 45 3-2
BRTR 242 54-64

CHURCH, EMORY NICHOLAS
(Bubba)
b.Sept.12,1925 Birmingham,Ala.
1950 Phi N P 39 8-6
1951 Phi N P 39 15-11
1952 Phi N P 2 0-0
1952 Cin N P 32 5-9
1953 cin N P 12 3-3
1953 Chi N P 27 4-5
1954 Chi N P 8 1-3
1955 Chi N P 3 0-0
BRTR 162 36-37

CHURCH, HIRAM LINCOLN
b.Central Square,N.Y.
1890 Bro a O 3 .125

CHURN, CLARENCE NOTTINGHAM
b.Feb.1,1930 Bridgetown,Va.
1957 Pit N P 5 0-0
1958 Cle A P 6 0-0
1959 LA N P 14 3-2
BRTR 25 3-2

CHURRY, JOHN
b.Nov.26,1901 Johnstown,Pa.
1924 Chi N C 6 .143
1925 Chi N C 3 .500
1926 Chi N C 2 .000
1927 Chi N C 1 1.000
BRTR 12 .278

CIAFFONE, LAWRENCE THOMAS
b.Aug.17,1924 Brooklyn,N.Y.
1951 St.L N O 5 .000
BRTR

Yr Cl Lea Pos G Rec

CICERO, JOSEPH FRANCIS
(Dode)
b.Nov.18,1910 Atlantic City,N.J.
1929 Bos A O 10 .313
1930 Bos A 3-O 18 .167
1945 Phi A O 12 .158
BRTR 40 .222

CICOTTE, ALVA WARREN
b.Dec.23,1929 Melvindale,Mich.
1957 NY A P 20 2-2
1958 Was A P 9 0-3
1958 Det A P 15 3-1
1959 Cle A P 26 3-1
1961 St.L N P 29 2-6
1962 Hou N P 5 0-0
BRTR 104 10-13

CICOTTE, EDWARD VICTOR
(Knuckles)
b.June 19,1884 Detroit,Mich.
1905 Det A P 4 4-0
1908 Bos A P 39 11-12
1909 Bos A P 26 13-5
1910 Bos A P 36 15-11
1911 Bos A P 35 11-14
1912 Bos A P 9 1-2
1912 Chi A P 20 9-8
1913 Chi A P 40 18-12
1914 Chi A P 42 11-16
1915 Chi A P 40 13-11
1916 Chi A P 44 15-7
1917 Chi A P 49 28-12
1918 Chi A P 38 12-19
1919 Chi A P 40 29-7
1920 Chi A P 37 21-10
BRTR 499 211-146

CIESLAK, THADDEUS WALTER
(Ted)
b.Nov.22,1916 Milwaukee,Wis.
1944 Phi N 3-O 85 .245
BRTR

CIHOCKI, ALBERT JOSEPH
b.May 7,1924 Nanticoke,Pa.
1945 Cle A 2-S-3 92 .212
BRTR

CIHOCKI, EDWARD JOSEPH
(Cy)
b.May 9,1909 Wilmington,Del.
1932 Phi A O 1 .000
1933 Phi A S 33 .144
BRTR 34 .143

CIMOLI, GINO NICHOLAS
b.Dec.18,1929 San Francisco,Cal.
1956 Bro N O 73 .111
1957 Bro N O 142 .293
1958 LA N O 109 .246
1959 St.L N O 143 .279
1960 Pit N O 101 .267
1961 Pit N O 21 .299
1961 Mil N O 37 .197
1962 KC A O 152 .275
BRTR 778 .269

CIOLA, LOUIS ALEXANDER
b.Sept.6,1922 Norfolk,Va.
1943 Phi A P 12 1-3
BRTR

CIPRIANI, FRANK DOMINICK
b.Apr.14,1941 Buffalo,N.Y.
1961 KC A O 13 .250
BRTR

CISAR, GEORGE
b.Aug.25,1915 Chicago,Ill.

Yr	Cl	Lea	Pos	G	Rec
1937	Bro	N	O	20	.207
	BRTR				

CISCO, GALEN BERNARD
b.Mar.7,1937 St.Mary's,O.

Yr	Cl	Lea	Pos	G	Rec
1961	Bos	A	P	18	2-4
1962	Bos	A	P	23	4-7
1962	NY	N	P	4	1-1
	BRTR			45	7-12

CISSELL, CHALMER WILLIAM
(Bill)
b.Jan.3,1904 Perryville,Mo.
d.Mar.15,1949

Yr	Cl	Lea	Pos	G	Rec
1928	Chi	A	S	125	.260
1929	Chi	A	S	152	.280
1930	Chi	A	2-S-3	141	.271
1931	Chi	A	2-S	109	.220
1932	Chi	A	S	12	.256
1932	Cle	A	2-S	131	.320
1933	Cle	A	2-S-3	112	.230
1934	Bos	A	2	102	.267
1937	Phi	A	2	34	.265
1938	NY	N	2	38	.268
	BRTR			956	.267

CLABAUGH, JOHN WILLIAM
(Moose)
b.Nov.13,1901 Albany,Mo.

Yr	Cl	Lea	Pos	G	Rec
1926	Bro	N	O	11	.071
	BLTR				

CLACK, ROBERT S.
(Gentleman Bob)
b.1851 Brooklyn,N.Y.
d.Oct.22,1933

Yr	Cl	Lea	Pos	G	Rec
1874	Atl	n	O	30	NR
1875	Atl	n	O	17	NR
1876	Cin	N	P-1-2-3-O	31	0-0 / .154
	BRTR			78	0-0 / NR

CLAIRE, DAVID MATTHEW
(Danny)
b.Nov.18,1897 Ludington,Mich.
d.Jan.7,1956

Yr	Cl	Lea	Pos	G	Rec
1920	Det	A	S	3	.000
	BRTR				

CLANCEY, WILLIAM EDWARD
b.Apr.12,1878 Redfield,N.Y.
d.Feb.10,1948

Yr	Cl	Lea	Pos	G	Rec
1905	Pit	N	1	56	.229
	TR				

CLANCY, ALBERT HARRISON
b.Aug.14,1888 Santa Fe,N.M.
d.Oct.17,1951

Yr	Cl	Lea	Pos	G	Rec
1911	St.L	A	3	3	.000
	BRTR				

CLANCY, JOHN WILLIAM
(Bud)
b.Sept.15,1900 Odell,Ill.

Yr	Cl	Lea	Pos	G	Rec
1924	Chi	A	1	13	.257
1925	Chi	A	1	4	.000
1926	Chi	A	1	12	.342
1927	Chi	A	1	130	.300
1928	Chi	A	1	130	.271
1929	Chi	A	1	92	.283
1930	Chi	A	1	68	.244
1932	Bro	N	1	53	.306
1934	Phi	N	1	20	.245
	BLTL			522	.281

CLANTON, EUCAL CURT
b.Feb.19,1898 Powell,Mo.

Yr	Cl	Lea	Pos	G	Rec
1922	Cle	A	1	1	.000
	BLTL				

CLAPP, AARON BRONSON
b.July 1856 Ithaca,N.Y.
d.Jan.13,1914

Yr	Cl	Lea	Pos	G	Rec
1879	Tro	N	1-O	34	.272
	TR				

CLAPP, JOHN EDGAR
b.July 17,1851 Ithaca,N.Y.
d.Dec.18,1904

Yr	Cl	Lea	Pos	G	Rec
1872	Man	n	C	14	NR
1873	Ath	n	C-2-S	43	NR
1874	Ath	n	C-S-O	39	NR
1875	Ath	n	C	59	.248
1876	St.L	N	C	64	.298
1877	St.L	N	C-1-O	60	.316
1878	Ind	N	M-1-O-	60	.296
1879	Buf	N	C	67	.265
1880	Cin	N	M-C-O	79	.280
1881	Cle	N	C-O	65	.253
1883	NY	N	M-C-O	19	.178
	BRTR			569	NR

CLARE, DANIEL J.
(Denny)
b.Brooklyn,N.Y.

Yr	Cl	Lea	Pos	G	Rec
1872	Atl	n	2	2	NR

CLARK, ALFRED ALOYSIUS
b.June 16,1923 S.Amboy,N.J.

Yr	Cl	Lea	Pos	G	Rec
1947	NY	A	O	24	.373
1948	Cle	A	1-3-O	81	.310
1949	Cle	A	1-O	35	.176
1950	Cle	A	O	59	.215
1951	Cle	A	O	3	.300
1951	Phi	A	3-O	56	.248
1952	Phi	A	1-O	71	.274
1953	Phi	A	O	20	.203
1953	Chi	A	1-O	9	.067
	BRTR			358	.262

CLARK, ARTHUR FRANKLIN
(Archie)
b.May 6,1865 Providence,R.I.
d.Nov.14,1949

Yr	Cl	Lea	Pos	G	Rec
1890	NY	N	C-2-3-O	101	.225
1891	NY	N	C	46	.188
				147	.214

CLARK, BAILEY EARL
b.Nov.6,1907 Washington,D.C.
d.Jan.16,1938

Yr	Cl	Lea	Pos	G	Rec
1927	Bos	N	O	13	.273
1928	Bos	N	O	28	.304
1929	Bos	N	O	84	.315
1930	Bos	N	O	82	.296
1931	Bos	N	O	16	.220
1932	Bos	N	O	50	.250
1933	Bos	N	O	7	.348
1934	St.L	A	O	13	.171
	BRTR			293	.291

CLARK, DANIEL CURRAN
b.Jan.18,1895 Meridian,Miss.
d.May 23,1937

Yr	Cl	Lea	Pos	G	Rec
1922	Det	A	2	83	.292
1924	Bos	A	3	104	.277
1927	St.L	N	O	58	.236
	BLTR			245	.277

CLARK, EDWARD C.
b.Cincinnati,O

Yr	Cl	Lea	Pos	G	Rec
1886	Ath	a	P	1	0-1
1891	Col	a	P	5	1-2
				6	1-3

CLARK, FREDERICK R.
b.Portland,Ore.

Yr	Cl	Lea	Pos	G	Rec
1902	Chi	N	1	12	.186
	TL				

CLARK, GEORGE C.
(Herkie)
b.1890

Yr	Cl	Lea	Pos	G	Rec
1913	NY	A	P	11	0-1
	BRTL				

CLARK, HARRY
(Pep)
b.Mar.20,1883 Paulding,O.

Yr	Cl	Lea	Pos	G	Rec
1903	Chi	A	3	15	.308
	BRTR				

CLARK, HARVEY DANIEL
(Ginger)
b.Mar.7,1879 Wooster,O.
d.May 10,1943

Yr	Cl	Lea	Pos	G	Rec
1902	Cle	A	P	1	1-0
	BRTR				

CLARK, JAMES
(Real name James Petrosky)
b.Sept.21,1927 Bagley,Pa.

Yr	Cl	Lea	Pos	G	Rec
1948	Was	A	S-3	9	.250
	BRTR				

CLARK, JAMES F.
b.Dec.26,1887 Brooklyn,N.Y.

Yr	Cl	Lea	Pos	G	Rec
1911	St.L	N	O	14	.176
1912	St.L	N	O	2	.000
	BRTR			16	.125

CLARK, JOHN CARROLL
(Cap)
b.Sept.19,1909 Snow Camp,N.C.
d.Feb.16,1957

Yr	Cl	Lea	Pos	G	Rec
1938	Phi	N	C	52	.257
	BLTR				

CLARK, MELVIN EARL
b.July 7,1926 Letart,W.Va.

Yr	Cl	Lea	Pos	G	Rec
1951	Phi	N	O	10	.323
1952	Phi	N	3-O	47	.335
1953	Phi	N	O	60	.298
1954	Phi	N	O	83	.240
1955	Phi	N	O	10	.156
1957	Det	A	O	5	.000
	BRTR			215	.277

CLARK, MICHAEL JOHN
b.Feb.12,1922 Camden,N.J.

Yr	Cl	Lea	Pos	G	Rec
1952	St.L	N	P	12	2-0
1953	St.L	N	P	23	1-0
	BRTR			35	3-0

CLARK, OWEN F.
(Spider)
b.Sept.16,1867 Brooklyn,N.Y.
d.Feb.8,1892

Yr	Cl	Lea	Pos	G	Rec
1889	Was	N	C	37	.255
1890	Buf	p	C-2-O	69	.268
	TR			106	.257

CLARK, PHILIP JAMES
b.Oct.3,1932 Albany,Ga.

Yr	Cl	Lea	Pos	G	Rec
1958	St.L	N	P	8	0-1
1959	St.L	N	P	7	0-1
	BRTR			15	0-2

CLARK, ROBERT H.
b.May 18,1864 Covington,Ky.
d.Aug.21,1919

Yr	Cl	Lea	Pos	G	Rec
1886	Bro	a	C	72	.228
1887	Bro	a	C	47	.289
1888	Bro	a	C	45	.245
1889	Bro	a	C	53	.265
1890	Bro	N	C	43	.218
1891	Cin	N	C	15	.132
1893	Lou	N	C	11	.103
	BRTR			286	.239

CLARK, ROBERT WILLIAM
b.Aug.22,1897 Newport,Pa.
d.May 18,1944

Yr	Cl	Lea	Pos	G	Rec
1920	Cle	A	P	11	1-2
1921	Cle	A	P	5	0-0
	BRTR			16	1-2

CLARK, ROYAL ELLIOTT
(Pepper)
b.May 11,1874 New Haven,Conn.
d.Nov.1,1925

Yr	Cl	Lea	Pos	G	Rec
1902	NY	N	O	20	.139

CLARK, WILLIAM OTIS
(Wee Willie)
b.Aug.16,1872 Pittsburgh,Pa.
d.Nov.1932

Yr	Cl	Lea	Pos	G	Rec
1895	NY	N	1	22	.261
1896	NY	N	1	65	.303
1897	NY	N	1	118	.282
1898	Pit	N	1	57	.310
1899	Pit	N	1	79	.282
				341	.289

CLARK, WILLIAM OTIS
(Otie)
b.May 22,1918 Boscobel,Wis.

Yr	Cl	Lea	Pos	G	Rec
1945	Bos	A	P	12	4-4

BRTR

CLARK, WILLIAM WATSON
(Watty)
b.May 16,1902 St.Joseph,La.

Yr	Cl	Lea	Pos	G	Rec
1924	Cle	A	P	12	1-3
1927	Bro	N	P	27	7-2
1928	Bro	N	P	40	12-9
1929	Bro	N	P	42	16-19
1930	Bro	N	P	44	13-13
1931	Bro	N	P	34	14-10
1932	Bro	N	P	40	20-12
1933	Bro	N	P	11	2-4
1933	NY	N	P	16	3-4
1934	NY	N	P	5	1-2
1934	Bro	N	P	17	2-0
1935	Bro	N	P	34	13-8
1936	Bro	N	P	33	7-11
1937	Bro	N	P	2	0-0
BLTL				357	111-97

CLARK, WILLIAM WINFIELD
b.Apr.11,1875 Circleville,O.
d.Apr.15,1959

Yr	Cl	Lea	Pos	G	Rec
1897	Lou	N	2	4	.176

BRTR

CLARKE, ALAN THOMAS
(Lefty)
b.Mar.8,1896 Linden,Md.

Yr	Cl	Lea	Pos	G	Rec
1921	Cin	N	P	1	0-1

BBTL

CLARKE, FRED CLIFFORD
b.Oct.3,1872 Winterset,Ia.
d.Aug.14,1960

Yr	Cl	Lea	Pos	G	Rec
1894	Lou	N	O	76	.275
1895	Lou	N	O	132	.354
1896	Lou	N	O	131	.327
1897	Lou	N	M-O	129	.406
1898	Lou	N	M-O	147	.318
1899	Lou	N	M-O	147	.348
1900	Pit	N	M-O	103	.281
1901	Pit	N	M-O	128	.316
1902	Pit	N	M-O	114	.321
1903	Pit	N	M-O	102	.351
1904	Pit	N	M-O	70	.306
1905	Pit	N	M-O	137	.299
1906	Pit	N	M-O	110	.309
1907	Pit	N	M-O	144	.289
1908	Pit	N	M-O	151	.265
1909	Pit	N	M-O	152	.287
1910	Pit	N	M-O	118	.263
1911	Pit	N	M-O	101	.324
1913	Pit	N	M-O	9	.077
1914	Pit	N	M-H	2	.000
1915	Pit	N	M-O	1	.500
BLTR				2204	.315

Non-playing manager Pit (N) 1912

CLARKE, HARRY CORSON
b.1861
d.Mar.3,1923

Yr	Cl	Lea	Pos	G	Rec
1889	Was	N	O	1	.000

CLARKE, HENRY TEFFT
b.Aug.4,1875 Bellevue,Neb.
d.Mar.28,1950

(Continued)

Yr	Cl	Lea	Pos	G	Rec
1897	Cle	N	P	8	3-5
1898	Chi	N	P	2	1-0
BRTR				10	4-5

CLARKE, JAY JUSTIN
(Nig)
b.Dec.15,1882 Amherstburg,Ont. Canada.
d.June 15,1949

Yr	Cl	Lea	Pos	G	Rec
1905	Cle	A	C	6	.182
1905	Det	A	C	2	.400
1905	Cle	A	C	37	.202
1906	Cle	A	C	57	.358
1907	Cle	A	C	120	.269
1908	Cle	A	C	97	.241
1909	Cle	A	C	55	.274
1910	Cle	A	C	21	.155
1911	St.L	A	C	82	.215
1919	Phi	N	C	26	.242
1920	Pit	N	C	3	.000
BBTR				506	.254

CLARKE, JOSHUA BALDWIN
(Pepper)
b.Mar.8,1879 Winfield,Kan.
d.July 2,1962

Yr	Cl	Lea	Pos	G	Rec
1898	Lou	N	O	6	.167
1905	St.L	N	2-O	46	.257
1908	Cle	A	O	131	.242
1909	Cle	A	O	4	.000
1911	Bos	N	O	30	.233
BLTR				217	.239

CLARKE, RICHARD GREY
b.Sept.26,1912 Fulton,Ala.

Yr	Cl	Lea	Pos	G	Rec
1944	Chi	A	3	63	.260

BRTR

CLARKE, RUFUS RIVERS
b.Apr.13,1900 Estill,S.C.

Yr	Cl	Lea	Pos	G	Rec
1923	Det	A	P	5	1-1
1924	Det	A	P	2	0-0
BRTR				7	1-1

CLARKE, SUMPTER ELLIS
b.Oct.18,1897 Savannah,Ga.

Yr	Cl	Lea	Pos	G	Rec
1920	Chi	N	3	1	.333
1923	Cle	A	O	1	.000
1924	Cle	A	O	45	.227
BRTR				47	.224

CLARKE, THOMAS ALOYSIUS
b.May 9,1888 New York,N.Y.
d.Aug.14,1945

Yr	Cl	Lea	Pos	G	Rec
1909	Cin	N	C	17	.250
1910	Cin	N	C	56	.278
1911	Cin	N	C	82	.241
1912	Cin	N	C	72	.281
1913	Cin	N	C	114	.264
1914	Cin	N	C	113	.262
1915	Cin	N	C	96	.288
1916	Cin	N	C	78	.237
1917	Cin	N	C	58	.291
1918	Chi	N	C	1	.000
BRTR				687	.265

CLARKE, VIBERT ERNESTO
b.June 8,1929 Colon, Panama

Yr	Cl	Lea	Pos	G	Rec
1955	Was	A	P	7	0-0

BLTL

CLARKE, WILLIAM H.
(Dad)
b.Jan.7,1865 Oswego,N.Y.
d.June 3,1911

Yr	Cl	Lea	Pos	G	Rec
1888	Chi	N	P	3	2-0
1891	Col	a	P	5	0-0
1894	NY	N	P	16	2-4
1895	NY	N	P	32	18-14
1896	NY	N	P	43	16-27
1897	NY	N	P	6	0-3
1897	Lou	N	P	7	3-3
1898	Lou	N	P	1	0-1
BBTR				113	41-52

CLARKE, WILLIAM JONES
(Boileryard)
b.Oct.18,1868 New York,N.Y.

Yr	Cl	Lea	Pos	G	Rec
1893	Bal	N	C	47	.194
1894	Bal	N	C	27	.270
1895	Bal	N	C	60	.297
1896	Bal	N	C	77	.290
1897	Bal	N	C	63	.274
1898	Bal	N	C	77	.245
1899	Bos	N	C	60	.229
1900	Bos	N	C	71	.320
1901	Was	A	C	109	.284
1902	Was	A	C	87	.262
1903	Was	A	C-1	126	.239
1904	Was	A	C-1	85	.213
1905	NY	N	1	27	.180
BRTR				916	.260

CLARKE, WILLIAM STUART
b.Jan.24,1907 Oakland,Cal.

Yr	Cl	Lea	Pos	G	Rec
1929	Pit	N	S-3	57	.264
1930	Pit	N	2	4	.444
BRTR				61	.273

CLARKSON, ARTHUR HAMILTON
(Dad)
b.Aug.31,1866 Cambridge,Mass.
d.Jan.6,1911

Yr	Cl	Lea	Pos	G	Rec
1891	NY	N	P	5	0-2
1892	Bos	N	P	1	0-0
1893	St.L	N	P	21	12-9
1894	St.L	N	P	27	9-18
1895	St.L	N	P	11	1-6
1895	Bal	N	P	17	13-4
1896	Bal	N	P	7	3-2
				89	39-41

CLARKSON, JAMES
b.Mar.13,1918 Columbia,S.C.

Yr	Cl	Lea	Pos	G	Rec
1952	Bos	N	S-3	14	.200

BRTR

CLARKSON, JOHN GIBSON
b.July 1,1861 Cambridge,Mass.
d.Feb.4,1909

Yr	Cl	Lea	Pos	G	Rec
1882	Wor	N	P-1	3	1-1 .364
1884	Chi	N	P-1-3-O	20	10-3 .261
1885	Chi	N	P-3-O	72	52-16 .215
1886	Chi	N	P	55	35-17
1887	Chi	N	P	61	38-21
1888	Bos	N	P	54	33-20
1889	Bos	N	P	72	48-19
1890	Bos	N	P	44	26-18
1891	Bos	N	P	55	34-19
1892	Bos	N	P	16	9-7
1892	Cle	N	P	27	17-10
1893	Cle	N	P	34	16-16
1894	Cle	N	P	16	8-8
BRTR				529	327-175 .225

CLARKSON, WALTER HAMILTON
b.Nov.3,1878 Cambridge,Mass.
d.Oct.10,1946

Yr	Cl	Lea	Pos	G	Rec
1904	NY	A	P	13	2-2
1905	NY	A	P	8	2-2
1906	NY	A	P	32	9-4
1907	NY	A	P	6	0-0
1907	Cle	A	P	16	5-7
1908	Cle	A	P	2	0-0
TR				77	18-15

CLARKSON, WILLIAM HENRY
(Blackie)
b.Sept.27,1899 Portsmouth,Va.

Yr	Cl	Lea	Pos	G	Rec
1927	NY	N	P	28	3-9
1928	NY	N	P	4	0-0
1928	Bos	N	P	19	0-2
1929	Bos	N	P	2	0-1
BRTR				53	3-12

CLARY, ELLIS
(Cat)
b.Sept.11,1916 Valdosta,Ga.

Yr	Cl	Lea	Pos	G	Rec
1942	Was	A	2	76	.275
1943	Was	A	3	73	.256
1943	St.L	A	2-S-3	23	.275
1944	St.L	A	2-3	25	.265
1945	St.L	A	2-3	26	.211
	BRTR			223	.263

CLASET, GOWELL SYLVESTER
(Lefty)
b.Nov.26,1907 Battle Creek,Mich.

Yr	Cl	Lea	Pos	G	Rec
1933	Phi	A	P	8	2-0
	BLTL				

CLAUSEN, FRED WILLIAM
(Fritz)
b.Apr.26,1869 New York,N.Y.
d.Feb.11,1960

Yr	Cl	Lea	Pos	G	Rec
1892	Lou	N	P	24	9-13
1893	Lou	N	P	9	1-3
1893	Chi	N	P	10	5-3
1894	Chi	N	P	2	0-1
1896	Lou	N	P	2	0-1
	BRTL			47	15-21

CLAUSS, ALBERT STANLEY
(Lefty)
b.June 24,1891 New Haven,Conn.
d.Sept.13,1952

Yr	Cl	Lea	Pos	G	Rec
1913	Det	A	P	4	0-2
	BRTL				

CLAY, DAIN ELMER
(Sniffy)
b.July 10,1919 Hicksville,O.

Yr	Cl	Lea	Pos	G	Rec
1943	Cin	N	O	49	.269
1944	Cin	N	O	110	.250
1945	Cin	N	O	153	.280
1946	Cin	N	O	121	.228
	BRTR			433	.258

CLAY, FREDERICK C.
(Bill)
b.1875 Baltimore,Md.
d.Oct.12,1917

Yr	Cl	Lea	Pos	G	Rec
1902	Phi	N	O	3	.250
	TR				

CLEARY, JOSEPH CHRISTOPHER
b.Dec.3,1920 Cork,Ireland

Yr	Cl	Lea	Pos	G	Rec
1945	Was	A	P	1	0-0
	BRTR				

CLEMENS, CHESTER SPURGEON
b.May 10,1918 San Fernando,Cal.

Yr	Cl	Lea	Pos	G	Rec
1939	Bos	N	O	9	.217
1944	Bos	N	O	19	.176
	BRTR			28	.200

CLEMENS, CLEMENT LAMBERT
(Real name
Clement Lambert Ulatowski)
b.Nov.21,1886 Chicago,Ill.

Yr	Cl	Lea	Pos	G	Rec
1914	Chi	F	C	12	.154
1915	Chi	F	C	11	.136
1916	Chi	N	C	10	.000
	BRTR			33	.111

CLEMENS, DOUGLAS HORACE
b.June 9,1939 Leesport,Pa.

Yr	Cl	Lea	Pos	G	Rec
1960	St.L	N	O	1	.000
1961	St.L	N	O	6	.167
1962	St.L	N	O	48	.237
	BLTR			55	.229

CLEMENSEN, JOHN WILLIAM
(Bill)
b.June 20,1919 New Brunswick,N.J.

(Continued)

Yr	Cl	Lea	Pos	G	Rec
1939	Pit	N	P	12	0-1
1941	Pit	N	P	2	1-0
1946	Pit	N	P	1	0-0
	BRTR			15	1-1

CLEMENT, WALLACE OAKES
b.July 21,1881 Auburn,Me.

Yr	Cl	Lea	Pos	G	Rec
1908	Phi	N	O	12	.242
1909	Phi	N	O	3	.000
1909	Bro	N	O	88	.256
	TR			103	.251

CLEMENTE, ROBERTO WALKER
b.Aug.18,1934 Carolina, Puerto Rico

Yr	Cl	Lea	Pos	G	Rec
1955	Pit	N	O	124	.255
1956	Pit	N	2-3-O	147	.311
1957	Pit	N	O	111	.253
1958	Pit	N	O	140	.289
1959	Pit	N	O	105	.296
1960	Pit	N	O	144	.314
1961	Pit	N	O	146	.351
1962	Pit	N	O	144	.312
	BRTR			1061	.300

CLEMENTS, EDWARD
b.Philadelphia,Pa.

Yr	Cl	Lea	Pos	G	Rec
1890	Pit	N	S	1	.000

CLEMENTS, JOHN T.
b.June 24,1864 Philadelphia,Pa.
d.May 23,1941

Yr	Cl	Lea	Pos	G	Rec
1884	Key	U	C-S-O	41	.289
1884	Phi	N	C	8	.240
1885	Phi	N	C-O	52	.191
1886	Phi	N	C	54	.205
1887	Phi	N	C	63	.306
1888	Phi	N	C	85	.247
1889	Phi	N	C	78	.284
1890	Phi	N	C	97	.315
1891	Phi	N	C	105	.305
1892	Phi	N	C	102	.270
1893	Phi	N	C	90	.290
1894	Phi	N	C	47	.343
1895	Phi	N	C	84	.389
1896	Phi	N	C	50	.362
1897	Phi	N	C	49	.239
1898	St.L	N	C	85	.268
1899	Cle	N	C	4	.167
1900	Bos	N	C	16	.307
	BLTL			1110	.288

CLEMONS, ROBERT E.
b.Oct.5,1891 Clemons,Ia.
d.Apr.19,1953

Yr	Cl	Lea	Pos	G	Rec
1914	St.L	A	O	8	.214
	BRTR				

CLEMONS, VERNON JAMES
(Fats)
b.Sept.8,1892 Clemons,Ia.
d.May 5,1959

Yr	Cl	Lea	Pos	G	Rec
1916	St.L	A	C	3	.000
1919	St.L	N	C	88	.264
1920	St.L	N	C	112	.281
1921	St.L	N	C	117	.320
1922	St.L	N	C	71	.256
1923	St.L	N	C	57	.285
1924	St.L	N	C	25	.321
	BRTR			473	.287

CLENDENON, DONN ALVIN
b.July 15,1935 Neosho,Mo.

Yr	Cl	Lea	Pos	G	Rec
1961	Pit	N	O	9	.314
1962	Pit	N	1-2-O	80	.302
	BRTR			89	.304

CLEVELAND, ELMER E.
b.1862 Washington,D.C.
d.Oct.8,1913

Yr	Cl	Lea	Pos	G	Rec
1884	Cin	U	2	26	.281
1888	NY	N	3	10	.270

(Continued)

Yr	Cl	Lea	Pos	G	Rec
1888	Pit	N	3	30	.204
1891	Col	a	3	12	.142
	BRTR			78	.228

CLEVENGER, TRUMAN EUGENE
(Gene)
b.July 9,1932 Visalia,Cal.

Yr	Cl	Lea	Pos	G	Rec
1954	Bos	A	P	25	2-4
1956	Was	A	P	20	0-0
1957	Was	A	P	52	7-6
1958	Was	A	P	55	9-9
1959	Was	A	P	50	8-5
1960	Was	A	P	53	5-11
1961	LA	A	P	12	2-1
1961	NY	A	P	21	1-1
1962	NY	A	P	22	2-0
	BRTR			310	36-37

CLIFT, HARLOND BENTON
(Darkie)
b.Aug.12,1912 El Reno,Okla.

Yr	Cl	Lea	Pos	G	Rec
1934	St.L	A	3	147	.260
1935	St.L	A	2-3	137	.295
1936	St.L	A	3	152	.302
1937	St.L	A	3	155	.306
1938	St.L	A	3	149	.290
1939	St.L	A	3	151	.270
1940	St.L	A	3	150	.273
1941	St.L	A	3	154	.255
1942	St.L	A	S-3	143	.274
1943	St.L	A	3	105	.232
1943	Was	A	3	8	.300
1944	Was	A	3	12	.159
1945	Was	A	3	119	.211
	BRTR			1582	.272

CLIFTON, HERMAN EARL
(Flea)
b.Dec.12,1909 Cincinnati,O.

Yr	Cl	Lea	Pos	G	Rec
1934	Det	A	2-3	16	.063
1935	Det	A	2-S-3	43	.255
1936	Det	A	2-S-3	13	.192
1937	Det	A	2-S-3	15	.116
	BRTR			87	.200

CLINE, JOHN
(Monk)
b.Louisville,Ky.

Yr	Cl	Lea	Pos	G	Rec
1882	Bal	a	2-S-3 O	45	.222
1884	Lou	a	S-O	94	.287
1885	Lou	a	3-O	2	.222
1888	KC	a	O	73	.243
1891	Lou	a	O	19	.304
				233	.277

CLINE, TYRONE ALEXANDER
b.June15,1939 Charleston,S.Car.

Yr	Cl	Lea	Pos	G	Rec
1960	Cle	A	O	7	.308
1961	Cle	A	O	12	.209
1962	Cle	A	O	118	.248
	BLTL			137	.248

CLINGMAN, WILLIAM FREDERICK
b.Nov.21,1869 Cincinnati,O
d.May 14,1958

Yr	Cl	Lea	Pos	G	Rec
1890	Cin	N	S	7	.258
1891	Cin	a	2	1	.200
1895	Pit	N	3	108	.261
1896	Lou	N	3	120	.230
1897	Lou	N	3	115	.232
1898	Lou	N	S-3	154	.262
1899	Lou	N	S	108	.267
1900	Chi	N	S	46	.201
1901	Was	A	S	137	.245
1903	Cle	A	2-S-3	21	.286
	BBTR			817	.248

CLINTON, JAMES LAWRENCE
(Big Jim)
b.Aug.10,1850 New York,N.Y.
d.Sept.3,1921

Yr	Cl	Lea	Pos	G	Rec
1872	Eck	n	M-2-S-3-O	20	NR
1873	Res	n	3-O	8	NR
1874	Atl	n	1-2-O	4	NR
1875	Atl	n	P-1-2-O	22	1-12 / NR
1876	Lou	N	P-O	16	0-1 / .338
1882	Wor	N	O	26	.163
1883	Bal	a	2-O	94	.305
1884	Bal	a	O	105	.281
1885	Cin	a	O	98	.239
1886	Bal	a	O	23	.183
		BRTR		416	1-13 / NR

CLINTON, LUCIEAN LOUIS
b.Oct.13,1937 Ponca City,Okla.

Yr	Cl	Lea	Pos	G	Rec
1960	Bos	A	O	96	.228
1961	Bos	A	O	17	.255
1962	Bos	A	O	114	.294
		BRTR		227	.265

CLOLO, CARLOS
(Played under name of Charles Louis Hall)

CLONINGER, TONY LEE
b.Aug.13,1940 Lincoln Co.,N.C.

Yr	Cl	Lea	Pos	G	Rec
1961	Mil	N	P	19	7-2
1962	Mil	N	P	24	8-3
		BRTR		43	15-5

CLOUGH, EDGAR GEORGE
(Big Ed)
b.Oct.28,1906 Wiconisco,Pa.
d.Jan.27,1944

Yr	Cl	Lea	Pos	G	Rec
1924	St.L	N	O	7	.071
1925	St.L	N	P	3	0-1
1926	St.L	N	P	1	0-0
		BLTL		11	0-1 / .111

CLOWERS, WILLIAM P.
b.Aug.14,1897 San Antonio,Tex.

Yr	Cl	Lea	Pos	G	Rec
1926	Bos	A	P	2	0-0

BLTL

CLYDE, THOMAS KNOX
b.Aug.17,1923 Wachapreague,Va.

Yr	Cl	Lea	Pos	G	Rec
1943	Phi	A	P	4	0-0

BRTR

CLYMER, OTIS EDGAR
b.Jan.27,1880 Pine Grove,Pa.
d.Feb.27,1926

Yr	Cl	Lea	Pos	G	Rec
1905	Pit	N	O	90	.296
1906	Pit	N	O	11	.224
1907	Pit	N	O	16	.227
1907	Was	A	O	57	.316
1908	Was	A	O	110	.253
1909	Was	A	O	45	.196
1913	Chi	N	O	30	.229
1913	Bos	N	O	14	.324
		BLTR		373	.267

CLYMER, WILLIAM JOHNSTON
(Derby Day Bill)
b.Dec.18,1873 Philadelphia,Pa.
d.Dec.26,1936

Yr	Cl	Lea	Pos	G	Rec
1891	Ath	a	S	3	.000

COAKLEY, ANDREW JAMES
(Also played under name of Jack McAllister)
b.Nov.20,1882 Providence,R.I.
(Jack McAllister)

Yr	Cl	Lea	Pos	G	Rec
1902	Phi	A	P	3	2-1

(Andrew James Coakley)

(Continued)

Yr	Cl	Lea	Pos	G	Rec
1903	Phi	A	P	6	0-3
1904	Phi	A	P	11	7-4
1905	Phi	A	P	34	20-8
1906	Phi	A	P	22	7-8
1907	Cin	N	P	37	17-16
1908	Cin	N	P	32	8-18
1908	Chi	N	P	4	2-0
1909	Chi	N	P	1	0-1
1911	NY	A	P	2	0-1
		BLTR		152	63-60

COAN, GILBERT FITZGERALD
(Citation)
b.May 18,1924 Monroe,N.C.

Yr	Cl	Lea	Pos	G	Rec
1946	Was	A	O	59	.209
1947	Was	A	O	11	.500
1948	Was	A	O	138	.232
1949	Was	A	O	111	.218
1950	Was	A	O	104	.303
1951	Was	A	O	135	.303
1952	Was	A	O	107	.205
1953	Was	A	O	68	.196
1954	Bal	A	O	94	.279
1955	**Bal**	**A**	**O**	**61**	**.238**
1955	**Chi**	**A**	**O**	**17**	**.176**
1955	**NY**	**N**	**O**	**9**	**.154**
1956	**NY**	**N**	**H**	**4**	**.000**
		BLTR		918	.254

COATES, JAMES ALTON
b.Aug.4,1932 Farnham,Va.

Yr	Cl	Lea	Pos	G	Rec
1956	**NY**	**A**	**P**	**2**	**0-0**
1959	NY	A	P	37	6-1
1960	NY	A	P	35	13-3
1961	NY	A	P	43	11-5
1962	NY	A	P	50	7-6
		BRTR		167	37-15

COBB, GEORGE WASHINGTON
b.San Francisco,Cal.

Yr	Cl	Lea	Pos	G	Rec
1892	Bal	N	P	49	9-38

COBB, HERBERT EDWARD
b.Aug.6,1904 Pinetops,N.C.

Yr	Cl	Lea	Pos	G	Rec
1929	St.L	A	P	1	0-0

BRTR

COBB, JOSEPH STANLEY
(Real name Joseph Stanley Serafin)
b.Jan.24,1895 Hudson,Pa.
d.Dec.24,1947

Yr	Cl	Lea	Pos	G	Rec
1918	Det	A	C	1	.000

BRTR

COBB, TYRUS RAYMOND
(Ty)
b.Dec.18,1886 Narrows,Banks Co.,Ga.
d.July 17,1961

Yr	Cl	Lea	Pos	G	Rec
1905	Det	A	O	41	.240
1906	Det	A	O	97	.320
1907	Det	A	O	150	.350
1908	Det	A	O	150	.324
1909	Det	A	O	156	.377
1910	Det	A	O	140	.385
1911	Det	A	O	146	.420
1912	Det	A	O	140	.410
1913	Det	A	2-O	122	.390
1914	Det	A	O	97	.368
1915	Det	A	O	156	.369
1916	Det	A	O	145	.371
1917	Det	A	O	152	.383
1918	Det	A	1-O	111	.382
1919	Det	A	O	124	.384
1920	Det	A	O	112	.334
1921	Det	A	M-O	128	.389
1922	Det	A	M-O	137	.401
1923	Det	A	M-O	145	.340
1924	Det	A	M-O	155	.338
1925	Det	A	M-P-O	121	0-0 / .378
1926	Det	A	M-O	79	.339
1927	Phi	A	O	134	.357
1928	Phi	A	O	95	.323
		BLTR		3033	0-0 / .367

COBLE, DAVID LAMAR
b.Dec.24,1915 Monroe,N.C.

Yr	Cl	Lea	Pos	G	Rec
1939	Phi	N	C	15	.280

BRTR

COCHRAN, ALVIN JACKSON
(Goat)
b.Jan.31,1891 Concord,Ga.
d.May 23,1947

Yr	Cl	Lea	Pos	G	Rec
1915	Cin	N	P	1	0-0

BRTR

COCHRAN, GEORGE LESLIE
b.Feb.12,1889 Rusk,Tex.

Yr	Cl	Lea	Pos	G	Rec
1918	Bos	A	3	25	.127

TR

COCHRANE, GORDON STANLEY
(Mickey)
b.Apr.6,1903 Bridgewater,Mass.
d.June 28,1962

Yr	Cl	Lea	Pos	G	Rec
1925	Phi	A	C	134	.331
1926	Phi	A	C	120	.273
1927	Phi	A	C	126	.338
1928	Phi	A	C	131	.293
1929	Phi	A	C	135	.331
1930	Phi	A	C	130	.357
1931	Phi	A	C	122	.349
1932	Phi	A	C	139	.293
1933	Phi	A	C	130	.322
1934	Det	A	M-C	129	.320
1935	Det	A	M-C	115	.319
1936	Det	A	M-C	44	.270
1937	Det	A	M-C	27	.306
		BLTR		1482	.320

Non-playing manager Det (A) 1938

COCKMAN, JAMES
b.Apr.26,1873 Guelph,Ont.,Canada.
d.Sept.28,1947

Yr	Cl	Lea	Pos	G	Rec
1905	NY	A	3	13	.076

TR

COCREHAM, EUGENE
b.Nov.14,1890 Luling,Tex.
d.Dec.27,1945

Yr	Cl	Lea	Pos	G	Rec
1913	Bos	N	P	1	0-1
1914	Bos	N	P	15	3-4
1915	Bos	N	P	1	0-0
		BRTR		17	3-5

COFFEY, JOHN FRANCIS
b.Jan.28,1888 New York,N.Y.

Yr	Cl	Lea	Pos	G	Rec
1909	Bos	N	S	73	.186
1918	Det	A	2	20	.209
1918	Bos	A	2-3	22	.188
		BRTR		115	.191

COFFEY, JOHN JOSEPH
b.Aug.8,1893 Oswaya,Pa.

Yr	Cl	Lea	Pos	G	Rec
1912	Det	A	3	1	.000

TR

COFFMAN, GEORGE DAVID
(Slick)
b.Dec.11,1910 Veto,Ala.

Yr	Cl	Lea	Pos	G	Rec
1937	Det	A	P	28	7-5
1938	Det	A	P	39	4-4
1939	Det	A	P	23	2-1
1940	St.L	A	P	32	2-2
		BRTR		122	15-12

COFFMAN, SAMUEL RICHARD
(Dick)
b.Dec.18,1906 Veto,Ala.

Yr	Cl	Lea	Pos	G	Rec
1927	Was	A	P	5	0-1
1928	St.L	A	P	29	4-5
1929	St.L	A	P	27	1-1
1930	St.L	A	P	38	8-18
1931	St.L	A	P	32	9-13
1932	St.L	A	P	9	5-3
1932	Was	A	P	22	1-6
1933	St.L	A	P	21	3-7
1934	St.L	A	P	40	9-10
1935	St.L	A	P	41	5-11
1936	NY	N	P	42	7-5
1937	NY	N	P	42	8-3
1938	NY	N	P	51	8-4
1939	NY	N	P	28	1-2

(Continued)

Yr	Cl	Lea	Pos	G	Rec
1940	Bos	N	P	31	1-5
1945	Phi	N	P	14	2-1
			BRTR	472	72-95

COGAN, RICHARD HENRY
b.Dec.5,1871 Paterson,N.J.
d.May 2,1948

Yr	Cl	Lea	Pos	G	Rec
1897	Bal	N	P	1	0-0
1899	Chi	N	P	8	2-3
1900	NY	N	P	3	0-0
				12	2-3

COGSWELL, EDWARD
b.Feb.25,1854 England
d.July 27,1888

Yr	Cl	Lea	Pos	G	Rec
1879	Bos	N	1	49	.322
1880	Tro	N	1	47	.301
1882	Wor	N	1	13	.122
			BR	109	.291

COHEN, ALTA ALBERT
(Schoolboy)
b.Dec.25,1910 New York,N.Y.

Yr	Cl	Lea	Pos	G	Rec
1931	Bro	N	O	1	.667
1932	Bro	N	O	9	.156
1933	Phi	N	O	19	.188
			BLTL	29	.194

COHEN, ANDREW HOWARD
b.Oct.25,1904 Baltimore,Md.

Yr	Cl	Lea	Pos	G	Rec
1926	NY	N	2-S	32	.257
1928	NY	N	2	129	.274
1929	NY	N	2	101	.294
			BRTR	262	.281

COHEN, HARRY
(Played under name of Harry Kane)

COHEN, HYMAN
b.Jan.29,1931 Brooklyn,N.Y.

Yr	Cl	Lea	Pos	G	Rec
1955	Chi	N	P	7	0-0
			BRTR		

COHEN, REUBEN
(Played under name of Reuben Ewing)

COHEN, SAMUEL ARTHUR
(Played under name of Samuel Arthur Bohne)

COHEN, SYDNEY HARRY
b.May 7,1908 Baltimore,Md.

Yr	Cl	Lea	Pos	G	Rec
1934	Was	A	P-O	4	1-1 / .273
1936	Was	A	P	19	0-2
1937	Was	A	P	33	2-4
			BBTL	56	3-7 / .152

COHN, PHILIP
(Played under name of Philip Cooney)

COKER, JIMMIE GOODWIN
b.Mar.28,1936 Holly Hill,S.C.

Yr	Cl	Lea	Pos	G	Rec
1958	Phi	N	C	2	.167
1960	Phi	N	C	81	.214
1961	Phi	N	C	11	.400
1962	Phi	N	H	5	.000
			BRTR	99	.227

COLAVITO, ROCCO DOMENICO
b.Aug.10,1933 Bronx,N.Y.

Yr	Cl	Lea	Pos	G	Rec
1955	Cle	A	O	5	.444
1956	Cle	A	O	101	.276
1957	Cle	A	O	134	.252
1958	Cle	A	P-1-O	143	0-0 / .303
1959	Cle	A	O	154	.257
1960	Det	A	O	145	.249
1961	Det	A	O	163	.290
1962	Det	A	O	161	.273
			BRTR	1006	.271

COLCOLOUGH, THOMAS BERNARD
b.Oct.8,1870 Charleston,S.C.
d.Dec.10,1919

Yr	Cl	Lea	Pos	G	Rec
1893	Pit	N	P	8	2-0
1894	Pit	N	P	19	7-7
1895	Pit	N	P	8	1-1
1899	NY	N	P	14	4-5
			BRTR	49	14-14

COLE, ALBERT GEORGE
(Bert)
b.July 1,1898 San Francisco,Cal.

Yr	Cl	Lea	Pos	G	Rec
1921	Det	A	P	30	7-4
1922	Det	A	P	27	1-6
1923	Det	A	P	58	13-5
1924	Det	A	P	33	3-9
1925	Det	A	P	14	2-3
1925	Cle	A	P	13	1-1
1927	Chi	A	P	27	1-4
			BLTL	202	28-32

COLE, DAVID BRUCE
b.Aug.29,1930 Williamsport,Md.

Yr	Cl	Lea	Pos	G	Rec
1950	Bos	N	P	4	0-1
1951	Bos	N	P	23	2-4
1952	Bos	N	P	22	1-1
1953	Mil	N	P	10	0-1
1954	Chi	N	P	19	3-8
1955	Phi	N	P	7	0-3
			BRTR	85	6-18

COLE, EDWARD WILLIAM
(Real name Edward William Kisleauskas)
b.Mar.25,1911 Wilkes-Barre,Pa.

Yr	Cl	Lea	Pos	G	Rec
1938	St.L	A	P	36	1-5
1939	St.L	A	P	6	0-2
			BRTR	42	1-7

COLE, LEONARD LESLIE
(King)
b.Apr.15,1886 Toledo,Ia.
d.Jan.6,1916

Yr	Cl	Lea	Pos	G	Rec
1909	Chi	N	P	1	1-0
1910	Chi	N	P	33	20-4
1911	Chi	N	P	32	18-7
1912	Chi	N	P	8	1-2
1912	Pit	N	P	12	2-2
1914	NY	A	P	25	11-9
1915	NY	A	P	10	2-3
			BRTR	121	55-27

COLE, RICHARD ROY
b.May 6,1926 Long Beach,Cal.

Yr	Cl	Lea	Pos	G	Rec
1951	St.L	N	2	15	.194
1951	Pit	N	2-S	42	.236
1953	Pit	N	1-2-S	97	.272
1954	Pit	N	2-S-3	138	.270
1955	Pit	N	2-S-3	77	.226
1956	Pit	N	2-S-3	72	.212
1957	Mil	N	1-2-3	15	.071
			BRTR	456	.249

COLE, WILLIS RUSSEL
b.Jan.6,1882 Milton Junction,Wis.

Yr	Cl	Lea	Pos	G	Rec
1909	Chi	A	O	46	.236
1910	Chi	A	O	22	.175
			BRTR	68	.216

COLEMAN, CURTIS HANCOCK
b.Feb.18,1888 Salem,Ore.

Yr	Cl	Lea	Pos	G	Rec
1912	NY	A	3	12	.263
			BLTR		

COLEMAN, CLARENCE
b.Aug.25,1937 Orlando,Fla.

Yr	Cl	Lea	Pos	G	Rec
1961	Phi	N	C	34	.128
1962	NY	N	C	136	.277
			BLTR	358	.283

COLEMAN, GERALD FRANCIS
b.Sept.14,1924 San Jose,Cal.

Yr	Cl	Lea	Pos	G	Rec
1949	NY	A	2-S	128	.275
1950	NY	A	2-S	153	.287

(Continued)

Yr	Cl	Lea	Pos	G	Rec
1951	NY	A	2-S	121	.249
1952	NY	A	2	11	.405
1953	NY	A	2-S	8	.200
1954	NY	A	2-S-3	107	.217
1955	NY	A	2-S-3	43	.229
1956	NY	A	2-S-3	80	.257
1957	NY	A	2-S-3	72	.268
			BRTR	723	.263

COLEMAN, GORDON CALVIN
b.July 5,1934 Rockville,Md.

Yr	Cl	Lea	Pos	G	Rec
1959	Cle	A	1	6	.533
1960	Cin	N	1	66	.271
1961	Cin	N	1	150	.287
1962	Cin	N	1	136	.277
			BLTR	358	.283

COLEMAN, JOHN
b.Bristol,Pa.

Yr	Cl	Lea	Pos	G	Rec
1890	Phi	N	P	1	0-0

COLEMAN, JOHN
b.Jefferson City,Mo.

Yr	Cl	Lea	Pos	G	Rec
1895	St.L	N	P	2	0-1

COLEMAN, JOHN FRANCIS
b.Mar.6,1863 Saratoga Springs,N.Y.
d.May 31,1922

Yr	Cl	Lea	Pos	G	Rec
1883	Phi	N	P-O	89	13-48 / .232
1884	Phi	N	P-1-O	43	5-14 / .245
1884	Ath	a	P-O	30	0-2 / .196
1885	Ath	a	P-O	97	1-3 / .309
1886	Ath	a	P-O	122	1-1 / .252
1886	Pit	a	O	10	.333
1887	Pit	N	O	115	.334
1888	Pit	N	1-O	115	.230
1889	Ath	a	P	6	3-2
1890	Pit	N	P	3	0-2
			BLTR	630	23-72 / .267

COLEMAN, JOSEPH PATRICK
b.July 30,1922 Medford,Mass.

Yr	Cl	Lea	Pos	G	Rec
1942	Phi	A	P	1	0-1
1946	Phi	A	P	4	0-2
1947	Phi	A	P	32	6-12
1948	Phi	A	P	33	14-13
1949	Phi	A	P	33	13-14
1950	Phi	A	P	15	0-5
1951	Phi	A	P	28	1-6
1953	Phi	A	P	21	3-4
1954	Bal	A	P	33	13-17
1955	Bal	A	P	6	0-1
1955	Det	A	P	17	2-1
			BRTR	223	52-76

COLEMAN, PARKE EDWARD
(Ed)
b.Dec.1,1902 Canby,Ore.

Yr	Cl	Lea	Pos	G	Rec
1932	Phi	A	O	26	.342
1933	Phi	A	O	102	.281
1934	Phi	A	O	101	.280
1935	Phi	A	O	10	.077
1935	St.L	A	O	108	.287
1936	St.L	A	O	92	.292
			BLTR	439	.285

COLEMAN, PIERCE D.
(Percy)
b.Cincinnati,O.

Yr	Cl	Lea	Pos	G	Rec
1897	St.L	N	P	12	1-5
1898	Cin	N	P	1	0-1
				13	1-6

COLEMAN, RAYMOND LEROY
b.June 4,1922 Dunsmuir,Cal.

Yr	Cl	Lea	Pos	G	Rec
1947	St.L	A	O	110	.259
1948	St.L	A	O	17	.172
1948	Phi	A	O	68	.243

(Continued)

Yr	Cl	Lea	Pos	G	Rec
1950	St.L	A	O	117	.271
1951	St.L	A	O	91	.282
1951	Chi	A	O	51	.276
1952	Chi	A	O	85	.215
1952	St.L	A	O	20	.196
	BLTR			559	.258

COLEMAN, ROBERT HUNTER
b.Sept.26,1890 Huntingburg,Ind.
d.July 16,1959

Yr	Cl	Lea	Pos	G	Rec
1913	Pit	N	C	24	.180
1914	Pit	N	C	73	.266
1916	Cle	A	C	19	.214
	BRTR			116	.241

Non-playing manager Bos (N) 1944-45

COLEMAN, WALTER GARY
b.July 31,1931 Troy,N.Y.

Yr	Cl	Lea	Pos	G	Rec
1955	NY	A	P	10	2-1
1956	NY	A	P	29	3-5
1957	KC	A	P	19	0-7
1959	KC	A	P	29	2-10
1959	Bal	A	P	3	0-0
1960	Bal	A	P	5	0-2
	BLTL			95	7-25

COLES, CADWALLADER R.
(Cad)
b.Jan.17,1885 Augusta,Ga.
d.June 30,1942

Yr	Cl	Lea	Pos	G	Rec
1914	KC	F	O	77	.253
	BLTR				

COLES, CHARLES EDWARD
b.June 27,1931 Fredericktown,Pa.

Yr	Cl	Lea	Pos	G	Rec
1958	Cin	N	O	5	.182
	BLTL				

COLGAN, WILLIAM H.
b.E.St. Louis,Ill.

Yr	Cl	Lea	Pos	G	Rec
1884	Pit	a	C	48	.166

COLIVER, WILLIAM J.
b.1867 Detroit,Mich.
d.Mar.24,1888

Yr	Cl	Lea	Pos	G	Rec
1885	Bos	N	O	1	.000

COLLAMORE, ALLAN EDWARD
b.June 5,1887 Worcester,Mass.

Yr	Cl	Lea	Pos	G	Rec
1911	Phi	A	P	2	0-0
1914	Cle	A	P	21	3-7
1915	Cle	A	P	13	2-5
	BRTR			36	5-12

COLLARD, EARL CLINTON
(Hap)
b.Aug.29,1900 Williams,Ariz.

Yr	Cl	Lea	Pos	G	Rec
1927	Cle	A	P	4	0-0
1928	Cle	A	P	1	0-0
1930	Phi	N	P	31	6-12
	BRTR			36	6-12

COLLIER, ORLIN EDWARD
b.Feb.17,1908 E.Prairie,Mo.
d.Sept.9,1944

Yr	Cl	Lea	Pos	G	Rec
1931	Det	A	P	2	0-1
	BRTR				

COLLIFLOWER, JAMES HARRY
b.Mar.11,1869 Petersville,Md.
d.Aug.12,1961

Yr	Cl	Lea	Pos	G	Rec
1899	Cle	N	P	21	1-11

COLLINS, CHARLES
(Chub)
b.1862 Dundas,Ont.,Canada
d.May 21,1914

Yr	Cl	Lea	Pos	G	Rec
1884	Buf	N	2-S	45	.177
1884	Ind	a	2	38	.229
1885	Det	N	S	14	.179
				97	.197

COLLINS, CYRIL WILSON
b.May 7,1889 Pulaski,Tenn.
d.Feb.28,1941

Yr	Cl	Lea	Pos	G	Rec
1913	Bos	N	O	16	.333
1914	Bos	N	O	27	.257
	BRTR			43	.263

COLLINS, DANIEL THOMAS
b.July 12,1854
d.Sept.21,1883

Yr	Cl	Lea	Pos	G	Rec
1874	Chi	n	P-S	3	1-1 NR
1876	Lou	N	O	7	.143
				10	1-1 NR

COLLINS, EDWARD TROWBRIDGE JR.
b.Nov.23,1916 Lansdowne,Pa.

Yr	Cl	Lea	Pos	G	Rec
1939	Phi	A	O	32	.238
1941	Phi	A	O	80	.242
1942	Phi	A	O	20	.235
	BLTR			132	.241

COLLINS, EDWARD TROWBRIDGE SR.
(Also played under name of Edward T. Sullivan)
b.May 2,1887 Millerton,N.Y.
d.Mar.25,1951

Yr	Cl	Lea	Pos	G	Rec
(Edward T. Sullivan)					
1906	Phi	A	3	6	.200
(Edward Trowbridge Collins)					
1907	Phi	A	S	14	.320
1908	Phi	A	2-S	102	.273
1909	Phi	A	2	153	.346
1910	Phi	A	2	153	.322
1911	Phi	A	2	132	.365
1912	Phi	A	2	153	.348
1913	Phi	A	2	148	.345
1914	Phi	A	2	152	.344
1915	Chi	A	2	155	.332
1916	Chi	A	2	155	.308
1917	Chi	A	2	156	.289
1918	Chi	A	2	97	.276
1919	Chi	A	2	140	.319
1920	Chi	A	2	153	.369
1921	Chi	A	2	139	.337
1922	Chi	A	2	154	.324
1923	Chi	A	2	145	.360
1924	Chi	A	2	152	.349
1925	Chi	A	M-2	118	.346
1926	Chi	A	M-2	106	.344
1927	Phi	A	2	95	.338
1928	Phi	A	S	36	.303
1929	Phi	A	H	9	.000
1930	Phi	A	H	3	.500
	BLTR			2826	.333

COLLINS, HARRY WARREN
(Rip)
b.Feb.26,1896 Weatherford,Tex.

Yr	Cl	Lea	Pos	G	Rec
1920	NY	A	P	36	14-8
1921	NY	A	P	28	11-5
1922	Bos	A	P	32	14-11
1923	Det	A	P	17	3-7
1924	Det	A	P	37	14-7
1925	Det	A	P	26	6-11
1926	Det	A	P	31	8-8
1927	Det	A	P	30	13-7
1929	St.L	A	P	26	11-6
1930	St.L	A	P	35	9-7
1931	St.L	A	P	17	5-5
	BBTR			315	108-82

COLLINS, HUBERT B.
b.Apr.15,1864 Louisville,Ky.
d.May 21,1892

Yr	Cl	Lea	Pos	G	Rec
1886	Lou	a	O	27	.287
1887	Lou	a	O	129	.349
1888	Lou	a	2-O	114	.321
1888	Bro	a	2	12	.295
1889	Bro	a	2	138	.268
1890	Bro	N	2	129	.278
1891	Bro	N	2-O	107	.284
1892	Bro	N	O	20	.302
	BRTR			676	.300

COLLINS, JAMES ANTHONY (Rip)
b.Mar.30,1905 Altoona,Pa.

Yr	Cl	Lea	Pos	G	Rec
1931	St.L	N	1	89	.301
1932	St.L	N	1-O	149	.279
1933	St.L	N	1	132	.310
1934	St.L	N	1	154	.333
1935	St.L	N	1	150	.313
1936	St.L	N	1	103	.292
1937	Chi	N	1	115	.274
1938	Chi	N	1	143	.267
1941	Pit	N	1-O	49	.210
	BBTL			1084	.296

COLLINS, JAMES JOSEPH
b.Jan.16,1873 Buffalo,N.Y.
d.Mar.6,1943

Yr	Cl	Lea	Pos	G	Rec
1895	Bos	N	3	11	.205
1895	Lou	N	3	93	.286
1896	Bos	N	3	83	.300
1897	Bos	N	3	133	.346
1898	Bos	N	3	152	.337
1899	Bos	N	3	151	.275
1900	Bos	N	3	142	.299
1901	Bos	A	M-3	138	.329
1902	Bos	A	M-3	105	.325
1903	Bos	A	M-3	130	.296
1904	Bos	A	M-3	156	.265
1905	Bos	A	M-3	131	.276
1906	Bos	A	M-3	37	.275
1907	Bos	A	3	41	.294
1907	Phi	A	3	100	.273
1908	Phi	A	3	115	.217
	BRTR			1718	.285

COLLINS, JOHN EDGAR (Zip)
b.May 2,1892 Brooklyn,N.Y.

Yr	Cl	Lea	Pos	G	Rec
1914	Pit	N	O	49	.242
1915	Pit	N	O	101	.293
1915	Bos	N	O	5	.308
1916	Bos	N	O	93	.209
1917	Bos	N	O	8	.148
1921	Phi	A	O	24	.282
	BLTL			280	.253

COLLINS, JOHN FRANCIS
(Shano)
b.Dec.4,1885 Charlestown,Mass.
d.Sept.10,1955

Yr	Cl	Lea	Pos	G	Rec
1910	Chi	A	1-O	97	.197
1911	Chi	A	1	106	.262
1912	Chi	A	1-O	153	.290
1913	Chi	A	O	148	.239
1914	Chi	A	O	154	.274
1915	Chi	A	1-O	153	.257
1916	Chi	A	O	143	.243
1917	Chi	A	O	82	.234
1918	Chi	A	O	103	.274
1919	Chi	A	O	63	.279
1920	Chi	A	1	133	.303
1921	Bos	A	O	141	.286
1922	Bos	A	O	135	.271
1923	Bos	A	O	97	.231
1924	Bos	A	1-O	89	.292
1925	Bos	A	O	2	.333
	BRTR			1799	.264

Non-playing manager Bos (A) 1931-32

COLLINS, JOSEPH EDWARD
(Real name
Joseph Edward Kollonige)
b.Dec.3,1922 Scranton,Pa.

Yr	Cl	Lea	Pos	G	Rec
1948	NY	A	H	5	.200
1949	NY	A	1	7	.100
1950	NY	A	1-O	108	.234
1951	NY	A	1-O	125	.286
1952	NY	A	1	122	.280
1953	NY	A	1-O	127	.269
1954	NY	A	1	130	.271
1955	NY	A	1-O	105	.234
1956	NY	A	1-O	100	.225
1957	NY	A	1-O	79	.201
	BLTL			908	.256

COLLINS, ORTH STEIN
(Buck)
b.Apr.27,1880 Lafayette,Ind.
d.Dec.13,1949

Yr	Cl	Lea	Pos	G	Rec
1904	NY	A	O	5	.352
1909	Was	A	P-O	8	0-0 / .000
	BLTR			13	0-0 / .250

COLLINS, PHILIP EUGENE
(Fidgety Phil)
b.Aug.27,1900 Rockford,Ill.
d.Aug.14,1948

Yr	Cl	Lea	Pos	G	Rec
1923	Chi	N	P	1	1-0
1929	Phi	N	P	59	9-7
1930	Phi	N	P	55	16-11
1931	Phi	N	P	44	12-16
1932	Phi	N	P	43	14-12
1933	Phi	N	P	43	8-13
1934	Phi	N	P	48	13-18
1935	Phi	N	P	3	0-2
1935	St.L	N	P	26	7-6
	BRTR			322	80-85

COLLINS, RAYMOND WILLISTON
b.Feb.11,1887 Colchester,Vt.

Yr	Cl	Lea	Pos	G	Rec
1909	Bos	A	P	12	4-3
1910	Bos	A	P	35	13-11
1911	Bos	A	P	31	11-12
1912	Bos	A	P	26	14-8
1913	Bos	A	P	30	19-8
1914	Bos	A	P	38	20-13
1915	Bos	A	P	25	5-7
	BLTL			197	86-62

COLLINS, ROBERT JOSEPH
b.Sept.19,1909 Pittsburgh,Pa.

Yr	Cl	Lea	Pos	G	Rec
1940	Chi	N	C	47	.208
1944	NY	A	C	3	.333
	BRTR			50	.211

COLLINS, THARON PATRICK
(Pat)
b.Sept.13,1896 Sweet Springs,Mo.
d.May 19,1960

Yr	Cl	Lea	Pos	G	Rec
1919	St.L	A	C	11	.143
1920	St.L	A	C	23	.214
1921	St.L	A	C	58	.243
1922	St.L	A	C	63	.307
1923	St.L	A	C	85	.177
1924	St.L	A	C	32	.315
1926	NY	A	C	102	.286
1927	NY	A	C	92	.275
1928	NY	A	C	70	.220
1929	Bos	N	C	7	.000
	BRTR			543	.254

COLLINS, WILLIAM J.
b.1867 Dublin,Ireland
d.June 8,1893

Yr	Cl	Lea	Pos	G	Rec
1887	Met	a	C	1	.250
1889	Ath	a	C	1	.200
1890	Ath	a	C	1	.000
1891	Cle	N	C	2	.000
1892	St.L	N	O	1	.000
	BR			6	.143

COLLINS, WILLIAM SHIRLEY
b.Mar.17,1884 Chesterton,Ind.

Yr	Cl	Lea	Pos	G	Rec
1910	Bos	N	O	151	.241
1911	Bos	N	O	17	.149
1911	Chi	N	O	7	.333
1913	Bro	N	O	32	.189
1914	Buf	F	O	20	.146
	BRTR			227	.224

COLLUM, JACK DEAN
b.June 21,1927 Victor,Ia.

Yr	Cl	Lea	Pos	G	Rec
1951	St.L	N	P	3	2-1

(Continued)

Yr	Cl	Lea	Pos	G	Rec
1952	St.L	N	P	2	0-0
1953	St.L	N	P	7	0-0
1953	Cin	N	P	30	7-11
1954	Cin	N	P	36	7-3
1955	Cin	N	P	32	9-8
1956	St.L	N	P	38	6-2
1957	Chi	N	P	9	1-1
1957	Bro	N	P	3	0-0
1958	LA	N	P	2	0-0
1962	Min	A	P	8	0-2
1962	Cle	A	P	1	0-0
	BLTL			171	32-28

COLMAN, FRANK LOYD
b.Mar.2,1918 London,Ont.,Canada

Yr	Cl	Lea	Pos	G	Rec
1942	Pit	N	O	10	.135
1943	Pit	N	O	32	.271
1944	Pit	N	1-O	99	.270
1945	Pit	N	1-O	77	.209
1946	Pit	N	1-O	26	.170
1946	NY	A	O	5	.267
1947	NY	A	O	22	.107
	BLTL			271	.228

COMBS, EARLE BRYAN
(Colonel)
b.May 14,1899 Pebworth,Ky.

Yr	Cl	Lea	Pos	G	Rec
1924	NY	A	O	24	.400
1925	NY	A	O	150	.343
1926	NY	A	O	145	.299
1927	NY	A	O	152	.356
1928	NY	A	O	149	.310
1929	NY	A	O	142	.345
1930	NY	A	O	137	.344
1931	NY	A	O	138	.318
1932	NY	A	O	143	.321
1933	NY	A	O	122	.298
1934	NY	A	O	63	.319
1935	NY	A	O	89	.282
	BLTR			1454	.325

COMBS, MERRILL RUSSELL
b.Dec.11,1919 Los Angeles,Cal.

Yr	Cl	Lea	Pos	G	Rec
1947	Bos	A	3	17	.221
1949	Bos	A	S-3	14	.208
1950	Bos	A	H	1	.000
1950	Was	A	S	37	.245
1951	Cle	A	S	19	.179
1952	Cle	A	2-S	52	.165
	BLTR			140	.202

COMELLAS, JORGE
b.Dec.18,1917 Havana,Cuba

Yr	Cl	Lea	Pos	G	Rec
1945	Chi	N	P	7	0-2
	BRTR				

COMISKEY, CHARLES ALBERT
(Commy)
b.Aug.19,1859 Chicago,Ill.
d.Oct.26,1931

Yr	Cl	Lea	Pos	G	Rec
1882	St.L	a	P-1	78	0-1 / .244
1883	St.L	a	M-1-O	95	.290
1884	St.L	a	1	108	.241
1885	St.L	a	M-1	83	.260
1886	St.L	a	M-1	131	.260
1887	St.L	a	M-1	125	.368
1888	St.L	a	M-1	137	.271
1889	St.L	a	M-1	137	.288
1890	Chi	p	M-1	88	.248
1891	St.L	a	M-1	139	.257
1892	Cin	N	M-1	140	.223
1893	Cin	N	M-1	62	.225
1894	Cin	N	M-1	59	.265
	BRTR			1382	0-1 / .269

COMMAND, JAMES DALTON
b.Oct.15,1929 Grand Rapids,Mich.

Yr	Cl	Lea	Pos	G	Rec
1954	Phi	N	3	9	.222
1955	Phi	N	H	5	.000
	BLTR			14	.174

COMOROSKY, ADAM ANTHONY
b.Dec.9,1904 Swoyersville,Pa.
d.Mar.2,1951

Yr	Cl	Lea	Pos	G	Rec
1926	Pit	N	O	8	.267
1927	Pit	N	O	18	.230
1928	Pit	N	O	51	.295
1929	Pit	N	O	127	.321
1930	Pit	N	O	152	.313
1931	Pit	N	O	99	.243
1932	Pit	N	O	108	.286
1933	Pit	N	O	64	.284
1934	Cin	N	O	127	.258
1935	Cin	N	O	59	.248
	BRTR			813	.285

COMPTON, ALBERT SEBASTIAN
(Bash)
b.Sept.28,1889 San Marcos,Tex.

Yr	Cl	Lea	Pos	G	Rec
1911	St.L	A	O	28	.272
1912	St.L	A	O	100	.280
1913	St.L	A	O	61	.180
1915	St.L	F	O	2	.250
1915	Bos	N	O	35	.241
1916	Bos	N	O	34	.202
1916	Pit	N	O	5	.100
1918	NY	N	O	21	.217
	BLTL			286	.239

COMPTON, HARRY LEROY
(Jack)
b.Mar.9,1882 Lancaster,O.

Yr	Cl	Lea	Pos	G	Rec
1911	Cin	N	P	8	1-1
	BRTR				

COMSTOCK, RALPH REMICK
b.Nov.24,1887 Toledo,O.

Yr	Cl	Lea	Pos	G	Rec
1913	Det	A	P	9	2-5
1915	Bos	A	P	3	1-0
1915	Pit	F	P	12	3-3
1918	Pit	N	P	15	5-6
	BRTR			39	11-14

CONATSER, CLINTON ASTOR
(Connie)
b.July 24,1921 Los Angeles,Cal

Yr	Cl	Lea	Pos	G	Rec
1948	Bos	N	O	90	.277
1949	Bos	N	O	53	.263
	BRTR			143	.271

CONDE, RAMON LUIS
b.Dec.29,1934 Juana Diaz,Puerto Rico

Yr	Cl	Lea	Pos	G	Rec
1962	Chi	A	3	14	.000
	BRTR				

CONE, H. B.
b.Texas

Yr	Cl	Lea	Pos	G	Rec
1915	Phi	A	P	1	0-0

CONE, J. FREDERICK
b.May 1848 Rockford,Ill.
d.Apr.13,1909

Yr	Cl	Lea	Pos	G	Rec
1871	Bos	n	O	18	NR

CONGALTON, WILLIAM MILLAR
(Bunk)
b.Jan.24,1875 Guelph,Ont.,Canada
d.Aug.19,1937

Yr	Cl	Lea	Pos	G	Rec
1902	Chi	N	O	47	.245
1905	Cle	A	O	12	.369
1906	Cle	A	O	117	.320
1907	Cle	A	O	9	.182
1907	Bos	A	O	124	.286
				309	.293

CONGER, RICHARD
b.Apr.3,1921 Los Angeles,Cal.

Yr	Cl	Lea	Pos	G	Rec
1940	Det	A	P	2	1-0
1941	Pit	N	P	2	0-0
1942	Pit	N	P	3	0-0
1943	Phi	N	P	13	2-7
	BRTR			20	3-7

CONKWRIGHT, ALLEN HOWARD
(Red)
b.Dec.4,1897 Sedalia,Mo.

Yr	Cl	Lea	Pos	G	Rec
1920	Det	A	P	5	2-1
	BRTR				

CONLAN, JOHN BERTRAND
(Jocko)
b.Dec.6,1902 Chicago,Ill.

Yr	Cl	Lea	Pos	G	Rec
1934	Chi	A	O	63	.249
1935	Chi	A	O	65	.286
	BLTL			128	.263

CONLEY, DONALD EUGENE
b.Nov.10,1930 Muskogee,Okla.

Yr	Cl	Lea	Pos	G	Rec
1952	Bos	N	P	4	0-3
1954	Mil	N	P	28	14-9
1955	Mil	N	P	22	11-7
1956	Mil	N	P	31	8-9
1957	Mil	N	P	35	9-9
1958	Mil	N	P	26	0-6
1959	Phi	N	P	25	12-7
1960	Phi	N	P	29	8-14
1961	Bos	A	P	33	11-14
1962	Bos	A	P	34	15-14
	BRTR			267	88-92

CONLEY, EDWARD J.
b.1864 Chicago,Ill.
d.Oct.17,1894

Yr	Cl	Lea	Pos	G	Rec
1884	Pro	N	P	8	4-4

CONLEY, JAMES PATRICK
(Snipe)
b.Apr.25,1894 Schuylkill Haven,Pa.

Yr	Cl	Lea	Pos	G	Rec
1914	Bal	F	P	21	4-6
1915	Bal	F	P	20	1-4
1918	Cin	N	P	5	2-0
	BRTR			46	7-10

CONLEY, ROBERT BURNS
b.Feb.1,1934 Newport News,Va.

Yr	Cl	Lea	Pos	G	Rec
1958	Phi	N	P	2	0-0
	BRTR				

CONLON, ARTHUR JOSEPH
b.Dec.10,1898 Woburn,Mass.

Yr	Cl	Lea	Pos	G	Rec
1923	Bos	N	2-S-3	59	.218
	BRTR				

CONN, ALBERT THOMAS
(Bert)
b.Sept.22,1879 Philadelphia,Pa.
d.Nov.2,1944

Yr	Cl	Lea	Pos	G	Rec
1898	Phi	N	P	1	0-0
1900	Phi	N	P	6	0-1
1901	Phi	N	2	5	.222
	TR			12	0-1 .267

CONNALLY, GEORGE WALTER
(Sarge)
b.Aug.31,1898 McGregor,Tex.

Yr	Cl	Lea	Pos	G	Rec
1921	Chi	A	P	5	0-1
1923	Chi	A	P	3	0-0
1924	Chi	A	P	44	7-13
1925	Chi	A	P	40	6-7
1926	Chi	A	P	31	6-5
1927	Chi	A	P	43	10-15
1928	Chi	A	P	28	2-5
1929	Chi	A	P	11	0-0
1931	Cle	A	P	17	5-5
1932	Cle	A	P	35	8-6
1933	Cle	A	P	41	5-3
1934	Cle	A	P	5	0-0
	BRTR			303	49-60

CONNALLY, MERVIN THOMAS
(Bud)
b.Apr.25,1901 San Francisco,Cal.

Yr	Cl	Lea	Pos	G	Rec
1925	Bos	A	S-3	43	.261
	BRTR				

CONNATSER, BROADUS MILBURN
(Bruce)
b.Sept.19,1902 Sevierville,Tenn.

Yr	Cl	Lea	Pos	G	Rec
1931	Cle	A	1	12	.286
1932	Cle	A	1	23	.233
	BRTR			35	.257

CONNAUGHTON, FRANK H.
b.Jan.1,1869 Clinton,Mass.
d.Dec.2,1942

Yr	Cl	Lea	Pos	G	Rec
1894	Bos	N	S	38	.337
1896	NY	N	S-O	83	.257
1906	Bos	N	2-S	12	.205
	BRTR			133	.278

CONNELL, EUGENE JOSEPH
b.May 10,1906 Hazleton,Pa.
d.Aug.31,1937

Yr	Cl	Lea	Pos	G	Rec
1931	Phi	N	C	6	.250
	BRTR				

CONNELL, JOSEPH BERNARD
b.Jan.16,1902 Bethlehem,Pa.

Yr	Cl	Lea	Pos	G	Rec
1926	NY	N	H	2	.000
	BLTL				

CONNELL, PETER J.
b.Brooklyn,N.Y.

Yr	Cl	Lea	Pos	G	Rec
1886	Met	a	3	1	.000

CONNELL, TERENCE G.
b.June 17,1855 Philadelphia,Pa.
d.Mar.25,1924

Yr	Cl	Lea	Pos	G	Rec
1874	Chi	n	P-C	1	0-0 .000

CONNELLY, JOHN M.
(Red)
b.1857
d.Mar.1,1896

Yr	Cl	Lea	Pos	G	Rec
1886	St.L	N	O	2	.000

CONNELLY, THOMAS MARTIN
b.Oct.20,1898 Chicago,Ill.

Yr	Cl	Lea	Pos	G	Rec
1920	NY	A	O	1	.000
1921	NY	A	O	4	.200
	BLTR			5	.167

CONNELLY, WILLIAM WIRT
(Wild Bill)
b.June 29,1925 Alberta,Va.

Yr	Cl	Lea	Pos	G	Rec
1945	Phi	A	P	2	1-1
1950	Chi	A	P	2	0-0
1950	Det	A	P	2	0-0
1952	NY	N	P	11	5-0
1953	NY	N	P	8	0-1
	BLTR			25	6-2

CONNOLLY, EDWARD JOSEPH
b.July 17,1908 Brooklyn,N.Y.

Yr	Cl	Lea	Pos	G	Rec
1929	Bos	A	C	5	.000
1930	Bos	A	C	27	.188
1931	Bos	A	C	42	.075
1932	Bos	A	C	75	.225
	BRTR			149	.178

CONNOLLY, JOSEPH ALOYSIUS
b.Feb.12,1888 N.Smithfield,R.I.
d.Sept.1,1943

Yr	Cl	Lea	Pos	G	Rec
1913	Bos	N	O	126	.281
1914	Bos	N	O	120	.306
1915	Bos	N	O	104	.298
1916	Bos	N	O	62	.227
	BLTR			412	.288

CONNOLLY, JOSEPH GEORGE
(Coaster)
b.June 4,1896 San Francisco,Cal.
(Continued)
d.Mar.30,1960

Yr	Cl	Lea	Pos	G	Rec
1921	NY	N	O	2	.000
1922	Cle	A	O	12	.244
1923	Cle	A	O	52	.303
1924	Bos	A	O	14	.100
	BRTR			80	.268

CONNOLLY, THOMAS FRANCIS
(Blackie)
b.Dec.30,1892 Boston,Mass.

Yr	Cl	Lea	Pos	G	Rec
1915	Was	A	3-O	50	.184
	BLTR				

CONNOR, JAMES MATTHEW
(Real name James Matthew O'Connor)
b.May 11,1865 Port Jervis,N.Y.
d.Sept.4,1950

Yr	Cl	Lea	Pos	G	Rec
1892	Chi	N	2	10	.057
1897	Chi	N	2	77	.296
1898	Chi	N	2	136	.225
1899	Chi	N	2-3	66	.206
				289	.235

CONNOR, JOHN
b.LaSalle,Ill.
d.Oct.13,1932

Yr	Cl	Lea	Pos	G	Rec
1884	Bos	N	P	7	1-4
1885	Buf	N	P	1	0-1
1885	Lou	a	P	4	1-3
				12	2-8

CONNOR, JOSEPH

Yr	Cl	Lea	Pos	G	Rec
1895	St.L	N	3	2	.000

CONNOR, JOSEPH FRANCIS
b.Dec.8,1874 Waterbury,Conn.
d.Nov.8,1957

Yr	Cl	Lea	Pos	G	Rec
1900	Bos	N	C	7	.200
1901	Mil	A	C-2-O	3[illegible]	.272
1901	Cle	A	C	38	.138
1905	NY	A	C-1	8	.271
	BRTR			91	.209

CONNOR, ROGER
b.July 1,1857 Waterbury,Conn.
d.Jan.4,1931

Yr	Cl	Lea	Pos	G	Rec
1880	Tro	N	3	83	.332
1881	Tro	N	1	84	.288
1882	Tro	N	1-3-O	79	.327
1883	NY	N	1	96	.361
1884	NY	N	2-3-O	112	.316
1885	NY	N	1	110	.371
1886	NY	N	1	118	.354
1887	NY	N	1	127	.382
1888	NY	N	1	134	.291
1889	NY	N	1	131	.316
1890	NY	p	1	123	.372
1891	NY	N	1	123	.293
1892	Phi	N	1	153	.285
1893	NY	N	1	135	.322
1894	NY	N	1-O	22	.293
1894	St.L	N	1	99	.318
1895	St.L	N	1	104	.326
1896	St.L	N	M-1	126	.282
1897	St.L	N	1	22	.229
	BLTL			1981	.327

CONNORS, JEREMIAH
b.Philadelphia,Pa.

Yr	Cl	Lea	Pos	G	Rec
1892	Phi	N	O	1	.000

CONNORS, JOSEPH P.
b.1850 N.Y.

Yr	Cl	Lea	Pos	G	Rec
1871	Tro	n	1-2-O	7	.182

CONNORS, JOSEPH P.
b.Philadelphia,Pa.

Yr	Cl	Lea	Pos	G	Rec
1884	Alt	U	P-3-O	3	0-1 .100
1884	KC	U	P-O	3	0-1 .091
				6	0-2 .095

CONNORS, KEVIN JOSEPH (Chuck)

b.Apr.10,1921 Brooklyn,N.Y.

Yr	Cl	Lea	Pos	G	Rec
1949	Bro	N	H	1	.000
1951	Chi	N	1	66	.239
		BLTL		67	.238

CONNORS, MERVYN JAMES (Mike)

b.Jan.23,1915 Berkeley,Cal.

Yr	Cl	Lea	Pos	G	Rec
1937	Chi	A	3	28	.233
1938	Chi	A	1	24	.355
		BRTR		52	.279

CONOVER, THEODORE (Huck)

b.Mar.10,1868 Lexington,Ky.

d.July 27,1910

Yr	Cl	Lea	Pos	G	Rec
1889	Cin	a	P	1	0-0

CONROY, BENJAMIN EDWARD

b.1871 Philadelphia,Pa.

Yr	Cl	Lea	Pos	G	Rec
1890	Ath	a	2-S	116	.175

CONROY, WILLIAM EDWARD (Wid)

b.Apr.5,1877 Philadelphia,Pa.

d.Dec.6,1959

Yr	Cl	Lea	Pos	G	Rec
1901	Mil	A	S	131	.269
1902	Pit	N	S-O	95	.241
1903	NY	A	3	125	.277
1904	NY	A	S-3	140	.249
1905	NY	A	S-3-O	101	.273
1906	NY	A	S-O	148	.245
1907	NY	A	S-O	140	.234
1908	NY	A	3	141	.237
1909	Was	A	3	139	.244
1910	Was	A	3-O	103	.254
1911	Was	A	3-O	106	.232
		BRTR		1369	.250

CONROY, WILLIAM FREDERICK (Pep)

b.Jan.9,1899 Chicago,Ill.

Yr	Cl	Lea	Pos	G	Rec
1923	Was	A	3	18	.133
		BRTR			

CONROY, WILLIAM GORDON

b.Feb.26,1915 Bloomington,Ill.

Yr	Cl	Lea	Pos	G	Rec
1935	Phi	A	C	1	.250
1936	Phi	A	C	1	.500
1937	Phi	A	C	26	.200
1942	Bos	A	C	83	.200
1943	Bos	A	C	39	.180
1944	Bos	A	C	19	.213
		BRTR		169	.199

CONSOLO, WILLIAM ANGELO

b.Aug.18,1934 Cleveland,O.

Yr	Cl	Lea	Pos	G	Rec
1953	Bos	A	2-3	47	.215
1954	Bos	A	2-S-3	91	.227
1955	Bos	A	2	8	.222
1956	Bos	A	2	48	.182
1957	Bos	A	2-S-3	68	.270
1958	Bos	A	2-S-3	46	.125
1959	Bos	A	S	10	.214
1959	Was	A	2-S	79	.213
1960	Was	A	2-S-3	100	.207
1961	Min	A	2-S-3	11	.000
1962	Phi	N	3	13	.400
1962	LA	A	2-S-3	28	.100
1962	KC	A	S	54	.240
		BRTR		603	.221

CONSTABLE, JAMES LEE

b.June 14,1933 Jonesboro,Tenn.

Yr	Cl	Lea	Pos	G	Rec
1956	NY	N	P	3	0-0
1957	NY	N	P	16	1-1
1958	SF	N	P	9	1-0
1958	Cle	A	P	6	0-1
1958	Was	A	P	15	0-1
1962	Mil	N	P	3	1-1
		BBTL		52	3-4

CONSUEGRA, SANDALIO SIMEON CASTELLON (Sandy)

b.Sept.3,1920 Santa Clara,Cuba

Yr	Cl	Lea	Pos	G	Rec
1950	Was	A	P	24	7-8
1951	Was	A	P	40	7-8

(Continued)

Yr	Cl	Lea	Pos	G	Rec
1952	Was	A	P	30	6-0
1953	Was	A	P	4	0-0
1953	Chi	A	P	29	7-5
1954	Chi	A	P-3	39	16-3 .229
1955	Chi	A	P	44	6-5
1956	Chi	A	P	28	1-2
1956	Bal	A	P	4	1-1
1957	Bal	A	P	5	0-0
1957	NY	N	P	4	0-0
		BRTR		251	51-32 .170

CONWAY, CHARLES C.

b.Apr.28,1886 Youngstown,O.

Yr	Cl	Lea	Pos	G	Rec
1911	Was	A	O	2	.333
		BRTR			

CONWAY, JACK CLEMENTS

b.July 30,1919 Bryan,Tex.

Yr	Cl	Lea	Pos	G	Rec
1941	Cle	A	S	2	.500
1946	Cle	A	2-S-3	68	.225
1947	Cle	A	2-S-3	34	.180
1948	NY	N	2-S-3	24	.245
		BRTR		128	.223

CONWAY, JAMES P.

b.Clifton,Pa.

Yr	Cl	Lea	Pos	G	Rec
1884	Bro	a	P-S-O	14	3-9 .133
1885	Ath	a	P-O	2	1-1 .167
1889	KC	a	P	41	18-19
		TR		57	22-29 .191

CONWAY, JEROME PATRICK

b.June 7,1901 Holyoke,Mass.

Yr	Cl	Lea	Pos	G	Rec
1920	Was	A	P	1	0-0
		BLTL			

CONWAY, OWEN SYLVESTER

b.Oct.23,1890 New York,N.Y.

d.Mar.13,1942

Yr	Cl	Lea	Pos	G	Rec
1915	Phi	A	3	4	.067
		TR			

CONWAY, PETER J.

b.Oct.30,1866 Burmont,Pa.

d.Jan.14,1903

Yr	Cl	Lea	Pos	G	Rec
1885	Buf	N	P-1-S	29	10-17 .111
1886	KC	N	P-O	52	5-16 .235
1886	Det	N	P	11	6-5
1887	Det	N	P	24	8-10
1888	Det	N	P	45	31-14
1889	Pit	N	P	3	2-1
		BR		164	62-63 .227

CONWAY, RICHARD BUTLER

b.Apr.25,1866 Lowell,Mass.

d.Sept.9,1926

Yr	Cl	Lea	Pos	G	Rec
1886	Bal	a	P	9	2-7
1887	Bos	N	P	39	9-15
1888	Bos	N	P	6	4-1
		BLTR		54	15-23

CONWAY, RICHARD DANIEL (Rip)

b.Apr.18,1896 White Bear,Minn.

Yr	Cl	Lea	Pos	G	Rec
1918	Bos	N	2	14	.167
		BLTR			

CONWAY, WILLIAM F.

b.Nov.28,1861 Lowell,Mass.

d.Dec.18,1943

Yr	Cl	Lea	Pos	G	Rec
1884	Phi	N	C	1	.000
1886	Bal	a	C	7	.142
				8	.111

CONWELL, EDWARD JAMES (Irish)

b.Jan.29,1890 Chicago,Ill.

Yr	Cl	Lea	Pos	G	Rec
1911	St.L	N	3	1	.000
		BRTR			

CONYERS, HERBERT LEROY

b.Jan.8,1921 Cowgill,Mo.

Yr	Cl	Lea	Pos	G	Rec
1950	Cle	A	1	7	.333
		BLTR			

CONZELMAN, JOSEPH HARRISON

b.July 14,1889 Bristol,Conn.

Yr	Cl	Lea	Pos	G	Rec
1913	Pit	N	P	2	0-1
1914	Pit	N	P	33	5-6
1915	Pit	N	P	18	1-1
		BRTR		53	6-8

COOGAN, DALE ROGER

b.Aug.14,1930 Los Angeles,Cal.

Yr	Cl	Lea	Pos	G	Rec
1950	Pit	N	1	53	.240
		BLTL			

COOGAN, DANIEL GEORGE

b.Feb.16,1875 Philadelphia,Pa.

d.Oct.28,1942

Yr	Cl	Lea	Pos	G	Rec
1895	Was	N	S	21	.203

COOK, EARL DAVIS

b.Dec.10,1911 Lemonville,Ont.,Canada

Yr	Cl	Lea	Pos	G	Rec
1941	Det	A	P	1	0-0
		BRTR			

COOK, FREDERICK RUSSELL

(Played under name of Frederick Russell Winchell)

COOK, JAMES FITCHIE

b.Nov.10,1879 Dundee,Ill.

d.June 17,1949

Yr	Cl	Lea	Pos	G	Rec
1903	Chi	N	O	8	.120
		TR			

COOK, LUTHER A. (Doc)

b.June 24,1889 Fort Worth,Tex.

Yr	Cl	Lea	Pos	G	Rec
1913	NY	A	O	20	.264
1914	NY	A	O	131	.283
1915	NY	A	O	132	.271
1916	NY	A	O	4	.100
		BLTR		287	.274

COOK, PAUL

b.May 5,1863 Caledonia,N.Y.

d.May 26,1905

Yr	Cl	Lea	Pos	G	Rec
1884	Phi	N	C	3	.083
1886	Lou	a	C-1	68	.205
1887	Lou	a	C-1	63	.267
1888	Lou	a	C	53	.200
1889	Lou	a	C	81	.236
1890	Bro	p	C-1	59	.242
1891	Lou	a	C	39	.232
1891	St.L	a	C	7	.179
		BRTR		373	.227

COOK, RAYMOND CLIFFORD

b.Aug.20,1936 Dallas,Tex.

Yr	Cl	Lea	Pos	G	Rec
1959	Cin	N	3	9	.381
1960	Cin	N	3-O	54	.208
1961	Cin	N	3	4	.000
1962	Cin	N	3	6	.000
1962	NY	N	3-O	40	.232
		BRTR		113	.223

COOK, ROLLIN EDWARD

b.Oct.5,1890 Toledo,O.

Yr	Cl	Lea	Pos	G	Rec
1915	St.L	A	P	5	0-0
		BRTR			

COOKE, ALLEN LINDSEY (Dusty)

b.June 23,1907 Swepsonville,N.C.

Yr	Cl	Lea	Pos	G	Rec
1930	NY	A	O	92	.255
1931	NY	A	O	27	.333
1932	NY	A	O	3	.000
1933	Bos	A	O	119	.291
1934	Bos	A	O	74	.244
1935	Bos	A	O	100	.306
1936	Bos	A	O	111	.273
1938	Cin	N	O	82	.275
		BLTR		608	.291

Non-playing manager Phi (N) 1948

COOKE, FREDERICK B.

b.Paulding,O.

Yr	Cl	Lea	Pos	G	Rec
1897	Cle	N	O	5	.295

COOLEY, DUFF C. (Sir Richard)
b.Mar.29,1873 Leavenworth,Kan.
d.Aug.9,1937

Yr	Cl	Lea	Pos	G	Rec
1893	St.L	N	O	26	.359
1894	St.L	N	O	52	.299
1895	St.L	N	O	132	.340
1896	St.L	N	O	40	.302
1896	Phi	N	O	64	.301
1897	Phi	N	O	131	.327
1898	Phi	N	O	148	.317
1899	Phi	N	1	94	.280
1900	Pit	N	1	65	.200
1901	Bos	N	O	60	.270
1902	Bos	N	1-O	134	.297
1903	Bos	N	O	138	.289
1904	Bos	N	O	122	.272
1905	Det	A	O	97	.247
			BLTR	1303	.295

COOMBS, CECIL LYSANDER
b.Mar.18,1888 Moweaqua,Ill.

Yr	Cl	Lea	Pos	G	Rec
1914	Chi	A	O	7	.173
			BRTR		

COOMBS, JOHN WESLEY
(Colby Jack)
b.Nov.18,1882 LeGrande,Ia.
d.Apr.15,1957

Yr	Cl	Lea	Pos	G	Rec
1906	Phi	A	P	24	10-11
1907	Phi	A	P	24	6-9
1908	Phi	A	P-O	78	7-5 .255
1909	Phi	A	P	37	12-11
1910	Phi	A	P	46	31-9
1911	Phi	A	P	52	28-12
1912	Phi	A	P	54	21-10
1913	Phi	A	P	1	0-0
1914	Phi	A	P	5	0-1
1915	Bro	N	P	29	15-10
1916	Bro	N	P	27	13-8
1917	Bro	N	P	32	7-11
1918	Bro	N	P-O	46	8-14 .168
1920	Det	A	P	2	0-0
			BBTR	457	158-111 .235

Non-playing manager Phi (N) 1919

COOMBS, RAYMOND FRANK
(Bobby)
b.Feb.2,1908 Goodwins Mills,Me.

Yr	Cl	Lea	Pos	G	Rec
1933	Phi	A	P	21	0-1
1943	NY	N	P	9	0-1
			BRTR	30	0-2

COONEY, JAMES EDWARD (Scoops)
b.Aug.24,1894 Cranston,R.I.

Yr	Cl	Lea	Pos	G	Rec
1917	Bos	A	2	11	.222
1919	NY	N	S	5	.214
1924	St.L	N	2-S-3	110	.295
1925	St.L	N	2-S-O	54	.273
1926	Chi	N	S	141	.251
1927	Chi	N	S	33	.242
1927	Phi	N	S	76	.270
1928	Bos	N	S	18	.137
			BRTR	448	.262

COONEY, JAMES JOHN
b.July 9,1865 Cranston,R.I.
d.July 2,1903

Yr	Cl	Lea	Pos	G	Rec
1890	Chi	N	S	135	.271
1891	Chi	N	S	118	.250
1892	Chi	N	S	84	.171
1892	Was	N	S	6	.154
			BRTR	343	.243

COONEY, JOHN WALTER
b.Mar.18,1901 Cranston,R.I.

Yr	Cl	Lea	Pos	G	Rec
1921	Bos	N	P	8	0-1
1922	Bos	N	P	4	1-2
1923	Bos	N	P-1-O	42	3-5 .379
1924	Bos	N	P-1-O	55	8-9 .254
1925	Bos	N	P-1-O	54	14-14 .320
1926	Bos	N	P-1	64	3-3 .302
1927	Bos	N	P	10	0-0

(Continued)

Yr	Cl	Lea	Pos	G	Rec
1928	Bos	N	P	33	3-7
1929	Bos	N	P-O	41	2-3 .319
1930	Bos	N	P	4	0-0
1935	Bro	N	O	10	.310
1936	Bro	N	O	130	.282
1937	Bro	N	O	120	.293
1938	Bos	N	1-O	120	.271
1939	Bos	N	O	118	.274
1940	Bos	N	1-O	108	.318
1941	Bos	N	1-O	123	.319
1942	Bos	N	1-O	74	.207
1943	Bro	N	1	37	.206
1944	Bro	N	O	7	.750
1944	NY	A	O	10	.125
			BRTL	1172	34-44 .286

Non-playing manager Bos (N) 1949

COONEY, PHILIP
(Real name Philip Cohn)
b.Sept.14,1886 Paterson,N.J.

Yr	Cl	Lea	Pos	G	Rec
1905	NY	A	3	1	.000
			BRTR		

COONEY, ROBERT DANIEL
b.July 12,1907 Glens Falls,N.Y.

Yr	Cl	Lea	Pos	G	Rec
1931	St.L	A	P	5	0-3
1932	St.L	A	P	24	1-2
			BRTR	29	1-5

COONEY, WILLIAM A. (Cush)
b.Apr.4,1887 Boston,Mass.
d.Nov.6,1928

Yr	Cl	Lea	Pos	G	Rec
1909	Bos	N	P	5	0-0
1910	Bos	N	P	8	0-0
			TR	13	0-0

COONS, WILBUR K.
b.Philadelphia,Pa.
d.Aug.30,1915

Yr	Cl	Lea	Pos	G	Rec
1875	Ath	n	C	3	NR
1876	Ath	N	C-O	54	.225
				57	NR

COOPER, ARLEY WILBUR
b.Feb.24,1892 Bearsville,W.Va.

Yr	Cl	Lea	Pos	G	Rec
1912	Pit	N	P	6	3-0
1913	Pit	N	P	30	5-3
1914	Pit	N	P	40	16-15
1915	Pit	N	P	38	5-16
1916	Pit	N	P	44	12-11
1917	Pit	N	P	41	17-11
1918	Pit	N	P	38	19-14
1919	Pit	N	P	36	19-13
1920	Pit	N	P	44	24-15
1921	Pit	N	P	38	22-14
1922	Pit	N	P	41	23-14
1923	Pit	N	P	39	17-19
1924	Pit	N	P	38	20-14
1925	Chi	N	P	32	12-14
1926	Chi	N	P	8	2-1
1926	Det	A	P	8	0-4
			BRTL	521	216-178

COOPER, CALVIN ASA
b.Aug.11,1924 Great Falls,S.C.

Yr	Cl	Lea	Pos	G	Rec
1948	Was	A	P	1	0-0
			BRTR		

COOPER, CLAUDE WILLIAM
b.Apr.1,1892 Troupe,Tex.

Yr	Cl	Lea	Pos	G	Rec
1913	NY	N	O	27	.300
1914	Bro	F	O	110	.239
1915	Bro	F	1-O	152	.291
1916	Phi	N	O	56	.192
1917	Phi	N	O	24	.103
			BLTL	369	.258

COOPER, GUY EVANS
b.Jan.28,1893 Rome,Ga.
d.Aug.2,1951

Yr	Cl	Lea	Pos	G	Rec
1914	NY	A	P	1	0-0
1914	Bos	A	P	10	1-1
1915	Bos	A	P	1	0-0
			BLTR	12	1-1

COOPER, MORTON CECIL
b.Mar.2,1913 Atherton,Mo.
d.Nov.17,1958

Yr	Cl	Lea	Pos	G	Rec
1938	St.L	N	P	4	2-1
1939	St.L	N	P	47	12-6
1940	St.L	N	P	38	11-12
1941	St.L	N	P	29	13-9
1942	St.L	N	P	37	22-7
1943	St.L	N	P	37	21-8
1944	St.L	N	P	34	22-7
1945	St.L	N	P	4	2-0
1945	Bos	N	P	20	7-4
1946	Bos	N	P	28	13-11
1947	Bos	N	P	10	2-5
1947	NY	N	P	8	1-5
1949	Chi	N	P	1	0-0
			BRTR	297	128-75

COOPER, ORGE PATTERSON
b.Nov.26,1917 Albemarle,N.C.

Yr	Cl	Lea	Pos	G	Rec
1946	Phi	A	P	1	0-0
1947	Phi	A	1	13	.250
			BRTR	14	0-0 .250

COOPER, WILLIAM WALKER
(Walk)
b.Jan.8,1915 Atherton,Mo.

Yr	Cl	Lea	Pos	G	Rec
1940	St.L	N	C	6	.316
1941	St.L	N	C	68	.245
1942	St.L	N	C	125	.281
1943	St.L	N	C	122	.319
1944	St.L	N	C	112	.317
1945	St.L	N	C	4	.389
1946	NY	N	C	87	.268
1947	NY	N	C	140	.305
1948	NY	N	C	91	.266
1949	NY	N	C	42	.211
1949	Cin	N	C	82	.280
1950	Cin	N	C	15	.191
1950	Bos	N	C	102	.329
1951	Bos	N	C	109	.313
1952	Bos	N	C	102	.235
1953	Mil	N	C	53	.219
1954	Pit	N	C	14	.200
1954	Chi	N	C	57	.310
1955	Chi	N	C	54	.279
1956	St.L	N	C	40	.265
1957	St.L	N	C	48	.269
			BRTR	1473	.285

COOPER, WILLIE G.
(Played under name of
William G. Nance)

COPELAND, MAYS
b.Aug.31,1913 Mountain View,Ark.

Yr	Cl	Lea	Pos	G	Rec
1935	St.L	N	P	1	0-0
			BRTR		

COPPOLA, HENRY PETER
b.Aug.6,1913 E. Douglas,Mass.

Yr	Cl	Lea	Pos	G	Rec
1935	Was	A	P	19	3-4
1936	Was	A	P	6	0-0
			BBTR	25	3-4

CORBETT, EUGENE LOUIS
b.Oct.25,1913 Winona,Minn.

Yr	Cl	Lea	Pos	G	Rec
1936	Phi	N	1	6	.143
1937	Phi	N	2-3	7	.333
1938	Phi	N	1	24	.080
			BLTR	37	.120

CORBETT, JOSEPH
b.Dec.4,1875 San Francisco,Cal.
d.May 3,1945

Yr	Cl	Lea	Pos	G	Rec
1895	Was	N	P	8	0-3
1896	Bal	N	P	8	3-1
1897	Bal	N	P	36	24-8
1904	St.L	N	P	14	5-9
			BRTR	66	32-21

CORBITT, CLAUDE ELLIOTT
b.July 21,1915 Sunbury,N.C.

Yr	Cl	Lea	Pos	G	Rec
1945	Bro	N	3	2	.500
1946	Cin	N	S	82	.248
1948	Cin	N	2-S-3	87	.256
1949	Cin	N	2-S-3	44	.181
			BRTR	215	.243

CORCORAN, ARTHUR A. (Bunny)
b.Virginia

Yr	Cl	Lea	Pos	G	Rec
1915	Phi	A	3	1	.000
			TR		

CORCORAN, JOHN A.
b.1873 Cincinnati,O.
d.Nov.1,1901

Yr	Cl	Lea	Pos	G	Rec
1895	Pit	N	S-3	6	.150

CORCORAN, JOHN H.
b.Lowell,Mass.

Yr	Cl	Lea	Pos	G	Rec
1884	Bro	a	C	52	.215

CORCORAN, LAWRENCE J.
b.Aug.10,1861 Brooklyn,N.Y.
d.Oct.14,1891

Yr	Cl	Lea	Pos	G	Rec
1880	Chi	N	P-S-O	70	43-14 .221
1881	Chi	N	P-S-O	47	31-14 .222
1882	Chi	N	P-3	41	27-13 .207
1883	Chi	N	P-2-S-O	66	31-21 .207
1884	Chi	N	P-S-O	63	35-23 .230
1885	Chi	N	P-S	7	5-2 .227
1885	NY	N	P-O	2	1-1 .375
1886	NY	N	O	1	.000
1886	Was	N	P-O	21	0-1 .185
1887	Ind	N	P	3	0-2
			TR	321	173-91 .218

CORCORAN, M.

Yr	Cl	Lea	Pos	G	Rec
1884	Chi	N	P	1	0-1

CORCORAN, MICHAEL JOSEPH
b.Aug.26,1882 Buffalo,N.Y.
d.Dec.9,1950

Yr	Cl	Lea	Pos	G	Rec
1910	Cin	N	3	14	.217
			BRTR		

CORCORAN, THOMAS W. (Corky)
Jan.4,1869. New Haven,Conn.
d.June 25,1960

Yr	Cl	Lea	Pos	G	Rec
1890	Pit	p	S	123	.219
1891	Ath	a	S	132	.252
1892	Bro	N	S	151	.237
1893	Bro	N	S	115	.281
1894	Bro	N	S	129	.302
1895	Bro	N	S	126	.277
1896	Bro	N	S	132	.299
1897	Cin	N	2-S	108	.288
1898	Cin	N	S	153	.244
1899	Cin	N	S	135	.279
1900	Cin	N	S	128	.242
1901	Cin	N	S	30	.184
1902	Cin	N	2-S	137	.251
1903	Cin	N	S	115	.246
1904	Cin	N	S	150	.230
1905	Cin	N	S	151	.248
1906	Cin	N	S	117	.207
1907	NY	N	2	62	.265
			BRTR	2196	.257

COREY, EDWARD N.
b.Apr.10,1900 Chicago,Ill.

Yr	Cl	Lea	Pos	G	Rec
1918	Chi	A	P	1	0-0
			BRTR		

COREY, FREDERICK HARRISON
b.1857 S.Kingston,R.I.
d.Nov.27,1912

Yr	Cl	Lea	Pos	G	Rec
1878	Pro	N	P-1-2	6	1-3 .125

(Continued)

Yr	Cl	Lea	Pos	G	Rec
1880	Wor	N	P-1-S-O	41	9-8 .162
1881	Wor	N	P-S-O	51	6-14 .221
1882	Wor	N	P-1-S-3-O	63	1-15 .247
1883	Ath	a	P-2-S-3-O	71	9-5 .254
1884	Ath	a	3	106	.273
1885	Ath	a	P-3	95	1-0 .252
			BRTR	433	27-45 .245

CORGAN, CHARLES HOWARD
d.Dec.3,1903 Wagoner,Okla.
d.June 13,1928

Yr	Cl	Lea	Pos	G	Rec
1925	Bro	N	S	14	.170
1927	Bro	N	2	19	.263
			BBTR	33	.221

CORHAN, ROY (Irish)
b.Oct.21,1887 Indianapolis,Ind.
d.Nov.24,1958

Yr	Cl	Lea	Pos	G	Rec
1911	Chi	A	S	43	.213
1916	St.L	N	S	92	.210
			BRTR	135	.211

CORKHILL, JOHN STEWART (Pop)
b.Apr.11,1858 Parkesburg,Pa.
d.Apr.4,1921

Yr	Cl	Lea	Pos	G	Rec
1883	Cin	a	2-S-O	86	.222
1884	Cin	a	P-1-S-3-O	111	1-0 .276
1885	Cin	a	P-1-O	112	1-4 .291
1886	Cin	a	P-1-S-O	129	0-0 .283
1887	Cin	a	P-O	127	0-0 .330
1888	Cin	a	P-1-2-O	118	0-0 .271
1888	Bro	a	O	19	.386
1889	Bro	a	O	138	.258
1890	Bro	N	O	51	.225
1891	Ath	a	O	83	.211
1891	Cin	N	O	1	.000
1891	Pit	N	O	41	.231
1892	Pit	N	O	67	.191
			BLTR	1083	2-4 .265

CORRIDEN, JOHN MICHAEL JR.
b.Jan.6,1920 Logansport,Ind.

Yr	Cl	Lea	Pos	G	Rec
1946	Bro	N	H	1	.000
			BLTR		

CORRIDEN, JOHN MICHAEL SR. (Red)
b.Sept.4,1887 Logansport,Ind.
d.Sept.28,1959

Yr	Cl	Lea	Pos	G	Rec
1910	St.L	A	S	26	.155
1912	Det	A	3	38	.203
1913	Chi	N	S	46	.175
1914	Chi	N	S	107	.230
1915	Chi	N	3	6	.000
			BRTR	223	.205

Non-playing manager Chi (A) 1950

CORRIDON, FRANK J. (Fiddler)
b.Nov.25,1880 Newport,R.I.
d.Feb.21,1941

Yr	Cl	Lea	Pos	G	Rec
1904	Chi	N	P	19	5-5
1904	Phi	N	P	12	6-5
1905	Phi	N	P	35	11-13
1907	Phi	N	P	38	17-14
1908	Phi	N	P	27	14-10
1909	Phi	N	P	27	11-7
1910	St.L	N	P	30	6-14
			BRTR	188	70-68

CORRIGAN, ...

Yr	Cl	Lea	Pos	G	Rec
1884	Chi	U	2-O	2	.143

CORTAZZO, JOHN FRANK (Jess)
b.Sept.26,1904 Wilmerding,Pa.

Yr	Cl	Lea	Pos	G	Rec
1923	Chi	A	H	1	.000
			BRTR		

CORWIN, ELMER NATHAN (Al)
b.Dec.3,1926 Newburgh,N.Y.

Yr	Cl	Lea	Pos	G	Rec
1951	NY	N	P	15	5-1
1952	NY	N	P	23	6-1
1953	NY	N	P	54	6-4
1954	NY	N	P	23	1-3
1955	NY	N	P	13	0-1
			BRTR	128	18-10

COSCARART, JOSEPH MARVIN
b.Nov.18,1911 Escondido,Cal.

Yr	Cl	Lea	Pos	G	Rec
1935	Bos	N	2-S-3	86	.236
1936	Bos	N	3	104	.245
			BRTR	190	.241

COSCARART, PETER JOSEPH
b.June 16,1916 Escondido,Cal.

Yr	Cl	Lea	Pos	G	Rec
1938	Bro	N	2	32	.152
1939	Bro	N	2	115	.277
1940	Bro	N	2	143	.237
1941	Bro	N	2-S	43	.127
1942	Pit	N	2-S	133	.228
1943	Pit	N	2-S-3	133	.242
1944	Pit	N	2-S-O	139	.264
1945	Pit	N	2-S	123	.242
1946	Pit	N	S	3	.500
			BRTR	864	.243

COSTELLO, DANIEL FRANCIS
(Dashing Dan)
b.Sept.9,1895 Jessup,Pa.
d.Mar.26,1936

Yr	Cl	Lea	Pos	G	Rec
1913	NY	A	H	2	.500
1914	Pit	N	O	21	.297
1915	Pit	N	O	71	.216
1916	Pit	N	O	60	.239
			BLTR	154	.243

COSTELLO, J. A.
(Real name Kenneth Leland Nash)

COTE, HENRY JOSEPH
b.Dec.20,1864 Troy,N.Y.
d.Apr.28,1940

Yr	Cl	Lea	Pos	G	Rec
1894	Lou	N	C	10	.313
1895	Lou	N	C	10	.265
				20	.288

COTE, WARREN PETER (Pete)
b.Aug.30,1902 Cambridge,Mass.

Yr	Cl	Lea	Pos	G	Rec
1926	NY	N	H	2	.000
			BRTR		

COTTER, EDWARD CHRISTOPHER
b.July 4,1904 Hartford,Conn.
d.June 14,1959

Yr	Cl	Lea	Pos	G	Rec
1926	Phi	N	S-3	17	.308
			BRTR		

COTTER, HARVEY LOUIS (Hooks)
b.May 22,1900 Holden,Mo.
d.Aug.6,1955

Yr	Cl	Lea	Pos	G	Rec
1922	Chi	N	1	1	1.000
1924	Chi	N	1	98	.261
			BLTL	99	.264

COTTER, RICHARD RAPHAEL
b.Oct.23,1890 Manchester,N.H.

Yr	Cl	Lea	Pos	G	Rec
1911	Phi	N	C	17	.283
1912	Chi	N	C	26	.278
			TR	43	.280

COTTER, DANIEL JOSEPH
b.Apr.14,1867 Boston,Mass.
d.Sept.14,1935

Yr	Cl	Lea	Pos	G	Rec
1890	Buf	p	P	1	0-1

COTTER, THOMAS B.
b.Sept.30,1866 Waltham,Mass.
d.Nov.22,1906

Yr	Cl	Lea	Pos	G	Rec
1891	Bos	a	C	5	.273

COTTIER, CHARLES KEITH

b.Jan.8,1936 Delta,Colo.

Yr	Cl	Lea	Pos	G	Rec
1959	Mil	N	2	10	.125
1960	Mil	N	2	95	.227
1961	Det	A	2-S	10	.286
1961	Was	A	2	101	.234
1962	Was	A	2	136	.242
	BRTR			352	.234

COTTRELL, ENSIGN STOVER

b.Aug.29,1888 Hoosick Falls,N.Y.

d.Feb.27,1947

Yr	Cl	Lea	Pos	G	Rec
1911	Pit	N	P	1	0-0
1912	Chi	N	P	1	0-0
1913	Phi	A	P	1	0-0
1914	Bos	N	P	1	0-1
1915	NY	A	P	7	0-1
	BLTL			11	0-2

COUCH, JOHN DANIEL

b.Mar.31,1891 Vaughn,Mont.

Yr	Cl	Lea	Pos	G	Rec
1917	Det	A	P	3	0-0
1922	Cin	N	P	43	16-9
1923	Cin	N	P	19	2-7
1923	Phi	N	P	12	2-4
1924	Phi	N	P	37	4-8
1925	Phi	N	P	34	5-6
	BLTR			148	29-34

COUGHLAN, EDWARD E.

b.Hartford,Conn.

Yr	Cl	Lea	Pos	G	Rec
1884	Buf	N	P-O	2	0-0 / .250

COUGHLIN, DENNIS F.

Yr	Cl	Lea	Pos	G	Rec
1872	Nat	n	2-S-3-O	7	NR

COUGHLIN, WILLIAM E. (Roscoe)

b.Feb.25,1866 Boston,Mass.

d.Mar.20,1951

Yr	Cl	Lea	Pos	G	Rec
1890	Chi	N	P	11	4-7
1891	NY	N	P	8	3-4
	TR			19	7-11

COUGHLIN, WILLIAM PAUL

b.Aug.12,1877 Scranton,Pa.

d.May 7,1943

Yr	Cl	Lea	Pos	G	Rec
1899	Was	N	3	5	.100
1901	Was	A	3	137	.277
1902	Was	A	2-S-3	121	.298
1903	Was	A	3	125	.251
1904	Was	A	3	64	.261
1904	Det	A	3	56	.355
1905	Det	A	3	138	.252
1906	Det	A	3	147	.235
1907	Det	A	3	134	.243
1908	Det	A	3	119	.215
	BRTR			1046	.252

COUGHTRY, JAMES MARLAN

b.Sept.11,1934 Hollywood,Cal.

Yr	Cl	Lea	Pos	G	Rec
1960	Bos	A	2-3	15	.158
1962	LA	A	2-3	11	.182
1962	KC	A	3	6	.182
1962	Cle	A	H	3	.500
	BLTR			35	.185

COULSON, ROBERT JACKSON

b.June 17,1887 Donora,Pa.

d.Sept.11,1953

Yr	Cl	Lea	Pos	G	Rec
1908	Cin	N	O	8	.333
1910	Bro	N	O	25	.247
1911	Bro	N	O	145	.234
1914	Pit	F	O	18	.203
	BRTR			196	.233

COUMBE, FREDERICK NICHOLAS
(Fritz)

b.Dec.13,1891 Antrim,Pa.

Yr	Cl	Lea	Pos	G	Rec
1914	Bos	A	P	14	1-2
1914	Cle	A	P	15	1-5
1915	Cle	A	P	35	4-7
1916	Cle	A	P	31	7-5
1917	Cle	A	P	35	8-6
1918	Cle	A	P	32	13-7
1919	Cle	A	P	8	1-1
1920	Cin	N	P-O	5	0-1 / .231
1921	Cin	N	P	31	3-4
	BLTL			206	38-38 / .199

COURTNEY, CLINTON DAWSON
(Scrap Iron)

b.Mar.16,1927 Hall Summit,La.

Yr	Cl	Lea	Pos	G	Rec
1951	NY	A	C	1	.000
1952	St.L	A	C	119	.286
1953	St.L	A	C	106	.251
1954	Bal	A	C	122	.270
1955	Chi	A	C	19	.378
1955	Was	A	C	75	.298
1956	Was	A	C	101	.300
1957	Was	A	C	91	.267
1958	Was	A	C	134	.251
1959	Was	A	C	72	.233
1960	Bal	A	C	83	.227
1961	KC	A	C	1	.000
1961	Bal	A	C	22	.267
	BLTR			946	.268

COURTNEY, ERNEST E.

b.1879 Des Moines,Ia.

Yr	Cl	Lea	Pos	G	Rec
1902	Bos	N	S-O	40	.212
1902	Bal	A	3	1	.500
1903	NY	A	S	25	.241
1903	Det	A	3	23	.253
1905	Phi	N	3	155	.275
1906	Phi	N	3	112	.236
1907	Phi	N	1-3	130	.243
1908	Phi	N	3	42	.181
	BLTR			528	.245

COURTNEY, HENRY SEYMOUR

b.Nov.19,1898 Asheville,N.C.

Yr	Cl	Lea	Pos	G	Rec
1919	Was	A	P	4	3-0
1920	Was	A	P	37	8-11
1921	Was	A	P	32	6-9
1922	Was	A	P	5	0-1
1922	Chi	A	P	18	5-6
	BLTL			96	22-27

COUSINEAU, EDWARD THOMAS

b.Dec.16,1899 Watertown,Mass.

d.July 14,1951

Yr	Cl	Lea	Pos	G	Rec
1923	Bos	N	C	1	1.000
1924	Bos	N	C	3	.000
1925	Bos	N	C	1	.000
	BRTR			5	.500

COVELESKI, HARRY FRANK
(Giant Killer)
(Real name
Harry Frank Kowalewski)

b.Apr.23,1886 Shamokin,Pa.

d.Aug.4,1950

Yr	Cl	Lea	Pos	G	Rec
1907	Phi	N	P	4	1-0
1908	Phi	N	P	6	4-1
1909	Phi	N	P	24	6-10
1910	Cin	N	P	7	1-1
1914	Det	A	P	42	22-12
1915	Det	A	P	50	23-13
1916	Det	A	P	44	21-10
1917	Det	A	P	16	4-6
1918	Det	A	P	3	0-1
	BBTL			196	82-54

COVELESKI, STANLEY ANTHONY
(Real name Stanislaus Kowalewski)

b.July 13,1890 Shamokin,Pa.

Yr	Cl	Lea	Pos	G	Rec
1912	Phi	A	P	3	2-1
1916	Cle	A	P	44	15-12
1917	Cle	A	P	46	19-14
1918	Cle	A	P	38	22-13
1919	Cle	A	P	43	24-12
1920	Cle	A	P	41	24-14
1921	Cle	A	P	43	23-13
1922	Cle	A	P	35	17-14
1923	Cle	A	P	33	13-14
1924	Cle	A	P	37	15-16
1925	Was	A	P	32	20-5
1926	Was	A	P	36	14-11
1927	Was	A	P	5	2-1
1928	NY	A	P	12	5-1
	BRTR			448	215-141

COVENEY, JOHN PATRICK

b.1880 S.Natick,Mass.

Yr	Cl	Lea	Pos	G	Rec
1903	st.L	N	C	3	.200
	TR				

COVINGTON, CHESTER ROGER
(Lefty)

b.Nov.6,1910 Cairo,Ill.

Yr	Cl	Lea	Pos	G	Rec
1944	Phi	N	P	19	1-1
	BBTL				

COVINGTON, CLARENCE CALVERT (Tex)

b.Nov.18,1894 Denison,Tex

d.Jan.4,1963

Yr	Cl	Lea	Pos	G	Rec
1913	St.L	A	1	20	.150
1917	Bos	N	1	17	.197
1918	Bos	N	O	3	.333
	BLTR			40	.178

COVINGTON, JOHN WESLEY

b.Mar.27,1932 Laurinburg,N.C.

Yr	Cl	Lea	Pos	G	Rec
1956	Mil	N	O	75	.283
1957	Mil	N	O	96	.284
1958	Mil	N	O	90	.330
1959	Mil	N	O	103	.279
1960	Mil	N	O	95	.249
1961	Mil	N	O	9	.190
1961	Chi	A	O	22	.288
1961	KC	A	O	17	.159
1961	Phi	N	O	57	.303
1962	Phi	N	O	116	.283
	BLTR			680	.283

COVINGTON, WILLIAM WILKES

b.Mar.19,1887 Henryville,Tenn.

d.Dec.10,1931

Yr	Cl	Lea	Pos	G	Rec
1911	Det	A	P	17	7-1
1912	Det	A	P	9	3-4
	BLTR			26	10-5

COX, ELMER JOSEPH (Dick)

b.Sept.30,1897 Pasadena,Cal.

Yr	Cl	Lea	Pos	G	Rec
1925	Bro	N	O	122	.329
1926	Bro	N	O	124	.296
	BRTR			246	.314

COX, ERNEST THOMPSON

b.Feb.19,1894 Birmingham,Ala.

Yr	Cl	Lea	Pos	G	Rec
1922	Chi	A	P	1	0-0
	BLTR				

COX, FRANK BERNHARDT (Runt)

b.Mar.17,1858 Waltham,Mass.

d.1928

Yr	Cl	Lea	Pos	G	Rec
1884	Det	N	S	27	.127

COX, GEORGE MELVIN

b.Nov.15,1904 Sherman,Tex.

Yr	Cl	Lea	Pos	G	Rec
1928	Chi	A	P	26	1-2
	BRTR				

COX, GLENN MELVIN

b.Feb.3,1931 Montebello,Cal.

Yr	Cl	Lea	Pos	G	Rec
1955	KC	A	P	2	0-2
1956	KC	A	P	3	0-2
1957	KC	A	P	10	1-0
1958	KC	A	P	2	0-0
	BRTR			17	1-4

COX, LESLIE WARREN

b.Aug.14,1905 Junction,Tex.

d.Oct.12,1934

Yr	Cl	Lea	Pos	G	Rec
1926	Chi	A	P	2	0-1
	BRTR				

COX, PLATEAU REX
b.Feb.16,1896 Hencher,N.C.

Yr	Cl	Lea	Pos	G	Rec
1920	Det	A	P	3	0-0
	BLTR				

COX, WILLIAM DONALD
b.June 23,1913 Ashmore,Ill.

Yr	Cl	Lea	Pos	G	Rec
1936	St.L	N	P	2	0-0
1937	Chi	A	P	3	1-0
1938	Chi	A	P	7	0-2
1938	St.L	A	P	24	1-4
1939	St.L	A	P	4	0-2
1940	St.L	A	P	13	0-1
	BRTR			53	2-9

COX, WILLIAM RICHARD
b.Aug.29,1919 Newport,Pa.

Yr	Cl	Lea	Pos	G	Rec
1941	Pit	N	S	10	.270
1946	Pit	N	S	121	.290
1947	Pit	N	S	132	.274
1948	Bro	N	2-S-3	88	.249
1949	Bro	N	3	100	.234
1950	Bro	N	2-S-3	119	.257
1951	Bro	N	S-3	142	.279
1952	Bro	N	2-S-3	116	.259
1953	Bro	N	2-S-3	100	.291
1954	Bro	N	2-S-3	77	.235
1955	Bal	A	2-S-3	53	.211
	BRTR			1058	.262

COYLE, WILLIAM CLAUDE
b.pittsburgh,Pa.

Yr	Cl	Lea	Pos	G	Rec
1893	Bos	N	P	1	0-1
	TR				

COYNE, ...

Yr	Cl	Lea	Pos	G	Rec
1914	Phi	A	3	1	.000
	TR				

COZART, CHARLES RHUBIN
b.Oct.17,1919 Lenoir,N.C.

Yr	Cl	Lea	Pos	G	Rec
1945	Bos	N	P	5	1-0
	BRTL				

CRABB, JAMES ROY
b.Aug.23,1890 Monticello,Ia.
d.Mar.30,1940

Yr	Cl	Lea	Pos	G	Rec
1912	Chi	A	P	2	0-0
1912	Phi	A	P	7	2-5
	BRTR			9	2-5

CRABLE, GEORGE E.
b.1886 Brooklyn,N.Y.

Yr	Cl	Lea	Pos	G	Rec
1910	Bro	N	P	2	0-0
	BLTL				

CRABTREE, C. C.
(Played under name of
Charles E. McDonald)

CRABTREE, ESTEL CRAYTON
b.Aug.19,1903 Crabtree,O.

Yr	Cl	Lea	Pos	G	Rec
1929	Cin	N	H	1	.000
1931	Cin	N	1-3-O	117	.269
1932	Cin	N	O	108	.274
1933	St.L	N	O	23	.265
1941	St.L	N	3-O	77	.341
1942	St.L	N	H	10	.333
1943	Cin	N	O	95	.276
1944	Cin	N	1-O	58	.286
	BLTR			489	.281

CRADDOCK, WALTER ANDERSON
b.Mar.25,1932 Pax,W.Va.

Yr	Cl	Lea	Pos	G	Rec
1955	KC	A	P	4	0-2
1956	KC	A	P	2	0-2
1958	KC	A	P	23	0-3
	BRTL			29	0-7

CRAFT, HARRY FRANCIS (Wildfire)
b.Apr.19,1915 Ellisville,Miss.

Yr	Cl	Lea	Pos	G	Rec
1937	Cin	N	O	10	.310
(Continued)					
1938	Cin	N	O	151	.270
1939	Cin	N	O	134	.257
1940	Cin	N	1-O	115	.244
1941	Cin	N	O	119	.249
1942	Cin	N	O	37	.177
	BRTR			566	.253

Non-Playing Manager KC(A)1957-59, Chi(N) 1961 and Hou(N)1962.

CRAFT, MAURICE M. (Mollie)
b.Nov.28,1896 Norfolk,Va.

Yr	Cl	Lea	Pos	G	Rec
1916	Was	A	P	3	0-1
1917	Was	A	P	8	0-0
1918	Was	A	P	3	0-0
1919	Was	A	P	16	0-3
	BRTR			30	0-4

CRAGHEAD, HOWARD OLIVER
b.May 25,1908 Fresno,Cal.

Yr	Cl	Lea	Pos	G	Rec
1931	Cle	A	P	4	0-0
1933	Cle	A	P	11	0-0
	BRTR			15	0-0

CRAIG, GEORGE McCARTHY
(Lefty)
b.Nov.15.1887 Philadelphia.Pa.
d.Apr.23,1911

Yr	Cl	Lea	Pos	G	Rec
1907	Phi	A	P	2	0-0
	TL				

CRAIG, ROGER LEE
b.Feb.17,1931 Durham,N.C.

Yr	Cl	Lea	Pos	G	Rec
1955	Bro	N	P	21	5-3
1956	Bro	N	P	35	12-11
1957	Bro	N	P	32	6-9
1958	LA	N	P	9	2-1
1959	LA	N	P	29	11-5
1960	LA	N	P	21	8-3
1961	LA	N	P	40	5-6
1962	NY	N	P	42	10-24
	BRTR			229	59-62

CRAMER, ROGER MAXWELL (Doc)
b.July 22,1906 Beach Haven,N.J.

Yr	Cl	Lea	Pos	G	Rec
1929	Phi	A	O	2	.000
1930	Phi	A	O	30	.232
1931	Phi	A	O	65	.260
1932	Phi	A	O	92	.336
1933	Phi	A	O	152	.295
1934	Phi	A	O	153	.311
1935	Phi	A	O	149	.332
1936	Bos	A	O	154	.292
1937	Bos	A	O	133	.305
1938	Bos	A	P-O	148	0-0 .301
1939	Bos	A	O	137	.311
1940	Bos	A	O	150	.303
1941	Was	A	O	154	.273
1942	Det	A	O	151	.263
1943	Det	A	O	140	.300
1944	Det	A	O	143	.292
1945	Det	A	O	141	.275
1946	Det	A	O	68	.294
1947	Det	A	O	73	.268
1948	Det	A	O	4	.000
	BLTR			2239	0-0 .296

CRAMER, WILLIAM B.
b.Brooklyn,N.Y.
d.Aug.12,1885

Yr	Cl	Lea	Pos	G	Rec
1883	NY	N	O	2	.125

CRAMER, WILLIAM WENDELL
b.1891 Bedford,Ind.

Yr	Cl	Lea	Pos	G	Rec
1912	Cin	N	P	1	0-0
	BRTR				

CRANDALL, DELMAR WESLEY
b.Mar.5,1930 Ontario,Cal.

Yr	Cl	Lea	Pos	G	Rec
1949	Bos	N	C	67	.263
1950	Bos	N	C-1	79	.220
1953	Mil	N	C	116	.272
(Continued)					
1954	Mil	N	C	138	.242
1955	Mil	N	C	133	.236
1956	Mil	N	C	112	.238
1957	Mil	N	C-1-O	118	.253
1958	Mil	N	C	131	.272
1959	Mil	N	C	150	.257
1960	Mil	N	C	142	.294
1961	Mil	N	C	15	.200
1962	Mil	N	C-1	107	.297
	BRTR			1308	.260

CRANDALL, JAMES OTIS (Doc)
b.Oct.8,1887 Wadena,Ind.
d.Aug.17,1951

Yr	Cl	Lea	Pos	G	Rec
1908	NY	N	P	32	12-12
1909	NY	N	P	30	6-4
1910	NY	N	P	43	17-4
1911	NY	N	P	50	15-5
1912	NY	N	P	50	13-7
1913	NY	N	P	31	4-4
1913	St.L	N	P	2	0-0
1913	NY	N	P	15	0-0
1914	St.L	F	P-2	115	12-9 .312
1915	St.L	F	P	81	21-15
1916	St.L	A	P	16	0-0
1918	Bos	N	P	14	1-2
	BRTR			479	101-62 .286

CRANE, EDWARD NICHOLAS
(Cannon-Ball)
b.May 1864 S.Boston,Mass.
d.Sept.19,1896

Yr	Cl	Lea	Pos	G	Rec
1884	Bos	U	P-C-O	99	0-2 .304
1885	Pro	N	P-O	1	0-0 .000
1885	Buf	N	O	13	.269
1886	Was	N	P-O	80	2-6 .171
1888	NY	N	P	12	5-6
1889	NY	N	P	28	14-10
1890	NY	p	P	44	16-23
1891	Cin	a	P-O	34	14-17 .145
1891	Cin	N	P	14	2-10
1892	NY	N	P	40	14-26
1893	NY	N	P	10	2-4
1893	Bro	N	P	3	0-2
	BRTR			378	69-106 .236

CRANE, SAMUEL BYREN (Lucky)
b.Sept.13,1894 Harrisburg,Pa
d.Nov.12,1955

Yr	Cl	Lea	Pos	G	Rec
1914	Phi	A	S	2	.000
1915	Phi	A	S	8	.087
1916	Phi	A	S	2	.250
1917	Was	A	S	32	.179
1920	Cin	N	2-S-3-O	54	.215
1921	Cin	N	S	73	.233
1922	Bro	N	S	3	.250
	BRTR			174	.208

CRANE, SAMUEL NEWHALL
b.Jan.2,1854 Springfield,Mass.
d.June 26,1925

Yr	Cl	Lea	Pos	G	Rec
1873	Res	n	2	1	NR
1875	Atl	n	1-O	21	NR
1880	Buf	N	M-2-O	10	.125
1883	Met	a	2-O	97	.234
1884	Cin	U	M-2	68	.231
1885	Det	N	2	68	.191
1886	Det	N	2	49	.139
1886	St.L	N	2	37	.175
1887	Was	N	2	7	.312
1890	NY	N	1-O	2	.000
1890	Pit	N	2-S	22	.200
1890	NY	N	2	2	.000
	BRTR			384	NR

CRAUSE, CLARENCE
(Played under name of
Clarence Cross)

CRAVATH, CLIFFORD CARLTON
(Gavvy)
b.Mar.23,1881 San Diego,Cal.

Yr	Cl	Lea	Pos	G	Rec
1908	Bos	A	O	94	.256
1909	Chi	A	O	18	.061
1909	Was	A	O	4	1.000
1912	Phi	N	O	130	.284
1913	Phi	N	O	147	.341
1914	Phi	N	O	149	.298
1915	Phi	N	O	150	.285
1916	Phi	N	O	137	.283
1917	Phi	N	O	140	.280
1918	Phi	N	O	121	.232
1919	Phi	N	M-O	83	.341
1920	Phi	N	M-O	46	.289
	BRTR			1219	.287

CRAVER, WILLIAM H.
b.1844 Troy,N.Y.
d.June 17,1901

Yr	Cl	Lea	Pos	G	Rec
1871	Tro	n	M-C-1-2-S	27	.303
1872	Bal	n	C-1-2-3-O	34	.343
1873	Bal	n	C-1-2-S-O	38	NR
1874	Phi	n	M-C-2	55	NR
1875	Cen	n	M-1-2-S-3	14	NR
1875	Ath	n	C-2	55	.314
1876	Mut	N	C-2	56	.222
1877	Lou	N	S	57	.263
	BRTR			336	NR

CRAWFORD, CHARLES LOWRIE
(Larry)
b.Apr.27,1914 Swissvale,Pa.

Yr	Cl	Lea	Pos	G	Rec
1937	Phi	N	P	6	0-0
	BLTL				

CRAWFORD, CLIFFORD RANKIN
(Pat)
b.Jan.28,1902 Society Hill,S.C.

Yr	Cl	Lea	Pos	G	Rec
1929	NY	N	1	65	.298
1930	NY	N	1-2	25	.276
1930	Cin	N	1-2	76	.290
1933	St.L	N	1-2-3	91	.268
1934	St.L	N	2-3	61	.271
	BLTR			318	.280

CRAWFORD, FORREST A.
b.May 10,1881 Rockdale,Tex.
d.Mar.27,1908

Yr	Cl	Lea	Pos	G	Rec
1906	St.L	N	S	45	.207
1907	St.L	N	S	7	.227
	TR			52	.210

CRAWFORD, GEORGE

Yr	Cl	Lea	Pos	G	Rec
1890	Ath	a	O	5	.111

CRAWFORD, GLENN MARTIN
b.Dec.2,1918 North Branch,Mich.

Yr	Cl	Lea	Pos	G	Rec
1945	St.L	N	O	4	.000
1945	Phi	N	2-S-O	82	.295
1946	Phi	N	H	1	.000
	BLTR			87	.291

CRAWFORD, KENNETH
b.Pittsburgh,Pa.

Yr	Cl	Lea	Pos	G	Rec
1915	Bal	F	1-O	23	.244

CRAWFORD, RUFUS (Jake)
b.Mar.30,1928 Campbell,Mo.

Yr	Cl	Lea	Pos	G	Rec
1952	St.L	A	O	7	.182
	BRTR				

CRAWFORD, SAMUEL EARL
(Wahoo Sam)
b.Apr.18,1880 Wahoo,Neb.

Yr	Cl	Lea	Pos	G	Rec
1899	Cin	N	O	31	.308
1900	Cin	N	O	96	.270
1901	Cin	N	O	124	.334
1902	Cin	N	O	140	.333
1903	Det	A	O	137	.332
1904	Det	A	O	150	.247
1905	Det	A	1-O	154	.297
1906	Det	A	1-O	145	.295
1907	Det	A	O	144	.323

(Continued)

Yr	Cl	Lea	Pos	G	Rec
1908	Det	A	1-O	152	.311
1909	Det	A	1-O	156	.314
1910	Det	A	O	154	.289
1911	Det	A	O	146	.378
1912	Det	A	O	149	.325
1913	Det	A	1-O	153	.316
1914	Det	A	O	157	.314
1915	Det	A	O	156	.299
1916	Det	A	O	100	.286
1917	Det	A	1-O	61	.173
	BLTL			2505	.309

CREAMER, GEORGE W.
(Real name George W. Triebel)
b.1855 Philadelphia,Pa.
d.June 27,1886

Yr	Cl	Lea	Pos	G	Rec
1878	Mil	N	2-O	50	.212
1879	Syr	N	2-S-O	15	.213
1880	Wor	N	2	83	.202
1881	Wor	N	2	79	.209
1882	Wor	N	2	81	.228
1883	Pit	a	2	89	.243
1884	Pit	a	M-2	100	.185
	BRTR			497	.216

CREE, WILLIAM FRANKLIN
(Birdie)
b.Oct.23,1882 Khedive,Pa.
d.Nov.8,1942

Yr	Cl	Lea	Pos	G	Rec
1908	NY	A	O	21	.269
1909	NY	A	O	104	.262
1910	NY	A	O	134	.287
1911	NY	A	O	137	.348
1912	NY	A	O	50	.332
1913	NY	A	O	147	.271
1914	NY	A	O	77	.309
1915	NY	A	O	74	.214
	BRTR			744	.292

CREEDEN, PATRICK FRANCIS
b.May 23,1907 Newburyport,Mass.

Yr	Cl	Lea	Pos	G	Rec
1931	Bos	A	2	5	.000
	BLTR				

CREEDON, CORNELIUS STEPHEN
b.July 21,1915 Danvers,Mass.

Yr	Cl	Lea	Pos	G	Rec
1943	Bos	N	H	5	.250
	BBTL				

CREEGAN, MARTIN
b.San Francisco,Cal.

Yr	Cl	Lea	Pos	G	Rec
1884	Was	U	C-1-3-O	9	.152

CREEL, JACK DALTON (Tex)
b.Apr.23,1917 Kyle,Tex

Yr	Cl	Lea	Pos	G	Rec
1945	St.L	N	P	35	5-4
	BRTR				

CREELY, AUGUST
b.St.Louis,Mo.

Yr	Cl	Lea	Pos	G	Rec
1890	St.L	a	S	4	.000

CREGAN, PETER (Peekskill Pete)

Yr	Cl	Lea	Pos	G	Rec
1899	NY	N	O	1	.000
1903	Cin	N	O	6	.111
	BRTR			7	.095

CREGER, BERNARD ODELL
b.Mar.21,1927 Wytheville,Va.

Yr	Cl	Lea	Pos	G	Rec
1947	St.L	N	S	15	.188
	BRTR				

CREMINS, ROBERT ANTHONY
b.Feb.15,1906 Pelham Manor,N.Y.

Yr	Cl	Lea	Pos	G	Rec
1927	Bos	A	P	4	0-0
	BLTL				

CRESPI, FRANK ANGELO JOSEPH
(Creepy)
b.Feb.16,1918 St.Louis,Mo.

Yr	Cl	Lea	Pos	G	Rec
1938	St.L	N	S	7	.263
1939	St.L	N	H	15	.172
1940	St.L	N	S-3	3	.273
1941	St.L	N	2	146	.279
1942	St.L	N	2-S	93	.243
	BRTR			264	.263

CRESS, WALKER JAMES
b.Mar.6,1918 Ben Hur,Va.

Yr	Cl	Lea	Pos	G	Rec
1948	Cin	N	P	31	0-1
1949	Cin	N	P	3	0-0
	BRTR			34	0-1

CRIGER, LOUIS
b.Feb.6,1872 Elkhart,Ind.
d.May 14,1934

Yr	Cl	Lea	Pos	G	Rec
1896	Cle	N	C	2	.000
1897	Cle	N	C	38	.230
1898	Cle	N	C	81	.273
1899	St.L	N	C	75	.256
1900	St.L	N	C	76	.266
1901	Bos	A	C	69	.240
1902	Bos	A	C-O	86	.259
1903	Bos	A	C	96	.197
1904	Bos	A	C	98	.217
1905	Bos	A	C	109	.198
1906	Bos	A	C	6	.214
1907	Bos	A	C	75	.181
1908	Bos	A	C	84	.190
1909	St.L	A	C	74	.170
1910	NY	A	C	27	.189
1912	St.L	A	C	1	.000
	BRTR			997	.223

CRIMIAN, JOHN MELVIN
b.Feb.17,1926 Philadelphia,Pa.

Yr	Cl	Lea	Pos	G	Rec
1951	St.L	N	P	11	1-0
1952	St.L	N	P	5	0-0
1956	KC	A	P	55	4-8
1957	Det	A	P	4	0-1
	BRTR			75	5-9

CRISCOLA, ANTHONY PAUL
b.July 9,1915 Walla Walla,Wash.

Yr	Cl	Lea	Pos	G	Rec
1942	St.L	A	O	91	.297
1943	St.L	A	O	29	.154
1944	Cin	N	O	64	.229
	BLTR			184	.248

CRISHAM, PATRICK LEWIS
b.June 4,1877 Amesbury,Mass.
d.June 12,1915

Yr	Cl	Lea	Pos	G	Rec
1899	Bal	N	1	44	.303

CRISP, JOSEPH SHELBY
b.July 8,1889 Higginsville,Mo.
d.Feb.5,1939

Yr	Cl	Lea	Pos	G	Rec
1910	St.L	A	C	1	.000
1911	St.L	A	C	1	1.000
	BRTR			2	.500

CRISS, DODE
b.Mar.12,1885 Sherman,Miss.
d.Sept.8,1955

Yr	Cl	Lea	Pos	G	Rec
1908	St.L	A	P-O	64	0-1 .341
1909	St.L	A	P	35	1-4
1910	St.L	A	P-O	70	2-1 .231
1911	St.L	A	P-O	58	0-2 .253
	BLTR			227	3-8 .276

CRISS, HARRY
(Played under name of Hugh I. Daly)

CRIST, CHESTER A.
b.Madisonville,O.

Yr	Cl	Lea	Pos	G	Rec
1906	Phi	N	C	5	.000
	TR				

CRISTALL, WILLIAM A.
b.Sept.12,1878 Buffalo,N.Y.
d.Jan.29,1939

Yr	Cl	Lea	Pos	G	Rec
1901	Cle	A	P	6	1-4
	TR				

CRISTANTE, LEO DANTE
b.Dec.10,1926 Detroit,Mich.

Yr	Cl	Lea	Pos	G	Rec
1951	Phi	N	P	10	1-1
1955	Det	A	P	20	0-1
	BRTR			30	1-2

CRITCHLEY, MORRIS A.

b.Pittsburgh,Pa.

d.Mar.7,1910

Yr	Cl	Lea	Pos	G	Rec
1882	Pit	a	P	1	1-0
1882	St.L	a	P	4	0-3
				5	1-3

CRITZ, HUGH MELVILLE

b.Sept.17,1900 Starkville,Miss.

Yr	Cl	Lea	Pos	G	Rec
1924	Cin	N	2-S	102	.322
1925	Cin	N	2	144	.277
1926	Cin	N	2	155	.270
1927	Cin	N	2	113	.278
1928	Cin	N	2	153	.296
1929	Cin	N	2-S	107	.247
1930	Cin	N	2	28	.231
1930	NY	N	2	124	.265
1931	NY	N	2	66	.290
1932	NY	N	2	151	.276
1933	NY	N	2	133	.246
1934	NY	N	2	137	.242
1935	NY	N	2	65	.187
		BRTR		1478	.268

CROCKER, CLAUDE ARTHUR

b.July 20,1925 Caroleen,N.C.

Yr	Cl	Lea	Pos	G	Rec
1944	Bro	N	P	2	0-0
1945	Bro	N	P	1	0-0
		BRTR		3	0-0

CROCKETT, DANIEL SOLOMON

b.Oct.5,1875 Lammoor,Va.

d.Feb.23,1961

Yr	Cl	Lea	Pos	G	Rec
1901	Det	A	1	28	.291

CROFT, ARTHUR F.

b.Jan.23,1855 St.Louis,Mo.

d.Mar.16,1884

Yr	Cl	Lea	Pos	G	Rec
1875	RS	n	O	19	NR
1877	St.L	N	1-2-O	54	.233
1878	Ind	N	1-O	57	.162
				130	NR

CROFT, HENRY T.

b.Chicago,Ill.

Yr	Cl	Lea	Pos	G	Rec
1899	Lou	N	O	1	.000
1899	Phi	N	2	2	.143
1901	Chi	N	O	3	.333
				6	.250

CROLIUS, FRED JOSEPH

b.Dec.16,1876 Jersey City,N.J.

d.Aug.25,1960

Yr	Cl	Lea	Pos	G	Rec
1901	Bos	N	O	50	.238
1902	Pit	N	O	9	.263
				59	.239

CROMPTON, EDWARD

b.Feb.12,1889 Liverpool,England

d.Sept.28,1930

Yr	Cl	Lea	Pos	G	Rec
1909	St.L	A	O	17	.157
1910	Cin	N	O	1	.000
		BLTL		18	.154

CROMPTON, HERBERT BRYAN

b.Nov.7,1912 Milan,Ill.

Yr	Cl	Lea	Pos	G	Rec
1937	Was	A	C	2	.333
1945	NY	A	C	36	.192
		BRTR		38	.196

CRONE, RAYMOND HAYES

b.Aug.7,1931 Memphis,Tenn.

Yr	Cl	Lea	Pos	G	Rec
1954	Mil	N	P	19	1-0
1955	Mil	N	P	33	10-9
1956	Mil	N	P	35	11-10
1957	Mil	N	P	11	3-1
1957	NY	N	P	25	4-8
1958	SF	N	P	14	1-2
		BRTR		137	30-30

CRONIN, DANIEL

b.1857 S.Boston,Mass.

d.Nov.30,1885

(Continued)

Yr	Cl	Lea	Pos	G	Rec
1884	Chi	U	2	1	.250
1884	KC	U	O	1	.000
				2	.111

CRONIN, JAMES JOHN

b.Aug.7,1906 Richmond,Cal.

Yr	Cl	Lea	Pos	G	Rec
1929	Phi	A	2	25	.232
	BBTR				

CRONIN, JOHN J.

b.May 26,1874 W.New Brighton,S.I., N.Y.

d.July 12,1929

Yr	Cl	Lea	Pos	G	Rec
1895	Bro	N	P	2	0-0
1898	Pit	N	P	4	2-2
1899	Cin	N	P	5	2-2
1901	Det	A	P	31	12-16
1902	Det	A	P	4	1-0
1902	Bal	A	P	9	2-5
1902	NY	N	P-O	19	5-6 .167
1903	NY	N	P	20	6-4
1904	Bro	N	P	40	11-22
		BRTR		134	41-57 .181

CRONIN, JOSEPH EDWARD

b.Oct.12,1906 San Francisco,Cal.

Yr	Cl	Lea	Pos	G	Rec
1926	Pit	N	2-S	38	.265
1927	Pit	N	S	12	.227
1928	Was	A	S	63	.243
1929	Was	A	S	145	.282
1930	Was	A	S	154	.346
1931	Was	A	S	156	.306
1932	Was	A	S	143	.318
1933	Was	A	M-S	152	.309
1934	Was	A	M-S	127	.284
1935	Bos	A	M-1-S	144	.295
1936	Bos	A	M-S-3	81	.281
1937	Bos	A	M-S	148	.307
1938	Bos	A	M-S	143	.325
1939	Bos	A	M-S	143	.308
1940	Bos	A	M-S-3	149	.285
1941	Bos	A	M-S-3-O	143	.311
1942	Bos	A	M-1-S-3	45	.304
1943	Bos	A	M-3	59	.312
1944	Bos	A	M-1	76	.241
1945	Bos	A	M-3	3	.375
		BRTR		2124	.302

Non-playing manager Bos (A) 1946-47

CRONIN, WILLIAM PATRICK

b.Dec.26,1902 West Newton,Mass.

Yr	Cl	Lea	Pos	G	Rec
1928	Bos	N	C	3	.000
1929	Bos	N	C	6	.111
1930	Bos	N	C	66	.253
1931	Bos	N	C	51	.206
		BRTR		126	.232

CROOKS, JOHN CHARLES

b.Nov.9,1866 St.Paul,Minn.

d.Jan.29,1918

Yr	Cl	Lea	Pos	G	Rec
1889	Col	a	2	12	.323
1890	Col	a	2	135	.221
1891	Col	a	2	138	.240
1892	St.L	N	2-3	127	.213
1893	St.L	N	3	128	.251
1895	Was	N	2	118	.291
1896	Was	N	2-3	24	.280
1896	Lou	N	2	37	.232
1898	St.L	N	2	71	.238
				790	.244

CROOKS, THOMAS

b.Washington,D.C.

Yr	Cl	Lea	Pos	G	Rec
1909	Was	A	1	3	.286
1910	Was	A	1	8	.182
		TR		11	.207

CROSBY, GEORGE W.

b.Chicago,Ill.

Yr	Cl	Lea	Pos	G	Rec
1884	Chi	N	P	3	1-2

CROSETTI, FRANK PETER JOSEPH (Crow)

b.Oct.4,1910 San Francisco,Cal.

Yr	Cl	Lea	Pos	G	Rec
1932	NY	A	S-3	115	.241
1933	NY	A	S	136	.253
1934	NY	A	S-3	138	.265
1935	NY	A	S	87	.256
1936	NY	A	S	151	.288
1937	NY	A	S	149	.234
1938	NY	A	S	157	.263
1939	NY	A	S	152	.233
1940	NY	A	S	145	.194
1941	NY	A	S-3	50	.223
1942	NY	A	2-S-3	74	.242
1943	NY	A	S	95	.233
1944	NY	A	S	55	.239
1945	NY	A	S	130	.238
1946	NY	A	S	28	.288
1947	NY	A	2-S	3	.000
1948	NY	A	2-S	17	.286
		BRTR		1682	.245

CROSS, AMOS C.

b.1861 Czechoslovakia

d.July 16,1888

Yr	Cl	Lea	Pos	G	Rec
1885	Lou	a	C	35	.295
1886	Lou	a	C-1	74	.276
1887	Lou	a	C	9	.257
				118	.280

CROSS, CLARENCE

(Real name Clarence Crause)

b.Mar.4,1856 St.Louis,Mo.

d.June 23,1931

Yr	Cl	Lea	Pos	G	Rec
1884	Alt	U	3	2	.572
1884	Key	U	S	2	.143
1884	KC	U	S	25	.212
1887	Met	a	S	16	.245
				45	.222

CROSS, FRANK A.

b.Cleveland,O.

Yr	Cl	Lea	Pos	G	Rec
1901	Cle	A	O	1	.600
		TR			

CROSS, GEORGE LEWIS (Lem)

b.Jan.9,1872 Manchester,N.H.

d.Apr.5,1929

Yr	Cl	Lea	Pos	G	Rec
1893	Cin	N	P	2	0-2
1894	Cin	N	P	9	2-4
				11	2-6

CROSS, JOFFRE JAMES (Jeff)

b.Aug.28,1918 Tulsa,Okla.

Yr	Cl	Lea	Pos	G	Rec
1942	St.L	N	S	1	.250
1946	St.L	N	2-S-3	49	.217
1947	St.L	N	2-S-3	51	.102
1948	St.L	N	H	2	.000
1948	Chi	N	2-S	16	.100
		BRTR		119	.162

CROSS, LAFAYETTE NAPOLEON (Lave)

b.May 11,1867 Milwaukee,Wis.

d.Sept.4,1927

Yr	Cl	Lea	Pos	G	Rec
1887	Lou	a	C	54	.327
1888	Lou	a	C	47	.213
1889	Ath	a	C	55	.226
1890	Phi	p	C	60	.299
1891	Ath	a	C-3-O	109	.302
1892	Phi	N	C-3-O	134	.262
1893	Phi	N	C-3	94	.302
1894	Phi	N	3	120	.388
1895	Phi	N	3	124	.277
1896	Phi	N	S-3	106	.261
1897	Phi	N	2-3	88	.261
1898	St.L	N	3	151	.319
1899	Cle	N	M-3	38	.263
1899	St.L	N	3	103	.304
1900	St.L	N	3	16	.300
1900	Bro	N	3	117	.292
1901	Phi	A	3	100	.331
1902	Phi	A	3	137	.339
1903	Phi	A	3	137	.292
1904	Phi	A	3	155	.290
1905	Phi	A	3	146	.266
1906	Was	A	3	130	.263
1907	Was	A	3	41	.199
		BRTR		2262	.293

Yr Cl Lea Pos G Rec

CROSS, MONTFORD MONTGOMERY
b.Aug.31,1869 Philadelphia,Pa.
d.June 21,1934
1892 Bal N S 15 .160
1894 Pit N S 13 .404
1895 Pit N S 108 .255
1896 St.L N S 124 .264
1897 St.L N S 130 .288
1898 Phi N S 149 .259
1899 Phi N S 153 .259
1900 Phi N S 130 .200
1901 Phi N S 139 .197
1902 Phi A S 137 .207
1903 Phi A S 138 .245
1904 Phi A S 153 .182
1905 Phi A S 78 .270
1906 Phi A S 134 .200
1907 Phi A S 77 .206
BRTR 1678 .233

CROSSIN, FRANK PATRICK
b.June 15,1891 Luzerne,Pa.
1912 St.L A C 7 .277
1913 St.L A C 3 .333
1914 St.L A C 43 .122
BRTR 53 .147

CROTHERS, DOUGLAS
b.St.Louis,Mo.
1884 KC U P 3 1-2
1885 Met a P 18 7-11
21 8-13

CROTTY, JOSEPH
b.Cincinnati,O.
1882 Lou a C 5 .100
1882 St.L a C-O 8 .133
1884 Cin U C 20 .287
1885 Lou a C 39 .172
1886 Met a C 12 .205
BR 84 .199

CROUCH, JACK ALBERT (Roxy)
b.Oct.12,1903 Salisbury,N.C.
1930 St.L A C 6 .143
1931 St.L A C 8 .000
1933 St.L A C 19 .167
1933 Cin N C 10 .125
BRTR 43 .125

CROUCH, WILLIAM ELMER
b.Aug.20,1910 Wilmington,Del.
1939 Bro N P 6 4-0
1941 Phi N P 20 2-3
1941 St.L N P 18 1-2
1945 St.L N P 6 1-0
BBTR 50 8-5

CROUCH, WILLIAM HENRY (Skip)
b.Dec.3,1886 Marshallton,Del.
d.Dec.22,1945
1910 St.L A P 1 0-0

CROUCHER, FRANK DONALD
(Dingle)
b.July 23,1914 San Antonio,Tex.
1939 Det A S 97 .269
1940 Det A 2-S-3 37 .105
1941 Det A S 136 .254
1942 Was A 2 26 .277
BRTR 296 .251

CROUSE, CLYDE ELLSWORTH
(Buck)
b.Jan.6,1897 Muncie,Ind.
1923 Chi A C 23 .257
1924 Chi A C 94 .259
1925 Chi A C 54 .352

Yr Cl Lea Pos G Rec

(Continued)
1926 Chi A C 49 .237
1927 Chi A C 85 .239
1928 Chi A C 78 .252
1929 Chi A C 45 .272
1930 Chi A C 42 .254
BLTR 470 .262

CROWDER ALVIN FLOYD (General)
b.Jan.11,1899 Winston-Salem,N.C.
1926 Was A P 19 7-4
1927 Was A P 15 4-7
1927 St.L A P 21 3-5
1928 St.L A P 41 21-5
1929 St.L A P 40 17-15
1930 St.L A P 13 3-7
1930 Was A P 27 15-9
1931 Was A P 44 18-11
1932 Was A P 51 26-13
1933 Was A P 52 24-15
1934 Was A P 29 4-10
1934 Det A P 9 5-1
1935 Det A P 33 16-10
1936 Det A P 9 4-3
BLTR 403 167-115

CROWE, GEORGE DANIEL
(Big George)
b.Mar.22,1923 Whiteland,Ind.
1952 Bos N 1 73 .258
1953 Mil N 1 47 .286
1955 Mil N 1 104 .281
1956 Cin N 1 77 .250
1957 Cin N 1 133 .271
1958 Cin N 1-2 111 .275
1959 St.L N 1 77 .301
1960 St.L N 1 73 .236
1961 St.L N H 7 .143
BLTL 702 .270

CROWELL, MINOT JOY (Cap)
b.Sept.5,1892 Roxbury,Mass.
d.Sept.30,1962
1915 Phi A P 10 2-6
1916 Phi A P 9 0-5
BRTR 19 2-11

CROWELL, WILLIAM THEODORE
b.Nov.6,1865 Cumminsville,O.
d.July 23,1935
1887 Cle a P 45 13-32
1888 Cle a P 18 0-12
1888 Lou a P 7 5-2
BRTR 70 18-46

CROWLEY, EDGAR JEWEL
b.Aug.20,1906 Watkinsville,Ga.
1928 Was A 3 2 .000
BRTR

CROWLEY, JOHN A.
b.Jan.12,1862 Lawrence,Mass.
d.Sept.23,1896
1884 Phi N C 44 .244

CROWLEY, WILLIAM MICHAEL
b.Apr.8,1857 Philadelphia,Pa.
d.July 14,1891
1875 Phi n 1-2-3-O 9 NR
1877 Lou N C-2-S-3-O 61 .281
1879 Buf N C-O 59 .282
1880 Buf N C-O 82 .261
1881 Bos N O 71 .254
1883 Ath a 1-O 24 .265
1883 Cle N O 11 .317
1884 Bos N O 103 .265
1885 Buf N O 92 .241
BRTR 512 NR

CROWSON, THOMAS WOODROW WILSON (Woody)
b.Sept.9,1918 Hartnett Co.,N.C.
d.Aug.14,1947
1945 Phi A P 1 0-0
BRTR

Yr Cl Lea Pos G Rec

CRUISE, WALTON EDWIN
b.May 6,1890 Sylacauga,Ala.
1914 St.L N O 95 .227
1916 St.L N O 3 .667
1917 St.L N O 153 .295
1918 St.L N O 70 .271
1919 St.L N 1-O 9 .095
1919 Bos N O 73 .216
1920 Bos N O 91 .278
1921 Bos N O 108 .346
1922 Bos N 1-O 104 .278
1923 Bos N O 21 .211
1924 Bos N O 9 .444
BLTR 736 .277

CRUM, CALVIN CARL
b.1892
1917 Bos N P 1 0-0
1918 Bos N P 1 0-1
BRTR 2 0-1

CRUMLING, EUGENE LEON
b.Apr.5,1922 Wrightsville,Pa.
1945 St.L N C 6 .083
BRTR

CRUMP, ARTHUR ELLIOTT
b.Nov.29,1901 Norfolk,Va.
1924 NY N O 1 .000
BLTL

CRUMPLER, RAY MAXTON
b.July 8,1895 Clinton,N.C.
1920 Det A P 4 1-0
1925 Phi N P 3 0-0
BLTL 7 1-0

CRUTCHER, RICHARD LOUIS
b.July 15,1891 Frankfort,Ky.
d.June 19,1952
1914 Bos N P 33 5-6
1915 Bos N P 14 2-2
BRTR 47 7-8

CUCCINELLO, ALFRED EDWARD
b.Aug.26,1915 Long Island City,N.Y.
1935 NY N 2-3 54 .248
BRTR

CUCCINELLO, ANTHONY FRANCIS
(Cooch)
b.Nov.8,1907 Long Island City,N.Y.
1930 Cin N 2-S-3 125 .312
1931 Cin N 2 154 .315
1932 Bro N 2 154 .281
1933 Bro N 2-3 134 .252
1934 Bro N 2-3 140 .261
1935 Bro N 2-3 102 .292
1936 Bos N 2 150 .308
1937 Bos N 2 152 .271
1938 Bos N 2 147 .265
1939 Bos N 2 81 .306
1940 Bos N 3 34 .270
1940 NY N 2-3 88 .208
1942 Bos N 2-3 40 .202
1943 Bos N 2-S-3 13 .000
1943 Chi A 3 34 .272
1944 Chi A 2-3 38 .262
1945 Chi A 3 118 .308
BRTR 1704 .280

CUCCURULLO, ARTHUR JOSEPH
(Cookie)
b.Feb.8,1919 Asbury Park,N.J.
1943 Pit N P 1 0-1
1944 Pit N P 36 2-1
1945 Pit N P 29 1-3
BLTL 66 3-5

CUDWORTH, JAMES ALARIC
b.Aug.22,1858 Fairhaven,Mass.
d.Dec.21,1943
1884 KC U P-1-O 29 { 0-0 / .134 }
BRTR

CUELLAR, CHARLES JESUS PATRICK (Charlie)
b.Sept.24,1917 Tampa,Fla.

Yr	Cl	Lea	Pos	G	Rec
1950	Chi	A	P	2	0-0
BRTR					

CUELLAR, MIGUEL SANTANA
b.May 8,1937 Santa Clara,Cuba

Yr	Cl	Lea	Pos	G	Rec
1959	Cin	N	P	2	0-0
BLTL					

CUETO, DAGOBERTO CONCEPCION
b.Aug.14,1937 San Luis,Cuba

Yr	Cl	Lea	Pos	G	Rec
1961	Min	A	P	7	1-3
BRTR					

CUETO, MANUEL MELO
b.Feb.8,1892 Havana,Cuba
d.Mar.1941

Yr	Cl	Lea	Pos	G	Rec
1914	St.L	F	S-3	15	.100
1917	Cin	N	C-2-O	56	.200
1918	Cin	N	C-2-S-O	47	.296
1919	Cin	N	3-O	29	.250
BRTR				147	.229

CUFF, JOHN J.
b.Jersey City,N.J.

Yr	Cl	Lea	Pos	G	Rec
1884	Bal	U	C	3	.083

CULBERSON, DELBERT LEON (Lee)
b.Aug.6,1919 Adairsville,Ga.

Yr	Cl	Lea	Pos	G	Rec
1943	Bos	A	O	80	.272
1944	Bos	A	O	75	.238
1945	Bos	A	O	97	.275
1946	Bos	A	3-O	59	.313
1947	Bos	A	3-O	47	.238
1948	Was	A	O	12	.172
BRTR				370	.266

CULLEN, JOHN J.
b.Marysville,Cal.

Yr	Cl	Lea	Pos	G	Rec
1884	Wil	U	S-O	9	.194

CULLEN, JOHN PATRICK
b.Oct.6,1939 Newark,N.J.

Yr	Cl	Lea	Pos	G	Rec
1962	NY	A	P	2	0-0
BRTR					

CULLENBINE, ROY JOSEPH
b.Oct.18,1914 Nashville,Tenn.

Yr	Cl	Lea	Pos	G	Rec
1938	Det	A	O	25	.284
1939	Det	A	O	75	.240
1940	Bro	N	O	22	.180
1940	St.L	A	1-O	86	.230
1941	St.L	A	1-O	149	.317
1942	St.L	A	O	38	.193
1942	Was	A	O	64	.286
1942	NY	A	1-O	21	.364
1943	Cle	A	1-O	138	.289
1944	Cle	A	O	154	.284
1945	Cle	A	3-O	8	.077
1945	Det	A	O	146	.277
1946	Det	A	1-O	113	.335
1947	Det	A	1	142	.224
BBTR				1181	.276

CULLER, RICHARD BROADUS
b.Jan.15,1915 High Point,N.C.

Yr	Cl	Lea	Pos	G	Rec
1936	Phi	A	2-S	9	.237
1943	Chi	A	2-S-3	53	.216
1944	Bos	N	S	8	.071
1945	Bos	N	S-3	136	.262
1946	Bos	N	S	134	.255
1947	Bos	N	S	77	.248
1948	Chi	N	2-S	48	.169
1949	NY	N	S	7	.000
BRTR				472	.244

CULLOP, HENRY NICHOLAS (Nick)
b.Oct.16,1900 St.Louis,Mo.

Yr	Cl	Lea	Pos	G	Rec
1926	NY	A	O	2	.500
1927	Was	A	O	15	.217
1927	Cle	A	P-O	32	0-0 .235
(Continued)					
1929	Bro	N	O	13	.195
1930	Cin	N	O	7	.182
1931	Cin	N	O	104	.263
BRTR				173	0-0 .249

CULLOP, NORMAN ANDREW
b.Sept.17,1887 Chilhowie,Va.
d.Apr.15,1961

Yr	Cl	Lea	Pos	G	Rec
1913	Cle	A	P	18	3-7
1914	Cle	A	P	1	0-1
1914	KC	F	P	41	14-19
1915	KC	F	P	40	22-11
1916	NY	A	P	27	13-6
1917	NY	A	P	30	5-9
1921	St.L	A	P	4	0-2
BLTL				161	57-55

CULLOTON, BERNARD ALOYSIUS (Bud)
b.May 19,1898 Kingston,N.Y.

Yr	Cl	Lea	Pos	G	Rec
1925	Pit	N	P	9	0-1
1926	Pit	N	P	4	0-0
BRTR				13	0-1

CULP, BENJAMIN BALDY
b.Jan.19,1914 Philadelphia,Pa.

Yr	Cl	Lea	Pos	G	Rec
1942	Phi	N	C	1	.000
1943	Phi	N	C	10	.208
1944	Phi	N	C	4	.000
BRTR				15	.192

CULP, WILLIAM EDWARD
b.June 11,1887 Bellaire, Ohio

Yr	Cl	Lea	Pos	G	Rec
1910	Phi	N	P	4	0-0
BBTR					

CUMMINGS, JOHN WILLIAM
b.Apr.1.1904 Pittsburgh,Pa.

Yr	Cl	Lea	Pos	G	Rec
1926	NY	N	C	7	.313
1927	NY	N	C	43	.363
1928	NY	N	C	33	.333
1929	NY	N	H	3	.333
1929	Bos	N	C	3	.167
BRTR				89	.338

CUMMINGS, WILLIAM ARTHUR (Candy)
b.Oct.17,1848 Ware,Mass.
d.May 17,1924

Yr	Cl	Lea	Pos	G	Rec
1872	Mut	n	P	54	31-21
1873	Bal	n	P-3	42	27-14 NR
1874	Phi	n	P	54	28-26
1875	Har	n	P-O	52	35-12 NR
1876	Har	N	P	24	15-8
1877	Cin	N	P-O	19	5-14 .200
BRTR				245	141-95 NR

CUNNINGHAM, BRUCE LEE
b.Sept.29,1906 San Francisco,Cal.

Yr	Cl	Lea	Pos	G	Rec
1929	Bos	N	P	19	4-6
1930	Bos	N	P	37	5-6
1931	Bos	N	P	34	3-12
1932	Bos	N	P	18	1-0
BRTR				108	13-24

CUNNINGHAM, ELLSWORTH ELMER (Bert)
b.Nov.25,1866 Wilmington,Del.
d.May 14,1952

Yr	Cl	Lea	Pos	G	Rec
1887	Bro	a	P	3	0-2
1888	Bal	a	P	51	22-29
1889	Bal	a	P	40	15-19
1890	Phi	p	P	15	3-10
1890	Buf	p	P	29	10-15
1891	Bal	a	P	31	11-14
1895	Lou	N	P	31	11-16
1896	Lou	N	P	24	7-14
1897	Lou	N	P	30	15-14
(Continued)					
1898	Lou	N	P	43	28-15
1899	Lou	N	P	43	18-16
1900	Chi	N	P	8	5-3
1901	Chi	N	P	1	0-1
BRTR				349	145-168

CUNNINGHAM, GEORGE H.
b.July 13,1894 Sturgeon Lake,Minn.

Yr	Cl	Lea	Pos	G	Rec
1916	Det	A	P	35	7-10
1917	Det	A	P	44	2-7
1918	Det	A	P-O	56	6-7 .223
1919	Det	A	P	26	1-1
1921	Det	A	O	1	.000
BRTR				162	16-25 .224

CUNNINGHAM, JOSEPH ROBERT
b.Aug.27,1931 Saddle River,N.J.

Yr	Cl	Lea	Pos	G	Rec
1954	St.L	N	1	85	.284
1956	St.L	N	1	4	.000
1957	St.L	N	1-O	122	.318
1958	St.L	N	1-O	131	.312
1959	St.L	N	1-O	144	.345
1960	St.L	N	1-O	139	.280
1961	St.L	N	1-O	113	.286
1962	Chi	A	1-O	149	.295
BLTL				887	.302

CUNNINGHAM, RAYMOND LEE
b.Jan.17,1908 Mesquite,Tex.

Yr	Cl	Lea	Pos	G	Rec
1931	St.L	N	3	3	.000
1932	St.L	N	2-3	11	.182
BRTR				14	.154

CUNNINGHAM, RUDOLPH (Mike)
b.Stroudsburg,Pa.

Yr	Cl	Lea	Pos	G	Rec
1906	Phi	A	P	6	0-0
TR					

CUNNINGHAM, WILLIAM ALOYSIUS
b.July 30,1895 San Francisco,Cal.
d.Sept.26,1953

Yr	Cl	Lea	Pos	G	Rec
1921	NY	N	O	40	.276
1922	NY	N	3-O	85	.327
1923	NY	N	2-O	79	.271
1924	Bos	N	O	114	.272
BRTR				318	.286

CUNNINGHAM, WILLIAM JOHN
b.June 9,1888 Schenectady,N.Y.
d.Feb.21,1946

Yr	Cl	Lea	Pos	G	Rec
1910	Was	A	2	22	.297
1911	Was	A	2	94	.190
1912	Was	A	2	8	.185
BRTR				124	.208

CUPPY, GEORGE JOSEPH (Nig)
(Real name George Maceo Koppe)
b.July 3,1869 Eaton,O.
d.July 27,1922

Yr	Cl	Lea	Pos	G	Rec
1892	Cle	N	P	43	27-16
1893	Cle	N	P	28	17-11
1894	Cle	N	P	41	21-16
1895	Cle	N	P	42	26-16
1896	Cle	N	P	41	25-15
1897	Cle	N	P	17	10-6
1898	Cle	N	P	16	9-7
1899	St.L	N	P	21	10-8
1900	Bos	N	P	17	8-4
1901	Bos	A	P	17	4-6
TR				283	157-105

CURLEY, WALTER JAMES (Doc)
b.Mar.12,1874 Upton,Mass.
d.Sept.23,1920

Yr	Cl	Lea	Pos	G	Rec
1899	Chi	N	2	10	.105
BRTR					

CURRAN, SIMON FRANCIS (Sam)
b.Oct.30,1874 Dorchester,Mass.
d.May 19,1936

Yr	Cl	Lea	Pos	G	Rec
1902	Bos	N	P	1	0-0

CURREN, PETER
b.Baltimore,Md.

Yr	Cl	Lea	Pos	G	Rec
1876	Ath	N	C-O	3	.333

CURRIE, CLARENCE F.
b.Dec. 30,1878 Glencoe,Ont.,Canada
d.July 15,1941

Yr	Cl	Lea	Pos	G	Rec
1902	Cin	N	P	10	3-4
1902	St.L	N	P	13	7-5
1903	St.L	N	P	22	4-12
1903	Chi	N	P	6	1-2
	BRTR			51	15-23

CURRIE, MURPHY
b.Aug.31,1893 Fayetteville,N.C.

Yr	Cl	Lea	Pos	G	Rec
1916	St.L	N	P	6	0-0
	BRTR				

CURRIE, WILLIAM CLEVELAND
b.Nov.29,1928 Leary,Ga.

Yr	Cl	Lea	Pos	G	Rec
1955	Was	A	P	3	0-0
	BRTR				

CURRIN, PERRY GILMORE
b.Sept.27,1928 Washington,D.C.

Yr	Cl	Lea	Pos	G	Rec
1947	St.L	A	S	3	.000
	BLTR				

CURRY, GEORGE ANTHONY
b.Dec.12,1938 Nassau,Bahama

Yr	Cl	Lea	Pos	G	Rec
1960	Phi	N	O	95	.261
1961	Phi	N	O	15	.194
	BLTL			110	.253

CURRY, GEORGE JAMES
(Soldier Boy)
b.Dec.23,1888 Bridgeport,Conn.

Yr	Cl	Lea	Pos	G	Rec
1911	St.L	A	P	3	0-3
	BRTR				

CURRY, JAMES L.
b.1889 Philadelphia,Pa.
d.Aug.1,1938

Yr	Cl	Lea	Pos	G	Rec
1909	Phi	A	2	1	.250
1911	NY	A	2	4	.182
1918	Det	A	2	5	.250
	BRTR			10	.229

CURRY, WESLEY
b.Philadelphia,Pa.

Yr	Cl	Lea	Pos	G	Rec
1884	Ric	a	P	2	0-2

CURTIS, CLIFTON GARFIELD
b.July 3,1883 Delaware,O.
d.Apr.23,1943

Yr	Cl	Lea	Pos	G	Rec
1909	Bos	N	P	10	4-5
1910	Bos	N	P	43	6-24
1911	Bos	N	P	12	1-8
1911	Chi	N	P	4	0-2
1911	Phi	N	P	8	3-1
1912	Phi	N	P	10	2-5
1912	Bro	N	P	19	4-7
1913	Bro	N	P	30	8-9
	BRTR			136	28-61

CURTIS, EDWIN R.
Non-playing manager Alt (U) 1884

CURTIS, EUGENE (Eude)
b.May 7,1877 Bethany,W.Va.
d.Jan.2,1918

Yr	Cl	Lea	Pos	G	Rec
1903	Pit	N	O	5	.421

CURTIS, FREDERICK

Yr	Cl	Lea	Pos	G	Rec
1905	NY	A	1	2	.222

CURTIS, HARRY ALBERT
b.Feb.19,1888 Portland,Me.
d.Aug.1,1951

Yr	Cl	Lea	Pos	G	Rec
1907	NY	N	C	6	.222
	TR				

CURTIS, JACK PATRICK
b.Jan.11,1937 Rhodhiss,N.C.

Yr	Cl	Lea	Pos	G	Rec
1961	Chi	N	P	31	10-13
(Continued)					
1962	Chi	N	P	4	0-2
1962	Mil	N	P	30	4-4
	BLTL			65	14-19

CURTIS, VERNON EUGENE
(Turkey)
b.May 24,1920 Cairo,Ill.

Yr	Cl	Lea	Pos	G	Rec
1943	Was	A	P	2	0-0
1944	Was	A	P	3	0-1
1946	Was	A	P	11	0-0
	BRTR			16	0-1

CURTISS, IRVIN DUANE (Tacks)
b.Dec.27,1861 Coldwater,Mich.
d.Feb.14,1945

Yr	Cl	Lea	Pos	G	Rec
1891	Cin	N	O	27	.266
1891	Was	a	O	29	.252
	BL			56	.257

CURTRIGHT, GUY PAXTON
b.Oct.18,1912 Henderson,Tex.

Yr	Cl	Lea	Pos	G	Rec
1943	Chi	A	O	138	.291
1944	Chi	A	O	72	.253
1945	Chi	A	O	98	.281
1946	Chi	A	O	23	.200
	BRTR			331	.276

CUSHMAN, CHARLES H.
b.May 25,1850 New York,N.Y.
d.June 29,1909
Non-playing manager Mil (a) 1891

CUSHMAN, EDGAR LEANDER
b.Mar.27,1852 Eagleville,O.
d.Sept.26,1915

Yr	Cl	Lea	Pos	G	Rec
1883	Buf	N	P-O	7	4-3 / .200
1884	Mil	U	P	4	4-0
1885	Ath	a	P	10	3-7
1885	Met	a	P	22	8-14
1886	Met	a	P	38	17-21
1887	Met	a	P	26	11-14
1890	Tol	a	P	39	17-20
	BRTL			146	64-79 / .177

CUSHMAN, HARVEY BARNES
b.July 5,1877 Rockland,Me.
d.Dec.27,1920

Yr	Cl	Lea	Pos	G	Rec
1902	Pit	N	P	4	0-4

CUSICK, ANTHONY DANIEL
b.1860 Fall River,Mass.

Yr	Cl	Lea	Pos	G	Rec
1884	Wil	U	C-2-S-3-O	11	.147
1884	Phi	N	C	9	.143
1885	Phi	N	C-O	39	.177
1886	Phi	N	C	27	.221
1887	Phi	N	C	7	.358
				93	.196

CUSICK, JOHN PETER
b.June 12,1928 Weehawken,N.J.

Yr	Cl	Lea	Pos	G	Rec
1951	Chi	N	S	65	.177
1952	Bos	N	S-3	49	.167
	BRTR			114	.174

CUTHBERT, EDGAR EDWARD (Ned)
b.June 20,1845 Philadelphia,Pa.
d.Feb.6,1905

Yr	Cl	Lea	Pos	G	Rec
1871	Ath	n	C-O	28	.278
1872	Ath	n	O	48	NR
1873	Phi	n	O	50	NR
1874	Chi	n	C-O	58	NR
1875	St.L	n	C-O	65	.266
1876	St.L	N	O	62	.242
1877	Cin	N	O	12	.175
1882	St.L	a	M-O	60	.219
1883	St.L	a	1-O	21	.158
1884	Bal	U	O	42	.193
	BRTR			446	NR

CUTSHAW, GEORGE WILLIAM
b.July 29,1887 Wilmington,Ill.

Yr	Cl	Lea	Pos	G	Rec
1912	Bro	N	2	102	.280
1913	Bro	N	2	147	.267
1914	Bro	N	2	153	.257
1915	Bro	N	2	154	.246
1916	Bro	N	2	154	.260
1917	Bro	N	2	135	.259
1918	Pit	N	2	126	.285
1919	Pit	N	2	139	.242
1920	Pit	N	2	131	.252
1921	Pit	N	2	98	.340
1922	Det	A	2	132	.267
1923	Det	A	2	45	.223
	BRTR			1516	.265

CUYLER, HAZEN SHIRLEY (Kiki)
b.Aug.30,1899 Harrisville,Mich.
d.Feb.11,1950

Yr	Cl	Lea	Pos	G	Rec
1921	Pit	N	O	1	.000
1922	Pit	N	H	1	.000
1923	Pit	N	O	11	.250
1924	Pit	N	O	117	.354
1925	Pit	N	O	153	.357
1926	Pit	N	O	157	.321
1927	Pit	N	O	85	.309
1928	Chi	N	O	133	.285
1929	Chi	N	O	139	.360
1930	Chi	N	O	156	.355
1931	Chi	N	O	154	.330
1932	Chi	N	O	110	.291
1933	Chi	N	O	70	.317
1934	Chi	N	O	142	.338
1935	Chi	N	O	45	.274
1935	Cin	N	O	62	.251
1936	Cin	N	O	144	.326
1937	Cin	N	O	117	.271
1938	Bro	N	O	82	.273
	BRTR			1879	.321

CVENGROS, MICHAEL JOHN
b.Dec.1,1901 Pana,Ill.

Yr	Cl	Lea	Pos	G	Rec
1922	NY	N	P	1	0-1
1923	Chi	A	P	41	12-13
1924	Chi	A	P	26	3-12
1925	Chi	A	P	22	3-9
1927	Pit	N	P	23	2-1
1929	Chi	N	P	33	5-4
	BLTL			146	25-40

CYPERT, ALFRED BOYD
b.Aug.8,1889 Little Rock,Ark.

Yr	Cl	Lea	Pos	G	Rec
1914	Cle	A	3	1	.000
	BRTR				

DAGENHARD, JOHN DOUGLAS
b.Apr.25,1917 Magnolia,O.

Yr	Cl	Lea	Pos	G	Rec
1943	Bos	N	P	2	1-0
	BRTR				

DAGLIA, PETER GEORGE
b.Feb.28,1906 Napa,Cal.
d.Mar.11,1952

Yr	Cl	Lea	Pos	G	Rec
1932	Chi	A	P	12	2-4
	BRTR				

DAGRES, ANGELO GEORGE
b.Aug.22,1934 Newburyport,Mass.

Yr	Cl	Lea	Pos	G	Rec
1955	Bal	A	O	8	.267
	BLTL				

DAHLEN, WILLIAM FREDERICK
(Bad Bill)
b.Jan.5,1871 Glens Falls,N.Y.
d.Dec.5,1950

Yr	Cl	Lea	Pos	G	Rec
1891	Chi	N	S-3-O	135	.263
1892	Chi	N	S-3	143	.294
1893	Chi	N	S-O	115	.311
1894	Chi	N	S-3	121	.362
1895	Chi	N	S	131	.273
1896	Chi	N	S	125	.361
1897	Chi	N	S	75	.296
1898	Chi	N	S	141	.290
1899	Bro	N	S	122	.276
1900	Bro	N	S	134	.259
1901	Bro	N	S	130	.261
1902	Bro	N	S	136	.267
1903	Bro	N	S	138	.262
1904	NY	N	S	145	.268

(Continued)

Yr	Cl	Lea	Pos	G	Rec
1905	NY	N	S	148	.242
1906	NY	N	S	143	.240
1907	NY	N	S	143	.207
1908	Bos	N	S	144	.239
1909	Bos	N	S	57	.233
1910	Bro	N	M-H	3	.000
1911	Bro	N	M-S	1	.000
	BRTR			2430	.277

Non-playing manager Bro (N) 1912-13.

DAHLGREN, ELLSWORTH TENNEY (Babe)
b.June 15,1912 San Francisco,Cal.

Yr	Cl	Lea	Pos	G	Rec
1935	Bos	A	1	149	.263
1936	Bos	A	1	16	.281
1937	NY	A	H	1	.000
1938	NY	A	1-3	27	.186
1939	NY	A	1	144	.235
1940	NY	A	1	155	.264
1941	Bos	N	1-3	44	.235
1941	Chi	N	1	99	.281
1942	Chi	N	1	17	.214
1942	St.L	A	H	2	.000
1942	Bro	N	1	17	.173
1943	Phi	N	C-1-S-3	136	.288
1944	Pit	N	1	158	.289
1945	Pit	N	1	144	.250
1946	St.L	A	1	28	.175
	BRTR			1137	.261

DAHLKE, JEROME ALEXANDER
b.June 8,1930 Wausau,Wis.

Yr	Cl	Lea	Pos	G	Rec
1956	Chi	A	P	5	0-0
	BRTR				

DAILEY, JOHN J.
b.Brooklyn,N.Y.
d.Jan.8,1898

Yr	Cl	Lea	Pos	G	Rec
1875	Nat	n	2-S-3	25	NR
1875	Atl	n	1-O	2	.125
				27	NR

DAILEY, SAMUEL L.
b.Mar.31,1905 Kansas City,Kan.

Yr	Cl	Lea	Pos	G	Rec
1929	Phi	N	P	20	2-2
	BLTR				

DAILEY, WILLIAM GARLAND
b.May 13,1935 Arlington,Va.

Yr	Cl	Lea	Pos	G	Rec
1961	Cle	A	P	12	1-0
1962	Cle	A	P	27	2-2
	BRTR			39	3-2

DAILY, CORNELIUS F. (Con)
b.Sept.11,1864 Blackstone,Mass.

Yr	Cl	Lea	Pos	G	Rec
1884	Key	U	C	2	.000
1885	Pro	N	C-1-O	59	.260
1886	Bos	N	C	50	.239
1887	Bos	N	C	33	.217
1888	Ind	N	C	57	.218
1889	Ind	N	C	60	.251
1890	Bro	p	C-1	46	.253
1891	Bro	N	C	53	.296
1892	Bro	N	C	78	.243
1893	Bro	N	C	58	.286
1894	Bro	N	C	65	.269
1895	Bro	N	C	40	.233
1896	Bro	N	C	1	.000
1896	Chi	N	C	9	.075
				611	.258

DAILY, EDWARD M.
b.Sept.7,1862 Providence,R.I.
d.Oct.21,1891

Yr	Cl	Lea	Pos	G	Rec
1885	Phi	N	P-O	49	26-22 .206
1886	Phi	N	P-O	78	13-9 .226
1887	Phi	N	P-O	25	0-4 .306
1887	Was	N	P-O	80	0-1 .296
1888	Was	N	P-O	110	2-4 .225
1889	Col	a	O	137	.254

(Continued)

Yr	Cl	Lea	Pos	G	Rec
1890	Bro	a	P-O	93	9-15 .250
1890	NY	N	P	4	2-1
1890	Lou	a	P-O	23	6-2 .244
1891	Lou	a	P-O	22	4-8 .277
1891	Was	a	P-O	17	0-0 .206
	BRTR			638	62-66 .250

DAILY, VINCENT P.
b.Dec.25,1864 Osceola,Pa.
d.Nov.14,1919

Yr	Cl	Lea	Pos	G	Rec
1890	Cle	N	O	64	.288

DAISEY, GEORGE K.

Yr	Cl	Lea	Pos	G	Rec
1884	Alt	U	O	1	.000

DALE, EMMETT EUGENE (Gene)
b.June 16,1889 St.Louis,Mo.
d.Mar.20,1958

Yr	Cl	Lea	Pos	G	Rec
1911	St.L	N	P	5	0-2
1912	St.L	N	P	20	0-5
1915	Cin	N	P	49	18-17
1916	Cin	N	P	17	3-4
	BRTR			91	21-28

DALEY, BUDDY LEO
b.Oct.7,1933 Orange,Cal.

Yr	Cl	Lea	Pos	G	Rec
1955	Cle	A	P	2	0-1
1956	Cle	A	P	14	1-0
1957	Cle	A	P	34	2-8
1958	KC	A	P	26	3-2
1959	KC	A	P	39	16-13
1960	KC	A	P	37	16-16
1961	KC	A	P	16	4-8
1961	NY	A	P	23	8-9
1962	NY	A	P	43	7-5
	BLTL			234	57-62

DALEY, JOHN FRANCIS
b.May 25,1889 Pittsburgh,Pa.

Yr	Cl	Lea	Pos	G	Rec
1912	St.L	A	S	17	.173
	BRTR				

DALEY, JUD LAWRENCE
b.Mar.14,1887 S.Coventry,Conn.

Yr	Cl	Lea	Pos	G	Rec
1911	Bro	N	O	16	.231
1912	Bro	N	O	61	.256
	BLTR			77	.250

DALEY, PETER HARVEY
b.Jan.14,1930 Grass Valley,Cal.

Yr	Cl	Lea	Pos	G	Rec
1955	Bos	A	C	17	.220
1956	Bos	A	C	59	.267
1957	Bos	A	C	78	.225
1958	Bos	A	C	27	.321
1959	Bos	A	C	65	.225
1960	KC	A	C-O	73	.263
1961	Was	A	C	72	.192
	BRTR			391	.239

DALEY, THOMAS FRANCIS (Pete)
b.Nov.13,1884 DuBois,Pa.
d.Dec.2,1934

Yr	Cl	Lea	Pos	G	Rec
1908	Cin	N	O	13	.108
1913	Phi	A	O	59	.260
1914	Phi	A	O	28	.241
1914	NY	A	O	67	.258
1915	NY	A	O	10	.250
	BLTR			177	.243

DALEY, WILLIAM
b.June 27,1868 Poughkeepsie,N.Y.
d.May 4,1922

Yr	Cl	Lea	Pos	G	Rec
1889	Bos	N	P	9	3-3
1890	Bos	p	P	47	20-12

(Continued)

Yr	Cl	Lea	Pos	G	Rec
1891	Bos	a	P	20	9-5
	TL			76	32-20

DALLESSANDRO, NICHOLAS DOMINIC (Dim Dom)
b.Oct.3,1913 Reading,Pa.

Yr	Cl	Lea	Pos	G	Rec
1937	Bos	A	O	68	.231
1940	Chi	N	O	107	.268
1941	Chi	N	O	140	.272
1942	Chi	N	O	96	.261
1943	Chi	N	O	87	.222
1944	Chi	N	O	117	.305
1946	Chi	N	O	65	.225
1947	Chi	N	O	66	.287
	BLTL			746	.267

DALRYMPLE, ABNER FRANK
b.Sept.9,1857 Warren,Ill.
d.Jan.25,1939

Yr	Cl	Lea	Pos	G	Rec
1878	Mil	N	O	60	.356
1879	Chi	N	O	67	.300
1880	Chi	N	O	84	.332
1881	Chi	N	O	81	.323
1882	Chi	N	O	84	.294
1883	Chi	N	O	80	.297
1884	Chi	N	O	110	.310
1885	Chi	N	O	113	.274
1886	Chi	N	O	82	.232
1887	Pit	N	O	92	.300
1888	Pit	N	O	56	.224
1891	Mil	a	O	31	.315
	BLTR			940	.293

DALRYMPLE, CLAYTON ERROL
b.Dec.3,1936 Chico,Cal.

Yr	Cl	Lea	Pos	G	Rec
1960	Phi	N	C	82	.272
1961	Phi	N	C	129	.220
1962	Phi	N	C	123	.276
	BLTR			334	.252

DALRYMPLE, MICHAEL
b St.Louis,Mo.

Yr	Cl	Lea	Pos	G	Rec
1915	St.L	A	3	3	.000
	TR				

DALTON, TALBOT PERCY (Jack)
b.July 3,1885 Henderson,Tenn.

Yr	Cl	Lea	Pos	G	Rec
1910	Bro	N	O	72	.227
1914	Bro	N	O	128	.319
1915	Buf	F	O	132	.294
1916	Det	A	O	8	.182
	BRTR			340	.287

DALY, BERT
b.Apr.8,1881 Bayonne,N.J.
d.Sept.4,1952

Yr	Cl	Lea	Pos	G	Rec
1903	Phi	A	2-S-3	10	.190
	TR				

DALY, GEORGE JOSEPH
b.July 28,1887 Buffalo,N.Y.
d.Dec.12,1957

Yr	Cl	Lea	Pos	G	Rec
1909	NY	N	P	3	0-3
	BRTR				

DALY, HUGH I. (One Arm)
(Real name Harry Criss)
b.1857 Baltimore,Md.

Yr	Cl	Lea	Pos	G	Rec
1882	Buf	N	P	29	15-14
1883	Cle	N	P-O	42	24-18 .109
1884	Chi	U	P-2-S-O	47	22-25 .235
1884	Pit	U	P	10	5-4
1884	Was	U	P	2	1-1
1885	St.L	N	P	11	3-8
1886	Was	N	P	6	0-6
1887	Cle	a	P	17	4-12
	BRTR			164	74-88 .155

DALY, JAMES J.
(Sun)
b.Jan.6,1865 Rutland,Vt.
d.Apr.30,1938

Yr	Cl	Lea	Pos	G	Rec
1891	Mil	a	O	1	.000
1892	Bal	N	O	13	.229
				14	.216

DALY, JOSEPH JOHN
b.Sept.21,1868 Philadelphia,Pa.
d.Mar.20,1943

Yr	Cl	Lea	Pos	G	Rec
1890	Ath	a	P	20	0-1
1891	Cle	N	O	1	.000
1892	Bos	N	C	1	.000
				22	0-1 / .175

DALY, THOMAS DANIEL
b.Dec.12,1891 St.John,N.B.,Canada.
d.Nov.7,1946

Yr	Cl	Lea	Pos	G	Rec
1913	Chi	A	C	1	.000
1914	Chi	A	O	61	.233
1915	Chi	A	C	29	.191
1916	Cle	A	C	31	.219
1918	Chi	N	C	1	.000
1919	Chi	N	C	25	.220
1920	Chi	N	C	44	.311
1921	Chi	N	C	51	.238
	BRTR			243	.239

DALY, THOMAS PETER
(Tido)
b.Feb.7,1866 Philadelphia,Pa.
d.Oct.29,1939

Yr	Cl	Lea	Pos	G	Rec
1887	Chi	N	C	74	.269
1888	Chi	N	C	65	.191
1889	Was	N	C	69	.300
1890	Bro	N	C	82	.243
1891	Bro	N	C	61	.293
1892	Bro	N	C-3-O	120	.255
1893	Bro	N	2-3	126	.306
1894	Bro	N	2	123	.338
1895	Bro	N	2	122	.289
1896	Bro	N	2	64	.280
1898	Bro	N	2	23	.329
1899	Bro	N	2	143	.312
1900	Bro	N	2	98	.313
1901	Bro	N	2	132	.310
1902	Chi	A	2	137	.231
1903	Chi	A	2	45	.201
1903	Cin	N	2	79	.293
	BBTR			1563	.284

DAM, ELBRIDGE RUST
(Bill)
b.Apr.4,1885 Cambridge,Mass.
d.June 22,1930

Yr	Cl	Lea	Pos	G	Rec
1909	Bos	N	O	1	.500

DAMMAN, WILLIAM HENRY A.
b.Aug.9,1872 Chicago,Ill.
d.Dec.6,1948

Yr	Cl	Lea	Pos	G	Rec
1897	Cin	N	P	16	7-5
1898	Cin	N	P	28	16-8
1899	Cin	N	P	9	2-1
	BLTL			53	25-14

DAMRAU, HARRY ROBERT
b.1892 New York,N.Y.

Yr	Cl	Lea	Pos	G	Rec
1915	Phi	A	3	16	.196
	BRTR				

DANEY, ARTHUR LEE
b.July 9,1905 Talihina,Okla.

Yr	Cl	Lea	Pos	G	Rec
1928	Phi	A	P	1	0-0
	BRTR				

DANFORTH, DAVID CHARLES
b.Mar.7,1890 Granger,Tex.

Yr	Cl	Lea	Pos	G	Rec
1911	Phi	A	P	14	5-2
1912	Phi	A	P	3	0-0
1916	Chi	A	P	28	6-5
1917	Chi	A	P	50	11-6
1918	Chi	A	P	39	6-15
1919	Chi	A	P	15	1-2

(Continued)

Yr	Cl	Lea	Pos	G	Rec
1922	St.L	A	P	20	5-2
1923	St.L	A	P	38	16-14
1924	St.L	A	P	41	15-12
1925	St.L	A	P	38	7-9
	BLTL			286	72-67

DANIEL, CHARLES EDWARD
b.Sept.17,1933 Bluffton,Ark.

Yr	Cl	Lea	Pos	G	Rec
1957	Det	A	P	1	0-0
	BRTR				

DANIEL, HANDLEY JACOB
(Jake)
b.Apr.22,1912 Roanoke,Ala.

Yr	Cl	Lea	Pos	G	Rec
1937	Bro	N	1	12	.185
	BLTL				

DANIELS, BENNIE
b.June 17,1932 Tuscaloosa,Ala.

Yr	Cl	Lea	Pos	G	Rec
1957	Pit	N	P	1	0-1
1958	Pit	N	P	8	0-3
1959	Pit	N	P	36	7-9
1960	Pit	N	P	10	1-3
1961	Was	A	P	32	12-11
1962	Was	A	P	44	7-16
	BLTR			131	27-43

DANIELS, BERTRAM ELMER
b.Oct.13,1882 Danville,Ill.
d.June 6,1958

Yr	Cl	Lea	Pos	G	Rec
1910	NY	A	1-3-O	95	.253
1911	NY	A	O	131	.286
1912	NY	A	O	133	.274
1913	NY	A	O	93	.216
1914	Cin	N	O	71	.219
	BRTR			523	.255

DANIELS, CHARLES L.
b.July 1,1861 Roxbury,Mass.

Yr	Cl	Lea	Pos	G	Rec
1884	Bos	U	P-O	3	0-2 / .273

DANIELS, FREDERICK CLINTON
b.Dec.28,1924 Gastonia,N.C.

Yr	Cl	Lea	Pos	G	Rec
1945	Phi	N	2-3	76	.200
	BRTR				

DANIELS, HAROLD JACK
b.Dec.21,1927 Chester,Pa.

Yr	Cl	Lea	Pos	G	Rec
1952	Bos	N	O	106	.187
	BLTL				

DANIELS, LAWRENCE LONG (Law)
b.1862 Newton,mass.
d.Jan.7,1929

Yr	Cl	Lea	Pos	G	Rec
1887	Bal	a	C	47	.287
1888	KC	a	C	61	.205
				108	.240

DANIELS, PETER J.
(Smiling Pete)
b.Apr.8,1864 County Cavan,Ireland
d.Feb.13,1928

Yr	Cl	Lea	Pos	G	Rec
1890	Pit	N	P	4	1-2
1898	St.L	N	P	10	1-6
				14	2-8

DANNER, HENRY FREDERICK
(Buck)
b.June 8,1891 Dedham,Mass.
d.Sept.19,1949

Yr	Cl	Lea	Pos	G	Rec
1915	Phi	A	S	3	.250
	BRTR				

DANNING, HARRY (The Horse)
b.Sept.6,1911 Los Angeles,Cal.

Yr	Cl	Lea	Pos	G	Rec
1933	NY	N	C	3	.000
1934	NY	N	C	53	.330
1935	NY	N	C	65	.243
1936	NY	N	C	32	.159
1937	NY	N	C	93	.288
1938	NY	N	C	120	.306
1939	NY	N	C	135	.313
1940	NY	N	C	140	.300

(Continued)

Yr	Cl	Lea	Pos	G	Rec
1941	NY	N	C-1	130	.244
1942	NY	N	C	119	.279
	BRTR			890	.285

DANNING, IKE
b.Jan.20,1905 Los Angeles,Cal.

Yr	Cl	Lea	Pos	G	Rec
1928	St.L	A	C	2	.500
	BRTR				

DANTONIO, JOHN JAMES
(Fats)
b.Dec.31,1919 New Orleans,La.

Yr	Cl	Lea	Pos	G	Rec
1944	Bro	N	C	3	.143
1945	Bro	N	C	47	.250
	BRTR			50	.244

DANZIG, HAROLD P.
(Babe)
b.Apr.30,1887 Binghamton,N.Y.

Yr	Cl	Lea	Pos	G	Rec
1909	Bos	A	1	6	.143
	BRTR				

DAPPER, CLIFFORD ROLAND
b.Jan.2,1920 Los Angeles,Cal.

Yr	Cl	Lea	Pos	G	Rec
1942	Bro	N	C	8	.471
	BRTR				

DARBY, GEORGE W.
(Deacon)
b.Alexandria,Va.

Yr	Cl	Lea	Pos	G	Rec
1893	Cin	N	P	4	2-1
1893	Phi	N	P	4	0-0
	BLTR			8	2-1

DARINGER, CLIFFORD CLARENCE
(Shanty)
b.Apr.10,1885 Hayden,Ind.

Yr	Cl	Lea	Pos	G	Rec
1914	KC	F	S-3	60	.247
	BLTR				

DARINGER, ROLLA HARRISON
b.Nov.15,1888 North Vernon,Ind.

Yr	Cl	Lea	Pos	G	Rec
1914	St.L	N	S	2	.500
1915	St.L	N	S	10	.087
	BLTR			12	.148

DARK, ALVIN RALPH
(Blackie)
b.Jan.7,1922 Comanche,Okla.

Yr	Cl	Lea	Pos	G	Rec
1946	Bos	N	S-O	15	.231
1948	Bos	N	S	137	.322
1949	Bos	N	S-3	130	.276
1950	NY	N	S	154	.279
1951	NY	N	S	156	.303
1952	NY	N	S	151	.301
1953	NY	N	P-2-S-3-O	155	0-0 / .300
1954	NY	N	S	154	.293
1955	NY	N	S	115	.282
1956	NY	N	S	48	.252
1956	St.L	N	S	100	.286
1957	St.L	N	S-3	140	.290
1958	St.L	N	S-3	18	.297
1958	Chi	N	3	114	.295
1959	Chi	N	1-S-3	136	.264
1960	Phi	N	1-3	55	.242
1960	Mil	N	1-2-3-O	50	.298
	BRTR			1828	.289

Non-playing manager San Francisco (N)1961-62

DARLING, DELL CONRAD
(Wienerwurst)
b.Dec.21,1863 Erie,Pa.
d.Nov.21,1904

Yr	Cl	Lea	Pos	G	Rec
1883	Buf	N	C	5	.158
1887	Chi	N	C-O	38	.411
1888	Chi	N	C	20	.213
1889	Chi	N	C	35	.191
1890	Chi	p	C-1	58	.259
1891	St.L	a	C	17	.137
	BR			173	.283

DARNELL, ROBERT JACK
b.Nov.6,1930 Wewoka,Okla.

Yr	Cl	Lea	Pos	G	Rec
1954	Bro	N	P	6	0-0
1956	Bro	N	P	1	0-0
	BRTR			7	0-0

DARRAGH, JAMES S.
b.1867 E.Liverpool,O.
d.Aug.12,1939

Yr	Cl	Lea	Pos	G	Rec
1891	Lou	a	P	1	1-0

DARROW, GEORGE F.
b.July 12,1905 Beloit,Kan.

Yr	Cl	Lea	Pos	G	Rec
1934	phi	N	P	17	2-6

BLTL

DARWIN, ARTHUR BOBBY LEE
b.Feb.16,1943 Los Angeles,Cal.

Yr	Cl	Lea	Pos	G	Rec
1962	LA	A	P	1	0-1

BRTR

DASHIELL, JOHN WALLACE
(Wally)
b.May 9,1901 Jewett,Tex.

Yr	Cl	Lea	Pos	G	Rec
1924	Chi	A	S	1	.000

BRTR

DASHNER, LEE CLARE
(Lefty)
b.Apr.25,1887 Renault,Ill.
d.Dec.16,1960

Yr	Cl	Lea	Pos	G	Rec
1913	Cle	A	P	1	0-0

BBTL

DASSO, FRANCIS JOSEPH NICHOLAS
b.Aug.31,1917 Chicago,Ill.

Yr	Cl	Lea	Pos	G	Rec
1945	Cin	N	P	16	4-5
1946	Cin	N	P	2	0-0
	BRTR			18	4-5

DAUB, DANIEL WILLIAM
b.Jan.12,1869 Middletown,O.

Yr	Cl	Lea	Pos	G	Rec
1892	Cin	N	P	5	1-1
1893	Bro	N	P	12	6-6
1894	Bro	N	P	28	10-15
1895	Bro	N	P	20	10-10
1896	Bro	N	P	27	14-11
1897	Bro	N	P	18	5-11
				110	46-54

DAUBERT, HARRY J.
b.Aug.7,1894 Detroit,Mich.

Yr	Cl	Lea	Pos	G	Rec
1915	Pit	N	S	1	.000

BRTR

DAUBERT, JACOB ELLSWORTH
b.May 15,1885 Llewellyn,Pa.
d.Oct.9,1924

Yr	Cl	Lea	Pos	G	Rec
1910	Bro	N	1	144	.264
1911	Bro	N	1	149	.307
1912	Bro	N	1	145	.308
1913	Bro	N	1	139	.350
1914	Bro	N	1	126	.329
1915	Bro	N	1	150	.301
1916	Bro	N	1	127	.316
1917	Bro	N	1	125	.261
1918	Bro	N	1	108	.308
1919	Cin	N	1	140	.276
1920	Cin	N	1	142	.304
1921	Cin	N	1	136	.306
1922	Cin	N	1	156	.336
1923	Cin	N	1	125	.292
1924	Cin	N	1	102	.281
	BLTL			2014	.303

DAUGHERTY, HAROLD RAY
(Doc)
b.Oct.12,1927 Paris,Pa.

Yr	Cl	Lea	Pos	G	Rec
1951	Det	A	H	1	.000

BRTR

DAUGHTERS, ROBERT FRANCIS
(Red)
b.Aug.5,1914 Cincinnati,O.

Yr	Cl	Lea	Pos	G	Rec
1937	Bos	A	H	1	.000

BRTR

DAUSS, GEORGE AUGUST
(Hooks)
b.Sept.22,1889 Indianapolis,Ind.

Yr	Cl	Lea	Pos	G	Rec
1912	Det	A	P	2	0-1
1913	Det	A	P	33	13-12
1914	Det	A	P	43	18-15
1915	Det	A	P	46	23-13
1916	Det	A	P	39	18-12
1917	Det	A	P	38	17-14
1918	Det	A	P	33	13-16
1919	Det	A	P	34	21-9
1920	Det	A	P	38	13-21
1921	Det	A	P	32	10-15
1922	Det	A	P	39	13-13
1923	Det	A	P	50	21-13
1924	Det	A	P	40	12-11
1925	Det	A	P	35	16-11
1926	Det	A	P	35	12-7
	BRTR			537	220-183

DAVALILLO, POMPEYO ROMERO (Yo-Yo)
b.July 5,1931 Cabimas,Venezuela

Yr	Cl	Lea	Pos	G	Rec
1953	Was	A	S	19	.293

BRTR

DAVENPORT, ARTHUR DAVID
(Davie)
b.Feb.2,1892 Alexandria,La.
d.Oct.16,1954

Yr	Cl	Lea	Pos	G	Rec
1914	Cin	N	P	10	2-2
1914	St.L	F	P	32	10-15
1915	St.L	F	P	51	22-18
1916	St.L	A	P	59	12-11
1917	St.L	A	P	47	17-17
1918	St.L	A	P	31	10-11
1919	St.L	A	P	24	2-11
	BRTR			254	75-85

DAVENPORT, CLAUDE EDWIN
b.May.28,1898 Runge,Tex.

Yr	Cl	Lea	Pos	G	Rec
1920	NY	N	P	1	0-0

BRTR

DAVENPORT, JAMES HOUSTON
b.Aug.17,1933 Siluria,Ala.

Yr	Cl	Lea	Pos	G	Rec
1958	SF	N	S-3	134	.256
1959	SF	N	S-3	123	.258
1960	SF	N	S-3	112	.251
1961	SF	N	3	137	.278
1962	SF	N	3	144	.297
	BRTR			650	.269

DAVENPORT, JOUBERT LUM
b.June 27,1900 Tucson,Ariz.

Yr	Cl	Lea	Pos	G	Rec
1921	Chi	A	P	15	0-3
1922	Chi	A	P	12	1-1
1923	Chi	A	P	2	0-0
1924	Chi	A	P	1	0-0
	BLTL			30	1-4

DAVIAULT, RAYMOND JOSEPH R.
b.May 27,1934 Montreal,Que.,Canada

Yr	Cl	Lea	Pos	G	Rec
1962	NY	N	P	36	1-5

BRTR

DAVIDSON, CLAUDE BOUCHER (Davey)
b.Oct.13,1896 Roxbury,Mass.
d.Apr.18,1956

Yr	Cl	Lea	Pos	G	Rec
1918	Phi	A	2	31	.185
1919	Was	A	3	2	.375
	BLTR			33	.202

DAVIDSON, HOMER HURD
b.Oct.14,1884 Cleveland,O.
d.July 26,1948

Yr	Cl	Lea	Pos	G	Rec
1908	Cle	A	C-O	9	.000

TR

DAVIDSON,MORDECAI H.
b.Nov.30,1846 Port Washington, O.
d.Sept.6,1940
Non-playing manager Lou(a)
1888-89

DAVIDSON, WILLIAM S.
(Davey)
b.May 10,1887 Lafayette,Ind.
d.Mar.14,1916

Yr	Cl	Lea	Pos	G	Rec
1909	Chi	N	O	2	.142
1910	Bro	N	O	131	.238
1911	Bro	N	O	74	.233
	BRTR			207	.235

DAVIE, GERALD LEE
b.Feb.10,1933 Detroit,Mich.

Yr	Cl	Lea	Pos	G	Rec
1959	Det	A	P	11	2-2

BRTR

DAVIES, GEORGE WASHINGTON
b.Feb.22,1868 Columbus,Wis
d.Sept.22,1906

Yr	Cl	Lea	Pos	G	Rec
1891	Mil	a	P	12	7-5
1892	Cle	N	P	25	10-15
1893	Cle	N	P	3	0-1
1893	NY	N	P	4	1-2
				44	18-23

DAVIES, LLOYD GARRISON
(Chick)
b.Mar.6,1892 Peabody,Mass.

Yr	Cl	Lea	Pos	G	Rec
1914	Phi	A	P	19	1-0
1915	Phi	A	P-O	56	0-2 / .182
1925	NY	N	P-O	4	0-0 / .000
1926	NY	N	P	38	2-4
	BLTL			117	3-6 / .196

DAVIS, ALFONZO DeFORD
(Lefty)
b.Feb.4,1875 Nashville,Tenn.
d.Feb.4,1919

Yr	Cl	Lea	Pos	G	Rec
1901	Bro	N	O	25	.209
1901	Pit	N	O	88	.308
1902	Pit	N	O	59	.291
1903	NY	A	O	108	.245
1907	Cin	N	O	70	.229
	BLTL			350	.264

DAVIS, CURTIS BENTON
(Coonskin)
b.Sept.7,1904 Greenfield,Mo.

Yr	Cl	Lea	Pos	G	Rec
1934	Phi	N	P	51	19-17
1935	Phi	N	P	46	16-14
1936	Phi	N	P	11	2-4
1936	Chi	N	P	24	11-9
1937	Chi	N	P	28	10-5
1938	St.L	N	P	40	12-8
1939	St.L	N	P	63	22-16
1940	St.L	N	P	14	0-4
1940	Bro	N	P	22	8-7
1941	Bro	N	P	31	13-7
1942	Bro	N	P	32	15-6
1943	Bro	N	P	31	10-13
1944	Bro	N	P	31	10-11
1945	Bro	N	P	24	10-10
1946	Bro	N	P	1	0-0
	BRTR			449	158-131

DAVIS, FRANK TALMADGE
(Dixie)
b.Oct.12,1890 Wilson Mills,N.C.
d.Feb.4,1944

Yr	Cl	Lea	Pos	G	Rec
1912	Cin	N	P	7	0-1
1915	Chi	A	P	2	0-0
1918	Phi	N	P	18	0-2
1920	St.L	A	P	38	18-12
1921	St.L	A	P	39	16-16
1922	St.L	A	P	25	11-6
1923	St.L	A	P	19	4-6
1924	St.L	A	P	29	11-13
1925	St.L	A	P	35	12-7
1926	St.L	A	P	27	4-8
	BRTR			239	76-71

DAVIS, GEORGE ALLEN
b.Mar.29,1890 Lancaster,N.Y.
d.June 4,1961

Yr	Cl	Lea	Pos	G	Rec
1912	NY	A	P	10	1-5

(Continued)

Yr	Cl	Lea	Pos	G	Rec
1913	Bos	N	P	2	0-0
1914	Bos	N	P	9	3-3
1915	Bos	N	P	15	3-3
	BRTR			36	7-11

DAVIS, GEORGE STACEY
b.Aug.23,1870 Cohoes,N.Y.

Yr	Cl	Lea	Pos	G	Rec
1890	Cle	N	O	134	.264
1891	Cle	N	P-3-O	136	0-0 / .292
1892	Cle	N	S-3-O	143	.253
1893	NY	N	3	133	.373
1894	NY	N	3	124	.345
1895	NY	N	M-3	110	.330
1896	NY	N	S-3	124	.315
1897	NY	N	S	131	.358
1898	NY	N	S	121	.306
1899	NY	N	S	111	.348
1900	NY	N	M-S	113	.325
1901	NY	N	M-S-3	130	.309
1902	Chi	A	1-S	132	.298
1903	NY	N	S	4	.250
1904	Chi	A	S	152	.256
1905	Chi	A	S	151	.278
1906	Chi	A	S	133	.277
1907	Chi	A	S	132	.238
1908	Chi	A	2-S	128	.217
1909	Chi	A	1	28	.132
	BBTR			2370	0-0 / .297

DAVIS, GEORGE WILLIS
(Kiddo)
b.Feb.12,1902 Bridgeport,Conn.

Yr	Cl	Lea	Pos	G	Rec
1926	NY	A	O	1	.000
1932	Phi	N	O	137	.309
1933	NY	N	O	126	.258
1934	St.L	N	O	16	.303
1934	Phi	N	O	100	.293
1935	NY	N	O	47	.264
1936	NY	N	O	47	.239
1937	NY	N	O	56	.263
1937	Cin	N	O	40	.257
1938	Cin	N	O	5	.278
	BRTR			575	.282

DAVIS, HARRY ALBERT
(Stinky)
b.May 7,1910 Shreveport,La.

Yr	Cl	Lea	Pos	G	Rec
1932	Det	A	1	140	.269
1933	Det	A	1	66	.214
1937	St.L	A	1	120	.276
	BLTL			326	.264

DAVIS, HARRY H. (Jasper)
b.July 19,1873 Philadelphia,Pa.
d.Aug.11,1947

Yr	Cl	Lea	Pos	G	Rec
1895	NY	N	1	7	.333
1896	NY	N	1	64	.254
1896	Pit	N	1-O	43	.206
1897	Pit	N	1-3	107	.309
1898	Pit	N	1	58	.290
1898	Lou	N	1-2-O	36	.227
1898	Was	N	1	1	.000
1899	Was	N	1	18	.188
1901	Phi	A	1	117	.307
1902	Phi	A	1-O	132	.308
1903	Phi	A	1	101	.298
1904	Phi	A	1	102	.308
1905	Phi	A	1	149	.284
1906	Phi	A	1	145	.292
1907	Phi	A	1	149	.266
1908	Phi	A	1	147	.248
1909	Phi	A	1	149	.268
1910	Phi	A	1	139	.248
1911	Phi	A	1	57	.197
1912	Cle	A	M-1	2	.000
1913	Phi	A	C-1	8	.444
1914	Phi	A	1	7	.333
1915	Phi	A	1	5	.167
1916	Phi	A	O	4	.167
1917	Phi	A	H	1	.000
	BRTR			1748	.277

DAVIS, HERMAN THOMAS
b.Mar.21,1939 Brooklyn,N.Y.

Yr	Cl	Lea	Pos	G	Rec
1959	LA	N	H	1	.000
1960	LA	N	3-O	110	.276
1961	LA	N	3-O	132	.278
1962	LA	N	3-O	163	.346
	BRTR			406	.308

DAVIS, ISAAC MARION
b.June 14,1895 Pueblo,Col.

Yr	Cl	Lea	Pos	G	Rec
1919	Was	A	S	7	.000
1924	Chi	A	S	10	.242
1925	Chi	A	S	146	.240
	BRTR			163	.235

DAVIS, JACKE SYLVESTA
b.Mar.5,1936 Carthage,Tex.

Yr	Cl	Lea	Pos	G	Rec
1962	Phi	N	O	48	.213
	BRTR				

DAVIS, JAMES BENNETT
b.Sept.15,1925 Red Bluff,Cal.

Yr	Cl	Lea	Pos	G	Rec
1954	Chi	N	P	46	11-7
1955	Chi	N	P	42	7-11
1956	Chi	N	P	46	5-7
1957	St.L	N	P	10	0-1
1957	NY	N	P	10	1-0
	BBTL			154	24-26

DAVIS, JAMES J. (Jumbo)
b.New York,N.Y.
d.Feb.1921

Yr	Cl	Lea	Pos	G	Rec
1884	KC	U	3	7	.222
1886	Bal	a	3	59	.185
1887	Bal	a	S-3	130	.345
1888	KC	a	3	122	.266
1889	KC	a	3	62	.258
1889	St.L	a	S-O	2	.000
1890	St.L	a	3	21	.250
1890	Bro	a	3	37	.284
1891	Was	a	3	18	.250
	BLTR			458	.278

DAVIS, JOHN A. (Daisy)
b.1858 Boston,Mass.

Yr	Cl	Lea	Pos	G	Rec
1884	St.L	a	P	28	11-12
1884	Bos	N	P-O	5	1-3 / .050
1885	Bos	N	P	11	5-6
				44	17-21 / .159

DAVIS, JOHN HUMPHREY
b.July 15,1916 Laurel Run,Pa.

Yr	Cl	Lea	Pos	G	Rec
1941	NY	N	3	21	.214
	BRTR				

DAVIS, J. IRA (Slats)
b.July 8,1870 Brooklyn,N.Y.
d.Dec.21,1942

Yr	Cl	Lea	Pos	G	Rec
1899	NY	N	1-S	6	.250

DAVIS, JOHN WILBUR (Bud)
b.Dec.7,1889 Merry Point,Va.

Yr	Cl	Lea	Pos	G	Rec
1915	Phi	A	P	20	1-2
	BLTR				

DAVIS, LAWRENCE COLUMBUS
(Crash)
b.July 14,1919 Canon,Ga.

Yr	Cl	Lea	Pos	G	Rec
1940	Phi	A	2-S	23	.269
1941	Phi	A	1-2	39	.219
1942	Phi	A	1-2-S	86	.224
	BRTR			148	.230

DAVIS, OTIS ALLEN (Scat)
b.Sept.24,1920 Charleston,Ark.

Yr	Cl	Lea	Pos	G	Rec
1946	Bro	N	H	1	.000
	BLTL				

DAVIS, RAYMOND THOMAS
(Peaches)
b.May 25,1910 Glass,Tex.

Yr	Cl	Lea	Pos	G	Rec
1936	Cin	N	P	26	8-8
1937	Cin	N	P	42	11-13
1938	Cin	N	P	29	7-12

(Continued)

Yr	Cl	Lea	Pos	G	Rec
1939	Cin	N	P	20	1-0
	BLTR			117	27-33

DAVIS, ROBERT BRANDON
b.Sept.10,1928 Wilmington,Del.

Yr	Cl	Lea	Pos	G	Rec
1952	Pit	N	O	55	.179
1953	Pit	N	O	12	.205
	BRTR			67	.187

DAVIS, ROBERT EDWARD
b.Sept.11,1933 New York,N.Y.

Yr	Cl	Lea	Pos	G	Rec
1958	KC	A	P	8	0-4
1960	KC	A	P	21	0-0
	BRTR			29	0-4

DAVIS, RONALD EVERETTE
b.Oct.21,1941 Roanoke Rapids,N.C.

Yr	Cl	Lea	Pos	G	Rec
1962	Hou	N	O	6	.214
	BBTR				

DAVIS, THOMAS J.

Yr	Cl	Lea	Pos	G	Rec
1890	Cle	N	O	1	.000

DAVIS, THOMAS OSCAR
(Tod)
b.July 24,1925 Los Angeles,Cal.

Yr	Cl	Lea	Pos	G	Rec
1949	Phi	A	2-S-3	31	.267
1951	Phi	A	2-3	11	.067
	BRTR			42	.233

DAVIS, VIRGIL LAWRENCE
(Spud)
b.Dec.20,1904 Birmingham,Ala.

Yr	Cl	Lea	Pos	G	Rec
1928	St.L	N	C	2	.200
1928	Phi	N	C	67	.282
1929	Phi	N	C	98	.342
1930	Phi	N	C	106	.313
1931	Phi	N	C	120	.326
1932	Phi	N	C	125	.336
1933	Phi	N	C	141	.349
1934	St.L	N	C	107	.300
1935	St.L	N	C-1	102	.317
1936	St.L	N	C	112	.273
1937	Cin	N	C	76	.268
1938	Cin	N	C	12	.167
1938	Phi	N	C	70	.247
1939	Phi	N	C	87	.307
1940	Pit	N	C	99	.326
1941	Pit	N	C	57	.252
1944	Pit	N	C	54	.301
1945	Pit	N	C	23	.242
	BRTR			1458	.308

Non-playing manager Pit (N) 1946

DAVIS, WILEY ANDERSON
b.Aug.1,1875 Blount Co.,Tenn.
d.Sept.24,1942

Yr	Cl	Lea	Pos	G	Rec
1896	Cin	N	P	2	0-0
	BRTR				

DAVIS, WILLIAM HENRY
b.Apr.15,1940 Phoenix,Ariz.

Yr	Cl	Lea	Pos	G	Rec
1960	LA	N	O	22	.318
1961	LA	N	O	128	.254
1962	LA	N	O	157	.285
	BLTL			307	.278

DAVIS, WOODROW WILSON
b.Apr.25,1913 Nicholls,Ga.

Yr	Cl	Lea	Pos	G	Rec
1938	Det	A	P	2	0-0
	BLTR				

DAWSON, RALPH FENTON
(Joe)
b.Mar.9,1898 Bow,Wash.

Yr	Cl	Lea	Pos	G	Rec
1924	Cle	A	P	4	1-2
1927	Pit	N	P	20	3-7
1928	Pit	N	P	31	7-7
1929	Pit	N	P	4	0-1
	BRTR			59	11-17

DAWSON, REXFORD PAUL
b.Feb.10,1889 Skagit Co.,Wash.
d.Oct.20,1958

Yr	Cl	Lea	Pos	G	Rec
1913	Was	A	P	1	0-0
	BLTR				

DAY, CLYDE HENRY
(Pea Ridge)
b.Aug.27,1899 Pea Ridge,Ark.
d.Mar.21,1934

Yr	Cl	Lea	Pos	G	Rec
1924	St.L	N	P	3	1-1
1925	St.L	N	P	17	2-4
1926	Cin	N	P	4	0-0
1931	Bro	N	P	22	2-2
	BRTR			46	5-7

DAY, JOHN B.
b.Mar.2,1847 Portland,Conn.
d.Jan.25,1925
Non-playing manager NY (N) 1899

DAY, WILLIAM
b.July 28,1867 Wilmington,Del.
d.Aug.16,1923

Yr	Cl	Lea	Pos	G	Rec
1889	Phi	N	P	3	0-3
1890	Phi	N	P	4	1-1
1890	Pit	N	P	7	0-7
				14	1-11

DEAGLE, LORENZO BURROUGHS
(Ren)
b.June 26,1858 New York,N.Y.
d.Dec.24,1937

Yr	Cl	Lea	Pos	G	Rec
1883	Cin	a	P-S	19	10-8 .130
1884	Cin	a	P	3	2-1
1884	Lou	a	P-O	12	4-6 .114
	BRTR			34	16-15 .109

DEAL, CHARLES ALBERT
b.Oct.30,1891 Wilkinsburg,Pa.

Yr	Cl	Lea	Pos	G	Rec
1912	Det	A	3	41	.225
1913	Det	A	3	16	.220
1913	Bos	N	3	10	.309
1914	Bos	N	3	79	.210
1915	St.L	F	3	65	.314
1916	St.L	A	3	23	.135
1916	Chi	N	3	2	.250
1917	Chi	N	3	135	.254
1918	Chi	N	3	119	.239
1919	Chi	N	3	116	.289
1920	Chi	N	3	129	.240
1921	Chi	N	3	115	.289
	BRTR			850	.256

DEAL, ELLIS FERGASON
(Cot)
b.Jan.23,1923 Arapaho,Okla.

Yr	Cl	Lea	Pos	G	Rec
1947	Bos	A	P	6	0-1
1948	Bos	A	P	4	1-0
1950	St.L	N	P	3	0-0
1954	St.L	N	P	33	2-3
	BBTR			46	3-4

DEAL, FREDERICK LINDSAY
b.Sept.3,1916 Lenoir,N.C.

Yr	Cl	Lea	Pos	G	Rec
1939	Bro	N	O	4	.000
	BLTR				

DEAL, JOHN WESLEY
(Snake)
b.Jan.21,1879 Conshohocken,Pa.
d.May 9,1944

Yr	Cl	Lea	Pos	G	Rec
1906	Cin	N	1	65	.208
	BRTR				

DEALEY, PATRICK E.
b.Moosup,Conn.

Yr	Cl	Lea	Pos	G	Rec
1884	St.P	U	C-O	5	.143
1885	Bos	N	C-1-S-3	34	.230
1886	Bos	N	C	14	.333
(Continued)					
1887	Was	N	C-S	56	.286
1890	Syr	a	P-C	18	0-1 .174
	BRTR			127	0-1 .256

DEAN, ALFRED LOVILL
(Chubby)
b.Aug.24,1916 Mt.Airy,N.C.

Yr	Cl	Lea	Pos	G	Rec
1936	Phi	A	1	111	.287
1937	Phi	A	P-1	104	1-0 .262
1938	Phi	A	P	16	2-1
1939	Phi	A	P	80	5-8
1940	Phi	A	P-1	67	6-13 .289
1941	Phi	A	P-1	27	2-4 .237
1941	Cle	A	P-1	17	1-4 .167
1942	Cle	A	P	70	8-11
1943	Cle	A	P	41	5-5
	BLTL			533	30-46 .274

DEAN, CHARLES WILSON
(Dorry)
b.Nov.6,1852 Cincinnati,O.
d.May 4,1935

Yr	Cl	Lea	Pos	G	Rec
1874	Bal	n	2-O	47	NR
1876	Cin	N	P-S-O	34	4-26 .257
	BRTR			81	4-26 NR

DEAN, JAMES HARRY
b.May 12,1915 Rockmart,Ga.

Yr	Cl	Lea	Pos	G	Rec
1941	Was	A	P	2	0-0
	BRTR				

DEAN, JAY HANNA
(Dizzy)
b.Jan.16,1911 Lucas,Ark.

Yr	Cl	Lea	Pos	G	Rec
1930	St.L	N	P	1	1-0
1932	St.L	N	P	47	18-15
1933	St.L	N	P	51	20-18
1934	St.L	N	P	51	30-7
1935	St.L	N	P	53	28-12
1936	St.L	N	P	51	24-13
1937	St.L	N	P	27	13-10
1938	Chi	N	P	13	7-1
1939	Chi	N	P	19	6-4
1940	Chi	N	P	10	3-3
1941	Chi	N	P	1	0-0
1947	St.L	A	P	1	0-0
	BRTR			325	150-83

DEAN, PAUL DEE
(Daffy)
b.Aug.14,1913 Lucas,Ark.

Yr	Cl	Lea	Pos	G	Rec
1934	St.L	N	P	39	19-11
1935	St.L	N	P	46	19-12
1936	St.L	N	P	17	5-5
1937	St.L	N	P	1	0-0
1938	St.L	N	P	5	3-1
1939	St.L	N	P	16	0-1
1940	NY	N	P	27	4-4
1941	NY	N	P	5	0-0
1943	St.L	A	P	3	0-0
	BRTR			159	50-34

DEAN, WAYLAND OGDEN
b.June 20,1903 Richwood,W.Va.
d.Apr.10,1930

Yr	Cl	Lea	Pos	G	Rec
1924	NY	N	P	26	6-12
1925	NY	N	P	33	10-7
1926	Phi	N	P	63	8-16
1927	Phi	N	P	3	0-1
1927	Chi	N	P	2	0-0
	BBTR			127	24-36

DEANE, JOHN HENRY
b.May 6,1846 Trenton,N.J.
d.May 31,1925

Yr	Cl	Lea	Pos	G	Rec
1871	Kek	n	M-O	5	NR

DEAR, PAUL STANFORD
(Buddy)
b.Dec.1,1905 Norfolk,Va.

Yr	Cl	Lea	Pos	G	Rec
1927	Was	A	2	2	.000
	BRTR				

DeARMOND, CHARLES HOMMER
b.Feb.13,1877 Okeana,O.
d.Dec.17,1933

Yr	Cl	Lea	Pos	G	Rec
1903	Cin	N	3	11	.297
	BRTR				

DEASLEY, JAMES (Sack)
b.Philadelphia,Pa.

Yr	Cl	Lea	Pos	G	Rec
1884	Was	U	S	31	.216
1884	KC	U	S	13	.175
				44	.207

DEASLEY, THOMAS H.
(Pat)
b.Nov.17,1857 Philadelphia,Pa.
d.Apr.1,1943

Yr	Cl	Lea	Pos	G	Rec
1681	Bos	N	C-1-S-O	43	.229
1882	Bos	N	C-S-O	66	.267
1883	St.L	a	C-O	53	.250
1884	St.L	a	C	73	.202
1885	NY	N	C-S	52	.256
1886	NY	N	C	38	.265
1887	NY	N	C	29	.362
1888	Was	N	C	34	.157
	BRTR			388	.246

DeBERRY, JOHN HERMAN
(Hank)
b.Dec.29,1893 Savannah,Tenn.
d.Sept.10,1951

Yr	Cl	Lea	Pos	G	Rec
1916	Cle	A	C	15	.273
1917	Cle	A	C	25	.273
1922	Bro	N	C	85	.301
1923	Bro	N	C	78	.285
1924	Bro	N	C	77	.243
1925	Bro	N	C	67	.259
1926	Bro	N	C	48	.287
1927	Bro	N	C	68	.234
1928	Bro	N	C	82	.252
1929	Bro	N	C	68	.262
1930	Bro	N	C	35	.295
	BRTR			648	.267

DeBERRY, JOSEPH H
b.Nov.29,1899 Southern Pines,N.C.
d.Oct.9,1944

Yr	Cl	Lea	Pos	G	Rec
1920	St.L	A	P	10	2-4
1921	St.L	A	P	10	0-1
	BLTR			20	2-5

DEBUS, ADAM JOSEPH
b.July 10,1893 Chicago,Ill.

Yr	Cl	Lea	Pos	G	Rec
1917	Pit	N	S-3	38	.229
	BRTR				

DeBUSSCHERE, DAVID ALBERT
b.Oct.16,1940 Detroit,Mich.

Yr	Cl	Lea	Pos	G	Rec
1962	Chi	A	P	12	0-0
	BRTR				

DECATUR, ARTHUR RUE
b.Jan.14,1894 Cleveland,O.

Yr	Cl	Lea	Pos	G	Rec
1922	Bro	N	P	29	3-4
1923	Bro	N	P	36	3-3
1924	Bro	N	P	31	10-9
1925	Bro	N	P	1	0-0
1925	Phi	N	P	25	4-13
1926	Phi	N	P	2	0-0
1927	Phi	N	P	29	3-5
	BRTR			153	23-34

DECKER, EDWARD HARRY
b.Sept.3,1854 Lockport,Ill.

Yr	Cl	Lea	Pos	G	Rec
1879	Syr	N	C-1-O	3	.100

(Continued)

Yr	Cl	Lea	Pos	G	Rec
1882	St.L	a	2	2	.250
1884	Ind	a	C	4	.286
1884	KC	U	C-O	23	.136
1886	Det	N	C-O	15	.203
1886	Was	N	C-3	6	.143
1889	Phi	N	C-2	11	.103
1890	Phi	N	C-1-O	5	.368
1890	Pit	N	C	90	.273
	BRTR			159	.236

DECKER, GEORGE A.
(Gentleman George)
b.June 1,1869 York,Pa.
d.June 9,1909

Yr	Cl	Lea	Pos	G	Rec
1892	Chi	N	2-O	79	.231
1893	Chi	N	1-2-O	81	.276
1894	Chi	N	1-O	89	.310
1895	Chi	N	O	70	.291
1896	Chi	N	1-O	106	.281
1897	Chi	N	1-O	109	.307
1898	St.L	N	1	64	.263
1898	Lou	N	1-O	42	.315
1899	Lou	N	1	38	.234
1899	Was	N	1-O	4	.000
				682	.281

DEDE, ARTHUR RICHARD
b.July 12,1895 Brooklyn,N.Y.

Yr	Cl	Lea	Pos	G	Rec
1916	Bro	N	C	1	.000
	BRTR				

DEDEAUX, RAOUL
b.Feb.17,1915 New Orleans,La.

Yr	Cl	Lea	Pos	G	Rec
1935	Bro	N	S	2	.250
	BRTR				

DEE, JAMES D.
b.Buffalo,N.Y.

Yr	Cl	Lea	Pos	G	Rec
1884	Pit	a	S	13	.136

DEE, MAURICE F.
(Shorty)
b.1891 Halifax,N.S.,Canada.

Yr	Cl	Lea	Pos	G	Rec
1915	St.L	A	S	1	.000
	TR				

DEEGAN, W. JOHN
(Dummy)
b.New York,N.Y.

Yr	Cl	Lea	Pos	G	Rec
1901	NY	N	P	2	0-2

DEERING, JOHN THOMAS
b.June 25,1878 Lynn,Mass.
d.Feb.15,1943

Yr	Cl	Lea	Pos	G	Rec
1903	Det	A	P	11	3-8
1903	NY	A	P	9	3-1
	TR			20	6-9

DeFATE, CLYDE (Tony)
b.Feb.22,1898 Kansas City,Mo.

Yr	Cl	Lea	Pos	G	Rec
1917	St.L	N	S	14	.143
1917	Det	A	2	3	.000
	BRTR			17	.133

DeGERICK, MICHAEL ARTHUR
b.Apr.1,1943 New York,N.Y.

Yr	Cl	Lea	Pos	G	Rec
1961	Chi	A	P	1	0-0
1962	Chi	A	P	1	0-0
	BRTR			2	0-0

DeGROFF, EDWARD ARTHUR
(Rube)
b.Sept.2,1879 Hyde Park,N.Y.
d.Dec.17,1955

Yr	Cl	Lea	Pos	G	Rec
1905	St.L	N	O	15	.250
1906	St.L	N	O	1	.000
				16	.233

DEHLMAN, HARMON J.
b.1850 Catasaqua,Pa.
d.Mar.13,1885

Yr	Cl	Lea	Pos	G	Rec
1872	Atl	n	1	36	NR

(Continued)

Yr	Cl	Lea	Pos	G	Rec
1873	Atl	n	1	54	NR
1874	Atl	n	1	53	NR
1875	St.L	n	1	64	.215
1876	St.L	N	1	64	.178
1877	St.L	N	1-O	32	.185
				303	NR

DEININGER, OTTO CHARLES
(Pep)
b.Oct.10,1877 Boston,Mass.
d.Sept.25,1950

Yr	Cl	Lea	Pos	G	Rec
1902	Bos	A	P	2	0-1
1908	Phi	N	O	1	.000
1909	Phi	N	O	46	.260
	BLTL			49	{ 0-1 .263

DEISEL, EDWARD (Pat)
b.Apr.29,1876 Ripley,O.
d.Apr.17,1948

Yr	Cl	Lea	Pos	G	Rec
1902	Bro	N	C	1	.667
1903	Cin	N	C	2	.000
	BRTR			3	.667

DEJAN, MIKE DAN
b.Jan.13,1915 Cleveland,O.
d.Feb.2,1953

Yr	Cl	Lea	Pos	G	Rec
1940	Cin	N	O	12	.188
	BLTL				

DEKONING, WILLIAM CALLAHAN
b.Dec.19,1919 Brooklyn,N.Y.

Yr	Cl	Lea	Pos	G	Rec
1945	NY	N	C	3	.000
	BRTR				

de la CRUZ, TOMAS
b.Sept.18,1914 Marianao,Cuba
d.Sept.6,1958

Yr	Cl	Lea	Pos	G	Rec
1944	Cin	N	P	36	9-9
	BRTR				

DELAHANTY, EDWARD JAMES
(Big Ed)
b.Oct.30,1867 Cleveland,O.
d.July 2,1903

Yr	Cl	Lea	Pos	G	Rec
1888	Phi	N	2	74	.227
1889	Phi	N	2-O	54	.292
1890	Cle	p	2-S-O	115	.296
1891	Phi	N	1-O	128	.249
1892	Phi	N	O	120	.312
1893	Phi	N	O	132	.370
1894	Phi	N	O	114	.400
1895	Phi	N	O	116	.399
1896	Phi	N	1-O	122	.394
1897	Phi	N	O	129	.377
1898	Phi	N	O	142	.334
1899	Phi	N	O	145	.408
1900	Phi	N	1	130	.319
1901	Phi	N	1-O	138	.357
1902	Was	A	1-O	123	.376
1903	Was	A	O	43	.338
	BRTR			1825	.346

DELAHANTY, FRANK GEORGE
(Pudgie)
b.Dec.29,1885 Cleveland,O.

Yr	Cl	Lea	Pos	G	Rec
1905	NY	A	1-O	9	.240
1906	NY	A	O	92	.238
1907	Cle	A	O	15	.173
1908	NY	A	O	37	.256
1914	Buf	F	O	79	.212
1914	Pit	F	O	42	.213
1915	Pit	F	O	14	.238
	BRTR			288	.219

DELAHANTY, JAMES CHRISTOPHER
b.June 20,1882 Cleveland,O.
d.Oct.17,1953

Yr	Cl	Lea	Pos	G	Rec
1901	Chi	N	3	16	.174
1902	NY	N	O	7	.231
1904	Bos	N	2-3	138	.285
1905	Bos	N	O	124	.258
1906	Cin	N	3	112	.280
1907	St.L	A	2-3	33	.219
1907	Was	A	2-3	108	.293
1908	Was	A	2	82	.317
1909	Was	A	2	88	.221
1909	Det	A	2	48	.253
1910	Det	A	2	106	.293
1911	Det	A	1-2	144	.339
1912	Det	A	2-3-O	78	.286
1914	Bro	F	2	74	.284
1915	Bro	F	1	16	.250
	BRTR			1174	.283

DELAHANTY, JOSEPH NICHOLAS
b.Oct.18,1875 Cleveland,O.
d.Jan.9,1936

Yr	Cl	Lea	Pos	G	Rec
1907	St.L	N	O	6	.303
1908	St.L	N	O	138	.255
1909	St.L	N	2-O	111	.214
	BRTR			255	.238

DELAHANTY, THOMAS JAMES
b.Mar.9,1872 Cleveland,O.
d.Jan.10,1951

Yr	Cl	Lea	Pos	G	Rec
1894	Phi	N	2	1	.250
1896	Cle	N	3	15	.216
1896	Pit	N	S	1	.333
1897	Lou	N	2	1	.333
	TR			18	.224

DE LA HOZ, MIGUEL A.
b.Oct.2,1939 Havana,Cuba

Yr	Cl	Lea	Pos	G	Rec
1960	Cle	A	S-3	49	.256
1961	Cle	A	2-S-3	61	.260
1962	Cle	A	2-3	12	.083
	BRTR			122	.252

DeLANCEY, WILLIAM L.
b.Cumminsville,O.

Yr	Cl	Lea	Pos	G	Rec
1890	Cle	N	2	36	.189

DeLANCEY, WILLIAM PINKNEY
b.Nov.28,1911 Greensboro,N.C.
d.Nov.28,1946

Yr	Cl	Lea	Pos	G	Rec
1932	St.L	N	C	8	.192
1934	St.L	N	C	93	.316
1935	St.L	N	C	103	.279
1940	St.L	N	C	15	.222
	BLTR			219	.289

DELANEY, ARTHUR D.
(Swede) (Real name
Arthur D. Helenius)
b.Jan.5,1897 Chicago,Ill.

Yr	Cl	Lea	Pos	G	Rec
1924	St.L	N	P	8	1-0
1928	Bos	N	P	39	9-17
1929	Bos	N	P	20	3-5
	BRTR			67	13-22

DEL GRECO, ROBERT GEORGE
b.Apr.7,1933 Pittsburgh,Pa.

Yr	Cl	Lea	Pos	G	Rec
1952	Pit	N	O	99	.217
1956	Pit	N	3-O	14	.200
1956	St.L	N	O	102	.215
1957	Chi	N	O	20	.200
1957	NY	A	O	8	.429
1958	NY	A	O	12	.200
1960	Phi	N	O	100	.237
1961	Phi	N	2-3-O	41	.259
1961	KC	A	O	74	.230
1962	KC	A	O	132	.254
	BRTR			602	.233

DELHI, LEE WILLIAM
(Flame)
b.Nov.5,1890 Los Angeles,Cal.

Yr	Cl	Lea	Pos	G	Rec
1912	Chi	A	P	1	0-0
	BRTR				

DELIS, JUAN FRANCISCO
b.Feb.27,1928 Santiago,Cuba

Yr	Cl	Lea	Pos	G	Rec
1955	Was	A	2-3-O	54	.189
	BRTR				

DELKER, EDWARD ALBERT
b.Apr.17,1907 Del Alto,Pa.

Yr	Cl	Lea	Pos	G	Rec
1929	St.L	N	2-S-3	22	.150
1931	St.L	N	3	1	.500
1932	St.L	N	2	20	.119
1932	Phi	N	2	30	.161
1933	Phi	N	2-3	25	.171
	BRTR			98	.155

DELL, WILLIAM GEORGE
(Wheezer)
b.June 11,1887 Tuscarora,Nev.

Yr	Cl	Lea	Pos	G	Rec
1912	St.L	N	P	3	0-0
1915	Bro	N	P	40	11-10
1916	Bro	N	P	32	8-9
1917	Bro	N	P	17	0-4
	BRTR			92	19-23

DELMAS, BERT CHARLES
b.May 5,1912 San Francisco,Cal.

Yr	Cl	Lea	Pos	G	Rec
1933	Bro	N	2	12	.250
	BLTR				

DELOCK, IVAN MARTIN
(Ike)
b.Nov.11,1929 Highland Park,Mich.

Yr	Cl	Lea	Pos	G	Rec
1952	Bos	A	P	39	4-9
1953	Bos	A	P	23	3-1
1955	Bos	A	P	29	9-7
1956	Bos	A	P	48	13-7
1957	Bos	A	P	49	9-8
1958	Bos	A	P	31	14-8
1959	Bos	A	P	28	11-6
1960	Bos	A	P	24	9-10
1961	Bos	A	P	28	6-9
1962	Bos	A	P	17	4-5
	BRTR			316	82-70

DEL SAVIO, GARTON ORVILLE
b.Nov.26,1914 New York,N.Y.

Yr	Cl	Lea	Pos	G	Rec
1943	Phi	N	S	4	.091
	BRTR				

DELSING, JAMES HENRY
b.Nov.13,1925 Rudolph,Wis.

Yr	Cl	Lea	Pos	G	Rec
1948	Chi	A	O	20	.190
1949	NY	A	O	9	.350
1950	NY	A	H	12	.400
1950	St.L	A	O	69	.263
1951	St.L	A	O	131	.249
1952	St.L	A	O	93	.255
1952	Det	A	O	33	.274
1953	Det	A	O	138	.288
1954	Det	A	O	122	.248
1955	Det	A	O	114	.239
1956	Det	A	O	10	.000
1956	Chi	A	O	55	.122
1960	KC	A	O	16	.250
	BLTR			822	.255

DeMAESTRI, JOSEPH PAUL
(Oats)
b.Dec.9,1928 San Francisco,Cal.

Yr	Cl	Lea	Pos	G	Rec
1951	Chi	A	2-S-3	56	.203
1952	St.L	A	2-S-3	81	.226
1953	Phi	A	S	111	.255
1954	Phi	A	2-S-3	146	.230
1955	KC	A	S	123	.249
1956	KC	A	2-S	133	.233
1957	KC	A	S	135	.245
1958	KC	A	S	139	.219
1959	KC	A	S	118	.244
1960	NY	A	2-S	49	.229
1961	NY	A	2-S-3	30	.146
	BRTR			1121	.236

DEMAREE, ALBERT WENTWORTH
b.Sept.8,1886 Quincy,Ill.
d.May 2,1962

Yr	Cl	Lea	Pos	G	Rec
1912	NY	N	P	2	1-0
1913	NY	N	P	31	13-4
1914	NY	N	P	38	10-17
1915	Phi	N	P	32	14-11

(Continued)

Yr	Cl	Lea	Pos	G	Rec
1916	Phi	N	P	39	19-14
1917	Chi	N	P	24	5-9
1917	NY	N	P	15	4-5
1918	NY	N	P	26	8-6
1919	Bos	N	P	25	6-6
	BLTR			232	80-72

DEMAREE, JOSEPH FRANKLIN
(Frank)
(Real name Joseph Franklin Dimaria)
b.June 10,1910 Woodland,Cal.
d.Aug.30,1958

Yr	Cl	Lea	Pos	G	Rec
1932	Chi	N	O	23	.250
1933	Chi	N	O	134	.272
1935	Chi	N	O	107	.325
1936	Chi	N	O	154	.350
1937	Chi	N	O	154	.324
1938	Chi	N	O	129	.273
1939	NY	N	O	150	.304
1940	NY	N	O	121	.302
1941	NY	N	O	16	.171
1941	Bos	N	O	48	.230
1942	Bos	N	O	64	.225
1943	St.L	N	O	39	.291
1944	St.L	A	O	16	.255
	BRTR			1155	.299

DEMARRIS, FRED
b.1865 Nashua,N.H.

Yr	Cl	Lea	Pos	G	Rec
1890	Chi	N	P	1	0-0
	TR				

DeMARS, WILLIAM LESTER
(Kid)
b.Aug.26,1925 Brooklyn,N.Y.

Yr	Cl	Lea	Pos	G	Rec
1948	Phi	A	2-S-3	18	.172
1950	St.L	A	S-3	61	.247
1951	St.L	A	S	1	.250
	BRTR			80	.237

DeMERIT, JOHN STEPHEN
b.Jan.8,1936 West Bend,Wis.

Yr	Cl	Lea	Pos	G	Rec
1957	Mil	N	O	33	.147
1958	Mil	N	O	3	.667
1959	Mil	N	O	11	.200
1961	Mil	N	O	32	.162
1962	NY	N	O	14	.188
	BRTR			93	.174

DEMETER, DONALD LEE
b.June 25,1935 Oklahoma City,Okla.

Yr	Cl	Lea	Pos	G	Rec
1956	Bro	N	O	3	.333
1958	LA	N	O	43	.189
1959	LA	N	O	139	.256
1960	LA	N	O	64	.274
1961	LA	N	O	15	.172
1961	Phi	N	1-O	106	.257
1962	Phi	N	2-3-O	153	.307
	BRTR			523	.270

DEMETER, STEVEN
b.Jan.27,1935 Homer City,Pa.

Yr	Cl	Lea	Pos	G	Rec
1959	Det	A	3	11	.111
1960	Cle	A	3	4	.000
	BRTR			15	.087

DeMILLER, HARRY
b.Nov.12,1867 Wooster,O.
d.Oct.19,1928

Yr	Cl	Lea	Pos	G	Rec
1892	St.L	N	S	1	.000

DEMMITT, CHARLES RAYMOND
(Ray)
b.Feb.2,1884 Illiopolis,Ill.
d.Feb.19,1956

Yr	Cl	Lea	Pos	G	Rec
1909	NY	A	O	119	.241
1910	St.L	A	O	10	.173
1914	Det	A	O	1	.000
1914	Chi	A	O	145	.258
1915	Chi	A	O	9	.000
1917	St.L	A	O	14	.283
1918	St.L	A	O	116	.281
1919	St.L	A	O	79	.238
	BLTR			493	.257

DeMONTREVILLE, EUGENE NAPOLEON
b.Mar.26,1874 St.Paul,Minn.
d.Feb.18,1935

Yr	Cl	Lea	Pos	G	Rec
1894	Pit	N	S	2	.250
1895	Was	N	S	12	.227
1896	Was	N	S	130	.349
1897	Was	N	2-S	132	.349
1898	Bal	N	2-S	151	.325
1899	Chi	N	2	83	.286
1899	Bal	N	2	60	.276
1900	Bro	N	2	63	.250
1901	Bos	N	2-3	140	.305
1902	Bos	N	2-S	123	.269
1903	Was	A	2	11	.292
1904	St.L	A	2	4	.111
	BRTR			911	.308

DeMONTREVILLE, LEON
(Lee)
b.Sept.23,1879 St.Paul,Minn.
d.Mar.22,1962

Yr	Cl	Lea	Pos	G	Rec
1903	St.L	N	S	20	.243
	TR				

DeMOTT, BENJAMIN HARRISON
b.Apr.2,1889 Green Village,N.J.

Yr	Cl	Lea	Pos	G	Rec
1910	Cle	A	P	9	0-3
1911	Cle	A	P	2	0-1
	BRTR			11	0-4

DEMPSEY, CORNELIUS FRANCIS
(Con)
b.Sept.16,1923 San Francisco,Cal.

Yr	Cl	Lea	Pos	G	Rec
1951	Pit	N	P	3	0-2
	BRTR				

DENIENS, ...

Yr	Cl	Lea	Pos	G	Rec
1914	Chi	F	C	1	.000

DENNEHY, THOMAS FRANCIS
(Tod)
b.May 12,1899 Philadelphia,Pa.

Yr	Cl	Lea	Pos	G	Rec
1923	Phi	N	O	9	.250
	BLTL				

DENNING, OTTO GEORGE
b.Dec.28,1913 Hays,Kan.

Yr	Cl	Lea	Pos	G	Rec
1942	Cle	A	C-O	92	.210
1943	Cle	A	1	37	.240
	BRTR			129	.215

DENNIS, WALTER L.
b.1853 Washington,D.C.
d.Sept.10,1889
Non-playing manager Was (N) 1887

DENNY, JEREMIAH D.
b.Mar.16,1859 New York,N.Y.
d.Aug.15,1927

Yr	Cl	Lea	Pos	G	Rec
1881	Pro	N	3	84	.240
1882	Pro	N	3	84	.246
1883	Pro	N	3	98	.274
1884	Pro	N	C-1-2-3	108	.251
1885	Pro	N	3	83	.223
1886	St.L	N	3	119	.257
1887	Ind	N	3	122	.340
1888	Ind	N	S-3	126	.261
1889	Ind	N	3	133	.282
1890	NY	N	3	114	.212
1891	NY	N	3	4	.250
1891	Cle	N	3	36	.229
1891	Phi	N	1-3	19	.301
1893	Lou	N	S	44	.251
1894	Lou	N	3	60	.274
	BRTR			1234	.263

DENT, ELLIOTT ESTILL
(Eddie)
b.Dec.8,1887 Baltimore,Md.

Yr	Cl	Lea	Pos	G	Rec
1909	Bro	N	P	6	2-4
1911	Bro	N	P	5	2-1
1912	Bro	N	P	1	0-0
	BRTR			12	4-5

DENTE, SAMUEL JOSEPH
(Blackie)
b.Apr.26,1922 Harrison,N.J.

Yr	Cl	Lea	Pos	G	Rec
1947	Bos	A	3	46	.232
1948	St.L	A	S-3	98	.270
1949	Was	A	S	153	.273
1950	Was	A	2-S	155	.239
1951	Was	A	2-S-3	88	.238
1952	Chi	A	1-2-S-3-O	62	.221
1953	Chi	A	S	2	.000
1954	Cle	A	2-S	68	.266
1955	Cle	A	2-S-3	73	.257
	BRTR			745	.252

DENZER, ROGER
b.Oct.5,1871 LeSueur Co.,Minn.
d.Sept.18,1949

Yr	Cl	Lea	Pos	G	Rec
1897	Chi	N	P	12	3-6
1901	NY	N	P	11	2-5
	TR			23	5-11

DePAUGHER, MICHAEL H.
b.San Francisco,Cal.

Yr	Cl	Lea	Pos	G	Rec
1884	Phi	N	C	2	.250

DePHILLIPS, ANTHONY ANDREW
b.Sept.20,1913 New York,N.Y.

Yr	Cl	Lea	Pos	G	Rec
1943	Cin	N	C	34	.100

BRTR

DERBY, EUGENE A.
b.Troy,N.Y.

Yr	Cl	Lea	Pos	G	Rec
1885	Bal	a	P-C-O	10	0-1 .129

DERBY, GEORGE H.
(Jonah)
b.July 6,1857 Webster,Mass.
d.July 4,1925

Yr	Cl	Lea	Pos	G	Rec
1881	Det	N	P-O	59	29-26 .186
1882	Det	N	P-O	38	16-20 .202
1883	Buf	N	P-O	15	3-11 .237
	BLTR			112	48-57 .199

DeREGO, ANTHONY J.
(Played under name of
Anthony J. Rego)

DERRICK, CLAUDE LESTER
(Deek)
b.June 11,1886 Clayton,Ga.

Yr	Cl	Lea	Pos	G	Rec
1910	Phi	A	S	2	.000
1911	Phi	A	2	36	.230
1912	Phi	A	S	21	.241
1913	NY	A	S	22	.292
1914	Cin	N	S	3	.333
1914	Chi	N	S	28	.219
	BRTR			112	.242

DERRINGER, SAMUEL PAUL
(Duke)
b.Oct.7,1906 Springfield,Ky.

Yr	Cl	Lea	Pos	G	Rec
1931	St.L	N	P	35	18-8
1932	St.L	N	P	39	11-14
1933	St.L	N	P	3	0-2
1933	Cin	N	P	33	7-25
1934	Cin	N	P	47	15-21
1935	Cin	N	P	45	22-13
1936	Cin	N	P	51	19-19
1937	Cin	N	P	43	10-14
1938	Cin	N	P	41	21-14
1939	Cin	N	P	38	25-7
1940	Cin	N	P	37	20-12
1941	Cin	N	P	29	12-14
1942	Cin	N	P	29	10-11
1943	Chi	N	P	32	10-14
1944	Chi	N	P	42	7-13
1945	Chi	N	P	35	16-11
	BRTR			579	223-212

DERRINGTON, CHARLES JAMES
b.Nov.29,1939 South Gate,Cal.

Yr	Cl	Lea	Pos	G	Rec
1956	Chi	A	P	1	0-1
1957	Chi	A	P	20	0-1
	BLTL			21	0-2

DERRY, ALVA RUSSELL
(Russ)
b.Oct.7,1917 Princeton,Mo.

Yr	Cl	Lea	Pos	G	Rec
1944	NY	A	O	38	.254
1945	NY	A	O	78	.225
1946	Phi	A	O	69	.207
1949	St.L	N	H	2	.000
	BLTR			187	.224

DESAUTELS, EUGENE ABRAHAM
(Red)
b.June 13,1907 Worcester,Mass.

Yr	Cl	Lea	Pos	G	Rec
1930	Det	A	C	42	.190
1931	Det	A	C	3	.091
1932	Det	A	C	28	.236
1933	Det	A	C	30	.143
1937	Bos	A	C	96	.243
1938	Bos	A	C	108	.291
1939	Bos	A	C	76	.243
1940	Bos	A	C	71	.225
1941	Cle	A	C	66	.201
1942	Cle	A	C	62	.247
1943	Cle	A	C	68	.205
1945	Cle	A	C	10	.111
1946	Phi	A	C	52	.215
	BRTR			712	.233

DeSHONG, JAMES BROOKLYN
b.Nov.30,1909 Harrisburg,Pa.

Yr	Cl	Lea	Pos	G	Rec
1932	Phi	A	P	6	0-0
1934	NY	A	P	31	6-7
1935	NY	A	P	29	4-1
1936	Was	A	P	35	18-10
1937	Was	A	P	37	14-15
1938	Was	A	P	31	5-8
1939	Was	A	P	7	0-3
	BRTR			176	47-44

DesJARDIEN, PAUL RAYMOND
(Shorty)
b.Aug.24,1893 Coffeyville,Kan.
d.Mar.7,1956

Yr	Cl	Lea	Pos	G	Rec
1916	Cle	A	P	1	0-0

BRTR

DESSAU, FRANK ROLLAND
(Rube)
b.Mar.29,1883 New Galilee,Pa.
d.May 6,1952

Yr	Cl	Lea	Pos	G	Rec
1907	Bos	N	P	2	0-1
1910	Bro	N	P	19	2-3
	BLTR			21	2-4

DETORE, GEORGE FRANCIS
b.Nov.11,1906 Utica,N.Y.

Yr	Cl	Lea	Pos	G	Rec
1930	Cle	A	3	3	.167
1931	Cle	A	S-3	30	.267
	BRTR			33	.250

DETWEILER, ROBERT STERLING
(Ducky)
b.Feb.15,1919 Trumbauersville,Pa.

Yr	Cl	Lea	Pos	G	Rec
1942	Bos	N	3	12	.318
1946	Bos	N	H	1	.000
	BRTR			13	.311

DEUTSCH, MELVIN ELLIOTT
b.July 26,1915 Caldwell,Tex.

Yr	Cl	Lea	Pos	G	Rec
1946	Bos	A	P	3	0-0

BRTR

DEVENS, CHARLES
b.Jan.1,1910 Milton,Mass.

Yr	Cl	Lea	Pos	G	Rec
1932	NY	A	P	1	1-0
1933	NY	A	P	14	3-3
1934	NY	A	P	1	1-0
	BRTR			16	5-3

DEVINE, WALTER JAMES
(Jim)
b.Oct.5,1858 Brooklyn,N.Y.
d.Jan.11,1905

Yr	Cl	Lea	Pos	G	Rec
1883	Bal	a	P-O	2	1-1 .222
1886	NY	N	O	1	.000
	TL			3	1-1 .167

DEVINE, WILLIAM PATRICK
(Mickey)
b.May 9,1892 Albany,N.Y.
d.Oct.1,1937

Yr	Cl	Lea	Pos	G	Rec
1918	Phi	N	C	4	.125
1920	Bos	A	C	8	.201
1925	NY	N	C-3	21	.273
	BRTR			33	.226

DEVINEY, JOHN HAROLD
(Hal)
b.Apr.11,1893 Newton,Mass.
d.Jan.4,1933

Yr	Cl	Lea	Pos	G	Rec
1920	Bos	A	P	1	0-0

BRTR

DeVIVEIROS, BERNARD JOHN
b.Apr.19,1901 Oakland,Cal.

Yr	Cl	Lea	Pos	G	Rec
1924	Chi	A	S	1	.000
1927	Det	A	S	24	.227
	BRTR			25	.217

DEVLIN, ARTHUR McARTHUR
b.Oct.16,1879 Washington,D.C.
d.Sept.18,1948

Yr	Cl	Lea	Pos	G	Rec
1904	NY	N	3	130	.281
1905	NY	N	3	153	.246
1906	NY	N	3	148	.299
1907	NY	N	3	143	.277
1908	NY	N	3	157	.253
1909	NY	N	3	143	.265
1910	NY	N	3	147	.260
1911	NY	N	3	95	.278
1912	Bos	N	1-S-3	124	.289
1913	Bos	N	3	73	.229
	BRTR			1313	.269

DEVLIN, JAMES ALEXANDER
b.1849 Philadelphia,Pa.
d.Oct.10,1883

Yr	Cl	Lea	Pos	G	Rec
1873	Phi	n	1-S-3-O	21	NR
1874	Chi	n	1-3-O	44	NR
1875	Chi	n	P-1-O	70	6-14 NR
1876	Lou	N	P	68	30-35
1877	Lou	N	P	61	35-25
	BRTR			264	71-74 NR

DEVLIN, JAMES H.
b.1867 Chicago,Ill.
d.Dec.20,1900

Yr	Cl	Lea	Pos	G	Rec
1886	NY	N	P	1	0-0
1887	Phi	N	P	2	0-2
1888	St.L	a	P	12	6-5
1889	St.L	a	P	9	4-2
	TL			24	10-9

DEVLIN, JAMES RAYMOND
b.Aug.25,1922 Plains,Pa.

Yr	Cl	Lea	Pos	G	Rec
1944	Cle	A	C	1	.000

BLTR

DeVOGT, REX EUGENE
b.Jan.4.1889 Clare,Mich.
d.Nov.9,1935

Yr	Cl	Lea	Pos	G	Rec
1913	Bos	N	C	3	.000

BRTR

DEVORE, JOSHUA
b.Nov.13,1887 Murray City,O.
d.Oct.5,1954

Yr	Cl	Lea	Pos	G	Rec
1908	NY	N	O	5	.167
1909	NY	N	O	23	.160
1910	NY	N	O	130	.304
1911	NY	N	O	149	.280
1912	NY	N	O	106	.275
1913	NY	N	O	16	.190
1913	Cin	N	O	66	.267
1913	Phi	N	O	23	.282
1914	Phi	N	O	30	.302
1914	Bos	N	O	51	.227
	BLTR			599	.278

DeVORMER, ALBERT E.
b.Aug.19,1891 Grand Rapids,Mich.

Yr	Cl	Lea	Pos	G	Rec
1918	Chi	A	C	8	.315
1921	NY	A	C	22	.347
1922	NY	A	C	24	.203
1923	Bos	A	C	74	.258
1927	NY	N	C	68	.248
	BRTR			196	.261

DEVOY, WALTER JOSEPH
b.Mar.14,1885 St.Louis,Mo.
d.Dec.17,1953

Yr	Cl	Lea	Pos	G	Rec
1909	St.L	A	O	19	.247

DEWALD, CHARLES H.
b.1867 Ashland,O.

Yr	Cl	Lea	Pos	G	Rec
1890	Cle	p	P	2	2-0
	TL				

DEXTER, CHARLES DANA
b.June 15,1876 Evansville,Ind.

Yr	Cl	Lea	Pos	G	Rec
1896	Lou	N	C-O	98	.284
1897	Lou	N	C-O	63	.292
1898	Lou	N	O	112	.311
1899	Lou	N	O	76	.262
1900	Chi	N	C	35	.201
1901	Chi	N	1-3-O	112	.278
1902	Chi	N	1-3-O	70	.227
1902	Bos	N	2-S-3-O	49	.257
1903	Bos	N	O	120	.223
	TR			735	.265

DIBUT, PEDRO
b.June 24,1901 Havana,Cuba.

Yr	Cl	Lea	Pos	G	Rec
1924	Cin	N	P	7	3-0
1925	Cin	N	P	1	0-0
	BRTR			8	3-0

DICKERMAN, LEO LOUIS
b.Oct.31,1897 De Soto,Mo.

Yr	Cl	Lea	Pos	G	Rec
1923	Bro	N	P	35	8-12
1924	Bro	N	P	7	0-0
1924	St.L	N	P	18	7-4
1925	St.L	N	P	29	4-11
	BRTR			89	19-27

DICKERSON, GEORGE CLARK
b.Dec.1,1892 Renner,Tex.
d.July 9,1938

Yr	Cl	Lea	Pos	G	Rec
1917	Cle	A	P	1	0-0
	BRTR				

DICKERSON, LEWIS PESSANO
(Buttercup)
b.Oct.11,1858 Tyaskin,Md.
d.July 23,1920

Yr	Cl	Lea	Pos	G	Rec
1878	Cin	N	O	30	.309
1879	Cin	N	O	80	.294
1880	Tro	N	S-O	30	.189
1880	Wor	N	O	31	.316
1881	Wor	N	O	80	.316
1883	Pit	a	2-S-O	80	.283
1884	St.L	U	3-O	46	.357
1884	Bal	a	O	13	.232
1884	Lou	a	O	8	.138
1885	Buf	N	S-O	5	.048
	BLTR			403	.286

DICKEY, GEORGE WILLARD
(Skeets)
b.July 10,1915 Kensett,Ark.

Yr	Cl	Lea	Pos	G	Rec
1935	Bos	A	C	5	.000
1936	Bos	A	C	10	.043
1941	Chi	A	C	32	.200
1942	Chi	A	C	59	.233
1946	Chi	A	C	37	.192
1947	Chi	A	C	83	.223
	BBTR			226	.204

DICKEY, WILLIAM MALCOLM
b.June 6,1907 Bastrop,La.

Yr	Cl	Lea	Pos	G	Rec
1928	NY	A	C	10	.200
1929	NY	A	C	130	.324
1930	NY	A	C	109	.339
1931	NY	A	C	130	.327
1932	NY	A	C	108	.310
1933	NY	A	C	130	.318
1934	NY	A	C	104	.322
1935	NY	A	C	120	.279
1936	NY	A	C	112	.362
1937	NY	A	C	140	.332
1938	NY	A	C	132	.313
1939	NY	A	C	128	.302
1940	NY	A	C	106	.247
1941	NY	A	C	109	.284
1942	NY	A	C	82	.295
1943	NY	A	C	85	.351
1946	NY	A	M-C	54	.261
	BLTR			1789	.313

DICKMAN, GEORGE EMERSON
b.Nov.12,1914 Buffalo,N.Y.

Yr	Cl	Lea	Pos	G	Rec
1936	Bos	A	P	1	0-0
1938	Bos	A	P	32	5-5
1939	Bos	A	P	48	8-3
1940	Bos	A	P	35	8-6
1941	Bos	A	P	9	1-1
	BRTR			125	22-15

DICKSHOT, JOHN OSCAR
(Ugly)
(Real name John Oscar Dicksus)
b.Jan.24,1912 Waukegan,Ill.

Yr	Cl	Lea	Pos	G	Rec
1936	Pit	N	O	9	.222
1937	Pit	N	O	82	.254
1938	Pit	N	O	29	.229
1939	NY	N	O	10	.235
1944	Chi	A	O	62	.253
1945	Chi	A	O	130	.302
	BRTR			322	.276

DICKSON, MURRY MONROE
b.Aug.21,1916 Tracy,Mo.

Yr	Cl	Lea	Pos	G	Rec
1939	St.L	N	P	1	0-0
1940	St.L	N	P	1	0-0
1942	St.L	N	P	37	6-3
1943	St.L	N	P	31	8-2
1946	St.L	N	P	47	15-6
1947	St.L	N	P	47	13-16
1948	St.L	N	P	43	12-16
1949	Pit	N	P	44	12-14
1950	Pit	N	P	52	10-15
1951	Pit	N	P	46	20-16
1952	Pit	N	P	47	14-21
1953	Pit	N	P	45	10-19
1954	Phi	N	P	40	10-20
1955	Phi	N	P	36	12-11
1956	Phi	N	P	3	0-3
1956	St.L	N	P	32	13-8
1957	St.L	N	P	14	5-3
1958	KC	A	P	28	9-5
1958	NY	A	P	6	1-2
1959	KC	A	P	38	2-1
	BRTR			638	172-181

DICKSON, WALTER R.
(Hickory)
b.1883 Greenville,Tex.
d.Dec.10,1918

Yr	Cl	Lea	Pos	G	Rec
1910	NY	N	P	12	1-0
1912	Bos	N	P	36	3-19

(Continued)

Yr	Cl	Lea	Pos	G	Rec
1913	Bos	N	P	19	6-7
1914	Pit	F	P	37	9-19
1915	Pit	F	P	24	7-5
	BRTR			128	26-50

DICKSUS, JOHN OSCAR
(Played under name of
John Oscar Dickshot)

DIDDLEBOCK, HENRY H.
b.June 27,1854 Philadelphia,Pa.
d.Feb.5,1900
Non-playing manager St.L (N) 1896.

DIEHL, ERNEST GUY
b.Cincinnati,O.
d.Nov.6,1958

Yr	Cl	Lea	Pos	G	Rec
1903	Pit	N	O	1	.333
1904	Pit	N	S-O	12	.162
1906	Bos	N	S	3	.545
1909	Bos	N	O	1	.500
	TR			17	.255

DIEHL, GEORGE KRAUSE
b.Feb.25,1918 Allentown,Pa.

Yr	Cl	Lea	Pos	G	Rec
1942	Bos	N	P	1	0-0
1943	Bos	N	P	1	0-0
	BRTR			2	0-0

DIERING, CHARLES EDWARD ALLEN
b.Feb.5,1923 St.Louis,Mo.

Yr	Cl	Lea	Pos	G	Rec
1947	St.L	N	O	105	.216
1948	St.L	N	O	7	.000
1949	St.L	N	O	131	.263
1950	St.L	N	O	89	.250
1951	St.L	N	O	64	.259
1952	NY	N	O	41	.174
1954	Bal	A	O	128	.258
1955	Bal	A	S-3-O	137	.256
1956	Bal	A	3-O	50	.186
	BRTR			752	.249

DIETRICH, WILLIAM JOHN
(Bullfrog)
b.Mar.29,1910 Philadelphia,Pa.

Yr	Cl	Lea	Pos	G	Rec
1933	Phi	A	P	8	0-1
1934	Phi	A	P	40	11-12
1935	Phi	A	P	44	7-13
1936	Phi	A	P	21	4-6
1936	Was	A	P	5	0-1
1936	Chi	A	P	14	4-4
1937	Chi	A	P	29	8-10
1938	Chi	A	P	8	2-4
1939	Chi	A	P	25	7-8
1940	Chi	A	P	23	10-6
1941	Chi	A	P	19	5-8
1942	Chi	A	P	26	6-11
1943	Chi	A	P	26	12-10
1944	Chi	A	P	36	16-17
1945	Chi	A	P	18	7-10
1946	Chi	A	P	11	3-3
1947	Phi	A	P	11	5-2
1948	Phi	A	P	4	1-2
	BRTR			368	108-128

DIETRICK, WILLIAM ALEXANDER
b.Apr.30,1902 Hanover Co.,Va.
d.May 6,1946

Yr	Cl	Lea	Pos	G	Rec
1927	Phi	N	S	5	.167
1928	Phi	N	O	52	.200
	BRTR			57	.198

DIETZ, LLOYD ARTHUR
(Dutch)
b.Feb.9,1912 Cincinnati,O.

Yr	Cl	Lea	Pos	G	Rec
1940	Pit	N	P	6	0-1
1941	Pit	N	P	33	7-2
1942	Pit	N	P	40	6-9
1943	Pit	N	P	10	0-3
1943	Phi	N	P	21	1-1
	BRTR			110	14-16

DIETZEL, LEROY LOUIS
(Roy)
b.Jan.9,1931 Baltimore,Md.

Yr	Cl	Lea	Pos	G	Rec
1954	Was	A	2-3	9	.238
	BRTR				

DIFANI, CLARENCE JOSEPH
(Jay)
b.Dec.21,1923 Crystal City,Mo.

Yr	Cl	Lea	Pos	G	Rec
1948	Was	A	H	2	.000
1949	Was	A	2	2	1.000
	BRTR			4	.333

DIGGS, REESE WILSON
b.Sept.22,1915 Mathews,Va.

Yr	Cl	Lea	Pos	G	Rec
1934	Was	A	P	4	1-2
	BBTR				

DIGNAN, STEPHEN E.
b.May 16,1859 Boston,Mass.
d.July 11,1881

Yr	Cl	Lea	Pos	G	Rec
1880	Bos	N	O	8	.324
1880	Wor	N	O	3	.300
				11	.318

DILLARD, DAVID DONALD
b.Jan.8,1937 Greenville,S.C.

Yr	Cl	Lea	Pos	G	Rec
1959	Cle	A	H	10	.400
1960	Cle	A	O	6	.143
1961	Cle	A	O	74	.272
1962	Cle	A	O	95	.230
	BLTR			185	.252

DILLARD, ROBERT LEE
(Pat)
b.June 12,1874 Chattanooga,Tenn.
d.July 22,1907

Yr	Cl	Lea	Pos	G	Rec
1900	St.L	N	3-O	44	.237

DILLHOEFER, WILLIAM MARTIN
(Pickles)
b.Oct.13,1894 Cleveland,O.
d.Feb.22,1922

Yr	Cl	Lea	Pos	G	Rec
1917	Chi	N	C	42	.126
1918	Phi	N	C	8	.090
1919	St.L	N	C	45	.213
1920	St.L	N	C	76	.263
1921	St.L	N	C	76	.241
	BRTR			247	.223

DILLINGER, HARLEY HUGH
b.Oct.30,1894 Pomeroy,O.
d.Jan.8, 1959

Yr	Cl	Lea	Pos	G	Rec
1914	Cle	A	P	10	0-1
	BRTL				

DILLINGER, ROBERT BERNARD
(Duke)
b.Sept.17,1918 Glendale,Cal.

Yr	Cl	Lea	Pos	G	Rec
1946	St.L	A	S-3	83	.280
1947	St.L	A	3	137	.294
1948	St.L	A	3	153	.321
1949	St.L	A	3	137	.324
1950	Phi	A	3	84	.309
1950	Pit	N	3	58	.288
1951	Pit	N	3	12	.233
1951	Chi	A	3	89	.301
	BRTR			753	.306

DILLON, FRANK EDWARD
(Pop)
b.Oct.17,1873 Normal,Ill.
d.Sept.12,1931

Yr	Cl	Lea	Pos	G	Rec
1899	Pit	N	1	30	.258
1900	Pit	N	1	5	.111
1901	Det	A	1	75	.298
1902	Det	A	1	66	.205
1902	Bal	A	1	2	.286
1904	Bro	N	1	134	.258
	BL			312	.255

DILLON, PACKARD ANDREW
b.St.Louis,Mo.
d.Jan.9,1890

Yr	Cl	Lea	Pos	G	Rec
1875	RS	n	C	3	NR

DiMAGGIO, DOMINIC PAUL
b.Feb.12,1918 San Francisco,Cal.

Yr	Cl	Lea	Pos	G	Rec
1940	Bos	A	O	108	.301
1941	Bos	A	O	144	.283
1942	Bos	A	O	151	.286
1946	Bos	A	O	142	.316
1947	Bos	A	O	136	.283
1948	Bos	A	O	155	.285
1949	Bos	A	O	145	.307
1950	Bos	A	O	141	.328
1951	Bos	A	O	146	.296
1952	Bos	A	O	128	.294
1953	Bos	A	H	3	.333
	BRTR			1399	.298

DiMAGGIO, JOSEPH PAUL
(Joltin' Joe)
b.Nov.25,1914 Martinez,Cal.

Yr	Cl	Lea	Pos	G	Rec
1936	NY	A	O	138	.323
1937	NY	A	O	151	.346
1938	NY	A	O	145	.324
1939	NY	A	O	120	.381
1940	NY	A	O	132	.352
1941	NY	A	O	139	.357
1942	NY	A	O	154	.305
1946	NY	A	O	132	.290
1947	NY	A	O	141	.315
1948	NY	A	O	153	.320
1949	NY	A	O	76	.346
1950	NY	A	1-O	139	.301
1951	NY	A	O	116	.263
	BRTR			1736	.325

DiMAGGIO, VINCENT PAUL
b.Sept.6,1912 Martinez,Cal.

Yr	Cl	Lea	Pos	G	Rec
1937	Bos	N	O	132	.256
1938	Bos	N	O	150	.228
1939	Cin	N	O	8	.071
1940	Cin	N	O	2	.250
1940	Pit	N	O	110	.289
1941	Pit	N	O	151	.267
1942	Pit	N	O	143	.238
1943	Pit	N	S-O	157	.248
1944	Pit	N	3-O	109	.240
1945	Phi	N	O	127	.257
1946	Phi	N	O	6	.211
1946	NY	N	O	15	.000
	BRTR			1110	.249

DIMARIA, JOSEPH FRANKLIN
(Played under name of
Joseph Franklin Demaree)

DIMITRIHOFF, DIMITRI
IVANOVICH (Played under
name of Alexander John Schauer)

DINGES, VANCE GEORGE
b.May 29,1917 Elizabeth,N.J.

Yr	Cl	Lea	Pos	G	Rec
1945	Phi	N	1-O	109	.287
1946	Phi	N	1-O	50	.308
	BLTL			159	.291

DINNEEN, WILLIAM HENRY
(Big Bill)
b.Apr.5,1876 Syracuse,N.Y.
d.Jan.13,1955

Yr	Cl	Lea	Pos	G	Rec
1898	Was	N	P	27	9-16
1899	Was	N	P	36	14-18
1900	Bos	N	P	37	21-16
1901	Bos	N	P	40	16-19
1902	Bos	A	P-O	44	21-20 / .134
1903	Bos	A	P	34	21-11
1904	Bos	A	P	39	24-15
1905	Bos	A	P	31	14-14
1906	Bos	A	P	28	8-19
1907	Bos	A	P	7	0-4
1907	St.L	A	P	22	7-11

(Continued)

Yr	Cl	Lea	Pos	G	Rec
1908	St.L	A	P	27	14-7
1909	St.L	A	P	17	6-7
	BRTR			389	175-177 / .193

DiPIETRO, ROBERT LOUIS PAUL
b.Sept.1,1927 San Francisco.Cal.

Yr	Cl	Lea	Pos	G	Rec
1951	Bos	A	O	4	.091
	BRTR				

DISCH, GEORGE CHARLES
b.Mar.15,1879 Benton Co.,Mo.

Yr	Cl	Lea	Pos	G	Rec
1905	Det	A	P	8	0-2

DISTEL, GEORGE ADAM
b.Apr.15,1896 Madison,Ind.

Yr	Cl	Lea	Pos	G	Rec
1918	St.L	N	2-S	8	.176
	BRTR				

DITMAR, ARTHUR JOHN
b.Apr.3,1929 Revere,Mass.

Yr	Cl	Lea	Pos	G	Rec
1954	Phi	A	P	14	1-4
1955	KC	A	P	35	12-12
1956	KC	A	P	44	12-22
1957	NY	A	P	46	8-3
1958	NY	A	P	38	9-8
1959	NY	A	P	38	13-9
1960	NY	A	P	36	15-9
1961	NY	A	P	12	2-3
1961	KC	A	P	20	0-5
1962	KC	A	P	6	0-2
	BRTR			289	72-77

DITTMER, JOHN DOUGLAS
b.Jan.10,1928 Elkader,Ia.

Yr	Cl	Lea	Pos	G	Rec
1952	Bos	N	2	93	.193
1953	Mil	N	2	138	.266
1954	Mil	N	2	66	.245
1955	Mil	N	2	38	.125
1956	Mil	N	2	44	.245
1957	Det	A	2-3	16	.227
	BLTR			395	.232

DIXON, JOHN CRAIG
(Sonny)
b.Nov.5,1924 Charlotte,N.C.

Yr	Cl	Lea	Pos	G	Rec
1953	Was	A	P	43	5-8
1954	Was	A	P	16	1-2
1954	Phi	A	P	38	5-7
1955	KC	A	P	2	0-0
1956	NY	A	P	3	0-1
	BBTR			102	11-18

DIXON, LEO MICHAEL
b.Sept.6,1897 Chicago,Ill.

Yr	Cl	Lea	Pos	G	Rec
1925	St.L	A	C	76	.224
1926	St.L	A	C	33	.191
1927	St.L	A	C	36	.194
1929	Cin	N	C	14	.167
	BRTR			159	.206

DOAK, WILLIAM LEOPOLD
(Spittin' Bill)
b.Jan.28,1891 Pittsburgh,Pa.
d.Nov.26,1954

Yr	Cl	Lea	Pos	G	Rec
1912	Cin	N	P	1	0-0
1913	St.L	N	P	15	2-8
1914	St.L	N	P	36	19-6
1915	St.L	N	P	38	16-18
1916	St.L	N	P	29	12-8
1917	St.L	N	P	44	16-20
1918	St.L	N	P	31	9-15
1919	St.L	N	P	31	13-14
1920	St.L	N	P	39	20-12
1921	St.L	N	P	32	15-6
1922	St.L	N	P	37	11-13
1923	St.L	N	P	30	8-13
1924	St.L	N	P	11	2-1
1924	Bro	N	P	21	11-5
1927	Bro	N	P	27	11-8
1928	Bro	N	P	28	3-8
1929	St.L	N	P	3	1-2
	BRTR			453	169-157

DOANE, WALTER RUDOLPH
b.Mar.12,1887 Bellevue,Ida.
d.Oct.20,1935

Yr	Cl	Lea	Pos	G	Rec
1909	Cle	A	P-O	4	0-1 .167
1910	Cle	A	P	6	0-0
	BLTR			10	0-1 .188

DOBB, JOHN KENNETH
(Lefty)
b.Nov.15,1901 Muskegon,Mich.

Yr	Cl	Lea	Pos	G	Rec
1924	Chi	A	P	2	0-0
	TL				

DOBBEK, DANIEL JOHN
b.Dec.6,1934 Ontonagon,Mich.

Yr	Cl	Lea	Pos	G	Rec
1959	Was	A	O	16	.250
1960	Was	A	O	110	.218
1961	Min	A	O	72	.168
	BLTR			198	.208

DOBBS, JOHN GORDON
b.June 3,1876 Chattanooga,Tenn.
d.Sept.9,1934

Yr	Cl	Lea	Pos	G	Rec
1901	Cin	N	O	108	.276
1902	Cin	N	O	63	.287
1902	Chi	N	O	59	.310
1903	Chi	N	O	16	.230
1903	Bro	N	O	110	.237
1904	Bro	N	O	95	.248
1905	Bro	N	O	123	.254
	BLTR			574	.263

DOBENS, RAYMOND JOSEPH
b.July 28,1906 Nashua,N.H.

Yr	Cl	Lea	Pos	G	Rec
1929	Bos	A	P	11	0-0
	BLTL				

DOBERNIC, ANDREW JOSEPH
(Jess)
b.Nov.20,1918 Mt.Olive,Ill.

Yr	Cl	Lea	Pos	G	Rec
1939	Chi	A	P	4	0-1
1948	Chi	N	P	54	7-2
1949	Chi	N	P	4	0-0
1949	Cin	N	P	14	0-0
	BRTR			76	7-3

DOBSON, JOSEPH GORDON
(Burrhead)
b.Jan.20,1917 Durant,Okla.

Yr	Cl	Lea	Pos	G	Rec
1939	Cle	A	P	35	2-3
1940	Cle	A	P	40	3-7
1941	Bos	A	P	27	12-5
1942	Bos	A	P	30	11-9
1943	Bos	A	P	25	7-11
1946	Bos	A	P	32	13-7
1947	Bos	A	P	33	18-8
1948	Bos	A	P	38	16-10
1949	Bos	A	P	33	14-12
1950	Bos	A	P	39	15-10
1951	Chi	A	P	28	7-6
1952	Chi	A	P	29	14-10
1953	Chi	A	P	23	5-5
1954	Bos	A	P	2	0-0
	BRTR			414	137-103

DOBY, LAWRENCE EUGENE
b.Dec.13,1924 Camden,S.C.

Yr	Cl	Lea	Pos	G	Rec
1947	Cle	A	1-2-S	29	.156
1948	Cle	A	O	121	.301
1949	Cle	A	O	147	.280
1950	Cle	A	O	142	.326
1951	Cle	A	O	134	.295
1952	Cle	A	O	140	.276
1953	Cle	A	O	149	.263
1954	Cle	A	O	153	.272
1955	Cle	A	O	131	.291
1956	Chi	A	O	140	.268
1957	Chi	A	O	119	.288
1958	Cle	A	O	89	.283
1959	Det	A	O	18	.218
1959	Chi	A	1-O	21	.241
	BLTR			1533	.283

DOCKINS, GEORGE WOODROW
(Lefty)
b.May 5,1917 Clyde,Kan.

Yr	Cl	Lea	Pos	G	Rec
1945	St.L	N	P	31	8-6
1947	Bro	N	P	4	0-0
	BLTL			35	8-6

DODD, ONA MELVIN
b.Oct.14,1886 Springtown,Tex.
d.Mar.31,1929

Yr	Cl	Lea	Pos	G	Rec
1912	Pit	N	2	5	.000
	BRTR				

DODGE, JOHN LEWIS
b.Apr.27,1893 Bolivar,Tenn.
d.June 19,1916

Yr	Cl	Lea	Pos	G	Rec
1912	Phi	N	2-S-3	30	.120
1913	Phi	N	3	3	.333
1913	Cin	N	3	94	.243
	BRTR			127	.215

DODGE, SAMUEL EDWARD
b.Dec.19,1899 Philadelphia,Pa.

Yr	Cl	Lea	Pos	G	Rec
1921	Bos	A	P	1	0-0
1922	Bos	A	P	3	0-1
	BRTR			4	0-1

DOE, ALFRED GEORGE
(Count)
b.Apr.18,1864 Gloucester,Mass.
d.Oct.4,1938

Yr	Cl	Lea	Pos	G	Rec
1890	Buf	p	P	1	0-1
1890	Pit	p	P	1	0-1
				2	0-2

DOERR, ROBERT PERSHING
b.Apr.7,1918 Los Angeles,Cal.

Yr	Cl	Lea	Pos	G	Rec
1937	Bos	A	2	55	.224
1938	Bos	A	2	145	.289
1939	Bos	A	2	127	.318
1940	Bos	A	2	151	.291
1941	Bos	A	2	132	.282
1942	Bos	A	2	144	.290
1943	Bos	A	2	155	.270
1944	Bos	A	2	125	.325
1946	Bos	A	2	151	.271
1947	Bos	A	2	146	.258
1948	Bos	A	2	140	.285
1949	Bos	A	2	139	.309
1950	Bos	A	2	149	.294
1951	Bos	A	2	106	.289
	BRTR			1865	.288

DOHENY, EDWARD R.
b.Nov.24,1874 Northfield,Vt.
d.Dec.29,1916

Yr	Cl	Lea	Pos	G	Rec
1895	NY	N	P	3	0-3
1896	NY	N	P	17	7-7
1897	NY	N	P	10	6-4
1898	NY	N	P	28	8-19
1899	NY	N	P	35	14-16
1900	NY	N	P	18	4-14
1901	NY	N	P	9	2-4
1901	Pit	N	P	11	6-3
1902	Pit	N	P	21	17-4
1903	Pit	N	P	27	16-8
	BLTL			179	80-82

DOLAN, ALVIN JAMES
(Cozy)
(Real name James Alberts)
b.Dec.6,1882 Oshkosh,Wis.
d.Dec.10,1958

Yr	Cl	Lea	Pos	G	Rec
1909	Cin	N	3	3	.167
1911	NY	A	3	19	.304
1912	NY	A	3	17	.200
1912	Phi	N	3	11	.280
1913	Phi	N	3	55	.262
1913	Pit	N	3	35	.203
1914	St.L	N	3-O	126	.240
1915	St.L	N	O	111	.280
1922	NY	N	H	1	.000
	BRTR			378	.252

DOLAN, E. L. (Biddy)

Yr	Cl	Lea	Pos	G	Rec
1914	Ind	F	1	31	.223
	BR				

DOLAN, JOHN
b.Sept.12,1867 Newport,Ky.
d.May 8,1948

Yr	Cl	Lea	Pos	G	Rec
1890	Cin	N	P	2	1-1
1891	Col	a	P	28	13-10
1893	St.L	N	P	3	0-2
1895	Chi	N	P	2	0-1
	TR			35	14-14

DOLAN, JOSEPH
b.Feb.24,1873 Baltimore,Md.
d.Mar.24,1938

Yr	Cl	Lea	Pos	G	Rec
1896	Lou	N	S	44	.219
1897	Lou	N	2-S	35	.210
1899	Phi	N	2	60	.256
1900	Phi	N	2-3	70	.194
1901	Phi	N	2	5	.071
1901	Phi	A	S-3	97	.219
	TR			311	.215

DOLAN, PATRICK HENRY
(Cozy)
b.Dec.3,1872 Cambridge,Mass.
d.Mar.29,1907

Yr	Cl	Lea	Pos	G	Rec
1892	Was	N	P	5	2-2
1895	Bos	N	P	23	11-9
1896	Bos	N	P	6	1-4
1900	Chi	N	O	13	.205
1901	Chi	N	O	43	.262
1901	Bro	N	O	62	.280
1902	Bro	N	O	140	.283
1903	Chi	A	1	28	.250
1903	Cin	N	O	93	.288
1904	Cin	N	1-O	126	.284
1905	Cin	N	1	22	.234
1905	Bos	N	O	112	.275
1906	Bos	N	O	152	.248
	BLTL			825	14-15 .271

DOLAN, THOMAS J.
b.Jan.10,1859 New York,N.Y.
d.Jan.16,1913

Yr	Cl	Lea	Pos	G	Rec
1879	Chi	N	C	1	.000
1882	Buf	N	C-3-O	22	.157
1883	St.L	a	P-C-O	78	0-0 .222
1884	St.L	a	C	35	.263
1884	St.L	U	C-3-O	20	.194
1885	St.L	N	C	3	.222
1886	St.L	N	C	15	.250
1886	Bal	a	C	37	.153
1888	St.L	a	C	11	.194
1891	St.L	a	C	1	.000
	TR			223	0-0 .203

DOLE, W. C.

Yr	Cl	Lea	Pos	G	Rec
1875	NH	n	O	1	NR

DOLJACK, FRANK JOSEPH
b.Oct.10,1908 Cleveland,O.
d.Jan.23,1948

Yr	Cl	Lea	Pos	G	Rec
1930	Det	A	O	20	.257
1931	Det	A	O	63	.278
1932	Det	A	O	8	.385
1933	Det	A	O	42	.286
1934	Det	A	O	56	.233
1943	Cle	A	O	3	.000
	BRTR			192	.269

DOLL, ARTHUR JAMES
(Moose)
b.May 7,1913 Chicago,Ill.

Yr	Cl	Lea	Pos	G	Rec
1935	Bos	N	C	3	.100
1936	Bos	N	P	1	0-1
1938	Bos	N	P	3	0-0
	BRTR			7	0-1 .154

DONAHUE, CHARLES MICHAEL (She)
b.June 29,1877 Oswego,N.Y.
d.Aug.28,1947

Yr	Cl	Lea	Pos	G	Rec
1904	St.L	N	S	4	.267
1904	Phi	N	S-3	56	.215
	BRTR			60	.219

DONAHUE, FRANCIS ROSTELL (Red)
b.Jan.23,1873 Waterbury,Conn.
d.Aug.25,1913

Yr	Cl	Lea	Pos	G	Rec
1893	NY	N	P	2	0-1
1895	St.L	N	P	1	0-1
1896	St.L	N	P	33	7-23
1897	St.L	N	P	44	11-33
1898	Phi	N	P	34	17-16
1899	Phi	N	P	34	22-7
1900	Phi	N	P	26	16-10
1901	Phi	N	P	35	20-13
1902	St.L	A	P	35	22-11
1903	St.L	A	P	14	6-4
1903	Cle	A	P	19	6-13
1904	Cle	A	P	35	18-14
1905	Cle	A	P	20	6-11
1906	Det	A	P	29	13-14
	BRTR			361	164-171

DONAHUE, JAMES AUGUSTUS
b.Jan.8,1862 Lockport,Ill.
d.Apr.19,1935

Yr	Cl	Lea	Pos	G	Rec
1886	Mets	a	C-O	50	.201
1887	Mets	a	C	60	.345
1888	KC	a	C	87	.241
1889	KC	a	C	67	.238
1891	Col	a	C	77	.217
	TR			341	.245

DONAHUE, JOHN AUGUSTUS (Jiggs)
b.July 13,1879 Springfield,O.
d.July 19,1913

Yr	Cl	Lea	Pos	G	Rec
1900	Pit	N	C	3	.200
1901	Pit	N	C	2	.000
1901	Mil	A	C	37	.305
1902	St.L	A	C-1	29	.250
1904	Chi	A	1	102	.251
1905	Chi	A	1	149	.287
1906	Chi	A	1	154	.257
1907	Chi	A	1	157	.259
1908	Chi	A	1	93	.204
1909	Chi	A	1	2	.000
1909	Was	A	1	84	.237
	BLTL			812	.256

DONAHUE, JOHN FRANCIS (Jiggs)
b.Apr.19,1894 Roxbury,Mass.
d.Oct.3,1949

Yr	Cl	Lea	Pos	G	Rec
1923	Bos	A	O	10	.343
	BBTR				

DONAHUE, JOHN STEPHEN MICHAEL (Deacon)
b.June 23,1922 Chicago,Ill.

Yr	Cl	Lea	Pos	G	Rec
1943	Phi	N	P	2	0-0
1944	Phi	N	P	6	0-2
	BRTR			8	0-2

DONAHUE, PATRICK WILLIAM
b.Nov.8,1884 Springfield,O.

Yr	Cl	Lea	Pos	G	Rec
1908	Bos	A	C	35	.198
1909	Bos	A	C	64	.239
1910	Bos	A	C	2	.000
1910	Phi	A	C	16	.143
1910	Cle	A	C	2	.167
	BRTR			119	.212

DONAHUE, TIMOTHY CORNELIUS (Bridget)
b.June 8,1870 Raynham,Mass.
d.June 12,1902

Yr	Cl	Lea	Pos	G	Rec
1891	Bos	a	C	3	.000
1895	Chi	N	C	62	.271
1896	Chi	N	C	54	.226
1897	Chi	N	C	53	.234
1898	Chi	N	C	117	.236
1899	Chi	N	C	90	.250
1900	Chi	N	C	65	.239
1902	Was	A	C	3	.250
	BLTR			447	.241

DONALD, RICHARD ATLEY (Swampy)
b.Aug.19,1912 Morton,Miss.

Yr	Cl	Lea	Pos	G	Rec
1938	NY	A	P	2	0-1
1939	NY	A	P	24	13-3
1940	NY	A	P	24	8-3
1941	NY	A	P	22	9-5
1942	NY	A	P	20	11-3
1943	NY	A	P	22	6-4
1944	NY	A	P	30	13-10*
1945	NY	A	P	9	5-4
	BLTR			153	65-33

DONALDS, EDWARD ALEXANDER (Skipper)
b.June 22,1885 Gallipolis,O.
d.July 3,1950

Yr	Cl	Lea	Pos	G	Rec
1912	Cin	N	P	1	1-0
	BRTR				

DONDERO, LEONARD PETER
b.Sept.12,1903 Newark,Cal.

Yr	Cl	Lea	Pos	G	Rec
1929	St.L	A	3	19	.194
	BRTR				

DONELY, JAMES B.
b.July 19,1865 New Haven,Conn.
d.Mar.5,1915

Yr	Cl	Lea	Pos	G	Rec
1884	KC	U	C-3	6	.130
1884	Ind	a	S-3	40	.249
1885	Det	N	1-3	55	.232
1886	KC	N	P-3	113	0-1 / .201
1887	Was	N	3	117	.229
1888	Was	N	3	122	.201
1889	Was	N	3	4	.154
1890	St.L	a	3	11	.344
1891	Col	a	3	17	.241
1896	Bal	N	3	104	.330
1897	Pit	N	3	43	.177
1897	NY	N	3	23	.205
1898	St.L	N	3	1	1.000
	BR			656	0-1 / .234

DONLIN, MICHAEL JOSEPH (Turkey Mike)
b.May 30,1878 Erie,Pa.
d.Sept.24,1933

Yr	Cl	Lea	Pos	G	Rec
1899	St.L	N	P-O	67	0-0 / .329
1900	St.L	N	1	77	.327
1901	Bal	A	1-O	122	.340
1902	Cin	N	P-S-O	33	0-0 / .294
1903	Cin	N	O	124	.351
1904	Cin	N	O	59	.356
1904	NY	N	O	37	.280
1905	NY	N	O	150	.356
1906	NY	N	O	30	.314
1908	NY	N	O	155	.334
1911	NY	N	O	12	.333
1911	Bos	N	O	56	.318
1912	Pit	N	O	77	.316
1914	NY	N	O	35	.161
	BLTL			1034	0-0 / .334

DONNELLY, EDWARD (Buck)
b.July 29,1880 Hampton,N.Y.
d.Nov.28,1957

Yr	Cl	Lea	Pos	G	Rec
1911	Bos	N	P	5	3-2
1912	Bos	N	P	38	5-10
	BRTR			43	8-12

DONNELLY, EDWARD VINCENT
b.Dec.10,1934 Allen,Mich.

Yr	Cl	Lea	Pos	G	Rec
1959	Chi	N	P	9	1-1
	BRTR				

DONNELLY, FRANKLIN MARION
b.Oct.7,1869 Tamaroa,Ill.
d.Feb.3,1953

Yr	Cl	Lea	Pos	G	Rec
1893	Chi	N	P	6	3-1
1894	Chi	N	P	1	0-0
				7	3-1

DONNELLY, SYLVESTER URBAN (Blix)
b.Jan.21,1915 Olivia,Minn.

Yr	Cl	Lea	Pos	G	Rec
1944	St.L	N	P	27	2-1
1945	St.L	N	P	31	8-10
1946	St.L	N	P	13	1-2
1946	Phi	N	P	12	3-4
1947	Phi	N	P	38	4-6
1948	Phi	N	P	26	5-7
1949	Phi	N	P	23	2-1
1950	Phi	N	P	14	2-4
1951	Bos	N	P	6	0-1
	BRTR			190	27-36

DONNELLY, T. J.

Yr	Cl	Lea	Pos	G	Rec
1871	Kek	n	3-O	9	.233
1873	Nat	n	2-S-O	30	NR
1874	Phi	n	2-S-O	5	NR
				44	NR

DONOHUE, JAMES THOMAS
b.Oct.31,1938 St.Louis,Mo.

Yr	Cl	Lea	Pos	G	Rec
1961	Det	A	P	14	1-1
1961	LA	A	P	38	4-6
1962	LA	A	P	12	1-0
1962	Min	A	P	6	0-1
	BRTR			70	6-8

DONOHUE, JOSEPH F.
b.1869 Syracuse,N.Y.
d.Nov.12,1894

Yr	Cl	Lea	Pos	G	Rec
1891	Phi	N	O	6	.317

DONOHUE, PETER JOSEPH
b.Nov.5,1900 Athens,Tex.

Yr	Cl	Lea	Pos	G	Rec
1921	Cin	N	P	21	7-6
1922	Cin	N	P	33	18-9
1923	Cin	N	P	42	21-15
1924	Cin	N	P	36	16-9
1925	Cin	N	P	43	21-14
1926	Cin	N	P	47	20-14
1927	Cin	N	P	33	6-16
1928	Cin	N	P	23	7-11
1929	Cin	N	P	32	10-13
1930	Cin	N	P	8	1-3
1930	NY	N	P	18	7-6
1931	NY	N	P	4	0-1
1931	Cle	A	P	2	0-0
1932	Bos	A	P	4	0-1
	BRTR			346	134-118

DONOSO, LINO GALATA
b.Sept.23,1922 Havana,Cuba

Yr	Cl	Lea	Pos	G	Rec
1955	Pit	N	P	25	4-6
1956	Pit	N	P	3	0-0
	BLTL			28	4-6

DONOVAN, FREDERICK M.
b.Cleveland,O.

Yr	Cl	Lea	Pos	G	Rec
1895	Cle	N	C	3	.083

DONOVAN, JEREMIAH FRANCIS
b.Aug.24,1875 Williamsport,Pa.
d.June 27,1938

Yr	Cl	Lea	Pos	G	Rec
1906	Phi	N	C	53	.199
	TR				

DONOVAN, MICHAEL B.
b.Oct.13,1883 New York,N.Y.
d.Feb.3,1938

Yr	Cl	Lea	Pos	G	Rec
1904	Cle	A	S	2	.000
1908	NY	A	3	5	.157
	TR			7	.143

DONOVAN, PATRICK JOSEPH
b.Mar.16,1865 County Cork,Ireland
d.Dec.25,1953

Yr	Cl	Lea	Pos	G	Rec
1890	Bos	N	O	32	.245
1890	Bro	N	O	26	.380
1891	Lou	a	O	98	.319
1891	Was	a	O	17	.200
1892	Was	N	O	40	.252
1892	Pit	N	O	88	.311
1893	Pit	N	O	110	.331
1894	Pit	N	O	133	.306
1895	Pit	N	O	126	.316
1896	Pit	N	O	129	.316
1897	Pit	N	M-O	120	.326
1898	Pit	N	O	147	.302
1899	Pit	N	M-O	123	.296
1900	St.L	N	O	127	.324
1901	St.L	N	M-O	129	.294
1902	St.L	N	M-O	126	.309
1903	St.L	N	M-O	105	.327
1904	Was	A	M-O	125	.239
1906	Bro	N	M-O	7	.238
1907	Bro	N	M-O	1	.000
	BLTL			1809	.304

Non-playing manager Bro (N) 1908 and Bos (A) 1910-11.

DONOVAN, RICHARD EDWARD
b.Dec.7,1927 Boston,Mass.

Yr	Cl	Lea	Pos	G	Rec
1950	Bos	N	P	10	0-2
1951	Bos	N	P	8	0-0
1952	Bos	N	P	7	0-2
1954	Det	A	P	2	0-0
1955	Chi	A	P	40	15-9
1956	Chi	A	P	44	12-10
1957	Chi	A	P	30	16-6
1958	Chi	A	P	34	15-14
1959	Chi	A	P	31	9-10
1960	Chi	A	P	33	6-1
1961	Was	A	P	24	10-10
1962	Cle	A	P	34	20-10
	BLTR			297	103-74

DONOVAN, THOMAS J.
b.Jan.1,1873 W. Troy,N.Y.

Yr	Cl	Lea	Pos	G	Rec
1901	Cle	A	O	18	.253

DONOVAN, WILLARD EARL
b.July 6,1916 Maywood,Ill.

Yr	Cl	Lea	Pos	G	Rec
1942	Bos	N	P	31	3-6
1943	Bos	N	P	7	1-0
	BRTL			38	4-6

DONOVAN, WILLIAM EDWARD
(Wild Bill)
b.Oct.13,1876 Lawrence,Mass.
d.Dec.9,1923

Yr	Cl	Lea	Pos	G	Rec
1898	Was	N	P-O	30	1-6 .178
1899	Bro	N	P	4	1-2
1900	Bro	N	P	5	1-2
1901	Bro	N	P	41	25-15
1902	Bro	N	1-P-2-O	46	17-15 .169
1903	Det	A	P	39	17-15
1904	Det	A	P	44	17-16
1905	Det	A	P	46	18-14
1906	Det	A	P	28	9-15
1907	Det	A	P	37	25-4
1908	Det	A	P	30	18-7
1909	Det	A	P	22	8-7
1910	Det	A	P	26	18-7
1911	Det	A	P	24	10-9
1912	Det	A	P	6	1-0
1915	NY	A	M-P	10	0-3
1916	NY	A	M-P	1	0-0
1918	Det	A	P	2	0-0
	BRTR			441	186-137 .196

Non-playing manager NY (A) 1917 and Phi (N) 1921

DOOIN, CHARLES SEBASTIAN
(Red)
b.June 12,1879 Cincinnati,O.
d.May 14,1952

Yr	Cl	Lea	Pos	G	Rec
1902	Phi	N	C-O	87	.228
1903	Phi	N	C	53	.218

(Continued)

Yr	Cl	Lea	Pos	G	Rec
1904	Phi	N	C	104	.242
1905	Phi	N	C	108	.250
1906	Phi	N	C	107	.245
1907	Phi	N	C	96	.211
1908	Phi	N	C	132	.248
1909	Phi	N	C	140	.224
1910	Phi	N	M-C	94	.242
1911	Phi	N	M-C	74	.328
1912	Phi	N	M-C	69	.234
1913	Phi	N	M-C	55	.256
1914	Phi	N	M-C	53	.178
1915	Cin	N	C	10	.323
1915	NY	N	C	46	.218
1916	NY	N	C	15	.118
	BRTR			1243	.240

DOOLAN, MICHAEL JOSEPH (Doc)
(Real name
Michael Joseph Doolittle)
b.May 7,1880 Ashland,Pa.
d.Nov.1,1951

Yr	Cl	Lea	Pos	G	Rec
1905	Phi	N	S	135	.254
1906	Phi	N	S	154	.230
1907	Phi	N	S	145	.204
1908	Phi	N	S	129	.234
1909	Phi	N	S	147	.219
1910	Phi	N	S	148	.263
1911	Phi	N	S	145	.238
1912	Phi	N	S	146	.258
1913	Phi	N	S	151	.218
1914	Bal	F	S	144	.245
1915	Bal	F	S	119	.195
1915	Chi	F	S	24	.256
1916	Chi	N	S	28	.211
1916	NY	N	S	18	.240
1918	Bro	N	2	92	.179
	BRTR			1725	.231

DOOLITTLE, MICHAEL JOSEPH
(Played under name of
Michael JOSEPH Doolan)

DOOMS, HARRY E. (Jack)
b.St.Louis,Mo.
d.Dec.1899

Yr	Cl	Lea	Pos	G	Rec
1892	Lou	N	O	1	.000

DORAN, JOHN F.
b.1870 N.J.

Yr	Cl	Lea	Pos	G	Rec
1891	Lou	a	P	17	5-9
	TL				

DORAN, THOMAS J. (Long Tom)
b.Dec.2,1880 Westchester Co.,N.Y.
d.June 22,1910

Yr	Cl	Lea	Pos	G	Rec
1904	Bos	A	C	5	.000
1905	Bos	A	C	3	.000
1905	Det	A	C	29	.165
1906	Bos	A	C	2	.000
	TR			39	.146

DORAN, WILLIAM JAMES
b.June 14,1900 San Francisco,Cal.

Yr	Cl	Lea	Pos	G	Rec
1922	Cle	A	3	3	.500
	BLTR				

DORGAN, JEREMIAH F.
b.1856 Meriden,Conn.
d.June 10,1891

Yr	Cl	Lea	Pos	G	Rec
1880	Wor	N	C-O	9	.229
1882	Ath	a	C-O	45	.287
1884	Ind	a	O	34	.294
1884	Bro	a	C	4	.308
1885	Det	N	O	39	.285
	TR			131	.286

DORGAN, MICHAEL CORNELIUS
b.Oct.2,1853 Middletown,Conn.
d.Apr.26,1909

Yr	Cl	Lea	Pos	G	Rec
1877	St.L	N	C-S-3-O	60	.308
1879	Syr	N	1-3-O	59	.266
1880	Pro	N	P-3-O	76	0-0 .246
1881	Wor	N	1-S-O	51	.264
1881	Det	N	1-3-O	8	.229

(Continued)

Yr	Cl	Lea	Pos	G	Rec
1883	NY	N	P-C-O	62	0-1 .235
1884	NY	N	P-C-2-O	79	8-6 .276
1885	NY	N	O	88	.325
1886	NY	N	O	118	.292
1887	NY	N	O	71	.295
1890	Syr	a	O	31	.219
	BRTR			703	8-7 .273

DORISH, HARRY (Fritz)
b.July 13,1923 Sweyersville,Pa.

Yr	Cl	Lea	Pos	G	Rec
1947	Bos	A	P	41	7-8
1948	Bos	A	P	9	0-1
1949	Bos	A	P	5	0-0
1950	St.L	A	P	30	4-9
1951	Chi	A	P-3	32	5-6 .258
1952	Chi	A	P	39	8-4
1953	Chi	A	P	55	10-6
1954	Chi	A	P	37	6-4
1955	Chi	A	P	13	2-0
1955	Bal	A	P	35	3-3
1956	Bal	A	P	13	0-0
1956	Bos	A	P	15	0-2
	BRTR			324	45-43 .157

DORMAN, CHARLES DWIGHT (Red)
b.Oct.3,1905 Jacksonville,Ill.

Yr	Cl	Lea	Pos	G	Rec
1928	Cle	A	O	25	.364
	BRTR				

DORMAN, CHARLES FREDERICK
(Dutch)
b.June 6,1902 Carlstadt,N.J.

Yr	Cl	Lea	Pos	G	Rec
1923	Chi	A	C	1	.500
	BRTR				

DORNER, AUGUSTUS
b.Aug.18,1876 Chambersburg,Pa.
d.May 4,1956

Yr	Cl	Lea	Pos	G	Rec
1902	Cle	A	P	4	3-1
1903	Cle	A	P	12	3-5
1906	Cin	N	P	2	0-0
1906	Bos	N	P	34	8-26
1907	Bos	N	P	36	12-16
1908	Bos	N	P	38	8-19
1909	Bos	N	P	5	1-2
	BRTR			131	35-69

DORR, CHARLES ALBERT (Bert)
b.Omaha,Neb.
d.June 19,1914

Yr	Cl	Lea	Pos	G	Rec
1882	St.L	a	P	8	3-5

DORSETT, CALVIN LEAVELL
(Preacher)
b.June 10,1916 Greenville,Tex.

Yr	Cl	Lea	Pos	G	Rec
1940	Cle	A	P	1	0-0
1941	Cle	A	P	5	0-1
1947	Cle	A	P	2	0-0
	BRTR			8	0-1

DORSEY, JEREMIAH
b.1885 Oakland,Cal.

Yr	Cl	Lea	Pos	G	Rec
1911	Pit	N	O	2	.000

DORSEY, JEREMIAH M.
b.Auburn,N.Y.

Yr	Cl	Lea	Pos	G	Rec
1884	Bal	U	P-O	2	0-1 .000

DOSCHER, JOHN HERMAN JR.
b.July 27,1880 Troy,N.Y.

Yr	Cl	Lea	Pos	G	Rec
1903	Chi	N	P	1	0-1
1903	Bro	N	P	3	0-0
1904	Bro	N	P	2	0-1
1905	Bro	N	P	11	1-5
1906	Bro	N	P	2	0-1
1908	Cin	N	P	6	1-3
	BLTL			25	2-11

DOSCHER, JOHN HERMAN, SR. (Herm)
b.Dec.20,1852 New York,N.Y.
d.Mar.20,1934

Yr	Cl	Lea	Pos	G	Rec
1872	Atl	n	O	6	NR
1873	Atl	n	O	1	NR
1875	Nat	n	S-3	21	NR
1879	Tro	N	3	46	.223
1881	Cle	N	3	5	.211
1882	Cle	N	3-O	25	.240
				104	NR

DOTTER, GARY RICHARD
b.Aug.7,1942 St.Louis,Mo.

Yr	Cl	Lea	Pos	G	Rec
1961	Min	A	P	2	0-0

BLTL

DOTTERER, HENRY JOHN
b.Nov.11,1931 Syracuse,N.Y.

Yr	Cl	Lea	Pos	G	Rec
1957	Cin	N	C	4	.083
1958	Cin	N	C	11	.250
1959	Cin	N	C	52	.267
1960	Cin	N	C	33	.228
1961	Was	A	C	7	.263
	BRTR			107	.248

DOTY, ELMER L. (Babe)
b.Dec.17,1867 Lyons,N.Y.
d.Nov.20,1929

Yr	Cl	Lea	Pos	G	Rec
1890	Tol	a	P	1	1-0

TR

DOUGHERTY, CHARLES
b.Feb.7,1862 Darlington,Wis.
d.Feb.18,1925

Yr	Cl	Lea	Pos	G	Rec
1884	Alt	U	2-S-3-O	23	.259

DOUGHERTY, PATRICK HENRY
b.Oct.27,1876 Bolivar, N.Y.
d.Apr.30,1940

Yr	Cl	Lea	Pos	G	Rec
1902	Bos	A	3-O	106	.335
1903	Bos	A	O	139	.332
1904	Bos	A	O	59	.268
1904	NY	A	O	96	.289
1905	NY	A	O	116	.263
1906	NY	A	O	12	.170
1906	Chi	A	O	75	.238
1907	Chi	A	O	148	.270
1908	Chi	A	O	138	.278
1909	Chi	A	O	139	.285
1910	Chi	A	O	127	.248
1911	Chi	A	O	76	.289
	BLTR			1231	.284

DOUGHERTY, THOMAS JAMES (Sugar Boy)
b.May 30,1881 Chicago,Ill.
d.Nov.6,1953

Yr	Cl	Lea	Pos	G	Rec
1904	Chi	A	P	1	0-0

BLTR

DOUGLAS, ASTYANAX SAUNDERS
b.Sept.19,1899 Covington,Tex.

Yr	Cl	Lea	Pos	G	Rec
1921	Cin	N	C	4	.143
1925	Cin	N	C	7	.176
	BLTR			11	.174

DOUGLAS. CHARLES WILLIAM
b.Feb.17.1935 Carrboro.N.C.

Yr	Cl	Lea	Pos	G	Rec
1957	Pit	N	P	11	3-3

BRTR

DOUGLAS, JOHN FRANKLIN
b.Sept.14,1918 Beckley,W.Va.

Yr	Cl	Lea	Pos	G	Rec
1945	Bro	N	1	5	.000

BLTL

DOUGLAS, PHILIP BROOKS (Shufflin' Phil)
b.June 17,1890 Cedartown,Ga.
d.Aug.1,1952

Yr	Cl	Lea	Pos	G	Rec
1912	Chi	A	P	3	0-1
1914	Cin	N	P	45	11-18
1915	Cin	N	P	8	1-5
1915	Bro	N	P	20	5-5

(Continued)

Yr	Cl	Lea	Pos	G	Rec
1915	Chi	N	P	4	1-1
1917	Chi	N	P	51	14-20
1918	Chi	N	P	25	10-9
1919	Chi	N	P	25	10-6
1919	NY	N	P	8	2-4
1920	NY	N	P	46	14-10
1921	NY	N	P	40	15-10
1922	NY	N	P	24	11-4
	BRTR			299	94-93

DOUGLAS, WILLIAM B. (Klondike)
b.May 10,1872 Boston,Pa.
d.Dec.13,1953

Yr	Cl	Lea	Pos	G	Rec
1896	St.L	N	O	79	.268
1897	St.L	N	C-1-O	127	.327
1898	Phi	N	1	146	.266
1899	Phi	N	C	72	.264
1900	Phi	N	C	45	.306
1901	Phi	N	C	47	.333
1902	Phi	N	C-1-O	107	.235
1903	Phi	N	1	97	.255
1904	Phi	N	1	3	.333
	BLTR			723	.278

DOUGLASS, LAWRENCE HOWARD
b.June 5,1892 Jellico,Tenn.

Yr	Cl	Lea	Pos	G	Rec
1915	Bal	F	P	2	1-0

DOUTHIT, TAYLOR LEE
b.Apr.22,1901 Little Rock,Ark.

Yr	Cl	Lea	Pos	G	Rec
1923	St.L	N	O	9	.185
1924	St.L	N	O	53	.277
1925	St.L	N	O	30	.274
1926	St.L	N	O	139	.308
1927	St.L	N	O	130	.262
1928	St.L	N	O	154	.295
1929	St.L	N	O	150	.336
1930	St.L	N	O	154	.303
1931	St.L	N	O	36	.331
1931	Cin	N	O	95	.262
1932	Cin	N	O	96	.243
1933	Cin	N	O	1	.000
1933	Chi	N	O	27	.225
	BRTR			1074	.291

DOW, CLARENCE G.
b.Oct.11,1854 Charlestown,Mass.
d.Mar.11,1893

Yr	Cl	Lea	Pos	G	Rec
1884	Bos	U	O	1	.333

DOWD, JAMES J. (Skip)
b.Feb.16,1889 Holyoke,Mass.

Yr	Cl	Lea	Pos	G	Rec
1910	Pit	N	P	1	0-0

DOWD, RAYMOND BERNARD (Snooks)
b.Dec.20,1897 Springfield,Mass.
d.Apr.4,1962

Yr	Cl	Lea	Pos	G	Rec
1919	Det	A	H	1	.000
1919	Phi	A	2-S-3	13	.158
1926	Bro	N	2	2	.000
	BRTR			16	.077

DOWD, THOMAS JEFFERSON (Buttermilk Tommy)
b.Apr.20,1869 Holyoke,Mass.
d.July 2,1933

Yr	Cl	Lea	Pos	G	Rec
1891	Bos	a	O	4	.167
1891	Was	a	2	105	.252
1892	Was	N	2-3-O	141	.246
1893	St.L	N	O	131	.294
1894	St.L	N	O	123	.267
1895	St.L	N	O	127	.325
1896	St.L	N	M-2-O	125	.266
1897	St.L	N	M-2-O	35	.267
1897	Phi	N	O	90	.290
1898	St.L	N	O	139	.243
1899	Cle	N	O	146	.275
1901	Bos	A	O	138	.270
	BRTR			1304	.272

DOWIE, JOSEPH E.
b.New Orleans,La.
d.Sept.3,1893

Yr	Cl	Lea	Pos	G	Rec
1889	Bal	a	O	20	.240

DOWLING, HENRY PETER (Pete)
b.Ky.
d.June 30,1905

Yr	Cl	Lea	Pos	G	Rec
1897	Lou	N	P	4	1-3
1898	Lou	N	P	35	13-17
1899	Lou	N	P	34	13-18
1901	Mil	A	P	10	3-5
1901	Cle	A	P	34	8-15
	TL			118	38-58

DOWLING, RODNEY J.
(Played under name of Robert J. Glenalvin)

DOWNEY, ALEXANDER C. (Red)
b.Feb.6,1889 Aurora,Ind.

Yr	Cl	Lea	Pos	G	Rec
1909	Bro	N	O	19	.256

DOWNEY, THOMAS EDWARD
b.Jan.1,1884 Lawrence,Mass.

Yr	Cl	Lea	Pos	G	Rec
1909	Cin	N	S	119	.231
1910	Cin	N	S-3	109	.270
1911	Cin	N	S	106	.261
1912	Phi	N	3	54	.292
1912	Chi	N	3	13	.182
1914	Buf	F	2-S	151	.223
1915	Buf	F	2-3	90	.199
	BRTR			642	.241

DOWNING, ALPHONSE ERWIN
b.June 28,1941 Trenton,N.J.

Yr	Cl	Lea	Pos	G	Rec
1961	NY	A	P	5	0-1
1962	NY	A	P	1	0-0
	BRTL			6	0-1

DOWNS, JEROME WILLIS (Red)
b.Aug.23,1883 Neola,Ia.
d.Oct.12,1939

Yr	Cl	Lea	Pos	G	Rec
1907	Det	A	2-O	105	.219
1908	Det	A	2	84	.221
1912	Bro	N	2	9	.250
1912	Chi	N	2	43	.263
	BRTR			241	.227

DOWSE, THOMAS J.
b.Aug.12,1867 New York,N.Y.

Yr	Cl	Lea	Pos	G	Rec
1890	Cle	N	O	40	.207
1891	Col	a	C	55	.217
1892	Lou	N	P-C	40	0-1 / .173
1892	Cin	N	C	1	.000
1892	Phi	N	C	16	.170
1892	Was	N	C-O	6	.261
	BRTR			158	0-1 / .196

DOYLE, CORNELIUS J.
b.1858 Holyoke,Mass.
d.Jan.18,1927

Yr	Cl	Lea	Pos	G	Rec
1883	Phi	N	O	16	.203
1890	Tol	a	3	1	.000
				17	.197

DOYLE, EDWARD H.
b.Ill.
d.Feb.6,1929

Yr	Cl	Lea	Pos	G	Rec
1882	St.L	a	P	3	0-3

DOYLE, HOWARD JAMES (Danny)
b.Jan.24,1917 McLoud,Okla.

Yr	Cl	Lea	Pos	G	Rec
1943	Bos	A	C	13	.209

BBTR

DOYLE, JAMES FRANCIS
b.Dec.25,1881 Syracuse,N.Y.
d.Feb.1,1912

Yr	Cl	Lea	Pos	G	Rec
1910	Cin	N	3	7	.191
1911	Chi	N	3	127	.282
	BRTR			134	.277

Yr Cl Lea Pos G Rec

DOYLE, JESS HERBERT
b.Apr.14,1898 Knoxville,Tenn.
d.Apr.15,1961
1925 Det A P 45 4-7
1926 Det A P 2 0-0
1927 Det A P 7 0-0
1931 St.L A P 1 0-0
BRTR 55 4-7

DOYLE, JOHN A.
b.N.S.,Canada
1884 Pit a O 23 .203

DOYLE, JOHN JOSEPH
b.Oct.25,1870 Killorglin,Ireland
d.Dec.31,1958
1889 Col a C 11 .355
1890 Col a P-C 76 {1-0 .272
1891 Cle N C-3-O 64 .263
1892 Cle N C-1-O 22 .300
1892 NY N C-2-O 86 .295
1893 NY N C-O 80 .322
1894 NY N 1 105 .369
1895 NY N M-1 78 .316
1896 Bal N 1 118 .345
1897 Bal N 1 114 .356
1898 Was N M-1-2 42 .285
1898 NY N 1 79 .297
1899 NY N 1 117 .308
1900 NY N 1 130 .273
1901 Chi N 1 73 .241
1902 NY N 1 50 .300
1902 Was A C-1-2-O 78 .238
1903 Bro N 1 139 .313
1904 Bro N 1 8 .227
1904 Phi N 1 64 .220
1905 NY A 1 1 .000
BRTR 1535 {1-0 .302

DOYLE, JOSEPH
b.Cincinnati,O.
1872 Nat n 2-S 8 NR

DOYLE, JOSEPH J.
b.Apr.9,1838 New York,N.Y.
d.Jan.7,1906
Non-playing manager Bro (a) 1885

DOYLE, JUDD BRUCE (Slow Joe)
b.Sept.15,1881 Clay Center,Kan.
d.Nov.21,1947
1906 NY A P 9 2-2
1907 NY A P 29 11-11
1908 NY A P 12 1-1
1909 NY A P 17 8-6
1910 NY A P 3 0-2
1910 Cin N P 5 0-0
BRTR 75 22-22

DOYLE, LAWRENCE JOSEPH
(Laughing Larry)
b.July 31,1886 Caseyville,Ill.
1907 NY N 2 69 .260
1908 NY N 2 102 .308
1909 NY N 2 144 .302
1910 NY N 2 151 .285
1911 NY N 2 141 .310
1912 NY N 2 143 .330
1913 NY N 2 132 .280
1914 NY N 2 145 .260
1915 NY N 2 150 .320
1916 NY N 2 113 .264
1916 Chi N 2 9 .436
1917 Chi N 2 135 .254
1918 NY N 2 75 .261
1919 NY N 2 113 .289
1920 NY N 2 137 .285
BLTR 1759 .290

DOYLE, WILLIAM CARL
b.July 30,1912 Knoxville,Tenn.
d.Sept.4,1951
1935 Phi A P 14 2-7
(Continued)
1936 Phi A P 8 0-3
1939 Bro N P 5 1-2
1940 Bro N P 3 0-0
1940 St.L N P 21 3-3
BRTR 51 6-15

DOZIER, WILLIAM JOSEPH (Buzz)
b.Aug.31,1927 Waco,Tex.
1947 Was A P 2 0-0
1949 Was A P 2 0-0
BRTR 4 0-0

DRABOWSKY, MYRON WALTER
(Moe)
b.July 21,1935 Ozanna,Poland
1956 Chi N P 9 2-4
1957 Chi N P 36 13-15
1958 Chi N P 22 9-11
1959 Chi N P 31 5-10
1960 Chi N P 33 3-1
1961 Mil N P 16 0-2
1962 Cin N P 23 2-6
1962 KC A P 10 1-1
BRTR 180 35-50

DRAKE, ...
1884 Was a O 2 .286

DRAKE, DELOS D.
b.Dec.3,1887 Girard,O.
1911 Det A O 95 .279
1914 St.L F 1-O 138 .252
1915 St.L F O 99 .265
BRTR 332 .264

DRAKE, LARRY FRANCIS
b.May 4,1921 Dallas,Tex.
1945 Phi A O 1 .000
1948 Was A O 4 .286
BLTR 5 .222

DRAKE, LOGAN GAFFNEY
b.Dec.26,1900 Spartanburg,S.C.
d.June 1,1940
1922 Cle A P 1 0-0
1923 Cle A P 4 0-0
1924 Cle A P 5 0-1
BRTR 10 0-1

DRAKE, SAMUEL HARRISON
b.Oct.7,1934 Little Rock,Ark.
1960 Chi N 2-3 15 .067
1961 Chi N O 13 .000
1962 NY N 2-3 25 .192
BBTR 53 .153

DRAKE, SOLOMON LOUIS
b.Oct.23,1930 N.Little Rock,Ark.
1956 Chi N O 65 .256
1959 LA N O 9 .250
1959 Phi N O 67 .145
BBTR 141 .232

DRAKE, THOMAS KENDALL
b.Aug.7,1914 Birmingham,Ala.
1939 Cle A P 8 0-1
1941 Bro N P-O 11 {1-1 .400
BRTR 19 {1-2 .286

DRAUBY, JACOB C.
b.1865 Harrisburg,Pa.
1892 Was N 3 10 .205

DREESEN, WILLIAM R.
b.July 26,1904 New York,N.Y.
1931 Bos N 3 48 .222
BLTR

DREISEWERD, CLEMENT JOHN
(Steamboat)
b.Jan.24,1916 Old Monroe,Mo.
1944 Bos A P 7 2-4
1945 Bos A P 2 0-1
1946 Bos A P 20 4-1
1948 St.L A P 13 0-2
1948 NY N P 4 0-0
BLTL 46 6-8

DRENNAN, K. JOHN
1904 Det A 1 1 .000

DRESCHER, WILLIAM CLAYTON
b.May 23,1921 Congers,N.Y.
1944 NY A C 4 .143
1945 NY A C 48 .270
1946 NY A C 5 .333
BLTR 57 .266

DRESSEN, CHARLES WALTER
b.Sept.20,1898 Decatur,Ill.
1925 Cin N 2-3-O 76 .274
1926 Cin N S-3-O 127 .266
1927 Cin N S-3 144 .292
1928 Cin N 3 135 .291
1929 Cin N 2-3 110 .244
1930 Cin N 2-3 33 .211
1931 Cin N 3 5 .067
1933 NY N 3 16 .222
BRTR 646 .272

Non-playing manager Cin (N) 1934-37 Bro (N) 1951-53 and Was (A) 1955-57 Mil (N(1960-61.

DRESSEN, LEE AUGUST
b.July 23,1889 Ellinwood,Kan.
d.June 30,1931
1914 St.L N 1 46 .233
1918 Det A 1 31 .178
BLTL 77 .205

DRESSER, EDWARD
1898 Bro N S 1 .250

DRESSER, ROBERT NICHOLSON
b.Oct.4,1878 Newton,Mass.
d.July 27,1924
1902 Bos N P 1 0-1
TL

DREW, DAVID
1884 Key U P-2 2 {0-0 .444
1884 Was U 1-S-O 13 .327
15 {0-0 .344

DREWS, FRANK JOHN
b.May 25,1918 Buffalo,N.Y.
1944 Bos N 2 46 .206
1945 Bos N 2 49 .204
BRTR 95 .205

DREWS, KARL AUGUST
b.Feb.22,1920 Eltingeville,S.I.,N.Y.
1946 NY A P 3 0-1
1947 NY A P 30 6-6
1948 NY A P 19 2-3
1948 St.L A P 20 3-2
1949 St.L A P 31 4-12
1951 Phi N P 5 1-0
1952 Phi N P 33 14-15
1953 Phi N P 47 9-10
1954 Phi N P 8 1-0
1954 Cin N P 22 4-4
BRTR 218 44-53

DRILL, LEWIS L.
b.May 9,1877 Browerville,Minn.
1902 Was A C-2-S-O 37 .272
1902 Bal A C-1 2 .250
1902 Was A C-2-S- 32 .250

Yr	Cl	Lea	Pos	G	Rec
1903	Was	A	C	51	.252
1904	Was	A	C	43	.394
1904	Det	A	C-1	51	.225
1905	Det	A	C	72	.261
	BRTR			288	.255

DRISCOLL, JOHN F. (Denny)
b.Nov.19,1855 Lowell,Mass.
d.July 11,1886

Yr	Cl	Lea	Pos	G	Rec
1880	Buf	N	P-O	18	1-3 .136
1882	Pit	a	P	22	13-9
1883	Pit	a	P-C-3-O	41	18-21 .185
1884	Lou	a	P-O	13	7-6 .167
1885	Buf	N	2	7	.158
				101	39-39 .160

DRISCOLL, JOHN LEO (Paddy)
b.Jan.11,1896 Evanston,Ill.
d.Mar.21,1953

Yr	Cl	Lea	Pos	G	Rec
1917	Chi	N	2	13	.107
	BRTR				

DRISCOLL, MICHAEL COLUMBUS
b.Oct.19,1892 N.Abington,Mass.
d.Mar.21,1953

Yr	Cl	Lea	Pos	G	Rec
1916	Phi	A	P	1	0-1
	BRTR				

DRISSEL, NICHOLAS MICHAEL (Mike)
b.Dec.19,1865 St.Louis,Mo.
d.Feb.26,1913

Yr	Cl	Lea	Pos	G	Rec
1885	St.L	a	C	6	.056
	BRTR				

DROHAN, DAVID
(Played under name of David Rowan)

DROHAN, THOMAS F.
b.Aug.26,1888 Fall River,Mass.
d.Sept.17,1926

Yr	Cl	Lea	Pos	G	Rec
1913	Was	A	P	2	0-0
	BRTR				

DROPO, WALTER (Moose)
b.Jan.30,1923 Moosup,Conn.

Yr	Cl	Lea	Pos	G	Rec
1949	Bos	A	1	11	.146
1950	Bos	A	1	136	.322
1951	Bos	A	1	99	.239
1952	Bos	A	1	37	.265
1952	Det	A	1	115	.279
1953	Det	A	1	152	.248
1954	Det	A	1	107	.281
1955	Chi	A	1	141	.280
1956	Chi	A	1	125	.266
1957	Chi	A	1	93	.256
1958	Chi	A	1	28	.192
1958	Cin	N	1	63	.290
1959	Cin	N	1	26	.103
1959	Bal	A	1-3	62	.278
1960	Bal	A	1-3	79	.268
1961	Bal	A	1	14	.259
	BRTR			1288	.270

DROTT, RICHARD FRED
b.July 1,1936 Cincinnati,Ohio

Yr	Cl	Lea	Pos	G	Rec
1957	Chi	N	P	38	15-11
1958	Chi	N	P	39	7-11
1959	Chi	N	P	8	1-2
1960	Chi	N	P	23	0-6
1961	Chi	N	P	35	1-4
1962	Hou	N	P	6	1-0
	BRTR			149	25-34

DRUCKE, LOUIS FRANK
b.Dec.3,1888 Waco,Tex.
d.Sept.22,1955

Yr	Cl	Lea	Pos	G	Rec
1909	NY	N	P	3	2-1
1910	NY	N	P	34	12-10

(Continued)

Yr	Cl	Lea	Pos	G	Rec
1911	NY	N	P	15	4-4
1912	NY	N	P	1	0-0
	TR			53	18-15

DRUHOT, CARL A. (Collie)
b.Sept.1,1882 Ohio
d.Feb.5,1918

Yr	Cl	Lea	Pos	G	Rec
1906	Cin	N	P	14	6-8
1906	St.L	N	P	5	2-1
1907	St.L	N	P	2	0-2
	BLTL			21	8-11

DRYSDALE, DONALD SCOTT
b.July 23,1936 Van Nuys,Cal.

Yr	Cl	Lea	Pos	G	Rec
1956	Bro	N	P	26	5-5
1957	Bro	N	P	37	17-9
1958	LA	N	P	47	12-13
1959	LA	N	P	46	17-13
1960	LA	N	P	41	15-14
1961	LA	N	P	40	13-10
1962	LA	N	P	43	25-9
	BRTR			280	104-73

DUBIEL, WALTER JOHN (Monk)
b.Feb.12,1920 Hartford,Conn.

Yr	Cl	Lea	Pos	G	Rec
1944	NY	A	P	31	13-13
1945	NY	A	P	26	10-9
1948	Phi	N	P	38	8-10
1949	Chi	N	P	33	6-9
1950	Chi	N	P	39	6-10
1951	Chi	N	P	22	2-2
1952	Chi	N	P	1	0-0
	BRTR			190	45-53

DUBUC, JEAN ARTHUR (Chauncey)
b.Sept.17,1888 St.Johnsbury,Vt.
d.Aug.29,1958

Yr	Cl	Lea	Pos	G	Rec
1908	Cin	N	P	16	5-6
1909	Cin	N	P	19	2-5
1912	Det	A	P	36	17-10
1913	Det	A	P	66	16-14
1914	Det	A	P	69	13-14
1915	Det	A	P	60	17-12
1916	Det	A	P	52	10-8
1918	Bos	A	P	5	0-1
1919	NY	N	P	37	6-4
	BRTR			360	86-74

DUDLEY, ELISE CLISE
b.Aug.8,1904 Graham,N.C.

Yr	Cl	Lea	Pos	G	Rec
1929	Bro	N	P	36	6-14
1930	Bro	N	P	21	2-4
1931	Phi	N	P	44	8-14
1932	Phi	N	P	23	1-1
1933	Pit	N	P	1	0-0
	BLTR			125	17-33

DUDLEY, ERNEST
(Played under name of Ernest Dudley Lee)

DUDRA, JOHN JOSEPH
b.May 27,1918 Assumption,Ill.

Yr	Cl	Lea	Pos	G	Rec
1941	Bos	N	1-2-S-3	14	.360
	BRTR				

DUFF, CECIL ELBA (Larry)
b.Nov.30,1896 Radersburg,Mont.

Yr	Cl	Lea	Pos	G	Rec
1922	Chi	A	P	3	1-1
	BLTR				

DUFF, PATRICK HENRY
b.May 6,1875 Providence,R.I.
d.Sept.11,1925

Yr	Cl	Lea	Pos	G	Rec
1906	Was	A	C	1	.000
	TR				

DUFFALO, JAMES FRANCIS
b.Nov.25,1936 Helvetia,Pa.

Yr	Cl	Lea	Pos	G	Rec
1961	SF	N	P	25	5-1
1962	SF	N	P	24	1-2
	BRTR			49	6-3

DUFFEE, CHARLES EDWARD (Home Run)
b.Jan.27,1866 Mobile,Ala.
d.Dec.24,1894

Yr	Cl	Lea	Pos	G	Rec
1889	St.L	a	O	137	.245
1890	St.L	a	O	98	.274
1891	Col	a	O	137	.302
1892	Was	N	O	129	.252
1893	Cin	N	O	4	.200
	BR			505	.266

DUFFY, BERNARD A.
b.Aug.18,1893 Vinson,Okla.
d.Feb.9,1962

Yr	Cl	Lea	Pos	G	Rec
1913	Pit	N	P	3	0-0
	BRTR				

DUFFY, EDWARD C.
b.1844 Ireland

Yr	Cl	Lea	Pos	G	Rec
1871	Chi	n	S-3	25	NR
1872	Eck	n	S	1	NR
				26	NR

DUFFY, HUGH
b.Nov.26,1866 Cranston,R.I.
d.Oct.19,1954

Yr	Cl	Lea	Pos	G	Rec
1888	Chi	N	O	71	.282
1889	Chi	N	O	136	.311
1890	Chi	p	O	137	.328
1891	Bos	a	O	127	.340
1892	Bos	N	O	146	.302
1893	Bos	N	O	131	.378
1894	Bos	N	O	124	.438
1895	Bos	N	O	131	.352
1896	Bos	N	O	131	.302
1897	Bos	N	O	134	.341
1898	Bos	N	O	151	.319
1899	Bos	N	O	147	.279
1900	Bos	N	O	50	.298
1901	Mil	A	M-O	78	.308
1904	Phi	N	M-O	16	.261
1905	Phi	N	M-O	15	.307
1906	Phi	N	M-H	1	.000
	BRTR			1726	.329

Non-playing manager Chi (A) 1910-11 and Bos (A) 1921-22.

DUGAN, DANIEL PHILLIP
b.Feb.22,1907 Plainfield,N.J.

Yr	Cl	Lea	Pos	G	Rec
1928	Chi	A	P	1	0-0
1929	Chi	A	P	19	1-4
	BLTL			20	1-4

DUGAN, E.

Yr	Cl	Lea	Pos	G	Rec
1884	KC	U	O	3	.000

DUGAN, EDWARD J.
b.1864 Brooklyn,N.Y.

Yr	Cl	Lea	Pos	G	Rec
1884	Ric	a	P-2	21	5-15 .114

DUGAN, JOSEPH ANTHONY (Jumping Joe)
b.May12,1897 Mahanoy City,Pa.

Yr	Cl	Lea	Pos	G	Rec
1917	Phi	A	S	43	.194
1918	Phi	A	2-S	120	.195
1919	Phi	A	S	104	.271
1920	Phi	A	2-S-3	123	.322
1921	Phi	A	3	119	.295
1922	Bos	A	S-3	84	.281
1922	NY	A	3	60	.294
1923	NY	A	3	146	.283
1924	NY	A	3	148	.302
1925	NY	A	3	102	.292
1926	NY	A	3	123	.288
1927	NY	A	3	112	.269
1928	NY	A	3	94	.276
1929	Bos	N	3	60	.304
1931	Det	A	3	8	.235
	BRTR			1446	.263

DUGAN, WILLIAM E.
b.1864 Kingston,N.Y.

Yr	Cl	Lea	Pos	G	Rec
1884	Ric	a	C	8	.040

DUGAS, AUGUSTIN JOSEPH (Gus)
b.Mar.24,1907 St.Jean deMatha,Que., Canada.

Yr	Cl	Lea	Pos	G	Rec
1930	Pit	N	O	9	.290
1932	Pit	N	O	55	.237
1933	Phi	N	1-O	37	.169
1934	Was	A	O	24	.053
	BLTL			125	.209

DUGDALE, DANIEL EDWARD
b.Oct.28,1866 Peoria,Ill.
d.Mar.9,1934

Yr	Cl	Lea	Pos	G	Rec
1886	KC	N	C	12	.175
1894	Was	N	C	33	.217
				45	.207

DUGEY, OSCAR JOSEPH (Jake)
b.Oct.25,1893 Palestine,Tex.

Yr	Cl	Lea	Pos	G	Rec
1913	Bos	N	S-3	5	.250
1914	Bos	N	2-O	58	.193
1915	Phi	N	2	42	.154
1916	Phi	N	2	41	.220
1917	Phi	N	2	44	.194
1920	Bos	N	H	5	.000
	BRTR			195	.194

DUGGAN, JAMES ELMER
b.June 3,1887 Franklin,Ind.
d.Dec.5,1951

Yr	Cl	Lea	Pos	G	Rec
1911	St.L	A	1	1	.000
	BRTL				

DUGGLEBY, WILLIAM JAMES (Frosty Bill)
b.Mar.17,1874 Utica,N.Y.
d.Aug.31,1944

Yr	Cl	Lea	Pos	G	Rec
1898	Phi	N	P	9	3-3
1901	Phi	N	P	33	19-12
1902	Phi	A	P	2	1-1
1902	Phi	N	P	31	11-17
1903	Phi	N	P	36	13-18
1904	Phi	N	P	32	12-14
1905	Phi	N	P	38	18-16
1906	Phi	N	P	42	13-19
1907	Phi	N	P	5	1-2
1907	Pit	N	P	9	0-2
	TR			237	91-104

DUKE, MARTIN F. (Duck)
b.Columbus,O.
d.Dec.31,1898

Yr	Cl	Lea	Pos	G	Rec
1891	Was	a	P	4	0-4
	TL				

DULIBA, ROBERT JOHN
b.Jan.9,1935 Glen Lyon,Pa.

Yr	Cl	Lea	Pos	G	Rec
1959	St.L	N	P	11	0-1
1960	St.L	N	P	27	4-4
1962	St.L	N	P	28	2-0
	BRTR			66	6-5

DUMONT, GEORGE HENRY (Pea Soup)
b.Nov.13,1895 Minneapolis,Minn.
d.Oct.13,1956

Yr	Cl	Lea	Pos	G	Rec
1915	Was	A	P	6	2-1
1916	Was	A	P	17	2-2
1917	Was	A	P	37	5-14
1918	Was	A	P	4	1-1
1919	Bos	A	P	13	0-4
	BRTR			77	10-22

DUMOVICH, NICHOLAS
b.Jan.2,1902 Los Angeles,Cal.

Yr	Cl	Lea	Pos	G	Rec
1923	Chi	N	P	28	3-5
	BLTL				

DUNCAN, JAMES WILLIAM
b.July 1,1871 Oil City,Pa.
d.Oct.16,1901

Yr	Cl	Lea	Pos	G	Rec
1899	Was	N	C	15	.234
1899	Cle	N	C	30	.231
				45	.232

DUNCAN, LOUIS BAIRD (Pat)
b.Oct.6,1893 Coalton,O.
d.July 17,1960

Yr	Cl	Lea	Pos	G	Rec
1915	Pit	N	O	3	.200
1919	Cin	N	O	31	.244
1920	Cin	N	O	154	.295
1921	Cin	N	O	145	.308
1922	Cin	N	O	151	.327
1923	Cin	N	O	147	.327
1924	Cin	N	O	96	.270
	BRTR			727	.307

DUNCAN, VERNON VAN DUKE
b.Jan.6,1890 Clayton,N.C.
d.June 1,1954

Yr	Cl	Lea	Pos	G	Rec
1913	Phi	N	O	8	.416
1914	Bal	F	O	157	.287
1915	Bal	F	3-O	146	.269
	BLTR			311	.280

DUNDON, AUGUSTUS J.
b.July 10,1875 Columbus,O.
d.Sept.1,1940

Yr	Cl	Lea	Pos	G	Rec
1904	Chi	A	2	108	.234
1905	Chi	A	2	106	.192
1906	Chi	A	2	33	.135
	TR			247	.204

DUNDON, EDWARD JOSEPH (Dummy)
b.July 10,1859 Columbus,O.
d.Aug.18,1893

Yr	Cl	Lea	Pos	G	Rec
1883	Col	a	P-2-O	26	3-16 .161
1884	Col	a	P-O	26	5-4 .140
	TR			52	8-20 .151

DUNGAN, SAMUEL MORRISON
b.Jan.29,1866 Ferndale,Cal.
d.Mar.16,1939

Yr	Cl	Lea	Pos	G	Rec
1892	Chi	N	O	113	.291
1893	Chi	N	O	107	.310
1894	Chi	N	O	10	.237
1894	Lou	N	O	8	.333
1900	Chi	N	O	6	.266
1901	Was	A	1-O	137	.324
	BR			381	.309

DUNHAM, LELAND HUFFIELD (Lee)
b.June 9,1902 Atlanta,Ill.
d.May 11,1961

Yr	Cl	Lea	Pos	G	Rec
1926	Phi	N	1	5	.250
	BLTL				

DUNHAM, WILEY H.
b.Piketon,O.

Yr	Cl	Lea	Pos	G	Rec
1902	St.L	N	P	7	2-3

DUNKLE, EDWARD PERKS (Davey)
b.Aug.30,1872 Homestead,Pa.
d.Nov.19,1941

Yr	Cl	Lea	Pos	G	Rec
1897	Phi	N	P	7	5-2
1898	Phi	N	P	9	1-5
1899	Was	N	P	4	0-2
1903	Chi	A	P	11	5-5
1903	Was	A	P	14	5-8
1904	Was	A	P	13	2-9
	TR			58	18-31

DUNLAP, FREDERICK C. (Sure Shot)
b.May 21,1859 Philadelphia,Pa.
d.Dec.1,1902

Yr	Cl	Lea	Pos	G	Rec
1880	Cle	N	2	84	.273
1881	Cle	N	2-3	78	.324
1882	Cle	N	2	82	.278
1883	Cle	N	2	90	.328
1884	St.L	U	M-P-2-O	81	0-0 .420
1885	St.L	N	M-2	106	.269
1886	St.L	N	2	73	.281
1886	Det	N	2	49	.284
1887	Det	N	2	64	.326
1888	Pit	N	2	81	.261

(Continued)

Yr	Cl	Lea	Pos	G	Rec
1889	Pit	N	M-2	121	.235
1890	Pit	N	2	17	.172
1890	NY	p	2	1	.000
1891	Was	a	2	7	.200
	BRTR			934	0-0 .295

DUNLAP, GRANT LESTER
b.Dec.20,1923 Stockton,Cal.

Yr	Cl	Lea	Pos	G	Rec
1953	St.L	N	O	16	.353
	BRTR				

DUNLAP, WILLIAM JAMES
b.May 1,1909 Three Rivers,Mass.

Yr	Cl	Lea	Pos	G	Rec
1929	Bos	N	O	10	.414
1930	Bos	N	O	16	.069
	BBTL			26	.241

DUNLEAVY, JOHN FRANCIS
b.Sept.14,1877 Harrison,N.J.

Yr	Cl	Lea	Pos	G	Rec
1903	St.L	N	P-O	52	6-8 .249
1904	St.L	N	P-O	51	1-4 .236
1905	St.L	N	O	119	.241
				222	7-12 .241

DUNLOP, GEORGE HENRY
b.July 19, 1888 Meriden,Conn.

Yr	Cl	Lea	Pos	G	Rec
1913	Cle	A	S-3	7	.222
1914	Cle	A	S	1	.000
	BRTR			8	.190

DUNN, JAMES WILLIAM
b.Feb.25,1931 Valdosta,Ga.

Yr	Cl	Lea	Pos	G	Rec
1952	Pit	N	P	3	0-0
	BRTR				

DUNN, JOHN JOSEPH
b.Oct.6,1872 Meadville,Pa.
d.Oct.22,1928

Yr	Cl	Lea	Pos	G	Rec
1897	Bro	N	P	34	16-9
1898	Bro	N	P	45	15-21
1899	Bro	N	P	39	21-12
1900	Bro	N	P	8	3-5
1900	Phi	N	P	10	4-5
1901	Phi	N	P	2	0-1
1901	Bal	A	P-S-3	96	3-3 .247
1902	NY	N	P-2-S-3-O	96	0-3 .211
1903	NY	N	2-S-3	72	.241
1904	NY	N	P-3	55	0-0 .309
	BRTR			457	62-59 .247

DUNN, JOSEPH EDWARD
b.Mar.11,1885 Springfield,O.
d.Mar.19,1944

Yr	Cl	Lea	Pos	G	Rec
1908	Bro	N	C	20	.172
1909	Bro	N	C	7	.160
	BRTR			27	.169

DUNN, STEPHEN
b.London,Ont.,Canada

Yr	Cl	Lea	Pos	G	Rec
1884	St.P	U	1-2	9	.242

DUNNING, ANDREW J.
b.New York,N.Y.

Yr	Cl	Lea	Pos	G	Rec
1889	Pit	N	P	2	0-2
1891	NY	N	P	1	0-0
				3	0-2

DUPEE, FRANK OLIVER
b.Apr.29,1877 Moncton,Vt.
d.Aug.14,1956

Yr	Cl	Lea	Pos	G	Rec
1901	Chi	A	P	1	0-0

DURBIN, BLAINE A. (Kid)
b.1887 Lamar,Mo.

Yr	Cl	Lea	Pos	G	Rec
1907	Chi	N	P	10	0-1
1908	Chi	N	O	14	.363
1909	Cin	N	P	6	0-0
1909	Pit	N	P	1	0-0
		BLTL		31	0-1 / .271

DUREN, RINOLD GEORGE (Ryne)
b.Feb.22,1930 Cazenovia,Wis.

Yr	Cl	Lea	Pos	G	Rec
1954	Bal	A	P	1	0-0
1957	KC	A	P	14	0-3
1958	NY	A	P	44	6-4
1959	NY	A	P	41	3-6
1960	NY	A	P	42	3-4
1961	NY	A	P	4	0-1
1961	LA	A	P	40	6-12
1962	LA	A	P	42	2-9
		BRTR		228	20-39

DURHAM, EDWARD FANT
b.Aug.17,1908 Chester,S.C.

Yr	Cl	Lea	Pos	G	Rec
1929	Bos	A	P	14	1-0
1930	Bos	A	P	33	4-15
1931	Bos	A	P	39	8-10
1932	Bos	A	P	35	6-13
1933	Chi	A	P	24	10-6
		BLTR		145	29-44

DURHAM, JAMES GARFIELD
b.Oct.7,1881 Douglass,Kan.

Yr	Cl	Lea	Pos	G	Rec
1902	Chi	A	P-O	5	1-1 / .066

DURHAM, JOSEPH VANN
b.July 31,1932 Newport News,Va.

Yr	Cl	Lea	Pos	G	Rec
1954	Bal	A	O	10	.225
1957	Bal	A	O	77	.185
1959	St.L	N	O	6	.000
		BRTR		93	.188

DURHAM, LOUIS G. (Bull)
b.1881 Bolivar,N.Y.

Yr	Cl	Lea	Pos	G	Rec
1904	Bro	N	P	2	1-0
1907	Was	A	P	2	0-0
1908	NY	N	P	1	0-0
1909	NY	N	P	4	0-0
		TR		9	1-0

DURNBAUGH, ROBERT EUGENE
b.Jan.15,1933 Dayton,O.

Yr	Cl	Lea	Pos	G	Rec
1957	Cin	N	S	2	.000
		BRTR			

DURNING, GEORGE WARREN
b.May 9,1902 Philadelphia,Pa.

Yr	Cl	Lea	Pos	G	Rec
1925	Phi	N	O	5	.357
		BRTR			

DURNING, RICHARD KNOTT
b.Oct.10,1892 Louisville,Ky.
d.Sept.23,1948

Yr	Cl	Lea	Pos	G	Rec
1917	Bro	N	P	1	0-0
1918	Bro	N	P	1	0-0
		BLTL		2	0-0

DUROCHER, LEO ERNEST (Lippy)
b.July 27,1905 W.Springfield,Mass.

Yr	Cl	Lea	Pos	G	Rec
1925	NY	A	S	2	.000
1928	NY	A	2-S	102	.270
1929	NY	A	S	106	.246
1930	Cin	N	2-S	119	.243
1931	Cin	N	S	121	.227
1932	Cin	N	S	143	.217
1933	Cin	N	S	16	.216
1933	St.L	N	S	123	.258
1934	St.L	N	S	146	.260
1935	St.L	N	S	143	.265
1936	St.L	N	S	136	.286
1937	St.L	N	S	135	.203
1938	Bro	N	S	141	.219
1939	Bro	N	M-S	116	.277
1940	Bro	N	M-2-S	62	.231
1941	Bro	N	M-2-S	18	.286
1943	Bro	N	M-S	6	.222

(Continued)

Yr	Cl	Lea	Pos	G	Rec
1945	Bro	N	M-2	2	.200
		BRTR		1637	.247

Non-playing manager Bro (N) 1942, 1944, 1946, 1948 and NY (N) 1948-55.

DURRETT, ELMER CHARLES (Red)
b.Feb.3,1921 Sherman,Tex.

Yr	Cl	Lea	Pos	G	Rec
1944	Bro	N	O	11	.156
1945	Bro	N	O	8	.125
		BLTL		19	.146

DURST, CEDRIC MONTGOMERY
b.Aug.23,1899 Austin,Tex.

Yr	Cl	Lea	Pos	G	Rec
1922	St.L	A	O	15	.333
1923	St.L	A	1-O	45	.212
1926	St.L	A	O	80	.237
1927	NY	A	O	65	.248
1928	NY	A	O	74	.252
1929	NY	A	O	92	.257
1930	NY	A	O	8	.188
1930	Bos	A	O	102	.243
		BLTL		481	.244

DURYEA, JAMES WHITNEY
(Cyclone Jim)
b.Sept.7,1862 Osage,Ia.
d.Aug.7,1942

Yr	Cl	Lea	Pos	G	Rec
1889	Cin	a	P-O	55	32-21 / .268
1890	Cin	N	P	32	17-13
1891	Cin	N	P	11	2-8
1891	St.L	a	P	4	1-1
1892	Cin	N	P-O	11	3-5 / .111
1892	Was	N	P	16	2-12
1893	Was	N	P	17	5-8
		BRTR		146	62-68 / .192

DUSAK, ERVIN FRANK (Four Sack)
b.July 29,1920 Chicago,Ill.

Yr	Cl	Lea	Pos	G	Rec
1941	St.L	N	O	6	.143
1942	St.L	N	3-O	12	.185
1946	St.L	N	2-3-O	100	.240
1947	St.L	N	3-O	111	.284
1948	St.L	N	P-2-S-3-O	114	0-0 / .209
1949	St.L	N	H	1	.000
1950	St.L	N	P-O	23	0-2 / .083
1951	St.L	N	P	5	0-0
1951	Pit	N	P-2-3-O	21	0-1 / .308
1952	Pit	N	O	20	.222
		BRTR		413	0-3 / .243

DUSER, CARL ROBERT
b.July 22,1932 Hazleton,Pa.

Yr	Cl	Lea	Pos	G	Rec
1956	KC	A	P	2	1-1
1958	KC	A	P	1	0-0
		BLTL		3	1-1

DUZEN, WILLIAM GEORGE
b.Feb.21,1870 Buffalo,N.Y.
d.Mar.11,1944

Yr	Cl	Lea	Pos	G	Rec
1890	Buf	p	P	2	0-2
		BRTR			

DWIGHT, ...
b.Chicago,Ill.

Yr	Cl	Lea	Pos	G	Rec
1884	KC	U	C-O	12	.268

DWYER, J. E. . . . .
b.Chicago,Ill.

Yr	Cl	Lea	Pos	G	Rec
1882	Cle	N	C-O	1	.000

DWYER, JOHN FRANCIS (Frank)
b.Mar.25,1868 Lee,Mass.
d.Feb.4,1943

Yr	Cl	Lea	Pos	G	Rec
1888	Chi	N	P	5	4-1
1889	Chi	N	P	33	16-12
1890	Chi	p	P	16	1-7
1891	Cin	a	P-2-O	34	13-18 / .250

(Continued)

Yr	Cl	Lea	Pos	G	Rec
1891	Mil	a	P	10	5-4
1892	St.L	N	P	14	2-6
1892	Cin	N	P	46	20-10
1893	Cin	N	P	32	18-14
1894	Cin	N	P	49	18-19
1895	Cin	N	P	34	18-13
1896	Cin	N	P	35	25-10
1897	Cin	N	P	35	17-12
1898	Cin	N	P	29	16-10
1899	Cin	N	P	5	0-5
		BRTR		377	173-141 / .233

Non-playing manager Det (A) 1902

DWYER, JOSEPH MICHAEL (Double)
b.Mar.27,1904 Orange,N.J.

Yr	Cl	Lea	Pos	G	Rec
1937	Cin	N	H	12	.273
		BBTL			

DYCK, JAMES ROBERT
b.Feb.3,1922 Omaha,Neb.

Yr	Cl	Lea	Pos	G	Rec
1951	St.L	A	3	4	.067
1952	St.L	A	3-O	122	.269
1953	St.L	A	3-O	112	.213
1954	Cle	A	H	2	1.000
1955	Bal	A	3-O	61	.279
1956	Bal	A	O	11	.217
1956	Cin	N	1-3	18	.091
		BRTR		330	.245

DYER, BENJAMIN FRANKLIN
b.Feb.13.1893 Chicago,Ill.
d.Aug.7,1959

Yr	Cl	Lea	Pos	G	Rec
1914	NY	N	2-S	7	.250
1915	NY	N	S-3	7	.211
1916	Det	A	S	4	.308
1917	Det	A	S	30	.209
1918	Det	A	P	13	0-0
1919	Det	A	3	44	.247
		BRTR		105	0-0 / .238

DYER, EDWIN HAWLEY
b.Oct.11,1900 Morgan City,La.

Yr	Cl	Lea	Pos	G	Rec
1922	St.L	N	P	6	0-0
1923	St.L	N	P-O	35	2-1 / .267
1924	St.L	N	P-O	50	8-11 / .237
1925	St.L	N	P	31	4-3
1926	St.L	N	P	6	1-0
1927	St.L	N	P	1	0-0
		BLTL		129	15-15 / .223

Non-playing manager St.L (N) 1946-50

DYGERT, JAMES HENRY (Sunny Jim)
b.July 5,1884 Utica,N.Y.
d.Feb.8,1936

Yr	Cl	Lea	Pos	G	Rec
1905	Phi	A	P	6	1-3
1906	Phi	A	P	35	11-13
1907	Phi	A	P	42	20-9
1908	Phi	A	P	41	11-15
1909	Phi	A	P	32	8-5
1910	Phi	A	P	19	4-4
		TR		175	55-49

DYKES, JAMES JOSEPH
b.Nov.10,1896 Philadelphia,Pa.

Yr	Cl	Lea	Pos	G	Rec
1918	Phi	A	2	59	.188
1919	Phi	A	2	17	.184
1920	Phi	A	2-3	142	.256
1921	Phi	A	2	155	.274
1922	Phi	A	3	145	.275
1923	Phi	A	2-S	124	.252
1924	Phi	A	2-3	110	.312
1925	Phi	A	2-S-3	122	.325
1926	Phi	A	2-3	124	.287
1927	Phi	A	P-1-3	121	0-0 / .324
1928	Phi	A	2-S-3	85	.277
1929	Phi	A	2-S-3	119	.327
1930	Phi	A	3	125	.301
1931	Phi	A	S-3	101	.273
1932	Phi	A	S-3	153	.265
1933	Chi	A	3	151	.260
1934	Chi	A	M-1-2-3	127	.268

(Continued)

Yr	Cl	Lea	Pos	G	Rec
1935	Chi	A	M-1-2-3	117	.288
1936	Chi	A	M-3	127	.267
1937	Chi	A	M-1-3	30	.306
1938	Chi	A	M-2	26	.303
1939	Chi	A	M-3	2	.000
			BRTR	2282	0-0 / .280

Non-playing manager Chi (A) 1940-46, Phi (A) 1951-53, Bal (A) 1954, Cin (N) 1958, Det (A) 1959-60 and Cle (A) 1960-61

DYLER, JOHN F.
b.Louisville,Ky.

Yr	Cl	Lea	Pos	G	Rec
1882	Lou	a	M-O	1	.000

EAGAN, CHARLES EUGENE (Truck)
b.Aug.10,1877 Oakland,Cal.
d.Mar.19,1949

Yr	Cl	Lea	Pos	G	Rec
1901	Pit	N	S	4	.083
1901	Cle	A	2-3	5	.176
				9	.138

EAGAN, WILLIAM (Bad Bill)
b.June 1,1869 Camden,N. J.
d.Feb.14,1905

Yr	Cl	Lea	Pos	G	Rec
1891	St.L	a	2	81	.222
1893	Chi	N	2	6	.300
1898	Pit	N	2	16	.328
				103	.240

EAGLE, WILLIAM
b.Rockville,Md.

Yr	Cl	Lea	Pos	G	Rec
1898	Was	N	O	4	.333

EAKLE, ...

Yr	Cl	Lea	Pos	G	Rec
1915	Bal	F	2	2	.286

EARL, HOWARD J.
b.Feb.25,1867 Palmyra,N.Y.
d.Dec.23,1916

Yr	Cl	Lea	Pos	G	Rec
1890	Chi	N	2-O	92	.247
1891	Mil	a	O	30	.254
				122	.248

EARLE, WILLIAM MOFFAT (Globetrotter)
b.Nov.10,1867 Philadelphia,Pa.
d.May 30,1946

Yr	Cl	Lea	Pos	G	Rec
1889	Cin	a	C-1-O	53	.269
1890	St.L	a	C	23	.212
1892	Pit	N	C	5	.500
1893	Pit	N	C	26	.317
1894	Lou	N	C	19	.377
1894	Bro	N	C-2	14	.321
			BRTR	140	.297

EARLEY, THOMAS FRANCIS ALOYSIUS
b.Feb.19,1918 Roxbury,Mass.

Yr	Cl	Lea	Pos	G	Rec
1938	Bos	N	P	2	1-0
1939	Bos	N	P	14	1-4
1940	Bos	N	P	4	2-0
1941	Bos	N	P	34	6-8
1942	Bos	N	P	27	6-11
1945	Bos	N	P	13	2-1
			BRTR	94	18-24

EARLY, JACOB WILLARD
b.May 19,1915 King's Mountain,N.C.

Yr	Cl	Lea	Pos	G	Rec
1939	Was	A	C	32	.262
1940	Was	A	C	80	.257
1941	Was	A	C	104	.287
1942	Was	A	C	104	.204
1943	Was	A	C	126	.258
1946	Was	A	C	64	.201
1947	St.L	A	C	87	.224
1948	Was	A	C	97	.220
1949	Was	A	C	53	.246
			BLTR	747	.241

EARNSHAW, GEORGE LIVINGSTON (Moose)
b.Feb.15,1900 New York,N.Y.

Yr	Cl	Lea	Pos	G	Rec
1928	Phi	A	P	26	7-7
1929	Phi	A	P	44	24-8
1930	Phi	A	P	49	22-13
1931	Phi	A	P	43	21-7
1932	Phi	A	P	36	19-13
1933	Phi	A	P	21	5-10
1934	Chi	A	P	33	14-11
1935	Chi	A	P	3	1-2
1935	Bro	N	P	25	8-12
1936	Bro	N	P	19	4-9
1936	St.L	N	P	20	2-1
			BRTR	319	127-93

EASON, MALCOLM WAYNE
b.Mar.13,1879 Brookville,Pa.

Yr	Cl	Lea	Pos	G	Rec
1900	Chi	N	P	1	1-0
1901	Chi	N	P	25	8-17
1902	Chi	N	P	6	1-1
1902	Bos	N	P	25	9-14
1903	Det	A	P	7	2-4
1905	Bro	N	P	29	5-20
1906	Bro	N	P	36	10-17
			TR	129	36-73

EAST, CARLTON W.
b.Aug.27,1893 Marletta,Va.
d.Jan.15,1953

Yr	Cl	Lea	Pos	G	Rec
1915	St.L	A	P	1	0-0
1924	Was	A	O	2	.333
			BLTR	3	0-0 / .286

EAST, GORDON HUGH
b.July 7,1919 Birmingham,Ala.

Yr	Cl	Lea	Pos	G	Rec
1941	NY	N	P	2	1-1
1942	NY	N	P	4	0-2
1943	NY	N	P	17	1-3
			BRTR	23	2-6

EAST, HARRY H.
b.St.Louis,Mo.

Yr	Cl	Lea	Pos	G	Rec
1882	Bal	a	3	1	.000

EADDY, DONALD JOHNSON
b.Feb. 16,1934 Grand Rapids,Mich.

Yr	Cl	Lea	Pos	G	Rec
1959	Chi	N	3	15	.000
			BRTR		

EARLEY, ARNOLD CARL
b.June 4,1933 Lincoln Park,Mich.

Yr	Cl	Lea	Pos	G	Rec
1960	Bos	A	P	2	0-1
1961	Bos	A	P	33	2-4
1962	Bos	A	P	38	4-5
			BLTL	73	6-10

EASTER, LUSCIOUS LUKE
b.Aug.4,1921 St.Louis,Mo.

Yr	Cl	Lea	Pos	G	Rec
1949	Cle	A	O	21	.222
1950	Cle	A	1-O	141	.280
1951	Cle	A	1	128	.270
1952	Cle	A	1	127	.263
1953	Cle	A	1	68	.303
1954	Cle	A	H	6	.167
			BLTR	491	.273

EASTERLING, PAUL
b.Sept.28,1905 Reidsville,Ga.

Yr	Cl	Lea	Pos	G	Rec
1928	Det	A	O	43	.325
1930	Det	A	O	29	.202
1938	Phi	A	O	4	.286
			BRTR	76	.275

EASTERLY, THEODORE HARRISON
b.Apr.20,1886 Lincoln,Neb.

Yr	Cl	Lea	Pos	G	Rec
1909	Cle	A	C	98	.261
1910	Cle	A	C-O	110	.306

(Continued)

Yr	Cl	Lea	Pos	G	Rec
1911	Cle	A	C-O	99	.324
1912	Cle	A	C	65	.296
1912	Chi	A	C	28	.364
1913	Chi	A	C	60	.235
1914	KC	F	C	134	.331
1915	KC	F	C	110	.267
			BLTR	704	.299

EASTERWOOD, ROY CHARLES
b.Jan.12,1915 Waxahachie,Tex.

Yr	Cl	Lea	Pos	G	Rec
1944	Chi	N	C	17	.212
			BRTR		

EASTON, JOHN DAVID
b.Mar.4,1933 Trenton.N.J.

Yr	Cl	Lea	Pos	G	Rec
1955	Phi	N	H	1	.000
1959	Phi	N	H	3	.000
			BRTR	4	.000

EASTON, JOHN E.
b.1867 Bridgeport,O.

Yr	Cl	Lea	Pos	G	Rec
1889	Col	a	P	4	1-0
1890	Col	a	P	37	14-13
1891	Col	a	P	15	5-10
1891	St.L	a	P	9	4-3
1891	Col	a	P-O	6	0-3 / .105
1892	St.L	N	P	5	2-3
1894	Pit	N	P	3	0-1
				79	26-33 / .194

EATON, ZEBULON VANCE (Red)
b.Feb.2,1920 Cooleemee,N.C.

Yr	Cl	Lea	Pos	G	Rec
1944	Det	A	P	9	0-0
1945	Det	A	P	26	4-2
			BRTR	35	4-2

EAVES, VALLIE ENNIS (Chief)
b.Sept.6,1911 Allen,Okla.

Yr	Cl	Lea	Pos	G	Rec
1935	Phi	A	P	3	1-2
1939	Chi	A	P	2	0-1
1940	Chi	A	P	5	0-2
1941	Chi	N	P	12	3-3
1942	Chi	N	P	2	0-0
			BRTR	24	4-8

EAYRS, EDWIN
b.Nov.10,1890 Blackstone,Mass.

Yr	Cl	Lea	Pos	G	Rec
1913	Pit	N	P	4	0-0
1920	Bos	N	P-O	87	1-2 / .328
1921	Bos	N	P	15	0-0
1921	Bro	N	P	8	0-0
			BLTL	114	1-2 / .306

EBBETS, CHARLES HERCULES
b.Oct.29,1859 New York,N.Y.
d.Apr.18,1925
Non-playing manager Bro (N) 1898.

EBRIGHT, HIRAM C. (Buck)
b.June 12,1859 Lancaster,Co.,Pa.
d.Oct.24,1916

Yr	Cl	Lea	Pos	G	Rec
1889	Was	N	3	15	.254
			BRTR		

ECCLES HARRY JOSIAH (Bugs)
b.July 9,1893 Kennedy,N.Y.
d.June 2,1955

Yr	Cl	Lea	Pos	G	Rec
1915	Phi	A	P	5	0-1
			BLTL		

ECHOLS, JOHN GRESHAM
b.Jan.9,1917 Atlanta,Ga.

Yr	Cl	Lea	Pos	G	Rec
1939	St.L	N	2	2	.000
			BRTR		

ECKERT, ALBERT GEORGE
b.May 17,1908 Milwaukee,Wis.

Yr	Cl	Lea	Pos	G	Rec
1930	Cin	N	P	2	0-1
1931	Cin	N	P	14	0-1
1935	St.L	N	P	2	0-0
			BLTL	18	0-2

ECKERT, CHARLES WILLIAM (Buzz)
b.Aug.8,1898 Philadelphia,Pa.

Yr	Cl	Lea	Pos	G	Rec
1919	Phi	A	P	2	0-1
1920	Phi	A	P	2	0-0
1922	Phi	A	P	21	0-2
			BRTR	25	0-3

ECKHARDT, OSCAR GEORGE (Ox)
b.Dec.23,1901 Yorktown,Tex.
d.Apr.22,1951

Yr	Cl	Lea	Pos	G	Rec
1932	Bos	N	H	8	.250
1936	Bro	N	O	16	.182
			BLTR	24	.192

EDELEN, EDWARD JOSEPH
b.Mar.16,1912 Bryantown,Md.

Yr	Cl	Lea	Pos	G	Rec
1932	Was	A	P	2	0-0
			BRTR		

EDELMAN, JOHN ROGERS
b.July 27,1935 Philadelphia,Pa.

Yr	Cl	Lea	Pos	G	Rec
1955	Mil	N	P	5	0-0
			BRTR		

EDEN, CHARLES M.
b.Jan.18,1855 Lexington,Ky.
d.Sept.17,1920

Yr	Cl	Lea	Pos	G	Rec
1877	Chi	N	O	15	.218
1879	Cle	N	O	81	.272
1884	Pit	a	P-O	32	0-1 .305
1885	Pit	a	P-O	98	1-2 .264
			BRTR	226	1-3 .269

EDINGTON, JACOB FRANK (Stump)
b.July 4,1891 Lyons,Ind.

Yr	Cl	Lea	Pos	G	Rec
1912	Pit	N	O	15	.302
			BLTL		

EDMONDSON, GEORGE HENDERSON
b.May 18,1896 Waxahachie,Tex.

Yr	Cl	Lea	Pos	G	Rec
1922	Cle	A	P	2	0-0
1923	Cle	A	P	1	0-0
1924	Cle	A	P	5	0-0
			BRTR	8	0-0

EDMONDSTON, SAMUEL SHERWOOD (Big Sam)
b.Aug.30,1883 Washington,D.C.

Yr	Cl	Lea	Pos	G	Rec
1906	Was	A	P	3	0-1
1907	Was	A	P	1	0-0
			BLTL	4	0-1

EDMONSON, EARL EDWARD (Eddie)
b.Nov.20,1889 Hopewell,Pa.

Yr	Cl	Lea	Pos	G	Rec
1913	Cle	A	1-O	2	.000
			BLTR		

EDMUNDSON, ROBERT E.
b.Lawrence,Kan.

Yr	Cl	Lea	Pos	G	Rec
1908	Was	A	O	26	.188

EDWARDS, ...

Yr	Cl	Lea	Pos	G	Rec
1875	Atl	n	O	1	NR

EDWARDS, ALBERT
b.1896 Freeport,L.I.,N.Y.

Yr	Cl	Lea	Pos	G	Rec
1915	Phi	A	2	2	.000
			TR		

EDWARDS, CHARLES BRUCE (Bull)
b.July 15,1923 Quincy,Ill.

Yr	Cl	Lea	Pos	G	Rec
1946	Bro	N	C	92	.267
1947	Bro	N	C	130	.296
1948	Bro	N	C-1-3 O	96	.276
1949	Bro	N	C-3-O	64	.209
1950	Bro	N	C-1	50	.183
1951	Bro	N	C	17	.250
(Continued)					
1951	Chi	N	C-1	51	.234
1952	Chi	N	C-2	50	.245
1954	Chi	N	H	4	.000
1955	Was	A	C-3	30	.175
1956	Cin	N	C-2-3	7	.200
			BRTR	591	.256

EDWARDS, FOSTER HAMILTON (Eddie)
b.Sept.1,1903 Holstein,Ia.

Yr	Cl	Lea	Pos	G	Rec
1925	Bos	N	P	1	0-0
1926	Bos	N	P	3	2-0
1927	Bos	N	P	33	2-8
1928	Bos	N	P	21	2-1
1930	NY	A	P	2	0-0
			BRTR	60	6-9

EDWARDS, HENRY ALBERT
b.Jan.29,1919 Elmwood Place,O.

Yr	Cl	Lea	Pos	G	Rec
1941	Cle	A	O	16	.221
1942	Cle	A	O	13	.250
1943	Cle	A	O	92	.276
1946	Cle	A	O	124	.301
1947	Cle	A	O	108	.260
1948	Cle	A	O	55	.269
1949	Cle	A	O	5	.267
1949	Chi	N	O	58	.290
1950	Chi	N	O	41	.364
1951	Bro	N	H	35	.226
1951	Cin	N	O	41	.315
1952	Cin	N	O	74	.283
1952	Chi	A	O	8	.333
1953	St.L	A	O	65	.198
			BLTL	735	.280

EDWARDS, HOWARD RODNEY
b.Dec.10,1937 Varney,W.Va.

Yr	Cl	Lea	Pos	G	Rec
1962	Cle	A	C	53	.273
			BRTR		

EDWARDS, JAMES CORBETTE (Little Joe)
b.Dec.14,1894 Banner,Miss.

Yr	Cl	Lea	Pos	G	Rec
1922	Cle	A	P	25	3-8
1923	Cle	A	P	38	10-10
1924	Cle	A	P	10	4-3
1925	Cle	A	P	13	0-3
1925	Chi	A	P	9	1-2
1926	Chi	A	P	32	6-9
1928	Cin	N	P	18	2-2
			BRTL	145	26-37

EDWARDS, JOHN ALBAN
b.June 10,1938 Columbus,O.

Yr	Cl	Lea	Pos	G	Rec
1961	Cin	N	C	52	.186
1962	Cin	N	C	133	.254
			BLTR	185	.238

EDWARDS, SHERMAN STANLEY
b.July 25,1910 Mt.Ida,Ark.

Yr	Cl	Lea	Pos	G	Rec
1934	Cin	N	P	1	0-0
			BRTR		

EELLS, HARRY A.
b.1882 Kansas City,Mo.

Yr	Cl	Lea	Pos	G	Rec
1906	Cle	A	P	14	4-5
			TR		

EGAN, ALOYSIUS JEROME (Wish)
b.June 16,1881 Everett,Mich.
d.Apr.13,1951

Yr	Cl	Lea	Pos	G	Rec
1902	Det	A	P	3	1-2
1905	St.L	N	P	23	5-16
1906	St.L	N	P	16	2-9
				42	8-27

EGAN, ARTHUR AUGUSTUS (Ben)
b.Nov.20,1883 Augusta,N.Y.

Yr	Cl	Lea	Pos	G	Rec
1908	Phi	A	C	2	.143
1912	Phi	A	C	48	.174
1914	Cle	A	C	29	.227
1915	Cle	A	C	42	.108
			BRTR	121	.164

EGAN, JAMES
b.1838 Ansonia,Conn.
d.Sept.26,1884

Yr	Cl	Lea	Pos	G	Rec
1882	Tro	N	P-C-O	29	4-6 .181

EGAN, JOHN JOSEPH (Rip)
b.July 9,1871 Philadelphia,Pa.
d.Dec.22,1950

Yr	Cl	Lea	Pos	G	Rec
1894	Was	N	P	1	0-0

EGAN, RICHARD JOSEPH
b.June 23,1884 Portland,Ore.
d.June 30,1947

Yr	Cl	Lea	Pos	G	Rec
1908	Cin	N	2	18	.206
1909	Cin	N	2	126	.275
1910	Cin	N	2	134	.245
1911	Cin	N	2	152	.249
1912	Cin	N	2	149	.247
1913	Cin	N	2-S	60	.282
1914	Bro	N	S	106	.226
1915	Bro	N	2	3	.000
1915	Bos	N	2-O	83	.264
1916	Bos	N	2	83	.223
			BRTR	914	.250

EGGERT, ELMER ALBERT
b.Jan.29,1903 Rochester,N.Y.

Yr	Cl	Lea	Pos	G	Rec
1927	Bos	A	P	5	0-0
			BRTR		

EGGLER, DAVID DANIEL
b.Apr.30,1851 Brooklyn,N.Y.
d.Apr.5,1902

Yr	Cl	Lea	Pos	G	Rec
1871	Mut	n	O	33	NR
1872	Mut	n	O	56	NR
1873	Mut	n	O	54	NR
1874	Phi	n	2-O	58	NR
1875	Ath	n	O	66	.288
1876	Ath	N	O	39	.295
1877	Chi	N	O	33	.265
1879	Buf	N	O	77	.208
1883	Bal	a	O	53	.194
1883	Buf	N	O	38	.245
1884	Buf	N	O	58	.198
1885	Buf	N	O	6	.083
			BRTR	572	NR

EGGLER, JOHN
b.Brooklyn,N.Y.

Yr	Cl	Lea	Pos	G	Rec
1872	Eck	n	1	15	NR

EHMKE, HOWARD JOHN
b.Apr.24,1894 Silver Creek,N.Y.
d.Mar.17,1959

Yr	Cl	Lea	Pos	G	Rec
1915	Buf	F	P	16	0-2
1916	Det	A	P	5	3-1
1917	Det	A	P	35	10-15
1919	Det	A	P	33	17-10
1920	Det	A	P	38	15-18
1921	Det	A	P	30	13-14
1922	Det	A	P	45	17-17
1923	Bos	A	P	43	20-17
1924	Bos	A	P	46	19-17
1925	Bos	A	P	34	9-20
1926	Bos	A	P	14	3-10
1926	Phi	A	P	21	12-4
1927	Phi	A	P	30	12-10
1928	Phi	A	P	23	9-8
1929	Phi	A	P	11	7-2
1930	Phi	A	P	3	0-1
			BRTR	427	166-166

EHRET, PHILIP SYDNEY (Red)
b.Aug.31,1868 Louisville,Ky.
d.July 28,1940

Yr	Cl	Lea	Pos	G	Rec
1888	KC	a	P-O	16	4-3 .186
1889	Lou	a	P	66	9-29
1890	Lou	a	P	42	24-13
1891	Lou	a	P	26	13-12
1892	Pit	N	P	40	18-19
1893	Pit	N	P	36	17-17
1894	Pit	N	P	41	18-22
1895	St.L	N	P	31	6-20
1896	Cin	N	P	33	18-15
1897	Cin	N	P	27	10-10
1898	Lou	N	P	12	3-7
			BRTR	370	140-167 .220

EHRHARDT, WELTON CLAUDE (Rube)
b.Nov.20,1894 Beecher,Ill.

Yr	Cl	Lea	Pos	G	Rec
1924	Bro	N	P	15	5-3
1925	Bro	N	P	36	10-14
1926	Bro	N	P	44	2-5
1927	Bro	N	P	46	3-7
1928	Bro	N	P	28	1-3
1929	Cin	N	P	24	1-2
	BRTR			193	22-34

EIBEL, HENRY H. (Hack)
b.Dec.6,1893 Brooklyn,N.Y.
d.Oct.16,1945

Yr	Cl	Lea	Pos	G	Rec
1912	Cle	A	O	1	.000
1920	Bos	A	P	29	0-0
	BL			30	0-0 / .174

EICHRODT, FREDERICK GEORGE
b.Jan.6,1903 Chicago,Ill.

Yr	Cl	Lea	Pos	G	Rec
1925	Cle	A	O	15	.230
1926	Cle	A	O	37	.313
1927	Cle	A	O	85	.221
1931	Chi	A	O	34	.214
	BRTR			171	.234

EISENHARDT, JACOB HENRY
b.Oct.3,1922 Perkasie,Pa.

Yr	Cl	Lea	Pos	G	Rec
1944	Cin	N	P	1	0-0
	BLTL				

EISENSTAT, HARRY
b.Oct.10,1915 Brooklyn,N.Y.

Yr	Cl	Lea	Pos	G	Rec
1935	Bro	N	P	2	0-1
1936	Bro	N	P	5	1-2
1937	Bro	N	P	13	3-3
1938	Det	A	P	32	9-6
1939	Det	A	P	10	2-2
1939	Cle	A	P	26	6-7
1940	Cle	A	P	27	1-4
1941	Cle	A	P	21	1-1
1942	Cle	A	P	29	2-1
	BLTL			165	25-27

EITELJORG, EDWARD HENRY
b.Oct.14,1871 Berlin,Germany.
d.Dec.7,1942

Yr	Cl	Lea	Pos	G	Rec
1890	Chi	N	P	1	0-0
1891	Was	a	P	8	2-6
				9	2-6

ELAND, ...

Yr	Cl	Lea	Pos	G	Rec
1873	Mar	n	O	1	.000

ELBERFELD, NORMAN ARTHUR (Kid)
b.Apr.13,1875 Pomeroy,O.
d.Jan.13,1944

Yr	Cl	Lea	Pos	G	Rec
1898	Phi	N	3	13	.228
1899	Cin	N	S	41	.259
1901	Det	A	S	122	.309
1902	Det	A	S	139	.265
1903	Det	A	S	35	.323
1903	NY	A	S	90	.290
1904	NY	A	S	122	.256
1905	NY	A	S	108	.262
1906	NY	A	S	99	.306
1907	NY	A	S	120	.271
1908	NY	A	M-S	19	.196
1909	NY	A	S-3	106	.237
1910	Was	A	3	127	.250
1911	Was	A	2-3	127	.272
1914	Bro	N	S	30	.226
	BRTR			1298	.270

ELDER, GEORGE REZIN
b.Mar.10,1923 Louisville,Ky.

Yr	Cl	Lea	Pos	G	Rec
1949	St.L	A	O	41	.250
	BLTR				

ELDER, HENRY KNOX (Heinie)
b.Aug.23,1890 Seattle,Wash.

Yr	Cl	Lea	Pos	G	Rec
1913	Det	A	P	1	0-0
	BLTL				

ELKO, PETER
b.June 17,1918 Wilkes-Barre,Pa.

Yr	Cl	Lea	Pos	G	Rec
1943	Chi	N	3	9	.133
1944	Chi	N	3	7	.227
	BRTR			16	.173

ELLAM, ROY
b.July 11,1887 Conshohocken,Pa.
d.Oct.28,1948

Yr	Cl	Lea	Pos	G	Rec
1909	Cin	N	S	10	.190
1918	Pit	N	S	26	.130
	BRTR			36	.143

ELLER, HORACE OWEN (Hod)
b.July 5,1894 Muncie,Ind.
d.July 18,1961

Yr	Cl	Lea	Pos	G	Rec
1917	Cin	N	P	37	10-5
1918	Cin	N	P	37	16-12
1919	Cin	N	P	38	19-9
1920	Cin	N	P-1-2	38	13-12
1921	Cin	N	P	13	.253 / 2-2
	BRTR			163	60-40 / .221

ELLERBE, FRANCIS ROGERS (Governor)
b.Dec.25,1895 Marion,S.C.

Yr	Cl	Lea	Pos	G	Rec
1919	Was	A	S	28	.276
1920	Was	A	S-3	101	.292
1921	Was	A	3	10	.200
1921	St.L	A	3	105	.288
1922	St.L	A	3	91	.246
1923	St.L	A	3	18	.184
1924	St.L	A	3	21	.194
1924	Cle	A	3	46	.261
	BRTR			420	.268

ELLICK, JOSEPH J.
b.1856 Cincinnati,O.

Yr	Cl	Lea	Pos	G	Rec
1875	RS	n	S-3-O	7	NR
1878	Mil	N	P-C-3	3	0-0 / .154
1880	Wor	N	3	5	.053
1884	Chi	U	C-2-S-O	72	.253
1884	Pit	U	M-S	18	.167
1884	KC	U	2-O	2	.000
1884	Bal	U	S-O	7	.148
				114	0-0 / NR

ELLIOT, LAWRENCE LEE
b.Mar.5,1938 San Diego,Cal.

Yr	Cl	Lea	Pos	G	Rec
1962	Pit	N	O	8	.300
	BLTL				

ELLIOTT, ALLEN CLIFFORD
b.Dec.25,1897 St.Louis,Mo.

Yr	Cl	Lea	Pos	G	Rec
1923	Chi	N	1	53	.250
1924	Chi	N	1	10	.143
	BLTR			63	.242

ELLIOTT, CARTER WARD
b.Nov.28,1897

Yr	Cl	Lea	Pos	G	Rec
1921	Chi	N	S	12	.250
	BLTR				

ELLIOTT, CLAUDE J.
b.Nov.17,1879 Pardeeville,Wis.
d.June 21,1923

Yr	Cl	Lea	Pos	G	Rec
1904	Cin	N	P	10	4-6
1904	NY	N	P	3	0-1
1905	NY	N	P	10	2-1
	BRTR			23	6-8

ELLIOTT, EUGENE BIRMINGHOUSE
b.Feb.8,1888 Fayette City,Pa.

Yr	Cl	Lea	Pos	G	Rec
1911	NY	A	3	5	.077
	BLTR				

ELLIOTT, HAROLD H. (Rowdy)
b.July 8,1890 Bloomington,Ill.
d.Feb.12,1934

Yr	Cl	Lea	Pos	G	Rec
1910	Bos	N	C	1	.000
1916	Chi	N	C	23	.255
1917	Chi	N	C	85	.251
1918	Chi	N	C	5	.000
1920	Bro	N	C	41	.241
	BRTR			155	.241

ELLIOTT, HARRY LEWIS
b.Dec.30,1925 San Francisco,Cal.

Yr	Cl	Lea	Pos	G	Rec
1953	St.L	N	O	24	.254
1955	St.L	N	O	68	.256
	BRTR			92	.256

ELLIOTT, HERBERT GLENN (Lefty)
b.Nov.11,1919 Sapulpa,Okla.

Yr	Cl	Lea	Pos	G	Rec
1947	Bos	N	P	11	0-1
1948	Bos	N	P	1	1-0
1949	Bos	N	P	22	3-4
	BLTL			34	4-5

ELLIOTT, HOWARD WILLIAM (Ace)
b.May 29,1903 Mt.Clemens,Mich.

Yr	Cl	Lea	Pos	G	Rec
1929	Phi	N	P	40	3-7
1930	Phi	N	P	48	6-11
1931	Phi	N	P	16	0-2
1932	Phi	N	P	16	2-4
	BRTR			120	11-24

ELLIOTT, JAMES THOMAS (Jumbo)
b.Oct.22,1900 St.Louis,Mo.

Yr	Cl	Lea	Pos	G	Rec
1923	St.L	A	P	1	0-0
1925	Bro	N	P	3	0-2
1927	Bro	N	P	30	6-13
1928	Bro	N	P	41	9-14
1929	Bro	N	P	6	1-2
1930	Bro	N	P	35	10-7
1931	Phi	N	P	52	19-14
1932	Phi	N	P	39	11-10
1933	Phi	N	P	36	6-10
1934	Phi	N	P	3	0-1
1934	Bos	N	P	7	1-1
	BRTL			253	63-74

ELLIOTT, ROBERT IRVING
b.Nov.26,1916 San Francisco,Cal.

Yr	Cl	Lea	Pos	G	Rec
1939	Pit	N	O	32	.333
1940	Pit	N	O	148	.292
1941	Pit	N	O	141	.273
1942	Pit	N	3-O	143	.297
1943	Pit	N	2-S-3	156	.315
1944	Pit	N	S-3	143	.298
1945	Pit	N	3-O	144	.290
1946	Pit	N	3-O	140	.263
1947	Bos	N	3	150	.317
1948	Bos	N	3	151	.283
1949	Bos	N	3	139	.280
1950	Bos	N	3	142	.305
1951	Bos	N	3	136	.285
1952	NY	N	3-O	98	.228
1953	St.L	A	3	48	.250
1953	Chi	A	3-O	67	.260
	BRTR			1978	.289

Non-playing manager Kansas 1960

ELLIS, BENJAMIN F.
b.Pottsville,Pa.

Yr	Cl	Lea	Pos	G	Rec
1896	Phi	N	S	4	.063

ELLIS, GEORGE WILLIAM (Rube)
b.Nov.17,1885 Los Angeles,Cal.
d.Mar.13,1938

Yr	Cl	Lea	Pos	G	Rec
1909	St.L	N	O	145	.268
1910	St.L	N	O	141	.258
1911	St.L	N	O	148	.250
1912	St.L	N	O	109	.269
	BLTL			543	.260

ELLIS, SAMUEL JOSEPH
b.Feb.11,1941 Youngstown,O.

Yr	Cl	Lea	Pos	G	Rec
1962	Cin	N	P	8	2-2
	BRTR				

ELLISON, GEORGE RUSSELL
b.1897

Yr	Cl	Lea	Pos	G	Rec
1920	Cle	A	P	1	0-0
	BRTR				

ELLISON, HERBERT SPENCER (Babe)
b.Nov.15,1896 Ola,Ark.
d.Aug.11,1955

Yr	Cl	Lea	Pos	G	Rec
1916	Det	A	3	2	.125

(Continued)

Yr	Cl	Lea	Pos	G	Rec
1917	Det	A	1	9	.172
1918	Det	A	2	7	.260
1919	Det	A	2	56	.216
1920	Det	A	1	61	.219
		BRTR		135	.215

ELLSWORTH, RICHARD CLARK
b.Mar.22,1940 Lusk,Wyo.

Yr	Cl	Lea	Pos	G	Rec
1958	Chi	N	P	1	0-1
1960	Chi	N	P	31	7-13
1961	Chi	N	P	37	10-11
1962	Chi	N	P	37	9-20
		BLTL		106	26-45

ELMORE, VERDO WILSON
b.Dec.10,1899 Gordo,Ala.

Yr	Cl	Lea	Pos	G	Rec
1924	St.L	A	O	7	.176
	BLTR				

ELROY, ALEJANDRO CARRASQUEL
(Played under name of Alejandro Carrasquel)

ELSH, EUGENE ROY
b.Mar.1,1896 Pennsgrove,N.J.

Yr	Cl	Lea	Pos	G	Rec
1923	Chi	A	O	81	.249
1924	Chi	A	O	60	.306
1925	Chi	A	1-O	32	.188
		BRTR		173	.262

ELSTON, DONALD RAY
b.Apr.6,1929 Campbellstown,O.

Yr	Cl	Lea	Pos	G	Rec
1953	Chi	N	P	2	0-1
1957	Bro	N	P	1	0-0
1957	Chi	N	P	39	6-7
1958	Chi	N	P	69	9-8
1959	Chi	N	P	65	10-8
1960	Chi	N	P	60	8-9
1961	Chi	N	P	58	6-7
1962	Chi	N	P	57	4-8
		BRTR		351	43-48

ELY, FREDERICK WILLIAM
(Bones)
b.June 7,1863 Girard,Pa.
d.Jan.10,1952

Yr	Cl	Lea	Pos	G	Rec
1884	Buf	N	P-O	1	0-1 .000
1886	Lou	a	P-O	10	0-4 .147
1890	Syr	a	S-O	118	.263
1891	Bro	N	S	31	.171
1892	Bal	N	P	1	0-1
1893	St.L	N	S	44	.263
1894	St.L	N	S	127	.305
1895	St.L	N	S	118	.260
1896	Pit	N	S	126	.287
1897	Pit	N	S	133	.282
1898	Pit	N	S	148	.210
1899	Pit	N	S	138	.288
1900	Pit	N	S	130	.242
1901	Pit	N	S	62	.219
1901	Phi	A	S	45	.223
1902	Was	A	S	105	.263
		BRTR		1337	0-6 .259

EMBREE, CHARLES WILLARD
(Red)
b.Aug.30,1919 El Monte,Cal.

Yr	Cl	Lea	Pos	G	Rec
1941	Cle	A	P	1	0-1
1942	Cle	A	P	19	3-4
1944	Cle	A	P	3	0-1
1945	Cle	A	P	8	4-4
1946	Cle	A	P	28	8-12
1947	Cle	A	P	28	8-10
1948	NY	A	P	20	5-3
1949	St.L	A	P	40	3-13
		BRTR		147	31-48

EMBREY, CHARLES AKIN (Slim)
b.Aug.17,1901 Columbia,Tenn.
d.Oct.10,1947

Yr	Cl	Lea	Pos	G	Rec
1923	Chi	A	P	1	0-0
		BRTR			

EMERSON, CHESTER ARTHUR
(Chuck)
b.Oct.27,1889 Stow,Me.

Yr	Cl	Lea	Pos	G	Rec
1911	Phi	A	O	7	.222
1912	Phi	A	H	1	.000
		BBTR		8	.211

EMERY, HERRICK SMITH (Spoke)
b.Dec.10,1898 Bay City,Mich.

Yr	Cl	Lea	Pos	G	Rec
1924	Phi	N	O	5	.667
		BRTR			

EMIG, CHARLES H.
b.Bellevue,Ky.

Yr	Cl	Lea	Pos	G	Rec
1896	Lou	N	P	1	0-1

EMMER, FRANK WILLIAM
b.Feb.17,1896 Crestline,O.

Yr	Cl	Lea	Pos	G	Rec
1916	Cin	N	2-S-3-O	42	.146
1926	Cin	N	S	80	.196
		BRTR		122	.182

EMMERICH, ROBERT G.
b.Aug.1,1897 New York,N.Y.
d.Nov.23,1948

Yr	Cl	Lea	Pos	G	Rec
1923	Bos	N	O	13	.083
		BRTR			

EMMERICH, WILLIAM PETER
(Slim)
b.Sept.29,1919 Allentown,Pa.

Yr	Cl	Lea	Pos	G	Rec
1945	NY	N	P	31	4-4
1946	NY	N	P	2	0-0
		BRTR		33	4-4

EMSLIE, ROBERT DANIEL
b.Jan.27,1859 Guelph,Ont.,Canada.
d.Apr.26,1943

Yr	Cl	Lea	Pos	G	Rec
1883	Bal	a	P-O	28	9-16 .153
1884	Bal	a	P	51	32-18
1885	Bal	a	P	13	2-10
1885	Ath	a	P-O	4	0-3 .083
			TR	96	43-47 .187

ENDICOTT, WILLIAM FRANKLIN
b.Sept.4,1918 Acorn,Mo.

Yr	Cl	Lea	Pos	G	Rec
1946	St.L	N	O	20	.200
		BLTL			

ENGEL, JOSEPH WILLIAM
b.Mar.12,1893 Washington,D.C.

Yr	Cl	Lea	Pos	G	Rec
1912	Was	A	P	15	1-5
1913	Was	A	P	30	8-9
1914	Was	A	P	30	7-5
1915	Was	A	P	11	1-3
1917	Cin	N	P	1	0-1
1919	Cle	A	P	1	0-0
1920	Was	A	P	1	0-0
		BRTL		89	17-23

ENGLE, ARTHUR CLYDE (Hack)
b.Mar.19,1884 Dayton,O.
d.Dec.26,1939

Yr	Cl	Lea	Pos	G	Rec
1909	NY	A	O	135	.278
1910	NY	A	3	6	.200
1910	Bos	A	3	105	.266
1911	Bos	A	1-3	146	.270
1912	Bos	A	1-2	57	.234
1913	Bos	A	1	143	.290
1914	Bos	A	1	55	.194
1914	Buf	F	3	32	.259
1915	Buf	F	2-3-O	141	.263
1916	Cle	A	3	11	.133
		BRTR		831	.266

ENGLE, CHARLES
b.Aug.27,1903 Brooklyn,N.Y.

Yr	Cl	Lea	Pos	G	Rec
1925	Phi	A	S	1	.000
1926	Phi	A	S	19	.105
1930	Pit	N	2-S-3	67	.264
		BRTR		87	.251

ENGLISH, CHARLES DEWIE
b.Apr.8,1910 Darlington,S.C.

Yr	Cl	Lea	Pos	G	Rec
1932	Chi	A	3	24	.317
1933	Chi	A	2	3	.444
1936	NY	N	2	6	.000
1937	Cin	N	2-3	17	.238
		BRTR		50	.287

ENGLISH, ELWOOD GEORGE
(Woody)
b.Mar.2,1907 Granville,O.

Yr	Cl	Lea	Pos	G	Rec
1927	Chi	N	S	87	.290
1928	Chi	N	S	116	.299
1929	Chi	N	S	144	.276
1930	Chi	N	S-3	156	.335
1931	Chi	N	S-3	156	.319
1932	Chi	N	S-3	127	.272
1933	Chi	N	S-3	105	.261
1934	Chi	N	S-3	109	.278
1935	Chi	N	S-3	34	.202
1936	Chi	N	S-3	64	.247
1937	Bro	N	2-S	129	.238
1938	Bro	N	3	34	.250
		BRTR		1261	.286

ENGLISH, GILBERT RAYMOND
b.July 2,1909 Trinity,N.C.

Yr	Cl	Lea	Pos	G	Rec
1931	NY	N	3	3	.000
1932	NY	N	S-3	59	.225
1936	Det	A	3	1	.000
1937	Det	A	2	18	.262
1937	Bos	N	3	79	.290
1938	Bos	N	3	53	.248
1944	Bro	N	2-S-3	27	.152
		BRTR		240	.245

ENNIS, DELMER
b.June 8,1925 Philadelphia,Pa.

Yr	Cl	Lea	Pos	G	Rec
1946	Phi	N	O	141	.313
1947	Phi	N	O	139	.275
1948	Phi	N	O	152	.290
1949	Phi	N	O	154	.302
1950	Phi	N	O	153	.311
1951	Phi	N	O	144	.267
1952	Phi	N	O	151	.289
1953	Phi	N	O	152	.285
1954	Phi	N	1-O	145	.261
1955	Phi	N	O	146	.296
1956	Phi	N	O	153	.260
1957	St.L	N	O	136	.286
1958	St.L	N	O	106	.261
1959	Cin	N	O	5	.333
1959	Chi	A	O	26	.219
		BRTR		1903	.284

ENNIS, RUSSELL ELWOOD (Hack)
b.Mar.10,1897 Superior,Wis.
d.Jan.21,1949

Yr	Cl	Lea	Pos	G	Rec
1926	Was	A	C	1	.000
		BRTR			

ENRIGHT, JOHN PERCY
b.1896 Ft.Worth,Tex.

Yr	Cl	Lea	Pos	G	Rec
1917	NY	A	P	1	0-1
		BRTR			

ENS, ANTON (Mutz)
b.Nov.8,1884 St.Louis,Mo.
d.June 28,1950

Yr	Cl	Lea	Pos	G	Rec
1912	Chi	A	1	3	.000
		BLTL			

ENS, JEWEL WILLOUGHBY
b.Aug.24,1889 St.Louis,Mo.
d.Jan.17,1950

Yr	Cl	Lea	Pos	G	Rec
1922	Pit	N	1-2-S-3	47	.295
1923	Pit	N	1-3	12	.267
1924	Pit	N	1	5	.300
1925	Pit	N	1	3	.200
		BRTR		67	.290

Non-playing manager Pit (N) 1929-31.

ENWRIGHT, CHARLES MICHAEL
b.Oct.6,1887 Sacramento,Cal.
d.Jan.19,1917

Yr	Cl	Lea	Pos	G	Rec
1909	St.L	N	S	3	.142
	BLTR				

ENZENROTH, CLARENCE HERMAN (Jack)
b.Nov.4,1889 Mineral Point,Wis.
d.Feb.21,1944

Yr	Cl	Lea	Pos	G	Rec
1914	St.L	A	C	3	.167
1914	KC	F	C	24	.166
1915	KC	F	C	14	.158
	BLTR			41	.165

ENZMANN, JOHN
b.Mar.4,1890 Brooklyn,N.Y.

Yr	Cl	Lea	Pos	G	Rec
1914	Bro	N	P	7	1-0
1918	Cle	A	P	30	5-7
1919	Cle	A	P	14	1-2
1920	Phi	N	P	17	2-3
	BRTR			68	9-12

EPPERLY, ALBERT PAUL (Tub)
b.May 7,1918 Glidden,Ia.

Yr	Cl	Lea	Pos	G	Rec
1938	Chi	N	P	9	2-0
1950	Bro	N	P	5	0-0
	BLTR			14	2-0

EPPS, AUBREY LEE (Yo-Yo)
b.Mar.3,1914 Memphis,Tenn.

Yr	Cl	Lea	Pos	G	Rec
1935	Pit	N	C	1	.750
	BRTR				

EPPS, HAROLD FRANKLIN
b.Mar.26,1914 Athens,Ga.

Yr	Cl	Lea	Pos	G	Rec
1938	St.L	N	O	17	.300
1940	St.L	N	O	11	.200
1943	St.L	A	O	8	.286
1944	St.L	A	O	22	.177
1944	Phi	A	O	67	.262
	BLTL			125	.253

ERAUTT, EDWARD LORENZ SEBASTIAN
b.Sept.26,1924 Portland,Ore.

Yr	Cl	Lea	Pos	G	Rec
1947	Cin	N	P	36	4-9
1948	Cin	N	P	2	0-0
1949	Cin	N	P	39	4-11
1950	Cin	N	P	33	4-2
1951	Cin	N	P	30	0-0
1953	Cin	N	P	4	0-0
1953	StL	N	P	20	3-1
	BRTR			164	15-23

ERAUTT, JOSEPH MICHAEL
b.Sept.1,1921 Vibank,Sask.,Canada.

Yr	Cl	Lea	Pos	G	Rec
1950	Chi	A	C	16	.222
1951	Chi	A	C	16	.160
	BRTR			32	.186

ERICKSON, DONALD LEE
b.Dec.13,1931 Springfield,Ill.

Yr	Cl	Lea	Pos	G	Rec
1958	Phil	N	P	9	0-1
	BRTR				

ERICKSON, ERIC GEORGE
b.Mar.13,1895 Gothenburg,Sweden.

Yr	Cl	Lea	Pos	G	Rec
1914	NY	N	P	1	0-1
1916	Det	A	P	7	0-2
1918	Det	A	P	12	4-5
1919	Det	A	P	3	0-2
1919	Was	A	P	20	5-10
1920	Was	A	P	39	12-16
1921	Was	A	P	32	8-10
1922	Was	A	P	30	4-12
	BRTR			144	33-58

ERICKSON, HAROLD JAMES
b.July 17,1919 Portland,Ore.

Yr	Cl	Lea	Pos	G	Rec
1953	Det	A	P	18	0-1
	BRTR				

ERICKSON, HENRY NELS
b.Nov.11,1908 Chicago,Ill.

Yr	Cl	Lea	Pos	G	Rec
1935	Cin	N	C	37	.261
	BRTR				

ERICKSON, PAUL WAKEFIELD (Li'l Abner)
b.Dec.14,1916 Zion,Ill.

Yr	Cl	Lea	Pos	G	Rec
1941	Chi	N	P	32	5-7
1942	Chi	N	P	18	1-6
1943	Chi	N	P	15	1-3
1944	Chi	N	P	33	5-9
1945	Chi	N	P	28	7-4
1946	Chi	N	P	32	9-7
1947	Chi	N	P	40	7-12
1948	Chi	N	P	3	0-0
1948	Phi	N	P	4	2-0
1948	NY	N	P	2	0-0
	BRTR			207	37-48

ERICKSON, RALPH LIEF
b.June 25,1906 Dubois,Ida.

Yr	Cl	Lea	Pos	G	Rec
1929	Pit	N	P	1	0-0
1930	Pit	N	P	7	1-0
	BLTL			8	1-0

ERMER, CALVIN COOLIDGE
b.Nov.10,1924 Baltimore,Md.

Yr	Cl	Lea	Pos	G	Rec
1947	Was	A	2	1	.000
	BRTR				

ERNAGA, FRANK JOHN
b.Aug.22,1930 Susanville,Cal.

Yr	Cl	Lea	Pos	G	Rec
1957	Chi	N	O	20	.314
1958	Chi	N	H	9	.125
	BRTR			29	.279

ERRICKSON, RICHARD MERRIWELL
b.Mar.5,1914 Vineland,N.J.

Yr	Cl	Lea	Pos	G	Rec
1938	Bos	N	P	34	9-7
1939	Bos	N	P	28	6-9
1940	Bos	N	P	34	12-13
1941	Bos	N	P	38	6-12
1942	Bos	N	P	21	2-5
1942	Chi	N	P	13	1-1
	BLTR			168	36-47

ERSKINE, CARL DANIEL
b.Dec.13,1926 Anderson,Ind.

Yr	Cl	Lea	Pos	G	Rec
1948	Bro	N	P	17	6-3
1949	Bro	N	P	22	8-1
1950	Bro	N	P	22	7-6
1951	Bro	N	P	46	16-12
1952	Bro	N	P	34	14-6
1953	Bro	N	P	43	20-6
1954	Bro	N	P	39	18-15
1955	Bro	N	P	42	11-8
1956	Bro	N	P	32	13-11
1957	Bro	N	P	21	5-3
1958	LA	N	P	32	4-4
1959	LA	N	P	10	0-3
	BRTR			360	122-78

ERSKINE, JAMES
(Played under name of James Erskine Mayer)

ERSKINE, SAMUEL FRANKEL
(Played under name of Samuel Frankel Mayer)

ERWIN, ROSS EMIL (Tex)
bDec.22,1885 Forney,Tex.
d.Apr.5,1953

Yr	Cl	Lea	Pos	G	Rec
1907	Det	A	C	4	.200
1910	Bro	N	C	68	.188
1911	Bro	N	C	74	.271
1912	Bro	N	C	59	.211
1913	Bro	N	C	20	.258
1914	Bro	N	C	7	.500
1914	Cin	N	C	14	.306
	BLTR			246	.237

ESCALERA, SATURNINO CUADRADO (Nino)
b.Nov.29,1929 Santurce,Porto Rico

Yr	Cl	Lea	Pos	G	Rec
1954	Cin	N	1-S-O	73	.159
	BLTR				

ESCHEN, JAMES GODRICH
b.Aug.21,1893 Brooklyn,N.Y.
d.Sept.27,1960

Yr	Cl	Lea	Pos	G	Rec
1915	Cle	A	O	15	.239
	BRTR				

ESCHEN, LAWRENCE EDWARD
b.Sept.22,1920 Suffern,N.Y.

Yr	Cl	Lea	Pos	G	Rec
1942	Phi	A	2-S	12	.000
	BRTR				

ESMOND, JAMES J.
b.Oct.8,1889 Albany, N.Y.
d.June 26,1948

Yr	Cl	Lea	Pos	G	Rec
1911	Cin	N	S	59	.273
1912	Cin	N	S	82	.195
1914	Ind	F	S	150	.295
1915	New	F	S	155	.258
	BRTR			446	.264

ESPER, CHARLES H. (Duke)
b.July 28,1868 Salem,N.J.
d.Aug.31,1910

Yr	Cl	Lea	Pos	G	Rec
1890	Ath	a	P	19	7-8
1890	Pit	N	P	2	0-2
1890	Phi	N	P	6	4-0
1891	Phi	N	P	34	20-13
1892	Phi	N	P	19	13-6
1892	Pit	N	P	11	1-0
1893	Was	N	P	40	12-26
1894	Was	N	P	15	6-9
1894	Bal	N	P	16	9-2
1895	Bal	N	P	27	12-12
1896	Bal	N	P	19	14-5
1897	St.L	N	P	8	1-6
1898	St.L	N	P	10	3-5
	TL			226	102-94

ESPOSITO, SAMUEL
b.Dec.15,1931 Chicago,Ill.

Yr	Cl	Lea	Pos	G	Rec
1952	Chi	A	S	1	.250
1955	Chi	A	3	3	.000
1956	Chi	A	2-S-3	81	.228
1957	Chi	A	2-S-3-O	94	.205
1958	Chi	A	2-S-3-O	98	.247
1959	Chi	A	2-S-3	69	.167
1960	Chi	A	2-S-3	57	.182
1961	Chi	A	2-S-3	63	.170
1962	Chi	A	2-S-3	75	.235
	BRTR			541	.207

ESSICK, WILLIAM EARL (Vinegar Bill)
b.Dec.18,1881 Grand Ridge,Ill.
d.Oct.11,1951

Yr	Cl	Lea	Pos	G	Rec
1906	Cin	N	P	6	1-1
1907	Cin	N	P	3	0-2
	TR			9	1-3

ESSEGIAN, CHARLES ABRAHAM
b.Aug.9,1931 Boston,Mass.

Yr	Cl	Lea	Pos	G	Rec
1958	Phi	N	O	39	.246
1959	St.L	N	O	17	.179
1959	LA	N	O	24	.304
1960	LA	N	O	52	.215
1961	Bal	A	O	1	.000
1961	KC	A	O	4	.333
1961	Cle	A	O	60	.289
1962	Cle	A	O	106	.274
	BRTR			303	.264

ESTALELLA, ROBERTO MENDEZ
b.Apr.25,1911 Cardenas,Cuba.

Yr	Cl	Lea	Pos	G	Rec
1935	Was	A	3	15	.314
1936	Was	A	H	13	.222
1939	Was	A	O	82	.275
1941	St.L	A	O	46	.241
1942	Was	A	3-O	133	.277
1943	Phi	A	O	117	.259
1944	Phi	A	1-O	140	.298

Yr Cl Lea Pos G Rec

(Continued)
1945 Phi A O 126 .299
1949 Phi A O 8 .250
BRTR 680 .282

ESTERBROOK, THOMAS JEFFERSON (Dude)
b.June 20,1860 New Brighton, S. I., N.Y.
d.Apr.30,1901
1880 Buf N C-1-2-S-O 63 .241
1882 Cle N 1-O 45 .246
1883 Met a 3 41 .250
1884 Met a 3 112 .408
1885 NY N 3-O 88 .256
1886 NY N 3 123 .264
1887 Met a S 26 .224
1888 Ind N 1 64 .219
1888 Lou a 1 23 .226
1889 Lou a 1 11 .309
1890 NY N 1 45 .289
1891 Bro N 2 3 .375
BRTR 644 .278

ESTERDAY, HENRY
b.Sept.16,1864 Philadelphia, Pa.
1884 Key U S 28 .250
1888 KC a S 114 .195
1889 Col a S 105 .175
1890 Col a S 52 .145
1890 Ath a S 19 .154
1890 Lou a S 7 .087
BRTR 306 .177

ESTOCK, GEORGE JOHN
b.Nov.2,1924 Stirling,N.J.
1951 Bos N P 37 0-1
BRTR

ESTRADA, CHARLES LEONARD
b.Feb.15,1938 San Luis Obispo,Cal.
1960 Bal A P 36 18-11
1961 Bal A P 33 15-9
1962 Bal A P 38 9-17
BRTR 107 42-37

ESTRADA, OSCAR
b.Feb.15,1904 Havana,Cuba.
1929 St.L A P 1 0-0
BLTL

ETCHEBARREN, ANDREW AUGUSTE
b.June 20,1943 La Puente,Cal.
1962 Bal A C 2 .333
BRTR

ETCHISON, CLARENCE HAMPTON (Buck)
b.Jan.27,1918 Baltimore,Md.
1943 Bos N 1 10 .316
1944 Bos N 1 109 .214
BLTL 119 .220

ETTEN, NICHOLAS RAYMOND THOMAS
b.Sept.19,1913 Chicago,Ill.
1938 Phi A 1 22 .259
1939 Phi A 1 43 .252
1941 Phi N 1 151 .311
1942 Phi N 1 139 .264
1943 NY A 1 154 .271
1944 NY A 1 154 .293
1945 NY A 1 152 .285
1946 NY A 1 108 .232
1947 Phi N 1 14 .244
BLTL 937 .277

EUBANK, JOHN FRANKLIN
b.Sept.9,1872 Servia,Ind.
d.Nov.3,1958

Yr Cl Lea Pos G Rec

(Continued)
1905 Det A P 7 2-0
1906 Det A P 26 4-10
1907 Det A P 15 2-3
BRTR 48 8-13

EUBANKS, UEL MELVIN (Poss)
b.Feb.14,1902 Quinlan,Tex.
d.Nov.22,1954
1922 Chi N P 2 0-0
BRTR

EUNICK, FERNANDAS BOWEN
b.Apr.22,1896 Baltimore,Md.
d.Dec.9,1959
1917 Cle A 3 1 .000
BRTR

EUSTACE, FRANK JOHN
b.Nov.7,1873 New York,N.Y.
d.Oct.20,1932
1896 Lou N S 25 .163

EVANS, ALFRED HUBERT
b.Sept.28,1916 Kenly,N.C.
1939 Was A C 7 .333
1940 Was A C 14 .320
1941 Was A C 53 .277
1942 Was A C 74 .229
1944 Was A C 14 .091
1945 Was A C 51 .260
1946 Was A C 88 .254
1947 Was A C 99 .241
1948 Was A C 93 .259
1949 Was A C 109 .271
1950 Was A C 90 .235
1951 Bos A C 12 .125
BRTR 704 .282

EVANS, CHICKERING F.
b.Sept.10,1888 Arlington,Vt.
1909 Bos N P 4 0-3
1910 Bos N P 13 1-1
BRTR 17 1-4

EVANS, J. FORD
d.Dec.1884
Non-playing manager
Cle (N) 1882.

EVANS, JACOB (Bloody Jake)
b.Baltimore,Md.
d.Feb.3,1907
1875 NH n O 1 NR
1879 Tro N O 70 .230
1880 Tro N P-S-O 47 {0-0 .255
1881 Tro N O 81 .242
1882 Wor N P-2-S-O 80 {0-1 .212
1883 Cle N P-2-3-O 89 {0-0 .235
1884 Cle N 2-S-O 80 .258
1885 Bal a O 20 .205
TR 468 {0-1 NR

EVANS, JOSEPH PATTON
b.May 15,1895 Meridian,Miss.
d.Aug.9,1953
1915 Cle A 3 42 .257
1916 Cle A 3 33 .146
1917 Cle A 3 132 .190
1918 Cle A 3 79 .263
1919 Cle A S 21 .071
1920 Cle A O 56 .349
1921 Cle A O 57 .333
1922 Cle A O 75 .269
1923 Was A 3-O 106 .263
1924 St.L A O 77 .254
1925 St.L A O 55 .314
BRTR 733 .259

EVANS, Le ROY
b.Mar.19,1874 Knoxville,Tenn.
1897 St.L N P 2 0-1
1897 Lou N P 9 5-4
1898 Was N P 7 3-3

Yr Cl Lea Pos G Rec

(Continued)
1899 Was N P 7 3-2
1902 NY N P 19 8-11
1902 Bro N P 13 5-C
1903 Bro N P 15 5-9
1903 St.L A P 7 1-5
BRTR 79 30-41

EVANS, LOUIS RICHARD (Steve)
b.Feb.17,1885 Cleveland,O.
d.Dec.28,1943
1908 NY N O 2 .333
1909 St.L N O 143 .259
1910 St.L N O 151 .241
1911 St.L N O 150 .294
1912 St.L N O 135 .283
1913 St.L N O 97 .249
1914 Bro F 1-O 145 .355
1915 Bro F O 63 .289
1915 Bal F O 87 .319
BLTL 973 .288

EVANS, RUSSELL EARL (Red)
b.Nov.12,1906 Chicago,Ill.
1936 Chi A P 18 0-3
1939 Bro N P 24 1-8
BRTR 42 1-11

EVANS, WILLIAM ARTHUR
b.Aug.3,1911 Elvine,Mo.
1932 Chi A P 7 0-0
BBTL

EVANS, WILLIAM JAMES
b.Feb.10,1894 Rockingham Co.,N.C.
1916 Pit N P 13 2-5
1917 Pit N P 8 0-4
1919 Pit N P 7 0-4
BRTR 28 2-13

EVANS, WILLIAM LAWRENCE
b.Mar.25,1919 Quanah,Tex.
1949 Chi A P 4 0-1
1951 Bos A P 9 0-0
BRTR 13 0-1

EVERETT, WILLIAM L. (Wild Bill)
b.Dec.13,1868 Ft.Wayne,Ind.
d.Jan.19,1938
1895 Chi N 3 133 .356
1896 Chi N 3-O 131 .333
1897 Chi N 3 90 .314
1898 Chi N 1 149 .325
1899 Chi N 1 136 .309
1900 Chi N 1 23 .236
1901 Was A 1 33 .189
TR 695 .320

EVERS, JOHN JOSEPH (Crab)
b.July 22,1883 Troy,N.Y.
d.Mar.28,1947
1902 Chi N 2-S 25 .225
1903 Chi N 2 123 .293
1904 Chi N 2 152 .265
1905 Chi N 2 99 .276
1906 Chi N 2 154 .255
1907 Chi N 2 151 .250
1908 Chi N 2 123 .300
1909 Chi N 2 126 .263
1910 Chi N 2 125 .263
1911 Chi N 2 44 .226
1912 Chi N 2 143 .341
1913 Chi N M-2 136 .285
1914 Bos N 2 139 .279
1915 Bos N 2 83 .263
1916 Bos N 2 71 .216
1917 Bos N 2 24 .176
1917 Phi N 2 56 .231
1922 Chi A 2 1 .000
1929 Bos N M-2 1 .000
BLTR 1776 .270
Non-playing manager Chi (N) 1921 and Chi (A) 1924.

EVERS, JOSEPH FRANCIS
b.Sept.10,1891 Troy,N.Y.
d.Jan.4,1949

Yr	Cl	Lea	Pos	G	Rec
1913	NY	N	3	1	.000
	BRTR				

EVERS, THOMAS FRANCIS
b.Mar.31,1852 Troy,N.Y.
d.Mar.23,1925

Yr	Cl	Lea	Pos	G	Rec
1882	Bal	a	2	1	.000
1884	Was	U	2	106	.234
				107	.232

EVERS, WALTER ARTHUR (Hoot)
b.Feb.8,1921 St.Louis,Mo.

Yr	Cl	Lea	Pos	G	Rec
1941	Det	A	O	1	.000
1946	Det	A	O	81	.266
1947	Det	A	O	126	.296
1948	Det	A	O	139	.314
1949	Det	A	O	132	.303
1950	Det	A	O	143	.323
1951	Det	A	O	116	.224
1952	Det	A	H	1	1.000
1952	Bos	A	O	106	.262
1953	Bos	A	O	99	.240
1954	Bos	A	O	6	.000
1954	NY	N	O	12	.091
1954	Det	A	O	30	.183
1955	Bal	A	O	60	.238
1955	Cle	A	O	39	.288
1956	Cle	A	H	3	.000
1956	Bal	A	O	48	.241
	BRTR			1142	.278

EWELL, ...
b.Washington,D.C.

Yr	Cl	Lea	Pos	G	Rec
1871	Cle	n	O	1	.000

EWING, GEORGE LEMUEL (Long Bob)
b.Apr.24,1873 New Hampshire,O.
d.June 20,1947

Yr	Cl	Lea	Pos	G	Rec
1902	Cin	N	P-O	19	5-6 .171
1903	Cin	N	P	31	14-13
1904	Cin	N	P	30	11-12
1905	Cin	N	P	42	21-12
1906	Cin	N	P	33	13-14
1907	Cin	N	P	44	17-19
1908	Cin	N	P	37	17-15
1909	Cin	N	P	31	11-12
1910	Phi	N	P	34	16-14
1911	Phi	N	P	4	0-2
1912	St.L	N	P	1	0-0
	BRTR			306	125-119 .195

EWING, JOHN (Long John)
b.June 1,1863 Cincinnati,O.
d.Apr.23,1893

Yr	Cl	Lea	Pos	G	Rec
1883	St.L	a	O	1	.000
1884	Cin	U	O	1	.000
1884	Was	U	O	1	.200
1888	Lou	a	P	21	8-13
1889	Lou	a	P	41	7-30
1890	NY	p	P	35	19-10
1891	NY	N	P	31	21-10
	TR			131	55-63 .186

EWING, REUBEN
(Real name Reuben Cohen)
b.Nov.30,1899 Russia.

Yr	Cl	Lea	Pos	G	Rec
1921	St.L	N	O	3	.000

EWING, WILLIAM (Buck)
b.Oct.17,1859 Hoaglands,O.
d.Oct.20,1906

Yr	Cl	Lea	Pos	G	Rec
1880	Tro	N	C-O	13	.152
1881	Tro	N	C-S-3-O	65	.243
1882	Tro	N	P-C-3	72	0-0 .273
1883	NY	N	C-2-S-O	85	.306
1884	NY	N	P-C-S-O	88	0-1 .278
1885	NY	N	P-C-1-S-3-O	81	0-1 .304
1886	NY	N	C-O	70	.309

(Continued)

Yr	Cl	Lea	Pos	G	Rec
1887	NY	N	2-3	76	.365
1888	NY	N	C-3	103	.306
1889	NY	N	P-C	96	0-0 .326
1890	NY	p	M-P-C	83	0-1 .349
1891	NY	N	C-2	14	.340
1892	NY	N	C-1	97	.319
1893	Cle	N	O	114	.371
1894	Cle	N	O	53	.255
1895	Cin	N	M-1	103	.316
1896	Cin	N	M-1	67	.282
1897	Cin	N	M-1	1	.000
	BRTR			1281	0-3 .311

Non-playing manager Cin (N) 1898-99 and NY (N) 1900.

EWOLDT, ARTHUR LEE (Sheriff)
b.Jan.8,1894 Paullina,Ia.

Yr	Cl	Lea	Pos	G	Rec
1919	Phi	A	3	9	.233
	BRTR				

EYRICH, GEORGE LINCOLN
b.Mar.3,1925 Reading,Pa.

Yr	Cl	Lea	Pos	G	Rec
1943	Phi	N	P	9	0-0
	BRTR				

EZZELL, HOMER ESTELL
b.Feb.28,1896 Victoria,Tex.

Yr	Cl	Lea	Pos	G	Rec
1923	St.L	A	3	88	.247
1924	Bos	A	S-3	90	.271
1925	Bos	A	2-3	58	.285
	BRTR			236	.265

FAATZ, JAY
b.Oct.24,1860 Weedsport,N.Y.
d.Apr.10,1923

Yr	Cl	Lea	Pos	G	Rec
1884	Pit	a	1	29	.230
1888	Cle	a	1	120	.264
1889	Cle	N	1	115	.230
1890	Buf	p	1	32	.200
	BRTR			296	.242

Non-playing manager Cle (p) 1890.

FABER, URBAN CHARLES (Red)
b.Sept.6,1888 Cascade,Ia.

Yr	Cl	Lea	Pos	G	Rec
1914	Chi	A	P	33	10-9
1915	Cni	A	P	49	24-13
1916	Chi	A	P	35	17-9
1917	Chi	A	P	41	16-13
1918	Chi	A	P	11	5-1
1919	Chi	A	P	25	11-9
1920	Chi	A	P	40	23-13
1921	Chi	A	P	43	25-15
1922	Chi	A	P	43	21-17
1923	Chi	A	P	33	14-11
1924	Chi	A	P	21	9-11
1925	Chi	A	P	34	12-11
1926	Chi	A	P	27	15-8
1927	Chi	A	P	18	4-7
1928	Chi	A	P	27	13-9
1929	Chi	A	P	31	13-13
1930	Chi	A	P	29	8-13
1931	Chi	A	P	44	10-14
1932	Chi	A	P	42	2-11
1933	Chi	A	P	36	3-4
	BBTR			662	255-211

FABRIQUE, ALBERT LaVERNE (Bunny)
b.Dec.23,1887 Clinton,Mich.
d.Jan.10,1960

Yr	Cl	Lea	Pos	G	Rec
1916	Bro	N	S	2	.000
1917	Bro	N	S	25	.205
	BBTR			27	.200

FACE, ELROY LEON (Roy)
b.Feb.20,1928 Stephentown,N.Y.

Yr	Cl	Lea	Pos	G	Rec
1953	Pit	N	P	43	6-8
1955	Pit	N	P	43	5-7
1956	Pit	N	P	69	12-13
1957	Pit	N	P	59	4-6
1958	Pit	N	P	57	5-2
1959	Pit	N	P	58	18-1
1960	Pit	N	P	68	10-8

(Continued)

Yr	Cl	Lea	Pos	G	Rec
1961	Pit	N	P	62	6-12
1962	Pit	N	P	63	8-7
	BRTR			522	74-64

FAETH, ANTHONY JOSEPH
b.July 9,1894 Aberdeen,S.C.

Yr	Cl	Lea	Pos	G	Rec
1919	Cle	A	P	6	0-0
1920	Cle	A	P	13	0-0
	BRTR			19	0-0

FAGAN, EVERETT JOSEPH
b.Jan.13,1919 Pottersville,N.J.

Yr	Cl	Lea	Pos	G	Rec
1943	Phi	A	P	18	2-6
1946	Phi	A	P	20	0-1
	BRTR			38	2-7

FAGAN, WILLIAM A. (Clinkers)
b.Lansingburg,N.Y.

Yr	Cl	Lea	Pos	G	Rec
1887	Met	a	P	6	1-4
1888	KC	a	P	18	6-11
				24	7-15

FAGIN, FREDERICK H.
b.Cincinnati,O.

Yr	Cl	Lea	Pos	G	Rec
1895	St.L	N	C	1	.333

FAHEY, FRANCIS R.
b.Jan.22,1896 Milford,Mass.
d.Mar.19,1954

Yr	Cl	Lea	Pos	G	Rec
1918	Phi	A	P	10	0-0

FAHEY, HOWARD SIMPSON
b.June 24,1892 Medford,Mass.

Yr	Cl	Lea	Pos	G	Rec
1912	Phi	A	S	5	.000
	BRTR				

FAHR, GERALD WARREN
b.Dec.9,1926 Marmaduke,Ark.

Yr	Cl	Lea	Pos	G	Rec
1951	Cle	A	P	5	0-0
	BRTR				

FAHRER, CLARENCE WILLIE (Pete)
b.Mar.10,1890 Holgate,Ohio

Yr	Cl	Lea	Pos	G	Rec
1914	Cin	N	P	5	0-0
	TR				

FAIN, FERRIS ROY (Burrhead)
b.May 29,1922 San Antonio,Tex.

Yr	Cl	Lea	Pos	G	Rec
1947	Phi	A	1	136	.291
1948	Phi	A	1	145	.281
1949	Phi	A	1	150	.263
1950	Phi	A	1	151	.282
1951	Phi	A	1-O	117	.344
1952	Phi	A	1	145	.327
1953	Chi	A	1	128	.256
1954	Chi	A	1	65	.302
1955	Det	A	1	58	.264
1955	Cle	A	1	56	.254
	BLTL			1151	.290

FAIRBANK, JAMES LEE
b.Mar.17,1881 Deansboro,N.Y.
d.Dec.27,1955

Yr	Cl	Lea	Pos	G	Rec
1903	Phi	A	P	1	0-0
1904	Phi	A	P	3	0-1
				4	0-1

FAIRCLOTH, JAMES LAMAR (Rags)
b.Aug.19,1892 Kenton,Tenn.

Yr	Cl	Lea	Pos	G	Rec
1919	Phi	N	P	2	0-0
	BRTR				

FAIRLY, RONALD RAY
b.July 12,1938 Macon,Ga.

Yr	Cl	Lea	Pos	G	Rec
1958	LA	N	O	15	.283
1959	LA	N	O	118	.238
1960	LA	N	O	14	.108
1961	LA	N	1-O	111	.322
1962	LA	N	1-O	147	.278
	BLTL			405	.284

FALCH, ANTON

Yr	Cl	Lea	Pos	G	Rec
1884	Mil	U	C-O	5	.471

FALK, BIBB AUGUST (Jockey)
b.Jan.27,1899 Austin,Tex.

Yr	Cl	Lea	Pos	G	Rec
1920	Chi	A	O	7	.294
1921	Chi	A	O	152	.285
1922	Chi	A	O	131	.298
1923	Chi	A	O	87	.307
1924	Chi	A	O	138	.352
1925	Chi	A	O	154	.301
1926	Chi	A	O	155	.345
1927	Chi	A	O	145	.327
1928	Chi	A	O	98	.290
1929	Cle	A	O	126	.310
1930	Cle	A	O	82	.325
1931	Cle	A	O	79	.304
	BLTL			1354	.314

FALK, CHESTER EMANUEL
b.May 15,1905 Austin,Tex.

Yr	Cl	Lea	Pos	G	Rec
1925	St.L	A	P	17	0-0
1926	St.L	A	P	19	4-4
1927	St.L	A	P	9	1-0
	BLTL			45	5-4

FALKENBERG, FREDERICK PETER (Cy)
b.Dec.17,1880 Chicago,Ill.
d.Apr.14,1961

Yr	Cl	Lea	Pos	G	Rec
1903	Pit	N	P	10	1-5
1905	Was	A	P	12	4-4
1906	Was	A	P	40	14-20
1907	Was	A	P	33	5-18
1908	Was	A	P	17	6-1
1908	Cle	A	P	8	2-5
1909	Cle	A	P	24	10-9
1910	Cle	A	P	37	14-13
1911	Cle	A	P	16	8-5
1913	Cle	A	P	36	23-10
1914	Ind	F	P	46	25-16
1915	New	F	P	16	4-6
1915	Bro	F	P	16	7-8
1917	Phi	A	P	15	2-6
	BRTR			326	125-126

FALLENSTEIN, EDWARD JOSEPH (Jack)
b.Dec.22,1908 Newark,N.J.

Yr	Cl	Lea	Pos	G	Rec
1931	Phi	N	P	24	0-0
1933	Bos	N	P	11	2-1
	BRTR			35	2-1

FALLON, GEORGE DECATUR (Flash)
b.July 8,1916 Jersey City,N.J.

Yr	Cl	Lea	Pos	G	Rec
1937	Bro	N	2	4	.250
1943	St.L	N	2	36	.231
1944	St.L	N	2-S-3	69	.199
1945	St.L	N	2-S	24	.236
	BRTR			133	.216

FALSEY, PETER JAMES
b.Apr.24,1891 New Haven,Conn.

Yr	Cl	Lea	Pos	G	Rec
1914	Pit	N	P	3	0-0
	BLTL				

FANNIN, CLIFFORD BRYSON (Mule)
b.May 13,1924 Louisa,Ky.

Yr	Cl	Lea	Pos	G	Rec
1945	St.L	A	P	5	0-0
1946	St.L	A	P	27	5-2
1947	St.L	A	P	26	6-8
1948	St.L	A	P	48	10-14
1949	St.L	A	P	37	8-14
1950	St.L	A	P	33	5-9
1951	St.L	A	P	8	0-2
1952	St.L	A	P	11	0-2
	BLTR			195	34-51

FANNING, JOHN JACOB
b.1863 S.Orange,N.J.
d.June 10,1917

(Continued)

Yr	Cl	Lea	Pos	G	Rec
1889	Ind	N	P	1	0-1
1894	Phi	N	P	6	1-3
				7	1-4

FANNING, WILLIAM JAMES
b.Sept.14,1927 Chicago,Ill.

Yr	Cl	Lea	Pos	G	Rec
1954	Chi	N	C	11	.184
1955	Chi	N	C	5	.000
1956	Chi	N	C	1	.250
1957	Chi	N	C	47	.180
	BRTR			64	.170

FANOVICH, FRANK JOSEPH
b.Jan.11,1922 New York,N.Y.

Yr	Cl	Lea	Pos	G	Rec
1949	Cin	N	P	29	0-2
1953	Phi	A	P	26	0-3
	BLTL			55	0-5

FANWELL, HARRY CLAYTON
b.Oct.16,1886 Carroll Co.,Md.

Yr	Cl	Lea	Pos	G	Rec
1910	Cle	A	P	17	2-9
		BLTR			

FARLEY, ROBERT JACOB
b.Nov.15,1937 Watsontown,Pa.

Yr	Cl	Lea	Pos	G	Rec
1961	SF	N	1-O	13	.100
1962	Chi	A	1	35	.189
1962	Det	A	1-O	36	.160
	BLTL			84	.163

FARLEY, THOMAS T.
b.Chicago,Ill.

Yr	Cl	Lea	Pos	G	Rec
1884	Was	a	O	13	.213

FARMER, ALBERT J.
d.1928

Yr	Cl	Lea	Pos	G	Rec
1908	Bro	N	C	12	.167
		TR			

FARMER, JOHN FLOYD
b.June 8,1892 Lebanon,Tenn.

Yr	Cl	Lea	Pos	G	Rec
1916	Pit	N	2-O	55	.271
1918	Cle	A	O	7	.222
	BRTR			62	.269

FARMER, WILLIAM
b.Philadelphia,Pa.

Yr	Cl	Lea	Pos	G	Rec
1888	Pit	N	C	2	.000
1888	Ath	a	C	3	.167
	BRTR			5	.125

FARRAR, SIDNEY DOUGLAS
b.Aug.10,1859 Paris Hill,Me.
d.May 7,1935

Yr	Cl	Lea	Pos	G	Rec
1883	Phi	N	1	98	.230
1884	Phi	N	1	110	.246
1885	Phi	N	1	111	.245
1886	Phi	N	1	118	.248
1887	Phi	N	1	115	.344
1888	Phi	N	1	130	.246
1889	Phi	N	1	130	.268
1890	Phi	p	1	127	.251
	TR			939	.262

FARRELL, CHARLES A. (Duke)
b.Aug.31,1866 Oakdale,Mass.
d.Feb.15,1925

Yr	Cl	Lea	Pos	G	Rec
1888	Chi	N	C-O	63	.232
1889	Chi	N	C-O	100	.263
1890	Chi	p	C-1	117	.296
1891	Bos	a	C-3-O	122	.304
1892	Pit	N	3-O	152	.230
1893	Was	N	C-3	122	.296
1894	NY	N	C	112	.282
1895	NY	N	C-3	89	.283
1896	NY	N	C	45	.279
1896	Was	N	C-3	37	.326
1897	Was	N	C	65	.327
1898	Was	N	C-1	88	.316
1899	Was	N	C	5	.333

(Continued)

Yr	Cl	Lea	Pos	G	Rec
1899	Bro	N	C	78	.294
1900	Bro	N	C	73	.277
1901	Bro	N	C-1	76	.293
1902	Bro	N	C-1	72	.237
1903	Bos	A	C	17	.404
1904	Bos	A	C	67	.219
1905	Bos	A	C	7	.238
	BRTR			1507	.280

FARRELL, EDWARD STEPHEN (Doc)
b.Dec.26,1902 Johnson City,N.Y.

Yr	Cl	Lea	Pos	G	Rec
1925	NY	N	2-S-3	27	.214
1926	NY	N	S	67	.287
1927	NY	N	S-3	42	.387
1927	Bos	N	2-S-3	110	.292
1928	Bos	N	S	134	.215
1929	Bos	N	2	5	.125
1929	NY	N	2-3	63	.213
1930	St.L	N	S	23	.213
1930	Chi	N	S	46	.292
1932	NY	A	2	26	.175
1933	NY	A	2-S	44	.269
1935	Bos	A	2	4	.286
	BRTR			591	.260

FARRELL, JOHN (Hartford Jack)
d.Feb.10,1914

Yr	Cl	Lea	Pos	G	Rec
1874	Har	n	O	3	NR

FARRELL, JOHN A. (Moose)
b.July 5,1857 Newark,N.J.
d.Nov.15,1916

Yr	Cl	Lea	Pos	G	Rec
1879	Syr	N	2	54	.304
1879	Pro	N	2	12	.260
1880	Pro	N	2	77	.270
1881	Pro	N	2-O	83	.237
1882	Pro	N	2	84	.254
1883	Pro	N	2	93	.304
1884	Pro	N	2-3	109	.220
1885	Pro	N	2	67	.206
1886	Phi	N	2	23	.171
1886	Was	N	2	42	.252
1887	Was	N	2-S	86	.264
1888	Bal	a	2-S	103	.197
1889	Bal	a	S	42	.204
	BRTR			875	.241

FARRELL, JOHN J.
b.June 16,1892 Chicago,Ill.
d.Mar.24,1918

Yr	Cl	Lea	Pos	G	Rec
1914	Chi	F	2	157	.240
1915	Chi	F	2	69	.213
	BBTR			226	.232

FARRELL, JOHN STEPHEN
b.Dec.4,1876 Covington,Ky.
d.May 14,1921

Yr	Cl	Lea	Pos	G	Rec
1901	Was	A	2-O	135	.277
1902	St.L	N	2-S	139	.255
1903	St.L	N	2	130	.272
1904	St.L	N	2	130	.255
1905	St.L	N	2	6	.182
	TR			540	.264

FARRELL, JOSEPH F.
b.1858 Brooklyn,N.Y.
d.Apr.18,1893

Yr	Cl	Lea	Pos	G	Rec
1882	Det	N	2-S-3	66	.246
1883	Det	N	3	98	.246
1884	Det	N	3	108	.225
1886	Bal	a	2-3	72	.212
				344	.233

FARRELL, MAJOR KERBY
b.Sept.3,1913 Leapwood,Tenn.

Yr	Cl	Lea	Pos	G	Rec
1943	Bos	N	P-1	85	0-1 / .268
1945	Chi	A	1	103	.258
	BLTL			188	0-1 / .262

Non-playing manager Cle (A) 1957

FARRELL, RICHARD JOSEPH
b.Apr.8,1934 Boston,Mass.

Yr	Cl	Lea	Pos	G	Rec
1956	Phi	N	P	1	0-1
1957	Phi	N	P	52	10-2
1958	Phi	N	P	54	8-9
1959	Phi	N	P	38	1-6
1960	Phi	N	P	59	10-6
1961	Phi	N	P	5	2-1
1961	LA	N	P	50	6-6
1962	Hou	N	P	43	10-20
	BRTR			302	47-51

FARRELL, W.

Yr	Cl	Lea	Pos	G	Rec
1883	Bal	a	S	2	.000

FARROW, JOHN JACOB
b.1852 Verplanck's Point,N.Y.
d.Dec.31,1914

Yr	Cl	Lea	Pos	G	Rec
1873	Res	n	C-1-3-O	10	NR
1874	Atl	n	C-2	27	NR
1884	Bro	a	C	16	.190
	TR			53	NR

FAST, ...
b.Milwaukee,Wis.

Yr	Cl	Lea	Pos	G	Rec
1887	Ind	N	P	4	0-1

FASZHOLZ, JOHN EDWARD
b.Apr.11,1927 St.Louis,Mo.

Yr	Cl	Lea	Pos	G	Rec
1953	St.L	N	P	4	0-0
	BRTR				

FAUL, WILLIAM A.
b.Apr.21,1940 Pleasant Plain,O.

Yr	Cl	Lea	Pos	G	Rec
1962	Det	A	P	1	0-0

FAULKNER, JAMES LeROY
b.July 27,1900 Beatrice,Neb.
d.June 2,1962

Yr	Cl	Lea	Pos	G	Rec
1927	NY	N	P	3	1-0
1928	NY	N	P	38	9-8
1930	Bro	N	P	2	0-0
	BBTL			43	10-8

FAUSETT, ROBERT SHAW (Buck)
b.Apr.8,1908 Sheridan,Ark.

Yr	Cl	Lea	Pos	G	Rec
1944	Cin	N	P-3	13	0-0 / .097
	BLTR				

FAUST, CHARLES VICTOR (Vic)
b.Oct.9,1880 Marion,Kan.
d.June 18,1915

Yr	Cl	Lea	Pos	G	Rec
1911	NY	N	P	2	0-0

FAUTSCH, JOSEPH R.
b.1889

Yr	Cl	Lea	Pos	G	Rec
1916	Chi	A	P	1	0-0
	BRTR				

FAUVER, CLAYTON KING
b.Aug.1,1872 N.Eaton,O.
d.Mar.3,1942

Yr	Cl	Lea	Pos	G	Rec
1899	Lou	N	P	1	1-0

FAZIO, ERNEST JOSEPH
b.Jan.25,1942 Oakland,Cal.

Yr	Cl	Lea	Pos	G	Rec
1962	Hou	N	S	12	.083
	BRTR				

FEAR, LUVERN CARL (Vern)
b.Aug.21,1924 Everly,Ia.

Yr	Cl	Lea	Pos	G	Rec
1952	Chi	N	P	4	0-0
	BRTR				

FEDEROFF, ALFRED
b.July 11,1925 Bairdford,Pa.

Yr	Cl	Lea	Pos	G	Rec
1951	Det	A	2	2	.000
1952	Det	A	2-S	74	.242
	BRTR			76	.238

FEE, JOHN
b.1870 Carbondale,Pa.
d.Mar.4,1913

Yr	Cl	Lea	Pos	G	Rec
1889	Ind	N	P	7	2-2

FEHRING, WILLIAM PAUL
b.May 31,1912 Columbus,Ind.

Yr	Cl	Lea	Pos	G	Rec
1934	Chi	A	C	1	.000
	BBTR				

FEINBERG, EDWARD
b.Sept.20,1918 Philadelphia,Pa.

Yr	Cl	Lea	Pos	G	Rec
1938	Phi	N	S-O	10	.150
1939	Phi	N	2-S	6	.222
	BBTR			16	.184

FELDERMAN, MARVIN WILFRED
b.Dec.17,1917 Bellevue,Ia.

Yr	Cl	Lea	Pos	G	Rec
1942	Chi	N	C	3	.167
	BRTR				

FELDMAN, HARRY
b.Nov.10,1919 New York,N.Y.
d.Mar. 16,1962

Yr	Cl	Lea	Pos	G	Rec
1941	NY	N	P	3	1-1
1942	NY	N	P	31	7-1
1943	NY	N	P	44	4-5
1944	NY	N	P	54	11-13
1945	NY	N	P	38	12-13
1946	NY	N	P	3	0-2
	BRTR			173	35-35

FELIX, AUGUST GUENTHER
b.May 24,1895 Cincinnati,Ohio
d.May 12,1960

Yr	Cl	Lea	Pos	G	Rec
1923	Bos	N	2-3-O	139	.273
1924	Bos	N	O	59	.211
1925	Bos	N	O	121	.307
1926	Bro	N	O	134	.280
1927	Bro	N	O	130	.265
	BRTR			583	.274

FELIX, HARRY
b.1877 Brooklyn,N.Y.
d.Oct.18,1961

Yr	Cl	Lea	Pos	G	Rec
1901	NY	N	P	1	0-0
1902	Phi	N	P-3	16	1-3 / .111
	TR			17	1-3 / .105

FELLER, JACK LELAND
b.Dec.10,1936 Adrian,Mich.

Yr	Cl	Lea	Pos	G	Rec
1958	Det	A	C	1	.000
	BRTR				

FELLER, ROBERT WILLIAM ANDREW
b.Nov.3,1918 Van Meter,Ia.

Yr	Cl	Lea	Pos	G	Rec
1936	Cle	A	P	14	5-3
1937	Cle	A	P	26	9-7
1938	Cle	A	P	39	17-11
1939	Cle	A	P	39	24-9
1940	Cle	A	P	43	27-11
1941	Cle	A	P	44	25-13
1945	Cle	A	P	9	5-3
1946	Cle	A	P	48	26-15
1947	Cle	A	P	42	20-11
1948	Cle	A	P	44	19-15
1949	Cle	A	P	36	15-14
1950	Cle	A	P	35	16-11
1951	Cle	A	P	33	22-8
1952	Cle	A	P	30	9-13
1953	Cle	A	P	25	10-7
1954	Cle	A	P	19	13-3
1955	Cle	A	P	25	4-4
1956	Cle	A	P	19	0-4
	BRTR			570	266-162

FELSCH, OSCAR EMIL (Happy)
b.Aug.22,1891 Milwaukee,Wis.

Yr	Cl	Lea	Pos	G	Rec
1915	Chi	A	O	121	.248
1916	Chi	A	O	146	.301
1917	Chi	A	O	152	.308
1918	Chi	A	O	53	.252
1919	Chi	A	O	135	.275

(Continued)

Yr	Cl	Lea	Pos	G	Rec
1920	Chi	A	O	142	.338
	BRTR			749	.290

FENNELLY, FRANCIS JOHN
b.Feb.18,1860 Fall River,Mass.
d.Aug.4,1920

Yr	Cl	Lea	Pos	G	Rec
1884	Was	a	2-S-O	62	.288
1884	Cin	a	S	28	.369
1885	Cin	a	S	112	.259
1886	Cin	a	S	132	.258
1887	Cin	a	S	134	.368
1888	Cin	a	2-S-O	112	.191
1888	Ath	a	S	15	.239
1889	Ath	a	S	137	.259
1890	Bro	a	S	47	.251
	BRTR			779	.278

FENNER, HORACE ALFRED (Hod)
b.July 12,1897 Martin,Mich.

Yr	Cl	Lea	Pos	G	Rec
1921	Chi	A	P	2	0-0
	BRTR				

FERENS, STANLEY
b.Mar.5,1919 Wendell,Pa.

Yr	Cl	Lea	Pos	G	Rec
1942	St.L	A	P	19	3-4
1946	St.L	A	P	34	2-9
	BBTL			53	5-13

FERGUSON, CHARLES AUGUSTUS
b.May 10,1875 Okemos,Mich.
d.May 17,1931

Yr	Cl	Lea	Pos	G	Rec
1901	Chi	N	P	1	0-0

FERGUSON, CHARLES J.
b.Apr.17,1863 Charlottesville,Va.
d.Apr.29,1888

Yr	Cl	Lea	Pos	G	Rec
1884	Phi	N	P-O	51	20-22 / .251
1885	Phi	N	P-O	59	26-19 / .306
1886	Phi	N	P-O	71	32-9 / .252
1887	Phi	N	P-2	69	21-10 / .412
	BBTR			250	99-60 / .313

FERGUSON, GEORGE CECIL
b.Aug.19,1886 Ellsworth,Ind.
d.Sept.5,1943

Yr	Cl	Lea	Pos	G	Rec
1906	NY	N	P	22	2-1
1907	NY	N	P	15	3-2
1908	Bos	N	P	37	11-11
1909	Bos	N	P	36	5-23
1910	Bos	N	P	26	7-7
1911	Bos	N	P	6	1-3
				142	29-47

FERGUSON, JAMES ALEXANDER (Alex)
b.Feb.16,1897 Montclair,N.J.

Yr	Cl	Lea	Pos	G	Rec
1918	NY	A	P	1	0-0
1921	NY	A	P	17	3-1
1922	Bos	A	P	39	9-16
1923	Bos	A	P	34	9-13
1924	Bos	A	P	41	14-17
1925	Bos	A	P	5	0-2
1925	NY	A	P	21	4-2
1925	Was	A	P	7	5-1
1926	Was	A	P	19	3-4
1927	Phi	N	P	31	8-16
1928	Phi	N	P	34	5-10
1929	Phi	N	P	5	1-2
1929	Bro	N	P	3	0-1
	BRTR			257	61-85

FERGUSON, ROBERT LESTER
b.Apr.18,1919 Birmingham,Ala.

Yr	Cl	Lea	Pos	G	Rec
1944	Cin	N	P	9	0-3
	BRTR				

FERGUSON, ROBERT V.
b.1845 Brooklyn,N.Y.
d.May 3,1894

Yr	Cl	Lea	Pos	G	Rec
1871	Mut	n	M-C-2-3	34	NR
1872	Atl	n	M-3	36	NR
1873	Atl	n	M-P-3	53	0-1 NR
1874	Atl	n	M-P-C-3	56	0-1 NR
1875	Har	n	M-3	84	NR
1876	Har	N	M-3	69	.264
1877	Har	N	M-P-3	58	1-1 .256
1878	Chi	N	M-S	60	.334
1879	Tro	N	M-3	29	.252
1880	Tro	N	M-2	82	.262
1881	Tro	N	M-2	84	.287
1882	Tro	N	M-2-S	79	.254
1883	Phi	N	M-P-2	85	0-0 .256
1884	Pit	a	M-1-3-O	10	.154
	BBTR			819	1-3 NR

Non-playing manager Met (a) 1886-87.

FERNANDES, EDWARD PAUL
b.Mar.11,1918 Oakland,Cal.

Yr	Cl	Lea	Pos	G	Rec
1940	Pit	N	C	28	.121
1946	Chi	A	C	14	.250
	BBTR			42	.185

FERNANDEZ, FROILAN (Nanny)
b.Oct.25,1918 Wilmington,Cal.

Yr	Cl	Lea	Pos	G	Rec
1942	Bos	N	3-O	145	.255
1946	Bos	N	S-3-O	115	.255
1947	Bos	N	S-3-O	83	.206
1950	Pit	N	3	65	.258
	BRTR			408	.248

FERNANDEZ, HUMBERTO PEREZ (Chico)
b.Mar.2,1932 Havana,Cuba

Yr	Cl	Lea	Pos	G	Rec
1956	Bro	N	S	34	.227
1957	Phi	N	S	149	.262
1958	Phi	N	S	148	.230
1959	Phi	N	2-S	45	.211
1960	Det	A	S	133	.241
1961	Det	A	S-3	133	.248
1962	Det	A	1-S-3	141	.249
	BRTR			783	.244

FERRARESE, DONALD HUGH
b.June 19,1929 Oakland,Cal.

Yr	Cl	Lea	Pos	G	Rec
1955	Bal	A	P	6	0-0
1956	Bal	A	P	36	4-10
1957	Bal	A	P	8	1-1
1958	Cle	A	P	28	3-4
1959	Cle	A	P	15	5-3
1960	Chi	A	P	5	0-1
1961	Phi	N	P-O	43	5-12 .171
1962	Phi	N	P	5	0-1
1962	St.L	N	P	38	1-4
	BRTL			184	19-36 .156

FERRAZZI, WILLIAM JOSEPH
b.Apr.19,1912 Quincy,Mass.

Yr	Cl	Lea	Pos	G	Rec
1935	Phi	A	P	3	1-2
	BRTR				

FERRELL, RICHARD BENJAMIN (Rick)
b.Oct.12,1905 Durham,N.C.

Yr	Cl	Lea	Pos	G	Rec
1929	St.L	A	C	64	.229
1930	St.L	A	C	101	.268
1931	St.L	A	C	117	.306
1932	St.L	A	C	126	.315
1933	St.L	A	C	22	.250
1933	Bos	A	C	118	.297
1934	Bos	A	C	132	.297
1935	Bos	A	C	133	.301

(Continued)

Yr	Cl	Lea	Pos	G	Rec
1936	Bos	A	C	121	.312
1937	Bos	A	C	18	.308
1937	Was	A	C	86	.229
1938	Was	A	C	135	.292
1939	Was	A	C	87	.281
1940	Was	A	C	103	.273
1941	Was	A	C	21	.273
1941	St.L	A	C	100	.252
1942	St.L	A	C	99	.223
1943	St.L	A	C	74	.239
1944	Was	A	C	99	.277
1945	Was	A	C	91	.266
1947	Was	A	C	37	.303
	BRTR			1884	.281

FERRELL, WESLEY CHEEK
b.Feb.2,1908 Greensboro,N.C.

Yr	Cl	Lea	Pos	G	Rec
1927	Cle	A	P	1	0-0
1928	Cle	A	P	2	0-2
1929	Cle	A	P	47	21-10
1930	Cle	A	P	53	25-13
1931	Cle	A	P	48	22-12
1932	Cle	A	P	55	23-13
1933	Cle	A	P-O	61	11-12 .271
1934	Bos	A	P	34	14-5
1935	Bos	A	P	75	25-14
1936	Bos	A	P	61	20-15
1937	Bos	A	P	18	3-6
1937	Was	A	P	53	11-13
1938	Was	A	P	26	13-8
1938	NY	A	P	5	2-2
1939	NY	A	P	3	1-2
1940	Bro	N	P	2	0-0
1941	Bos	N	P	4	2-1
	BRTR			548	193-128 .280

FERRICK, THOMAS JEROME
b.Jan.6,1915 New York,N.Y.

Yr	Cl	Lea	Pos	G	Rec
1941	Phi	A	P	36	8-10
1942	Cle	A	P	31	3-2
1946	Cle	A	P	9	0-0
1946	St.L	A	P	25	4-1
1947	Was	A	P	31	1-7
1948	Was	A	P	37	2-5
1949	St.L	A	P	51	6-4
1950	St.L	A	P	16	1-3
1950	NY	A	P	30	8-4
1951	NY	A	P	9	1-1
1951	Was	A	P	22	2-0
1952	Was	A	P	27	4-3
	BRTR			324	40-40

FERRIS, ALBERT SAYLES (Hobe)
b.Dec.7,1877 Providence,R.I.
d.Mar.18,1938

Yr	Cl	Lea	Pos	G	Rec
1901	Bos	A	2	138	.251
1902	Bos	A	2	133	.251
1903	Bos	A	2	141	.250
1904	Bos	A	2	156	.221
1905	Bos	A	2	141	.220
1906	Bos	A	2	130	.244
1907	Bos	A	2	143	.241
1908	St.L	A	3	148	.270
1909	St.L	A	2-3	148	.216
	BRTR			1278	.240

FERRISS, DAVID MEADOW (Boo)
b.Dec.5,1921 Shaw,Miss.

Yr	Cl	Lea	Pos	G	Rec
1945	Bos	A	P	61	21-10
1946	Bos	A	P	45	25-6
1947	Bos	A	P	52	12-11
1948	Bos	A	P	31	7-3
1949	Bos	A	P	4	0-0
1950	Bos	A	P	1	0-0
	BLTR			194	65-30

FERRY, ALFRED JOSEPH (Cy)
b.Sept.27,1878 Hudson,N.Y.
d.Sept.27,1938

Yr	Cl	Lea	Pos	G	Rec
1904	Det	A	P	3	0-1
1905	Cle	A	P	1	0-0
	BRTR			4	0-1

FERRY, JOHN FRANCIS
b.Apr.7,1887 Pittsfield,Mass.
d.Aug.29,1954

Yr	Cl	Lea	Pos	G	Rec
1910	Pit	N	P	6	1-2
1911	Pit	N	P	26	6-4
1912	Pit	N	P	11	2-0
1913	Pit	N	P	4	1-0
	BRTR			47	10-6

FERSON, ALEXANDER (Colonel)
b.July 14,1866 Philadelphia,Pa.

Yr	Cl	Lea	Pos	G	Rec
1889	Was	N	P	35	17-17
1890	Buf	p	P	10	1-5
1892	Bal	N	P	2	0-1
	TR			47	18-23

FESSENDEN, WALLACE C.
b.Watertown,Mass.
Non-playing manager Syr (a) 1890.

FETTE, LOUIS HENRY WILLIAM
b.Mar.15,1907 Alma,Mo.

Yr	Cl	Lea	Pos	G	Rec
1937	Bos	N	P	36	20-10
1938	Bos	N	P	33	11-13
1939	Bos	N	P	27	10-10
1940	Bos	N	P	7	0-5
1940	Bro	N	P	2	0-0
1945	Bos	N	P	5	0-2
	BRTR			110	41-40

FETZER, WILLY McKINNON
b.June 24,1884 Concord,N.C.

Yr	Cl	Lea	Pos	G	Rec
1906	Phi	A	O	1	.000

FEWSTER, WILSON LLOYD (Chick)
b.Nov.10,1895 Baltimore,Md.
d.Apr.16,1945

Yr	Cl	Lea	Pos	G	Rec
1917	NY	A	2	11	.222
1918	NY	A	2	5	.500
1919	NY	A	S-O	81	.283
1920	NY	A	S	21	.286
1921	NY	A	2-O	66	.280
1922	NY	A	2-O	44	.228
1922	Bos	A	O	23	.316
1923	Bos	A	2-S	90	.236
1924	Cle	A	2	101	.267
1925	Cle	A	2-3	93	.248
1926	Bro	N	2	105	.243
1927	Bro	N	H	4	.000
	BRTR			644	.258

FICK, JOHN RALPH
b.May 18,1921 Baltimore,Md.
d.June 9,1958

Yr	Cl	Lea	Pos	G	Rec
1944	Phi	N	P	4	0-0
	BLTL				

FIEBER, CLARENCE THOMAS
b.Sept.4,1913 San Francisco,Cal.

Yr	Cl	Lea	Pos	G	Rec
1932	Chi	A	P	3	1-0
	BLTL				

FIELD, JAMES C.
b.Apr.24,1863 Philadelphia,Pa.
d.May 13,1953

Yr	Cl	Lea	Pos	G	Rec
1883	Col	a	1	75	.239
1884	Col	a	1	105	.229
1885	Pit	a	1	56	.245
1885	Bal	a	1	38	.213
1890	Roc	a	1	51	.190
1898	Was	N	1	5	.095
				330	.228

FIELD, SAMUEL JAY
b.Oct.12,1848 Philadelphia,Pa.
d.Oct.28,1904

Yr	Cl	Lea	Pos	G	Rec
1875	Cen	n	C-O	3	NR
1875	Nat	n	C-O	5	NR
1876	Cin	N	C-2	4	.000
	BRTR			12	NR

FIELDS, GEORGE W.

Yr	Cl	Lea	Pos	G	Rec
1872	Man	n	S-3-O	13	NR

FIELDS, JOHN JAMES (Jocko)
b.Oct.20,1864 Cork,Ireland.
d.Oct.14,1950

Yr	Cl	Lea	Pos	G	Rec
1887	Pit	N	O	39	.298
1888	Pit	N	O	44	.195
1889	Pit	N	C-O	74	.311
1890	Pit	p	C-2-O	127	.277
1891	Pit	N	C	19	.239
1891	Phi	N	C	8	.233
1892	NY	N	C	17	.268
	BRTR			328	.274

FIENE, LOUIS HENRY (Big Finn)
b.Dec.29,1884 Ft.Dodge,Ia.

Yr	Cl	Lea	Pos	G	Rec
1906	Chi	A	P	6	1-1
1907	Chi	A	P	4	0-1
1908	Chi	A	P	1	0-1
1909	Chi	A	P	15	2-2
	BRTR			26	3-5

FIFIELD, JOHN PROCTOR
b.Oct.5,1871 Enfield,N.H.
d.Nov.27,1939

Yr	Cl	Lea	Pos	G	Rec
1897	Phi	N	P	24	4-20
1898	Phi	N	P	20	11-9
1899	Phi	N	P	13	3-8
1899	Was	N	P-3	7	2-4 .200
				64	20-41 .200

FIGGEMEIER, FRANK Y.
b.Apr.25,1873 St.Louis,Mo.

Yr	Cl	Lea	Pos	G	Rec
1894	Phi	N	P		0-1

FILE, LAWRENCE SAMUEL
b.May 18,1922 Chester,Pa.

Yr	Cl	Lea	Pos	G	Rec
1940	Phi	N	S-3	7	.077
	BRTR				

FILES, CHARLES EDWARD (Eddie)
b.May 19,1883 Portland,Me.
d.May 10,1954

Yr	Cl	Lea	Pos	G	Rec
1908	Phi	A	P	2	0-0
	BRTR				

FILIPOWICZ, STEPHEN CHARLES (Flip)
b.June 28,1921 Donora,Pa.

Yr	Cl	Lea	Pos	G	Rec
1944	NY	N	C-O	15	.195
1945	NY	N	O	35	.205
1948	Cin	N	O	7	.346
	BRTR			57	.223

FILLEY, MARCUS LUCIUS
b.Feb.28,1912 Troy,N.Y.

Yr	Cl	Lea	Pos	G	Rec
1934	Was	A	P	1	0-0
	BRTR				

FILLINGIM, DANA
b.Nov.6,1893 Seale,Ala.
d.Feb. 3,1961

Yr	Cl	Lea	Pos	G	Rec
1915	Phi	A	P	8	0-4
1918	Bos	N	P	14	7-6
1919	Bos	N	P	32	6-13
1920	Bos	N	P	38	12-21
1921	Bos	N	P	45	15-10
1922	Bos	N	P	25	5-9
1923	Bos	N	P	36	1-9
1925	Phi	N	P	5	1-0
	BLTR			203	47-72

FINCHER, WILLIAM ALLEN
b.May 26,1894 Atlanta,Ga.
d.May 8,1946

Yr	Cl	Lea	Pos	G	Rec
1916	St.L	A	P	12	0-1
	BRTR				

FINE, BENJAMIN J.
Non-playing manager St.L. (N) 1885.

FINE, THOMAS MORGAN
b.Oct.10,1914 Cleburne,Tex.

Yr	Cl	Lea	Pos	G	Rec
1947	Bos	A	P	9	1-2
1950	St.L	A	P	16	0-1
	BBTR			25	1-3

FINIGAN, JAMES LEROY
b.Aug.19,1928 Quincy,Ill.

Yr	Cl	Lea	Pos	G	Rec
1954	Phi	A	3	136	.302
1955	KC	A	2-3	150	.255
1956	KC	A	2-3	91	.216
1957	Det	A	2-3	64	.270
1958	SF	N	2-3	23	.200
1959	Bal	A	2-S-3	48	.252
	BRTR			512	.264

FINK, HERMAN ADAM
b.Aug.22,1911 Landis,N.C.

Yr	Cl	Lea	Pos	G	Rec
1935	Phi	A	P	5	0-3
1936	Phi	A	P	34	8-16
1937	Phi	A	P	28	2-1
	BRTR			67	10-20

FINLAYSON, PEMBROKE
b.July 31,1888 Cheraw,S.C.
d.Mar.6,1912

Yr	Cl	Lea	Pos	G	Rec
1908	Bro	N	P	1	0-0
1909	Bro	N	P	1	0-0
	BRTR			2	0-0

FINLEY, ROBERT EDWARD
b.Nov.25,1915 Ennis,Tex.

Yr	Cl	Lea	Pos	G	Rec
1943	Phi	N	C	28	.259
1944	Phi	N	C	94	.249
	BRTR			122	.252

FINLEY, WILLIAM JAMES
b.Oct.4,1863 New York,N.Y.
d.Oct.6,1912

Yr	Cl	Lea	Pos	G	Rec
1886	NY	N	C-O	13	.188

FINN, CORNELIUS FRANCIS (Mickey)
b.Jan.24,1902 Brooklyn,N.Y.
d.July 7,1933

Yr	Cl	Lea	Pos	G	Rec
1930	Bro	N	2	87	.278
1931	Bro	N	2	118	.274
1932	Bro	N	3	65	.238
1933	Phi	N	2	51	.237
	BRTR			321	.262

FINNERAN, JOSEPH IGNATIUS (Happy)
b.Oct.29,1892 E.Orange,N.J.
d.Feb.3,1942

Yr	Cl	Lea	Pos	G	Rec
1912	Phi	N	P	14	0-2
1913	Phi	N	P	3	0-0
1914	Bro	F	P	23	12-11
1915	Bro	F	P	34	10-12
1918	Det	A	P	6	1-2
1918	NY	A	P	23	3-6
	BRTR			103	26-33

FINNEY, HAROLD WILSON
b.July 30,1907 LaFayette,Ala.

Yr	Cl	Lea	Pos	G	Rec
1931	Pit	N	C	10	.308
1932	Pit	N	C	31	.212
1933	Pit	N	C	56	.233
1834	Pit	N	C	5	.000
1936	Pit	N	C	21	.000
	BRTR			123	.203

FINNEY, LOUIS KLOPSCHE
b.Aug.13,1910 Buffalo,Ala.

Yr	Cl	Lea	Pos	G	Rec
1931	Phi	A	O	9	.376
1933	Phi	A	O	74	.267
1934	Phi	A	1-O	92	.279
1935	Phi	A	1-O	109	.273
1936	Phi	A	1-O	151	.302
1937	Phi	A	1-O	92	.251
1938	Phi	A	1-O	122	.275
1939	Phi	A	O	9	.136
1939	Bos	A	1-O	95	.325
1940	Bos	A	1-O	130	.320
1941	Bos	A	1-O	127	.288
1942	Bos	A	1-O	113	.285
1944	Bos	A	1-O	68	.287
1945	Bos	A	H	2	.000
1945	St.L	A	1-3-O	57	.277
1946	St.L	A	O	16	.300
1947	Phi	N	H	4	.000
	BLTR			1270	.287

FIRTH, THEODORE JOHN
b.Philadelphia,Pa.
d.Apr.18,1885

Yr	Cl	Lea	Pos	G	Rec
1884	Ric	a	P	1	0-1

FISCHER, CHARLES WILLIAM (Carl)
b.Nov.5,1905 Medina,N.Y.

Yr	Cl	Lea	Pos	G	Rec
1930	Was	A	P	8	1-1
1931	Was	A	P	46	13-9
1932	Was	A	P	12	3-2
1932	St.L	A	P	24	3-7
1933	Det	A	P	35	11-15
1934	Det	A	P	20	6-4
1935	Det	A	P	3	0-1
1935	Chi	A	P	24	5-5
1937	Cle	A	P	2	0-1
1937	Was	A	P	17	4-5
	BBTL			191	46-50

FISCHER, HENRY WILLIAM
b.Jan.11,1940 Yonkers,N.Y.

Yr	Cl	Lea	Pos	G	Rec
1962	Mil	N	P	2	.333

FISCHER, REUBEN WALTER
b.Sept.19,1918 Carlock,S.D.

Yr	Cl	Lea	Pos	G	Rec
1941	NY	N	P	2	1-0
1943	NY	N	P	22	5-10
1944	NY	N	P	38	6-14
1945	NY	N	P	31	3-8
1946	NY	N	P	15	1-2
	BRTR			108	16-34

FISCHER, WILLIAM CHARLES
b.Mar.2,1891 New York,N.Y.
d.Sept.4,1945

Yr	Cl	Lea	Pos	G	Rec
1913	Bro	N	C	62	.267
1914	Bro	N	C	43	.257
1915	Chi	F	C	105	.326
1916	Chi	N	C	65	.197
1916	Pit	N	C	42	.254
1917	Pit	N	C	95	.286
	BLTR			412	.273

FISCHER, WILLIAM CHARLES
b.Oct.11,1930 Marathon,Wis.

Yr	Cl	Lea	Pos	G	Rec
1956	Chi	A	P	3	0-0
1957	Chi	A	P	33	7-8
1958	Chi	A	P	17	2-3
1958	Det	A	P	22	2-4
1958	Was	A	P	3	0-3
1959	Was	A	P	34	9-11
1960	Was	A	P	20	3-5
1960	Det	A	P	20	5-3
1961	Det	A	P	26	3-2
1961	KC	A	P	15	1-0
1962	KC	A	P	29	2-3
	BRTR			222	34-42

FISHBURNE, SAMUEL
b.June 2,1895 Haverhill,Mass.

Yr	Cl	Lea	Pos	G	Rec
1919	St.L	N	1-2	9	.333
	BRTR				

FISHEL, LEO
b.Dec.13,1877 Babylon,L.I.,N.Y.

Yr	Cl	Lea	Pos	G	Rec
1899	NY	N	P	1	0-1

FISHER, ...
b.Johnstown,Pa.

Yr	Cl	Lea	Pos	G	Rec
1884	Key	U	P-1	10	1-7 .222
1884	Wil	U	S-O	8	.069
1885	Buf	N	P	1	0-1
				19	1-8 .143

FISHER, AUGUST HARRIS
b.Oct.21,1885 Pottsborough,Tex.

Yr	Cl	Lea	Pos	G	Rec
1911	Cle	A	C	70	.261
1912	NY	A	C	4	.200
	BLTR			74	.258

FISHER, CHAUNCEY BURR
(Whoa Bill)
b.Jan.8,1872 Anderson,Ind.
d.Apr.27,1939

Yr	Cl	Lea	Pos	G	Rec
1893	Cle	N	P	3	0-2
1894	Cle	N	P	3	0-2
1894	Cin	N	P	12	2-10
1896	Cin	N	P	20	9-7
1897	Bro	N	P	18	8-7
1901	NY	N	P	1	0-1
1901	St.L	N	P	1	0-0
	BRTR			58	19-29

FISHER, CLARENCE HENRY
b.Aug.27,1897 Letart,W.Va.

Yr	Cl	Lea	Pos	G	Rec
1919	Was	A	P	2	0-0
1920	Was	A	P	2	0-1
	BRTR			4	0-1

FISHER, DONALD RAYMOND
b.Feb.6,1916 Cleveland,O.

Yr	Cl	Lea	Pos	G	Rec
1945	NY	N	P	2	1-0
	BRTR				

FISHER, EDDIE GENE
b.July 16,1936 Shreveport,La.

Yr	Cl	Lea	Pos	G	Rec
1959	SF	N	P	17	2-6
1960	SF	N	P	3	1-0
1961	SF	N	P	15	0-2
1962	Chi	A	P	57	9-5
	BRTR			92	12-13

FISHER, GEORGE ALOYS (Showboat)
b.Jan.16,1899 Jennings,Ia.

Yr	Cl	Lea	Pos	G	Rec
1923	Was	A	O	13	.240
1924	Was	A	O	15	.219
1930	St.L	N	O	92	.374
1932	St.L	A	O	18	.182
	BLTR			138	.335

FISHER, HARRY C.
b.Philadelphia,Pa.

Yr	Cl	Lea	Pos	G	Rec
1884	KC	U	S-3	10	.195
1884	Chi	U	3	1	.667
1884	Cle	N	C-2	6	.130
1889	Lou	a	O	1	.000
				18	.147

FISHER, HARRY DEVEREUX
b.Jan.3,1926 Newbury,Ont.,Canada

Yr	Cl	Lea	Pos	G	Rec
1951	Pit	N	H	3	.000
1952	Pit	N	P	15	1-2
	BLTR			18	1-2 / .278

FISHER, JOHN GUS (Red)
b.June 22,1887 New York,N.Y.
d.Feb.1,1940

Yr	Cl	Lea	Pos	G	Rec
1910	St.L	A	O	23	.125
	TR				

FISHER, JOHN HOWARD
b.Mar.4,1939 Frostburg,Md.

Yr	Cl	Lea	Pos	G	Rec
1959	Bal	A	P	27	1-6
1960	Bal	A	P	40	12-11
1961	Bal	A	P	36	10-13
1962	Bal	A	P	33	7-9
	BRTR			136	30-39

FISHER, MAURICE WAYNE
b.Feb.16,1931 Wells Co.,Ind.

Yr	Cl	Lea	Pos	G	Rec
1955	Cin	N	P	1	0-0
	BRTR				

FISHER, NEWTON
b.July 28,1874 Chattanooga,Tenn.
d.Feb.1947

Yr	Cl	Lea	Pos	G	Rec
1898	Phi	N	C	9	.154
	BRTR				

FISHER, RAYMOND LYLE (Chic)
b.Oct.4,1887 Middlebury,Vt.

Yr	Cl	Lea	Pos	G	Rec
1910	NY	A	P	15	5-3
1911	NY	A	P	29	10-11

(Continued)

Yr	Cl	Lea	Pos	G	Rec
1912	NY	A	P	16	2-8
1913	NY	A	P	37	11-17
1914	NY	A	P	28	10-12
1915	NY	A	P	30	18-11
1916	NY	A	P	31	11-8
1917	NY	A	P	23	8-9
1919	Cin	N	P	26	14-5
1920	Cin	N	P	33	10-11
	BRTR			268	99-95

FISHER, ROBERT TECUMSEH
b.Nov.3,1887 Nashville,Tenn.

Yr	Cl	Lea	Pos	G	Rec
1912	Bro	N	S	82	.233
1913	Bro	N	S	132	.262
1914	Chi	N	S	15	.300
1915	Chi	N	S	147	.287
1916	Cin	N	2-S-O	61	.272
1918	St.L	N	2	63	.317
1919	St.L	N	2	3	.273
	BRTR			503	.276

FISHER, THOMAS CHALMERS (Red)
b.Nov.1,1881 Anderson,Ind.

Yr	Cl	Lea	Pos	G	Rec
1902	Det	A	P	1	0-0
1904	Bos	N	P	36	6-16
	BRTR			37	6-16

FISHER, WILBUR McCULLOUGH
b.July 18,1894 Chesapeake,O.

Yr	Cl	Lea	Pos	G	Rec
1916	Pit	N	H	1	.000

FISHER, WILLIAM CHARLES
(Cherokee)
b.1844 Philadelphia,Pa.
d.Sept.26,1912

Yr	Cl	Lea	Pos	G	Rec
1871	Rok	n	P-1-O	25	5-17 / NR
1872	Bal	n	P-3-O	45	8-3 / .237
1873	Ath	n	P-1-O	49	2-2 / NR
1874	Har	n	P-S-3-O	52	13-22 / NR
1875	Phi	n	P-O	40	22-17 / .231
1876	Cin	N	P-1-S-O	35	4-20 / .248
1877	Chi	N	3	1	.000
1878	Pro	N	P	1	0-1
	BRTR			248	54-82 / NR

FISK, MAXIMILIAN PATRICK
b.1888 Roseland,Ind.

Yr	Cl	Lea	Pos	G	Rec
1914	Chi	F	P	35	12-12
	BRTR				

FISLER, WESTON DICKSON
b.July 5,1841 Camden,N.J.
d.Dec.26,1922

Yr	Cl	Lea	Pos	G	Rec
1871	Ath	n	1-2	28	.333
1872	Ath	n	2	48	NR
1873	Ath	n	1-2	43	NR
1874	Ath	n	1-2	37	.343
1875	Ath	n	1-2-O	57	.276
1876	Ath	N	1-2-O	59	.286
				272	NR

FITTERY, PAUL
b.Oct.10,1891 Lebanon,Pa.

Yr	Cl	Lea	Pos	G	Rec
1914	Cin	N	P	11	0-2
1917	Phi	N	P	19	1-1
	BLTL			30	1-3

FITZBERGER, CHARLES CASPAR
b.Feb.13,1905 Baltimore,Md.

Yr	Cl	Lea	Pos	G	Rec
1928	Bos	N	H	7	.286
	BLTL				

FITZGERALD, DENNIS S.
b.Boston,Mass.

Yr	Cl	Lea	Pos	G	Rec
1890	Ath	a	S	2	.429

FITZ GERALD, EDWARD RAYMOND
b.May 21,1924 Santa Ynez,Cal.

Yr	Cl	Lea	Pos	G	Rec
1948	Pit	N	C	102	.267
1949	Pit	N	C	75	.263
1950	Pit	N	C	6	.067
1951	Pit	N	C	55	.227

(Continued)

Yr	Cl	Lea	Pos	G	Rec
1952	Pit	N	C-3	51	.233
1953	Pit	N	C	6	.118
1953	Was	A	C	88	.250
1954	Was	A	C	115	.289
1955	Was	A	C	74	.237
1956	Was	A	C	64	.304
1957	Was	A	C	45	.272
1958	Was	A	C-1	58	.263
1959	Was	A	C	19	.194
1959	Cle	A	C	49	.271
	BRTR			807	.260

FITZGERALD, HOWARD CHUMNEY
(Lefty)
b.May 16,1902 Eagle Lake,Tex.

Yr	Cl	Lea	Pos	G	Rec
1922	Chi	N	O	10	.330
1924	Chi	N	O	7	.158
1926	Bos	A	O	31	.258
	BLTL			48	.259

FITZGERALD, JOHN FRANCIS
b.Sept.15,1934 Brooklyn,N.Y.

Yr	Cl	Lea	Pos	G	Rec
1958	SF	N	P	1	0-0
	BLTL				

FITZGERALD, JOHN H.
b.May 30,1870 Natick,Mass.

Yr	Cl	Lea	Pos	G	Rec
1891	Bos	a	P	6	2-1

FITZGERALD, JOHN T.
b.Leadville,Col.

Yr	Cl	Lea	Pos	G	Rec
1890	Roc	a	P	12	3-8
1891	Lou	a	P	32	12-17
1892	Lou	N	P	4	1-3
				48	16-28

FITZGERALD, JUSTIN HOWARD
(Mike)
b.June 22,1890 San Mateo,Cal.
d.Jan.17,1945

Yr	Cl	Lea	Pos	G	Rec
1911	NY	A	O	16	.270
1918	Phi	N	O	66	.293
	BLTR			82	.288

FITZGERALD, MATTHEW WILLIAM
b.Aug.31,1880 Albany,N.Y.
d.Sept.22,1949

Yr	Cl	Lea	Pos	G	Rec
1906	NY	N	C	4	.500
1907	NY	N	C	6	.133
	TR			10	.200

FITZGERALD, RAYMOND FRANCIS
b.Dec.5,1904 Westfield,Mass.

Yr	Cl	Lea	Pos	G	Rec
1931	Cin	N	H	1	.000
	BRTR				

FITZKE, PAUL FREDERICK HERMAN
b.July 30,1900 La Crosse,Wis.
d.June 30,1950.

Yr	Cl	Lea	Pos	G	Rec
1924	Cle	A	P	1	0-0
	BRTR				

FITZPATRICK, EDWARD HENRY
b.Dec.9,1889 Phillipsburg,Pa.

Yr	Cl	Lea	Pos	G	Rec
1915	Bos	N	2-O	105	.221
1916	Bos	N	2-O	83	.213
1917	Bos	N	2-3-O	63	.253
	BRTR			251	.227

FITZSIMMONS, ...

Yr	Cl	Lea	Pos	G	Rec
1872	Eck	n	C	2	NR

FITZSIMMONS,
FREDERICK LANDIS (Fat Freddie)
b.July 28,1901 Mishawaka,Ind.

Yr	Cl	Lea	Pos	G	Rec
1925	NY	N	P	10	6-3
1926	NY	N	P	37	14-10
1927	NY	N	P	42	17-10
1928	NY	N	P	40	20-9
1929	NY	N	P	37	15-11
1930	NY	N	P	41	19-7
1931	NY	N	P	35	18-11
1932	NY	N	P	35	11-11

(Continued)

Yr	Cl	Lea	Pos	G	Rec
1933	NY	N	P	36	16-11
1934	NY	N	P	38	18-14
1935	NY	N	P	18	4-8
1936	NY	N	P	28	10-7
1937	NY	N	P	6	2-2
1937	Bro	N	P	13	4-8
1938	Bro	N	P	27	11-8
1939	Bro	N	P	27	7-9
1940	Bro	N	P	20	16-2
1941	Bro	N	P	13	6-1
1942	Bro	N	P	1	0-0
1943	Bro	N	P	9	3-4
		BRTR		513	217-146

Non-playing manager Phi (N) 1943-45.

FITZSIMMONS, THOMAS WILLIAM
b.Apr.6,1890 Oakland,Cal.

Yr	Cl	Lea	Pos	G	Rec
1919	Bro	N	3	4	.000
		BRTR			

FLACK, MAX JOHN
b.Feb.5,1891 Belleville,Ill.

Yr	Cl	Lea	Pos	G	Rec
1914	Chi	F	O	135	.253
1915	Chi	F	O	141	.315
1916	Chi	N	O	141	.258
1917	Chi	N	O	131	.248
1918	Chi	N	O	123	.257
1919	Chi	N	O	116	.294
1920	Chi	N	O	135	.302
1921	Chi	N	O	133	.301
1922	Chi	N	O	17	.222
1922	St.L	N	O	66	.292
1923	St.L	N	O	128	.291
1924	St.L	N	O	67	.263
1925	St.L	N	O	79	.249
		BLTL		1412	.279

FLAGER, WALTER LEONARD
b.Nov.3,1921 Chicago Heights,Ill.

Yr	Cl	Lea	Pos	G	Rec
1945	Cin	N	S	21	.212
1945	Phi	N	2-S	49	.250
		BLTR		70	.241

FLAGSTEAD, IRA (Pete)
b.Sept.22,1893 Montague,Mich.
d.Mar.13,1940

Yr	Cl	Lea	Pos	G	Rec
1917	Det	A	O	4	.000
1919	Det	A	O	97	.331
1920	Det	A	O	110	.235
1921	Det	A	S-O	85	.305
1922	Det	A	O	44	.308
1923	Det	A	O	1	.000
1923	Bos	A	O	102	.312
1924	Bos	A	O	149	.304
1925	Bos	A	O	148	.280
1926	Bos	A	O	98	.299
1927	Bos	A	O	131	.285
1928	Bos	A	O	140	.290
1929	Bos	A	O	16	.325
1929	Was	A	O	16	.143
1929	Pit	N	O	26	.280
1930	Pit	N	O	44	.250
		BRTR		1211	.290

FLAHERTY, P. J.
b.Worcester,Mass.

Yr	Cl	Lea	Pos	G	Rec
1881	Wor	N	O	1	.000
		BLTL			

FLAHERTY, PATRICK HENRY
b.June 24,1862 St.Louis,Mo.
d.Jan.30,1946

Yr	Cl	Lea	Pos	G	Rec
1894	Lou	N	3	38	.295

FLAHERTY, PATRICK JOSEPH
b.June 29,1876 Carnegie,Pa.

Yr	Cl	Lea	Pos	G	Rec
1899	Lou	N	P	7	2-3
1900	Pit	N	P	4	0-1
1903	Chi	A	P	39	11-25
1904	Chi	A	P	5	3-2
1904	Pit	N	P	31	19-9
1905	Pit	N	P	29	10-10
1907	Bos	N	P	35	12-15

(Continued)

Yr	Cl	Lea	Pos	G	Rec
1908	Bos	N	P	31	12-18
1910	Phi	N	P-O	2	0-0
					.500
1911	Bos	N	P-O	23	0-2
					.287
		BLTL		206	69-85
					.196

FLAIR, ALBERT DELL (Broadway)
b.July 24,1918 New Orleans,La.

Yr	Cl	Lea	Pos	G	Rec
1941	Bos	A	1	10	.200
		BLTL			

FLANAGAN, CHARLES JAMES
b.Dec.13,1891 Oakland,Cal.
d.Jan.8,1930

Yr	Cl	Lea	Pos	G	Rec
1913	St.L	A	3	4	.000
		BRTR			

FLANAGAN, EDWARD F. (Sleepy)
b.Sept.15,1861 Lowell,Mass.
d.Nov.10,1926

Yr	Cl	Lea	Pos	G	Rec
1887	Ath	a	1	19	.277
1889	Lou	a	1	23	.247
				42	.255

FLANAGAN, JAMES PAUL (Steamer)
b.Apr.20,1881 Wilkes-Barre,Pa.
d.Apr.21,1947

Yr	Cl	Lea	Pos	G	Rec
1905	Pit	N	O	7	.280

FLANIGAN, RAYMOND ARTHUR
b.Jan.8,1923 Morgantown,W.Va.

Yr	Cl	Lea	Pos	G	Rec
1946	Cle	A	P	3	0-1
		BRTR			

FLANIGAN, THOMAS ANTHONY
b.Sept.6,1934 Cincinnati,O.

Yr	Cl	Lea	Pos	G	Rec
1954	Chi	A	P	2	0-0
1958	St.L	N	P	1	0-0
		BRTL		3	0-0

FLASKAMPER, RAYMOND HAROLD
b.Oct.31,1901 St.Louis,Mo.

Yr	Cl	Lea	Pos	G	Rec
1927	Chi	A	S	26	.221
		BBTR			

FLATER, JOHN
b.Sept.22,1883 Westminster,Md.

Yr	Cl	Lea	Pos	G	Rec
1908	Phi	A	P	5	1-3
		TR			

FLEET, FRANK H.
b.1848 New York,N.Y.
d.June 13,1900

Yr	Cl	Lea	Pos	G	Rec
1871	Mut	n	P	1	0-1
1872	Eck	n	2-3-O	11	NR
1873	Res	n	P-1-2-S-3	21	0-3
					NR
1874	Atl	n	C-2-O	19	NR
1875	St.L	n	P	3	2-1
1875	Atl	n	P-C-2-S	25	0-1
					NR
				80	2-6
					NR

FLEITAS, ANGEL FELIX HUSTA
b.Nov.10,1918 Los Abrens,Cuba.

Yr	Cl	Lea	Pos	G	Rec
1948	Was	A	S	15	.077
		BRTR			

FLEMING, LESLIE FLETCHERD (Bill)
b.July 31,1913 Los Angeles,Cal.

Yr	Cl	Lea	Pos	G	Rec
1940	Bos	A	P	10	1-2
1941	Bos	A	P	16	1-1
1942	Chi	N	P	33	5-6
1943	Chi	N	P	11	0-1
1944	Chi	N	P	40	9-10
1946	Chi	N	P	14	0-1
		BRTR		124	16-21

FLEMING, LESLIE HARVEY (Moe)
b.Aug.7,1915 Singleton,Tex.

Yr	Cl	Lea	Pos	G	Rec
1939	Det	A	O	8	.000
1941	Cle	A	1	2	.250
1942	Cle	A	1	156	.292
1945	Cle	A	1-O	42	.329
1946	Cle	A	1-O	99	.278
1947	Cle	A	1	103	.242
1949	Pit	N	1	24	.258
		BLTL		434	.277

FLEMING, THOMAS VINCENT (Sleuth)
b.1879 Bustleton,Pa.

Yr	Cl	Lea	Pos	G	Rec
1899	NY	N	O	20	.257
1902	Phi	N	O	5	.375
1904	Phi	N	O	2	.000
				27	.261

FLETCHER, ARTHUR
b.Jan.5,1885 Collinsville,Ill.
d.Feb.6,1950

Yr	Cl	Lea	Pos	G	Rec
1909	NY	N	S	29	.214
1910	NY	N	S	44	.224
1911	NY	N	S-3	108	.319
1912	NY	N	S	129	.282
1913	NY	N	S	136	.297
1914	NY	N	S	135	.286
1915	NY	N	S	149	.254
1916	NY	N	S	133	.286
1917	NY	N	S	151	.260
1918	NY	N	S	124	.263
1919	NY	N	S	127	.277
1920	NY	N	S	41	.254
1920	Phi	N	S	102	.297
1922	Phi	N	S	110	.280
		BRTR		1518	.277

Non-playing manager Phi (N) 1923-26 and N.Y. (A) 1929.

FLETCHER, ELBURT PRESTON
b.Mar.18,1916 Dorchester,Mass.

Yr	Cl	Lea	Pos	G	Rec
1934	Bos	N	1	8	.500
1935	Bos	N	1	39	.236
1937	Bos	N	1	148	.247
1938	Bos	N	1	147	.272
1939	Bos	N	1	35	.245
1939	Pit	N	1	102	.303
1940	Pit	N	1	147	.273
1941	Pit	N	1	151	.288
1942	Pit	N	1	145	.289
1943	Pit	N	1	154	.283
1946	Pit	N	1	148	.256
1947	Pit	N	1	69	.242
1949	Bos	N	1	122	.261
		BLTL		1415	.271

FLETCHER, O. FRANK
b.1891

Yr	Cl	Lea	Pos	G	Rec
1914	Phi	N	H	1	.000
		BRTR			

FLETCHER, SAMUEL S.

Yr	Cl	Lea	Pos	G	Rec
1909	Bro	N	P	1	0-1
1912	Cin	N	P	2	0-0
		TR		3	0-1

FLETCHER, THOMAS WAYNE
b.June 28,1942 Elmira,N.Y.

Yr	Cl	Lea	Pos	G	Rec
1962	Det	A	P	1	0-0
		BLTL			

FLETCHER, VANOIDE
b.Aug.6,1928 East Bend,N.C.

Yr	Cl	Lea	Pos	G	Rec
1955	Det	A	P	9	0-0
		BRTR			

FLICK, ELMER HARRISON
b.Jan.11,1876 Bedford,O.

Yr	Cl	Lea	Pos	G	Rec
1898	Phi	N	O	133	.319
1899	Phi	N	O	125	.343
1900	Phi	N	O	138	.378
1901	Phi	N	O	138	.336
1902	Phi	A	O	11	.324
1902	Cle	A	O	110	.293
1903	Cle	A	O	142	.299
1904	Cle	A	O	149	.303

(Continued)

Yr	Cl	Lea	Pos	G	Rec
1905	Cle	A	O	131	.306
1906	Cle	A	O	157	.311
1907	Cle	A	O	147	.302
1908	Cle	A	O	9	.212
1909	Cle	A	O	66	.255
1910	Cle	A	O	24	.265
BLTR				1480	.315

FLICK, LEWIS MILLER (Noisy)
b.Feb.18,1915 Bristol,Tenn.

Yr	Cl	Lea	Pos	G	Rec
1943	Phi	A	O	1	.600
1944	Phi	A	O	19	.114
BLTL				20	.175

FLINN, DON RAPHIEL
b.Nov.17,1892 Huckaby,Tex.
d.Mar.9,1959

Yr	Cl	Lea	Pos	G	Rec
1917	Pit	N	O	14	.298

BRTR

FLINT, FRANK SYLVESTER (Silver)
b.Aug.3,1855 Philadelphia,Pa.
d.Jan.14,1892

Yr	Cl	Lea	Pos	G	Rec
1875	RS	n	C-3	17	NR
1878	Ind	N	C	60	.228
1879	Chi	N	C	75	.290
1880	Chi	N	C-O	71	.167
1881	Chi	N	C-1-O	80	.310
1882	Chi	N	C-O	81	.250
1883	Chi	N	C-O	84	.265
1884	Chi	N	C	71	.207
1885	Chi	N	C-O	67	.208
1886	Chi	N	C	49	.202
1887	Chi	N	C	48	.282
1888	Chi	N	C	22	.181
1889	Chi	N	C	15	.232
BRTR				740	NR

FLITCRAFT, HILDRETH MILTON (Hilly)
b.Aug.21,1923 Woodstown,N.J.

Yr	Cl	Lea	Pos	G	Rec
1942	Phi	N	P	3	0-0

BLTL

FLOHR, MORITZ HERMAN (Dutch)
b.Aug.15,1911 Canisteo,N.Y.

Yr	Cl	Lea	Pos	G	Rec
1934	Phi	A	P	15	0-2

BLTL

FLOOD, CURTIS CHARLES
b.Jan.18,1938 Houston,Tex.

Yr	Cl	Lea	Pos	G	Rec
1956	Cin	N	H	5	.000
1957	Cin	N	2-3	3	.333
1958	St.L	N	3-O	121	.261
1959	St.L	N	2-O	121	.255
1960	St.L	N	3-O	140	.237
1961	St.L	N	O	132	.322
1962	St.L	N	O	151	.296
BRTR				673	.277

FLOOD, TIMOTHY A.
b.Mar.13,1877 Montgomery City,Mo.
d.June 15,1929

Yr	Cl	Lea	Pos	G	Rec
1899	St.L	N	2	9	.333
1902	Bro	N	2-O	131	.228
1903	Bro	N	2	87	.249
BRTR				227	.239

FLORENCE, PAUL ROBERT (Pep)
b.Apr.23,1901 Chicago,Ill.

Yr	Cl	Lea	Pos	G	Rec
1926	NY	N	C	76	.229

BBTR

FLORES, JESSE SANDOVAL
b.Nov.2,1916 Guadalajara,Mexico.

Yr	Cl	Lea	Pos	G	Rec
1942	Chi	N	P	4	0-1
1943	Phi	A	P	31	12-14
1944	Phi	A	P	27	9-11
1945	Phi	A	P	29	7-10
1946	Phi	A	P	29	9-7
1947	Phi	A	P	28	4-13
1950	Cle	A	P	28	3-3
BRTR				176	44-59

FLOWERS, BENNETT
b.June 15,1927 Goldsboro,N.C.

Yr	Cl	Lea	Pos	G	Rec
1951	Bos	A	P	1	0-0
1953	Bos	A	P	32	1-4
1955	Det	A	P	4	0-0
1955	St.L	N	P	4	1-0
1956	St.L	N	P	3	1-1
1956	Phi	N	P	32	0-2
BRTR				76	3-7

FLOWERS, CHARLES RICHARD
b.1850 Philadelphia,Pa.
d.Oct.5,1892

Yr	Cl	Lea	Pos	G	Rec
1871	Tro	n	2-S	21	.303
1872	Ath	n	S	3	NR
				24	NR

FLOWERS, CHARLES WESLEY (Wes)
b.Aug.13,1913 Wynne,Ark.

Yr	Cl	Lea	Pos	G	Rec
1940	Bro	N	P	5	1-1
1944	Bro	N	P	9	1-1
BLTL				14	2-2

FLOWERS, D'ARCY RAYMOND (Jake)
b.Mar.16,1902 Cambridge,Md.
d.Dec.27,1962

Yr	Cl	Lea	Pos	G	Rec
1923	St.L	N	2-S-3	13	.094
1926	St.L	N	2	40	.270
1927	Bro	N	S	67	.234
1928	Bro	N	2	103	.274
1929	Bro	N	2	46	.200
1930	Bro	N	2	89	.320
1931	Bro	N	2-S	22	.226
1931	St.L	N	2-S	45	.248
1932	St.L	N	3	67	.255
1933	Bro	N	2-S-3-O	78	.233
1934	Cin	N	H	13	.333
BRTR				583	.255

FLOYD, LESLIE ROE (Bubba)
b.June 23,1917 Dallas,Tex.

Yr	Cl	Lea	Pos	G	Rec
1944	Det	A	H	3	.444

BRTR

FLUHRER, JOHN L.
(Also played under name of Wm. G. Morris)
b.Jan.3,1893 Adrian,Mich.
d.July 17,1946

Yr	Cl	Lea	Pos	G	Rec
1915	Chi	N	O	7	.400

BRTR

FLYNN, CORNELIUS FRANCIS XAVIER (Carney)
b.Jan.23,1875 Cincinnati,O.
d.Feb.10,1947

Yr	Cl	Lea	Pos	G	Rec
1894	Cin	N	P	2	0-1
1896	NY	N	P	3	0-0
1896	Was	N	P	4	0-1
BLTL				9	0-2

FLYNN, EDWARD J.
b.Chicago,Ill.

Yr	Cl	Lea	Pos	G	Rec
1887	Cle	a	3	7	.215

FLYNN, GEORGE A. (Dibby)
b.May 24,1870 Chicago,Ill.
d.Dec.28,1901

Yr	Cl	Lea	Pos	G	Rec
1896	Chi	N	O	29	.267

FLYNN, JOHN A. (Jocko)
b.June 30,1864 Lawrence,Mass.
d.Dec.30,1907

Yr	Cl	Lea	Pos	G	Rec
1886	Chi	N	P-O	56	24-6 .200
1887	Chi	N	O	1	.000
				57	24-6 .200

FLYNN, JOHN ANTHONY
b.Sept.7,1883 Providence,R.I.
d.Mar.23,1935

Yr	Cl	Lea	Pos	G	Rec
1910	Pit	N	1	93	.274
1911	Pit	N	1-3	32	.214
1912	Was	A	1	20	.169
BRTR				145	.251

FLYNN, JOSEPH
b.Philadelphia,Pa.

Yr	Cl	Lea	Pos	G	Rec
1884	Key	U	C-1-S-O	50	.244
1884	Bos	U	C-1-O	9	.233
				59	.242

FLYNN, MICHAEL E.
b.Lowell,Mass.

Yr	Cl	Lea	Pos	G	Rec
1891	Bos	a	C	1	.000

FLYNN, WILLIAM (Clipper)
b.1850 N.Y.
d.Nov.11,1881

Yr	Cl	Lea	Pos	G	Rec
1871	Tro	n	1-3-O	29	.311
1872	Oly	n	1	9	NR
				38	NR

FLYTHE, STUART McGUIRE
b.Dec.5,1911 Conway,N.C.

Yr	Cl	Lea	Pos	G	Rec
1936	Phi	A	P	17	0-0

BRTR

FODGE, EUGENE ARLEN
b.July 9,1931 South Bend,Ind.

Yr	Cl	Lea	Pos	G	Rec
1958	Chi	N	P	16	1-1

BRTR

FOGARTY, JAMES G.
b.Feb.12,1864 San Francisco,Cal.
d.May 20,1891

Yr	Cl	Lea	Pos	G	Rec
1884	Phi	N	P-2-S-3-O	95	0-0 .211
1885	Phi	N	2-S-3-O	111	.231
1886	Phi	N	O	76	.292
1887	Phi	N	O	126	.365
1888	Phi	N	O	120	.235
1889	Phi	N	O	128	.258
1890	Phi	p	M-O	91	.251
BR				747	0-0 .268

FOGARTY, JOSEPH J.
b.San Francisco,Cal.

Yr	Cl	Lea	Pos	G	Rec
1885	St.L	N	O	2	.125

FOGEL, HORACE S.
b.Mar.2,1861 Macungie,Pa.
d.Nov.15,1928
Non-playing manager Ind (N) 1887 and N.Y. (N) 1902.

FOHL, LEO ALEXANDER
b.Nov.28,1879 Pittsburgh,Pa.

Yr	Cl	Lea	Pos	G	Rec
1902	Pit	N	C	1	.000
1903	Cin	N	C	4	.357
BLTR				5	.294

Non-playing manager Cle (A) 1915-19, St.L (A) 1921-23 and Bos (A) 1924-26.

FOILES, HENRY LEE
b.June 10,1929 Richmond,Va.

Yr	Cl	Lea	Pos	G	Rec
1953	Cin	N	C	5	.154
1953	Cle	A	C	7	.143
1955	Cle	A	C	62	.261
1956	Cle	A	C	1	.000
1956	Pit	N	C	79	.212
1957	Pit	N	C	109	.270
1958	Pit	N	C	104	.205
1959	Pit	N	C	53	.225
1960	KC	A	C	6	.571
1960	Cle	A	C	24	.279
1960	Det	A	C	26	.250
1961	Bal	A	C	43	.274
1962	Cin	N	C	43	.275
BRTR				562	.245

FOLEY, CHARLES JOSEPH (Curry)
b.Jan.20,1858 Milltown,Ireland
d.Oct.20,1898

Yr	Cl	Lea	Pos	G	Rec
1879	Bos	N	P-O	35	5-8 .313
1880	Bos	N	P-1-O	78	14-14 .285
1881	Buf	N	P-1-O	83	2-4 .256
1882	Buf	N	P-O	84	0-0 .305
1883	Buf	N	P-O	23	1-0 .270
1885	Pro	N	P	1	0-1
	TL			304	22-27 .283

FOLEY, RAYMOND KIRWIN
b.June 23,1907 Missouri City,Mo.

Yr	Cl	Lea	Pos	G	Rec
1928	NY	N	H	2	.000
	BLTR				

FOLEY, THOMAS J.
b.Aug.16,1842 Cashel,Ireland.
d.Nov.3,1926

Yr	Cl	Lea	Pos	G	Rec
1871	Chi	n	M-C-3-O	18	NR

FOLEY, WILLIAM B.
b.Nov.15,1855 Chicago,Ill.
d.Nov.12,1916

Yr	Cl	Lea	Pos	G	Rec
1875	Chi	n	3	3	NR
1876	Cin	N	C-3	56	.226
1877	Cin	N	3	56	.188
1878	Mil	N	C-3	55	.271
1879	Cin	N	2-3-O	55	.213
1881	Det	N	2-3	5	.118
1884	Chi	U	3	18	.294
	BRTR			250	NR

FONDY, DEE VIRGIL
b.Oct.31,1924 Slaton,Tex.

Yr	Cl	Lea	Pos	G	Rec
1951	Chi	N	1	49	.271
1952	Chi	N	1	145	.300
1953	Chi	N	1	150	.309
1954	Chi	N	1	141	.285
1955	Chi	N	1	150	.265
1956	Chi	N	1	137	.269
1957	Chi	N	1	11	.314
1957	Pit	N	1	95	.313
1958	Cin	N	1-O	89	.218
	BLTL			967	.283

FONSECA, LEWIS ALBERT
b.Jan.21,1899 Oakland,Cal.

Yr	Cl	Lea	Pos	G	Rec
1921	Cin	N	1-2-O	82	.276
1922	Cin	N	2	81	.361
1923	Cin	N	1-2	65	.278
1924	Cin	N	1-2	20	.228
1925	Phi	N	1-2	126	.319
1927	Cle	A	1-2	112	.311
1928	Cle	A	1-3	75	.327
1929	Cle	A	1	148	.369
1930	Cle	A	1	40	.279
1931	Cle	A	1	26	.370
1931	Chi	A	1-2-O	121	.299
1932	Chi	A	M-P-O	18	0-0 .135
1933	Chi	A	M-1	23	.203
	BRTR			937	0-0 .316

Non-playing manager Chi (A) 1934.

FORAN, JAMES H.
b.1848 N.Y.

Yr	Cl	Lea	Pos	G	Rec
1871	Kek	n	1-O	19	NR

FORCE, DAVID W. (Wee Davey)
b.July 27,1849 New York,N.Y.
d.June 21,1918

Yr	Cl	Lea	Pos	G	Rec
1871	Oly	n	S-3	32	NR
1872	Tro	n	S-3	25	NR
1872	Bal	n	3	19	NR
1873	Bal	n	P-S-3	48	1-1 NR
1874	Chi	n	S-3-O	59	NR
1875	Ath	n	S	77	.312

(Continued)

Yr	Cl	Lea	Pos	G	Rec
1876	Ath	N	S	60	.228
1877	St.L	N	S-3	58	.258
1879	Buf	N	S	78	.209
1880	Buf	N	2-S	78	.162
1881	Buf	N	2-S-3-O	75	.179
1882	Buf	N	2-S-3	73	.241
1883	Buf	N	2-S-3	95	.213
1884	Buf	N	2-S	102	.208
1885	Buf	N	2-S-3	71	.225
1886	Was	N	S	68	.181
	BRTR			1018	1-1 NR

FORD, E. L.
b.Richmond,Va.

Yr	Cl	Lea	Pos	G	Rec
1884	Ric	a	1-S	2	.000

FORD, EDWARD CHARLES (Whitey)
b.Oct.21,1928 New York,N.Y.

Yr	Cl	Lea	Pos	G	Rec
1950	NY	A	P	20	9-1
1953	NY	A	P	33	18-6
1954	NY	A	P	34	16-8
1955	NY	A	P	39	18-7
1956	NY	A	P	31	19-6
1957	NY	A	P	24	11-5
1958	NY	A	P	30	14-7
1959	NY	A	P	35	16-10
1960	NY	A	P	33	12-9
1961	NY	A	P	39	25-4
1962	NY	A	P	38	17-8
	BLTL			356	175-71

FORD, EUGENE MATTHEW
b.June 23,1913 Ft.Dodge,Ia.

Yr	Cl	Lea	Pos	G	Rec
1936	Bos	N	P	2	0-0
1938	Chi	A	P	4	0-0
	BRTR			6	0-0

FORD, EUGENE WYMAN
b.Apr.16,1881 Milton,N.S.Canada.

Yr	Cl	Lea	Pos	G	Rec
1905	Det	A	P	7	0-2
	BRTR				

FORD, HORACE HILLS (Hod)
b.July 23,1897 New Haven,Conn.

Yr	Cl	Lea	Pos	G	Rec
1919	Bos	N	2	10	.214
1920	Bos	N	2-S	88	.241
1921	Bos	N	2-S	152	.279
1922	Bos	N	2-S	143	.271
1923	Bos	N	2-S	111	.271
1924	Phi	N	2	145	.272
1925	Bro	N	S	66	.273
1926	Cin	N	S	57	.279
1927	Cin	N	2-S	115	.274
1928	Cin	N	S	149	.241
1929	Cin	N	2-S	148	.276
1930	Cin	N	2-S	132	.231
1931	Cin	N	2-S-3	84	.229
1932	St.L	N	S	1	.000
1932	Bos	N	2-S	40	.274
1933	Bos	N	S	5	.067
	BRTR			1446	.263

FORD, RUSSELL WILLIAM
b.Apr.25,1883 Brandon,Man.,Canada.
d.Jan.24,1960

Yr	Cl	Lea	Pos	G	Rec
1909	NY	A	P	1	0-0
1910	NY	A	P	36	26-6
1911	NY	A	P	37	22-11
1912	NY	A	P	39	13-21
1913	NY	A	P	30	11-18
1914	Buf	F	P	30	21-6
1915	Buf	F	P	20	5-9
	BRTR			193	98-71

FORD, THOMAS W.
b.Chattanooga,Tenn.

Yr	Cl	Lea	Pos	G	Rec
1890	Col	a	P	1	0-1
1890	Bro	a	P-S.	10	0-6 .034
				11	0-7 .032

FOREMAN, AUGUST (Happy)
b.July 20,1897 Memphis,Tenn.
d.Feb.13,1953

Yr	Cl	Lea	Pos	G	Rec
1924	Chi	A	P	5	0-0
1926	Bos	A	P	3	0-0
	BLTL			8	0-0

FOREMAN, FRANCIS ISAIAH (Monkey)
b.May 1,1863 Baltimore,Md.
d.Nov.19,1957

Yr	Cl	Lea	Pos	G	Rec
1884	Chi	U	P-O	3	1-0 .091
1884	KC	U	P	1	0-1
1885	Bal	a	P-O	3	2-1 .286
1889	Bal	a	P	54	25-21
1890	Cin	N	P	24	13-11
1891	Cin	N	P	1	0-0
1891	Was	a	P	49	22-22
1892	Was	N	P	11	2-5
1892	Bal	N	P	5	0-2
1893	NY	N	P	2	0-1
1895	Cin	N	P	25	11-14
1896	Cin	N	P	22	12-6
1901	Bos	A	P	1	0-1
1901	Bal	A	P	23	13-7
1902	Bal	A	P	2	0-2
	BLTL			226	101-94 .227

FOREMAN, JOHN DAVIS (Brownie)
b.Aug.6,1875 Baltimore,Md.
d.Oct.10,1926

Yr	Cl	Lea	Pos	G	Rec
1895	Pit	N	P	19	8-7
1896	Pit	N	P	9	3-4
1896	Cin	N	P	5	2-3
	BLTL			33	13-14

FOREMAN, WILLIAM
b.Pa.

Yr	Cl	Lea	Pos	G	Rec
1909	Was	A	P	2	0-2
1910	Was	A	P	1	0-0
				3	0-2

FORNIELES, JOSE MIGUEL TORRES (Mike)
b.Jan.18,1932 Havana,Cuba.

Yr	Cl	Lea	Pos	G	Rec
1952	Was	A	P	4	2-2
1953	Chi	A	P	39	8-7
1954	Chi	A	P	16	1-2
1955	Chi	A	P	28	6-3
1956	Chi	A	P	6	0-1
1956	Bal	A	P	33	4-7
1957	Bal	A	P	16	2-6
1957	Bos	A	P	26	8-7
1958	Bos	A	P	37	4-6
1959	Bos	A	P	46	5-3
1960	Bos	A	P	70	10-5
1961	Bos	A	P	57	9-8
1962	Bos	A	P	42	3-6
	BRTR			420	62-63

FORSTER, THOMAS W.
b.May 1,1858 New York,N.Y.
d.July 17,1946

Yr	Cl	Lea	Pos	G	Rec
1882	Det	N	2-3	20	.098
1884	Pit	a	S-3	35	.212
1885	Met	a	2	57	.220
1886	Met	a	2	84	.205
				196	.200

FORSYTHE, CLARENCE
b.St.Louis,Mo.

Yr	Cl	Lea	Pos	G	Rec
1915	Bal	F	3	1	.000
	TR				

FORTUNE, GARRETT REESE (Gary)
b.Oct.11,1894 High Point,N.C.

Yr	Cl	Lea	Pos	G	Rec
1916	Phi	N	P	1	0-1
1918	Phi	N	P	8	0-2
1920	Bos	A	P	14	0-2
	BRTR			23	0-5

FOSS, GEORGE DUEWARD (Deeby)
b.June 16,1898 Register,Va.

Yr	Cl	Lea	Pos	G	Rec
1921	Was	A	3	4	.000
	BRTR				

FOSS, LAWRENCE CURTIS
b.Apr.18,1936 Castleton,Kans.

Yr	Cl	Lea	Pos	G	Rec
1961	Pit	N	P	3	1-1
1962	NY	N	P	5	0-1
	BRTR			8	1-2

FOSTER, CLARENCE FRANCIS (Pop)
b.Apr.8,1878 New Haven,Conn.
d.Apr.16,1944

Yr	Cl	Lea	Pos	G	Rec
1898	NY	N	O	31	.281
1899	NY	N	O	88	.305
1900	NY	N	O	20	.286
1901	Was	A	O	104	.271
1901	Chi	A	O	11	.281
	TR			254	.285

FOSTER, EDWARD CUNNINGHAM (Kid)
b.Feb.13,1888 Chicago,Ill.
d.Jan.15,1937

Yr	Cl	Lea	Pos	G	Rec
1910	NY	A	S	30	.132
1912	Was	A	3	154	.285
1913	Was	A	3	106	.247
1914	Was	A	3	156	.282
1915	Was	A	2-3	154	.275
1916	Was	A	2-3	158	.253
1917	Was	A	2-3	143	.235
1918	Was	A	3	129	.283
1919	Was	A	3	120	.263
1920	Bos	A	2-3	117	.259
1921	Bos	A	2-3	120	.284
1922	Bos	A	3	48	.211
1922	St.L	A	3	37	.306
1923	St.L	A	2	27	.180
	BRTR			1499	.264

FOSTER, EDWARD LEE
d.Mar.2,1929

Yr	Cl	Lea	Pos	G	Rec
1908	Cle	A	P	6	1-0

FOSTER, ELMER E.
b.Aug.15,1861 Minneapolis,Minn.
d.July 22,1946

Yr	Cl	Lea	Pos	G	Rec
1884	Ath	a	C-O	3	.167
1884	Key	U	C	1	.333
1886	Met	a	O	18	.206
1888	NY	N	O	37	.147
1889	NY	N	O	2	.000
1890	Chi	N	O	27	.247
1891	Chi	N	O	4	.187
	TR			92	.191

FOSTER, GEORGE (Rube)
b.Jan.5,1889 Lehigh,Okla.

Yr	Cl	Lea	Pos	G	Rec
1913	Bos	A	P	20	3-4
1914	Bos	A	P	30	14-8
1915	Bos	A	P	40	20-9
1916	Bos	A	P	38	14-7
1917	Bos	A	P	17	8-7
	BRTR			145	59-35

FOSTER, OSCAR E. (Reddy)
b.1867 Richmond,Va.
d.Dec.19,1908

Yr	Cl	Lea	Pos	G	Rec
1896	NY	N	O	1	.000

FOTHERGILL, ROBERT ROY (Fatty)
b.Aug.16,1897 Massillon,O.
d.Mar.20,1938

Yr	Cl	Lea	Pos	G	Rec
1922	Det	A	O	42	.322
1923	Det	A	O	101	.315
1924	Det	A	O	54	.301
1925	Det	A	O	71	.353
1926	Det	A	O	110	.367
1927	Det	A	O	143	.359
1928	Det	A	O	111	.317
1929	Det	A	O	115	.350
1930	Det	A	O	54	.254
1930	Chi	A	O	52	.311
1931	Chi	A	O	108	.282
1932	Chi	A	O	116	.295
1933	Bos	A	O	28	.344
	BRTR			1105	.326

FOURNIER, F. HENRY (Frenchy)
b.Syracuse,N.Y.

Yr	Cl	Lea	Pos	G	Rec
1894	Cin	N	P	6	1-3
	TL				

FOURNIER, JACQUES FRANK (Jack)
b.Sept.29,1892 Au Sable,Mich.

Yr	Cl	Lea	Pos	G	Rec
1912	Chi	A	1	35	.192
1913	Chi	A	1-O	68	.234
1914	Chi	A	1	109	.311
1915	Chi	A	1-O	126	.322
1916	Chi	A	1	105	.240
1917	Chi	A	H	1	.000
1918	NY	A	1	27	.350
1920	St.L	N	1	141	.306
1921	St.L	N	1	149	.343
1922	St.L	N	P-1	128	0-0 .294
1923	Bro	N	1	133	.351
1924	Bro	N	1	154	.334
1925	Bro	N	1	145	.350
1926	Bro	N	1	87	.284
1927	Bos	N	1	122	.283
	BLTR			1530	0-0 .313

FOUSER, WILLIAM C.
b.1855 Philadelphia,Pa.
d.Mar.1,1919

Yr	Cl	Lea	Pos	G	Rec
1876	Ath	N	2-O	21	.135

FOUTZ, DAVID LUTHER (Scissors)
b.Sept.7,1856 Carroll Co.,Md.
d.Mar.5,1897

Yr	Cl	Lea	Pos	G	Rec
1884	St.L	a	P-O	32	15-6 .233
1885	St.L	a	P-1	65	33-14 .250
1886	St.L	a	P-O	89	41-16 .282
1887	St.L	a	P-O	103	24-12 .393
1888	Bro	a	P-1-O	140	12-7 .283
1889	Bro	a	P-1	138	4-0 .286
1890	Bro	N	P-1	129	3-1 .302
1891	Bro	N	P-1	130	3-3 .262
1892	Bro	N	P-O	53	12-9 .199
1893	Bro	N	M-1-O	130	.272
1894	Bro	N	M-1	73	.310
1895	Bro	N	M-O	28	.304
1896	Bro	N	M-1-O	2	.250
	TR			1112	147-68 .286

FOUTZ, FRANK HAYES
b.Apr.8,1877 Baltimore,Md.

Yr	Cl	Lea	Pos	G	Rec
1901	Bal	A	1	20	.236
	BRTR				

FOWLER, JESSE PETER
b.Oct.30,1898 Spartanburg,S.C.

Yr	Cl	Lea	Pos	G	Rec
1924	St.L	N	P	13	1-1
	BRTL				

FOWLER, JOHN ARTHUR
b.July 23,1923 Converse,S.C.

Yr	Cl	Lea	Pos	G	Rec
1954	Cin	N	P	40	12-10
1955	Cin	N	P	46	11-10
1956	Cin	N	P	45	11-11
1957	Cin	N	P	33	3-0
1959	LA	N	P	36	3-4
1961	LA	A	P	53	5-8
1962	LA	A	P	48	4-3
	BRTR			301	49-46

FOWLER, JOSEPH CHESTER (Gink)
b.Nov.11,1900 Waco,Tex.

Yr	Cl	Lea	Pos	G	Rec
1923	Cin	N	S	11	.333
1924	Cin	N	2-S-3	59	.333
1925	Cin	N	S	6	.400
1926	Bos	A	3	2	.125
	BLTR			78	.326

FOWLER, RICHARD JOHN
b.Mar.30,1921 Toronto,Ont.,Canada.

Yr	Cl	Lea	Pos	G	Rec
1941	Phi	A	P	4	1-2
1942	Phi	A	P	32	6-11

(Continued)

Yr	Cl	Lea	Pos	G	Rec
1945	Phi	A	P	11	1-2
1946	Phi	A	P	32	9-16
1947	Phi	A	P	36	12-11
1948	Phi	A	P	29	15-8
1949	Phi	A	P	31	15-11
1950	Phi	A	P	11	1-5
1951	Phi	A	P	22	5-11
1952	Phi	A	P	18	1-2
	BRTR			226	66-79

FOX, CHARLES FRANCIS (Irish)
b.Oct.7,1922 New York,N.Y.

Yr	Cl	Lea	Pos	G	Rec
1942	NY	N	C	3	.429
	BRTR				

FOX, ERVIN (Pete)
b.Mar.8,1909 Evansville,Ind.

Yr	Cl	Lea	Pos	G	Rec
1933	Det	A	O	128	.288
1934	Det	A	O	128	.285
1935	Det	A	O	131	.321
1936	Det	A	O	73	.305
1937	Det	A	O	148	.331
1938	Det	A	O	155	.293
1939	Det	A	O	141	.295
1940	Det	A	O	93	.289
1941	Bos	A	O	73	.302
1942	Bos	A	O	77	.262
1943	Bos	A	O	127	.288
1944	Bos	A	O	121	.315
1945	Bos	A	O	66	.245
	BRTR			1461	.298

FOX, GEORGE (Paddy)
d.May 8,1914

Yr	Cl	Lea	Pos	G	Rec
1899	Pit	N	C	13	.243

FOX, GEORGE B.
b.1869 Pottstown,Pa.
d.May 6,1914

Yr	Cl	Lea	Pos	G	Rec
1891	Lou	a	3	6	.105

FOX, HENRY H.

Yr	Cl	Lea	Pos	G	Rec
1902	Phi	N	P	1	0-0

FOX, HOWARD FRANCIS
b.Mar.1,1921 Coburg,Ore.
d.Oct.9,1955

Yr	Cl	Lea	Pos	G	Rec
1944	Cin	N	P	2	0-0
1945	Cin	N	P	45	8-13
1946	Cin	N	P	4	0-0
1948	Cin	N	P	35	6-9
1949	Cin	N	P	41	6-19
1950	Cin	N	P	35	11-8
1951	Cin	N	P	40	9-14
1952	Phi	N	P	13	2-7
1954	Bal	A	P	38	1-2
	BRTR			253	43-72

FOX, JACOB NELSON (Nellie)
b.Dec.25,1927 St.Thomas,Pa.

Yr	Cl	Lea	Pos	G	Rec
1947	Phi	A	2	7	.000
1948	Phi	A	2	3	.154
1949	Phi	A	2	88	.255
1950	Chi	A	2	130	.247
1951	Chi	A	2	147	.313
1952	Chi	A	2	152	.296
1953	Chi	A	2	154	.285
1954	Chi	A	2	155	.319
1955	Chi	A	2	154	.311
1956	Chi	A	2	154	.296
1957	Chi	A	2	155	.317
1958	Chi	A	2	155	.300
1959	Chi	A	2	156	.306
1960	Chi	A	2	150	.289
1961	Chi	A	2	159	.251
1962	Chi	A	2	157	.267
	BLTR			2076	.292

FOX, JOHN JOSEPH
b.Feb.7,1859 Roxbury,Mass.
d.Apr.18,1893

Yr	Cl	Lea	Pos	G	Rec
1881	Bos	N	P-1-O	30	6-8 .178
1883	Bal	a	P-1-O	23	6-14 .168

(Continued)

Yr	Cl	Lea	Pos	G	Rec
1884	Pit	a	P-S	8	1-6 .240
1886	Was	N	P	1	0-1
				62	13-29 .179

FOX, JOHN PAUL
b.May 21,1885 Reading,Pa.

Yr	Cl	Lea	Pos	G	Rec
1908	Phi	A	O	8	.209
BRTR					

FOX, TERRENCE EDWARD
b.July 31,1935 Chicago,Ill.

Yr	Cl	Lea	Pos	G	Rec
1960	Mil	N	P	5	0-0
1961	Det	A	P	39	5-2
1962	Det	A	P	47	3-1
BRTR				91	8-3

FOX, WILLIAM H.
b.Jan.15,1872 Sturbridge,Mass.
d.May 6,1946

Yr	Cl	Lea	Pos	G	Rec
1897	Was	N	2-S	4	.250
1901	Cin	N	2	44	.183
BRTR				48	.191

FOXEN, WILLIAM A.
b.May 31,1884 Tenafly,N.J.
d.Apr.17,1937

Yr	Cl	Lea	Pos	G	Rec
1908	Phi	N	P	22	7-7
1909	Phi	N	P	18	3-7
1910	Phi	N	P	16	5-5
1910	Chi	N	P	2	0-0
1911	Chi	N	P	3	1-1
BLTL				61	16-20

FOXX, JAMES EMORY (Beast)
b.Oct.22,1907 Sudlersville,Md.

Yr	Cl	Lea	Pos	G	Rec
1925	Phi	A	C	10	.667
1926	Phi	A	C	26	.313
1927	Phi	A	1	61	.323
1928	Phi	A	C-1-3	118	.328
1929	Phi	A	1	149	.354
1930	Phi	A	1	153	.335
1931	Phi	A	1-3	139	.291
1932	Phi	A	1-3	154	.364
1933	Phi	A	1	149	.356
1934	Phi	A	1	150	.334
1935	Phi	A	C-1-3	147	.346
1936	Bos	A	1-O	155	.338
1937	Bos	A	1	150	.285
1938	Bos	A	1	149	.349
1939	Bos	A	P-1	124	0-0 .360
1940	Bos	A	C-1-3	144	.297
1941	Bos	A	1-3-O	135	.300
1942	Bos	A	1	30	.270
1942	Chi	N	C-1	70	.205
1944	Chi	N	C-3	15	.050
1945	Phi	N	P-1-3	89	1-0 .268
BRTR				2317	1-0 .325

FOYTACK, PAUL EUGENE
b.Nov.16,1930 Scranton,Pa.

Yr	Cl	Lea	Pos	G	Rec
1953	Det	A	P	6	0-0
1955	Det	A	P	22	0-1
1956	Det	A	P	43	15-13
1957	Det	A	P	38	14-11
1958	Det	A	P	39	15-13
1959	Det	A	P	39	14-14
1960	Det	A	P	29	2-11
1961	Det	A	P	32	11-10
1962	Det	A	P	29	10-7
BRTR				277	81-80

FRANCE, OSMAN B.
b.Oct.4,1859 Greentown,O.
d.May 2,1947

Yr	Cl	Lea	Pos	G	Rec
1890	Chi	N	P	1	0-0

FRANCIS, EARL COLEMAN
b.July 14,1935 Slab Fork,W.Va.

Yr	Cl	Lea	Pos	G	Rec
1960	Pit	N	P	7	1-0
1961	Pit	N	P	23	2-8
1962	Pit	N	P	36	9-8
BRTR				66	12-16

FRANCIS, RAY JAMES
b.Mar.8,1893 Sherman,Tex.
d.July 14,1932

Yr	Cl	Lea	Pos	G	Rec
1922	Was	A	P	39	7-18
1923	Det	A	P	37	4-8
1925	NY	A	P	4	0-0
1925	Bos	A	P	6	0-2
BLTL				86	11-28

FRANCONA, JOHN PATSY
b.Nov.4,1933 Aliquippa,Pa.

Yr	Cl	Lea	Pos	G	Rec
1956	Bal	A	1-O	139	.258
1957	Bal	A	1-O	97	.233
1958	Chi	A	O	41	.258
1958	Det	A	1-O	45	.246
1959	Cle	A	1-O	122	.363
1960	Cle	A	1-O	147	.292
1961	Cle	A	1-O	155	.301
1962	Cle	A	1	158	.272
BLTL				904	.286

FRANK, CHARLES
b.May 30,1870 Mobile,Ala.
d.May 24,1922

Yr	Cl	Lea	Pos	G	Rec
1893	St.L	N	O	40	.331
1894	St.L	N	O	80	.246
				120	.272

FRANK, FREDERICK
b.Mar.11,1874 Dayton,O.
d.Mar.27,1950

Yr	Cl	Lea	Pos	G	Rec
1898	Cle	N	O	17	.208

FRANKHOUSE, FREDERICK MELOY
b.Apr.9,1904 Port Royal,Pa.

Yr	Cl	Lea	Pos	G	Rec
1927	St.L	N	P	8	5-1
1928	St.L	N	P	22	3-2
1929	St.L	N	P	34	7-2
1930	St.L	N	P	9	2-3
1930	Bos	N	P	27	7-6
1931	Bos	N	P	26	8-8
1932	Bos	N	P	40	4-6
1933	Bos	N	P	43	16-15
1934	Bos	N	P	37	17-9
1935	Bos	N	P	40	11-15
1936	Bro	N	P	42	13-10
1937	Bro	N	P	39	10-13
1938	Bro	N	P	31	3-5
1939	Bos	N	P	23	0-2
BRTR				421	106-97

FRANKLIN, ...

Yr	Cl	Lea	Pos	G	Rec
1884	Was	U	O	1	.000

FRANKLIN, JAMES WILFORD (Jack)
b.Oct.20,1919 Paris,Ill.

Yr	Cl	Lea	Pos	G	Rec
1944	Bro	N	P	1	0-0
BRTR					

FRANKLIN, MURRAY ASHER (Moe)
b.Apr.1,1914 Chicago,Ill.

Yr	Cl	Lea	Pos	G	Rec
1941	Det	A	S-3	13	.300
1942	Det	A	2-S	48	.260
BRTR				61	.262

FRANKS, HERMAN LOUIS
b.Jan.4,1914 Price,Utah.

Yr	Cl	Lea	Pos	G	Rec
1939	St.L	N	C	17	.059
1940	Bro	N	C	65	.183
1941	Bro	N	C-O	57	.201
1947	Phi	A	C	8	.200
1948	Phi	A	C	40	.224
1949	NY	N	C	1	.667
BLTR				188	.195

FRASER, CHARLES CARROLTON (Chick)
b.Mar.17,1874 Scotland.
d.May 8,1940

Yr	Cl	Lea	Pos	G	Rec
1896	Lou	N	P	43	13-25
1897	Lou	N	P	36	15-17
1898	Lou	N	P	26	7-19
1898	Cle	N	P	6	2-3

(Continued)

Yr	Cl	Lea	Pos	G	Rec
1899	Phi	N	P	37	21-13
1900	Phi	N	P	26	16-10
1901	Phi	A	P	43	20-15
1902	Phi	N	P	27	12-13
1903	Phi	N	P	32	12-17
1904	Phi	N	P	44	13-24
1905	Bos	N	P	45	15-21
1906	Cin	N	P	31	10-20
1907	Chi	N	P	22	8-5
1908	Chi	N	P	26	11-9
1909	Chi	N	P	1	0-0
BRTR				445	175-211

FRASIER, VICTOR PATRICK
b.Aug.5,1906 Ruston,La.

Yr	Cl	Lea	Pos	G	Rec
1931	Chi	A	P	46	13-15
1932	Chi	A	P	29	3-13
1933	Chi	A	P	10	1-1
1933	Det	A	P	20	5-5
1934	Det	A	P	8	1-3
1937	Bos	N	P	3	0-0
1939	Chi	A	P	10	0-1
BRTR				126	23-38

FRAZER, GEORGE KASSON
b.Jan.7,1861 Syracuse,N.Y.
d.Feb.5,1913
Non-playing manager Syr (a) 1890.

FRAZIER, JOSEPH FILMORE
b.Oct.6,1922 Liberty,N.C..

Yr	Cl	Lea	Pos	G	Rec
1947	Cle	A	O	9	.071
1954	St.L	N	1-O	81	.295
1955	St.L	N	O	58	.200
1956	St.L	N	O	14	.211
1956	Cin	N	O	10	.235
1956	Bal	A	O	45	.257
BLTR				217	.241

FREDERICK, JOHN HENRY
b.Jan.26,1901 Denver,Col.

Yr	Cl	Lea	Pos	G	Rec
1929	Bro	N	O	148	.328
1930	Bro	N	O	142	.334
1931	Bro	N	O	146	.270
1932	Bro	N	O	118	.299
1933	Bro	N	O	147	.308
1934	Bro	N	O	104	.296
BLTL				805	.307

FREED, EDWARD CHARLES
b.Aug.22,1919 Centre Valley,Pa.

Yr	Cl	Lea	Pos	G	Rec
1942	Phi	N	O	13	.303
BRTR					

FREEHAN, WILLIAM ASHLEY
b.Nov.29,1941 Detroit,Mich.

Yr	Cl	Lea	Pos	G	Rec
1961	Det	A	C	4	.400
BRTR					

FREEMAN, ALEXANDER VERNON (Buck)
b.July 5,1896 Mart,Tex.

Yr	Cl	Lea	Pos	G	Rec
1921	Chi	N	P	38	9-10
1922	Chi	N	P	11	0-1
BBTR				49	9-11

FREEMAN, HARVEY B. (Poke)
b.Oct.22,1899 Otsego,Mich.

Yr	Cl	Lea	Pos	G	Rec
1921	Phi	A	P	18	1-4
BRTR					

FREEMAN, HERSHELL BASKIN (Buster)
b.July 1,1928 Gadsden,Ala.

Yr	Cl	Lea	Pos	G	Rec
1952	Bos	A	P	4	1-0
1953	Bos	A	P	18	1-4
1955	Bos	A	P	2	0-0
1955	Cin	N	P-3	53	7-4 .167
1956	Cin	N	P	64	14-5
1957	Cin	N	P	52	7-2
1958	Cin	N	P	3	0-0
1958	Chi	N	P	9	0-1
BRTR				205	30-16 .143

FREEMAN, JAMES JEREMIAH (Jerry)
b.1882

Yr	Cl	Lea	Pos	G	Rec
1908	Was	A	1	154	.252
1909	Was	A	1	19	.167
				173	.245

FREEMAN, JOHN EDWARD
b.Jan.24,1901 Boston,Mass.
d.Apr.14,1958

Yr	Cl	Lea	Pos	G	Rec
1927	Bos	A	O	4	.000
	BRTR				

FREEMAN, JOHN F. (Buck)
b.Oct.30,1871 Catasaqua,Pa.
d.June 25,1949

Yr	Cl	Lea	Pos	G	Rec
1891	Was	a	P	6	0-0
1898	Was	N	O	29	.368
1899	Was	N	O	155	.318
1900	Bos	N	1-O	109	.300
1901	Bos	A	1	129	.346
1902	Bos	A	O	138	.311
1903	Bos	A	O	141	.285
1904	Bos	A	O	157	.278
1905	Bos	A	1-O	130	.240
1906	Bos	A	1-O	121	.250
1907	Bos	A	O	4	.167
	BLTL			1119	0-0 .294

FREEMAN, JULIUS B.
b.1869 Omaha,Neb.

Yr	Cl	Lea	Pos	G	Rec
1888	St.L	a	P	1	0-1

FREEMAN, MARK PRICE
b.Dec.7,1930 Memphis,Tenn.

Yr	Cl	Lea	Pos	G	Rec
1959	KC	A	P	3	0-0
1959	NY	A	P	1	0-0
1960	Chi	N	P	30	3-3
	BRTR			34	3-3

FREESE, EUGENE LEWIS
b.Jan.8,1934 Wheeling,W.Va.

Yr	Cl	Lea	Pos	G	Rec
1955	Pit	N	2-3	134	.253
1956	Pit	N	2-3	65	.208
1957	Pit	N	2-3-O	114	.283
1958	Pit	N	3	17	.167
1958	St.L	N	2-S-3	62	.257
1959	Phi	N	2-3	132	.268
1960	Chi	A	3	127	.273
1961	Cin	N	2-3	152	.277
1962	Cin	N	3	18	.143
	BRTR			821	.262

FREESE, GEORGE WALTER (Bud)
b.Sept.12,1926 Wheeling,W.Va.

Yr	Cl	Lea	Pos	G	Rec
1953	Det	A	H	1	.000
1955	Pit	N	3	51	.257
1961	Chi	N	H	9	.286
	BRTR			61	.257

FREEZE, CARL ALEXANDER (Jake)
b.Apr.25,1900 Ft.Smith,Ark.

Yr	Cl	Lea	Pos	G	Rec
1925	Chi	A	P	2	0-0
	BRTR				

FREGOSI, JAMES LOUIS
b.Apr.4,1942 San Francisco,Cal.

Yr	Cl	Lea	Pos	G	Rec
1961	LA	A	S	11	.222
1962	LA	A	S	58	.291
	BRTR			69	.282

FREIBERGER, VERNON DONALD
b.Nov.19,1923 Detroit,Mich.

Yr	Cl	Lea	Pos	G	Rec
1941	Cle	A	1	2	.125
	BRTL				

FREIGAU, HOWARD EARL (Ty)
b.Aug.1,1902 Dayton,O.
d.July 18,1932

Yr	Cl	Lea	Pos	G	Rec
1922	St.L	N	S-3	3	.000
1923	St.L	N	1-2-S-3-O	113	.263

(Continued)

Yr	Cl	Lea	Pos	G	Rec
1924	St.L	N	3	98	.269
1925	St.L	N	S	9	.154
1925	Chi	N	1-S-3	117	.307
1926	Chi	N	3	140	.270
1927	Chi	N	3	30	.233
1928	Bro	N	S-3	17	.206
1928	Bos	N	2-S	52	.257
	BRTR			579	.272

FREITAS, TONY
b.May 5,1908 Mill Valley,Cal.

Yr	Cl	Lea	Pos	G	Rec
1932	Phi	A	P	23	12-5
1933	Phi	A	P	19	2-4
1934	Cin	N	P	31	6-12
1935	Cin	N	P	31	5-10
1936	Cin	N	P	4	0-2
	BRTL			108	25-33

FRENCH, CHARLES CALVIN
b.Oct,12,1883 Indianapolis,Ind.
d.Mar.30,1962

Yr	Cl	Lea	Pos	G	Rec
1909	Bos	A	2-S	51	.251
1910	Bos	A	2	9	.200
1910	Chi	A	2	45	.165
	BLTR			105	.207

FRENCH, FRANK ALEXANDER (Pat)
b.Sept.22,1893 Dover,N.H.

Yr	Cl	Lea	Pos	G	Rec
1917	Phi	A	O	4	.000
	BBTR				

FRENCH, LAWRENCE HERBERT
b.Nov.1,1908 Visalia,Cal.

Yr	Cl	Lea	Pos	G	Rec
1929	Pit	N	P	30	7-5
1930	Pit	N	P	42	17-18
1931	Pit	N	P	39	15-13
1932	Pit	N	P	47	18-16
1933	Pit	N	P	47	18-13
1934	Pit	N	P	49	12-18
1935	Chi	N	P	42	17-10
1936	Chi	N	P	43	18-9
1937	Chi	N	P	42	16-10
1938	Chi	N	P	43	10-19
1939	Chi	N	P	36	15-8
1940	Chi	N	P	40	14-14
1941	Chi	N	P	26	5-14
1941	Bro	N	P	6	0-0
1942	Bro	N	P	38	15-4
	BBTL			570	197-171

FRENCH, RAYMOND EDWARD
b.Jan.9,1897 Alameda,Cal.

Yr	Cl	Lea	Pos	G	Rec
1920	NY	A	S	2	.000
1923	Bro	N	S	43	.219
1924	Chi	A	S	37	.179
	BRTR			82	.193

FRENCH, WALTER EDWARD (Piggy)
b.July 12,1899 Moorestown,N.J.

Yr	Cl	Lea	Pos	G	Rec
1923	Phi	A	O	16	.231
1925	Phi	A	O	67	.370
1926	Phi	A	O	112	.305
1927	Phi	A	O	109	.304
1928	Phi	A	O	49	.257
1929	Phi	A	O	45	.267
	BLTR			398	.303

FRENCH, WILLIAM
b.Baltimore,Md.

Yr	Cl	Lea	Pos	G	Rec
1873	Mar	n	P-1-O	5	0-1 NR

FREY, BENJAMIN RUDOLPH
b.Apr.6,1906 Dexter,Mich.
d.Nov.1,1937

Yr	Cl	Lea	Pos	G	Rec
1929	Cin	N	P	3	1-2
1930	Cin	N	P	44	11-18
1931	Cin	N	P	34	8-12
1932	St.L	N	P	2	0-2
1932	Cin	N	P	28	4-10
1933	Cin	N	P	38	6-4
1934	Cin	N	P	41	11-16
1935	Cin	N	P	38	6-10
1936	Cin	N	P	32	10-8
	BRTR			260	57-82

FREY, LINUS REINHARD (Lonny)
b.Aug.23,1912 St.Louis,Mo.

Yr	Cl	Lea	Pos	G	Rec
1933	Bro	N	S	34	.319
1934	Bro	N	S-3	125	.284
1935	Bro	N	2-S	131	.262
1936	Bro	N	2-S	148	.279
1937	Chi	N	2-S	78	.278
1938	Cin	N	2-S	124	.265
1939	Cin	N	2	125	.291
1940	Cin	N	2	150	.266
1941	Cin	N	2	146	.254
1942	Cin	N	2	141	.266
1943	Cin	N	2	144	.263
1946	Cin	N	2-O	111	.246
1947	Chi	N	2	24	.209
1947	NY	A	2	24	.179
1948	NY	A	H	1	.000
1948	NY	N	2	29	.255
	BLTR			1535	.269

FRIBERG, BERNARD ALBERT (Barney)
b.Aug.18,1899 Manchester,N.H.
d.Dec.8,1958

Yr	Cl	Lea	Pos	G	Rec
1919	Chi	N	O	8	.200
1920	Chi	N	2-O	50	.211
1922	Chi	N	1-2-3-O	97	.311
1923	Chi	N	3	146	.318
1924	Chi	N	3	142	.279
1925	Chi	N	1-3	44	.257
1925	Phi	N	P-2-S-3-O	91	0-0 .270
1926	Phi	N	2	144	.268
1927	Phi	N	3	111	.233
1928	Phi	N	S	52	.202
1929	Phi	N	S-O	128	.301
1930	Phi	N	2-S-O	105	.341
1931	Phi	N	2-3	103	.261
1932	Phi	N	2	61	.240
1933	Bos	A	2-S-3	17	.317
	BRTR			1299	0-0 .280

FRICANO, MARION JOHN
b.July 15,1923 Brant,N.Y.

Yr	Cl	Lea	Pos	G	Rec
1952	Phi	A	P	2	1-0
1953	Phi	A	P	46	9-12
1954	Phi	A	P	42	5-11
1955	KC	A	P	10	0-0
	BRTR			100	15-23

FRICKEN, ANTHONY (Hon)
b.Brooklyn,N.Y.
d.Nov.30,1903

Yr	Cl	Lea	Pos	G	Rec
1890	Bos	N	P	1	0-1

FRIDAY, GRIER WILLIAM (Skipper)
b.Oct.24,1896 Lincolnton,N.C.

Yr	Cl	Lea	Pos	G	Rec
1923	Was	A	P	7	0-1
	BRTR				

FRIDLEY, JAMES RILEY
b.Sept.6,1924 Philippi,W.Va.

Yr	Cl	Lea	Pos	G	Rec
1952	Cle	A	O	62	.251
1954	Bal	A	O	85	.246
1958	Cin	N	O	5	.222
	BRTR			152	.248

FRIED, ARTHUR EDWIN (Cy)
b.July 23,1897 San Antonio,Tex.

Yr	Cl	Lea	Pos	G	Rec
1920	Det	A	P	2	0-0
	BLTL				

FRIEDRICH, ROBERT GEORGE
b.Aug.30,1909 Cincinnati,O.

Yr	Cl	Lea	Pos	G	Rec
1932	Was	A	P	2	0-0
	BRTR				

FRIEL, PATRICK HENRY
b.June 11,1860 Lewisburg,W.Va.
d.Jan.15,1924

Yr	Cl	Lea	Pos	G	Rec
1890	Syr	a	O	62	.238
1891	Ath	a	O	2	.286
				64	.243

FRIEL, WILLIAM EDWARD
b.Apr.1,1876 Renovo,Pa.
d.Dec.24,1959

Yr	Cl	Lea	Pos	G	Rec
1901	Mil	A	3-O	106	.271
1902	St.L	A	P-C-1-2-S-3-O	79	0-0 / .239
1903	St.L	A	2-3	98	.223
			BLTR	283	0-0 / .245

FRIEND, DANIEL SEBASTIAN
b.May 19,1873 Chillicothe,O.
d.June 1,1942

Yr	Cl	Lea	Pos	G	Rec
1895	Chi	N	P	5	2-2
1896	Chi	N	P	33	19-14
1897	Chi	N	P	24	12-11
1898	Chi	N	P	2	0-2
			TL	64	33-29

FRIEND, FRANK B.
b.Washington,D.C.
d.Sept.8,1897

Yr	Cl	Lea	Pos	G	Rec
1896	Lou	N	C	2	.200

FRIEND, OWEN LACEY (Red)
b.Mar.21,1927 Granite City,Ill.

Yr	Cl	Lea	Pos	G	Rec
1949	St.L	A	2	2	.375
1950	St.L	A	2-S-3	119	.237
1953	Det	A	2	31	.177
1953	Cle	A	2-S-3	34	.235
1955	Bos	A	2-S	14	.262
1955	Chi	N	S-3	6	.100
1956	Chi	N	H	2	.000
			BRTR	208	.227

FRIEND, ROBERT BARTMESS (Warrior)
b.Nov.24,1930 Lafayette,Ind.

Yr	Cl	Lea	Pos	G	Rec
1951	Pit	N	P	34	6-10
1952	Pit	N	P	35	7-17
1953	Pit	N	P	32	8-11
1954	Pit	N	P	35	7-12
1955	Pit	N	P	44	14-9
1956	Pit	N	P	49	17-17
1957	Pit	N	P	40	14-18
1958	Pit	N	P	38	22-14
1959	Pit	N	P	35	8-19
1960	Pit	N	P	38	18-12
1961	Pit	N	P	41	14-19
1962	Pit	N	P	39	18-14
			BRTR	460	153-172

FRIERSON, ROBERT LAWRENCE (Buck)
b.July 29,1917 Chicota,Tex.

Yr	Cl	Lea	Pos	G	Rec
1941	Cle	A	O	5	.273
			BRTR		

FRIES, PETER J.

Yr	Cl	Lea	Pos	G	Rec
1883	Col	a	P	3	0-3
1884	Ind	a	O	1	.250
			TL	4	0-3 / .267

FRILL, JOHN EDMOND
b.Apr.3,1879 Reading,Pa.
d.Sept.29,1918

Yr	Cl	Lea	Pos	G	Rec
1910	NY	A	P	10	2-2
1912	St.L	A	P	3	1-0
1912	Cin	N	P	3	1-0
			BRTL	16	4-2

FRINK, FREDERICK FERDINAND
b.Aug.25,1911 Macon,Ga.

Yr	Cl	Lea	Pos	G	Rec
1934	Phi	N	O	2	.000
			BRTR		

FRISBEE, CHARLES A.
b.Feb.2,1875 Dows,Ia.

Yr	Cl	Lea	Pos	G	Rec
1899	Bos	N	O	39	.331
1900	NY	N	O	4	.153
				43	.316

FRISCH, FRANK FRANCIS (The Fordham Flash)
b.Sept.9,1898 New York,N.Y.

Yr	Cl	Lea	Pos	G	Rec
1919	NY	N	2-S-3	54	.226
1920	NY	N	3	110	.280
1921	NY	N	2-3	153	.341
1922	NY	N	2-S-3	132	.326
1923	NY	N	2-3	151	.348
1924	NY	N	2-S-3	145	.328
1925	NY	N	2-S-3	120	.331
1926	NY	N	2	135	.314
1927	St.L	N	2	153	.337
1928	St.L	N	2	141	.300
1929	St.L	N	2-3	138	.334
1930	St.L	N	2-3	133	.346
1931	St.L	N	2	131	.311
1932	St.L	N	2-3	115	.292
1933	St.L	N	M-2-S	147	.303
1934	St.L	N	M-2-3	140	.305
1935	St.L	N	M-2-3	103	.294
1936	St.L	N	M-2-3	93	.274
1937	St.L	N	M-2	17	.219
			BBTR	2311	.316

Non-playing manager St.L (N) 1938, Pit (N) 1940-46 and Chi (N) 1949-51.

FRISK, JOHN EMIL
b.Oct.15,1875 Kalkaska,Mich.
d.Jan.27,1922

Yr	Cl	Lea	Pos	G	Rec
1899	Cin	N	P	9	3-6
1901	Det	A	P	19	5-3
1905	St.L	A	O	127	.261
1907	St.L	A	H	5	.250
			BLTR	160	8-9 / .266

FRITZ, CHARLES CORNELIUS
b.June 18,1882 Mobile,Ala.
d.July 31,1944

Yr	Cl	Lea	Pos	G	Rec
1907	Phi	A	P	1	1-0
			TL		

FRITZ, HARRY KOCH (Dutchman)
b.Sept.30,1890 Philadelphia,Pa.

Yr	Cl	Lea	Pos	G	Rec
1913	Phi	A	3	5	.000
1914	Chi	F	3	63	.229
1915	Chi	F	3	72	.240
			BRTR	140	.228

FROATS, WILLIAM JOHN
b.Oct.20,1930 New York,N.Y.

Yr	Cl	Lea	Pos	G	Rec
1955	Det	A	P	1	0-0
			BLTL		

FROCK, SAMUEL W.
b.Dec.23,1883 Baltimore,Md.
d.Nov.3,1925

Yr	Cl	Lea	Pos	G	Rec
1907	Bos	N	P	5	1-3
1909	Pit	N	P	8	2-1
1910	Pit	N	P	1	0-0
1910	Bos	N	P	45	12-19
1911	Bos	N	P	4	0-1
			BRTR	63	15-24

FROELICH, WILLIAM PALMER (Ben)
b.Nov.12,1887 Pittsburgh,Pa.
d.Sept.1,1916

Yr	Cl	Lea	Pos	G	Rec
1909	Phi	N	C	1	.000
			TR		

FROMME, ARTHUR HENRY
b.Sept.3,1883 Quincy,Ill.
d.Aug.24,1956

Yr	Cl	Lea	Pos	G	Rec
1906	St.L	N	P	5	1-4
1907	St.L	N	P	23	5-13
1908	St.L	N	P	20	5-13
1909	Cin	N	P	37	19-13
1910	Cin	N	P	11	3-4
1911	Cin	N	P	38	10-11
1912	Cin	N	P	43	16-19
1913	Cin	N	P	9	1-4
1913	NY	N	P	26	11-6
1914	NY	N	P	38	9-5
1915	NY	N	P	4	0-1
			BRTR	254	80-93

FRY, JOHNSON
b.Nov.21,1901 Huntington,W.Va.
d.Apr.7,1959

Yr	Cl	Lea	Pos	G	Rec
1923	Cle	A	P	1	0-0
			BRTR		

FRYE, CHARLES ANDREW
b.July 17,1914 Hickory,N.C.
d.May 25,1945

Yr	Cl	Lea	Pos	G	Rec
1940	Phi	N	P	18	0-6
			BRTR		

FUCHS, CHARLES THOMAS
b.Nov.18,1912 Union City,N.J.

Yr	Cl	Lea	Pos	G	Rec
1942	Det	A	P	9	3-3
1943	Phi	N	P	17	2-7
1943	St.L	A	P	13	0-0
1944	Bro	N	P	8	1-0
			BBTR	47	6-10

FUCHS, EMIL EDWIN (Judge)
b.Apr.17,1878 New York,N.Y.
d.Dec.5,1961
Non-playing manager Bos (N) 1929.

FUHR, OSCAR LAWRENCE
b.Aug.22,1893 Defiance,Mo.

Yr	Cl	Lea	Pos	G	Rec
1921	Chi	N	P	1	0-0
1924	Bos	A	P	23	3-6
1925	Bos	A	P	38	0-6
			BLTL	62	3-12

FUHRMAN, ALFRED GEORGE (Ollie)
b.July 20,1896 Jordan,Minn.

Yr	Cl	Lea	Pos	G	Rec
1922	Phi	A	C	7	.333
			BLTR		

FULGHUM, JAMES LAVOISIER (Dot)
b.July 4,1900 Valdosta,Ga.
d.Nov.1,1947

Yr	Cl	Lea	Pos	G	Rec
1921	Phi	A	S	2	.000
			BRTR		

FULLER, CHARLES F. (Nig)

Yr	Cl	Lea	Pos	G	Rec
1902	Bro	N	C	3	.000
			BRTR		

FULLER, EDWARD A.
b.Mar.22,1869 Washington,D.C.

Yr	Cl	Lea	Pos	G	Rec
1886	Was	N	P	1	0-1

FULLER, FRANK EDWARD (Rabbit)
b.Jan.1,1895 Detroit,Mich.

Yr	Cl	Lea	Pos	G	Rec
1915	Det	A	2	14	.156
1916	Det	A	2	20	.100
1923	Bos	A	2	6	.238
			BLTR	40	.177

FULLER, HENRY W. (Harry)
b.Dec.5,1862 Cincinnati,O.
d.Dec.12,1895

Yr	Cl	Lea	Pos	G	Rec
1891	St.L	a	3	1	.000

FULLER, WILLIAM BENJAMIN (Shorty)
b.Oct.10,1867 Cincinnati,O.
d.Apr.11,1904

Yr	Cl	Lea	Pos	G	Rec
1888	Was	N	S	49	.182
1889	St.L	a	S	140	.228
1890	St.L	a	S	130	.271
1891	St.L	a	2-S	135	.219
1892	NY	N	S	138	.236
1893	NY	N	S	130	.247
1894	NY	N	S	95	.282
1895	NY	N	S	126	.227
1896	NY	N	S	17	.180
			BRTR	960	.239

FULLERTON, CURTIS HOOPER
b.Sept.13,1898 Ellsworth,Me.

Yr	Cl	Lea	Pos	G	Rec
1921	Bos	A	P	4	0-1
1922	Bos	A	P	31	1-4
1923	Bos	A	P	37	2-15
1924	Bos	A	P	33	7-12
1925	Bos	A	P	4	0-3
1933	Bos	A	P	6	0-2
	BLTR			115	10-37

FULLIS, CHARLES PHILIP (Chick)
b.Feb.27,1904 Girardville,Pa.
d.Mar.28,1946

Yr	Cl	Lea	Pos	G	Rec
1928	NY	N	O	11	.000
1929	NY	N	O	86	.288
1930	NY	N	O	13	.000
1931	NY	N	O	89	.328
1932	NY	N	O	96	.298
1933	Phi	N	3-O	151	.309
1934	Phi	N	O	28	.225
1934	St.L	N	O	69	.261
1936	St.L	N	O	47	.281
	BRTR			590	.295

FULMER, CHARLES J.
b.Feb.13,1851 Philadelphia,Pa.
d.Feb.15,1940

Yr	Cl	Lea	Pos	G	Rec
1871	Rok	n	1-S	16	NR
1872	Mut	n	S-3	34	NR
1873	Phi	n	C-S	49	NR
1874	Phi	n	S-3	57	NR
1875	Phi	n	S-3	68	.222
1876	Lou	N	M-S	66	.272
1879	Buf	N	2	75	.266
1880	Buf	N	2	11	.152
1882	Cin	a	M-S	79	.277
1883	Cin	a	S	82	.247
1884	Cin	a	S-3-O	30	.177
1884	St.L	a	2	1	.000
	TR			568	NR

FULMER, CHRISTOPHER
b.July 4,1858 Tamaqua,Pa.
d.Nov.9,1931

Yr	Cl	Lea	Pos	G	Rec
1875	Alt	n	O	1	.500
1884	Was	U	C-1-O	47	.282
1886	Bal	a	C	79	.251
1887	Bal	a	C	56	.368
1888	Bal	a	C	51	.179
1889	Bal	a	C	16	.278
				250	.275

FULTZ, DAVID LEWIS
b.May 29,1875 Staunton,Va.
d.Oct.30,1959

Yr	Cl	Lea	Pos	G	Rec
1898	Phi	N	O	16	.196
1899	Phi	N	S-3	2	.400
1899	Bal	N	3-O	54	.304
1901	Phi	A	2-O	132	.295
1902	Phi	A	2-O	129	.300
1903	NY	A	O	78	.240
1904	NY	A	O	96	.278
1905	NY	A	O	122	.232
	BRTR			629	.275

FUNK, ELIAS CALVIN (Liz)
b.Oct.28,1904 La Cygne,Kan.

Yr	Cl	Lea	Pos	G	Rec
1929	NY	A	H	1	.000
1930	Det	A	O	140	.275
1932	Chi	A	O	122	.259
1933	Chi	A	O	10	.222
	BLTL			273	.267

FUNK, FRANKLIN RAY
b.Aug.30,1935 Washington,D.C.

Yr	Cl	Lea	Pos	G	Rec
1960	Cle	A	P	9	4-2
1961	Cle	A	P	56	11-11
1962	Cle	A	P	47	2-1
	BRTR			112	17-14

FUNKHOUSER, LEONIDAS P.
b.Dec.13,1860 St. Louis,Mo.
d.June 11,1912
(Played under name of Leonidas P. Lee)

FURILLO, CARL ANTHONY (Rocky)
b.Mar.8,1922 Stony Creek Mills,Pa.

Yr	Cl	Lea	Pos	G	Rec
1946	Bro	N	O	117	.284
1947	Bro	N	O	124	.295
1948	Bro	N	O	108	.297
1949	Bro	N	O	142	.324
1950	Bro	N	O	153	.305
1951	Bro	N	O	158	.295
1952	Bro	N	O	134	.247
1953	Bro	N	O	132	.344
1954	Bro	N	O	150	.294
1955	Bro	N	O	140	.314
1956	Bro	N	O	149	.289
1957	Bro	N	O	119	.306
1958	LA	N	O	122	.290
1959	LA	N	O	50	.290
1960	LA	N	O	8	.200
	BRTR			1806	.299

FURNISS, THOMAS
b.Conn.
Non-playing manager Bos (U) 1884.

FUSSELBACH, EDWARD L.
b.July 4,1858 Philadelphia,Pa.

Yr	Cl	Lea	Pos	G	Rec
1882	St.L	a	P-C-O	35	0-2 .219
1884	Bal	U	C	65	.286
1885	Ath	a	C	5	.316
1888	Lou	a	O	1	.250
				106	0-2 .267

FUSSELL, FREDERICK MORRIS
b.Oct.7,1897 Sheridan,Mo.

Yr	Cl	Lea	Pos	G	Rec
1922	Chi	N	P	3	1-1
1923	Chi	N	P	28	3-5
1928	Pit	N	P	28	8-9
1929	Pit	N	P	21	2-2
	BLTL			80	14-17

FUSSELMAN, LESTER LeROY
b.Mar.7,1921 Pryor,Okla.

Yr	Cl	Lea	Pos	G	Rec
1952	St.L	N	C	32	.159
1953	St.L	N	C	11	.250
	BRTR			43	.169

GABLER, FRANK HAROLD (Gabbo)
bNov.6,1911 E.Highlands,Cal.

Yr	Cl	Lea	Pos	G	Rec
1935	NY	N	P	26	2-1
1936	NY	N	P	43	9-8
1937	NY	N	P	6	0-0
1937	Bos	N	P	19	4-7
1938	Bos	N	P	1	0-0
1938	Chi	A	P	18	1-7
	BRTR			113	16-23

GABLER, JOHN RICHARD
b.Oct.2,1930 Kansas City,Mo.

Yr	Cl	Lea	Pos	G	Rec
1959	NY	A	P	3	1-1
1960	NY	A	P	21	3-3
1961	Was	A	P	34	3-8
	BLTR			58	7-12

GABLER, WILLIAM LOUIS
b.Aug.4,1931 St.Louis,Mo.

Yr	Cl	Lea	Pos	G	Rec
1958	Chi	N	H	3	.000
	BLTR				

GABLES, KENNETH HARLIN
b.Jan.21,1919 Walnut Grove,Mo.

Yr	Cl	Lea	Pos	G	Rec
1945	Pit	N	P	29	11-7
1946	Pit	N	P	32	2-4
1947	Pit	N	P	1	0-0
	BRTR			62	13-11

GABRIELSON, LEONARD GARY
b.Feb.14,1940 Oakland,Cal.

Yr	Cl	Lea	Pos	G	Rec
1960	Mil	N	O	4	.000
	BLTR				

GABRIELSON, LEONARD HILBOURNE
b.Sept.8,1916 Oakland,Cal.

Yr	Cl	Lea	Pos	G	Rec
1939	Phi	N	1	5	.222
	BLTL				

GADDY, JOHN WILSON
b.Feb.5,1916 Wadesboro,N.C.

Yr	Cl	Lea	Pos	G	Rec
1938	Bro	N	P	2	2-0
	BRTR				

GAEDEL, EDWARD CARL
b.June 8,1925 Chicago,Ill.
d.June 19,1961

Yr	Cl	Lea	Pos	G	Rec
1951	St.L	A	H	1	.000
	BR				

GAFFKE, FABIAN SEBASTIAN
b.Aug.5,1913 Milwaukee,Wis.

Yr	Cl	Lea	Pos	G	Rec
1936	Bos	A	O	15	.127
1937	Bos	A	O	54	.288
1938	Bos	A	C-O	15	.100
1939	Bos	A	O	1	.000
1941	Cle	A	O	4	.250
1942	Cle	A	O	40	.164
	BRTR			129	.227

GAFFNEY, JOHN H.
b.June 29,1855 Roxbury,Mass.
d.Aug.8,1913
Non-playing manager Wash (N) 1886-87.

GAGNIER, EDWARD J.
b.Apr.16,1883 Paris,France.
d.Sept.13,1946

Yr	Cl	Lea	Pos	G	Rec
1914	Bro	F	S	94	.182
1915	Bro	F	S	19	.260
1915	Buf	F	2	2	.000
	BRTR			115	.191

GAGNON, HAROLD DENNIS (Chick)
b.Sept.27,1897 Millbury,Mass.

Yr	Cl	Lea	Pos	G	Rec
1922	Det	A	S	9	.250
1924	Was	A	S	4	.200
	BRTR			13	.222

GAGUS, CHARLES
b.San Francisco,Cal.

Yr	Cl	Lea	Pos	G	Rec
1884	Was	U	P-S-O	42	11-9 .240

GAINES, ARNESTA
b.Nov.22,1936 Bryan,Tex.

Yr	Cl	Lea	Pos	G	Rec
1960	Cin	N	O	11	.200
1961	Cin	N	O	5	.000
1962	Cin	N	O	64	.231
	BRTR			80	.214

GAINES, WILLARD ROLAND (Nemo)
b.Dec.23,1897 Fairfax Co.,Va.

Yr	Cl	Lea	Pos	G	Rec
1921	Was	A	P	4	0-0
	BLTL				

GAINOR, DELOS CHARLES (Sheriff)
b.Nov.10,1886 Elkins,W.Va.
d.Jan.29,1947

Yr	Cl	Lea	Pos	G	Rec
1909	Det	A	1	2	.200
1911	Det	A	1	70	.302
1912	Det	A	1	51	.240
1913	Det	A	1	104	.270
1914	Det	A	1	1	.000
1914	Bos	A	1	38	.238
1915	Bos	A	1	82	.295
1916	Bos	A	1	56	.253
1917	Bos	A	1	52	.308
1919	Bos	A	1-O	47	.237
1922	St.L	N	1-O	43	.268
	BRTR			546	.273

GAISER, FRED JACOB
b.Apr.8,1885 Stuttgart,Germany
d.Nov.14,1918

Yr	Cl	Lea	Pos	G	Rec
1908	St.L	N	P	1	0-0

GALAN, AUGUST JOHN
b.May 25,1912 Berkeley,Cal.

Yr	Cl	Lea	Pos	G	Rec
1934	Chi	N	2	66	.260
1935	Chi	N	O	154	.314
1936	Chi	N	O	145	.264
1937	Chi	N	O	147	.252
1938	Chi	N	O	110	.286
1939	Chi	N	O	148	.304
1940	Chi	N	2-O	68	.230
1941	Chi	N	O	65	.208
1941	Bro	N	O	17	.259
1942	Bro	N	1-2-O	69	.263
1943	Bro	N	1-O	139	.287
1944	Bro	N	2-O	151	.318
1945	Bro	N	1-3-O	152	.307
1946	Bro	N	1-3-O	99	.310
1947	Cin	N	O	124	.314
1948	Cin	N	O	54	.286
1949	NY	N	1-O	22	.059
1949	Phi	A	O	12	.308
BBTR				1742	.287

GALATZER, MILTON
b.May 4,1909 Chicago,Ill.

Yr	Cl	Lea	Pos	G	Rec
1933	Cle	A	1-O	57	.238
1934	Cle	A	O	49	.270
1935	Cle	A	O	93	.301
1936	Cle	A	O	49	.237
1939	Cin	N	1	3	.000
BLTL				251	.268

GALAZEWSKI, STANLEY JOSEPH
(Played under name of
Stanley Joseph Galle)

GALEHOUSE, DENNIS WARD
b.Dec.7,1911 Marshallville,O.

Yr	Cl	Lea	Pos	G	Rec
1934	Cle	A	P	1	0-0
1935	Cle	A	P	5	1-0
1936	Cle	A	P	36	8-7
1937	Cle	A	P	36	9-14
1938	Cle	A	P	36	7-8
1939	Bos	A	P	30	9-10
1940	Bos	A	P	25	6-6
1941	St.L	A	P	30	9-10
1942	St.L	A	P	32	12-12
1943	St.L	A	P	31	11-11
1944	St.L	A	P	24	9-10
1946	St.L	A	P	30	8-12
1947	St.L	A	P	9	1-3
1947	Bos	A	P	21	11-7
1948	Bos	A	P	27	8-8
1949	Bos	A	P	2	0-0
BRTR				375	109-118

GALLAGHER, D. F.

Yr	Cl	Lea	Pos	G	Rec
1901	Cle	A	O	2	.000

GALLAGHER, DOUGLAS EUGENE
b.Feb.21,1940 Fremont,O.

Yr	Cl	Lea	Pos	G	Rec
1962	Det	A	P	9	0-4
BRTL					

GALLAGHER, EDWARD JOHN
(Jackie)
b.July 23,1903 Providence,R.I.

Yr	Cl	Lea	Pos	G	Rec
1923	Cle	A	O	1	1.000
BLTR					

GALLAGHER, EDWARD MICHAEL
(Lefty)
b.Nov.28,1910 Dorchester,Mass.

Yr	Cl	Lea	Pos	G	Rec
1932	Bos	A	P	9	0-3
BBTL					

GALLAGHER, JAMES E.
b.Findlay,O.
d.Mar.29,1894

Yr	Cl	Lea	Pos	G	Rec
1886	Was	N	S	1	.200

GALLAGHER, JOHN C.
b.1894 Pittsburgh,Pa.

Yr	Cl	Lea	Pos	G	Rec
1915	Bal	F	2	40	.200
BRTR					

GALLAGHER, JOSEPH EMMETT
(Muscles)
b.Mar.7,1914 Buffalo,N.Y.

Yr	Cl	Lea	Pos	G	Rec
1939	NY	A	O	14	.244
1939	St.L	A	O	71	.282
1940	St.L	A	O	23	.271
1940	Bro	N	O	57	.264
BRTR				165	.273

GALLAGHER, LAWRENCE KIRBY (Gil)
b.Sept.5,1896 Washington,D.C.
d.Jan.6,1957

Yr	Cl	Lea	Pos	G	Rec
1922	Bos	N	S	7	.045
BBTR					

GALLAGHER, WILLIAM H.
b.1875 Lowell,Mass.

Yr	Cl	Lea	Pos	G	Rec
1896	Phi	N	S	14	.327

GALLAGHER, WILLIAM JOHN
b.Philadelphia,Pa.

Yr	Cl	Lea	Pos	G	Rec
1883	Bal	a	P-S-O	16	0-3 .159
1883	Phi	N	O	2	.000
1884	Key	U	P	3	1-2
TL				21	1-5 .133

GALLE, STANLEY JOSEPH
(Real name Stanley
Joseph Galazewski)
b.Feb.7,1919 Milwaukee,Wis.

Yr	Cl	Lea	Pos	G	Rec
1942	Was	A	3	13	.111
BRTR					

GALLIA, MELVIN ALLYS
(Bert)
b.Oct.14,1891 Beeville,Tex.

Yr	Cl	Lea	Pos	G	Rec
1912	Was	A	P	2	0-0
1913	Was	A	P	23	1-5
1914	Was	A	P	2	0-0
1915	Was	A	P	43	16-10
1916	Was	A	P	49	17-13
1917	Was	A	P	44	9-13
1918	St.L	A	P	19	7-6
1919	St.L	A	P	34	12-14
1920	St.L	A	P	2	0-1
1920	Phi	N	P	19	2-6
BBTR				237	64-68

GALLIGAN, JOHN T.
b.1868 Easton,Pa.
d.July 17,1906

Yr	Cl	Lea	Pos	G	Rec
1889	Lou	a	O	31	.167

GALLIVAN, PHILIP JOSEPH
b.May 29,1907 Seattle,Wash.

Yr	Cl	Lea	Pos	G	Rec
1931	Bro	N	P	6	0-1
1932	Chi	A	P	13	1-3
1934	Chi	A	P	35	4-7
BRTR				54	5-11

GALLOWAY, CLARENCE EDWARD
(Chick)
b.Aug.4,1896 Clinton,S.C

Yr	Cl	Lea	Pos	G	Rec
1919	Phi	A	S	17	.143
1920	Phi	A	S	98	.202
1921	Phi	A	S-3	131	.265
1922	Phi	A	S	155	.324
1923	Phi	A	S	134	.278
1924	Phi	A	S	129	.276
1925	Phi	A	S	149	.241
1926	Phi	A	S	133	.240
1927	Phi	A	S	77	.265
1928	Det	A	S-3	53	.264
BRTR				1076	.264

GALLOWAY, JAMES CATO
(Bad News)
b.Sept.16,1887 Iredell,Tex.
d.May 3,1950

Yr	Cl	Lea	Pos	G	Rec
1912	St.L	N	2	21	.185
BBTR					

GALVIN, JAMES F. (Pud)
b.Dec.25,1856 St.Louis,Mo.
d.Mar.7.1902

Yr	Cl	Lea	Pos	G	Rec
1875	St.L	N	P-O	11	4-2 .146
1879	Buf	N	P	66	37-27
1880	Buf	N	P-O	64	20-34 .211
1881	Buf	N	P-O	62	29-24 .211
1882	Buf	N	P-O	54	28-22 .213
1883	Buf	N	P-O	79	44-29 .220
1884	Buf	N	P	68	46-21
1885	Buf	N	M-P	32	12-19
1885	Pit	a	P-O	11	3-8 .108
1886	Pit	a	P	50	29-21
1887	Pit	N	P	49	28-20
1888	Pit	N	P	50	23-25
1889	Pit	N	P	40	23-17
1890	Pit	p	P	26	11-14
1891	Pit	N	P	28	15-13
1892	Pit	N	P	11	5-6
1892	St.L	N	P	15	5-6
BBTR				716	362-308 .203

GALVIN, JAMES JOSEPH
b.Aug.11,1907 Somerville,Mass.

Yr	Cl	Lea	Pos	G	Rec
1930	Bos	A	H	2	.000
BRTR					

GALVIN, LOUIS
b.Haverhill,Mass.
d.June 17,1895

Yr	Cl	Lea	Pos	G	Rec
1884	St.P	U	P	3	0-2

GAMBLE, LEE JESSE
b.June 28,1910 Renovo,Pa.

Yr	Cl	Lea	Pos	G	Rec
1935	Cin	N	O	2	.500
1938	Cin	N	O	53	.320
1939	Cin	N	O	72	.267
1940	Cin	N	O	38	.143
BLTR				165	.266

GAMBLE, ROBERT
b.1867 Hazleton,Pa.

Yr	Cl	Lea	Pos	G	Rec
1888	Ath	a	P	1	0-1

GAMMON, JOHN FRANCIS
(Played under name of
John Francis Smith)

GAMMONS, JOHN ASHLEY
(Daff)
b.Mar.17,1876 New Bedford,Mass.

Yr	Cl	Lea	Pos	G	Rec
1901	Bos	N	O	26	.211

GANDIL, CHARLES ARNOLD
(Chick)
b.Jan.19,1889 St.Paul,Minn.

Yr	Cl	Lea	Pos	G	Rec
1910	Chi	A	1	77	.193
1912	Was	A	1	117	.305
1913	Was	A	1	147	.318
1914	Was	A	1	145	.259
1915	Was	A	1	136	.291
1916	Cle	A	1	146	.259
1917	Chi	A	1	149	.273
1918	Chi	A	1	114	.271
1919	Chi	A	1	115	.290
BRTR				1146	.276

GANDY, ROBERT BRINKLEY
b.Aug.25,1893 Jacksonville,Fla.
d.June 19,1945

Yr	Cl	Lea	Pos	G	Rec
1916	Phi	N	O	1	.000
BLTR					

GANLEY, ROBERT STEPHEN
b.Apr.23,1875 Lowell,Mass.
d.Oct.10,1945

Yr	Cl	Lea	Pos	G	Rec
1905	Pit	N	O	32	.315
1906	Pit	N	O	134	.258
1907	Was	A	O	154	.276
1908	Was	A	O	150	.239
1909	Was	A	O	16	.209
1909	Phi	A	O	83	.207
BLTL				569	.254

GANNON, JAMES EDWARD
(Gussie)
b.Nov.26,1873 Erie,Pa.

Yr	Cl	Lea	Pos	G	Rec
1895	Pit	N	P	1	0-0

GANNON, WILLIAM G.
b.New Haven,Conn.

Yr	Cl	Lea	Pos	G	Rec
1898	St.L	N	P	1	0-1
1901	Chi	N	O	15	.159
				16	0-1 .167

GANTENBEIN, JOSEPH STEPHEN
(Sep)
b.Aug.25,1916 San Francisco,Cal.

Yr	Cl	Lea	Pos	G	Rec
1939	Phi	A	2-3	111	.290
1940	Phi	A	1-S-3-O	75	.239
	BLTR			186	.272

GANZEL, CHARLES WILLIAM
b.June 18,1862 Waterford,Wis.
d.Apr.7,1914

Yr	Cl	Lea	Pos	G	Rec
1884	St.P	U	C-O	7	.208
1885	Phi	N	C-O	33	.168
1886	Phi	N	C	1	.000
1886	Det	N	C	53	.276
1887	Det	N	C	55	.285
1888	Det	N	C-2	93	.248
1889	Bos	N	C-O	71	.265
1890	Bos	N	C	38	.269
1891	Bos	N	C	68	.259
1892	Bos	N	C	51	.270
1893	Bos	N	C-O	69	.282
1894	Bos	N	C	65	.278
1895	Bos	N	C	74	.265
1896	Bos	N	C	44	.262
1897	Bos	N	C	27	.274
	BRTR			749	.264

GANZEL, FOSTER PERE
(Babe)
b.May 22,1901 Malden,Mass.

Yr	Cl	Lea	Pos	G	Rec
1927	Was	A	O	13	.437
1928	Was	A	O	10	.077
	BRTR			23	.311

GANZEL, JOHN HENRY
b.Apr.7,1875 Racine,Wis.
d.Jan.14,1959

Yr	Cl	Lea	Pos	G	Rec
1898	Pit	N	1	14	.111
1900	Chi	N	1	78	.272
1901	NY	N	1	139	.220
1903	NY	A	1	129	.285
1904	NY	A	1	129	.261
1907	Cin	N	1	143	.254
1908	Cin	N	M-1	108	.250
	BRTR			740	.253

Non-playing manager Bro (F) 1915.

GARAGIOLA, JOSEPH HENRY
b.Feb.12,1926 St.Louis,Mo.

Yr	Cl	Lea	Pos	G	Rec
1946	St.L	N	C	74	.237
1947	St.L	N	C	77	.257
1948	St.L	N	C	24	.107
1949	St.L	N	C	81	.261
1950	St.L	N	C	34	.318
1951	St.L	N	C	27	.194
1951	Pit	N	C	72	.255
1952	Pit	N	C	118	.273
1953	Pit	N	C	27	.233
1953	Chi	N	C	74	.272
1954	Chi	N	C	63	.281
1954	NY	N	C	5	.273
	BLTR			676	.257

GARBACH, NATHANIEL MICHAEL
(Played under name of
Nathaniel Michael Garbark)

GARBACH, ROBERT MICHAEL
(Played under name of
Robert Michael Garbark)

GARBARK, NATHANIEL MICHAEL
(Mike) (Real name
Nathaniel Michael Garbach)
b.Feb.3,1916 Houston,Tex.

Yr	Cl	Lea	Pos	G	Rec
1944	NY	A	C	89	.261
1945	NY	A	C	60	.216
	BRTR			149	.244

GARBARK, ROBERT MICHAEL
(Real name Robert
Michael Garbach)
b.Nov.13,1909 Houston,Tex.

Yr	Cl	Lea	Pos	G	Rec
1934	Cle	A	C	5	.000
1935	Cle	A	C	6	.333
1937	Chi	N	C	1	.000
1938	Chi	N	C	23	.259
1939	Chi	N	C	24	.143
1944	Phi	A	C	18	.261
1945	Bos	A	C	68	.261
	BRTR			145	.248

GARBER, ROBERT MITCHELL
b.Sept.10,1928 Hunkers,Pa.

Yr	Cl	Lea	Pos	G	Rec
1956	Pit	N	P	2	0-0
	BRTR				

GARBOWSKI, ALEXANDER
b.June 25,1925 Yonkers,N.Y.

Yr	Cl	Lea	Pos	G	Rec
1952	Det	A	H	2	.000
	BRTR				

GARCIA, EDWARD MIGUEL
(Mike)
b.Nov.17,1923 San Gabriel,Cal.

Yr	Cl	Lea	Pos	G	Rec
1948	Cle	A	P	1	0-0
1949	Cle	A	P	41	14-5
1950	Cle	A	P	33	11-11
1951	Cle	A	P	47	20-13
1952	Cle	A	P	46	22-11
1953	Cle	A	P	38	18-9
1954	Cle	A	P	45	19-8
1955	Cle	A	P	38	11-13
1956	Cle	A	P	35	11-12
1957	Cle	A	P	38	12-8
1958	Cle	A	P	6	1-0
1959	Cle	A	P	29	3-6
1960	Chi	A	P	15	0-0
1961	Was	A	P	16	0-1
	BRTR			428	142-97

GARCIA, RAMON GARCIA
b.Mar.5,1924 LaEsperanza,Cuba.

Yr	Cl	Lea	Pos	G	Rec
1948	Was	A	P	4	0-0
	BRTR				

GARCIA, VINICIO UZCANGA
(Chico)
b.Dec.13,1928 Vera Cruz,Mexico

Yr	Cl	Lea	Pos	G	Rec
1954	Bal	A	2	39	.113
	BRTR				

GARDELLA, ALFRED STEVE
b.Jan.11,1918 New York,N.Y.

Yr	Cl	Lea	Pos	G	Rec
1945	NY	N	1-O	17	.077
	BLTL				

GARDELLA, DANIEL LEWIS
b.Feb.26,1920 New York,N.Y.

Yr	Cl	Lea	Pos	G	Rec
1944	NY	N	O	47	.250
1945	NY	N	1-O	121	.272
1950	St.L	N	H	1	.000
	BLTL			169	.268

GARDINER, ARTHUR CECIL
b.Dec.26,1899 Brooklyn,N.Y.

Yr	Cl	Lea	Pos	G	Rec
1923	Phi	N	P	1	0-0
	BRTR				

GARDNER, ALEXANDER
b.Apr.28,1861 Toronto,Ont.,Canada
d.June 18,1926

Yr	Cl	Lea	Pos	G	Rec
1884	Was	a	C	1	.000

GARDNER, EARL M.
b.Jan.24,1885 Sparta,Ill.
d.Mar.2,1943

Yr	Cl	Lea	Pos	G	Rec
1908	NY	A	2	20	.213
1909	NY	A	2	22	.329
1910	NY	A	2	86	.244
1911	NY	A	2	102	.263
1912	NY	A	2	43	.281
	BRTR			273	.263

GARDNER, FRANKLIN W.
(Gid)
b.Aug.1,1859 E.Cambridge,Mass.
d.Aug.1,1914

Yr	Cl	Lea	Pos	G	Rec
1879	Tro	N	P	2	0-2
1880	Cle	N	P-O	10	2-7 .200
1883	Bal	a	P-2-3-O	42	1-0 .290
1884	Bal	A	O	41	.203
1884	Chi	U	P-3-O	20	0-0 .173
1884	Pit	U	2-O	16	.254
1884	Bal	U	S	1	.250
1885	Bal	a	P-2	44	0-1 .219
1887	Ind	N	2-O	18	.306
1888	Was	N	2	2	.200
				196	3-10 .238

GARDNER, FREDERICK
b.Palmer,Mass.

Yr	Cl	Lea	Pos	G	Rec
1887	Bal	a	P	4	0-1

GARDNER, GLENN MILESO
b.Jan.25,1916 Burnsville,N.C.

Yr	Cl	Lea	Pos	G	Rec
1945	St.L	N	P	17	3-1
	BRTR				

GARDNER, HARRY
b.Sept.20,1888 Portland,Ore.
d.Aug.2,1961

Yr	Cl	Lea	Pos	G	Rec
1911	Pit	N	P	13	1-1
1912	Pit	N	P	1	0-0
	TR			14	1-1

GARDNER, JAMES ANDERSON
b.Oct.4,1874 Pittsburgh,Pa.
d.Apr.24,1905

Yr	Cl	Lea	Pos	G	Rec
1895	Pit	N	P	10	8-2
1897	Pit	N	P	28	5-5
1898	Pit	N	P	32	10-13
1899	Pit	N	P	7	1-1
1902	Chi	N	P	3	1-2
	TR			80	25-23

GARDNER, RAYMOND VINCENT
b.Oct.25,1901 Frederick,Md.

Yr	Cl	Lea	Pos	G	Rec
1929	Cle	A	S	82	.262
1930	Cle	A	S	33	.077
	BRTR			115	.253

GARDNER, WILLIAM FREDERICK
b.July 19,1927 New London,Conn.

Yr	Cl	Lea	Pos	G	Rec
1954	NY	N	2-S-3	62	.213
1955	NY	N	2-S-3	59	.203
1956	Bal	A	2-S-3	144	.231
1957	Bal	A	2-S	154	.262
1958	Bal	A	2-S	151	.225
1959	Bal	A	2-S-3	140	.217
1960	Was	A	2-S	145	.257
1961	Min	A	2-3	45	.234
1961	NY	A	2-3	41	.212
1962	NY	A	2-3	4	.000
1962	Bos	A	2-S-3	53	.271
	BRTR			998	.238

GARDNER, WILLIAM LAWRENCE
(Larry)
b.May 13,1886 Enosburg Falls,Vt.

Yr	Cl	Lea	Pos	G	Rec
1908	Bos	A	3	3	.300
1909	Bos	A	3	19	.297
1910	Bos	A	2	113	.283

(Continued)

Yr	Cl	Lea	Pos	G	Rec
1911	Bos	A	2-3	138	.284
1912	Bos	A	3	143	.315
1913	Bos	A	3	131	.282
1914	Bos	A	3	155	.259
1915	Bos	A	3	127	.258
1916	Bos	A	3	148	.308
1917	Bos	A	3	146	.265
1918	Phi	A	3	127	.285
1919	Cle	A	3	139	.300
1920	Cle	A	3	154	.310
1921	Cle	A	3	153	.319
1922	Cle	A	3	137	.285
1923	Cle	A	3	52	.253
1924	Cle	A	3	38	.200
	BLTR			1923	.289

GARFIELD, WILLIAM MILTON
b.Oct.26,1867 Elyria,O.
d.Dec.16,1941

Yr	Cl	Lea	Pos	G	Rec
1889	Pit	N	P	4	0-2
1890	Cle	N	P	8	1-7
	TR			12	1-9

GARIBALDI, ARTHUR E.
b.Aug.21,1909 San Francisco,Cal.

Yr	Cl	Lea	Pos	G	Rec
1936	St.L	N	2-3	71	.276
	BRTR				

GARIBALDI, ROB ROY
b.Mar.3,1942 Stockton,Cal.

Yr	Cl	Lea	Pos	G	Rec
1962	SF	N	P	9	0-0
	BRTR				

GARLAND, LOUIS LYMAN
b.July 16,1905 Archie,Mo.

Yr	Cl	Lea	Pos	G	Rec
1931	Chi	A	P	7	0-2
	BRTR				

GARMS, DEBS C. (Tex)
b.June 26,1908 Bangs,Tex.

Yr	Cl	Lea	Pos	G	Rec
1932	St.L	A	O	34	.284
1933	St.L	A	O	78	.317
1934	St.L	A	O	91	.293
1935	St.L	A	O	10	.267
1937	Bos	N	3-O	125	.259
1938	Bos	N	3-O	117	.315
1939	Bos	N	3-O	132	.298
1940	Pit	N	3-O	103	.355
1941	Pit	N	3-O	83	.264
1943	St.L	N	S-3-O	90	.257
1944	St.L	N	3-O	73	.201
1945	St.L	N	3-O	74	.336
	BLTR			1010	.293

GARONI, WILLIAM
b.July 28,1877 Ft.Lee,N.J.
d.Sept.9,1914

Yr	Cl	Lea	Pos	G	Rec
1899	NY	N	P	3	0-1

GARRETT, CLARENCE RAYMOND
b.Mar.6,1891 Reader,W.Va.

Yr	Cl	Lea	Pos	G	Rec
1915	Cle	A	P	4	2-2
	BRTR				

GARRIOTT, CECIL VIRGIL
b.Aug.15,1916 Harristown,Ill.

Yr	Cl	Lea	Pos	G	Rec
1946	Chi	N	H	6	.000
	BLTR				

GARRISON, CLIFFORD GARRY
b.Aug.13,1906 Meeker,Okla.

Yr	Cl	Lea	Pos	G	Rec
1928	Bos	A	P	6	0-0
	BRTR				

GARRISON, ROBERT FORD
(Rocky)
b.Aug.29,1915 Greenville,S.C.

Yr	Cl	Lea	Pos	G	Rec
1943	Bos	A	O	36	.279
1944	Bos	A	O	13	.245
1944	Phi	A	O	121	.269
1945	Phi	A	O	6	.304
1946	Phi	A	O	9	.108
	BRTR			185	.262

GARRITY, FRANCIS JOSEPH
(Hank)
b.Feb.4,1908 Boston,Mass.
d.Sept.3,1962

Yr	Cl	Lea	Pos	G	Rec
1931	Chi	A	C	8	.214
	BRTR				

GARRY, JAMES THOMAS
b.Sept.21,1869 Great Barrington,Mass.
d.Jan.15,1917

Yr	Cl	Lea	Pos	G	Rec
1893	Bos	N	P	1	0-1

GARVER, NED FRANKLIN
b.Dec.25,1925 Ney,O.

Yr	Cl	Lea	Pos	G	Rec
1948	St.L	A	P	46	7-11
1949	St.L	A	P	55	12-17
1950	St.L	A	P-O	51	13-18 / .286
1951	St.L	A	P	49	20-12
1952	St.L	A	P	24	7-10
1952	Det	A	P	1	1-0
1953	Det	A	P	30	11-11
1954	Det	A	P	36	14-11
1955	Det	A	P	33	12-16
1956	Det	A	P	6	0-2
1957	KC	A	P	24	6-13
1958	KC	A	P	31	12-11
1959	KC	A	P	32	10-13
1960	KC	A	P	28	4-9
1961	LA	A	P	12	0-3
	BRTR			458	129-157

GARVIN, VIRGIL LEE
b.Jan.1,1874 Navasota,Tex.
d.June 16,1908

Yr	Cl	Lea	Pos	G	Rec
1896	Phi	N	P	2	0-1
1899	Chi	N	P	22	9-13
1900	Chi	N	P	28	11-17
1901	Mil	A	P	37	8-21
1902	Chi	A	P	23	9-10
1902	Bro	N	P	2	1-1
1903	Bro	N	P	38	15-18
1904	Bro	N	P	23	6-15
1904	NY	A	P	2	0-1
	TR			177	59-97

GASPAR, HARRY LAMBERT
b.Apr.28,1884 Kingsley,Ia.
d.May 14,1940

Yr	Cl	Lea	Pos	G	Rec
1909	Cin	N	P	44	19-11
1910	Cin	N	P	48	15-17
1911	Cin	N	P	44	10-17
1912	Cin	N	P	7	1-3
	BRTR			143	45-48

GASSAWAY, CHARLES CASON
(Sheriff)
b.Aug.12,1918 Gassaway,Tenn.

Yr	Cl	Lea	Pos	G	Rec
1944	Chi	N	P	2	0-1
1945	Phi	A	P	24	4-7
1946	Cle	A	P	13	1-1
	BLTL			39	5-9

GASTALL, THOMAS EVERETT
b.June 13,1933 Fall River,Mass.
d.Sept.20,1956

Yr	Cl	Lea	Pos	G	Rec
1955	Bal	A	C	20	.148
1956	Bal	A	C	32	.196
	BRTR			52	.181

GASTFIELD, EDWARD
b.Chicago,Ill.
d.Dec.1,1899

Yr	Cl	Lea	Pos	G	Rec
1884	Det	N	C-1-O	22	.063
1885	Det	N	P	1	0-0
1885	Chi	N	C	1	.000
				24	0-0 / .059

GASTON, ALEXANDER NATHANIEL
b.Mar.12,1893 New York,N.Y.

Yr	Cl	Lea	Pos	G	Rec
1920	NY	N	C	4	.100
1921	NY	N	C	20	.227
1922	NY	N	C	16	.192
1923	NY	N	C	22	.205
1926	Bos	A	C	98	.223
1929	Bos	A	C	55	.224
	BRTR			215	.218

GASTON, NATHANIEL MILTON
(Milt)
b.Jan.27,1896 Ridgefield Park,N.J.

Yr	Cl	Lea	Pos	G	Rec
1924	NY	A	P	28	5-3
1925	St.L	A	P	42	15-14
1926	St.L	A	P	32	10-18
1927	St.L	A	P	37	13-17
1928	Was	A	P	28	6-12
1929	Bos	A	P	39	12-19
1930	Bos	A	P	38	13-20
1931	Bos	A	P	23	2-13
1932	Chi	A	P	28	7-17
1933	Chi	A	P	30	8-12
1934	Chi	A	P	29	6-19
	BBTR			354	97-164

GASTON, WELCOME THORNBURG
b.Dec.19,1874 Senecaville,O.
d.Dec.13,1944

Yr	Cl	Lea	Pos	G	Rec
1898	Bro	N	P	2	1-1
1899	Bro	N	P	1	0-1
	TL			3	1-2

GASTREICH, HENRY CARL
(Played under name of
Henry Carl Gastright)

GASTRIGHT, HENRY CARL
(Real name Henry Carl Gastreich)
b.Mar.29,1865 Covington,Ky.
d.Oct.9,1937

Yr	Cl	Lea	Pos	G	Rec
1889	Col	a	P	31	11-13
1890	Col	a	P	50	26-14
1891	Col	a	P	35	12-19
1892	Was	N	P	12	2-6
1893	Pit	N	P	9	3-2
1893	Bos	N	P	20	12- 4
1894	Bro	N	P	16	3-4
1896	Cin	N	P	2	0-1
	BRTR			175	69-63

GATINS, FRANK ANTHONY
b.1871 Johnstown,Pa.
d.Nov.8,1911

Yr	Cl	Lea	Pos	G	Rec
1898	Was	N	S	16	.250
1901	Bro	N	3	49	.229
				65	.234

GAULE, MICHAEL JOHN
b.Aug.4,1869 Baltimore,Md.
d.Jan.24,1918

Yr	Cl	Lea	Pos	G	Rec
1889	Lou	a	O	1	.000
	BLTL				

GAUTREAU, WALTER PAUL
(Doc)
b.July 26,1904 Cambridge,Mass.

Yr	Cl	Lea	Pos	G	Rec
1925	Phi	A	2	4	.000
1925	Bos	N	2	68	.262
1926	Bos	N	2	79	.267
1927	Bos	N	2	87	.246
1928	Bos	N	2	23	.278
	BRTR			261	.257

GAUTREAUX, SIDNEY ALLEN
(Pudge)
b.May 4,1913 New Orleans,La.

Yr	Cl	Lea	Pos	G	Rec
1936	Bro	N	C	75	.268
1937	Bro	N	C	11	.100
	BBTR			86	.247

GAVERN, JOHN

Yr	Cl	Lea	Pos	G	Rec
1872	Atl	n	2	1	.000
1874	Atl	n	2	1	.000
				2	.000

GAW, GEORGE JOSEPH
(Chippy)
b.Mar.13,1892 Newton,Mass.

Yr	Cl	Lea	Pos	G	Rec
1920	Chi	N	P	6	1-1
	TR				

GAZELLA, MICHAEL
b.Oct.13,1896 Olyphant,Pa.

Yr	Cl	Lea	Pos	G	Rec
1923	NY	A	2-S-3	8	.077
1926	NY	A	S-3	66	.232
1927	NY	A	3	54	.278
1928	NY	A	3	32	.232
	BRTR			160	.241

GEAR, DALE DUDLEY
b.Feb.2,1876 Lone Elm,Kan.
d.Sept.23,1951

Yr	Cl	Lea	Pos	G	Rec
1896	Cle	N	P	2	0-2
1897	Cle	N	O	7	.167
1901	Was	A	P-O	58	3-11 .236
				67	3-13 .239

GEARHART, LLOYD WILLIAM
(Gary)
b.Aug.10,1923 New Lebanon,O.

Yr	Cl	Lea	Pos	G	Rec
1947	NY	N	O	73	.246
	BRTL				

GEARIN, DENNIS JOHN
(Dinty)
b.Oct.14,1897 Providence,R.I.
d.Mar.11,1959

Yr	Cl	Lea	Pos	G	Rec
1923	NY	N	P	6	1-1
1924	NY	N	P	10	1-2
1924	Bos	N	P	1	0-1
	BLTL			17	2-4

GEARY, EUGENE FRANCIS JOSEPH (Huck)
b.Jan.22,1917 Buffalo,N.Y.

Yr	Cl	Lea	Pos	G	Rec
1942	Pit	N	S	9	.227
1943	Pit	N	S	46	.151
	BLTR			55	.160

GEARY, ROBERT NORTON
(Speed)
b.May 10,1893 Cincinnati,O.

Yr	Cl	Lea	Pos	G	Rec
1918	Phi	A	P	16	3-5
1919	Phi	A	P	9	0-3
1921	Cin	N	P	10	1-1
	BRTR			35	4-9

GEBRIAN, PETER (Gabe)
b.Aug.10,1923 Bayonne,N.J.

Yr	Cl	Lea	Pos	G	Rec
1947	Chi	A	P	27	2-3
	BRTR				

GEDEON, ELMER JOHN
b.Apr.15,1917 Cleveland,O.
d.Apr.15,1944

Yr	Cl	Lea	Pos	G	Rec
1939	Was	A	O	5	.200
	BRTR				

GEDEON, ELMER JOSEPH
(Joe)
b.Dec.6,1894 San Francisco,Cal.
d.May 19,1941

Yr	Cl	Lea	Pos	G	Rec
1913	Was	A	P-O	26	0-0 .188
1914	Was	A	O	4	.000
1916	NY	A	2	122	.211
1917	NY	A	2	33	.239
1918	St.L	A	2	123	.213
1919	St.L	A	2	120	.254
1920	St.L	A	2	153	.292
	BRTR			581	0-0 .244

GEDNEY, ALFRED W.
(Count)
b.May 10,1849 Brooklyn,N.Y.
d.Mar.26,1922

Yr	Cl	Lea	Pos	G	Rec
1872	Tro	n	O	9	NR
1872	Eck	n	O	16	NR
1873	Mut	n	O	54	NR
1874	Ath	n	1-O	54	NR
1875	Mut	n	P-O	68	1-0 NR
				201	1-0 NR

GEE, JOHN ALEXANDER
(Whiz)
b.Dec.7,1915 Syracuse,N.Y.

Yr	Cl	Lea	Pos	G	Rec
1939	Pit	N	P	3	1-2
1941	Pit	N	P	3	0-2
1943	Pit	N	P	15	4-4
1944	Pit	N	P	4	0-0
1944	NY	N	P	4	0-0
1945	NY	N	P	2	0-0
1946	NY	N	P	13	2-4
	BLTL			44	7-12

GEER, WILLIAM HENRY HARRISON
b.Aug.13,1849 Syracuse,N.Y.
d.Jan.5,1922

Yr	Cl	Lea	Pos	G	Rec
1874	Mut	n	O	2	NR
1875	NH	n	2-S-3-O	37	NR
1878	Cin	N	2-S	62	.215
1880	Wor	N	S-O	2	.000
1884	Key	U	S	8	.226
1884	Bro	a	S	107	.226
1885	Lou	a	S	14	.113
	TR			232	NR

GEHRIG, HENRY LOUIS
(Lou)
b.June 19,1903 New York,N.Y.
d.June 2,1941

Yr	Cl	Lea	Pos	G	Rec
1923	NY	A	1	13	.423
1924	NY	A	1	10	.500
1925	NY	A	1-O	126	.295
1926	NY	A	1	155	.313
1927	NY	A	1	155	.373
1928	NY	A	1	154	.374
1929	NY	A	1	154	.300
1930	NY	A	1	154	.379
1931	NY	A	1	155	.341
1932	NY	A	1	155	.349
1933	NY	A	1	152	.334
1934	NY	A	1-S	154	.363
1935	NY	A	1	149	.329
1936	NY	A	1	155	.354
1937	NY	A	1	157	.351
1938	NY	A	1	157	.295
1939	NY	A	1	8	.143
	BLTL			2163	.340

GEHRING, HENRY
b.Jan.24,1881 St.Paul,Minn.
d.Apr.18,1912

Yr	Cl	Lea	Pos	G	Rec
1907	Was	A	P	20	3-7
1908	Was	A	P	5	0-1
				25	3-8

GEHRINGER, CHARLES LEONARD
b.May 11,1903 Fowlerville,Mich.

Yr	Cl	Lea	Pos	G	Rec
1924	Det	A	2	5	.545
1925	Det	A	2	8	.167
1926	Det	A	2	123	.277
1927	Det	A	2	133	.317
1928	Det	A	2	154	.320
1929	Det	A	2	155	.339
1930	Det	A	2	154	.330
1931	Det	A	2	101	.311
1932	Det	A	2	151	.298
1933	Det	A	2	155	.325
1934	Det	A	2	154	.356
1935	Det	A	2	150	.330
1936	Det	A	2	154	.354
1937	Det	A	2	144	.371
1938	Det	A	2	152	.306
1939	Det	A	2	118	.325
1940	Det	A	2	139	.313
1941	Det	A	2	127	.220
1942	Det	A	2	45	.267
	BLTR			2322	.320

GEHRMAN PAUL ARTHUR
(Dutch)
b.May 3,1914 Mt.Angel,Ore.

Yr	Cl	Lea	Pos	G	Rec
1937	Cin	N	P	2	0-1
	BRTR				

GEIER, PHILIP LOUIS
(Little Phil)
b.Nov.5,1875 Washington,D.C.

Yr	Cl	Lea	Pos	G	Rec
1896	Phi	N	O	17	.232
1897	Phi	N	2-O	88	.285
1900	Cin	N	O	29	.273
1901	Phi	A	O	50	.236
1901	Mil	A	O	10	.184
1904	Bos	N	O	148	.243
	BLTR			342	.252

GEIGER, GARY MERLE
b.Apr.4,1937 Sand Ridge,Ill.

Yr	Cl	Lea	Pos	G	Rec
1958	Cle	A	P-3-O	91	0-0 .231
1959	Bos	A	O	120	.245
1960	Bos	A	O	77	.302
1961	Bos	A	O	140	.232
1962	Bos	A	O	131	.249
	BLTR			559	.249

GEISS, EMIL M.
b.Chicago,Ill.

Yr	Cl	Lea	Pos	G	Rec
1882	Bal	a	P-O	13	4-9 .159
1887	Chi	N	P	3	0-1
	BR			16	4-10 .140

GEISS, WILLIAM
b.1860 Chicago,Ill.

Yr	Cl	Lea	Pos	G	Rec
1884	Det	N	P-1-2-O	75	0-0 .177
1891	St.L	a	2	76	.323
				151	0-0 .253

GELBERT, CHARLES MAGNUS
b.Jan.26,1906 Scranton,Pa.

Yr	Cl	Lea	Pos	G	Rec
1929	St.L	N	S	146	.262
1930	St.L	N	S	139	.304
1931	St.L	N	S	131	.289
1932	St.L	N	S	122	.268
1935	St.L	N	2-S-3	62	.292
1936	St.L	N	S-3	93	.229
1937	Cin	N	2-S-3	43	.193
1937	Det	A	S	20	.085
1939	Was	A	S-3	68	.255
1940	Was	A	P-2-5-3	22	0-0 .370
1940	Bos	A	3	30	.198
	BRTR			876	0-0 .267

GENEWICH, JOSEPH EDWARD
b.Jan.15,1898 Mishawaka,Ind.

Yr	Cl	Lea	Pos	G	Rec
1922	Bos	N	P	6	0-2
1923	Bos	N	P	43	13-14
1924	Bos	N	P	34	10-19
1925	Bos	N	P	34	12-10
1926	Bos	N	P	37	8-16
1927	Bos	N	P	40	11-8
1928	Bos	N	P	13	3-7
1928	NY	N	P	26	11-4
1929	NY	N	P	25	3-7
1930	NY	N	P	21	2-5
	BRTR			279	73-92

GENINS, C. FRANK
(Frenchy)
b.Nov.2,1866 St.Louis,Mo.
d.Sept.30,1922

Yr	Cl	Lea	Pos	G	Rec
1892	Cin	N	S	31	.195
1892	St.L	N	S	14	.167
1895	Pit	N	3-O	64	.253
1901	Cle	A	O	26	.232
	TR			135	.228

GENOVESE, GEORGE MICHAEL
b.Feb.22,1923 Staten Island,N.Y.

Yr	Cl	Lea	Pos	G	Rec
1950	Was	A	H	3	.000
	BLTR				

GENTILE, JAMES EDWARD
b.June 3,1934 San Francisco,Cal.

Yr	Cl	Lea	Pos	G	Rec
1957	Bro	N	1	4	.167
1958	LA	N	1	12	.133
1960	Bal	A	1	138	.292
1961	Bal	A	1	148	.302
1962	Bal	A	1	152	.251
	BLTL			454	.276

GENTILE, SAMUEL CHRISTOPHER
b.Oct.12,1916 Charlestown,Mass.

Yr	Cl	Lea	Pos	G	Rec
1943	Bos	N	H	8	.250

BLTR

GENTRY, HARVEY WILLIAM
b.May 27,1926 Winston-Salem,N.C.

Yr	Cl	Lea	Pos	G	Rec
1954	NY	N	H	5	.250

BLTR

GENTRY, JAMES RUFFUS (Rufe)
b.May 18,1918 Winston-Salem,N.C.

Yr	Cl	Lea	Pos	G	Rec
1943	Det	A	P	4	1-3
1944	Det	A	P	37	12-14
1946	Det	A	P	2	0-0
1947	Det	A	P	1	0-0
1948	Der	A	P	4	0-0
	BRTR			48	13-17

GEORGE, ALEXANDER THOMAS
b.Sept.27,1938 Kansas City,Mo.

Yr	Cl	Lea	Pos	G	Rec
1955	KC	A	S	5	.100

BLTR

GEORGE, CHARLES PETER (Greek)
b.Dec.25,1912 Waycross,Ga.

Yr	Cl	Lea	Pos	G	Rec
1935	Cle	A	C	2	.000
1936	Cle	A	C	23	.195
1938	Bro	N	C	7	.200
1941	Chi	N	C	35	.156
1945	Phi	A	C	51	.174
	BRTR			118	.177

GEORGE, THOMAS EDWARD (Lefty)
b.Aug.13,1886 Pittsburgh,Pa.
d.May 13,1955

Yr	Cl	Lea	Pos	G	Rec
1911	St.L	A	P	27	3-10
1912	Cle	A	P	9	0-5
1915	Cin	N	P	7	2-2
1918	Bos	N	P	10	1-5
	BLTL			53	6-22

GEORGE, WILLIAM M.
b.Jan.27,1865 Bellaire,O.
d.Aug.23,1916

Yr	Cl	Lea	Pos	G	Rec
1887	NY	N	P	13	3-9
1888	NY	N	P-O	9	2-1 .230
1889	NY	N	O	3	.267
1889	Col	a	P-O	5	0-0 .308
	BRTL			30	5-10 .220

GEORGY, OSCAR JOHN
b.Nov.25,1918 New Orleans,La.

Yr	Cl	Lea	Pos	G	Rec
1938	NY	N	P	1	0-0

BRTR

GERAGHTY, BENJAMIN RAYMOND
b.July 19,1914 Jersey City,N.J.

Yr	Cl	Lea	Pos	G	Rec
1936	Bro	N	S	51	.194
1943	Bos	N	2-S-3	8	.000
1944	Bos	N	2-3	11	.250
	BRTR			70	.199

GERARD, DAVID FREDERICK
b.Aug.6,1936 New York,N.Y.

Yr	Cl	Lea	Pos	G	Rec
1962	Chi	N	P	39	2-3

BRTR

GERBER, WALTER (Spooks)
b.Aug.18,1891 Columbus,O.
d.June 19,1951

Yr	Cl	Lea	Pos	G	Rec
1914	Pit	N	S	17	.241
1915	Pit	N	S-3	56	.194
1917	St.L	A	S	14	.308
1918	St.L	A	S	56	.240
1919	St.L	A	S	140	.227
1920	St.L	A	S	154	.279
1921	St.L	A	S	114	.278
1922	St.L	A	S	153	.267
1923	St.L	A	S	154	.281
1924	St.L	A	S	148	.272
1925	St.L	A	S	72	.272
1926	St.L	A	S	131	.270
1927	St.L	A	S	142	.224
1928	St.L	A	S	6	.222
1928	Bos	A	S	104	.217
1929	Bos	A	2-S	61	.165
	BRTR			1522	.257

GERBERMAN, GEORGE ALOIS
b.Mar.8,1942 El Campo,Tex.

Yr	Cl	Lea	Pos	G	Rec
1962	Chi	N	P	1	0-0

BRTR

GERHARDT, JOSEPH JOHN (Moveup)
b.Feb.14,1855 Washington,D.C.
d.Mar.11,1922

Yr	Cl	Lea	Pos	G	Rec
1872	Nat	n	2	1	NR
1873	Nat	n	S	13	NR
1874	Bal	n	S	14	NR
1875	Mut	n	2-S-3-O	59	NR
1876	Lou	N	1-2	65	.258
1877	Lou	N	1-2-S-O	59	.304
1878	Cin	N	2	61	.303
1879	Cin	N	1-2-3	78	.199
1881	Det	N	2-3	80	.242
1883	Lou	a	M-2	77	.270
1884	Lou	a	M-2	108	.220
1885	NY	N	2	112	.155
1886	NY	N	2	123	.190
1887	NY	N	3	1	.000
1887	Met	a	2	85	.277
1890	Bro	a	2	97	.211
1890	St.L	a	2-3	37	.260
1891	Lou	a	2	2	.000
	BRTR			1072	NR

GERHEAUSER, ALBERT
b.June 24,1917 St.Louis,Mo.

Yr	Cl	Lea	Pos	G	Rec
1943	Phi	N	P	38	10-19
1944	Phi	N	P	32	8-16
1945	Pit	N	P	32	5-10
1946	Pit	N	P-O	36	2-2 .333
1948	St.L	A	P	14	0-3
	BLTL			152	25-50 .209

GERKEN, GEORGE HERBERT
b.July 28,1903 Chicago,Ill.

Yr	Cl	Lea	Pos	G	Rec
1927	Cle	A	O	6	.214
1928	Cle	A	O	38	.226
	BRTR			44	.225

GERKIN, STEPHEN PAUL (Splinter)
b.Nov.19,1915 Grafton,W.Va.

Yr	Cl	Lea	Pos	G	Rec
1945	Phi	A	P	21	0-12

BRTR

GERLACH, JOHN GLENN
b.May 11,1917 Shullsburg,Wis.

Yr	Cl	Lea	Pos	G	Rec
1938	Chi	A	S	9	.280
1939	Chi	A	3	3	1.000
	BRTR			12	.333

GERMAN, LESTER S.
b.June 2,1869 Baltimore,Md.

Yr	Cl	Lea	Pos	G	Rec
1890	Bal	a	P	16	4-10
1893	NY	N	P	20	10-8
1894	NY	N	P	19	7-8
1895	NY	N	P	31	7-13
1896	NY	N	P	3	1-1
1896	Was	N	P	23	2-18
1897	Was	N	P-2	19	4-3 .311
				131	35-61 .252

GERNER, EDWIN FREDERICK
b.July 22,1897 Philadelphia,Pa.

Yr	Cl	Lea	Pos	G	Rec
1919	Cin	N	P	5	1-0

BLTL

GERNERT, RICHARD EDWARD
b.Sept.12,1929 Reading,Pa.

Yr	Cl	Lea	Pos	G	Rec
1952	Bos	A	1	102	.243
1953	Bos	A	1	139	.253
1954	Bos	A	1	14	.261
1955	Bos	A	1	7	.200
1956	Bos	A	1-O	106	.291
1957	Bos	A	1-O	99	.237
1958	Bos	A	1	122	.237
1959	Bos	A	1-O	117	.262
1960	Chi	N	1-O	52	.250
1960	Det	A	1-O	21	.300
1961	Det	A	1	6	.200
1961	Cin	N	1	40	.302
1962	Hou	N	1	10	.208
	BRTR			835	.254

GERTENRICH, LOUIS WILHELM
b.May 4,1875 Chicago,Ill.
d.Oct.23,1933

Yr	Cl	Lea	Pos	G	Rec
1901	Mil	A	O	2	.333
1903	Pit	N	O	1	.000
				3	.143

GERVAIS, LUCIEN EDWARD (Lefty)
b.July 6,1890 Grover,Wis.

Yr	Cl	Lea	Pos	G	Rec
1913	Bos	N	P	6	0-1

BLTL

GESSLER, HARRY HOMER (Doc)
b.Dec.23,1880 Indiana,Pa.
d.Dec.26,1924

Yr	Cl	Lea	Pos	G	Rec
1903	Det	A	O	29	.238
1903	Bro	N	O	43	.247
1904	Bro	N	O	89	.290
1905	Bro	N	1	119	.290
1906	Bro	N	1	9	.242
1906	Chi	N	O	22	.253
1908	Bos	A	O	128	.308
1909	Bos	A	O	111	.299
1909	Was	A	O	17	.182
1910	Was	A	O	145	.259
1911	Was	A	O	128	.282
	BLTR			840	.280

Non-playing manager Pit (F) 1914.

GESSNER, CHARLES J.
b.Philadelphia,Pa.

Yr	Cl	Lea	Pos	G	Rec
1886	Ath	a	P	1	0-1

GETTEL, ALLEN JONES
b.Sept.17,1917 Norfolk,Va.

Yr	Cl	Lea	Pos	G	Rec
1945	NY	A	P	27	9-8
1946	NY	A	P	26	6-7
1947	Cle	A	P	34	11-10
1948	Cle	A	P	5	0-1
1948	Chi	A	P-2	24	8-10 .241
1949	Chi	A	P	19	2-5
1949	Was	A	P	16	0-2
1951	NY	N	P	30	1-2
1955	St.L	N	P	8	1-0
	BRTR			189	38-45 .228

GETTIG, CHARLES H.
(Sandow) (Real name Charles H. Gettinger)
b.1875 Cumberland, Md.

Yr	Cl	Lea	Pos	G	Rec
1896	NY	N	P	6	1-0
1897	NY	N	P-S	20	1-1 .203
1898	NY	N	P-O	55	5-4 .248
1899	NY	N	P	31	7-8
				112	14-13 .239

GETTINGER, CHARLES H.
(Played under name of Charles H. Gettig)

GETTINGER, THOMAS L.
b.1870 Mobile, Ala.

Yr	Cl	Lea	Pos	G	Rec
1889	St.L	a	O	3	.455
1890	St.L	a	O	59	.260
1895	Lou	N	P-O	60	0-1 .281
BLTL				122	0-1 .277

GETTMAN, JACOB JOHN
(Quick)
b.Oct.25, 1875 Frank, Russia
d.Oct.4, 1956

Yr	Cl	Lea	Pos	G	Rec
1897	Was	N	O	37	.315
1898	Was	N	O	140	.279
1899	Was	N	O	16	.226
BBTL				193	.280

GETZ, GUSTAVE
b.Aug.3, 1889 Pittsburgh, Pa.

Yr	Cl	Lea	Pos	G	Rec
1909	Bos	N	3	40	.223
1910	Bos	N	3	47	.194
1914	Bro	N	3	55	.248
1915	Bro	N	3	130	.258
1916	Bro	N	3	40	.219
1917	Cin	N	2-3	7	.286
1918	Cle	A	3	6	.066
1918	Pit	N	3	7	.200
BRTR				332	.219

GETZEIN, CHARLES H.
(Pretzels)
b.Feb.14, 1864 Chicago, Ill.
d.June 19, 1932

Yr	Cl	Lea	Pos	G	Rec
1884	Det	N	P	17	5-12
1885	Det	N	P-O	39	12-26 .211
1886	Det	N	P	43	31-11
1887	Det	N	P	43	29-13
1888	Det	N	P	45	18-26
1889	Ind	N	P	41	19-22
1890	Bos	N	P	42	23-17
1891	Bos	N	P-O	13	4-6 .189
1891	Cle	N	P	1	0-1
1892	St.L	N	P	14	5-9
BRTR				298	146-143 .207

GEYER, JACOB BOWMAN
(Rube)
b.Mar.22, 1885 Pittsburgh, Pa.

Yr	Cl	Lea	Pos	G	Rec
1910	St.L	N	P	4	0-1
1911	St.L	N	P	29	9-6
1912	St.L	N	P	41	7-14
1913	St.L	N	P	30	1-5
TR				104	17-26

GEYGAN, JAMES EDWARD
(Chappie)
b.June 3, 1903 Columbus, O.

Yr	Cl	Lea	Pos	G	Rec
1924	Bos	A	S	33	.256
1925	Bos	A	S	3	.182
1926	Bos	A	3	4	.300
BRTR				40	.252

GHARRITY, EDWARD PATRICK
(Patsy)
b.Mar.13, 1892 Parnell, Ia.

Yr	Cl	Lea	Pos	G	Rec
1916	Was	A	C-1	39	.228
1917	Was	A	1	76	.284
1918	Was	A	C	4	.250
1919	Was	A	C-O	111	.271
1920	Was	A	C-1	131	.245
1921	Was	A	C	121	.310
1922	Was	A	C	96	.256
1923	Was	A	C-1	93	.207
1929	Was	A	H	3	.000
1930	Was	A	1	2	.000
BRTR				676	.249

GIALLOMBARDO, ROBERT PAUL
b.May 20, 1938 Brooklyn, N.Y.

Yr	Cl	Lea	Pos	G	Rec
1958	LA	N	P	8	1-1
BLTL					

GIANNINI, JOSEPH FRANCIS
b.Sept.8, 1888 San Francisco, Cal.
d.Sept.26, 1942

Yr	Cl	Lea	Pos	G	Rec
1911	Bos	A	S	1	.500
BLTR					

GIARD, JOSEPH OSCAR
(Peco)
b.Oct.7, 1898 Ware, Mass.
d.July 10, 1956

Yr	Cl	Lea	Pos	G	Rec
1925	St.L	A	P	30	10-5
1926	St.L	A	P	22	3-10
1927	NY	A	P	16	0-0
BLTL				68	13-15

GIBBON, JOSEPH CHARLES
b.Apr.10, 1935 Hickory, Miss.

Yr	Cl	Lea	Pos	G	Rec
1960	Pit	N	P	27	4-2
1961	Pit	N	P	31	13-10
1962	Pit	N	P	19	3-4
BRTL				77	20-16

GIBBS, JERRY DEAN
b.Nov.7, 1938 Grenada, Miss.

Yr	Cl	Lea	Pos	G	Rec
1962	NY	A	3	2	.000
BLTR					

GIBSON, CHARLES E.
b.1877 Philadelphia, Pa.

Yr	Cl	Lea	Pos	G	Rec
1905	St.L	A	C	1	.000
TR					

GIBSON, CHARLES GRIFFIN
b.Nov.21, 1899 LaGrange, Ga.

Yr	Cl	Lea	Pos	G	Rec
1924	Phi	A	C	12	.133
BRTR					

GIBSON, CHARLES ROBERT
b.Aug.20, 1869 Duncansville, Pa.

Yr	Cl	Lea	Pos	G	Rec
1890	Chi	N	P	1	1-0
1890	Pit	N	P-O	3	0-2 .231
				4	1-2 .176

GIBSON, FRANK GILBERT
b.Sept.27, 1890 Omaha, Neb.
d.Apr.27, 1961

Yr	Cl	Lea	Pos	G	Rec
1913	Det	A	C	20	.140
1921	Bos	N	C	63	.264
1922	Bos	N	C-1	66	.299
1923	Bos	N	C	41	.300
1924	Bos	N	C-1-3	90	.310
1925	Bos	N	C-1	104	.278
1926	Bos	N	C	24	.340
1927	Bos	N	C	60	.222
BBTR				468	.274

GIBSON, GEORGE (Moon)
b.July 22, 1880 London, Ont., Canada.

Yr	Cl	Lea	Pos	G	Rec
1905	Pit	N	C	44	.178
1906	Pit	N	C	81	.178
1907	Pit	N	C	110	.220
1908	Pit	N	C	140	.228
1909	Pit	N	C	150	.265

(Continued)

Yr	Cl	Lea	Pos	G	Rec
1910	Pit	N	C	143	.259
1911	Pit	N	C	98	.209
1912	Pit	N	C	95	.240
1913	Pit	N	C	48	.280
1914	Pit	N	C	102	.285
1915	Pit	N	C	120	.251
1916	Pit	N	C	33	.202
1917	NY	N	C	35	.171
1918	NY	N	C	4	.500
BRTR				1203	.236

Non-playing manager Pit (N) 1920-22, Chi (N) 1925 and Pit (N) 1932-34.

GIBSON, LEIGHTON B.
b.1866 Lancaster, Pa.

Yr	Cl	Lea	Pos	G	Rec
1888	Ath	a	C	1	.000
TR					

GIBSON, NORWOOD R.
b.Mar.11, 1877 Peoria, Ill.
d.July 7, 1959

Yr	Cl	Lea	Pos	G	Rec
1903	Bos	A	P	25	11-9
1904	Bos	A	P	33	17-14
1905	Bos	A	P	24	5-10
1906	Bos	A	P	5	0-2
TR				87	33-35

GIBSON, ROBERT
b.Nov.9, 1935 Omaha, Neb.

Yr	Cl	Lea	Pos	G	Rec
1959	St.L	N	P	21	3-5
1960	St.L	N	P	40	3-6
1961	St.L	N	P	40	13-12
1962	St.L	N	P	42	15-13
BRTR				143	34-36

GIBSON, SAMUEL BRAXTON
b.Aug.5, 1900 High Point, N.C.

Yr	Cl	Lea	Pos	G	Rec
1926	Det	A	P	36	12-9
1927	Det	A	P	33	11-12
1928	Det	A	P	20	5-8
1930	NY	A	P	2	0-1
1932	NY	N	P	41	4-8
BLTR				132	32-38

GICK, GEORGE EDWARD
b.Oct.18, 1915 Dunnington, Ind.

Yr	Cl	Lea	Pos	G	Rec
1937	Chi	A	P	1	0-0
1938	Chi	A	P	1	0-0
BBTR				2	0-0

GIEBEL, JOSEPH HENRY
b.Nov.30, 1891 Washington, D.C.

Yr	Cl	Lea	Pos	G	Rec
1913	Phi	A	C	1	.333
BRTR					

GIEBELL, FLOYD KARL
b.Dec.10, 1914 Pennsboro, W.Va.

Yr	Cl	Lea	Pos	G	Rec
1939	Det	A	P	9	1-1
1940	Det	A	P	2	2-0
1941	Det	A	P	17	0-0
BLTR				28	3-1

GIEL, PAUL ROBERT
b.Feb.29, 1932 Winona, Minn.

Yr	Cl	Lea	Pos	G	Rec
1954	NY	N	P	6	0-0
1955	NY	N	P	34	4-4
1958	SF	N	P	29	4-5
1959	Pit	N	P	4	0-0
1960	Pit	N	P	16	2-0
1961	Min	A	P	15	1-0
1961	KC	A	P	1	0-0
BRTR				105	11-9

GIFFORD, JAMES H.
b.Oct.18, 1845 Warren, N.Y.
d.Dec.19, 1901
Non-playing manager Ind (a) 1884 and Met (a) 1885-86.

GIGGIE, ROBERT THOMAS
b.Aug.13, 1933 Dorchester, Mass.

Yr	Cl	Lea	Pos	G	Rec
1959	Mil	N	P	13	1-0

(Continued)

Yr	Cl	Lea	Pos	G	Rec
1960	Mil	N	P	3	0-0
1960	KC	A	P	10	1-0
1962	KC	A	P	4	1-1
	BRTR			30	3-1

GILBERT, ANDREW
b.July 18,1916 Latrobe,Pa.

Yr	Cl	Lea	Pos	G	Rec
1942	Bos	A	O	6	.091
1946	Bos	A	O	2	.000
	BRTR			8	.083

GILBERT, BENNETT HAROLD ROCHEFORT (Played under name of Bennett Harold Rochefort)

GILBERT, CHARLES MADER
b.July 8,1919 New Orleans,La.

Yr	Cl	Lea	Pos	G	Rec
1940	Bro	N	O	57	.246
1941	Chi	N	O	39	.279
1942	Chi	N	O	74	.184
1943	Chi	N	O	8	.150
1946	Chi	N	O	15	.077
1946	Phi	N	O	88	.242
1947	Phi	N	O	83	.237
	BLTL			364	.229

GILBERT, DREW EDWARD
b.July 26,1935 Knoxville,Tenn.

Yr	Cl	Lea	Pos	G	Rec
1959	Cin	N	O	7	.150
	BLTR				

GILBERT, HAROLD JOSEPH (Tookie)
b.Apr.4,1929 New Orleans,La.

Yr	Cl	Lea	Pos	G	Rec
1950	NY	N	1	113	.220
1953	NY	N	1	70	.169
	BLTR			183	.203

GILBERT, HARRY

Yr	Cl	Lea	Pos	G	Rec
1890	Pit	N	2	2	.250

GILBERT, JOHN G.
b.Jan.8,1864 Pottstown,Pa.
d.Nov.12,1903

Yr	Cl	Lea	Pos	G	Rec
1890	Pit	N	S	2	.000

GILBERT, JOHN ROBERT (Jackrabbit)
b.Sept.14,1875 Rhinebeck,N.Y.
d.July 7,1941

Yr	Cl	Lea	Pos	G	Rec
1898	Was	N	O	2	.167
1898	NY	N	O	1	.250
1904	Pit	N	O	25	.241
				28	.237

GILBERT, LAWRENCE WILLIAM
b.Dec.2,1891 New Orleans,La.

Yr	Cl	Lea	Pos	G	Rec
1914	Bos	N	O	72	.268
1915	Bos	N	O	45	.151
	BLTL			117	.230

GILBERT, PETER
b.Sept,6,1867 Baltic,Conn.
d.Jan.1,1912

Yr	Cl	Lea	Pos	G	Rec
1890	Bal	a	3	29	.262
1891	Bal	a	3	137	.229
1892	Bal	N	3	4	.200
1894	Bro	N	3	6	.000
1894	Lou	N	3	28	.287
	TR			204	.234

GILBERT, WALTER JOHN
b.Dec.19,1901 Oscoda,Mich.
d.Sept.8,1958

Yr	Cl	Lea	Pos	G	Rec
1928	Bro	N	3	39	.203
1929	Bro	N	3	143	.304
1930	Bro	N	3	150	.294
1931	Bro	N	3	145	.266
1932	Cin	N	3	114	.214
	BRTR			591	.269

GILBERT, WILLIAM
b.Havre de Grace,Md.

Yr	Cl	Lea	Pos	G	Rec
1892	Bal	N	P	2	0-1

GILBERT, WILLIAM OLIVER
b.June 21,1876 Trenton,N.J.
d.Aug.8,1927

Yr	Cl	Lea	Pos	G	Rec
1901	Mil	A	2	127	.269
1902	Bal	A	S	130	.243
1903	NY	N	2	128	.252
1904	NY	N	2	146	.253
1905	NY	N	2	115	.247
1906	NY	N	2	98	.231
1908	St.L	N	2	89	.214
1909	St.L	N	2	12	.172
	BRTR			845	.246

GILE, DONALD LOREN
b.Apr.19,1935 Modesto,Cal.

Yr	Cl	Lea	Pos	G	Rec
1959	Bos	A	C	3	.200
1960	Bos	A	C-1	29	.176
1961	Bos	A	C-1	8	.278
1962	Bos	A	1	18	.049
	BRTR			58	.150

GILHAM, GEORGE LEWIS
b.Sept.8,1899 Shamokin,Pa.
d.Apr.25,1937

Yr	Cl	Lea	Pos	G	Rec
1920	St.L	N	C	1	.000
1921	St.L	N	C	1	.000
	BRTR			2	.000

GILHOOLEY, FRANK PATRICK (Flash)
b.June 10,1892 Toledo,O.
d.July 11,1959

Yr	Cl	Lea	Pos	G	Rec
1911	St.L	N	O	1	.000
1912	St.L	N	O	13	.224
1913	NY	A	O	24	.341
1914	NY	A	O	1	.667
1915	NY	A	O	1	.000
1916	NY	A	O	58	.278
1917	NY	A	O	54	.242
1918	NY	A	O	112	.276
1919	Bos	A	O	48	.241
	BLTR			312	.271

GILKS, ROBERT JAMES
b.July 2,1867 Cincinnati,O.
d.Aug.20,1944

Yr	Cl	Lea	Pos	G	Rec
1887	Cle	a	P-O	22	6-5 .333
1888	Cle	a	3-O	118	.232
1889	Cle	N	O	52	.238
1890	Cle	N	P-O	130	2-2 .213
1893	Bal	N	O	15	.274
	BRTR			337	8-7 .234

GILL, EDWARD JAMES
b.Aug.7,1895 Somerville,Mass.

Yr	Cl	Lea	Pos	G	Rec
1919	Was	A	P	16	1-1
	BRTR				

GILL, GEORGE LLOYD
b.Feb.13,1909 Catchings,Miss.

Yr	Cl	Lea	Pos	G	Rec
1937	Det	A	P	31	11-4
1938	Det	A	P	24	12-9
1939	Det	A	P	3	0-1
1939	St.L	A	P	27	1-12
	BRTR			85	24-26

GILL, HAROLD EDMUND (Haddie)
b.Jan.23,1899 Brockton,Mass.
d.Aug.1,1932

Yr	Cl	Lea	Pos	G	Rec
1923	Cin	N	P	1	0-0
	BLTL				

GILL, JAMES C.
b.St.Louis,Mo.

Yr	Cl	Lea	Pos	G	Rec
1889	St.L	a	2-O	2	.250

GILL, JOHN WESLEY (Patcheye)
b.Mar.27,1906 Nashville,Tenn.

Yr	Cl	Lea	Pos	G	Rec
1927	Cle	A	O	21	.216
1928	Cle	A	H	2	.000
1931	Was	A	O	8	.267
1934	Was	A	O	13	.245
1935	Chi	N	H	3	.333
1936	Chi	N	O	71	.253
	BLTR			118	.245

GILL, WARREN DARST
b.Dec.21,1878 Ladoga,Ind.
d.Nov.26,1952

Yr	Cl	Lea	Pos	G	Rec
1908	Pit	N	1	25	.224
	TR				

GILLELAND, SAMUEL (Played under name of Samuel Gillen)

GILLEN, SAMUEL (Real name Samuel Gilleland)
b.1870 Allegheny,Pa.
d.May 13,1905

Yr	Cl	Lea	Pos	G	Rec
1893	Pit	N	S	3	.000
1897	Phi	N	S	74	.258
				77	.253

GILLEN, THOMAS J.
b.May 18,1862 Philadelphia,Pa.
d.Jan.26,1889

Yr	Cl	Lea	Pos	G	Rec
1884	Key	U	C-O	28	.149
1884	Phi	N	C	1	.333
1886	Det	N	C	2	.400
				31	.154

GILLENWATER, CARDEN EDISON
b.May 13,1918 Riceville,Tenn.

Yr	Cl	Lea	Pos	G	Rec
1940	St.L	N	O	7	.160
1943	Bro	N	O	8	.176
1945	Bos	N	O	144	.288
1946	Bos	N	O	99	.228
1948	Was	A	O	77	.244
	BRTR			335	.260

GILLENWATER, CLARAL LEWIS
b.May 20,1900 Sims,Ind.

Yr	Cl	Lea	Pos	G	Rec
1923	Chi	A	P	5	1-3
	BRTR				

GILLESPIE, JAMES
b.Buffalo,N.Y.

Yr	Cl	Lea	Pos	G	Rec
1890	Buf	p	O	1	.000

GILLESPIE, JOHN PATRICK
b.Feb.25,1900 Oakland,Cal.
d.Feb.15,1954

Yr	Cl	Lea	Pos	G	Rec
1922	Cin	N	P	31	3-3
	BRTR				

GILLESPIE, PATRICK PETER (Pete)
b.Nov.30,1851 Carbondale,Pa.
d.May 5,1910

Yr	Cl	Lea	Pos	G	Rec
1880	Tro	N	O	82	.242
1881	Tro	N	O	83	.277
1882	Tro	N	O	72	.265
1883	NY	N	O	95	.314
1884	NY	N	O	97	.264
1885	NY	N	O	102	.292
1886	NY	N	O	98	.272
1887	NY	N	O	74	.293
	BL			703	.279

GILLESPIE, PAUL ALLEN
b.Sept.18,1920 Cartersville,Ga.

Yr	Cl	Lea	Pos	G	Rec
1942	Chi	N	C	5	.250
1944	Chi	N	C	9	.269
1945	Chi	N	C-O	75	.288
	BLTR			89	.283

GILLESPIE, ROBERT WILLIAM
(Bunch)
b.Oct.8,1918 Columbus,O.

Yr	Cl	Lea	Pos	G	Rec
1944	Det	A	P	7	0-1
1947	Chi	A	P	25	5-8
1948	Chi	A	P	25	0-4
1950	Bos	A	P	1	0-0
	BRTR			58	5-13

GILLIAM, JAMES WILLIAM (Junior)
b.Oct.17,1928 Nashville,Tenn.

Yr	Cl	Lea	Pos	G	Rec
1953	Bro	N	2	151	.278
1954	Bro	N	2-O	146	.282
1955	Bro	N	2-O	147	.249
1956	Bro	N	2-O	153	.300
1957	Bro	N	2-O	149	.250
1958	LA	N	2-3-O	147	.261
1959	LA	N	2-3-O	145	.282
1960	LA	N	2-3	151	.248
1961	LA	N	2-3-O	144	.244
1962	LA	N	2-3-O	160	.270
	BBTR			1493	.267

GILLIGAN, ANDREW BERNARD
(Barney)
b.Jan.3,1857 Cambridge,Mass.
d.Apr.1,1934

Yr	Cl	Lea	Pos	G	Rec
1875	Atl	n	C-O	2	NR
1879	Cle	N	C-O	52	.170
1880	Cle	N	C-S-O	28	.179
1881	Pro	N	C-2-S-O	45	.218
1882	Pro	N	C-S	55	.223
1883	Pro	N	C	72	.198
1884	Pro	N	C-1-3	80	.244
1885	Pro	N	C-S-O	69	.214
1886	Was	N	C	82	.190
1887	Was	N	C	27	.242
1888	Det	N	C	1	.200
	BRTR			513	NR

GILLIGAN, JOHN PATRICK
b.Oct.18,1885 Chicago

Yr	Cl	Lea	Pos	G	Rec
1909	St.L	A	P	3	1-2
1910	St.L	A	P	9	0-3
	BBTR			12	1-5

GILLIS, GRANT
b.Jan.24,1901 Grove Hill,Ala.

Yr	Cl	Lea	Pos	G	Rec
1927	Was	A	S	10	.222
1928	Was	A	S	24	.253
1929	Bos	A	2	28	.247
	BRTR			62	.245

GILMAN, PITKIN CLARK
b.Mar.14,1864 Laporte,O.
d.Aug.17,1950

Yr	Cl	Lea	Pos	G	Rec
1884	Cle	N	O	2	.100
1893	Cle	N	3	2	.285
	BLTL			4	.176

GILMORE, ERNEST GROVER
b.Oct.31,1889 Chicago,Ill.
d.Nov.25,1919

Yr	Cl	Lea	Pos	G	Rec
1914	KC	F	O	138	.282
1915	KC	F	O	119	.282
	BLTL			257	.282

GILMORE, FRANK T.
b.Apr.27,1864 Webster,Mass.
d.July 22,1929

Yr	Cl	Lea	Pos	G	Rec
1886	Was	N	P	9	4-4
1887	Was	N	P	27	7-20
1888	Was	N	P	13	1-10
	BR			49	12-34

GILMORE, JAMES
b.Baltimore,Md.

Yr	Cl	Lea	Pos	G	Rec
1875	Nat	n	C-2-3	5	NR

GILMORE, LEONARD PRESTON
(Meow)
b.Nov.3,1918 Clinton,Ind.

Yr	Cl	Lea	Pos	G	Rec
1944	Pit	N	P	1	0-1
	BRTR				

GILPATRICK, GEORGE F.
b.Feb.28,1875 Holden,Mo.
d.Dec.15,1941

Yr	Cl	Lea	Pos	G	Rec
1898	St.L	N	P	7	0-1

GILROY, ...

Yr	Cl	Lea	Pos	G	Rec
1874	Chi	n	C	8	NR
1875	Ath	n	O	1	.000
				9	NR

GILROY, JOHN N.
b.Oct.26,1875 Washington,D.C.
d.Aug.4,1897

Yr	Cl	Lea	Pos	G	Rec
1895	Was	N	P	11	1-4
1896	Was	N	P	1	0-0
				12	1-4

GING, WILLIAM JOSEPH
b.Nov.7,1872 Elmira,N.Y.
d.Sept.14,1950

Yr	Cl	Lea	Pos	G	Rec
1899	Bos	N	P	1	1-0

GINGRAS, JOSEPH JOHN E.
b.Jan.10,1893 New York,N.Y.
d.Sept.6,1947

Yr	Cl	Lea	Pos	G	Rec
1915	KC	F	P	2	0-0
	BRTR				

GINN, TINSLEY RUCKER
b.Sept.26,1891 Royston,Ga.
d.Aug.30,1931

Yr	Cl	Lea	Pos	G	Rec
1914	Cle	A	O	2	.000

GINSBERG, MYRON NATHAN
(Joe)
b.Oct.11,1926 New York,N.Y.

Yr	Cl	Lea	Pos	G	Rec
1948	Det	A	C	11	.361
1950	Det	A	C	36	.232
1951	Det	A	C	102	.260
1952	Det	A	C	113	.221
1953	Det	A	C	18	.302
1953	Cle	A	C	46	.284
1954	Cle	A	C	3	.500
1956	KC	A	C	71	.246
1956	Bal	A	C	15	.071
1957	Bal	A	C	85	.274
1958	Bal	A	C	61	.211
1959	Bal	A	C	65	.181
1960	Bal	A	C	14	.267
1960	Chi	A	C	28	.253
1961	Chi	A	C	6	.000
1961	Bos	A	C	10	.250
1962	NY	N	C	2	.000
	BLTR			695	.241

GIONFRIDDO, ALBERT FRANCIS
b.Mar.8,1922 Dysart,Pa.

Yr	Cl	Lea	Pos	G	Rec
1944	Pit	N	O	4	.167
1945	Pit	N	O	122	.284
1946	Pit	N	O	64	.255
1947	Pit	N	H	1	.000
1947	Bro	N	O	37	.177
	BLTL			228	.266

GIORDANO, THOMAS ARTHUR
b.Oct.9,1925 Newark,N.J.

Yr	Cl	Lea	Pos	G	Rec
1953	Phi	A	2	11	.175
	BRTR				

GIRARD, CHARLES A.
b.1886 Brooklyn,N.Y.

Yr	Cl	Lea	Pos	G	Rec
1910	Phi	N	P	7	1-2

GIULIANI, ANGELO JOHN
(Tony)
b.Nov.24,1912 St.Paul,Minn.

Yr	Cl	Lea	Pos	G	Rec
1936	St.L	A	C	71	.217
1937	St.L	A	C	19	.302
1938	Was	A	C	46	.217
1939	Was	A	C	54	.250
1940	Bro	N	C	1	.000
1941	Bro	N	C	3	.000
1943	Was	A	C	49	.226
	BRTR			243	.233

GIUSTI, DAVID JOHN
b.Nov.27,1939 Seneca Falls,N.Y.

Yr	Cl	Lea	Pos	G	Rec
1962	Hou	N	P	26	2-3
	BRTR				

GLADD, JAMES WALTER
b.Oct.2,1922 Ft.Gibson,Okla.

Yr	Cl	Lea	Pos	G	Rec
1946	NY	N	C	4	.091
	BRTR				

GLADDING, FRED EARL
b.June 28,1936 Flat Rock,Mich.

Yr	Cl	Lea	Pos	G	Rec
1961	Det	A	P	8	1-0
1962	Det	A	P	6	0-0
	BLTR			14	1-0

GLADE, FREDERICK MONROE
(Lucky)
b.Jan.25,1876 Dubuque,Ia.
d.Nov.21,1934

Yr	Cl	Lea	Pos	G	Rec
1902	Chi	N	P	1	0-1
1904	St.L	A	P	36	19-15
1905	St.L	A	P	32	6-24
1906	St.L	A	P	35	15-15
1907	St.L	A	P	32	13-9
1908	NY	A	P	5	0-4
	BRTR			141	53-68

GLADMAN, JOHN H. (Buck)
b.1864 Wahington,D.C.

Yr	Cl	Lea	Pos	G	Rec
1883	Phi	N	3	1	.000
1884	Was	a	3	56	.158
1886	Was	N	3	44	.138
				101	.149

GLADU, ROLAND EDWIN
b.May 10,1913 Montreal,Que.,Canada.

Yr	Cl	Lea	Pos	G	Rec
1944	Bos	N	3-O	21	.242
	BLTR				

GLAISER, JOHN BURKE
b.July 28,1897 Yoakum,Tex.
d.Mar.7,1959

Yr	Cl	Lea	Pos	G	Rec
1920	Det	A	P	9	0-0
	BLTR				

GLASS, THOMAS JOSEPH
b.Apr.29,1902 Greensboro,N.C.

Yr	Cl	Lea	Pos	G	Rec
1925	Phi	A	P	2	1-0
	BRTR				

GLASSCOCK, JOHN WESLEY
(Pebbly Jack)
b.July 22,1859 Wheeling,W.Va.
d.Feb.24,1947

Yr	Cl	Lea	Pos	G	Rec
1879	Cle	N	2-3	80	.209
1880	Cle	N	S	76	.247
1881	Cle	N	2-S	84	.260
1882	Cle	N	S	82	.285
1883	Cle	N	2-S	93	.290
1884	Cle	N	P-2-S	72	{ 0-0 .249
1884	Cin	U	2-S	39	.388
1885	St.L	N	2-S	111	.280
1886	St.L	N	S	121	.325
1887	Ind	N	S	121	.349
1888	Ind	N	S	112	.269
1889	Ind	N	M-S	134	.359
1890	NY	N	S	124	.336
1891	NY	N	S	95	.243
1892	St.L	N	S	139	.273
1893	St.L	N	S	48	.301
1893	Pit	N	S	66	.380
1894	Pit	N	S	86	.282
1895	Lou	N	S	18	.373
1895	Was	N	S	25	.233
	BRTR			1726	{ 0-0 .297

GLAVENICH, LUKE FRANK
b.Jan.17,1894 New Chicago,Cal.
d.May 22,1935

Yr	Cl	Lea	Pos	G	Rec
1913	Cle	A	P	1	0-0

GLAVIANO, THOMAS GIATANO
(Rabbit)
b.Oct.26,1923 Sacramento,Cal.

Yr	Cl	Lea	Pos	G	Rec
1949	St.L	N	2-3	87	.267
1950	St.L	N	2-S-3	115	.285
1951	St.L	N	2-O	54	.183
1952	St.L	N	2-3	80	.241
1953	Phi	N	2-S-3	53	.203
	BRTR			389	.257

GLAZE, DANIEL RALPH
b.Mar.13,1882 Denver,Col.

Yr	Cl	Lea	Pos	G	Rec
1906	Bos	A	P	22	4-6
1907	Bos	A	P	32	9-13
1908	Bos	A	P	10	2-2
	BRTR			64	15-21

GLAZNER, CHARLES FRANKLIN
(Whitey)
b.Sept.17,1893 Sycamore,Ala.

Yr	Cl	Lea	Pos	G	Rec
1920	Pit	N	P	2	0-0
1921	Pit	N	P	36	14-5
1922	Pit	N	P	33	11-12
1923	Pit	N	P	7	2-1
1923	Phi	N	P	28	7-14
1924	Phi	N	P	35	7-16
	BRTR			141	41-48

GLEASON, HARRY GEORGE
b.Aug.17,1882 Philadelphia,Pa.

Yr	Cl	Lea	Pos	G	Rec
1901	Bos	A	3	1	1.000
1902	Bos	A	2-3-O	66	.224
1904	St.L	A	S-3	45	.214
1905	St.L	A	3	150	.217
	TR			262	.217

GLEASON, JOHN DAY
b.July 14,1854 St.Louis,Mo.
d.Sept.4,1944

Yr	Cl	Lea	Pos	G	Rec
1877	St.L	N	O	1	.250
1882	St.L	a	3-O	78	.262
1883	St.L	a	3-O	9	.205
1883	Lou	a	S-3	84	.276
1884	St.L	U	3	77	.312
1885	St.L	N	3	2	.143
1886	Ath	a	3	76	.195
	BRTR			327	.262

GLEASON, JOSEPH PAUL
b.July 9,1895 New York,N.Y.

Yr	Cl	Lea	Pos	G	Rec
1920	Wa	A	P	2	0-0
1922	Was	A	P	8	2-2
	BRTR			10	2-2

GLEASON, WILLIAM
b.1868 Cleveland,O.
d.Dec.2,1893

Yr	Cl	Lea	Pos	G	Rec
1890	Cle	p	P	1	0-1

GLEASON, WILLIAM G.
b.Nov.12,1858 St.Louis,Mo.
d.July 21,1932

Yr	Cl	Lea	Pos	G	Rec
1882	St.L	a	S	79	.286
1883	St.L	a	S	95	.274
1884	St.L	a	S	110	.269
1885	St.L	a	S	112	.253
1886	St.L	a	S	126	.267
1887	St.L	a	S	135	.336
1888	Ath	a	S	123	.224
1889	Lou	a	S	15	.216
	BRTR			795	.275

GLEASON, WILLIAM J. (Kid)
b.Oct.26,1866 Camden,N.J.
d.Jan.2,1933

Yr	Cl	Lea	Pos	G	Rec
1888	Phi	N	P	24	7-17
1889	Phi	N	P	28	9-14
1890	Phi	N	P	58	39-17
1891	Phi	N	P	60	24-19
1892	St.L	N	P	63	16-24
1893	St.L	N	P	55	21-25
1894	St.L	N	P	10	2-6
1894	Bal	N	P	23	15-6
1895	Bal	N	P-2	107	{ 3-1 / .323

(Continued)

Yr	Cl	Lea	Pos	G	Rec
1896	NY	N	2	133	.292
1897	NY	N	2	134	.311
1898	NY	N	2	149	.222
1899	NY	N	2	148	.267
1900	NY	N	2	111	.257
1901	Det	A	2	136	.278
1902	Det	A	2	118	.247
1903	Phi	N	2	106	.284
1904	Phi	N	2	153	.274
1905	Phi	N	2	155	.247
1906	Phi	N	2	135	.227
1907	Phi	N	2	35	.143
1908	Phi	N	2-O	2	.000
	BLTR			1943	{ 136-136 / .262

Non-playing manager Chi (A) 1919-23.

GLEASON, WILLIAM PATRICK
b.Sept.8,1893 Chicago,Ill.
d.Jan.9,1957

Yr	Cl	Lea	Pos	G	Rec
1916	Pit	N	2	1	.000
1917	Pit	N	2	14	.167
1921	St.L	A	2	26	.257
	BRTR			41	.220

GLEESON, JAMES JOSEPH
(Gee Gee)
b.Mar.5,1912 Kansas City,Mo.

Yr	Cl	Lea	Pos	G	Rec
1936	Cle	A	O	41	.259
1939	Chi	N	O	111	.223
1940	Chi	N	O	129	.313
1941	Cin	N	O	102	.233
1942	Cin	N	O	9	.200
	BBTR			392	.263

GLEICH, FRANK ELMER
(Inch)
b.Mar.7,1901 Columbus,O.
d.Mar.27,1949

Yr	Cl	Lea	Pos	G	Rec
1919	NY	A	O	4	.333
1920	NY	A	O	24	.122
	BLTR			28	.156

GLENALVIN, ROBERT J.
(Real name Rodney J. Dowling)
b.Jan.17,1868 Indianapolis,Ind.
d.Mar.24,1944

Yr	Cl	Lea	Pos	G	Rec
1890	Chi	N	2	66	.268
1893	Chi	N	2	16	.400
	TR			82	.294

GLENDON, MARTIN H.
(Buns)
b.1876 Chicago,Ill.

Yr	Cl	Lea	Pos	G	Rec
1902	Cin	N	P	1	0-1
1903	Cle	A	P	3	1-2
				4	1-3

GLENN, BURDETTE (Bob)
b.June 16,1894 W.Sunbury,Pa.

Yr	Cl	Lea	Pos	G	Rec
1920	St.L	N	P	2	0-0

GLENN, EDWARD C. (Mouse)
b.Sept.19,1860 Richmond,Va.
d.Feb.10,1892

Yr	Cl	Lea	Pos	G	Rec
1884	Ric	a	O	42	.250
1886	Pit	a	O	71	.182
1888	KC	a	O	3	.000
1888	Bos	N	O	19	.154
	BRTR			135	.196

GLENN, EDWARD D.
b.1876 Ludlow,Ky.
d.Dec.7,1911

Yr	Cl	Lea	Pos	G	Rec
1898	NY	N	S	2	.167
1902	Chi	N	S	2	.000
				4	.158

GLENN, HARRY M.
b.June 9,1890 Shelburn,Ind.
d.Oct.12,1918

Yr	Cl	Lea	Pos	G	Rec
1915	St.L	N	C	6	.312
	BLTR				

GLENN, JOHN
b.July 10,1928 Moultrie,Ga.

Yr	Cl	Lea	Pos	G	Rec
1960	St.L	N	O	32	.258
	BRTR				

GLENN, JOHN W.
b.1849 Rochester,N.Y.
d.Nov.10,1888

Yr	Cl	Lea	Pos	G	Rec
1871	Oly	n	O	25	NR
1872	Oly	n	O	9	NR
1872	Nat	n	O	1	NR
1873	Nat	n	1	39	NR
1874	Chi	n	1-3-O	54	NR
1875	Chi	n	1-O	70	NR
1876	Chi	N	1-O	66	.292
1877	Chi	N	1-O	50	.228
	BRTR			314	NR

GLENN, JOSEPH CHARLES
(Gabby) (Real name Joseph Charles Gurzensky)
b.Nov.19,1908 Dickson City,Pa.

Yr	Cl	Lea	Pos	G	Rec
1932	NY	A	C	6	.125
1933	NY	A	C	5	.143
1935	NY	A	C	17	.233
1936	NY	A	C	44	.271
1937	NY	A	C	25	.283
1938	NY	A	C	41	.260
1939	St.L	A	C	88	.273
1940	Bos	A	C	22	.128
	BRTR			248	.252

GLIATTO, SALVADOR MICHAEL
b.May 7,1905 Chicago,Ill.

Yr	Cl	Lea	Pos	G	Rec
1930	Cle	A	P	10	0-0
	BBTR				

GLOCKSON, NORMAN STANLEY
b.June 15,1894 Blue Island,Ill.

Yr	Cl	Lea	Pos	G	Rec
1914	Cin	N	C	7	.000
	BRTR				

GLOSSOP, ALBAN
b.July 23,1915 Christopher,Ill.

Yr	Cl	Lea	Pos	G	Rec
1939	NY	N	2	10	.188
1940	NY	N	2	27	.209
1940	Bos	N	2-S-3	60	.236
1942	Phi	N	2-3	121	.225
1943	Bro	N	2-S-3	87	.171
1946	Chi	N	2-S	4	.000
	BBTR			309	.209

GLYNN, WILLIAM VINCENT
b.Jan.30,1926 Sussex,N.J.

Yr	Cl	Lea	Pos	G	Rec
1949	Phi	N	1	8	.200
1952	Cle	A	1	44	.272
1953	Cle	A	1-O	147	.243
1954	Cle	A	1-O	111	.251
	BLTL			310	.249

GOAR, JOSHUA MERCER
(Jot)
b.Jan.31,1870 New Lisbon,Ind.
d.Apr.4,1947

Yr	Cl	Lea	Pos	G	Rec
1896	Pit	N	P	3	0-0
1898	Cin	N	P	1	0-0
	BRTR			4	0-0

GOCHNAUR, JOHN PETER
b.Sept.12,1875 Altoona,Pa.
d.Sept.27,1929

Yr	Cl	Lea	Pos	G	Rec
1901	Bro	N	S	3	.363
1902	Cle	A	S	126	.183
1903	Cle	A	S	136	.181
	BRTR			265	.184

GODAR, JOHN MICHAEL
b.Oct.25,1864 Cincinnati,O.
d.June 23,1949

Yr	Cl	Lea	Pos	G	Rec
1892	Bal	N	O	5	.333

GODWIN, JOHN HENRY
b.Mar.10,1877 E.Liverpool,O.
d.May 5,1956

Yr	Cl	Lea	Pos	G	Rec
1905	Bos	A	2	16	.304
1906	Bos	A	3	66	.187
	TR			82	.209

GOEBEL, EDWIN
b.Sept.1,1899 Brooklyn,N.Y.

Yr	Cl	Lea	Pos	G	Rec
1922	Was	A	O	37	.271
	BRTR				

GOECKEL, WILLIAM JOHN
b.Sept.3,1871 Wilkes-Barre,Pa.
d.Nov.1,1922

Yr	Cl	Lea	Pos	G	Rec
1899	Phi	N	1	35	.283

GOETZ, GEORGE BURT
b.Greencastle,Ind.

Yr	Cl	Lea	Pos	G	Rec
1889	Bal	a	P	1	1-0

GOETZ, JOHN HARDY
b.Oct.24,1937 Goetzville,Mich.

Yr	Cl	Lea	Pos	G	Rec
1960	Chi	N	P	4	0-0
	BRTR				

GOLDEN, JAMES EDWARD
b.Mar.20,1936 Eldon,Miss.

Yr	Cl	Lea	Pos	G	Rec
1960	LA	N	P	1	1-0
1961	LA	N	P	28	1-1
1962	Hou	N	P	43	7-11
	BLTR			72	9-12

GOLDEN, MICHAEL HENRY
b.Sept.11,1851 Chelsea,Mass.
d.Jan.11,1929

Yr	Cl	Lea	Pos	G	Rec
1875	Wes	n	P	13	1-12
1875	Chi	n	P-O	38	6-8 NR
1878	Mil	N	P-O	54	3-15 .209
	BRTR			105	10-35 NR

GOLDEN, ROY K.
b.July 12,1888 Chicago,Ill.
d.Oct.4,1961

Yr	Cl	Lea	Pos	G	Rec
1910	St.L	N	P	7	2-3
1911	St.L	N	P	30	4-9
	TR			37	6-12

GOLDMAN, JONAH JOHN
b.Aug.29,1906 New York,N.Y.

Yr	Cl	Lea	Pos	G	Rec
1928	Cle	A	S	7	.238
1930	Cle	A	S-3	111	.242
1931	Cle	A	S	30	.129
	BRTR			148	.224

GOLDSBERRY, GORDON FREDERICK
b.Aug.30,1927 Sacramento,Cal.

Yr	Cl	Lea	Pos	G	Rec
1949	Chi	A	1	39	.248
1950	Chi	A	1-O	82	.268
1951	Chi	A	1	10	.091
1952	St.L	A	1-O	86	.229
	BLTL			217	.241

GOLDSBY, WALTON HUGH
b.Jan.1,1862 Evansville,Ind.
d.Jan.11,1914

Yr	Cl	Lea	Pos	G	Rec
1884	St.L	a	O	5	.211
1884	Was	a	O	6	.375
1884	Ric	a	O	10	.222
1886	Was	N	O	6	.111
1888	Bal	a	O	44	.227
				71	.233

GOLDSMITH, FRED E.
b.May 15,1852 New Haven,Conn.
d.Mar.28,1939

Yr	Cl	Lea	Pos	G	Rec
1879	Tro	N	P-1-O	9	2-4 .231
1880	Chi	N	P-1-O	35	22-3 .260
1881	Chi	N	P-O	40	25-13 .240
1882	Chi	N	P-1	44	28-16 .229
1883	Chi	N	P-1-O	60	28-18 .221
1884	Chi	N	P-O	22	8-12 .135
1884	Bal	a	P-1	4	3-1 .167
	BRTR			214	116-67 .225

GOLDSMITH, HAROLD EUGENE
b.Aug.18,1898 Peconic,N.Y.

Yr	Cl	Lea	Pos	G	Rec
1926	Bos	N	P	19	5-7
1927	Bos	N	P	22	1-3
1928	Bos	N	P	4	0-0
1929	St.L	N	P	2	0-0
	BRTR			47	6-10

GOLDSMITH, WALLACE
b.1849 Baltimore,Md.

Yr	Cl	Lea	Pos	G	Rec
1871	Kek	n	C-S-3	19	NR
1872	Oly	n	2-S	9	NR
1873	Mar	n	2	1	.000
1875	Wes	n	3	13	NR
1875	NH	n	2	1	NR
				43	NR

GOLDSTEIN, ISADORE
b.June 6,1908 New York,N.Y.

Yr	Cl	Lea	Pos	G	Rec
1932	Det	A	P	16	3-2
	BBTR				

GOLDSTEIN, LESLIE ELMER (Lonnie)
b.May 13,1919 Austin,Tex.

Yr	Cl	Lea	Pos	G	Rec
1943	Cin	N	1	5	.200
1946	Cin	N	H	6	.000
	BLTL			11	.100

GOLDY, PURNAL WILLIAM
b.Nov.28,1937 Camden,N.J.

Yr	Cl	Lea	Pos	G	Rec
1962	Det	A	O	20	.299
	BRTR				

GOLETZ, STANLEY (Stosh)
b.May 21,1918 Crescent,O.

Yr	Cl	Lea	Pos	G	Rec
1941	Chi	A	H	5	.600
	BLTL				

GOLIAT, MIKE MITCHEL
b.Nov.3,1919 Yatesboro,Pa.

Yr	Cl	Lea	Pos	G	Rec
1949	Phi	N	1-2	55	.212
1950	Phi	N	2	145	.234
1951	Phi	N	2-3	41	.225
1951	St.L	A	2	5	.182
1952	St.L	A	2	3	.000
	BRTR			249	.225

GOLVIN, WALTER GEORGE
b.Feb.1,1894 North Platte,Neb.

Yr	Cl	Lea	Pos	G	Rec
1922	Chi	N	1	2	.000
	BLTL				

GOMEZ, JOSE LUIS RODRIGUEZ (Chile)
b.Sept.23,1910 Villaunion,Mexico.

Yr	Cl	Lea	Pos	G	Rec
1935	Phi	N	2-S	67	.230
1936	Phi	N	2-S	108	.232
1942	Was	A	2	25	.192
	BRTR			200	.226

GOMEZ, PEDRO W. MARTINEZ
b.Apr.20,1923 Central Preston,Cuba.

Yr	Cl	Lea	Pos	G	Rec
1944	Was	A	2-S	8	.286
	BRTR				

GOMEZ, RUBEN COLON
b.July 13,1927 Arroyo,Porto Rico

Yr	Cl	Lea	Pos	G	Rec
1953	NY	N	P	61	13-11
1954	NY	N	P	49	17-9
1955	NY	N	P	42	9-10
1956	NY	N	P-O	52	7-17 .183
1957	NY	N	P-O	54	15-13 .184
1958	SF	N	P	48	10-12
1959	Phi	N	P	24	3-8
1960	Phi	N	P	22	0-3
1962	Cle	A	P	16	1-2
1962	Min	A	P	6	1-1
	BRTR			374	76-86 .199

GOMEZ, VERNON LOUIS (Lefty)
b.Nov.26,1909 Rodeo,Cal.

Yr	Cl	Lea	Pos	G	Rec
1930	NY	A	P	15	2-5
1931	NY	A	P	40	21-9
1932	NY	A	P	37	24-7
1933	NY	A	P	35	16-10
1934	NY	A	P	38	26-5
1935	NY	A	P	34	12-15
1936	NY	A	P	31	13-7
1937	NY	A	P	34	21-11
1938	NY	A	P	32	18-12
1939	NY	A	P	26	12-8
1940	NY	A	P	9	3-3
1941	NY	A	P	23	15-5
1942	NY	A	P	13	6-4
1943	Was	A	P	1	0-1
	BLTL			368	189-102

GONDER, JESSE LEMAR
b.Jan.20,1936 Monticello,Ark.

Yr	Cl	Lea	Pos	G	Rec
1960	NY	A	C	7	.286
1961	NY	A	H	15	.333
1962	Cin	N	H	4	.000
	BLTR			26	.261

GONZALEZ, ANDRES ANTONIO
b.Aug.28,1936 Camaguey,Cuba.

Yr	Cl	Lea	Pos	G	Rec
1960	Cin	N	O	39	.212
1960	Phi	N	O	78	.299
1961	Phi	N	O	126	.277
1962	Phi	N	O	118	.302
	BLTR			361	.285

GONZALES, EUSEBIO MIGUEL
b.July 13,1892 Havana,Cuba.

Yr	Cl	Lea	Pos	G	Rec
1918	Bos	A	S-3	3	.400
	BRTR				

GONZALES, JOSEPH MADRID
b.Mar.19,1915 San Francisco,Cal.

Yr	Cl	Lea	Pos	G	Rec
1937	Bos	A	P	3	1-2
	BRTR				

GONZALES, JULIO ENRIQUE
b.Dec.20,1920 Havana,Cuba.

Yr	Cl	Lea	Pos	G	Rec
1949	Was	A	P	13	0-0
	BRTR				

GONZALES, WENCESLAO O'REILLY
b.Sept.28,1925 Quivican,Cuba

Yr	Cl	Lea	Pos	G	Rec
1955	Was	A	P	1	0-0
	BLTL				

GONZALEZ, MIGUEL ANGEL CORDERO (Mike)
b.Sept.24,1892 Havana,Cuba.

Yr	Cl	Lea	Pos	G	Rec
1912	Bos	N	C	1	.000
1914	Cin	N	C	95	.233
1915	St.L	N	C-1	51	.227
1916	St.L	N	C-1	118	.239
1917	St.L	N	C-1	106	.262
1918	St.L	N	C-1-O	117	.252
1919	NY	N	C-1	58	.190
1920	NY	N	C	11	.231
1921	NY	N	C-1	13	.375
1924	St.L	N	C	120	.296
1925	St.L	N	C-1	22	.310
1925	Chi	N	C	70	.264
1926	Chi	N	C	80	.249
1927	Chi	N	C	39	.241
1928	Chi	N	C	49	.272
1929	Chi	N	C	60	.240
1931	St.L	N	C	15	.105
1932	St.L	N	C	17	.143
	BRTR			1042	.254

Non-playing manager St.L (N) 1938 and 1940.

GONZZLE, CLAUDE
b.Niles,O.

Yr	Cl	Lea	Pos	G	Rec
1903	St.L	A	2	1	.000
	TR				

GOOCH, CHARLES FURMAN
b.June 5,1904 Smyrna,Tenn.

Yr	Cl	Lea	Pos	G	Rec
1929	Was	A	1-S-3	39	.281
	BRTR				

GOOCH, JOHN BEVERLY
b.Nov.9,1898 Smyrna,Tenn.

Yr	Cl	Lea	Pos	G	Rec
1921	Pit	N	C	13	.237
1922	Pit	N	C	105	.328
1923	Pit	N	C	66	.277
1924	Pit	N	C	70	.290
1925	Pit	N	C	79	.298
1926	Pit	N	C	86	.271
1927	Pit	N	C	101	.258
1928	Pit	N	C	31	.238
1928	Bro	N	C	42	.317
1929	Bro	N	H	1	.000
1929	Cin	N	C	92	.300
1930	Cin	N	C	82	.243
1933	Bos	A	C	37	.182
	BBTR			805	.276

GOOCH, LEE CURRIN
b.Feb.23,1890 Oxford,N.C.

Yr	Cl	Lea	Pos	G	Rec
1915	Cle	A	H	2	.667
1917	Phi	A	O	17	.288
	BRTR			19	.295

GOOD, EUGENE J.
b.Dec.13,1882 Boston,Mass.
d.Aug.6,1947

Yr	Cl	Lea	Pos	G	Rec
1906	Bos	N	O	34	.151

GOOD, RALPH NELSON
(Holy)
b.Apr.25,1886 Monticello,Me.

Yr	Cl	Lea	Pos	G	Rec
1910	Bos	N	P	2	0-0
	BRTR				

GOOD, WILBUR DAVID
(Lefty)
b.Sept.28,1885 Jefferson Co.,Pa.

Yr	Cl	Lea	Pos	G	Rec
1905	NY	A	P	5	0-1
1908	Cle	A	O	46	.279
1909	Cle	A	O	94	.214
1910	Bos	N	O	23	.337
1911	Bos	N	O	43	.267
1911	Chi	N	O	58	.269
1912	Chi	N	O	39	.143
1913	Chi	N	O	49	.253
1914	Chi	N	O	154	.272
1915	Chi	N	O	128	.253
1916	Phi	N	O	75	.250
1918	Chi	A	O	35	.250
	BLTL			749	0-1 / .258

GOODALL, HERBERT FRANK
b.Aug.10,1866 Mansfield,Pa.
d.Jan.20,1938

Yr	Cl	Lea	Pos	G	Rec
1890	Lou	a	P	18	10-6

GOODELL, JOHN HENRY WILLIAM
b.Apr.5,1907 Muskogee,Okla.

Yr	Cl	Lea	Pos	G	Rec
1928	Chi	A	P	2	0-0
	BRTL				

GOODENOUGH, WILLIAM B.
b.St.Louis,Mo.
d.May 24,1905

Yr	Cl	Lea	Pos	G	Rec
1893	St.L	N	O	10	.178

GOODFELLOW, MICHAEL J.
b.Oct.3,1866 Port Jervis,N.Y.
d.Feb.12,1920

Yr	Cl	Lea	Pos	G	Rec
1887	St.L	a	C	1	.000
1888	Cle	a	O	69	.250
				70	.246

GOODMAN, IVAL RICHARD
b.July 23,1908 Northview,Mo.

Yr	Cl	Lea	Pos	G	Rec
1935	Cin	N	O	148	.269
1936	Cin	N	O	136	.284
1937	Cin	N	O	147	.273
1938	Cin	N	O	145	.292
1939	Cin	N	O	124	.323
1940	Cin	N	O	136	.258
1941	Cin	N	O	42	.268
1942	Cin	N	O	87	.243
1943	Chi	N	O	80	.320
1944	Chi	N	O	62	.262
	BLTR			1107	.281

GOODMAN, JACOB
b.Sept.14,1853 Lancaster,Pa.
d.Mar.9,1890

Yr	Cl	Lea	Pos	G	Rec
1878	Mil	N	1	59	.246
1882	Pit	a	1	10	.316
				69	.256

GOODMAN, WILLIAM DALE
b.Mar.22,1926 Concord,N.C.

Yr	Cl	Lea	Pos	G	Rec
1947	Bos	A	O	12	.182
1948	Bos	A	1-2-3	127	.310
1949	Bos	A	1	122	.298
1950	Bos	A	1-2-S-3-O	110	.354
1951	Bos	A	1-2-3-O	141	.297
1952	Bos	A	1-2-3-O	138	.306
1953	Bos	A	1-2	128	.313
1954	Bos	A	1-2-3-O	127	.303
1955	Bos	A	1-2-O	149	.294
1956	Bos	A	2	105	.293
1957	Bos	A	H	18	.063
1957	Bal	A	1-2-S 3-O	73	.308
1958	Chi	A	1-2-S 3	116	.299
1957	Bal	A	1-2-S-3-O	73	.308
1958	Chi	A	1-2-S-3	116	.299
1959	Chi	A	2-3	104	.250
1960	Chi	A	2-3	30	.234
1961	Chi	A	1-2-3	41	.255
1962	Hou	N	2-3	82	.255
	BLTR			1623	.300

GOODWIN, ARTHUR INGRAM
b.Feb.27,1876 Whitley Township,Pa.
d.June 19,1943

Yr	Cl	Lea	Pos	G	Rec
1905	NY	A	P	1	0-0

GOODWIN, CLAIRE VERNON
(Pep)
b.Dec.19,1894 Pocatello,Ida.

Yr	Cl	Lea	Pos	G	Rec
1914	KC	F	S-3	111	.243
1915	KC	F	2-S	81	.235
	BLTR			192	.240

GOODWIN, CLYDE SAMUEL
b.Nov.12,1886 Athens Co.,O.

Yr	Cl	Lea	Pos	G	Rec
1906	Was	A	P	3	0-2
	BRTR				

GOODWIN, JAMES PATRICK
b.Aug.15,1926 St.Louis,Mo.

Yr	Cl	Lea	Pos	G	Rec
1948	Chi	A	P	8	0-0
	BLTL				

GOODWIN, MARVIN MARDO
b.Jan.16,1893 Richmond,Vt.
d.Oct.22,1925

Yr	Cl	Lea	Pos	G	Rec
1916	Was	A	P	3	0-0
1917	St.L	N	P	14	6-4
1919	St.L	N	P	34	11-9
1920	St.L	N	P	32	3-8
1921	St.L	N	P	14	1-2
1922	St.L	N	P	2	0-0
1925	Cin	N	P	4	0-2
	BRTR			103	21-25

GOOLSBY, RAYMOND DANIEL
(Ox)
b.Sept.5,1919 Florala,Ala.

Yr	Cl	Lea	Pos	G	Rec
1946	Was	A	O	3	.000
	BRTR				

GORBOUS, GLEN EDWARD
b.July 8,1930 Drumheller,Alta.,Canada

Yr	Cl	Lea	Pos	G	Rec
1955	Cin	N	O	8	.333
1955	Phi	N	O	91	.237
1956	Phi	N	O	15	.182
1957	Phi	N	H	3	.500
	BLTR			117	.238

GORCZYCA, JOHN JOSEPH PERRY (Played under name of John Joseph Perry Gorsica)

GORDON, JOSEPH LOWELL
(Flash)
b.Feb.18,1915 Los Angeles,Cal.

Yr	Cl	Lea	Pos	G	Rec
1938	NY	A	2	127	.255
1939	NY	A	2	151	.284
1940	NY	A	2	155	.281
1941	NY	A	2	156	.276
1942	NY	A	2	147	.322
1943	NY	A	2	152	.249
1946	NY	A	2	112	.210
1947	Cle	A	2	155	.272
1948	Cle	A	2-S	144	.280
1949	Cle	A	2	148	.251
1950	Cle	A	2	119	.236
	BRTR			1566	.268

Non-playing Manager Cle(A)1958-60, Det(A)1960, KC(A)1961

GORDON, SIDNEY
b.Aug.13,1918 Brooklyn,N.Y.

Yr	Cl	Lea	Pos	G	Rec
1941	NY	N	O	9	.258
1942	NY	N	3	6	.316
1943	NY	N	1-2-3-O	131	.251
1946	NY	N	3-O	135	.293
1947	NY	N	O	130	.273
1948	NY	N	3-O	142	.299
1949	NY	N	1-3-O	141	.284
1950	Bos	N	3-O	134	.304
1951	Bos	N	3-O	150	.287
1952	Bos	N	3-O	144	.289
1953	Mil	N	O	140	.274
1954	Pit	N	3-O	131	.306
1955	Pit	N	3-O	16	.170
1955	NY	N	3-O	66	.243
	BRTR			1475	.283

GORDONIER, RAYMOND CHARLES
b.Apr.11,1896 Rochester,N.Y.

Yr	Cl	Lea	Pos	G	Rec
1921	Bro	N	P	3	1-0
1922	Bro	N	P	5	0-0
	BBTR			8	1-0

GORE, GEORGE F.
(Piano Legs)
b.May 3,1852 Saccarappa,Me.
d.Sept.16,1933

Yr	Cl	Lea	Pos	G	Rec
1879	Chi	N	O	60	.268
1880	Chi	N	1-O	75	.365
1881	Chi	N	1-S-O	73	.297
1882	Chi	N	O	84	.318
1883	Chi	N	O	91	.334
1884	Chi	N	O	101	.316
1885	Chi	N	O	109	.312
1886	Chi	N	O	118	.304
1887	NY	N	O	111	.348
1888	NY	N	O	64	.220
1889	NY	N	O	119	.305
1890	NY	p	O	93	.335
1891	NY	N	O	130	.285
1892	NY	N	O	53	.254
1892	St.L	N	O	20	.200
	BLTR			1301	.308

GORIN, CHARLES PERRY
b.Feb.2,1928 Waco,Tex.

Yr	Cl	Lea	Pos	G	Rec
1954	Mil	N	P	5	0-1
1955	Mil	N	P	2	0-0
	BLTL			7	0-1

GORMAN, HERBERT ALLEN
b.Dec.18,1925 San Francisco,Cal.
d.Apr.5,1953

Yr	Cl	Lea	Pos	G	Rec
1952	St.L	N	H	1	.000
	BLTL				

GORMAN, HOWARD PAUL
b.May 14,1913 Pittsburgh,Pa.

Yr	Cl	Lea	Pos	G	Rec
1937	Phi	N	O	13	.211
1938	Phi	N	H	1	.000
	BLTL			14	.200

GORMAN, JOHN F.
(Stooping Jack)
b.St.Louis,Mo.
d.Sept.9,1889

Yr	Cl	Lea	Pos	G	Rec
1883	St.L	a	C-O	1	.000
1884	KC	U	1-3-O	33	.275
1884	Pit	a	P-3-O	8	1-2 / .133
				42	1-2 / .256

GORMAN, THOMAS ALOYSIUS
b.Jan.4,1926 New York,N.Y.

Yr	Cl	Lea	Pos	G	Rec
1952	NY	A	P	12	6-2
1953	NY	A	P	40	4-5
1954	NY	A	P	23	0-0
1955	KC	A	P	57	7-6
1956	KC	A	P	52	9-10
1957	KC	A	P	38	5-9
1958	KC	A	P	50	4-4
1959	KC	A	P	17	1-0
		BRTR		289	36-36

GORMAN, THOMAS DAVID
b.Mar.16,1919 New York,N.Y.

Yr	Cl	Lea	Pos	G	Rec
1939	NY	N	P	4	0-0
		BRTL			

GORMLEY, EDWARD
b.Lansford,Pa.

Yr	Cl	Lea	Pos	G	Rec
1891	Phi	N	P	1	0-1
		TL			

GORNICKI, HENRY FRANK
b.Jan.14,1915 Niagara Falls,N.Y.

Yr	Cl	Lea	Pos	G	Rec
1941	St.L	N	P	4	1-0
1941	Chi	N	P	1	0-0
1942	Pit	N	P	25	5-6
1943	Pit	N	P	42	9-13
1946	Pit	N	P	7	0-0
		BRTR		79	15-19

GORSICA, JOHN JOSEPH PERRY (Real name John Joseph Perry Gorczyca)
b.Mar.29,1915 Bayonne,N.J.

Yr	Cl	Lea	Pos	G	Rec
1940	Det	A	P	29	7-7
1941	Det	A	P	33	9-11
1942	Det	A	P	31	3-2
1943	Det	A	P	36	4-5
1944	Det	A	P	40	6-14
1946	Det	A	P	14	0-0
1947	Det	A	P	31	2-0
		BRTR		214	31-39

GORYL, JOHN ALBERT
b.Oct.21,1933 Lonsdale,R.I.

Yr	Cl	Lea	Pos	G	Rec
1957	Chi	N	3	9	.211
1958	Chi	N	2-3	83	.242
1959	Chi	N	2-3	25	.188
1962	Min	A	2-S	37	.192
		BRTR		154	.227

GOSLIN, LEON ALLEN
(Goose)
b.Oct.16,1900 Salem,N.J.

Yr	Cl	Lea	Pos	G	Rec
1921	Was	A	O	14	.260
1922	Was	A	O	101	.324
1923	Was	A	O	150	.300
1924	Was	A	O	154	.344
1925	Was	A	O	150	.335
1926	Was	A	O	147	.354
1927	Was	A	O	148	.334
1928	Was	A	O	135	.379
1929	Was	A	O	145	.288
1930	Was	A	O	47	.270
1930	St.L	A	O	101	.327
1931	St.L	A	O	151	.328
1932	St.L	A	O	150	.299
1933	Was	A	O	132	.297
1934	Det	A	O	151	.305
1935	Det	A	O	147	.292
1936	Det	A	O	147	.315
1937	Det	A	O	79	.238
1938	Was	A	O	38	.158
		BLTR		2287	.316

GOSS, HOWARD WAYNE
b.Nov.1,1934 Wewoka,Okla.

Yr	Cl	Lea	Pos	G	Rec
1962	Pit	N	O	89	.243
		BRTR			

GOSSETT, JOHN STAR
(Dick)
b.Aug.21,1891 Dennison,O.

Yr	Cl	Lea	Pos	G	Rec
1913	NY	A	C	39	.162
1914	NY	A	C	10	.090
		BRTR		49	.151

GOTAY, JULIO SANCHEZ
b.June 9,1939 Fajardo,Puerto Rico

Yr	Cl	Lea	Pos	G	Rec
1960	St.L	N	S-3	3	.375
1961	St.L	N	S	10	.244
1962	St.L	N	2-S-3-O	127	.255
		BRTR		140	.256

GOULAIT, THEODORE L.
b.1891

Yr	Cl	Lea	Pos	G	Rec
1912	NY	N	P	1	0-0
		BRTR			

GOULD, ALBERT FRANK
(Pudgy)
b.Jan.20,1893 Muscatine,Ia.

Yr	Cl	Lea	Pos	G	Rec
1916	Cle	A	P	30	5-7
1917	Cle	A	P	27	4-4
		BRTR		57	9-11

GOULD, CHARLES HARVEY
b.Aug.21,1847 Cincinnati,O.
d.Apr.10,1917

Yr	Cl	Lea	Pos	G	Rec
1871	Bos	n	1-O	33	NR
1872	Bos	n	1-O	44	.256
1874	Bal	n	C-1	33	NR
1875	NH	n	M-1-O	27	NR
1876	Cin	N	M-P-1	61	0-0 / .246
1877	Cin	N	1-O	24	.275
		BRTR		222	0-0 / NR

GOULISH, NICHOLAS EDWARD
b.Nov.13,1917 Punxsutawney,Pa.

Yr	Cl	Lea	Pos	G	Rec
1944	Phi	N	H	1	.000
1945	Phi	N	O	13	.273
		BLTL		14	.250

GOWDY, HARRY (Hank)
b.Aug.24,1889 Columbus,O.

Yr	Cl	Lea	Pos	G	Rec
1910	NY	N	1	5	.214
1911	NY	N	1	4	.250
1911	Bos	N	1	29	.289
1912	Bos	N	C	44	.271
1913	Bos	N	C	3	.600
1914	Bos	N	C	128	.243
1915	Bos	N	C	118	.247
1916	Bos	N	C	118	.252
1917	Bos	N	C	49	.214
1919	Bos	N	C-1	78	.279
1920	Bos	N	C	80	.243
1921	Bos	N	C	64	.299
1922	Bos	N	C-1	92	.316
1923	Bos	N	C	23	.125
1923	NY	N	C	53	.328
1924	NY	N	C	87	.325
1925	NY	N	C	47	.325
1929	Bos	N	C	10	.438
1930	Bos	N	C	16	.200
		BRTR		1048	.270

Non-playing manager Cin (N) 1946.

GRABER, RODNEY BLAINE
b.June 20,1931 Marshallville,O.

Yr	Cl	Lea	Pos	G	Rec
1958	Cle	A	O	4	.125
		BLTL			

GRABOWSKI, ALBERT FRANCIS
b.Sept.6,1903 Syracuse,N.Y.

Yr	Cl	Lea	Pos	G	Rec
1929	St.L	N	P	6	3-2
1930	St.L	N	P	35	6-4
		BLTL		41	9-6

GRABOWSKI, JOHN PATRICK
(Nig)
b.Jan.7,1900 Ware,Mass.
d.May 23,1946

Yr	Cl	Lea	Pos	G	Rec
1924	Chi	A	C	20	.250
1925	Chi	A	C	21	.304
1926	Chi	A	C	48	.262
1927	NY	A	C	70	.277
1928	NY	A	C	75	.238
1929	NY	A	C	22	.203
1931	Det	A	C	40	.235
		BRTR		296	.252

GRABOWSKI, REGINALD JOHN
b.July 16,1909 Syracuse,N.Y.
d.Apr.2,1955

Yr	Cl	Lea	Pos	G	Rec
1932	Phi	N	P	14	2-2
1933	Phi	N	P	10	1-3
1934	Phi	N	P	27	1-3
		BRTR		51	4-8

GRACE, JOSEPH LaVERNE
b.Jan.5,1914 Gorham,Ill.

Yr	Cl	Lea	Pos	G	Rec
1938	St.L	A	O	12	.340
1939	St.L	A	O	74	.304
1940	St.L	A	C-O	80	.258
1941	St.L	A	C-O	115	.309
1946	St.L	A	O	48	.230
1946	Was	A	O	77	.302
1947	Was	A	O	78	.248
		BLTR		484	.283

GRACE, ROBERT EARL
b.Feb.24,1907 Barlow,Ky.

Yr	Cl	Lea	Pos	G	Rec
1929	Chi	N	C	27	.250
1931	Chi	N	C	7	.111
1931	Pit	N	C	47	.280
1932	Pit	N	C	115	.274
1933	Pit	N	C	93	.289
1934	Pit	N	C	95	.270
1935	Pit	N	C	77	.263
1936	Phi	N	C	86	.249
1937	Phi	N	C	80	.211
		BLTR		627	.263

GRADY, JOHN J.
b.1860 Lowell,Mass.
d.1893

Yr	Cl	Lea	Pos	G	Rec
1884	Alt	U	1-O	9	.289

GRADY, MICHAEL WILLIAM
b.Dec.23,1869 Kennett Square,Pa.
d.Dec.3,1943

Yr	Cl	Lea	Pos	G	Rec
1894	Phi	N	C	50	.363
1895	Phi	N	C	33	.336
1896	Phi	N	C	62	.333
1897	Phi	N	1	4	.154
1897	St.L	N	1	83	.281
1898	NY	N	C-O	83	.293
1899	NY	N	C-3	83	.336
1900	NY	N	C	75	.222
1901	Was	A	C-1	94	.286
1904	St.L	N	C	92	.313
1905	St.L	N	C-1	91	.286
1906	St.L	N	C-1	92	.250
		BRTR		842	.296

GRAFF, FREDERICK GOTTLEIB
b.Aug.25,1889 Canton,O.

Yr	Cl	Lea	Pos	G	Rec
1913	St.L	A	3	4	.400
		BRTR			

GRAFF, JOHN F.
b.Philadelphia,Pa.

Yr	Cl	Lea	Pos	G	Rec
1893	Was	N	P	2	0-1

GRAFF, LOUIS GEORGE
b.1866 Philadelphia,Pa.

Yr	Cl	Lea	Pos	G	Rec
1890	Syr	a	C	1	.400

GRAFF, MILTON EDWARD
b.Dec.30,1930 Saxonburg,Pa.

Yr	Cl	Lea	Pos	G	Rec
1957	KC	A	2	56	.181
1958	KC	A	2	5	.000
BLTR				61	.179

GRAFFEN, S. MASON
b.1845 Philadelphia, Pa.
d.Nov.18,1883
Non-playing manager St.L (n) 1875 and St.L (N) 1876.

GRAHAM, ARCHIBALD WRIGHT
(Moonlight)
b.Nov.11,1881 Fayetteville,N.C.

Yr	Cl	Lea	Pos	G	Rec
1905	NY	N	O	1	.000

GRAHAM, ARTHUR WILLIAM
(Skinny)
b.Aug.12,1911 Somerville,Mass.

Yr	Cl	Lea	Pos	G	Rec
1934	Bos	A	O	13	.234
1935	Bos	A	O	8	.300
BLTR				21	.246

GRAHAM, BARNEY
b.Philadelphia,Pa.
d.Dec.31,1896

Yr	Cl	Lea	Pos	G	Rec
1889	Ath	a	3	4	.167

GRAHAM, BERNARD
b.Milwaukee,Wis.

Yr	Cl	Lea	Pos	G	Rec
1884	Chi	U	O	2	.500
1884	Bal	U	1-O	42	.271
				44	.303

GRAHAM, BERT
b.Apr.3,1886 Danville,Ill.

Yr	Cl	Lea	Pos	G	Rec
1910	St.L	A	1-2	8	.115
BBTR					

GRAHAM, CHARLES HENRY
b.Apr.24,1878 Santa Clara,Cal.
d.Aug.29,1948

Yr	Cl	Lea	Pos	G	Rec
1906	Bos	A	C	30	.233
BRTR					

GRAHAM, DAWSON FRANK (Tiny)
b.Sept.9,1892 Nashville,Tenn.

Yr	Cl	Lea	Pos	G	Rec
1914	Cin	N	1	25	.230
BRTR					

GRAHAM, GEORGE FREDERICK
(Peaches)
b.Mar.23,1880 Aledo,Ill.
d.July 25,1939

Yr	Cl	Lea	Pos	G	Rec
1902	Cle	A	2	2	.333
1903	Chi	N	P	1	0-1
1908	Bos	N	C	67	.274
1909	Bos	N	C	81	.239
1910	Bos	N	C	91	.282
1911	Bos	N	C	33	.273
1911	Chi	N	C	36	.239
1912	Phi	N	C	24	.288
BRTR				335	0-1 / .265

GRAHAM, JOHN BERNARD
b.Dec.24,1916 Minneapolis,Minn.

Yr	Cl	Lea	Pos	G	Rec
1946	Bro	N	1	2	.200
1946	NY	N	1-O	100	.219
1949	St.L	A	1	137	.238
BLTL				239	.231

GRAHAM, KYLE B.
b.Aug.14,1899 Bessemer,Ala.

Yr	Cl	Lea	Pos	G	Rec
1924	Bos	N	P	5	0-4
1925	Bos	N	P	34	7-12
1926	Bos	N	P	15	3-3
1929	Det	A	P	13	1-3
BRTR				67	11-22

GRAHAM, OSCAR M.
b.1877 Manilla,Ia.
d.Sept.16,1931

Yr	Cl	Lea	Pos	G	Rec
1907	Was	A	P	26	4-10
TL					

GRAHAM, ROY VINCENT
b.Feb.22,1899 San Francisco,Cal.

Yr	Cl	Lea	Pos	G	Rec
1922	Chi	A	C	5	.000
1923	Chi	A	C	36	.195
BRTR				41	.188

GRAHAM, WILLIAM

Yr	Cl	Lea	Pos	G	Rec
1908	St.L	A	P	21	6-7
1909	St.L	A	P	34	8-14
1910	St.L	A	P	9	0-8
TL				64	14-29

GRAMMAS, ALEXANDER PETER
b.Apr.3,1928 Birmingham,Ala.

Yr	Cl	Lea	Pos	G	Rec
1954	St.L	N	S-3	142	.264
1955	St.L	N	S	128	.240
1956	St.L	N	S	6	.250
1956	Cin	N	2-S-3	77	.243
1957	Cin	N	2-S-3	73	.303
1958	Cin	N	2-S-3	105	.218
1959	St.L	N	S	131	.269
1960	St.L	N	2-S-3	102	.245
1961	St.L	N	2-S-3	89	.212
1962	St.L	N	2-S	21	.111
1962	Chi	N	2-S-3	23	.233
BRTR				897	.248

GRAMPP, HENRY ECKHARDT
b.Sept.28,1903 New York,N.Y.

Yr	Cl	Lea	Pos	G	Rec
1927	Chi	N	P	2	0-0
1929	Chi	N	P	1	0-1
BRTR				3	0-1

GRANEY, JOHN GLADSTONE
b. June 10, 1886 St. Thomas, Ont., Canada.

Yr	Cl	Lea	Pos	G	Rec
1908	Cle	A	P	2	0-0
1910	Cle	A	O	116	.236
1911	Cle	A	O	146	.269
1912	Cle	A	O	78	.242
1913	Cle	A	O	148	.267
1914	Cle	A	O	130	.265
1915	Cle	A	O	116	.260
1916	Cle	A	O	155	.241
1917	Cle	A	O	146	.228
1918	Cle	A	O	70	.237
1919	Cle	A	O	128	.234
1920	Cle	A	O	62	.296
1921	Cle	A	O	68	.299
1922	Cle	A	O	37	.155
BLTL				1402	0-0 / .250

GRANT, EDWARD LESLIE
(Harvard Eddie)
b.May 21,1883 Franklin,Mass.
d.Oct.5,1918

Yr	Cl	Lea	Pos	G	Rec
1905	Cle	A	2	2	.375
1907	Phi	N	3	74	.243
1908	Phi	N	3	147	.244
1909	Phi	N	3	154	.269
1910	Phi	N	3	152	.268
1911	Cin	N	3	133	.223
1912	Cin	N	S-3	96	.239
1913	Cin	N	3	27	.213
1913	NY	N	3	27	.200
1914	NY	N	2-S-3	88	.277
1915	NY	N	3	87	.208
BLTR				987	.249

GRANT, GEORGE ADDISON
b.Jan.6,1903 E.Tallassee,Ala.

Yr	Cl	Lea	Pos	G	Rec
1923	St.L	A	P	4	0-0
1924	St.L	A	P	22	1-2
1925	St.L	A	P	12	0-2
1927	Cle	A	P	25	4-6

(Continued)

Yr	Cl	Lea	Pos	G	Rec
1928	Cle	A	P	29	10-8
1929	Cle	A	P	12	0-2
1931	Pit	N	P	11	0-0
BRTR				115	15-20

GRANT, JAMES CHARLES
b.Oct.6,1918 Racine,Wis.

Yr	Cl	Lea	Pos	G	Rec
1942	Chi	A	3	12	.167
1943	Chi	A	3	58	.259
1943	Cle	A	3	15	.136
1944	Cle	A	2-3	61	.273
BLTR				146	.246

GRANT, JAMES RONALD
b.Aug.4,1894 Ft.Dodge,Ia.

Yr	Cl	Lea	Pos	G	Rec
1923	Phi	N	P	2	0-0
BRTL					

GRANT, JAMES TIMOTHY
(Mudcat)
b.Aug.13,1935 Lacoochee,Fla.

Yr	Cl	Lea	Pos	G	Rec
1958	Cle	A	P	54	10-11
1959	Cle	A	P	42	10-7
1960	Cle	A	P	47	9-8
1961	Cle	A	P	48	15-9
1962	Cle	A	P	30	7-10
BRTR				221	51-45

GRANTHAM, GEORGE FARLEY
(Boots)
b.May 20,1900 Galena,Kan.
d.Mar.16,1954

Yr	Cl	Lea	Pos	G	Rec
1922	Chi	N	3	7	.174
1923	Chi	N	2	152	.281
1924	Chi	N	2-3	127	.316
1925	Pit	N	1	114	.326
1926	Pit	N	1	141	.319
1927	Pit	N	1-2	151	.305
1928	Pit	N	1	124	.323
1929	Pit	N	1-2-O	110	.307
1930	Pit	N	2	146	.324
1931	Pit	N	1-2	127	.305
1932	Cin	N	1-2	126	.292
1933	Cin	N	1-2	87	.204
1934	NY	N	1-3	32	.241
BLTR				1444	.302

GRASMICK, LOUIS JUNIOR
b.Sept.11,1924 Baltimore,Md.

Yr	Cl	Lea	Pos	G	Rec
1948	Phi	N	P	2	0-0
BRTR					

GRASSO, NEWTON MICHAEL
(Mickey)
b.May 10,1920 Newark,N.J.

Yr	Cl	Lea	Pos	G	Rec
1946	NY	N	C	7	.136
1950	Was	A	C	75	.287
1951	Was	A	C	52	.206
1952	Was	A	C	115	.216
1953	Was	A	C	61	.209
1954	Cle	A	C	4	.333
1955	NY	N	C	8	.000
BRTR				322	.226

GRATE, DONALD
b.Sept.27,1923 Greenfield,O.

Yr	Cl	Lea	Pos	G	Rec
1945	Phi	N	P	5	0-1
1946	Phi	N	P	3	1-0
BRTR				8	1-1

GRAULICH, LEWIS
b.Camden,N.J.

Yr	Cl	Lea	Pos	G	Rec
1891	Phi	N	C-1	7	.309

GRAVES, FRANK M.
b.Nov.2,1860 Cincinnati,O.

Yr	Cl	Lea	Pos	G	Rec
1886	St.L	N	C	41	.152

Yr Cl Lea Pos G Rec

GRAVES, JOSEPH EBENEZER
b.Feb.27,1906 Marblehead,Mass.
1926 Chi N 3 2 .000
BRTR

GRAVES, SAMUEL SIDNEY
(Sid)
b.Nov.30,1901 Marblehead,Mass.
1927 Bos N O 7 .250
BRTR

GRAY, CHARLES
b.1867 Indianapolis,Ind.
1890 Pit N P 5 0-3

GRAY, GEORGE EDWARD
(Chummy)
b.July 17,1873 Rockland,Me.
d.Aug.14,1913
1899 Pit N P 9 4-3
TR

GRAY, JAMES D. (Reddy)
1890 Pit p 3 2 .222
1890 Pit N S 1 .000
1893 Pit N S 2 .500
5 .300

GRAY, JAMES W.
1884 Pit a 3 1 1.000

GRAY, JOHN LEONARD
b.Dec.11,1927 W.Palm Beach,Fla.
1954 Phi A P 19 3-12
1955 KC A P 8 0-3
1957 Cle A P 7 1-3
1958 Phi N P 15 0-0
BRTR 49 4-18

GRAY, MILTON MARSHALL
b.Feb.21,1916 Louisville,Ky.
1937 Was A C 2 .000
BRTR

GRAY, PETER WYSHNER
(Real name Peter Wyshner)
b.Mar.6,1917 Nanticoke,Pa.
1945 St.L A O 77 .218
BLTL

GRAY, RICHARD BENJAMIN
b.July 11,1931 Jefferson,Pa.
1958 LA N 3 58 .249
1959 LA N 3 21 .154
1959 St.L N 2-S-3 36 .314
O
1960 St.L N 2-3 9 .000
BRTR 124 .240

GRAY, SAMUEL DAVID
(Dolly)
b.Oct.15,1897 Van Alstyne,Tex.
d.Apr.16,1953
1924 Phi A P 34 8-7
1925 Phi A P 32 16-8
1926 Phi A P 38 11-12
1927 Phi A P 37 9-6
1928 St.L A P 35 20-12
1929 St.L A P 43 18-15
1930 St.L A P 27 4-15
1931 St.L A P 43 11-24
1932 St.L A P 52 7-12
1933 St.L A P 38 7-4
BRTR 379 111-115

GRAY, STANLEY
b.Sept.20,1887 Brownwood,Tex.
1912 Pit N 1 7 .250

GRAY, THEODORE GLENN
b.Dec.31,1924 Detroit,Mich.
1946 Det A P 3 0-2
1948 Det A P 26 6-2
1949 Det A P 36 10-10
1950 Det A P 27 10-7
1951 Det A P 35 7-14

Yr Cl Lea Pos G Rec

(Continued)
1952 Det A P 36 12-17
1953 Det A P 32 10-15
1954 Det A P 19 3-5
1955 Chi A P 2 0-0
1955 Cle A P 2 0-0
1955 NY A P 1 0-0
1955 Bal A P 9 1-2
BBTL 228 59-74

GRAY, WILLIAM
b.Jan.4,1872 Pittsburgh,Pa.
d.Sept.7,1933
1903 Pit N O 2 .333

GRAY, WILLIAM DENTON
(Dolly)
b.Dec.4,1878 Houghton,Mich.
d.Apr.4,1956
1909 Was A P 47 5-19
1910 Was A P 35 8-19
1911 Was A P 29 2-12
BLTL 111 15-50

GRBA, ELI
b.Aug.9,1934 Chicago,Ill.
1959 NY A P 19 2-5
1960 NY A P 27 6-4
1961 LA A P 42 11-13
1962 LA A P 42 8-9
BRTR 130 27-31

GREASON, WILLIAM HENRY
b.Sept.3,1926 Atlanta,Ga.
1954 St.L N P 3 0-1
BRTR

GREEN, EDWARD (Danny)
b.Nov.6,1876 Burlington,N.J.
d.Nov.9,1914
1898 Chi N O 47 .328
1899 Chi N O 114 .296
1900 Chi N O 100 .299
1901 Chi N O 132 .317
1902 Chi A O 129 .318
1903 Chi A O 136 .313
1904 Chi A O 148 .266
1905 Chi A O 112 .243
BL 918 .296

GREEN, EDWARD M.
b.1850 Philadelphia,Pa.
d.Mar.22,1917
1890 Ath a P 39 7-14

GREEN, ELIJAH JERRY
b.Oct.27,1934 Oakland,Cal.
1959 Bos A 2-S 50 .233
1960 Bos A 2-S 133 .242
1961 Bos A 2-S 88 .260
1962 Bos A 2-S 56 .231
BBTR 327 .244

GREEN, EUGENE LEROY
b.June 26,1933 Los Angeles,Cal.
1957 St.L N O 6 .200
1958 St.L N C-O 137 .281
1959 St.L N C-O 30 .189
1960 Bal A O 1 .250
1961 Was A C-O 110 .280
1962 Cle A 1-O 66 .280
BRTR 350 .273

GREEN, FRED ALLAN
b.Sept.14,1933 Titusville,N.J.
1959 Pit N P 17 1-2
1960 Pit N P 45 8-4
1961 Pit N P 13 0-0
1962 Was A P 5 0-1
BRTL 80 9-7

Yr Cl Lea Pos G Rec

GREEN, GEORGE DALLAS
b.Aug.4,1934 Newport,Del.
1960 Phi N P 24 3-6
1961 Phi N P 42 2-4
1962 Phi N P 47 6-6
BLTR 113 11-16

GREEN, HARVEY G.
b.Feb.9,1915 Kenosha,Wis.
1935 Bro N P 2 0-0
BRTR

GREEN, JAMES R.
b.Cleveland,O.
1884 Was U 3-O 10 .139

GREEN, JOSEPH HENRY
b.Sept.17,1897 Philadelphia,Pa.
1924 Phi A H 1 .000
TR

GREEN, JUNE F.
b.June 25,1902 Greensboro,N.C.
1928 Phi N P 11 0-0
1929 Phi N P 21 0-0
BLTR 32 0-0

GREEN, LEONARD CHARLES
b.Jan.6,1933 Detroit,Mich.
1957 Bal A O 19 .182
1958 Bal A O 69 .231
1959 Bal A O 27 .292
1959 Was A O 88 .242
1960 Was A O 127 .294
1961 Min A O 156 .285
1962 Min A O 158 .271
BLTL 644 .273

GREENBERG, HENRY BENJAMIN
(Hammerin' Hank)
b.Jan.1,1911 New York,N.Y.
1930 Det A H 1 .000
1933 Det A 1 117 .301
1934 Det A 1 153 .339
1935 Det A 1 152 .328
1936 Det A 1 12 .348
1937 Det A 1 154 .337
1938 Det A 1 155 .315
1939 Det A 1 138 .312
1940 Det A O 148 .340
1941 Det A O 19 .269
1945 Det A O 78 .311
1946 Det A 1 142 .277
1947 Pit N 1 125 .249
BRTR 1394 .313

GREENE, NELSON GEORGE
b.Sept.20,1900 Philadelphia,Pa.
1924 Bro N P 4 0-1
1925 Bro N P 11 2-0
BLTL 15 2-1

GREENE, PATRICK JOSEPH
(Also played under name
of Patrick Foley)
b.Mar.20,1875 Providence,R.I.
d.Oct.20,1934
(Patrick Foley)
1902 Phi N 3 19 .188
(Patrick Joseph Greene)
1903 NY A 3 4 .308
1903 Det A 3 1 .000
24 .200

GREENFIELD, KENT
b.July 1,1904 Guthrie,Ky.
1924 NY N P 1 0-1
1925 NY N P 29 12-8
1926 NY N P 39 13-12
1927 NY N P 12 2-2
1927 Bos N P 27 11-14
1928 Bos N P 32 3-11
1929 Bos N P 6 0-0
1929 Bro N P 7 0-0
BRTR 153 41-48

GREENGRASS, JAMES RAYMOND
b.Oct.24,1927 Addison,N.Y.

Yr	Cl	Lea	Pos	G	Rec
1952	Cin	N	O	18	.309
1953	Cin	N	O	154	.285
1954	Cin	N	O	139	.280
1955	Cin	N	O	13	.103
1955	Phi	N	3-O	94	.272
1956	Phi	N	O	86	.205
		BRTR		504	.269

GREENIG, JOHN A.
(Played under name of John A. Greening)

GREENING, JOHN A.
(Real name John A. Greenig)
b.Philadelphia,Pa.

Yr	Cl	Lea	Pos	G	Rec
1888	Was	N	P	1	0-1

GREENWOOD, ROBERT CHANDLER
b.Mar.13,1928 Cananea,Mexico

Yr	Cl	Lea	Pos	G	Rec
1954	Phi	N	P	12	1-2
1955	Phi	N	P	1	0-0
		BRTL		13	1-2

GREENWOOD, WILLIAM F.
b.1857 Philadelphia,Pa.
d.May 2,1902

Yr	Cl	Lea	Pos	G	Rec
1882	Ath	a	2-O	7	.290
1884	Bro	a	2	92	.220
1887	Bal	a	2	119	.326
1888	Bal	a	2-S	113	.202
1889	Col	a	2	118	.219
1890	Roc	a	2	121	.226
		BRTL		570	.246

GREER, EDWARD C.
b.Philadelphia,Pa.
d.Feb.4,1890

Yr	Cl	Lea	Pos	G	Rec
1885	Bal	a	C-O	55	.199
1886	Bal	a	C-O	10	.139
1886	Ath	a	O	72	.197
1887	Ath	a	O	3	.182
1887	Bro	a	O	88	.302
		BR		228	.237

GREGG, DAVID CHARLES
(Highpockets)
b.Mar.14,1891 Chehalis,Wash.

Yr	Cl	Lea	Pos	G	Rec
1913	Cle	A	P	1	0-0

BRTR

GREGG, HAROLD DANA
(Skeets)
b.July 11,1921 Anaheim,Cal.

Yr	Cl	Lea	Pos	G	Rec
1943	Bro	N	P	5	0-3
1944	Bro	N	P	42	9-16
1945	Bro	N	P	42	18-13
1946	Bro	N	P	26	6-4
1947	Bro	N	P	37	4-5
1948	Pit	N	P	22	2-4
1949	Pit	N	P	8	1-1
1950	Pit	N	P	5	0-1
1952	NY	N	P	16	0-1
		BRTR		203	40-48

GREGG, SYLVEANUS AUGUSTUS
(Vean)
b.Oct.27,1885 Chehalis,Wash.

Yr	Cl	Lea	Pos	G	Rec
1911	Cle	A	P	34	23-7
1912	cle	A	P	33	20-13
1913	Cle	A	P	37	20-13
1914	Cle	A	P	15	9-3
1914	Bos	A	P	12	3-4
1915	Bos	A	P	18	5-3
1916	Bos	A	P	21	2-5
1918	Phi	A	P	30	8-14
1925	Was	A	P	26	2-2
		BRTL		226	92-64

GREGORY, FRANK E.
b.July 25,1890 Greene Co.,Wis.
d.Nov.5,1955

Yr	Cl	Lea	Pos	G	Rec
1912	Cin	N	P	4	2-0

BRTR

GREGORY, HOWARD WATTERSON
b.Nov.18,1886 Hannibal,Mo.

Yr	Cl	Lea	Pos	G	Rec
1911	St.L	A	P	3	0-1

BLTR

GREGORY, PAUL EDWIN
b.June 9,1908 Tomnolen,Miss.

Yr	Cl	Lea	Pos	G	Rec
1932	Chi	A	P	33	5-3
1933	Chi	A	P	23	4-11
		BRTR		56	9-14

GREISENBECK, CARLOS TIMOTHY
(Tim)
b.Dec.10,1898 San Antonio,Tex.
d.Mar.25,1953

Yr	Cl	Lea	Pos	G	Rec
1920	St.L	N	C	5	.331

BRTR

GREMMINGER, LORENZO EDWARD
(Battleship)
b.Mar.30,1874 Canton,O.
d.May 26,1942

Yr	Cl	Lea	Pos	G	Rec
1895	Cle	N	3	19	.275
1902	Bos	N	3	140	.250
1903	Bos	N	3	140	.264
1904	Det	A	3	82	.215
		TR		381	.249

GREMP, LEWIS EDWARD
(Buddy)
b.Aug.5,1919 Denver,Col.

Yr	Cl	Lea	Pos	G	Rec
1940	Bos	N	1	4	.222
1941	Bos	N	C-1-2	37	.240
1942	Bos	N	1-3	72	.217
		BRTR		113	.224

GREVELL, WILLIAM
b.Mar.5,1898 Williamstown,N.J.
d.June 20,1923

Yr	Cl	Lea	Pos	G	Rec
1919	Phi	A	P	5	0-0

BRTR

GREY, WILLIAM TOBIN
b.Apr.15,1871 Philadelphia,Pa.
d.Dec.8,1932

Yr	Cl	Lea	Pos	G	Rec
1890	Phi	N	C	32	.242
1891	Phi	N	C	18	.264
1895	Cin	N	3	47	.301
1896	Cin	N	C	35	.216
1898	Pit	N	3	137	.232
				269	.246

GREYSON, ...

Yr	Cl	Lea	Pos	G	Rec
1873	Nat	n	P	8	1-7

GRIFFETH, LEON CLIFFORD
b.May 20,1925 Carmel,N.Y.

Yr	Cl	Lea	Pos	G	Rec
1946	Phi	A	P	10	0-0

BBTL

GRIFFIN, FRANCIS ARTHUR
(Pug)
b.Apr.24,1896 Lincoln,Neb.
d.Oct.12,1951

Yr	Cl	Lea	Pos	G	Rec
1917	Phi	A	1	18	.200
1920	NY	N	O	5	.250
		BRTR		23	.207

GRIFFIN, IVY MOORE
b.Dec.25,1897 Mobile,Ala.
d.Aug.25,1957

Yr	Cl	Lea	Pos	G	Rec
1919	Phi	A	1	17	.294
1920	Phi	A	1	129	.238
1921	Phi	A	1	39	.321
		BLTR		185	.257

GRIFFIN, JOHN LINTON
(Hank)
b.1886

Yr	Cl	Lea	Pos	G	Rec
1911	Chi	N	P	1	0-0
1911	Bos	N	P	15	0-6
1912	Bos	N	P	3	0-0
		BRTR		19	0-6

GRIFFIN, MARTIN JOHN
b.Sept.2,1901 San Francisco,Cal.
d.Nov.19,1951

Yr	Cl	Lea	Pos	G	Rec
1928	Bos	A	P	12	0-3

BRTR

GRIFFIN, MICHAEL JOSEPH
b.Mar.20,1865 Utica,N.Y.
d.Apr.10,1908

Yr	Cl	Lea	Pos	G	Rec
1887	Bal	a	O	136	.368
1888	Bal	a	O	137	.261
1889	Bal	a	S-O	137	.280
1890	Phi	p	O	115	.290
1891	Bro	N	O	133	.272
1892	Bro	N	O	129	.276
1893	Bro	N	O	93	.304
1894	Bro	N	O	106	.365
1895	Bro	N	O	132	.335
1896	Bro	N	O	122	.315
1897	Bro	N	O	134	.320
1898	Bro	N	M-O	134	.296
		BLTR		1508	.308

GRIFFIN, PATRICK RICHARD
b.May 13,1893 Niles,O.

Yr	Cl	Lea	Pos	G	Rec
1914	Cin	N	P	1	0-0

BRTR

GRIFFIN, THOMAS W.
b.Rockford,Ill.

Yr	Cl	Lea	Pos	G	Rec
1884	Mil	U	1	11	.295

GRIFFIN, TOBIAS CHARLES
(Sandy)
b.Oct.24,1860 Fayetteville,N.Y.
d.June 5,1926

Yr	Cl	Lea	Pos	G	Rec
1884	NY	N	O	15	.164
1890	Roc	a	O	107	.305
1891	Was	a	M-O	19	.273
1893	St.L	N	O	23	.204
				164	.269

GRIFFITH, BERT JOSEPH
(Buck)
b.Mar.3,1897 St.Louis,Mo.

Yr	Cl	Lea	Pos	G	Rec
1922	Bro	N	1-O	106	.308
1923	Bro	N	O	79	.294
1924	Was	A	O	6	.111
		BRTR		191	.299

GRIFFITH, CLARK CALVIN
(Old Fox)
b.Nov.20,1869 Stringtown,Mo.
d.Oct.27,1955

Yr	Cl	Lea	Pos	G	Rec
1891	St.L	a	P	27	11-8
1891	Bos	a	P	9	3-1
1893	Chi	N	P	3	1-1
1894	Chi	N	P	41	21-11
1895	Chi	N	P	39	25-14
1896	Chi	N	P	36	23-11
1897	Chi	N	P	46	18-18
1898	Chi	N	P	37	25-12
1899	Chi	N	P	39	21-13
1900	Chi	N	P	30	14-13
1901	Chi	A	M-P	35	24-8
1902	Chi	A	M-P-O	34	15-9 / .220
1903	NY	A	M-P	25	14-10
1904	NY	A	M-P	16	6-5
1905	NY	A	M-P	35	6-5
1906	NY	A	M-P	17	2-2
1907	NY	A	M-P	5	0-0
1909	Cin	N	M-P	1	0-1
1910	Cin	N	M-H	1	.000
1912	Was	A	M-P	1	0-0
1913	Was	A	M-P	1	0-0
1914	Was	A	M-P	1	0-0
		BRTR		469	228-142 / .233

Non-playing manager NY (A) 1908,Cin (N) 1911 and Was (A) 1915-20.

GRIFFITH, EDWARD

Yr	Cl	Lea	Pos	G	Rec
1892	Chi	N	P	1	0-0

TL

GRIFFITH, FRANK WESLEY
b.Nov.18,1872 Gilman,Ill.
d.Dec.13,1908

Yr	Cl	Lea	Pos	G	Rec
1894	Cle	N	P	7	3-3

GRIFFITH, THOMAS HERMAN
b.Oct.26,1889 Prospect,O.

Yr	Cl	Lea	Pos	G	Rec
1913	Bos	N	O	37	.252
1914	Bos	N	O	16	.104
1915	Cin	N	O	160	.307
1916	Cin	N	O	155	.266
1917	Cin	N	O	115	.270
1918	Cin	N	O	118	.265
1919	Bro	N	O	125	.281
1920	Bro	N	O	93	.260
1921	Bro	N	O	129	.312
1922	Bro	N	O	99	.316
1923	Bro	N	O	131	.293
1924	Bro	N	O	140	.251
1925	Bro	N	O	7	.000
1925	Chi	N	O	76	.285
	BLTR			1401	.279

GRIGGS, ARTHUR J.
b.July 14,1884 Topeka,Kan.
d.Dec.19,1938

Yr	Cl	Lea	Pos	G	Rec
1909	St.L	A	1-O	108	.280
1910	st.L	A	1-2-O	123	.236
1911	Cle	A	1	27	.250
1912	Cle	A	1	89	.304
1914	Bro	F	1	38	.282
1915	Bro	F	1	27	.275
1918	Det	A	1	28	.364
	BRTR			440	.276

GRIGGS, HAROLD LLOYD
b.Aug.24,1928 Atlanta,Ga.

Yr	Cl	Lea	Pos	G	Rec
1956	Was	A	P	36	1-6
1957	Was	A	P	2	0-1
1958	Was	A	P	32	3-11
1959	Was	A	P	37	2-8
	BRTR			107	6-26

GRIGSBY, DENVER CLARENCE
b.Mar.25,1901 Sapulpa,Okla.

Yr	Cl	Lea	Pos	G	Rec
1923	Chi	N	O	24	.292
1924	Chi	N	O	124	.299
1925	Chi	N	O	51	.255
	BLTR			199	.289

GRIM, JOHN HELM
b.Aug.9,1867 Lebanon,Ky.
d.July 28,1961

Yr	Cl	Lea	Pos	G	Rec
1888	Phi	N	2	2	.143
1890	Roc	a	P-C-S	50	{ 2-0 .254
1891	Mil	a	C	28	.233
1892	Lou	N	C	95	.254
1893	Lou	N	C	92	.287
1894	Lou	N	C-2	107	.290
1895	Bro	N	C	90	.288
1896	Bro	N	C	80	.269
1897	Bro	N	C	76	.261
1898	Bro	N	C	50	.275
1899	Bro	N	C	14	.271
	TR			684	{ 2-0 .272

GRIM, ROBERT ANTON
b.Mar.8,1930 New York,N.Y.

Yr	Cl	Lea	Pos	G	Rec
1954	NY	A	P	37	20-6
1955	NY	A	P	26	7-5
1956	NY	A	P	26	6-1
1957	NY	A	P	46	12-8
1958	NY	A	P	11	0-1
1958	KC	A	P	26	7-6
1959	KC	A	P	40	6-10
1960	Cle	A	P	3	0-1
1960	Cin	N	P	26	2-2
1960	St.L	N	P	15	1-0
1962	KC	A	P	12	0-1
	BRTR			268	61-41

GRIMES, BURLEIGH ARLAND
b.Aug.18,1893 Clear Lake,Wis.

(Continued)

Yr	Cl	Lea	Pos	G	Rec
1916	Pit	N	P	6	2-3
1917	Pit	N	P	42	3-16
1918	Bro	N	P	41	19-9
1919	Bro	N	P	26	10-11
1920	Bro	N	P	43	23-11
1921	Bro	N	P	37	22-13
1922	Bro	N	P	36	17-14
1923	Bro	N	P	40	21-18
1924	Bro	N	P	40	22-13
1925	Bro	N	P	34	12-19
1926	Bro	N	P	31	12-13
1927	NY	N	P	39	19-8
1928	Pit	N	P	48	25-14
1929	Pit	N	P	33	17-7
1930	Bos	N	P	11	3-5
1930	St.L	N	P	23	13-6
1931	St.L	N	P	29	17-9
1932	Chi	N	P	30	6-11
1933	Chi	N	P	17	3-6
1933	St.L	N	P	4	0-1
1934	St.L	N	P	4	2-1
1934	Pit	N	P	8	1-2
1934	NY	A	P	10	1-2
	BRTR			632	270-212

Non-playing manager Bro (N) 1937-38.

GRIMES, EDWARD ADELBERT
b.Sept.8,1905 Chicago,Ill.

Yr	Cl	Lea	Pos	G	Rec
1931	St.L	A	3	43	.263
1932	St.L	A	3	31	.235
	BRTR			74	.248

GRIMES, JOHN C.
b.July 7,1876 Cleveland,O.
d.Sept.14,1913

Yr	Cl	Lea	Pos	G	Rec
1897	St.L	N	P	3	0-2

GRIMES, OSCAR RAY JR.
b.Apr.13,1915 Minerva,O.

Yr	Cl	Lea	Pos	G	Rec
1938	Cle	A	1-2	4	.200
1939	Cle	A	1-2-S	119	.269
1940	Cle	A	1-3	11	.000
1941	Cle	A	1-2-3	77	.238
1942	Cle	A	1-2-S-3	51	.179
1943	NY	A	1-S	9	.150
1944	NY	A	S-3	116	.279
1945	NY	A	1-3	142	.265
1946	NY	A	2-S	14	.205
1946	Phi	A	2-S-3	59	.262
	BRTR			602	.256

GRIMES, OSCAR RAY SR.
b.Sept.11 1893 Minerva,O.
d.May 25,1953

Yr	Cl	Lea	Pos	G	Rec
1920	Bos	A	1	1	.250
1921	Chi	N	1	147	.321
1922	Chi	N	1	138	.354
1923	Chi	N	1	64	.329
1924	Chi	N	1	51	.299
1926	Phi	N	1	32	.297
	BRTR			433	.329

GRIMES, ROY AUSTIN
b.Sept.11,1893 Minerva,O.
d.Sept.13,1954

Yr	Cl	Lea	Pos	G	Rec
1920	NY	N	2	21	.158
	BRTR				

GRIMM, CHARLES JOHN
(Jolly Cholly)
b.Aug.25,1898 St.Louis,Mo.

Yr	Cl	Lea	Pos	G	Rec
1916	Phi	A	O	12	.091
1918	St.L	N	1-3-O	50	.220
1919	Pit	N	1	14	.318
1920	Pit	N	1	148	.227
1921	Pit	N	1	151	.274
1922	Pit	N	1	154	.292
1923	Pit	N	1	152	.345
1924	Pit	N	1	151	.288
1925	Chi	N	1	141	.306
1926	Chi	N	1	147	.277
1927	Chi	N	1	147	.311
1928	Chi	N	1	147	.294
1929	Chi	N	1	120	.298
1930	Chi	N	1	114	.289
1931	Chi	N	1	146	.331
1932	Chi	N	M-1	149	.307

(Continued)

Yr	Cl	Lea	Pos	G	Rec
1933	Chi	N	M-1	107	.247
1934	Chi	N	M-1	75	.296
1935	Chi	N	M-1	2	.000
1936	Chi	N	M-1	39	.250
	BLTL			2166	.290

Non-playing manager Chi (N) 1937-38, 1944-49, Bos (N) 1952 and Mil (N) 1953-56, Chi (N) 1960.

GRIMSHAW, MYRON FREDERICK (Moose)
b.Nov.30,1875 St.Johnsville,N.Y.
d.Dec.11,1936

Yr	Cl	Lea	Pos	G	Rec
1905	Bos	A	1	85	.239
1906	Bos	A	1	110	.290
1907	Bos	A	1-O	64	.204
	BRTR			259	.256

GRIMSLEY, ROSS ALBERT
b.June 4,1924 Americus,Kan.

Yr	Cl	Lea	Pos	G	Rec
1951	Chi	A	P	7	0-0
	BLTL				

GRINER, DANIEL DEXTER
(Rusty)
b.Mar.7,1889 Centerville,Tenn.
d.June 3,1950

Yr	Cl	Lea	Pos	G	Rec
1912	St.L	N	P	12	3-4
1913	St.L	N	P	34	10-22
1914	st.L	N	P	37	9-13
1915	St.L	N	P	39	5-11
1916	St.L	N	P	4	0-0
1918	Bro	N	P	12	1-5
	BLTR			138	28-55

GRISSOM, LEO THEO
b.Oct.23,1907 Sherman,Tex.

Yr	Cl	Lea	Pos	G	Rec
1934	Cin	N	P	4	0-1
1935	Cin	N	P	3	1-1
1936	Cin	N	P	6	1-1
1937	Cin	N	P	51	12-17
1938	Cin	N	P	14	2-3
193[illegible]	Cin	N	P	33	9-7
1940	NY	A	P	5	0-0
1940	Bro	N	P	14	2-5
1941	Bro	N	P	4	0-0
1941	Phi	N	P	29	2-13
	BBTL			163	29-48

GRISSOM, MARVIN EDWARD
b.Mar.31,1918 Los Molinos,Cal.

Yr	Cl	Lea	Pos	G	Rec
1946	NY	N	P	4	0-2
1949	Det	A	P	27	2-4
1952	Chi	A	P	28	12-10
1953	Bos	A	P	13	2-6
1953	NY	N	P	21	4-2
1954	NY	N	P	56	10-7
1955	NY	N	P	55	5-4
1956	NY	N	P	43	1-1
1957	NY	N	P	55	4-4
1958	SF	N	P	51	7-5
1959	St.L	N	P	3	0-0
	BRTR			356	47-45

GROAT, RICHARD MORROW
b.Nov.4,1930 Swissvale,Pa.

Yr	Cl	Lea	Pos	G	Rec
1952	Pit	N	S	95	.284
1955	Pit	N	S	151	.267
1956	Pit	N	S-3	142	.273
1957	Pit	N	S-3	125	.315
1958	Pit	N	S	151	.300
1959	Pit	N	S	147	.275
1960	Pit	N	S	138	.325
1961	Pit	S	S-3	148	.275
1962	Pit	N	S	161	.294
	BRTR			1258	.290

GROB, CONRAD GEORGE
b.Nov.9,1932 Cross Plains,Wis.

Yr	Cl	Lea	Pos	G	Rec
1956	Was	A	P	37	4-5
	BLTR				

GRODZICKI, JOHN
b.Feb.26,1919 Nanticoke,Pa.

Yr	Cl	Lea	Pos	G	Rec
1941	St.L	N	P	5	2-1
1946	st.L	N	P	3	0-0
1947	St.L	N	P	16	0-1
	BRTR			24	2-2

GROH, HENRY KNIGHT
(Heinie)
b.Sept.18,1889 Rochester,N.Y.

Yr	Cl	Lea	Pos	G	Rec
1912	NY	N	2	27	.271
1913	NY	N	2	4	.000
1913	Cin	N	2	117	.282
1914	Cin	N	2	139	.288
1915	Cin	N	2-3	160	.290
1916	Cin	N	2-S-3	149	.269
1917	Cin	N	2-3	156	.304
1918	Cin	N	M-3	126	.320
1919	Cin	N	3	122	.310
1920	Cin	N	3	145	.298
1921	Cin	N	3	97	.331
1922	NY	N	3	115	.265
1923	NY	N	3	123	.290
1924	NY	N	3	145	.281
1925	NY	N	2-3	25	.231
1926	NY	N	3	12	.229
1927	Pit	N	3	14	.286
	BRTR			1676	.292

GROH, LEWIS CARL
(Silver)
b.Oct.16,1883 Rochester,N.Y.
d.Oct.20,1960

Yr	Cl	Lea	Pos	G	Rec
1919	Phi	A	3	4	.000
	BRTR				

GROMEK, STEPHEN JOSEPH
b.Jan.15,1920 Hamtramck,Mich.

Yr	Cl	Lea	Pos	G	Rec
1941	Cle	A	P	9	1-1
1942	Cle	A	P	14	2-0
1943	Cle	A	P	3	0-0
1944	Cle	A	P	44	10-9
1945	Cle	A	P	37	19-9
1946	Cle	A	P	37	5-15
1947	Cle	A	P	30	3-5
1948	Cle	A	P	38	9-3
1949	Cle	A	P	27	4-6
1950	Cle	A	P	31	10-7
1951	Cle	A	P	27	7-4
1952	Cle	A	P	30	7-7
1953	Cle	A	P	5	1-1
1953	Det	A	P	19	6-8
1954	Det	A	P	36	18-16
1955	Det	A	P	28	13-10
1956	Det	A	P	40	8-6
1957	Det	A	P	15	0-1
	BBTR			470	123-108

GROOM, ROBERT
b.Sept.12,1884 Belleville,Ill.
d.Feb.19,1948

Yr	Cl	Lea	Pos	G	Rec
1909	Was	A	P	46	6-26
1910	Was	A	P	34	12-17
1911	Was	A	P	38	13-17
1912	Was	A	P	42	24-13
1913	Was	A	P	36	15-16
1914	St.L	F	P	40	13-20
1915	St.L	F	P	30	11-11
1916	St.L	A	P	41	13-9
1917	St.L	A	P	38	8-19
1918	Cle	A	P	14	2-2
	BRTR			359	117-150

GROSART, GEORGE ALBERT
b.1879 Meadville,Pa.
d.Apr.18,1902

Yr	Cl	Lea	Pos	G	Rec
1901	Bos	N	O	7	.125

GROSS, DONALD JOHN
b.June 30,1931 Weidman,Mich.

Yr	Cl	Lea	Pos	G	Rec
1955	Cin	N	P	17	4-5
1956	Cin	N	P	19	3-0
1957	Cin	N	P	43	7-9
1958	Pit	N	P	40	5-7
1959	Pit	N	P	21	1-1
1960	Pit	N	P	5	0-0
	BLTL			145	20-22

GROSS, EMIL M.
b.1859 Chicago,Ill.

Yr	Cl	Lea	Pos	G	Rec
1879	Pro	N	C	30	.379
1880	Pro	N	C	84	.255
1881	Pro	N	C	51	.274
1883	Phi	N	C-O	56	.312
1884	Chi	U	C-O	23	.326
1886	St.L	N	C	1	.000
				245	.291

GROSS, EWELL (Turkey)
b.Feb.23,1896 Mesquite,Tex.
d.Jan.11,1936

Yr	Cl	Lea	Pos	G	Rec
1925	Bos	A	S	9	.094
	BRTR				

GROSSKLOSS, HOWARD HOFFMAN (Howdie)
b.Apr.9,1907 Pittsburgh,Pa.

Yr	Cl	Lea	Pos	G	Rec
1930	Pit	N	S	2	.333
1931	Pit	N	2	53	.280
1932	Pit	N	S	17	.100
	BRTR			72	.261

GROSSMAN, HARLEY JOSEPH
b.May 5,1930 Evansville,Ind.

Yr	Cl	Lea	Pos	G	Rec
1952	Was	A	P	1	0-0
	BRTR				

GROTH, EDWARD JOHN
b.Dec.24,1885 Cedarburg,Wis.
d.May 23,1950

Yr	Cl	Lea	Pos	G	Rec
1904	Chi	N	P	3	0-2

GROTH, ERNEST WILLIAM
b.May 3,1922 Beaver Falls,Pa.

Yr	Cl	Lea	Pos	G	Rec
1947	Cle	A	P	2	0-0
1948	Cle	A	P	2	0-0
1949	Chi	A	P	3	0-1
	BRTR			7	0-1

GROTH, JOHN THOMAS
b.July 23,1926 Chicago,Ill.

Yr	Cl	Lea	Pos	G	Rec
1946	Det	A	O	4	.000
1947	Det	A	O	2	.250
1948	Det	A	O	6	.471
1949	Det	A	O	103	.293
1950	Det	A	O	157	.306
1951	Det	A	O	118	.299
1952	Det	A	O	141	.284
1953	St.L	A	O	141	.253
1954	Chi	A	O	125	.275
1955	Chi	A	O	32	.338
1955	Was	A	O	63	.219
1956	KC	A	O	95	.258
1957	KC	A	O	55	.254
1957	Det	A	O	38	.291
1958	Det	A	O	88	.281
1959	Det	A	O	55	.235
1960	Det	A	O	25	.368
	BRTR			1248	.279

GROVE, ORVAL LeROY
b.Aug.29,1919 Mineral,Kan.

Yr	Cl	Lea	Pos	G	Rec
1940	Chi	A	P	3	0-0
1941	Chi	A	P	2	0-0
1942	Chi	A	P	12	4-6
1943	Chi	A	P	32	15-9
1944	Chi	A	P	34	14-15
1945	Chi	A	P	33	14-12
1946	Chi	A	P	33	8-13
1947	Chi	A	P	25	6-8
1948	Chi	A	P	32	2-10
1949	Chi	A	P	1	0-0
	BRTR			207	63-73

GROVE, ROBERT MOSES
(Lefty)
b.Mar.6,1900 Lonaconing,Md.

Yr	Cl	Lea	Pos	G	Rec
1925	Phi	A	P	45	10-12
1926	Phi	A	P	45	13-13
1927	Phi	A	P	51	20-13
1928	Phi	A	P	39	24-8
1929	Phi	A	P	42	20-6
1930	Phi	A	P	50	28-5

(Continued)

Yr	Cl	Lea	Pos	G	Rec
1931	Phi	A	P	41	31-4
1932	Phi	A	P	44	25-10
1933	Phi	A	P	45	24-8
1934	Bos	A	P	22	8-8
1935	Bos	A	P	35	20-12
1936	Bos	A	P	35	17-12
1937	Bos	A	P	32	17-9
1938	Bos	A	P	24	14-4
1939	Bos	A	P	25	15-4
1940	Bos	A	P	23	7-6
1941	Bos	A	P	21	7-7
	BLTL			619	300-141

GROVER, CHARLES BERT
(Bugs)
b.June 20,1891 Vanceton,O.

Yr	Cl	Lea	Pos	G	Rec
1913	Det	A	P	2	0-0
	BLTR				

GROVER, ROY ARTHUR
b.Jan.17,1893 Snohomish,Wash.

Yr	Cl	Lea	Pos	G	Rec
1916	Phi	A	2	20	.272
1917	Phi	A	2	141	.224
1919	Phi	A	2	22	.232
1919	Was	A	2	24	.187
	BRTR			207	.226

GRUBB, HARVEY HERBERT
b.Sept.18,1891 Greensboro,N.C.

Yr	Cl	Lea	Pos	G	Rec
1912	Cle	A	3	1	.000
	BRTR				

GRUBBS, THOMAS DILLARD
b.Feb.22,1894 Mt.Sterling,Ky.

Yr	Cl	Lea	Pos	G	Rec
1920	NY	N	P	1	0-1
	BRTR				

GRUBE, FRANKLIN THOMAS
(Hans)
b.Jan.7,1905 Easton,Pa.
d.July 2,1945

Yr	Cl	Lea	Pos	G	Rec
1931	Chi	A	C	88	.219
1932	Chi	A	C	93	.282
1933	Chi	A	C	85	.230
1934	St.L	A	C	65	.288
1935	St.L	A	C	3	.333
1935	Chi	A	C	9	.368
1936	Chi	A	C	33	.161
1941	St.L	A	C	18	.154
	BRTR			394	.244

GRUBER, HENRY JOHN
b.Dec.14,1864 New Haven,Conn.

Yr	Cl	Lea	Pos	G	Rec
1887	Det	N	P	9	5-3
1888	Det	N	P	27	11-13
1889	Cle	N	P	23	7-16
1890	Cle	p	P	50	21-20
1891	Cle	N	P	38	16-21
	BRTR			147	60-73

GRUNWALD, ALFRED HENRY
b.Feb.13,1930 Los Angeles,Cal.

Yr	Cl	Lea	Pos	G	Rec
1955	Pit	N	P	3	0-0
1959	KC	A	P	7	0-1
	BLTL			11	0-1

GRYSKA, SIGMUND STANLEY
b.Nov.4,1915 Chicago,Ill.

Yr	Cl	Lea	Pos	G	Rec
1938	St.L	A	S	7	.476
1939	St.L	A	S	18	.265
	BRTR			25	.329

GRZENDA, JOSEPH CHARLES
b.June 8,1937 Moosic,Pa.

Yr	Cl	Lea	Pos	G	Rec
1961	Det	A	P	4	1-0
	BRTL				

GUDAT, MARVIN JOHN
b.Aug.27,1904 Weser,Tex.
d.Mar.2,1954

Yr	Cl	Lea	Pos	G	Rec
1929	Cin	N	P	9	1-1
1932	Chi	N	P-O	60	0-0 .255
	BLTL			69	1-1 .250

GUERRA, FERMIN ROMERO
(Mike)
b.Oct.11,1912 Havana,Cuba.

Yr	Cl	Lea	Pos	G	Rec
1937	Was	A	C	1	.000
1944	Was	A	C-O	75	.281
1945	Was	A	C	56	.210
1946	Was	A	C	41	.253
1947	Phi	A	C	72	.215
1948	Phi	A	C	53	.211
1949	Phi	A	C	98	.265
1950	Phi	A	C	87	.282
1951	Bos	A	C	10	.156
1951	Was	A	C	72	.200
			BRTR	565	.242

GUESE, THEODORE (Whitey)
b.Jan.23,1873 New Bremen,O.
d.Apr.8,1951

Yr	Cl	Lea	Pos	G	Rec
1901	Cin	N	P	6	1-4
			BRTR		

GUINEY, BENJAMIN FRANKLIN
b.Nov.16,1858 Detroit,Mich.
d.Dec.5,1930

Yr	Cl	Lea	Pos	G	Rec
1883	Det	N	2-O	1	.200
1884	Det	N	C	2	.000
				3	.083

GUINTINI, BENJAMIN JOHN
b.Jan.13,1920 Los Banos,Cal.

Yr	Cl	Lea	Pos	G	Rec
1946	Pit	N	O	2	.000
1950	Phi	A	O	3	.000
			BRTR	5	.000

GUISE, WITT ORISON
(Lefty)
b.Sept.18,1909 Driggs,Ark.

Yr	Cl	Lea	Pos	G	Rec
1940	Cin	N	P	2	0-0
			BLTL		

GUISTO, LOUIS JOSEPH
b.Jan.16,1894 Napa,Cal.

Yr	Cl	Lea	Pos	G	Rec
1916	Cle	A	1	6	.158
1917	Cle	A	1	73	.185
1921	Cle	A	1	2	.500
1922	Cle	A	1	35	.250
1923	Cle	A	1	40	.181
			BRTR	156	.196

GULLEY, THOMAS JEFFERSON
b.Dec.25,1899 Brookhaven,Miss.

Yr	Cl	Lea	Pos	G	Rec
1923	Cle	A	O	3	.500
1924	Cle	A	O	8	.150
1926	Chi	A	O	16	.229
			BLTR	27	.224

GULLIC, THEODORE JASPER
b.Jan.2,1907 Koshkoning,Mo.

Yr	Cl	Lea	Pos	G	Rec
1930	St.L	A	O	92	.250
1933	St.L	A	1-3-O	104	.243
			BRTR	196	.247

GUMBERT, ADDISON COURTNEY
b.Oct.10,1868 Pittsburgh,Pa.
d.Apr.23,1925

Yr	Cl	Lea	Pos	G	Rec
1888	Chi	N	P	7	3-3
1889	Chi	N	P	49	14-13
1890	Bos	p	P	45	22-9
1891	Chi	N	P	29	17-10
1892	Chi	N	P	48	23-18
1893	Pit	N	P	24	13-6
1894	Pit	N	P	33	18-14
1895	Bro	N	P	26	11-15
1896	Bro	N	P	5	0-4
1896	Phi	N	P	11	6-4
			TR	277	127-96

GUMBERT, HARRY EDWARD
(Gunboat)
b.Nov.5,1911 Elizabeth,Pa.

Yr	Cl	Lea	Pos	G	Rec
1935	NY	N	P	6	1-2
1936	NY	N	P	39	11-3
1937	NY	N	P	34	10-11

(Continued)

Yr	Cl	Lea	Pos	G	Rec
1938	NY	N	P	40	15-13
1939	NY	N	P	37	18-11
1940	NY	N	P	35	12-14
1941	NY	N	P	5	1-1
1941	St.L	N	P	34	11-5
1942	St.L	N	P	38	9-5
1943	St.L	N	P	21	10-5
1944	St.L	N	P	10	4-2
1944	Cin	N	P	24	10-8
1946	Cin	N	P	36	6-8
1947	Cin	N	P	46	10-10
1948	Cin	N	P	61	10-8
1949	Cin	N	P	29	4-3
1949	Pit	N	P	16	1-4
1950	Pit	N	P	1	0-0
			BRTR	512	143-113

GUMBERT, WILLIAM SKEEN
b.Aug.8,1865 Pittsburgh,Pa.
d.Apr.13,1946

Yr	Cl	Lea	Pos	G	Rec
1890	Pit	N	P	10	4-4
1892	Pit	N	P	7	3-2
1893	Lou	N	P	1	0-0
				18	7-6

GUMPERT, RANDALL PENNINGTON
b.Jan.23,1918 Monocacy,Pa.

Yr	Cl	Lea	Pos	G	Rec
1936	Phi	A	P	22	1-2
1937	Phi	A	P	10	0-0
1938	Phi	A	P	4	0-2
1946	NY	A	P	33	11-3
1947	NY	A	P	25	4-1
1948	NY	A	P	15	1-0
1948	Chi	A	P	16	2-6
1949	Chi	A	P	34	13-16
1950	Chi	A	P	41	5-12
1951	Chi	A	P	37	9-8
1952	Bos	A	P	10	1-0
1952	Was	A	P	20	4-9
			BRTR	267	51-59

GUNKEL, WOODWARD WILLIAM
(Red)
b.Apr.15,1894 Sheffield,Ill.
d.Apr.19,1954

Yr	Cl	Lea	Pos	G	Rec
1916	Cle	A	P	1	0-0
			BBTR		

GUNKLE, FREDERICK W.
b.Cleveland,O.

Yr	Cl	Lea	Pos	G	Rec
1879	Cle	N	C-O	1	.000

GUNNING, HYLAND
b.Aug.6,1888 Maplewood,N.J.

Yr	Cl	Lea	Pos	G	Rec
1911	Bos	A	1	4	.111
			BLTR		

GUNNING, THOMAS FRANCIS
b.Mar.4,1862 Newmarket,N.H.
d.Mar.17,1931

Yr	Cl	Lea	Pos	G	Rec
1884	Bos	N	C	12	.095
1885	Bos	N	C	48	.184
1886	Bos	N	C	27	.224
1887	Phi	N	C	27	.293
1888	Ath	a	C	23	.217
1889	Ath	a	C	5	.375
				142	.216

GUNSON, JOSEPH BROOK
b.Mar.23,1863 Philadelphia,Pa.
d.Nov.15,1942

Yr	Cl	Lea	Pos	G	Rec
1884	Was	U	C-O	44	.158
1889	KC	a	C	34	.198
1892	Bal	N	C-O	85	.223
1893	St.L	N	C	37	.280
1893	Cle	N	C	21	.296
			TR	221	.223

GURZENSKY, JOSEPH CHARLES (Played under name of Joseph Charles Glenn)

GUST, ERNEST

Yr	Cl	Lea	Pos	G	Rec
1911	St.L	A	1	3	.000

GUSTINE, FRANK WILLIAM
b.Feb.20,1920 Hoopeston,Ill.

Yr	Cl	Lea	Pos	G	Rec
1939	Pit	N	3	22	.186

(Continued)

Yr	Cl	Lea	Pos	G	Rec
1940	Pit	N	2	133	.281
1941	Pit	N	2-3	121	.270
1942	Pit	N	C-2-S-3	115	.229
1943	Pit	N	1-2-S	112	.290
1944	Pit	N	2-S-3	127	.230
1945	Pit	N	C-2-S	128	.280
1946	Pit	N	2-S-3	131	.259
1947	Pit	N	3	156	.297
1948	Pit	N	3	131	.267
1949	Chi	N	2-3	76	.226
1950	St.L	A	3	9	.158
			BRTR	1261	.265

GUTH, CHARLES J.
b.1856 Chicago,Ill.
d.July 1883

Yr	Cl	Lea	Pos	G	Rec
1880	Chi	N	P	1	1-0

GUTIERREZ, RENE VALDES
(Played under name of Rene Gutierrez Valdes)

GUTTERIDGE, DONALD JOSEPH
b.June 19,1913 Pittsburg,Kan.

Yr	Cl	Lea	Pos	G	Rec
1936	St.L	N	3	23	.319
1937	St.L	N	3	119	.271
1938	St.L	N	S-3	142	.255
1939	St.L	N	3	148	.269
1940	St.L	N	3	69	.269
1942	St.L	A	2-3	147	.255
1943	St.L	A	2	132	.273
1944	St.L	A	2	148	.245
1945	St.L	A	2-O	143	.238
1946	Bos	A	2-3	22	.234
1947	bos	A	2-3	54	.168
1948	Pit	N	H	4	.000
			BRTR	1151	.256

GYSELMAN, RICHARD REYNALD
b.Apr.6,1911 San Francisco,Cal.

Yr	Cl	Lea	Pos	G	Rec
1933	Bos	N	2-S-3	58	.239
1934	Bos	N	3	24	.167
			BRTR	82	.225

HAAS, BERTHOLD JOHN
b.Feb.8,1914 Naperville,Ill.

Yr	Cl	Lea	Pos	G	Rec
1937	Bro	N	1	16	.400
1938	Bro	N	H	1	.000
1942	Cin	N	1-3-O	154	.239
1943	Cin	N	1-3-O	101	.262
1946	Cin	N	1-3	140	.264
1947	Cin	N	1-O	135	.286
1948	Phi	N	1-3	95	.282
1949	Phi	N	H	2	.000
1949	NY	N	1-3	54	.260
1951	Chi	A	1-3-O	23	.163
			BRTR	721	.264

HAAS, BRUNO PHILIP
(Boon)
b.May 5,1891 Worcester,Mass.
d.June 5,1952

Yr	Cl	Lea	Pos	G	Rec
1915	Phi	A	P	12	0-2
			BBTL		

HAAS, GEORGE EDWIN
b.May 26,1935 Paducah,Ky.

Yr	Cl	Lea	Pos	G	Rec
1957	Chi	N	O	14	.208
1958	Mil	N	O	9	.357
1960	Mil	N	O	32	.219
			BLTR	55	.243

HAAS, GEORGE WILLIAM
(Mule)
b.Oct.15,1903 Montclair,N.J.

Yr	Cl	Lea	Pos	G	Rec
1925	Pit	N	O	4	.000
1928	Phi	A	O	91	.280
1929	Phi	A	O	139	.313
1930	Phi	A	O	132	.299
1931	Phi	A	O	102	.323
1932	Phi	A	O	143	.305
1933	Chi	A	O	146	.287
1934	Chi	A	O	106	.268
1935	Chi	A	O	92	.291
1936	Chi	A	O	119	.284

(Continued)

Yr	Cl	Lea	Pos	G	Rec
1937	Chi	A	1	54	.207
1938	Phi	A	O	40	.205
	BLTR			1168	.292

HABENICHT, ROBERT JULIUS
(Hobby)
b.Feb.13,1926 St.Louis,Mo.

Yr	Cl	Lea	Pos	G	Rec
1951	St.L	N	P	3	0-0
1953	St.L	A	P	1	0-0
	BRTR			4	0-0

HABERER, EMIL KARL
b.Feb.2.1878 Cincinnati,O.
d.Oct.19,1951

Yr	Cl	Lea	Pos	G	Rec
1901	Cin	N	1	6	.167
1903	Cin	N	C	5	.154
1909	Cin	N	C	5	.187
	BRTR			16	.178

HACH, IRVIN (Major)
b.June 6,1873 Louisville,Ky.
d.Aug.13,1936

Yr	Cl	Lea	Pos	G	Rec
1897	Lou	N	2-3	15	.163

HACK, STANLEY CAMFIELD
b.Dec. 6,1909 Sacramento,Cal.

Yr	Cl	Lea	Pos	G	Rec
1932	Chi	N	3	72	.236
1933	Chi	N	3	20	.350
1934	Chi	N	3	111	.289
1935	Chi	N	1-3	124	.311
1936	Chi	N	1-3	149	.298
1937	Chi	N	3	154	.297
1938	Chi	N	3	152	.320
1939	Chi	N	3	156	.298
1940	Chi	N	3	149	.317
1941	Chi	N	1-3	151	.317
1942	Chi	N	3	140	.300
1943	Chi	N	3	144	.289
1944	Chi	N	1-3	98	.282
1945	Chi	N	1-3	150	.323
1946	Chi	N	3	92	.285
1947	Chi	N	3	76	.271
	BLTR			1938	.301

Non-playing manager Chi (N) 1954-56 and St.L (N) 1958

HACKER, WARREN LOUIS
b.Nov.21,1924 Marissa,Ill.

Yr	Cl	Lea	Pos	G	Rec
1948	Chi	N	P	3	0-1
1949	Chi	N	P	32	5-8
1950	Chi	N	P	5	0-1
1951	Chi	N	P	2	0-0
1952	Chi	N	P	34	15-9
1953	Chi	N	P	42	12-19
1954	Chi	N	P	43	6-13
1955	Chi	N	P	35	11-15
1956	Chi	N	P	34	3-13
1957	Cin	N	P	15	3-2
1957	Phi	N	P	20	4-4
1958	Phi	N	P	9	0-1
1961	Chi	A	P	42	3-3
	BRTR			316	62-89

HACKETT, CHARLES M.
b. Holyoke,Mass.
Non-playing manager Cleveland (N) 1884 and Bro (a) 1885.

HACKETT, JAMES JOSEPH
b.Oct.1,1877 Jacksonville,Ill.
d.Mar.28,1961

Yr	Cl	Lea	Pos	G	Rec
1902	St.L	N	P-O	6	0-1 .285
1903	St.L	N	P-1	96	1-3 .228
	BRTR			102	1-7 .233

HACKETT, MORTIMER MARTIN
(Mertie)
b.Nov.11,1859 Cambridge,Mass.
d.Feb.22,1938

Yr	Cl	Lea	Pos	G	Rec
1883	Bos	N	C-O	46	.234
1884	Bos	N	C-3	68	.203
1885	Bos	N	C	33	.182
1886	KC	N	C	62	.217

(Continued)

Yr	Cl	Lea	Pos	G	Rec
1887	Ind	N	C	41	.272
	TR			250	.222

HACKETT, WALTER HENRY
b.Aug.15,1857 Cambridge,Mass.
d.Oct.2,1920

Yr	Cl	Lea	Pos	G	Rec
1884	Bos	U	S	102	.248
1885	Bos	N	2-S	35	.184
				137	.233

HADDIX, HARVEY (Kitten)
b.Sept.18,1925 Medway,O.

Yr	Cl	Lea	Pos	G	Rec
1952	St.L	N	P-O	9	2-2 .214
1953	St.L	N	P	48	20-9
1954	St.L	N	P	61	18-13
1955	St.L	N	P	37	12-16
1956	St.L	N	P	5	1-0
1956	Phi	N	P	46	12-8
1957	Phi	N	P	41	10-13
1958	Cin	N	P	42	8-7
1959	Pit	N	P	31	12-12
1960	Pit	N	P	29	11-10
1961	Pit	N	P	31	10-6
1962	Pit	N	P	28	9-6
	BLTL			408	125-102 .218

HADDOCK, GEORGE SILAS
(Gentleman George)
b.Dec.25,1866 Portsmouth,N.H.
d.Apr.19,1926

Yr	Cl	Lea	Pos	G	Rec
1888	Was	N	P	2	0-2
1889	Was	N	P	33	10-19
1890	Buf	p	P-O	42	9-26 .240
1891	Bos	a	P	58	33-11
1892	Bro	N	P	44	31-13
1893	Bro	N	P	26	8-10
1894	Phi	N	P	10	4-3
1894	Was	N	P-O	5	0-4 .250
	TR			220	95-88 .219

HADDOW, JOHN FALCNOR
(Played under name of John B. Black)

HADLEY, IRVING DARIUS
(Bump)
b.July 5,1904 Lynn,Mass.
d.Feb.14,1963

Yr	Cl	Lea	Pos	G	Rec
1926	Was	A	P	1	0-0
1927	Was	A	P	30	14-6
1928	Was	A	P	33	12-13
1929	Was	A	P	37	6-16
1930	Was	A	P	42	15-11
1931	Was	A	P	55	11-10
1932	Chi	A	P	3	1-1
1932	St.L	A	P	40	13-20
1933	St.L	A	P	45	15-20
1934	St.L	A	P	39	10-16
1935	Was	A	P	35	10-15
1936	NY	A	P	31	14-4
1937	NY	A	P	29	11-8
1938	NY	A	P	29	9-8
1939	NY	A	P	26	12-6
1940	NY	A	P	25	3-5
1941	NY	N	P	3	1-0
1941	Phi	A	P	25	4-6
	BRTR			528	161-165

HADLEY, KENT WILLIAM
b.Dec.17,1934 Pocatello,Ida.

Yr	Cl	Lea	Pos	G	Rec
1958	KC	A	1	3	.182
1959	KC	A	1	113	.253
1960	NY	A	1	55	.203
	BLTL			171	.242

HAEFFNER, WILLIAM BERNARD
b.July 18,1895 Philadelphia,Pa.

Yr	Cl	Lea	Pos	G	Rec
1915	Phi	A	C	3	.250
1920	Pit	N	C	54	.194

(Continued)

Yr	Cl	Lea	Pos	G	Rec
1928	NY	N	C	2	.000
	BRTR			59	.194

HAEFNER, MILTON ARNOLD
(Mickey)
b.Oct.9,1912 Lenzburg,Ill.

Yr	Cl	Lea	Pos	G	Rec
1943	Was	A	P	36	11-5
1944	Was	A	P	31	12-15
1945	Was	A	P	37	16-14
1946	Was	A	P	33	14-11
1947	Was	A	P	31	10-14
1948	Was	A	P	28	5-13
1949	Was	A	P	20	5-5
1949	Chi	A	P	14	4-6
1950	Chi	A	P	24	1-6
1950	Bos	N	P	8	0-2
	BLTL			262	78-91

HAFEY, CHARLES JAMES
(Chick)
b.Feb.12,1903 Berkeley,Cal.

Yr	Cl	Lea	Pos	G	Rec
1924	St.L	N	O	24	.253
1925	St.L	N	O	93	.302
1926	St.L	N	O	78	.271
1927	St.L	N	O	103	.330
1928	St.L	N	O	138	.337
1929	St.L	N	O	134	.339
1930	St.L	N	O	120	.336
1931	St.L	N	O	122	.349
1932	Cin	N	O	83	.344
1933	Cin	N	O	144	.303
1934	Cin	N	O	140	.293
1935	Cin	N	O	15	.339
1937	Cin	N	O	89	.261
	BRTR			1283	.317

HAFEY, DANIEL ALBERT
(Bud)
b.Aug.6,1912 Berkeley,Cal.

Yr	Cl	Lea	Pos	G	Rec
1935	Chi	A	H	2	.000
1935	Pit	N	O	58	.228
1936	Pit	N	O	39	.212
1939	Cin	N	O	6	.154
1939	Phi	N	P-O	18	0-0 .176
	BRTR			123	0-0 .213

HAFEY, THOMAS FRANCIS
(Heave-o)
b.July 12,1913 Berkeley,Cal.

Yr	Cl	Lea	Pos	G	Rec
1939	NY	N	3	70	.242
1944	St.L	A	1-O	8	.357
	BRTR			78	.248

HAFFORD, LEO EDGAR
b.Sept.17,1883 Somerville,Mass.
d.Oct.2,1911

Yr	Cl	Lea	Pos	G	Rec
1906	Cin	N	P	3	0-0

HAGAN, ARTHUR F.
(Cut)
b.1863 Lonsdale,R.I.

Yr	Cl	Lea	Pos	G	Rec
1883	Phi	N	P	17	1-16
1883	Buf	N	P-O	2	0-2 .000
1884	Buf	N	P	3	1-2
				22	2-20 .115

HAGEMAN, KURT R. MORRIS (Casey)
b.May 12,1888 Pittsburgh,Pa.

Yr	Cl	Lea	Pos	G	Rec
1911	Bos	A	P	2	0-2
1912	Bos	A	P	2	0-0
1914	St.L	N	P	12	2-4
1914	Chi	N	P	16	1-1
	BRTR			32	3-7

Yr	Cl	Lea	Pos	G	Rec

HAGERMAN, ZERIAH ZEQUIEL
(Rip)
b.June 20,1889 Linden,Kans.
d.Jan.29,1930

Yr	Cl	Lea	Pos	G	Rec
1909	Chi	N	P	13	4-4
1914	Cle	A	P	35	9-15
1915	Cle	A	P	28	7-13
1916	Cle	A	P	2	0-0
	BRTR			78	20-32

HAGUE, WILLIAM L.
(Real name William L. Haug)
b.1852 Philadelphia,Pa.

Yr	Cl	Lea	Pos	G	Rec
1875	St.L	n	1-3	59	.206
1876	Lou	N	3	67	.264
1877	Lou	N	3	59	.267
1878	Pro	N	3	60	.207
1879	Pro	N	3	50	.227
	BRTR			295	.231

HAHN, EDGAR WILLIAM
b.Aug.27,1880 Nevada,O.
d.Nov.29,1941

Yr	Cl	Lea	Pos	G	Rec
1905	NY	A	O	43	.319
1906	NY	A	O	11	.091
1906	Chi	A	O	130	.227
1907	Chi	A	O	156	.255
1908	Chi	A	O	122	.251
1909	Chi	A	O	76	.182
1910	Chi	A	O	15	.113
	BLTR			553	.237

HAHN, FRANK GEORGE
(Noodles)
b.Apr.29,1879 Nashville,Tenn.
d.Feb.6,1960

Yr	Cl	Lea	Pos	G	Rec
1899	Cin	N	P	38	23-8
1900	Cin	N	P	40	16-21
1901	Cin	N	P	41	22-19
1902	Cin	N	P-1-O	37	23-12 .183
1903	Cin	N	P	34	22-12
1904	Cin	N	P	35	15-18
1905	Cin	N	P	12	5-3
1906	NY	A	P	6	3-2
	BLTL			243	129-95 .178

HAHN, FREDERICK ALOYS
b.Feb.16,1929 Nyack,N.Y.

Yr	Cl	Lea	Pos	G	Rec
1952	St.L	N	P	1	0-0
	BRTL				

HAHN, RICHARD FREDERICK
b.July 24,1917 Canton,O.

Yr	Cl	Lea	Pos	G	Rec
1940	Was	A	C	1	.000
	BRTR				

HAID, HAROLD AUGUSTINE
b.Dec.21,1897 Barberton,O.
d.Aug.13,1952

Yr	Cl	Lea	Pos	G	Rec
1919	St.L	A	P	1	0-0
1928	St.L	N	P	27	2-2
1929	St.L	N	P	38	9-9
1930	St.L	N	P	21	3-2
1931	Bos	N	P	27	0-2
1933	Chi	A	P	6	0-0
	BRTR			120	14-15

HAIGH, EDWARD E.
b.Feb.5,1867 Philadelphia,Pa.
d.Feb.14,1953

Yr	Cl	Lea	Pos	G	Rec
1892	St.L	N	O	1	.250

HAINES, HENRY LUTHER
(Hinkey)
b.Dec.23,1899 Red Lion,Pa.

Yr	Cl	Lea	Pos	G	Rec
1923	NY	A	O	28	.160
	BRTR				

HAINES, JESSE JOSEPH
(Pop)
b.July 22,1893 Clayton,O.

Yr	Cl	Lea	Pos	G	Rec
1918	Cin	N	P	1	0-0
1920	St.L	N	P	48	13-20
1921	St.L	N	P	39	18-12
1922	St.L	N	P-1	30	11-9 .167

(Continued)

Yr	Cl	Lea	Pos	G	Rec
1923	St.L	N	P	37	20-13
1924	St.L	N	P	35	8-19
1925	St.L	N	P	29	13-14
1926	St.L	N	P	33	13-4
1927	St.L	N	P	38	24-10
1928	St.L	N	P	33	20-8
1929	St.L	N	P	28	13-10
1930	St.L	N	P	29	13-8
1931	St.L	N	P	19	12-3
1932	St.L	N	P	20	3-5
1933	St.L	N	P	33	9-6
1934	St.L	N	P	37	4-4
1935	St.L	N	P	30	6-5
1936	St.L	N	P	25	7-5
1937	St.L	N	P	16	3-3
	BRTR			560	210-158 .186

HAIRSTON, SAMUEL
b.Jan,20,1925 Crawford,Miss.

Yr	Cl	Lea	Pos	G	Rec
1951	Chi	A	C	4	.400
	BRTR				

HAISLIP, JAMES C.
b.1890

Yr	Cl	Lea	Pos	G	Rec
1913	Phi	N	P	1	0-0
	BRTR				

HAJDUK, CHESTER
b.July 21,1919 Chicago,Ill.

Yr	Cl	Lea	Pos	G	Rec
1941	Chi	A	H	1	.000
	BRTR				

HALAS, GEORGE STANLEY
b.Feb.2,1895 Chicago,Ill.

Yr	Cl	Lea	Pos	G	Rec
1919	NY	A	O	12	.091
	BBTR				

HALDEMAN, JOHN AVERY
b.Dec.2,1855 Pee Wee Valley,Ky.
d.Sept.17,1899

Yr	Cl	Lea	Pos	G	Rec
1877	Lou	N	2	1	.000
	BRTR				

HALE, ARVEL ODELL
(Bad News)
b.Aug.10,1908 Hosston,La.

Yr	Cl	Lea	Pos	G	Rec
1931	Cle	A	2-3	25	.283
1933	Cle	A	2-3	98	.276
1934	Cle	A	2	143	.302
1935	Cle	A	2-3	150	.304
1936	Cle	A	3	153	.316
1937	Cle	A	2-3	154	.267
1938	Cle	A	2	130	.278
1939	Cle	A	2	108	.312
1940	Cle	A	3	48	.220
1941	Bos	A	2-3	12	.208
1941	NY	N	2	41	.196
	BRTR			1062	.289

HALE, GEORGE WAGNER
b.Aug.3,1894 Dexter,Kan.

Yr	Cl	Lea	Pos	G	Rec
1914	St.L	A	C	5	.271
1916	St.L	A	O	4	.000
1917	St.L	A	C	38	.197
1918	St.L	A	C	12	.133
	BRTR			59	.184

HALE, ROBERT HOUSTON
b.Nov.7,1933 Sarasota,Fla.

Yr	Cl	Lea	Pos	G	Rec
1955	Bal	A	1	67	.357
1956	Bal	A	1	85	.237
1957	Bal	A	1	42	.250
1958	Bal	A	1	19	.350
1959	Bal	A	1	40	.185
1960	Cle	A	1	70	.300
1961	Cle	A	H	42	.167
1961	NY	A	1	11	.154
	BLTL			376	.273

HALE, ROY L.
b.Feb.18,1880 Dowagiac,Mich.
d.Feb.1,1946

Yr	Cl	Lea	Pos	G	Rec
1902	Bos	N	P	8	0-3
1902	Bal	A	P	3	0-1
				11	0-4

HALE, SAMUEL DOUGLAS
b.Sept.10,1896 Glen Rose,Tex.

Yr	Cl	Lea	Pos	G	Rec
1920	Det	A	3-O	76	.293
1921	Det	A	O	9	.000
1923	Phi	A	3	115	.288
1924	Phi	A	3	80	.318
1925	Phi	A	2-3	110	.345
1926	Phi	A	3	111	.281
1927	Phi	A	3	131	.313
1928	Phi	A	3	88	.309
1929	Phi	A	3	101	.277
1930	St.L	A	3	62	.274
	BRTR			883	.302

HALEY, FRED
b.Wheeling,W.Va.

Yr	Cl	Lea	Pos	G	Rec
1880	Tro	N	C	2	.000

HALEY, RAYMOND TIMOTHY
b.Jan.23,1891 Danbury, Iowa

Yr	Cl	Lea	Pos	G	Rec
1915	Bos	A	C	5	.143
1916	Bos	A	C	1	.000
1916	Phi	A	C	34	.220
1917	Phi	A	C	41	.276
	BRTR			81	.250

HALL, ARCHIBALD W. (Al)
b.Worcester,Mass.

Yr	Cl	Lea	Pos	G	Rec
1879	Tro	N	O	66	.255
1880	Cle	N	O	2	.125
1887	Met	a	O	3	.214
				71	.250

HALL, CHARLES LOUIS
(Sea Lion)
(Real name Carlos Clolo)
b.May 6,1888 Kerrville,Tex.
d.Dec.6,1943

Yr	Cl	Lea	Pos	G	Rec
1906	Cin	N	P	16	3-6
1907	Cin	N	P	12	4-3
1909	Bos	A	P	11	6-4
1910	Bos	A	P	47	12-9
1911	Bos	A	P	39	8-7
1912	Bos	A	P	32	15-8
1913	Bos	A	P	33	4-4
1916	St.L	N	P	10	0-4
1918	Det	A	P	6	0-1
	BRTR			206	52-46

HALL, GEORGE W.
b.1849 Brooklyn,N.Y.

Yr	Cl	Lea	Pos	G	Rec
1871	Oly	n	O	32	NR
1872	Bal	n	1-O	53	.317
1873	Bal	n	O	35	NR
1874	Bos	n	O	47	.321
1875	Ath	n	O	77	.298
1876	Ath	N	O	60	.355
1877	Lou	N	O	61	.322
	BL			365	NR

HALL, HERBERT S.
b.1894

Yr	Cl	Lea	Pos	G	Rec
1918	Det	A	O	3	.000
	BBTR				

HALL, IRVIN GLADSTONE
b.Oct.7,1918 Alberton,Md.

Yr	Cl	Lea	Pos	G	Rec
1943	Phi	A	2-S-3	151	.256
1944	Phi	A	1-2-S	143	.268
1945	Phi	A	2	151	.261
1946	Phi	A	2-S	63	.249
	BRTR			508	.261

HALL, JAMES
d.Jan.30,1886

Yr	Cl	Lea	Pos	G	Rec
1872	Atl	n	2-O	14	NR
1874	Atl	n	2	2	NR
1875	Wes	n	O	1	NR
				17	NR

Yr	Cl	Lea	Pos	G	Rec

HALL, JOHN SYLVESTER
b.Jan.9,1924 Muskogee,Okla.

1948	Bro	N	P	3	0-0
	BRTR				

HALL, LEWIS C.
b.1888 Omaha,Neb.

1911	Phi	N	P	7	0-1

HALL, MARCUS
b.Aug.12,1887 Joplin,Mo.
d.Feb.24,1915

1910	St.L	A	P	8	1-7
1913	Det	A	P	28	9-12
1914	Det	A	P	18	4-6
	BRTR			54	14-25

HALL, RICHARD WALLACE
b.Sept.27,1930 St.Louis,Mo.

1952	Pit	N	3-O	26	.138
1953	Pit	N	2	7	.167
1954	Pit	N	O	112	.239
1955	Pit	N	P-O	21	6-6 / .175
1956	Pit	N	P-1	33	0-7 / .345
1957	Pit	N	P	10	0-0
1959	Pit	N	P	2	0-0
1960	KC	A	P	32	8-13
1961	Bal	A	P	30	7-5
1962	Bal	A	P	44	6-6
	BRTR			317	27-37 / .201

HALL, ROBERT LEWIS
b.Dec.22,1923 Swissvale,Pa.

1949	Bos	N	P	31	6-4
1950	Bos	N	P	21	0-2
1953	Pit	N	P	37	3-12
	BRTR			89	9-18

HALL, ROBERT PRILL
b.1878 Baltimore,Md.
d.Dec.1,1950

1904	Phi	N	S-3	46	.160
1905	NY	N	O	1	.333
1905	Bro	N	O	52	.236
	TR			99	.203

HALL, RUSSELL P.
b.Sept.29,1871 Shelbyville,Ky.
d.July 1,1937

1898	St.L	N	S	39	.252
1901	Cle	A	S	1	.500
	TR			40	.259

HALL, WILLIAM BERNARD
b.Feb.22,1892 Charleston,W.Va.

1913	Bro	N	P	3	0-0
	BRTR				

HALL, WILLIAM LEMUEL
b.July 30,1928 Moultrie,Ga.

1954	Pit	N	C	5	.000
1956	Pit	N	C	1	.000
1958	Pit	N	C	51	.284
	BLTR			57	.262

HALLA, JOHN ARTHUR
b.May 13,1884 St.Louis,Mo.
d.Sept.30,1947

1905	Cle	A	P	3	0-1
	BLTL				

HALLAHAN, WILLIAM ANTHONY
(Wild Bill)
b.Aug.4,1902 Binghamton,N.Y.

1925	St.L	N	P	6	1-0
1926	St.L	N	P	19	1-4
1929	St.L	N	P	20	4-4
1930	St.L	N	P	35	15-9
1931	St.L	N	P	37	19-9
1932	St.L	N	P	28	12-7
1933	St.L	N	P	37	16-13
1934	St.L	N	P	32	8-12
1935	St.L	N	P	40	15-8
1936	St.L	N	P	9	2-2

(Continued)

1936	Cin	N	P	23	5-9
1937	Cin	N	P	21	3-9
1938	Phi	N	P	21	1-8
	BRTL			328	102-94

HALLER, THOMAS FRANK
b.June 23,1937 Lockport,Ill.

1961	SF	N	C	30	.145
1962	SF	N	C	99	.261
	BLTR			129	.239

HALLETT, JACK PRICE
b.Nov.13,1913 Toledo,O.

1940	Chi	A	P	2	1-1
1941	Chi	A	P	22	5-5
1942	Pit	N	P	3	0-1
1943	Pit	N	P	9	1-2
1946	Pit	N	P	35	5-7
1948	NY	N	P	2	0-0
	BRTR			73	12-16

HALLIDAY, NEWTON
b.1897

1916	Pit	N	1	1	.000
	BRTR				

HALLIGAN, WILLIAM E.
(Jocko)
b.Dec.8,1867 Avon,N.Y.
d.Feb.13,1945

1890	Buf	p	C-O	53	.268
1891	Cin	N	O	61	.311
1892	Cin	N	1-O	26	.287
1892	Bal	N	1-O	44	.269
				184	.287

HALLINAN, EDWARD S.
b.Aug.23,1889 San Francisco,Cal.
d.Aug.24,1940

1911	St.L	A	2-S	52	.207
1912	St.L	A	S	27	.221
	BRTR			79	.212

HALLINAN, JAMES H.
b.May 27,1849 Ireland.
d.Oct.28,1879

1871	Kek	n	S	5	NR
1875	Wes	n	S	13	NR
1875	Mut	n	2-S-3	44	NR
1876	Mut	N	S	54	.277
1877	Cin	N	2	16	.370
1877	Chi	N	O	19	.281
1878	Chi	N	2-O	15	.231
1878	Ind	N	O	3	.250
	BLTL			169	NR

HALLMAN, WILLIAM HARRY
b.Mar.15,1876 Philadelphia,Pa.
d.Apr.23,1950

1901	Mil	A	O	139	.256
1903	Chi	A	O	64	.213
1906	Pit	N	O	23	.270
1907	Pit	N	O	84	.222
				310	.240

HALLMAN, WILLIAM WHITE
b.Mar.30,1867 Pittsburgh,Pa.
d.Sept.11,1920

1888	Phi	N	2	16	.206
1889	Phi	N	S	119	.253
1890	Phi	p	C-2-3-O	85	.278
1891	Ath	a	2	140	.288
1892	Phi	N	2	136	.292
1893	Phi	N	2	132	.328
1894	Phi	N	2	119	.327
1895	Phi	N	2	124	.315
1896	Phi	N	2	120	.318
1897	Phi	N	2	31	.248
1897	St.L	N	M-2	81	.252
1898	Bro	N	2	133	.245
1901	Cle	A	S	5	.211

(Continued)

1901	Phi	N	2-3	122	.194
1902	Phi	N	3	73	.245
1903	Phi	N	2-3	57	.212
	BRTR			1493	.276

HALLSTROM, CHARLES E.
b. Chicago,Ill.

1885	Pro	N	P	1	0-1

HALPIN, JAMES NATHANIEL
b.Oct.4,1863 England.
d.Jan.4,1893

1882	Wor	N	3	2	.000
1884	Was	U	S	44	.182
1885	Det	N	S	15	.129
				61	.163

HALT, ALVA WILLIAM
b. Sandusky,O.

1914	Bro	F	S	80	.235
1915	Bro	F	S-3	151	.245
1918	Cle	A	3	26	.174
	BRTR			257	.237

HAM, RALPH A.
b.1850 Troy,N.Y.
d.Feb.13,1905

1871	Rok	n	S-3-O	25	NR
1872	Man	n	S	1	NR
				26	NR

HAMBRICK, CHARLES H.
(Played under name of Charles H. Hamburg)

HAMBURG, CHARLES H.
(Real name Charles H. Hambrick)
b.Nov.22,1863 Louisville,Ky.

1890	Lou	a	O	134	.265

HAMBY, JAMES SANFORD
(Cracker)
b.July 29,1900 Wilkesboro,N.C.

1926	NY	N	C	1	.000
1927	NY	N	C	21	.192
	BRTR			22	.182

HAMILL, JOHN CHARLES
b.1850 New York,N.Y.
d.Dec.6,1911

1884	Was	a	P	21	2-16

HAMILTON, EARL A.
b.July 19.1892 Gibson City,Ill.

1911	St.L	A	P	32	5-12
1912	St.L	A	P	36	11-14
1913	St.L	A	P	25	13-12
1914	St.L	A	P	43	16-18
1915	St.L	A	P	35	9-17
1916	St.L	A	P	20	4-6
1916	Det	A	P	5	2-3
1917	St.L	A	P	27	0-9
1918	Pit	N	P	6	6-0
1919	Pit	N	P	28	8-11
1920	Pit	N	P	39	10-13
1921	Pit	N	P	35	13-15
1922	Pit	N	P	33	11-7
1923	Pit	N	P	28	7-9
1924	Phi	N	P	3	0-1
	BLTL			395	115-147

HAMILTON, JACK EDWIN
b.Dec.25,1938 Burlington,Ia.

1962	Phi	N	P	41	9-12
	BRTR				

HAMILTON, STEVE ABSHER
b.Nov.30,1935 Columbia,Ky.

1961	Cle	A	P	2	0-0
1962	Was	A	P	43	3-8
	BLTL			45	3-8

HAMILTON, THOMAS BALL
b.Sept.29,1925 Altoona,Kan.

Yr	Cl	Lea	Pos	G	Rec
1952	Phi	A	1	9	.200
1953	Phi	A	1-O	58	.196
	BLTR			67	.197

HAMILTON, WILLIAM ROBERT
(Sliding Billy)
b.Feb.16,1866 Newark,N.J.
d.Dec.16,1940

Yr	Cl	Lea	Pos	G	Rec
1888	KC	a	O	35	.250
1889	KC	a	O	137	.301
1890	Phi	N	O	123	.324
1891	Phi	N	O	133	.388
1892	Phi	N	O	136	.330
1893	Phi	N	O	82	.395
1894	Phi	N	O	131	.399
1895	Phi	N	O	121	.393
1896	Bos	N	O	131	.363
1897	Bos	N	O	125	.344
1898	Bos	N	O	109	.367
1899	Bos	N	O	81	.306
1900	Bos	N	O	135	.332
1901	Bos	N	O	99	.292
	BLTR			1578	.344

HAMLIN, KENNETH LEE
b.June 18,1935 Detroit,Mich.

Yr	Cl	Lea	Pos	G	Rec
1957	Pit	N	S	2	.000
1959	Pit	N	S	3	.125
1960	KC	A	S	140	.224
1961	LA	A	S	42	.209
1962	Was	A	2-S	98	.253
	BRTR			285	.232

HAMLIN, LUKE DANIEL
(Hot Potato)
b.July 3,1906 Terris Center,Mich.

Yr	Cl	Lea	Pos	G	Rec
1933	Det	A	P	3	1-0
1934	Det	A	P	20	2-3
1937	Bro	N	P	41	11-13
1938	Bro	N	P	44	12-15
1939	Bro	N	P	40	20-13
1940	Bro	N	P	35	9-8
1941	Bro	N	P	30	8-8
1942	Pit	N	P	23	4-4
1944	Phi	A	P	29	6-12
	BLTR			265	73-76

HAMMOND, WALTER CHARLES
(Jack)
b.Feb.26,1892 Amsterdam,N.Y.
d.Mar.4,1942

Yr	Cl	Lea	Pos	G	Rec
1915	Cle	A	2	35	.214
1922	Cle	A	2	1	.250
1922	Pit	N	2	9	.273
	BRTR			45	.232

HAMNER, GRANVILLE WILBUR
b.Apr.26,1927 Richmond,Va.

Yr	Cl	Lea	Pos	G	Rec
1944	Phi	N	S	21	.247
1945	Phi	N	S	14	.171
1946	Phi	N	S	2	.143
1947	Phi	N	S	2	.286
1948	Phi	N	2-S-3	129	.260
1949	Phi	N	S	154	.263
1950	Phi	N	S	157	.270
1951	Phi	N	S	150	.255
1952	Phi	N	S	151	.275
1953	Phi	N	2-S	154	.276
1954	Phi	N	2-S	152	.299
1955	Phi	N	2-S	104	.257
1956	Phi	N	P-2-S	122	0-1 / .224
1957	Phi	N	P-2-S	133	0-0 / .227
1958	Phi	N	2-S-3	35	.301
1959	Phi	N	S-3	21	.297
1959	Cle	A	2-S-3	27	.164
1962	KC	A	P	3	0-1
	BRTR			1531	0-2 / .262

HAMNER, RALPH CONANT
(Bruz)
b.Sept.12,1916 Gibsland,La.

(Continued)

Yr	Cl	Lea	Pos	G	Rec
1946	Chi	A	P	25	2-7
1947	Chi	N	P	3	1-2
1948	Chi	N	P	27	5-9
1949	Chi	N	P	6	0-2
	BRTR			61	8-20

HAMNER, WESLEY GARVIN
b.Mar.18,1924 Richmond,Va.

Yr	Cl	Lea	Pos	G	Rec
1945	Phi	N	2-S-3	32	.198
	BRTR				

HAMON, FREDERICK

Yr	Cl	Lea	Pos	G	Rec
1922	Cle	A	P	1	0-0

HAMRIC, ODBERT HERMAN
b.Mar.1,1928 Clarksburg,W.Va.

Yr	Cl	Lea	Pos	G	Rec
1955	Bro	N	H	2	.000
1958	Bal	A	H	8	.125
	BLTR			10	.111

HAMRICK, RAYMOND BERNARD
b.Aug.1,1921 Nashville,Tenn.

Yr	Cl	Lea	Pos	G	Rec
1943	Phi	N	2-S	44	.200
1944	Phi	N	S	74	.205
	BRTR			118	.204

HANCKEN, MORRIS MEDLOCK
(Buddy)
b.Aug.30,1914 Birmingham,Ala.

Yr	Cl	Lea	Pos	G	Rec
1940	Phi	A	C	1	.000
	BRTR				

HANCOCK, FRED JAMES
b.Mar.28,1921 Allenport,Pa.

Yr	Cl	Lea	Pos	G	Rec
1949	Chi	A	S-3-O	39	.135
	BRTR				

HANDIBOE, ALOYSIUS JAMES
(Coalyard Mike)
b.July 21,1887 Washington,D.C.
d.Jan.31,1953

Yr	Cl	Lea	Pos	G	Rec
1911	NY	A	O	5	.067
	BLTL				

HANDIBOE, JAMES EDWARD
b.July 17,1866 Columbus,O.
d.Nov.8,1942

Yr	Cl	Lea	Pos	G	Rec
1886	Pit	a	P-O	14	7-7 / .114

HANDLEY, EUGENE LOUIS
b.Nov.25,1914 St. Louis,Mo.

Yr	Cl	Lea	Pos	G	Rec
1946	Phi	A	2-S-3	89	.251
1947	Phi	A	2-S-3	36	.256
	BRTR			125	.252

HANDLEY, LEE ELMER
(Jeep)
b.July 31,1913 St. Louis,Mo.

Yr	Cl	Lea	Pos	G	Rec
1936	Cin	N	2	24	.308
1937	Pit	N	2	127	.250
1938	Pit	N	3	139	.268
1939	Pit	N	3	101	.285
1940	Pit	N	2-3	98	.281
1941	Pit	N	3	124	.288
1944	Pit	N	2-S-3	40	.221
1945	Pit	N	3	98	.298
1946	Pit	N	2-3	116	.238
1947	Phi	N	2-S-3	101	.253
	BRTR			968	.269

HANEBRINK, HARRY ALOYSIUS
b.Nov.12,1927 St. Louis,Mo.

Yr	Cl	Lea	Pos	G	Rec
1953	Mil	N	2-3	51	.238
1957	Mil	N	3	6	.286
1958	Mil	N	3-O	63	.188
1959	Phi	N	2-3-O	57	.258
	BLTR			177	.224

HANEY, FRED GIRARD
(Pudge)
b.Apr.25,1898 Albuquerque,N.Mex.

Yr	Cl	Lea	Pos	G	Rec
1922	Det	A	1-3	81	.352
1923	Det	A	2-S-3	142	.282

(Continued)

Yr	Cl	Lea	Pos	G	Rec
1924	Det	A	3	86	.309
1925	Det	A	3	114	.279
1926	Bos	A	3	138	.221
1927	Bos	A	3	47	.276
1927	Chi	N	H	4	.000
1929	St.L	N	3	10	.115
	BRTR			622	.275

Non-playing manager St.L (A) 1939-41 Pit (N) 1953-55 and Mil (N) 1956-59

HANFORD, CHARLES JOSEPH
b.June 3,1882 Tunstall,England.

Yr	Cl	Lea	Pos	G	Rec
1914	Buf	F	O	156	.287
1915	Chi	F	O	74	.239
	BRTR			230	.276

HANIFIN, PATRICK JAMES
b.1868 Nova Scotia,Canada
d.Nov.5,1908

Yr	Cl	Lea	Pos	G	Rec
1897	Bro	N	O	9	.200

HANKINS, DONALD WAYNE
b.Feb.9,1903 Pendleton,Ind.

Yr	Cl	Lea	Pos	G	Rec
1927	Det	A	P	20	2-1
	BRTR				

HANKINS, JAY NELSON
b.Nov.7,1930 St.Louis Co.,Mo.

Yr	Cl	Lea	Pos	G	Rec
1961	KC	A	O	76	.185
	BLTR				

HANKINSON, FRANK EDWARD
b.1854 New York,N.Y.
d.Apr.5,1911

Yr	Cl	Lea	Pos	G	Rec
1878	Chi	N	P-3	57	0-1 / .268
1879	Chi	N	P-O	41	14-9 / .183
1880	Cle	N	P-3-O	68	1-1 / .209
1881	Tro	N	S-3	84	.196
1883	NY	N	3	91	.221
1884	NY	N	3	101	.235
1885	Met	a	3	96	.241
1886	Met	a	3	136	.240
1887	Met	a	3	127	.315
1888	KC	a	2	37	.175
	BRTR			838	15-11 / .239

HANLEY, JAMES PATRICK
b.Providence,R.I.

Yr	Cl	Lea	Pos	G	Rec
1913	NY	A	P	1	0-0

HANLON, EDWARD HUGH
(Ned)
b.Aug.22,1857 Montville,Conn.
d.Apr.14,1937

Yr	Cl	Lea	Pos	G	Rec
1880	Cle	N	S-3-O	72	.247
1881	Det	N	3-O	75	.278
1882	Det	N	3-O	79	.236
1883	Det	N	2-O	97	.245
1884	Det	N	O	112	.268
1885	Det	N	3-O	106	.301
1886	Det	N	O	126	.234
1887	Det	N	O	118	.316
1888	Det	N	O	108	.265
1889	Pit	N	M-O	115	.238
1890	Pit	p	M-O	119	.284
1891	Pit	N	M-O	115	.274
1892	Bal	N	M-O	8	.233
	BL			1250	.266

Non-playing manager Bal (N) 1893-98, Bro (N) 1899-1905 and Cin (N) 1906-07.

HANLON, WILLIAM
(Big Bill)
b.Cal.

Yr	Cl	Lea	Pos	G	Rec
1903	Chi	N	1	8	.045

HANNA, JOHN
b.Philadelphia,Pa.

Yr	Cl	Lea	Pos	G	Rec
1884	Was	a	C-O	24	.113
1884	Ric	a	C-S	22	.206
				46	.162

HANNAH, JAMES HARRISON
(Truck)
b.June 5,1892 Larimore,N.Dak.

Yr	Cl	Lea	Pos	G	Rec
1918	NY	A	C	90	.220
1919	NY	A	C	75	.238
1920	NY	A	C	79	.247
BRTR				244	.235

HANNAH, JAMES JOHN
b.Jan.7,1940 Jersey City,N.J.

Yr	Cl	Lea	Pos	G	Rec
1962	Was	A	P	42	2-4
BRTR					

HANNIFAN, JOHN JOSEPH
b.Feb.25,1883 Holyoke,Mass.
d.Oct.27,1945

Yr	Cl	Lea	Pos	G	Rec
1906	Phi	A	H	1	.000
1906	NY	N	S-3	10	.200
1907	NY	N	1	49	.228
1908	NY	N	2	1	.000
1908	Bos	N	3	79	.206
TR				140	.214

HANNING, LOY VERNON
b.Oct.18,1917 Bunker,Mo.

Yr	Cl	Lea	Pos	G	Rec
1939	St.L	A	P	4	0-1
1942	St.L	A	P	11	1-1
BRTR				15	1-2

HANSEN, ANDREW VIGGO
(Swede)
b.Nov.12,1924 Lake Worth,Fla.

Yr	Cl	Lea	Pos	G	Rec
1944	NY	N	P	24	3-3
1945	NY	N	P	23	4-3
1947	NY	N	P	27	1-5
1948	NY	N	P	36	5-3
1949	NY	N	P	33	2-6
1950	NY	N	P	31	0-1
1951	Phi	N	P	24	3-1
1952	Phi	N	P	43	5-6
1953	Phi	N	P	30	0-2
BRTR				271	23-30

HANSEN, DOUGLAS WILLIAM
b.Dec.16,1928 Los Angeles,Cal.

Yr	Cl	Lea	Pos	G	Rec
1951	Cle	A	H	3	.000
BRTR					

HANSEN, RONALD LAVERN
b.Apr.5,1938 Oxford,Neb.

Yr	Cl	Lea	Pos	G	Rec
1958	Bal	A	S	12	.000
1959	Bal	A	S	2	.000
1960	Bal	A	S	153	.255
1961	Bal	A	2-S	155	.248
1962	Bal	A	S-3	71	.172
BRTR				393	.235

HANSEN, ROY EMIL
(Snipe)
b.Feb.21,1907 Chicago,Ill.

Yr	Cl	Lea	Pos	G	Rec
1930	Phi	N	P	22	0-7
1932	Phi	N	P	39	10-10
1933	Phi	N	P	33	6-14
1934	Phi	N	P	50	6-12
1935	Phi	N	P	2	0-1
1935	St.L	A	P	10	0-1
BBTL				156	22-45

HANSFORD, F. C.

Yr	Cl	Lea	Pos	G	Rec
1898	Bro	N	P	1	0-1
TL					

HANSKI, DONALD THOMAS
(Real name Donald Thomas Hanyzewski)
b.Feb.27,1918 LaPorte,Ind.
d.Sept.2,1957

Yr	Cl	Lea	Pos	G	Rec
1943	Chi	A	P-1	9	{ 0-0 .238
1944	Chi	A	P	2	0-0
BLTL				11	{ 0-0 .227

HANSON, EARL SYLVESTER
(Ollie)
b.Jan.19,1896 Holbrook,Mass.

Yr	Cl	Lea	Pos	G	Rec
1921	Chi	N	P	2	0-2
BRTR					

HANSON, JOSEPH
b.St.Louis,Mo.

Yr	Cl	Lea	Pos	G	Rec
1913	NY	A	C	1	.000
TR					

HANSON, RAYMOND
b.Mar.6,1898 Beloit,Wis.

Yr	Cl	Lea	Pos	G	Rec
1918	Was	A	P	5	1-0
BRTR					

HANYZEWSKI, DONALD THOMAS
(Played under name of Donald Thomas Hanski)

HANYZEWSKI, EDWARD MICHAEL
b.Sept.18,1920 Union Mills,Ind.

Yr	Cl	Lea	Pos	G	Rec
1942	Chi	N	P	6	1-1
1943	Chi	N	P	33	8-7
1944	Chi	N	P	14	2-5
1945	Chi	N	P	2	0-0
1946	Chi	N	P	3	1-0
BRTR				58	12-13

HAPPENNY, JOHN CLIFFORD
b.May 18,1901 Waltham,Mass.

Yr	Cl	Lea	Pos	G	Rec
1923	Chi	A	2	32	.221
BRTR					

HARBIDGE, WILLIAM ARTHUR
(Yaller Bill)
b.Mar.29,1855 Philadelphia,Pa.
d.Mar.17,1924

Yr	Cl	Lea	Pos	G	Rec
1875	Har	n	C-1-2-O	50	NR
1876	Har	N	C-O	30	.211
1877	Har	N	C-2-O	41	.222
1878	Chi	N	C-O	53	.298
1879	Chi	N	C-O	1	.000
1880	Tro	N	C-O	8	.370
1882	Tro	N	C-1-O	32	.187
1883	Phi	N	C-2-S-3-O	73	.221
1884	Cin	U	O	65	.271
BLTL				353	NR

HARDER, MELVIN LeROY
(Chief)
b.Oct.15,1909 Beemer,Neb.

Yr	Cl	Lea	Pos	G	Rec
1928	Cle	A	P	23	0-2
1929	Cle	A	P	11	1-0
1930	Cle	A	P	36	11-10
1931	Cle	A	P	40	13-14
1932	Cle	A	P	39	15-13
1933	Cle	A	P	44	15-17
1934	Cle	A	P	44	20-12
1935	Cle	A	P	42	22-11
1936	Cle	A	P	36	15-15
1937	Cle	A	P	38	15-12
1938	Cle	A	P	39	17-10
1939	Cle	A	P	29	15-9
1940	Cle	A	P	31	12-11
1941	Cle	A	P	15	5-4
1942	Cle	A	P	29	13-14
1943	Cle	A	P	19	8-7
1944	Cle	A	P	30	12-10
1945	Cle	A	P	11	3-7
1946	Cle	A	P	13	5-4
1947	Cle	A	P	15	6-4
BRTR				584	223-186

Non-playing manager Cle (A) 1961

HARDESTY, SCOTT D.
b.Dayton,O.

Yr	Cl	Lea	Pos	G	Rec
1899	NY	N	S	21	.228

HARDIE, LEWIS W.
b.Aug.24,1864 New York,N.Y.

Yr	Cl	Lea	Pos	G	Rec
1884	Phi	N	C	2	.143
1886	Chi	N	C	16	.176
1890	Bos	N	C-O	47	.227
1891	Bal	a	O	15	.232
				80	.223

HARDIN, WILLIAM EDGAR
(Bud)
b.June 14,1923 Shelby,N.C.

Yr	Cl	Lea	Pos	G	Rec
1952	Chi	N	2-S	3	.143
BRTR					

HARDING, CHARLES H.
b.Jan.3,1891 Nashville,Tenn.

Yr	Cl	Lea	Pos	G	Rec
1913	Det	A	P	1	0-0
BRTR					

HARDING, LOUIS EDWARD
b.San Francisco,Cal.

Yr	Cl	Lea	Pos	G	Rec
1886	St.L	a	C	1	.000

HARDY, CARROLL WILLIAM
b.May 18,1833 Sturgis,S.Dak.

Yr	Cl	Lea	Pos	G	Rec
1958	Cle	A	O	27	.204
1959	Cle	A	O	32	.208
1960	Cle	A	O	29	.111
1960	Bos	A	O	73	.243
1961	Bos	A	O	85	.263
1962	Bos	A	O	115	.215
BRTR				361	.230

HARDY, DAVID ALEXANDER
(Alex)
b.1877 Toronto,Ont.,Canada
d.Apr.22,1940

Yr	Cl	Lea	Pos	G	Rec
1902	Chi	N	P	4	2-2
1903	Chi	N	P	3	1-1
TL				7	3-3

HARDY, FRANCIS JOSEPH
b.Jan,6,1923 Marmarth,N.Dak.

Yr	Cl	Lea	Pos	G	Rec
1951	NY	N	P	2	0-0
BRTR					

HARDY, HARRY
b.Nov.5,1875 Steubenville,O.
d.Sept.4,1943

Yr	Cl	Lea	Pos	G	Rec
1905	Was	A	P	8	3-1
1906	Was	A	P	5	0-3
				13	3-4

HARDY, JOHN DOOLITTLE
b.June 23,1880 Cleveland,O.

Yr	Cl	Lea	Pos	G	Rec
1903	Cle	A	O	5	.150
1907	Chi	N	C	1	.250
1909	Was	A	C	10	.167
1910	Was	A	C	7	.375
TR				23	.196

HARGRAVE, EUGENE FRANKLIN (Bubbles)
b.July 15,1892 New Haven,Ind.

Yr	Cl	Lea	Pos	G	Rec
1913	Chi	N	C	3	.333
1914	Chi	N	C	23	.222
1915	Chi	N	C	15	.158
1921	Cin	N	C	93	.289
1922	Cin	N	C	98	.315
1923	Cin	N	C	118	.333
1924	Cin	N	C	98	.301
1925	Cin	N	C	87	.300
1926	Cin	N	C	105	.353
1927	Cin	N	C	102	.308
1928	Cin	N	C	65	.295
1930	NY	A	C	45	.278
BRTR				852	.310

HARGRAVE, WILLIAM McKINLEY
(Pinky)
b.Jan.31,1896 New Haven,Ind.
d.Oct.3,1942

Yr	Cl	Lea	Pos	G	Rec
1923	Was	A	C	33	.288
1924	Was	A	C	24	.152
1925	Was	A	C	5	.333
1925	St.L	A	C	67	.284
1926	St.L	A	C	92	.281
1928	Det	A	C	121	.275
1929	Det	A	C	76	.330
1930	Det	A	C	55	.286
1930	Was	A	C	10	.179
1931	Was	A	C	40	.325
1932	Bos	N	C	82	.263
1933	Bos	N	C	45	.178
BBTR				650	.278

HARGREAVES, CHARLES RUSSELL
b.Dec.14,1898 Trenton,N.J.

Yr	Cl	Lea	Pos	G	Rec
1923	Bro	N	C	20	.281
1924	Bro	N	C	15	.407
1925	Bro	N	C-1	45	.277
1926	Bro	N	C	85	.250
1927	Bro	N	C	46	.286
1928	Bro	N	C	20	.197
1928	Pit	N	C	79	.285
1929	Pit	N	C	102	.268
1930	Pit	N	C	11	.226
	BRTR			423	.270

HARGROVE, WILLIAM PATRICK (Pat)
b.May 10,1896 Palmyra Court House, Kan.

Yr	Cl	Lea	Pos	G	Rec
1918	Chi	A	H	2	.000
	BRTR				

HARKINS, JOHN JOSEPH
b.Apr.12,1859 Newark,N.J.
d.Nov.20,1940

Yr	Cl	Lea	Pos	G	Rec
1884	Cle	N	P-S-3-O	60	12-32 / .205
1885	Bro	a	P	43	14-21
1886	Bro	a	P	41	14-16
1887	Bro	a	P	27	10-14
1888	Bal	a	P	1	0-1
	TR			172	50-84 / .235

HARKNESS, FREDERICK HARVEY (Specs)
b.Dec.13,1887 Los Angeles,Cal.
d.May 18,1952

Yr	Cl	Lea	Pos	G	Rec
1910	Cle	A	P	26	10-7
1911	Cle	A	P	12	2-2
	BRTR			38	12-9

HARKNESS, THOMAS WILLIAM
b.Dec.23,1937 Lachine,Que.,Canada

Yr	Cl	Lea	Pos	G	Rec
1961	LA	N	1	5	.500
1962	LA	N	1	92	.258
	BLTL			97	.286

HARLEY, HENRY RISK
b.Aug.18,1874 Springfield,O.

Yr	Cl	Lea	Pos	G	Rec
1905	Bos	N	P	7	2-4
	BRTR				

HARLEY, RICHARD JOSEPH
b.Sept.25,1872 Philadelphia, Pa.
d.Apr.3,1952

Yr	Cl	Lea	Pos	G	Rec
1897	St.L	N	O	89	.288
1898	St.L	N	O	142	.248
1899	Cle	N	O	145	.250
1900	Cin	N	O	5	.450
1901	Cin	N	O	133	.268
1902	Det	A	O	124	.276
1903	Chi	N	O	103	.231
	BLTR			741	.261

HARMAN, WILLIAM BELL
b.Jan.2,1919 Bridgewater,Va.

Yr	Cl	Lea	Pos	G	Rec
1941	Phi	N	P-C	15	0-0 / .071
	BRTR				

HARMON, CHARLES BYRON
b.Apr.23,1926 Washington,Ind.

Yr	Cl	Lea	Pos	G	Rec
1954	Cin	N	1-3	94	.238
1955	Cin	N	1-3-O	96	.253
1956	Cin	N	1-O	13	.000
1956	St.L	N	1-3-O	20	.000
1957	St.L	N	O	9	.333
1957	Phi	N	1-3-O	57	.256
	BRTR			289	.238

HARMON, ROBERT GREEN
b.Oct.15.1887 Liberal,Mo.
d.Nov.27,1961

Yr	Cl	Lea	Pos	G	Rec
1909	St.L	N	P	21	6-11
1910	St.L	N	P	43	13-15
1911	St.L	N	P	51	23-16
1912	St.L	N	P	46	18-18

(Continued)

Yr	Cl	Lea	Pos	G	Rec
1913	St.L	N	P	46	8-21
1914	Pit	N	P	44	13-17
1915	Pit	N	P	42	16-17
1916	Pit	N	P	35	8-11
1918	Pit	N	P	18	2-7
	BLTR			346	107-133

HARPER, CHARLES WILLIAM (Jack)
b.Apr.2,1878 Franklin,Pa.
d.Sept.30,1950

Yr	Cl	Lea	Pos	G	Rec
1899	Cle	N	P	5	1-4
1900	St.L	N	P	1	0-1
1901	St.L	N	P	36	23-13
1902	St.L	A	P	29	17-10
1903	Cin	N	P	17	7-7
1904	Cin	N	P	35	24-8
1905	Cin	N	P	26	9-14
1906	Cin	N	P	5	0-3
1906	Chi	N	P	1	0-0
	BRTR			155	81-60

HARPER, GEORGE B.
b.Aug.17,1866 Milwaukee,Wis.
d.Dec.11,1931

Yr	Cl	Lea	Pos	G	Rec
1894	Phi	N	P	12	5-3
1896	Bro	N	P	16	4-8
				28	9-11

HARPER, GEORGE WASHINGTON
b.June 24,1892 Arlington,Ky.

Yr	Cl	Lea	Pos	G	Rec
1916	Det	A	O	44	.161
1917	Det	A	O	47	.205
1918	Det	A	O	69	.243
1922	Cin	N	O	128	.339
1923	Cin	N	O	61	.256
1924	Cin	N	O	28	.270
1924	Phi	N	O	109	.295
1925	Phi	N	O	132	.349
1926	Phi	N	O	56	.314
1927	NY	N	O	145	.331
1928	NY	N	O	19	.228
1928	St.L	N	O	99	.305
1929	Bos	N	O	136	.291
	BLTR			1073	.303

HARPER, HARRY CLAYTON
b.Apr.24,1895 Hackensack,N.J.

Yr	Cl	Lea	Pos	G	Rec
1913	Was	A	P	4	0-0
1914	Was	A	P	22	2-1
1915	Was	A	P	19	5-4
1916	Was	A	P	36	15-10
1917	Was	A	P	31	11-12
1918	Was	A	P	36	11-10
1919	Was	A	P	35	6-21
1920	Bos	A	P	27	5-14
1921	NY	A	P	8	4-3
1923	Bro	N	P	1	0-1
	BLTL			219	60-76

HARPER, JOHN WESLEY
b.Aug.5,1893 Hendricks,W.Va.
d.June 18,1927

Yr	Cl	Lea	Pos	G	Rec
1915	Phi	A	P	3	0-1
	BRTR				

HARPER, THOMAS
b.Oct.14,1940 Oak Grove,La.

Yr	Cl	Lea	Pos	G	Rec
1962	Cin	N	3	6	.174
	BRTR				

HARPER, WILLIAM HOMER (Blue Sleeve)
b.June 14.1889 Bertrand,Mo.
d.June 17,1951

Yr	Cl	Lea	Pos	G	Rec
1911	St.L	A	P	2	0-0
	BBTR				

HARRELL, OSCAR MARTIN (Slim)
b.July 31,1890 Grandview,Tex.

Yr	Cl	Lea	Pos	G	Rec
1912	Phi	A	P	1	0-0
	BRTR				

HARRELL, RAYMOND JAMES (Cowboy)
b.Feb.16,1912 Petrolia, Tex.

(Continued)

Yr	Cl	Lea	Pos	G	Rec
1935	St.L	N	P	11	1-1
1937	St.L	N	P	35	3-7
1938	St.L	N	P	32	2-3
1939	Chi	N	P	4	0-2
1939	Phi	N	P	22	3-7
1940	Pit	N	P	3	0-0
1945	NY	N	P	12	0-0
	BRTR			119	9-20

HARRELL, WILLIAM
b.July 18,1928 Troy,N.Y.

Yr	Cl	Lea	Pos	G	Rec
1955	Cle	A	S	13	.421
1957	Cle	A	2-S-3	22	.263
1958	Cle	A	2-S-3-O	101	.218
1961	Bos	A	1-S-3	37	.162
	BRTR			173	.231

HARRINGTON, ANDREW FRANCIS
b.Nov.13,1888 Wakefield,Mass.
d.Nov.12,1938

Yr	Cl	Lea	Pos	G	Rec
1913	Cin	N	P	1	0-0
	BRTR				

HARRINGTON, ANDREW MATTHEW
b.Feb.12,1904 Mountain View,Cal.

Yr	Cl	Lea	Pos	G	Rec
1925	Det	A	2	1	.000
	BRTR				

HARRINGTON, JEREMIAH PETER
b.Aug.12,1869 Keokuk,Ia.
d.Apr.17,1913

Yr	Cl	Lea	Pos	G	Rec
1890	Cin	N	C	65	.246
1891	Cin	N	C	90	.229
1892	Cin	N	C	18	.213
1893	Lou	N	C	10	.121
	TR			183	.228

HARRINGTON, JOSEPH C.
b.Dec.21,1869 Fall River,Mass.
d.Sept.13,1933

Yr	Cl	Lea	Pos	G	Rec
1895	Bos	N	2	18	.299
1896	Bos	N	3	53	.203
				71	.229

HARRINGTON, WILLIAM WOMBLE
b.Oct.3,1927 Sanford,N.C.

Yr	Cl	Lea	Pos	G	Rec
1953	Phi	A	P	1	0-0
1955	KC	A	P	34	3-3
1956	KC	A	P	23	2-2
	BRTR			58	5-5

HARRIS, BENJAMIN F.
b.1889 Nashville,Tenn.

Yr	Cl	Lea	Pos	G	Rec
1914	KC	F	P	27	7-7
1915	KC	F	P	1	0-0
	BRTR			28	7-7

HARRIS, BOYD GAIL
b.Oct.15,1931 Abingdon,Va.

Yr	Cl	Lea	Pos	G	Rec
1955	NY	N	1	79	.232
1956	NY	N	1	12	.132
1957	NY	N	1	90	.240
1958	Det	A	1	134	.273
1959	Det	A	1	114	.221
1960	Det	A	1	8	.000
	BLTL			437	.240

HARRIS, CHALMER LUMAN (Lum)
b.Jan.17,1915 New Castle,Ala.

Yr	Cl	Lea	Pos	G	Rec
1941	Phi	A	P	33	4-4
1942	Phi	A	P	26	11-15
1943	Phi	A	P	32	7-21
1944	Phi	A	P	23	10-9
1946	Phi	A	P	34	3-14
1947	Was	A	P	3	0-0
	BRTR			151	35-63

HARRIS, CHARLES (Bubba)
b.Jan.17,1925 Birmingham,Ala.

Yr	Cl	Lea	Pos	G	Rec
1948	Phi	A	P	45	5-2
1949	Phi	A	P	37	1-1
1951	Phi	A	P	3	0-0
1951	Cle	A	P	2	0-0
BRTR				87	6-3

HARRIS, CHARLES JENKINS
b.Oct.21,1877 Macon,Ga.

Yr	Cl	Lea	Pos	G	Rec
1899	Bal	N	3	21	.283

HARRIS, DAVID STANLEY (Sheriff)
b.July 27,1902 Greensboro,N.C.

Yr	Cl	Lea	Pos	G	Rec
1925	Bos	N	O	92	.265
1928	Bos	N	O	7	.118
1930	Chi	A	O	33	.235
1930	Was	A	O	73	.320
1931	Was	A	O	77	.312
1932	Was	A	O	81	.327
1933	Was	A	1-3-O	82	.260
1934	Was	A	O	97	.251
BRTR				542	.281

HARRIS, FRANK W.
b.Nov.2,1858 Pittsburgh,Pa.
d.Nov.26,1939

Yr	Cl	Lea	Pos	G	Rec
1884	Alt	U	1-O	24	.242

HARRIS, HERBERT
b.Apr.24,1913 Whiting,Ind.

Yr	Cl	Lea	Pos	G	Rec
1936	Phi	N	P	4	0-0
BLTL					

HARRIS, JOSEPH (Moon)
b.May 20,1892 Coulters,Pa.
d.Dec.10,1959

Yr	Cl	Lea	Pos	G	Rec
1914	NY	A	O	2	.000
1917	Cle	A	1	112	.304
1919	Cle	A	1	62	.375
1922	Bos	A	1-O	119	.316
1923	Bos	A	O	142	.335
1924	Bos	A	1	133	.301
1925	Bos	A	1	9	.150
1925	Was	A	1-O	99	.324
1926	Was	A	1-O	92	.307
1927	Pit	N	1	129	.326
1928	Pit	N	1	16	.391
1928	Bro	N	O	55	.236
BRTR				970	.317

HARRIS, JOSEPH WHITE
b.Feb.1,1882 Melrose,Mass.

Yr	Cl	Lea	Pos	G	Rec
1905	Bos	A	P	3	1-2
1906	Bos	A	P	30	2-21
1907	Bos	A	P	12	0-7
TR				45	3-30

HARRIS, MAURICE CHARLES (Mickey)
b.Jan.30.1917 New York,N.Y.

Yr	Cl	Lea	Pos	G	Rec
1940	Bos	A	P	13	4-2
1941	Bos	A	P	35	8-14
1946	Bos	A	P	34	17-9
1947	Bos	A	P	15	5-4
1948	Bos	A	P	20	7-10
1949	Bos	A	P	7	2-3
1949	Was	A	P	23	2-12
1950	Was	A	P	53	5-9
1951	Was	A	P	41	6-8
1952	Was	A	P	1	0-0
1952	Cle	A	P	29	3-0
BLTL				271	59-71

HARRIS, ROBERT ARTHUR
b.May 1,1916 Gillette,Wyo.

Yr	Cl	Lea	Pos	G	Rec
1938	Det	A	P	3	1-0
1939	Det	A	P	5	1-1
1939	St.L	A	P	29	3-12
1940	St.L	A	P	35	11-15
1941	St.L	A	P	34	12-14
1942	St.L	A	P	6	1-5
1942	Phi	A	P	16	1-5
BRTR				128	30-52

HARRIS, ROBERT NED
b.July 9,1916 Ames,Ia.

Yr	Cl	Lea	Pos	G	Rec
1941	Det	A	O	26	.213
1942	Det	A	O	121	.271
1943	Det	A	O	114	.254
1946	Det	A	H	1	.000
BLTL				262	.259

HARRIS, SPENCER ANTHONY
b.Aug.12,1900 Duluth,Minn.

Yr	Cl	Lea	Pos	G	Rec
1925	Chi	A	O	56	.283
1926	Chi	A	O	80	.252
1929	Was	A	O	6	.214
1930	Phi	A	O	22	.184
BLTL				164	.250

HARRIS, STANLEY RAYMOND (Bucky)
b.Nov.8,1896 Port Jervis,N.Y.

Yr	Cl	Lea	Pos	G	Rec
1919	Was	A	2	8	.214
1920	Was	A	2	137	.300
1921	Was	A	2	154	.289
1922	Was	A	2	154	.269
1923	Was	A	2	145	.282
1924	Was	A	M-2	143	.268
1925	Was	A	M-2	144	.287
1926	Was	A	M-2	141	.283
1927	Was	A	M-2	128	.267
1928	Was	A	M-2	99	.204
1929	Det	A	M-2	7	.091
1931	Det	A	M-2	4	.125
BRTR				1264	.274

Non-playing manager Det (A) 1930, 1932-33, Bos (A) 1934, Was (A) 1935-42, Phi (N) 1943, NY (A) 1947-48, Was (A) 1950-54 and Det (A) 1955-56.

HARRIS, WILLIAM MILTON
b.June 23,1900 Wylie,Tex.

Yr	Cl	Lea	Pos	G	Rec
1923	Cin	N	P	22	3-2
1924	Cin	N	P	3	0-0
1931	Pit	N	P	4	2-2
1932	Pit	N	P	37	10-9
1933	Pit	N	P	31	4-4
1934	Pit	N	P	11	0-0
1938	Bos	A	P	13	5-5
BRTR				121	24-22

HARRIS, WILLIAM THOMAS
b.Dec.3,1930 Marysville,N.B.,Canada

Yr	Cl	Lea	Pos	G	Rec
1957	Bro	N	P	1	0-1
1959	LA	N	P	1	0-0
BLTR				2	0-1

HARRISON, ...

Yr	Cl	Lea	Pos	G	Rec
1875	NH	n	C	1	NR

HARRISON, LEO J. (Ben)

Yr	Cl	Lea	Pos	G	Rec
1901	Was	A	O	1	.000

HARRISON, ROBERT LEE
b.Sept.22,1930 St.Louis,Mo.

Yr	Cl	Lea	Pos	G	Rec
1955	Bal	A	P	1	0-0
1956	Bal	A	P	1	0-0
BLTR				2	0-0

HARRISS, WILLIAM BRYAN (Slim)
b.Dec.11,1897 Brownwood,Tex.

Yr	Cl	Lea	Pos	G	Rec
1920	Phi	A	P	31	9-14
1921	Phi	A	P	39	11-16
1922	Phi	A	P	47	9-20
1923	Phi	A	P	46	10-16
1924	Phi	A	P	36	6-10
1925	Phi	A	P	46	19-12
1926	Phi	A	P	12	3-5
1926	Bos	A	P	21	6-10
1927	Bos	A	P	44	14-21
1928	Bos	A	P	27	8-11
BRTR				349	95-135

HARRIST, EARL (Irish)
b.Aug.20,1920 Dubach,La.

Yr	Cl	Lea	Pos	G	Rec
1945	Cin	N	P	14	2-4
1947	Chi	A	P	33	3-8
1948	Chi	A	P	11	1-3
1948	Was	A	P	23	3-3
1952	St.L	A	P	36	2-8

(Continued)

Yr	Cl	Lea	Pos	G	Rec
1953	Chi	A	P	7	1-0
1953	Det	A	p	8	0-2
BRTR				132	12-28

HARSHANY, SAMUEL
b.May 1,1910 Madison,Ill.

Yr	Cl	Lea	Pos	G	Rec
1937	St.L	A	C	5	.091
1938	St.L	A	C	11	.292
1939	St.L	A	C	42	.241
1940	St.L	A	C	3	.000
BRTR				61	.238

HARSHMAN, JOHN ELVIN
b.July 12,1927 San Diego,Cal.

Yr	Cl	Lea	Pos	G	Rec
1948	NY	N	1	5	.250
1950	NY	N	1	9	.125
1952	NY	N	P	3	0-2
1954	Chi	A	P-1	36	14-8 / .143
1955	Chi	A	P	32	11-7
1956	Chi	A	P	36	15-11
1957	Chi	A	P	30	8-8
1958	Bal	A	P-O	47	12-15 / .195
1959	Bal	A	P	15	0-6
1959	Bos	A	P	9	2-3
1959	Cle	A	P	21	5-1
1960	Cle	A	P	15	2-4
BLTL				258	69-65 / .179

HARSTAD, OSCAR THEANDER
b.May 24,1892 Parkland,Wash.

Yr	Cl	Lea	Pos	G	Rec
1915	Cle	A	P	32	3-6

HART, JAMES A.
b.July 10,1855 Girard,Pa.
d.July 18.1919
Non-playing manager Lou (a) 1885-86 and Bos (N) 1889.

HART, JAMES HENRY (Hub)
b.Feb.2,1878 Everett,Mass.
d.Oct.10,1960

Yr	Cl	Lea	Pos	G	Rec
1905	Chi	A	C	11	.125
1906	Chi	A	C	17	.162
1907	Chi	A	C	29	.271
BLTR				57	.217

HART, JOSEPH L.

Yr	Cl	Lea	Pos	G	Rec
1890	St.L	a	P	28	12-9

HART, THOMAS HENRY (Bushy)
b.June 15,1869 Canaan,N.Y.
d.Sept.17,1939

Yr	Cl	Lea	Pos	G	Rec
1891	Was	a	C-O	8	.130

HART, WARREN F.

Yr	Cl	Lea	Pos	G	Rec
1901	Bal	A	1	58	.312

HART, WILLIAM FRANKLIN
b.July 19,1865 Louisville,Ky.
d.Sept.19,1936

Yr	Cl	Lea	Pos	G	Rec
1886	Ath	a	P	23	9-13
1887	Ath	a	P	3	1-2
1892	Bro	N	P	29	7-10
1895	Pit	N	P	31	14-15
1896	St.L	N	P	46	13-26
1897	St.L	N	P	43	9-23
1898	Pit	N	P	15	6-9
1901	Cle	A	P	20	6-12
				210	65-110

HART, WILLIAM WOODROW
b.Mar.4,1915 Wisconisco,Pa.

Yr	Cl	Lea	Pos	G	Rec
1943	Bro	N	S	8	.158
1944	Bro	N	S-3	29	.178
1945	Bro	N	S-3	58	.230
BRTR				95	.207

HARTER, FRANK PIERCE
b.Sept.19,1886 Keyesport,Ill.
d.Apr.14,1959

(Continued)

Yr	Cl	Lea	Pos	G	Rec
1912	Cin	N	P	6	1-2
1913	Cin	N	P	17	1-1
1914	Ind	F	P	6	1-2
	BRTR			29	3-5

HARTFORD, BRUCE
b.May 14,1892 Chicago,Ill.

Yr	Cl	Lea	Pos	G	Rec
1914	Cle	A	S	8	.181
	BRTR				

HARTJE, CHRISTIAN HENRY
b.Aug.25,1915 San Francisco,Cal.
d.June 26,1946

Yr	Cl	Lea	Pos	G	Rec
1939	Bro	N	C	9	.313
	BRTR				

HARTLEY, GROVER ALLEN
(Slick)
b.July 2,1888 Osgood,Ind.

Yr	Cl	Lea	Pos	G	Rec
1911	NY	N	C	10	.222
1912	NY	N	C	25	.235
1913	NY	N	C	23	.316
1914	St.L	F	C	86	.286
1915	St.L	F	C	117	.271
1916	St.L	A	C	89	.225
1917	St.L	A	C	19	.231
1924	NY	N	C	4	.286
1925	NY	N	C-1	46	.316
1926	NY	N	C	13	.048
1927	Bos	A	C	103	.275
1929	Cle	A	C	24	.273
1930	Cle	A	C	1	.750
1934	St.L	A	C	5	.333
	BRTR			565	.267

HARTLEY, WALTER SCOTT
(Chick)
b.Aug.22,1880 Philadelphia,Pa.
d.July 18,1948

Yr	Cl	Lea	Pos	G	Rec
1902	NY	N	O	1	.000

HARTMAN, CHARLES OTTO
b.Aug.10,1888 Los Angeles,Cal.

Yr	Cl	Lea	Pos	G	Rec
1908	Bos	A	P	1	0-0

HARTMAN, FREDERICK ORRIN
(Dutch)
b.Apr.25,1868 Allegheny,Pa.
d.Nov.11,1938

Yr	Cl	Lea	Pos	G	Rec
1894	Pit	N	3	49	.311
1897	St.L	N	3	126	.301
1898	NY	N	3	122	.267
1899	NY	N	3	52	.241
1901	Chi	A	3	120	.313
1902	St.L	N	1-S-3	112	.221
	TR			581	.278

HARTMAN, J. C.
b.Apr.15,1934 Cottonton,Ala.

Yr	Cl	Lea	Pos	G	Rec
1962	Hou	N	S	51	.223
	BRTR				

HARTMAN, ROBERT LOUIS
b.Aug.28,1937 Kenosha,Wis.

Yr	Cl	Lea	Pos	G	Rec
1959	Mil	N	P	3	0-0
1962	Cle	A	P	8	0-1
	BRTL			11	0-1

HARTNETT, CHARLES LEO
(Gabby)
b.Dec.20,1900 Woonsocket,R.I.

Yr	Cl	Lea	Pos	G	Rec
1922	Chi	N	C	31	.194
1923	Chi	N	C-1	85	.268
1924	Chi	N	C	111	.299
1925	Chi	N	C	117	.289
1926	Chi	N	C	93	.275
1927	Chi	N	C	127	.294
1928	Chi	N	C	120	.302
1929	Chi	N	C	25	.273
1930	Chi	N	C	141	.339
1931	Chi	N	C	116	.282
1932	Chi	N	C	121	.271
1933	Chi	N	C	140	.276
1934	Chi	N	C	130	.299

(Continued)

Yr	Cl	Lea	Pos	G	Rec
1935	Chi	N	C	116	.344
1936	Chi	N	C	121	.307
1937	Chi	N	C	110	.354
1938	Chi	N	M-C	88	.274
1939	Chi	N	M-C	97	.278
1940	Chi	N	M-C-1	37	.266
1941	NY	N	C	64	.300
	BRTR			1990	.298

HARTNETT, PATRICK J.
(Happy)
b.Oct.20,1863 S.Boston,Mass.
d.Apr.10,1935

Yr	Cl	Lea	Pos	G	Rec
1890	St.L	a	1	13	.200

HARTRANFT, RAYMOND CHARLES

Yr	Cl	Lea	Pos	G	Rec
1913	Phi	N	P	1	0-0

HARTSEL, TULLOS FREDERICK
(Topsy)
b.June 26,1874 Polk,O.
d.Oct.14,1944

Yr	Cl	Lea	Pos	G	Rec
1898	Lou	N	O	21	.319
1899	Lou	N	O	20	.261
1900	Cin	N	O	18	.328
1901	Chi	N	O	140	.339
1902	Phi	A	O	137	.286
1903	Phi	A	O	98	.311
1904	Phi	A	O	147	.249
1905	Phi	A	O	148	.276
1906	Phi	A	O	144	.255
1907	Phi	A	O	143	.280
1908	Phi	A	O	129	.243
1909	Phi	A	O	83	.270
1910	Phi	A	O	90	.221
1911	Phi	A	O	25	.237
	BLTL			1343	.276

HARTSFIELD, ROY THOMAS
(Spec)
b.Oct.25,1925 Chattahoochee,Ga.

Yr	Cl	Lea	Pos	G	Rec
1950	Bos	N	2	107	.277
1951	Bos	N	2	120	.271
1952	Bos	N	2	38	.262
	BRTR			265	.273

HARTUNG, CLINTON CLARENCE
(Floppy)
b.Aug.10,1922 Hondo,Tex.

Yr	Cl	Lea	Pos	G	Rec
1947	NY	N	P-O	34	9-7 .309
1948	NY	N	P	43	8-8
1949	NY	N	P	38	9-11
1950	NY	N	P-1-C	32	3-3 .302
1951	NY	N	O	21	.205
1952	NY	N	O	28	.218
	BRTR			196	29-29 .212

HARTZELL, ROY ALLEN
b.July 6,1881 Golden,Colo.
d.Nov.5,1961

Yr	Cl	Lea	Pos	G	Rec
1906	St.L	A	3	113	.213
1907	St.L	A	2-3	60	.236
1908	St.L	A	S-O	115	.265
1909	St.L	A	S-O	152	.271
1910	St.L	A	S-3-O	151	.218
1911	NY	A	3	144	.296
1912	NY	A	3-O	123	.272
1913	NY	A	2-3-O	141	.259
1914	NY	A	O	137	.233
1915	NY	A	O	119	.251
1916	NY	A	O	33	.187
	BLTR			1288	.252

HARVEL, LUTHER RAYMOND
b.Sept.30,1905 Cambria,Ill.

Yr	Cl	Lea	Pos	G	Rec
1928	Cle	A	O	40	.220
	BRTR				

HARVEY, ERWIN K.
b.Jan. 5,1878 Saratoga,Cal.

Yr	Cl	Lea	Pos	G	Rec
1900	Chi	N	P	2	0-0
1901	Chi	A	P-O	17	2-1 .256
1901	Cle	A	P-O	44	0-7 .351
1902	Cle	A	O	12	.369
				75	2-8 .336

HASBROUCK, ROBERT LYNDON
(Ziggy)
b.nov.21,1893 Grundy Center,Ia.

Yr	Cl	Lea	Pos	G	Rec
1916	Chi	A	1	8	.125
1917	Chi	A	2	2	.000
	BRTR			10	.111

HASENMAYER, DONALD IRVIN
b,Apr.4,1927 Roslyn,Pa.

Yr	Cl	Lea	Pos	G	Rec
1945	Phi	N	2-3	5	.111
1946	Phi	N	3	6	.083
	BRTR			11	.100

HASH, HERBERT HOWARD
b.Feb.13,1912 Woolwine,Va.

Yr	Cl	Lea	Pos	G	Rec
1940	Bos	A	p	35	7-7
1941	Bos	A	P	4	1-0
	BRTR			39	8-7

HASLIN, MICHAEL JOSEPH
b.Oct.31,1910 Wilkes-Barre,Pa.

Yr	Cl	Lea	Pos	G	Rec
1933	Phi	N	2	26	.236
1934	Phi	N	2-3	72	.265
1935	Phi	N	2-S-3	110	.265
1936	Phi	N	2-3	16	.344
1936	Bos	N	2-3	36	.279
1937	NY	N	2-S-3	27	.190
1938	NY	N	2-3	31	.324
	BRTR			318	.272

HASNEY, PETER JAMES
b.May 26,1865 England
d.May 24,1908

Yr	Cl	Lea	Pos	G	Rec
1890	Ath	a	O	2	.125

HASSAMAER, WILLIAM LOUIS
(Roaring Bill)
b.July 26,1864 St.Louis,Mo.
d.May 29,1910

Yr	Cl	Lea	Pos	G	Rec
1894	Was	N	3-O	116	.326
1895	Was	N	O	89	.278
1895	Lou	N	1-O	20	.198
1896	Lou	N	1	26	.248
				251	.291

HASSETT, JOHN ALOYSIUS
(Buddy)
b.sept.5,1911 New York,N.Y.

Yr	Cl	Lea	Pos	G	Rec
1936	Bro	N	1	156	.310
1937	Bro	N	1	137	.304
1938	Bro	N	O	115	.293
1939	Bos	N	1-O	147	.309
1940	bos	N	1-O	124	.234
1941	Bos	N	1	118	.296
1942	NY	A	1	132	.284
	BLTL			929	.292

HASSLER, JOSEPH FREDERICK
b.Apr.7,1905 Ft.Smith,Ark.

Yr	Cl	Lea	Pos	G	Rec
1928	Phi	A	S	28	.265
1929	Phi	A	S	4	.000
1930	St.L	A	S	5	.250
	BRTR			37	.239

HASSON, CHARLES EUGENE
(Gene)
b.July 20,1915 Connellsville,Pa.

Yr	Cl	Lea	Pos	G	Rec
1937	Phi	A	1	28	.306
1938	Phi	A	1	19	.275
	BLTL			47	.293

HASTINGS, CHARLES MORTON
b.1871 Ironton,Ohio

Yr	Cl	Lea	Pos	G	Rec
1893	Cle	N	P	16	4-6
1896	Pit	N	P	17	5-9
1897	Pit	N	P	15	7-3
1898	Pit	N	P	18	4-9
				66	20-27

HASTINGS, WINFIELD SCOTT
b.Aug.10,1847 Hillsboro,O.
d.Aug.15,1907

Yr	Cl	Lea	Pos	G	Rec
1871	Rok	n	P-C-2	24	0-1 NR
1872	Cle	n	M-C-2-O	21	NR
1872	Bal	n	C-2	14	NR
1873	Bal	n	C-1-2-O	31	NR
1874	Har	n	C-2-O	52	NR
1875	Chi	n	C-2-O	66	NR
1876	Lou	N	O	67	.254
1877	Cin	N	C-O	20	.141
	BRTR			295	0-1 NR

HASTY, ROBERT KELLER
b.May 3,1896 Canton,Ga.

Yr	Cl	Lea	Pos	G	Rec
1919	Phi	A	P	2	0-2
1920	Phi	A	P	19	1-3
1921	Phi	A	P	35	5-16
1922	Phi	A	P	28	9-14
1923	Phi	A	P	44	13-15
1924	Phi	A	P	18	1-3
	BRTR			146	29-53

HATFIELD, FRED JAMES
b.Mar.18,1925 Lanett,Ala,

Yr	Cl	Lea	Pos	G	Rec
1950	Bos	A	3	10	.250
1951	Bos	A	3	80	.172
1952	Bos	A	3	20	.286
1952	Det	A	S-3	111	.237
1953	Det	A	2-S-3	109	.254
1954	Det	A	2-3	81	.294
1955	Det	A	2-S-3	122	.232
1956	Det	A	2	8	.250
1956	Chi	A	2-S-3	106	.262
1957	Chi	A	3	69	.202
1958	Cle	A	3	3	.125
1958	Cin	N	2-3	3	.000
	BLTR			722	.241

HATFIELD, GILBERT (Colonel)
b.Jan.27,1855 Hoboken,N.J.
d.May 27,1921

Yr	Cl	Lea	Pos	G	Rec
1885	Buf	N	2-3	11	.125
1887	NY	N	3	2	.429
1888	NY	N	3	27	.181
1889	NY	N	P-S	32	0-0 .184
1890	NY	p	S-3	48	.301
1890	Bos	p	S	3	.143
1890	NY	N	P-S-3	20	0-2 .244
1891	Was	a	P-S-3	132	0-2 .258
1893	Bro	N	3	33	.315
1895	Lou	N	S	5	.196
	TR			313	0-2 .246

HATFIELD, JOHN VAN BUREN
b.1847
d.Feb.21,1909

Yr	Cl	Lea	Pos	G	Rec
1871	Mut	n	2-3-O	34	NR
1872	Mut	n	2	56	NR
1873	Mut	n	2-3	53	NR
1874	Mut	n	3-O	64	NR
1875	Mut	n	O	1	NR
1876	Mut	N	2	1	.250
				209	NR

HATHAWAY, RAY WILSON
b.Oct.13,1919 Greenville,O.

Yr	Cl	Lea	Pos	G	Rec
1945	Bro	N	P	4	0-1
	BRTR				

HATTEN, JOSEPH HILARIAN
b.Nov.17,1917 Bancroft,Ia.

Yr	Cl	Lea	Pos	G	Rec
1946	Bro	N	P	42	14-11
1947	Bro	N	P	42	17-8
1948	Bro	N	P	43	13-10
1949	Bro	N	P	39	12-8
1950	Bro	N	P	27	2-2
1951	Bro	N	P	11	1-0
1951	Chi	N	P	23	2-6
1952	Chi	N	P	17	4-4
	BRTL			244	65-49

HATTER, CLYDE MELNO
b.Aug.7,1908 Poplar Hill,Ky.
d.Oct.16,1937

Yr	Cl	Lea	Pos	G	Rec
1935	Det	A	P	8	0-0
1937	Det	A	P	3	1-0
	BRTL			11	1-0

HATTON, GRADY EDGEBERT
b.Oct.7,1922 Beaumont,Tex.

Yr	Cl	Lea	Pos	G	Rec
1946	Cin	N	3-O	116	.271
1947	Cin	N	3	146	.281
1948	Cin	N	2-S-3-O	133	.240
1949	Cin	N	3	137	.263
1950	Cin	N	2-S-3	130	.260
1951	Cin	N	3-O	96	.254
1952	Cin	N	2	128	.213
1953	Cin	N	1-2-3	83	.233
1954	Cin	N	H	1	.000
1954	Chi	A	1-3	13	.167
1954	Bos	A	1-S-3	99	.281
1955	Bos	A	2-3	126	.245
1956	Bos	A	H	5	.400
1956	St.L	N	2-3	44	.247
1956	Bal	A	2-3	27	.148
1960	Chi	N	2	28	.342
	BLTR			1312	.254

HAUG, WILLIAM L.
(Played under name of
William L. Hague)

HAUGHER, JOHN ARTHUR
b.Nov.18,1893 Delhi,O.
d.Aug.3,1944

Yr	Cl	Lea	Pos	G	Rec
1912	Cle	A	O	15	.056
	BLTR				

HAUGHEY, CHRISTOPHER FRANCIS
b.Oct.3,1925 Astoria,N.Y.

Yr	Cl	Lea	Pos	G	Rec
1943	Bro	N	P	1	0-1
	BRTR				

HAUGSTAD, PHILIP DONALD
b.Feb.23,1924 Black River Falls,Wis.

Yr	Cl	Lea	Pos	G	Rec
1947	bro	N	P	6	1-0
1948	Bro	N	P	1	0-0
1951	Bro	N	P	21	0-1
1952	Cin	N	P	9	0-0
	BRTR			37	1-1

HAUSER, ARNOLD J.
(Pee Wee)
b.Sept.25,1888 Chicago,Ill.

Yr	Cl	Lea	Pos	G	Rec
1910	St.L	N	S	118	.205
1911	St.L	N	S	136	.241
1912	St.L	N	S	133	.259
1913	St.L	N	S	22	.289
1915	Chi	F	S	20	.222
	BRTR			429	.238

HAUSER, JOSEPH JOHN
b.Jan.12,1899 Milwaukee,Wis.

Yr	Cl	Lea	Pos	G	Rec
1922	Phi	A	1	111	.323
1923	Phi	A	1	146	.307
1924	Phi	A	1	149	.288
1926	Phi	A	1	91	.192
1928	Phi	A	1	95	.260
1929	Cle	A	1	37	.250
	BLTL			629	.284

HAUSMANN, CLEMENS RAYMOND
b.Aug.17,1919 Houston,Tex.

Yr	Cl	Lea	Pos	G	Rec
1944	Bos	A	P	32	4-7
1945	Bos	A	P	31	5-7
1949	Phi	A	P	1	0-0
	BRTR			64	9-14

HAUSMANN, GEORGE JOHN
b.Feb.11,1917 St.Louis,Mo.

Yr	Cl	Lea	Pos	G	Rec
1944	NY	N	2	131	.268
1945	NY	N	2	154	.279
1949	NY	N	2	16	.128
	BRTR			301	.268

HAWES, ROY LEE
b.July 5,1928 Shiloh,Ill.

Yr	Cl	Lea	Pos	G	Rec
1951	Was	A	1	3	.167
	BLTL				

HAWES, WILLIAM HILDRETH
b.Nov.24,1853 Nashua,N.H.
d.June 16,1940

Yr	Cl	Lea	Pos	G	Rec
1879	Bos	N	O	37	.200
1884	Cin	U	1-O	68	.260
	BRTR			105	.240

HAWK, EDWARD
b.May 11,1890 Neosho,Mo.
d.Mar.26,1936

Yr	Cl	Lea	Pos	G	Rec
1911	St.L	A	P	5	1-4
	BLTR				

HAWKE, WILLIAM VICTOR
(Dick)
b.Apr.28,1870 Wilmington,Del.
d.Dec.12,1902

Yr	Cl	Lea	Pos	G	Rec
1892	St.L	N	P	15	4-5
1893	St.L	N	P	3	0-1
1893	Bal	N	P	28	11-17
1894	Bal	N	P	25	16-9
				71	31-32

HAWKES, THORNDIKE PROCTOR
b.Oct.15,1852 Danvers,Mass.
d.Feb.3,1929

Yr	Cl	Lea	Pos	G	Rec
1879	Tro	N	2	63	.206
1884	Was	a	2	38	.256
				101	.226

HAWKINS, WYNN FIRTH
b.Feb.20,1936 E.Palestine,O.

Yr	Cl	Lea	Pos	G	Rec
1960	Cle	A	P	15	4-4
1961	Cle	A	P	30	7-9
1962	Cle	A	P	3	1-0
	BRTR			48	12-13

HAWKS, NELSON LOUIS
(Chicken)
b.Feb.3,1897 San Francisco,Cal.

Yr	Cl	Lea	Pos	G	Rec
1921	NY	A	O	41	.288
1925	Phi	N	1	105	.322
	BLTL			146	.316

HAWLEY, EMERSON P.
(Pink)
b.dec.5,1872 Beaver Dam,Wis.
d.Sept.19,1938

Yr	Cl	Lea	Pos	G	Rec
1892	St.L	N	P	19	6-13
1893	St.L	N	P	33	5-17
1894	St.L	N	P	48	18-25
1895	Pit	N	P	53	29-21
1896	Pit	N	P	48	21-21
1897	Pit	N	P	37	18-19
1898	Cin	N	P	42	26-12
1899	Cin	N	P	33	14-17
1900	NY	N	P	39	18-20
1901	Mil	A	P	28	7-13
	BLTR			380	162-178

HAWLEY, SCOTT

Yr	Cl	Lea	Pos	G	Rec
1894	Bos	N	P	1	0-0

HAWORTH, HOWARD HOMER
b.Aug.27,1895 Newberg,Ore.

Yr	Cl	Lea	Pos	G	Rec
1915	Cle	A	C	7	.142
	BLTR				

HAYDEN. EUGENE FRANKLIN
b.Apr.14.1935 San Francisco.Cal.

Yr	Cl	Lea	Pos	G	Rec
1958	Cin	N	P	3	0-0
	BLTL				

HAYDEN, JOHN FRANCIS
b.Oct.21,1880 Bryn Mawr,Pa.
d.Aug.3,1942

Yr	Cl	Lea	Pos	G	Rec
1901	Phi	A	O	51	.266
1906	Bos	A	O	85	.248
1908	Chi	N	O	11	.200
				147	.251

HAYES, FRANK WITMAN
(Blimp)
b.Oct.13,1914 Jamesburg,N.J.
d.June 22,1955

Yr	Cl	Lea	Pos	G	Rec
1933	Phi	A	C	3	.000
1934	Phi	A	C	92	.226
1936	Phi	A	C	144	.271
1937	Phi	A	C	60	.261
1938	Phi	A	C	99	.291
1939	Phi	A	C	124	.283
1940	Phi	A	C-1	136	.308
1941	Phi	A	C	126	.280
1942	Phi	A	C	21	.238
1942	St.L	A	C	56	.252
1943	St.L	A	C-1	88	.188
1944	Phi	A	C-1	155	.248
1945	Phi	A	C	32	.227
1945	Cle	A	C	119	.236
1946	Cle	A	C	51	.256
1946	Chi	A	C	53	.212
1947	Bos	A	C	5	.154
	BRTR			1364	.259

HAYES, JAMES MILLARD
b.Feb.11,1913 Montevallo,Ala.

Yr	Cl	Lea	Pos	G	Rec
1935	Was	A	P	7	2-4
	BLTR				

HAYES, JOHN J.
b.June 27,1861 Brooklyn,N.Y.

Yr	Cl	Lea	Pos	G	Rec
1882	Wor	N	C-S-3-O	78	.269
1883	Pit	a	C-2-S-O	83	.263
1884	Pit	a	C-1-2-O	34	.220
1884	Bro	a	C-O	15	.220
1885	Bro	a	C	42	.132
1886	Was	N	C	26	.184
1887	Bal	a	C	8	.143
1890	Bro	p	C	12	.191
	TR			298	.232

HAYES, MICHAEL
b.Cleveland,O.

Yr	Cl	Lea	Pos	G	Rec
1876	Mut	N	O	5	.182

HAYES, MINTER CARNEY
(Jackie)
b.July 19,1906 Clanton,Ala.

Yr	Cl	Lea	Pos	G	Rec
1827	Was	A	S-3	10	.241
1928	Was	A	2-S	60	.257
1929	Was	A	2-3	123	.276
1930	Was	A	2	51	.283
1931	Was	A	2	38	.222
1932	Chi	A	2-S-3	117	.257
1933	Chi	A	2	138	.258
1934	Chi	A	2	62	.257
1935	Chi	A	2	89	.267
1936	Chi	A	2-S	108	.312
1937	Chi	A	2	143	.229
1938	Chi	A	2	62	.328
1939	Chi	A	2	72	.249
1940	Chi	A	2	18	.195
	BRTR			1091	.265

HAYHURST, ELIAS HICKS
b.1826 Philadelphia,Pa.
d.Dec.18,1882
Non-playing manager Ath (n) 1871-75.

HAYNES, JOSEPH WALTON
b.Sept.21,1917 Lincolnton,Ga.

Yr	Cl	Lea	Pos	G	Rec
1939	Was	A	P	27	8-12
1940	Was	A	P	22	3-6
1941	Chi	A	P	8	0-0
1942	Chi	A	P	40	8-5
1943	Chi	A	P	35	7-2
1944	Chi	A	P	33	5-6
1945	Chi	A	P	15	5-5
1946	Chi	A	P	32	7-9
1947	Chi	A	P	29	14-6
1948	Chi	A	P	27	9-10
1949	Was	A	P	37	2-9
1950	Was	A	P	27	7-5
1951	Was	A	P	26	1-4
1952	was	A	P	22	0-3
	BRTR			380	76-82

HAYWORTH, MYRON CLAUDE
(Red)
b.May 14,1915 High Point,N.C.

Yr	Cl	Lea	Pos	G	Rec
1944	St.L	A	C	89	.223
1945	St.L	A	C	56	.194
	BRTR			145	.212

HAYWORTH, RAYMOND HALL
b.Jan.29,1905 High Point,N.C.

Yr	Cl	Lea	Pos	G	Rec
1926	Det	A	C	12	.273
1929	Det	A	C	14	.255
1930	Det	A	C	77	.278
1931	Det	A	C	88	.256
1932	Det	A	C	108	.293
1933	Det	A	C	134	.245
1934	Det	A	C	54	.293
1935	Det	A	C	51	.309
1936	Det	A	C	81	.240
1937	Det	A	C	30	.269
1938	Det	A	C	8	.211
1938	Bro	N	C	5	.000
1939	Bro	N	C	21	.154
1939	NY	N	C	5	.231
1942	St.L	A	H	1	1.000
1944	Bro	N	C	7	.000
1945	Bro	N	C	2	.000
	BRTR			698	.265

HAZINSKI, STANLEY FRANK
(Played under name of
Stanley Frank Rogers)

HAZLE, ROBERT SIDNEY
b.Dec.9,1930 Laurens,S.C.

Yr	Cl	Lea	Pos	G	Rec
1955	Cin	N	O	6	.231
1957	Mil	N	O	41	.403
1958	Mil	N	O	20	.179
1958	Det	A	O	43	.241
	BLTR			110	.310

HAZLETON, WILLARD CARPENTER (Doc)
b.Aug.28,1876 Strafford,Vt.
d.Mar.17,1941

Yr	Cl	Lea	Pos	G	Rec
1901	St.L	N	1	7	.125
1902	St.L	N	1	7	.130
				14	.128

HEAD, EDWARD MARVIN
b.Jan.25,1920 Selma,La.

Yr	Cl	Lea	Pos	G	Rec
1940	Bro	N	P	14	1-2
1942	Bro	N	P	36	10-6
1943	Bro	N	P	47	9-10
1944	Bro	N	P	9	4-3
1946	Bro	N	P	13	3-2
	BRTR			119	27-23

HEAD, RALPH
b.Aug.30,1894 Tallapoosa,Ga.
d.Oct.8,1962

Yr	Cl	Lea	Pos	G	Rec
1923	Phi	N	P	35	2-9
	BRTR				

HEALEY, FRANCIS JEREMIAH
b.June 29,1911 Holyoke,Mass.

Yr	Cl	Lea	Pos	G	Rec
1930	NY	N	O	7	.000
1931	NY	N	C	6	.143
1932	NY	N	C	14	.250
1934	St.L	N	C	15	.308
	BRTR			42	.241

HEALEY, THOMAS
b.Cranston,R.I.
d.Feb.6,1891

Yr	Cl	Lea	Pos	G	Rec
1878	Pro	N	P	2	0-2
1878	Ind	N	P-O	13	7-5 .204
				15	7-7 .185

HEALY, JOHN J. (Egyptian)
b.Oct.27,1866 Cairo,Ill.
d.Mar.16,1899

Yr	Cl	Lea	Pos	G	Rec
1885	St.L	N	P	8	1-7
1886	St.L	N	P	42	17-24
1887	Ind	N	P	40	12-28
1888	Ind	N	P	37	12-24
1889	Was	N	P	15	1-14
1889	Chi	N	P	7	3-4
1890	Tol	a	P	47	22-19
1891	Bal	a	P	23	8-12
1892	Bal	N	P	9	2-5
1892	Lou	N	P	8	1-1
	BRTR			236	79-138

HEALY, THOMAS FITZGERALD
b.Oct.30,1895 Altoona,Pa.

Yr	Cl	Lea	Pos	G	Rec
1915	Phi	A	3	23	.221
1916	Phi	A	3	6	.261
	BRTR			29	.230

HEARD, CHARLES H.
b.Jan.30,1872 Philadelphia,Pa.
d.Feb.20,1945

Yr	Cl	Lea	Pos	G	Rec
1890	Pit	N	P	12	0-6

HEARD, JEHOSIE
b.Jan.17,1925 Atlanta,Ga.

Yr	Cl	Lea	Pos	G	Rec
1954	Bal	A	P	2	0-0
	BLTL				

HEARN, ...

Yr	Cl	Lea	Pos	G	Rec
1872	Oly	n	S-O	2	NR

HEARN, BUNN
b.May 21,1891 Chapel Hill,N.C.
d.Oct.11,1959

Yr	Cl	Lea	Pos	G	Rec
1910	St.L	N	P	5	1-3
1911	St.L	N	P	2	0-0
1913	NY	N	P	2	1-1
1915	Pit	F	P	26	6-11
1918	Bos	N	P	17	5-6
1920	Bos	N	P	11	0-3
	BLTL			63	13-24

HEARN, EDMUND
b.Sept.17,1888 Ventura,Cal.
d.Sept.8,1952

Yr	Cl	Lea	Pos	G	Rec
1910	Bos	A	3	2	.000
	TR				

HEARN, ELMER LAFAYETTE
b.Jan.13,1904 Brooklyn,N.Y.

Yr	Cl	Lea	Pos	G	Rec
1926	Bos	N	P	34	4-9
1927	Bos	N	P	8	0-2
1928	Bos	N	P	7	1-0
1929	Bos	N	P	10	2-0
	BLTL			59	7-11

HEARN, JAMES TOLBERT
b.Apr.11,1923 Atlanta,Ga.

Yr	Cl	Lea	Pos	G	Rec
1947	St.L	N	P	37	12-7
1948	St.L	N	P	36	8-6
1949	St.L	N	P	17	1-3
1950	St.L	N	P	6	0-1
1950	NY	N	P	16	11-3

(Continued)

Yr	Cl	Lea	Pos	G	Rec
1951	NY	N	P	34	17-9
1952	NY	N	P	37	14-7
1953	NY	N	P	37	9-12
1954	NY	N	P	29	8-8
1955	NY	N	P	41	14-16
1956	NY	N	P	32	5-11
1957	Phi	N	P	36	5-1
1958	Phi	N	P	39	5-3
1959	Phi	N	P	6	0-2
BRTR				403	109-89

HEARNE, HUGH J.
b.Apr.18,1874 Troy,N.Y.

Yr	Cl	Lea	Pos	G	Rec
1901	Bro	N	C	2	.500
1902	Bro	N	C	62	.281
1903	Bro	N	C	19	.281
BRTR				83	.284

HEATH, JOHN GEOFFREY
(Jeff)
b.Apr.1,1916 Ft.William,Ont.,Canada.

Yr	Cl	Lea	Pos	G	Rec
1936	Cle	A	O	12	.341
1937	Cle	A	O	20	.230
1938	Cle	A	O	126	.343
1939	Cle	A	O	121	.292
1940	Cle	A	O	100	.219
1941	Cle	A	O	151	.340
1942	Cle	A	O	147	.278
1943	Cle	A	O	118	.274
1944	Cle	A	O	60	.331
1945	Cle	A	O	102	.305
1946	Was	A	O	48	.283
1946	St.L	A	O	86	.275
1947	St.L	A	O	141	.251
1948	Bos	N	O	115	.319
1949	Bos	N	O	36	.306
BLTR				1383	.293

HEATH, MINOR WILSON
(Mickey)
b.Oct.30,1904 Toledo,O.

Yr	Cl	Lea	Pos	G	Rec
1931	Cin	N	1	7	.269
1932	Cin	N	1	39	.201
BLTL				46	.213

HEATH, SPENCER PAUL
b.Nov.5,1895 Chicago,Ill.
d.Jan.1930

Yr	Cl	Lea	Pos	G	Rec
1920	Chi	A	P	4	0-0
BBTR					

HEATH, THOMAS GEORGE
b.Aug,18,1913 Akron,Col.

Yr	Cl	Lea	Pos	G	Rec
1935	St.L	A	C	47	.237
1937	St.L	A	C	17	.233
1938	St.L	A	C	70	.227
BRTR				134	.230

HEATHCOTE, CLIFTON EARL
b.Jan.24,1898 Glen Rock,Pa.
d.Jan.19,1939

Yr	Cl	Lea	Pos	G	Rec
1918	St.L	N	1-O	88	.259
1919	St.L	N	1-O	114	.279
1920	St.L	N	O	133	.284
1921	St.L	N	O	62	.244
1922	St.L	N	O	34	.245
1922	Chi	N	O	76	.276
1923	Chi	N	O	117	.249
1924	Chi	N	O	113	.309
1925	Chi	N	O	109	.263
1926	Chi	N	O	139	.276
1927	Chi	N	O	83	.294
1928	Chi	N	O	67	.285
1929	Chi	N	O	82	.313
1930	Chi	N	O	70	.260
1931	Cin	N	O	90	.258
1932	Cin	N	O	8	.000
1932	Phi	N	1	30	.282
BLTL				1415	.275

HEBERT, WALLACE ANDREW
(Preacher)
b.Aug.21,1908 Lake Charles,La.

Yr	Cl	Lea	Pos	G	Rec
1931	St.L	A	P	23	6-7
1932	St.L	A	P	35	1-12
1933	St.L	A	P	33	4-6
1943	Pit	N	P	35	10-11
BLTL				126	21-36

HECKER, GUY JACKSON
b.Apr.3,1856 Youngville,Pa.
d.Dec.3,1938

Yr	Cl	Lea	Pos	G	Rec
1882	Lou	a	P-1-O	78	7-5 .285
1883	Lou	a	P-1-O	79	28-25 .264
1884	Lou	a	P	79	52-20
1885	Lou	a	P-1	72	30-24 .274
1886	Lou	a	P-1	84	27-23 .342
1887	Lou	a	P-1	91	19-12 .374
1888	Lou	a	P-1	55	8-17 .255
1889	Lou	a	P-1	82	5-11 .277
1890	Pit	N	M-P-1	86	2-12 .226
BRTR				706	178-149 .292

HECKINGER, MICHAEL VINCENT
b.Feb.14,1890 Chicago,Ill.

Yr	Cl	Lea	Pos	G	Rec
1912	Chi	N	C	2	.000
1913	Chi	N	C	2	.000
1913	Bro	N	C	9	.222
BRTR				13	.143

HEDGEPETH, HARRY MALCOLM
b.Sept.4,1888 Fayetteville,N.C.

Yr	Cl	Lea	Pos	G	Rec
1913	Was	A	P	1	0-0
BLTL					

HEFFNER, DONALD HENRY
(Jeep)
b.Feb.8,1911 Rouzerville,Pa.

Yr	Cl	Lea	Pos	G	Rec
1934	NY	A	2	72	.261
1935	NY	A	2	10	.306
1936	NY	A	2-S-3	19	.229
1937	NY	A	2-S	60	.249
1938	St.L	A	2	141	.245
1939	St.L	A	2-S	110	.267
1940	St.L	A	2	126	.236
1941	St.L	A	2	110	.233
1942	St.L	A	1-2	19	.167
1943	St.L	A	1-2	18	.121
1943	Phi	A	1-2	52	.208
1944	Det	A	2	6	.211
BRTR				743	.241

HEFLIN, RANDOLPH RUTHERFORD
b.Sept.11,1919 Fredericksburg,Va.

Yr	Cl	Lea	Pos	G	Rec
1945	Bos	A	P	20	4-10
1946	Bos	A	P	5	0-1
BLTR				25	4-11

HEGAN, JAMES EDWARD
b.Aug.3,1920 Lynn,Mass.

Yr	Cl	Lea	Pos	G	Rec
1941	Cle	A	C	16	.319
1942	Cle	A	C	68	.194
1946	Cle	A	C	88	.236
1947	Cle	A	C	135	.249
1948	Cle	A	C	144	.248
1949	Cle	A	C	152	.224
1950	Cle	A	C	131	.219
1951	Cle	A	C	133	.238
1952	Cle	A	C	112	.225
1953	Cle	A	C	112	.217
1954	Cle	A	C	139	.234
1955	Cle	A	C	116	.220
1956	Cle	A	C	122	.222
1957	Cle	A	C	58	.216

(Continued)

Yr	Cl	Lea	Pos	G	Rec
1958	Det	A	C	45	.192
1958	Phi	N	C	25	.220
1959	Phi	N	C	25	.196
1959	SF	N	C	21	.133
1960	Chi	N	C	24	.209
BRTR				1666	.228

HEHL, HERMAN JACOB
(Jake)
b.Dec.8,1899 Brooklyn,N.Y.

Yr	Cl	Lea	Pos	G	Rec
1918	Bro	N	P	1	0-0
BRTR					

HEIDRICK, JOHN EMMETT (Snags)
b.July 6,1876 Queenstown,Pa.
d.Jan.20,1916

Yr	Cl	Lea	Pos	G	Rec
1898	Cle	N	O	19	.293
1899	St.L	N	O	147	.329
1900	St.L	N	O	83	.301
1901	St.L	N	O	115	.339
1902	St.L	A	P-S-3-O	110	0-0 .288
1903	St.L	A	O	121	.281
1904	St.L	A	O	133	.269
1908	St.L	A	O	26	.215
				754	0-0 .299

HEIFER. FRANKLIN (Heck)
b.Jan.18,1854 Reading,Pa.
d.Aug.29,1893

Yr	Cl	Lea	Pos	G	Rec
1875	Bos	n	1-O	11	.333

HEILBRONER, LOUIS WILBUR
b.July 4,1861 Ft.Wayne,Ind.
d.Dec.21,1933
Non-playing manager St.L (N) 1900.

HEILEMAN, JOHN GEORGE
(Chink)
b.Aug.10,1872 Cincinnati,O.
d.July 19,1940

Yr	Cl	Lea	Pos	G	Rec
1901	Cin	N	3	5	.133
TR					

HEILMANN, HARRY EDWIN
(Slug)
b.Aug.3,1894 San Francisco,Cal.
d.July 9,1951

Yr	Cl	Lea	Pos	G	Rec
1914	Det	A	1-O	67	.225
1916	Det	A	1-O	136	.282
1917	Det	A	1-O	150	.281
1918	Det	A	O	79	.276
1919	Det	A	1	140	.320
1920	Det	A	1-O	145	.309
1921	Det	A	O	149	.394
1922	Det	A	O	118	.356
1923	Det	A	O	144	.403
1924	Det	A	O	153	.346
1925	Det	A	O	150	.393
1926	Det	A	O	141	.367
1927	Det	A	O	141	.398
1928	Det	A	1-O	151	.328
1929	Det	A	O	125	.344
1930	Cin	N	1-O	142	.333
1932	Cin	N	1	15	.258
BRTR				2146	.342

HEIM, VAL RAYMOND
b.Nov.4,1920 Plymouth,Wis.

Yr	Cl	Lea	Pos	G	Rec
1942	Chi	A	O	13	.200
BLTR					

HEIMACH, FRED AMOS
(Lefty)
b.Jan.27,1901 Camden,N.J.

Yr	Cl	Lea	Pos	G	Rec
1920	Phi	A	P	1	0-1
1921	Phi	A	P	1	1-0
1922	Phi	A	P	37	7-11
1923	Phi	A	P	63	6-12
1924	Phi	A	P	58	14-12
1925	Phi	A	P	15	0-1
1926	Phi	A	P	14	1-0
1926	Bos	A	P	26	2-9
1928	NY	A	P	18	2-3
1929	NY	A	P	36	11-6
1930	Bro	N	P	13	0-2
1931	Bro	N	P	39	9-7
1932	Bro	N	P	37	9-4
1933	Bro	N	P	10	0-1
BLTL				368	62-69

Yr Cl Lea Pos G Rec

HEINE, WILLIAM H.
(Pete)
b.Sept.22,1901 Elmira,N.Y.
1921 NY N 2 1 .000
BLTR

HEINTZELMAN, KENNETH ALPHONSE
b.Oct.14,1915 Peruque,Mo.
1937 Pit N P 1 1-0
1938 Pit N P 1 0-0
1939 Pit N P 17 1-1
1940 Pit N P 41 8-8
1941 Pit N P 35 11-11
1942 Pit N P 27 8-11
1946 Pit N P 32 8-12
1947 Pit N P 2 0-0
1947 Phi N P 24 7-10
1948 Phi N P 27 6-11
1949 Phi N P 33 17-10
1950 Phi N P 23 3-9
1951 Phi N P 35 6-12
1952 Phi N P 23 1-3
BRTL 321 77-98

HEINTZMAN, JOHN P.
b.Sept.27,1865 Louisville,Ky.
d.Nov.19,1914
1886 Lou a 1 1 .000

HEISE, CLARENCE EDWARD
(Lefty)
b.Aug.7,1907 Topeka,Kan.
1934 St.L N P 1 0-0
BLTL

HEISE, JAMES EDWARD
b.Sept.3,1932 Scottdale,Pa.
1957 Was A P 8 0-3
BRTR

HEISER, LE ROY BARTON
b.June 22,1942 Baltimore,Md.
1961 Was A P 3 0-0
BRTR

HEISMANN, CHRISTIAN ERNEST (Crese)
b.Apr.16,1880 Cincinnati,O.
d.Nov.19,1951
1901 Cin N P 3 0-1
1902 Cin N P 5 2-1
1902 Bal A P 3 0-3
BLTL 11 2-5

HEIST, ALFRED MICHAEL
b.Oct.5,1927 Brooklyn,N.Y.
1960 Chi N O 41 .275
1961 Chi N O 109 .255
1962 Hou N O 27 .222
177 .255

HEITMAN, HENRY ANTHONY
b.Oct.6,1897 New York,N.Y.
1918 Bro N P 1 0-1
BRTR

HEITMULLER, WILLIAM FREDERICK (Heinie)
b.1883 San Francisco,Cal.
d.Oct.8,1912
1909 Phi A O 64 .286
1910 Phi A O 31 .243
95 .271

HELD, MELVIN NICHOLAS
b.Apr.12,1929 Edon,O.
1956 Bal A P 4 0-0
BRTR

HELD, WOODSON GEORGE
b.Mar.25,1932 Sacramento,Cal.
1954 NY A S-3 4 .000
1957 NY A H 1 .000
1957 KC A O 92 .239

(Continued)
1958 KC A S-3-O 47 .214
1958 Cle A S-3-O 67 .194
1959 Cle A 2-5-3-O 143 .251
1960 Cle A S 109 .258
1961 Cle A S 146 .267
1962 Cle A 5-3-O 139 .249
BRTR 748 .248

HELENIUS, ARTHUR D.
(Played under name of Arthur D. Delaney)

HELF, HENRY HARTZ
b.Aug.26,1913 Austin,Tex.
1938 Cle A C 6 .077
1940 Cle A C 1 .000
1946 St.L A C 71 .192
BRTR 78 .184

HELFRICH, EMORY WILBUR
(Ty)
b.Oct.9,1890 Pleasantville,N.J.
d.Mar.18,1955
1915 Bro F 2 40 .245
BRTR

HELLINGS, ...
1875 Atl n 2 1 .250

HELLMAN, ANTHONY J.
b.1861 Cincinnati,O.
d.Mar.29,1898
1886 Bal a C 1 .000

HELMBOLD, HORACE
b.Philadelphia,Pa.
1890 Ath a P 1 1-0

HELTZEL, WILLIAM WADE
(Heinie)
b.Dec.21,1913 York,Pa.
1943 Bos N 3 29 .151
1944 Phi N S 11 .182
BRTR 40 .157

HEMAN, RUSSELL FREDERICK
b.Feb.10,1933 Olive,Cal.
1961 Cle A P 6 0-0
1961 LA A P 6 0-0
BRTR 12 0-0

HEMINGWAY, EDSON M.
b.May 8,1893 Sheridan,Mich.
1914 St.L A 3 4 .000
1917 NY N 1 7 .320
1918 Phi N 1-2-3 33 .213
BBTR 44 .225

HEMMING, GEORGE EARL
b.Dec.15,1868 Carrollton,O
d.June 3,1930
1890 Cle p P 3 0-3
1890 Bro p P 16 7-5
1891 Bro N P 22 8-14
1892 Cin N P 1 0-0
1892 Lou N P 4 2-1
1893 Lou N P 43 18-18
1894 Lou N P 32 11-20
1894 Bal N P 15 5-0
1895 Bal N P 31 18-12
1896 Bal N P 25 15-7
1897 Lou N P 8 3-5
BRTR 203 87-85

HEMP, WILLIAM H.
(Ducky)
b.Dec.27,1867 St.Louis,Mo.
d.Mar.6,1923
1887 Lou a O 1 .250
1890 Pit N O 21 .213
1890 Syr a O 9 .156
31 .200

HEMPHILL, CHARLES JUDSON
(Eagle Eye)
b.Apr.20,1876 Greenville,Mich.
d.June 22,1953
1899 St.L N O 11 .243
1899 Cle N O 51 .280
1901 Bos A O 137 .269
1902 Cle A O 25 .272
1902 St.L A O 103 .317
1903 St.L A O 106 .238
1904 St.L A O 114 .253
1906 St.L A O 154 .289
1907 St.L A O 153 .259
1908 NY A O 142 .297
1909 NY A O 73 .243
1910 NY A O 102 .239
1911 NY A O 69 .284
BLTL 1240 .271

HEMPHILL, FRANK VERNON
b.May 13,1878 Greenville,Mich.
d.Nov.16,1950
1906 Chi A O 13 .075
1909 Was A O 1 .000
BRTR 14 .070

HEMSLEY, RALSTON BURDETT
(Rollie)
b.June 24,1907 Syracuse,O.
1928 Pit N C 50 .271
1929 Pit N C 88 .269
1930 Pit N C 104 .253
1931 Pit N C 10 .171
1931 Chi N C 66 .309
1932 Chi N C 60 .238
1933 Cin N C 49 .190
1933 St.L A C 32 .242
1934 St.L A C-O 123 .309
1935 St.L A C 144 .290
1936 St.L A C 116 .263
1937 St.L A C 100 .222
1938 Cle A C 66 .296
1939 Cle A C 107 .263
1940 Cle A C 119 .267
1941 Cle A C 98 .240
1942 Cin N C 36 .113
1942 NY A C 31 .294
1943 NY A C 62 .239
1944 NY A C 81 .268
1946 Phi N C 49 .223
1947 Phi N C 2 .333
BRTR 1593 .262

HEMUS, SOLOMON JOSEPH
b.Apr.17,1924 Phoenix,Ariz.
1949 St.L N 2 20 .333
1950 St.L N 3 11 .133
1951 St.L N 2-S 120 .281
1952 St.L N S-3 151 .268
1953 St.L N 2-S 154 .279
1954 St.L N 2-S-3 124 .304
1955 St.L N 2-S-3 96 .243
1956 St.L N H 8 .200
1956 Phi N 2-3 78 .289
1957 Phi N 2 70 .185
1958 Phi N 2-3 105 .284
1959 St.L N M-2-3 24 .235
BLTR 961 .273
Non-playing manager St.L (N) 1960-61.

HENDERSON, ALBERT H.
b.Baltimore,Md.
Non-playing manager Balt (n) 1872-74.

HENDERSON, BERNARD
(Barnyard)
b.Apr.12,1899 Douglassville,Tex.
1921 Cle A P 3 0-1
BLTR

HENDERSON, EDWARD J.
b.1890 New York,N.Y.
1914 Pit F P 6 0-3
1914 Ind F P 1 1-0
BLTL 7 1-3

HENDERSON, JAMES HARDING
(Hardie)
b.Oct.31,1862 Philadelphia, Pa.
d.Feb.6,1903

Yr	Cl	Lea	Pos	G	Rec
1883	Phi	N	P-O	2	0-0 .250
1883	Bal	a	P-S-3-O	50	10-30 .151
1884	Bal	a	P	54	27-22
1885	Bal	a	P	61	26-35
1886	Bal	a	P	19	3-16
1886	Bro	a	P	14	10-4
1887	Bro	a	P	14	4-9
1888	Pit	N	P	5	1-4
		BRTR		219	81-119 .208

HENDERSON, WILLIAM C.
Non-playing manager Bal (U) 1884.

HENDERSON, WILLIAM MAXWELL
b.Nov.4,1902 Pensacola, Fla.

Yr	Cl	Lea	Pos	G	Rec
1930	NY	A	P	3	0-0
		BRTR			

HENDLEY, CHARLES ROBERT
b.Apr.30,1939 Macon, Ga.

Yr	Cl	Lea	Pos	G	Rec
1961	Mil	N	P	19	5-7
1962	Mil	N	P	36	11-13
		BRTL		55	16-20

HENDRICK, HARVEY (Gink)
b.Nov.9,1897 Mason, Tenn.
d.Oct.29,1941

Yr	Cl	Lea	Pos	G	Rec
1923	NY	A	O	37	.273
1924	NY	A	O	40	.263
1925	Cle	A	1-O	25	.286
1927	Bro	N	1-O	128	.310
1928	Bro	N	3-O	126	.318
1929	Bro	N	1-O	110	.354
1930	Bro	N	O	68	.257
1931	Bro	N	H	1	.000
1931	Cin	N	1	137	.315
1932	St.L	N	3	28	.250
1932	Cin	N	1	94	.327
1933	Chi	N	1-3-O	69	.291
1934	Phi	N	O	59	.293
		BLTR		922	.308

HENDRICKS, EDWARD
b.1887 Benton Harbor, Mich.

Yr	Cl	Lea	Pos	G	Rec
1910	NY	N	P	4	0-1

HENDRICKS, JOHN CALHOUN
b.Apr.9,1876 Joliet, Ill.
d.May 13,1943

Yr	Cl	Lea	Pos	G	Rec
1902	NY	N	O	7	.240
1902	Chi	N	O	2	.500
1903	Was	A	O	32	.183
		BLTL		41	.211

Non-playing manager St.L (N) 1918 and Cin (N) 1924-29.

HENDRICKSON, DONALD WILLIAMSON
b.July 14,1915 Kewanna, Ind.

Yr	Cl	Lea	Pos	G	Rec
1945	Bos	N	P	37	4-8
1946	Bos	N	P	2	0-1
		BBTR		39	4-9

HENDRIX, CLAUDE RAYMOND
b.Apr.13,1889 Olathe, Kan.
d.Mar.22,1944

Yr	Cl	Lea	Pos	G	Rec
1911	Pit	N	P	22	4-6
1912	Pit	N	P	46	24-9
1913	Pit	N	P	53	14-15
1914	Chi	F	P	48	29-10
1915	Chi	F	P	46	16-15
1916	Chi	N	P	45	8-16
1917	Chi	N	P	48	10-12
1918	Chi	N	P	35	20-7
1919	Chi	N	P	36	10-14
1920	Chi	N	P	34	9-12
		BRTR		413	144-116

HENDRYX, TIMOTHY GREEN
b.Jan.31,1891 LeRoy, Ill.
d.Aug.14,1957

Yr	Cl	Lea	Pos	G	Rec
1911	Cle	A	O	3	.285
1912	Cle	A	O	23	.243
1915	NY	A	O	13	.200
1916	NY	A	O	15	.290
1917	NY	A	O	125	.249
1918	St.L	A	O	88	.279
1920	Bos	A	O	99	.328
1921	Bos	A	O	49	.241
		BRTR		415	.240

HENGLE, EDWARD S.
b.Chicago, Ill.
Non-playing manager Chi (U) 1884.

HENGLE, EMORY J.
(Moxie)
b 1858

Yr	Cl	Lea	Pos	G	Rec
1884	Chi	U	2	18	.222
1884	St.P	U	2	9	.132
1885	Buf	N	2-O	7	.154
				34	.172

HENION, LAFAYETTE M.
b.1899 San Diego, Cal.

Yr	Cl	Lea	Pos	G	Rec
1919	Bro	N	P	1	0-0
		BRTR			

HENLEY, GAIL CURTICE
b.Oct.15,1929 Wichita, Kan.

Yr	Cl	Lea	Pos	G	Rec
1954	Pit	N	O	14	.300
		BLTR			

HENLEY, WELDON
b.Oct.25,1880 Jasper, Ga.
d.Nov.16,1960

Yr	Cl	Lea	Pos	G	Rec
1903	Phi	A	P	30	12-9
1904	Phi	A	P	36	14-16
1905	Phi	A	P	25	4-12
1907	Bro	N	P	7	1-5
		BRTR		98	31-42

HENLINE, WALTER JOHN
(Butch)
b.Dec.20,1898 Ft.Wayne, Ind.
d.Oct.9,1957

Yr	Cl	Lea	Pos	G	Rec
1921	NY	N	C	1	.000
1921	Phi	N	C	33	.306
1922	Phi	N	C	125	.316
1923	Phi	N	C-O	111	.324
1924	Phi	N	C-O	115	.284
1925	Phi	N	C-O	93	.304
1926	Phi	N	C	99	.283
1927	Bro	N	C	67	.266
1928	Bro	N	C	55	.212
1929	Bro	N	C	27	.242
1930	Chi	A	C	3	.125
1931	Chi	A	C	11	.067
		BRTR		740	.291

HENNESSEY, GEORGE
(Three Star)
b.Oct.28,1914 Bethlehem, Pa.

Yr	Cl	Lea	Pos	G	Rec
1937	St.L	A	P	5	0-1
1942	Phi	N	P	5	1-1
1945	Chi	N	P	2	0-0
		BRTR		12	1-2

HENNESSY, LESTER J.
b.Dec.12,1893 Lynn, Mass.

Yr	Cl	Lea	Pos	G	Rec
1913	Det	A	2	14	.133
		BRTR			

HENNING, PETER HERMAN
b.Dec.28,1887 Crown Point, Ind.
d.Nov.9,1939

Yr	Cl	Lea	Pos	G	Rec
1914	KC	F	P	23	5-9
1915	KC	F	P	40	9-15
		BRTR		63	14-24

HENRICH, FRANK WILDE
(Fritz)
b.May 8,1899 Cincinnati, O.

Yr	Cl	Lea	Pos	G	Rec
1924	Phi	N	O	36	.211
		BLTL			

HENRICH, ROBERT EDWARD
b.Dec.14,1938 Lawrence, Kan.

Yr	Cl	Lea	Pos	G	Rec
1957	Cin	N	2-S-3-O	29	.200
1958	Cin	N	S	5	.000
1959	Cin	N	S	14	.000
		BRTR		48	.125

HENRICH, THOMAS DAVID
b.Feb.20,1913 Massillon, O.

Yr	Cl	Lea	Pos	G	Rec
1937	NY	A	O	67	.320
1938	NY	A	O	131	.270
1939	NY	A	O	99	.277
1940	NY	A	1-O	90	.307
1941	NY	A	O	144	.277
1942	NY	A	1-O	127	.267
1946	NY	A	1-O	150	.251
1947	NY	A	1-O	142	.287
1948	NY	A	1-O	146	.308
1949	NY	A	1-O	115	.287
1950	NY	A	1	73	.272
		BLTL		1284	.282

HENRIKSEN, OLAF (Swede)
b.Apr.26,1888 Kirkerup, Denmark.
d.Oct.17,1962

Yr	Cl	Lea	Pos	G	Rec
1911	Bos	A	O	27	.366
1912	Bos	A	O	37	.321
1913	Bos	A	O	30	.375
1914	Bos	A	O	61	.253
1915	Bos	A	O	73	.196
1916	Bos	A	O	68	.202
1917	Bos	A	O	15	.083
		BLTL		311	.267

HENRY, EARL CLIFFORD
(Hook)
b.June 10,1917 Roseville, O.

Yr	Cl	Lea	Pos	G	Rec
1944	Cle	A	P	4	1-1
1945	Cle	A	P	16	0-3
		BLTL		20	1-4

HENRY, FRANK JOHN
(Dutch)
b.May 12,1902 Cleveland, O.

Yr	Cl	Lea	Pos	G	Rec
1921	St.L	A	P	1	0-0
1922	St.L	A	P	4	0-0
1923	Bro	N	P	17	4-6
1924	Bro	N	P	16	1-2
1927	NY	N	P	45	11-6
1928	NY	N	P	17	3-6
1929	NY	N	P	27	5-6
1929	Chi	A	P	2	1-0
1930	Chi	A	P	35	2-17
		BLTL		164	27-43

HENRY, FREDERICK MARSHALL
(Snake)
b.July 19,1897 Richmond, Va.

Yr	Cl	Lea	Pos	G	Rec
1922	Bos	N	1	18	.197
1923	Bos	N	1	11	.111
		BLTL		29	.187

HENRY, GEORGE WASHINGTON
b.Aug.10,1863 Philadelphia, Pa.
d.Dec.30,1934

Yr	Cl	Lea	Pos	G	Rec
1893	Cin	N	O	21	.273
		BRTR			

HENRY, JAMES FRANCIS
b.June 26,1912 Danville, Va.

Yr	Cl	Lea	Pos	G	Rec
1936	Bos	A	P	22	5-1
1937	Bos	A	P	3	1-0
1939	Phi	N	P	9	0-1
		BRTR		34	6-2

HENRY, JOHN MICHAEL
b.Sept.2,1864 Springfield, Mass.
d.June 11,1939.

Yr	Cl	Lea	Pos	G	Rec
1884	Cle	N	P-O	9	1-4 .154
1885	Bal	a	P-O	10	2-6 .273
1886	Was	N	P	4	1-3
1890	NY	N	O	37	.243
				60	4-13 .241

HENRY, JOHN PARK
b.Dec.28,1888 Amherst,Mass.
d.Nov.24,1941

Yr	Cl	Lea	Pos	G	Rec
1910	Was	A	C	29	.149
1911	Was	A	C-1	85	.203
1912	Was	A	C	63	.194
1913	Was	A	C	96	.226
1914	Was	A	C	91	.169
1915	Was	A	C	95	.220
1916	Was	A	C	117	.249
1917	Was	A	C	65	.190
1918	Bos	N	C	43	.206
	BRTR			684	.207

HENRY, RONALD BAXTER
b.Aug.7,1936 Chester,Pa.

Yr	Cl	Lea	Pos	G	Rec
1961	Min	A	C-1	20	.143
	BRTR				

HENRY, WILLIAM RODMAN
b.Oct.15,1927 Alice,Tex.

Yr	Cl	Lea	Pos	G	Rec
1952	Bos	A	P	14	5-4
1953	Bos	A	P	21	5-5
1954	Bos	A	P	25	3-7
1955	Bos	A	P	17	2-4
1958	Chi	N	P	44	5-4
1959	Chi	N	P	65	9-8
1960	Cin	N	P	51	1-5
1961	Cin	N	P	48	2-1
1962	Cin	N	P	40	4-2
	BLTL			325	36-40

HENSHAW, ROY JOHN
b.July 29,1911 Chicago,Ill.

Yr	Cl	Lea	Pos	G	Rec
1933	Chi	N	P	21	2-1
1935	Chi	N	P	31	13-5
1936	Chi	N	P	39	6-5
1937	Bro	N	P	43	5-12
1938	St.L	N	P	27	5-11
1942	Det	A	P	23	2-4
1943	Det	A	P	26	0-2
1944	Det	A	P	7	0-0
	BRTL			217	33-40

HENSIEK, PHILIP FRANK
b.Oct.13,1901 St.Louis,Mo.

Yr	Cl	Lea	Pos	G	Rec
1935	Was	A	P	6	0-3
	BRTR				

HERBERT, ERNIE ALBERT
b.Jan.30,1887 Breckenridge,Mo.

Yr	Cl	Lea	Pos	G	Rec
1913	Cin	N	P	6	0-0
1914	St.L	F	P	25	1-0
1915	St.L	F	P	12	1-0
	BRTR			43	2-0

HERBERT, FREDERICK
(Real name Herbert Frederick Kemman)
b.Mar.4,1887 LaGrange,Ill.

Yr	Cl	Lea	Pos	G	Rec
1915	NY	N	P	2	1-1
	BRTR				

HERBERT, RAYMOND ERNEST
b.Dec.15,1929 Detroit,Mich.

Yr	Cl	Lea	Pos	G	Rec
1950	Det	A	P	8	1-2
1951	Det	A	P	5	4-0
1953	Det	A	P	43	4-6
1954	Det	A	P	42	3-6
1955	KC	A	P	24	1-8
1958	KC	A	P	42	8-8
1959	KC	A	P	37	11-11
1960	KC	A	P	37	14-15
1961	KC	A	P	13	3-6
1961	Chi	A	P	35	20-9
	BRTR			307	78-77

HERCHENROEDER, NICHOLAS
(Played under name of Nicholas Reeder)

HERMAN, ARTHUR
b.May 11,1871 Louisville,Ky.
d.Sept.20,1955

Yr	Cl	Lea	Pos	G	Rec
1896	Lou	N	P	13	3-5
1897	Lou	N	P	3	0-0
				16	3-5

HERMAN, FLOYD CAVES
(Babe)
b.June 26,1903 Buffalo,N.Y.

Yr	Cl	Lea	Pos	G	Rec
1926	Bro	N	1-O	137	.319
1927	Bro	N	1	130	.272
1928	Bro	N	O	134	.340
1929	Bro	N	O	146	.381
1930	Bro	N	O	153	.393
1931	Bro	N	O	151	.313
1932	Cin	N	O	148	.326
1933	Chi	N	O	137	.289
1934	Chi	N	O	125	.304
1935	Pit	N	1-O	26	.235
1935	Cin	N	1-O	92	.335
1936	Cin	N	1-O	119	.279
1937	Det	A	O	17	.300
1945	Bro	N	O	37	.265
	BLTL			1552	.323

HERMAN, WILLIAM JENNINGS BRYAN
b.July 7,1909 New Albany,Ind.

Yr	Cl	Lea	Pos	G	Rec
1931	Chi	N	2	25	.327
1932	Chi	N	2	154	.314
1933	Chi	N	2	153	.279
1934	Chi	N	2	113	.303
1935	Chi	N	2	154	.341
1936	Chi	N	2	153	.334
1937	Chi	N	2	138	.335
1938	Chi	N	2	152	.277
1939	Chi	N	2	156	.307
1940	Chi	N	2	135	.292
1941	Chi	N	2	11	.194
1941	Bro	N	2	133	.291
1942	Bro	N	1-2	155	.256
1943	Bro	N	2-3	153	.330
1946	Bro	N	2-3	47	.288
1946	Bos	N	1-2-3	75	.306
1947	Pit	N	M-1-2	15	.213
	BRTR			1922	.304

HERMANN, ...

Yr	Cl	Lea	Pos	G	Rec
1918	Bro	N	P	1	0-0

HERMANN, ALBERT BARTEL
b.Mar.28,1901 Milltown,N.J.

Yr	Cl	Lea	Pos	G	Rec
1923	Bos	N	1-2-3	31	.237
1924	Bos	N	H	1	.000
	BRTR			32	.235

HERMANSKI, EUGENE VICTOR
b.May 11,1921 Pittsfield,Mass.

Yr	Cl	Lea	Pos	G	Rec
1943	Bro	N	O	18	.300
1946	Bro	N	O	64	.200
1947	Bro	N	O	79	.275
1948	Bro	N	O	133	.290
1949	Bro	N	O	87	.299
1950	Bro	N	O	94	.298
1951	Bro	N	O	31	.250
1951	Chi	N	O	75	.282
1952	Chi	N	O	99	.255
1953	Chi	N	O	18	.150
1953	Pit	N	O	41	.177
	BLTR			739	.272

HERNANDEZ, EVELIO LOPEZ
b.Dec.24,1930 San Miguel Del Papron, Cuba

Yr	Cl	Lea	Pos	G	Rec
1956	Was	A	P	4	1-1
1957	Was	A	P	14	0-0
	BRTR			18	1-1

HERNANDEZ, RUDOLPH ALBERT
b.Dec.10,1931 Santiago,D.R.

Yr	Cl	Lea	Pos	G	Rec
1960	Was	A	P	24	4-1
1961	Was	A	P	7	0-1
	BRTR			31	4-2

HERNANDEZ, SALVADOR RAMOS (Chico)
b.Jan.3,1916 Havana,Cuba.

Yr	Cl	Lea	Pos	G	Rec
1942	Chi	N	C	47	.229
1943	Chi	N	C	43	.270
	BRTR			90	.250

HERNON, THOMAS H.
b.Nov.4,1866 E.Bridgewater,Mass.
d.Feb.4,1902

Yr	Cl	Lea	Pos	G	Rec
1897	Chi	N	O	4	.111

HEROUX, GEORGE L.
(Played under name of George L. Wheeler)

HERR, EDWARD JOSEPH
b.May 18,1862 St.Louis,Mo.
d.July 18,1943

Yr	Cl	Lea	Pos	G	Rec
1887	Cle	a	3	11	.360
1888	St.L	a	S	43	.266
1890	St.L	a	2-O	12	.233
	BRTR			66	.249

HERRELL, WALTER W.
b.Washington,D.C.

Yr	Cl	Lea	Pos	G	Rec
1911	Was	A	P	1	0-0

HERRERA, JUAN FRANCISCO
b.June 16,1934 Havana,Cuba

Yr	Cl	Lea	Pos	G	Rec
1958	Phi	N	1-3	29	.270
1960	Phi	N	1-2	145	.281
1961	Phi	N	1	126	.258
	BRTR			300	.271

HERRERA, PROCOPIO RODRIGUEZ
b.July 26,1926 Nuevo Laredo,Mexico.

Yr	Cl	Lea	Pos	G	Rec
1951	St.L	A	P	3	0-0
	BRTR				

HERRERA, RAMON
(Mike)
b.Dec.19,1897 Havana,Cuba.

Yr	Cl	Lea	Pos	G	Rec
1925	Bos	A	2	10	.385
1926	Bos	A	2-3	74	.257
	BRTR			84	.275

HERRIAGE, WILLIAM TROY
b.Dec.20,1930 Tipton,Okla.

Yr	Cl	Lea	Pos	G	Rec
1956	KC	A	P	34	1-13
	BRTR				

HERRIN, THOMAS EDWARD
b.Sept.12,1929 Shreveport,La.

Yr	Cl	Lea	Pos	G	Rec
1954	Bos	A	P	14	1-2
	BRTR				

HERRING, ARTHUR L.
(Red)
b.Mar.10,1907 Altus,Okla.

Yr	Cl	Lea	Pos	G	Rec
1929	Det	A	P	4	2-1
1930	Det	A	P	23	3-3
1931	Det	A	P	35	7-13
1932	Det	A	P	12	1-2
1933	Det	A	P	24	1-2
1934	Bro	N	P	14	2-4
1939	Chi	A	P	7	0-0
1944	Bro	N	P	12	3-4
1945	Bro	N	P	23	7-4
1946	Bro	N	P	35	7-2
1947	Pit	N	P	11	1-3
	BRTR			200	34-38

HERRING, HERBERT LEE
b.July 22,1891 Danville,Ark.

Yr	Cl	Lea	Pos	G	Rec
1912	Was	A	P	1	0-0
	BRTR				

HERRING, SILAS CLARKE (Lefty)
b.Mar.4,1880 Philadelphia,Pa.

Yr	Cl	Lea	Pos	G	Rec
1899	Was	N	P	2	0-0
1904	Was	A	O	15	.174
	BLTL			17	0-0 / .191

HERRING, WILLIAM FRANCIS
b.Oct.31,1893 New York,N.Y.
d.Sept.10,1962

Yr	Cl	Lea	Pos	G	Rec
1915	Bro	F	P	3	0-1

HERRMANN, LeROY GEORGE
b.Feb.27,1908 Steward,Ill.

Yr	Cl	Lea	Pos	G	Rec
1932	Chi	N	P	7	2-1
1933	Chi	N	P	9	0-1
1935	Cin	N	P	29	3-5
	BRTR			45	5-7

HERRNSTEIN, JOHN ELLETT
b.Mar.31,1938 Hampton,Va.

Yr	Cl	Lea	Pos	G	Rec
1962	Phi	N	O	6	.200
	BLTL				

HERRSCHER, RICHARD FRANKLIN
b.Nov.3,1931 St. Louis,Mo.

Yr	Cl	Lea	Pos	G	Rec
1962	NY	N	1-5-3-O	35	.220
	BRTR				

HERSH, EARL WALTER
b.May 21,1932 Manchester,Md.

Yr	Cl	Lea	Pos	G	Rec
1956	Mil	N	O	7	.231
	BLTL				

HERSHBERGER, NORMAN MICHAEL
b.Oct.19,1939 Massilon,O.

Yr	Cl	Lea	Pos	G	Rec
1961	Chi	A	O	15	.309
1962	Chi	A	O	148	.262
	BRTR			163	.268

HERSHBERGER, WILLARD McKEE
b.May 28,1911 Lemon Cove,Cal.
d.Aug.3,1940

Yr	Cl	Lea	Pos	G	Rec
1938	Cin	N	C-2	49	.275
1939	Cin	N	C	63	.345
1940	Cin	N	C	48	.309
	BRTR			160	.316

HERSHEY, FRANK
b.Sept.13,1878 Gorham,N.Y.

Yr	Cl	Lea	Pos	G	Rec
1905	Bos	N	P	2	0-1

HERTWECK, NEAL CHARLES
b.Nov.22,1931 St.Louis,Mo.

Yr	Cl	Lea	Pos	G	Rec
1952	St.L	N	1	2	.000
	BLTL				

HERZOG, CHARLES LINCOLN
(Buck)
b.July 9,1885 Baltimore,Md.
d.Sept.4,1953

Yr	Cl	Lea	Pos	G	Rec
1908	NY	N	2	59	.300
1909	NY	N	O	38	.185
1910	Bos	N	3	105	.250
1911	Bos	N	3	79	.310
1911	NY	N	3	69	.267
1912	NY	N	3	140	.263
1913	NY	N	3	96	.286
1914	Cin	N	M-S	138	.281
1915	Cin	N	M-1-S	155	.264
1916	Cin	N	M-S-3-O	79	.267
1916	NY	N	2-S-3	77	.261
1917	NY	N	2	114	.235
1918	Bos	N	1-2-S	118	.228
1919	Bos	N	2	73	.276
1919	Chi	N	2	52	.280
1920	Chi	N	2-3	91	.193
	BRTR			1483	.259

HERZOG, DORREL NORMAN
(Whitey)
b.Nov.9,1931 New Athens,Ill.

Yr	Cl	Lea	Pos	G	Rec
1956	Was	A	1-O	117	.245
1957	Was	A	O	36	.167
1958	Was	A	O	8	.000
1958	KC	A	1-3-O	88	.240
1959	KC	A	1-O	38	.293
1960	KC	A	1-O	83	.266
1961	Bal	A	O	113	.291
1962	Bal	A	O	99	.266
	BLTL			582	.260

HESLIN, THOMAS
(Played under name of Thomas Hess)

HESS, OTTO C.
b.Nov.13,1878 Berne,Switzerland.
d.Feb.24,1926

Yr	Cl	Lea	Pos	G	Rec
1902	Cle	A	P	7	2-3
1904	Cle	A	P	34	9-7
1905	Cle	A	P-O	54	10-12 .251
1906	Cle	A	P	53	20-17
1907	Cle	A	P	19	6-6
1908	Cle	A	P	9	1-0
1912	Bos	N	P	33	12-17
1913	Bos	N	P	35	7-17
1914	Bos	N	P	31	5-6
1915	Bos	N	P	5	0-1
	BLTL			280	72-86 .214

HESS, THOMAS
(Real Name Thomas Heslin)
b.Aug.15,1875 Brooklyn,N.Y.
d.Dec.15,1945

Yr	Cl	Lea	Pos	G	Rec
1892	Bal	N	C	1	.000

HESSELBACHER, GEORGE EDWARD
b.Jan.18,1895 Philadelphia, Pa.

Yr	Cl	Lea	Pos	G	Rec
1916	Phi	A	P	6	0-4
	BRTR				

HESTERFER, LAWRENCE
b.June 20,1878 Newark,N.J.
d.Sept.22,1943

Yr	Cl	Lea	Pos	G	Rec
1901	NY	N	P	1	0-1

HETKI, JOHN EDWARD
b.May 12,1922 Leavenworth,Kan.

Yr	Cl	Lea	Pos	G	Rec
1945	Cin	N	P	5	1-2
1946	Cin	N	P	32	6-6
1947	Cin	N	P	37	3-4
1948	Cin	N	P	3	0-1
1950	Cin	N	P	22	1-2
1952	St.L	A	P	3	0-1
1953	Pit	N	P	54	3-6
1954	Pit	N	P	58	4-4
	BRTR			214	18-26

HETLING, AUGUST JULIUS
(Gus)
b.Nov.21,1885 St.Louis,Mo.

Yr	Cl	Lea	Pos	G	Rec
1906	Det	A	3	2	.143
	BRTR				

HEUBLE, GEORGE A.
b.1849 Paterson,N.J.
d.Feb.1896

Yr	Cl	Lea	Pos	G	Rec
1871	Ath	n	1-O	15	.261
1872	Oly	n	O	4	NR
1876	Mut	N	1	1	.000
				20	NR

HEUSSER, EDWARD BURLTON
b.May 7,1909 Murray,Utah.
d.Mar.1,1956

Yr	Cl	Lea	Pos	G	Rec
1935	St.L	N	P	33	5-5
1936	St.L	N	P	42	7-3
1938	Phi	N	P	1	0-0
1940	Phi	A	P	41	6-13
1943	Cin	N	P	26	4-3
1944	Cin	N	P	30	13-11
1945	Cin	N	P	31	11-16
1946	Cin	N	P	29	7-14
1948	Phi	N	P	33	3-2
	BBTR			266	56-67

HEVING, JOHN ALOYSIUS
b.Apr.29,1898 Mentor,Ky.

Yr	Cl	Lea	Pos	G	Rec
1920	St.L	A	C	1	.000
1924	Bos	A	C	45	.284
1925	Bos	A	C	45	.168
1928	Bos	A	C	82	.259
1929	Bos	A	C	76	.319
1930	Bos	A	C	75	.277
1931	Phi	A	C	42	.239
1932	Phi	A	C	33	.273
	BRTR			399	.265

HEVING, JOSEPH WILLIAM
b.Sept.2,1904 Covington,Ky.

Yr	Cl	Lea	Pos	G	Rec
1930	NY	N	P	41	7-5
1931	NY	N	P	22	1-6
1933	Chi	A	P	40	7-5
1934	Chi	A	P	33	1-7
1937	Cle	A	P	40	8-4
1938	Cle	A	P	3	1-1
1938	Bos	A	P	16	8-1
1939	Bos	A	P	46	11-3
1940	Bos	A	P	39	12-7
1941	Cle	A	P	27	5-2
1942	Cle	A	P	27	5-3
1943	Cle	A	P	30	1-1
1944	Cle	A	P	63	8-3
1945	Bos	N	P	3	1-0
	BRTR			430	76-48

HEWITT, CHARLES JACOB
(Jake)
b.June 6,1871 Maidsville,W.Va.

Yr	Cl	Lea	Pos	G	Rec
1895	Pit	N	P	3	1-0
	TL				

HEWITT, WALTER F.
Non-playing manager Was (N) 1888.

HEYDON, MICHAEL EDWARD
b.July 15,1874 Indianapolis.Ind.
d.Oct.13,1913

Yr	Cl	Lea	Pos	G	Rec
1898	Bal	N	C	3	.111
1899	Was	N	C	3	.000
1901	St.L	N	C	14	.244
1904	Chi	A	C	5	.100
1905	Was	A	C	77	.192
1906	Was	A	C	49	.159
1907	Was	A	C	62	.183
	TR			213	.182

HEYNER, JOHN
b.Hyde Park,Ill.

Yr	Cl	Lea	Pos	G	Rec
1890	Pit	N	P	1	0-0

HIBBARD, JOHN DENISON
b.Dec.2,1864 Chicago,Ill.
d.Nov.17,1937

Yr	Cl	Lea	Pos	G	Rec
1884	Chi	N	P	2	1-1

HICKEY, JAMES ROBERT
b.Oct.22,1920 N.Abington,Mass.

Yr	Cl	Lea	Pos	G	Rec
1942	Bos	N	P	1	0-1
1944	Bos	N	P	8	0-0
	BRTR			9	0-1

HICKEY, JOHN W.
b.Nov.3,1881 Minneapolis,Minn.
d.Dec.28,1941

Yr	Cl	Lea	Pos	G	Rec
1904	Cle	A	P	3	0-3
	BRTR				

HICKEY, MICHAEL EDWARD
b.Dec.25,1871 Chicopee,Mass.
d.June 11,1918

Yr	Cl	Lea	Pos	G	Rec
1899	Bos	N	2	1	.333
1901	Chi	N	3	10	.176
	BRTR			11	.212

HICKMAN, CHARLES TAYLOR
(Piano Legs)
b.Mar.4,1876 Dunkirk,N.Y.
d.Apr.19,1934

Yr	Cl	Lea	Pos	G	Rec
1897	Bos	N	P	2	0-0
1898	Bos	N	P	17	2-2
1899	Bos	N	P	18	7-0
1900	NY	N	3	125	.313
1901	NY	N	P-S-3-O	101	3-5 .287
1902	Bos	A	O	28	.308
1902	Cle	A	P-1	102	0-1 .376
1903	Cle	A	1	130	.330
1904	Cle	A	1	85	.415
1904	Det	A	1	41	.254
1905	Det	A	1-O	59	.221
1905	Was	A	2	88	.311
1906	Was	A	1-O	120	.284
1907	Was	A	P-1-2	60	0-0 .300
1907	Chi	A	2	21	.226

Yr Cl Lea Pos G Rec

(Continued)
1908 Cle A 1-O 65 .234

BRTR 1062 {12-8 .302}

HICKMAN, DAVID JAMES
b.May 19,1894 Union City,Tenn.
1915 Bal F O 20 .210
1916 Bro N O 9 .200
1917 Bro N O 114 .219
1918 Bro N O 53 .234
1919 Bro N O 57 .192

BRTR 253 .218

HICKMAN, ERNEST L.
b.1856 E.St.Louis,Ill.
d.Nov.22,1891
1884 KC U P 18 3-13

HICKMAN, JAMES LUCIUS
b.May 10,1937 Henning, Tenn.
1962 NY N O 140 .245
BRTR

HICKS, CLARENCE WALTER
b.Feb.15,1927 Belvedere,Cal.
1956 Det A 2-S-3 26 .213
BBTR

HICKS, NATHANIEL WOODHULL
b.Apr.19,1845 Brooklyn,N.Y.
d.Apr.21,1907
1872 Mut n C-O 56 NR
1873 Mut n C 28 NR
1874 Phi n C-O 58 NR
1875 Mut n M-C-O 62 NR
1876 Mut N C 45 .250
1877 Cin N C 8 .187

BRTR 257 NR

HICKS, WILLIAM JOSEPH
b.Apr.7,1933 Ivy,Va.
1959 Chi A O 6 .429
1960 Chi A O 36 .191
1961 Was A O 12 .172
1962 Was A O 102 .224

BLTR 156 .218

HIGBE, WALTER KIRBY
b.Apr.8,1915 Columbia,S.C.
1937 Chi N P 1 1-0
1938 Chi N P 2 0-0
1939 Chi N P 9 2-1
1939 Phi N P 34 10-14
1940 Phi N P 41 14-19
1941 Bro N P 48 22-9
1942 Bro N P 38 16-11
1943 Bro N P 35 13-10
1946 Bro N P 42 17-8
1947 Bro N P 4 2-0
1947 Pit N P 46 11-17
1948 Pit N P 56 8-7
1949 Pit N P 7 0-2
1949 NY N P 37 2-0
1950 NY N P 18 0-3

BRTR 418 118-101

HIGBEE, MAHLON JESSE
b.Aug.16,1901 Louisville,Ky.
1922 NY N O 3 .400
BRTR

HIGBY, ...
1872 Atl n O 1 .000

HIGDON, WILLIAM TRAVIS
b.Apr.27,1925 Camp Hill,Ala.
1949 Chi A O 11 .304
BLTR

HIGGINBOTHAM, IRVING CLINTON
b.Apr.26,1882 Homer,Neb.

Yr Cl Lea Pos G Rec

(Continued)
d.June 12,1959
1906 St.L N P 7 1-6
1908 St.L N P 19 3-8
1909 St.L N P 3 1-0
1909 Chi N P 19 5-2

TR 48 10-16

HIGGINS, FESTUS EDWARD
b.1893 Cincinnati,O.
d.Oct.4,1924
1909 St.L N P 16 3-3
1910 St.L N P-O 2 {0-1 .400}

BRTR 18 {3-4 .231}

HIGGINS, MICHAEL FRANKLIN
(Pinkey)
b.May 27,1909 Red Oak,Tex.
1930 Phi A 2-S-3 14 .250
1933 Phi A 3 152 .314
1934 Phi A 3 144 .330
1935 Phi A 3 133 .296
1936 Phi A 3 146 .289
1937 Bos A 3 153 .302
1938 Bos A 3 139 .303
1939 Det A 3 132 .276
1940 Det A 3 131 .271
1941 Det A 3 147 .298
1942 Det A 3 143 .267
1943 Det A 3 138 .277
1944 Det A 3 148 .297
1946 Det A 3 18 .217
1946 Bos A 3 64 .275

BRTR 1802 .292

Non-playing manager Bos (A) 1955-59 and 1960-62

HIGGINS, ROBERT STONE
b.Sept.23,1886 Fayetteville,Tenn.
d.May 25,1941
1909 Cle A C 8 .087
1911 Bro N C 4 .300
1912 Bro N C 1 .000

BRTR 13 .143

HIGGINS, WILLIAM H.
b.Oct.3,1862 Wilmington,Del.
d.Sept.23,1926
1888 Bos N 2 14 .167
1890 St.L a 2 64 .251
1890 Syr a 2 1 .250

TR 79 .236

HIGH, ANDREW AIRD
(Handy Andy)
b.Nov.21,1897 Ava,Ill.
1922 Bro N 2-S-3 153 .283
1923 Bro N 2-S-3 123 .270
1924 Bro N 2-S-3 144 .328
1925 Bro N 2-S-3 44 .200
1925 Bos N 2-3 60 .288
1926 Bos N 2-3 130 .296
1927 Bos N 3 113 .302
1928 St.L N 2-3 111 .285
1929 St.L N 2-3 146 .295
1930 St.L N 3 72 .279
1931 St.L N 2-3 63 .267
1932 Cin N 2-3 84 .188
1933 Cin N 2-3 24 .209
1934 Phi N 3 47 .206

BLTR 1314 .284

HIGH, CHARLES EDWIN
b.Dec.1,1898 Ava,Ill.
d.Sept.11,1960
1919 Phi A O 11 .077
1920 Phi A O 17 .308

BLTR 28 .242

HIGH, EDWARD (Lefty)
1901 Det A P 5 3-2
TL

Yr Cl Lea Pos G Rec

HIGH, HUGH JENKINS
(Bunny)
b.Oct.24,1890 Pottstown,Pa.
d.Nov.16,1962
1913 Det A O 80 .230
1914 Det A O 80 .266
1915 NY A O 119 .258
1916 NY A O 115 .263
1917 NY A O 103 .236
1918 NY A O 6 .000

BLTL 503 .250

HIGHAM, RICHARD
b.1852 England.
d.Mar.18,1905
1871 Mut n C-2-O 22 NR
1872 Bal n C-1-2-3-O 46 .347
1873 Mut n 2-O 23 NR
1873 Atl n 2 1 NR
1873 Mut n C-3-O 26 NR
1874 Mut n M-C-2-O 65 NR
1875 Chi n C-2-O 44 NR
1875 Mut n C-1-2-O 14 NR
1876 Har N C-O 67 .325
1878 Pro N O 60 .315
1880 Tro N C-O 1 .200

BLTR 369 NR

HILAND, JOHN W.
b.Philadelphia,Pa.
1885 Phi N 2 3 .000

HILCHER, WALTER FRANK
(Whitey)
b.Feb.28,1909 Chicago,Ill.
1931 Cin N P 2 0-1
1932 Cin N P 11 0-3
1935 Cin N P 4 2-0
1936 Cin N P 14 1-2

BRTR 31 3-6

HILDEBRAND, GEORGE ALBERT
b.Sept.6,1882 San Francisco,Cal.
d.May 30,1960
1902 Bro N O 11 .227

HILDEBRAND, ORAL CLYDE
b.Apr.13,1907 Indianapolis,Ind.
1931 Cle A P 5 2-1
1932 Cle A P 27 8-6
1933 Cle A P 36 16-11
1934 Cle A P 33 11-9
1935 Cle A P 34 9-8
1936 Cle A P 36 10-11
1937 St.L A P 30 8-17
1938 St.L A P 24 8-10
1939 NY A P 21 10-4
1940 NY A P 13 1-1

BRTR 259 83-78

HILDEBRAND, PALMER MARION
b.Dec.23,1884 Shauck,O.
d.Jan.25,1960
1913 St.L N C 26 .164
BRTR

HILDEBRAND, R. E.
1902 Chi N O 1 .000

HILGERINK, WILLIAM EDWARD
Played under name of
William Edward Hilly

HILL, BELDEN L.
b.Aug.24,1863 Kewanee,Ill.
d.Oct.23,1934
1890 Bal a 3 9 .133

HILL, CARMEN PROCTOR
(Specs)
b.Oct.1,1895 Royalton,Minn.
1915 Pit N P 8 2-1
1916 Pit N P 2 0-0
1918 Pit N P 6 2-3
1919 Pit N P 4 0-0
1922 NY N P 8 2-1

(Continued)

Yr	Cl	Lea	Pos	G	Rec
1926	Pit	N	P	6	3-3
1927	Pit	N	P	44	22-11
1928	Pit	N	P	36	16-10
1929	Pit	N	P	27	2-3
1929	St.L	N	P	3	0-0
1930	St.L	N	P	4	0-1
			BRTR	148	49-33

HILL, CLIFFORD J.
(Red)

b.Jan.25,1894 Marshall,Tex.
d.Aug.13,1938

Yr	Cl	Lea	Pos	G	Rec
1917	Phi	A	P	1	0-0
			BBTL		

HILL, DAVID BURNHAM

b.Nov.11,1938 Milwaukee,Wis.

Yr	Cl	Lea	Pos	G	Rec
1957	KC	A	P	2	0-0
			BRTL		

HILL, HUBBELL JOHNSON

b.Aug.5,1892 Neb.
d.Nov.19,1918

Yr	Cl	Lea	Pos	G	Rec
1915	Cle	A	P	1	0-0

HILL, HUGH ELLIS

b.July 21,1879 Ringgold,Ga.

Yr	Cl	Lea	Pos	G	Rec
1903	Cle	A	H	1	.000
1904	St.L	N	O	23	.226
				24	.223

HILL, HUNTER BENJAMIN

b.June 21,1879 Austin,Tex.
d.Feb.22,1959

Yr	Cl	Lea	Pos	G	Rec
1903	St.L	A	3	86	.249
1904	St.L	A	3	58	.220
1904	Was	A	3	77	.229
1905	Was	A	3	103	.209
			TR	324	.219

HILL, JESSE TERRILL

b.Jan.20,1907 Yates,Mo.

Yr	Cl	Lea	Pos	G	Rec
1935	NY	A	O	107	.293
1936	Was	A	O	85	.305
1937	Was	A	O	33	.217
1937	Phi	A	O	70	.293
			BRTR	295	.289

HILL, JOHN CLINTON

b.Oct.16,1912 Powder Springs,Ga.

Yr	Cl	Lea	Pos	G	Rec
1939	Bos	N	H	2	.500
			BLTR		

HILL, WILLIAM C.
(Still Bill)

b.Aug.2,1874 Chattanooga,Tenn.
d.Jan.28,1938

Yr	Cl	Lea	Pos	G	Rec
1896	Lou	N	P	39	10-29
1897	Lou	N	P	26	6-18
1898	Cin	N	P	28	13-15
1899	Cle	N	P-O	11	3-6 / .121
1899	Bal	N	P	8	3-4
1899	Bro	N	P	1	1-0
			BLTL	113	36-72 / .166

HILLEBRAND, HOMER HILLER HENRY

b.Oct.10,1879 LeMars,Ia.

Yr	Cl	Lea	Pos	G	Rec
1905	Pit	N	P-1	36	4-2 / .236
1906	Pit	N	P	7	3-2
1908	Pit	N	P	1	0-0
				44	7-4 / .238

HILLER, CHARLES JOSEPH

b.Oct.1,1935 Johnsburg,Ill.

Yr	Cl	Lea	Pos	G	Rec
1961	SF	N	2	70	.238
1962	SF	N	2	161	.276
			BLTR	231	.265

HILLER, FRANK WALTER
(Dutch)

b.July 13,1920 Newark,N.J.

(Continued)

Yr	Cl	Lea	Pos	G	Rec
1946	NY	A	P	3	0-2
1948	NY	A	P	22	5-2
1949	NY	A	P	4	0-2
1950	Chi	N	P	38	12-5
1951	Chi	N	P	24	6-12
1952	Cin	N	P	29	5-8
1953	NY	N	P	19	2-1
			BRTR	139	30-32

HILLER, HARVEY MAX

b.May 12,1893 E.Mauch Chunk,Pa.
d.Dec.27,1956

Yr	Cl	Lea	Pos	G	Rec
1920	Bos	A	3	17	.172
1921	Bos	A	O	1	.000
			BRTR	18	.167

HILLEY, EDWARD GARFIELD

b.June 17,1879 Cleveland,O.
d.Nov.14,1956

Yr	Cl	Lea	Pos	G	Rec
1903	Phi	A	3	1	.333
			BRTR		

HILLIS, MALCOLM DAVID
(Mack)

b.July 23,1901 Cambridge,Mass.

Yr	Cl	Lea	Pos	G	Rec
1924	NY	A	2	1	.000
1928	Pit	N	2	11	.250
			BRTR	12	.243

HILLMAN, DARIUS DUTTON

b.Sept.14,1927 Dungannon,Va.

Yr	Cl	Lea	Pos	G	Rec
1955	Chi	N	P	26	0-0
1956	Chi	N	P	2	0-2
1957	Chi	N	P	36	6-11
1958	Chi	N	P	32	4-8
1959	Chi	N	P	42	8-11
1960	Bos	A	P	16	0-3
1961	Bos	A	P	28	3-2
1962	Cin	N	P	2	0-0
1962	NY	N	P	13	0-0
			BRTR	197	21-37

HILLY, WILLIAM EDWARD
(Real name William Edward Hilgerink)

b.Feb.24,1887 Fostoria,O.
d.July 25,1953

Yr	Cl	Lea	Pos	G	Rec
1914	Phi	N	O	8	.300
			BRTR		

HILSEY, CHARLES

b.1864 Philadelphia,Pa.

Yr	Cl	Lea	Pos	G	Rec
1883	Phi	N	P	3	0-3
1884	Ath	a	P-O	6	2-1 / .261
				9	2-4 / .235

HILT, BENJAMIN FRANKLIN

b.Philadelphia,Pa.
Non-playing manager Phi (p) 1890.

HIMES, JOHN H.

Yr	Cl	Lea	Pos	G	Rec
1905	St.L	N	O	12	.156
1906	St.L	N	O	40	.271
				52	.250

HIMSL, AVITUS BERNARD

b.Apr.2,1917 Plevna,Mont.
Non-playing manager Chicago (N) 1961-62.

HINCHMAN, HARRY SIBLEY

b.Aug.4,1878 Philadelphia,Pa.
d.Jan,19,1933

Yr	Cl	Lea	Pos	G	Rec
1907	Cle	A	2	15	.216
			BBTR		

HINCHMAN, WILLIAM WHITE

b.Apr.4.1883 Providence,Pa.
d.Feb.21,1963

Yr	Cl	Lea	Pos	G	Rec
1905	Cin	N	O	17	.255

(Continued)

Yr	Cl	Lea	Pos	G	Rec
1906	Cin	N	O	16	.204
1907	Cle	A	O	152	.228
1908	Cle	A	S-O	137	.231
1909	Cle	A	O	139	.258
1915	Pit	N	O	156	.307
1916	Pit	N	1-O	152	.315
1917	Pit	N	1-O	69	.189
1918	Pit	N	1-O	50	.234
1920	Pit	N	O	18	.188
			BRTR	906	.233

HINES, HENRY F. (Hunkey)

b.Sept.29,1870 Elgin,Ill.
d.Jan.2,1928

Yr	Cl	Lea	Pos	G	Rec
1895	Bro	N	O	2	.250

HINES, MICHAEL P.

b.1864 Ireland.
d.Mar.14,1910

Yr	Cl	Lea	Pos	G	Rec
1883	Bos	N	C-O	61	.228
1884	Bos	N	C	34	.181
1885	Bos	N	C-O	14	.250
1885	Bro	a	C	2	.167
1885	Pro	N	C	1	.000
1888	Bos	N	C	3	.167
			TL	115	.213

HINES, PAUL A.

b.Mar.1,1852 Washington,D.C.
d.July 10,1935

Yr	Cl	Lea	Pos	G	Rec
1872	Nat	n	1-3	10	NR
1873	Nat	n	C-2-O	39	NR
1874	Chi	n	2-S-O	59	NR
1875	Chi	n	2-O	69	NR
1876	Chi	N	O	64	.330
1877	Chi	N	2-O	60	.280
1878	Pro	N	O	60	.351
1879	Pro	N	O	84	.357
1880	Pro	N	1-2-O	82	.306
1881	Pro	N	2-O	79	.283
1882	Pro	N	1-O	84	.308
1883	Pro	N	1-O	97	.298
1884	Pro	N	P-1-O	112	0-0 / .304
1885	Pro	N	1-2-S-3-O	98	.270
1886	Was	N	3-O	121	.312
1887	Was	N	O	123	.370
1888	Ind	N	O	132	.280
1889	Ind	N	1	121	.304
1890	Pit	N	1-O	31	.172
1890	Bos	N	O	69	.266
1891	Was	a	O	54	.266
			BRTR	1648	0-0 / NR

HINKLE, DANIEL GORDON
(Gordie)

b.Apr.3,1905 Toronto,O.

Yr	Cl	Lea	Pos	G	Rec
1934	Bos	A	C	27	.173
			BRTR		

HINRICHS, PAUL EDWIN

b.Aug.31,1925 Marengo,Ia.

Yr	Cl	Lea	Pos	G	Rec
1951	Bos	A	P	4	0-0
			BRTR		

HINRICHS, WILLIAM LOUIS
(Dutch)

b.Apr.27,1889 Orange,Cal.

Yr	Cl	Lea	Pos	G	Rec
1910	Was	A	P	3	0-1
			BRTR		

HINSON, JAMES PAUL

b.May 9,1907 Van Leer,Tenn.

Yr	Cl	Lea	Pos	G	Rec
1928	Bos	A	H	3	.000
			BRTR		

HINTON, CHARLES EDWARD

b.May 3,1936 Rocky Mount,N.C.

Yr	Cl	Lea	Pos	G	Rec
1961	Was	A	O	106	.260
1962	Was	A	2-S-O	151	.310
			BRTR	257	.291

HINTON, JOHN R.

b.Altoona,Pa.

Yr	Cl	Lea	Pos	G	Rec
1901	Bos	N	3	4	.071
			TR		

HISNER, HARLEY PARNELL
b.Nov.6,1926 Ft.Wayne,Ind.

Yr	Cl	Lea	Pos	G	Rec
1951	Bos	A	P	1	0-1
	BRTR				

HITCHCOCK, JAMES FRANKLIN
b.June 28,1913 Inverness,Ala.
d.June 23,1959

Yr	Cl	Lea	Pos	G	Rec
1938	Bos	N	S	28	.171
	BRTR				

HITCHCOCK, WILLIAM CLYDE
b.July 31,1918 Inverness,Ala.

Yr	Cl	Lea	Pos	G	Rec
1942	Det	A	S-3	85	.211
1946	Det	A	2	3	.000
1946	Was	A	S-3	98	.212
1947	St.L	A	1-2-S-3	80	.222
1948	Bos	A	2-3	49	.298
1949	Bos	A	1-2	55	.204
1950	Phi	A	2-S	115	.273
1951	Phi	A	1-2-3	77	.306
1952	Phi	A	1-3	119	.246
1953	Det	A	2-S-3	22	.211
	BRTR			703	.243

Non-playing manager Det (A) 1960 and Bal (A) 1961-62

HITT, BRUCE O.
b.Mar.14,1898 Comanche,Tex.

Yr	Cl	Lea	Pos	G	Rec
1917	St.L	N	P	2	0-0
	BRTR				

HITT, ROY WESLEY
b.June 22,1884 Carleton,Neb.
d.Feb.9,1956

Yr	Cl	Lea	Pos	G	Rec
1907	Cin	N	P	21	6-10
	TL				

HITTLE, LLOYD ELDON
(Red)
b.Feb.21,1924 Acampo,Cal.

Yr	Cl	Lea	Pos	G	Rec
1949	Was	A	P	36	5-7
1950	Was	A	P	11	2-4
	BRTL			47	7-11

HOAG, MYRIL OLIVER
b.Mar.8,1908 Davis,Cal.

Yr	Cl	Lea	Pos	G	Rec
1931	NY	A	O	44	.143
1932	NY	A	O	46	.370
1934	NY	A	O	97	.267
1935	NY	A	3-O	48	.255
1936	NY	A	O	45	.301
1937	NY	A	O	106	.301
1938	NY	A	O	85	.277
1939	St.L	A	P-O	129	{ 0-0 .295
1940	St.L	A	O	76	.262
1941	St.L	A	O	1	.000
1941	Chi	A	O	106	.255
1942	Chi	A	O	113	.240
1944	Chi	A	O	17	.229
1944	Cle	A	O	67	.285
1945	Cle	A	P-O	40	{ 0-0 .211
	BRTR			1020	{ 0-0 .271

HOAK, DONALD ALBERT
b.Feb.5,1928 Roulette,Pa.

Yr	Cl	Lea	Pos	G	Rec
1954	Bro	N	3	88	.245
1955	Bro	N	3	94	.240
1956	Chi	N	3	121	.215
1957	Cin	N	2-3	149	.293
1958	Cin	N	S-3	114	.261
1959	Pit	N	3	155	.294
1960	Pit	N	3	155	.282
1961	Pit	N	3	145	.298
1962	Pit	N	3	121	.241
	BRTR			1142	.268

HOBAUGH, EDWARD RUSSELL
b.June 27,1934 Kittanning,Pa.

Yr	Cl	Lea	Pos	G	Rec
1961	Was	A	P	27	7-9
1962	Was	A	P	26	2-1
	BRTR			53	9-10

HOBBIE, GLEN FREDERICK
b.Apr.24,1936 Witt,Ill.

Yr	Cl	Lea	Pos	G	Rec
1957	Chi	N	P	2	0-0
1958	Chi	N	P	55	10-6
1959	Chi	N	P	46	16-13
1960	Chi	N	P	46	16-20
1961	Chi	N	P	36	7-13
1962	Chi	N	P	42	5-14
	BRTR			227	54-66

HOBBS, WILLIAM LEE
(Smokey)
b.May 7,1893 Grant's Lick,Ky.
d.Jan.5,1945

Yr	Cl	Lea	Pos	G	Rec
1913	Cin	N	2	2	.000
1916	Cin	N	S	6	.182
	BRTR			8	.133

HOBLITZEL, RICHARD CARLETON (Doc)
b.Oct.26,1888 Waverly,W.Va.

Yr	Cl	Lea	Pos	G	Rec
1908	Cin	N	1	32	.254
1909	Cin	N	1	142	.308
1910	Cin	N	1	155	.278
1911	Cin	N	1	158	.289
1912	Cin	N	1	148	.294
1913	Cin	N	1	137	.285
1914	Cin	N	1	78	.210
1914	Bos	A	1	68	.319
1915	Bos	A	1	124	.283
1916	Bos	A	1	130	.259
1917	Bos	A	1	120	.257
1918	Bos	A	1	25	.159
	BRTR			1317	.278

HOCH, CYRUS
(Played under name of William E. Hooker)

HOCH, HARRY KELLER
b.Jan.9,1887 Woodside,Del.

Yr	Cl	Lea	Pos	G	Rec
1908	Phi	N	P	3	2-1
1914	St.L	A	P	12	0-2
1915	St.L	A	P	12	0-3
	BRTR			27	2-6

HOCK, EDWARD FRANCIS
b.Mar.27,1900 Franklin Furnace,O.

Yr	Cl	Lea	Pos	G	Rec
1920	St.L	N	O	1	.000
1923	Cin	N	O	2	.000
1924	Cin	N	O	16	.100
	BLTL			19	.100

HOCKETT, ORIS LEON
b.Sept.29,1909 Bluffton,Ind.

Yr	Cl	Lea	Pos	G	Rec
1938	Bro	N	O	21	.329
1939	Bro	N	O	9	.231
1941	Cle	A	O	2	.333
1942	Cle	A	O	148	.250
1943	Cle	A	O	141	.276
1944	Cle	A	O	124	.289
1945	Chi	A	O	106	.293
	BLTR			551	.276

HOCKETTE, GEORGE EDWARD
(Lefty)
b.Apr.7,1909 Perth,Miss.

Yr	Cl	Lea	Pos	G	Rec
1934	Bos	A	P	3	2-1
1935	Bos	A	P	23	2-3
	BLTL			26	4-4

HODAPP, URBAN JOHN
(Johnny)
b.Sept.26,1905 Cincinnati,O.

Yr	Cl	Lea	Pos	G	Rec
1925	Cle	A	3	37	.238
1926	Cle	A	3	3	.200
1927	Cle	A	3	79	.304
1928	Cle	A	1-3	116	.323
1929	Cle	A	2	90	.327
1930	Cle	A	2	154	.354
1931	Cle	A	2	122	.295
1932	Cle	A	H	7	.188
1932	Chi	A	O	68	.222

(Continued)

Yr	Cl	Lea	Pos	G	Rec
1933	Bos	A	1-2	115	.312
	BRTR			791	.311

HODERLEIN, MELVIN ANTHONY
b.June 24,1923 Mt.Carmel,O.

Yr	Cl	Lea	Pos	G	Rec
1951	Bos	A	2-3	9	.357
1952	Was	A	2	72	.269
1953	Was	A	2-S	23	.191
1954	Was	A	2-S	14	.160
	BBTR			118	.252

HODES, CHARLES
b.1848 New York,N.Y.
d.Feb.14,1875

Yr	Cl	Lea	Pos	G	Rec
1871	Chi	n	C-S-3	28	NR
1872	Tro	n	C-S-3-O	13	NR
1874	Atl	n	2-O	21	NR
1875	Mut	n	C	1	NR
				63	NR

HODGE, CLARENCE CLEMET
(Shovel)
b.July 6,1894 Clayton,Ala.

Yr	Cl	Lea	Pos	G	Rec
1920	Chi	A	P	4	1-1
1921	Chi	A	P	36	6-8
1922	Chi	A	P	35	7-6
	BLTR			75	14-15

HODGE, EDWARD BURTON
(Bert)
b.May 25,1918 Neuberts,Tenn.

Yr	Cl	Lea	Pos	G	Rec
1942	Phi	N	3	8	.182
	BLTR				

HODGES, GILBERT RAYMOND
b.Apr.4,1924 Princeton,Ind.

Yr	Cl	Lea	Pos	G	Rec
1943	Bro	N	3	1	.000
1947	Bro	N	C	28	.156
1948	Bro	N	C-1	134	.249
1949	Bro	N	1	156	.285
1950	Bro	N	1	153	.283
1951	Bro	N	1	158	.268
1952	Bro	N	1	153	.254
1953	Bro	N	1-O	141	.302
1954	Bro	N	1	154	.304
1955	Bro	N	1-O	150	.289
1956	Bro	N	C-1-O	153	.265
1957	Bro	N	1-2-3	150	.299
1958	LA	N	C-1-3-O	141	.259
1959	LA	N	1-3	124	.276
1960	LA	N	1-3	101	.198
1961	LA	N	1	109	.242
1962	NY	N	1	54	.252
	BRTR			2060	.273

HODGIN, ELMER RALPH
b.Feb.10,1916 Greensboro,N.C.

Yr	Cl	Lea	Pos	G	Rec
1939	Bos	N	O	32	.208
1943	Chi	A	3-O	117	.314
1944	Chi	A	3-O	121	.295
1946	Chi	A	O	87	.252
1947	Chi	A	O	59	.294
1948	Chi	A	O	114	.266
	BLTR			530	.285

HODKEY, ALOYSIUS JOSEPH
b.Nov.3,1918 Lorain,O.

Yr	Cl	Lea	Pos	G	Rec
1946	Phi	N	P	2	0-1
	BLTL				

HODNET, CHARLES
b.St.Louis,Mo.

Yr	Cl	Lea	Pos	G	Rec
1883	St.L	a	P-O	4	{ 1-1 .154
1884	St.L	U	P	15	12-1
				19	{ 13-2 .121

HODSON, GEORGE S.
b.1876 Hartford,Conn.

Yr	Cl	Lea	Pos	G	Rec
1894	Bos	N	P	11	4-3
1895	Phi	N	P	4	0-2
				15	4-5

HOEFT, WILLIAM FREDERICK
b.May 17,1932 Oshkosh,Wis.

Yr	Cl	Lea	Pos	G	Rec
1952	Det	A	P	34	2-7
1953	Det	A	P	30	9-14
1954	Det	A	P	35	7-15
1955	Det	A	P	36	16-7
1956	Det	A	P	42	20-14
1957	Det	A	P	42	9-11
1958	Det	A	P	43	10-9
1959	Det	A	P	3	1-1
1959	Bos	A	P	7	0-3
1959	Bal	A	P	16	1-1
1960	Bal	A	P	19	2-1
1961	Bal	A	P	35	7-4
1962	Bal	A	P	57	4-8
	BLTL			399	88-95

HOELSKOETTER, ARTHUR H.
(Also played under name of Arthur H. Hostetter)
b.Sept.30,1882 St.Louis,Mo.
d.Aug.3,1954

Yr	Cl	Lea	Pos	G	Rec
1905	St.L	N	P-3	24	0-0 .241
1906	St.L	N	P-S-3	94	1-1 .224
1907	St.L	N	1-2	118	.247
1908	St.L	N	C	45	.232
	TR			281	1-1 .236

HOERNSCHEMEYER, LEOPOLD CHRISTOPHER
(Played under name of Lee Magee)

HOERST, FRANK JOSEPH
(Lefty)
b.Aug.11,1917 Philadelphia,Pa.

Yr	Cl	Lea	Pos	G	Rec
1940	Phi	N	P	6	1-0
1941	Phi	N	P	37	3-10
1942	Phi	N	P	33	4-16
1946	Phi	N	P	18	1-6
1947	Phi	N	P	4	1-1
	BLTL			98	10-33

HOEY, FREDERICK C.
b.New York,N.Y.
d.Dec.7,1933
Non-playing manager N.Y. (N) 1899.

HOEY, JOHN B.
b.Nov.10,1881 Watertown,Mass.

Yr	Cl	Lea	Pos	G	Rec
1906	Bos	A	O	94	.244
1907	Bos	A	O	39	.219
1908	Bos	A	O	13	.139
				146	.230

HOFF, CHESTER CORNELIUS
(Red)
b.May 8,1891 Ossining,N.Y.

Yr	Cl	Lea	Pos	G	Rec
1911	NY	A	P	5	0-2
1912	NY	A	P	5	0-1
1913	NY	A	P	2	0-0
1915	St.L	A	P	11	2-2
	BLTL			23	2-5

HOFFER, WILLIAM LEOPOLD
(Chick)
b.Nov.8,1870 Cedar Rapids,Ia.
d.July 21,1959

Yr	Cl	Lea	Pos	G	Rec
1895	Bal	N	P	38	29-8
1896	Bal	N	P	35	26-7
1897	Bal	N	P	41	22-10
1898	Bal	N	P-O	5	0-5 .235
1898	Pit	N	P	4	3-0
1899	Pit	N	P	30	8-9
1901	Cle	A	P	17	6-7

(Continued)

Yr	Cl	Lea	Pos	G	Rec
	BRTR			170	94-46 .230

HOFFERTH, STEWART EDWARD
(Stew)
b.Jan.27,1915 Logansport,Ind.

Yr	Cl	Lea	Pos	G	Rec
1944	Bos	N	C	66	.200
1945	Bos	N	C	50	.235
1946	Bos	N	C	20	.207
	BRTR			136	.216

HOFFMAN, CHARLES (Hickey)
b.Oct.27,1856 Cleveland,O.
d.Oct.27,1915

Yr	Cl	Lea	Pos	G	Rec
1879	Cle	N	C	1	.000

HOFFMAN, CLARENCE CASPER
(Red)
b.Jan.28,1904 Belleville,Ill.

Yr	Cl	Lea	Pos	G	Rec
1929	Chi	A	O	107	.258
	BRTR				

HOFFMAN, DANIEL JOHN
b.Mar.10,1880 Canton,Conn.
d.Mar.14,1922

Yr	Cl	Lea	Pos	G	Rec
1903	Phi	A	O	73	.235
1904	Phi	A	O	53	.305
1905	Phi	A	O	119	.262
1906	Phi	A	O	7	.217
1906	NY	A	O	100	.257
1907	NY	A	O	136	.253
1908	St.L	A	O	99	.251
1909	St.L	A	O	110	.269
1910	St.L	A	O	106	.237
1911	St.L	A	O	24	.210
	BLTL			827	.255

HOFFMAN, EDWARD H.
(Tex)
b.Nov.30,1893 San Antonio,Tex.
d.May 19,1947

Yr	Cl	Lea	Pos	G	Rec
1915	Cle	A	3	9	.153
	BBTR				

HOFFMAN, FRANK J.
b.Houston,Tex.

Yr	Cl	Lea	Pos	G	Rec
1888	KC	a	P	12	3-9

HOFFMAN, HARRY C.
(Izzy)
b.Jan.5,1875 Bridgeport,N.J.
d.Nov.13,1942

Yr	Cl	Lea	Pos	G	Rec
1904	Was	A	O	10	.067
1907	Bos	N	O	19	.279
				29	.224

HOFFMAN, LAWRENCE CHARLES
b.July 18,1882 Chicago,Ill.
d.Dec.29,1948

Yr	Cl	Lea	Pos	G	Rec
1901	Chi	N	3	5	.315
	TR				

HOFFMAN, RAYMOND LAMONT
b.June 14,1918 Detroit,Mich.

Yr	Cl	Lea	Pos	G	Rec
1942	Was	A	3	7	.053
	BLTR				

HOFFMAN, WILLIAM JOSEPH
b.Mar.3,1918 Philadelphia,Pa.

Yr	Cl	Lea	Pos	G	Rec
1939	Phi	N	P	3	0-0
	BLTL				

HOFFMEISTER, JESSE H.
b.Toledo,O.

Yr	Cl	Lea	Pos	G	Rec
1897	Pit	N	3	47	.312

HOFFNER, WILLIAM
b.Danville,Pa.

Yr	Cl	Lea	Pos	G	Rec
1888	KC	a	P	2	0-2

HOFFORD, JOHN WILLIAM
b.Philadelphia,Pa.

Yr	Cl	Lea	Pos	G	Rec
1885	Pit	a	P	3	0-2
1886	Pit	a	P	9	3-6
				12	3-8

HOFMAN, ARTHUR F.
(Circus Solly)
b.Oct.29,1882 St.Louis,Mo.
d.Mar.11,1956

Yr	Cl	Lea	Pos	G	Rec
1903	Pit	N	O	3	.000
1904	Chi	N	O	7	.269
1905	Chi	N	2	83	.237
1906	Chi	N	1-O	60	.256
1907	Chi	N	1-S-O	134	.268
1908	Chi	N	1-2-O	116	.243
1909	Chi	N	O	153	.285
1910	Chi	N	1-O	135	.325
1911	Chi	N	1-O	143	.252
1912	Chi	N	O	36	.272
1912	Pit	N	O	17	.283
1913	Pit	N	O	28	.229
1914	Bro	F	1-2-O	147	.291
1915	Buf	F	O	108	.233
1916	NY	A	O	6	.296
1916	Chi	N	O	5	.313
	BRTR			1181	.269

HOFMAN, ROBERT GEORGE
b.Oct.5,1926 St.Louis,Mo.

Yr	Cl	Lea	Pos	G	Rec
1949	NY	N	2	19	.208
1952	NY	N	1-2-3	32	.286
1953	NY	N	2-3	74	.266
1954	NY	N	1-2-3	71	.224
1955	NY	N	C-1-2-3	96	.266
1956	NY	N	C-1-2-3	47	.179
1957	NY	N	H	2	.000
	BRTR			341	.248

HOFMANN, FRED
b.June 10,1894 St.Louis,Mo.

Yr	Cl	Lea	Pos	G	Rec
1919	NY	A	C	1	.000
1920	NY	A	C	15	.292
1921	NY	A	C	23	.177
1922	NY	A	C	37	.297
1923	NY	A	C	72	.290
1924	NY	A	C	62	.175
1925	NY	A	C	3	.000
1927	Bos	A	C	87	.272
1928	Bos	A	C	78	.226
	BRTR			378	.237

HOGAN, GEORGE EMMET
b.Sept.25,1885 Marion,O.
d.Feb.28,1922

Yr	Cl	Lea	Pos	G	Rec
1914	KC	F	P	4	0-1

HOGAN, HARRY S
b.Nov.1,1875 Syracuse,N.Y.
d.Jan.25,1934

Yr	Cl	Lea	Pos	G	Rec
1901	Cle	A	O	1	.000

HOGAN, JAMES FRANCIS
(Shanty)
b.Mar.21,1906 Somerville,Mass.

Yr	Cl	Lea	Pos	G	Rec
1925	Bos	N	O	9	.286
1926	Bos	N	C	4	.286
1927	Bos	N	C	71	.288
1928	NY	N	C	131	.333
1929	NY	N	C	102	.300
1930	NY	N	C	122	.339
1931	NY	N	C	123	.301
1932	NY	N	C	140	.287
1933	Bos	N	C	96	.253
1934	Bos	N	C	92	.262
1935	Bos	N	C	59	.301
1936	Was	A	C	19	.323
1937	Was	A	C	21	.152
	BRTR			989	.295

HOGAN, KENNETH TIMOTHY
b.Oct.9,1902 Cleveland,O.

Yr	Cl	Lea	Pos	G	Rec
1921	Cin	N	O	1	.000
1923	Cle	A	O	1	.000
1924	Cle	A	O	1	.000
	BLTR			3	.000

HOGAN, MARTIN T.
b.Oct.25,1871 Wensbury,England.
d.Aug.16,1923

Yr	Cl	Lea	Pos	G	Rec
1894	Cin	N	O	6	.174
1894	St.L	N	O	23	.288
1895	St.L	N	O	5	.150
				34	.244

HOGAN, ROBERT EDWARD
b.St.Louis,Mo.

Yr	Cl	Lea	Pos	G	Rec
1882	St.L	a	P	1	0-1
1884	Mil	U	O	11	.077
1887	Met	a	O	32	.377
1888	Cle	a	O	77	.236
	BR			121	0-1 / .277

HOGAN, WILLIAM HENRY
(Happy)
b.Sept.14,1884 San Juan,Cal.

Yr	Cl	Lea	Pos	G	Rec
1911	Phi	A	O	7	.105
1911	St.L	A	O	123	.260
1912	StL	A	O	107	.214
				237	.236

HOGG, CARTER BRADLEY
(Brad)
b.Mar.26,1888 Buena Vista,Ga.
d.May 15,1935

Yr	Cl	Lea	Pos	G	Rec
1911	Bos	N	P	8	0-3
1912	Bos	N	P	10	1-1
1915	Chi	N	P	2	1-0
1918	Phi	N	P	39	13-13
1919	Phi	N	P	25	5-12
	BRTR			84	20-29

HOGG, WILBERT GEORGE
b.Apr.21,1913 Detroit,Mich.

Yr	Cl	Lea	Pos	G	Rec
1934	Bro	N	3	2	.000
	BRTR				

HOGG, WILLIAM (Buffalo Bill)
b.1880 Port Huron,Mich.
d.Dec.8,1909

Yr	Cl	Lea	Pos	G	Rec
1905	NY	A	P	39	9-16
1906	NY	A	P	28	14-13
1907	NY	A	P	27	11-8
1908	NY	A	P	24	4-16
				118	38-53

HOGRIEVER, GEORGE C.
b.Mar.17,1869 Cincinnati,O.
d.Jan.26,1961

Yr	Cl	Lea	Pos	G	Rec
1895	Cin	N	O	67	.278
1901	Mil	A	O	54	.243
	BRTR			121	.261

HOGSETT, ELON CHESTER
(Chief)
b.Nov.2,1903 Brownell,Kan.

Yr	Cl	Lea	Pos	G	Rec
1929	Det	A	P	4	1-2
1930	Det	A	P	33	9-8
1931	Det	A	P	22	3-9
1932	Det	A	P	48	11-9
1933	Det	A	P	45	6-10
1934	Det	A	P	26	3-2
1935	Det	A	P	40	6-6
1936	Det	A	P	3	0-1
1936	St.L	A	P	43	13-15
1937	St.L	A	P	40	6-19
1938	Was	A	P	32	5-6
1944	Det	A	P	3	0-0
	BLTL			339	63-87

HOGUE, CALVIN GREY
b.Oct.24,1927 Dayton,O.

Yr	Cl	Lea	Pos	G	Rec
1952	Pit	N	P	19	1-8
1953	Pit	N	P	3	1-1
1954	Pit	N	P	3	0-1
	BRTR			25	2-10

HOGUE, ROBERT CLINTON
b.Apr.5,1921 Miami,Fla.

Yr	Cl	Lea	Pos	G	Rec
1948	Bos	N	P	40	8-2
1949	Bos	N	P	33	2-2
1950	Bos	N	P	36	3-5
1951	Bos	N	P	3	0-0
1951	St.L	A	P	18	1-1
1951	NY	A	P	7	1-0
1952	NY	A	P	27	3-5
1952	St.L	A	P	8	0-1
	BRTR			172	18-16

HOHMAN, WILLIAM HENRY
b.Nov.27,1903 Baltimore,Md.

Yr	Cl	Lea	Pos	G	Rec
1927	Phi	N	O	7	.278
	BRTR				

HOHNHURST, EDWARD HENRY
b.Jan.31,1885 Cincinnati,O.
d.Mar.28,1916

Yr	Cl	Lea	Pos	G	Rec
1910	Cle	A	1	17	.323
1912	Cle	A	1	15	.209
	BLTL			32	.267

HOLBERT, WILLIAM H.
b.Mar.14,1855 Baltimore,Md.
d.Mar.1,1935

Yr	Cl	Lea	Pos	G	Rec
1876	Lou	N	C	12	.256
1878	Mil	N	C-O	44	.184
1879	Syr	N	C-O	57	.199
1879	Tro	N	C	4	.267
1880	Tro	N	C-O	60	.188
1881	Tro	N	C-O	44	.274
1882	Tro	N	C-1-3-O	68	.186
1883	Met	a	C-2-O	71	.238
1884	Met	a	C	65	.208
1885	Met	a	C	55	.190
1886	Met	a	C	48	.216
1887	Met	a	C	70	.252
1888	Bro	a	C	15	.115
	BRTR			613	.213

HOLBOROW, WALTER ALBERT
b.Nov.30,1913 New York,N.Y.

Yr	Cl	Lea	Pos	G	Rec
1944	Was	A	P	1	0-0
1945	Was	A	P	15	1-1
1948	Phi	A	P	5	1-2
	BRTR			21	2-3

HOLBRIGHTER, EDWARD
b.Auburn,N.Y.

Yr	Cl	Lea	Pos	G	Rec
1882	Ath	a	P	1	0-1

HOLBROOK, JAMES MARBURY
(Sammy)
b.July 17,1910 Meridian,Miss.

Yr	Cl	Lea	Pos	G	Rec
1935	Was	A	C	52	.259
	BRTR				

HOLCOMBE, KENNETH EDWARD
b.Aug.23,1918 Burnsville,N.Car.

Yr	Cl	Lea	Pos	G	Rec
1945	NY	A	P	23	3-3
1948	Cin	N	P	2	0-0
1950	Chi	A	P	24	3-10
1951	Chi	A	P	28	11-12
1952	Chi	A	P	7	0-5
1952	St.L	A	P	12	0-2
1953	Bos	A	P	3	1-0
	BRTR			99	18-32

HOLDEN, JOSEPH FRANCIS
(Socks)
b.June 4,1913 St.Clair,Pa.

Yr	Cl	Lea	Pos	G	Rec
1934	Phi	N	C	10	.071
1935	Phi	N	C	6	.111
1936	Phi	N	H	1	.000
	BLTR			17	.083

HOLDEN, WILLIAM PAUL
b.Oct.17,1889 Albany,Ga.

Yr	Cl	Lea	Pos	G	Rec
1913	NY	A	O	18	.302
1914	NY	A	O	50	.182
1914	Cin	N	O	11	.214
	BRTR			79	.211

HOLDSWORTH, JAMES
(Long Jim)
b.N.Y.

Yr	Cl	Lea	Pos	G	Rec
1872	Cle	n	S	21	NR
1872	Eck	n	S	2	NR
1873	Mut	n	S	54	NR
1874	Phi	n	S-3-O	56	NR
1875	Mut	n	S-O	69	NR
1876	Mut	N	O	52	.264
1877	Har	N	O	55	.254
1882	Tro	N	O	1	.000
1884	Ind	a	O	5	.100
	BRTR			315	NR

HOLKE, WALTER HENRY
(Union Man)
b.Dec.25,1892 St.Louis,Mo.
d.Oct.12,1954

Yr	Cl	Lea	Pos	G	Rec
1914	NY	N	1	2	.333
1916	NY	N	1	34	.351
1917	NY	N	1	153	.277
1918	NY	N	1	88	.252
1919	Bos	N	1	137	.292
1920	Bos	N	1	144	.294
1921	Bos	N	1	150	.261
1922	Bos	N	1	105	.291
1923	Phi	N	P-1	147	0-0 / .311
1924	Phi	N	1	148	.300
1925	Phi	N	1	39	.244
1925	Cin	N	1	65	.280
	BBTL			1212	0-0 / .287

HOLLAHAN, WILLIAM CHARLES
b.Nov.22,1897 New York,N.Y.

Yr	Cl	Lea	Pos	G	Rec
1920	Was	A	3	3	.167
	BRTR				

HOLLAND, HOWARD ARTHUR
(Mulligan)
b.Jan,6,1903 Franklin,Va.

Yr	Cl	Lea	Pos	G	Rec
1926	Cin	N	P	3	0-0
1927	NY	N	P	2	1-0
1929	St.L	N	P	8	0-1
	BRTR			13	1-1

HOLLAND, ROBERT CLYDE
(Dutch)
b.Oct.12,1903 Nashville,N.C.

Yr	Cl	Lea	Pos	G	Rec
1932	Bos	N	O	39	.295
1933	Bos	N	O	13	.258
1934	Cle	A	O	50	.250
	BRTR			102	.273

HOLLAND, WILLARD A.
b.Ft.Wayne,Ind.

Yr	Cl	Lea	Pos	G	Rec
1889	Bal	a	S	40	.182

HOLLAND, WILLIAM DAVID
(Dutch)
b.June 4,1915 Fuquay Springs,N.C.

Yr	Cl	Lea	Pos	G	Rec
1939	Was	A	P	3	0-1
	BLTL				

HOLLEY, EDWARD EDGAR
b.July 23,1901 Benton,Ky.

Yr	Cl	Lea	Pos	G	Rec
1928	Chi	N	P	13	0-0
1932	Phi	N	P	34	11-14
1933	Phi	N	P	30	13-15
1934	Phi	N	P	16	1-8
1934	Pit	N	P	5	0-3
	BRTR			98	25-40

HOLLIDAY, JAMES WEAR
(Bug)
b.Feb.8,1867 St.Louis,Mo.
d.Feb.15,1910

Yr	Cl	Lea	Pos	G	Rec
1889	Cin	a	O	135	.343
1890	Cin	N	O	131	.270
1891	Cin	N	O	110	.318
1892	Cin	N	P-O	149	0-1 / .286
1893	Cin	N	O	122	.332
1894	Cin	N	O	122	.383
1895	Cin	N	O	31	.301
1896	Cin	N	O	22	.346
1897	Cin	N	O	53	.328
1898	Cin	N	O	26	.240
	BRTR			901	0-1 / .319

HOLLING, CARL
b.July 9,1896 Dana,Cal.

Yr	Cl	Lea	Pos	G	Rec
1921	Det	A	P	35	3-7
1922	Det	A	P	7	1-1
	BRTR			42	4-8

HOLLINGSHEAD, JOHN SAMUEL
(Also played under name of
Samuel John Holly)
b.Jan.17,1853 Washington,D.C.

(Continued)
d.Oct.6,1926

Yr	Cl	Lea	Pos	G	Rec
1872	Nat	n	2	8	NR
1873	Nat	n	2-O	30	NR
1875	Nat	n	O	17	NR
				55	NR

Non-playing manager Was (a) 1884.

HOLLINGSWORTH, ALBERT WAYNE (Boots)
b.Feb.25,1908 St.Louis,Mo.

Yr	Cl	Lea	Pos	G	Rec
1935	Cin	N	P	39	6-13
1936	Cin	N	P	34	9-10
1937	Cin	N	P	46	9-15
1938	Cin	N	P	9	2-2
1938	Phi	N	P	24	5-16
1939	Phi	N	P	15	1-9
1939	Bro	N	P	9	1-2
1940	Was	A	P	3	1-0
1942	St.L	A	P	36	10-6
1943	St.L	A	P	36	6-13
1944	St.L	A	P	26	5-7
1945	St.L	A	P	28	12-9
1946	St.L	A	P	5	0-0
1946	Chi	A	P	21	3-2
		BLTL		331	70-104

HOLLINGSWORTH, JOHN BERNARD
b.Dec.26,1896 Knoxville,Tenn.

Yr	Cl	Lea	Pos	G	Rec
1922	Pit	N	P	9	0-0
1923	Was	A	P	17	3-7
1924	Bro	N	P	2	1-0
1928	Bos	N	P	7	0-2
		BRTR		35	4-9

HOLLISON, JOHN HENRY
b.May 3,1871 Chicago,Ill.

Yr	Cl	Lea	Pos	G	Rec
1892	Chi	N	P	1	0-1
	TL				

HOLLMIG, STANLEY ERNEST
b.Jan.2,1926 Fredericksburg,Tex.

Yr	Cl	Lea	Pos	G	Rec
1949	Phi	N	O	81	.255
1950	Phi	N	O	11	.250
1951	Phi	N	H	2	.000
		BRTR		94	.253

HOLLOCHER, CHARLES JACOB
b.June 11,1896 St.Louis,Mo.
d.Aug.14,1940

Yr	Cl	Lea	Pos	G	Rec
1918	Chi	N	S	131	.316
1919	Chi	N	S	115	.270
1920	Chi	N	S	80	.319
1921	Chi	N	S	140	.289
1922	Chi	N	S	152	.339
1923	Chi	N	S	66	.342
1924	Chi	N	S	76	.245
		BLTR		760	.304

HOLLOMAN, ALVA LEE (Bobo)
b.Mar.7,1926 Thomaston,Ga.

Yr	Cl	Lea	Pos	G	Rec
1953	St.L	A	P	22	3-7
	BRTR				

HOLLOWAY, JAMES MADISON
b.Sept.22,1908 Plaquemine,La.

Yr	Cl	Lea	Pos	G	Rec
1929	Phi	N	P	3	0-0
	BRTR				

HOLLOWAY, KENNETH EUGENE
b.Aug.8,1897 Barwick,Ga.

Yr	Cl	Lea	Pos	G	Rec
1922	Det	A	P	1	0-0
1923	Det	A	P	42	11-10
1924	Det	A	P	49	14-6
1925	Det	A	P	38	13-4
1926	Det	A	P	36	4-5
1927	Det	A	P	36	11-12
1928	Det	A	P	30	4-8
1929	Cle	A	P	25	6-5
1930	Cle	A	P	12	1-1
1930	NY	A	P	16	0-0
		BRTR		285	64-51

HOLLY, EDWARD WILLIAM
b.July 6,1886 Chicago,Ill.

Yr	Cl	Lea	Pos	G	Rec
1906	St.L	N	S	9	.067
1907	St.L	N	S	150	.229
1914	Pit	F	S	100	.246
1915	Pit	F	S	16	.262
		BRTR		275	.232

HOLLY, SAMUEL JOHN
(Also played under real name of John Samuel Hollingshead)

HOLM, ROSCOE ALBERT (Wattie)
b.Dec.28,1901 Peterson,Ia.
d.May 19,1950

Yr	Cl	Lea	Pos	G	Rec
1924	St.L	N	C-3-O	81	.294
1925	St.L	N	O	13	.207
1926	St.L	N	O	55	.285
1927	St.L	N	O	110	.286
1928	St.L	N	3	102	.277
1929	St.L	N	O	64	.233
1932	St.L	N	O	11	.176
		BRTR		436	.275

HOLM, WILLIAM FREDERICK
b.July 21,1912 Chicago,Ill.

Yr	Cl	Lea	Pos	G	Rec
1943	Chi	N	C	7	.067
1944	Chi	N	C	54	.148
1945	Bos	A	C	58	.185
		BRTR		119	.156

HOLMES, EDWARD M.

Yr	Cl	Lea	Pos	G	Rec
1918	Phi	A	P	2	0-0
	TR				

HOLMES, FREDERICK
b.Chicago,Ill.

Yr	Cl	Lea	Pos	G	Rec
1903	NY	A	1	1	.000
1904	Chi	N	C	1	.333
		TR		2	.333

HOLMES, HOWARD ELBERT
b.July 8,1883 Dayton,O.
d.Sept.18,1945

Yr	Cl	Lea	Pos	G	Rec
1906	St.L	N	C	9	.185
	TR				

HOLMES, JAMES SCOTT
b.Aug.2,1882 Lawrenceburg,Ky.

Yr	Cl	Lea	Pos	G	Rec
1906	Phi	A	P	3	0-1
1908	Bro	N	P	13	1-4
				16	1-5

HOLMES, JAMES WILLIAM (Ducky)
b.Jan.28,1869 Des Moines,Ia.
d.Aug.6,1932

Yr	Cl	Lea	Pos	G	Rec
1895	Lou	N	P-O	39	1-0 / .382
1896	Lou	N	P-O	37	0-2 / .276
1897	Lou	N	S	2	.000
1897	NY	N	O	78	.288
1898	St.L	N	O	23	.276
1898	Bal	N	O	112	.280
1899	Bal	N	O	138	.315
1901	Det	A	O	130	.294
1902	Det	A	O	92	.253
1903	Was	A	2-3-O	21	.229
1903	Chi	A	O	86	.279
1904	Chi	A	O	67	.308
1905	Chi	A	O	92	.201
		BLTR		917	1-2 / .283

HOLMES, THOMAS FRANCIS (Kelly)
b.Mar.29,1918 Brooklyn,N.Y.

Yr	Cl	Lea	Pos	G	Rec
1942	Bos	N	O	141	.278
1943	Bos	N	O	152	.270
1944	Bos	N	O	155	.309
1945	Bos	N	O	154	.352
1946	Bos	N	O	149	.310
1947	Bos	N	O	150	.309
1948	Bos	N	O	139	.325
1949	Bos	N	O	117	.266
1950	Bos	N	O	105	.298
1951	Bos	N	M-O	27	.172
1952	Bro	N	O	31	.111
		BLTL		1320	.302

Non-playing manager Bos (N) 1952.

HOLSHOUSER, HERMAN ALEXANDER
b.Jan.20,1907 Rockwell,N.C.

Yr	Cl	Lea	Pos	G	Rec
1930	St.L	A	P	25	0-1
	BRTR				

HOLT, JAMES EMMETT MADISON (Red)
b.July 25,1899 Dayton,Tenn.
d.Feb.2,1961

Yr	Cl	Lea	Pos	G	Rec
1925	Phi	A	1	27	.273
	BLTL				

HONAN, MARTIN
b.Chicago,Ill.

Yr	Cl	Lea	Pos	G	Rec
1890	Chi	N	C	1	.000
1891	Chi	N	C	5	.167
				6	.133

HOOD, AUBREY LINCOLN (Abe)
b.Jan.31,1903 Cumnock,N.C.

Yr	Cl	Lea	Pos	G	Rec
1925	Bos	N	2	5	.286
	BLTR				

HOOD, WALLACE JAMES JR.
b.Sept.24,1925 Los Angeles,Cal.

Yr	Cl	Lea	Pos	G	Rec
1949	NY	A	P	2	0-0
	BRTR				

HOOD, WALLACE JAMES SR.
b.Feb.9,1896 Whittier,Cal.

Yr	Cl	Lea	Pos	G	Rec
1920	Bro	N	O	7	.154
1920	Pit	N	O	2	.000
1921	Bro	N	O	56	.262
1922	Bro	N	O	2	.000
		BRTR		67	.238

HOOK, JAMES WESLEY
b.Nov.18,1936 Waukegan,Ill.

Yr	Cl	Lea	Pos	G	Rec
1957	Cin	N	P	3	0-1
1958	Cin	N	P	1	0-1
1959	Cin	N	P	19	5-5
1960	Cin	N	P	36	11-18
1961	Cin	N	P	22	1-3
1962	NY	N	P	41	8-19
		BRTR		122	25-47

HOOKER, WILLIAM E. (Cy)
(Real name Cyrus Hoch)
b.1880 Richmond,Va.
d.Aug.21,1911

Yr	Cl	Lea	Pos	G	Rec
1902	Cin	N	P	1	0-1
1903	Cin	N	P	1	0-0
				2	0-1

HOOKS, ALEXANDER MARCUS
b.Aug.29,1908 Edgewood,Tex.

Yr	Cl	Lea	Pos	G	Rec
1935	Phi	A	1	15	.227
	BLTL				

HOOPER, HARRY BARTHOLOMEW
b.Aug.24,1887 Santa Clara Co.,Cal.

Yr	Cl	Lea	Pos	G	Rec
1909	Bos	A	O	81	.282
1910	Bos	A	O	155	.267
1911	Bos	A	O	130	.311
1912	Bos	A	O	147	.242
1913	Bos	A	O	148	.289
1914	Bos	A	O	141	.258
1915	Bos	A	O	149	.235
1916	Bos	A	O	151	.271
1917	Bos	A	O	151	.256
1918	Bos	A	O	126	.289
1919	Bos	A	O	128	.267
1920	Bos	A	O	139	.312
1921	Chi	A	O	108	.327
1922	Chi	A	O	152	.304
1923	Chi	A	O	145	.288

(Continued)

Yr	Cl	Lea	Pos	G	Rec
1924	Chi	A	O	130	.328
1925	Chi	A	O	127	.265
	BLTR			2308	.281

HOOPER, MICHAEL H.
b.1845 Baltimore,Md.

Yr	Cl	Lea	Pos	G	Rec
1873	Mar	n	C-O	3	NR

HOOPER, ROBERT NELSON
b.May 30,1922 Leamington,Ont.,Canada.

Yr	Cl	Lea	Pos	G	Rec
1950	Phi	A	P	45	15-10
1951	Phi	A	P	38	12-10
1952	Phi	A	P	43	8-15
1953	Cle	A	P	43	5-4
1954	Cle	A	P	17	0-0
1955	Cin	N	P	8	0-2
	BRTR			194	40-41

HOOVER, CHARLES E.
b.Sept.21,1865 Mound City,Ill.

Yr	Cl	Lea	Pos	G	Rec
1888	KC	a	C	3	.200
1889	KC	a	C	71	.247
	TR			74	.245

HOOVER, RICHARD LLOYD
b.Dec.11,1925 Columbus,O.

Yr	Cl	Lea	Pos	G	Rec
1952	Bos	N	P	2	0-0
	BLTL				

HOOVER, ROBERT JOSEPH
b.Apr.15,1916 Brawley,Cal.

Yr	Cl	Lea	Pos	G	Rec
1943	Det	A	S	144	.243
1944	Det	A	2-S	120	.236
1945	Det	A	S	74	.257
	BRTR			338	.243

HOOVER, WILLIAM J.
(Buster)
b.1863 Philadelphia,Pa.

Yr	Cl	Lea	Pos	G	Rec
1884	Key	U	P-1-2-S-O	61	0-0 / .355
1884	Phi	N	O	9	.211
1886	Bal	a	O	40	.213
1892	Cin	N	O	14	.176
	BRTR			124	0-0 / .285

HOPE, SAMUEL
b.Dec.4,1878 Brooklyn,N.Y.
d.June 30,1946

Yr	Cl	Lea	Pos	G	Rec
1907	Phi	A	P	1	0-0

HOPKINS, JOHN WINTON
(Sis)
b.Jan.3,1883 Phoebus,Va.
d.Oct.5,1929

Yr	Cl	Lea	Pos	G	Rec
1902	Pit	N	C	1	1.000
1907	St.L	N	O	15	.136
	BRTR			16	.174

HOPKINS, MEREDITH HILLIARD
(Marty)
b.Feb.22,1907 Wolfe City,Tex.

Yr	Cl	Lea	Pos	G	Rec
1934	Phi	N	3	10	.120
1934	Chi	A	3	67	.214
1935	Chi	A	2-3	59	.222
	BRTR			136	.211

HOPKINS, PAUL HENRY
b.Sept.25,1904 Chester,Conn.

Yr	Cl	Lea	Pos	G	Rec
1927	Was	A	P	2	1-0
1929	Was	A	P	7	0-1
1929	St.L	A	P	2	0-0
	BRTR			11	1-1

HOPP, JOHN LEONARD
b.July 18,1916 Hastings,Neb.

Yr	Cl	Lea	Pos	G	Rec
1939	St.L	N	1	6	.500
1940	St.L	N	1-O	80	.270
1941	St.L	N	1-O	134	.303
1942	St.L	N	1	95	.258
1943	St.L	N	1-O	91	.224
1944	St.L	N	1-O	139	.336
1945	St.L	N	1-O	124	.289
1946	Bos	N	1-O	129	.333
1947	Bos	N	O	134	.288
1948	Pit	N	1-O	120	.278
1949	Pit	N	1-O	105	.318
1949	Bro	N	1-O	8	.000
1950	Pit	N	1-O	106	.340
1950	NY	A	1-O	19	.333
1951	NY	A	1	46	.206
1952	NY	A	1	15	.160
1952	Det	A	1-O	42	.217
	BLTL			1393	.296

HOPPER, C. F. (Lefty)
b.Ridgewood,N.J.

Yr	Cl	Lea	Pos	G	Rec
1898	Bro	N	P	2	0-2
	TL				

HOPPER, JAMES McDANIEL
b.Sept.1,1919 Charlotte,N.C.

Yr	Cl	Lea	Pos	G	Rec
1946	Pit	N	P	2	0-1
	BRTR				

HOPPER, WILLIAM BOOTH
(Bird Dog)
b.Oct.26,1890 Jackson,Tenn.

Yr	Cl	Lea	Pos	G	Rec
1913	St.L	N	P	3	0-3
1914	St.L	N	P	3	0-0
1915	Was	A	P	13	0-1
	BRTR			19	0-4

HORAN, JOHN J.
b.Chicago,Ill.

Yr	Cl	Lea	Pos	G	Rec
1884	Chi	U	P-O	20	3-3 / .080

HORAN, JOSEPH PATRICK
(Shags)
b.Sept.7,1894 St.Louis,Mo.

Yr	Cl	Lea	Pos	G	Rec
1924	NY	A	O	22	.290
	BRTR				

HORAZDOVSKY, ALBERT
(Played under name of Albert Nelson)

HORLEN, JOEL EDWARD
b.Aug.14,1937 San Antonio,Tex.

Yr	Cl	Lea	Pos	G	Rec
1961	Chi	A	P	5	1-3
1962	Chi	A	P	20	7-6
	BRTR			25	8-9

HORNE, BERLYN DALE
(Sonny)
bApr12,1899 Bachman,O

Yr	Cl	Lea	Pos	G	Rec
1929	Chi	N	P	11	1-1
	BBTR				

HORNER, WILLIAM FRANK
(Jack)
b.Sept.21,1863 Baltimore,Md.
d.July 14,1910

Yr	Cl	Lea	Pos	G	Rec
1894	Bal	N	P	2	0-1

HORNSBY, ROGERS (Rajah)
b.Apr.27,1896 Winters,Tex.
d.Jan.5,1963

Yr	Cl	Lea	Pos	G	Rec
1915	St.L	N	S	18	.246
1916	St.L	N	1-S-3	139	.313
1917	St.L	N	S	145	.327
1918	St.L	N	S-O	115	.281
1919	St.L	N	1-2-S-3	138	.318
1920	St.L	N	2	149	.370
1921	St.L	N	2	154	.397
1922	St.L	N	2	154	.401
1923	St.L	N	1-2	107	.384
1924	St.L	N	2	143	.424
1925	St.L	N	M-2	138	.403
1926	St.L	N	M-2	134	.317

(Continued)

Yr	Cl	Lea	Pos	G	Rec
1927	NY	N	2	155	.361
1928	Bos	N	M-2	140	.387
1929	Chi	N	2	156	.380
1930	Chi	N	M-2	42	.308
1931	Chi	N	M-2-3	100	.331
1932	Chi	N	M-O	19	.224
1933	St.L	N	2	46	.325
1933	St.L	A	M-H	11	.333
1934	St.L	A	M-3-O	24	.304
1935	St.L	A	M-1-2-3	10	.208
1936	St.L	A	M-1	2	.400
1937	St.L	A	M-2	20	.321
	BRTR			2259	.358

Non-playing manager St.L (A) 1952 and Cin (N) 1952-53.

HORNUNG, MICHAEL JOSEPH
(Ubbo)
b.June 12,1857 Carthage,N.Y.
d.Oct.30,1931

Yr	Cl	Lea	Pos	G	Rec
1879	Buf	N	O	78	.266
1880	Buf	N	P-1-2-O	82	0-0 / .262
1881	Bos	N	O	83	.240
1882	Bos	N	1-O	84	.301
1883	Bos	N	O	98	.278
1884	Bos	N	1-O	110	.266
1885	Bos	N	O	25	.201
1886	Bos	N	O	94	.257
1887	Bos	N	O	97	.299
1888	Bos	N	O	107	.239
1889	Bal	a	O	135	.227
1890	NY	N	1-O	120	.238
	BRTR			1113	0-0 / .259

HORSEY, HANSON
b.Nov.26,1889 Elkton,Md.
d.Dec.1,1949

Yr	Cl	Lea	Pos	G	Rec
1912	Cin	N	P	1	0-0
	BRTR				

HORSTMAN, OSCAR THEODORE
b.Apr.27,1892 Alma,Mo.

Yr	Cl	Lea	Pos	G	Rec
1917	St.L	N	P	35	9-4
1918	St.L	N	P	9	0-2
1919	St.L	N	P	6	0-1
	BRTR			50	9-7

HORTON, ELMER E.
(Herky Jerky)
b.Sept.4,1869 Hamilton,O.

Yr	Cl	Lea	Pos	G	Rec
1896	Pit	N	P	3	0-2
1898	Bro	N	P	1	0-1
				4	0-3

HOSKINS, DAVID TAYLOR
b.Aug.3,1925 Greenwood,Miss.

Yr	Cl	Lea	Pos	G	Rec
1953	Cle	A	P	38	9-3
1954	Cle	A	P	15	0-1
	BLTR			53	9-4

HOST, EUGENE EARL
b.Jan.1,1933 Leeper,Pa.

Yr	Cl	Lea	Pos	G	Rec
1956	Det	A	P	1	0-0
1957	KC	A	P	11	0-2
	BBTL			12	0-2

HOSTETTER, ARTHUR
(Also played under name of Arthur Hoelskoetter)

HOSTETLER, CHARLES CLOYD
b.Sept.2,1905 Uniontown,Pa.

Yr	Cl	Lea	Pos	G	Rec
1944	Det	A	O	90	.298
1045	Det	A	O	42	.159
	BLTR			132	.278

HOTALING, PETER JAMES
(Monkey)
b.Dec.16,1856 Mohawk,N.Y.
d.July 3,1928

Yr	Cl	Lea	Pos	G	Rec
1879	Cin	N	C-2-3-O	80	.278

(Continued)

Yr	Cl	Lea	Pos	G	Rec
1880	Cle	N	O	77	.240
1881	Wor	N	C-O	76	.306
1882	Bos	N	O	83	.253
1883	Cle	N	O	97	.255
1884	Cle	N	2-O	101	.242
1885	Bro	a	O	95	.277
1887	Cle	a	O	127	.367
1888	Cle	a	O	97	.250
	BRTR			833	.279

HOUCK, BYRON
b.Aug.28,1887 Prosper,Minn.

Yr	Cl	Lea	Pos	G	Rec
1912	Phi	A	P	25	8-8
1913	Phi	A	P	35	15-6
1914	Phi	A	P	3	0-0
1914	Bro	F	P	18	2-6
1918	St.L	A	P	26	2-4
	BRTR			107	27-24

HOUCK, STEPHEN ARNOLD DOUGLAS (Sadie)
b.1856 Washinton,D.C.

Yr	Cl	Lea	Pos	G	Rec
1879	Bos	N	S-O	80	.264
1880	Bos	N	O	12	.170
1880	Pro	N	O	48	.197
1881	Det	N	S	75	.279
1883	Det	N	S	98	.251
1884	Ath	a	S	110	.302
1885	Ath	a	S	92	.259
1886	Bal	a	S	61	.203
1886	Was	N	S	51	.215
1887	Met	a	S	10	.222
	BRTR			637	.254

HOUK, RALPH GEORGE (Major)
b.Aug.9,1919 Lawrence,Kan.

Yr	Cl	Lea	Pos	G	Rec
1947	NY	A	C	41	.272
1948	NY	A	C	14	.276
1949	NY	A	C	5	.571
1950	NY	A	C	10	.111
1951	NY	A	C	3	.200
1952	NY	A	C	9	.333
1953	NY	A	C	8	.222
1954	NY	A	H	1	.000
	BRTR			91	.272

Non-playing manager New York (A) 1961-62.

HOUSE, HENRY FRANK (Pig)
b.Feb.18,1930 Bessemer,Ala.

Yr	Cl	Lea	Pos	G	Rec
1950	Det	A	C	5	.400
1951	Det	A	C	18	.220
1954	Det	A	C	114	.250
1955	Det	A	C	102	.259
1956	Det	A	C	94	.240
1957	Det	A	C	106	.259
1958	KC	A	C	76	.252
1959	KC	A	C	98	.238
1960	Cin	N	C	23	.179
1961	Det	A	C	17	.227
	BLTR			653	.248

HOUSE, WILFRED E.
b.1891 Cabool,Mo.

Yr	Cl	Lea	Pos	G	Rec
1913	Det	A	P	16	1-2
	BRTR				

HOUSEHOLDER, CHARLES F.
b.1856 Harrisburg,Pa.
d.Oct.10,1884

Yr	Cl	Lea	Pos	G	Rec
1884	Chi	U	P-S-3-O	64	0-0 / .232
1884	Pit	U	O	16	.270
				80	0-0 / .240

HOUSEHOLDER, CHARLES W.
b.1856 Harrisburg,Pa.
d.Dec.26,1908

Yr	Cl	Lea	Pos	G	Rec
1882	Bal	a	C-1	73	.244

(Continued)

Yr	Cl	Lea	Pos	G	Rec
1884	Bro	a	C-1	76	.242
	BLTR			149	.243

HOUSEHOLDER, EDWARD H.
b.Oct.12,1869 Pittsburgh,Pa.
d.July 3,1924

Yr	Cl	Lea	Pos	G	Rec
1903	Bro	N	O	12	.209

HOUSEMAN, FRANK
b.Baltimore,Md.

Yr	Cl	Lea	Pos	G	Rec
1886	Bal	a	P	1	0-1

HOUSEMAN, JOHN FRANKLIN
b.Jan.10,1870 Holland, Mich.
d.Nov.4,1922

Yr	Cl	Lea	Pos	G	Rec
1894	Chi	N	S	4	.353
1897	St.L	N	2-O	76	.232
				80	.239

HOUSER, BENJAMIN FRANKLIN
b.Nov.30,1883 Shenandoah,Pa.
d.Jan.15,1952

Yr	Cl	Lea	Pos	G	Rec
1910	Phi	A	1	34	.189
1911	Bos	N	1	20	.254
1912	Bos	N	1	108	.286
	BLTL			162	.267

HOUSER, JOSEPH
b.1892 Steubenville,O.

Yr	Cl	Lea	Pos	G	Rec
1914	Buf	F	P	8	0-1
	BLTL				

HOUSTON, HARRY
b.Arkadelphia,Ark.

Yr	Cl	Lea	Pos	G	Rec
1906	Phi	N	C	2	.000
	TR				

HOUTTEMAN, ARTHUR JOSEPH
b.Aug.7,1927 Detroit,Mich.

Yr	Cl	Lea	Pos	G	Rec
1945	Det	A	P	13	0-2
1946	Det	A	P	1	0-1
1947	Det	A	P	23	7-2
1948	Det	A	P	43	2-16
1949	Det	A	P	36	15-10
1950	Det	A	P	41	19-12
1952	Det	A	P	36	8-20
1953	Det	A	P	16	2-6
1953	Cle	A	P	23	7-7
1954	Cle	A	P	32	15-7
1955	Cle	A	P	35	10-6
1956	Cle	A	P	23	2-2
1957	Cle	A	P	3	0-0
1957	Bal	A	P	5	0-0
	BRTR			330	87-91

HOUTZ, CHARLES
b.St.Louis,Mo.

Yr	Cl	Lea	Pos	G	Rec
1875	RS	n	1	19	NR
1884	Pit	a	1-O	9	.226
				28	NR

HOUTZ, FRED FRITZ (Lefty)
b.Sept.4,1875 Connersville,Ind.

Yr	Cl	Lea	Pos	G	Rec
1899	Cin	N	O	5	.176
	BLTL				

HOVLIK, EDWARD C.
b.Aug.10,1892 Cleveland,O.
d.Mar.20,1955

Yr	Cl	Lea	Pos	G	Rec
1918	Was	A	P	8	2-1
1919	Was	A	P	3	0-0
	BRTR			11	2-1

HOVLIK, JOSEPH
b.Aug.16,1884 Czechoslovakia.
d.Nov.3,1951

Yr	Cl	Lea	Pos	G	Rec
1909	Was	A	P	3	0-0
1910	Was	A	P	1	0-0
1911	Chi	A	P	12	2-0
	BRTR			16	2-0

HOWARD, DAVID AUSTIN
b.May 1,1889 Washington,D.C.
d.Jan.26,1956

Yr	Cl	Lea	Pos	G	Rec
1912	Was	A	H	1	.000
1915	Bro	F	2	20	.222
	BRTR			21	.222

HOWARD, EARL N.
b.June 25,1896 Everett,Pa.
d.Apr.1937

Yr	Cl	Lea	Pos	G	Rec
1918	St.L	N	P	1	0-0

HOWARD, ELSTON GENE
b.Feb.23,1930 St. Louis,Mo.

Yr	Cl	Lea	Pos	G	Rec
1955	NY	A	C-O	97	.290
1956	NY	A	C-O	98	.262
1957	NY	A	C-1-O	110	.253
1958	NY	A	C-1-O	103	.314
1959	NY	A	C-1-O	125	.273
1960	NY	A	C-O	107	.245
1961	NY	A	C-1	129	.348
1962	NY	A	C	136	.279
	BRTR			905	.285

HOWARD, FRANK OLIVER
b.Aug.8,1936 Columbus,Ohio

Yr	Cl	Lea	Pos	G	Rec
1958	LA	N	O	8	.241
1959	LA	N	O	9	.143
1960	LA	N	1-O	117	.268
1961	LA	N	1-O	92	.296
1962	LA	N	O	141	.296
	BRTR			367	.282

HOWARD, GEORGE ELMER (Del)
b.Dec.24,1880 Kenney,Ill.
d.Dec.24,1956

Yr	Cl	Lea	Pos	G	Rec
1905	Pit	N	1-O	119	.292
1906	Bos	N	2-O	147	.261
1907	Bos	N	O	48	.273
1907	Chi	N	1-O	41	.230
1908	Chi	N	1-O	89	.279
1909	Chi	N	1	57	.197
	BLTR			501	.262

HOWARD, IVAN CHESTER
b.Oct.12,1882 Kenney,Ill.

Yr	Cl	Lea	Pos	G	Rec
1914	St.L	A	1-3	81	.244
1915	St.L	A	1-3-O	113	.278
1916	Cle	A	2	81	.187
1917	Cle	A	3	27	.102
	BBTR			302	.233

HOWARD, LEE VINCENT
b.Nov.11,1923 Staten Island,N.Y.

Yr	Cl	Lea	Pos	G	Rec
1946	Pit	N	P	3	0-1
1947	Pit	N	P	2	0-0
	BLTL			5	0-1

HOWARD, PAUL JOSEPH
b.May 20,1884 Boston,Mass.

Yr	Cl	Lea	Pos	G	Rec
1909	Bos	A	O	6	.230
	BRTR				

HOWE, CALVIN EARL
b.Nov.27,1925 Rock Falls,Ill.

Yr	Cl	Lea	Pos	G	Rec
1952	Chi	N	P	1	0-0
	BLTL				

HOWE, JOHN (Shorty)
b.New York,N.Y.

Yr	Cl	Lea	Pos	G	Rec
1890	NY	N	2	17	.172
1893	NY	N	3	1	.500
				18	.203

HOWE, LESTER CURTIS
b.Aug.24,1895 Brooklyn,N.Y.

Yr	Cl	Lea	Pos	G	Rec
1923	Bos	A	P	13	1-0
1924	Bos	A	P	4	1-0
	BRTR			17	2-0

HOWELL, HARRY (Handsome Harry)
b.Nov.14,1876 Brooklyn,N.Y.
d.May 22,1956

(Continued)

Yr	Cl	Lea	Pos	G	Rec
1898	Bro	N	P	2	2-0
1899	Bal	N	P	28	14-7
1900	Bro	N	P	21	6-3
1901	Bal	A	P	54	14-21
1902	Bal	A	P-1-2-S-3-O	96	9-14 .266
1903	NY	A	P	41	10-7
1904	St.L	A	P	35	13-21
1905	St.L	A	P	41	14-21
1906	St.L	A	P	36	15-13
1907	St.L	A	P	44	16-15
1908	St.L	A	P	41	18-18
1909	St.L	A	P	18	1-1
1910	St.L	A	P	1	0-0
		BRTR		458	132-141 .217

HOWELL, HOMER ELLIOTT
(Dixie)
b.Apr.24,1919 Louisville,Ky.

Yr	Cl	Lea	Pos	G	Rec
1947	Pit	N	C	76	.276
1949	Cin	N	C	64	.244
1950	Cin	N	C	82	.223
1951	Cin	N	C	77	.251
1952	Cin	N	C	17	.189
1953	Bro	N	H	1	.000
1955	Bro	N	C	16	.262
1956	Bro	N	C	7	.231
		BRTR		340	.246

HOWELL, MILLARD FILLMORE
(Dixie)
b.Jan.7,1920 Bowman,Ky.
d.Mar.18,1960

Yr	Cl	Lea	Pos	G	Rec
1940	Cle	A	P	3	0-0
1949	Cin	N	P	9	0-1
1955	Chi	A	P	35	8-3
1956	Chi	A	P	34	5-6
1957	Chi	A	P	42	6-5
1958	Chi	A	P	1	0-0
		BLTR		124	19-15

HOWELL, MURRAY DONALD
(Red)
b.Jan.29,1909 Atlanta,Ga.
d.Oct.1,1950

Yr	Cl	Lea	Pos	G	Rec
1941	Cle	A	H	11	.286
		BRTR			

HOWELL, ROLAND BOATNER
b.Jan.3,1892 Napoleonville,La.

Yr	Cl	Lea	Pos	G	Rec
1912	St.L	N	P	3	0-0

HOWERTON, WILLIAM RAY
b.Dec.12,1921 Lompoc,Cal.

Yr	Cl	Lea	Pos	G	Rec
1949	St.L	N	O	9	.308
1950	St.L	N	O	110	.281
1951	St.L	N	O	24	.262
1951	Pit	N	3-O	80	.274
1952	Pit	N	3	13	.320
1952	NY	N	O	11	.067
		BLTR		247	.274

HOWLEY, DANIEL PHILIP
(Howling Dan)
b.Oct.16,1885 E.Weymouth,Mass.
d.Mar.10,1944

Yr	Cl	Lea	Pos	G	Rec
1913	Phi	N	C	26	.125
		TR			

Non-playing manager St.L(A) 1927-29 and Cin(N) 1930-32.

HOWSER, RICHARD DALTON
b.May 14,1937 Miami,Fla.

Yr	Cl	Lea	Pos	G	Rec
1961	KC	A	S	158	.280
1962	KC	A	S	83	.238
		BRTR		241	.266

HOY, WILLIAM ELLSWORTH
(Dummy)
b.May 23,1862 Houckstown,O.
d.Dec.15,1961

Yr	Cl	Lea	Pos	G	Rec
1888	Was	N	O	136	.274
1889	Was	N	O	127	.282
1890	Buf	p	O	122	.299

(Continued)

Yr	Cl	Lea	Pos	G	Rec
1891	St.L	a	O	139	.288
1892	Was	N	O	149	.279
1893	Was	N	O	130	.259
1894	Cin	N	O	128	.312
1895	Cin	N	O	107	.274
1896	Cin	N	O	121	.296
1897	Cin	N	O	128	.290
1898	Lou	N	O	148	.318
1899	Lou	N	O	155	.306
1901	Chi	A	O	130	.293
1902	Cin	N	O	72	.294
		BLTR		1792	.291

HOYLE, ROLAND EDISON
(Tex)
b.July 17,1923 Carbondale,Pa.

Yr	Cl	Lea	Pos	G	Rec
1952	Phi	A	P	3	0-0
		BRTR			

HOYT, WAITE CHARLES
(Schoolboy)
b.Sept.9,1899 Brooklyn,N.Y.

Yr	Cl	Lea	Pos	G	Rec
1918	NY	N	P	1	0-0
1919	Bos	A	P	13	4-6
1920	Bos	A	P	22	6-6
1921	NY	A	P	43	19-13
1922	NY	A	P	37	19-12
1923	NY	A	P	37	17-9
1924	NY	A	P	46	18-13
1925	NY	A	P	46	11-14
1926	NY	A	P	39	16-12
1927	NY	A	P	36	22-7
1928	NY	A	P	42	23-7
1929	NY	A	P	30	10-9
1930	NY	A	P	8	2-2
1930	Det	A	P	26	9-8
1931	Det	A	P	16	3-8
1931	Phi	A	P	16	10-5
1932	Bro	N	P	8	1-3
1932	NY	N	P	18	5-7
1933	Pit	N	P	36	5-7
1934	Pit	N	P	48	15-6
1935	Pit	N	P	39	7-11
1936	Pit	N	P	22	7-5
1937	Pit	N	P	11	1-2
1937	Bro	N	P	27	7-7
1938	Bro	N	P	6	0-3
		BRTR		673	237-182

HUBBARD, ALLEN
b.Dec.9,1860 Westfield,Mass.
d.Dec.14,1930

Yr	Cl	Lea	Pos	G	Rec
1883	Ath	a	C-S	2	.286

HUBBELL, CARL OWEN
(King Carl)
b.June 22,1903 Carthage,Mo.

Yr	Cl	Lea	Pos	G	Rec
1928	NY	N	P	20	10-6
1929	NY	N	P	39	18-11
1930	NY	N	P	37	17-12
1931	NY	N	P	36	14-12
1932	NY	N	P	40	18-11
1933	NY	N	P	45	23-12
1934	NY	N	P	49	21-12
1935	NY	N	P	42	23-12
1936	NY	N	P	42	26-6
1937	NY	N	P	39	22-8
1938	NY	N	P	24	13-10
1939	NY	N	P	29	11-9
1940	NY	N	P	31	11-12
1941	NY	N	P	26	11-9
1942	NY	N	P	24	11-8
1943	NY	N	P	12	4-4
		BRTL		535	253-154

HUBBELL, WILBERT WILLIAM
b.June 17,1897 Henderson,Colo.

Yr	Cl	Lea	Pos	G	Rec
1919	NY	N	P	2	1-1
1920	NY	N	P	14	0-1
1920	Phi	N	P	24	9-9
1921	Phi	N	P	36	9-16
1922	Phi	N	P	35	7-15
1923	Phi	N	P	23	1-6
1924	Phi	N	P	36	10-9
1925	Phi	N	P	2	0-0
1925	Bro	N	P	33	3-6
		BRTR		205	40-63

HUBBS, KENNETH DOUGLASS
b.Dec.23,1941 Riverside,Cal.

Yr	Cl	Lea	Pos	G	Rec
1961	Chi	N	2	10	.179
1962	Chi	N	2	160	.260
		BRTR		170	.257

HUBER, CLARENCE BILL
b.Oct.27,1897 Tyler,Tex.

Yr	Cl	Lea	Pos	G	Rec
1920	Det	A	3	10	.205
1921	Det	A	3	1	.000
1925	Phi	N	3	124	.284
1926	Phi	N	3	118	.245
		BRTR		253	.266

HUBER, OTTO
b.Mar.12,1917 Garfield,N.J.

Yr	Cl	Lea	Pos	G	Rec
1939	Bos	N	2-3	11	.273
		BRTR			

HUCKLEBERRY, EARL EUGENE
b.May 23,1910 Konawa,Okla.

Yr	Cl	Lea	Pos	G	Rec
1935	Phi	A	P	1	1-0
		BRTR			

HUDGENS, JAMES PRICE
b.Aug.24,1902 Newburg,Mo.

Yr	Cl	Lea	Pos	G	Rec
1923	St.L	N	1-2	6	.250
1925	Cin	N	1	3	.429
1926	Cin	N	1	17	.250
		BLTR		26	.282

HUDLIN, GEORGE WILLIS
(Ace)
b.May 23,1906 Wagoner,Okla.

Yr	Cl	Lea	Pos	G	Rec
1926	Cle	A	P	8	1-3
1927	Cle	A	P	43	18-12
1928	Cle	A	P	42	14-14
1929	Cle	A	P	40	17-15
1930	Cle	A	P	37	13-16
1931	Cle	A	P	44	15-14
1932	Cle	A	P	33	12-8
1933	Cle	A	P	34	5-13
1934	Cle	A	P	36	15-10
1935	Cle	A	P	37	15-11
1936	Cle	A	P	27	1-5
1937	Cle	A	P	35	12-11
1938	Cle	A	P	29	8-8
1939	Cle	A	P	27	9-10
1940	Cle	A	P	4	2-1
1940	Was	A	P	8	1-2
1940	St.L	A	P	6	0-1
1940	NY	N	P	1	0-1
1944	St.L	A	P	1	0-1
		BRTR		492	158-156

HUDSON, HAL CAMPBELL
(Bud)
b.May 4,1927 Grosse Point,Mich.

Yr	Cl	Lea	Pos	G	Rec
1952	St.L	A	P	3	0-0
1952	Chi	A	P	2	0-0
1953	Chi	A	P	1	0-0
		BLTL		6	0-0

HUDSON, JOHN WILSON
(Mr. Chips)
b.June 30,1915 Bryan,Tex.

Yr	Cl	Lea	Pos	G	Rec
1936	Bro	N	S	6	.167
1937	Bro	N	S	13	.185
1938	Bro	N	2	135	.261
1939	Bro	N	2-S	109	.254
1940	Bro	N	2-S-3	85	.218
1941	Chi	N	2-S-3	50	.202
1945	NY	N	2-3	28	.000
		BRTR		426	.242

HUDSON, NATHANIEL P.
b.Jan.12,1859 Chicago,Ill.
d.Mar.14,1928

Yr	Cl	Lea	Pos	G	Rec
1886	St.L	a	P	40	16-13
1887	St.L	a	P	13	3-5
1888	St.L	a	P	55	26-10
1889	St.L	a	P-O	13	2-2 .245
		TR		121	47-30 .255

Yr Cl Lea Pos G Rec

HUDSON, SIDNEY CHARLES
b.Jan.3,1917 Oliver Springs,Tenn.

Yr	Cl	Lea	Pos	G	Rec
1940	Was	A	P	38	17-16
1941	Was	A	P	33	13-14
1942	Was	A	P	36	10-17
1946	Was	A	P	31	8-11
1947	Was	A	P	20	6-9
1948	Was	A	P	39	4-16
1949	Was	A	P	40	8-17
1950	Was	A	P	31	14-14
1951	Was	A	P	24	5-12
1952	Was	A	P	7	3-4
1952	Bos	A	P	21	7-9
1953	Bos	A	P	30	6-9
1954	Bos	A	P	33	3-4
	BRTR			383	104-152

HUELSMAN, FRANK ELMER
b.June 5,1874 St.Louis,Mo.
d.June 9,1959

Yr	Cl	Lea	Pos	G	Rec
1897	St.L	N	S	2	.286
1904	Chi	A	O	3	.167
1904	Det	A	O	4	.333
1904	Chi	A	H	1	.000
1904	St.L	A	O	20	.221
1904	Was	A	O	84	.331
1905	Was	A	O	121	.271
	BRTR			235	.256

HUENKE, ALBERT JOHN
b.June 26,1891 New Bremen,O.

Yr	Cl	Lea	Pos	G	Rec
1914	NY	N	P	1	0-0
	BRTR				

HUFF, GOERGE A. (Gee)
b.June 11,1872 Champaign,Ill.
d.Oct.1,1936
Non-playing manager Bos (A) 1907.

HUFFMAN, BENJAMIN FRANKLIN
b.June 26,1914 Rileyville,Va.

Yr	Cl	Lea	Pos	G	Rec
1937	St.L	A	C	76	.273
	BLTR				

HUG, EDWARD AMBROSE
b.July 14,1880 Fayetteville,O.
d.May 11,1953.

Yr	Cl	Lea	Pos	G	Rec
1903	Bro	N	C	1	.000
	BRTR				

HUGGINS, MILLER JAMES
b.Mar.27,1879 Cincinnati,O.
d.Sept.25,1929

Yr	Cl	Lea	Pos	G	Rec
1904	Cin	N	2	140	.263
1905	Cin	N	2	149	.273
1906	Cin	N	2	146	.292
1907	Cin	N	2	156	.248
1908	Cin	N	2	135	.239
1909	Cin	N	2-3	46	.213
1910	St.L	N	2	151	.265
1911	St.L	N	2	136	.261
1912	St.L	N	2	120	.304
1913	St.L	N	M-2	121	.285
1914	St.L	N	M-2	148	.263
1915	St.L	N	M-2	107	.241
1916	St.L	N	M-2	18	.333
	BBTR			1573	.265

Non-playing manager St.L (N) 1917 and N Y (A) 1918-29.

HUGHES, EDWARD

Yr	Cl	Lea	Pos	G	Rec
1902	Chi	N	O	1	.000

HUGHES, EDWARD
b.Chicago,Ill.

Yr	Cl	Lea	Pos	G	Rec
1902	Chi	A	C	1	.250
	TR				

HUGHES, EDWARD H.
b.1880 Chicago,Ill.

Yr	Cl	Lea	Pos	G	Rec
1905	Bos	A	P	6	3-0
1906	Bos	A	P	2	0-0
				8	3-0

HUGHES, JAMES JAY
b.Jan.22,1874 Sacramento,Cal.
d.June 2,1924

Yr	Cl	Lea	Pos	G	Rec
1898	Bal	N	P	49	21-11
1899	Bro	N	P	35	25-5
1901	Bro	N	P	30	17-12
(Continued)					
1902	Bro	N	P-O	29	15-11 / .202
				143	78-39 / .223

HUGHES, JAMES ROBERT
b.Mar.21,1923 Chicago,Ill.

Yr	Cl	Lea	Pos	G	Rec
1952	Bro	N	P	6	2-1
1953	Bro	N	P	48	4-3
1954	Bro	N	P	60	8-4
1955	Bro	N	P	24	0-2
1956	Bro	N	P	5	0-0
1956	Chi	N	P	25	1-3
1957	Chi	A	P	4	0-0
	BRTR			172	15-13

HUGHES, MICHAEL F.
b.Oct.25,1866 New York,N.Y.
d.Apr.10,1931

Yr	Cl	Lea	Pos	G	Rec
1888	Bro	a	P	39	25-13
1889	Bro	a	P	19	10-6
1890	Bro	N	P	8	3-5
1890	Ath	a	P	6	1-5
	TR			72	39-29

HUGHES, ROY JOHN (Jeep)
b.Jan.11,1911 Cincinnati,O.

Yr	Cl	Lea	Pos	G	Rec
1935	Cle	A	2-S-3	82	.293
1936	Cle	A	2	152	.295
1937	Cle	A	2-3	104	.277
1938	St.L	A	2	58	.281
1939	St.L	A	2-S	17	.087
1939	Phi	N	2	65	.228
1940	Phi	N	2	1	.000
1944	Chi	N	S-3	126	.287
1945	Chi	N	1-2-S-3	69	.261
1946	Phi	N	1-2-S-3	89	.236
	BRTR			763	.273

HUGHES, THOMAS EDWARD
b.Sept. 13,1934 Amcan,C.Z.,Panama

Yr	Cl	Lea	Pos	G	Rec
1959	St.L	N	P	2	0-2
	BLTR				

HUGHES, THOMAS FRANKLIN
b.Aug.6,1907 Emmet,Ark.

Yr	Cl	Lea	Pos	G	Rec
1930	Det	A	O	17	.373
	BLTR				

HUGHES, THOMAS J. (Long Tom)
b.Nov.26,1878 Chicago,Ill.
d.Feb.8,1956

Yr	Cl	Lea	Pos	G	Rec
1900	Chi	N	P	3	1-1
1901	Chi	N	P	33	10-23
1902	Bal	A	P	15	7-8
1902	Bos	A	P	8	2-4
1903	Bos	A	P	32	21-7
1904	NY	A	P	23	7-12
1904	Was	A	P	16	2-14
1905	Was	A	P	39	16-16
1906	Was	A	P	30	7-17
1907	Was	A	P	36	7-13
1908	Was	A	P	43	18-15
1909	Was	A	P	22	4-8
1911	Was	A	P	34	11-17
1912	Was	A	P	30	13-10
1913	Was	A	P	28	4-12
	TR			392	130-176

HUGHES, THOMAS L. (Salida Tom)
b.Jan.28,1885 Coal Creek,Colo.

Yr	Cl	Lea	Pos	G	Rec
1906	NY	A	P	3	0-0
1907	NY	A	P	3	2-1
1909	NY	A	P	25	7-8
1910	NY	A	P	23	7-9
1914	Bos	N	P	2	1-0
1915	Bos	N	P	50	16-14
1916	Bos	N	P	40	16-3
1917	Bos	N	P	13	5-3
(Continued)					
1918	Bos	N	P	3	0-2
	BRTR			162	54-40

HUGHES, THOMAS OWEN
b.Oct.7,1919 Wilkes-Barre,Pa.

Yr	Cl	Lea	Pos	G	Rec
1941	Phi	N	P	37	9-14
1942	Phi	N	P	42	12-18
1946	Phi	N	P	29	6-9
1947	Phi	N	P	32	4-11
1948	Cin	N	P	12	0-4
	BRTR			152	31-56

HUGHES, VERNON ALEXANDER
b.Apr.15,1893 Etna,Pa.
d.Sept.26,1961

Yr	Cl	Lea	Pos	G	Rec
1914	Bal	F	P	3	0-0
	BLTL				

HUGHES, WILLIAM NESBERT
b.Nov.18,1897 Philadelphia,Pa.

Yr	Cl	Lea	Pos	G	Rec
1921	Pit	N	P	1	0-0
	BRTR				

HUGHES, WILLIAM W.
b.Apr.10,1862 Leavenworth,Kan.
d.Aug.25,1943

Yr	Cl	Lea	Pos	G	Rec
1884	Was	U	1-O	14	.122
1885	Ath	a	P-O	4	0-2 / .188
				18	0-2 / .138

HUGHEY, JAMES ULYSSES
(Coldwater Jim)
b.Mar.8,1869 Coldwater,Mich.
d.Mar.29,1945

Yr	Cl	Lea	Pos	G	Rec
1891	Mil	a	P	2	1-1
1893	Chi	N	P	1	0-1
1896	Pit	N	P	21	6-8
1897	Pit	N	P	20	6-13
1898	St.L	N	P	34	7-24
1899	Cle	N	P	35	4-29
1900	St.L	N	P	20	5-8
	TR			133	29-84

HUGHSON, CECIL CARLTON
(Tex)
b.Feb.9,1916 Kyle,Tex.

Yr	Cl	Lea	Pos	G	Rec
1941	Bos	A	P	12	5-3
1942	Bos	A	P	38	22-6
1943	Bos	A	P	35	12-15
1944	Bos	A	P	28	18-5
1946	Bos	A	P	39	20-11
1947	Bos	A	P	29	12-11
1948	Bos	A	P	15	3-1
1949	Bos	A	P	29	4-2
	BRTR			225	96-54

HUGHSON, GEORGE H.
b.Aug.1,1834 Erie Co.,N.Y.
d.Apr.22,1912
Non-playing manager Buf (N) 1885.

HUHN, EMIL HUGO
b.Mar.10,1892 North Vernon,Ind.
d.Sept.5,1925

Yr	Cl	Lea	Pos	G	Rec
1915	New	F	C-1	124	.227
1916	Cin	N	C-1-O	37	.255
1917	Cin	N	C-1	23	.196
	BRTR			184	.229

HULEN, WILLIAM FRANKLIN
b.Mar.12,1869 Dixon,Cal.
d.Oct.2,1947

Yr	Cl	Lea	Pos	G	Rec
1896	Phi	N	S	85	.268
1899	Was	N	S	19	.147
	TL			104	.248

HULIHAN, HARRY JOSEPH
b.Apr.18,1899 Rutland,Vt.

Yr	Cl	Lea	Pos	G	Rec
1922	Bos	N	P	7	2-3
	BRTL				

HULSWITT, RUDOLPH EDWARD
b.Feb.23,1877 Newport,Ky.
d.Jan.16,1950

Yr	Cl	Lea	Pos	G	Rec
1899	Lou	N	S	1	.000
1902	Phi	N	S	128	.272
1903	Phi	N	S	138	.247
1904	Phi	N	S	113	.244
1908	Cin	N	S	119	.228
1909	St.L	N	S	77	.280
1910	St.L	N	S	32	.248
	BRTR			608	.253

HULVEY, JAMES HENSEL (Hank)
b.July 18,1898 Mt.Sidney,Va.

Yr	Cl	Lea	Pos	G	Rec
1923	PHI	A	P	1	0-1
	BBTR				

HUMMEL, JOHN EDWIN
(Silent John)
b.Apr.4,1883 Bloomsburg,Pa.

Yr	Cl	Lea	Pos	G	Rec
1905	Bro	N	2	30	.266
1906	Bro	N	1-2-O	86	.199
1907	Bro	N	2-O	97	.234
1908	Bro	N	2-O	154	.241
1909	Bro	N	1-2-S-	145	.280
1910	Bro	N	2	153	.244
1911	Bro	N	2	133	.270
1912	Bro	N	2-O	122	.282
1913	Bro	N	S-O	67	.242
1914	Bro	N	1-O	73	.264
1915	Bro	N	O	53	.230
1918	NY	A	O	22	.295
	BRTR			1135	.254

HUMPHERIES, ALBERT (Bert)
b.Sept.21,1880 California,Pa.
d.Sept.21,1945

Yr	Cl	Lea	Pos	G	Rec
1910	Phi	N	P	5	0-0
1911	Phi	N	P	11	3-3
1911	Cin	N	P	14	4-1
1912	Cin	N	P	30	9-11
1913	Chi	N	P	28	16-4
1914	Chi	N	P	35	10-11
1915	Chi	N	P	31	8-13
				154	50-43

HUMPHREY, ALFRED W.
b.Feb.28,1886 Ashtabula,O.
d.May 13,1961

Yr	Cl	Lea	Pos	G	Rec
1911	Bro	N	O	8	.143
	BLTR				

HUMPHREYS, ROBERT WILLIAM
b.Aug.18,1936 Covington,Va.

Yr	Cl	Lea	Pos	G	Rec
1962	Det	A	P	4	0-1
	BRTR				

HUMPHREYS, WILLIAM BYRON
b.June 17,1911 Vienna,Mo.

Yr	Cl	Lea	Pos	G	Rec
1938	Bos	A	P	2	0-0
	BRTR				

HUMPHRIES, JOHN HENRY
b.Nov.12,1861 North Gower,Ont.,Canada
d.Nov.29,1933

Yr	Cl	Lea	Pos	G	Rec
1883	NY	N	C-O	26	.117
1884	Was	a	C-O	48	.178
1884	NY	N	C	19	.093
	TL			93	.146

HUMPHRIES, JOHN WILLIAM
b.June 23,1915 Clifton Forge,Va.

Yr	Cl	Lea	Pos	G	Rec
1938	Cle	A	P	45	9-8
1939	Cle	A	P	15	2-4
1940	Cle	A	P	19	0-2
1941	Chi	A	P	14	4-2
1942	Chi	A	P	28	12-12
1943	Chi	A	P	28	11-11
1944	Chi	A	P	30	8-10
1945	Chi	A	P	22	6-14
1946	Phi	N	P	10	0-0
	BRTR			211	52-63

HUNGLING, BERNARD HERMAN
b.Mar.5,1896 Dayton,O.

Yr	Cl	Lea	Pos	G	Rec
1922	Bro	N	C	39	.255
1923	Bro	N	C	2	.000

(Continued)

Yr	Cl	Lea	Pos	G	Rec
1930	St.L	A	C	10	.323
	BRTR			51	.241

HUNNEFIELD, WILLIAM FENTON
(Wild Bill)
b.Jan.5,1899 Dedham,Mass.

Yr	Cl	Lea	Pos	G	Rec
1926	Chi	A	2-S-3	131	.274
1927	Chi	A	2-S	112	.285
1928	Chi	A	2	94	.294
1929	Chi	A	2	47	.181
1930	Chi	A	S	31	.272
1931	Cle	A	S	21	.239
1931	Bos	N	2	11	.286
1931	NY	N	2	64	.270
	BBTR			511	.272

HUNT, BENJAMIN FRANKLIN
(High Pockets)
b.1888 Eufaula,Okla.

Yr	Cl	Lea	Pos	G	Rec
1910	Bos	A	P	7	2-4
1913	St.L	N	P	2	0-1
	BLTL			9	2-5

HUNT, KENNETH LAWRENCE
b.July 13,1934 Grand Forks,N.Dak.

Yr	Cl	Lea	Pos	G	Rec
1959	NY	A	O	6	.333
1960	NY	A	O	25	.273
1961	LA	A	2-O	149	.255
1962	LA	A	1	13	.182
	BRTR			193	.256

HUNT, KENNETH RAYMOND
b.Dec.14,1938 Ogden,Utah

Yr	Cl	Lea	Pos	G	Rec
1961	Cin	N	P	29	9-10
	BRTR				

HUNT, OLIVER JOEL
b.Oct.11,1905 Texico,N.Mex.

Yr	Cl	Lea	Pos	G	Rec
1931	St.L	N	O	4	.000
1932	St.L	N	O	12	.190
	BRTR			16	.182

HUNT, RICHARD M.
b.1847 N.Y.

Yr	Cl	Lea	Pos	G	Rec
1872	Eck	n	2-O	9	NR

HUNTER, EDWARD FRANKLIN
b.Feb.6,1907 Cincinnati,O.

Yr	Cl	Lea	Pos	G	Rec
1933	Cin	N	3	1	.000
	BRTR				

HUNTER, FREDERICK CREIGHTON
(Newt)
b.Jan.5,1884 Chillicothe,O.

Yr	Cl	Lea	Pos	G	Rec
1911	Pit	N	1	61	.254
	BRTR				

HUNTER, GEORGE HARRISON
b.July 8,1886 Buffalo,N.Y.

Yr	Cl	Lea	Pos	G	Rec
1909	Bro	N	P-O	39	4-10 / .228
1910	Bro	N	O	1	.000
	BR			40	4-10 / .228

HUNTER, GORDON WILLIAM
(Billy)
b.June 4,1928 Punxsutawney,Pa.

Yr	Cl	Lea	Pos	G	Rec
1953	St.L	A	S	154	.219
1954	Bal	A	S	125	.243
1955	NY	A	S	98	.227
1956	NY	A	S-3	39	.280
1957	KC	A	2-S-3	116	.191
1958	KC	A	2-S	22	.155
1958	Cle	A	S-3	76	.195
	BRTR			630	.219

HUNTER, HERBERT HARRISON
b.Dec.25,1895 E.Boston,Mass.

Yr	Cl	Lea	Pos	G	Rec
1916	NY	N	3	21	.250
1916	Chi	N	H	2	.000
1917	Chi	N	2-3	3	.000

(Continued)

Yr	Cl	Lea	Pos	G	Rec
1920	Bos	A	O	4	.083
1921	St.L	N	1	9	.000
	BLTR			39	.163

HUNTER, ROBERT LEMUEL (Lem)
b.Jan.14,1863 Warren,O.
d.Nov.9,1956

Yr	Cl	Lea	Pos	G	Rec
1883	Cle	N	P-O	1	0-0 / .250
	TR				

HUNTER, WILLARD MITCHELL
b.Mar.18,1935 Newark,N.J.

Yr	Cl	Lea	Pos	G	Rec
1962	LA	N	P	1	0-0
1962	NY	N	P	27	1-6
	BRTL			28	1-6

HUNTER, WILLIAM ELLSWORTH
b.July 8,1886 Buffalo,N.Y.
d.Apr.10,1934

Yr	Cl	Lea	Pos	G	Rec
1912	Cle	A	O	21	.165
	BLTL				

HUNTER, WILLIAM ROBERT
b.St.Thomas,Ont.,Canada.

Yr	Cl	Lea	Pos	G	Rec
1884	Lou	a	C	2	.429

HUNTZINGER, WALTER HENRY
b.Feb.6,1899 Pottsville,Pa.

Yr	Cl	Lea	Pos	G	Rec
1923	NY	N	P	2	0-1
1924	NY	N	P	12	1-1
1925	NY	N	P	26	5-1
1926	St.L	N	P	9	0-4
1926	Chi	N	P	11	1-1
	BRTR			60	7-8

HURD, THOMAS CARR
b.May 27,1924 Danville,Va.

Yr	Cl	Lea	Pos	G	Rec
1954	Bos	A	P	16	2-0
1955	Bos	A	P	43	8-6
1956	Bos	A	P	40	3-4
	BRTR			99	13-10

HURLEY, JEREMIAH F.
b.June 15,1864 E.Boston,Mass.
d.Sept.17,1950

Yr	Cl	Lea	Pos	G	Rec
1889	Bos	N	C	1	.000
1890	Pit	p	C	8	.273
1891	Cin	a	C-1-O	26	.220
	TR			35	.227

HURLEY, PATRICK

Yr	Cl	Lea	Pos	G	Rec
1901	Cin	N	C	7	.062
1907	Bro	N	C	1	.000
	TR			8	.056

HURLEY, WILLIAM F. (Dick)
b.1847

Yr	Cl	Lea	Pos	G	Rec
1872	Oly	n	O	2	.000

HURST, FRANK O'DONNELL (Don)
b.Aug.12,1905 Maysville,Ky.
d.Dec.6,1952

Yr	Cl	Lea	Pos	G	Rec
1928	Phi	N	1	107	.285
1929	Phi	N	1	154	.304
1930	Phi	N	1	119	.327
1931	Phi	N	1	137	.305
1932	Phi	N	1	150	.339
1933	Phi	N	1	147	.267
1934	Phi	N	1	40	.262
1934	Chi	N	1	51	.199
	BLTL			905	.292

HURST, TIMOTHY CARROLL
b.June 30,1865 Ashland,Pa.
d.June 4,1915.
Non-playing manager St.L (N) 1898.

HUSTA, CARL LAWRENCE (Sox)
b.Apr.8,1902 Egg Harbor,N.J.
d.Nov.6,1951

Yr	Cl	Lea	Pos	G	Rec
1925	Phi	A	S	6	.136
	BRTR				

HUSTED, WILLIAM J.
b.Oct.9,1867 Gloucester,N.J.

Yr	Cl	Lea	Pos	G	Rec
1890	Phi	p	P	19	5-10

HUSTING, BERTHOLD JUNEAU
(Pete)
b.Mar.6,1878 Fond du Lac,Wis.
d.Sept.3,1948

Yr	Cl	Lea	Pos	G	Rec
1900	Pit	N	P	2	0-0
1901	Mil	A	P	35	9-15
1902	Bos	A	P	1	0-1
1902	Phi	A	P	32	14-5
	BRTR			70	23-21

HUSTON, WARREN LLEWELLYN
b.Oct.31,1913 Newton,Mass.

Yr	Cl	Lea	Pos	G	Rec
1937	Phi	A	2-S	38	.130
1944	Bos	N	2-S-3	33	.200
	BRTR			71	.165

HUTCHESON, JOSEPH JOHNSON
(Slug)
b.Feb.5,1905 Springtown,Tex.

Yr	Cl	Lea	Pos	G	Rec
1933	Bro	N	O	55	.234
	BLTR				

HUTCHINGS, JOHN RICHARD JOSEPH
b.Apr.14,1916 Chicago,Ill.

Yr	Cl	Lea	Pos	G	Rec
1940	Cin	N	P	19	2-1
1941	Cin	N	P	8	0-0
1941	Bos	N	P	36	1-6
1942	Bos	N	P	20	1-0
1944	Bos	N	P	14	1-4
1945	Bos	N	P	57	7-6
1946	Bos	N	P	1	0-1
	BBTR			155	12-18

HUTCHINSON, EDWARD F.
b.1870 Pittsburgh,Pa.

Yr	Cl	Lea	Pos	G	Rec
1890	Chi	N	2	7	.107

HUTCHINSON, FREDERICK CHARLES
b.Aug.12,1919 Seattle,Wash.

Yr	Cl	Lea	Pos	G	Rec
1939	Det	A	P	13	3-6
1940	Det	A	P	17	3-7
1941	Det	A	H	2	.000
1946	Det	A	P	40	14-11
1947	Det	A	P	56	18-10
1948	Det	A	P	76	13-11
1949	Det	A	P	38	15-7
1950	Det	A	P	44	17-8
1951	Det	A	P	47	10-10
1952	Det	A	M-P	17	2-1
1953	Det	A	M-P-1	4	0-0 .167
	BLTR			354	95-71 .263

Non-playing manager Det (A) 1954, St.L (N) 1956-58 and Cin (N) 1959-62.

HUTCHINSON, IRA KENDALL
b.Aug.21,1910 Chicago,Ill.

Yr	Cl	Lea	Pos	G	Rec
1933	Chi	A	P	1	0-0
1937	Bos	N	P	31	4-6
1938	Bos	N	P	36	9-8
1939	Bro	N	P	41	5-2
1940	St.L	N	P	20	4-2
1941	St.L	N	P	29	1-5
1944	Bos	N	P	40	9-7
1945	Bos	N	P	11	2-3
	BRTR			209	34-33

HUTCHINSON, JAMES F.
b.1863
d.Dec.24,1941

Yr	Cl	Lea	Pos	G	Rec
1884	KC	U	P	2	1-1

HUTCHINSON, WILLIAM FOREST
(Wild Bill)
b.Dec.17,1861 New Haven,Conn.
d.Mar.19,1926

Yr	Cl	Lea	Pos	G	Rec
1889	Chi	N	P	37	16-17
1890	Chi	N	P	68	42-26
1891	Chi	N	P	64	43-19

(Continued)

Yr	Cl	Lea	Pos	G	Rec
1892	Chi	N	P	71	37-33
1893	Chi	N	P	41	16-24
1894	Chi	N	P	34	16-18
1895	Chi	N	P	34	13-18
1897	St.L	N	P	6	1-4
	TR			355	184-159

HUTSON, ROY LEE
b.Feb.27,1902 Scotland Co.,Mo.

Yr	Cl	Lea	Pos	G	Rec
1925	Bro	N	O	7	.500
	BLTR				

HYATT, ROBERT HAMILTON (Ham)
b.Nov.1,1884 Buncombe Co.,N.C.

Yr	Cl	Lea	Pos	G	Rec
1909	Pit	N	O	49	.299
1910	Pit	N	1	41	.263
1912	Pit	N	O	46	.289
1913	Pit	N	O	63	.333
1914	Pit	N	O	74	.215
1915	St.L	N	1-O	106	.268
1918	NY	A	O	53	.229
	BLTR			432	.267

HYDE, RICHARD ELDE
b.Aug.3,1928 Hindsboro,Ill.

Yr	Cl	Lea	Pos	G	Rec
1955	Was	A	P	3	0-0
1957	Was	A	P	52	4-3
1958	Was	A	P	53	10-3
1959	Was	A	P	37	2-5
1960	Was	A	P	9	0-1
1961	Bal	A	P	15	1-2
	BRTR			169	17-14

HYNDMAN, JAMES WILLIAM
b.1864 Kingston,Pa.

Yr	Cl	Lea	Pos	G	Rec
1886	Ath	a	P	1	0-1

HYNES, PATRICK J.
b.Mar.12,1884 St.Louis,Mo.
d.Mar.12,1907

Yr	Cl	Lea	Pos	G	Rec
1903	St.L	N	P	1	0-1
1904	St.L	A	P-O	66	1-0 .240
				67	1-1 .237

IBURG, HERMAN EDWARD
(Ham)
b.Oct.30,1878 San Francisco,Cal.
d.Feb.11,1945

Yr	Cl	Lea	Pos	G	Rec
1902	Phi	N	P	30	11-19
	TR				

IMLAY, HARRY MILLER
(Doc)
b.Jan.12,1889 Allentown,N.J.
d.Oct.7,1948

Yr	Cl	Lea	Pos	G	Rec
1913	Phi	N	P	9	0-1
	BRTR				

INGERSOLL, ROBERT RANDOLPH
b.Jan.8,1889 Rapid City,S.D.
d.Jan.13,1927

Yr	Cl	Lea	Pos	G	Rec
1914	Cin	N	P	4	0-0
	BRTR				

INGERTON, WILLIAM JOHN
(Scotty)
b.Apr.19,1886 Peninsula,O.
d.June 15.1956

Yr	Cl	Lea	Pos	G	Rec
1911	Bos	N	3-O	133	.250
	BRTR				

INGRAHAM, CHARLES
b.1860 Youngstown,O.

Yr	Cl	Lea	Pos	G	Rec
1883	Bal	a	C	1	.250

INGRAM, MELVIN DAVID
b.July 4,1904 Asheville,N.C.

Yr	Cl	Lea	Pos	G	Rec
1929	Pit	N	H	3	.000
	BRTR				

INKS, ALBERT PRESTON
(Bert)
(Real name Albert Preston Inkstein)
b.Jan.27,1871 Ligonier, Ind.
d.Oct.3, 1941

Yr	Cl	Lea	Pos	G	Rec
1891	Bro	N	P	13	3-9
1892	Bro	N	P	9	5-1
1892	Was	N	P	8	2-4
1894	Bal	N	P	16	8-5
1894	Lou	N	P	11	2-6
1895	Lou	N	P	27	7-19
1896	Phi	N	P	5	0-1
1896	Cin	N	P	3	1-1
	BLTL			92	28-46

INKSTEIN, ALBERT PRESTON
(Played under name of Albert Preston Inks)

IOTT, CLARENCE EUGENE
(Hooks)
b.Dec.3,1919 Mountain Grove,Mo.

Yr	Cl	Lea	Pos	G	Rec
1941	St.L	A	P	2	0-0
1947	St.L	A	P	4	0-1
1947	NY	N	P	20	3-8
	BBTL			26	3-9

IOTT, JOHN
(Happy)
b.Bangor,Me.

Yr	Cl	Lea	Pos	G	Rec
1903	Cle	A	O	3	.200

IRELAN, HAROLD
(Grump)
b.Aug.5,1890 Burnettsville,Ind.
d.July 16,1944

Yr	Cl	Lea	Pos	G	Rec
1914	Phi	N	2	67	.236
	BRTR				

IRVIN, MONFORD MERRILL
(Monte)
b.Feb.25,1919 Columbia,Ala.

Yr	Cl	Lea	Pos	G	Rec
1949	NY	N	1-3-O	36	.224
1950	NY	N	1-3-O	110	.300
1951	NY	N	1-O	151	.312
1952	NY	N	O	46	.310
1953	NY	N	O	124	.329
1954	NY	N	1-3-O	135	.262
1955	NY	N	O	51	.253
1956	Chi	N	O	111	.271
	BRTR			764	.293

IRVIN, WILLIAM EDWARD
(Ed)
b.1892 Philadelphia,Pa.
d.Feb.18,1916

Yr	Cl	Lea	Pos	G	Rec
1912	Det	A	C	1	.667
	TR				

IRWIN, ARTHUR ALBERT (Doc)
b.Feb.14,1858 Toronto,Ont.,Canada
d.July 16,1921

Yr	Cl	Lea	Pos	G	Rec
1880	Wor	N	C-S-3	83	.260
1881	Wor	N	S	49	.266
1882	Wor	N	1-S-3	84	.220
1883	Pro	N	2-S	98	.285
1884	Pro	N	P-S	99	0-0 .245
1885	Pro	N	2-S	59	.179
1886	Phi	N	S	101	.233
1887	Phi	N	S	99	.339
1888	Phi	N	S	124	.220
1889	Phi	N	S	18	.219
1889	Was	N	M-S	85	.233
1890	Bos	p	S	96	.264
1891	Bos	a	M-S	5	.154
1894	Phi	N	M-S	1	.000
	BLTR			1001	0-0 .252

Non-playing manager Was (N) 1892, Phi (N) 1895, NY (N) 1896 and Was (N) 1898-99.

IRWIN, CHARLES E.
b.Feb.15,1869 Sheffield,Ill.
d.Sept.21,1925

(Continued)

Yr	Cl	Lea	Pos	G	Rec
1893	Chi	N	S	21	.324
1894	Chi	N	S-3	130	.302
1895	Chi	N	S	3	.200
1896	Cin	N	3	127	.295
1897	Cin	N	3	134	.293
1898	Cin	N	3	135	.240
1899	Cin	N	3	87	.231
1900	Cin	N	S-3	85	.271
1901	Cin	N	3	67	.226
1901	Bro	N	3	64	.223
1902	Bro	N	S-3	131	.273
		BLTR		984	.269

IRWIN, JOHN
b.July 21,1861 Toronto,Ont.,Canada.
d.Feb.28,1934

Yr	Cl	Lea	Pos	G	Rec
1882	Wor	N	1	1	.000
1884	Bos	U	3	104	.235
1886	Ath	a	S	2	.333
1887	Was	N	S	8	.382
1888	Was	N	S	37	.222
1889	Was	N	3	58	.289
1890	Buf	p	1-3	77	.220
1891	Bos	a	3-O	20	.192
1891	Lou	a	3	14	.038
1896	Bal	N	2	1	.500
		BLTR		322	.242

IRWIN, THOMAS ANDREW
b.Dec.20,1914 Atloona,Pa.

Yr	Cl	Lea	Pos	G	Rec
1938	Cle	A	S	3	.111

BRTR

IRWIN, WALTER KINGSLEY
b.Sept.23,1897 Henrietta,Pa.

Yr	Cl	Lea	Pos	G	Rec
1921	St.L	N	H	4	.000

BBTR

IRWIN, WILLIAM FRANKLIN
b.Sept.17,1859 Neville,O.
d.Aug.7,1933

Yr	Cl	Lea	Pos	G	Rec
1886	Cin	a	P	2	0-2

BRTR

ISBELL, WILLIAM FRANK
(Bald Eagle)
b.Aug.21,1875 Delavan,N.Y.
d.July 15,1941

Yr	Cl	Lea	Pos	G	Rec
1898	Chi	N	P-O	41	4-6 / .235
1901	Chi	A	1	137	.261
1902	Chi	A	P-C-1-S	137	1-0 / .256
1903	Chi	A	1-3	138	.259
1904	Chi	A	1-2	94	.208
1905	Chi	A	2-O	94	.296
1906	Chi	A	2	143	.279
1907	Chi	A	P-2	125	0-0 / .243
1908	Chi	A	P-1-2	84	0-0 / .247
1909	Chi	A	1	120	.224
		BLTR		1113	5-6 / .254

JABLONOWSKI, PETER WILLIAM
(Also played under name of Peter William Appleton)
b.May 20,1904 Terryville,Conn.

Yr	Cl	Lea	Pos	G	Rec
1927	Cin	N	P	6	2-1
1928	Cin	N	P-O	32	3-4 / .323
1930	Cle	A	P	39	8-7
1931	Cle	A	P	30	4-4
1932	Cle	A	P	4	0-0
1932	Bos	A	P	11	0-3
1933	NY	A	P	1	0-0
(Peter Wm. Appleton)					
1936	Was	A	P	38	14-9
1937	Was	A	P	35	8-15
1938	Was	A	P	43	7-9
1939	Was	A	P	40	5-10
1940	Chi	A	P	25	4-0
1941	Chi	A	P	13	0-3
1942	Chi	A	P	4	0-0
1942	St.L	A	P	14	1-1
1945	St.L	A	P	2	0-0
1945	Was	A	P	6	1-0
		BRTR		343	57-66 / .233

JABLONSKI, RAYMOND LEO (Jabbo)
b.Dec.17,1926 Chicago,Ill.

Yr	Cl	Lea	Pos	G	Rec
1953	St.L	N	3	157	.268
1954	St.L	N	1-3	152	.296
1955	Cin	N	3-O	74	.240
1956	Cin	N	2-3	130	.256
1957	NY	N	1-3-O	107	.289
1958	SF	N	3-O	86	.230
1959	St.L	N	S-3	60	.253
1959	KC	A	3	25	.262
1960	KC	A	3	21	.219
		BRTR		812	.268

JACKLITSCH, FREDERICK LAWRENCE
b.May 24,1876 Brooklyn,N.Y.
d.July 18,1937

Yr	Cl	Lea	Pos	G	Rec
1900	Phi	N	C	5	.181
1901	Phi	N	C	31	.252
1902	Phi	N	C-O	27	.200
1903	Bro	N	C	55	.267
1904	Bro	N	C	23	.234
1905	NY	A	C	1	.000
1907	Phi	N	C	65	.213
1908	Phi	N	C	30	.221
1909	Phi	N	C	19	.310
1910	Phi	N	C	17	.196
1914	Bal	F	C	122	.275
1915	Bal	F	C	48	.237
1917	Bos	N	C	1	.000
		BRTR		444	.243

JACKSON, ALVIN NEIL
b.Dec.25,1935 Waco,Tex.

Yr	Cl	Lea	Pos	G	Rec
1959	Pit	N	P	8	0-0
1961	Pit	N	P	5	1-0
1962	NY	N	P	44	8-20
		BLTL		57	9-20

JACKSON, CHARLES HERBERT
b.Feb.7,1895 Granite City,Ill.

Yr	Cl	Lea	Pos	G	Rec
1915	Chi	A	H	1	.000
1917	Pit	N	O	41	.240
		BLTL		42	.238

JACKSON, CHARLES W.
b.1882 Iowa.

Yr	Cl	Lea	Pos	G	Rec
1905	Det	A	P	2	0-2

JACKSON, SAMUEL
b.Mar.24,1849 Ripon,England.
d.Aug.4,1930

Yr	Cl	Lea	Pos	G	Rec
1871	Bos	n	2-O	16	NR
1872	Atl	n	O	3	NR
		BRTR		19	NR

JACKSON, GEORGE CHRISTOPHER
(Hickory)
b.Oct.14,1886 Blum,Tex.

Yr	Cl	Lea	Pos	G	Rec
1911	Bos	N	O	39	.347
1912	Bos	N	O	110	.262
1913	Bos	N	O	3	.300
		BRTR		152	.285

JACKSON, HENRY EVERETT
b.June 23,1861 Union City,Ind.
d.Sept.14,1932

Yr	Cl	Lea	Pos	G	Rec
1887	Ind	N	1	10	.263

JACKSON, JAMES BENNER
b.Nov.28,1877 Philadelphia,Pa.
d.Oct.8,1955

Yr	Cl	Lea	Pos	G	Rec
1901	Bal	A	O	97	.254
1902	NY	N	O	35	.193
1905	Cle	A	O	108	.257
1906	Cle	A	O	105	.214
		BRTR		345	.236

JACKSON, JOHN LEWIS
b.July 15,1911 Wynnefield,Pa.

Yr	Cl	Lea	Pos	G	Rec
1933	Phi	N	P	10	2-2

BRTR

JACKSON, JOSEPH JEFFERSON
(Shoeless Joe)
b.July 16,1887 Brandon Mills,S.C.
d.Dec.5,1951

Yr	Cl	Lea	Pos	G	Rec
1908	Phi	A	O	5	.131
1909	Phi	A	O	5	.177
1910	Cle	A	O	20	.387
1911	Cle	A	O	147	.408
1912	Cle	A	O	152	.395
1913	Cle	A	O	148	.373
1914	Cle	A	O	122	.338
1915	Cle	A	1-O	82	.326
1915	Chi	A	O	46	.269
1916	Chi	A	O	155	.341
1917	Chi	A	O	146	.301
1918	Chi	A	O	17	.354
1919	Chi	A	O	139	.351
1920	Chi	A	O	146	.382
		BLTR		1330	.356

JACKSON, LAWRENCE CURTIS
b.June 2,1931 Nampa,Idaho

Yr	Cl	Lea	Pos	G	Rec
1955	St.L	N	P	37	9-14
1956	St.L	N	P	51	2-2
1957	St.L	N	P	41	15-9
1958	St.L	N	P	50	13-13
1959	St.L	N	P	54	14-13
1960	St.L	N	P	52	18-13
1961	St.L	N	P	34	14-11
1962	St.L	N	P	36	16-11
		BRTR		355	101-86

JACKSON, LOUIS CLARENCE
b.July 26,1935 Riverton,La.

Yr	Cl	Lea	Pos	G	Rec
1958	Chi	N	O	24	.171
1959	Chi	N	H	6	.250
		BLTR		30	.179

JACKSON, RANSOM JOSEPH (Randy)
b.Feb.10,1926 Little Rock,Ark.

Yr	Cl	Lea	Pos	G	Rec
1950	Chi	N	3	34	.225
1951	Chi	N	3	145	.275
1952	Chi	N	3-O	116	.232
1953	Chi	N	3	139	.285
1954	Chi	N	3	126	.273
1955	Chi	N	3	138	.265
1956	Bro	N	3	101	.274
1957	Bro	N	3	48	.198
1958	LA	N	3	35	.185
1958	Cle	A	3	29	.242
1959	Cle	A	3	3	.143
1959	Chi	N	3-O	41	.243
		BRTR		955	.261

JACKSON, RONALD ALLEN
b.Oct.22,1933 Kalamazoo,Mich.

Yr	Cl	Lea	Pos	G	Rec
1954	Chi	A	1	40	.280
1955	Chi	A	1	40	.203
1956	Chi	A	1	22	.214
1957	Chi	A	1	13	.317
1958	Chi	A	1	61	.233
1959	Chi	A	1	10	.214
1960	Bos	A	1	10	.226
		BRTR		196	.245

JACKSON, TRAVIS CALVIN
(Stonewall)
b.Nov.2,1903 Waldo,Ark.

Yr	Cl	Lea	Pos	G	Rec
1922	NY	N	S	3	.000
1923	NY	N	2-S-3	96	.275
1924	NY	N	S	151	.302
1925	NY	N	S	112	.285
1926	NY	N	S	111	.327
1927	NY	N	S	127	.318
1928	NY	N	S	150	.270
1929	NY	N	S	149	.294
1930	NY	N	S	116	.339
1931	NY	N	S	145	.310
1932	NY	N	S	52	.256
1933	NY	N	S-3	53	.246
1934	NY	N	S	137	.268
1935	NY	N	3	128	.301
1936	NY	N	3	126	.230
		BRTR		1656	.290

JACKSON, WILLIAM RILEY
b.Apr.4,1885 Pittsburgh,Pa.
d.Sept.26,1958

Yr	Cl	Lea	Pos	G	Rec
1914	Chi	F	1	17	.040
1915	Chi	F	1	48	.165
	BLTL			65	.139

JACOBS, ANTHONY ROBERT
b.Aug.5,1925 Dixmoor,Ill.

Yr	Cl	Lea	Pos	G	Rec
1948	Chi	N	P	1	0-0
1955	St.L	N	P	1	0-0
	BRTR			2	0-0

JACOBS, ARTHUR EVAN
b.Aug.28,1903 Luckey,O.

Yr	Cl	Lea	Pos	G	Rec
1939	Cin	N	P	1	0-0
	BLTL				

JACOBS, FORREST VANDERGRIFT (Spook)
b.Nov.4,1925 Cheswold,Del.

Yr	Cl	Lea	Pos	G	Rec
1954	Phi	A	2	132	.258
1955	KC	A	2	13	.261
1956	KC	A	2	32	.216
1956	Pit	N	2	11	.162
	BRTR			188	.247

JACOBS, LAMAR GARY
b.June 9,1937 Youngstown,O.

Yr	Cl	Lea	Pos	G	Rec
1960	Was	A	H	6	.000
1961	Min	A	O	4	.250
	BRTR			10	.200

JACOBS, MORRIS ELMORE (Mike)

Yr	Cl	Lea	Pos	G	Rec
1902	Chi	N	S	5	.210

JACOBS, NEWTON SMITH (Bucky)
b.Mar.21,1913 Altavista,Va.

Yr	Cl	Lea	Pos	G	Rec
1937	Was	A	P	11	1-1
1939	Was	A	P	2	0-0
1940	Was	A	P	9	0-1
	BRTR			22	1-2

JACOBS, OTTO ALBERT
b.Apr.19,1889 Chicago,Ill.

Yr	Cl	Lea	Pos	G	Rec
1918	Chi	A	C	29	.205
	BRTR				

JACOBS, RAYMOND F.
b.Jan.2,1902 Salt Lake City,Utah.
d.Apr.4,1952

Yr	Cl	Lea	Pos	G	Rec
1928	Chi	N	H	2	.000
	BRTR				

JACOBS, WILLIAM ELMER
b.Aug.10,1892 Salem,Mo.
d.Feb.10,1958

Yr	Cl	Lea	Pos	G	Rec
1914	Phi	N	P	14	1-3
1916	Pit	N	P	34	6-10
1917	Pit	N	P	38	6-19
1918	Pit	N	P	8	0-1
1918	Phi	N	P	18	9-5
1919	Phi	N	P	17	6-10
1919	St.L	N	P	17	3-6
1920	St.L	N	P	23	4-8
1924	Chi	N	P	38	11-12
1925	Chi	N	P	18	2-3
1927	Chi	A	P	25	2-4
	BRTR			250	50-81

JACOBSON, ALBERT L. (Beany)
b.June 5,1881 Port Washington,Wis.
d.Jan.31,1933

Yr	Cl	Lea	Pos	G	Rec
1904	Was	A	P	33	5-23
1905	Was	A	P	22	8-9
1906	St.L	A	P	25	9-9
1907	St.L	A	P	7	1-5
1907	Bos	A	P	2	0-0
	TL			89	23-46

JACOBSON, MERWIN JOHN WILLIAM (Jake)
b.Mar.7,1894 New Britain,Conn.

Yr	Cl	Lea	Pos	G	Rec
1915	NY	N	O	8	.083
1916	Chi	N	O	4	.231
1926	Bro	N	O	110	.247
1927	Bro	N	O	11	.000
	BLTL			133	.230

JACOBSON, WILLIAM CHESTER (Baby Doll)
b.Aug.16,1890 Cable,Ill.

Yr	Cl	Lea	Pos	G	Rec
1915	Det	A	O	38	.215
1915	St.L	A	O	33	.209
1917	St.L	A	O	148	.248
1919	St.L	A	O	120	.323
1920	St.L	A	O	154	.355
1921	St.L	A	1-O	151	.352
1922	St.L	A	O	145	.317
1923	St.L	A	O	147	.309
1924	St.L	A	O	152	.318
1925	St.L	A	O	142	.341
1926	St.L	A	O	50	.290
1926	Bos	A	O	98	.302
1927	Bos	A	O	45	.245
1927	Cle	A	O	32	.252
1927	Phi	A	O	17	.229
	BRTR			1472	.311

JACOBUS, STUART LOUIS (Larry)
b.Dec.13,1896 Cincinnati,O.

Yr	Cl	Lea	Pos	G	Rec
1918	Cin	N	P	5	0-1
	BBTR				

JACOBY, HARRY
b.Philadelphia,Pa.

Yr	Cl	Lea	Pos	G	Rec
1882	Bal	a	3-O	31	.213
1885	Bal	a	2	11	.143
				42	.195

JAEGER, CHARLES THOMAS
b.Apr.17,1875 Ottawa,Ill.
d.Sept.27,1942

Yr	Cl	Lea	Pos	G	Rec
1904	Det	A	P	8	2-3

JAEGER, JOSEPH P.
b.Mar.3,1896 St.Cloud,Minn.

Yr	Cl	Lea	Pos	G	Rec
1920	Chi	N	P	2	0-0
	BRTR				

JAHN, ARTHUR CHARLES
b.Dec.2,1897 Struble,Ia.
d.Jan.9,1948

Yr	Cl	Lea	Pos	G	Rec
1925	Chi	N	O	58	.301
1928	NY	N	O	10	.276
1928	Phi	N	O	36	.223
	BRTR			104	.278

JAKUCKI, SIGMUND JACK
b.Aug.20,1911 Camden,N.J.

Yr	Cl	Lea	Pos	G	Rec
1936	St.L	A	P	7	0-3
1944	St.L	A	P	36	13-9
1945	St.L	A	P	30	12-10
	BRTR			73	25-22

JAMERSON, CHARLEY DEWEY (Lefty)
b.Jan.26,1900 Enfield,Ill.

Yr	Cl	Lea	Pos	G	Rec
1924	Bos	A	P	1	0-0
	BLTL				

JAMES, BERTON HULON (Bob)
b.July 7,1886 Adamsville,Ky.

Yr	Cl	Lea	Pos	G	Rec
1909	St.L	N	O	6	.285
	BLTR				

JAMES, CHARLES WESLEY
b.Dec.22,1937 St.Louis,Mo.

Yr	Cl	Lea	Pos	G	Rec
1960	St.L	N	O	43	.180
1961	St.L	N	O	108	.255
1962	St.L	N	O	129	.276
	BRTR			280	.260

JAMES, JAMES McCUTCHEN
(Played under name of James McCutchen McJames)
b.July 23,1933 Bonner's Ferry,Idaho

JAMES, JOHN PHILLIP
b.July 23,1933 Bonner's Ferry,Idaho

Yr	Cl	Lea	Pos	G	Rec
1958	NY	A	P	1	0-0
1960	NY	A	P	28	5-1
1961	NY	A	P	1	0-0
1961	LA	A	P	43	0-2
	BLTR			73	5-3

JAMES, ROBERT BYRNE (Bernie)
b.Sept.2,1905 Angleton,Tex.

Yr	Cl	Lea	Pos	G	Rec
1929	Bos	N	2	46	.307
1930	Bos	N	2	8	.182
1933	NY	N	2-S-3	60	.224
	BBTR			114	.257

JAMES, WILLIAM A. (Lefty)
b.July 1,1890 Glenroy,O.
d.May 3,1933

Yr	Cl	Lea	Pos	G	Rec
1912	Cle	A	P	6	0-1
1913	Cle	A	P	11	2-2
1914	Cle	A	P	11	0-3
	BLTL			28	2-6

JAMES, WILLIAM HENRY (Big Bill)
b.Jan.20,1888 Ann Arbor,Mich.
d.May 24,1942

Yr	Cl	Lea	Pos	G	Rec
1911	Cle	A	P	8	3-4
1912	Cle	A	P	3	0-0
1914	St.L	A	P	38	15-14
1915	St.L	A	P	34	6-10
1915	Det	A	P	11	7-3
1916	Det	A	P	30	7-12
1917	Det	A	P	34	13-10
1918	Det	A	P	19	6-11
1919	Det	A	P	3	3-0
1919	Bos	A	P	14	2-5
1919	Chi	A	P	5	3-1
	BBTR			199	65-70

JAMES, WILLIAM LAWRENCE (Seattle Bill)
b.Mar.12,1892 Placer Co.,Cal.

Yr	Cl	Lea	Pos	G	Rec
1913	Bos	N	P	24	6-10
1914	Bos	N	P	49	26-7
1915	Bos	N	P	14	5-4
1919	Bos	N	P	1	0-0
	BRTR			88	37-21

JAMIESON, CHARLES DEVINE (Cuckoo)
b.Feb.7,1893 Paterson,N.J.

Yr	Cl	Lea	Pos	G	Rec
1915	Was	A	O	17	.279
1916	Was	A	P-O	64	0-0 .248
1917	Was	A	P-O	20	0-0 .171
1917	Phi	A	O	85	.267
1918	Phi	A	P-O	110	1-1 .202
1919	Cle	A	O	26	.353
1920	Cle	A	O	108	.319
1921	Cle	A	O	140	.310
1922	Cle	A	P-O	145	0-0 .323
1923	Cle	A	O	152	.345
1924	Cle	A	O	143	.358
1925	Cle	A	O	138	.296
1926	Cle	A	O	143	.299
1927	Cle	A	O	127	.309
1928	Cle	A	O	112	.307
1929	Cle	A	O	102	.291
1930	Cle	A	O	103	.301
1931	Cle	A	O	28	.302
1932	Cle	A	O	16	.063
	BLTL			1779	1-1 .303

JANOWICZ, VICTOR FELIX
b.Feb.26,1930 Elyria,O.

Yr	Cl	Lea	Pos	G	Rec
1953	Pit	N	C	42	.252
1954	Pit	N	3-O	41	.151
	BRTR			83	.214

JANSEN, LAWRENCE JOSEPH
b.July 16,1920 Forest Grove,Ore.

Yr	Cl	Lea	Pos	G	Rec
1947	NY	N	P	42	21-5
1948	NY	N	P	42	18-12
1949	NY	N	P	37	15-16
1950	NY	N	P	40	19-13
1951	NY	N	P	39	23-11
1952	NY	N	P	34	11-11
1953	NY	N	P	36	11-16
1954	NY	N	P	13	2-2
1956	Cin	N	P	8	2-3
	BRTR			291	122-89

JANSEN, RAYMOND W.
b.1890 St.Louis,Mo.

Yr	Cl	Lea	Pos	G	Rec
1910	St.L	A	3	1	.800
	BRTR				

JANTZEN, WALTER C. (Heinie)
b.1890

Yr	Cl	Lea	Pos	G	Rec
1912	St.L	A	O	31	.185
	BRTR				

JANVRIN, HAROLD CHANDLER
b.Aug.27,1892 Haverhill,Mass.
d.Mar.2,1962

Yr	Cl	Lea	Pos	G	Rec
1911	Bos	A	3	10	.153
1913	Bos	A	S-3	86	.206
1914	Bos	A	1-2-S	143	.238
1915	Bos	A	S-3	99	.269
1916	Bos	A	2-S	117	.223
1917	Bos	A	2	55	.197
1919	Was	A	2	61	.178
1919	St.L	N	2	7	.214
1920	St.L	N	1-S-O	87	.274
1921	St.L	N	1	18	.281
1921	Bro	N	1-S	44	.196
1922	Bro	N	1-2-S-3-O	30	.298
	BRTR			757	.232

JARVIS, LeROY GILBERT
b.June 27,1926 Oklahoma City,Okla.

Yr	Cl	Lea	Pos	G	Rec
1944	Bro	N	C	1	.000
1946	Pit	N	C	2	.250
1947	Pit	N	C	18	.156
	BRTR			21	.160

JASPER, HARRY W. (Hi)
b.May 24,1887 St.Louis,Mo.
d.May 22,1937

Yr	Cl	Lea	Pos	G	Rec
1914	Chi	A	P	16	1-0
1915	Chi	A	P	3	1-1
1916	St.L	N	P	21	5-6
1919	Cle	A	P	12	4-5
	BRTR			52	11-12

JAVERY, ALVA WILLIAM
(Beartracks)
b.June 5,1918 Worcester,Mass.

Yr	Cl	Lea	Pos	G	Rec
1940	Bos	N	P	29	2-4
1941	Bos	N	P	34	10-11
1942	Bos	N	P	42	12-16
1943	Bos	N	P	41	17-16
1944	Bos	N	P	40	10-19
1945	Bos	N	P	17	2-7
1946	Bos	N	P	2	0-1
	BRTR			205	53-74

JAVIER, MANUEL JULIEN LIRANZO
b.Aug.9,1936 San Francisco De Macoris,D.R.

Yr	Cl	Lea	Pos	G	Rec
1960	St.L	N	2	119	.237
1961	St.L	N	2	113	.279
1962	St.L	N	2-S	155	.263
	BRTR			387	.260

JAY, JOSEPH RICHARD
b.Aug.15,1935 Middletown,Conn.

Yr	Cl	Lea	Pos	G	Rec
1953	Mil	N	P	3	1-0
1954	Mil	N	P	15	1-0
1955	Mil	N	P	12	0-0
1957	Mil	N	P	1	0-0
1958	Mil	N	P	18	7-5
1959	Mil	N	P	34	6-11
1960	Mil	N	P	32	9-8
1961	Cin	N	P	34	21-10
1962	Cin	N	P	39	21-14
	BRTR			188	66-48

JEANES, ERNEST LEE (Tex)
b.Dec.19,1900 Maypearl,Tex.

Yr	Cl	Lea	Pos	G	Rec
1921	Cle	A	O	4	.500
1922	Cle	A	P	1	0-0
1925	Was	A	O	15	.263
1926	Was	A	O	21	.233
1927	NY	N	P	11	0-0
	BRTR			52	0-0 .278

JEFFCOAT, GEORGE EDWARD
b.Dec.24,1913 New Brookland,S.C.

Yr	Cl	Lea	Pos	G	Rec
1936	Bro	N	P	40	5-6
1937	Bro	N	P	21	1-3
1939	Bro	N	P	1	0-0
1943	Bos	N	P	8	1-2
	BRTR			70	7-11

JEFFCOAT, HAROLD BENTLY
b.Sept.6,1924 W.Columbia,S.C.

Yr	Cl	Lea	Pos	G	Rec
1948	Chi	N	O	134	.279
1949	Chi	N	O	108	.245
1950	Chi	N	O	66	.235
1951	Chi	N	O	113	.273
1952	Chi	N	O	102	.219
1953	Chi	N	O	106	.235
1954	Chi	N	P-O	56	5-6 .258
1955	Chi	N	P	52	8-6
1956	Cin	N	P	49	8-2
1957	Cin	N	P	53	12-13
1958	Cin	N	P-O	50	6-8 .556
1959	Cin	N	P	17	0-1
1959	St.L	N	P	12	0-1
	BRTR			918	39-37 .253

JEFFRIES, IRVINE FRANKLIN
b.Sept.10,1905 Louisville,Ky.

Yr	Cl	Lea	Pos	G	Rec
1930	Chi	A	S-3	40	.237
1931	Chi	A	3	79	.224
1934	Phi	N	2	56	.246
	BRTR			175	.234

JELINCICH, FRANK ANTHONY
(Jelly)
b.Sept.3,1919 San Jose,Cal.

Yr	Cl	Lea	Pos	G	Rec
1941	Chi	N	O	4	.125
	BRTR				

JENKINS, JOHN ROBERT
b.July 7,1897 Bosworth,Mo.

Yr	Cl	Lea	Pos	G	Rec
1922	Chi	A	2-S	5	.000
	BRTR				

JENKINS, JOSEPH DANIEL
b.Oct.12,1891 Shelbyville,Tenn.

Yr	Cl	Lea	Pos	G	Rec
1914	St.L	A	C	19	.125
1917	Chi	A	C	10	.111
1919	Chi	A	C	11	.167
	BRTR			40	.136

JENKINS, THOMAS GRIFFITH (Tut)
b.Apr.10,1898 Camden,Ala.

Yr	Cl	Lea	Pos	G	Rec
1925	Bos	A	O	15	.297
1926	Bos	A	O	21	.180
1926	Phi	A	O	6	.174
1929	St.L	A	O	21	.182
1930	St.L	A	O	2	.250
1931	St.L	A	O	81	.265
1932	St.L	A	O	25	.323
	BLTR			171	.259

JENKINS, WARREN WASHINGTON
b.Dec.22,1942 Covington,Va.

Yr	Cl	Lea	Pos	G	Rec
1962	Was	A	P	3	0-1
	BRTR				

JENNINGS, ALFRED (Alamazoo)
b.1851 Newport,Ky.
d.Nov.2,1894

Yr	Cl	Lea	Pos	G	Rec
1878	Mil	N	C	1	.000

JENNINGS, HUGH AMBROSE
(Ee-Yah)
b.Apr.2,1869 Pittston,Pa.
d.Feb.1,1928

Yr	Cl	Lea	Pos	G	Rec
1891	Lou	a	1-S	87	.286
1892	Lou	N	S	152	.232
1893	Lou	N	S	23	.148
1893	Bal	N	S	15	.241
1894	Bal	N	S	128	.332
1895	Bal	N	S	131	.386
1896	Bal	N	S	129	.397
1897	Bal	N	S	115	.353

(Continued)

Yr	Cl	Lea	Pos	G	Rec
1898	Bal	N	2-S	143	.325
1899	Bro	N	1	10	.200
1899	Bal	N	2	2	.375
1899	Bro	N	1-S	51	.320
1900	Bro	N	1	112	.270
1901	Phi	N	1	81	.274
1902	Phi	N	1-2-S	78	.277
1903	Bro	N	O	6	.235
1907	Det	A	M-S	2	.250
1908	Det	A	M-H	1	.000
1909	Det	A	M-1	2	.500
1912	Det	A	M-H	1	.000
1918	Det	A	M-1	1	.000
	BRTR			1270	.314

Non-playing manager Det (A) 1910-11, 1913-17 and 1919-20

JENNINGS, WILLIAM LEE
b.Sept.28,1925 St.Louis,Mo.

Yr	Cl	Lea	Pos	G	Rec
1951	St.L	A	S	64	.179
	BRTR				

JENSEN, FORREST DUCENUS
(Woody)
b.Aug.11,1909 Bremerton,Wash.

Yr	Cl	Lea	Pos	G	Rec
1931	Pit	N	O	73	.243
1932	Pit	N	O	7	.000
1933	Pit	N	O	70	.296
1934	Pit	N	O	88	.290
1935	Pit	N	O	143	.324
1936	Pit	N	O	153	.283
1937	Pit	N	O	124	.279
1938	Pit	N	O	68	.200
1939	Pit	N	O	12	.167
	BLTL			738	.285

JENSEN, JACK EUGENE
b.Mar.9,1927 San Francisco,Cal.

Yr	Cl	Lea	Pos	G	Rec
1950	NY	A	O	45	.171
1951	NY	A	O	56	.298
1952	NY	A	O	7	.105
1952	Was	A	O	144	.286
1953	Was	A	O	147	.266
1954	Bos	A	O	152	.276
1955	Bos	A	O	152	.275
1956	Bos	A	O	151	.315
1957	Bos	A	O	145	.281
1958	Bos	A	O	154	.286
1959	Bos	A	O	148	.277
1961	Bos	A	O	137	.263
	BRTR			1438	.279

JENSEN, WILLIAM
b.Nov.23,1888 New Haven,Conn.

Yr	Cl	Lea	Pos	G	Rec
1912	Det	A	P	4	1-2
1914	Phi	A	P	2	0-1
	BLTR			6	1-3

JESSEE, DANIEL EDWARD
b.Feb.22,1901 Olive Hill,Ky.

Yr	Cl	Lea	Pos	G	Rec
1929	Cle	A	H	1	.000
	BLTR				

JESTER, VIRGIL MILTON
b.July 23,1927 Denver,Colo.

Yr	Cl	Lea	Pos	G	Rec
1952	Bos	N	P	19	3-5
1953	Mil	N	P	2	0-0
	BRTR			21	3-5

JETHROE, SAMUEL (Jet)
b.Jan.20,1922 E.St.Louis,Ill.

Yr	Cl	Lea	Pos	G	Rec
1950	Bos	N	O	141	.273
1951	Bos	N	O	148	.280
1952	Bos	N	O	151	.232
1954	Pit	N	O	2	.000
	BBTR			442	.261

JEWETT, NATHAN W.
b.1842

Yr	Cl	Lea	Pos	G	Rec
1872	Eck	n	C	2	NR

JIMINEZ, MANUEL EMILIO
b.Nov.19,1938 San Pedro,D.R.

Yr	Cl	Lea	Pos	G	Rec
1962	KC	A	O	139	.301

JOHNS, AUGUST FRANCIS
b.Sept.10,1899 St.Louis,Mo.

Yr	Cl	Lea	Pos	G	Rec
1926	Det	A	P	35	6-4
1927	Det	A	P	1	0-0
			BBTL	36	6-4

JOHNS, OLIVER TRACY
b.Aug.21,1879 Trenton,O.
d.June 17,1961

Yr	Cl	Lea	Pos	G	Rec
1905	Cin	N	P	4	1-0
			BLTL		

JOHNS, THOMAS P.
b.Baltimore,Md.

Yr	Cl	Lea	Pos	G	Rec
1873	Mar	n	O	1	.000

JOHNS, WILLIAM R. (Pete)
b.Jan.17,1889 Cleveland,O.

Yr	Cl	Lea	Pos	G	Rec
1915	Chi	A	3	28	.210
1918	St.L	A	1	46	.180
			BRTR	74	.196

JOHNSON, ABRAHAM
b.London,Ont.,Canada

Yr	Cl	Lea	Pos	G	Rec
1893	Chi	N	P	1	0-0

JOHNSON, ADAM RANKIN JR.
b.Mar.1,1917 Hayden,Ariz.

Yr	Cl	Lea	Pos	G	Rec
1941	Phi	A	P	7	1-0
			BRTR		

JOHNSON, ADAM RANKIN SR. (Tex)
b.Feb.4,1888 Burnet,Tex.

Yr	Cl	Lea	Pos	G	Rec
1914	Bos	A	P	15	4-9
1914	Chi	F	P	17	9-5
1915	Chi	F	P	11	2-5
1915	Bal	F	P	20	7-10
1918	St.L	N	P	6	1-1
			BRTR	69	23-30

JOHNSON, ALBERT J.
b.Chicago,Ill.

Yr	Cl	Lea	Pos	G	Rec
1896	Lou	N	2	24	.232
1897	Lou	N	2	44	.251
				68	.245

JOHNSON, ARTHUR GILBERT
b.Feb.15,1901 Warren,Pa.

Yr	Cl	Lea	Pos	G	Rec
1927	NY	N	P	1	0-0
			BBTL		

JOHNSON, ARTHUR HENRY (Lefty)
b.July 16,1916 Winchester,Mass.

Yr	Cl	Lea	Pos	G	Rec
1940	Bos	N	P	2	0-1
1941	Bos	N	P	44	7-15
1942	Bos	N	P	4	0-0
			BLTL	50	7-16

JOHNSON, BENJAMIN FRANKLIN
b.May 16,1931 Greenwood,S.Car.

Yr	Cl	Lea	Pos	G	Rec
1959	Chi	N	P	4	0-0
1960	Chi	N	P	17	2-1
			BRTR	21	2-1

JOHNSON, CALEB CLARK
b.May 23,1844 Fulton,Ill.
d.Mar.7,1925

Yr	Cl	Lea	Pos	G	Rec
1871	Cle	n	2-S-O	16	NR

JOHNSON, CHARLES CLEVELAND (Home Run)
b.Mar.12,1885 Slatington,Pa.
d.Aug.28,1940

Yr	Cl	Lea	Pos	G	Rec
1908	Phi	N	O	5	.214

JOHNSON, CHESTER LILLIS
b.Aug.,1918 Redmond,Wash.

Yr	Cl	Lea	Pos	G	Rec
1946	St.L	A	P	5	0-0
			BLTL		

JOHNSON, CLIFFORD (Connie)
b.Dec.7,1922 Stone Mountain,Ga.

Yr	Cl	Lea	Pos	G	Rec
1953	Chi	A	P	15	4-4
1955	Chi	A	P	19	7-4
1956	Chi	A	P	5	0-1

(Continued)

Yr	Cl	Lea	Pos	G	Rec
1956	Bal	A	P	26	9-10
1957	Bal	A	P	35	14-11
1958	Bal	A	P	26	6-9
			BRTR	126	40-39

JOHNSON, DARRELL DEAN
b.Aug.25,1928 Ord,Neb.

Yr	Cl	Lea	Pos	G	Rec
1952	St.L	A	C	29	.282
1952	Chi	A	C	22	.108
1957	NY	A	C	21	.217
1958	NY	A	C	5	.250
1960	St.L	N	C	8	.000
1961	Phi	N	C	21	.230
1961	Cin	N	C	20	.315
1962	Cin	N	C	2	.000
1962	Bal	A	C	6	.182
			BRTR	134	.234

JOHNSON, DERON ROGER
b.July 17,1938 San Diego,Cal.

Yr	Cl	Lea	Pos	G	Rec
1960	NY	A	3	6	.500
1961	NY	A	3	13	.105
1961	KC	A	1-3-O	83	.216
1962	KC	A	1-3-O	17	.105
			BRTR	119	.206

JOHNSON, DONALD ROY
b.Nov.12,1926 Portland,Ore.

Yr	Cl	Lea	Pos	G	Rec
1947	NY	A	P	15	4-3
1950	NY	A	P	8	1-0
1950	St.L	A	P	25	5-6
1951	St.L	A	P	6	0-1
1951	Was	A	P	21	7-11
1952	Was	A	P	29	0-5
1954	Chi	A	P	46	8-7
1955	Bal	A	P	31	2-4
1958	SF	N	P	17	0-1
			BRTR	198	27-38

JOHNSON, DONALD SPORI (Pep)
b.Dec.7,1911 Chicago,Ill.

Yr	Cl	Lea	Pos	G	Rec
1943	Chi	N	2	10	.190
1944	Chi	N	2	154	.278
1945	Chi	N	2	138	.302
1946	Chi	N	2	83	.242
1947	Chi	N	2-3	120	.259
1948	Chi	N	2-3	6	.250
			BRTR	511	.268

JOHNSON, EARL DOUGLASS (Lefty)
b.Apr.2,1919 Redmond,Wash.

Yr	Cl	Lea	Pos	G	Rec
1940	Bos	A	P	18	6-2
1941	Bos	A	P	17	4-5
1946	Bos	A	P	29	5-4
1947	Bos	A	P	46	12-11
1948	Bos	A	P	35	10-4
1949	Bos	A	P	19	3-6
1950	Bos	A	P	11	0-0
1951	Det	A	P	6	0-0
			BLTL	181	40-32

JOHNSON, EDWIN CYRIL
b.Mar.31,1900 Morganfield,Ky.

Yr	Cl	Lea	Pos	G	Rec
1920	Was	A	1-O	4	.230
			BLTR		

JOHNSON, ELLIS WATT
b.Dec.8,1892 Minneapolis,Minn.

Yr	Cl	Lea	Pos	G	Rec
1912	Chi	A	P	5	0-0
1915	Chi	A	P	1	0-0
1917	Phi	A	P	4	0-2
			BRTR	10	0-2

JOHNSON, ELMER ELLSWORTH
b.June 12,1885 Frankfort,Ind.

Yr	Cl	Lea	Pos	G	Rec
1914	NY	N	C	11	.166
			BRTR		

JOHNSON, ERNEST RUDOLPH
b.Apr.29,1888 Chicago,Ill.
d.May 1,1952

Yr	Cl	Lea	Pos	G	Rec
1912	Chi	A	S	18	.262
1915	St.L	F	S	152	.244
1916	St.L	A	S	74	.229
1917	St.L	A	2-S	80	.248

(Continued)

Yr	Cl	Lea	Pos	G	Rec
1918	St.L	A	S	29	.265
1921	Chi	A	S	142	.295
1922	Chi	A	S	145	.254
1923	Chi	A	S	12	.189
1923	NY	A	S	19	.447
1924	NY	A	2	64	.353
1925	NY	A	2-S-3	76	.282
			BLTR	811	.267

JOHNSON, ERNEST THORWALD
b.June 16,1924 Brattleboro,Vt.

Yr	Cl	Lea	Pos	G	Rec
1950	Bos	N	P	16	2-0
1952	Bos	N	P	29	6-3
1953	Mil	N	P	36	4-3
1954	Mil	N	P	40	5-2
1955	Mil	N	P	40	5-7
1956	Mil	N	P	36	4-3
1957	Mil	N	P	30	7-3
1958	Mil	N	P	15	3-1
1959	Bal	A	P	31	4-1
			BRTR	273	40-23

JOHNSON, FREDERICK EDWARD (Cactus)
b.Mar.5,1897 Handley,Tex.

Yr	Cl	Lea	Pos	G	Rec
1922	NY	N	P	2	0-2
1923	NY	N	P	3	2-0
1938	St.L	A	P	17	3-7
1939	St.L	A	P	5	0-1
			BRTR	27	5-10

JOHNSON, GEORGE MURPHY (Chief)
b.Mar.25,1887 Winnebago,Neb.
d.June 12,1922

Yr	Cl	Lea	Pos	G	Rec
1913	Cin	N	P	44	14-16
1914	Cin	N	P	1	0-0
1914	KC	F	P	20	9-10
1915	KC	F	P	39	17-17
			BRTR	104	40-43

JOHNSON, HENRY WARD
b.May 21,1906 Bradenton,Fla.

Yr	Cl	Lea	Pos	G	Rec
1925	NY	A	P	24	1-3
1926	NY	A	P	1	0-0
1928	NY	A	P	31	14-9
1929	NY	A	P	13	3-3
1930	NY	A	P	51	14-11
1931	NY	A	P	40	13-8
1932	NY	A	P	6	2-2
1933	Bos	A	P	26	8-6
1934	Bos	A	P	31	6-8
1935	Bos	A	P	13	2-1
1936	Phi	A	P	3	0-2
1939	Cin	N	P	20	0-3
			BBTR	259	63-56

JOHNSON, JOHN CLIFFORD (Swede)
b.Sept.29,1914 Belmore,O.

Yr	Cl	Lea	Pos	G	Rec
1944	NY	A	P	22	0-2
1945	Chi	A	P	29	3-0
			BLTL	51	3-2

JOHNSON, JOHN LOUIS (Youngy)
(Real name John Louis Mercer)
b.Nov.18,1869 N.Cohocton,N.Y.
d.Jan.28,1941

Yr	Cl	Lea	Pos	G	Rec
1894	Phi	N	P	4	1-3

JOHNSON, JOHN RALPH (Spud)
b.1860 Chicago,Ill.

Yr	Cl	Lea	Pos	G	Rec
1889	Col	a	3-O	117	.285
1890	Col	a	O	137	.354
1891	Cle	N	O	80	.263
				334	.337

JOHNSON, KENNETH CARSTENSEN (Hook)
b.Jan.14,1923 Topeka,Kan.

Yr	Cl	Lea	Pos	G	Rec
1947	St.L	N	P	2	1-0
1948	St.L	N	P	20	2-4
1949	St.L	N	P	21	0-1
1950	St.L	N	P	2	0-0
1950	Phi	N	P	21	4-1

(Continued)

Yr	Cl	Lea	Pos	G	Rec
1951	Phi	N	P	36	5-8
1952	Det	A	P	9	0-0
		BLTL		111	12-14

JOHNSON, KENNETH TRAVIS
b.June 16,1933 W.Palm Beach,Fla.

Yr	Cl	Lea	Pos	G	Rec
1958	KC	A	P	2	0-0
1959	KC	A	P	2	1-1
1960	KC	A	P	42	5-10
1961	KC	A	P	6	0-4
1961	Cin	N	P	15	6-2
1962	Hou	N	P	33	7-16
		BRTR		100	19-33

JOHNSON, LLOYD WILLIAM (Eppa)
b.Dec.24,1910 Santa Rosa,Cal.

Yr	Cl	Lea	Pos	G	Rec
1934	Pit	N	P	1	0-0
		BLTL			

JOHNSON, LOUIS BROWN
b.Sept.22,1934 Lexington,Ky.

Yr	Cl	Lea	Pos	G	Rec
1960	Chi	N	O	34	.206
1961	LA	A	O	1	.000
1962	Mil	N	O	61	.282
		BRTR		96	.254

JOHNSON, OTIS L.
b.Nov.5,1883 Muncie,Ind.
d.Nov.9,1915

Yr	Cl	Lea	Pos	G	Rec
1911	NY	A	2-S	71	.234
		BBTR			

JOHNSON, PAUL OSCAR
b.Sept.2,1896 N.Grosvenordale,Conn.

Yr	Cl	Lea	Pos	G	Rec
1918	Bos	N	H	1	.000
1920	Phi	A	O	18	.208
1921	Phi	A	O	48	.315
		BRTR		67	.276

JOHNSON, RICHARD ALLAN
b.Feb.15,1932 Dayton,Ohio

Yr	Cl	Lea	Pos	G	Rec
1958	Chi	N	H	8	.000
		BL			

JOHNSON, ROBERT LEE
(Indian Bob)
b.Nov.26,1906 Pryor,Okla.

Yr	Cl	Lea	Pos	G	Rec
1933	Phi	A	O	142	.290
1934	Phi	A	O	141	.307
1935	Phi	A	O	147	.299
1936	Phi	A	2-O	153	.292
1937	Phi	A	O	138	.306
1938	Phi	A	O	152	.313
1939	Phi	A	O	150	.338
1940	Phi	A	O	138	.268
1941	Phi	A	1-O	149	.275
1942	Phi	A	O	149	.291
1943	Was	A	1-3-O	117	.265
1944	Bos	A	O	144	.324
1945	Bos	A	O	143	.280
		BRTR		1863	.296

JOHNSON, ROBERT WALLACE
b.Mar.4,1936 Omaha,Neb.

Yr	Cl	Lea	Pos	G	Rec
1960	KC	A	2-5-3	76	.205
1961	Was	A	2-5-3	61	.295
1962	Was	A	2-5-3-O	135	.288
		BRTR		272	.275

JOHNSON, ROY (Hardrock)
b.Oct.1,1895 Madill,Okla.

Yr	Cl	Lea	Pos	G	Rec
1918	Phi	A	P	10	1-5
		BRTR			

Non-playing manager Chi (N) 1944.

JOHNSON, ROY CLEVELAND
b.Feb.23,1904 Spavinaw,Okla.

Yr	Cl	Lea	Pos	G	Rec
1929	Det	A	O	148	.314
1930	Det	A	O	125	.275
1931	Det	A	O	151	.279
1932	Det	A	O	49	.254
1932	Bos	A	O	94	.296
1933	Bos	A	O	133	.313
1934	Bos	A	O	143	.320
1935	Bos	A	O	145	.315

(Continued)

Yr	Cl	Lea	Pos	G	Rec
1936	NY	A	O	63	.265
1937	NY	A	O	12	.294
1937	Bos	N	O	85	.277
1938	Bos	N	O	7	.172
		BLTR		1155	.296

JOHNSON, RUSSELL CONWELL
(Jing)
b.Oct.9,1894 Parker Ford,Pa.
d.Dec.6,1950

Yr	Cl	Lea	Pos	G	Rec
1916	Phi	A	P	12	2-9
1917	Phi	A	P	35	9-12
1919	Phi	A	P	35	9-14
1927	Phi	A	P	17	4-2
1928	Phi	A	P	3	0-0
		BRTR		102	24-37

JOHNSON, SILAS KENNETH
b.Oct.5,1908 Marseilles,Ill.

Yr	Cl	Lea	Pos	G	Rec
1928	Cin	N	P	3	0-0
1929	Cin	N	P	1	0-0
1930	Cin	N	P	35	3-1
1931	Cin	N	P	42	11-19
1932	Cin	N	P	42	13-15
1933	Cin	N	P	34	7-18
1934	Cin	N	P	46	7-22
1935	Cin	N	P	30	5-11
1936	Cin	N	P	2	0-0
1936	St.L	N	P	12	5-3
1937	St.L	N	P	38	12-12
1938	St.L	N	P	6	0-3
1940	Phi	N	P	37	5-14
1941	Phi	N	P	39	5-12
1942	Phi	N	P	39	8-19
1943	Phi	N	P	21	8-3
1946	Phi	N	P	1	0-0
1946	Bos	N	P	28	6-5
1947	Bos	N	P	36	6-8
		BRTR		492	101-165

JOHNSON, STANLEY LUCIUS
b.Feb.12,1937 Dallas,Tex.

Yr	Cl	Lea	Pos	G	Rec
1960	Chi	A	O	5	.167
1961	KC	A	O	3	.000
		BLTL		8	.111

JOHNSON, SYLVESTER W.
b.Dec.31,1900 Portland,Ore.

Yr	Cl	Lea	Pos	G	Rec
1922	Det	A	P	29	7-3
1923	Det	A	P	37	12-7
1924	Det	A	P	29	5-4
1925	Det	A	P	6	0-2
1926	St.L	N	P	19	0-3
1927	St.L	N	P	2	0-0
1928	St.L	N	P	34	8-4
1929	St.L	N	P	42	13-7
1930	St.L	N	P	32	12-10
1931	St.L	N	P	32	11-9
1932	St.L	N	P	32	5-14
1933	St.L	N	P	35	3-3
1934	Cin	N	P	2	0-0
1934	Phi	N	P	42	5-9
1935	Phi	N	P	37	10-8
1936	Phi	N	P	39	5-7
1937	Phi	N	P	32	4-10
1938	Phi	N	P	22	2-7
1939	Phi	N	P	22	8-8
1940	Phi	N	P	17	2-2
		BRTR		542	112-117

JOHNSON, THOMAS G.
b.Scranton,Pa.

Yr	Cl	Lea	Pos	G	Rec
1897	Phi	N	P	5	0-2
1899	NY	N	P	1	0-0
				6	0-2

JOHNSON, VICTOR OSCAR
b.Aug.3,1920 Eau Claire,Wis.

Yr	Cl	Lea	Pos	G	Rec
1944	Bos	A	P	7	0-3
1945	Bos	A	P	26	6-4
1946	Cle	A	P	9	0-1
		BRTL		42	6-8

JOHNSON, WALTER PERRY
(Barney)
b.Nov.6,1887 Humboldt,Kan.
d.Dec.10,1946

Yr	Cl	Lea	Pos	G	Rec
1907	Was	A	P	14	5-9
1908	Was	A	P	36	14-14
1909	Was	A	P	40	13-25
1910	Was	A	P	45	25-17
1911	Was	A	P	42	23-15
1912	Was	A	P	53	32-12
1913	Was	A	P	51	36-7
1914	Was	A	P	54	28-18
1915	Was	A	P	64	27-13
1916	Was	A	P	59	25-20
1917	Was	A	P	57	23-16
1918	Was	A	P	65	23-13
1919	Was	A	P	56	20-14
1920	Was	A	P	35	8-10
1921	Was	A	P	38	17-14
1922	Was	A	P	43	15-16
1923	Was	A	P	42	17-12
1924	Was	A	P	39	23-7
1925	Was	A	P	36	20-7
1926	Was	A	P	35	15-16
1927	Was	A	P	26	5-6
		BRTR		930	414-281

Non-playing manager Was (A) 1929-32 and Cle (A) 1933-35.

JOHNSON, WILLIAM L.
b.July 30,1894 Chicago,Ill.

Yr	Cl	Lea	Pos	G	Rec
1916	Phi	A	O	4	.267
1917	Phi	A	O	48	.174
		BLTR		52	.185

JOHNSON, WILLIAM RUSSELL (Bull)
b.Aug.30,1918 Montclair,N.J.

Yr	Cl	Lea	Pos	G	Rec
1943	NY	A	3	155	.280
1946	NY	A	3	85	.260
1947	NY	A	3	132	.285
1948	NY	A	3	127	.294
1949	NY	A	1-2-3	113	.249
1950	NY	A	1-3	108	.260
1951	NY	A	3	15	.300
1951	St.L	N	3	124	.262
1952	St.L	N	3	94	.252
1953	St.L	N	3	11	.200
		BRTR		964	.271

JOHNSON, WILLIAM T. (Sleepy Bill)
b.Chester,Pa.
d.1921

Yr	Cl	Lea	Pos	G	Rec
1884	Key	U	O	1	.000
1887	Ind	N	O	11	.190
1890	Bal	a	O	24	.354
1891	Bal	a	O	127	.269
1892	Bal	N	O	4	.133
		BLTL		167	.264

JOHNSTON, JAMES HARLE
b.Dec.10,1889 Cleveland,Tenn.

Yr	Cl	Lea	Pos	G	Rec
1911	Chi	A	O	1	.000
1914	Chi	N	O	50	.228
1916	Bro	N	O	118	.252
1917	Bro	N	O	103	.270
1918	Bro	N	1-2-3-O	123	.281
1919	Bro	N	1-2-S-O	117	.281
1920	Bro	N	3	155	.291
1921	Bro	N	3	152	.325
1922	Bro	N	2-S-3	138	.319
1923	Bro	N	2-S-3	151	.325
1924	Bro	N	1-2-S-3-O	86	.298
1925	Bro	N	1-S-3-O	123	.297
1926	Bos	N	3-O	23	.246
1926	NY	N	O	37	.232
		BRTR		1377	.294

JOHNSTON, JOHN THOMAS
b.Mar.28,1890 Longview,Tex.
d.Mar.7,1940

Yr	Cl	Lea	Pos	G	Rec
1913	St.L	A	O	109	.226
		BLTR			

JOHNSTON, RICHARD FREDERICK
b.Apr.6,1863 Kingston,N.Y.
d.Apr.4,1934

Yr	Cl	Lea	Pos	G	Rec
1884	Ric	a	S-O	39	.286
1885	Bos	N	O	26	.238
1886	Bos	N	O	109	.239
1887	Bos	N	O	124	.283
1888	Bos	N	O	135	.295
1889	Bos	N	O	131	.228
1890	Bos	p	O	2	.111
1890	NY	p	O	75	.257
1891	Cin	a	O	99	.219
	BRTR			740	.256

JOHNSTON, WHEELER ROGERS
(Doc)
b.Sept.9,1887 Cleveland,Tenn.
d.Feb.18,1961

Yr	Cl	Lea	Pos	G	Rec
1909	Cin	N	1	3	.000
1912	Cle	A	1	43	.280
1913	Cle	A	1	133	.255
1914	Cle	A	1	103	.244
1915	Pit	N	1	147	.265
1916	Pit	N	1	114	.213
1918	Cle	A	1	74	.227
1919	Cle	A	1	102	.305
1920	Cle	A	1	147	.292
1921	Cle	A	1	118	.297
1922	Phi	A	1	71	.250
	BLTL			1055	.274

JOHNSTON, WILFRED IVY
b.July 9,1901 Charlotte,N.C.

Yr	Cl	Lea	Pos	G	Rec
1924	Bro	N	2	4	.250
	BRTR				

JOINER, ROY MERRILL (Pop)
b.Oct.30,1907 Red Bluff,Cal.

Yr	Cl	Lea	Pos	G	Rec
1934	Chi	N	P	20	0-1
1935	Chi	N	P	2	0-0
1940	NY	N	P	30	3-2
	BLTL			52	3-3

JOK, STANLEY EDWARD
b.May 3,1926 Buffalo,N.Y.

Yr	Cl	Lea	Pos	G	Rec
1954	Phi	N	H	3	.000
1954	Chi	A	3	3	.167
1955	Chi	A	3-O	6	.250
	BRTR			12	.158

JOLLEY, SMEAD POWELL (Guinea)
b.Jan.14,1902 El Dorado,Ark.

Yr	Cl	Lea	Pos	G	Rec
1930	Chi	A	O	152	.313
1931	Chi	A	O	54	.300
1932	Chi	A	O	12	.357
1932	Bos	A	O	137	.309
1933	Bos	A	O	118	.282
	BLTR			473	.305

JOLLY, DAVID
b.Oct.14,1924 Stony Point,N.C.

Yr	Cl	Lea	Pos	G	Rec
1953	Mil	N	P	24	0-1
1954	Mil	N	P	48	11-6
1955	Mil	N	P	36	2-3
1956	Mil	N	P	29	2-3
1957	Mil	N	P	23	1-1
	BRTR			160	16-14

JONES, ...
b.Syracuse,N.Y.

Yr	Cl	Lea	Pos	G	Rec
1882	Bal	a	C-O	4	.067
1884	Key	U	C-O	4	.154
				8	.107

JONES, ALBERT EDWARD (Cowboy)
b.Aug.23,1874 Golden,Colo.
d.Feb 9,1958

Yr	Cl	Lea	Pos	G	Rec
1898	Cle	N	P	8	4-4
1899	St.L	N	P	14	6-5
1900	St.L	N	P	38	13-20
1901	St.L	N	P	10	2-6
	BLTL			70	25-35

JONES, ALEXANDER H.
b.1867 Bradford,Pa.

Yr	Cl	Lea	Pos	G	Rec
1889	Pit	N	P	1	1-0
1892	Lou	N	P	18	6-12
1892	Was	N	P	7	1-2
1894	Phi	N	P	1	1-0
1903	Det	A	P	2	0-2
	TL			29	9-16

JONES, ARTHUR LENOX
b.Feb.7,1907 Kershaw,S.C.

Yr	Cl	Lea	Pos	G	Rec
1932	Bro	N	P	1	0-0
	BRTR				

JONES, CARROLL ELMER (Deacon)
b.Dec.20,1893 Arcadia,Kan.
d.Dec.28,1952

Yr	Cl	Lea	Pos	G	Rec
1916	Det	A	P	1	0-0
1917	Det	A	P	24	4-4
1918	Det	A	P	22	2-2
	BRTR			47	6-6

JONES, CHARLES C. (Casey)
b.June 2,1876 Butler,Pa.
d.Apr.2,1947

Yr	Cl	Lea	Pos	G	Rec
1901	Bos	A	O	10	.119
1904	Chi	A	O	5	.235
1905	Was	A	O	142	.208
1906	Was	A	O	131	.241
1907	Was	A	O	121	.265
1908	St.L	A	O	74	.232
	TR			483	.233

JONES, CHARLES F.
b.New York,N.Y.

Yr	Cl	Lea	Pos	G	Rec
1884	Bro	a	2-3	24	.188
1885	Met	a	3	1	.250
				25	.191

JONES, CHARLES LEANDER
(Bumpus)
b.Jan.1870 Cedarville,O.
d.June 25,1938

Yr	Cl	Lea	Pos	G	Rec
1892	Cin	N	P	1	1-0
1893	Cin	N	P	6	1-3
1893	NY	N	P	4	0-1
	BRTR			11	2-4

JONES, CHARLES WESLEY (Baby)
(Real name Charles Wesley Rippay)
b.Apr.30,1850 Alamance Co.,N.C.

Yr	Cl	Lea	Pos	G	Rec
1873	Mar	n	O	1	NR
1874	Bal	n	C-O	5	NR
1875	Wes	n	O	12	NR
1875	Har	n	O	1	.000
1876	Cin	N	O	64	.279
1877	Cin	N	1-O	20	.329
1877	Chi	N	O	2	.375
1877	Cin	N	O	35	.330
1878	Cin	N	O	62	.297
1879	Bos	N	O	83	.315
1880	Bos	N	O	64	.297
1883	Cin	a	O	85	.285
1884	Cin	a	O	113	.322
1885	Cin	a	O	112	.327
1886	Cin	a	O	127	.274
1887	Cin	a	O	41	.374
1887	Met	a	O	63	.302
1888	KC	a	O	6	.250
	BRTR			896	NR

JONES, COBURN D.
b.Aug.21,1907 Denver,Colo.

Yr	Cl	Lea	Pos	G	Rec
1928	Pit	N	S	1	.500
1929	Pit	N	S	25	.254
	BBTR			26	.262

JONES, DALE ELDON (Nubs)
b.Dec.17,1918 Marquette,Neb.

Yr	Cl	Lea	Pos	G	Rec
1941	Phi	N	P	2	0-1
	BRTR				

JONES, DANIEL ALBION
(Jumping Jack)
b.Oct.23,1860 Litchfield,Conn.
d.Oct.19,1936

(Continued)

Yr	Cl	Lea	Pos	G	Rec
1883	Det	N	P-O	11	6-4 .243
1883	Ath	a	P	7	5-2
	TR			18	11-6 .197

JONES, DAVID JEFFERSON
(Kangaroo)
b.June 30,1880 Cambria,Wis.

Yr	Cl	Lea	Pos	G	Rec
1901	Mil	A	O	14	.169
1902	St.L	A	O	14	.224
1902	Chi	N	O	63	.310
1903	Chi	N	O	130	.282
1904	Chi	N	O	97	.244
1906	Det	A	O	84	.260
1907	Det	A	O	126	.273
1908	Det	A	O	56	.207
1909	Det	A	O	69	.279
1910	Det	A	O	113	.265
1911	Det	A	O	98	.273
1912	Det	A	O	97	.294
1913	Chi	A	O	12	.288
1914	Pit	F	O	97	.272
1915	Pit	F	O	14	.327
1918	Det	A	O	2	.000
	BLTR			1086	.270

JONES, DECATUR POINDEXTER
(Dick)
b.May 22,1904 Meadville,Miss.

Yr	Cl	Lea	Pos	G	Rec
1926	Was	A	P	5	2-1
1927	Was	A	P	2	0-0
	BLTR			7	2-1

JONES, EARL LESLIE (Lefty)
b.June 11,1919 Fresno,Cal.

Yr	Cl	Lea	Pos	G	Rec
1945	St.L	A	P	10	0-0
	BLTL				

JONES, ELIJAH ALBERT
b.Jan.27,1882 Oxford,Mich.
d.Apr.28,1943

Yr	Cl	Lea	Pos	G	Rec
1907	Det	A	P	4	0-2
1909	Det	A	P	2	1-1
	BRTR			6	1-3

JONES, FIELDER ALLISON
b.Aug.13,1874 Shinglehouse,Pa.
d.Mar.13,1934

Yr	Cl	Lea	Pos	G	Rec
1896	Bro	N	O	102	.353
1897	Bro	N	O	135	.322
1898	Bro	N	O	147	.304
1899	Bro	N	O	95	.286
1900	Bro	N	O	136	.309
1901	Chi	A	O	133	.325
1902	Chi	A	O	135	.318
1903	Chi	A	O	137	.304
1904	Chi	A	M-O	150	.245
1905	Chi	A	M-O	153	.245
1906	Chi	A	M-O	144	.230
1907	Chi	A	M-O	154	.261
1908	Chi	A	M-O	149	.253
1914	St.L	F	M-H	5	.333
1915	St.L	F	M-O	5	.000
	BLTR			1780	.287

Non-playing manager St.L (A) 1916-18

JONES, FRANK M.
b.Duluth,Minn.

Yr	Cl	Lea	Pos	G	Rec
1884	Det	N	2-S-O	34	.209

JONES, GORDON BASSETT
b.Apr.2,1930 Portland,Ore.

Yr	Cl	Lea	Pos	G	Rec
1954	St.L	N	P	11	4-4
1955	St.L	N	P	15	1-4
1956	St.L	N	P	5	0-2
1957	NY	N	P	10	0-1
1958	SF	N	P	11	3-1
1959	SF	N	P	31	3-2
1960	Bal	A	P	29	1-1
1961	Bal	A	P	3	0-0
1962	KC	A	P	21	3-2
	BRTR			136	15-17

Yr	Cl	Lea	Pos	G	Rec

JONES, GROVER WILLIAM
b.Apr.18,1934 White Plains, N.Y.

Yr	Cl	Lea	Pos	G	Rec
1962	Chi	A	1	18	.321
BRTR					

JONES, HAROLD MARION
b.Apr.9,1938 Louisiana, Mo.

Yr	Cl	Lea	Pos	G	Rec
1961	Cle	A	1	12	.171
1962	Cle	A	1	5	.313
BRTR				17	.216

JONES, HENRY M. (Baldy)
b.Cadillac, Mich.

Yr	Cl	Lea	Pos	G	Rec
1890	Pit	N	P	4	2-2

JONES, HOWARD (Cotton)
b.Jan.1,1889 Irwin, Pa.

Yr	Cl	Lea	Pos	G	Rec
1921	St.L	N	O	3	.000
BLTL					

JONES, JAMES MURRELL (Jake)
b.Nov.23,1920 Epps, La.

Yr	Cl	Lea	Pos	G	Rec
1941	Chi	A	1	3	.000
1942	Chi	A	1	7	.150
1946	Chi	A	1	24	.266
1947	Chi	A	1	45	.240
1947	Bos	A	1	109	.235
1948	Bos	A	1	36	.200
BRTR				224	.229

JONES, JAMES TILFORD (Sheriff)
b.Dec.25,1878 London, Ky.
d.May 6,1953

Yr	Cl	Lea	Pos	G	Rec
1897	Lou	N	P	2	0-0
1901	NY	N	P-O	21	0-1 / .209
1902	NY	N	O	65	.236
				88	0-1 / .229

JONES, JESSE FRANK (Broadway)
b.Nov.15,1898

Yr	Cl	Lea	Pos	G	Rec
1923	Phi	N	P	3	0-0
BRTR					

JONES, JOHN PAUL
b.Aug.25,1894 Arcadia, La.

Yr	Cl	Lea	Pos	G	Rec
1919	NY	N	P	2	0-0
1920	Bos	N	P	3	1-0
BRTR				5	1-0

JONES, JOHN WILLIAM
b.July 11,1899 St.Louis, Mo.
d.May 13,1961

Yr	Cl	Lea	Pos	G	Rec
1924	Bro	N	S	10	.108
BRTR					

JONES, JOHN WILLIAM
b.May 13,1902 Coatesville, Pa.
d.Nov.3,1956

Yr	Cl	Lea	Pos	G	Rec
1923	Phi	A	O	1	.250
1932	Phi	A	O	4	.167
BLTL				5	.200

JONES, KENNETH FREDERICK
b.Apr.13,1904 Dover, N.J.

Yr	Cl	Lea	Pos	G	Rec
1924	Det	A	P	1	0-0
1930	Bos	N	P	8	0-1
BRTR				9	0-1

JONES, MACK
b.Nov.6,1938 Atlanta, Ga.

Yr	Cl	Lea	Pos	G	Rec
1961	Mil	N	O	28	.231
1962	Mil	N	O	91	.255
BLTR				119	.249

JONES, MAURICE MORRIS (Red)
b.Nov.2,1914 Timpson, Tex.

Yr	Cl	Lea	Pos	G	Rec
1940	St.L	N	O	12	.091
BLTR					

JONES, MICHAEL
b.Hamilton, Ont., Canada
d.Mar.24,1894

Yr	Cl	Lea	Pos	G	Rec
1890	Lou	a	P	4	4-0

JONES, OSCAR WINFIELD
(Flip Flap)
b.Jan.21,1879 London Grove, Pa.
d.Oct.8,1946

Yr	Cl	Lea	Pos	G	Rec
1903	Bro	N	P	38	19-14
1904	Bro	N	P	46	18-26
1905	Bro	N	P	30	7-14
BRTR				114	44-54

JONES, PERCY LEE
b.Oct.28,1899 Harwood, Tex.

Yr	Cl	Lea	Pos	G	Rec
1920	Chi	N	P	4	0-0
1921	Chi	N	P	32	3-5
1922	Chi	N	P	44	8-9
1925	Chi	N	P	28	6-6
1926	Chi	N	P	30	12-7
1927	Chi	N	P	30	7-8
1928	Chi	N	P	39	10-6
1929	Bos	N	P	36	7-15
1930	Pit	N	P	9	0-1
BBTL				252	53-57

JONES, ROBERT WALTER (Ducky)
b.Dec.2,1889 Clayton, Cal.

Yr	Cl	Lea	Pos	G	Rec
1917	Det	A	2	46	.156
1918	Det	A	3	75	.275
1919	Det	A	3	127	.260
1920	Det	A	3	81	.249
1921	Det	A	3	141	.303
1922	Det	A	3	124	.257
1923	Det	A	3	100	.250
1924	Det	A	3	110	.272
1925	Det	A	3	50	.236
BLTR				854	.265

JONES, RYERSON L.
(Angel Sleeves)
b.Cincinnati, O.

Yr	Cl	Lea	Pos	G	Rec
1883	Lou	a	S-O	2	.000
1884	Cin	U	S	55	.265
TR				57	.258

JONES, SAMUEL
b.Dec.14,1925 Stewartsville, O.

Yr	Cl	Lea	Pos	G	Rec
1951	Cle	A	P	2	0-1
1952	Cle	A	P	14	2-3
1955	Chi	N	P	36	14-20
1956	Chi	N	P	33	9-14
1957	St.L	N	P	28	12-9
1958	St.L	N	P	35	14-13
1959	SF	N	P	59	21-14
1960	SF	N	P	39	18-14
1961	SF	N	P	37	8-8
1962	Det	A	P	30	2-4
BRTR				304	100-101

JONES, SAMUEL POND (Sad Sam)
b.July 26,1892 Woodsfield, O.

Yr	Cl	Lea	Pos	G	Rec
1914	Cle	A	P	1	0-0
1915	Cle	A	P	48	3-8
1916	Bos	A	P	13	0-1
1917	Bos	A	P	9	0-1
1918	Bos	A	P	24	16-5
1919	Bos	A	P	35	13-20
1920	Bos	A	P	44	13-16
1921	Bos	A	P	43	23-16
1922	NY	A	P	45	13-13
1923	NY	A	P	39	21-8
1924	NY	A	P	36	9-6
1925	NY	A	P-O	46	15-21 / .162
1926	NY	A	P	44	9-8
1927	St.L	A	P	32	8-14
1928	Was	A	P	37	17-7
1929	Was	A	P	28	9-9
1930	Was	A	P	30	15-7
1931	Was	A	P	30	9-10
1932	Chi	A	P	39	10-15
1933	Chi	A	P	37	10-12
1934	Chi	A	P	31	8-12
1935	Chi	A	P	22	8-7
BRTR				713	229-216 / .197

JONES, SHELDON LESLIE
(Available)
b.Feb.2,1922 Tecumseh, Neb.

Yr	Cl	Lea	Pos	G	Rec
1946	NY	N	P	6	1-2
1947	NY	N	P	15	2-2
1948	NY	N	P	55	16-8
1949	NY	N	P	42	15-12
1950	NY	N	P	40	13-16
1951	NY	N	P	41	6-11
1952	Bos	N	P	39	1-4
1953	Chi	N	P	22	0-2
BRTR				260	54-57

JONES, SHERMAN JARVIS
b.Feb.10,1936 Hertford Co., N.C.

Yr	Cl	Lea	Pos	G	Rec
1960	SF	N	P	16	1-1
1961	Cin	N	P	24	1-1
1962	NY	N	P	8	0-4
BLTR				48	2-6

JONES, THOMAS
b.Jan.22,1877 Honesdale, Pa.
d.June 21,1923

Yr	Cl	Lea	Pos	G	Rec
1902	Bal	A	1-2	37	.283
1904	St.L	A	1-2	156	.241
1905	St.L	A	1	135	.242
1906	St.L	A	1	144	.252
1907	St.L	A	1	155	.250
1908	St.L	A	1	155	.248
1909	St.L	A	1	97	.254
1909	Det	A	1	44	.271
1910	Det	A	1	135	.255
BRTR				1058	.250

JONES, VERNAL LEROY (Nippy)
b.June 29,1925 Los Angeles, Cal.

Yr	Cl	Lea	Pos	G	Rec
1946	St.L	N	2	16	.333
1947	St.L	N	2-O	23	.247
1948	St.L	N	1	132	.254
1949	St.L	N	1	110	.300
1950	St.L	N	1	13	.231
1951	St.L	N	1	80	.263
1952	Phi	N	1	8	.167
1957	Mil	N	1-O	30	.266
BRTR				412	.267

JONES, WILLIAM D. (Midget)
b.Apr.8,1888 Hartland, N.B., Canada

Yr	Cl	Lea	Pos	G	Rec
1911	Bos	N	O	18	.216
1912	Bos	N	O	2	.500
BLTR				20	.226

JONES, WILLIE EDWARD
(Puddin' Head)
b.Aug.16,1925 Dillon, S.C.

Yr	Cl	Lea	Pos	G	Rec
1947	Phi	N	3	18	.226
1948	Phi	N	3	17	.333
1949	Phi	N	3	149	.245
1950	Phi	N	3	157	.267
1951	Phi	N	3	148	.285
1952	Phi	N	3	147	.250
1953	Phi	N	3	149	.225
1954	Phi	N	3	142	.271
1955	Phi	N	3	146	.258
1956	Phi	N	3	149	.277
1957	Phi	N	3	133	.218
1958	Phi	N	1-3	118	.271
1959	Phi	N	3	72	.249
1959	Cle	A	3	11	.222
1959	Cin	N	3	72	.249
1960	Cin	N	2-3	79	.268
1961	Cin	N	3	9	.000
BRTR				1691	.258

JONES, WILLIAM RODERICK (Tex)
b.Aug.4,1885 Marion, Kan.
d.Feb.26,1938

Yr	Cl	Lea	Pos	G	Rec
1911	Chi	A	1	9	.193
BRTR					

JONNARD, CLARENCE JAMES (Bubber)
b.Nov.23,1897 Nashville,Tenn.

Yr	Cl	Lea	Pos	G	Rec
1920	Chi	A	C	2	.000
1922	Pit	N	C	10	.238
1926	Phi	N	C	19	.118
1927	Phi	N	C	53	.294
1929	St.L	N	C	18	.097
1935	Phi	N	C	1	.000
	BRTR			103	.230

JONNARD, CLAUDE ALFRED
b.Nov.23,1897 Nashville,Tenn.
d.Aug.27,1959

Yr	Cl	Lea	Pos	G	Rec
1921	NY	N	P	1	0-0
1922	NY	N	P	33	6-1
1923	NY	N	P	45	4-3
1924	NY	N	P	34	4-5
1926	St.L	A	P	12	0-2
1929	Chi	N	P	12	0-1
	BRTR			137	14-12

JOOST, EDWIN DAVID
b.June 5,1916 San Francisco,Cal.

Yr	Cl	Lea	Pos	G	Rec
1936	Cin	N	2-S	13	.154
1937	Cin	N	2	6	.083
1939	Cin	N	2-S	42	.252
1940	Cin	N	2-S-3	88	.216
1941	Cin	N	1-2-S-3	152	.253
1942	Cin	N	2-S	142	.224
1943	Bos	N	2-S-3	124	.185
1945	Bos	N	2-3	35	.248
1947	Phi	A	S	151	.206
1948	Phi	A	S	135	.250
1949	Phi	A	S	144	.263
1950	Phi	A	S	131	.233
1951	Phi	A	S	140	.289
1952•	Phi	A	S	146	.244
1953	Phi	A	S	51	.249
1954	Phi	A	M-2-S-3	19	.362
1955	Bos	A	2-S-3	55	.193
	BRTR			1574	.239

JORDAN, ADOLPH OTTO (Dutch)
b.Jan.5,1880 Pittsburgh,Pa.

Yr	Cl	Lea	Pos	G	Rec
1903	Bro	N	2-3	77	.236
1904	Bro	N	2	85	.179
	BRTR			162	.208

JORDAN, BAXTER BYERLY (Buck)
b.Jan.16,1907 Cooleemee,N.C.

Yr	Cl	Lea	Pos	G	Rec
1927	NY	N	H	5	.200
1929	NY	N	1	2	.500
1931	Was	A	1	9	.222
1932	Bos	N	1	49	.321
1933	Bos	N	1	152	.286
1934	Bos	N	1	124	.311
1935	Bos	N	1-3-O	130	.279
1936	Bos	N	1	138	.323
1937	Bos	N	1	8	.250
1937	Cin	N	1	98	.282
1938	Cin	N	H	9	.286
1938	Phi	N	1-3	87	.300
	BLTR			811	.299

JORDAN, CHARLES T.
b.Oct.4,1871 Baltimore,Md.
d.June 1,1928

Yr	Cl	Lea	Pos	G	Rec
1896	Phi	N	P	1	0-0

JORDAN, HARRY J.
b.Titusville,Pa.

Yr	Cl	Lea	Pos	G	Rec
1894	Pit	N	P	1	1-0
1895	Pit	N	P	2	0-2
				3	1-2

JORDAN, JAMES WILLIAM (Lord)
b.Jan.13,1908 Tucapau,S.C.
d.Dec.4,1957

Yr	Cl	Lea	Pos	G	Rec
1933	Bro	N	2-S	70	.256
1934	Bro	N	2-S	97	.266
1935	Bro	N	2-S-3	94	.278
1936	Bro	N	2	115	.234
	BRTR			376	.257

JORDAN, MICHAEL J. (Witty)

Yr	Cl	Lea	Pos	G	Rec
1890	Pit	N	O	37	.096

JORDAN, MILTON MIGNOT
b.May 24,1927 Mineral Springs,Pa.

Yr	Cl	Lea	Pos	G	Rec
1953	Det	A	P	8	0-1
	BRTR				

JORDAN, NILES CHAPMAN
b.Dec.1,1926 Lyman,Wash.

Yr	Cl	Lea	Pos	G	Rec
1951	Phi	N	P	5	2-3
1952	Cin	N	P	3	0-1
	BLTL			8	2-4

JORDAN, RAYMOND WILLIS (Rip)
b.Sept.28,1889 Portland,Me.
d.June 5,1960

Yr	Cl	Lea	Pos	G	Rec
1912	Chi	A	P	4	0-0
1919	Was	A	P	1	0-0
	BLTR			5	0-0

JORDAN, THOMAS JEFFERSON
b.Sept.5,1919 Lawton,Okla.

Yr	Cl	Lea	Pos	G	Rec
1944	Chi	A	C	14	.267
1946	Chi	A	C	10	.267
1946	Cle	A	C	14	.200
1948	St.L	A	H	1	.000
	BRTR			39	.240

JORDAN, TIMOTHY JOSEPH
b.Feb.14,1879 New York,N.Y.
d.Sept.13,1949

Yr	Cl	Lea	Pos	G	Rec
1901	Was	A	1	5	.250
1901	Bal	A	1	1	.000
1902	Bal	A	O	1	.000
1903	NY	A	1	2	.125
1906	Bro	N	1	126	.262
1907	Bro	N	1	143	.274
1908	Bro	N	1	146	.247
1909	Bro	N	1	95	.273
1910	Bro	N	H	5	.200
	BLTR			524	.261

JORGENS, ARNDT LUDWIG (Art)
b.May 18,1905 Modum,Norway.

Yr	Cl	Lea	Pos	G	Rec
1929	NY	A	C	18	.324
1930	NY	A	C	16	.367
1931	NY	A	C	46	.270
1932	NY	A	C	55	.219
1933	NY	A	C	21	.220
1934	NY	A	C	58	.208
1935	NY	A	C	36	.238
1936	NY	A	C	31	.273
1937	NY	A	C	13	.130
1938	NY	A	C	9	.235
1939	NY	A	C	3	.000
	BRTR			306	.238

JORGENS, ORVILLE EDWARD
b.June 4,1909 Rockford,Ill.

Yr	Cl	Lea	Pos	G	Rec
1935	Phi	N	P	53	10-15
1936	Phi	N	P	39	8-8
1937	Phi	N	P	52	3-4
	BRTR			144	21-27

JORGENSEN, JOHN DONALD (Spider)
b.Nov.3,1919 Folsom,Cal.

Yr	Cl	Lea	Pos	G	Rec
1947	Bro	N	3	129	.274
1948	Bro	N	3	31	.300
1949	Bro	N	3	53	.269
1950	Bro	N	3	2	.000
1950	NY	N	3	24	.135
1951	NY	N	3-O	28	.235
	BLTR			267	.266

JORGENSON, CARL (Pinky)
b.Nov.21,1916 Corcoran,Cal.

Yr	Cl	Lea	Pos	G	Rec
1937	Cin	N	O	6	.286
	BRTR				

JOSEPHS, JOSEPH E.
(Played under name of Joseph E. Borden)

JOSS, ADRIAN (Addie)
b.Apr.12,1880 Juneau,Wis.
d.Apr.14,1911

Yr	Cl	Lea	Pos	G	Rec
1902	Cle	A	P-1	33	17-13 / .116
1903	Cle	A	P	34	18-13
1904	Cle	A	P	28	14-8
1905	Cle	A	P	34	19-12
1906	Cle	A	P	36	21-9
1907	Cle	A	P	42	27-11
1908	Cle	A	P	42	24-11
1909	Cle	A	P	33	14-13
1910	Cle	A	P	13	5-5
	BRTR			295	159-95 / .145

JOURDAN, THEODORE CHARLES
b.Sept.5,1895 New Orleans,La.
d.Sept.23,1961

Yr	Cl	Lea	Pos	G	Rec
1916	Chi	A	H	3	.000
1917	Chi	A	1	17	.148
1918	Chi	A	1	7	.100
1920	Chi	A	1	48	.240
	BLTL			75	.214

JOY, ALOYSIUS C.
b.Washington,D.C.

Yr	Cl	Lea	Pos	G	Rec
1884	Was	U	1	35	.190

JOYCE, MICHAEL
(Real name Michael Joyce O'Neill)

JOYCE, MICHAEL LEWIS
b.Feb.12,1941 Detroit,Mich.

Yr	Cl	Lea	Pos	G	Rec
1962	Chi	A	P	25	2-1
	BRTR				

JOYCE, ROBERT EMMETT
b.Jan.14,1915 Stockton,Cal.

Yr	Cl	Lea	Pos	G	Rec
1939	Phi	A	P	30	3-5
1946	NY	N	P	14	3-4
	BRTR			44	6-9

JOYCE, WILLIAM MICHAEL (Scrappy)
b.Sept.21,1865 St.Louis,Mo.
d.May 8,1941

Yr	Cl	Lea	Pos	G	Rec
1890	Bro	p	3	133	.269
1891	Bos	a	3	65	.317
1892	Bro	N	3	97	.249
1894	Was	N	3	98	.344
1895	Was	N	3	128	.308
1896	Was	N	3	80	.309
1896	NY	N	M-3	49	.350
1897	NY	N	M-3	110	.305
1898	NY	N	M-1	143	.253
	BLTR			903	.293

JUDD, RALPH WESLEY
b.Dec.7,1901 Toledo,O.

Yr	Cl	Lea	Pos	G	Rec
1927	Was	A	P	1	0-0
1929	NY	N	P	18	3-0
1930	NY	N	P	2	0-0
	BLTR			21	3-0

JUDD, THOMAS WILLIAM OSCAR (Ossie)
b.Feb.14,1910 London,Ont.,Canada

Yr	Cl	Lea	Pos	G	Rec
1941	Bos	A	P	10	0-0
1942	Bos	A	P	36	8-10
1943	Bos	A	P	27	11-6
1944	Bos	A	P	10	1-1
1945	Bos	A	P	2	0-1
1945	Phi	N	P	27	5-4
1946	Phi	N	P	46	11-12
1947	Phi	N	P	44	4-15
1948	Phi	N	P	4	0-2
	BLTL			206	40-51

JUDE, FRANK
b.1884 Minn.

Yr	Cl	Lea	Pos	G	Rec
1906	Cin	N	O	80	.208
	BRTR				

JUDGE, JOSEPH IGNATIUS
b.May 25,1894 Brooklyn,N.Y.
d.Mar.11,1963

Yr	Cl	Lea	Pos	G	Rec
1915	Was	A	1	12	.353
1916	Was	A	1	103	.220
1917	Was	A	1	102	.285
1918	Was	A	1	130	.261
1919	Was	A	1	135	.288
1920	Was	A	1	126	.333
1921	Was	A	1	153	.301
1922	Was	A	1	148	.295
1923	Was	A	1	113	.314
1924	Was	A	1	140	.324
1925	Was	A	1	112	.314
1926	Was	A	1	134	.291
1927	Was	A	1	137	.308
1928	Was	A	1	153	.306
1929	Was	A	1	143	.315
1930	Was	A	1	126	.326
1931	Was	A	1	35	.284
1932	Was	A	1	82	.258
1933	Bro	N	1	42	.214
1933	Bos	A	1	34	.288
1934	Bos	A	1	10	.333
		BLTL		2170	.298

JUDNICH, WALTER FRANKLIN
b.Jan.24,1917 San Francisco,Cal.

Yr	Cl	Lea	Pos	G	Rec
1940	St.L	A	O	137	.303
1941	St.L	A	O	146	.284
1942	St.L	A	O	132	.313
1946	St.L	A	O	142	.262
1947	St.L	A	1-O	144	.258
1948	Cle	A	1-O	79	.257
1949	Pit	N	O	10	.229
		BLTL		790	.281

JUDSON, HOWARD KOLLS
b.Feb.16,1926 Hebron,Ill.

Yr	Cl	Lea	Pos	G	Rec
1948	Chi	A	P	41	4-5
1949	Chi	A	P	26	1-14
1950	Chi	A	P	46	2-3
1951	Chi	A	P	27	5-6
1952	Chi	A	P	21	0-1
1953	Cin	N	P	10	0-1
1954	Cin	N	P	37	5-7
		BRTR		208	17-37

JUDY, LYLE LeROY
b.Nov.15,1913 Lawrenceville,Ill.

Yr	Cl	Lea	Pos	G	Rec
1935	St.L	N	2	8	.000
		BRTR			

JUELICH, JOHN WALTER (Red)
b.Sept.20,1916 St.Louis,Mo.

Yr	Cl	Lea	Pos	G	Rec
1939	Pit	N	2	17	.239
		BRTR			

JUMONVILLE, GEORGE BENEDICT
b.May 16,1917 Mobile,Ala.

Yr	Cl	Lea	Pos	G	Rec
1940	Phi	N	S-3	11	.088
1941	Phi	N	2-S	6	.429
		BRTR		17	.146

JUNGELS, KENNETH PETER (Curly)
b.June 23,1916 Aurora,Ill.

Yr	Cl	Lea	Pos	G	Rec
1937	Cle	A	P	2	0-0
1938	Cle	A	P	9	1-0
1940	Cle	A	P	2	0-0
1941	Cle	A	P	6	0-0
1942	Pit	N	P	9	0-0
		BRTR		28	1-0

JURGES, WILLIAM FREDERICK
b.May 9,1908 Brooklyn,N.Y.

Yr	Cl	Lea	Pos	G	Rec
1931	Chi	N	2-3	88	.201
1932	Chi	N	S	115	.253
1933	Chi	N	S	143	.269
1934	Chi	N	S	100	.246
1935	Chi	N	S	146	.241
1936	Chi	N	S	118	.280
1937	Chi	N	S	129	.298
1938	Chi	N	S	137	.245
1939	NY	N	S	138	.285
1940	NY	N	S	63	.252
1941	NY	N	S	134	.293

(Continued)

Yr	Cl	Lea	Pos	G	Rec
1942	NY	N	S	127	.256
1943	NY	N	S-3	136	.229
1944	NY	N	2-S-3	85	.211
1945	NY	N	S-3	61	.324
1946	Chi	N	2-S-3	82	.222
1947	Chi	N	S	14	.200
		BRTR		1816	.258

Non-playing manager Bos (A) 1959-60

JURISICH, ALVIN JOSEPH
b.Aug.25,1921 New Orleans,La.

Yr	Cl	Lea	Pos	G	Rec
1944	St.L	N	P	30	7-9
1945	St.L	N	P	27	3-3
1946	Phi	N	P	13	4-3
1947	Phi	N	P	34	1-7
		BRTR		104	15-22

JUST, JOSEPH ERWIN
(Real Name Joseph Erwin Juszczak)
b.Jan.8,1916 Milwaukee,Wis.

Yr	Cl	Lea	Pos	G	Rec
1944	Cin	N	C	11	.182
1945	Cin	N	C	14	.147
		BRTR		25	.156

JUSTIS, WALTER (Smoke)
b.Aug.17,1883 Lawrenceburg,Ind.
d.Oct.4,1941

Yr	Cl	Lea	Pos	G	Rec
1905	Det	A	P	2	0-0

JUSZCZAK, JOSEPH ERWIN
(Played under name of Joseph Erwin Just)

JUUL, EARL HERBERT (Herb)
b.May 21,1893 Chicago,Ill.
d.Jan.4,1942

Yr	Cl	Lea	Pos	G	Rec
1914	Bro	F	P	9	0-3
		BRTR			

JUUL, HERBERT VICTOR
b.Feb.2,1886 Chicago,Ill.
d.Nov.14,1928

Yr	Cl	Lea	Pos	G	Rec
1911	Cin	N	P	2	0-0
		TL			

KAAT, JAMES LEE
b.Nov.7,1938 Zeeland, Mich.

Yr	Cl	Lea	Pos	G	Rec
1959	Was	A	P	3	0-2
1960	Was	A	P	13	1-5
1961	Min	A	P	47	9-17
1962	Min	A	P	48	18-14
		BLTL		111	28-38

KADING, JOHN FRED
b.Nov.17,1884 Waukesha,Wis.

Yr	Cl	Lea	Pos	G	Rec
1910	Pit	N	1	8	.304
1914	Chi	F	H	3	.000
				11	.292

KAFORA, FRANK JACOB (Jake)
b.Oct.16,1889 Detroit,Mich.
d.Mar.,1928

Yr	Cl	Lea	Pos	G	Rec
1913	Pit	N	C	1	.000
1914	Pit	N	C	21	.130
		BRTR		22	.125

KAHDOT, ISAAC LEONARD
b.Oct.22,1901 Sacred Heart,Okla.

Yr	Cl	Lea	Pos	G	Rec
1922	Cle	A	P	4	0-0
		BRTR			

KAHL, NICHOLAS ALEXANDER
b.Apr.10,1879 Coulterville,Ill.
d.Feb.7.1924

Yr	Cl	Lea	Pos	G	Rec
1905	Cle	A	2	38	.221
		BRTR			

KAHLE, ROBERT WAYNE
b.Nov.23,1915 Newcastle,Ind.

Yr	Cl	Lea	Pos	G	Rec
1938	Bos	N	H	8	.333
		BRTR			

KAHLER, GEORGE RANNELS (Krum)
b.Sept.6,1889 Athens,O.
d.Feb.14,1924

Yr	Cl	Lea	Pos	G	Rec
1910	Cle	A	P	12	6-4
1911	Cle	A	P	30	9-8
1912	Cle	A	P	32	12-19
1913	Cle	A	P	24	5-11
1914	Cle	A	P	2	0-1
		BRTR		100	32-43

KAHN, OWEN EARLE
b.June 11,1905 Richmond,Va.

Yr	Cl	Lea	Pos	G	Rec
1930	Bos	N	H	1	.000
		BRTR			

KAHOE, MICHAEL JOSEPH
b.Sept.3,1873 Yellow Springs,O.
d.May 14,1949

Yr	Cl	Lea	Pos	G	Rec
1895	Cin	N	C	3	.000
1899	Cin	N	C	14	.167
1900	Cin	N	C	49	.186
1901	Cin	N	C	4	.267
1901	Chi	N	C	65	.215
1902	Chi	N	C-S-3	7	.222
1902	St.L	A	C	54	.251
1903	St.L	A	C	74	.185
1904	St.L	A	C	71	.215
1905	Phi	N	C	15	.255
1907	Chi	N	C	4	.286
1907	Was	A	C	17	.191
1908	Was	A	C	17	.185
1909	Was	A	C	4	.125
		BRTR		398	.211

KAISER, ALFRED E. (Deerfoot)
b.Aug.3,1886 Cincinnati,Ohio

Yr	Cl	Lea	Pos	G	Rec
1911	Chi	N	O	26	.250
1911	Bos	N	O	66	.203
1912	Bos	N	O	4	.000
1914	Ind	F	O	59	.226
		BRTR		155	.215

KAISER, CLYDE DONALD
b.Feb.3,1935 Byng,Okla.

Yr	Cl	Lea	Pos	G	Rec
1955	Chi	N	P	11	0-0
1956	Chi	N	P	27	4-9
1957	Chi	N	P	20	2-6
		BRTR		58	6-15

KAISERLING, GEORGE
b.Aug.15,1890 Steubenville,O.
d.Mar.2,1918

Yr	Cl	Lea	Pos	G	Rec
1914	Ind	F	P	36	17-10
1915	New	F	P	38	15-16
		BRTR		74	32-26

KALAHAN, JOHN JOSEPH
b.Sept.30,1878 Philadelphia,Pa.

Yr	Cl	Lea	Pos	G	Rec
1903	Phi	A	C	1	.000
		TR			

KALBFUS, CHARLES HENRY
b.Dec.28,1864 Washington,D.C.
d.Nov.18,1941

Yr	Cl	Lea	Pos	G	Rec
1884	Was	U	O	1	.200

KALFASS, WILLIAM PHILIP
b.Mar.3,1916 New York,N.Y.

Yr	Cl	Lea	Pos	G	Rec
1937	Phi	A	P	3	1-0
		BRTL			

KALIN, FRANK BRUNO (Fats)
(Real name Frank Bruno Kalinkiewicz)
b.Oct.3,1917 Steubenville,O.

Yr	Cl	Lea	Pos	G	Rec
1940	Pit	N	O	3	.000
1943	Chi	A	H	4	.000
		BRTR		7	.000

KALINE, ALBERT WILLIAM
b.Dec.19,1934 Baltimore,Md.

Yr	Cl	Lea	Pos	G	Rec
1953	Det	A	O	30	.250

(Continued)

Yr	Cl	Lea	Pos	G	Rec
1954	Det	A	O	138	.276
1955	Det	A	O	152	.340
1956	Det	A	O	153	.314
1957	Det	A	O	149	.295
1958	Det	A	O	146	.313
1959	Det	A	O	136	.327
1960	Det	A	O	147	.278
1961	Det	A	3-O	153	.324
1962	Det	A	O	100	.304
	BRTR			1304	.308

KALINKIEWICZ, FRANK BRUNO
(Played under name of Frank Bruno Kalin)

KALLIO, RUDOLPH
b.Dec.14,1892 Portland,Ore.

Yr	Cl	Lea	Pos	G	Rec
1918	Det	A	P	31	8-13
1919	Det	A	P	12	0-0
1925	Bos	A	P	7	1-4
	BRTR			50	9-17

KAMM, WILLIAM EDWARD
b.Feb.2,1900 San Francisco,Cal.

Yr	Cl	Lea	Pos	G	Rec
1923	Chi	A	3	149	.292
1924	Chi	A	3	147	.254
1925	Chi	A	3	152	.279
1926	Chi	A	3	143	.294
1927	Chi	A	3	148	.270
1928	Chi	A	3	155	.308
1929	Chi	A	3	147	.268
1930	Chi	A	3	111	.269
1931	Chi	A	3	18	.254
1931	Cle	A	3	114	.295
1932	Cle	A	3	148	.286
1933	Cle	A	3	133	.282
1934	Cle	A	3	121	.269
1935	Cle	A	3	6	.333
	BRTR			1692	.281

KAMP, ALPHONSE FRANCIS (Ike)
b.Sept.5,1901 Roxbury,Mass.
d.Feb.26,1955

Yr	Cl	Lea	Pos	G	Rec
1924	Bos	N	P	1	0-1
1925	Bos	N	P	24	2-4
	BBTL			25	2-5

KAMPOURIS, ALEXIS WILLIAM
b.Nov.13,1912 Sacramento,Cal.

Yr	Cl	Lea	Pos	G	Rec
1934	Cin	N	2	19	.197
1935	Cin	N	2-S	148	.246
1936	Cin	N	2	122	.239
1937	Cin	N	2	146	.249
1938	Cin	N	2	21	.257
1938	NY	N	2	82	.246
1939	NY	N	2-3	74	.249
1941	Bro	N	2	16	.314
1942	Bro	N	2	10	.238
1943	Bro	N	2	19	.227
1943	Was	A	2-3-O	51	.207
	BRTR			708	.243

KANE, FRANCIS THOMAS (Sugar)
(Real name Francis Thomas Kiley)
b.Mar.9,1895 Whitman,Mass.

Yr	Cl	Lea	Pos	G	Rec
1915	Bro	F	O	3	.200
1919	NY	A	O	1	.000
	BLTR			4	.182

KANE, HARRY (Klondike)
(Real name Harry Cohen)
b.July 27,1883 Hamburg,Ark.
d.Sept.15,1932

Yr	Cl	Lea	Pos	G	Rec
1902	St.L	A	P	4	0-1
1903	Det	A	P	3	0-2
1905	Phi	N	P	2	1-1
1906	Phi	N	P	6	1-2
	TL			15	2-6

KANE, JAMES J.
b.Nov.27,1882 Scranton,Pa.
d.Oct.2,1947

Yr	Cl	Lea	Pos	G	Rec
1908	Pit	N	1	40	.241
	BLTL				

KANE, JEREMIAH
b.1867 Collinsville,Ill.

Yr	Cl	Lea	Pos	G	Rec
1890	St.L	a	C-1	8	.160
	BRTR				

KANE, JOHN FRANCIS
b.Oct.24,1883 Pittsburg,Kan.
d.Jan.28,1934

Yr	Cl	Lea	Pos	G	Rec
1907	Cin	N	3-O	75	.248
1908	Cin	N	O	127	.213
1909	Chi	N	1	15	.089
1910	Chi	N	O	30	.242
	BRTR			247	.220

KANE, JOHN FRANCIS
b.Feb.19,1900 Chicago,Ill.

Yr	Cl	Lea	Pos	G	Rec
1925	Chi	A	2-S	14	.179
	BBTR				

KANE, THOMAS JOSEPH
b.Dec.15,1908 Chicago,Ill.

Yr	Cl	Lea	Pos	G	Rec
1938	Bos	N	2	2	.000
	BRTR				

KANEHL, RODERICK EDWIN
b.Apr.1,1934 Wichita, Kan.

Yr	Cl	Lea	Pos	G	Rec
1962	NY	N	1-2-S-3-O	133	.248
	BRTR				

KANTLEHNER, ERVINE L. (Peanuts)
b.July 31,1892 San Jose,Cal.

Yr	Cl	Lea	Pos	G	Rec
1914	Pit	N	P	21	3-2
1915	Pit	N	P	29	5-12
1916	Pit	N	P	34	5-15
1916	Phi	N	P	3	0-0
	BLTL			87	13-29

KAPPEL, HENRY
b.1862 Philadelphia,Pa.
d.Aug.27,1905

Yr	Cl	Lea	Pos	G	Rec
1887	Cin	a	2-S-3-O	24	.294
1888	Cin	a	2-S-3	35	.254
1889	Col	a	S-3	49	.269
	BRTR			108	.272

KAPPEL, JOSEPH
b.1857 Philadelphia,Pa.
d.July 8,1929

Yr	Cl	Lea	Pos	G	Rec
1884	Phi	N	C	4	.067
1890	Ath	a	S	57	.240
				61	.227

KARDOW, PAUL OTTO (Tex)
b.Sept.19,1915 Humble,Tex.

Yr	Cl	Lea	Pos	G	Rec
1936	Cle	A	P	2	0-0
	BRTR				

KARGER, EDWIN
b.May 6,1883 San Angelo,Tex.
d.Sept.9,1957

Yr	Cl	Lea	Pos	G	Rec
1906	Pit	N	P	5	2-3
1906	St.L	N	P	25	5-16
1907	St.L	N	P	39	15-19
1908	St.L	N	P	22	4-9
1909	Cin	N	P	9	1-3
1909	Bos	A	P	12	5-2
1910	Bos	A	P	27	11-7
1911	Bos	A	P	25	5-8
	BRTL			164	48-67

KARL, ANTON ANDREW (Andy)
b.Apr.8,1914 Mt.Vernon,N.Y.

Yr	Cl	Lea	Pos	G	Rec
1943	Bos	A	P	11	1-1
1943	Phi	N	P	11	1-2
1944	Phi	N	P	42	3-2
1945	Phi	N	P	67	8-8
1946	Phi	N	P	39	3-7
1947	Bos	N	P	27	2-3
	BRTR			197	18-23

KARLON, WILLIAM JOHN (Hank)
b.Jan.21,1909 Palmer,Mass.

Yr	Cl	Lea	Pos	G	Rec
1930	NY	A	O	2	.000
	BRTR				

KAROW, MARTIN GREGORY
b.July 18,1904 Braddock,Pa.

Yr	Cl	Lea	Pos	G	Rec
1927	Bos	A	S-3	6	.200
	BRTR				

KARPEL, HERBERT
b.Dec.27,1918 Brooklyn,N.Y.

Yr	Cl	Lea	Pos	G	Rec
1946	NY	A	P	2	0-0
	BLTL				

KARR, BENJAMIN JOYCE (Baldy)
b.Nov.28,1893 Mt.Pleasant,Miss.

Yr	Cl	Lea	Pos	G	Rec
1920	Bos	A	P	57	3-8
1921	Bos	A	P	43	8-7
1922	Bos	A	P	66	5-12
1925	Cle	A	P	46	11-12
1926	Cle	A	P	31	5-6
1927	Cle	A	P	22	3-3
	BLTR			265	35-48

KARST, JOHN GOTTLIEB
b.Oct.15,1893 Philadelphia,Pa.

Yr	Cl	Lea	Pos	G	Rec
1915	Bro	N	3	1	.000
	TR				

KASKO, EDWARD MICHAEL
b.June 27,1932 Linden,N.J.

Yr	Cl	Lea	Pos	G	Rec
1957	St.L	N	2-S-3	134	.273
1958	St.L	N	2-S	104	.220
1959	Cin	N	2-S-3	118	.283
1960	Cin	N	2-S-3	126	.292
1961	Cin	N	2-S-3	126	.271
1962	Cin	N	S-3	134	.278
	BRTR			742	.273

KATOLL, JOHN (Big John)
b.June 24,1875 Etnon,O.
d.June 18,1955

Yr	Cl	Lea	Pos	G	Rec
1898	Chi	N	P	2	0-1
1899	Chi	N	P	3	1-1
1901	Chi	A	P	27	13-12
1902	Chi	A	P	1	0-0
1902	Bal	A	P-O	15	3-10 .152
	BRTR			48	17-24 .135

KATT, RAYMOND FREDERICK
b.May 9,1927 New Braunfels,Tex.

Yr	Cl	Lea	Pos	G	Rec
1952	NY	N	C	9	.222
1953	NY	N	C	8	.172
1954	NY	N	C	86	.255
1955	NY	N	C	124	.215
1956	NY	N	C	37	.228
1956	St.L	N	C	47	.259
1957	NY	N	C	72	.230
1958	St.L	N	C	19	.171
1959	St.L	N	C	15	.292
	BRTR			417	.232

KATZ, ROBERT CLYDE
b.Jan.30,1911 Lancaster,Pa.

Yr	Cl	Lea	Pos	G	Rec
1944	Cin	N	P	6	0-1
	BRTR				

KAUFF, BENJAMIN MICHAEL
b.Jan.5,1891 Middleport,O.
d.Nov.17,1961

Yr	Cl	Lea	Pos	G	Rec
1912	NY	A	O	5	.272
1914	Ind	F	O	154	.366
1915	Bro	F	O	136	.344
1916	NY	N	O	154	.264
1917	NY	N	O	153	.308
1918	NY	N	O	67	.315
1919	NY	N	O	135	.277
1920	NY	N	O	55	.274
	BLTL			859	.310

KAUFFMAN, HOWARD RICHARD (Dick)
b.June 22,1888 Milton,Pa.
d.Apr.17,1948

(Continued)

Yr	Cl	Lea	Pos	G	Rec
1914	St.L	A	1	6	.333
1915	St.L	A	1	37	.258
	BRTR			43	.266

KAUFMANN, ANTHONY CHARLES
b.Dec.16,1900 Chicago,Ill.

Yr	Cl	Lea	Pos	G	Rec
1921	Chi	N	P	2	1-0
1922	Chi	N	P	38	7-13
1923	Chi	N	P	33	14-10
1924	Chi	N	P	35	16-11
1925	Chi	N	P	31	13-13
1926	Chi	N	P	30	9-7
1927	Chi	N	P	9	3-3
1927	Phi	N	P	8	0-3
1927	St.L	N	P	1	0-0
1928	St.L	N	P	5	0-0
1929	NY	N	O	39	.031
1930	St.L	N	P	2	0-1
1931	St.L	N	P	20	1-1
1935	St.L	N	P	7	0-0
	BRTR			260	64-62 .220

KAVANAGH, CHARLES HUGH
(Silk)
b.June 9,1893 Chicago,Ill.

Yr	Cl	Lea	Pos	G	Rec
1914	Chi	A	O	5	.250
	BRTR				

KAVANAGH, LEO DANIEL
b.Aug.9,1894 Chicago,Ill.
d.Aug.10,1950

Yr	Cl	Lea	Pos	G	Rec
1914	Chi	F	S	5	.273
	BRTR				

KAVANAGH, MARTIN JOSEPH
b.June 13,1891 Harrison,N.J.
d.July 28,1960

Yr	Cl	Lea	Pos	G	Rec
1914	Det	A	2	127	.248
1915	Det	A	1-2	113	.295
1916	Det	A	2	58	.141
1916	Cle	A	2	19	.250
1917	Cle	A	2	14	.000
1918	Cle	A	1	13	.211
1918	St.L	N	2	12	.181
1918	Det	A	1	13	.273
	BRTR			369	.249

KAVANAUGH, ...

Yr	Cl	Lea	Pos	G	Rec
1872	Eck	n	1-O	5	NR

KAY, WALTER B. (King Bill)
b.Feb.14,1878 New Castle,Va.
d.Dec.3,1945

Yr	Cl	Lea	Pos	G	Rec
1907	Was	A	O	25	.333

KAZAK, EDWARD TERRANCE
(Real name
Edward Terrance Tkaczuk)
b.July 18,1920 Steubenville,O.

Yr	Cl	Lea	Pos	G	Rec
1948	St.L	N	3	6	.273
1949	St.L	N	2-3	92	.304
1950	St.L	N	3	93	.256
1951	St.L	N	3	11	.182
1952	St.L	N	3	3	.000
1952	Cin	N	1	13	.067
	BRTR			218	.273

KAZANSKI, THEODORE STANLEY
b.Jan.25,1934 Hamtramck,Mich.

Yr	Cl	Lea	Pos	G	Rec
1953	Phi	N	S	95	.217
1954	Phi	N	S	39	.135
1955	Phi	N	S-3	9	.083
1956	Phi	N	2-S	117	.211
1957	Phi	N	2-S-3	62	.265
1958	Phi	N	2-S-3	95	.228
	BRTR			417	.217

KEANE, JOHN JOSEPH
b.Nov.3,1911 St.Louis,Mo.
Non-playing manager St.L (N) 1961-62

KEARNS, EDWARD JOSEPH (Ted)
b.Jan.1,1900 Trenton,N.J.

(Continued)

Yr	Cl	Lea	Pos	G	Rec
1924	Chi	N	1	4	.250
1925	Chi	N	1	3	.500
	BRTR			7	.278

KEARNS, THOMAS J. (Dasher)
b.Nov.9,1859 Rochester,N.Y.
d.Dec.7,1938

Yr	Cl	Lea	Pos	G	Rec
1880	Buf	N	C-O	9	.091
1882	Det	N	2	4	.308
1884	Det	N	2	18	.211
				31	.188

KEARNS, W. A.
b.Chicago,Ill.

Yr	Cl	Lea	Pos	G	Rec
1901	Bal	A	P	4	1-0

KEARSE, EDWARD PAUL
b.Feb.23,1918 San Francisco,Cal.

Yr	Cl	Lea	Pos	G	Rec
1942	NY	A	C	11	.192
	BRTR				

KEAS, EDWARD JAMES
b.Feb.2,1863 Dubuque,Ia.
d.Jan.12,1940

Yr	Cl	Lea	Pos	G	Rec
1888	Cle	a	P	6	3-3

KEATING, EDWARD
b.Pittsburgh,Pa.

Yr	Cl	Lea	Pos	G	Rec
1887	Bal	a	P	1	0-1

KEATING, RAYMOND HERBERT
b.July 21,1891 Bridgeport,Conn.

Yr	Cl	Lea	Pos	G	Rec
1912	NY	A	P	5	0-3
1913	NY	A	P	22	6-12
1914	NY	A	P	33	7-11
1915	NY	A	P	11	3-6
1916	NY	A	P	14	5-6
1918	NY	A	P	15	2-2
1919	Bos	N	P	24	7-11
	BRTR			124	30-51

KEATING, WALTER FRANCIS
(Chick)
b.Aug.8,1891 Philadelphia,Pa.
d.July 13,1959

Yr	Cl	Lea	Pos	G	Rec
1913	Chi	N	S	2	.200
1914	Chi	N	S	20	.100
1915	Chi	N	S	4	.000
1926	Phi	N	S	4	.000
	BRTR			30	.087

KECK, FRANK JOSEPH (Cactus)
b.Jan.13,1899 St.Louis,Mo.

Yr	Cl	Lea	Pos	G	Rec
1922	Cin	N	P	27	7-6
1923	Cin	N	P	35	3-6
	BRTR			62	10-12

KEEFE, DAVID EDWIN
b.Jan.9,1897 Williston,Vt.

Yr	Cl	Lea	Pos	G	Rec
1917	Phi	A	P	3	1-0
1918	Phi	A	P	1	0-1
1919	Phi	A	P	2	0-1
1920	Phi	A	P	32	6-7
1921	Phi	A	P	44	2-9
1922	Cle	A	P	18	0-0
	BLTR			100	9-18

KEEFE, GEORGE W.
b.Jan.7,1867 Washington,D.C.

Yr	Cl	Lea	Pos	G	Rec
1886	Was	N	P	4	0-3
1887	Was	N	P	1	0-1
1888	Was	N	P	13	6-7
1889	Was	N	P	27	8-18
1890	Buf	p	P	25	5-17
1891	Was	a	P	5	0-5
	BLTL			75	19-51

KEEFE, JOHN T.
b.Pittsburgh,Pa.

Yr	Cl	Lea	Pos	G	Rec
1890	Syr	a	P	44	14-23

KEEFE, ROBERT FRANCIS
b.June 16,1882 Folsom,Cal.

Yr	Cl	Lea	Pos	G	Rec
1907	NY	A	P	19	4-4
1911	Cin	N	P	39	12-13
1912	Cin	N	P	17	1-3
	BRTR			75	17-20

KEEFE, TIMOTHY J. (Smiling Tim)
b.Jan.1,1856 Cambridge,Mass.
d.Apr.23,1933

Yr	Cl	Lea	Pos	G	Rec
1880	Tro	N	P	12	6-6
1881	Tro	N	P	46	19-27
1882	Tro	N	P-3-O	51	17-26 .225
1883	Met	a	P-O	70	41-26 .220
1884	Met	a	P	62	35-18
1885	NY	N	P-O	46	32-13 .162
1886	NY	N	P	64	42-20
1887	NY	N	P	56	35-20
1888	NY	N	P	51	35-12
1889	NY	N	P	43	30-13
1890	NY	p	P	30	17-8
1891	NY	N	P	8	2-5
1891	Phi	N	P	9	3-6
1892	Phi	N	P	36	21-14
1893	Phi	N	P	20	10-10
	BRTR			604	345-224 .199

KEEGAN, EDWARD CHARLES
b.July 8,1939 Camden,N.J.

Yr	Cl	Lea	Pos	G	Rec
1959	Phi	N	P	3	0-3
1961	KC	A	P	6	0-0
1962	Phi	N	P	5	0-0
	BRTR			14	0-3

KEEGAN, ROBERT CHARLES
b.Aug.4,1920 Rochester,N.Y.

Yr	Cl	Lea	Pos	G	Rec
1953	Chi	A	P	22	7-5
1954	Chi	A	P	32	16-9
1955	Chi	A	P	18	2-5
1956	Chi	A	P	20	5-7
1957	Chi	A	P	30	10-8
1958	Chi	A	P	14	0-2
	BRTR			136	40-36

KEELER, WILLIAM HENRY
(Wee Willie)
b.Mar.3,1872 Brooklyn,N.Y.
d.Jan.1,1923

Yr	Cl	Lea	Pos	G	Rec
1892	NY	N	3	13	.306
1893	NY	N	2-S-O	7	.364
1893	Bro	N	3	19	.340
1894	Bal	N	O	128	.367
1895	Bal	N	O	131	.394
1896	Bal	N	O	127	.392
1897	Bal	N	O	128	.432
1898	Bal	N	O	128	.379
1899	Bro	N	O	143	.376
1900	Bro	N	O	137	.366
1901	Bro	N	O	136	.355
1902	Bro	N	O	132	.342
1903	NY	A	O	132	.318
1904	NY	A	O	143	.343
1905	NY	A	O	149	.302
1906	NY	A	O	152	.304
1907	NY	A	O	107	.234
1908	NY	A	O	91	.263
1909	NY	A	O	99	.264
1910	NY	N	O	17	.300
	BLTL			2119	.345

KEELEY, BURTON ELWOOD
b.Nov.2,1888 Wilmington,Ill.
d.May 4,1952

Yr	Cl	Lea	Pos	G	Rec
1908	Was	A	P	31	6-11
1909	Was	A	P	2	0-0
	BRTR			33	6-11

KEELY, ROBERT WILLIAM
b.Aug.22,1916 St.Louis,Mo.

Yr	Cl	Lea	Pos	G	Rec
1944	St.L	N	C	1	.000
1945	St.L	N	C	1	.000
	BRTR			2	.000

KEEN, HOWARD VICTOR (Vic)
b.Mar.16,1900 Philadelphia,Pa.

Yr	Cl	Lea	Pos	G	Rec
1918	Phi	A	P	1	1-0
1921	Chi	N	P	5	0-3
1922	Chi	N	P	7	1-2
1923	Chi	N	P	35	12-8
1924	Chi	N	P	40	15-14
1925	Chi	N	P	30	2-6
1926	St.L	N	P	26	10-9
1927	St.L	N	P	21	2-1
	BRTR			165	43-43

KEENAN, HARRY LEON (Kid)
b.1875 Louisville,Ky.
d.June 11,1903

Yr	Cl	Lea	Pos	G	Rec
1891	Cin	a	P	1	0-1
	TR				

KEENAN, JAMES W.
b.Feb.10,1858 New Haven,Conn.
d.Sept.21,1926

Yr	Cl	Lea	Pos	G	Rec
1875	NH	n	C-3	3	NR
1880	Buf	N	C	2	.125
1882	Pit	a	C-S-O	24	.206
1884	Ind	a	C-1	68	.305
1885	Cin	a	P-C-1-O	32	0-0 / .282
1886	Cin	a	P-C-1-O	43	0-0 / .278
1887	Cin	a	C-1	47	.297
1888	Cin	a	C-1	84	.229
1889	Cin	a	C-1-3	87	.287
1890	Cin	N	C	54	.138
1891	Cin	N	C-1	75	.203
	BRTR			519	0-0 / NR

KEENAN, JAMES WILLIAM (Sparkplug)
b.May 25,1889 Avon,N.Y.

Yr	Cl	Lea	Pos	G	Rec
1920	Phi	N	P	1	0-0
1921	Phi	N	P	15	1-2
	BLTL			16	1-2

KEENE, WILLIAM BROWN (Rebel)
b.1891 Atlanta,Ga.

Yr	Cl	Lea	Pos	G	Rec
1911	Pit	N	1	5	.000
	BRTR				

KEENER, JOSHUA HARRY
b.1869 Easton,Pa.
d.Mar.5,1912

Yr	Cl	Lea	Pos	G	Rec
1896	Phi	N	P	15	2-10

KEERL, GEORGE HENRY
b.Apr.10,1847 Baltimore,Md.
d.Sept.9,1923

Yr	Cl	Lea	Pos	G	Rec
1875	Chi	n	2	6	NR

KEESEY, JAMES WARD
b.Oct.27,1903 Perryville,Md.
d.Sept.5,1951

Yr	Cl	Lea	Pos	G	Rec
1925	Phi	A	1	5	.400
1930	Phi	A	1	11	.250
	BRTR			16	.294

KEFFER, C. FRANK
b.Philadelphia,Pa.
d.Oct.1,1932

Yr	Cl	Lea	Pos	G	Rec
1890	Syr	a	P	1	0-1

KEHN, CHESTER LAURENCE
b.Oct.30,1921 San Diego,Cal.

Yr	Cl	Lea	Pos	G	Rec
1942	Bro	N	P	3	0-0
	BRTR				

KEIFER, SHERMAN C. (Katie)
b.1892

Yr	Cl	Lea	Pos	G	Rec
1914	Ind	F	P	1	1-0
	BBTR				

KEINZIL, WILLIAM
b.Philadelphia,Pa.

Yr	Cl	Lea	Pos	G	Rec
1882	Ath	a	O	9	.297
1884	Key	U	O	61	.260
				70	.265

KEISTER, WILLIAM HOFFMAN (Wagon Tongue)
b.Aug.17,1874 Baltimore,Md.
(Continued)
d.Aug.19,1924

Yr	Cl	Lea	Pos	G	Rec
1896	Bal	N	2	13	.224
1898	Bos	N	2-S	9	.200
1899	Bal	N	2-S	134	.331
1900	St.L	N	2	128	.298
1901	Bal	A	S	114	.328
1902	Was	A	2-S-3-O	119	.303
1903	Phi	N	O	100	.320
	BLTR			617	.312

KELB, GEORGE FRANCIS (Pugger)
b.July 17,1870 Toledo,O.
d.Oct.20,1936

Yr	Cl	Lea	Pos	G	Rec
1898	Cle	N	P	3	0-1
	TL				

KELIHER, MAURICE MICHAEL (Mickey)
b.Jan.11,1890 Washington,D.C.
d.Sept.5,1930

Yr	Cl	Lea	Pos	G	Rec
1911	Pit	N	1	3	.000
1912	Pit	N	H	2	.000
	BLTL			5	.000

KELL, EVERETT LEE (Skeeter)
b.Oct.11,1929 Swifton,Ark.

Yr	Cl	Lea	Pos	G	Rec
1952	Phi	A	2	75	.221
	BRTR				

KELL, GEORGE CLYDE
b.Aug.23,1922 Swifton,Ark.

Yr	Cl	Lea	Pos	G	Rec
1943	Phi	A	3	1	.200
1944	Phi	A	3	139	.268
1945	Phi	A	3	147	.272
1946	Phi	A	3	26	.299
1946	Det	A	1-3	105	.327
1947	Det	A	3	152	.320
1948	Det	A	3	92	.304
1949	Det	A	3	134	.343
1950	Det	A	3	157	.340
1951	Det	A	3	147	.319
1952	Det	A	3	39	.296
1952	Bos	A	3	75	.319
1953	Bos	A	3-O	134	.307
1954	Bos	A	3	26	.258
1954	Chi	A	1-3-O	71	.283
1955	Chi	A	1-3-O	128	.312
1956	Chi	A	1-3	21	.313
1956	Bal	A	1-2-3	102	.261
1957	Bal	A	1-3	99	.297
	BRTR			1795	.306

KELLEHER, ALBERT ALOYSIUS (Duke)
b.Sept.30,1893 New York,N.Y.

Yr	Cl	Lea	Pos	G	Rec
1916	NY	N	C	1	.000
	TR				

KELLEHER, FRANCIS EUGENE
b.Aug.22,1916 San Francisco,Cal.

Yr	Cl	Lea	Pos	G	Rec
1942	Cin	N	O	38	.182
1943	Cin	N	O	9	.000
	BRTR			47	.167

KELLEHER, HAROLD JOSEPH
b.June 24,1914 Philadelphia,Pa.

Yr	Cl	Lea	Pos	G	Rec
1935	Phi	N	P	3	2-0
1936	Phi	N	P	14	0-5
1937	Phi	N	P	30	2-4
1938	Phi	N	P	6	0-0
	BRTR			53	4-9

KELLEHER, JOHN PATRICK
b.Sept.13,1893 Brookline,Mass.
d.Aug.21,1960

Yr	Cl	Lea	Pos	G	Rec
1912	St.L	N	3	6	.363
1916	Bro	N	S-3	2	.000
1921	Chi	N	2-3	95	.309
1922	Chi	N	1-S-3	63	.259

(Continued)

Yr	Cl	Lea	Pos	G	Rec
1923	Chi	N	1-2-S-3	66	.306
1924	Bos	N	3	1	.000
	BRTR			233	.293

KELLER, CHARLES ERNEST (King Kong)
b.Sept.12,1916 Middletown,Md.

Yr	Cl	Lea	Pos	G	Rec
1939	NY	A	O	111	.334
1940	NY	A	O	138	.286
1941	NY	A	O	140	.298
1942	NY	A	O	152	.292
1943	NY	A	O	141	.271
1945	NY	A	O	44	.301
1946	NY	A	O	150	.275
1947	NY	A	O	45	.238
1948	NY	A	O	83	.267
1949	NY	A	O	60	.250
1950	Det	A	O	50	.314
1951	Det	A	O	54	.258
1952	NY	A	O	2	.000
	BLTR			1170	.286

KELLER, HAROLD KEFAUVER
b.July 7,1927 Middletown,Md.

Yr	Cl	Lea	Pos	G	Rec
1949	Was	A	H	3	.333
1950	Was	A	C	11	.214
1952	Was	A	C	11	.174
	BLTR			25	.204

KELLERT, FRANK WILLIAM
b.July 6,1924 Oklahoma City,Okla.

Yr	Cl	Lea	Pos	G	Rec
1953	St.L	A	1	2	.000
1954	Bal	A	1	10	.206
1955	Bro	N	1	39	.325
1956	Chi	N	1	71	.186
	BRTR			122	.231

KELLETT, ALFRED HENRY
b.Oct.30,1902 Red Bank,N.J.
d.July 14,1960

Yr	Cl	Lea	Pos	G	Rec
1923	Phi	A	P	5	0-1
1924	Bos	A	P	1	0-0
				6	0-1

KELLETT, DONALD STAFFORD (Red)
b.July 15,1909 Brooklyn,N.Y.

Yr	Cl	Lea	Pos	G	Rec
1934	Bos	A	2-S-3	9	.000
	BRTR				

KELLEY, HARRY LeROY
b.Feb.13,1906 Parkin,Ark.
d.Mar.23,1958

Yr	Cl	Lea	Pos	G	Rec
1925	Was	A	P	6	1-1
1926	Was	A	P	7	0-0
1936	Phi	A	P	36	15-12
1937	Phi	A	P	41	13-21
1938	Phi	A	P	4	0-2
1938	Was	A	P	38	9-8
1939	Was	A	P	15	4-3
	BRTR			147	42-47

KELLEY, JOSEPH JAMES
b.Dec.9,1871 Cambridge,Mass.
d.Aug.14,1943

Yr	Cl	Lea	Pos	G	Rec
1891	Bos	N	O	12	.244
1891	Pit	N	O	2	.143
1892	Pit	N	O	56	.245
1892	Bal	N	O	10	.250
1893	Bal	N	O	124	.312
1894	Bal	N	O	129	.391
1895	Bal	N	O	131	.370
1896	Bal	N	O	130	.370
1897	Bal	N	O	129	.389
1898	Bal	N	O	124	.328
1899	Bro	N	O	144	.329
1900	Bro	N	1-O	118	.318
1901	Bro	N	1	120	.309
1902	Bal	A	1-3-O	60	.311
1902	Cin	N	M-2-S-3-O	37	.327
1903	Cin	N	M-O	104	.316
1904	Cin	N	M-1	123	.281
1905	Cin	N	M-O	87	.277

Yr Cl Lea Pos G Rec

(Continued)
1906 Cin N O 127 .228
1908 Bos N M-O 62 .259
BRTR 1829 .321

KELLEY, MICHAEL JOSEPH
b.Dec.2,1875 Otter River,Mass.
d.June 6,1955
1899 Lou N 1 76 .247

KELLIHER, FRANK MORTIMER
b.May 23,1899 Somerville,Mass.
d.Mar.4,1956
1919 Was A H 1 .000

KELLNER, ALEXANDER RAYMOND
b.Aug.26,1924 Tucson,Ariz.
1948 Phi A P 13 0-0
1949 Phi A P 38 20-12
1950 Phi A P 36 8-20
1951 Phi A P 33 11-14
1952 Phi A P 34 12-14
1953 Phi A P 25 11-12
1954 Phi A P 27 6-17
1955 KC A P 30 11-8
1956 KC A P 21 7-4
1957 KC A P 28 6-5
1958 KC A P 8 0-2
1958 Cin N P 18 7-3
1959 St.L N P 12 2-1
BRTL 323 101-112

KELLNER, WALTER JOSEPH
bApr.26,1929 Tucson,Ariz.
1952 Phi A P 1 0-0
1953 Phi A P 2 0-0
BRTR 3 0-0

KELLOGG, ALBERT C.
d.Sept.1912
1908 Phi A P 3 0-2

KELLOGG, NATHANIEL M.
b.Manchester,N.H.
1885 Det N S 5 .118

KELLOGG, RAYMOND NELSON
(Played under name of
Raymond N. Nelson)

KELLOGG, WILLIAM DEARSTYNE
b.May 25,1884 Albany,N.Y.
1914 Cin N 1 71 .175
BRTR

KELLUM, WINFORD ANSLEY
b.Apr.11,1876 Waterford,Ont.,Canada
d.Aug.10,1951
1901 Bos A P 6 2-3
1904 Cin N P 36 16-8
1905 St.L N P 11 3-3
BLTL 53 21-14

KELLY, ALBERT MICHAEL (Red)
b.Nov.15,1884 Livingston, Co.,Ill.
1910 Chi A O 14 .155
TR

KELLY, CHARLES H.
1883 Phi N 3 2 .143
1886 Ath a S 1 .000
3 .100

KELLY, EDWARD L.
b.1890 Spokane,Wash.
1914 Bos A P 3 0-0
BRTR

KELLY, GEORGE LANGE
(High Pockets)
b.Sept.10,1896 San Francisco,Cal.
1915 NY N 1 17 .158
1916 NY N 1 49 .158
1917 NY N P-1-0 11 {1-0 .000}
1917 Pit N 1 8 .087
1919 NY N 1 32 .290

Yr Cl Lea Pos G Rec

(Continued)
1920 NY N 1 155 .266
1921 NY N 1 149 .308
1922 NY N 1 151 .327
1923 NY N 1 145 .307
1924 NY N 1-2-3-O 144 .324
1925 NY N 1-2-O 147 .309
1926 NY N 1-2 136 .303
1927 Cin N 1-2-O 61 .270
1928 Cin N 1-O 116 .296
1929 Cin N 1 147 .293
1930 Cin N 1 51 .288
1930 Chi N 1 39 .331
1932 Bro N 1 64 .243
BRTR 1622 {1-0 .297}

KELLY, HERBERT BARRETT
b.June 4,1892 Mobile,Ala.
1914 Pit N P 5 0-2
1915 Pit N P 5 1-1
BLTL 10 1-3

KELLY, JAMES ROBERT
(Real name Robert John Taggart)
b.Feb.1,1890 Bloomfield,N.J.
1914 Pit N O 32 .227
1915 Pit F O 148 .290
(Robert John Taggart)
1918 Bos N O 35 .329
BLTR 215 .294

KELLY, JOHN
1871 Kek n O 18 NR

KELLY, JOHN B.
b.San Francisco,Cal.
1907 St.L N O 52 .188

KELLY, JOHN FRANCIS (Kick)
b.1859 Paterson,N.J.
d.Apr.13,1908
1879 Syr N C-1 9 .125
1882 Cle N C 29 .134
1883 Bal a C-O 46 .224
1883 Phi N O 1 .000
1884 Cin U C 39 .253
1884 Was U C-O 4 .357
BRTR 128 .211

KELLY, JOHN O. (Honest John)
b.1856 New York,N.Y.
d.Mar.27,1926
Non-playing manager Lou (a) 1887.

KELLY, JOSEPH HERBERT
b.Sept.23,1889 Weir City,Kan.
1914 Pit N O 141 .222
1916 Chi N O 54 .254
1917 Bos N O 116 .222
1918 Bos N O 47 .232
1919 Bos N O 18 .141
BRTR 376 .224

KELLY, JOSEPH JAMES
b.Apr.23,1901 New York,N.Y.
1926 Chi N O 65 .335
1928 Chi N 1 32 .212
BLTL 97 .307

KELLY, MICHAEL J.
b.Nov.9,1902 St. Louis,Mo.
1926 Phi N P 4 0-0
BRTR

KELLY, MICHAEL JOSEPH (King)
b.Dec.31,1857 Troy,N.Y.
d.Nov.8,1894
1878 Cin N C-3-O 61 .281
1879 Cin N C-3-O 77 .348
1880 Chi N P-C-S-3-O 82 {0-0 .292}
1881 Chi N C-3-O 80 .323

Yr Cl Lea Pos G Rec

(Continued)
1882 Chi N C-1-S-3-O 84 .305
1883 Chi N P-C-2-3-O 98 {0-0 .253}
1884 Chi N P-C-1-2-S-3-O 107 {0-0 .341}
1885 Chi N C-1-2-3-O 107 .287
1886 Chi N C-O 118 .388
1887 Bos N C-2-O 114 .394
1888 Bos N C-O 105 .318
1889 Bos N C-O 125 .293
1890 Bos p M-C-S 90 .324
1891 Cin a M-P-C-1-2-S-3-O 74 {0-1 .280}
1891 Bos a C 3 .200
1891 Bos N O 24 .239
1892 Bos N C 72 .201
1893 NY N C 16 .314
BRTR 1437 {0-1 .313}

KELLY, REYNOLDS CLARENCE
b.Nov.18,1900 San Francisco,Cal.
1923 Phi A P 1 0-0
BRTR

KELLY, ROBERT BROWN (Speed)
b.Aug.19,1884 Bryan,O.
d.May 6,1949
1909 Was A 3 17 .143
BRTR

KELLY, ROBERT EDWARD
b.Oct.4,1927 Cleveland,O.
1951 Chi N P 35 7-4
1952 Chi N P 31 4-9
1953 Chi N P 14 0-1
1953 Cin N P 28 1-2
1958 Cin N P 2 0-0
1958 Cle A P 13 0-2
BRTR 123 12-18

KELLY, WILLIAM HENRY
b.Dec.28,1899 Syracuse,N.Y.
1920 Phi A 1 8 .181
1928 Phi N 1 23 .169
BRTR 31 .171

KELLY, WILLIAM J.
b.1889 Baltimore,Md.
1910 St.L N C 2 .000
1911 Pit N C 6 .125
1912 Pit N C 48 .318
1913 Pit N C 48 .268
BRTR 104 .290

KELSEY, GEORGE W.
b.Ohio.
1907 Pit N C 2 .400
TR

KELTNER, KENNETH FREDERICK
(Butch)
b.Oct.31,1916 Milwaukee,Wis.
1937 Cle A 3 1 .000
1938 Cle A 3 149 .276
1939 Cle A 3 154 .325
1940 Cle A 3 149 .254
1941 Cle A 3 149 .269
1942 Cle A 3 152 .287
1943 Cle A 3 110 .260
1944 Cle A 3 149 .295
1946 Cle A 3 116 .241
1947 Cle A 3 151 .257
1948 Cle A 3 153 .297
1949 Cle A 3 80 .232
1950 Bos A 1-3 13 .321
BRTR 1526 .276

KELTY, JOHN E. JOSEPH (Chief)
b.1867 Jersey City,N.J.
1890 Pit N O 59 .236

KEMMAN, HERBERT FREDERICK
(Played under name of
Frederick Herbert)

KEMMER, WILLIAM E.

Yr	Cl	Lea	Pos	G	Rec
1895	Lou	N	3	10	.139

KEMMERER, RUSSELL PAUL
(Rusty)
b.Nov.1,1931 Pittsburgh,Pa.

Yr	Cl	Lea	Pos	G	Rec
1954	Bos	A	P	19	5-3
1955	Bos	A	P	7	1-1
1957	Bos	A	P	1	0-0
1957	Was	A	P	39	7-11
1958	Was	A	P	40	6-15
1959	Was	A	P	37	8-17
1960	Was	A	P	3	0-2
1960	Chi	A	P	36	6-3
1961	Chi	A	P	47	3-3
1962	Chi	A	P	20	2-1
1962	Hou	N	P	36	5-3
		BRTR		285	43-59

KEMMLER, RUDOLPH
b.Chicago,Ill.

Yr	Cl	Lea	Pos	G	Rec
1879	Pro	N	C	2	.143
1881	Cle	N	C	1	.000
1882	Cin	a	C-O	3	.091
1882	Pit	a	C-O	25	.218
1883	Col	a	C-O	85	.202
1884	Col	a	C	61	.202
1885	Pit	a	C	18	.191
1886	St.L	a	C	35	.150
1889	Col	a	C	8	.134
		BRTR		238	.195

KEMNER, HERMAN JOHN (Dutch)
b.Mar.4,1899 Quincy,Ill.

Yr	Cl	Lea	Pos	G	Rec
1929	Cin	N	P	9	0-0
		BRTR			

KENDERS, ALBERT DANIEL GEORGE
b.Apr.4,1937 Barrington,N.J.

Yr	Cl	Lea	Pos	G	Rec
1961	Phi	N	C	10	.174
		BRTR			

KENNA, EDWARD ALOYSIUS
b.Sept.19,1901 San Francisco,Cal.

Yr	Cl	Lea	Pos	G	Rec
1928	Was	A	C	41	.297
		BRTR			

KENNA, EDWARD BENNINGHAUS
(Poet)
b.Oct.10,1877 Charleston,W.Va.
d.Mar.22,1912

Yr	Cl	Lea	Pos	G	Rec
1902	Phi	A	P	3	1-1
		TR			

KENNEDY, CHARLES
b.Cohocton,N.Y.
d.Aug.19,1897

Yr	Cl	Lea	Pos	G	Rec
1884	Cin	U	S-3-O	13	.213
		BRTR			

KENNEDY, EDWARD
b.Apr.1,1856 Carbondale,Pa.
d.May 22,1905

Yr	Cl	Lea	Pos	G	Rec
1883	Met	a	O	97	.215
1884	Met	a	O	103	.184
1885	Met	a	O	96	.222
1886	Bro	a	O	6	.181
				302	.209

KENNEDY, JAMES C.
b.1867 New York,N.Y.
d.Apr.20,1904
Non-playing manager Bro (a) 1890.

KENNEDY, JOHN EDWARD
b.May 29,1941 Chicago,Ill.

Yr	Cl	Lea	Pos	G	Rec
1962	Was	A	S-3	14	.262

KENNEDY, JOHN IRVIN
b.Nov.23,1934 Sumter,S.C.

Yr	Cl	Lea	Pos	G	Rec
1957	Phi	N	3	5	.000
		BRTR			

KENNEDY, LLOYD VERNON
(Vern)
b.Mar.20,1907 Kansas City,Mo.

Yr	Cl	Lea	Pos	G	Rec
1934	Chi	A	P	3	0-2
1935	Chi	A	P	31	11-11

(Continued)

Yr	Cl	Lea	Pos	G	Rec
1936	Chi	A	P	36	21-9
1937	Chi	A	P	32	14-13
1938	Det	A	P	37	12-9
1939	Det	A	P	4	0-3
1939	St.L	A	P	34	9-17
1940	St.L	A	P	35	12-17
1941	St.L	A	P	6	2-4
1941	Was	A	P	18	1-7
1942	Cle	A	P	33	4-8
1943	Cle	A	P	38	10-7
1944	Cle	A	P	15	2-5
1944	Phi	N	P	14	1-5
1945	Phi	N	P	13	0-3
1945	Cin	N	P	24	5-12
		BBTR		373	104-132

KENNEDY, MICHAEL JOSEPH
(Doc)
b.Aug.11,1855 Brooklyn,N.Y.
d.May 29,1920

Yr	Cl	Lea	Pos	G	Rec
1879	Cle	N	C	47	.285
1880	Cle	N	C	66	.200
1881	Cle	N	C-3-O	38	.313
1882	Cle	N	C	1	.250
1883	Buf	N	C-1-O	5	.286
				157	.257

KENNEDY, MONTIA CALVIN
b.May 11,1922 Amelia,Va.

Yr	Cl	Lea	Pos	G	Rec
1946	NY	N	P	38	9-10
1947	NY	N	P	34	9-12
1948	NY	N	P	26	3-9
1949	NY	N	P	39	12-14
1950	NY	N	P	36	5-4
1951	NY	N	P	29	1-2
1952	NY	N	P	34	3-4
1953	NY	N	P	19	0-0
		BRTL		255	42-55

KENNEDY, RAYMOND LINCOLN
b.May 19,1895 Pittsburgh,Pa.

Yr	Cl	Lea	Pos	G	Rec
1916	St.L	A	C	1	.000
		BRTR			

KENNEDY, ROBERT DANIEL
b.Aug.18,1920 Chicago,Ill.

Yr	Cl	Lea	Pos	G	Rec
1939	Chi	A	3	3	.250
1940	Chi	A	3	154	.252
1941	Chi	A	3	76	.206
1942	Chi	A	3-O	113	.231
1946	Chi	A	3-O	113	.258
1947	Chi	A	3-O	115	.262
1948	Chi	A	O	30	.248
1948	Cle	A	1-2-O	66	.301
1949	Cle	A	3-O	121	.276
1950	Cle	A	O	146	.291
1951	Cle	A	O	108	.246
1952	Cle	A	3-O	22	.300
1953	Cle	A	O	100	.236
1954	Cle	A	O	1	.000
1954	Bal	A	3-O	106	.251
1955	Bal	A	1-3-O	26	.143
1955	Chi	A	1-3-O	83	.304
1956	Chi	A	3	8	.077
1956	Det	A	3-O	69	.232
1957	Chi	A	H	4	.000
1957	Bro	N	3-O	19	.129
		BRTR		1483	.254

KENNEDY, SHERMAN MONTGOMERY (Snapper)
b.Nov.1,1877 Conneaut,O.
d.1944

Yr	Cl	Lea	Pos	G	Rec
1902	Chi	N	O	1	.000

KENNEDY, THEODORE A.
b.Feb.1865 Henry,Ill.
d.Oct.31,1907

Yr	Cl	Lea	Pos	G	Rec
1885	Chi	N	P-3	9	7-2 .065
1886	Ath	a	P	22	5-15
1886	Lou	a	P	4	0-4
		BL		35	12-21 .043

KENNEDY, WILLIAM AULTON
(Lefty)
b.Mar.14,1921 Carnesville,Ga.

Yr	Cl	Lea	Pos	G	Rec
1948	Cle	A	P	6	1-0
1948	St.L	A	P	26	7-8
1949	St.L	A	P	48	4-11
1950	St.L	A	P	1	0-0
1951	St.L	A	P	19	1-5
1952	Chi	A	P	47	2-2
1953	Bos	A	P	16	0-0
1956	Cin	N	P	1	0-0
1957	Cin	N	P	8	0-2
		BLTL		172	15-28

KENNEDY, WILLIAM GORMAN
b.Dec.22,1918 Alexandria,Va.

Yr	Cl	Lea	Pos	G	Rec
1942	Was	A	P	8	0-1
1946	Was	A	P	21	1-2
1947	Was	A	P	2	0-0
		BLTL		31	1-3

KENNEDY, WILLIAM V. (Brickyard)
b.Oct.7,1868 Bellaire,O.
d.Sept.23,1915

Yr	Cl	Lea	Pos	G	Rec
1892	Bro	N	P	22	13-8
1893	Bro	N	P	45	25-18
1894	Bro	N	P	44	24-20
1895	Bro	N	P	36	19-13
1896	Bro	N	P	37	15-22
1897	Bro	N	P	42	19-21
1898	Bro	N	P	38	16-22
1899	Bro	N	P	37	18-8
1900	Bro	N	P	37	22-15
1901	Bro	N	P	14	3-5
1902	NY	N	P	6	1-4
1903	Pit	N	P	18	9-6
		TR		376	184-162

KENNEY, ...

Yr	Cl	Lea	Pos	G	Rec
1872	Atl	n	2-O	5	.000

KENNEY, ARTHUR JOSEPH
b.Apr.29,1917 Milford,Mass.

Yr	Cl	Lea	Pos	G	Rec
1938	Bos	N	P	2	0-0
		BLTL			

KENT, EDWARD C.
b.N.Y.

Yr	Cl	Lea	Pos	G	Rec
1884	Tol	a	P	1	0-1
		TL			

KENT, MAURICE ALLEN
b.Sept.17,1885 Marshalltown,Ia.

Yr	Cl	Lea	Pos	G	Rec
1912	Bro	N	P	20	5-5
1913	Bro	N	P	5	0-0
		BBTR		25	5-5

KENWORTHY, RICHARD LEE
b.Apr.1,1941 Red Oak,Ia.

Yr	Cl	Lea	Pos	G	Rec
1962	Chi	A	2	3	.000
		BRTR			

KENWORTHY, WILLIAM JENNINGS
(Duke)
b.July 4,1887 Cambridge,O.
d.Sept.21,1950

Yr	Cl	Lea	Pos	G	Rec
1912	Was	A	O	12	.289
1914	KC	F	2	146	.316
1915	KC	F	2	121	.299
1917	St.L	A	2	5	.100
		BBTR		284	.305

KENZIE, WALTER H.
b.1859 Chicago,Ill.

Yr	Cl	Lea	Pos	G	Rec
1882	Det	N	S	13	.094
1884	Chi	N	S-3	19	.158
1884	St.L	a	2	2	.125
				34	.133

KEOUGH, RICHARD MARTIN
b.Apr.14,1935 Oakland,Cal.

Yr	Cl	Lea	Pos	G	Rec
1956	Bos	A	H	3	.000

Yr Cl Lea Pos G Rec

(Continued)
1957 Bos A O 9 .059
1958 Bos A 1-O 68 .220
1959 Bos A 1-O 96 .243
1960 Bos A O 38 .248
1960 Cle A O 65 .248
1961 Was A 1-O 135 .249
1962 Cin N 1-O 111 .278
BLTL 525 .247

KERIAZAKOS, CONSTANTINE NICHOLAS (Gus)
b.July 28,1931 W.Orange,N.J.
1950 Chi A P 1 0-1
1954 Was A P 22 2-3
1955 KC A P 5 0-1
BRTR 28 2-5

KERINS, JOHN NELSON
b.Dec.22,1858 Indianapolis,Ind.
d.Sept.15,1919
1884 Ind a 1 93 .210
1885 Lou a C-1 113 .243
1886 Lou a C-1 119 .268
1887 Lou a C-1 112 .360
1888 Lou a M-C-O 81 .239
1889 Lou a C-O 2 .333
1889 Bal a C-1-S-O 16 .283
1890 St.L a C 19 .136
BRTR 555 .267

KERKSIECK, WAYMAN WILLIAM
b.Dec.6,1916 Ulm,Ark.
1939 Phi N P 25 0-2
BBTR

KERLIN, ORIE MILTON
b.Jan.23,1891 Summerfield,La.
1915 Pit F C 3 .000
TR

KERN, WILLIAM GEORGE
b.Feb.28,1933 Coplay,Pa.
1962 KC A O 8 .250

KERNAN, JOSEPH
b.Baltimore,Md.
1873 Mar n 2-O 2 NR

KERNS, DANIEL P.
b.Philadelphia,Pa.
1920 Phi A H 1 .000

KERNS, RUSSELL ELDON
b.Nov.10,1920 Fremont,O.
1945 Det A H 1 .000
BLTR

KERR, JOHN FRANCIS
b.Nov.26,1900 San Francisco,Cal.
1923 Det A S 19 .214
1924 Det A 3-O 17 .273
1929 Chi A 2 127 .258
1930 Chi A 2-S 70 .289
1931 Chi A 2 128 .268
1932 Was A 2-S 51 .273
1933 Was A 2-3 28 .200
1934 Was A 3 31 .272
BBTR 471 .266

KERR, JOHN JONAS (Doc)
b.Baltimore,Md.
d.June 9,1937
1914 Pit F C 41 .254
1914 Bal F C 14 .265
1915 Bal F C 3 .333
BRTR 58 .260

KERR, JOHN JOSEPH (Buddy)
b.Nov.6,1922 Astoria,N.Y.
1943 NY N S 27 .286
1944 NY N S 150 .267
1945 NY N S 149 .249

(Continued)
1946 NY N S-3 145 .250
1947 NY N S 138 .287
1948 NY N S 144 .240
1949 NY N S 90 .209
1950 Bos N S 155 .227
1951 Bos N 2-S 69 .186
BRTR 1067 .249

KERR, JOHN MELVILLE (Mel)
b.May 22,1904 Souris, Man., Canada.
1925 Chi N H 1 .000
BLTL

KERR, RICHARD HENRY (Dickie)
b.July 3,1893 St.Louis,Mo.
1919 Chi A P 39 13-8
1920 Chi A P 46 21-9
1921 Chi A P 45 19-17
1925 Chi A P 13 0-1
BLTL 143 53-35

KERWIN, DANIEL P.
b.July 9,1879 Philadelphia,Pa.
1903 Cin N O 1 .750
BLTL

KESSLER, HENRY (Lucky)
b.1847 Brooklyn,N.Y.
d.Jan.9,1900
1873 Atl n 1 1 NR
1874 Atl n C-2-3-O 14 NR
1875 Atl n 2-S-O 25 NR
1876 Cin N S-3-O 59 .251
1877 Cin N C-1 6 .100
BRTR 105 NR

KETCHAM, FREDERICK L.
b.July 27,1875 Elmira,N.Y.
d.Mar.12,1908
1899 Lou N O 15 .311
1901 Phi A O 5 .227
BLTR 20 .289

KETCHUM, AUGUST FRANKLIN
b.Mar.21,1898 Rockwall,Tex.
1922 Phi A P 6 0-1
BRTR

KETTER, PHILIP
b.Hutchinson,Kan.
1912 St.L A C 2 .333
TR

KEUPPER, HENRY
b.1888 Egypt,Ill.
1914 St.L F P 38 7-20
BLTL

KIBBIE, HORACE KENT
b.July 18,1903 Ft.Worth,Tex.
1925 Bos N 2-S 11 .268
BRTR

KIBBLE, JOHN WESTLY (Happy)
b.Jan.2,1892 Seatonville,Ill.
1912 Cle A 2-3 5 .000
BLTR

KIEFER, JOSEPH WILLIAM (Harlem Joe)
b.July 19,1899 W.Leyden,N.Y.
1920 Chi A P 2 0-1
1925 Bos A P 2 0-2
1926 Bos A P 11 0-3
BRTR 15 0-6

KIELY, LEO PATRICK (Kiki)
b.Nov.30,1929 Hoboken,N.J.
1951 Bos A P 18 7-7
1954 Bos A P 28 5-8
1955 Bos A P 33 3-3
1956 Bos A P 23 2-2
1958 Bos A P 47 5-2
1959 Bos A P 41 3-3
1960 KC A P 20 1-2
BLTL 210 26-27

KILDUFF, PETER JOHN
b.Apr.4,1894 Weir City,Kan.
d.Feb.14,1930
1917 NY N 2-S 31 .205
1917 Chi N 2-S 56 .277
1918 Chi N 2 30 .204
1919 Chi N 2-S 31 .273
1919 Bro N 2-3 32 .301
1920 Bro N 2 141 .272
1921 Bro N 2 107 .268
BRTR 428 .270

KILEEN, EVANS HENRY
b.Feb.27,1936 Elmont,N.Y.
1959 KC A P 4 0-0
BRTR

KILEY, FRANCIS THOMAS
(Played under name of Francis Thomas Kane)

KILEY, JOHN FREDERICK
b.Cambridge,Mass.
1884 Was a O 14 .203
1891 Bos N P 1 0-1
BLTL 15 {0-1 / .197}

KILHULLEN, JOSEPH ISADORE (Pat)
b.May 3,1888 Carbondale,Pa.
d.Nov.2,1922
1914 Pit N C 1 .000
TR

KILLEBREW, HARMON CLAYTON
b.June 29,1936 Payette,Ida.
1954 Was A 2 9 .308
1955 Was A 2-3 38 .200
1956 Was A 2-3 44 .222
1957 Was A 2-3 9 .290
1958 Was A 3 13 .194
1959 Was A 3-O 153 .242
1960 Was A 1-3 124 .276
1961 Min A 1-3-O 150 .288
1962 Min A 1-O 155 .243
BRTR 695 .257

KILLEEN, HENRY
b.1871 Troy,N.Y.
1891 Cle N P 1 0-1

KILLEFER, WADE HAMPTON (Red)
b.Apr.13,1884 Bloomingdale,Mich.
d.Sept.4,1958
1907 Det A O 1 .000
1908 Det A 2 28 .213
1909 Det A 2 23 .302
1909 Was A O 40 .160
1910 Was A 2 106 .229
1914 Cin N O 42 .277
1915 Cin N 1-O 155 .272
1916 Cin N O 70 .244
1916 NY N H 2 .500
BRTR 467 .248

KILLEFER, WILLIAM LAVIER (Reindeer Bill)
b.Oct.10,1888 Bloomingdale,Mich.
d.June 2,1960
1909 St.L A C 11 .172
1910 St.L A C 74 .124
1911 Phi N C 6 .188
1912 Phi N C 85 .224
1913 Phi N C 120 .244
1914 Phi N C 98 .234
1915 Phi N C 105 .238
1916 Phi N C 97 .217
1917 Phi N C 125 .274
1918 Chi N C 104 .233
1919 Chi N C 103 .286
1920 Chi N C 62 .220
1921 Chi N M-C 45 .323
BRTR 1035 .239
Non-playing manager Chi (N) 1922-25 and St.L (A) 1930-33.

Yr	Cl	Lea	Pos	G	Rec

KILLEN, FRANK BISSELL
(Lefty)
b.Nov.30,1870 Pittsburgh,Pa.
d.Dec.4,1939

Yr	Cl	Lea	Pos	G	Rec
1891	Mil	a	P	11	8-3
1892	Was	N	P	54	29-25
1893	Pit	N	P	47	33-14
1894	Pit	N	P	24	14-10
1895	Pit	N	P	14	7-6
1896	Pit	N	P	50	31-19
1897	Pit	N	P	41	16-23
1898	Pit	N	P	22	10-12
1898	Was	N	P-O	20	7-9 .268
1899	Was	N	P	5	0-2
1899	Bos	N	P	12	7-5
1900	Chi	N	P	6	3-3
	TL			306	165-131 .246

KILLIAN, EDWIN HENRY
(Twilight)
b.Nov.12,1876 Racine,Wis.
d.July 18,1928

Yr	Cl	Lea	Pos	G	Rec
1903	Cle	A	P	10	3-5
1904	Det	A	P	40	15-20
1905	Det	A	P	39	22-14
1906	Det	A	P	20	9-6
1907	Det	A	P	46	25-13
1908	Det	A	P	28	11-10
1909	Det	A	P	25	11-9
1910	Det	A	P	11	4-3
	BLTL			219	100-80

KILLILAY, JOHN WILLIAM
bMay 24,1887 Leavenworth,Kan

Yr	Cl	Lea	Pos	G	Rec
1911	Bos	A	P	14	4-3
	BRTR				

KILROY, MATTHEW ALOYSIUS
(Matches)
b.June 21,1866 Philadelphia,Pa.
d.Mar.2,1940

Yr	Cl	Lea	Pos	G	Rec
1886	Bal	a	P	69	29-34
1887	Bal	a	P	73	46-20
1888	Bal	a	P	43	16-21
1889	Bal	a	P	65	28-25
1890	Bos	p	P	31	10-13
1891	Cin	a	P-O	8	1-4 190
1892	Was	N	P	4	1-1
1893	Lou	N	P	5	3-2
1894	Lou	N	P	6	0-6
1898	Chi	N	P	25	6-6
	TL			329	140-132 .242

KILROY, MICHAEL JOSEPH
b.Nov.4,1869 Philadelphia,Pa.

Yr	Cl	Lea	Pos	G	Rec
1888	Bal	a	P	1	0-1
1891	Phi	N	P	3	0-1
	TR			4	0-2

KIMBALL, EUGENE
b.Aug.31,1850 Rochester,NY
d.Aug.2,1882

Yr	Cl	Lea	Pos	G	Rec
1871	Cle	n	2-S-O	29	NR

KIMBALL, NEWEL W.
(Newt)
b.Mar.27,1915 Logan,Utah

Yr	Cl	Lea	Pos	G	Rec
1937	Chi	N	P	2	0-0
1938	Chi	N	P	1	0-0
1940	Bro	N	P	21	3-1
1940	StL	N	P	2	1-0
1941	Bro	N	P	15	3-1
1942	Bro	N	P	14	2-0
1943	Bro	N	P	5	1-1
1943	Phi	N	P	34	1-6
	BRTR			94	11-9

KIMBER, SAMUEL JACKSON
b.Oct.29,1852 Philadelphia,Pa.
d.Nov.6,1925

Yr	Cl	Lea	Pos	G	Rec
1884	Bro	a	P	41	18-20
1885	Pro	N	P	1	0-1
				42	18-21

KIMBERLIN, HARRY LIDDLE
(Mule Trader)
b.Mar.13,1909 Sullivan,Mo.

Yr	Cl	Lea	Pos	G	Rec
1936	St.L	A	P	13	0-0
1937	St.L	A	P	3	0-2
1938	St.L	A	P	1	0-0
1939	St.L	A	P	17	1-2
	BRTR			34	1-4

KIMBLE, RICHARD LOUIS
b.July 27,1917 Buchtel,O.

Yr	Cl	Lea	Pos	G	Rec
1945	Was	A	S	20	.245
	BLTR				

KIME, HAROLD LEE
(Lefty)
b.Mar.15,1899 W.Salem,O.

Yr	Cl	Lea	Pos	G	Rec
1920	St.L	N	P	4	0-0
	BLTL				

KIMMICK, WALTER LYONS
b.May 30,1898 Turtle Creek,Pa.

Yr	Cl	Lea	Pos	G	Rec
1919	St.L	N	S	2	.000
1921	Cin	N	3	3	.167
1922	Cin	N	2-S-3	39	.247
1923	Cin	N	2-S-3	29	.225
1925	Phi	N	2-S-3	70	.305
1926	Phi	N	1-S-3	20	.214
	BRTR			163	.261

KIMSEY, CLYDE ELIAS
(Chad)
b.Aug.6,1905 Copperhill,Tenn.
d.Dec.3,1942

Yr	Cl	Lea	Pos	G	Rec
1929	St.L	A	P	29	3-6
1930	St.L	A	P	60	6-10
1931	St.L	A	P	47	4-6
1932	St.L	A	P	34	4-2
1932	Chi	A	P	7	1-1
1933	Chi	A	P	28	4-1
1936	Det	A	P	22	2-3
	BLTR			227	24-29

KINDALL, GERALD DONALD
b.May 27,1935 St. Paul,Minn.

Yr	Cl	Lea	Pos	G	Rec
1956	Chi	N	S	32	.164
1957	Chi	N	2-S-3	72	.160
1958	Chi	N	2	3	.167
1960	Chi	N	2-S	89	.240
1961	Chi	N	2-S	96	.242
1962	Cle	A	2	154	.232
	BRTR			446	.223

KINDER, ELLIS RAYMOND
(Old Folks)
b.July 26,1914 Atkins,Ark.

Yr	Cl	Lea	Pos	G	Rec
1946	St.L	A	P	33	3-3
1947	St.L	A	P	34	8-15
1948	Bos	A	P	28	10-7
1949	Bos	A	P	43	23-6
1950	Bos	A	P	48	14-12
1951	Bos	A	P	63	11-2
1952	Bos	A	P	23	5-6
1953	Bos	A	P	69	10-6
1954	Bos	A	P	48	8-8
1955	Bos	A	P	43	5-5
1956	St.L	N	P	22	2-0
1956	Chi	A	P	29	3-1
1957	Chi	A	P	1	0-0
	BRTR			484	102-71

KINER, RALPH McPHERRAN
b.Oct.27,1922 Santa Rita,N.Mex.

Yr	Cl	Lea	Pos	G	Rec
1946	Pit	N	O	144	.247
1947	Pit	N	O	152	.313
1948	Pit	N	O	156	.265
1949	Pit	N	O	152	.310
1950	Pit	N	O	150	.272
1951	Pit	N	1-O	151	.309
1952	Pit	N	O	149	.244
1953	Pit	N	O	41	.270
1953	Chi	N	O	117	.283

(Continued)

Yr	Cl	Lea	Pos	G	Rec
1954	Chi	N	O	147	.285
1955	Cle	A	O	113	.243
	BRTR			1472	.279

KING, CHARLES FREDERICK
(Silver)
(Real name
Charles Frederick Koenig)
b.Jan.11,1868 St.Louis,Mo.
d.May 19,1938

Yr	Cl	Lea	Pos	G	Rec
1886	KC	N	P	7	1-3
1887	St.L	a	P	62	34-11
1888	St.L	a	P	66	44-21
1889	St.L	a	P	54	33-17
1890	Chi	p	P	57	33-20
1891	Pit	N	P	48	17-31
1892	NY	N	P	52	24-24
1893	NY	N	P	15	5-3
1893	Cin	N	P	13	7-6
1896	Was	N	P	16	10-6
1897	Was	N	P	18	9-9
	BRTR			408	217-151

KING, CHARLES GILBERT
b.Nov.10,1930 Paris,Tenn.

Yr	Cl	Lea	Pos	G	Rec
1954	Det	A	O	11	.214
1955	Det	A	O	7	.238
1956	Det	A	O	7	.222
1958	Chi	N	O	8	.250
1959	Chi	N	O	7	.000
1959	St.L	N	O	5	.429
	BRTR			45	.237

KING, CLYDE EDWARD
b.May 23,1925 Goldsboro,N.C.

Yr	Cl	Lea	Pos	G	Rec
1944	Bro	N	P	14	2-1
1945	Bro	N	P	43	5-5
1947	Bro	N	P	29	6-5
1948	Bro	N	P	9	0-1
1951	Bro	N	P	48	14-7
1952	Bro	N	P	23	2-0
1953	Cin	N	P	35	3-6
	BBTR			201	32-25

KING, EDWARD LEE
b.Mar.28,1894 New Britain,Conn.
d.Sept.7,1938

Yr	Cl	Lea	Pos	G	Rec
1916	Phi	A	O	42	.188
1919	Bos	N	O	2	.000
	BRTR			44	.186

KING, FREDERICK

Yr	Cl	Lea	Pos	G	Rec
1901	Mil	A	C	1	.500

KING, JAMES HUBERT
b.Aug.27,1932 Elkins,Ark.

Yr	Cl	Lea	Pos	G	Rec
1955	Chi	N	O	113	.256
1956	Chi	N	O	118	.249
1957	St.L	N	O	22	.314
1958	SF	N	O	34	.214
1961	Was	A	O	110	.270
1962	Was	A	O	132	.243
	BLTR			529	.254

KING, LEE
b.Dec.26,1894 Fairmont,W.Va.

Yr	Cl	Lea	Pos	G	Rec
1916	Pit	N	O	8	.111
1917	Pit	N	O	111	.249
1918	Pit	n	O	36	.232
1919	NY	N	O	21	.100
1920	NY	N	O	93	.276
1921	NY	N	O	39	.223
1921	Phi	N	O	64	.269
1922	Phi	N	O	19	.226
1922	NY	N	1-O	20	.176
	BRTR			411	.247

KING, LYNN PAUL (Dig)
b.Nov.28,1907 Villisca,Ia.

Yr	Cl	Lea	Pos	G	Rec
1935	St.L	N	O	8	.182
1936	St.L	N	O	78	.190
1939	St.L	N	O	89	.235
	BLTR			175	.208

KING, MARSHAL NEY
(Mart)
b.1849 Troy,N.Y.
d.Oct.19,1911

Yr	Cl	Lea	Pos	G	Rec
1871	Chi	n	C-S-O	20	NR
1872	Tro	n	O	2	.000
				22	NR

KING, NELSON JOSEPH
b.Mar.15,1928 Shenandoah,Pa.

Yr	Cl	Lea	Pos	G	Rec
1954	Pit	N	P	4	0-0
1955	Pit	N	P	17	1-3
1956	Pit	N	P	38	4-1
1957	Pit	N	P	36	2-1
	BRTR			95	7-5

KING, SAMUEL WARREN
b.Danvers,Mass.
d.Oct.28,1891

Yr	Cl	Lea	Pos	G	Rec
1883	Phi	N	C	1	.000
1884	Was	a	1	12	.174
				13	.174

KING, STEPHEN F.
b.May 17,1852 Peabody,Mass.
d.July 8,1895

Yr	Cl	Lea	Pos	G	Rec
1871	Tro	n	O	29	NR
1872	Tro	n	O	25	NR
1874	Phi	n	O	12	NR
				66	NR

KINGDON, WESTCOTT WILLIAM
b.July 4,1900 Los Angeles,Cal.

Yr	Cl	Lea	Pos	G	Rec
1932	Was	A	S-3	18	.324
	BRTR				

KINGMAN, HARRY LEES
b.Apr.3,1892 Pomona,Cal.

Yr	Cl	Lea	Pos	G	Rec
1914	NY	A	1	4	.000
	BLTL				

KINLOCK, WALTER
b.1878 St.Joseph,Mo.

Yr	Cl	Lea	Pos	G	Rec
1895	St.L	N	3	1	.333

KINNEY, WALTER WILLIAM
b.Sept.9,1894 Denison,Tex.

Yr	Cl	Lea	Pos	G	Rec
1918	Bos	A	P	6	0-0
1919	Phi	A	P	57	9-15
1920	Phi	A	P	13	2-4
1923	Phi	A	P	5	0-1
	BLTL			81	11-20

KINSELLA, EDWARD WILLIAM
(Rube)
b.Jan.15,1880 Bloomington,Ill.

Yr	Cl	Lea	Pos	G	Rec
1905	Pit	N	P	3	0-1
1910	St.L	A	P	10	1-3
	TR			13	1-4

KINSELLA, ROBERT FRANCIS
b.Jan.5,1899 Springfield,Ill.
d.Dec.30,1951

Yr	Cl	Lea	Pos	G	Rec
1919	NY	N	O	3	.222
1920	NY	N	O	1	.333
	BLTR			4	.250

KINSLER, ...
b.Staten Island,N.Y.

Yr	Cl	Lea	Pos	G	Rec
1893	NY	N	O	1	.000

KINSLOW, THOMAS F.
b.Jan.12,1866 Washington,D.C.
d.Feb.22,1901

Yr	Cl	Lea	Pos	G	Rec
1886	Was	N	C	3	.333
1887	Met	a	C	2	.000
1890	Bro	p	C	63	.277
1891	Bro	N	C	59	.238
1892	Bro	N	C	63	.309
1893	Bro	N	C	77	.259
1894	Bro	N	C	61	.298
1895	Pit	N	C	17	.230
1896	Lou	N	C	8	.280
1898	Was	N	C	3	.111
1898	St.L	N	C	14	.278
	TR			370	.271

KINZY, HARRY HERSEL
(Slim)
b.July 19,1910 Hallsville,Tex.

Yr	Cl	Lea	Pos	G	Rec
1934	Chi	A	P	13	0-1
	BRTR				

KIPP, FRED LEO
b.Oct.1,1931 Piqua,Kan.

Yr	Cl	Lea	Pos	G	Rec
1957	Bro	N	P	1	0-0
1958	LA	N	P	42	6-6
1959	LA	N	P	2	0-0
1960	NY	A	P	4	0-1
	BLTL			49	6-7

KIPPER, THORNTON JOHN
b.Sept.27,1928 Bagley,Wis.

Yr	Cl	Lea	Pos	G	Rec
1953	Phi	N	P	20	3-3
1954	Phi	N	P	11	0-0
1955	Phi	N	P	24	0-1
	BRTR			55	3-4

KIPPERT, EDWARD A.
b.Jan.3,1880 Detroit,Mich.

Yr	Cl	Lea	Pos	G	Rec
1914	Cin	N	O	2	.000
	BRTR				

KIRBY, JAMES HERSCHEL
b.May 5,1923 Nashville,Tenn.

Yr	Cl	Lea	Pos	G	Rec
1949	Chi	N	H	3	.500
	BRTR				

KIRBY. JOHN J.
b.Jan.13,1865 St.Louis,Mo.
d.Oct.6,1931

Yr	Cl	Lea	Pos	G	Rec
1884	KC	U	P-O	2	{0-1 / .167
1885	St.L	N	P	14	5-8
1886	St.L	N	P	41	12-25
1887	Ind	N	P	8	1-7
1887	Cle	a	P	5	0-5
1888	KC	a	P	6	1-5
	TR			76	{19-51 / .108

KIRBY. LARUE V.
b.Dec.30,1889 Eureka,Mich.

Yr	Cl	Lea	Pos	G	Rec
1912	NY	N	P	3	1-0
1914	St.L	F	O	51	.253
1915	St.L	F	O	59	.212
	BRTR			113	{1-0 / .233

KIRCHER, MICHAEL ANDREW
b.Sept.30,1897 Rochester,N.Y.

Yr	Cl	Lea	Pos	G	Rec
1919	Phi	A	P	2	0-0
1920	St.L	N	P	9	2-1
1921	St.L	N	P	3	0-1
	BRTL			14	2-2

KIRK, THOMAS DANIEL
b.Sept.27,1927 Philadelphia,Pa.

Yr	Cl	Lea	Pos	G	Rec
1947	Phi	A	H	1	.000
	BLTL				

KIRK, WILLIAM PARTLEMORE
b.July 19,1936 Coatesville,Pa.

Yr	Cl	Lea	Pos	G	Rec
1961	KC	A	P	1	0-0
	BLTL				

KIRKE, JAY
b.June 16,1888 Fleischmann's,N.Y.

Yr	Cl	Lea	Pos	G	Rec
1910	Det	A	2	8	.192
1911	Bos	N	O	20	.360
1912	Bos	N	O	103	.320
1913	Bos	N	O	18	.237
1914	Cle	A	O	67	.273
1915	Cle	A	1	87	.310
1918	NY	N	1	17	.250
	BLTR			320	.301

KIRKLAND, WILLIE CHARLES
b.Feb.17,1934 Siluria,Ala.

Yr	Cl	Lea	Pos	G	Rec
1958	SF	N	O	122	.258
1959	SF	N	O	126	.272

(Continued)

Yr	Cl	Lea	Pos	G	Rec
1960	SF	N	O	146	.252
1961	Cle	A	O	146	.259
1962	Cle	A	O	137	.200
	BLTR			677	.250

KIRKPATRICK, EDGAR LEON
b.Oct.8,1944 Spokane,Wash.

Yr	Cl	Lea	Pos	G	Rec
1962	LA	A	C	3	.000
	BLTR				

KIRKPATRICK, ENOS CLAIRE
b.Dec.9,1889 Pittsburgh,Pa.

Yr	Cl	Lea	Pos	G	Rec
1912	Bro	N	3	32	.191
1913	Bro	N	1	48	.247
1914	Bal	F	3	55	.259
1915	Bal	F	2-3	60	.241
	BRTR			195	.239

KIRRENE, JOSEPH JOHN
b.Oct.4,1931 San Francisco,Cal.

Yr	Cl	Lea	Pos	G	Rec
1950	Chi	A	3	1	.250
1954	Chi	A	3	9	.304
	BRTR			10	.296

KIRSCH, HARRY
b.1891 Pittsburgh,Pa.

Yr	Cl	Lea	Pos	G	Rec
1910	Cle	A	P	2	0-0
	TR				

KISH, ERNEST ALEXANDER
b.Feb.6,1919 Washington,D.C.

Yr	Cl	Lea	Pos	G	Rec
1945	Phi	A	O	43	.245
	BLTR				

KISLEAUSKAS, EDWARD WILLIAM
(Played under name of
Edward William Cole)

KISSINGER, CHARLES SAMUEL
(Rube)
b.Dec.13,1876 Adrian,Mich.
d.July 14,1941

Yr	Cl	Lea	Pos	G	Rec
1902	Det	A	P	5	1-4
1903	Det	A	P	16	7-9
	BRTR			21	8-13

KISSINGER, WILLIAM FRANCIS
(Shang)
b.Aug.15.1871 Dayton,Ky.
d.Apr.20.1929

Yr	Cl	Lea	Pos	G	Rec
1895	Bal	N	P	6	1-1
1895	St.L	N	P	23	5-10
1896	St.L	N	P	22	2-13
1897	St.L	N	P	11	0-4
	BRTR			62	8-28

KITSON. FRANK R.
b.Apr.11,1872 Hopkins,Mich.
d.Apr.14,1930

Yr	Cl	Lea	Pos	G	Rec
1898	Bal	N	P	23	8-5
1899	Bal	N	P	40	20-16
1900	Bro	N	P	33	14-13
1901	Bro	N	P	32	19-11
1902	Bro	N	P	31	19-12
1903	Det	A	P	36	15-15
1904	Det	A	P	27	10-12
1905	Det	A	P	33	8-17
1906	Was	A	P	33	6-14
1907	Was	A	P	5	0-1
1907	NY	A	P	11	3-2
	BRTR			304	122-118

KITSOS, CHRISTOPHER ANESTOS
b.Feb.2,1929 New York,N.Y.

Yr	Cl	Lea	Pos	G	Rec
1954	Chi	N	S	1	.000
	BBTR				

KITTREDGE, MALACHI J. (Jedediah)
b.Oct.12,1869 Clinton,Mass.
d.Sept.12,1927

Yr	Cl	Lea	Pos	G	Rec
1890	Chi	N	C	96	.201

(Continued)

Yr	Cl	Lea	Pos	G	Rec
1891	Chi	N	C	70	.202
1892	Chi	N	C	66	.187
1893	Chi	N	C	67	.245
1894	Chi	N	C	50	.317
1895	Chi	N	C	58	.244
1896	Chi	N	C	61	.223
1897	Chi	N	C	77	.198
1898	Lou	N	C	88	.250
1899	Lou	N	C	46	.174
1899	Was	N	C	41	.158
1901	Bos	N	C	113	.247
1902	Bos	N	C	72	.233
1903	Bos	N	C	30	.212
1903	Was	A	C	59	.218
1904	Was	A	M-C	80	.242
1905	Was	A	C	77	.163
1906	Was	A	C	22	.191
1906	Cle	A	C	5	.100
	BRTR			1178	.220

KLAERNER, HUGO EMIL
b.Oct.15,1908 Fredericksburg,Tex.

Yr	Cl	Lea	Pos	G	Rec
1934	Chi	A	P	3	0-2
	BRTR				

KLAUS, WILLIAM JOSEPH
b.Dec.9,1928 Spring Grove,Ill.

Yr	Cl	Lea	Pos	G	Rec
1952	Bos	N	S	7	.000
1953	Mil	N	H	2	.000
1955	Bos	A	S-3	135	.283
1956	Bos	A	S-3	135	.271
1957	Bos	A	S	127	.252
1958	Bos	A	S	61	.159
1959	Bal	A	2-S-3	104	.249
1960	Bal	A	2-S-3	46	.209
1961	Was	A	2-S-3-O	91	.227
1962	Phi	N	2-S-3	102	.206
	BRTR			810	.251

KLAWITTER, ALBERT C.

Yr	Cl	Lea	Pos	G	Rec
1909	NY	N	P	6	1-1
1910	NY	N	P	1	0-0
1913	Det	A	P	6	1-2
	BRTR			13	2-3

KLEE, OLLIE CHESTER
b.May 20,1900 Dayton,O.

Yr	Cl	Lea	Pos	G	Rec
1925	Cin	N	O	3	.000
	BLTL				

KLEIN, CHARLES HERBERT
(Chuck)
b.Oct.7,1905 Indianapolis,Ind.
d.Mar.28,1958

Yr	Cl	Lea	Pos	G	Rec
1928	Phi	N	O	64	.360
1929	Phi	N	O	149	.356
1930	Phi	N	O	156	.386
1931	Phi	N	O	148	.337
1932	Phi	N	O	154	.348
1933	Phi	N	O	152	.368
1934	Chi	N	O	115	.301
1935	Chi	N	O	119	.293
1936	Chi	N	O	29	.294
1936	Phi	N	O	117	.309
1937	Phi	N	O	115	.325
1938	Phi	N	O	129	.247
1939	Phi	N	O	25	.191
1939	Pit	N	O	85	.300
1940	Phi	N	O	116	.218
1941	Phi	N	O	50	.123
1942	Phi	N	H	14	.071
1943	Phi	N	H	12	.100
1944	Phi	N	O	4	.143
	BLTR			1753	.320

KLEIN, LOUIS FRANK
b.Oct.22,1918 New Orleans,La.

Yr	Cl	Lea	Pos	G	Rec
1943	St.L	N	2-S	154	.287
1945	St.L	N	2-S-3-O	19	.228
1946	St.L	N	2	23	.194
1949	St.L	N	2-S-3	58	.219
1951	Cle	A	H	2	.000
1951	Phi	A	2	49	.229
	BRTR			305	.259

Non-playing manager Chicago (N) 1961

KLEINE, HAROLD JOHN
b.June 8,1923 St.Louis,Mo.
d.Dec.10,1957

Yr	Cl	Lea	Pos	G	Rec
1944	Cle	A	P	14	1-2
1945	Cle	A	P	3	0-0
	BLTL			17	1-2

KLEINHANS, THEODORE OTTO
b.Apr.8,1904 Deer Park,Wis.

Yr	Cl	Lea	Pos	G	Rec
1934	Phi	N	P	5	0-0
1934	Cin	N	P	25	2-6
1936	NY	A	P	19	1-1
1937	Cin	N	P	7	1-2
1938	Cin	N	P	1	0-0
	BRTL			57	4-9

KLEINKE, NORBERT GEORGE
(Nub)
b.May 19,1912 Fond du Lac,Wis.
d.Mar.16,1950

Yr	Cl	Lea	Pos	G	Rec
1935	St.L	N	P	4	0-0
1937	St.L	N	P	5	1-1
	BRTR			9	1-1

KLEINOW, JOHN PETER (Red)
b.July 20,1879 Milwaukee,Wis.
d.Oct.9,1929

Yr	Cl	Lea	Pos	G	Rec
1904	NY	A	C	67	.200
1905	NY	A	C	88	.221
1906	NY	A	C	96	.220
1907	NY	A	C	90	.264
1908	NY	A	C	96	.168
1909	NY	A	C	78	.228
1910	NY	A	C	5	.455
1910	Bos	A	C	51	.149
1911	Bos	A	C	8	.214
1911	Phi	N	C	4	.125
	BRTR			583	.212

KLEPFER, EDWARD LLOYD
(Big Ed)
b.Mar.17,1888 Warren,Pa.
d.Aug.9,1950

Yr	Cl	Lea	Pos	G	Rec
1911	NY	A	P	2	0-0
1913	NY	A	P	8	0-1
1915	Chi	A	P	2	0-0
1915	Cle	A	P	9	2-6
1916	Cle	A	P	31	6-7
1917	Cle	A	P	41	14-4
1919	Cle	A	P	5	0-0
	BRTR			98	22-18

KLIEMAN, EDWARD FREDERICK
(Specs)
b.Mar.21,1918 Norwood,O.

Yr	Cl	Lea	Pos	G	Rec
1943	Cle	A	P	1	0-1
1944	Cle	A	P	47	11-13
1945	Cle	A	P	38	5-8
1946	Cle	A	P	9	0-0
1947	Cle	A	P	58	5-4
1948	Cle	A	P	44	3-2
1949	Was	A	P	2	0-0
1949	Chi	A	P	18	2-0
1950	Phi	A	P	5	0-0
	BRTR			222	26-28

KLIMCHOCK, LOUIS STEPHEN
b.Oct.15,1939 Hostetter,Pa.

Yr	Cl	Lea	Pos	G	Rec
1958	KC	A	2	2	.200
1959	KC	A	2	17	.273
1960	KC	A	2	10	.300
1961	KC	A	1-2-S-O	57	.215
1962	Mil	N	H	8	.000
	BLTR			94	.228

KLINE, JOHN ROBERT
b.Jan.27,1929 St.Petersburg,Fla.

Yr	Cl	Lea	Pos	G	Rec
1955	Was	A	P-2-S-3	77	0-0
	BRTR				.221

KLINE, ROBERT GEORGE (Junior)
b.Dec.1,1909 Enterprise,O.

Yr	Cl	Lea	Pos	G	Rec
1930	Bos	A	P	1	0-0
1931	Bos	A	P	28	5-5
1932	Bos	A	P	47	11-13
1933	Bos	A	P	46	7-8
1934	Phi	A	P	20	6-2
1934	Was	A	P	6	1-0
	BRTR			148	30-28

KLINE, RONALD LEE
b.Mar.9,1932 Callery,Pa.

Yr	Cl	Lea	Pos	G	Rec
1952	Pit	N	P	27	0-7
1955	Pit	N	P-3	37	6-13 .132
1956	Pit	N	P	44	14-18
1957	Pit	N	P	40	9-16
1958	Pit	N	P	33	13-16
1959	Pit	N	P	38	11-13
1960	St.L	N	P	34	4-9
1961	LA	A	P	26	3-6
1961	Det	A	P	10	5-3
1962	Det	A	P	36	3-6
	BRTR			325	68-107 .097

KLING, JOHN G. (Noisy)
b.Nov.13,1875 Kansas City,Mo.
d.Jan.31,1947

Yr	Cl	Lea	Pos	G	Rec
1900	Chi	N	C	15	.294
1901	Chi	N	C	70	.266
1902	Chi	N	C-S	113	.286
1903	Chi	N	C	132	.297
1904	Chi	N	C	120	.243
1905	Chi	N	C	110	.218
1906	Chi	N	C	99	.312
1907	Chi	N	C	100	.284
1908	Chi	N	C	125	.276
1910	Chi	N	C	86	.269
1911	Chi	N	C	27	.175
1911	Bos	N	C	75	.224
1912	Bos	N	M-C	81	.317
1913	Cin	N	C	80	.273
	BRTR			1233	.271

KLING RUDOLPH A.
b.Mar.23,1875 St.Louis,Mo.
d.Mar.14,1937

Yr	Cl	Lea	Pos	G	Rec
1902	St.L	N	S	4	.200
	TR				

KLING, WILLIAM
b.Jan.14,1867 Kansas City,Mo.
d.Aug.25,1934

Yr	Cl	Lea	Pos	G	Rec
1891	Phi	N	P	13	4-3
1892	Bal	N	P	2	0-1
1895	Lou	N	P	1	0-0
	BLTR			16	4-4

KLINGER, JOSEPH JOHN
b.Aug.2,1902 Canonsburg,Pa.
d.July 31,1960 Canonsburg,Pa

Yr	Cl	Lea	Pos	G	Rec
1927	NY	N	O	3	.400
1930	Chi	A	C-1	4	.375
	BRTR			7	.389

KLINGER, ROBERT HAROLD
b.June 4,1908 Allenton,Mo.

Yr	Cl	Lea	Pos	G	Rec
1938	Pit	N	P	28	12-5
1939	Pit	N	P	37	14-17
1940	Pit	N	P	39	8-13
1941	Pit	N	P	35	9-4
1942	Pit	N	P	37	8-11
1943	Pit	N	P	33	11-8
1946	Bos	A	P	28	3-2
1947	Bos	A	P	28	1-1
	BRTR			265	66-61

KLIPPSTEIN, JOHN CALVIN
b.Oct.17,1927 Washington,D.C.

Yr	Cl	Lea	Pos	G	Rec
1950	Chi	N	P	35	2-9
1951	Chi	N	P	35	6-6
1952	Chi	N	P	41	9-14
1953	Chi	N	P	48	10-11
1954	Chi	N	P	36	4-11
1955	Cin	N	P	39	9-10
1956	Cin	N	P	37	12-11
1957	Cin	N	P	46	8-11
1958	Cin	N	P	12	3-2
1958	LA	N	P	45	3-5

(Continued)

Yr	Cl	Lea	Pos	G	Rec
1959	LA	N	P	28	4-0
1960	Cle	A	P	49	5-5
1961	Was	A	P	42	2-2
1962	Cin	N	P	40	7-6
		BRTR		533	84-103

KLOBEDANZ, FREDERICK A. (Duke)
b.June 13,1873 Waterbury,Conn.

Yr	Cl	Lea	Pos	G	Rec
1896	Bos	N	P	11	6-4
1897	Bos	N	P	38	25-8
1898	Bos	N	P	32	19-10
1899	Bos	N	P	5	1-4
1902	Bos	N	P	1	1-0
		BLTL		87	52-26

KLOPP, STANLEY HAROLD
b.Dec.22,1913 Robesonia,Pa.

Yr	Cl	Lea	Pos	G	Rec
1944	Bos	N	P	24	1-2
		BRTR			

KLOZA, JOHN CLARENCE (Nap)
b.Nov.2,1904 Milwaukee,Wis.

Yr	Cl	Lea	Pos	G	Rec
1931	St.L	A	O	3	.143
1932	St.L	A	O	19	.154
		BRTR		22	.150

KLUGMAN, JOSEPH
b.Mar.16,1895 St.Louis,Mo.
d.July 18,1951.

Yr	Cl	Lea	Pos	G	Rec
1921	Chi	N	2	6	.286
1922	Chi	N	2	7	.250
1924	Bro	N	2-S	31	.165
1925	Cle	A	1-2-3	38	.333
		BRTR		77	.251

KLUMPP, ELMER EDWARD
b.Aug.26,1906 St.Louis,Mo.

Yr	Cl	Lea	Pos	G	Rec
1934	Was	A	C	12	.133
1937	Bro	N	C	5	.091
		BRTR		17	.115

KLUSMAN, WILLIAM F.
b.Mar.24,1865 Cincinnati,O.
d.June 24,1907

Yr	Cl	Lea	Pos	G	Rec
1888	Bos	N	2	28	.168
1890	St.L	a	1	15	.275
		BRTR		43	.206

KLUSZEWSKI, THEODORE BERNARD
b.Sept.10,1924 Argo,Ill.

Yr	Cl	Lea	Pos	G	Rec
1947	Cin	N	1	9	.100
1948	Cin	N	1	113	.275
1949	Cin	N	1	136	.309
1950	Cin	N	1	134	.307
1951	Cin	N	1	154	.259
1952	Cin	N	1	135	.320
1953	Cin	N	1	149	.316
1954	Cin	N	1	149	.326
1955	Cin	N	1	153	.314
1956	Cin	N	1	138	.302
1957	Cin	N	1	69	.268
1958	Pit	N	1	100	.292
1959	Pit	N	1	60	.262
1959	Chi	A	1	31	.297
1960	Chi	A	1	81	.293
1961	LA	A	1	107	.243
		BLTL		1718	.298

KLUTTZ, CLYDE FRANKLIN
b.Dec.12,1918 Salisbury,N.C.

Yr	Cl	Lea	Pos	G	Rec
1942	Bos	N	C	72	.267
1943	Bos	N	C	66	.246
1944	Bos	N	C	81	.279
1945	Bos	N	C	25	.296
1945	NY	N	C	73	.279
1946	NY	N	C	5	.375
1946	St.L	N	C	52	.265
1947	Pit	N	C	73	.302
1948	Pit	N	C	94	.221
1951	St.L	A	C	4	.500
1951	Was	A	C	53	.308
1952	Was	A	C	58	.229
		BRTR		656	.268

KNABE, FRANZ OTTO (Dutch)
b.June 12,1884 Carrick,Pa.

Yr	Cl	Lea	Pos	G	Rec
1905	Pit	N	3	3	.300
1907	Phi	N	2	126	.255
1908	Phi	N	2	151	.218
1909	Phi	N	2	111	.234
1910	Phi	N	2	136	.261
1911	Phi	N	2	142	.237
1912	Phi	N	2	126	.282
1913	Phi	N	2	148	.263
1914	Bal	F	M-2	146	.228
1915	Bal	F	M-2	100	.251
1916	Pit	N	2	28	.193
1916	Chi	N	2	51	.274
		BRTR		1268	.247

KNAUPP, HENRY ANTONE (Cotton)
b.Aug.13,1889 San Antonio,Tex.

Yr	Cl	Lea	Pos	G	Rec
1910	Cle	A	S	18	.236
1911	Cle	A	S	13	.102
		BRTR		31	.184

KNAUSS, FRANK H.
b.1868 Cleveland,O.

Yr	Cl	Lea	Pos	G	Rec
1890	Col	a	P	33	21-11
1891	Cle	N	P	3	0-3
1892	Cin	N	P	1	0-1
1894	Cle	N	P	2	1-1
1895	NY	N	P	1	0-0
		BLTL		40	22-16

KNEISCH, RUDOLPH FRANK
b.Apr.10,1900 Baltimore,Md.

Yr	Cl	Lea	Pos	G	Rec
1926	Det	A	P	2	0-1
		BRTL			

KNELL, PHILIP H.
b.1865 Mill Valley,Cal.

Yr	Cl	Lea	Pos	G	Rec
1888	Pit	N	P	4	1-2
1890	Phi	p	P	35	20-11
1891	Col	a	P	66	27-27
1892	Was	N	P	15	9-10
1892	Phi	N	P	18	4-6
1894	Pit	N	P	4	0-0
1894	Lou	N	P	30	7-22
1895	Lou	N	P	14	0-6
1895	Cle	N	P	14	5-4
		BRTL		200	73-88

KNELME, WILLIAM J.
(Played under name of William J. Kuehne)

KNEPPER, CHARLES
b.Anderson,Ind.

Yr	Cl	Lea	Pos	G	Rec
1899	Cle	N	P	27	4-22

KNERR, WALLACE LUTHER (Lou)
b.Aug.21,1921 Lancaster,Pa.

Yr	Cl	Lea	Pos	G	Rec
1945	Phi	A	P	28	5-11
1946	Phi	A	P	30	3-16
1947	Was	A	P	6	0-0
		BRTR		64	8-27

KNETZER, ELMER ELLSWORTH (Baron)
b.July 22,1887 Carrick,Pa.

Yr	Cl	Lea	Pos	G	Rec
1909	Bro	N	P	5	1-3
1910	Bro	N	P	20	7-5
1911	Bro	N	P	35	11-12
1912	Bro	N	P	33	7-9
1914	Pit	F	P	34	20-12
1915	Pit	F	P	41	18-14
1916	Bos	N	P	2	0-2
1916	Cin	N	P	37	5-12
1917	Cin	N	P	11	0-0
		BRTR		218	69-69

KNICKERBOCKER AUSTIN JAY
b.Oct.15,1918 Bangall,N.Y.

Yr	Cl	Lea	Pos	G	Rec
1947	Phi	A	O	21	.250
		BRTR			

KNICKERBOCKER, WILLIAM HART
b.Dec.29,1911 Los Angeles,Cal.

Yr	Cl	Lea	Pos	G	Rec
1933	Cle	A	S	80	.226
1934	Cle	A	S	146	.317
1935	Cle	A	S	132	.298
1936	Cle	A	S	155	.294
1937	St.L	A	S	121	.261

Yr	Cl	Lea	Pos	G	Rec
1938	NY	A	2	46	.250
1939	NY	A	2-S	6	.154
1940	NY	A	S-3	45	.242
1941	Chi	A	2	89	.245
1942	Phi	A	2-S	87	.253
		BRTR		907	.277

KNIGHT, ALONZO P. (Lon)
b.June 16,1853 Philadelphia,Pa.
d.Apr.23,1932

Yr	Cl	Lea	Pos	G	Rec
1875	Ath	n	P	13	6-5
1876	Ath	N	P-1-O	55	10-23 .248
1880	Wor	N	O	48	.242
1881	Det	N	1-2-O	83	.270
1882	Det	N	1-O	83	.204
1883	Ath	a	M-2-3-O	97	.237
1884	Ath	a	P-O	110	0-1 .275
1885	Ath	a	M-O	28	.186
1885	Pro	N	P-O	25	0-0 .160
		BRTR		542	16-29 .246

KNIGHT, ELMA RUSSELL (Jack)
b.Jan.12,1895 Pittsboro,Miss.

Yr	Cl	Lea	Pos	G	Rec
1922	St.L	N	P	1	0-0
1925	Phi	N	P	40	7-6
1926	Phi	N	P	40	3-12
1927	Bos	N	P	3	0-0
		BLTR		84	10-18

KNIGHT, GEORGE HENRY
b.Nov.24,1855 Lakeville,Conn.
d.Oct.4,1912

Yr	Cl	Lea	Pos	G	Rec
1875	NH	n	P	1	1-0

KNIGHT, JOHN WESLEY (Schoolboy)
b.Oct.6,1886 Philadelphia,Pa.

Yr	Cl	Lea	Pos	G	Rec
1905	Phi	A	S	88	.234
1906	Phi	A	3	74	.194
1907	Phi	A	3	40	.212
1907	Bos	A	3	98	.215
1909	NY	A	1-2-S	116	.236
1910	NY	A	1-S	117	.312
1911	NY	A	1-2-S	132	.268
1912	Was	A	2	32	.161
1913	NY	A	1-2	70	.236
		BRTR		767	.239

KNIGHT, JONAS WILLIAM (Quiet Joe)
b.Sept.28,1858 Ft.Stanley,Ont.,Canada.
d.Oct.18,1938

Yr	Cl	Lea	Pos	G	Rec
1884	Phi	N	P	6	2-4
1890	Cin	N	O	127	.312
		BLTL		133	2-4 .307

KNISELY, PETER C.
b.Aug.11,1887 Waynesboro,Pa.
d.July 1,1948

Yr	Cl	Lea	Pos	G	Rec
1912	Cin	N	O	21	.328
1913	Chi	N	O	2	.000
1914	Chi	N	O	37	.130
1915	Chi	N	O	64	.246
		BRTR		124	.235

KNODE, KENNETH THOMSON (Mike)
b.Nov.8,1895 Westminster,Md.

Yr	Cl	Lea	Pos	G	Rec
1920	St.L	N	O	42	.231
		BRTR			

KNODE, ROBERT TROXELL (Ray)
b.Jan.28,1901 Westminster,Md.

Yr	Cl	Lea	Pos	G	Rec
1923	Cle	A	1	22	.289
1924	Cle	A	1	11	.243
1925	Cle	A	1	45	.250
1926	Cle	A	1	31	.333
		BLTL		109	.266

KNOLL, CHARLES ELMER (Punch)
b.Oct.7,1881 Evansville,Ind.
d.Feb.7,1960

Yr	Cl	Lea	Pos	G	Rec
1905	Was	A	O	79	.213
	BRTR				

KNOLLS, OSCAR EDWARD (Hub)
b.Dec.18,1883 Medaryville,Ind.
d.July 1,1946

Yr	Cl	Lea	Pos	G	Rec
1906	Bro	N	P	2	0-0
	TR				

KNOTHE, GEORGE BERTRAM
b.Jan.12,1900 Bayonne,N.J.

Yr	Cl	Lea	Pos	G	Rec
1932	Phi	N	2	6	.083
	BRTR				

KNOTHE, WILFRED EDGAR (Fritz)
b.May 1,1904 Passaic,N.J.

Yr	Cl	Lea	Pos	G	Rec
1932	Bos	N	3	89	.238
1933	Bos	N	S-3	44	.228
1933	Phi	N	2-3	41	.150
	BRTR			174	.220

KNOTT, JOHN HENRY
b.Mar.2,1907 Dallas,Tex.

Yr	Cl	Lea	Pos	G	Rec
1933	St.L	A	P	20	1-8
1934	St.L	A	P	45	10-3
1935	St.L	A	P	48	11-8
1936	St.L	A	P	47	9-17
1937	St.L	A	P	38	8-18
1938	St.L	A	P	7	1-2
1938	Chi	A	P	20	5-10
1939	Chi	A	P	25	11-6
1940	Chi	A	P	25	11-9
1941	Phi	A	P	27	13-11
1942	Phi	A	P	20	2-10
1946	Phi	A	P	3	0-1
	BRTR			325	82-103

KNOTTS, JOSEPH
b.Biddeford,Me.

Yr	Cl	Lea	Pos	G	Rec
1907	Bos	N	C	3	.000
	TR				

KNOUFF, EDWARD
b.1867 Philadelphia,Pa.
d.Sept.14,1900

Yr	Cl	Lea	Pos	G	Rec
1885	Ath	a	P-O	14	7-6 .204
1886	Bal	a	P	1	0-1
1887	Bal	a	P	8	0-6
1887	St.L	a	P-O	16	4-3 .190
1888	St.L	a	P	9	5-4
1888	Cle	a	P-2	10	6-4 .143
1889	Ath	a	P	3	2-0
	BRTR			61	24-24 .194

KNOWDELL, JACOB AUGUSTUS
b.Brooklyn,N.Y.

Yr	Cl	Lea	Pos	G	Rec
1874	Atl	n	C-O	23	NR
1875	Atl	n	C-S-O	42	NR
1878	Mil	N	C-O	4	.000
				69	NR

KNOWLES, JAMES (Darby)
b.1859 Toronto,Ont.,Canada.
d.Mar.1904

Yr	Cl	Lea	Pos	G	Rec
1884	Pit	a	1	46	.228
1884	Bro	a	1-3	41	.237
1886	Was	N	2-3	115	.212
1887	Met	a	3	16	.262
1890	Roc	a	3	124	.281
1892	NY	N	3	15	.169
				357	.240

KNOWLSON, THOMAS H.
b.1895 Ridgway,Pa.

Yr	Cl	Lea	Pos	G	Rec
1915	Phi	A	P	18	4-7
	BBTR				

KNOWLTON, WILLIAM YOUNG
b.Aug.18,1892 Philadelphia,Pa.
d.Feb.25,1944

Yr	Cl	Lea	Pos	G	Rec
1920	Phi	A	P	1	0-1
	BRTR				

KNOX, ANDREW JACKSON (Dasher)
b.Jan.5,1864 Philadelphia,Pa.
d.Sept.14,1940

Yr	Cl	Lea	Pos	G	Rec
1890	Ath	a	1	21	.250
	BRTR				

KNOX, CLIFFORD H. (Bud)
b.Jan.7,1902 Ft.Dodge,Ia.

Yr	Cl	Lea	Pos	G	Rec
1924	Pit	N	C	6	.222
	BBTR				

KOBACK, NICHOLAS NICHOLIA
b.July 19,1935 Hartford,Conn.

Yr	Cl	Lea	Pos	G	Rec
1953	Pit	N	C	7	.125
1954	Pit	N	C	4	.000
1955	Pit	N	C	5	.286
	BRTR			16	.121

KOCH, BARNEY
b.Mar.23,1923 Campbell,Neb.

Yr	Cl	Lea	Pos	G	Rec
1944	Bro	N	2-S	33	.219
	BRTR				

KOCHER, BRADLEY WILSON
b.Jan.16,1888 White Haven,Pa.

Yr	Cl	Lea	Pos	G	Rec
1912	Det	A	C	24	.206
1915	NY	N	C	4	.455
1916	NY	N	C	34	.108
	BRTR			62	.179

KOECHER, RICHARD FINLAY (Highpockets)
b.Mar.30,1926 Philadelphia,Pa.

Yr	Cl	Lea	Pos	G	Rec
1946	Phi	N	P	1	0-1
1947	Phi	N	P	3	0-2
1948	Phi	N	P	3	0-1
	BLTL			7	0-4

KOEHLER, BERNARD JAMES (Ben)
b.Jan.26,1877 Schoerndorn,Germany
d.May 21,1961

Yr	Cl	Lea	Pos	G	Rec
1905	St.L	A	O	142	.237
1906	St.L	A	O	66	.220
	BRTR			208	.233

KOEHLER, HORACE LEVERING (Pip)
b.Jan.16,1902 Gilbert,Pa.

Yr	Cl	Lea	Pos	G	Rec
1925	NY	N	O	12	.000
	BRTR				

KOENECKE, LEONARD GEORGE
b.Jan.18,1906 Baraboo,Wis.
d.Sept.17,1935

Yr	Cl	Lea	Pos	G	Rec
1932	NY	N	O	42	.255
1934	Bro	N	O	123	.320
1935	Bro	N	O	100	.283
	BLTR			265	.297

KOENIG, CHARLES FREDERICK
(Played under name of
Charles Frederick King)

KOENIG, MARK ANTHONY
b.July 19,1902 San Francisco,Cal.

Yr	Cl	Lea	Pos	G	Rec
1925	NY	A	S	28	.205
1926	NY	A	S	147	.271
1927	NY	A	S	123	.285
1928	NY	A	S	132	.319
1929	NY	A	S-3	116	.292
1930	NY	A	S	21	.243
1930	Det	A	P-S	76	0-1 .236
1931	Det	A	P-2-S	106	0-0 .253
1932	Chi	N	S	33	.353
1933	Chi	N	2-S-3	80	.284
1934	Cin	N	1-2-S-3	151	.272
1935	NY	N	2-S-3	107	.283
1936	NY	N	S	42	.276
	BBTR			1162	0-1 .279

KOENIGSMARK, WILLIS T.
b.1886

Yr	Cl	Lea	Pos	G	Rec
1919	St.L	N	P	1	0-0
	BRTR				

KOESTNER, ELMER JOSEPH (Bob)
b.Nov.30,1885 Piper City,Ill.
d.Oct.27,1959

Yr	Cl	Lea	Pos	G	Rec
1910	Cle	A	P	27	5-10
1914	Chi	N	P	4	0-0
1914	Cin	N	P	5	0-0
	BRTR			36	5-10

KOHLER, HENRY
b.Baltimore,Md.

Yr	Cl	Lea	Pos	G	Rec
1871	Kek	n	1-3	3	.167
1873	Mar	n	3	6	NR
1874	Bal	n	C-1	5	NR
				14	NR

KOHLMAN, JOSEPH JAMES (Blackie)
b.Jan.28,1913 Philadelphia,Pa.

Yr	Cl	Lea	Pos	G	Rec
1937	Was	A	P	2	1-0
1938	Was	A	P	7	0-0
	BRTR			9	1-0

KOKOS, RICHARD JEROME
(Real name
Richard Jerome Kokoszka)
b.Feb.28,1928 Chicago,Ill.

Yr	Cl	Lea	Pos	G	Rec
1948	St.L	A	O	71	.298
1949	St.L	A	O	143	.261
1950	St.L	A	O	143	.261
1953	St.L	A	O	107	.241
1954	Bal	A	O	11	.200
	BLTL			475	.263

KOKOSZKA, RICHARD JEROME
(Played under name of
Richard Jerome Kokos)

KOLB, GARY ALAN
b.Mar.13,1940 Rock Falls, Ill.

Yr	Cl	Lea	Pos	G	Rec
1960	St.L	N	O	9	.000
1962	St.L	N	O	6	.357
	BLTR			15	.294

KOLB, EDWARD WILLIAM
b.July 20,1880 Cincinnati,O.

Yr	Cl	Lea	Pos	G	Rec
1899	Cle	N	P	1	0-1
	BRTR				

KOLLONIGE, JOSEPH EDWARD
(Played under name of
Joseph Edward Collins)

KOLLOWAY, DONALD MARTIN
b.Aug.4,1918 Posen,Ill.

Yr	Cl	Lea	Pos	G	Rec
1940	Chi	A	2	10	.225
1941	Chi	A	1-2	71	.271
1942	Chi	A	1-2	147	.273
1943	Chi	A	2	85	.216
1946	Chi	A	2-3	123	.280
1947	Chi	A	1-2-3	124	.278
1948	Chi	A	2-3	119	.273
1949	Chi	A	3	4	.000
1949	Det	A	1-2-3	126	.294
1950	Det	A	1-2	125	.289
1951	Det	A	1	78	.255
1952	Det	A	1-2	65	.243
1953	Phi	A	3	2	.000
	BRTR			1079	.271

KOLP, RAYMOND CARL (Jockey)
b.Oct.1,1899 New Berlin,O.

Yr	Cl	Lea	Pos	G	Rec
1921	St.L	A	P	39	8-7
1922	St.L	A	P	32	14-4
1923	St.L	A	P	34	5-12
1924	St.L	A	P	25	5-7
1927	Cin	N	P	24	3-3
1928	Cin	N	P	44	13-10

(Continued)

Yr	Cl	Lea	Pos	G	Rec
1929	Cin	N	P	30	8-10
1930	Cin	N	P	37	7-12
1931	Cin	N	P	30	4-9
1932	Cin	N	P	32	6-10
1933	Cin	N	P	30	6-9
1934	Cin	N	P	28	0-2
		BRTR		385	79-95

KOLSETH, KARL DICKEY
b.Dec.25,1892 Somerville,Mass.
d.May 3,1956

Yr	Cl	Lea	Pos	G	Rec
1915	Bal	F	1	6	.217
		BLTR			

KOLSTAD, HAROLD EVERETTE
b.June 1,1935 Rice Lake, Wis.

Yr	Cl	Lea	Pos	G	Rec
1962	Bos	A	P	27	0-2
		BRTR			

KOMMERS, FREDERICK RAYMOND
b.Mar.31,1886 Chicago,Ill.
d.June 14,1943

Yr	Cl	Lea	Pos	G	Rec
1913	Pit	N	O	40	.232
1914	St.L	F	O	75	.308
1914	Bal	F	O	17	.220
		BLTR		132	.271

KONETCHY, EDWARD JOSEPH
(Big Ed)
b.Sept.3,1885 LaCrosse,Wis.
d.May 27,1947

Yr	Cl	Lea	Pos	G	Rec
1907	St.L	N	1	91	.251
1908	St.L	N	1	154	.248
1909	St.L	N	1	152	.286
1910	St.L	N	P-1	144	0-0 / .302
1911	St.L	N	1	158	.289
1912	St.L	N	1	143	.314
1913	St.L	N	P-1	140	1-0 / .276
1914	Pit	N	1	154	.249
1915	Pit	F	1	152	.310
1916	Bos	N	1	158	.260
1917	Bos	N	1	130	.272
1918	Bos	N	P-1-O	119	0-1 / .236
1919	Bro	N	1	132	.298
1920	Bro	N	1	131	.308
1921	Bro	N	1	55	.269
1921	Phi	N	1	72	.321
		BRTR		2085	1-1 / .281

KONIKOWSKI, ALEXANDER JAMES
(Whitey)
b.June 8,1928 Throop,Pa.

Yr	Cl	Lea	Pos	G	Rec
1948	NY	N	P	22	2-3
1951	NY	N	P	3	0-0
1954	NY	N	P	10	0-0
		BRTR		35	2-3

KONNICK, MICHAEL ALOYSIUS
b.Jan.13,1889 Glen Lyon,Pa.

Yr	Cl	Lea	Pos	G	Rec
1909	Cin	N	C	2	.400
1910	Cin	N	S	1	.000
		BRTR		3	.250

KONOPKA, BRUCE BRUNO
b.Sept.16,1919 Hammond,Ind.

Yr	Cl	Lea	Pos	G	Rec
1942	Phi	A	1	5	.300
1943	Phi	A	H	2	.000
1946	Phi	A	1-O	38	.237
		BLTL		45	.238

KONSTANTY, CASIMER JAMES
(Jim)
b.Mar.2,1917 Strykersville,N.Y.

Yr	Cl	Lea	Pos	G	Rec
1944	Cin	N	P	20	6-4
1946	Bos	N	P	10	0-1
1948	Phi	N	P	6	1-0
1949	Phi	N	P	53	9-5
1950	Phi	N	P	74	16-7

(Continued)

Yr	Cl	Lea	Pos	G	Rec
1951	Phi	N	P	58	4-11
1952	Phi	N	P	42	5-3
1953	Phi	N	P	48	14-10
1954	Phi	N	P	33	2-3
1954	NY	A	P	9	1-1
1955	NY	A	P	45	7-2
1956	NY	A	P	8	0-0
1956	St.L	N	P	27	1-1
		BRTR		433	66-48

KOOB, ERNEST GERALD
b.Sept.11,1892 Keeler,Mich.
d.Nov.12,1941

Yr	Cl	Lea	Pos	G	Rec
1915	St.L	A	P	28	5-6
1916	St.L	A	P	33	11-8
1917	St.L	A	P	39	6-14
1919	St.L	A	P	24	2-4
		BLTL		124	24-32

KOONCE, CALVIN LEE
b.Nov.18,1940 Fayetteville,N.C.

Yr	Cl	Lea	Pos	G	Rec
1962	Chi	N	P	35	10-10
		BRTR			

KOONS, HARRY M.
b.1863 Philadelphia, Pa.

Yr	Cl	Lea	Pos	G	Rec
1884	Ath	U	C-3	21	.213
1884	Chi	U	3	1	.000
				22	.205

KOPF, WALTER HENRY
b.July 10,1899 New Britain,Conn.

Yr	Cl	Lea	Pos	G	Rec
1921	NY	N	3	2	.333
		BBTR			

KOPF, WILLIAM LORENZ (Larry)
(Also played under name of Fred Brady)
b.Nov.3,1890 Bristol,Conn.
(Fred Brady)

Yr	Cl	Lea	Pos	G	Rec
1913	Cle	A	2-3	6	.300
(Wm. Lorenz Kopf)					
1914	Phi	A	2	35	.189
1915	Phi	A	S-3	118	.225
1916	Cin	N	S	11	.275
1917	Cin	N	S	148	.255
1919	Cin	N	S	135	.270
1920	Cin	N	2-S-3-O	126	.245
1921	Cin	N	S	107	.218
1922	Bos	N	2-S-3	126	.266
1923	Bos	N	2-S	39	.275
		BBTR		851	.249

KOPLITZ, HOWARD DEAN
b.May 4,1938 Oshkosh,Wis.

Yr	Cl	Lea	Pos	G	Rec
1961	Det	A	P	4	2-0
1962	Det	A	P	12	3-0
		BRTR		16	5-0

KOPP, MERLIN H.
b.Jan.2,1892 Toledo,O.
d.May 7,1960

Yr	Cl	Lea	Pos	G	Rec
1915	Was	A	O	16	.250
1918	Phi	A	O	96	.234
1919	Phi	A	O	75	.226
		BLTR		187	.230

KOPPE, GEORGE MACEO
(Played under name of George Maceo Cuppy)

KOPPE, JOSEPH
(Real name Joseph Kopchia)
b.Oct.19,1931 Detroit,Mich.

Yr	Cl	Lea	Pos	G	Rec
1958	Mil	N	S	16	.444
1959	Phi	N	2-S	126	.261
1960	Phi	N	S-3	58	.171
1961	Phi	N	S	6	.000
1961	LA	A	2-S-3	91	.251
1962	LA	A	2-S-3	128	.227
		BRTR		425	.238

KOPSHAW, GEORGE CHARLES
b.Apr.21,1900 Passaic,N.J.
d.Dec.26,1934

Yr	Cl	Lea	Pos	G	Rec
1923	St.L	N	C	2	.200
		BBTR			

KORCHECK, STEPHEN JOSEPH
b.Aug.11,1932 McClellandtown,Pa.

Yr	Cl	Lea	Pos	G	Rec
1954	Was	A	C	2	.143
1955	Was	A	C	13	.278
1958	Was	A	C	21	.078
1959	Was	A	C	22	.157
		BRTR		58	.159

KORES, ARTHUR EMIL
b.July 22,1887 Milwaukee,Wis.

Yr	Cl	Lea	Pos	G	Rec
1915	St.L	F	3	60	.229
		BRTR			

KORWAN, JAMES (Long Jim)
b.Mar.4,1874 Brooklyn,N.Y.
d.Aug.1899

Yr	Cl	Lea	Pos	G	Rec
1894	Bro	N	P	1	0-0
1897	Chi	N	P	5	1-2
				6	1-2

KOSHOREK, CLEMENT JOHN
b.June 20,1926 Royal Oak,Mich.

Yr	Cl	Lea	Pos	G	Rec
1952	Pit	N	2-S-3	98	.261
1953	Pit	N	H	1	.000
		BRTR		99	.260

KOSKI, WILLIAM JOHN
b.Feb.6,1932 Madera,Cal.

Yr	Cl	Lea	Pos	G	Rec
1951	Pit	N	P	13	0-1
		BRTR			

KOSLO, GEORGE BERNARD (Dave)
(Real name George Bernard Koslowski)
b.Mar.31,1920 Menasha,Wis.

Yr	Cl	Lea	Pos	G	Rec
1941	NY	N	P	4	1-2
1942	NY	N	P	19	3-6
1946	NY	N	P	41	14-19
1947	NY	N	P	39	15-10
1948	NY	N	P	35	8-10
1949	NY	N	P	39	11-14
1950	NY	N	P	40	13-15
1951	NY	N	P	39	10-9
1952	NY	N	P	41	10-7
1953	NY	N	P	37	6-12
1954	Bal	A	P	3	0-1
1954	Mil	N	P	12	1-1
1955	Mil	N	P	1	0-1
		BLTL		350	92-107

KOSLOWSKI, GEORGE BERNARD
(Played under name of George Bernard Koslo)

KOSMAN, MICHAEL THOMAS
b.Dec.10,1917 Detroit,Mich.

Yr	Cl	Lea	Pos	G	Rec
1944	Cin	N	H	1	.000
		BR			

KOSTAL, JOSEPH

Yr	Cl	Lea	Pos	G	Rec
1896	Lou	N	C	2	.000

KOSTER, FREDERICK CHARLES
(Fritz)
b.Dec.21,1906 Louisville,Ky.

Yr	Cl	Lea	Pos	G	Rec
1931	Phi	N	O	76	.225
		BLTL			

KOSTRO, FRANK JOSEPH
b.Aug.4,1937 Windber,Pa.

Yr	Cl	Lea	Pos	G	Rec
1962	Det	A	3	16	.268
		BRTR			

KOUFAX, SANFORD
b.Dec.30,1935 Brooklyn,N.Y.

Yr	Cl	Lea	Pos	G	Rec
1955	Bro	N	P	12	2-2
1956	Bro	N	P	16	2-4
1957	Bro	N	P	34	5-4
1958	LA	N	P	40	11-11
1959	LA	N	P	35	8-6
1960	LA	N	P	37	8-13
1961	LA	N	P	42	18-13

(Continued)

Yr	Cl	Lea	Pos	G	Rec
1962	LA	N	P	28	14-7
	BRTL			244	68-60

KOUKALIK, JOSEPH
b.Mar.3,1880 Chicago,Ill.

Yr	Cl	Lea	Pos	G	Rec
1904	Bro	N	P	1	0-1

KOUPAL, LOUIS LADDIE
b.Dec.19,1898 Tabor,S.Dak.

Yr	Cl	Lea	Pos	G	Rec
1925	Pit	N	P	7	0-0
1926	Pit	N	P	6	0-2
1928	Bro	N	P	17	1-0
1929	Bro	N	P	18	0-1
1929	Phi	N	P	15	5-5
1930	Phi	N	P	13	0-4
1937	St.L	A	P	26	4-9
	BRTR			102	10-21

KOWALEWSKI, HARRY FRANK
(Played under name of
Harry Frank Coveleski)

KOWALEWSKI, STANISLAUS W.
(Played under name of
Stanley Coveleski)

KOWALIK, FABIAN LORENZ
b.Apr.22,1909 Falls City,Tex
d.Aug.14,1954

Yr	Cl	Lea	Pos	G	Rec
1932	Chi	A	P	6	0-1
1935	Chi	N	P	20	2-2
1936	Chi	N	P	6	0-2
1936	Phi	N	P	42	1-5
1936	Bos	N	P	2	0-1
	BBTR			76	3-11

KOY, ERNEST ANYZ (Chief)
b.Sept.17,1912 Sealy,Tex.

Yr	Cl	Lea	Pos	G	Rec
1938	Bro	N	O	142	.299
1939	Bro	N	O	125	.278
1940	Bro	N	O	24	.229
1940	St.L	N	O	93	.310
1941	St.L	N	O	13	.200
1941	Cin	N	O	67	.250
1942	Cin	N	H	3	.000
1942	Phi	N	O	91	.244
	BRTR			558	.279

KOZAR, ALBERT KENNETH
b.July 5,1922 McKee's Rocks,Pa.

Yr	Cl	Lea	Pos	G	Rec
1948	Was	A	2	150	.250
1949	Was	A	2	105	.269
1950	Was	A	2	20	.200
1950	Chi	A	2-3	10	.300
	BRTR			285	.254

KRACHER, JOSEPH PETER (Jug)
b.Nov.4,1915 Philadelphia, Pa.

Yr	Cl	Lea	Pos	G	Rec
1939	Phi	N	C	5	.200
	BRTR				

KRAFT, CLARENCE OTTO
(Big Boy)
b.June 9,1887 Evansville,Ind.
d.Mar.26,1958

Yr	Cl	Lea	Pos	G	Rec
1914	Bos	N	1-3	3	.333
	BRTR				

KRAKAUSKAS, JOSEPH VICTOR LAWRENCE
b.Mar.28,1916 Montreal,Que.,Canada.
d.Dec.8,1961

Yr	Cl	Lea	Pos	G	Rec
1937	Was	A	P	5	4-1
1938	Was	A	P	29	7-5
1939	Was	A	P	39	11-17
1940	Was	A	P	32	1-6
1941	Cle	A	P	12	1-2
1942	Cle	A	P	3	0-0
1946	Cle	A	P	29	2-5
	BLTL			149	26-36

KRALICK, JOHN FRANCIS
b.June 1,1936 Youngstown,O.

Yr	Cl	Lea	Pos	G	Rec
1959	Was	A	P	6	0-0
1960	Was	A	P	35	8-6
1961	Min	A	P	33	13-11
1962	Min	A	P	39	12-11
	BLTL			113	33-28

KRALY, STEVE CHARLES
b.Apr.18,1930 Whiting,Ind.

Yr	Cl	Lea	Pos	G	Rec
1953	NY	A	P	5	0-2
	BLTL				

KRAMER, JOHN HENRY
b.Jan.5,1918 New Orleans,La.

Yr	Cl	Lea	Pos	G	Rec
1939	St.L	A	P	40	9-16
1940	St.L	A	P	16	3-7
1941	St.L	A	P	29	4-3
1943	St.L	A	P	3	0-0
1944	St.L	A	P	33	17-13
1945	St.L	A	P	29	10-15
1946	St.L	A	P	31	13-11
1947	St.L	A	P	33	11-16
1948	Bos	A	P	29	18-5
1949	Bos	A	P	21	6-8
1950	NY	N	P	35	3-6
1951	NY	N	P	4	0-0
1951	NY	A	P	19	1-3
	BRTR			322	95-103

KRANEPOOL, EDWARD EMIL
b.Nov.8,1944 New York,N.Y.

Yr	Cl	Lea	Pos	G	Rec
1962	NY	N	1	3	.167
	BLTL				

KRAPP, EUGENE (Rubber)
b.May 12,1888 Rochester,N.Y.
d.Apr.13,1923

Yr	Cl	Lea	Pos	G	Rec
1911	Cle	A	P	36	12-8
1912	Cle	A	P	9	2-5
1914	Buf	F	P	37	16-14
1915	Buf	F	P	34	9-19
	BRTR			116	39-46

KRAUS, JOHN WILLIAM (Tex)
b.Apr.26,1918 San Antonio,Tex.

Yr	Cl	Lea	Pos	G	Rec
1943	Phi	N	P	35	9-15
1945	Phi	N	P	19	4-9
1946	NY	N	P	17	2-1
	BRTL			71	15-25

KRAUSE, HARRY WILLIAM (Hal)
b.July 12,1887 San Francisco,Cal.
d.Oct.23,1940

Yr	Cl	Lea	Pos	G	Rec
1908	Phi	A	P	4	1-1
1909	Phi	A	P	32	18-8
1910	Phi	A	P	16	6-6
1911	Phi	A	P	28	11-7
1912	Phi	A	P	3	0-3
1912	Cle	A	P	3	0-1
	BRTL			86	36-24

KRAUSSE, LEWIS BERNARD
b.June 8,1912 Media,Pa.

Yr	Cl	Lea	Pos	G	Rec
1931	Phi	A	P	3	1-0
1932	Phi	A	P	20	4-1
	BRTR			23	5-1

KRAUSSE, LEWIS BERNARD, JR.
b.Apr.25,1943 Chester,Pa.

Yr	Cl	Lea	Pos	G	Rec
1961	KC	A	P	13	2-5
	BRTR				

KRAVITZ, DANIEL
b.Dec.21,1930 Lopez,Pa.

Yr	Cl	Lea	Pos	G	Rec
1956	Pit	N	C-3	32	.265
1957	Pit	N	C	19	.146
1958	Pit	N	C	45	.240
1959	Pit	N	C	52	.253
1960	Pit	N	C	8	.000
1960	KC	A	C	59	.234
	BLTR			215	.236

KREEVICH, MICHAEL ANDREAS
b.June 10,1910 Mt.Olive,Ill.

Yr	Cl	Lea	Pos	G	Rec
1931	Chi	N	O	5	.167
1935	Chi	A	3	6	.435
1936	Chi	A	O	137	.307
1937	Chi	A	O	144	.302
1938	Chi	A	O	129	.297
1939	Chi	A	O	145	.323
1940	Chi	A	O	144	.265
1941	Chi	A	O	121	.232
1942	Phi	A	O	116	.255
1943	St.L	A	O	60	.255
1944	St.L	A	O	105	.301
1945	St.L	A	O	84	.237
1945	Was	A	O	45	.272
	BRTR			1241	.282

KREHMEYER, CHARLES L.
b.July 4,1857 St.Louis,Mo.
d.Feb.10,1926

Yr	Cl	Lea	Pos	G	Rec
1884	St.L	a	C-O	20	.257
1885	Lou	a	C-1-O	7	.212
1885	St.L	N	C-O	1	.000
				28	.250

KREITNER, ALBERT JOSEPH
(Mickey)
b.Oct.10,1922 Nashville,Tenn.

Yr	Cl	Lea	Pos	G	Rec
1943	Chi	N	C	3	.375
1944	Chi	N	C	39	.152
	BRTR			42	.172

KREITZ, RALPH WESLEY (Red)
b.Nov.13,1886 Plum Creek,Neb.
d.July 20,1941.

Yr	Cl	Lea	Pos	G	Rec
1911	Chi	A	C	7	.176
	BRTR				

KREMER, REMY (Ray)
b.Mar.23,1893 Oakland,Cal.

Yr	Cl	Lea	Pos	G	Rec
1924	Pit	N	P	42	18-10
1925	Pit	N	P	40	17-8
1926	Pit	N	P	37	20-6
1927	Pit	N	P	35	19-8
1928	Pit	N	P	34	15-13
1929	Pit	N	P	34	18-10
1930	Pit	N	P	39	20-12
1931	Pit	N	P	30	11-15
1932	Pit	N	P	11	4-3
1933	Pit	N	P	7	1-0
	BRTR			309	143-85

KRESS, CHARLES STEVEN (Buck)
b.Dec.9,1921 Philadelphia, Pa.

Yr	Cl	Lea	Pos	G	Rec
1947	Cin	N	1	11	.148
1949	Cin	N	1	27	.207
1949	Chi	A	1	97	.278
1950	Chi	A	1	3	.000
1954	Det	A	1-O	24	.189
1954	Bro	N	1	13	.083
	BLTL			175	.249

KRESS, RALPH (Red)
b.Jan.2,1907 Columbia,Cal.
d.Nov.29,1962

Yr	Cl	Lea	Pos	G	Rec
1927	St.L	A	S	7	.304
1928	St.L	A	S	150	.273
1929	St.L	A	S	147	.305
1930	St.L	A	S-3	154	.313
1931	St.L	A	1-S-3-O	150	.311
1932	St.L	A	3	14	.191
1932	Chi	A	S-3-O	135	.283
1933	Chi	A	1-O	129	.248
1934	Chi	A	O	8	.286
1934	Was	A	1-O	56	.228
1935	Was	A	P-1-2-S-O	84	0-0 / .298
1936	Was	A	2-S	109	.284
1938	St.L	A	S	150	.302
1939	St.L	A	S	13	.279
1939	Det	A	S	51	.242
1940	Det	A	S-3	33	.222
1946	NY	N	P	1	0-0
	BRTR			1391	0-0 / .286

KRETLOW, LOUIS HENRY (Lena)
b.June 27,1923 Apache,Okla.

Yr	Cl	Lea	Pos	G	Rec
1946	Det	A	P	1	1-0
1948	Det	A	P	5	2-1

(Continued)

Yr	Cl	Lea	Pos	G	Rec
1949	Det	A	P	25	3-2
1950	St.L	A	P	10	0-2
1950	Chi	A	P	11	0-0
1951	Chi	A	P	26	6-9
1952	Chi	A	P	19	4-4
1953	Chi	A	P	9	0-0
1953	St.L	A	P	22	1-5
1954	Bal	A	P	32	6-11
1955	Bal	A	P	15	0-4
1956	KC	A	P	25	4-9
	BRTR			200	27-47

KREUTZER, FRANKLIN

b.Feb.1,1939 Buffalo,N.Y.

Yr	Cl	Lea	Pos	G	Rec
1961	Chi	A	P	1	0-0
	BRTL				

KRICHELL, PAUL BERNARD

b.Dec.19,1882 New York,N.Y.

d.June 4,1957

Yr	Cl	Lea	Pos	G	Rec
1911	St.L	A	C	28	.232
1912	St.L	A	C	57	.217
	BRTR			85	.222

KRIEG, WILLIAM F.

b.Jan.29,1859 Petersburg,Ill.

d.Mar.25,1930

Yr	Cl	Lea	Pos	G	Rec
1884	Chi	U	C-1-O	59	.231
1884	Pit	U	C-O	10	.350
1885	Chi	N	C-O	1	.000
1885	Bro	a	C	17	.150
1886	Was	N	1	27	.255
1887	Was	N	1	24	.304
	TR			138	.248

KRIEGER, ...

Yr	Cl	Lea	Pos	G	Rec
1884	KC	U	P	1	0-1

KRIEGER, KURT FERDINAND (Dutch)

b.Sept.16,1926 Traisen,Austria.

Yr	Cl	Lea	Pos	G	Rec
1949	St.L	N	P	1	0-0
1951	St.L	N	P	2	0-0
	BRTR			3	0-0

KRIST, HOWARD WILBUR (Spud)

b.Feb.28,1916 W.Henrietta,N.Y.

Yr	Cl	Lea	Pos	G	Rec
1937	St.L	N	P	6	3-1
1938	St.L	N	P	2	0-0
1941	St.L	N	P	37	10-0
1942	St.L	N	P	35	13-3
1943	St.L	N	P	34	11-5
1946	St.L	N	P	15	0-2
	BLTR			129	37-11

KROCK, AUGUST H.

b.May 9,1866 Milwaukee,Wis.

d.Mar.22,1905

Yr	Cl	Lea	Pos	G	Rec
1888	Chi	N	P	39	25-14
1889	Chi	N	P	8	4-4
1889	Ind	N	P	7	5-2
1889	Was	N	P	7	1-6
1890	Buf	p	P	4	0-3
	TL			65	35-29

KROH, FLOYD H. (Rube)

b.1883 Friendship,N.Y.

Yr	Cl	Lea	Pos	G	Rec
1906	Bos	A	P	1	1-0
1907	Bos	A	P	7	0-4
1908	Chi	N	P	2	0-0
1909	Chi	N	P	17	9-4
1910	Chi	N	P	6	3-1
1912	Bos	N	P	3	0-0
	BLTL			36	13-9

KRONER, JOHN HAROLD

b.Nov.13,1908 St.Louis,Mo.

Yr	Cl	Lea	Pos	G	Rec
1935	Bos	A	3	2	.250
1936	Bos	A	2-S-3	84	.292
1937	Cle	A	2-3	86	.237
1938	Cle	A	2	51	.248
	BRTR			223	.262

KROUSE, WILLIAM

b.Aurora,Ill.

Yr	Cl	Lea	Pos	G	Rec
1901	Cin	N	2	1	.250
	TR				

KRSNICH, ROCCO PETER (Rocky)

b.Dec.4,1927 W.Allis,Wis.

Yr	Cl	Lea	Pos	G	Rec
1949	Chi	A	3	16	.218
1952	Chi	A	3	40	.231
1953	Chi	A	3	64	.202
	BRTR			120	.215

KRSNICH, MICHAEL

b.Sept.24,1931 W.Allis,Wis.

Yr	Cl	Lea	Pos	G	Rec
1960	Mil	N	O	4	.333
1962	Mil	N	1-3-O	11	.083
	BRTR			15	.190

KRUEGER, ARTHUR T.

b.Mar.16,1881 San Antonio,Tex.

d.Nov.28,1949

Yr	Cl	Lea	Pos	G	Rec
1907	Cin	N	O	96	.233
1910	Cle	A	O	62	.170
1910	Bos	N	O	1	.000
1914	KC	F	O	122	.250
1915	KC	F	O	80	.234
	BRTR			361	.228

KRUEGER, ERNEST GEORGE

b.Dec.27,1891 Chicago,Ill.

Yr	Cl	Lea	Pos	G	Rec
1913	Cle	A	C	5	.000
1915	NY	A	C	10	.172
1917	NY	N	C	8	.000
1917	Bro	N	C	31	.272
1918	Bro	N	C	30	.289
1919	Bro	N	C	80	.248
1920	Bro	N	C	52	.288
1921	Bro	N	C	65	.264
1925	Cin	N	C	37	.307
	BRTR			318	.264

KRUEGER, OOMPAUL ARTHUR

b.Sept. 17, 1876 Chicago, Ill.

d.Feb.20,1961

Yr	Cl	Lea	Pos	G	Rec
1899	Cle	N	3	13	.227
1900	St.L	N	2	12	.400
1901	St.L	N	3	142	.274
1902	St.L	N	S-3	125	.264
1903	Pit	N	S-O	71	.246
1904	Pit	N	S-O	75	.194
1905	Phi	N	P-S	30	{ 0-1 .184
	BRTR			468	{ 0-1 .250

KRUG, HENRY C.

b.Dec.4,1876 San Francisco,Cal.

d.Jan.14,1908

Yr	Cl	Lea	Pos	G	Rec
1902	Phi	N	2-S-3-O	53	.225
	TR				

KRUG, MARTIN JOHN

b.Sept.10,1888 Coblenz,Germany.

Yr	Cl	Lea	Pos	G	Rec
1912	Bos	A	S	15	.308
1922	Chi	N	2-S-3	127	.275
	BRTR			142	.278

KRUGER, ABRAHAM

b.Feb.14,1886 Morris Run,Pa.

d.July 4,1962

Yr	Cl	Lea	Pos	G	Rec
1908	Bro	N	P	1	0-1
	BRTR				

KRUMM, ALBERT

b.Columbus,O.

Yr	Cl	Lea	Pos	G	Rec
1889	Pit	N	P	1	0-1

KRYHOSKI, RICHARD DAVID

b.Mar.24,1925 Leonia,N.J.

Yr	Cl	Lea	Pos	G	Rec
1949	NY	A	1	54	.294
1950	Det	A	1	53	.219
1951	Det	A	1	119	.287
1952	St.L	A	1	111	.243
1953	St.L	A	1	104	.278
1954	Bal	A	1	100	.260
1955	KC	A	1	28	.213
	BLTL			569	.264

KUBEK, ANTHONY CHRISTOPHER

b.Oct.12,1936 Milwaukee,Wis.

Yr	Cl	Lea	Pos	G	Rec
1957	NY	A	2-S-3-O	127	.297
1958	NY	A	1-2-S-O	138	.265
1959	NY	A	2-S-3-O	132	.279
1960	NY	A	S-O	147	.273
1961	NY	A	S	153	.276
1962	NY	A	S-O	45	.314
	BLTR			742	.279

KUBISZYN, JOHN HENRY

b.Dec.19,1936 Buffalo,N.Y.

Yr	Cl	Lea	Pos	G	Rec
1961	Cle	A	2-S-3	25	.214
1962	Cle	A	S-3	25	.169
	BRTR			50	.188

KUCAB, JOHN ALBERT

b.Dec.17,1919 Olyphant,Pa.

Yr	Cl	Lea	Pos	G	Rec
1950	Phi	A	P	4	1-1
1951	Phi	A	P	30	4-3
1952	Phi	A	P	28	0-1
	BRTR			62	5-5

KUCKS, JOHN CHARLES

b.July 27,1933 Stanhope,N.J.

Yr	Cl	Lea	Pos	G	Rec
1955	NY	A	P	29	8-7
1956	NY	A	P	34	18-9
1957	NY	A	P	37	8-10
1958	NY	A	P	34	8-8
1959	NY	A	P	9	0-1
1959	KC	A	P	33	8-11
1960	KC	A	P	31	4-10
	BRTR			207	54-56

KUCZEK, STANISLAW LEO (Steve)

b.Dec.28,1924 Amsterdam,N.Y.

Yr	Cl	Lea	Pos	G	Rec
1949	Bos	N	H	1	1.000
	BRTR				

KUCZYNSKI, BERNARD CARL (Bert)

b.Jan.8,1920 Philadelphia,Pa.

Yr	Cl	Lea	Pos	G	Rec
1943	Phi	A	P	6	0-1
	BRTR				

KUEHNE, WILLIAM J.

(Real name William J. Knelme)

b.Oct.24,1863 Leipzig,Germany.

d.Oct.27,1921

Yr	Cl	Lea	Pos	G	Rec
1883	Col	a	2-S-3-O	96	.222
1884	Col	a	3	110	.238
1885	Pit	a	3	105	.216
1886	Pit	a	3-O	117	.211
1887	Pit	N	S	101	.322
1888	Pit	N	S-3	137	.234
1889	Pit	N	3	97	.246
1890	Pit	p	3	126	.243
1891	Col	a	3	56	.214
1891	Lou	a	3	40	.275
1892	Lou	N	3	76	.164
1892	St.L	N	S-3	6	.167
1892	Cin	N	3	6	.217
1892	St.L	N	3	1	.000
	TR			1074	.236

KUENN, HARVEY EDWARD

b.Dec.4,1930 Milwaukee,Wis.

Yr	Cl	Lea	Pos	G	Rec
1952	Det	A	S	19	.325
1953	Det	A	S	155	.308
1954	Det	A	S	155	.306
1955	Det	A	S	145	.306
1956	Det	A	S-O	146	.332
1957	Det	A	1-S-3	151	.277
1958	Det	A	O	139	.319
1959	Det	A	O	139	.353
1960	Cle	A	O	126	.308
1961	SF	N	S-3-O	131	.265
1962	SF	N	3-O	130	.304
	BRTR			1436	.309

KUHEL, JOSEPH ANTHONY

b.June 25,1906 Cleveland,O.

Yr	Cl	Lea	Pos	G	Rec
1930	Was	A	1	18	.286

(Continued)

Yr	Cl	Lea	Pos	G	Rec
1931	Was	A	1	139	.269
1932	Was	A	1	101	.291
1933	Was	A	1	153	.322
1934	Was	A	1	63	.289
1935	Was	A	1	151	.261
1936	Was	A	1	149	.321
1937	Was	A	1	136	.283
1938	Chi	A	1	117	.267
1939	Chi	A	1	139	.300
1940	Chi	A	1	155	.280
1941	CHI	A	1	153	.250
1942	Chi	A	1	115	.249
1943	Chi	A	1	153	.213
1944	Was	A	1	139	.278
1945	Was	A	1	142	.285
1946	Was	A	1	14	.150
1946	Chi	A	1	64	.273
1947	Chi	A	H	4	.000
	BLTL			2105	.277

Non-playing manager Was (A) 1948-49.

KUHN, BERNARD DANIEL (Bub)
b.Oct.12,1899 Vicksburg,Mich.
d.Nov.20,1956

Yr	Cl	Lea	Pos	G	Rec
1924	Cle	A	P	1	0-1
	BLTR				

KUHN, KENNETH HAROLD
b.Mar.20,1937 Louisville,Ky.

Yr	Cl	Lea	Pos	G	Rec
1955	Cle	A	S	4	.333
1956	Cle	A	2-S	27	.273
1957	Cle	A	2-S-3	40	.170
	BLTR			71	.210

KUHN, WALTER CHARLES (Red)
b.Feb.2,1884 Fresno,Cal.
d.June 14,1935

Yr	Cl	Lea	Pos	G	Rec
1912	Chi	A	C	75	.202
1913	Chi	A	C	26	.160
1914	Chi	A	C	17	.275
	BRTR			118	.205

KUHNS, CHARLES B.
b.Freeport,Pa.
d.July 15,1922

Yr	Cl	Lea	Pos	G	Rec
1897	Pit	N	3	2	.000
1899	Bos	N	S-3	6	.267
				8	.217

KULL, JOHN A.
b.June 24,1882 Shenandoah,Pa.
d.Mar.30,1936

Yr	Cl	Lea	Pos	G	Rec
1909	Phi	A	P	1	1-0
	TL				

KUME, JOHN MICHAEL
b.May 19,1926 Premier,W.Va.

Yr	Cl	Lea	Pos	G	Rec
1955	KC	A	P	6	0-2
	BRTR				

KUNKEL, WILLIAM GUSTAVE JAMES
b.July 7,1936 Hoboken,N.J.

Yr	Cl	Lea	Pos	G	Rec
1961	KC	A	P	58	3-4
1962	KC	A	P	9	0-0
	BRTR			67	3-4

KUNZ, EARL DEWEY (Pinches)
b.Dec.25,1899 Sacramento,Cal.

Yr	Cl	Lea	Pos	G	Rec
1923	Pit	N	P	21	1-2
	BRTR				

KUROWSKI, GEORGE JOHN
(Whitey)
b.Apr.19,1918 Reading,Pa.

Yr	Cl	Lea	Pos	G	Rec
1941	St.L	N	3	5	.333
1942	St.L	N	S-3-O	115	.254
1943	St.L	N	S-3	139	.287
1944	St.L	N	2-S-3	149	.270
1945	St.L	N	S-3	133	.323
1946	St.L	N	3	142	.301
1947	St.L	N	3	146	.310
1948	St.L	N	3	77	.214
1949	St.L	N	3	10	.143
	BRTR			916	.286

KUSEL, EDWARD
b.Feb.15,1886 Cleveland,O.
d.Oct.20,1948

Yr	Cl	Lea	Pos	G	Rec
1909	St.L	A	P	3	0-3

KUSH, EMIL BENEDICT
b.Nov.4,1917 Chicago,Ill.

Yr	Cl	Lea	Pos	G	Rec
1941	Chi	N	P	2	0-0
1942	Chi	N	P	1	0-0
1946	Chi	N	P	40	9-2
1947	Chi	N	P	47	8-3
1948	Chi	N	P	34	1-4
1949	Chi	N	P	26	3-3
	BRTR			150	21-12

KUSTUS, JULIUS (Joe)
b.Detroit,Mich.

Yr	Cl	Lea	Pos	G	Rec
1909	Bro	N	O	50	.145
	BRTR				

KUTINA, JOSEPH PETER
b.Jan.16,1885 Chicago,Ill.
d.Apr.13,1945

Yr	Cl	Lea	Pos	G	Rec
1911	St.L	A	1	26	.259
1912	St.L	A	1	67	.205
	BRTR			93	.222

KUTYNA, MARION JOHN
b.Nov.14,1932 Philadelphia,Pa.

Yr	Cl	Lea	Pos	G	Rec
1959	KC	A	P	4	0-0
1960	KC	A	P	51	3-2
1961	Was	A	P	50	6-8
1962	Was	A	P	54	5-6
	BRTR			159	14-16

KUZAVA, ROBERT LeROY
b.May 28,1923 Wyandotte,Mich.

Yr	Cl	Lea	Pos	G	Rec
1946	Cle	A	P	2	1-0
1947	Cle	A	P	4	1-1
1949	Chi	A	P	29	10-6
1950	Chi	A	P	10	1-3
1950	Was	A	P	22	8-7
1951	Was	A	P	8	3-3
1951	NY	A	P	24	8-4
1952	NY	A	P	28	8-8
1953	NY	A	P	33	6-5
1954	NY	A	P	20	1-3
1954	Bal	A	P	4	1-3
1955	Bal	A	P	6	0-1
1955	Phi	N	P	17	1-0
1957	Pit	N	P	4	0-0
1957	St.L	N	P	3	0-0
	BBTL			214	49-44

KVASNAK, ALEXANDER
b.Jan.11,1921 Sagamore,Pa.

Yr	Cl	Lea	Pos	G	Rec
1942	Was	A	O	5	.182
	BRTR				

KWIETNIEWSKI, CASIMIR EUGENE
(Played under name of Casimir Éugene Michaels)

KYLE, ANDREW EWING
b.Oct.29,1889 Toronto,Ont.,Canada

Yr	Cl	Lea	Pos	G	Rec
1912	Cin	N	O	8	.350
	BLTL				

LAABS, CHESTER PETER
b.Apr.30,1912 Milwaukee,Wis.

Yr	Cl	Lea	Pos	G	Rec
1937	Det	A	O	72	.240
1938	Det	A	O	64	.237
1939	Det	A	O	5	.313
1939	St.L	A	O	95	.300
1940	St.L	A	O	105	.271
1941	St.L	A	O	118	.278
1942	St.L	A	O	144	.275
1943	St.L	A	O	151	.250
1944	St.L	A	O	66	.234
1945	St.L	A	O	35	.239
1946	St.L	A	O	80	.261
1947	Phi	A	O	15	.219
	BRTR			950	.262

LABINE, CLEMENT WALTER
b.Aug.6,1926 Lincoln,R.I.

Yr	Cl	Lea	Pos	G	Rec
1950	Bro	N	P	1	0-0

(Continued)

Yr	Cl	Lea	Pos	G	Rec
1951	Bro	N	P	14	5-1
1952	Bro	N	P	26	8-4
1953	Bro	N	P	37	11-6
1954	Bro	N	P	47	7-6
1955	Bro	N	P	60	13-5
1956	Bro	N	P	62	10-6
1957	Bro	N	P	58	5-7
1958	LA	N	P	52	6-6
1959	LA	N	P	56	5-10
1960	LA	N	P	13	0-1
1960	Det	A	P	14	0-3
1960	Pit	N	P	15	3-0
1961	Pit	N	P	56	4-1
1962	NY	N	P	3	0-0
	BRTR			514	74-56

LaCHANCE, GEORGE
(Candy)
b.Feb.15,1870 Waterbury,Conn.
d.Aug.18,1932

Yr	Cl	Lea	Pos	G	Rec
1893	Bro	N	C	11	.176
1894	Bro	N	1	65	.329
1895	Bro	N	1	128	.320
1896	Bro	N	1	89	.280
1897	Bro	N	1	125	.308
1898	Bro	N	1-S	135	.243
1899	Bal	N	1	126	.307
1901	Cle	A	1	133	.306
1902	Bos	A	1	138	.275
1903	Bos	A	1	141	.258
1904	Bos	A	1	157	.231
1905	Bos	A	1	12	.128
				1260	.281

LACY, ...

Yr	Cl	Lea	Pos	G	Rec
1873	Mar	n	S	1	NR

LACY, OSCEOLA GUY
b.June 12,1898 Cleveland,Tenn.
d.Nov.19,1953

Yr	Cl	Lea	Pos	G	Rec
1926	Cle	A	2	13	.167
	BRTR				

LADD, ARTHUR CLIFFORD HIRAM
(Hi)
b.Feb.9,1870 Willimantic,Conn.
d.May 7,1948

Yr	Cl	Lea	Pos	G	Rec
1898	Pit	N	O	1	.000
1898	Bos	N	O	1	.000
				2	.000

LADE, DOYLE MARION
(Porky)
b.Feb.17,1921 Fairbury,Neb.

Yr	Cl	Lea	Pos	G	Rec
1946	Chi	N	P	3	0-2
1947	Chi	N	P	35	11-10
1948	Chi	N	P	19	5-6
1949	Chi	N	P	36	4-5
1950	Chi	N	P	34	5-6
	BRTR			127	25-29

LADEW, STEPHEN
b.St. Louis,Mo.

Yr	Cl	Lea	Pos	G	Rec
1889	KC	a	P	2	0-0

LAFATA, JOSEPH JOSEPH
b.Aug.4,1921 Detroit,Mich.

Yr	Cl	Lea	Pos	G	Rec
1947	NY	N	O	62	.221
1948	NY	N	H	1	.000
1949	NY	N	1	64	.236
	BLTL			127	.229

LAFFERTY, FRANK BERNARD
(Flip)
b.May 4,1854 Scranton,Pa.
d.Feb.8,1910

Yr	Cl	Lea	Pos	G	Rec
1876	Ath	N	P	1	0-1
1877	Lou	N	O	4	.059
	TR			5	0-1 / .050

LAFITTE, EDWARD FRANCIS
b.Apr.7,1887 New Orleans,La.

Yr	Cl	Lea	Pos	G	Rec
1909	Det	A	P	3	0-1
1911	Det	A	P	31	11-8
1912	Det	A	P	1	0-0
1914	Bro	F	P	40	18-15
1915	Bro	F	P	17	7-9
1915	Buf	F	P	14	2-2
	BRTR			106	38-35

LaFOREST, BYRON JOSEPH
(Ty)
b.Apr.18,1919 Edmundston,N.B., Canada
d.May 5,1947

Yr	Cl	Lea	Pos	G	Rec
1945	Bos	A	3-O	52	.250
	BRTR				

LAGGER, EDWIN JOSEPH
b.July 14,1912 Joliet,Ill.

Yr	Cl	Lea	Pos	G	Rec
1934	Phi	A	P	8	0-0
	BRTR				

LAJESKIE, RICHARD
b.Jan.8,1926 Passaic,N.J.

Yr	Cl	Lea	Pos	G	Rec
1946	NY	N	2	6	.200
	BRTR				

LAJOIE, NAPOLEON
(Larry)
b.Sept.5,1875 Woonsocket,R.I.
d.Feb.7,1959

Yr	Cl	Lea	Pos	G	Rec
1896	Phi	N	1	39	.328
1897	Phi	N	1-O	126	.363
1898	Phi	N	2	147	.328
1899	Phi	N	2	72	.379
1900	Phi	N	2	102	.346
1901	Phi	A	2	131	.422
1902	Phi	A	2	1	.200
1902	Cle	A	2	86	.369
1903	Cle	A	1-2	126	.355
1904	Cle	A	2-S	140	.381
1905	Cle	A	M-2	65	.329
1906	Cle	A	M-2-3	152	.355
1907	Cle	A	M-2	137	.299
1908	Cle	A	M-2	157	.289
1909	Cle	A	M-2	128	.324
1910	Cle	A	2	159	.384
1911	Cle	A	1-2	90	.365
1912	Cle	A	1-2	117	.368
1913	Cle	A	2	137	.335
1914	Cle	A	1-2	121	.258
1915	Phi	A	2	129	.280
1916	Phi	A	2	113	.246
	BRTR			2475	.339

LAKE, EDWARD ERVING
(Sparky)
b.Mar.18,1917 Antioch,Cal.

Yr	Cl	Lea	Pos	G	Rec
1939	St.L	N	S	2	.250
1940	St.L	N	2-S	32	.212
1941	St.L	N	2-S-3	45	.105
1943	Bos	A	S	75	.199
1944	Bos	A	P-2-S-3	57	0-0 .206
1945	Bos	A	S	133	.279
1946	Det	A	S	155	.254
1947	Det	A	S	158	.211
1948	Det	A	2-3	64	.263
1949	Det	A	2-S-3	94	.196
1950	Det	A	S-3	20	.000
	BRTR			835	0-0 .231

LAKE, FREDERICK LOVETT
b.Oct.16,1866 Nova Scotia,Canada
d.Nov.24,1931

Yr	Cl	Lea	Pos	G	Rec
1891	Bos	N	C	5	.142
1894	Lou	N	C	16	.292
1897	Bos	N	C	17	.272
1898	Pit	N	1	5	.083
1910	Bos	N	M-H	3	.000
				46	.238

Non-playing manager Bos (A) 1908-09.

LAKE, JOSEPH HENRY
b.Jan.6,1883 Brooklyn,N.Y.
d.June 30,1950

Yr	Cl	Lea	Pos	G	Rec
1908	NY	A	P	44	9-21
1909	NY	A	P	32	14-11
1910	St.L	A	P	37	11-18
1911	St.L	A	P	30	10-15
1912	St.L	A	P	15	3-10
1912	Det	A	P	22	9-9
1913	Det	A	P	24	8-7
	BRTR			204	64-91

LAKEMAN, ALBERT WESLEY
(Moose)
b.Dec.31,1919 Cincinnati,O.

Yr	Cl	Lea	Pos	G	Rec
1942	Cin	N	C	20	.158
1943	Cin	N	C	22	.255
1944	Cin	N	H	1	.000
1945	Cin	N	C	76	.256
1946	Cin	N	C	23	.133
1947	Cin	N	H	2	.000
1947	Phi	N	C-1	55	.159
1948	Phi	N	P-C	32	0-0 .162
1949	Bos	N	1	3	.167
1954	Det	A	C	5	.000
	BRTR			239	0-0 .203

LALLY, DANIEL J.
(Bud)
b.Aug.12,1867 Jersey City,N.J.
d.Apr.14,1936

Yr	Cl	Lea	Pos	G	Rec
1891	Pit	N	O	41	.225
1897	St.L	N	O	87	.278
	BRTR			128	.263

LaMABE, JOHN ALEXANDER
b.Oct.3,1936 Farmingdale,N.Y.

Yr	Cl	Lea	Pos	G	Rec
1962	Pit	N	P	43	3-1
	BRTR				

LaMACCHIA, ALFRED ANTHONY
b.July 22,1921 St.Louis,Mo.

Yr	Cl	Lea	Pos	G	Rec
1943	St.L	A	P	1	0-1
1945	St.L	A	P	5	2-0
1946	St.L	A	P	8	0-0
1946	Was	A	P	2	0-1
	BRTR			16	2-2

LaMANNA, FRANK
b.Aug.22,1919 Watertown,Pa.

Yr	Cl	Lea	Pos	G	Rec
1940	Bos	N	P	5	1-0
1941	Bos	N	P-O	47	5-4 .281
1942	Bos	N	P	10	0-1
	BRTR			62	6-5 .256

LAMANNO, RAYMOND SIMON
b.Nov.17,1919 Oakland,Cal.

Yr	Cl	Lea	Pos	G	Rec
1941	Cin	N	C	1	.000
1942	Cin	N	C	111	.264
1946	Cin	N	C	85	.243
1947	Cin	N	C	118	.257
1948	Cin	N	C	127	.242
	BRTR			442	.252

LAMANSKE, FRANK JAMES
b.Sept.30,1906 Oglesby,Ill.

Yr	Cl	Lea	Pos	G	Rec
1935	Bro	N	P	2	0-0
	BLTL				

LAMAR, PIERRE
(Pete)
b.1874 Hoboken,N.J.
d.Oct.24,1931

Yr	Cl	Lea	Pos	G	Rec
1902	Chi	N	C	2	.222
1907	Cin	N	C	1	.000
	TR			3	.182

LAMAR, WILLIAM HARMONG
(Good Time)
b.Mar.21,1897 Rockville,Md.

Yr	Cl	Lea	Pos	G	Rec
1917	NY	A	O	11	.244
1918	NY	A	O	28	.227
1919	NY	A	O	11	.188
1919	Bos	A	O	48	.291
1920	Bro	N	O	24	.273
1921	Bro	N	O	3	.333
1924	Phi	A	O	87	.330
1925	Phi	A	O	138	.356
1926	Phi	A	O	116	.284
1927	Phi	A	O	84	.299
	BBTR			550	.310

LaMASTER, WAYNE LEE
b.Feb.13,1908 Sellersburg,Ind.

Yr	Cl	Lea	Pos	G	Rec
1937	Phi	N	P	51	15-19
1938	Phi	N	P	18	4-7
1938	Bro	N	P	5	0-1
	BLTL			74	19-27

LAMB, LYMAN RAYMOND
b.Mar.17,1895 Lincoln,Neb.
d.Oct.5,1955

Yr	Cl	Lea	Pos	G	Rec
1920	St.L	A	O	9	.375
1921	St.L	A	3	45	.253
	BRTR			54	.272

LAMBERT, CLAYTON PATRICK
b.Mar.26,1917 Summit,Ill.

Yr	Cl	Lea	Pos	G	Rec
1946	Cin	N	P	23	2-2
1947	Cin	N	P	3	0-0
	BRTR			26	2-2

LAMBERT, EUGENE MARION
b.Apr.26,1921 Crenshaw,Miss.

Yr	Cl	Lea	Pos	G	Rec
1941	Phi	N	P	2	0-1
1942	Phi	N	P	1	0-0
	BRTR			3	0-1

LAMBETH, SAMUEL OTIS
b.May 13,1892 Berlin,Kan.

Yr	Cl	Lea	Pos	G	Rec
1916	Cle	A	P	16	4-3
1917	Cle	A	P	26	7-6
1918	Cle	A	P	2	0-0
	BRTR			44	11-9

LAMLINE, FREDERICK ARTHUR
b.Aug.14,1891 Port Huron,Mich.

Yr	Cl	Lea	Pos	G	Rec
1912	Chi	A	P	1	0-0
1915	St.L	N	P	4	0-0
	BRTR			5	0-0

LaMOTTE, ROBERT EUGENE
b.Feb.15,1898 Savannah,Ga.

Yr	Cl	Lea	Pos	G	Rec
1920	Was	A	S	4	.000
1921	Was	A	S	16	.195
1922	Was	A	3	68	.252
1925	St.L	A	S-3	97	.273
1926	St.L	A	S	36	.202
	BRTR			221	.253

LAMPE, HENRY JOSEPH
b.Sept.19,1872 Boston,Mass.
d.Sept.16,1936

Yr	Cl	Lea	Pos	G	Rec
1894	Bos	N	P	2	0-1
1895	Phi	N	P	7	0-2
				9	0-3

LANAHAN, RICHARD ANTHONY
b.Sept.27,1913 Washington,D.C.

Yr	Cl	Lea	Pos	G	Rec
1935	Was	A	P	3	0-3
1937	Was	A	P	6	0-1
1940	Pit	N	P	40	6-8
1941	Pit	N	P	7	0-1
	BLTL			56	6-13

LAND, DOC BURRELL
(Played under name of William Gilbert Land)

LAND, GROVER CLEVELAND
b.Sept.22,1884 Frankfort,Ky.
d.July 22,1958

Yr	Cl	Lea	Pos	G	Rec
1908	Cle	A	C	7	.230
1909	Cle	A	C	1	.500
1910	Cle	A	C	34	.207
1911	Cle	A	C	35	.140
1913	Cle	A	C	17	.235
1914	Bro	F	C	103	.282
1915	Bro	F	C	96	.261
	BRTR			293	.247

LAND, WILLIAM GILBERT
(Real name Doc Burrell Land)
b.May 14,1903 Geiger,Ala.

Yr	Cl	Lea	Pos	G	Rec
1929	Was	A	O	1	.000
	BLTL				

LANDENBERGER, KENNETH HENRY
(Red)
b.July 29,1928 Cleveland,O.
d.July 28,1960

Yr	Cl	Lea	Pos	G	Rec
1952	Chi	A	1	2	.200
	BLTL				

LANDIS, JAMES HENRY
b.Mar.9,1934 Fresno,Cal.

Yr	Cl	Lea	Pos	G	Rec
1957	Chi	A	O	96	.212
1958	Chi	A	O	142	.277
1959	Chi	A	O	149	.272
1960	Chi	A	O	148	.253
1961	Chi	A	O	140	.283
1962	Chi	A	O	149	.228
	BRTR			824	.258

LANDIS, SAMUEL H.
(Doc)
b.Aug.16,1854 Philadelphia,Pa.

Yr	Cl	Lea	Pos	G	Rec
1882	Ath	a	P-O	3	1-1 / .167
1882	Bal	a	P-O	51	11-28 / .160
				54	12-29 / .161

LANDRITH, HOBERT NEAL
b.Mar.16,1930 Decatur,Ill.

Yr	Cl	Lea	Pos	G	Rec
1950	Cin	N	C	4	.214
1951	Cin	N	C	4	.385
1952	Cin	N	C	15	.260
1953	Cin	N	C	52	.240
1954	Cin	N	C	48	.198
1955	Cin	N	C	43	.253
1956	Chi	N	C	111	.221
1957	St.L	N	C	75	.243
1958	St.L	N	C	70	.215
1959	SF	N	C	109	.251
1960	SF	N	C	71	.242
1961	SF	N	C	43	.239
1962	NY	N	C	23	.289
1962	Bal	A	C	60	.222
	BLTR			728	.237

LANDRUM, DONALD LEROY
b.Feb.16,1936 Santa Rosa,Cal.

Yr	Cl	Lea	Pos	G	Rec
1957	Phi	N	O	2	.143
1960	St.L	N	O	13	.245
1961	St.L	N	2-O	28	.167
1962	St.L	N	O	32	.314
1962	Chi	N	O	83	.282
	BLTL			158	.258

LANDRUM, JESSE GLENN
b.Sept.11,1914 Crockett,Tex.

Yr	Cl	Lea	Pos	G	Rec
1938	Chi	A	2	4	.000
	BRTR				

LANDRUM, JOSEPH BUTLER
b.Dec.13,1928 Columbia,S.C.

Yr	Cl	Lea	Pos	G	Rec
1950	Bro	N	P	7	0-0
1952	Bro	N	P	9	1-3
	BRTR			16	1-3

LANE, GEORGE M. (Chappy)
b.Pittsburgh,Pa.
d.1896

Yr	Cl	Lea	Pos	G	Rec
1882	Pit	a	C-1-O	54	.167
1884	Tol	a	1-O	56	.231
				110	.200

LANE, JAMES HUNTER
b.July 20,1900 Pulaski,Tenn.

Yr	Cl	Lea	Pos	G	Rec
1924	Bos	N	2-3	7	.067
	BRTR				

LANE, JERALD HAL
b.Feb.7,1926 Windham,N.Y.

Yr	Cl	Lea	Pos	G	Rec
1953	Was	A	P	20	1-4
1954	Cin	N	P	3	1-0
1955	Cin	N	P	7	0-2
	BRTR			30	2-6

LANE, RICHARD HARRISON
b.June 28,1927 Detroit,Mich.

Yr	Cl	Lea	Pos	G	Rec
1949	Chi	A	O	12	.119
	BRTR				

LANFORD, LEWIS GROVER
b.Jan.8,1886 Woodruff,S.Car.

Yr	Cl	Lea	Pos	G	Rec
1907	Was	A	P	2	0-0

LANFRANCONI, WALTER OSWALD
b.Nov.9,1917 Barre,Vt.

Yr	Cl	Lea	Pos	G	Rec
1941	Chi	N	P	2	0-1
1947	Bos	N	P	37	4-4
	BRTR			39	4-5

LANG, DONALD CHARLES
b.Mar.15,1917 Selma,Cal.

Yr	Cl	Lea	Pos	G	Rec
1938	Cin	N	2-3	21	.260
1948	St.L	N	2-3	117	.269
	BRTR			138	.268

LANG, MARTIN JOHN
b.Sept.27,1907 Hooper,Neb.

Yr	Cl	Lea	Pos	G	Rec
1930	Pit	N	P	2	0-0
	BRTL				

LANGE, FRANK H.
b.Oct.28,1883 Columbus,Wis.
d.Dec.26,1945

Yr	Cl	Lea	Pos	G	Rec
1910	Chi	A	P	33	9-4
1911	Chi	A	P	54	8-8
1912	Chi	A	P	36	10-10
1913	Chi	A	P	16	1-4
	BRTR			139	28-26

LANGE, IRWIN
b.1888 Germany

Yr	Cl	Lea	Pos	G	Rec
1914	Chi	F	P	31	12-11
	BR				

LANGE, WILLIAM ALEXANDER
(Little Eva)
b.June 6,1871 San Francisco,Cal.
d.July 23,1950

Yr	Cl	Lea	Pos	G	Rec
1893	Chi	N	2-O	116	.288
1894	Chi	N	O	112	.324
1895	Chi	N	O	122	.388
1896	Chi	N	O	123	.333
1897	Chi	N	O	117	.352
1898	Chi	N	O	111	.332
1899	Chi	N	O	107	.324
	BRTR			808	.336

LANGFORD, ELTON J.
b.May 21,1901 Briggs,Tex.

Yr	Cl	Lea	Pos	G	Rec
1926	Bos	A	O	1	.000
1927	Cle	A	O	20	.269
1928	Cle	A	O	110	.276
	BLTR			131	.275

LANGSFORD, ROBERT WILLIAM
(Real Name
Robert William Lankswert)
b.Louisville,Ky.
d.Jan.10,1907

Yr	Cl	Lea	Pos	G	Rec
1899	Lou	N	S	1	.000
	TL				

LANIER, HUBERT MAX
b.Aug.18,1915 Denton,N.C.

Yr	Cl	Lea	Pos	G	Rec
1938	St.L	N	P	18	0-3
1939	St.L	N	P	7	2-1
1940	St.L	N	P	35	9-6
1941	St.L	N	P	35	10-8
1942	St.L	N	P	34	13-8
1943	St.L	N	P	32	15-7

(Continued)

Yr	Cl	Lea	Pos	G	Rec
1944	St.L	N	P	33	17-12
1945	St.L	N	P	4	2-2
1946	St.L	N	P	6	6-0
1949	St.L	N	P	15	5-4
1950	St.L	N	P	27	11-9
1951	St.L	N	P	31	11-9
1952	NY	N	P	38	7-12
1953	NY	N	P	3	0-0
1953	St.L	A	P	10	0-1
	BRTL			328	108-82

LANKSWERT, ROBERT WILLIAM
(Played under name of Robert William Langsford)

LANNING, JOHN YOUNG
(Tobacco John)
b.Sept.6,1911 Asheville,N.C.

Yr	Cl	Lea	Pos	G	Rec
1936	Bos	N	P	28	7-11
1937	Bos	N	P	32	5-7
1938	Bos	N	P	32	8-7
1939	Bos	N	P	37	5-6
1940	Pit	N	P	38	8-4
1941	Pit	N	P	34	11-11
1942	Pit	N	P	34	6-8
1943	Pit	N	P	12	4-1
1945	Pit	N	P	1	0-0
1946	Pit	N	P	27	4-5
1947	Bos	N	P	3	0-0
	BRTR			278	58-60

LANNING, LESTER ALFRED
b.May 13,1895 Harvard,Ill.
d.June 13,1962

Yr	Cl	Lea	Pos	G	Rec
1916	Phi	A	P-O	19	0-3 / .182
	BLTL				

LANNING, THOMAS NEWTON
b.Apr.22,1909 Biltmore,N.C.

Yr	Cl	Lea	Pos	G	Rec
1938	Phi	N	P	3	0-1
	BLTL				

LANSING, EUGENE HEWETT
b.Jan.11,1898 Rensselaer,N.Y.
d.Jan.18,1945

Yr	Cl	Lea	Pos	G	Rec
1922	Bos	N	P	15	0-1
	BRTR				

LaPALME, PAUL EDMORE
b.Dec.14,1923 Springfield,Mass.

Yr	Cl	Lea	Pos	G	Rec
1951	Pit	N	P	22	1-5
1952	Pit	N	P	31	1-2
1953	Pit	N	P	35	8-16
1954	Pit	N	P	33	4-10
1955	St.L	N	P	56	4-3
1956	St.L	N	P	1	0-0
1956	Cin	N	P	11	2-4
1956	Chi	A	P	29	3-1
1957	Chi	A	P	36	1-4
	BLTL			254	24-45

LAPAN, PETER NELSON
b.June 25,1891 Easthampton,Mass.
d.Jan.5,1953

Yr	Cl	Lea	Pos	G	Rec
1922	Was	A	C	11	.324
1923	Was	A	C	2	.000
	BRTR			13	.306

LAPIHUSKA, ANDREW (Apples)
b.Nov.1,1922 Leesburg,N.J.

Yr	Cl	Lea	Pos	G	Rec
1942	Phi	N	P	3	0-2
1943	Phi	N	P	1	0-0
	BLTR			4	0-2

LaPOINTE, RALPH JOHN
b.Jan.8,1922 Winooski,Vt.

Yr	Cl	Lea	Pos	G	Rec
1947	Phi	N	S	56	.308
1948	St.L	N	2-S-3	87	.225
	BRTR			143	.266

LaPORTE, FRANK B.
b.Feb.6,1882 Ulrichsville,O.
d.Sept.25,1939

Yr	Cl	Lea	Pos	G	Rec
1905	NY	A	2	11	.375
1906	NY	A	3	123	.264

(Continued)

Yr	Cl	Lea	Pos	G	Rec
1907	NY	A	3-O	130	.270
1908	Bos	A	2-3	60	.245
1908	NY	A	2	41	.253
1909	NY	A	2	89	.298
1910	NY	A	2-O	124	.264
1911	St.L	A	2	136	.314
1912	St.L	A	3-O	80	.308
1912	Was	A	2	39	.316
1913	Was	A	2-3-O	80	.250
1914	Ind	F	2	133	.311
1915	New	F	2	148	.251
	BRTR			1194	.281

LAPP, JOHN WALKER
b.Sept.10,1884 Frazer,Pa.
d.Feb.6,1920

Yr	Cl	Lea	Pos	G	Rec
1908	Phi	A	C	13	.143
1909	Phi	A	C	21	.336
1910	Phi	A	C	71	.234
1911	Phi	A	C	68	.353
1912	Phi	A	C	90	.292
1913	Phi	A	C	84	.228
1914	Phi	A	C	69	.231
1915	Phi	A	C	112	.272
1916	Chi	A	C	40	.208
	BLTR			568	.263

LaRIVIERE, EDMOND WINGO (Tink)
(Played under name of Edmund Wingo)

LARKER, NORMAN HOWARD
b.Dec.27,1930 Beaver Meadows,Pa.

Yr	Cl	Lea	Pos	G	Rec
1958	LA	N	1-O	99	.277
1959	LA	N	1-O	108	.289
1960	LA	N	1-O	133	.323
1961	LA	N	1-O	97	.270
1962	Hou	N	1-O	147	.263
	BLTL			584	.285

LARKIN, EDWARD FRANCIS
b.July 1,1885 Wyalusing,Pa.
d.Mar.28,1934

Yr	Cl	Lea	Pos	G	Rec
1909	Phi	A	C	2	.167
	BRTR				

LARKIN, FRANK (Terry)
b.New York,N.Y.

Yr	Cl	Lea	Pos	G	Rec
1876	Mut	N	P	1	0-1
1877	Har	N	P-2-3	58	29-25 .228
1878	Chi	N	P	57	29-26
1879	Chi	N	P	58	30-23
1880	Tro	N	P-S-O	5	0-5 .118
1884	Was	U	3	17	.257
1884	Ric	a	2	39	.179
	BRTR			235	88-80 .242

LARKIN, HENRY E. (Ted)
b.Jan.12,1863 Reading,Pa.
d.Jan.31,1942

Yr	Cl	Lea	Pos	G	Rec
1884	Ath	a	O	87	.296
1885	Ath	a	O	108	.338
1886	Ath	a	O	139	.327
1887	Ath	a	1-O	125	.374
1888	Ath	a	1	135	.283
1889	Ath	a	1	133	.324
1890	Cle	p	M-1	125	.327
1891	Ath	a	1-O	133	.277
1892	Was	N	1	116	.282
1893	Was	N	1	81	.322
	BRTR			1182	.313

LARKIN, STEPHEN PATRICK
b.Dec.9,1910 Cincinnati,O.

Yr	Cl	Lea	Pos	G	Rec
1934	Det	A	P	2	0-0
	BRTR				

LARMORE, ROBERT McKAHAN
b.Dec.6,1896 Anderson,Ind.

Yr	Cl	Lea	Pos	G	Rec
1918	St.L	N	S	4	.285
	TR				

LaROQUE, SAMUEL H. J.
b.Feb.26,1864 St. Mathias,Que., Canada.

Yr	Cl	Lea	Pos	G	Rec
1888	Det	N	2	2	.444
1890	Pit	N	2-S	111	.242
1891	Pit	N	2	1	.000
1891	Lou	a	2	9	.333
				123	.249

LaROSS, HARRY RAYMOND (Spike)
b.Jan.2,1891 Easton,Pa.

Yr	Cl	Lea	Pos	G	Rec
1914	Cin	N	O	22	.229

LARSEN, DONALD JAMES
b.Aug.7,1929 Michigan City,Ind.

Yr	Cl	Lea	Pos	G	Rec
1953	St.L	A	P-O	50	7-12 .284
1954	Bal	A	P	44	3-21
1955	NY	A	P	21	9-2
1956	NY	A	P	45	11-5
1957	NY	A	P	31	10-4
1958	NY	A	P	28	9-6
1959	NY	A	P	29	6-7
1960	KC	A	P	23	1-10
1961	KC	A	P-O	18	1-0 .300
1961	Chi	A	P	25	7-2
1962	SF	N	P	52	5-4
	BRTR			366	69-73 .252

LARSEN, ERLING ARTHUR (Swede)
b.Nov.15,1913 Jersey City,N.J.

Yr	Cl	Lea	Pos	G	Rec
1936	Bos	N	2	3	.000
	BRTR				

LARY, ALFRED ALLEN
b.Sept.26,1929 Northport,Ala.

Yr	Cl	Lea	Pos	G	Rec
1954	Chi	N	P	2	0-0
1955	Chi	N	H	4	.000
1962	Chi	N	P	23	0-1
	BRTR			29	0-1 .250

LARY, FRANK STRONG
b.Apr.10,1931 Northport,Ala.

Yr	Cl	Lea	Pos	G	Rec
1954	Det	A	P	3	0-0
1955	Det	A	P	36	14-15
1956	Det	A	P	41	21-13
1957	Det	A	P	40	11-16
1958	Det	A	P	39	16-15
1959	Det	A	P	32	17-10
1960	Det	A	P	39	15-15
1961	Det	A	P	42	23-9
1962	Det	A	P	22	2-6
	BRTR			294	119-99

LARY, LYNFORD HOBART
(Broadway)
b.Jan.28,1906 Armona,Cal.

Yr	Cl	Lea	Pos	G	Rec
1929	NY	A	S-3	80	.309
1930	NY	A	S	117	.289
1931	NY	A	S	155	.280
1932	NY	A	S	91	.232
1933	NY	A	1-S-3-O	52	.220
1934	NY	A	S	1	.000
1934	Bos	A	1-S	129	.241
1935	Was	A	S	39	.194
1935	St.L	A	S	93	.288
1936	St.L	A	S	155	.289
1937	Cle	A	S	156	.290
1938	Cle	A	S	141	.268
1939	Cle	A	S	3	.000
1939	Bro	N	S-3	29	.161
1939	St.L	N	S-3	34	.187
1940	St.L	A	2-S	27	.056
	BRTR			1302	.269

LASLEY, WILLARD ALMOND
b.July 13,1902 Marietta,O.

Yr	Cl	Lea	Pos	G	Rec
1924	St.L	A	P	2	0-0
	BBTR				

LASORDA, THOMAS CHARLES
b.Sept.22,1927 Norristown,Pa.

Yr	Cl	Lea	Pos	G	Rec
1954	Bro	N	P	4	0-0
1955	Bro	N	P	4	0-0
1956	KC	A	P	19	0-4
	BLTL			27	0-4

LASSETTER, DONALD O'NEAL
b.Mar.27,1933 Newnan,Ga.

Yr	Cl	Lea	Pos	G	Rec
1957	St.L	N	O	4	.154
	BRTR				

LATHAM, GEORGE WARREN (Juice)
b:Sept.6,1852 Utica,N.Y.
d.May 26,1914.

Yr	Cl	Lea	Pos	G	Rec
1875	Bos	n	1	16	.320
1875	NH	n	1-S-3	20	NR
1877	Lou	N	1	59	.290
1882	Ath	a	1	75	.300
1883	Lou	a	1-2-S	90	.248
1884	Lou	a	1	78	.161
	BRTR			338	NR

LATHAM, WALTER ARLINGTON
(Arlie)
b.Mar.15,1859 W.Lebanon,N.H.
d.Nov.29,1952

Yr	Cl	Lea	Pos	G	Rec
1880	Buf	N	C-S-O	22	.125
1883	St.L	a	3	97	.228
1884	St.L	a	3	110	.276
1885	St.L	a	3	110	.213
1886	St.L	a	3	134	.303
1887	St.L	a	3	136	.307
1888	St.L	a	3	133	.264
1889	St.L	a	3	118	.254
1890	Chi	p	3	52	.241
1890	Cin	N	3	41	.250
1891	Cin	N	3	135	.271
1892	Cin	N	3	150	.239
1893	Cin	N	3	125	.296
1894	Cin	N	3	130	.313
1895	Cin	N	3	110	.310
1896	St.L	N	M-3	8	.229
1899	Was	N	2	6	.143
1909	NY	N	2	4	.000
	BRTR			1621	.266

LATHERS, CHARLES TEN EYCK
(Chick)
b.Oct.22,1888 Detroit,Mich.

Yr	Cl	Lea	Pos	G	Rec
1910	Det	A	3	41	.232
1911	Det	A	3	29	.222
	TR			70	.228

LATHROP, WILLIAM GEORGE
b.Aug.12,1891 Hanover,Wis.
d.Nov.20,1958

Yr	Cl	Lea	Pos	G	Rec
1913	Chi	A	P	6	0-0
1914	Chi	A	P	16	1-2
	BRTR			22	1-2

LATIMER, CLIFFORD WESLEY
(Tacks)
b.Nov.30,1875 Loveland,O.
d.Apr.24,1936

Yr	Cl	Lea	Pos	G	Rec
1898	NY	N	C	3	.400
1899	Lou	N	C	8	.280
1900	Pit	N	C	4	.333
1901	Bal	A	C	1	.250
1902	Bro	N	C	8	.041
	TR			24	.209

LATMAN, ARNOLD BARRY
b.May 21,1936 Los Angeles, Cal.

Yr	Cl	Lea	Pos	G	Rec
1957	Chi	A	P	7	1-2
1958	Chi	A	P	13	3-0
1959	Chi	A	P	37	8-5
1960	Cle	A	P	31	7-7
1961	Cle	A	P	45	13-5
1962	Cle	A	P	45	8-13
	BRTR			178	40-32

LATTIMORE, WILLIAM HERSHEL
b.May 5,1884 Roxton,Tex.
d.Oct.8,1920

Yr	Cl	Lea	Pos	G	Rec
1908	Cle	A	P	4	1-2
	BLTL				

LAU, CHARLES RICHARD
b.Apr.12,1933 Romulus,Mich.

Yr	Cl	Lea	Pos	G	Rec
1956	Det	A	C	3	.222
1958	Det	A	C	30	.147
1959	Det	A	C	2	.167
1960	Mil	N	C	21	.189
1961	Mil	N	C	28	.207
1961	Bal	A	C	17	.170
1962	Bal	A	C	81	.294
	BLTR			182	.229

LAUDER, WILLIAM
b.Feb.23,1874 New York,N.Y.
d.May 20,1933

Yr	Cl	Lea	Pos	G	Rec
1898	Phi	N	3	97	.272
1899	Phi	N	3	149	.263
1901	Phi	A	3	2	.125
1902	NY	N	3-O	126	.239
1903	NY	N	3	108	.281
	TR			482	.262

LAUER, JOHN CHARLES (Chuck)
b.1865 Pittsburgh,Pa.

Yr	Cl	Lea	Pos	G	Rec
1884	Pit	a	P-1-O	13	0-2 .109
1889	Pit	N	C	4	.231
1890	Chi	N	C	2	.375
	TR			19	0-2 .179

LAUGHLIN, BENJAMIN

Yr	Cl	Lea	Pos	G	Rec
1873	Res	n	2-3	11	NR

LAUTERBORN, WILLIAM BERNARD
b.June 12,1878 Hornell,N.Y.

Yr	Cl	Lea	Pos	G	Rec
1904	Bos	N	2	20	.275
1905	Bos	N	2-3	57	.185
	TR			77	.208

LAVAGETTO, HARRY ARTHUR (Cookie)
b.Dec.1,1914 Oakland,Cal.

Yr	Cl	Lea	Pos	G	Rec
1934	Pit	N	2	87	.220
1935	Pit	N	2-3	78	.290
1936	Pit	N	2-3	60	.244
1937	Bro	N	2-3	149	.282
1938	Bro	N	3	137	.273
1939	Bro	N	3	153	.300
1940	Bro	N	3	118	.257
1941	Bro	N	3	132	.277
1946	Bro	N	3	88	.236
1947	Bro	N	1-3	41	.261
	BRTR			1043	.269

Non-playing manager Was(A) 1957-60, and Minnesota(A) 1961

LAVAN, JOHN LEONARD (Doc)
b.Oct.28,1890 Grand Rapids,Mich.
d.May 30,1952

Yr	Cl	Lea	Pos	G	Rec
1913	St.L	A	S	46	.147
1913	Phi	A	S	6	.067
1914	St.L	A	S	74	.263
1915	St.L	A	S	157	.218
1916	St.L	A	S	110	.236
1917	St.L	A	S	118	.239
1918	Was	A	S	117	.278
1919	St.L	N	S	100	.242
1920	St.L	N	S	142	.289
1921	St.L	N	S	150	.259
1922	St.L	N	S-3	89	.227
1923	St.L	N	1-2-S-3	50	.198
1924	St.L	N	2-S	4	.000
	BRTR			1163	.246

LAVENDER, JAMES SANFORD
b.Mar.26,1885 Montezuma,Ga.
d.Jan.12,1960

Yr	Cl	Lea	Pos	G	Rec
1912	Chi	N	P	42	16-13
1913	Chi	N	P	40	10-14
1914	Chi	N	P	37	11-11
1915	Chi	N	P	41	10-16
1916	Chi	N	P	36	10-14
1917	Phi	N	P	28	6-8
	BRTR			224	63-76

LAVIGNE, ARTHUR DAVID
b.Jan.26,1885 Worcester,Mass.
d.July 18,1950

Yr	Cl	Lea	Pos	G	Rec
1914	Buf	F	C	45	.200
	BRTR				

LAVIN, JOHN
b.Bay City,Mich.

Yr	Cl	Lea	Pos	G	Rec
1884	St.L	a	O	16	.204

LAW, VERNON SANDERS
b.Mar.12,1930 Meridian,Ida.

Yr	Cl	Lea	Pos	G	Rec
1950	Pit	N	P	27	7-9
1951	Pit	N	P	28	6-9
1954	Pit	N	P-O	50	9-13 .231
1955	Pit	N	P	44	10-10
1956	Pit	N	P	39	8-16
1957	Pit	N	P	34	10-8
1958	Pit	N	P	36	14-12
1959	Pit	N	P	38	18-9
1960	Pit	N	P	35	20-9
1961	Pit	N	P	11	3-4
1962	Pit	N	P	23	10-7
	BRTR			365	115-106 .197

LAWING, GARLAND FREDERICK
b.Aug.29,1919 Gastonia,N.C.

Yr	Cl	Lea	Pos	G	Rec
1946	Cin	N	O	2	.000
1946	NY	N	O	8	.167
	BRTR			10	.133

LAWLOR, MICHAEL H.
b.Troy,N.Y.
d.Aug.3,1918

Yr	Cl	Lea	Pos	G	Rec
1880	Tro	N	C	4	.100
1884	Was	U	C	2	.000
				6	.059

LAWRENCE, BROOKS ULYSSES (Bull)
b.Jan.30,1925 Springfield,O.

Yr	Cl	Lea	Pos	G	Rec
1954	St.L	N	P	35	15-6
1955	St.L	N	P	46	3-8
1956	Cin	N	P	49	19-10
1957	Cin	N	P	49	16-13
1958	Cin	N	P	46	8-13
1959	Cin	N	P	43	7-12
1960	Cin	N	P	7	1-0
	BRTR			275	69-62

LAWRENCE, ROBERT ANDREW (Larry)
b.Dec.14,1899 Brooklyn,N.Y.

Yr	Cl	Lea	Pos	G	Rec
1924	Chi	A	P	1	0-0
	BRTR				

LAWRENCE, WILLIAM HENRY
b.Mar.11,1906 San Mateo,Cal.

Yr	Cl	Lea	Pos	G	Rec
1932	Det	A	O	25	.217
	BRTR				

LAWRY, OTIS CARROLL
b.Nov.1,1893 Fairfield,Me.

Yr	Cl	Lea	Pos	G	Rec
1916	Phi	A	2	41	.203
1917	Phi	A	2	30	.164
	BLTR			71	.191

LAWSON, ALBERT W.
b.Bloomington,Ill.

Yr	Cl	Lea	Pos	G	Rec
1890	Bos	N	P	1	0-1
1890	Pit	N	P	2	0-1
	BRTR			3	0-2

LAWSON, ALFRED VOYLE (Roxie)
b.Apr.13,1906 Donnellson,Ia.

Yr	Cl	Lea	Pos	G	Rec
1930	Cle	A	P	7	1-2
1931	Cle	A	P	17	0-2
1933	Det	A	P	4	0-1
1935	Det	A	P	7	3-1
1936	Det	A	P	41	8-6
1937	Det	A	P	37	18-7
1938	Det	A	P	27	8-9

(Continued)

Yr	Cl	Lea	Pos	G	Rec
1939	Det	A	P	2	1-1
1939	St.L	A	P	37	3-7
1940	St.L	A	P	30	5-3
	BRTR			209	47-39

LAWSON, ROBERT BAKER
b.Aug.23,1876 Brookneal,Va.

Yr	Cl	Lea	Pos	G	Rec
1901	Bos	N	P	10	2-2
1902	Bal	A	P	3	0-2
				13	2-4

LAYDEN, EUGENE FRANCIS
b.Mar.14,1894 Pittsburgh,Pa.

Yr	Cl	Lea	Pos	G	Rec
1915	NY	A	O	3	.286
	BLTL				

LAYDON, PETER JOHN
b.Dec.30,1919 Dallas,Tex.

Yr	Cl	Lea	Pos	G	Rec
1948	St.L	A	O	41	.250
	BRTR				

LAYNE, HERMAN
b.Feb.13,1901 New Haven,W.Va.

Yr	Cl	Lea	Pos	G	Rec
1927	Pit	N	O	11	.000
	BRTR				

LAYNE, IVORIA HILLIS (Tony)
b.Feb.23,1919 Whitwell,Tenn.

Yr	Cl	Lea	Pos	G	Rec
1941	Was	A	3	13	.280
1944	Was	A	2-3	33	.195
1945	Was	A	3	61	.299
	BLTR			107	.264

LAYTON, LESTER LEE
b.Nov.18,1921 Nardin,Okla.

Yr	Cl	Lea	Pos	G	Rec
1948	NY	N	O	63	.231
	BRTR				

LAZOR, JOHN PAUL
b.Sept.9,1912 Taylor,Wash.

Yr	Cl	Lea	Pos	G	Rec
1943	Bos	A	O	83	.226
1944	Bos	A	C-O	16	.083
1945	Bos	A	O	101	.310
1946	Bos	A	O	23	.138
	BLTR			223	.263

LAZZERI, ANTHONY MICHAEL (Poosh 'Em Up)
b.Dec.6,1903 San Francisco,Cal.
d.Aug.6,1946

Yr	Cl	Lea	Pos	G	Rec
1926	NY	A	2	155	.275
1927	NY	A	2-S	153	.309
1928	NY	A	2	116	.332
1929	NY	A	2	147	.354
1930	NY	A	2-3	143	.303
1931	NY	A	2-3	135	.267
1932	NY	A	2	141	.300
1933	NY	A	2	139	.294
1934	NY	A	2-3	123	.267
1935	NY	A	2-S	130	.273
1936	NY	A	2	150	.287
1937	NY	A	2	126	.244
1938	Chi	N	S	54	.267
1939	Bro	N	2-3	14	.282
1939	NY	N	3	13	.295
	BRTR			1739	.292

LEACH, FREDERICK M.
b.Nov.23,1897 Springfield,Mo.

Yr	Cl	Lea	Pos	G	Rec
1923	Phi	N	O	52	.260
1924	Phi	N	O	8	.464
1925	Phi	N	O	65	.312
1926	Phi	N	O	129	.329
1927	Phi	N	O	140	.306
1928	Phi	N	1-O	145	.304
1929	NY	N	O	113	.290
1930	NY	N	O	126	.327
1931	NY	N	O	129	.309
1932	Bos	N	O	84	.247
	BLTR			991	.307

LEACH, THOMAS WILLIAM
b.Nov.4,1877 French Creek,N.Y.

Yr	Cl	Lea	Pos	G	Rec
1898	Lou	N	3	3	.300
1899	Lou	N	S-3	106	.289
1900	Pit	N	3	45	.215

(Continued)

Yr	Cl	Lea	Pos	G	Rec
1901	Pit	N	3	93	.298
1902	Pit	N	3	135	.280
1903	Pit	N	3	127	.298
1904	Pit	N	3	146	.257
1905	Pit	N	3-O	131	.257
1906	Pit	N	3-O	126	.286
1907	Pit	N	3-O	149	.303
1908	Pit	N	3	152	.259
1909	Pit	N	O	151	.261
1910	Pit	N	O	133	.270
1911	Pit	N	O	102	.238
1912	Pit	N	O	28	.299
1912	Chi	N	O	82	.240
1913	Chi	N	O	131	.287
1914	Chi	N	3-O	153	.263
1915	Cin	N	O	107	.224
1918	Pit	N	S-O	30	.194
	BRTR			2130	.270

LEADLEY, ROBERT H.
b.Detroit,Mich.
Non-playing manager Det (N) 1888 and Cle (N) 1890-91.

LEAHY, DANIEL C.
b.Aug.8,1870 Nashville,Tenn.
b.Dec.25,1915

Yr	Cl	Lea	Pos	G	Rec
1896	Phi	N	S	2	.333

LEAHY, THOMAS JOSEPH
b.June 2,1869 New Haven,Conn.
d.June 12,1951

Yr	Cl	Lea	Pos	G	Rec
1897	Pit	N	O	23	.242
1897	Was	N	C-2-3-O	20	.426
1898	Was	N	C	15	.182
1901	Mil	A	C	33	.240
1901	Phi	A	C	3	.294
1905	St.L	N	C	29	.227
	TR			123	.256

LEAR, CHARLES BERNARD (King)
b.Jan.23,1891 Greencastle,Pa.

Yr	Cl	Lea	Pos	G	Rec
1914	Cin	N	P	17	1-2
1915	Cin	N	P	40	6-10
	BRTR			57	7-12

LEAR, FREDERICK FRANCIS
b.Apr.7,1894 New York,N.Y.
d.Oct.13,1955

Yr	Cl	Lea	Pos	G	Rec
1915	Phi	A	3	2	.000
1918	Chi	N	2	2	.000
1919	Chi	N	2	40	.224
1920	NY	N	3	31	.253
	BRTR			75	.235

LEARD, WILLIAM WALLACE
b.Oct.14,1885 Oneida,N.Y.

Yr	Cl	Lea	Pos	G	Rec
1917	Bro	N	2	3	.000
	TR				

LEARY, FRANCIS PATRICK
b.Feb.26,1881 Wayland,Mass.
d.Oct.4,1907

Yr	Cl	Lea	Pos	G	Rec
1907	Cin	N	P	2	1-1

LEARY, JOHN J.
b.1858 New Haven,Conn.

Yr	Cl	Lea	Pos	G	Rec
1880	Bos	N	P-O	1	0-1 .000
1881	Det	N	P-O	3	0-2 .273
1882	Pit	a	P-1-2-3-O	61	1-0 .293
1882	Bal	a	P-O	4	2-1 .167
1883	Lou	a	S	40	.183
1883	Bal	a	2	3	.182
1884	Alt	U	P-3-O	8	0-3 .088
1884	Chi	U	P-2-3-O	10	0-0 .184
				130	3-7 .230

LEARY, JOHN LOUIS
b.May 2,1891 Waltham,Mass.
d.Aug.18,1961

Yr	Cl	Lea	Pos	G	Rec
1914	St.L	A	1	144	.265
1915	St.L	A	1	75	.243
	BRTR			219	.258

LEATHERS, HAROLD LANGFORD
b.Dec.2,1898 Los Angeles,Cal.

Yr	Cl	Lea	Pos	G	Rec
1920	Chi	N	S	7	.319
	BLTR				

LEBER, EMIL BOHMIEL
b.May 15,1881 Cleveland,O.
d.Nov.6,1924

Yr	Cl	Lea	Pos	G	Rec
1905	Cle	A	3	2	.000
	TR				

LeBOURVEAU, DeWITT WILEY (Bevo)
b.Aug.24,1896 Dana,Cal.
d.Dec.10,1947

Yr	Cl	Lea	Pos	G	Rec
1919	Phi	N	O	17	.270
1920	Phi	N	O	84	.257
1921	Phi	N	O	93	.295
1922	Phi	N	O	74	.269
1929	Phi	A	O	12	.312
	BLTR			280	.275

LeCLAIRE, GEORGE L.
b.1889 Milton,Vt.

Yr	Cl	Lea	Pos	G	Rec
1914	Pit	F	P	17	5-2
1915	Pit	F	P	14	3-2
1915	Buf	F	P	1	0-0
1915	Bal	F	P	17	0-6
	TR			49	8-10

LEDBETTER, RALPH OVERTON
b.Dec.8,1894 Rutherford College,N.Car.

Yr	Cl	Lea	Pos	G	Rec
1915	Det	A	P	1	0-0
	BRTR				

LEDWITH, MICHAEL
b.Brooklyn,N.Y.

Yr	Cl	Lea	Pos	G	Rec
1874	Atl	n	C	1	NR

LEE, CLIFFORD WALKER
b.Aug.4,1896 Lexington,Neb.

Yr	Cl	Lea	Pos	G	Rec
1919	Pit	N	C-O	42	.196
1920	Pit	N	C	37	.237
1921	Phi	N	1-O	88	.308
1922	Phi	N	1-3-O	122	.322
1923	Phi	N	1-O	107	.321
1924	Phi	N	1-O	21	.250
1924	Cin	N	O	6	.333
1925	Cle	A	O	77	.322
1926	Cle	A	O	21	.175
	BRTR			521	.300

LEE, DONALD EDWARD
b.Feb.26,1934 Globe,Ariz.

Yr	Cl	Lea	Pos	G	Rec
1957	Det	A	P	11	1-3
1958	Det	A	P	1	0-0
1960	Was	A	P	44	8-7
1961	Min	A	P	37	3-6
1962	Min	A	P	9	3-3
1962	LA	A	P	27	8-8
	BRTR			129	23-27

LEE, ERNEST DUDLEY (Dud)
(Also played under name of Ernest Dudley)
b.Aug.22,1900 Denver,Col.

Yr	Cl	Lea	Pos	G	Rec
	(Ernest Dudley)				
1920	St.L	A	S	1	1.000
1921	St.L	A	2-S	72	.167
	(Ernest Dudley Lee)				
1924	Bos	A	S	94	.253
1925	Bos	A	S	84	.224
1926	Bos	A	S	2	.143
	BLTR			253	.223

LEE, HAROLD BURNHAM (Sheriff)
b.Feb.15,1906 Ludlow,Miss.

Yr	Cl	Lea	Pos	G	Rec
1930	Bro	N	O	22	.162

(Continued)

Yr	Cl	Lea	Pos	G	Rec
1931	Phi	N	O	44	.221
1932	Phi	N	O	149	.303
1933	Phi	N	O	46	.287
1933	Bos	N	O	88	.221
1934	Bos	N	O	139	.292
1935	Bos	N	O	112	.303
1936	Bos	N	O	152	.253
	BRTR			752	.275

LEE, LEONIDAS P.
(Real name Leonidas P. Funkhouser)
b.Dec.13,1860 St.Louis,Mo.
d.June 11,1912

Yr	Cl	Lea	Pos	G	Rec
1877	St.L	N	S-O	4	.278

LEE, MICHAEL R.
b.May 19,1941 Bell,Cal.

Yr	Cl	Lea	Pos	G	Rec
1960	Cle	A	P	7	0-0
	BLTL				

LEE, ROY EDWIN
b.Sept.28,1918 Elmira,N.Y.

Yr	Cl	Lea	Pos	G	Rec
1945	NY	N	P	3	0-2
	BLTL				

LEE, THOMAS F.
b.June 9,1862 Milwaukee,Wis.
d.Mar.4,1886

Yr	Cl	Lea	Pos	G	Rec
1884	Chi	N	P-S	6	1-4 .125
1884	Bal	U	P-1-S-3-O	21	5-8 .300
				27	6-12 .260

LEE, THORNTON STARR (Lefty)
b.Sept.13,1906 Sonoma,Cal.

Yr	Cl	Lea	Pos	G	Rec
1933	Cle	A	P	3	1-1
1934	Cle	A	P	24	1-1
1935	Cle	A	P	32	7-10
1936	Cle	A	P	43	3-5
1937	Chi	A	P	30	12-10
1938	Chi	A	P	34	13-12
1939	Chi	A	P	33	15-11
1940	Chi	A	P	28	12-13
1941	Chi	A	P	35	22-11
1942	Chi	A	P	11	2-6
1943	Chi	A	P	19	5-9
1944	Chi	A	P	15	3-9
1945	Chi	A	P	29	15-12
1946	Chi	A	P	7	2-4
1947	Chi	A	P	21	3-7
1948	NY	N	P	11	1-3
	BLTL			375	117-124

LEE, WILLIAM CRUTCHER (Big Bill)
b.Oct.21,1909 Plaquemine,La.

Yr	Cl	Lea	Pos	G	Rec
1934	Chi	N	P	40	13-14
1935	Chi	N	P	39	20-6
1936	Chi	N	P	43	18-11
1937	Chi	N	P	42	14-15
1938	Chi	N	P	44	22-9
1939	Chi	N	P	37	19-15
1940	Chi	N	P	37	9-17
1941	Chi	N	P	28	8-14
1942	Chi	N	P	32	13-13
1943	Chi	N	P	13	3-7
1943	Phi	N	P	13	1-5
1944	Phi	N	P	31	10-11
1945	Phi	N	P	13	3-6
1945	Bos	N	P	16	6-3
1946	Bos	N	P	25	10-9
1947	Chi	N	P	14	0-2
	BRTR			467	169-157

LEE, WILLIAM JOSEPH
b.Jan.9,1895 Bayonne,N.J.

Yr	Cl	Lea	Pos	G	Rec
1915	St.L	A	3-O	18	.186
1916	St.L	A	O	7	.182
	BRTR			25	.186

LEE, WYATT ARNOLD (Watty)
b.Aug.12,1879 Lynch's Station,Va.

Yr	Cl	Lea	Pos	G	Rec
1901	Was	A	P	42	16-16
1902	Was	A	P-O	108	4-6 .261
1903	Was	A	P-O	76	8-13 .207
1904	Pit	N	P	8	1-2
TL				234	29-37 .247

LEEK, EUGENE HAROLD
b.July 15,1937 San Diego,Cal.

Yr	Cl	Lea	Pos	G	Rec
1959	Cle	A	S-3	13	.222
1961	LA	A	S-3-O	57	.226
1962	LA	A	3	7	.143
BRTR				77	.221

LEES, GEORGE EDWARD
b.Feb.2,1895 Bethlehem,Pa.

Yr	Cl	Lea	Pos	G	Rec
1921	Chi	A	C	20	.214
BRTR					

LEEVER, SAMUEL W. (Deacon)
b.Dec.23,1871 Goshen,O.
d.May 19,1953

Yr	Cl	Lea	Pos	G	Rec
1898	Pit	N	P	4	1-0
1899	Pit	N	P	50	20-23
1900	Pit	N	P	28	15-13
1901	Pit	N	P	19	14-5
1902	Pit	N	P-O	26	16-7 .178
1903	Pit	N	P	36	25-7
1904	Pit	N	P	34	18-12
1905	Pit	N	P	33	19-6
1906	Pit	N	P	36	22-7
1907	Pit	N	P	31	14-9
1908	Pit	N	P	38	15-7
1909	Pit	N	P	19	8-1
1910	Pit	N	P	26	6-5
BRTR				380	193-102 .186

LeFEBVRE, WILFRID HENRY (Bill)
b.Nov.11,1915 Natick,R.I.

Yr	Cl	Lea	Pos	G	Rec
1938	Bos	A	P	1	0-0
1939	Bos	A	P	7	1-1
1943	Was	A	P	7	2-0
1944	Was	A	P-1	60	2-4 .258
BLTL				75	5-5 .276

LeFEVRE, ALFRED MODESTO
b.Sept.16,1898 New York,N.Y.

Yr	Cl	Lea	Pos	G	Rec
1920	NY	N	2-S	17	.148
BLTR					

LEFLER, WADE HAMPTON
b.June 5,1897 Cooleemee,N.C.

Yr	Cl	Lea	Pos	G	Rec
1924	Bos	N	H	1	.000
1924	Was	A	O	5	.625
BL				6	.556

LEGETT, LOUIS ALFRED (Doc)
b.June 1,1901 New Orleans,La.

Yr	Cl	Lea	Pos	G	Rec
1929	Bos	N	C	39	.160
1933	Bos	A	C	8	.200
1934	Bos	A	C	19	.289
1935	Bos	A	H	2	.000
BRTR				68	.208

LEHANE, MICHAEL PATRICK
b.Rhode Island

Yr	Cl	Lea	Pos	G	Rec
1884	Was	U	S-3	3	.333
1890	Col	a	1	140	.185
1891	Col	a	1	137	.217
				280	.204

LEHENEY, REGIS FRANCIS
b.Jan.5,1908 Pittsburgh,Pa.

Yr	Cl	Lea	Pos	G	Rec
1932	Bos	A	P	2	0-0
BLTL					

LEHEW, JAMES ANTHONY
b.Aug.19,1937 Baltimore,Md.

Yr	Cl	Lea	Pos	G	Rec
1961	Bal	A	P	2	0-0
1962	Bal	A	P	6	0-0
BRTR				8	0-0

LEHMAN, KENNETH KARL
b.June 10,1928 Seattle,Wash.

Yr	Cl	Lea	Pos	G	Rec
1952	Bro	N	P	4	1-2
1956	Bro	N	P	25	2-3
1957	Bro	N	P	3	0-0
1957	Bal	A	P	33	8-3
1958	Bal	A	P	31	2-1
1961	Phi	N	P	42	1-1
BLTL				138	14-10

LEHNER, PAUL EUGENE (Peanuts)
b.July 1,1920 Dolomite,Ala.

Yr	Cl	Lea	Pos	G	Rec
1946	St.L	A	O	16	.222
1947	St.L	A	O	135	.248
1948	St.L	A	1-O	103	.276
1949	St.L	A	1-O	104	.229
1950	Phi	A	O	114	.309
1951	Phi	A	O	9	.143
1951	Chi	A	O	23	.208
1951	St.L	A	O	21	.134
1951	Cle	A	O	12	.231
1952	Bos	A	O	3	.667
BLTL				540	.257

LEHR, CLARENCE EMANUEL
b.May 16,1887 Escanaba,Mich.
d.Jan.31,1948

Yr	Cl	Lea	Pos	G	Rec
1911	Phi	N	2-S-O	12	.148
TR					

LEHR, NORMAN CARL MICHAEL
b.May 28,1901 Rochester,N.Y.

Yr	Cl	Lea	Pos	G	Rec
1926	Cle	A	P	4	0-0
TR					

LEIBER, HENRY EDWARD
b.Jan.17,1912 Phoenix,Ariz.

Yr	Cl	Lea	Pos	G	Rec
1933	NY	N	O	6	.200
1934	NY	N	O	63	.241
1935	NY	N	O	154	.331
1936	NY	N	O	101	.279
1937	NY	N	O	51	.293
1938	NY	N	O	98	.269
1939	Chi	N	O	112	.310
1940	Chi	N	1-O	117	.302
1941	Chi	N	1-O	53	.216
1942	NY	N	P-O	58	0-1 .218
BRTR				813	0-1 .288

LEIBOLD, HARRY LORAN (Nemo)
b.Feb.17,1892 Butler,Ind.

Yr	Cl	Lea	Pos	G	Rec
1913	Cle	A	O	84	.260
1914	Cle	A	O	114	.264
1915	Cle	A	O	56	.246
1915	Chi	A	O	37	.284
1916	Chi	A	O	45	.244
1917	Chi	A	O	125	.236
1918	Chi	A	O	116	.250
1919	Chi	A	O	122	.302
1920	Chi	A	O	108	.220
1921	Bos	A	O	123	.306
1922	Bos	A	O	81	.258
1923	Bos	A	O	11	.111
1923	Was	A	O	96	.305
1924	Was	A	O	84	.293
1925	Was	A	3-O	56	.273
BLTR				1258	.266

LEIFER, ELMER EDWIN
b.May 23,1893 Clarington,O.

Yr	Cl	Lea	Pos	G	Rec
1921	Chi	A	O	9	.300

LEIFIELD, ALBERT PETER (Lefty)
b.Sept.5,1883 Trenton,Ill.

Yr	Cl	Lea	Pos	G	Rec
1905	Pit	N	P	8	5-2
1906	Pit	N	P	37	18-13
1907	Pit	N	P	40	20-16
1908	Pit	N	P	34	15-14
1909	Pit	N	P	32	19-8
1910	Pit	N	P	40	15-13
1911	Pit	N	P	43	16-16
1912	Pit	N	P	6	1-2
1912	Chi	N	P	13	7-2
1913	Chi	N	P	6	0-1
1918	St.L	A	P	15	2-6
1919	St.L	A	P	19	6-4
1920	St.L	A	P	4	0-0
BLTL				297	124-97

LEIGHTON, JOHN ATKINSON
b.Oct.4,1861 Peabody,Mass.
d.Oct.31,1956

Yr	Cl	Lea	Pos	G	Rec
1890	Syr	a	O	7	.266

LEINHAUSER, WILLIAM CHARLES
b.Nov.4,1893 Philadelphia,Pa.

Yr	Cl	Lea	Pos	G	Rec
1912	Det	A	O	1	.000

LEIP, EDGAR ELLSWORTH
b.Nov.29,1914 Trenton,N.J.

Yr	Cl	Lea	Pos	G	Rec
1939	Was	A	2	9	.344
1940	Pit	N	2	3	.200
1941	Pit	N	2-3	15	.200
1942	Pit	N	H	3	.000
BRTR				30	.274

LEIPER, JOHN HENRY THOMAS
b.Dec.23,1867 Chester,Pa.

Yr	Cl	Lea	Pos	G	Rec
1891	Col	a	P	6	2-3

LEITH, WILLIAM (Shady Bill)
b.May 31,1874 Matteawan,N.Y.
d.July 16,1940

Yr	Cl	Lea	Pos	G	Rec
1899	Was	N	P	1	0-0

LEITNER, GEORGE ALOYSIUS (Doc)
b.Sept.14,1865 Piermont,N.Y.
d.May 18,1937

Yr	Cl	Lea	Pos	G	Rec
1887	Ind	N	P	9	2-7

LEITNER, GEORGE MICHAEL (Dummy)
b.June 19,1871 Baltimore,Md.
d.Feb.20,1960

Yr	Cl	Lea	Pos	G	Rec
1901	Phi	A	P	1	0-0
1901	NY	N	P	2	0-2
1902	Cle	A	P	1	0-1
1902	Chi	A	P	1	0-0
				5	0-3

LEJA, FRANK JOHN
b.Feb.7,1936 Holyoke,Mass.

Yr	Cl	Lea	Pos	G	Rec
1954	NY	A	1	12	.200
1955	NY	A	1	7	.000
1962	LA	A	1	7	.000
BLTL				26	.043

LeJEUNE, SHELDON ALDENBURY (Larry)
b.July 22,1885 Chicago,Ill.
d.Apr.21,1952

Yr	Cl	Lea	Pos	G	Rec
1911	Bro	N	O	6	.157
1915	Pit	N	O	18	.169
				24	.167

LELIVELT, JOHN FRANK
b.Nov.14,1885 Chicago,Ill.
d.Jan.20,1941

Yr	Cl	Lea	Pos	G	Rec
1909	Was	A	O	91	.292
1910	Was	A	O	110	.265
1911	Was	A	O	72	.320
1912	NY	A	O	36	.362
1913	NY	A	O	18	.214
1913	Cle	A	O	16	.409
1914	Cle	A	O	32	.328
BLTL				375	.301

LELIVELT, WILLIAM JOHN
b.Oct.21,1886 Chicago,Ill.

Yr	Cl	Lea	Pos	G	Rec
1909	Det	A	P	4	0-2
1910	Det	A	P	1	0-1
BRTR				5	0-3

LEMASTER, DENVER CLAYTON
b.Feb.25,1939 Corona,Cal.

Yr	Cl	Lea	Pos	G	Rec
1962	Mil	N	P	17	3-4
	BRTL				

LEMAY, RICHARD PAUL
b.Aug.28,1938 Cincinnati,O.

Yr	Cl	Lea	Pos	G	Rec
1961	SF	N	P	27	3-6
1962	SF	N	P	9	0-1
	BLTL			36	3-7

LEMBO, STEPHEN NEAL
b.Nov.13,1926 Brooklyn,N.Y.

Yr	Cl	Lea	Pos	G	Rec
1950	Bro	N	C	5	.167
1952	Bro	N	C	2	.200
	BRTR			7	.182

LEMON, JAMES ROBERT
b.Mar.23,1928 Covington,Va.

Yr	Cl	Lea	Pos	G	Rec
1950	Cle	A	O	12	.176
1953	Cle	A	1-O	16	.174
1954	Was	A	O	37	.234
1955	Was	A	O	10	.200
1956	Was	A	O	146	.271
1957	Was	A	1-O	137	.284
1958	Was	A	O	142	.246
1959	Was	A	O	147	.279
1960	Was	A	O	148	.269
1961	Min	A	O	129	.258
1962	Min	A	O	12	.176
	BRTR			936	.264

LEMON, ROBERT GRANVILLE
b.Sept.22,1920 San Bernardino,Cal.

Yr	Cl	Lea	Pos	G	Rec
1941	Cle	A	3	5	.250
1942	Cle	A	3	5	.000
1946	Cle	A	P-O	55	4-5 .180
1947	Cle	A	P-O	47	11-5 .321
1948	Cle	A	P	52	20-14
1949	Cle	A	P	46	22-10
1950	Cle	A	P	72	23-11
1951	Cle	A	P	56	17-14
1952	Cle	A	P	54	22-11
1953	Cle	A	P	51	21-15
1954	Cle	A	P	40	23-7
1955	Cle	A	P	49	18-10
1956	Cle	A	P	43	20-14
1957	Cle	A	P	25	6-11
1958	Cle	A	P	15	0-1
	BLTR			615	207-128 .222

LENHARDT, DONALD EUGENE (Footsie)
b.Oct.4,1922 Alton,Ill.

Yr	Cl	Lea	Pos	G	Rec
1950	St.L	A	1-3-O	139	.273
1951	St.L	A	1-O	31	.262
1951	Chi	A	1-O	64	.266
1952	Bos	A	O	30	.295
1952	Det	A	O	45	.188
1952	St.L	A	1-O	18	.271
1953	St.L	A	3-O	97	.317
1954	Bal	A	1-O	13	.152
1954	Bos	A	3-O	44	.273
	BRTR			481	.271

LENNON, EDWARD FRANCIS
b.Aug.17,1897 Philadelphia,Pa.
d.Sept.13,1947

Yr	Cl	Lea	Pos	G	Rec
1928	Phi	N	P	5	0-0
	BRTR				

LENNON, ROBERT ALBERT
b.Sept.15,1928 Brooklyn,N.Y.

Yr	Cl	Lea	Pos	G	Rec
1954	NY	N	H	3	.000
1956	NY	N	O	26	.182
1957	Chi	N	O	9	.143
	BLTL			38	.165

LENNON, WILLIAM F.
b.1848 Brooklyn,N.Y.

Yr	Cl	Lea	Pos	G	Rec
1871	Kek	n	M-C	11	NR
1872	Nat	n	C	10	NR
1873	Mar	n	C-1	5	NR
				26	NR

LENNOX, JAMES EDGAR (Eggie)
b.Nov.3,1885 Camden, N.J.
d.Oct.26,1939

Yr	Cl	Lea	Pos	G	Rec
1906	Phi	A	3	6	.059
1909	Bro	N	3	121	.262
1910	Bro	N	3	100	.259
1912	Chi	N	3	27	.235
1914	Pit	F	3	124	.317
1915	Pit	F	3	55	.321
	BRTR			433	.276

LENTZ, ...

Yr	Cl	Lea	Pos	G	Rec
1872	Eck	n	C	4	NR

LEON, ISIDORE JUAN
b.Feb.19,1915 Havana,Cuba.

Yr	Cl	Lea	Pos	G	Rec
1945	Phi	N	P	14	0-4
	BRTR				

LEONARD, ...

Yr	Cl	Lea	Pos	G	Rec
1892	St.L	N	O	1	.000

LEONARD, ANDREW JACKSON
b.June 1,1846 Ireland.
d.Aug.22,1903

Yr	Cl	Lea	Pos	G	Rec
1871	Oly	n	2-S-O	31	NR
1872	Bos	n	2-3-O	46	.349
1873	Bos	n	2-S-O	58	.327
1874	Bos	n	2-S-O	71	.342
1875	Bos	n	2-S-3-O	80	.323
1876	Bos	N	2-O	64	.277
1877	Bos	N	S-O	58	.286
1878	Bos	N	O	60	.259
1880	Cin	N	2-S-O	33	.210
1882	St.L	a	O	1	.250
	BRTR			502	NR

LEONARD, ELMER ELLSWORTH
b.Nov.12,1888 Napa,Cal.

Yr	Cl	Lea	Pos	G	Rec
1911	Phi	A	P	5	2-2
	BRTR				

LEONARD, EMIL JOHN (Dutch)
b.Mar.25,1909 Auburn,Ill.

Yr	Cl	Lea	Pos	G	Rec
1933	Bro	N	P	10	2-3
1934	Bro	N	P	44	14-11
1935	Bro	N	P	43	2-9
1936	Bro	N	P	16	0-0
1938	Was	A	P	33	12-15
1939	Was	A	P	34	20-8
1940	Was	A	P	35	14-19
1941	Was	A	P	34	18-13
1942	Was	A	P	6	2-2
1943	Was	A	P	31	11-13
1944	Was	A	P	32	14-14
1945	Was	A	P	31	17-7
1946	Was	A	P	26	10-10
1947	Phi	N	P	32	17-12
1948	Phi	N	P	34	12-17
1949	Chi	N	P	33	7-16
1950	Chi	N	P	35	5-1
1951	Chi	N	P	41	10-6
1952	Chi	N	P	45	2-2
1953	Chi	N	P	45	2-3
	BRTR			640	191-181

LEONARD, HUBERT BENJAMIN (Dutch)
b.July 26,1892 Lorraine Co.,O.
d.July 11,1952

Yr	Cl	Lea	Pos	G	Rec
1913	Bos	A	P	39	14-16
1914	Bos	A	P	32	19-5
1915	Bos	A	P	32	15-7
1916	Bos	A	P	48	18-12
1917	Bos	A	P	37	16-17
1918	Bos	A	P	16	8-6
1919	Det	A	P	29	14-13
1920	Det	A	P	28	10-17
1921	Det	A	P	36	11-13
1924	Det	A	P	9	3-2
1925	Det	A	P	18	11-4
	BLTL			324	139-112

LEONARD, JOSEPH HOWARD
b.Nov.14,1893 W.Chicago,Ill.
d.May 4,1920

Yr	Cl	Lea	Pos	G	Rec
1914	Pit	N	3	53	.198
1916	Cle	A	3	3	.000
1916	Was	A	3	42	.274
1917	Was	A	1-3	99	.192
1919	Was	A	2-3	71	.258
1920	Was	A	H	1	.000
	BLTR			269	.226

LEOPOLD, RUDOLPH MATAS
b.July 27,1907 Grand Cane,La.

Yr	Cl	Lea	Pos	G	Rec
1928	Chi	A	P	2	0-0
	BLTL				

LEOVICH, JOHN JOSEPH
b.May 5,1918 Portland,Ore.

Yr	Cl	Lea	Pos	G	Rec
1941	Phi	A	C	1	.500
	BRTR				

LEPCIO, THADDEUS STANLEY (Ted)
b.July 28,1930 Utica,N.Y.

Yr	Cl	Lea	Pos	G	Rec
1952	Bos	A	2-S-3	84	.263
1953	Bos	A	2-S-3	66	.236
1954	Bos	A	2-S-3	116	.256
1955	Bos	A	3	51	.231
1956	Bos	A	2-3	83	.261
1957	Bos	A	2	79	.241
1958	Bos	A	2	50	.199
1959	Bos	A	2	3	.333
1959	Det	A	2-S-3	76	.279
1960	Phi	N	2-S-3	69	.227
1961	Chi	A	3	5	.000
1961	Min	A	2-S-3	47	.170
	BRTR			729	.245

LePINE, LOUIS JOSEPH (Pete)
b.Sept.5,1876 Montreal,Que.,Canada.
d.Dec.4,1949

Yr	Cl	Lea	Pos	G	Rec
1902	Det	A	1-O	29	.202
	BLTL				

LEPPERT, DON EUGENE
b.Nov.20,1930 Memphis,Tenn.

Yr	Cl	Lea	Pos	G	Rec
1955	Bal	A	2	40	.114
	BLTR				

LEPPERT, DONALD GEORGE
b.Oct.19,1932 Indianapolis,Ind.

Yr	Cl	Lea	Pos	G	Rec
1961	Pit	N	C	22	.267
1962	Pit	N	C	45	.266
	BLTR			67	.266

LERCHEN, BERTRAM ROE
b.Apr.4,1889 Detroit,Mich.

Yr	Cl	Lea	Pos	G	Rec
1910	Bos	A	S	6	.067
	TR				

LERCHEN, GEORGE EDWARD
b.Dec.1,1922 Detroit,Mich.

Yr	Cl	Lea	Pos	G	Rec
1952	Det	A	O	14	.156
1953	Cin	N	O	22	.294
	BBTR			36	.204

LERIAN, WALTER IRVIN (Peck)
b.Mar.3,1903 Baltimore,Md.
d.Oct.22,1929

Yr	Cl	Lea	Pos	G	Rec
1928	Phi	N	C	96	.272
1929	Phi	N	C	105	.223
	BRTR			201	.246

Yr Cl Lea Pos G Rec

LeROY, LOUIS PAUL
b.Feb.18,1879 Red Springs,Wis.
d.Oct.10,1944
1905 NY A P 3 2-1
1906 NY A P 11 2-0
1910 Bos A P 1 0-0
TR 15 4-1

LESLIE, ROY REID
b.Aug.23,1894 Bailey,Tex.
1917 Chi N 1 7 .211
1919 St.L N 1 12 .208
1922 Phi N 1 141 .270
BRTR 160 .266

LESLIE, SAMUEL ANDREW (Sambo)
b.July 26,1906 Moss Point,Miss.
1929 NY N O 1 .000
1930 NY N H 2 .500
1931 NY N 1 53 .302
1932 NY N 1 77 .293
1933 NY N 1 40 .321
1933 Bro N 1 96 .283
1934 Bro N 1 146 .332
1935 Bro N 1 142 .308
1936 NY N 1 117 .295
1937 NY N 1 72 .309
1938 NY N 1 76 .253
BLTL 822 .304

LETCHAS, CHARLIE
b.Oct.3,1915 Thomasville,Ga.
1939 Phi N 2 12 .227
1941 Was A 2 2 .125
1944 Phi N 2-S-3 116 .238
1946 Phi N 2 6 .231
BRTR 136 .234

LETCHER, THOMAS F.
b.Harvard,Neb.
1891 Mil a O 6 .130

LEVAN, JESSE ROY
b.July 15,1926 Reading,Pa.
1947 Phi N O 2 .444
1954 Was A 1-3 7 .300
1955 Was A H 16 .188
BLTR 25 .286

LEVERENZ, WALTER FRANK (Tiny)
b.July 21,1888 Chicago,Ill.
1913 St.L A P 28 6-17
1914 St.L A P 26 1-12
1915 St.L A P 5 1-2
BLTL 59 8-31

LEVERETT, GORHAM VANCE (Dixie)
b.Mar.29,1894 Georgetown,Tex.
d.Feb.20,1957
1922 Chi A P 33 13-10
1923 Chi A P 38 10-13
1924 Chi A P 21 2-3
1926 Chi A P 6 1-1
1929 Bos N P 24 3-7
BRTR 122 29-34

LEVERETTE, HORACE WILLIAM
b.Feb.4,1889 Shreveport,La.
d.Apr.10,1958
1920 St.L A P 3 0-2
BRTR

LEVEY, JAMES JULIUS
b.Sept.13,1906 Pittsburgh,Pa.
1930 St.L A S 8 .243
1931 St.L A S 139 .209
1932 St.L A S 152 .280
1933 St.L A S 141 .195
BBTR 440 .230

Yr Cl Lea Pos G Rec

LEVIS, CHARLES T.
b.St.Louis,Mo.
1884 Bal U M-1-3 88 .228
1884 Was U 1 1 .000
1884 Ind a 1 3 .200
1885 Bal a 1 1 .333
93 .226

LEVSEN, EMIL HENRY (Dutch)
b.Apr.29,1900 Wyoming,Ia.
1923 Cle A P 3 0-0
1924 Cle A P 4 1-1
1925 Cle A P 4 1-2
1926 Cle A P 33 16-13
1927 Cle A P 25 3-7
1928 Cle A P 11 0-3
BRTR 80 21-26

LEVY, EDWARD CLARENCE
(Real name Edward Clarence Whitner)
b.Oct.28,1916 Birmingham,Ala.
1940 Phi N H 1 .000
1942 NY A 1 13 .122
1944 NY A O 40 .242
BRTR 54 .215

LEWANDOWSKI, DANIEL WILLIAM
b.Jan.6,1928 Buffalo,N.Y.
1951 St.L N P 2 0-1
BRTR

LEWIS, ...
b.Brooklyn,N.Y.
1890 Buf p P 1 0-0

LEWIS, EDWARD MORGAN (Parson)
b.Dec.25,1872 Machynlleth,Wales.
d.May 24,1936
1896 Bos N P 6 1-4
1897 Bos N P 35 20-12
1898 Bos N P 34 25-8
1899 Bos N P 28 17-11
1900 Bos N P 26 13-12
1901 Bos A P 38 17-16
167 93-63

LEWIS, FREDERICK MILLER
b.Oct.13,1858 Buffalo,N.Y.
d.June 5,1945
1881 Bos N O 27 .195
1883 Phi N O 38 .242
1883 St.L a O 50 .295
1884 St.L a O 72 .322
1884 St.L U O 8 .281
1885 St.L N O 45 .292
1886 Cin a O 67 .325
BBTR 307 .296

LEWIS, GEORGE EDWARD (Duffy)
b.Apr.18,1888 San Francisco,Cal.
1910 Bos A O 151 .283
1911 Bos A O 130 .307
1912 Bos A O 154 .284
1913 Bos A O 149 .298
1914 Bos A O 146 .278
1915 Bos A O 152 .291
1916 Bos A O 152 .268
1917 Bos A O 150 .302
1919 NY A O 141 .272
1920 NY A O 107 .271
1921 Was A O 27 .186
BLTL 1459 .284

LEWIS, JOHN D.
b.1888 Pittsburgh,Pa.
1911 Bos A 2 18 .271
1914 Pit F 2 117 .234
1915 Pit F 2 77 .268
BRTR 212 .249

LEWIS, JOHN KELLY (Buddy)
b.Aug.10,1916 Gastonia,N.C.
1935 Was A 3 8 .107
1936 Was A 3 143 .291
1937 Was A 3 156 .314
1938 Was A 3 151 .296
1939 Was A 3 140 .319
1940 Was A 3-O 148 .317
1941 Was A 3-O 149 .297
1945 Was A O 69 .333
1946 Was A O 150 .292

Yr Cl Lea Pos G Rec

(Continued)
1947 Was A O 140 .261
1949 Was A O 95 .245
BLTR 1349 .297

LEWIS, PHILIP
b.Oct.7,1883 Pittsburgh,Pa.
d.Aug.8,1959
1905 Bro N S 118 .254
1906 Bro N S 135 .243
1907 Bro N S 136 .248
1908 Bro N S 116 .219
BRTR 505 .242

LEWIS, WILLIAM BURTON (Bert)
b.Oct.3,1895 Tonawanda,N.Y.
d.Mar.24,1950
1924 Phi N P 12 0-0
BRTR

LEWIS, WILLIAM HENRY
b.Oct.15,1905 Ripley,Tenn.
1933 St.L N C 15 .400
1935 Bos N C 6 .000
1936 Bos N C 29 .306
BRTR 50 .327

LEZOTTE, ABEL
b.Apr.13,1870 Lewiston,Me.
1896 Pit N 1 7 .104

LIBBY, STEPHEN AUGUSTUS
b.Dec.8,1853 Scarborough,Me.
1879 Buf N 1 1 .000

LIBKE, ALBERT WALTER
b.Sept.12,1919 Tacoma,Wash.
1945 Cin N P-1-O 130 {0-0 .283}
1946 Cin N P-O 124 {0-0 .253}
BLTR 254 {0-0 .268}

LIDDLE, DONALD EUGENE
b.May 25,1926 Mt.Carmel,Ill.
1953 Mil N P 31 7-6
1954 NY N P 29 9-4
1955 NY N P 33 10-4
1956 NY N P 11 1-2
1956 St.L N P 15 1-2
BLTL 119 28-18

LIEBER, CHARLES EDWIN (Dutch)
b.Feb.1,1909 Alameda,Cal.
1935 Phi A P 19 1-1
1936 Phi A P 3 0-1
BRTR 22 1-2

LIEBHARDT, GLENN IGNATIUS
b.July31,1910 Cleveland,O.
1930 Phi A P 5 0-1
1936 St.L A P 24 0-0
1938 St.L A P 2 0-0
BRTR 31 0-1

LIEBHARDT, GLENN JOHN
b.Mar.10,1883 Milton,Ind.
d.July 13,1956
1906 Cle A P 2 2-0
1907 Cle A P 38 18-14
1908 Cle A P 38 15-16
1909 Cle A P 12 1-5
90 36-35

LIESE, FREDERICK RICHARD
1910 Bos N P 4 0-0

LIFSIT, HENRY LANDERS
(Played under name of
Henry Landers Bostick)

LILLARD, ROBERT EUGENE (Gene)
b.Nov.12,1913 Santa Barbara,Cal.
1936 Chi N S-3 19 .206
1939 Chi N P 23 3-5
1940 St.L N P 2 0-1
BRTR 44 {3-6 .182}

LILLARD, WILLIAM BEVERLY
b.Jan.10,1918 Goleta,Cal.

Yr	Cl	Lea	Pos	G	Rec
1939	Phi	A	S	7	.316
1940	Phi	A	2-S	73	.238
			BRTR	80	.244

LILLIE, JAMES J.
b.1862 New Haven,Conn.
d.Nov.9,1890

Yr	Cl	Lea	Pos	G	Rec
1883	Buf	N	P-2-3-O	50	0-0 .231
1884	Buf	N	P-C-O	110	0-1 .219
1885	Buf	N	1-S-O	112	.248
1886	KC	N	O	114	.175
				386	0-1 .217

LILLIS, ROBERT PERRY
b.June 2,1930 Altadena,Cal.

Yr	Cl	Lea	Pos	G	Rec
1958	LA	N	S	20	.391
1959	LA	N	S	30	.229
1960	LA	N	2-S-3	48	.267
1961	LA	N	2-S-3	19	.111
1961	St.L	N	2-S	86	.217
1962	Hou	N	2-S-3	129	.249
			BRTR	332	.251

LIMMER, LOUIS
b.Mar.10,1927 New York,N.Y.

Yr	Cl	Lea	Pos	G	Rec
1951	Phi	A	1	94	.159
1954	Phi	A	1	115	.231
			BLTL	209	.202

LINCOLN, EZRA PERRY
b.Nov.17,1868 Raynham,Mass.
d.May 7,1951

Yr	Cl	Lea	Pos	G	Rec
1890	Cle	N	P	15	3-10
1890	Syr	a	P	3	0-3
			TL	18	3-13

LIND, HENRY CARL
b.Sept.19,1904 New Orleans,La.
d.Aug.4,1946

Yr	Cl	Lea	Pos	G	Rec
1927	Cle	A	2	12	.135
1928	Cle	A	2	154	.294
1929	Cle	A	2	66	.240
1930	Cle	A	2	24	.247
			BRTR	256	.272

LINDAMAN, VIVIAN ALEXANDER
b.Oct.28,1877 Charles City,Ia.
d.Feb.13,1927

Yr	Cl	Lea	Pos	G	Rec
1906	Bos	N	P	39	12-23
1907	Bos	N	P	34	11-15
1908	Bos	N	P	43	12-16
1909	Bos	N	P	15	1-6
			BLTL	131	36-60

LINDBECK, EMERIT DESMOND
b.Aug.27,1935 Kewanee,Ill.

Yr	Cl	Lea	Pos	G	Rec
1960	Det	A	H	2	.000

BLTR

LINDE, LYMAN GILBERT
b.Sept.20,1920 Beaver Dam,Wis.

Yr	Cl	Lea	Pos	G	Rec
1947	Cle	A	P	1	0-0
1948	Cle	A	P	3	0-0
			BRTR	4	0-0

LINDELL, JOHN HARLAN
b.Aug.30,1916 Greeley,Col.

Yr	Cl	Lea	Pos	G	Rec
1941	NY	A	H	1	.000
1942	NY	A	P	27	2-1
1943	NY	A	O	122	.245
1944	NY	A	O	149	.300
1945	NY	A	O	41	.283
1946	NY	A	1-O	102	.259
1947	NY	A	O	127	.275
1948	NY	A	O	88	.317
1949	NY	A	O	78	.242
1950	NY	A	O	7	.190
1950	St.L	N	O	36	.186

(Continued)

Yr	Cl	Lea	Pos	G	Rec
1953	Pit	N	P-1	58	5-16 .286
1953	Phi	N	P-O	11	1-1 .389
1954	Phi	N	H	7	.200
			BRTR	854	8-18 .273

LINDEMANN, ERNEST
b.June 10,1883 New York,N.Y.
d.Dec.27,1951

Yr	Cl	Lea	Pos	G	Rec
1907	Bos	N	P	1	0-0

BRTR

LINDEN, WALTER CHARLES
b.Mar.27,1925 Chicago,Ill.

Yr	Cl	Lea	Pos	G	Rec
1950	Bos	N	C	3	.400

BRTR

LINDERMANN, ROBERT J.
b.Chester,Pa.

Yr	Cl	Lea	Pos	G	Rec
1901	Phi	A	O	3	.100

LINDQUIST, CARL EMIL
b.May 9,1920 Morris Run,Pa.

Yr	Cl	Lea	Pos	G	Rec
1943	Bos	N	P	2	0-2
1944	Bos	N	P	5	0-0
			BRTR	7	0-2

LINDSAY, CHRISTIAN H. (Pinky
b.July 21,1878 Monaca,Pa.
d.Jan.25,1941

Yr	Cl	Lea	Pos	G	Rec
1905	Det	A	1	88	.267
1906	Det	A	1-2	141	.224
				229	.240

LINDSAY, WILLIAM GIBBON
b.Feb.24,1887 Madison,N.C.

Yr	Cl	Lea	Pos	G	Rec
1911	Cle	A	3	19	.242

BLTR

LINDSEY, JAMES KENDRICK
b.Jan.24,1900 Greensburg,La.

Yr	Cl	Lea	Pos	G	Rec
1922	Cle	A	P	29	4-5
1924	Cle	A	P	3	0-0
1929	St.L	N	P	2	1-1
1930	St.L	N	P	39	7-5
1931	St.L	N	P	35	6-4
1932	St.L	N	P	33	3-3
1933	St.L	N	P	1	0-0
1934	Cin	N	P	4	0-0
1934	St.L	N	P	11	0-1
1937	Bro	N	P	20	0-1
			BRTR	177	21-20

LINDSTROM, AXEL OLOF
b.Aug.26,1895 Gustafsberg,Sweden.
d.June 24,1940

Yr	Cl	Lea	Pos	G	Rec
1916	Phi	A	P	1	0-0

LINDSTROM, CHARLES WILLIAM
b.Sept.7,1936 Chicago,Ill.

Yr	Cl	Lea	Pos	G	Rec
1958	Chi	A	C	1	1.000

BRTR

LINDSTROM, FREDERICK CHARLES
b.Nov.21,1905 Chicago,Ill.

Yr	Cl	Lea	Pos	G	Rec
1924	NY	N	2-3	52	.253
1925	NY	N	2-S-3	104	.287
1926	NY	N	3	140	.302
1927	NY	N	3-O	138	.306
1928	NY	N	3	153	.358
1929	NY	N	3	130	.319
1930	NY	N	3	148	.379
1931	NY	N	O	78	.300
1932	NY	N	O	144	.271
1933	Pit	N	O	138	.310
1934	Pit	N	O	97	.290
1935	Chi	N	3-O	90	.275
1936	Bro	N	O	26	.264
			BRTR	1438	.311

LINHART, CARL JAMES
b.Dec.14,1929 Zborov,Czechoslovakia.

Yr	Cl	Lea	Pos	G	Rec
1952	Det	A	H	3	.000

BLTR

LINKE, EDWARD KARL (Babe)
b.Nov.9,1911 Chicago,Ill.

Yr	Cl	Lea	Pos	G	Rec
1933	Was	A	P	3	1-0
1934	Was	A	P	8	2-2
1935	Was	A	P	40	11-7
1936	Was	A	P	13	1-5
1937	Was	A	P	37	6-1
1938	St.L	A	P	21	1-7
			BRTR	122	22-22

LINKE, FREDERICK L. (Laddie)

Yr	Cl	Lea	Pos	G	Rec
1910	Cle	A	P	22	5-6
1910	St.L	A	P	3	0-0
				25	5-6

LINT, ROYCE JAMES
b.Jan.1,1921 Birmingham,Ala.

Yr	Cl	Lea	Pos	G	Rec
1954	St.L	N	P	31	2-3

BLTL

LINTON, CLAUDE C. (Bob)
b.Apr.18,1903 Emerson,Ark.

Yr	Cl	Lea	Pos	G	Rec
1929	Pit	N	C	17	.111

BLTR

LINZ, PHILIP FRANCIS
b.June 4,1939 Baltimore,Md.

Yr	Cl	Lea	Pos	G	Rec
1962	NY	A	2-S-3-O	71	.287

BRTR

Li PETRI, MICHAEL ANGELO
b.July 6,1930 Brooklyn,N.Y.

Yr	Cl	Lea	Pos	G	Rec
1956	Phi	N	P	6	0-0
1958	Phi	N	P	4	0-0
			BRTR	10	0-0

LIPON, JOHN JOSEPH (Skids)
b.Nov.10,1922 Martin's Ferry,O.

Yr	Cl	Lea	Pos	G	Rec
1942	Det	A	S	34	.191
1946	Det	A	S-3	14	.300
1948	Det	A	2-S-3	121	.290
1949	Det	A	S	127	.251
1950	Det	A	S	147	.293
1951	Det	A	S	129	.265
1952	Det	A	S	39	.221
1952	Bos	A	S-3	79	.205
1953	Bos	A	S	60	.214
1953	St.L	A	2-3	7	.222
1954	Cin	N	H	1	.000
			BRTR	758	.259

LIPP, THOMAS C.
b.1871 Baltimore,Md.

Yr	Cl	Lea	Pos	G	Rec
1897	Phi	N	P	1	0-1

LIPSCOMB, GERARD (Nig)
b.Feb.24,1911 Rutherfordton,N.C.

Yr	Cl	Lea	Pos	G	Rec
1937	St.L	A	P-2	36	0-0 .323

BRTR

LISENBEE, HORACE MILTON (Hod)
b.Sept.23,1901 Clarksville,Tenn.

Yr	Cl	Lea	Pos	G	Rec
1927	Was	A	P	39	18-9
1928	Was	A	P	16	2-6
1929	Bos	A	P	5	0-0
1930	Bos	A	P	37	10-17
1931	Bos	A	P	41	5-12
1932	Bos	A	P	19	0-4
1936	Phi	A	P	19	1-7
1945	Cin	N	P	31	1-3
			BRTR	207	37-58

LISKA, ADOLPH JAMES
b.July 10,1906 Dwight,Neb.

Yr	Cl	Lea	Pos	G	Rec
1929	Was	A	P	24	3-9
1930	Was	A	P	32	9-7
1931	Was	A	P	2	0-1
1932	Phi	N	P	8	2-0
1933	Phi	N	P-O	47	3-1 .071
			BRTR	113	17-18 .108

LISTER, MORRIS ELMER (Pete)
b.July 21,1881 Savanna,Ill.
d.May 12,1948

Yr	Cl	Lea	Pos	G	Rec
1907	Cle	A	1	22	.277

LITTLE, GEORGE HARRY
b.St.Louis,Mo.
d.Jan.25,1892

Yr	Cl	Lea	Pos	G	Rec
1877	St.L	N	O	1	.200
1877	Lou	N	2	1	.000
1877	St.L	N	O	2	.143
				4	.133

LITTLE, WILLIAM ARTHUR (Jack)
b.Mar.12,1891 Mart,Tex.

Yr	Cl	Lea	Pos	G	Rec
1912	NY	A	O	3	.250

LITTLEFIELD, RICHARD BERNARD
b.Mar.18,1926 Detroit,Mich.

Yr	Cl	Lea	Pos	G	Rec
1950	Bos	A	P	15	2-2
1951	Chi	A	P	4	1-1
1952	Det	A	P	28	0-3
1952	St.L	A	P	7	2-3
1953	St.L	A	P	38	7-12
1954	Bal	A	P	3	0-0
1954	Pit	N	P	23	10-11
1955	Pit	N	P	35	5-12
1956	Pit	N	P	6	0-0
1956	St.L	N	P	3	0-2
1956	NY	N	P	31	4-4
1957	Chi	N	P	48	2-3
1958	Mil	N	P	4	0-1
BLTL				245	33-54

LITTLEJOHN, CHARLES CARLISLE
b.Oct.6,1901 Irene,Tex.

Yr	Cl	Lea	Pos	G	Rec
1927	St.L	N	P	15	3-1
1928	St.L	N	P	12	2-1
BRTR				27	5-2

LITTRELL, JACK NAPIER
b.Jan.22,1929 Louisville,Ky.

Yr	Cl	Lea	Pos	G	Rec
1952	Phi	A	S-3	4	.000
1954	Phi	A	S	9	.300
1955	KC	A	1-2-S	37	.200
1957	Chi	A	2-S-3	61	.190
BRTR				111	.204

LITWHILER, DANIEL WEBSTER
b.Aug.31,1917 Ringtown,Pa.

Yr	Cl	Lea	Pos	G	Rec
1940	Phi	N	O	36	.345
1941	Phi	N	O	151	.305
1942	Phi	N	O	151	.271
1943	Phi	N	O	36	.258
1943	St.L	N	O	80	.279
1944	St.L	N	O	140	.264
1946	St.L	N	H	6	.000
1946	Bos	N	3-O	79	.292
1947	Bos	N	O	91	.261
1948	Bos	N	O	13	.273
1948	Cin	N	3-O	106	.275
1949	Cin	N	3-O	102	.291
1950	Cin	N	O	54	.259
1951	Cin	N	O	12	.276
BRTR				1057	.281

LIVELY, EVERETT ADRIAN (Buddy)
b.Feb.14,1925 Birmingham,Ala.

Yr	Cl	Lea	Pos	G	Rec
1947	Cin	N	P	38	4-7
1948	Cin	N	P	10	0-0
1949	Cin	N	P	31	4-6
BRTR				79	8-13

LIVELY, HENRY EVERETT (Jack)
b.May 29,1885 Joppa,Ala.

Yr	Cl	Lea	Pos	G	Rec
1911	Det	A	P	20	7-5
BR					

LIVENGOOD, WESLEY AMOS
b.July 18,1911 Winston-Salem,N.C.

Yr	Cl	Lea	Pos	G	Rec
1939	Cin	N	P	5	0-0
BRTR					

LIVINGSTON, PATRICK JOSEPH (Paddy)
b.Jan.14,1880 Cleveland,O.

Yr	Cl	Lea	Pos	G	Rec
1901	Cle	A	C	1	.000
1906	Cin	N	C	47	.158
1909	Phi	A	C	64	.234
1910	Phi	A	C	37	.208
1911	Phi	A	C	27	.239
1912	Cle	A	C	19	.234
1917	St.L	N	C	7	.200
BRTR				202	.208

LIVINGSTON, THOMPSON ORVILLE (Mickey)
b.Nov.15,1914 Newberry,S.C.

Yr	Cl	Lea	Pos	G	Rec
1938	Was	A	C	2	.750
1941	Phi	N	C-1	95	.203
1942	Phi	N	C-1	89	.205
1943	Phi	N	C-1	84	.249
1943	Chi	N	C-1	36	.261
1945	Chi	N	C-1	71	.254
1946	Chi	N	C	66	.256
1947	Chi	N	C	19	.212
1947	NY	N	C	5	.167
1948	NY	N	C	45	.212
1949	NY	N	C	19	.298
1949	Bos	N	C	28	.234
1951	Bro	N	C	2	.400
BRTR				561	.238

LIVINGSTONE, ALBANY
b.N.Y.
d.Jan.21,1914

Yr	Cl	Lea	Pos	G	Rec
1901	NY	N	P	2	0-2

LLEWELLYN, CLEMENT MANLEY
b.Mar.1,1895 Dobson,N.C.

Yr	Cl	Lea	Pos	G	Rec
1922	NY	A	P	1	1-0
BLTR					

LOAN, WILLIAM JOSEPH (Mike)
b.Sept.27,1895 Philadelphia,Pa.

Yr	Cl	Lea	Pos	G	Rec
1912	Phi	N	C	1	.500
TR					

LOANE, ROBERT KENNETH
b.Aug.6,1914 Berkeley,Cal.

Yr	Cl	Lea	Pos	G	Rec
1939	Was	A	O	3	.000
1940	Bos	N	O	13	.227
BRTR				16	.161

LOBERT, FRANK JOHN
b.Nov.26,1883 Williamsport,Pa.
d.May 29,1932

Yr	Cl	Lea	Pos	G	Rec
1914	Bal	F	3	10	.167
TR					

LOBERT, JOHN BERNARD (Hans)
b.Oct.18,1881 Wilmington,Del.

Yr	Cl	Lea	Pos	G	Rec
1903	Pit	N	3	5	.077
1905	Chi	N	3	14	.196
1906	Cin	N	S-3	76	.310
1907	Cin	N	S	147	.246
1908	Cin	N	S-3-O	155	.293
1909	Cin	N	3	122	.212
1910	Cin	N	3	90	.309
1911	Phi	N	3	147	.285
1912	Phi	N	3	65	.327
1913	Phi	N	3	150	.300
1914	Phi	N	3	135	.275
1915	NY	N	3	106	.251
1916	NY	N	3	48	.224
1917	NY	N	3	50	.192
BRTR				1310	.275

Non-playing manager Phi (N) 1938 and 1942.

LOCK, DON WILSON
b.July 27,1936 Wichita,Kan.

Yr	Cl	Lea	Pos	G	Rec
1962	Was	A	O	71	.253
BRTR					

LOCKE, CHARLES EDWARD
b.May 5,1932 Malden,Mo.

Yr	Cl	Lea	Pos	G	Rec
1955	Bal	A	P	2	0-0
BRTR					

LOCKE, LAWRENCE DONALD
b.Mar.3,1934 Rowes Run,Pa.

Yr	Cl	Lea	Pos	G	Rec
1959	Cle	A	P	24	3-2
1960	Cle	A	P	35	3-5
1961	Cle	A	P	37	4-4
1962	St.L	N	P	1	0-0
1962	Phi	N	P	5	1-0
BRTR				102	11-11

LOCKE, MARSHALL
b.Indianapolis,Ind.

Yr	Cl	Lea	Pos	G	Rec
1874	Bal	n	S	1	.000
1884	Ind	a	O	7	.241
				8	.233

LOCKHEAD, HARRY P.
b.California

Yr	Cl	Lea	Pos	G	Rec
1899	Cle	N	S	146	.223
1901	Det	A	S	1	.500
1901	Phi	A	S	9	.088
TR				156	.217

LOCKMAN, CARROLL WALTER (Whitey)
b.July 25,1926 Lowell,N.C.

Yr	Cl	Lea	Pos	G	Rec
1945	NY	N	O	32	.341
1947	NY	N	H	2	.500
1948	NY	N	O	146	.286
1949	NY	N	O	151	.301
1950	NY	N	O	129	.295
1951	NY	N	1-O	153	.282
1952	NY	N	1	154	.290
1953	NY	N	1-O	150	.295
1954	NY	N	1-O	148	.251
1955	NY	N	1-O	147	.273
1956	NY	N	1-O	48	.272
1956	St.L	N	1-O	70	.249
1957	NY	N	1-O	133	.248
1958	SF	N	1-2-O	92	.238
1959	Bal	A	1-2-O	38	.217
1959	Cin	N	1-2-3-O	52	.262
1960	Cin	N	1	21	.200
BLTR				1666	.279

LOCKLIN, STUART CARLTON
b.July 22,1928 Appleton,Wis.

Yr	Cl	Lea	Pos	G	Rec
1955	Cle	A	O	16	.167
1956	Cle	A	O	9	.167
BLTL				25	.167

LOCKWOOD, MILO HATHAWAY
b.Apr.7,1858 Cleveland,O.
d.Oct.9,1897

Yr	Cl	Lea	Pos	G	Rec
1884	Was	U	P-3-O	20	1-9 / .209

LODIGIANI, DARIO ANTONIO
b.June 6,1916 San Francisco,Cal.

Yr	Cl	Lea	Pos	G	Rec
1938	Phi	A	2-3	93	.280
1939	Phi	A	2-3	121	.260
1940	Phi	A	H	1	.000
1941	Chi	A	3	87	.239
1942	Chi	A	2-3	59	.280
1946	Chi	A	3	44	.245
BRTR				405	.260

LOEPP, GEORGE HERBERT
b.Sept.11,1903 Detroit,Mich.

Yr	Cl	Lea	Pos	G	Rec
1928	Bos	A	O	15	.176
1930	Was	A	O	50	.276
BRTR				65	.249

LOES, WILLIAM
b.Dec.13,1929 Long Island City,N.Y.

Yr	Cl	Lea	Pos	G	Rec
1950	Bro	N	P	10	0-0
1952	Bro	N	P	39	13-8
1953	Bro	N	P	32	14-8
1954	Bro	N	P	28	13-5
1955	Bro	N	P	22	10-4
1956	Bro	N	P	1	0-1
1956	Bal	A	P	21	2-7

(Continued)

Yr	Cl	Lea	Pos	G	Rec
1957	Bal	A	P	31	12-7
1958	Bal	A	P	32	3-9
1959	Bal	A	P	37	4-7
1960	SF	N	P	37	3-2
1961	SF	N	P	26	6-5
	BRTR			316	80-63

LOFTUS, FRANCIS PATRICK
b.Mar.10,1900 Scranton,Pa.

Yr	Cl	Lea	Pos	G	Rec
1926	Was	A	P	1	0-0
	BRTR				

LOFTUS, RICHARD JOSEPH
b.Mar.7,1901 Concord,Mass.

Yr	Cl	Lea	Pos	G	Rec
1924	Bro	N	1-O	46	.272
1925	Bro	N	O	51	.237
	BLTR			97	.250

LOFTUS, THOMAS JOSEPH
b.Nov.15,1856 St.Louis,Mo.
d.Apr.16,1910

Yr	Cl	Lea	Pos	G	Rec
1877	St.L	N	O	3	.182
1883	St.L	a	O	6	.160
				9	.167

Non-playing manager Cle (a) 1888,Cle (N) 1889,Cin (N) 1890-91,Chi (N) 1900-01 and Was (A) 1902-03.

LOGAN, JOHN (Yatcha)
b.Mar.23,1927 Endicott,N.Y.

Yr	Cl	Lea	Pos	G	Rec
1951	Bos	N	S	62	.219
1952	Bos	N	S	117	.283
1953	Mil	N	S	150	.273
1954	Mil	N	S	154	.275
1955	Mil	N	S	154	.297
1956	Mil	N	S	148	.281
1957	Mil	N	S	129	.273
1958	Mil	N	S	145	.226
1959	Mil	N	S	138	.291
1960	Mil	N	S	136	.245
1961	Mil	N	S	18	.105
1961	Pit	N	S-3	27	.231
1962	Pit	N	3	44	.300
	BRTR			1422	.270

LOGAN, ROBERT DEAN
(Lefty)
b.Feb.8,1910 Thompson,Neb.

Yr	Cl	Lea	Pos	G	Rec
1935	Bro	N	P	2	0-1
1937	Det	A	P	1	0-0
1937	Chi	N	P	4	0-0
1938	Chi	N	P	14	0-2
1941	Cin	N	P	2	0-1
1945	Bos	N	P	34	7-11
	BRTL			57	7-15

LOHMAN, GEORGE F. (Pete)
b.Oct.21,1864 Lake Elmo,Minn.
d.Nov.21,1928

Yr	Cl	Lea	Pos	G	Rec
1891	Was	a	C	32	.200

LOHR, HOWARD SYLVESTER
b.June 3,1892 Philadelphia,Pa.

Yr	Cl	Lea	Pos	G	Rec
1914	Cin	N	O	18	.213
1916	Cle	A	O	3	.143
	BRTR			21	.204

LOHRKE, JACK WAYNE
(Lucky)
b.Feb.25,1924 Los Angeles,Cal.

Yr	Cl	Lea	Pos	G	Rec
1947	NY	N	3	112	.240
1948	NY	N	2-3	97	.250
1949	NY	N	2-S-3	55	.267
1950	NY	N	2-3	30	.186
1951	NY	N	S-3	23	.200
1952	Phi	N	2-S-3	25	.207
1953	Phi	N	2-S-3	12	.154
	BRTR			354	.242

LOHRMAN, WILLIAM LeROY
b.May 22,1913 Brooklyn,N.Y.

Yr	Cl	Lea	Pos	G	Rec
1934	Phi	N	P	4	0-1
1937	NY	N	P	2	1-0
1938	NY	N	P	31	9-6
1939	NY	N	P	38	12-13
1940	NY	N	P	31	10-15
1941	NY	N	P	33	9-10
1942	St.L	N	P	5	1-1
1942	NY	N	P	26	13-4
1943	NY	N	P	21	5-6
1943	Bro	N	P	6	0-2
1944	Bro	N	P	3	0-0
1944	Cin	N	P	2	0-1
	BRTR			202	60-59

LOLLAR, JOHN SHERMAN
(Sherm)
b.Aug.23,1924 Durham,Ark.

Yr	Cl	Lea	Pos	G	Rec
1946	Cle	A	C	28	.242
1947	NY	A	C	11	.219
1948	NY	A	C	22	.211
1949	StL	A	C	109	.261
1950	StL	A	C	126	.280
1951	St.L	A	C-3	98	.252
1952	Chi	A	C	132	.240
1953	Chi	A	C-1	113	.287
1954	Chi	A	C	107	.244
1955	Chi	A	C	138	.261
1956	Chi	A	C	136	.293
1957	Chi	A	C	101	.256
1958	Chi	A	C	127	.273
1959	Chi	A	C-1	140	.265
1960	Chi	A	C	129	.252
1961	Chi	A	C	116	.282
1962	Chi	A	C	84	.268
	BRTR			1717	.265

LOMBARDI, ERNESTO NATALI
(Schnozz)
b.Apr.6,1908 Oakland,Cal.

Yr	Cl	Lea	Pos	G	Rec
1931	Bro	N	C	73	.297
1932	Cin	N	C	118	.303
1933	Cin	N	C	107	.283
1934	Cin	N	C	132	.305
1935	Cin	N	C	120	.343
1936	Cin	N	C	121	.333
1937	Cin	N	C	120	.334
1938	Cin	N	C	129	.342
1939	Cin	N	C	130	.287
1940	Cin	N	C	109	.319
1941	Cin	N	C	117	.264
1942	Bos	N	C	105	.330
1943	NY	N	C	104	.305
1944	NY	N	C	117	.255
1945	NY	N	C	115	.307
1946	NY	N	C	88	.290
1947	NY	N	C	48	.282
	BRTR			1853	.306

LOMBARDI, VICTOR ALVIN
b.Sept.20,1922 Berkeley,Cal.

Yr	Cl	Lea	Pos	G	Rec
1945	Bro	N	P	45	10-11
1946	Bro	N	P	43	13-10
1947	Bro	N	P	36	12-11
1948	Pit	N	P	39	10-9
1949	Pit	N	P	43	5-5
1950	Pit	N	P	42	0-5
	BLTL			248	50-51

LOMBARDO, LOUIS
b.Nov.18,1928 Carlstadt,N.J.

Yr	Cl	Lea	Pos	G	Rec
1948	NY	N	P	2	0-0
	BLTL				

LONERGAN, WALTER E.
b.Sept.22,1885 S.Boston,Mass.
d.Jan.23,1958

Yr	Cl	Lea	Pos	G	Rec
1911	Bos	A	2-S-3	9	.269
	BRTR				

LONG, DANIEL W.
b.Aug.27,1867 Boston,Mass.
d.Apr.30,1929

Yr	Cl	Lea	Pos	G	Rec
1888	Lou	a	O	1	.000
1890	Bal	a	O	21	.177
				22	.173

LONG, HERMAN C.
(Flying Dutchman)
b.Apr.13,1866 Chicago,Ill.
d.Sept.17,1909

Yr	Cl	Lea	Pos	G	Rec
1889	KC	a	S	136	.280
1890	Bos	N	S	101	.250
1891	Bos	N	S	139	.287
1892	Bos	N	S	151	.286
1893	Bos	N	S	128	.294
1894	Bos	N	S	103	.324
1895	Bos	N	S	124	.319
1896	Bos	N	S	119	.334
1897	Bos	N	S	106	.327
1898	Bos	N	S	142	.275
1899	Bos	N	S	145	.257
1900	Bos	N	S	124	.256
1901	Bos	N	S	138	.238
1902	Bos	N	2-S	120	.227
1903	NY	A	S	22	.225
1903	Det	A	2-S	69	.218
1904	Phi	N	2	1	.250
	BLTR			1868	.280

LONG, JAMES ALBERT
b.June 29,1898 Ft.Dodge,Ia.

Yr	Cl	Lea	Pos	G	Rec
1922	Chi	A	C	3	.000
	BRTR				

LONG, JAMES M.
b.Nov.15,1862 Louisville,Ky.
d.Dec.12.1932

Yr	Cl	Lea	Pos	G	Rec
1891	Lou	a	O	6	.240
1893	Bal	N	O	55	.225
				61	.227

LONG, LESTER
b.July 12,1888 Summit,N.J.

Yr	Cl	Lea	Pos	G	Rec
1911	Phi	A	P	4	0-0
	BRTR				

LONG, NELSON (Red)
b.Sept.28,1876 Hamilton,Ont.,Canada.
d.Aug.11,1929

Yr	Cl	Lea	Pos	G	Rec
1902	Bos	N	P	1	0-0

LONG, RICHARD DALE
b.Feb.6,1926 Springfield,Mo.

Yr	Cl	Lea	Pos	G	Rec
1951	Pit	N	1	10	.167
1951	St.L	A	1-O	34	.238
1955	Pit	N	1	131	.291
1956	Pit	N	1	148	.263
1957	Pit	N	1	7	.182
1957	Chi	N	1	123	.305
1958	Chi	N	C-1	142	.271
1959	Chi	N	1	110	.236
1960	SF	N	1	37	.167
1960	NY	A	1	26	.366
1961	Was	A	1	123	.249
1962	Was	A	1	67	.241
1962	NY	A	1	41	.298
	BLTL			999	.267

LONG, THOMAS AUGUSTUS
b.June 1,1890 Mitchum,Ala.

Yr	Cl	Lea	Pos	G	Rec
1911	Was	A	O	14	.208
1912	Was	A	O	1	.000
1915	St.L	N	O	140	.294
1916	St.L	N	O	119	.293
1917	St.L	N	O	144	.232
	BRTR			418	.269

LONG, THOMAS FRANCIS
b.Apr.22,1898 Memphis,Tenn.

Yr	Cl	Lea	Pos	G	Rec
1924	Bro	N	P	1	0-0
	BLTL				

LONNETT, JOSEPH PAUL
b.Feb.7,1927 Beaver Falls,Pa.

Yr	Cl	Lea	Pos	G	Rec
1956	Phi	N	C	16	.182
1957	Phi	N	C	67	.169
1958	Phi	N	C	17	.140
1959	Phi	N	C	43	.172
	BRTR			143	.166

LOOK, DEAN ZACHARY
b.July 23,1937 Lansing,Mich.

Yr	Cl	Lea	Pos	G	Rec
1961	Chi	A	O	3	.000

BRTR

LOOS, PETER
b.Philadelphia,Pa.

Yr	Cl	Lea	Pos	G	Rec
1901	Phi	A	P	1	0-1

LOPAT, EDMUND WALTER
(Real name Edmund Walter Lopatynski)
b.June 21,1918 New York,N.Y.

Yr	Cl	Lea	Pos	G	Rec
1944	Chi	A	P	30	11-10
1945	Chi	A	P	32	10-13
1946	Chi	A	P	30	13-13
1947	Chi	A	P	35	16-13
1948	NY	A	P	34	17-11
1949	NY	A	P	31	15-10
1950	NY	A	P	36	18-8
1951	NY	A	P	31	21-9
1952	NY	A	P	20	10-5
1953	NY	A	P	26	16-4
1954	NY	A	P	26	12-4
1955	NY	A	P	16	4-8
1955	Bal	A	P	10	3-4
	BLTL			357	166-112

LOPATA, STANLEY EDWARD
(Stash)
b.Sept.12,1925 Delray,Mich.

Yr	Cl	Lea	Pos	G	Rec
1948	Phi	N	C	6	.133
1949	Phi	N	C	83	.271
1950	Phi	N	C	58	.209
1951	Phi	N	C	3	.000
1952	Phi	N	C	57	.274
1953	Phi	N	C	81	.239
1954	Phi	N	C-1	86	.290
1955	Phi	N	C-1	99	.271
1956	Phi	N	C-1	146	.267
1957	Phi	N	C	116	.237
1958	Phi	N	C	86	.248
1959	Mil	N	C-1	25	.104
1960	Mil	N	C	7	.125
	BRTR			853	.254

LOPATKA, ARTHUR JOSEPH
b.May 28,1920 Chicago,Ill.

Yr	Cl	Lea	Pos	G	Rec
1945	St.L	N	P	4	1-0
1946	Phi	N	P	4	0-1
	BBTL			8	1-1

LOPATYNSKI, EDMUND WALTER (Played under name of Edmund Walter Lopat)

LOPEZ, ALFONSO RAMON
b.Aug.20,1908 Tampa,Fla.

Yr	Cl	Lea	Pos	G	Rec
1928	Bro	N	C	3	.000
1930	Bro	N	C	128	.309
1931	Bro	N	C	111	.269
1932	Bro	N	C	126	.275
1933	Bro	N	C-2	126	.301
1934	Bro	N	C	140	.275
1935	Bro	N	C	128	.251
1936	Bos	N	C	128	.242
1937	Bos	N	C	105	.204
1938	Bos	N	C	71	.267
1939	Bos	N	C	131	.252
1940	Bos	N	C	36	.294
1940	Pit	N	C	59	.259
1941	Pit	N	C	114	.265
1942	Pit	N	C	103	.256
1943	Pit	N	C-3	118	.263
1944	Pit	N	C	115	.230
1945	Pit	N	C	91	.218
1946	Pit	N	C	56	.307
1947	Cle	A	C	61	.262
	BRTR			1950	.261

Non-playing manager Cle (A) 1951-56 and Chi (A) 1957-62

LOPEZ, HECTOR HEADLEY
b.July 8,1932 Colon,Panama

Yr	Cl	Lea	Pos	G	Rec
1955	KC	A	2-3	128	.290
1956	KC	A	2-S-3-O	151	.273
1957	KC	A	2-3-O	121	.294
1958	KC	A	2-S-3-O	151	.261

(Continued)

Yr	Cl	Lea	Pos	G	Rec
1959	KC	A	2	35	.281
1959	NY	A	3-O	112	.283
1960	NY	A	2-3-O	131	.284
1961	NY	A	O	93	.222
1962	NY	A	2-3-O	106	.275
	BRTR			1028	.275

LORD, BRISTOL ROBOTHAM
(Briscoe)
b.Sept.12,1883 Upland,Pa.

Yr	Cl	Lea	Pos	G	Rec
1905	Phi	A	O	66	.239
1906	Phi	A	P-O	118	0-0 .233
1907	Phi	A	O	57	.182
1909	Cle	A	O	69	.269
1910	Cle	A	O	57	.226
1910	Phi	A	O	69	.274
1911	Phi	A	O	134	.310
1912	Phi	A	O	96	.238
1913	Bos	N	O	73	.251
	BRTR			739	0-0 .256

LORD, CARLTON
b.Jan.7,1900 Pa.

Yr	Cl	Lea	Pos	G	Rec
1923	Phi	N	3	17	.234

BRTR

LORD, HARRY DONALD
b.Mar.8,1882 Porter,Me.
d.Aug.9,1948

Yr	Cl	Lea	Pos	G	Rec
1907	Bos	A	3	10	.184
1908	Bos	A	3	145	.259
1909	Bos	A	3	136	.311
1910	Bos	A	3	77	.243
1910	Chi	A	3	44	.310
1911	Chi	A	3	141	.321
1912	Chi	A	3-O	151	.267
1913	Chi	A	3	150	.263
1914	Chi	A	3	21	.189
1915	Buf	F	M-3	97	.273
	BLTR			972	.278

LORENZEN, ADOLPH ANDREAS
b.Jan.12,1893 Davenport,Ia.

Yr	Cl	Lea	Pos	G	Rec
1913	Det	A	P	1	0-0

BLTL

LOTZ, JOSEPH PETER (Smokey)
b.Jan.2,1892 Remsen,Ia.

Yr	Cl	Lea	Pos	G	Rec
1916	St.L	N	P	12	0-3

BRTR

LOUDELL, ARTHUR
b.1885

Yr	Cl	Lea	Pos	G	Rec
1910	Det	A	P	5	1-1

BR

LOUDEN, WILLIAM (Baldy)
b.Aug.27,1885 Piedmont,W.Va.
d.Dec.8,1935

Yr	Cl	Lea	Pos	G	Rec
1907	NY	A	3	2	.167
1912	Det	A	2	121	.241
1913	Det	A	2	72	.241
1914	Buf	F	S	127	.313
1915	Buf	F	2-S-3	137	.280
1916	Cin	N	2-S	134	.219
	BRTR			593	.261

LOUDENSLAGER, CHARLES E.
b.Baltimore,Md.

Yr	Cl	Lea	Pos	G	Rec
1904	Bro	N	2	1	.000

TR

LOUGHLIN, WILLIAM H.
b.Baltimore,Md.

Yr	Cl	Lea	Pos	G	Rec
1883	Bal	a	O	1	.400

LOUGHRAN, ...
b.New York,N.Y.

Yr	Cl	Lea	Pos	G	Rec
1884	NY	N	C-O	8	.120

LOVE, ELMER HAUGHTON
(Slim)
b.Aug.1,1893 Love,Miss.
d.Nov.30,1942

Yr	Cl	Lea	Pos	G	Rec
1913	Was	A	P	5	2-0

(Continued)

Yr	Cl	Lea	Pos	G	Rec
1916	NY	A	P	20	2-0
1917	NY	A	P	33	6-5
1918	NY	A	P	38	13-12
1919	Det	A	P	22	5-4
1920	Det	A	P	1	0-0
	BLTL			119	28-21

LOVELACE, GROVER THOMAS
b.Sept.8,1898 Wolfe City,Tex.

Yr	Cl	Lea	Pos	G	Rec
1922	Pit	N	O	1	.000

BRTR

LOVENGUTH, LYNN RICHARD
b.Nov.29,1923 Camden,N.J.

Yr	Cl	Lea	Pos	G	Rec
1955	Phi.	N	P	14	0-1
1957	St.L	N	P	3	0-1
	BLTR			17	0-2

LOVETT, JOHN
b.May 6,1878 Monday,O.
d.Dec.6,1937

Yr	Cl	Lea	Pos	G	Rec
1903	St.L	N	P	3	0-0

LOVETT, LEONARD WALKER
b.July 17,1852 Lancaster Co.,Pa.
d.Nov.18,1922

Yr	Cl	Lea	Pos	G	Rec
1873	Res	n	P	1	0-1
1875	Cen	n	O	5	NR
	BRTR			6	0-1 NR

LOVETT, MERRITT MARWOOD
b.June 15,1912 Chicago,Ill.

Yr	Cl	Lea	Pos	G	Rec
1933	Chi	A	H	1	.000

BRTR

LOVETT, THOMAS JOSEPH
b.Dec.7,1863 Providence,R.I.
d.Mar.20,1928

Yr	Cl	Lea	Pos	G	Rec
1885	Ath	a	P	16	7-8
1889	Bro	a	P	30	18-10
1890	Bro	N	P	44	31-11
1891	Bro	N	P	42	24-18
1893	Bro	N	P	18	3-6
1894	Bos	N	P	15	7-4
	BR			165	90-57

LOW, FLETCHER
b.Apr.7,1893 Essex,Mass.

Yr	Cl	Lea	Pos	G	Rec
1915	Bos	N	3	1	.250

BRTR

LOWDERMILK, GROVER CLEVELAND
b.Jan.15,1886 Sandborn,Ind.

Yr	Cl	Lea	Pos	G	Rec
1909	St.L	N	P	7	0-2
1911	St.L	N	P	11	0-1
1912	Chi	N	P	2	0-1
1915	St.L	A	P	38	9-18
1915	Det	A	P	7	4-1
1916	Det	A	P	2	0-0
1916	Cle	A	P	10	1-5
1917	St.L	A	P	3	2-1
1918	St.L	A	P	13	2-6
1919	St.L	A	P	7	0-0
1919	Chi	A	P	20	5-5
1920	Chi	A	P	3	0-0
	BRTR			123	23-40

LOWDERMILK, LOUIS B.
b.Feb.23,1889 Sandborn,Ind.

Yr	Cl	Lea	Pos	G	Rec
1911	St.L	N	P	16	3-4
1912	St.L	N	P	4	1-1
				20	4-5

LOWE, ...

Yr	Cl	Lea	Pos	G	Rec
1884	Det	N	C	1	.250

LOWE, CHARLES
b.Baltimore,Md.

Yr	Cl	Lea	Pos	G	Rec
1872	Atl	n	2	6	NR

LOWE, GEORGE WESLEY
b.Apr.25,1895 Ridgefield Park,N.J.

Yr	Cl	Lea	Pos	G	Rec
1920	Cin	N	P	1	0-0

LOWE, ROBERT LINCOLN
(Link)
b.July 10,1868 Allegheny,Pa.
d.Dec.8,1951

Yr	Cl	Lea	Pos	G	Rec
1890	Bos	N	S-O	52	.280
1891	Bos	N	2-O	124	.281
1892	Bos	N	O	124	.244
1893	Bos	N	2	120	.316
1894	Bos	N	2	133	.341
1895	Bos	N	2	99	.301
1896	Bos	N	2	73	.320
1897	Bos	N	2	121	.314
1898	Bos	N	2	147	.272
1899	Bos	N	2	152	.267
1900	Bos	N	2	127	.279
1901	Bos	N	2-3	129	.259
1902	Chi	N	2-3	121	.260
1903	Chi	N	2	28	.267
1904	Pit	N	H	1	.000
1904	Det	A	M-2	140	.205
1905	Det	A	3-O	58	.193
1906	Det	A	2-S	41	.207
1907	Det	A	3	17	.243
			BRTR	1807	.275

LOWN, OMAR JOSEPH
(Turk)
b.May 30,1924 Brooklyn,N.Y.

Yr	Cl	Lea	Pos	G	Rec
1951	Chi	N	P	31	4-9
1952	Chi	N	P	33	4-11
1953	Chi	N	P	49	8-7
1954	Chi	N	P	16	0-2
1956	Chi	N	P	61	9-8
1957	Chi	N	P	67	5-7
1958	Chi	N	P	4	0-0
1958	Cin	N	P	11	0-2
1958	Chi	A	P	27	3-3
1959	Chi	A	P	60	9-2
1960	Chi	A	P	45	2-3
1961	Chi	A	P	60	7-5
1962	Chi	A	P	42	4-2
			BRTR	506	55-61

LOWREY, HARRY LEE
(Peanuts)
b.Aug.27,1918 Culver City,Cal.

Yr	Cl	Lea	Pos	G	Rec
1942	Chi	N	O	27	.190
1943	Chi	N	2-S-O	130	.292
1945	Chi	N	S-O	143	.283
1946	Chi	N	3-O	144	.257
1947	Chi	N	2-3-O	115	.281
1948	Chi	N	2-S-3-O	129	.294
1949	Chi	N	3-O	38	.270
1949	Cin	N	O	89	.224
1950	Cin	N	2-O	91	.227
1950	St.L	N	2-3-O	17	.268
1951	St.L	N	2-3-O	114	.303
1952	St.L	N	3-O	132	.286
1953	St.L	N	2-3-O	104	.269
1954	St.L	N	O	74	.115
1955	Phi	N	1-2-O	54	.189
			BRTR	1401	.273

LOWRY, JOHN D.
b.Baltimore,Md.

Yr	Cl	Lea	Pos	G	Rec
1875	Nat	n	O	6	NR

LOWRY, SAMUEL JOSEPH
b.Mar.25,1920 Philadelphia,Pa.

Yr	Cl	Lea	Pos	G	Rec
1942	Phi	A	P	1	0-0
1943	Phi	A	P	5	0-0
			BRTR	6	0-0

LUBY, HUGH MAX (Hal)
b.June 13,1913 Blackfoot,Ida.

Yr	Cl	Lea	Pos	G	Rec
1936	Phi	A	2	9	.184
1944	NY	N	1-2-3	111	.254
			BRTR	120	.247

LUBY, JOHN PERKINS (Pat)
b.1868 Charleston,S.C.
d.Apr.24,1899

Yr	Cl	Lea	Pos	G	Rec
1890	Chi	N	P-1-O	30	20-8
					.342

(Continued)

Yr	Cl	Lea	Pos	G	Rec
1891	Chi	N	P	24	10-12
1892	Chi	N	P	40	9-21
1895	Lou	N	P	15	1-5
			TR	109	40-46
					.250

LUCADELLO, JOHN
b.Feb.22,1919 Thurbur,Tex.

Yr	Cl	Lea	Pos	G	Rec
1938	St.L	A	3	7	.150
1939	St.L	A	2	9	.233
1940	St.L	A	2	17	.317
1941	St.L	A	2-S-3-O	107	.279
1946	St.L	A	2-3	87	.248
1947	NY	A	2	12	.083
			BBTR	239	.264

LUCAS, CHARLES FREDERICK
(Red)
b.Apr.28,1902 Columbia,Tenn.

Yr	Cl	Lea	Pos	G	Rec
1923	NY	N	P	3	0-0
1924	Bos	N	P-3	33	1-4
					.333
1925	Bos	N	2	6	.150
1926	Cin	N	P-2	66	8-5
					.303
1927	Cin	N	P-2-S-O	80	18-11
					.313
1928	Cin	N	P	39	13-9
1929	Cin	N	P	76	19-12
1930	Cin	N	P	80	14-16
1931	Cin	N	P	97	14-13
1932	Cin	N	P	76	13-17
1933	Cin	N	P	75	10-16
1934	Pit	N	P	68	10-9
1935	Pit	N	P	47	8-6
1936	Pit	N	P	69	15-4
1937	Pit	N	P	59	8-10
1938	Pit	N	P	33	6-3
			BLTR	907	157-135
					.281

LUCAS, FREDERICK WARRINGTON
b.Jan.19,1905 Vineland,N.J.

Yr	Cl	Lea	Pos	G	Rec
1935	Phi	N	O	20	.265
		BRTR			

LUCAS, HENRY V.
b.Apr.25,1895 Ridgefield Park,N.J.
d.Nov.15,1910
Non-playing manager St.L (N) 1885.

LUCAS, JOHN CHARLES
b.Feb.10,1908 Glen Carbon,Ill.

Yr	Cl	Lea	Pos	G	Rec
1931	Bos	A	O	3	.000
1932	Bos	A	O	1	.000
			BRTL	4	.000

LUCAS, J. R. C.
Non-playing manager St.L (N) 1877.

LUCAS, RAYMOND WESLEY
b.Oct.2,1908 Springfield,O.

Yr	Cl	Lea	Pos	G	Rec
1929	NY	N	P	3	0-0
1930	NY	N	P	6	0-0
1931	NY	N	P	1	0-0
1933	Bro	N	P	2	0-0
1934	Bro	N	P	10	1-1
			BRTR	22	1-1

LUCE, FRANK EDWARD
b.Dec.6,1899 Spencer,O.
d.Feb.3,1942

Yr	Cl	Lea	Pos	G	Rec
1923	Pit	N	O	9	.500
		BLTR			

LUCEY, JOSEPH EARL
b.Mar.27,1900 Holyoke,Mass.

Yr	Cl	Lea	Pos	G	Rec
1920	NY	A	2	3	.000
1925	Bos	A	P-S	10	0-1
					.133
			BRTR	13	0-1
					.118

LUCID, CORNELIUS CONRAD
(Con)
b.Feb.24,1869 Dublin,Ireland.

Yr	Cl	Lea	Pos	G	Rec
1893	Lou	N	P	2	0-1
1894	Bro	N	P	10	4-3
1895	Bro	N	P	21	11-6
1895	Phi	N	P	10	6-3
1896	Phi	N	P	5	1-4
1897	St.L	N	P	6	1-5
				54	23-22

LUCIER, LOUIS JOSEPH
b.Mar.23,1918 Northbridge,Mass.

Yr	Cl	Lea	Pos	G	Rec
1943	Bos	A	P	16	3-4
1944	Bos	A	P	3	0-0
1944	Phi	N	P	1	0-0
1945	Phi	N	P	13	0-1
			BRTR	33	3-5

LUCKEY, HOWARD J.
b.Philadelphia,Pa.

Yr	Cl	Lea	Pos	G	Rec
1890	Ath	a	P	1	0-0

LUDERUS, FREDERICK WILLIAM
b.Sept.12,1886 Milwaukee,Wis.
d.Jan.4.1961

Yr	Cl	Lea	Pos	G	Rec
1909	Chi	N	1	11	.305
1910	Chi	N	1	17	.204
1910	Phi	N	1	19	.294
1911	Phi	N	1	146	.301
1912	Phi	N	1	148	.257
1913	Phi	N	1	155	.262
1914	Phi	N	1	121	.248
1915	Phi	N	1	141	.315
1916	Phi	N	1	146	.281
1917	Phi	N	1	154	.261
1918	Phi	N	1	125	.288
1919	Phi	N	1	138	.293
1920	Phi	N	1	16	.156
			BLTR	1337	.277

LUDOLPH, WILLIAM FRANCIS
(Wee Willie)
b.Jan.21,1900 San Francisco,Cal.
d.Apr.7,1952

Yr	Cl	Lea	Pos	G	Rec
1924	Det	A	P	3	0-0
		BRTR			

LUDWIG, WILLIAM LAWRENCE
b.May 27,1882 Louisville,Ky.
d.Sept.5,1947

Yr	Cl	Lea	Pos	G	Rec
1908	St.L	N	C	62	.182
		TR			

LUEBBE, ROY JOHN
b.Sept.17,1901 Parkersburg,Ia.

Yr	Cl	Lea	Pos	G	Rec
1925	NY	A	C	8	.000
		BBTR			

LUEBKE, RICHARD RAYMOND
b.Apr.8,1935 Chicago,Ill.

Yr	Cl	Lea	Pos	G	Rec
1962	Bal	A	P	10	0-1
		BRTL			

LUFF, HENRY T.
b.Philadelphia,Pa.

Yr	Cl	Lea	Pos	G	Rec
1875	NH	n	P-3-O	38	1-7
					NR
1882	Det	N	2-O	3	.273
1882	Cin	a	1-O	28	.223
1883	Lou	a	1-O	6	.174
1884	Key	U	1-O	24	.266
1884	KC	U	3-O	5	.053
				104	1-7
					NR

LUHRSEN, WILLIAM FERDINAND
b.Apr.14,1884 Buckley,Ill.

Yr	Cl	Lea	Pos	G	Rec
1913	Pit	N	P	5	3-1
		BRTR			

LUKENS, ALBERT P.
b.1872 Vineland,N.J.

Yr	Cl	Lea	Pos	G	Rec
1894	Phi	N	P	3	0-1

LUKON, EDWARD PAUL
b.Aug.5,1920 Burgettstown,Pa.

Yr	Cl	Lea	Pos	G	Rec
1941	Cin	N	O	23	.267
1945	Cin	N	O	2	.125
1946	Cin	N	O	102	.250
1947	Cin	N	O	86	.205
			BLTL	213	.236

LUMENTI, RAPHAEL ANTHONY
(Ralph)
b.Dec.21,1936 Milford,Mass.

Yr	Cl	Lea	Pos	G	Rec
1957	Was	A	P	3	0-1
1958	Was	A	P	8	1-2
1959	Was	A	P	2	0-0
	BLTL			13	1-3

LUMLEY, HARRY G. (Judge)
b.Sept.29,1880 Forest City,Pa.
d.May 22,1938

Yr	Cl	Lea	Pos	G	Rec
1904	Bro	N	O	150	.279
1905	Bro	N	O	129	.293
1906	Bro	N	O	131	.324
1907	Bro	N	O	118	.267
1908	Bro	N	O	116	.216
1909	Bro	N	M-O	52	.250
1910	Bro	N	O	8	.100
				704	.275

LUMPE, JERRY DEAN
b.June 2,1933 Lincoln,Mo.

Yr	Cl	Lea	Pos	G	Rec
1956	NY	A	S-3	20	.258
1957	NY	A	S-3	40	.340
1958	NY	A	2-S-3	81	.254
1959	NY	A	2-S-3	18	.222
1959	KC	A	2-S-3	108	.243
1960	KC	A	2-S	146	.272
1961	KC	A	2	148	.293
1962	KC	A	2-S	156	.301
	BLTR			717	.279

LUNA, GUILLERMO ROMERO
(Memo)
b.June 25,1930 Tacubaya,Mexico

Yr	Cl	Lea	Pos	G	Rec
1954	St.L	N	P	1	0-1
	BLTL				

LUND, DONALD ANDREW
b.May 18,1923 Detroit,Mich.

Yr	Cl	Lea	Pos	G	Rec
1945	Bro	N	H	4	.000
1947	Bro	N	O	11	.300
1948	Bro	N	O	27	.188
1948	St.L	A	O	63	.248
1949	Det	A	H	2	.000
1952	Det	A	O	8	.304
1953	Det	A	O	131	.257
1954	Det	A	O	35	.130
	BRTR			281	.240

LUNDBOM, JOHN FREDERICK
b.Mar.10,1877 Manistee,Mich.
d.Oct.31,1949

Yr	Cl	Lea	Pos	G	Rec
1902	Cle	A	P	8	2-1
	TL				

LUNDGREN, CARL LEONARD
b.Feb.16,1880 Marengo,Ill.
d.Aug.21,1934

Yr	Cl	Lea	Pos	G	Rec
1902	Chi	N	P-S	19	9-9 .106
1903	Chi	N	P	27	11-9
1904	Chi	N	P	31	17-10
1905	Chi	N	P	23	13-4
1906	Chi	N	P	28	17-6
1907	Chi	N	P	28	18-7
1908	Chi	N	P	23	6-9
1909	Chi	N	P	2	0-1
	BRTR			181	91-55 .157

LUNDGREN, EBIN DELMAR
(Del)
b.Sept.21,1900 Lindsborg,Kan.

Yr	Cl	Lea	Pos	G	Rec
1924	Pit	N	P	8	0-1
1926	Bos	A	P	18	0-2
1927	Bos	A	P	30	5-12
	BRTR			56	5-15

LUNTE, HARRY AUGUST
b.Sept.15,1893 St.Louis,Mo.

Yr	Cl	Lea	Pos	G	Rec
1919	Cle	A	S	26	.195
1920	Cle	A	S	23	.197
	BRTR			49	.196

LUPIEN, ULYSSES JOHN
(Tony)
b.Apr.23,1917 Chelmsford,Mass.

Yr	Cl	Lea	Pos	G	Rec
1940	Bos	A	1	10	.474
1942	Bos	A	1	128	.281
1943	Bos	A	1	154	.255
1944	Phi	N	1	153	.283
1945	Phi	N	1	15	.315
1948	Chi	A	1	154	.246
	BLTL			614	.268

LUPLOW, ALVIN DAVID
b.Mar.13,1939 Saginaw,Mich.

Yr	Cl	Lea	Pos	G	Rec
1961	Cle	A	O	5	.056
1962	Cle	A	O	97	.277
	BLTR			102	.265

LUQUE, ADOLFO
b.Aug.4,1890 Havana,Cuba.
d.July 3,1957

Yr	Cl	Lea	Pos	G	Rec
1914	Bos	N	P	2	0-1
1915	Bos	N	P	2	0-0
1918	Cin	N	P	13	6-3
1919	Cin	N	P-3	31	10-3 .125
1920	Cin	N	P	37	13-9
1921	Cin	N	P	42	17-19
1922	Cin	N	P	39	13-23
1923	Cin	N	P	43	27-8
1924	Cin	N	P-O	33	10-15 .178
1925	Cin	N	P	37	16-18
1926	Cin	N	P	34	13-16
1927	Cin	N	P	29	13-12
1928	Cin	N	P	33	11-10
1929	Cin	N	P	32	5-16
1930	Bro	N	P	31	14-8
1931	Bro	N	P	19	7-6
1932	NY	N	P	38	6-7
1933	NY	N	P	35	8-2
1934	NY	N	P	26	4-3
1935	NY	N	P	2	1-0
	BRTR			558	194-179 .227

LUSH, ERNEST BENJAMIN
b.Oct.31,1884 Bridgeport,Conn.
d.Feb.26,1937

Yr	Cl	Lea	Pos	G	Rec
1910	St.L	N	O	1	.000
	TL				

LUSH, JOHN CHARLES
b.Oct.8,1885 Williamsport,Pa.
d.Nov.18,1946

Yr	Cl	Lea	Pos	G	Rec
1904	Phi	N	P-1-O	102	0-5 .276
1905	Phi	N	P	6	2-0
1906	Phi	N	P-O	61	18-15 .264
1907	Phi	N	P	12	5-6
1907	St.L	N	P	16	5-9
1908	St.L	N	P	38	11-18
1909	St.L	N	P	45	11-18
1910	St.L	N	P	36	14-13
	BLTL			316	66-84 253

LUSH, WILLIAM LUCAS
b.Nov.10,1873 Bridgeport,Conn.
d.Aug.28,1951

Yr	Cl	Lea	Pos	G	Rec
1895	Was	N	O	5	.210
1896	Was	N	O	91	.245
1897	Was	N	O	2	.000
1901	Bos	N	O	7	.185
1902	Bos	N	3-O	118	.231
1903	Det	A	O	117	.278
1904	Cle	A	O	138	.272
	BBTR			478	.254

LUSKEY, CHARLES MELTON
b.Apr.6,1876 Washington,D.C.

Yr	Cl	Lea	Pos	G	Rec
1901	Was	A	C-O	11	.195

LUTENBERG, CHARLES WILLIAM
b.Oct.4,1864 Quincy,Ill.
d.Dec.24,1938

Yr	Cl	Lea	Pos	G	Rec
1894	Lou	N	1	70	.192

LUTTRELL, LYLE KENNETH
b.Feb.22,1930 Bloomington,Ill.

Yr	Cl	Lea	Pos	G	Rec
1956	Was	A	S	38	.189
1957	Was	A	S	19	.200
	BRTR			57	.192

LUTZ, LOUIS WILLIAM
(Red)
b.Dec.17,1898 Cincinnati,O.

Yr	Cl	Lea	Pos	G	Rec
1922	Cin	N	C	1	1.000
	BRTR				

LUTZ, ROLLIN JOSEPH
b.Feb.18,1925 Keokuk,Ia.

Yr	Cl	Lea	Pos	G	Rec
1951	St.L	A	1	14	.167
	BLTL				

LUTZKE, WALTER JOHN
(Rube)
b.Nov.17,1897 Milwaukee,Wis.
d.Mar.6,1938

Yr	Cl	Lea	Pos	G	Rec
1923	Cle	A	3	143	.256
1924	Cle	A	3	106	.243
1925	Cle	A	2-3	81	.219
1926	Cle	A	3	142	.261
1927	Cle	A	3	100	.251
	BRTR			572	.249

LYLE, JAMES CLAUDE
b.July 24,1902 Lake,Miss.

Yr	Cl	Lea	Pos	G	Rec
1925	Was	A	P	1	0-0
	BRTR				

LYNCH, ADRIAN RYAN
b.Feb.9,1897 Laurens,Ia.
d.Mar.16,1934

Yr	Cl	Lea	Pos	G	Rec
1920	St.L	A	P	5	2-0
	BRTR				

LYNCH, GERALD THOMAS
b.July 17,1930 Bay City,Mich.

Yr	Cl	Lea	Pos	G	Rec
1954	Pit	N	O	98	.239
1955	Pit	N	C-O	88	.284
1956	Pit	N	O	19	.158
1957	Cin	N	C-O	67	.258
1958	Cin	N	O	122	.312
1959	Cin	N	O	117	.269
1960	Cin	N	O	102	.289
1961	Cin	N	O	96	.315
1962	Cin	N	O	114	.281
	BLTR			823	.281

LYNCH, HENRY W.
b.Binghamton,N.Y.
d.Nov.23,1925

Yr	Cl	Lea	Pos	G	Rec
1893	Chi	N	O	4	.214

LYNCH, JOHN H.
b.Feb.5,1857 New York,N.Y.
d.Apr.20,1923

Yr	Cl	Lea	Pos	G	Rec
1881	Buf	N	P-O	23	10-9 .166
1883	Met	a	P	29	13-16
1884	Met	a	P	54	39-14
1885	Met	a	P	45	23-21
1886	Met	a	P	51	20-30
1887	Met	a	P	23	7-15
1890	Bro	a	P	2	0-2
	BRTR			227	112-107 .151

LYNCH, MATTHEW DANIEL
(Dummy)
b.Feb.7,1927 Dallas,Tex.

Yr	Cl	Lea	Pos	G	Rec
1948	Chi	N	2	7	.286
	BRTR				

LYNCH, MICHAEL JOSEPH
b.Sept.10,1876 St.Paul,Minn.
d.Apr.2,1947

Yr	Cl	Lea	Pos	G	Rec
1902	Chi	N	O	7	.166

LYNCH, MICHAEL JOSEPH
b.June 28,1880 Holyoke,Mass.
d.Apr.2,1927

Yr	Cl	Lea	Pos	G	Rec
1904	Pit	N	P	27	14-11
1905	Pit	N	P	33	17-7
1906	Pit	N	P	18	6-5

Yr	Cl	Lea	Pos	G	Rec

(Continued)

Yr	Cl	Lea	Pos	G	Rec
1907	Pit	N	P	7	2-2
1907	NY	N	P	12	3-6
		TL		97	42-31

LYNCH, THOMAS JAMES
b.Apr.3,1860 Bennington,Vt.
d.Mar.28,1955

Yr	Cl	Lea	Pos	G	Rec
1884	Chi	N	P-1	5	3-2 / .000
1884	Wil	U	C-1-O	16	.281
1884	Phi	N	P-C-O	12	0-1 / .318
1885	Phi	N	2-O	13	.189
		BLTR		46	3-3 / .256

LYNCH, WALTER EDWARD
b.Apr.15,1897 Buffalo,N.Y.

Yr	Cl	Lea	Pos	G	Rec
1922	Bos	A	C	3	.667

TR

LYNN, BYRD
b.Mar.13,1889 Unionville,Ill.
d.Feb.5,1940

Yr	Cl	Lea	Pos	G	Rec
1916	Chi	A	C	31	.225
1917	Chi	A	C	35	.222
1918	Chi	A	C	4	.142
1919	Chi	A	C	29	.227
1920	Chi	A	C	16	.320
		BRTR		115	.237

LYNN, JAPHET MONROE
(Red)
b.Dec.27,1913 Kenney,Tex.

Yr	Cl	Lea	Pos	G	Rec
1939	Det	A	P	4	0-1
1939	NY	N	P	26	1-0
1940	NY	N	P	33	4-3
1944	Chi	N	P	22	5-4
		BRTR		85	10-8

LYNN, JEROME
b.Apr.20,1916 Scranton,Pa.

Yr	Cl	Lea	Pos	G	Rec
1937	Was	A	2	1	.667

BRTR

LYON, RUSSELL MAYO
b.Jan.26,1913 Ball Ground,Ga.

Yr	Cl	Lea	Pos	G	Rec
1944	Cle	A	C	7	.182

BRTR

LYONS, ALBERT HAROLD
b.July 18,1918 St.Joseph,Mo.

Yr	Cl	Lea	Pos	G	Rec
1944	NY	A	P	19	0-0
1946	NY	A	P	2	0-1
1947	NY	A	P	8	1-0
1947	Pit	N	P	15	1-2
1948	Bos	N	P-O	16	1-0 / .167
		BRTR		60	3-3 / .293

LYONS, DENNIS PATRICK ALOYSIUS
b.Mar.12,1866 Cincinnati,O.
d.Jan.2,1929

Yr	Cl	Lea	Pos	G	Rec
1885	Pro	N	3	4	.125
1886	Ath	a	3	32	.226
1887	Ath	a	3	137	.469
1888	Ath	a	3	111	.325
1889	Ath	a	3	131	.327
1890	Ath	a	3	88	.351
1891	St.L	a	3	120	.312
1892	NY	N	3	108	.260
1893	Pit	N	3	131	.318
1894	Pit	N	3	72	.311
1895	St.L	N	3	33	.290
1896	Pit	N	3	116	.306
1897	Pit	N	1	36	.206
		BRTR		1119	.325

LYONS, EDWARD HOYT
(Mouse)
b.May12,1923 Winston-Salem,N.C.

Yr	Cl	Lea	Pos	G	Rec
1947	Was	A	2	7	.154

BRTR

LYONS, GEORGE TONY
b.Jan.25,1891 Bible Grove,Ill.

Yr	Cl	Lea	Pos	G	Rec
1920	St.L	N	P	7	2-1
1924	St.L	A	P	26	3-2
		BRTR		33	5-3

LYONS, HARRY P.
b.1866 Chester,Pa.
d.June 30,1912

Yr	Cl	Lea	Pos	G	Rec
1887	Phi	N	O	1	.200
1887	St.L	a	2	2	.125
1888	St.L	a	O	123	.190
1889	NY	N	O	5	.100
1890	Roc	a	O	132	.264
1892	NY	N	O	96	.245
1893	NY	N	O	46	.272
				405	.236

LYONS, HERSCHEL E.
b.July 23,1915 Fresno,Cal.

Yr	Cl	Lea	Pos	G	Rec
1941	St.L	N	P	1	0-0

BRTR

LYONS, PATRICK JERRY
b.1860 Canada.
d.Jan.20,1914

Yr	Cl	Lea	Pos	G	Rec
1890	Cle	N	2	11	.052

LYONS, TERENCE HILBERT
b.Dec.14,1908 New Holland,O.

Yr	Cl	Lea	Pos	G	Rec
1929	Phi	N	1	1	.000

BRTR

LYONS, THEODORE AMAR
b.Dec.28,1900 Lake Charles,La.

Yr	Cl	Lea	Pos	G	Rec
1923	Chi	A	P	9	2-1
1924	Chi	A	P	41	12-11
1925	Chi	A	P	43	21-11
1926	Chi	A	P	41	18-16
1927	Chi	A	P	41	22-14
1928	Chi	A	P	49	15-14
1929	Chi	A	P	40	14-20
1930	Chi	A	P	57	22-15
1931	Chi	A	P	42	4-6
1932	Chi	A	P	49	10-15
1933	Chi	A	P	51	10-21
1934	Chi	A	P	50	11-13
1935	Chi	A	P	29	15-8
1936	Chi	A	P	26	10-13
1937	Chi	A	P	23	12-7
1938	Chi	A	P	24	9-11
1939	Chi	A	P	21	14-6
1940	Chi	A	P	22	12-8
1941	Chi	A	P	22	12-10
1942	Chi	A	P	20	14-6
1946	Chi	A	M-P	5	1-4
		BBTR		705	260-230

Non-playing manager Chi (A) 1947-48.

LYONS, TOBY A.
b.Boston,Mass.

Yr	Cl	Lea	Pos	G	Rec
1890	Syr	a	P	3	1-2

LYSTON, WILLIAM EDWARD
b.1863 Baltimore,Md.
d.1944

Yr	Cl	Lea	Pos	G	Rec
1891	Col	a	P	1	0-0
1894	Cle	N	P	1	0-1
				2	0-1

LYTLE, EDWARD BENSON
(Dad)
b.Mar.10,1862 Racine,Wis.
d.Dec.21,1950

Yr	Cl	Lea	Pos	G	Rec
1890	Chi	N	O	1	.000
1890	Pit	N	2-O	15	.123
				16	.115

MAAS, DUANE FREDERICK
b.Jan.1,1931 Utica,Mich.

Yr	Cl	Lea	Pos	G	Rec
1955	Det	A	P	18	5-6
1956	Det	A	P	26	0-7
1957	Det	A	P	45	10-14
1958	KC	A	P	10	4-5
1958	NY	A	P	22	7-3

(Continued)

Yr	Cl	Lea	Pos	G	Rec
1959	NY	A	P	38	14-8
1960	NY	A	P	35	5-1
1961	NY	A	P	1	0-0
		BRTR		195	45-44

MABE, ROBERT LEE
b.Oct.8,1929 Danville,Va.

Yr	Cl	Lea	Pos	G	Rec
1958	St.L	N	P	32	3-9
1959	Cin	N	P	18	4-2
1960	Bal	A	P	2	0-0
		BRTR		52	7-11

MacDONALD, HARVEY FORSYTH
b.May 18,1904 New York,N.Y.

Yr	Cl	Lea	Pos	G	Rec
1928	Phi	N	O	13	.250

BLTL

MACDONALD, WILLIAM PAUL
b.Mar.28,1929 Alameda,Cal.

Yr	Cl	Lea	Pos	G	Rec
1950	Pit	N	P	32	8-10
1953	Pit	N	P	4	0-1
		BRTR		36	8-11

MACE, HARRY L. (Jimmy)
b.Washington,D.C.

Yr	Cl	Lea	Pos	G	Rec
1891	Was	a	P	5	0-4

MACEY, ...
b.Columbus,O.

Yr	Cl	Lea	Pos	G	Rec
1890	Ath	a	C	1	.000

MacFAYDEN, DANIEL KNOWLES
(Deacon)
b.June 10,1905 N.Truro,Mass.

Yr	Cl	Lea	Pos	G	Rec
1926	Bos	A	P	3	0-1
1927	Bos	A	P	37	5-8
1928	Bos	A	P	35	9-15
1929	Bos	A	P	32	10-18
1930	Bos	A	P	36	11-14
1931	Bos	A	P	35	16-12
1932	Bos	A	P	12	2-10
1932	NY	A	P	16	7-5
1933	NY	A	P	25	3-2
1934	NY	A	P	22	4-3
1935	Cin	N	P	7	1-2
1935	Bos	N	P	28	5-13
1936	Bos	N	P	37	17-13
1937	Bos	N	P	32	14-14
1938	Bos	N	P	29	14-9
1939	Bos	N	P	33	8-14
1940	Pit	N	P	35	5-4
1941	Was	A	P	5	0-1
1943	Bos	N	P	10	2-1
		BRTR		469	133-159

MACIARZ, JOSEPH JOHN
(Played under name of
Joseph John Mack)

MACK, CORNELIUS (Connie)
(Real name Cornelius McGillicuddy)
b.Dec.22,1862 E.Brookfield,Mass.
d.Feb.8,1956

Yr	Cl	Lea	Pos	G	Rec
1886	Was	N	C	10	.361
1887	Was	N	C	80	.220
1888	Was	N	C	85	.186
1889	Was	N	C-1-O	97	.292
1890	Buf	p	C	123	.268
1891	Pit	N	C	71	.210
1892	Pit	N	C	86	.257
1893	Pit	N	C	36	.325
1894	Pit	N	M-C	63	.257
1895	Pit	N	M-C	14	.362
1896	Pit	N	M-C-1	30	.207
		BRTR		695	.252

Non-playing manager Phi (A) 1901-1950.

MACK, DENNIS JOSEPH
(Real name Dennis Joseph McCrohan)
b.1851 Easton,Pa.
d.Apr.10,1888

Yr	Cl	Lea	Pos	G	Rec
1871	Rok	n	P-1-S	25	0-1 / NR
1872	Ath	n	1-S	48	NR

(Continued)

Yr	Cl	Lea	Pos	G	Rec
1873	Phi	n	1-2-O	45	NR
1874	Phi	n	1	56	NR
1876	St.L	N	S	48	.204
1880	Buf	N	2-S	17	.203
1882	Lou	a	2-S-O	72	.193
1883	Pit	a	1-S	60	.200
	BRTR			371	0-1 NR

MACK, EARLE THADDEUS
(Real name
Earle Thaddeus McGillicuddy)
b.Feb.1,1889 Spencer,Mass.

Yr	Cl	Lea	Pos	G	Rec
1910	Phi	A	C	1	.500
1911	Phi	A	3	2	.000
1914	Phi	A	1	2	.000
	BRTR			5	.133

MACK, FRANK GEORGE (Stubby)
b.Feb.2,1900 Oklahoma City,Okla.

Yr	Cl	Lea	Pos	G	Rec
1922	Chi	A	P	8	2-2
1923	Chi	A	P	12	0-1
1925	Chi	A	P	8	0-0
	BRTR			28	2-3

MACK, JOSEPH (Reddy)
(Real name Joseph McNamara)
b.May 2,1866 Ireland
d.Dec.30,1916

Yr	Cl	Lea	Pos	G	Rec
1885	Lou	a	2	11	.244
1886	Lou	a	2	137	.244
1887	Lou	a	2	128	.410
1888	Lou	a	2	110	.228
1889	Bal	a	2	136	.236
1890	Bal	a	2	26	.272
				548	.285

MACK, JOSEPH JOHN
(Real name Joseph John Maciarz)
b.July 4,1915 Chicago,Ill.

Yr	Cl	Lea	Pos	G	Rec
1945	Bos	N	1	66	.231
	BBTL				

MACK, RAYMOND JAMES
(Real name
Raymond James Mlckovsky)
b.Aug.31,1916 Cleveland,O.

Yr	Cl	Lea	Pos	G	Rec
1938	Cle	A	2	2	.333
1939	Cle	A	2	36	.152
1940	Cle	A	2	146	.283
1941	Cle	A	2	145	.228
1942	Cle	A	2	143	.225
1943	Cle	A	2	153	.220
1944	Cle	A	2	83	.232
1946	Cle	A	2	61	.205
1947	NY	A	H	1	.000
1947	Chi	N	2	21	.218
	BRTR			791	.232

MACK, WILLIAM FRANCIS
b.Feb.12,1885 Elmira,N.Y.

Yr	Cl	Lea	Pos	G	Rec
1908	Chi	N	P	2	0-0

MacKENZIE, ERIC HUGH
b.Aug.29,1932 Glendon,Alta.,Canada

Yr	Cl	Lea	Pos	G	Rec
1955	KC	A	C	1	.000
	BLTR				

MacKENZIE, HENRY GORDON
b.July 9,1937 St.Petersburg,Fla.

Yr	Cl	Lea	Pos	G	Rec
1961	KC	A	C	11	.125
	BRTR				

MacKENZIE, KENNETH PURVIS
b.Mar.10,1934 Gore Bay,Ont.,Canada

Yr	Cl	Lea	Pos	G	Rec
1960	Mil	N	P	9	0-1
1961	Mil	N	P	5	0-1
1962	NY	N	P	42	5-4
	BRTL			56	5-6

MACKIEWICZ, FELIX THADDEUS
b.Nov.20,1917 Chicago,Ill.

Yr	Cl	Lea	Pos	G	Rec
1941	Phi	A	O	5	.285
1942	Phi	A	O	6	.214
1943	Phi	A	O	9	.063
1945	Cle	A	O	120	.273
1946	Cle	A	O	78	.260
1947	Cle	A	O	2	.000
1947	Was	A	O	3	.167
	BRTR			223	.259

MACKINSON, JOHN JOSEPH
b.Oct.29,1923 Orange,N.J.

Yr	Cl	Lea	Pos	G	Rec
1953	Phi	A	P	1	0-0
1955	St.L	N	P	9	0-1
	BBTR			10	0-1

MacLEOD, WILLIAM DANIEL
b.May 13,1942 Gloucester,Mass.

Yr	Cl	Lea	Pos	G	Rec
1962	Bos	A	P	2	0-1
	BLTL				

MACON, MAX CULLEN
b.Oct.14,1915 Pensacola,Fla.

Yr	Cl	Lea	Pos	G	Rec
1938	St.L	N	P	46	4-11
1940	Bro	N	P	2	1-0
1942	Bro	N	P	26	5-3
1943	Bro	N	P-1	45	7-5 .164
1944	Bos	N	P-1-O	106	0-0 .273
1947	Bos	N	P	1	0-0
	BLTL			226	17-19 .265

MacPHEE, WALTER SCOTT (Waddy)
b.Dec.23,1902 Brooklyn,N.Y.

Yr	Cl	Lea	Pos	G	Rec
1922	NY	N	3	2	.286
	BRTR				

MacPHERSON, HARRY WILLIAM
b.July 10,1926 N.Andover,Mass.

Yr	Cl	Lea	Pos	G	Rec
1944	Bos	N	P	1	0-0
	BRTR				

MACULLAR, JAMES F. (Little Mac)
b.Jan.16,1855 Boston,Mass.
d.Apr.8,1924

Yr	Cl	Lea	Pos	G	Rec
1879	Syr	N	S-O	63	.213
1882	Cin	a	O	79	.282
1883	Cin	a	S-O	14	.151
1884	Bal	a	S	108	.193
1885	Bal	a	S	100	.202
1886	Bal	a	S	76	.227
	BRTL			440	.210

MADDEN, ...
b.Pittsburgh,Pa.

Yr	Cl	Lea	Pos	G	Rec
1914	Pit	F	C	2	.500

MADDEN, EUGENE
b.June 5,1892 Elm Grove,W.Va.
d.Apr.6,1949

Yr	Cl	Lea	Pos	G	Rec
1916	Pit	N	O	1	.000
	BLTR				

MADDEN, LEONARD JOSEPH
b.July 2,1890 Toledo,O.
d.Sept.9,1949

Yr	Cl	Lea	Pos	G	Rec
1912	Chi	N	P	6	0-1
	BLTL				

MADDEN, MICHAEL JOSEPH (Kid)
b.Oct.22,1866 Portland,Me.
d.Mar.16,1896

Yr	Cl	Lea	Pos	G	Rec
1887	Bos	N	P	37	22-14
1888	Bos	N	P	19	7-12
1889	Bos	N	P	21	10-10
1890	Bos	p	P	14	3-2
1891	Bos	a	P	4	0-2
1891	Bal	a	P-O	36	14-10 .257
	TL			131	56-50 .281

MADDEN, THOMAS FRANCIS
b.Sept.14,1882 Boston,Mass.
d.Jan.20,1954

Yr	Cl	Lea	Pos	G	Rec
1909	Bos	A	C	12	.168
1910	Bos	A	C	14	.400
1911	Bos	A	C	4	.200
1911	Phi	N	C	22	.276
	BRTR			52	.285

MADDEN, THOMAS J. (Bunny)
b.1884

Yr	Cl	Lea	Pos	G	Rec
1906	Bos	N	O	4	.267
1910	NY	A	O	1	.000
				5	.250

MADDERN, JAMES CLARENCE
b.Sept.26,1921 Bisbee,Ariz.

Yr	Cl	Lea	Pos	G	Rec
1946	Chi	N	O	3	.000
1948	Chi	N	O	80	.252
1949	Chi	N	1	10	.333
1951	Cle	A	O	11	.167
	BRTR			104	.248

MADDOX, NICHOLAS
b.Nov.9,1886 Gavanstown,Md.
d.Nov.27,1954

Yr	Cl	Lea	Pos	G	Rec
1907	Pit	N	P	6	5-1
1908	Pit	N	P	36	23-8
1909	Pit	N	P	31	13-8
1910	Pit	N	P	20	2-3
	TR			93	43-20

MADIGAN, ANTHONY J. (Pony)
b.1868 Washington,D.C.
d.Dec.1954

Yr	Cl	Lea	Pos	G	Rec
1886	Was	N	P	14	1-13
	TR				

MADISON, ARTHUR M.
b.Jan.14,1871 Clarksburg,Mass.
d.Jan.27,1933

Yr	Cl	Lea	Pos	G	Rec
1895	Phi	N	2-S	10	.400
1899	Pit	N	2-S	33	.269
				43	.288

MADISON, DAVID PLEDGER
b.Feb.1,1924 Brooksville,Miss.

Yr	Cl	Lea	Pos	G	Rec
1950	NY	A	P	1	0-0
1952	St.L	A	P	31	4-2
1952	Det	A	P	10	1-1
1953	Det	A	P	32	3-4
	BRTR			74	8-7

MADJESKI, EDWARD WILLIAM
(Real name
Edward William Majewski)
b.July 24,1909 Far Rockaway,N.Y.

Yr	Cl	Lea	Pos	G	Rec
1932	Phi	A	C	17	.229
1933	Phi	A	C	51	.282
1934	Phi	A	C	8	.375
1934	Chi	A	C	85	.221
1937	NY	N	C	5	.200
	BRTR			166	.241

MADRID, SALVADOR
b.June 9,1920 El Paso,Tex.

Yr	Cl	Lea	Pos	G	Rec
1947	Chi	N	S	8	.125
	BRTR				

MAESTRI, HECTOR ANIBAL
b.Apr.19,1935 Havana,Cuba

Yr	Cl	Lea	Pos	G	Rec
1960	Was	A	P	1	0-0
1961	Was	A	P	1	0-1
	BRTR			2	0-1

MAGEE, LEO CHRISTOPHER
(Real name
Leopold Christopher
Hoernschemeyer)
b.June 4,1889 Cincinnati,O.

Yr	Cl	Lea	Pos	G	Rec
1911	St.L	N	2	21	.261
1912	St.L	N	2-O	128	.290
1913	St.L	N	2-O	137	.267
1914	St.L	N	1-O	142	.284
1915	Bro	F	M-2	121	.330

(Continued)

Yr	Cl	Lea	Pos	G	Rec
1916	NY	A	O	131	.257
1917	NY	A	O	51	.220
1917	St.L	A	O	36	.165
1918	Cin	N	2-3	119	.290
1919	Bro	N	2	45	.238
1919	Chi	N	S	79	.292
		BBTR		1010	.276

MAGEE SHERWOOD ROBERT
b.Aug.6,1884 Clarendon, Pa.
d.Mar.13,1929

Yr	Cl	Lea	Pos	G	Rec
1904	Phi	N	O	95	.277
1905	Phi	N	O	155	.299
1906	Phi	N	O	154	.282
1907	Phi	N	O	139	.328
1908	Phi	N	O	142	.283
1909	Phi	N	O	143	.270
1910	Phi	N	O	154	.331
1911	Phi	N	O	120	.288
1912	Phi	N	O	132	.306
1913	Phi	N	O	138	.306
1914	Phi	N	1-S-O	146	.314
1915	Bos	N	1-O	156	.280
1916	Bos	N	O	122	.241
1917	Bos	N	O	72	.255
1917	Cin	N	1-O	45	.324
1918	Cin	N	1-2-O	115	.297
1919	Cin	N	2-3-O	56	.215
		BRTR		2084	.291

MAGEE, WILLIAM M.
b.Jan.11,1868 S.Boston, Mass.

Yr	Cl	Lea	Pos	G	Rec
1897	Lou	N	P	20	4-13
1898	Lou	N	P	35	16-14
1899	Lou	N	P	11	4-6
1899	Phi	N	P	10	3-5
1899	Was	N	P	5	1-4
1901	St.L	N	P	1	0-1
1901	NY	N	P	6	0-3
1902	NY	N	P	3	0-0
1902	Phi	N	P	8	2-4
				99	30-50

MAGGERT, HARL VESS
b.Feb.13,1883 Cromwell, Ind.
d.Jan.7,1963

Yr	Cl	Lea	Pos	G	Rec
1907	Pit	N	O	3	.000
1912	Phi	A	O	72	.256
		BLTR		75	.250

MAGGERT, HARL WARREN
b.May 4,1914 Los Angeles, Cal.

Yr	Cl	Lea	Pos	G	Rec
1938	Bos	N	O	66	.281
		BRTR			

MAGLIE, SALVATORE ANTHONY
b.Apr.26,1917 Niagara Falls, N.Y.

Yr	Cl	Lea	Pos	G	Rec
1945	NY	N	P	14	5-4
1950	NY	N	P	47	18-4
1951	NY	N	P	42	23-6
1952	NY	N	P	35	18-8
1953	NY	N	P	27	8-9
1954	NY	N	P	34	14-6
1955	NY	N	P	23	9-5
1955	Cle	A	P	10	0-2
1956	Cle	A	P	2	0-0
1956	Bro	N	P	28	13-5
1957	Bro	N	P	19	6-6
1957	NY	A	P	6	2-0
1958	NY	A	P	7	1-1
1958	St.L	N	P	10	2-6
		BRTR		304	119-62

MAGNER, ESMUND BURKE (Stubby)
b.Feb.20,1888 Kalamazoo, Mich.
d.Sept.6,1956

Yr	Cl	Lea	Pos	G	Rec
1911	NY	A	2	12	.194
		BRTR			

MAGNER, WILLIAM JOHN
b.July 15,1858 Birmingham, England.
d.June 27,1923

Yr	Cl	Lea	Pos	G	Rec
1879	Cin	N	O	1	.000

MAGOON, GEORGE HENRY (Topsy)
b.May 27,1875 St.Albans, Me.
d.Dec.6,1943

Yr	Cl	Lea	Pos	G	Rec
1898	Bro	N	S	93	.227
1899	Bal	N	S	61	.252
1899	Chi	N	S	59	.235
1901	Cin	N	S	128	.251
1902	Cin	N	2-S	44	.275
1903	Cin	N	2	41	.216
1903	Chi	A	2	94	.227
		BRTR		520	.240

MAGUIRE, FREDERICK EDWARD
b.May 10,1900 Roxbury, Mass.
d.Nov.3,1961

Yr	Cl	Lea	Pos	G	Rec
1922	NY	N	2	5	.333
1923	NY	N	2-3	41	.200
1928	Chi	N	2	140	.279
1929	Bos	N	2	138	.252
1930	Bos	N	2	146	.267
1931	Bos	N	2	148	.228
		BRTR		618	.252

MAGUIRE, JACK
b.Feb.5,1925 St.Louis, Mo.

Yr	Cl	Lea	Pos	G	Rec
1950	NY	N	1-O	29	.175
1951	NY	N	O	16	.400
1951	Pit	N	2-3	8	.000
1951	St.L	A	2-3-O	41	.244
		BRTR		94	.240

MAGUIRE, JAMES A.
b.Feb.4,1875 Dunkirk, N.Y.
d.Jan.27,1917

Yr	Cl	Lea	Pos	G	Rec
1901	Cle	A	S	18	.232
		TR			

MAHADY, JAMES B.
b.Apr.22,1902 Cortland, N.Y.
d.Aug.9,1936

Yr	Cl	Lea	Pos	G	Rec
1921	NY	N	2	1	.000
		BRTR			

MAHAFFEY, ARTHUR
b.June 4,1938 Cincinnati, O.

Yr	Cl	Lea	Pos	G	Rec
1960	Phi	N	P	14	7-3
1961	Phi	N	P	36	11-19
1962	Phi	N	P	42	19-14
		BRTR		92	37-36

MAHAFFEY, LEE ROY (Popeye)
b.Feb.9,1903 Belton, S.C.

Yr	Cl	Lea	Pos	G	Rec
1926	Pit	N	P	4	0-0
1927	Pit	N	P	2	1-0
1930	Phi	A	P	33	9-5
1931	Phi	A	P	30	15-4
1932	Phi	A	P	37	13-13
1933	Phi	A	P	33	13-10
1934	Phi	A	P	37	6-7
1935	Phi	A	P	27	8-4
1936	St.L	A	P	21	2-6
		BRTR		224	67-49

MAHAFFY, LOUIS W.
b.1874 Madison, Wis.

Yr	Cl	Lea	Pos	G	Rec
1898	Lou	N	P	2	0-1

MAHAN, ARTHUR LEO
b.June 8,1914 Somerville, Mass.

Yr	Cl	Lea	Pos	G	Rec
1940	Phi	N	P-1	146	0-0 / .244
		BLTL			

MAHANEY, DANIEL J.
b.Mar.20,1864 Springfield, Mass.
d.Feb.1,1904

Yr	Cl	Lea	Pos	G	Rec
1892	Cin	N	C	5	.190
1895	Was	N	C	6	.167
		BRTR		11	.182

MAHARG, WILLIAM
b.Mar.19,1887 Philadelphia, Pa.

Yr	Cl	Lea	Pos	G	Rec
1912	Det	A	3	1	.000
1916	Phi	N	O	1	.000
		TR		2	.000

MAHER, F.
b.Philadelphia, Pa.

Yr	Cl	Lea	Pos	G	Rec
1902	Phi	N	S	2	.000
		TR			

MAHER, THOMAS
b.Philadelphia, Pa.

Yr	Cl	Lea	Pos	G	Rec
1902	Phi	N	O	1	.000

MAHON, ALFRED GEORGE
b.Sept.23,1910 St.Edward, Neb.

Yr	Cl	Lea	Pos	G	Rec
1930	Phi	A	P	3	0-0
		BLTL			

MAHONEY, CHRISTOPHER JOHN
b.June 11,1886 Milton, Mass.
d.July 15,1954

Yr	Cl	Lea	Pos	G	Rec
1910	Bos	A	P	3	0-1
		BR			

MAHONEY, DANIEL JOSEPH
b.Sept.6,1888 Lewiston, Me.
d.Sept.28,1960

Yr	Cl	Lea	Pos	G	Rec
1911	Cin	N	H	1	.000

MAHONEY, GEORGE W. (Big Mike)
b.Dec.5,1873 Boston, Mass.
d.Jan.3,1940

Yr	Cl	Lea	Pos	G	Rec
1897	Bos	N	C	2	.500
1898	St.L	N	1	2	.000
				4	.111

MAHONEY, JAMES THOMAS
b.May 26,1934 Englewood, N.J.

Yr	Cl	Lea	Pos	G	Rec
1959	Bos	A	S	31	.130
1961	Was	A	2-S	43	.241
1962	Cle	A	2-S-3	41	.243
		BRTR		115	.229

MAHONEY, ROBERT PAUL
b.June 20,1928 LeRoy, Minn.

Yr	Cl	Lea	Pos	G	Rec
1951	Chi	A	P	3	0-0
1951	St.L	A	P	30	2-5
1952	St.L	A	P	3	0-0
		BRTR		36	2-5

MAIER, ROBERT PHILIP
b.Sept.5,1917 Dunellen, N.J.

Yr	Cl	Lea	Pos	G	Rec
1945	Det	A	3-O	132	.263
		BRTR			

MAILHO, EMIL PIERRE (Lefty)
b.Dec.16,1909 Berkeley, Cal.

Yr	Cl	Lea	Pos	G	Rec
1936	Phi	A	O	21	.056
		BLTL			

MAILS, JOHN WALTER (Duster)
b.Oct.1,1896 San Quentin, Cal.

Yr	Cl	Lea	Pos	G	Rec
1915	Bro	N	P	2	0-1
1916	Bro	N	P	11	0-1
1920	Cle	A	P	9	7-0
1921	Cle	A	P	34	14-8
1922	Cle	A	P	26	4-7
1925	St.L	N	P	21	7-7
1926	St.L	N	P	1	0-1
		BLTL		104	32-25

MAIN, FORREST HARRY (Woody)
b.Feb.12,1922 Delano, Cal.

Yr	Cl	Lea	Pos	G	Rec
1948	Pit	N	P	17	1-1
1950	Pit	N	P	12	1-0
1952	Pit	N	P	48	2-12
1953	Pit	N	P	2	0-0
		BRTR		79	4-13

MAIN, MILES GRANT
b.May 13,1884 Montrose, Mich.

Yr	Cl	Lea	Pos	G	Rec
1914	Det	A	P	29	6-6
1915	KC	F	P	32	13-14
1918	Phi	N	P	9	2-2
		BLTR		70	21-22

MAINS, JAMES ROYAL
b.June 12,1922 Bridgton, Me.

Yr	Cl	Lea	Pos	G	Rec
1943	Phi	A	P	1	0-1
		BRTR			

MAINS, WILLARD EBEN
(Grasshopper)
b.July 7,1868 N.Windham, Me.
d.May 23,1923

Yr	Cl	Lea	Pos	G	Rec
1888	Chi	N	P	2	1-1
1891	Cin	a	P-O	27	12-10 .280
1891	Mil	a	P	2	0-2
1896	Bos	N	P	10	3-2
		TR		41	16-15 .306

MAISEL, FREDERICK CHARLES
(Fritz)
b.Dec.23,1889 Catonsville, Md.

Yr	Cl	Lea	Pos	G	Rec
1913	NY	A	3	51	.257
1914	NY	A	3	149	.239
1915	NY	A	3	135	.281
1916	NY	A	O	53	.228
1917	NY	A	2	113	.198
1918	St.L	A	3	90	.232
		BRTR		591	.242

MAISEL, GEORGE JOHN
b.Mar.12,1892 Catonsville, Md.

Yr	Cl	Lea	Pos	G	Rec
1913	St.L	A	O	11	.157
1916	Det	A	3	8	.000
1921	Chi	N	O	111	.310
1922	Chi	N	O	38	.190
		BRTR		168	.281

MAJESKI, HENRY (Heeney)
b.Dec.13,1916 Staten Island, N.Y.

Yr	Cl	Lea	Pos	G	Rec
1939	Bos	N	3	106	.272
1940	Bos	N	H	3	.000
1941	Bos	N	3	19	.145
1946	NY	A	3	8	.083
1946	Phi	A	3	78	.250
1947	Phi	A	2-S-3	141	.280
1948	Phi	A	S-3	148	.310
1949	Phi	A	3	114	.277
1950	Chi	A	3	122	.309
1951	Chi	A	3	12	.257
1951	Phi	A	3	89	.285
1952	Phi	A	3	34	.256
1952	Cle	A	2-3	36	.296
1953	Cle	A	2-3-O	50	.300
1954	Cle	A	2-3	57	.281
1955	Cle	A	2-3	36	.188
1955	Bal	A	2-3	16	.171
		BRTR		1069	.279

MAJEWSKI, EDWARD WILLIAM
(Played under name of
Edward William Madjeski)

MAKOSKY, FRANK
b.Jan.20,1912 Boonton, N.J.

Yr	Cl	Lea	Pos	G	Rec
1937	NY	A	P	26	5-2

BRTR

MAKOWSKY, HARRY DUQUESNE
(Played under name of
Harry Duquesne Markell)

MALARKEY, JOHN S. (Liz)
b.May 10,1872 Springfield, O.
d.Oct.29,1949

Yr	Cl	Lea	Pos	G	Rec
1894	Was	N	P	4	2-1
1895	Was	N	P	22	0-8
1896	Was	N	P	1	0-1
1899	Chi	N	P	1	0-1
1902	Bos	N	P-2	20	9-11 .210
1903	Bos	N	P	32	11-15
				80	22-37 .172

MALARKEY, WILLIAM JOHN
b.Nov.26,1878 Port Byron, Ill.
d.Dec.12,1956

Yr	Cl	Lea	Pos	G	Rec
1908	NY	N	P	15	0-2

BRTR

MALAY, CHARLES FRANCIS
b.June 13,1879 Brooklyn, N.Y.
d.Sept.18,1949

Yr	Cl	Lea	Pos	G	Rec
1905	Bro	N	2-O	101	.252

BBTR

MALAY, JOSEPH CHARLES
b.Oct.25,1905 Brooklyn, N.Y.

Yr	Cl	Lea	Pos	G	Rec
1933	NY	N	1	8	.125
1935	NY	N	H	1	1.000
		BLTL		9	.160

MALINOSKY, ANTHONY FRANCIS
b.Oct.5,1913 Collinsville, Ill.

Yr	Cl	Lea	Pos	G	Rec
1937	Bro	N	S-3	35	.228

BRTR

MALIS, CYRUS SOL
b.Feb.26,1907 Philadelphia, Pa.

Yr	Cl	Lea	Pos	G	Rec
1934	Phi	N	P	1	0-0

BRTR

MALKMUS, ROBERT EDWARD
b.July 4,1931 Newark, N.J.

Yr	Cl	Lea	Pos	G	Rec
1957	Mil	N	2	13	.091
1958	Was	A	2-S-3	41	.186
1959	Was	A	H	6	.000
1960	Phi	N	2-S-3	79	.211
1961	Phi	N	2-S-3	121	.231
1962	Phi	N	S	8	.200
		BRTR		268	.214

MALLETT, GERALD GORDON
b.Sept.18,1935 Bonne Terre, Mo.

Yr	Cl	Lea	Pos	G	Rec
1959	Bos	A	O	4	.267

BRTR

MALLETTE, MALCOLM FRANCIS
b.Jan.30,1923 Syracuse, N.Y.

Yr	Cl	Lea	Pos	G	Rec
1950	Bro	N	P	2	0-0

BLTL

MALLON, LESLIE CLYDE
b.Nov.21,1907 Dallas, Tex.

Yr	Cl	Lea	Pos	G	Rec
1931	Phi	N	2	122	.309
1932	Phi	N	2	103	.259
1934	Bos	N	2	42	.295
1935	Bos	N	2-3-O	116	.274
		BRTR		383	.283

MALLONEE, HOWARD BENNETT
(Ben)
b.Mar.31,1898 Baltimore, Md.

Yr	Cl	Lea	Pos	G	Rec
1921	Phi	A	O	7	.261

BLTL

MALLONEE, JULES W.
b.1902

Yr	Cl	Lea	Pos	G	Rec
1925	Chi	A	O	2	.000

BLTR

MALLORY, JAMES BAUGH
(Sunny Jim)
b.Sept.1,1918 Lawrenceville, Va.

Yr	Cl	Lea	Pos	G	Rec
1940	Was	A	O	4	.167
1945	St.L	N	O	13	.233
1945	NY	N	O	37	.298
		BRTR		54	.268

MALLOY, ALEXANDER
b.Oct.31,1886 Laurel Hill, N.C.

Yr	Cl	Lea	Pos	G	Rec
1910	St.L	A	P	7	0-6

MALLOY, HERMAN
b.Massillon, O.

Yr	Cl	Lea	Pos	G	Rec
1907	Det	A	P	1	0-1
1908	Det	A	P	3	0-2
				4	0-3

MALLOY, ROBERT PAUL
b.May 28,1918 Canonsburg, Pa.

Yr	Cl	Lea	Pos	G	Rec
1943	Cin	N	P	6	0-0
1944	Cin	N	P	9	1-1
1946	Cin	N	P	27	2-5
1947	Cin	N	P	1	0-0
1949	St.L	A	P	5	1-1
		BBTR		48	4-7

MALMBERG, HARRY WILLIAM
b.July 31,1926 Fairfield, Ala.

Yr	Cl	Lea	Pos	G	Rec
1955	Det	A	2	67	.216

BRTR

MALONE, ...

Yr	Cl	Lea	Pos	G	Rec
1872	Eck	n	P-O	2	0-1 NR

MALONE, EDWARD RUSSELL
b.June-16,1920 Chicago, Ill.

Yr	Cl	Lea	Pos	G	Rec
1949	Chi	A	C	55	.271
1950	Chi	A	C	31	.225
		BRTR		86	.257

MALONE, FERGUSON G.
b.1842 Ireland.
d.Jan.18,1905

Yr	Cl	Lea	Pos	G	Rec
1871	Ath	n	C	27	.366
1872	Ath	n	C-1	41	NR
1873	Phi	n	C-S	52	NR
1874	Chi	n	C	47	NR
1875	Phi	n	C-1-O	27	.228
1876	Ath	N	C	22	.229
1884	Key	U	M-C	1	.250
		BRTL		217	NR

MALONE, LEWIS ALOYSIUS
b.Mar.13,1897 Baltimore, Md.

Yr	Cl	Lea	Pos	G	Rec
1915	Phi	A	2	76	.204
1916	Phi	A	S	5	.000
1917	Bro	N	H	1	.000
1919	Bro	N	2-S-3	51	.204
		BRTR		133	.202

MALONE, PERCE LEIGH (Pat)
b.Sept.25,1902 Altoona, Pa.
d.May 13,1943

Yr	Cl	Lea	Pos	G	Rec
1928	Chi	N	P	42	18-13
1929	Chi	N	P	40	22-10
1930	Chi	N	P	45	20-9
1931	Chi	N	P	36	16-9
1932	Chi	N	P	37	15-17
1933	Chi	N	P	31	10-14
1934	Chi	N	P	34	14-7
1935	NY	A	P	29	3-5
1936	NY	A	P	35	12-4
1937	NY	A	P	28	4-4
		BBTR		357	134-92

MALONEY, CHARLES MICHAEL

Yr	Cl	Lea	Pos	G	Rec
1908	Bos	N	P	1	0-0

MALONEY, JAMES WILLIAM
b.June 2,1940 Fresno, Cal.

Yr	Cl	Lea	Pos	G	Rec
1960	Cin	N	P	11	2-6
1961	Cin	N	P-O	30	6-7 .379
1962	Cin	N	P	24	9-7
		BLTR		65	17-20 .233

MALONEY, JOHN
d.July 21,1890

Yr	Cl	Lea	Pos	G	Rec
1876	Mut	N	O	2	.286
1877	Har	N	O	1	.250
				3	.273

MALONEY, PATRICK WILLIAM
b.Jan.19,1888 Grosvenordale, Conn.

Yr	Cl	Lea	Pos	G	Rec
1912	NY	A	O	22	.215

MALONEY, WILLIAM ALPHONSE
b.June 5,1878 Lewiston, Me.
d.Sept.2,1960

Yr	Cl	Lea	Pos	G	Rec
1901	Mil	A	C-O	84	.297
1902	St.L	A	C-O	30	.203
1902	Cin	N	C-O	24	.228
1905	Chi	N	O	145	.260
1906	Bro	N	O	151	.221
1907	Bro	N	O	144	.229
1908	Bro	N	O	107	.195
		BLTR		685	.236

MALOY, PAUL A. (Biff)
b.June 4,1892 Tiffin, O.

Yr	Cl	Lea	Pos	G	Rec
1913	Bos	A	P	2	0-0

BRTR

MALTZBERGER, GORDON RALPH
b.Sept.4,1912 Utopia,Tex.

Yr	Cl	Lea	Pos	G	Rec
1943	Chi	A	P	37	7-4
1944	Chi	A	P	46	10-5
1946	Chi	A	P	19	2-0
1947	Chi	A	P	33	1-4
		BRTR		135	20-13

MALZONE, FRANK JAMES
b.Feb.28,1930 Bronx,N.Y.

Yr	Cl	Lea	Pos	G	Rec
1955	Bos	A	3	6	.350
1956	Bos	A	3	27	.165
1957	Bos	A	3	153	.292
1958	Bos	A	3	155	.295
1959	Bos	A	3	154	.280
1960	Bos	A	3	152	.271
1961	Bos	A	3	151	.266
1962	Bos	A	3	156	.283
		BRTR		954	.278

MAMAUX, ALBERT LEON
b.May 30,1894 Pittsburgh,Pa.
d.Jan.2,1963

Yr	Cl	Lea	Pos	G	Rec
1913	Pit	N	P	1	0-0
1914	Pit	N	P	13	5-2
1915	Pit	N	P	38	21-8
1916	Pit	N	P	45	21-15
1917	Pit	N	P	16	2-11
1918	Bro	N	P	2	0-1
1919	Bro	N	P	30	10-12
1920	Bro	N	P	41	12-8
1921	Bro	N	P	12	3-3
1922	Bro	N	P	37	1-4
1923	Bro	N	P	5	0-2
1924	NY	A	P	14	1-1
		BRTR		254	76-67

MANCUSO, AUGUST RODNEY (Blackie)
b.Dec.5,1905 Galveston,Tex.

Yr	Cl	Lea	Pos	G	Rec
1928	St.L	N	C	11	.184
1930	St.L	N	C	76	.366
1931	St.L	N	C	67	.262
1932	St.L	N	C	103	.284
1933	NY	N	C	144	.264
1934	NY	N	C	122	.245
1935	NY	N	C	128	.298
1936	NY	N	C	139	.301
1937	NY	N	C	86	.279
1938	NY	N	C	52	.348
1939	Chi	N	C	80	.231
1940	Bro	N	C	60	.229
1941	St.L	N	C	106	.229
1942	St.L	N	C	5	.077
1942	NY	N	C	39	.193
1943	NY	N	C	94	.198
1944	NY	N	C	78	.251
1945	Phi	N	C	70	.199
		BRTR		1460	.265

MANCUSO, FRANK OCTAVIUS
b.May 23,1918 Houston,Tex.

Yr	Cl	Lea	Pos	G	Rec
1944	St.L	A	C	88	.205
1945	St.L	A	C	119	.268
1946	St.L	A	C	87	.240
1947	Was	A	C	43	.229
		BRTR		337	.241

MANDA, CARL ALAN
b.Nov.16,1888 Little River,Kan.

Yr	Cl	Lea	Pos	G	Rec
1914	Chi	A	2	9	.333
		BRTR			

MANDERS, HAROLD CARL
b.June 14,1917 Waukee,Ia.

Yr	Cl	Lea	Pos	G	Rec
1941	Det	A	P	8	1-0
1942	Det	A	P	18	2-0
1946	Det	A	P	2	0-0
1946	Chi	N	P	2	0-1
		BRTR		30	3-1

MANGAN, JAMES DANIEL
b.Sept.24,1929 San Francisco,Cal.

Yr	Cl	Lea	Pos	G	Rec
1952	Pit	N	C	11	.154
1954	Pit	N	C	14	.192
1956	NY	N	C	20	.100
		BRTR		45	.153

MANGUM, LEO ALLEN (Blackie)
b.May 24,1898 Durham,N.C.

Yr	Cl	Lea	Pos	G	Rec
1924	Chi	A	P	13	1-4
1925	Chi	A	P	7	1-0
1928	NY	N	P	1	0-0
1932	Bos	N	P	7	0-0
1933	Bos	N	P	25	4-3
1934	Bos	N	P	29	5-3
1935	Bos	N	P	3	0-0
		BRTR		85	11-10

MANGUS, GEORGE GRAHAM
b.1891

Yr	Cl	Lea	Pos	G	Rec
1912	Phi	N	O	10	.200
		BLTR			

MANION, CLYDE JENNINGS (Pete)
b.Oct.30,1896 St.Louis,Mo.

Yr	Cl	Lea	Pos	G	Rec
1920	Det	A	C	32	.275
1921	Det	A	C	11	.111
1922	Det	A	C	42	.275
1923	Det	A	C	23	.136
1924	Det	A	C	14	.231
1926	Det	A	C	75	.198
1927	Det	A	H	1	.000
1928	St.L	A	C	76	.226
1929	St.L	A	C	35	.243
1930	St.L	A	C	57	.216
1932	Cin	N	C	49	.207
1933	Cin	N	C	36	.167
1934	Cin	N	C	25	.185
		BRTR		476	.218

MANLOVE, CHARLES HALE
b.Oct.8,1862 Philadelphia,Pa.
d.Feb.12,1952

Yr	Cl	Lea	Pos	G	Rec
1884	Alt	U	C	1	.750
1884	NY	N	C	2	.000
		TR		3	.231

MANN, BEN GARTH
b.Nov.6,1918 Brandon,Tex.

Yr	Cl	Lea	Pos	G	Rec
1944	Chi	N	H	1	.000
		BRTR			

MANN, FRED I.
b.Apr.1,1858 Sutton,Vt.
d.Apr.7,1916

Yr	Cl	Lea	Pos	G	Rec
1882	Wor	N	1-3	19	.241
1882	Ath	a	3	29	.224
1883	Col	a	1-S-3-O	96	.230
1884	Col	a	O	99	.276
1885	Pit	a	O	100	.253
1886	Pit	a	O	117	.259
1887	Cle	a	O	64	.375
1887	Ath	a	O	55	.310
		BL		579	.277

MANN, JOHN LEO
b.Feb.4,1898 Fontanet,Ind.

Yr	Cl	Lea	Pos	G	Rec
1928	Chi	A	3	6	.286
		BRTR			

MANN, LESLIE (Major)
b.Nov.18,1893 Lincoln,Neb.
d.Jan.15,1962

Yr	Cl	Lea	Pos	G	Rec
1913	Bos	N	O	120	.253
1914	Bos	N	O	126	.247
1915	Chi	F	O	135	.306
1916	Chi	N	O	127	.272
1917	Chi	N	O	117	.273
1918	Chi	N	O	129	.288
1919	Chi	N	O	80	.227
1919	Bos	N	O	40	.285
1920	Bos	N	O	115	.276
1921	St.L	N	O	97	.328
1922	St.L	N	O	84	.347
1923	St.L	N	O	38	.371
1923	Cin	N	O	8	.000
1924	Bos	N	O	32	.275
1925	Bos	N	O	60	.342
1926	Bos	N	O	50	.302
1927	Bos	N	O	29	.258
1927	NY	N	O	29	.328
1928	NY	N	O	82	.264
		BRTR		1498	.282

MANNING, ERNEST DEVON
b.Oct.9,1890 Florala,Ala.

Yr	Cl	Lea	Pos	G	Rec
1914	St.L	A	P	7	0-0
		BLTR			

MANNING, JAMES BENJAMIN
b.July 21,1943 L'Anse,Mich.

Yr	Cl	Lea	Pos	G	Rec
1962	Min	A	P	5	0-0
		BRTR			

MANNING, JAMES H.
b.Jan.31,1862 Fall River,Mass.
d.Oct.1929

Yr	Cl	Lea	Pos	G	Rec
1884	Bos	N	2-S-3-O	84	.241
1885	Bos	N	S-O	84	.206
1885	Det	N	S	20	.269
1886	Det	N	O	26	.185
1887	Det	N	O	13	.250
1889	KC	a	M-2-O	132	.204
		TR		359	.217

Non-playing manager Was (A) 1901.

MANNING, JOHN E.
b.Dec.20,1853 Braintree,Mass.
d.Aug.15,1929

Yr	Cl	Lea	Pos	G	Rec
1873	Bos	n	1-O	33	.311
1874	Bal	n	P-2-S	42	4-15 NR
1874	Har	n	3	1	NR
1875	Bos	n	P-1-3-O	77	14-2 .285
1876	Bos	N	P-O	70	15-6 .258
1877	Cin	N	P-1-2-S-O	58	0-4 .315
1878	Bos	N	P-O	60	1-0 .254
1880	Cin	N	1-O	48	.216
1881	Buf	N	O	1	.000
1883	Phi	N	O	97	.265
1884	Phi	N	O	103	.272
1885	Phi	N	O	107	.256
1886	Bal	a	O	137	.227
		BRTR		834	34-27 NR

MANNING, TIMOTHY E.
b.Chicago,Ill.

Yr	Cl	Lea	Pos	G	Rec
1882	Pro	N	C-S	19	.105
1883	Bal	a	2	35	.233
1884	Bal	a	2	91	.207
1885	Bal	a	2	43	.201
1885	Pro	N	S	10	.086
				198	.193

MANNING, WALTER S. (Rube)
b.Apr.29,1883 Chambersburg,Pa.
d.Apr.23,1930

Yr	Cl	Lea	Pos	G	Rec
1907	NY	A	P	1	0-1
1908	NY	A	P	44	13-16
1909	NY	A	P	26	7-11
1910	NY	A	P	16	2-4
		TR		87	22-32

MANNO, DONALD
b.May 4,1918 Williamsport,Pa.

Yr	Cl	Lea	Pos	G	Rec
1940	Bos	N	O	3	.286
1941	Bos	N	1-3-O	22	.167
		BRTR		25	.189

MANSELL, JOHN
b.1861 Auburn,N.Y.
d.Feb.20,1925

Yr	Cl	Lea	Pos	G	Rec
1882	Ath	a	O	32	.237

MANSELL, MICHAEL R.
b.Jan.15,1859 Auburn,N.Y.
d.Dec.4,1902

Yr	Cl	Lea	Pos	G	Rec
1879	Syr	N	O	66	.211
1880	Cin	N	O	53	.192
1882	Pit	a	O	73	.283
1883	Pit	a	O	90	.240
1884	Pit	a	O	27	.131
1884	Ath	a	O	20	.194
1884	Ric	a	O	29	.301
		BL		358	.235

MANSELL, THOMAS E. (Brick)
b.Jan.1,1855 Auburn,N.Y.
d.Oct.6,1934

Yr	Cl	Lea	Pos	G	Rec
1879	Tro	N	O	39	.242
1879	Syr	N	O	1	.250
1883	Det	N	P-O	34	0-0 .213
1883	St.L	a	O	28	.370
1884	Cin	a	O	65	.244
1884	Col	a	O	23	.211
	BL			190	0-0 .254

MANSKE, LOUIS
b.July 4,1884 Milwaukee,Wis.

Yr	Cl	Lea	Pos	G	Rec
1906	Pit	N	P	2	0-0

MANTILLA, FELIX LAMELA
b.July 29,1934 Isabela,Puerto Rico

Yr	Cl	Lea	Pos	G	Rec
1956	Mil	N	S-3	35	.283
1957	Mil	N	2-S-3-O	71	.236
1958	Mil	N	2-S-3-O	85	.221
1959	Mil	N	2-S-3-O	103	.215
1960	Mil	N	2-S-O	63	.257
1961	Mil	N	2-S-3-O	45	.215
1962	NY	N	2-S-3	141	.275
	BRTR			543	.245

MANTLE, MICKEY CHARLES (Muscles)
b.Oct.20,1931 Spavinaw,Okla.

Yr	Cl	Lea	Pos	G	Rec
1951	NY	A	O	96	.267
1952	NY	A	3-O	142	.311
1953	NY	A	S-O	127	.295
1954	NY	A	2-S-O	146	.300
1955	NY	A	S-O	147	.306
1956	NY	A	O	150	.353
1957	NY	A	O	144	.365
1958	NY	A	O	150	.304
1959	NY	A	O	144	.285
1960	NY	A	O	153	.275
1961	NY	A	O	153	.317
1962	NY	A	O	123	.321
	BBTR			1675	.309

MANUEL, MOXIE

Yr	Cl	Lea	Pos	G	Rec
1905	Was	A	P	3	0-0
1908	Chi	A	P	17	2-4
				20	2-4

MANUSH, FRANK BENJAMIN
b.Sept.18,1886 Tuscumbia,Ala.

Yr	Cl	Lea	Pos	G	Rec
1908	Phi	A	3	23	.156
	BRTR				

MANUSH, HENRY EMMETT (Heinie)
b.July 20,1901 Tuscumbia,Ala.

Yr	Cl	Lea	Pos	G	Rec
1923	Det	A	O	109	.334
1924	Det	A	O	120	.289
1925	Det	A	O	99	.303
1926	Det	A	O	136	.377
1927	Det	A	O	152	.299
1928	St.L	A	O	154	.378
1929	St.L	A	O	142	.355
1930	St.L	A	O	49	.328
1930	Was	A	O	88	.362
1931	Was	A	O	146	.307
1932	Was	A	O	149	.342
1933	Was	A	O	153	.336
1934	Was	A	O	137	.349
1935	Was	A	O	119	.273
1936	Bos	A	O	82	.291
1937	Bro	N	O	132	.333
1938	Bro	N	O	17	.235
1938	Pit	N	O	15	.308
1939	Pit	N	O	10	.000
	BLTL			2009	.331

MANVILLE, RICHARD WESLEY
b.Dec.31,1925 Des Moines,Ia.

Yr	Cl	Lea	Pos	G	Rec
1950	Bos	N	P	1	0-0
1952	Chi	N	P	11	0-0
	BRTR			12	0-0

MAPEL, ROLLA HAMILTON
b.Mar.9,1890 Lee's Summitt,Mo.

Yr	Cl	Lea	Pos	G	Rec
1919	St.L	A	P	4	0-3
	BLTL				

MAPES, CLIFFORD FRANKLIN
b.Mar.13,1922 Sutherland,Neb.

Yr	Cl	Lea	Pos	G	Rec
1948	NY	A	O	53	.250
1949	NY	A	O	111	.247
1950	NY	A	O	108	.247
1951	NY	A	O	45	.216
1951	St.L	A	O	56	.274
1952	Det	A	O	86	.197
	BLTR			459	.242

MAPLE, HOWARD ALBERT
b.July 20,1903 Adrian,Mo.

Yr	Cl	Lea	Pos	G	Rec
1932	Was	A	C	44	.244
	BLTR				

MAPPES, GEORGE RICHARD (Dick)
b.Dec.25,1865 St.Louis,Mo.
d.Feb.20,1934

Yr	Cl	Lea	Pos	G	Rec
1885	Bal	a	2	6	.211
1886	St.L	N	C	6	.143
				12	.182

MARANDA, GEORGES HENRI
b.Jan.15,1932 Levis,Que.,Canada

Yr	Cl	Lea	Pos	G	Rec
1960	SF	N	P	17	1-4
1962	Min	A	P	32	1-3
	BRTR			49	2-7

MARANVILLE, WALTER JAMES VINCENT (Rabbit)
b.Nov.11,1891 Springfield,Mass.
d.Jan.5,1954

Yr	Cl	Lea	Pos	G	Rec
1912	Bos	N	S	26	.209
1913	Bos	N	S	143	.247
1914	Bos	N	S	156	.246
1915	Bos	N	S	149	.244
1916	Bos	N	S	155	.235
1917	Bos	N	S	142	.260
1918	Bos	N	S	11	.316
1919	Bos	N	S	131	.267
1920	Bos	N	S	134	.266
1921	Pit	N	S	153	.294
1922	Pit	N	2-S	155	.294
1923	Pit	N	S	141	.277
1924	Pit	N	2	152	.266
1925	Chi	N	M-2-S	75	.233
1926	Bro	N	2-S	78	.235
1927	St.L	N	S	9	.241
1928	St.L	N	S	112	.240
1929	Bos	N	S	146	.284
1930	Bos	N	S	142	.281
1931	Bos	N	2-S	145	.260
1932	Bos	N	2	149	.235
1933	Bos	N	2	143	.218
1935	Bos	N	2	23	.149
	BRTR			2670	.258

MARBERRY, FREDERICK (Firpo)
b.Nov.30,1898 Streetman,Tex.

Yr	Cl	Lea	Pos	G	Rec
1923	Was	A	P	11	4-0
1924	Was	A	P	50	11-12
1925	Was	A	P	55	8-6
1926	Was	A	P	64	11-7
1927	Was	A	P	56	10-7
1928	Was	A	P	48	13-13
1929	Was	A	P	49	19-12
1930	Was	A	P	33	15-5
1931	Was	A	P	45	16-4
1932	Was	A	P	54	8-4
1933	Det	A	P	37	16-11
1934	Det	A	P	38	15-5
1935	Det	A	P	5	0-1
1936	NY	N	P	1	0-0
1936	Was	A	P	5	0-2
	BRTR			551	146-89

MARBET, WALTER

Yr	Cl	Lea	Pos	G	Rec
1913	St.L	N	P	3	0-1

MARCHILDON, PHILIP JOSEPH (Babe)
b.Oct.25,1916 Penetanguishene,Ont., Canada.

Yr	Cl	Lea	Pos	G	Rec
1940	Phi	A	P	2	0-2
1941	Phi	A	P	30	10-15
1942	Phi	A	P	38	17-14
1945	Phi	A	P	3	0-1
1946	Phi	A	P	36	13-16
1947	Phi	A	P	35	19-9
1948	Phi	A	P	33	9-15
1949	Phi	A	P	7	0-3
1950	Bos	A	P	1	0-0
	BRTR			185	68-75

MARCUM, JOHN ALFRED (Footsie)
b.Sept.9,1908 Campbellsburg,Ky.

Yr	Cl	Lea	Pos	G	Rec
1933	Phi	A	P	5	3-2
1934	Phi	A	P	58	14-11
1935	Phi	A	P	64	17-12
1936	Bos	A	P	48	8-13
1937	Bos	A	P	51	13-11
1938	Bos	A	P	19	5-6
1939	St.L	A	P	16	2-5
1939	Chi	A	P	38	3-3
	BLTR			299	65-63

MARCZLEWICZ, CHARLES ANTHONY
(Played under name of Charles Anthony Marshall)

MARES, ...

Yr	Cl	Lea	Pos	G	Rec
1894	Lou	N	O	1	.000

MARGONERI, JOSEPH EMANUEL
b.Jan.13,1930 Smithton,Pa.

Yr	Cl	Lea	Pos	G	Rec
1956	NY	N	P	23	6-6
1957	NY	N	P	13	1-1
	BLTL			36	7-7

MARICHAL, JUAN ANTONIO SANCHEZ
b.Oct.24,1937 Laguna Verde,D.R.

Yr	Cl	Lea	Pos	G	Rec
1960	SF	N	P	11	6-2
1961	SF	N	P	30	13-10
1962	SF	N	P	38	18-11
	BRTR			79	37-23

MARION, DONALD G. M. (Rube)
b.1890
d.Jan.19,1933

Yr	Cl	Lea	Pos	G	Rec
1914	Bro	F	P	17	3-3
1915	Bro	F	P	32	12-9
	BRTR			49	15-12

MARION, JOHN WYETH (Red)
b.Mar.14,1915 Richburg,S.C.

Yr	Cl	Lea	Pos	G	Rec
1935	Was	A	O	4	.182
1943	Was	A	O	14	.176
	BRTR			18	.179

MARION, MARTIN WHITFORD (Slats)
b.Dec.1,1917 Richburg,S.C.

Yr	Cl	Lea	Pos	G	Rec
1940	St.L	N	S	125	.278
1941	St.L	N	S	155	.252
1942	St.L	N	S	147	.276
1943	St.L	N	S	129	.280
1944	St.L	N	S	144	.267
1945	St.L	N	S	123	.277
1946	St.L	N	S	146	.233
1947	St.L	N	S	149	.272
1948	St.L	N	S	144	.252
1949	St.L	N	S	134	.272
1950	St.L	N	S	106	.247
1952	St.L	A	M-S	67	.247
1953	St.L	A	M-3	3	.000
	BRTR			1572	.263

Non-playing manager St.L (N) 1951 and Chi (A) 1954-56.

MARIS, ROGER EUGENE
b.Sept.10,1934 Hibbing,Minn.

Yr	Cl	Lea	Pos	G	Rec
1957	Cle	A	O	116	.235
1958	Cle	A	O	51	.225
1958	KC	A	O	99	.247

(Continued)

Yr	Cl	Lea	Pos	G	Rec
1959	KC	A	O	122	.273
1960	NY	A	O	136	.283
1961	NY	A	O	161	.269
1962	NY	A	O	157	.256
	BLTR			842	.260

MARKELL, HARRY DUQUESNE
(Real name
Harry Duquesne Makowsky)
b.Aug.17,1923 Paris,France

Yr	Cl	Lea	Pos	G	Rec
1951	St.L	A	P	5	1-1
	BRTR				

MARKLAND, CLENETH EUGENE
b.Dec.26,1919 Detroit,Mich.

Yr	Cl	Lea	Pos	G	Rec
1950	Phi	A	2	5	.125
	BRTR				

MARKLE, CLIFFORD MONROE
b.May 3,1894 Pittsburgh,Pa.

Yr	Cl	Lea	Pos	G	Rec
1915	NY	A	P	3	2-0
1916	NY	A	P	11	4-3
1921	Cin	N	P	10	2-6
1922	Cin	N	P	25	4-5
1924	NY	A	P	7	0-3
	BRTR			56	12-17

MARLOWE, RICHARD BURTON
b.May 27,1929 Hickory,N.C.

Yr	Cl	Lea	Pos	G	Rec
1951	Det	A	P	2	0-1
1952	Det	A	P	4	0-2
1953	Det	A	P	42	6-7
1954	Det	A	P	38	5-4
1955	Det	A	P	4	1-0
1956	Det	A	P	7	1-1
1956	Chi	A	P	1	0-0
	BRTR			98	13-15

MARNIE, HARRY SYLVESTER
b.July 6,1918 Philadelphia,Pa.

Yr	Cl	Lea	Pos	G	Rec
1940	Phi	N	2	11	.176
1941	Phi	N	2-S-3	61	.241
1942	Phi	N	2-S-3	24	.167
	BRTR			96	.221

MAROLEWSKI, FRED DANIEL
b.Oct.6,1929 Chicago,Ill.

Yr	Cl	Lea	Pos	G	Rec
1953	St.L	N	1	1	.000
	BRTR				

MARONEY, JAMES FRANCIS
b.Dec.4,1883 S.Boston,Mass.
d.Feb.1929

Yr	Cl	Lea	Pos	G	Rec
1906	Bos	N	P	3	0-3
1910	Phi	N	P	12	1-2
1912	Chi	N	P	10	1-1
	BLTL			25	2-6

MARQUARD, RICHARD WILLIAM
(Rube)
b.Oct.9,1889 Cleveland,O.

Yr	Cl	Lea	Pos	G	Rec
1908	NY	N	P	1	0-1
1909	NY	N	P	29	5-13
1910	NY	N	P	13	4-4
1911	NY	N	P	45	24-7
1912	NY	N	P	43	26-11
1913	NY	N	P	42	23-10
1914	NY	N	P	39	12-22
1915	NY	N	P	27	9-8
1915	Bro	N	P	6	2-2
1916	Bro	N	P	36	13-6
1917	Bro	N	P	37	19-12
1918	Bro	N	P	34	9-18
1919	Bro	N	P	8	3-3
1920	Bro	N	P	28	10-7
1921	Cin	N	P	39	17-14
1922	Bos	N	P	39	11-15
1923	Bos	N	P	38	11-14
1924	Bos	N	P	6	1-2
1925	Bos	N	P	26	2-8
	BBTL			536	201-177

MARQUARDT, ALBERT LUDWIG
(Ollie)
b.Sept.22,1904 Toledo,O.

Yr	Cl	Lea	Pos	G	Rec
1931	Bos	A	2	17	.179
	BRTR				

MARQUEZ, LUIS ANGEL
b.Oct.26,1925 Aguadilla,Porto Rico

Yr	Cl	Lea	Pos	G	Rec
1951	Bos	N	O	68	.197
1954	Chi	N	O	17	.083
1954	Pit	N	O	14	.111
	BRTR			99	.182

MARQUIS, JAMES MILBURN
b.Nov.18,1900 Yoakum,Tex.

Yr	Cl	Lea	Pos	G	Rec
1925	NY	A	P	2	0-0
	BRTR				

MARQUIS, ROBERT RUDOLPH
b.Dec.23,1924 Oklahoma City,Okla.

Yr	Cl	Lea	Pos	G	Rec
1953	Cin	N	O	40	.273
	BLTL				

MARQUIS, ROGER J.
b.Apr.5,1937 Holycke,Mass.

Yr	Cl	Lea	Pos	G	Rec
1955	Bal	A	O	1	.000
	BLTL				

MARR, CHARLES W. (Lefty)
b.Sept.19,1862 Cincinnati,O.
d.Jan.11,1912

Yr	Cl	Lea	Pos	G	Rec
1886	Cin	a	O	7	.269
1889	Col	a	S-3-O	139	.303
1890	Cin	N	3-O	130	.299
1891	Cin	N	O	72	.244
1891	Cin	a	O	14	.204
	BLTL			362	.289

MARRERO,
CONRADO EUGENIO RAMOS
b.May 1,1917 Sagua La Grande,Cuba.

Yr	Cl	Lea	Pos	G	Rec
1950	Was	A	P	27	6-10
1951	Was	A	P	25	11-9
1952	Was	A	P	22	11-8
1953	Was	A	P	22	8-7
1954	Was	A	P	22	3-6
	BRTR			118	39-40

MARRIOTT, WILLIAM EARL
b.Apr.18,1894 Pratt,Kan.

Yr	Cl	Lea	Pos	G	Rec
1917	Chi	N	H	3	.000
1920	Chi	N	2	14	.279
1921	Chi	N	2	30	.316
1925	Bos	N	3-O	103	.268
1926	Bro	N	3	109	.267
1927	Bro	N	3	6	.111
	BLTR			265	.268

MARROW, CHARLES KENNON (Buck)
b.Aug.29,1909 Tarboro,N.C.

Yr	Cl	Lea	Pos	G	Rec
1932	Det	A	P	18	2-5
1937	Bro	N	P	6	1-2
1938	Bro	N	P	15	0-1
	BRTR			39	3-8

MARS, EDWARD

Yr	Cl	Lea	Pos	G	Rec
1890	Syr	a	P	17	9-6

MARSANS, ARMANDO
b.Oct.3,1887 Matanzas,Cuba.

Yr	Cl	Lea	Pos	G	Rec
1911	Cin	N	O	36	.261
1912	Cin	N	O	110	.317
1913	Cin	N	1-O	118	.297
1914	Cin	N	O	36	.298
1914	St.L	F	O	9	.350
1915	St.L	F	O	36	.177
1916	St.L	A	O	151	.254
1917	St.L	A	O	75	.230
1917	NY	A	O	25	.227
1918	NY	A	O	37	.236
	BRTR			633	.269

MARSH, FRED FRANCIS
b.Jan.5,1924 Valley Falls,Kan.

Yr	Cl	Lea	Pos	G	Rec
1949	Cle	A	H	1	.000
1951	St.L	A	2-S-3	130	.243
1952	St.L	A	2-S	11	.217
1952	Was	A	2-O	9	.042

(Continued)

Yr	Cl	Lea	Pos	G	Rec
1952	St.L	A	S-3	76	.286
1953	Chi	A	1-2-S-3	67	.200
1954	Chi	A	1-S-3-O	62	.306
1955	Bal	A	2-S-3	89	.218
1956	Bal	A	2-S-3	20	.125
	BRTR			465	.239

MARSHALL, CHARLES ANTHONY
(Real name
Charles Anthony Marczlewicz)
b.Aug.28,1919 Wilmington,Del.

Yr	Cl	Lea	Pos	G	Rec
1941	St.L	N	C	1	.000
	BRTR				

MARSHALL, CLARENCE WESTLY
(Cuddles)
b.Apr.28,1925 Bellingham,Wash.

Yr	Cl	Lea	Pos	G	Rec
1946	NY	A	P	23	3-4
1948	NY	A	P	1	0-0
1949	NY	A	P	21	3-0
1950	St.L	A	P	28	1-3
	BRTR			73	7-7

MARSHALL, EDWARD HERBERT
(Doc)
b.June 4,1906 New Albany,Miss.

Yr	Cl	Lea	Pos	G	Rec
1929	NY	N	2	5	.400
1930	NY	N	2-S	78	.309
1931	NY	N	2-S	68	.201
1932	NY	N	S	68	.248
	BRTR			219	.259

MARSHALL, JOSEPH H.
b.Troy,N.Y.
d.1932

Yr	Cl	Lea	Pos	G	Rec
1903	Pit	N	2-O	9	.261
1906	St.L	N	O	27	.158
				36	.178

MARSHALL, MILO MAX
b.Sept.18,1913 Shenandoah,Ia.

Yr	Cl	Lea	Pos	G	Rec
1942	Cin	N	O	131	.255
1943	Cin	N	O	132	.236
1944	Cin	N	O	66	.245
	BLTR			329	.245

MARSHALL, ROY DeVERNE (Rube)
b.Jan.19,1890 Salineville,O.

Yr	Cl	Lea	Pos	G	Rec
1912	Phi	N	P	2	0-1
1913	Phi	N	P	13	1-3
1914	Phi	N	P	27	6-7
1915	Buf	F	P	21	2-1
	BRTR			63	9-12

MARSHALL, RUFUS JAMES
b.May 25,1932 Danville,Ill.

Yr	Cl	Lea	Pos	G	Rec
1958	Bal	A	1-O	85	.215
1958	Chi	N	1-O	26	.272
1959	Chi	N	1-O	108	.252
1960	SF	N	1-O	75	.237
1961	SF	N	1-O	44	.222
1962	NY	N	1-O	17	.344
1962	Pit	N	1	55	.220
	BLTL			410	.242

MARSHALL, WILLARD WARREN
b.Feb.8,1921 Richmond,Va.

Yr	Cl	Lea	Pos	G	Rec
1942	NY	N	O	116	.257
1946	NY	N	O	131	.282
1947	NY	N	O	155	.291
1948	NY	N	O	143	.272
1949	NY	N	O	141	.307
1950	Bos	N	O	105	.235

(Continued)

Yr	Cl	Lea	Pos	G	Rec
1951	Bos	N	O	136	.281
1952	Bos	N	O	21	.227
1952	Cin	N	O	107	.267
1953	Cin	N	O	122	.266
1954	Chi	A	O	47	.254
1955	Chi	A	O	22	.171
	BLTR			1246	.274

MARSHALL, WILLIAM HENRY
b.Feb.14,1909 Dorchester,Mass.

Yr	Cl	Lea	Pos	G	Rec
1931	Bos	A	H	1	.000
1934	Cin	N	2	6	.125
	BRTR			7	.125

MARSHALL, WILLIAM RIDDLE (Doc)
b.Sept.22.1875 Butler.Pa.
d.Dec.11,1959

Yr	Cl	Lea	Pos	G	Rec
1904	Phi	N	C	8	.100
1904	NY	N	C	1	.000
1904	Bos	N	C	13	.209
1904	NY	N	H	10	.353
1906	NY	N	C-O	29	.167
1906	St.L	N	C	38	.276
1907	St.L	N	C	83	.202
1908	St.L	N	C	6	.071
1908	Chi	N	C	9	.300
1909	Bro	N	C	47	.202
	BRTR			244	.210

MARTEL, LEON ALPHONSE (Doc)
b.Jan.29,1883 Boston,Mass.
d.Oct.11,1947

Yr	Cl	Lea	Pos	G	Rec
1909	Phi	N	C	24	.268
1910	Bos	N	1	10	.000
	TR			34	.211

MARTIN, ALBERT
(Played under name of Albert May)

MARTIN, ALFRED MANUEL (Billy)
(Real name Alfred Manuel Pesano)
b.May 16,1928 Berkeley,Cal.

Yr	Cl	Lea	Pos	G	Rec
1950	NY	A	2-3	34	.250
1951	NY	A	2-S-3-O	51	.259
1952	NY	A	2	109	.267
1953	NY	A	2-S	149	.257
1955	NY	A	2-S	20	.300
1956	NY	A	2-3	121	.264
1957	NY	A	2-3	43	.241
1957	KC	A	2-S-3	73	.257
1958	Det	A	S-3	131	.255
1959	Cle	A	2-3	73	.260
1960	Cin	N	2	103	.246
1961	Mil	N	H	6	.000
1961	Min	A	2-S	108	.246
	BRTR			1021	.257

MARTIN, ALPHONSE CASE
b.Aug.4,1845 New York,N.Y.
d.May 24,1933

Yr	Cl	Lea	Pos	G	Rec
1872	Tro	n	P-O	25	1-2 / NR
1872	Eck	n	P-O	16	1-7 / NR
1873	Mut	n	P-C-O	30	0-2 / NR
1874	Atl	n	2-O	7	NR
1875	Atl	n	O	5	NR
				83	2-11 / NR

MARTIN, BARNEY ROBERT
b.Mar.3,1923 Columbia,S.C.

Yr	Cl	Lea	Pos	G	Rec
1953	Cin	N	P	1	0-0
	BRTR				

MARTIN, BORIS MICHAEL (Babe)
(Real name
Boris Michael Martinovich)
b.Mar.28,1921 Seattle,Wash.

(Continued)

Yr	Cl	Lea	Pos	G	Rec
1944	St.L	A	O	2	.750
1945	St.L	A	1-O	54	.200
1946	St.L	A	C	3	.222
1948	Bos	A	C	4	.500
1949	Bos	A	C	2	.000
1953	St.L	A	C	4	.000
	BRTR			69	.214

MARTIN, ELWOOD GOODE (Speed)
b.Sept.15,1893 Wawawai,Wash.

Yr	Cl	Lea	Pos	G	Rec
1917	St.L	A	P	10	0-3
1918	Chi	N	P	9	5-2
1919	Chi	N	P	35	8-8
1920	Chi	N	P	35	4-15
1921	Chi	N	P	37	11-15
1922	Chi	N	P	1	1-0
	BRTR			127	29-43

MARTIN, FRANK
b.1877 Chicago,Ill.

Yr	Cl	Lea	Pos	G	Rec
1897	Lou	N	2	2	.222
1898	Chi	N	2	1	.000
1899	NY	N	3	17	.254
				20	.235

MARTIN, FREDERICK TURNER
b.June 27,1915 Cameron,Okla.

Yr	Cl	Lea	Pos	G	Rec
1946	St.L	N	P	6	2-1
1949	St.L	N	P	21	6-0
1950	St.L	N	P	31	4-2
	BRTR			58	12-3

MARTIN, HAROLD WINTHROP (Doc)
b.Sept.23,1887 Roxbury,Mass.
d.Apr.15,1935

Yr	Cl	Lea	Pos	G	Rec
1908	Phi	A	P	1	0-1
1911	Phi	A	P	11	1-3
1912	Phi	A	P	2	0-0
	BRTR			14	1-4

MARTIN, HERSHEL RAY
b.Sept.19,1909 Birmingham,Ala.

Yr	Cl	Lea	Pos	G	Rec
1937	Phi	N	O	141	.283
1938	Phi	N	O	120	.298
1939	Phi	N	O	111	.282
1940	Phi	N	O	33	.253
1944	NY	A	O	85	.302
1945	NY	A	O	117	.267
	BBTR			607	.285

MARTIN, JOHN CHRISTOPHER
b.Apr.19,1889 Plainfield,N.J.

Yr	Cl	Lea	Pos	G	Rec
1912	NY	A	S	69	.225
1914	Bos	N	3	33	.212
1914	Phi	N	S	83	.253
	BRTR			185	.237

MARTIN, JOHN LEONARD (Pepper)
b.Feb.29,1904 Temple,Okla.

Yr	Cl	Lea	Pos	G	Rec
1928	St.L	N	O	39	.308
1930	St.L	N	O	6	.000
1931	St.L	N	O	123	.300
1932	St.L	N	3-O	85	.238
1933	St.L	N	3	145	.316
1934	St.L	N	P-3	110	0-0 / .289
1935	St.L	N	3-O	135	.299
1936	St.L	N	P-3-O	143	0-0 / .309
1937	St.L	N	O	98	.304
1938	St.L	N	O	91	.294
1939	St.L	N	3-O	88	.306
1940	St.L	N	3-O	86	.316
1944	St.L	N	O	40	.279
	BRTR			1189	0-0 / .298

MARTIN, JOSEPH CLIFTON
b.Dec.13,1936 Axton,Va.

Yr	Cl	Lea	Pos	G	Rec
1959	Chi	A	3	3	.250
1960	Chi	A	1-3	7	.100
1961	Chi	A	1-3	110	.230
1962	Chi	A	C-3	18	.077
	BLTR			138	.210

MARTIN, JOSEPH SAMUEL
b.Jan.1,1876 Hollidaysburg,Pa.

Yr	Cl	Lea	Pos	G	Rec
1903	Was	A	2-3-O	36	.208
1903	St.L	A	3-O	44	.231
	TR			80	.221

MARTIN, MORRIS WEBSTER (Lefty)
b.Sept.3,1922 Dixon,Mo.

Yr	Cl	Lea	Pos	G	Rec
1949	Bro	N	P	10	1-3
1951	Phi	A	P	35	11-4
1952	Phi	A	P	5	0-2
1953	Phi	A	P	58	10-12
1954	Phi	A	P	13	2-4
1954	Chi	A	P	35	5-4
1955	Chi	A	P	37	2-3
1956	Chi	A	P	10	1-0
1956	Bal	A	P	9	1-1
1957	St.L	N	P	4	0-0
1958	St.L	N	P	17	3-1
1958	Cle	A	P	14	2-0
1959	Chi	N	P	3	0-0
	BLTL			250	38-34

MARTIN, PATRICK FRANCIS
b.Apr.13,1894 Brooklyn,N.Y.

Yr	Cl	Lea	Pos	G	Rec
1919	Phi	A	P	2	0-2
1920	Phi	A	P	8	1-4
	BLTL			10	1-6

MARTIN, PAUL CHARLES
b.Mar.9,1932 Fayette City,Pa.

Yr	Cl	Lea	Pos	G	Rec
1955	Pit	N	P	8	0-1
	BRTR				

MARTIN, RAYMOND JOSEPH
b.Mar.13,1925 Norwood,Mass.

Yr	Cl	Lea	Pos	G	Rec
1943	Bos	N	P	2	0-0
1947	Bos	N	P	1	1-0
1948	Bos	N	P	2	0-0
	BRTR			5	1-0

MARTIN, STUART McGUIRE
b.Nov.17,1913 Rich Square,N.C.

Yr	Cl	Lea	Pos	G	Rec
1936	St.L	N	2	92	.298
1937	St.L	N	2	90	.260
1938	St.L	N	2	114	.278
1939	St.L	N	2-3	120	.268
1940	St.L	N	3-O	112	.238
1941	Pit	N	1-2-3	88	.304
1942	Pit	N	1-2-S	42	.225
1943	Chi	N	1-2-3	64	.220
	BLTR			722	.268

MARTIN, WILLIAM GLOYD
b.Feb.13,1894 Washington,D.C.
d.Sept.15,1949

Yr	Cl	Lea	Pos	G	Rec
1914	Bos	N	S	1	.000
	BRTR				

MARTIN, WILLIAM JOSEPH (Smokey Joe)
b.July 28,1911 Seymour,Mo.
d.Sept.28,1960

Yr	Cl	Lea	Pos	G	Rec
1936	NY	N	3	7	.267
1938	Chi	A	H	1	.000
	BRTR			8	.267

MARTINA, JOSEPH JOHN (Oyster Joe)
b.July 8,1889 New Orleans,La.
d.Mar.22,1962

Yr	Cl	Lea	Pos	G	Rec
1924	Was	A	P	25	6-8
	BRTR				

MARTINEZ, HECTOR
b.May 11,1939 Las Villas,Cuba

Yr	Cl	Lea	Pos	G	Rec
1962	KC	A	H	37	.167
	BRTR				

MARTINEZ, ORLANDO
b.Aug.23,1941 Havana,Cuba

Yr	Cl	Lea	Pos	G	Rec
1962	Min	A	S-3	37	.167
	BRTR				

MARTINEZ, ROGELIO ULLOA
b.Nov.5,1918 Cidra,Cuba.

Yr	Cl	Lea	Pos	G	Rec
1950	Was	A	P	2	0-1
BRTR					

MARTINI, GUIDO
b.July 1,1913 Birmingham,Ala.

Yr	Cl	Lea	Pos	G	Rec
1935	Phi	A	P	3	0-2
BRTR					

MARTINOVICH, BORIS MICHAEL
(Played under name of Boris Michael Martin)

MARTY, JOSEPH ANTON
b:Sept.1,1913 Sacramento,Cal.

Yr	Cl	Lea	Pos	G	Rec
1937	Chi	N	O	88	.290
1938	Chi	N	O	76	.243
1939	Chi	N	O	23	.132
1939	Phi	N	P-O	91	0-0 .254
1940	Phi	N	O	123	.270
1941	Phi	N	O	137	.268
BRTR				538	0-0 .261

MARTYN, ROBERT GORDON
b.Aug.15,1930 Weiser,Ida.

Yr	Cl	Lea	Pos	G	Rec
1957	KC	A	O	58	.267
1958	KC	A	O	95	.261
1959	KC	A	H	1	.000
BLTR				154	.263

MASI, PHILIP SAMUEL
b.Jan.6,1917 Chicago,Ill.

Yr	Cl	Lea	Pos	G	Rec
1939	Bos	N	C	46	.254
1940	Bos	N	C	63	.196
1941	Bos	N	C	87	.222
1942	Bos	N	C-O	57	.218
1943	Bos	N	C	80	.273
1944	Bos	N	C-1-3	89	.275
1945	Bos	N	C-1	114	.272
1946	Bos	N	C	133	.267
1947	Bos	N	C	126	.304
1948	Bos	N	C	113	.253
1949	Bos	N	C	37	.210
1949	Pit	N	C-1	48	.274
1950	Chi	A	C	122	.279
1951	Chi	A	C	84	.271
1952	Chi	A	C	30	.254
BRTR				1229	.264

MASKREY, HARRY H.
b.Dec.21,1861 Mercer,Pa.
d.Aug.17,1930

Yr	Cl	Lea	Pos	G	Rec
1882	Lou	a	O	1	.000

MASKREY, SAMUEL LEECH
b.Feb.16,1856 Mercer,Pa.
d.Apr.1,1922

Yr	Cl	Lea	Pos	G	Rec
1882	Lou	a	M-2-O	76	.225
1883	Lou	a	M-S-O	96	.190
1884	Lou	a	O	107	.247
1885	Lou	a	O	110	.230
1886	Lou	a	O	5	.158
1886	Cin	a	O	27	.204
				421	.227

MASON, ADELBERT WILLIAM (Del)
b.Oct.29,1883 Lockport,N.Y.
d.Dec.31,1962

Yr	Cl	Lea	Pos	G	Rec
1904	Was	A	P	5	0-3
1906	Cin	N	P	2	0-1
1907	Cin	N	P	25	5-12
BRTR				32	5-16

MASON, CHARLES E.
b.June 25,1853 New Orleans,La.
d.Oct.21,1936

Yr	Cl	Lea	Pos	G	Rec
1875	Cen	n	1-O	12	NR
1875	Nat	n	O	8	NR
1883	Ath	a	M-O	1	.500
TR				21	NR

Non-playing manager Ath (a) 1882 and 1884-87.

MASON, ERNEST
b.New Orleans,La.
d.Aug.1904

Yr	Cl	Lea	Pos	G	Rec
1894	St.L	N	P	4	0-2

MASON, HENRY
b.June 19,1931 Marshall,Mo.

Yr	Cl	Lea	Pos	G	Rec
1958	Phi	N	P	1	0-0
1960	Phi	N	P	3	0-0
BRTR				4	0-0

MASSA, GORDON RICHARD
b.Sept.2,1935 Cincinnati,O.

Yr	Cl	Lea	Pos	G	Rec
1957	Chi	N	C	6	.467
1958	Chi	N	H	2	.000
BLTR				8	.412

MASSEY, ROY H.
b.Oct.9,1892 Sevierville,Tenn.
d.June 24,1956

Yr	Cl	Lea	Pos	G	Rec
1918	Bos	N	1-S-3-O	66	.291
TR					

MASSEY, WILLIAM HARRY
(Big Bill)
b.Jan.1871 Philadelphia,Pa.
d.Oct.9,1940

Yr	Cl	Lea	Pos	G	Rec
1894	Cin	N	1	13	.294

MASSEY, WILLIAM HERBERT
(Mike)
b.Sept.28,1893 Galveston,Tex.

Yr	Cl	Lea	Pos	G	Rec
1917	Bos	N	2	31	.198
BLTR					

MASTERS, WALTER THOMAS
b.Mar.28,1907 Pen Argyl,Pa.

Yr	Cl	Lea	Pos	G	Rec
1931	Was	A	P	3	0-0
1937	Phi	N	P	1	0-0
1939	Phi	A	P	4	0-0
BRTR				8	0-0

MASTERSON, PAUL NICKALIS
b.Oct.16,1915 Chicago,Ill.

Yr	Cl	Lea	Pos	G	Rec
1940	Phi	N	P	2	0-0
1941	Phi	N	P	2	1-0
1942	Phi	N	P	4	0-0
BLTL				8	1-0

MASTERSON, WALTER EDWARD
b.June 22,1920 Philadelphia,Pa.

Yr	Cl	Lea	Pos	G	Rec
1939	Was	A	P	24	2-2
1940	Was	A	P	31	3-13
1941	Was	A	P	34	4-3
1942	Was	A	P	26	5-9
1945	Was	A	P	4	1-2
1946	Was	A	P	29	5-6
1947	Was	A	P	36	12-16
1948	Was	A	P	33	8-15
1949	Was	A	P	11	3-2
1949	Bos	A	P	18	3-4
1950	Bos	A	P	33	8-6
1951	Bos	A	P	30	3-0
1952	Bos	A	P	5	1-1
1952	Was	A	P	24	9-8
1953	Was	A	P	29	10-12
1956	Det	A	P	35	1-1
BRTR				402	78-100

MATARAZZO, LEONARD
b.Sept.12,1928 New Castle,Pa.

Yr	Cl	Lea	Pos	G	Rec
1952	Phi	A	P	1	0-0
BRTR					

MATHES, JOSEPH JOHN
b.July 28,1891 Milwaukee,Wis.

Yr	Cl	Lea	Pos	G	Rec
1912	Phi	A	3	4	.154
1914	St.L	F	2	24	.298
1916	Bos	N	2	2	.000
BBTR				30	.276

MATHEWS, EDWIN LEE
b.Oct.13,1931 Texarkana,Tex.

Yr	Cl	Lea	Pos	G	Rec
1952	Bos	N	3	145	.242
1953	Mil	N	3	157	.302
1954	Mil	N	3-O	138	.290
1955	Mil	N	3	141	.289
1956	Mil	N	3	151	.272
1957	Mil	N	3	148	.292
1958	Mil	N	3	149	.251
1959	Mil	N	3	148	.306
1960	Mil	N	3	153	.277
1961	Mil	N	3	152	.306
1962	Mil	N	1-3	152	.265
BLTR				1634	.282

MATHEWS, NELSON ELMER
b.July 21,1941 Columbia,Ill.

Yr	Cl	Lea	Pos	G	Rec
1960	Chi	N	O	3	.250
1961	Chi	N	O	3	.111
1962	Chi	N	O	15	.306
BRTR				21	.273

MATHEWS, ROBERT T.
b.Nov.21,1851 Baltimore,Md.
d.Apr.17,1898

Yr	Cl	Lea	Pos	G	Rec
1871	Kek	n	P	19	6-13
1872	Bal	n	P-3-O	49	26-16 .223
1873	Mut	n	P-O	26	10-15 NR
1873	Atl	n	P	1	1-0
1873	Mut	n	P	26	19-7
1874	Mut	n	P	65	42-23
1875	Mut	n	P	70	29-38
1876	Mut	N	P	56	21-34
1877	Cin	N	P-S-O	15	3-12 .169
1879	Pro	N	P-O	42	11-5 .200
1881	Pro	N	P-O	15	4-7 .155
1881	Bos	N	P-O	19	1-0 .169
1882	Bos	N	P-S-O	45	19-14 .224
1883	Ath	a	P-O	44	30-14 .173
1884	Ath	a	P	49	30-18
1885	Ath	a	P	48	30-17
1886	Ath	a	P	23	13-9
1887	Ath	a	P	8	3-5
BRTR				620	298-247 NR

MATHEWS, WILLIAM C.
b.Pottsville,Pa.

Yr	Cl	Lea	Pos	G	Rec
1909	Bos	A	P	5	0-0

MATHEWSON, CHRISTOPHER
(Big Six)
b.Aug.12,1880 Factoryville,Pa.
d.Oct.7,1925

Yr	Cl	Lea	Pos	G	Rec
1900	NY	N	P	6	0-2
1901	NY	N	P	37	20-16
1902	NY	N	P-1-O	41	13-18 .200
1903	NY	N	P	45	30-13
1904	NY	N	P	48	33-12
1905	NY	N	P	43	32-8
1906	NY	N	P	38	22-12
1907	NY	N	P	41	24-12
1908	NY	N	P	56	37-11
1909	NY	N	P	37	25-6
1910	NY	N	P	38	27-9
1911	NY	N	P	45	26-13
1912	NY	N	P	43	23-12
1913	NY	N	P	40	25-11
1914	NY	N	P	41	24-13
1915	NY	N	P	27	8-14
1916	NY	N	P	12	3-4
1916	Cin	N	M-P	1	1-0
BRTR				639	373-186 .214

Non-playing manager Cin (N) 1917-18.

MATHEWSON, HENRY
b.Dec.24,1886 Factoryville,Pa.
d.July 1,1917

Yr	Cl	Lea	Pos	G	Rec
1906	NY	N	P	2	0-0
1907	NY	N	P	1	0-0
				3	0-1

MATHIAS, CARL LYNWOOD
b.June 13,1936 Bechtelsville,Pa.

Yr	Cl	Lea	Pos	G	Rec
1960	Cle	A	P	7	0-1
1961	Was	A	P	4	0-1
		BRTL		11	0-2

MATHISON, I. I.

Yr	Cl	Lea	Pos	G	Rec
1902	Bal	A	S-3	28	.275

TR

MATTERN, ALONZO ALBERT
b.June 16,1883 W.Rush,N.Y.
d.Nov.6,1958

Yr	Cl	Lea	Pos	G	Rec
1908	Bos	N	P	5	1-2
1909	Bos	N	P	47	15-21
1910	Bos	N	P	51	16-19
1911	Bos	N	P	33	4-15
1912	Bos	N	P	2	0-1
		BLTR		138	36-58

MATTERSON, C. V.
b.Ohio

Yr	Cl	Lea	Pos	G	Rec
1884	St.L	U	P-O	1	1-0 .000

MATTESON, HENRY EDSON
b.Sept.7,1884 Guy's Mills,Pa.
d.Aug.31,1943

Yr	Cl	Lea	Pos	G	Rec
1914	Phi	N	P	15	3-2
1918	Was	A	P	14	5-3
		BRTR		29	8-5

MATTHEWS, JAMES VINCENT
b.Sept.29,1899 Baltimore,Md.

Yr	Cl	Lea	Pos	G	Rec
1922	Bos	N	P	3	0-1

BRTL

MATTHEWS, ROBERT
b.Camden,N.J.

Yr	Cl	Lea	Pos	G	Rec
1891	Ath	a	O	1	.333

MATTHEWS, WID CURRY
b.Oct.20,1896 Raleigh,Ill.

Yr	Cl	Lea	Pos	G	Rec
1923	Phi	A	O	129	.274
1924	Was	A	O	53	.302
1925	Was	A	O	10	.444
		BLTL		192	.284

MATTHEWSON, DALE WESLEY
b.May 15,1923 Catasaqua,Pa.

Yr	Cl	Lea	Pos	G	Rec
1943	Phi	N	P	12	0-3
1944	Phi	N	P	17	0-0
		BRTR		29	0-3

MATTHIAS, STEPHEN J.
b.Mitchellville,Md.

Yr	Cl	Lea	Pos	G	Rec
1884	Chi	U	S	35	.274

MATTICK, ROBERT JAMES
b.Dec.5,1916 Sioux City,Ia.

Yr	Cl	Lea	Pos	G	Rec
1938	Chi	N	S	1	1.000
1939	Chi	N	S	51	.287
1940	Chi	N	S-3	128	.218
1941	Cin	N	2-S-3	20	.183
1942	Cin	N	S	6	.200
		BRTR		206	.233

MATTICK, WALTER JOSEPH
(Chink)
b.Mar.12,1887 St.Louis,Mo.

Yr	Cl	Lea	Pos	G	Rec
1912	Chi	A	O	88	.260
1913	Chi	A	O	68	.188
1918	St.L	N	O	8	.142
		BRTR		164	.227

MATTIMORE, MICHAEL J.
b.1859 Renovo,Pa.
d.Apr.29,1931

Yr	Cl	Lea	Pos	G	Rec
1887	NY	N	P	8	3-4
1888	Ath	a	P	41	15-10
1889	Ath	a	P-O	23	2-2 .257
1889	KC	a	P-O	19	1-1 .147
1890	Bro	a	P-O	33	6-14 .126
		BLTR		124	27-31 .206

MATTINGLY, LAWRENCE EARL
b.Nov.4,1904 Charles Co.,Md.

Yr	Cl	Lea	Pos	G	Rec
1931	Bro	N	P	8	0-1

BRTR

MATTIS, RALPH L.
b.1891 St.Marys,Pa.

Yr	Cl	Lea	Pos	G	Rec
1914	Pit	F	O	35	.247

BRTR

MATTOX, CLOY MITCHELL
b.Nov.24,1905 Leesville,Va.

Yr	Cl	Lea	Pos	G	Rec
1929	Phi	A	C	3	.167

BLTR

MATTOX, JAMES POWELL
b.Dec.17,1897 Leesville,Va.

Yr	Cl	Lea	Pos	G	Rec
1922	Pit	N	C	29	.294
1923	Pit	N	C	22	.188
		BLTR		51	.253

MATUZAK, HARRY GEORGE
b.Jan.27,1911 Omer,Mich.

Yr	Cl	Lea	Pos	G	Rec
1934	Phi	A	P	11	0-3
1936	Phi	A	P	6	0-1
		BRTR		17	0-4

MAUCH, EUGENE WILLIAM (Skip)
b.Nov.18,1925 Salina,Kan.

Yr	Cl	Lea	Pos	G	Rec
1944	Bro	N	S	5	.133
1947	Pit	N	2-S	16	.300
1948	Bro	N	2-S	12	.154
1948	Chi	N	2-S	53	.203
1949	Chi	N	2-S-3	72	.247
1950	Bos	N	2-S-3	48	.231
1951	Bos	N	2-S-3	19	.100
1952	St.L	N	S	7	.000
1956	Bos	A	2	7	.320
1957	Bos	A	2	65	.270
		BRTR		304	.239

Non-playing manager Phi(N) 1960-62

MAUCK, ALFRED MARIS (Hal)
b.Mar.6,1869 Princeton,Ind.
d.Apr.27,1921

Yr	Cl	Lea	Pos	G	Rec
1893	Chi	N	P	18	8-9

MAUL, ALBERT JOSEPH
(Smiling Al)
b.Oct.9,1866 Philadelphia,Pa.
d.May 3,1958

Yr	Cl	Lea	Pos	G	Rec
1884	Key	U	P	1	0-1
1887	Phi	N	P-O	16	5-2 .450
1888	Pit	N	P-1-O	73	0-1 .211
1889	Pit	N	P-O	67	1-3 .276
1890	Pit	p	P-O	44	17-11 .265
1891	Pit	N	P-O	40	1-2 .194
1893	Was	N	P	39	10-23
1894	Was	N	P	35	11-15
1895	Was	N	P	20	11-6
1896	Was	N	P	9	5-2
1897	Was	N	P	1	0-0
1897	Bal	N	P	1	0-0
1898	Bal	N	P	29	20-7
1899	Bro	N	P	4	2-0
1900	Phi	N	P	5	2-3

(Continued)

Yr	Cl	Lea	Pos	G	Rec
1901	NY	N	P	3	0-2
		BRTR		387	85-78 .251

MAULDIN, MARSHALL REESE
b.Nov.5,1914 Atlanta,Ga.

Yr	Cl	Lea	Pos	G	Rec
1934	Chi	A	3	10	.263

BRTR

MAUN, ERNEST GERALD
b.Feb.3,1901 Clearwater,Kan.

Yr	Cl	Lea	Pos	G	Rec
1924	NY	N	P	22	1-1
1926	Phi	N	P	14	1-4
		BLTR		36	2-5

MAUNEY, RICHARD
b.Jan.26,1920 Concord,N.C.

Yr	Cl	Lea	Pos	G	Rec
1945	Phi	N	P	22	6-10
1946	Phi	N	P	25	6-4
1947	Phi	N	P	15	0-0
		BRTR		62	12-14

MAUPIN, HENRY C.
b.Louisville,Mo.

Yr	Cl	Lea	Pos	G	Rec
1898	St.L	N	P	2	0-2
1899	Cle	N	P	5	0-3
				7	0-5

MAURIELLO, RALPH
b.Aug.25,1934 Brooklyn,N.Y.

Yr	Cl	Lea	Pos	G	Rec
1958	LA	N	P	3	1-1

BRTR

MAURO, CARMEN LOUIS
b.Nov.10,1926 St.Paul,Minn.

Yr	Cl	Lea	Pos	G	Rec
1948	Chi	N	O	3	.200
1950	Chi	N	O	62	.227
1951	Chi	N	O	13	.172
1953	Bro	N	O	8	.000
1953	Was	A	O	17	.174
1953	Phi	A	3-O	64	.267
		BLTR		167	.231

MAVIS, ROBERT HENRY
b.Apr.8,1920 Milwaukee,Wis.

Yr	Cl	Lea	Pos	G	Rec
1949	Det	A	H	1	.000

BLTR

MAXVILL, CHARLES DALLAN
b.Feb.18,1939 Granite City,Ill.

Yr	Cl	Lea	Pos	G	Rec
1962	St.L	N	S-3	79	.222

BRTR

MAXWELL, CHARLES RICHARD
(Smokey)
b.Apr.8,1927 Lawton,Mich.

Yr	Cl	Lea	Pos	G	Rec
1950	Bos	A	O	2	.000
1951	Bos	A	O	49	.188
1952	Bos	A	1-O	8	.067
1954	Bos	A	O	74	.250
1955	Bal	A	H	4	.000
1955	Det	A	1-O	55	.266
1956	Det	A	O	141	.326
1957	Det	A	O	138	.276
1958	Det	A	1-O	131	.272
1959	Det	A	O	145	.251
1960	Det	A	O	134	.237
1961	Det	A	O	79	.229
1962	Det	A	1-O	30	.194
1962	Chi	A	1-3-O	69	.296
		BLTL		1059	.266

MAXWELL, J. ALBERT (Bert)
b.Texarkana,Ark.

Yr	Cl	Lea	Pos	G	Rec
1906	Pit	N	P	1	0-1
1908	Phi	A	P	4	0-0
1911	NY	N	P	4	1-2
1914	Bro	F	P	12	3-4
		BBTR		21	4-7

MAY, ALBERT
(Real name Martin)

Yr	Cl	Lea	Pos	G	Rec
1872	Eck	n	2	6	NR

MAY, FRANK SPRUELL (Jakie)
b.Nov.23,1895 Wendell,N.C.

Yr	Cl	Lea	Pos	G	Rec
1917	St.L	N	P	15	0-0
1918	St.L	N	P	29	5-6
1919	St.L	N	P	28	3-12
1920	St.L	N	P	16	1-4

Yr	Cl	Lea	Pos	G	Rec
(Continued)					
1921	St.L	N	P	5	1-3
1924	Cin	N	P	38	3-3
1925	Cin	N	P	36	8-9
1926	Cin	N	P	45	13-9
1927	Cin	N	P	44	15-12
1928	Cin	N	P	21	3-5
1929	Cin	N	P	41	10-14
1930	Cin	N	P	26	3-11
1931	Chi	N	P	31	5-5
1932	Chi	N	P	35	2-2
		BRTL		410	72-95

MAY, MERRILL GLEND (Pinky)
b.Jan.18,1911 Laconia,Ind.

Yr	Cl	Lea	Pos	G	Rec
1939	Phi	N	3	135	.287
1940	Phi	N	S-3	136	.293
1941	Phi	N	3	142	.267
1942	Phi	N	3	115	.238
1943	Phi	N	3	137	.282
		BRTR		665	.275

MAY, WILLIAM HERBERT
(Buckshot)
b.Dec.13,1899 Bakersfield,Cal.

Yr	Cl	Lea	Pos	G	Rec
1924	Pit	N	P	1	0-0
		BRTR			

MAYE, ARTHUR LEE
b.Dec.11,1934 Tuscaloosa,Ala.

Yr	Cl	Lea	Pos	G	Rec
1959	Mil	N	O	51	.300
1960	Mil	N	O	41	.301
1961	Mil	N	O	110	.271
1962	Mil	N	O	99	.244
		BLTR		301	.268

MAYER, EDWARD H.
b.Aug.16,1866 Marshall,Ill.

Yr	Cl	Lea	Pos	G	Rec
1890	Phi	N	3	117	.241
1891	Phi	N	3-O	65	.201
				182	.217

MAYER, EDWIN DAVID
b.Nov.30,1931 San Francisco,Cal.

Yr	Cl	Lea	Pos	G	Rec
1957	Chi	N	P	3	0-0
1958	Chi	N	P	19	2-2
		BLTL		22	2-2

MAYER, JAMES ERSKINE
(Real name James Erskine)
b.Jan.16,1891 Atlanta,Ga.
d.Mar.10,1957

Yr	Cl	Lea	Pos	G	Rec
1912	Phi	N	P	7	0-1
1913	Phi	N	P	39	9-9
1914	Phi	N	P	48	21-19
1915	Phi	N	P	43	21-15
1916	Phi	N	P	28	7-7
1917	Phi	N	P	28	11-6
1918	Phi	N	P	13	7-4
1918	Pit	N	P	15	9-3
1919	Pit	N	P	18	5-3
1919	Chi	A	P	6	1-3
		BRTR		245	91-70

MAYER, SAMUEL FRANKEL
(Real name Samuel Frankel Erskine)
b.Feb.28,1893 Atlanta,Ga.
d.July 1,1962

Yr	Cl	Lea	Pos	G	Rec
1915	Was	A	P-1-O	11	0-0 / .231
		BRTL			

MAYER, WALTER A.
b.Aug.3,1889 Cincinnati,O.
d.Nov.18,1951

Yr	Cl	Lea	Pos	G	Rec
1911	Chi	A	C	1	.000
1912	Chi	A	C	9	.000
1914	Chi	A	C	39	.165
1915	Chi	A	C	22	.222
1917	Bos	A	C	4	.167
1918	Bos	A	C	26	.224
1919	St.L	A	C	30	.226
		BRTR		131	.183

MAYES, ALBERT B. (Paddy)
b.1688

Yr	Cl	Lea	Pos	G	Rec
1911	Phi	N	O	5	.000
		BLTR			

MAYNARD, JAMES WALTER
(Buster)
b.Mar.25,1915 Henderson,N.C.

Yr	Cl	Lea	Pos	G	Rec
1940	NY	N	O	7	.276
1942	NY	N	2-3-O	89	.247
1943	NY	N	3-O	121	.206
1946	NY	N	O	7	.000
		BRTR		224	.221

MAYNARD, LeROY EVANS (Chick)
b.Nov.2,1896 Turner Falls,Mass.
d.Jan.31,1957

Yr	Cl	Lea	Pos	G	Rec
1922	Bos	A	S	12	.125
		TR			

MAYNARD, RICHARD WHEELER
(Played under name of
Richard Wheeler)

MAYO, EDWARD JOSEPH (Hotshot)
(Real name Edward Joseph Mayoski)
b.Apr.15,1912 Holyoke,Mass.

Yr	Cl	Lea	Pos	G	Rec
1936	NY	N	3	46	.199
1937	Bos	N	3	65	.227
1938	Bos	N	S-3	8	.214
1943	Phi	A	3	128	.219
1944	Det	A	2-S	154	.249
1945	Det	A	2	134	.285
1946	Det	A	2	51	.252
1947	Det	A	2	142	.279
1948	Det	A	2-3	106	.249
		BLTR		834	.253

MAYO, JOHN LEWIS
b.July 25,1926 Litchfield,Ill.

Yr	Cl	Lea	Pos	G	Rec
1948	Phi	N	O	12	.229
1949	Phi	N	O	45	.128
1950	Phi	N	O	18	.222
1951	Phi	N	O	9	.143
1952	Phi	N	1-O	50	.244
1953	Phi	N	O	5	.000
		BLTR		139	.213

MAYOSKI, EDWARD JOSEPH
(Played under name of
Edward Joseph Mayo)

MAYS, ALBERT C.
b.May 17,1865 Canal Dover,O.
d.May 7,1905

Yr	Cl	Lea	Pos	G	Rec
1885	Lou	a	P	17	6-11
1886	Met	a	P	41	11-27
1887	Met	a	P	62	17-34
1888	Bro	a	P	18	9-9
1889	Col	a	P	22	9-9
1890	Col	a	P	1	0-1
		BR		161	52-91

MAYS, CARL WILLIAM
b.Nov.1,1893 Liberty,Ky.

Yr	Cl	Lea	Pos	G	Rec
1915	Bos	A	P	38	4-6
1916	Bos	A	P	48	18-13
1917	Bos	A	P	35	22-9
1918	Bos	A	P	38	21-13
1919	Bos	A	P	22	8-12
1919	NY	A	P	13	5-2
1920	NY	A	P	45	26-11
1921	NY	A	P	51	27-9
1922	NY	A	P	35	12-14
1923	NY	A	P	23	5-2
1924	Cin	N	P	38	20-9
1925	Cin	N	P	12	3-5
1926	Cin	N	P	39	19-12
1927	Cin	N	P	14	3-7
1928	Cin	N	P	14	4-1
1929	NY	N	P	37	7-2
		BLTR		502	204-127

MAYS, WILLIE HOWARD
(Say Hey)
b.May 6,1931 Westfield,Ala.

Yr	Cl	Lea	Pos	G	Rec
1951	NY	N	O	121	.274
1952	NY	N	O	34	.236
1954	NY	N	O	151	.345
1955	NY	N	O	152	.319
1956	NY	N	O	152	.296
1957	NY	N	O	152	.333
1958	SF	N	O	152	.347
(Continued)					
1959	SF	N	O	151	.313
1960	SF	N	O	153	.319
1961	SF	N	O	154	.308
1962	SF	N	O	162	.304
		BRTR		1534	.315

MAZEROSKI, WILLIAM STANLEY
b.Sept.5,1936 Wheeling,W.Va.

Yr	Cl	Lea	Pos	G	Rec
1956	Pit	N	2	81	.243
1957	Pit	N	2	148	.283
1958	Pit	N	2	152	.275
1959	Pit	N	2	135	.241
1960	Pit	N	2	151	.273
1961	Pit	N	2	152	.265
1962	Pit	N	2	159	.271
		BRTR		978	.261

MAZZERA, MELVIN LEONARD
(Mike)
b.Jan.31,1914 Stockton,Cal.

Yr	Cl	Lea	Pos	G	Rec
1935	St.L	A	O	12	.233
1937	St.L	A	H	7	.286
1938	St.L	A	O	86	.279
1939	St.L	A	O	34	.297
1940	Phi	N	1-O	69	.237
		BLTL		208	.268

McADAMS, GEORGE D. JOHN (Jack)
b.Dec.17,1886 Benton,Ark.
d.May 21,1937

Yr	Cl	Lea	Pos	G	Rec
1911	St.L	N	P	6	0-0
		BRTR			

McAFEE, WILLIAM FORT
b.Sept.7,1907 Smithville,Ga.
d.July 8,1958

Yr	Cl	Lea	Pos	G	Rec
1930	Chi	N	P	2	0-0
1931	Bos	N	P	18	0-1
1932	Was	A	P	8	6-1
1933	Was	A	P-2	27	3-2 / .267
1934	St.L	A	P	28	1-0
		BRTR		83	10-4 / .173

McALEER, JAMES ROBERT
(Loafer)
b.July 10,1864 Youngstown,O.
d.Apr.29,1931

Yr	Cl	Lea	Pos	G	Rec
1889	Cle	N	O	109	.235
1890	Cle	p	O	86	.272
1891	Cle	N	O	135	.246
1892	Cle	N	O	150	.241
1893	Cle	N	O	91	.253
1894	Cle	N	O	64	.298
1895	Cle	N	O	132	.291
1896	Cle	N	O	116	.288
1897	Cle	N	O	23	.224
1898	Cle	N	O	104	.235
1901	Cle	A	M-O	3	.125
1902	St.L	A	M-O	2	.667
		BRTR		1015	.259

Non-playing manager St. L. (A) 1903-09 and Was (A) 1910-11.

McALEESE, JOHN JAMES
b.Aug.22,1879 Sharon,Pa.

Yr	Cl	Lea	Pos	G	Rec
1901	Chi	A	P	1	0-0
1909	St.L	A	O	85	.213
				86	0-0 / .213

McALLESTER, WILLIAM LUSK
b.Dec.29,1889 Chattanooga,Tenn.

Yr	Cl	Lea	Pos	G	Rec
1913	St.L	A	C	46	.153
		BRTR			

McALLISTER, JACK
(Real name Andrew James Coakley)

McALLISTER, LEWIS WILLIAM
(Sport)
b.July 23,1874 Austin,Miss.
d.July 18,1962

Yr	Cl	Lea	Pos	G	Rec
1896	Cle	N	P-C-O	7	0-0 / .185

(Continued)

Yr	Cl	Lea	Pos	G	Rec
1897	Cle	N	P-O	40	2-3 .211
1898	Cle	N	P	16	3-3
1899	Cle	N	P-O	110	0-1 .238
1901	Det	A	C-1	91	.287
1902	Det	A	C-1-2-S-3-O	20	.200
1902	Bal	A	1-2-3	3	.091
1902	Det	A	C-1-2 S-3-O	44	.209
1903	Det	A	C-S	78	.264
	BBTR			409	5-7 .245

McANANY, JAMES
b.Sept.4,1936 Los Angeles,Cal.

Yr	Cl	Lea	Pos	G	Rec
1958	Chi	A	O	5	.000
1959	Chi	A	O	67	.276
1960	Chi	A	H	3	.000
1961	Chi	N	O	11	.300
1962	Chi	N	H	7	.000
	BRTR			93	.253

McARTHUR, MALCOLM
b.1862 Detroit,Mich.

Yr	Cl	Lea	Pos	G	Rec
1884	Ind	a	P	6	1-5
	TR				

McARTHUR, OLIVER ALEXANDER (Happy)
b.Feb.1,1893 Vernon,Ala.

Yr	Cl	Lea	Pos	G	Rec
1914	Pit	N	P	1	0-0
	BRTR				

McATEE, MICHAEL JAMES (Butch)
b.1846 Lansingburg,N.Y.
d.Oct.18,1876

Yr	Cl	Lea	Pos	G	Rec
1871	Chi	n	1	26	NR
1872	Tro	n	1	25	NR
				51	NR

McAULEY, JAMES EARL (Ike)
b.Aug.19,1893 Wichita,Kan.
d.Apr.6,1928

Yr	Cl	Lea	Pos	G	Rec
1914	Pit	N	2-S-3	15	.125
1915	Pit	N	S	5	.133
1916	Pit	N	S	4	.250
1917	St.L	N	S	3	.286
1925	Chi	N	S	37	.280
	BRTR			64	.246

McAULIFFE, EUGENE LEO
b.Feb.28,1872 Randolph,Mass.
d.Apr.29,1953

Yr	Cl	Lea	Pos	G	Rec
1904	Bos	N	C	1	.500
	TR				

McAULIFFE, RICHARD JOHN
b.Nov.29,1939 Hartford,Conn.

Yr	Cl	Lea	Pos	G	Rec
1960	Det	A	S	8	.259
1961	Det	A	S-3	80	.256
1962	Det	A	2-S-3	139	.263
	BLTR			227	.261

McAVOY, GEORGE H.

Yr	Cl	Lea	Pos	G	Rec
1914	Phi	N	H	1	.000

McAVOY, JAMES EUGENE (Wicky)
b.Oct.22,1894 Rochester,N.Y.

Yr	Cl	Lea	Pos	G	Rec
1913	Phi	A	C	4	.111
1914	Phi	A	C	8	.111
1915	Phi	A	C	68	.190
1917	Phi	A	C	10	.250
1918	Phi	A	C	83	.244
1919	Phi	A	C	62	.141
	BRTR			235	.199

McAVOY, THOMAS JOHN
b.Aug.12,1937 Brooklyn,N.Y.

Yr	Cl	Lea	Pos	G	Rec
1959	Was	A	P	1	0-0
	BLTL				

McBEAN, ALVIN O'NEAL
b.May 15,1938 Charlotte Amalie,V.I.

Yr	Cl	Lea	Pos	G	Rec
1961	Pit	N	P	28	3-2
1962	Pit	N	P	34	15-10
	BRTR			62	18-12

McBEE, PRYOR EDWARD
b.June 20,1902 McAlester,Okla.

Yr	Cl	Lea	Pos	G	Rec
1926	Chi	A	P	1	0-0
	BRTL				

McBRIDE, ALGERNON BRIGGS
b.May 23,1869 Martinsville,Ind.
d.Jan.10,1956

Yr	Cl	Lea	Pos	G	Rec
1896	Chi	N	O	9	.233
1898	Cin	N	O	120	.300
1899	Cin	N	O	62	.352
1900	Cin	N	O	109	.277
1901	Cin	N	O	30	.254
1901	NY	N	O	62	.277
	BLTL			392	.294

McBRIDE, GEORGE FLORIAN
b.Nov.20,1880 Milwaukee,Wis.

Yr	Cl	Lea	Pos	G	Rec
1901	Mil	A	S	1	.250
1905	Pit	N	S-3	25	.218
1905	St.L	N	S	81	.253
1906	St.L	N	S	90	.169
1908	Was	A	S	155	.232
1909	Was	A	S	155	.234
1910	Was	A	S	154	.230
1911	Was	A	S	154	.236
1912	Was	A	S	152	.226
1913	Was	A	S	150	.214
1914	Was	A	S	156	.203
1915	Was	A	S	146	.204
1916	Was	A	S	139	.227
1917	Was	A	S	50	.192
1918	Was	A	S	18	.132
1919	Was	A	S	15	.200
1920	Was	A	S	14	.219
	BRTR			1655	.218

Non-playing manager Was (A) 1921.

McBRIDE, JAMES DICKSON (Dick)
b.1845 Philadelphia,Pa.
d.Oct.10,1916

Yr	Cl	Lea	Pos	G	Rec
1871	Ath	n	P	25	20-5
1872	Ath	n	P	48	31-15
1873	Ath	n	P-O	48	24-21 NR
1874	Ath	n	P	55	33-22
1875	Ath	n	P	59	43-14
1876	Bos	N	P	4	0-4
	TR			239	151-81 NR

McBRIDE, JOHN F.

Yr	Cl	Lea	Pos	G	Rec
1890	Ath	a	O	1	.000

McBRIDE, PETER WILLIAM
b.July 9,1875 Adams,Mass.
d.July 3,1944

Yr	Cl	Lea	Pos	G	Rec
1898	Cle	N	P	1	0-1
1899	St.L	N	P	11	2-5
				12	2-6

McBRIDE, KENNETH FAYE
b.Aug.12,1935 Huntsville,Ala.

Yr	Cl	Lea	Pos	G	Rec
1959	Chi	A	P	11	0-1
1960	Chi	A	P	5	0-1
1961	LA	A	P	45	12-15
1962	LA	A	P	24	11-5
	BRTR			85	23-22

McBRIDE, THOMAS RAYMOND
b.Nov.2,1915 Bonham,Tex.

Yr	Cl	Lea	Pos	G	Rec
1943	Bos	A	O	26	.240
1944	Bos	A	1-O	71	.245
1945	Bos	A	1-O	100	.305
1946	Bos	A	O	61	.301
1947	Bos	A	O	2	.200
1947	Was	A	3-O	56	.271
1948	Was	A	O	92	.257
	BRTR			408	.275

McCABE, JAMES ARTHUR (Swat)
b.Nov.20,1881 Towanda,Pa.
d.Dec.9,1944

Yr	Cl	Lea	Pos	G	Rec
1909	Cin	N	O	4	.461
1910	Cin	N	O	13	.257
	BL			17	.313

McCABE, RALPH HERBERT (Mack)
b.Oct.21,1920 Napanee,Ont.,Canada

Yr	Cl	Lea	Pos	G	Rec
1946	Cle	A	P	1	0-1
	BRTR				

McCABE, RICHARD JAMES
b.Feb.21,1896 Mamaroneck,N.Y.
d.Apr.11,1950

Yr	Cl	Lea	Pos	G	Rec
1918	Bos	A	P	3	0-1
1922	Chi	A	P	3	1-0
	BRTR			6	1-1

McCABE, TIMOTHY J.
b.Oct.19,1894 Graniteville,Mo.

Yr	Cl	Lea	Pos	G	Rec
1915	St.L	A	P	7	3-1
1916	St.L	A	P	13	3-0
1917	St.L	A	P	1	0-0
1918	St.L	A	P	2	0-0
	BRTR			23	6-1

McCABE, WILLIAM FRANCIS
b.Oct.28,1894 Chicago,Ill.

Yr	Cl	Lea	Pos	G	Rec
1918	Chi	N	2-O	29	.178
1919	Chi	N	S-3-O	33	.155
1920	Chi	N	O	3	.500
1920	Bro	N	O	41	.147
	BBTR			106	.161

McCAFFREY, CHARLES P. (Sparrow)
b.Philadelphia,Pa.
d.May,1894

Yr	Cl	Lea	Pos	G	Rec
1889	Col	a	C	2	.167
1890	Ath	a	C	1	.250
				3	.200

McCAFFREY, HARRY
b.Nov.25,1858 St.Louis,Mo.
d.Apr.19,1928

Yr	Cl	Lea	Pos	G	Rec
1882	St.L	a	1-2-3-O	37	.268
1883	St.L	a	O	5	.053
1885	Cin	a	P	1	1-0
				43	1-0 .237

McCAHAN, WILLIAM GLENN
b.June 7,1921 Philadelphia,Pa.

Yr	Cl	Lea	Pos	G	Rec
1946	Phi	A	P	4	1-1
1947	Phi	A	P	29	10-5
1948	Phi	A	P	17	4-7
1949	Phi	A	P	7	1-1
	BRTR			57	16-14

McCALL, BRIAN ALLEN
b.Jan.25,1943 Kentfield,Cal.

Yr	Cl	Lea	Pos	G	Rec
1962	Chi	A	O	4	.375
	BLTL				

McCALL, JOHN WILLIAM (Windy)
b.July 18,1925 San Francisco,Cal.

Yr	Cl	Lea	Pos	G	Rec
1948	Bos	A	P	1	0-1
1949	Bos	A	P	5	0-0
1950	Pit	N	P	2	0-0
1954	NY	N	P	33	2-5
1955	NY	N	P	42	6-5
1956	NY	N	P	46	3-4
1957	NY	N	P	5	0-0
	BLTL			134	11-15

McCALL, ROBERT LEONARD (Dutch)
b.Dec.25,1920 Columbia,Tenn.

Yr	Cl	Lea	Pos	G	Rec
1948	Chi	N	P	30	4-13
	BBTL				

Yr Cl Lea Pos G Rec

McCALLISTER, JACK
b.Jan.19,1879 Marietta,O.
d.Oct.18,1946
Non-playing manager Cle (A) 1927.

McCANDLESS, JOHN C.
b.1895 Pittsburgh,Pa.
1914 Bal F O 11 .258
1915 Bal F O 116 .218
BLTR 127 .221

McCANN, HENRY EUGENE (Mike)
b.June 13,1876 Baltimore,Md.
d.Apr.26,1943
1901 Bro N P 6 2-3
1902 Bro N P 3 1-2
TR 9 3-5

McCANN, ROBERT EMMETT
b.Mar.4,1902 Philadelphia,Pa.
d.Apr.15,1937
1920 Phi A S 10 .286
1921 Phi A S 52 .223
1926 Bos A S 6 .000
BRTR 68 .222

McCARDELL, ROGER MORTON
b.Aug.29,1932 Gorsuch Mills,Md.
1959 SF N C 4 .000
BRTR

McCARREN, WILLIAM JOSEPH
b.Nov.4,1897 Honesdale,Pa.
1923 Bro N 3-O 69 .245
BRTR

McCARTHY, ALEXANDER GEORGE
b.May 12,1888 Bradley,Ill.
1910 Pit N S 3 .084
1911 Pit N S 46 .240
1912 Pit N 2 111 .277
1913 Pit N S 31 .203
1914 Pit N 3 57 .150
1915 Pit N 2 21 .204
1915 Chi N S 23 .264
1916 Chi N 2-S 37 .245
1916 Pit N 2-S 50 .197
1917 Pit N 3 49 .219
BRTR 428 .229

McCARTHY, ARCHIBALD J.
b.Ypsilanti,Mich.
1902 Det A P 10 1-7

McCARTHY, JEROME FRANCIS
b.May 23,1923 Brooklyn,N.Y.
1948 St.L A 1 2 .333
BLTL

McCARTHY, JOHN A.
b.Mar.26,1869 Gilbertville,Mass.
d.Sept.11,1931
1893 Cin N O 48 .285
1894 Cin N 1-O 40 .267
1898 Pit N O 137 .289
1899 Pit N O 139 .307
1900 Chi N O 123 .296
1901 Cle A O 86 .314
1902 Cle A O 95 .276
1903 Cle A O 109 .265
1903 Chi N O 24 .277
1904 Chi N O 115 .264
1905 Chi N O 43 .276
1906 Bro N O 86 .304
1907 Bro N O 25 .220
BLTL 1070 .286

McCARTHY, JOHN JOSEPH
b.Jan.7,1913 Chicago,Ill.
1934 Bro N 1 17 .179
1935 Bro N 1 22 .250
1936 NY N 1 4 .438
1937 NY N 1 114 .279
1938 NY N 1 134 .272
1939 NY N 1 50 .262
1940 NY N 1 51 .239
1941 NY N 1-O 14 .325
1943 Bos N 1 78 .304
1946 Bos N 1 2 .143

Yr Cl Lea Pos G Rec

(Continued)
1948 NY N 1 56 .263
BLTL 542 .277

McCARTHY, JOSEPH N.
b.Dec.25,1881 Syracuse,N.Y.
d.Jan.12,1937
1905 NY A C 1 .000
1906 St.L N C 14 .237
TR 15 .225

McCARTHY, JOSEPH VINCENT (Marse Joe)
b.Apr.21,1887 Philadelphia,Pa.
Non-playing manager Chi (N) 1926-30, NY (A) 1931-46 and Bos (A) 1948-50.

McCARTHY, THOMAS FRANCIS MICHAEL
b.July 24,1864 S.Boston,Mass.
d.Aug.5,1922
1884 Bos U P-O 53 {0-7 .218}
1885 Bos N O 40 .182
1886 Phi N O 8 .185
1887 Phi N O 18 .208
1888 St.L a P-O 131 {0-0 .276}
1889 St.L a O 139 .297
1890 St.L a M-O 133 .332
1891 St.L a O 135 .302
1892 Bos N O 152 .244
1893 Bos N O 116 .360
1894 Bos N O 126 .349
1895 Bos N O 116 .291
1896 Bro N O 101 .253
BRTR 1268 {0-7 .294}

McCARTHY, THOMAS PATRICK
b.May 22, 1884 Ft.Wayne,Ind.
d.Mar.28,1933
1908 Cin N P 1 0-1
1908 Pit N P 2 0-0
1908 Bos N P 14 7-3
1909 Bos N P 8 0-5
25 7-9

McCARTHY, WILLIAM JOHN
b.Boston,Mass.
1905 Bos N C 1 .000
1907 Cin N C 3 .125
TR 4 .091

McCARTHY, WILLIAM THOMAS
b.Apr.11,1882 Ashland,Mass.
d.May 29,1939
1906 Bos N P 1 0-0

McCARTON, FRANK
b.New York,N.Y.
1872 Man n O 15 NR

McCARTY, GEORGE LEWIS (Lew)
b.Nov.17,1888 Catawissa,Pa.
d.June 19,1930
1913 Bro N C 9 .192
1914 Bro N C 90 .254
1915 Bro N C 84 .239
1916 Bro N C-1 55 .311
1916 NY N C 25 .400
1917 NY N C 56 .247
1918 NY N C 86 .269
1919 NY N C 85 .281
1920 NY N C 36 .132
1920 St.L N C 5 .286
1921 St.L N C 1 .000
BRTR 532 .277

McCARTY, JOHN A.
b.St.Louis,Mo.
1889 KC a P 20 8-6
TR

Yr Cl Lea Pos G Rec

McCARVER, JAMES TIMOTHY
b.Oct.16,1941 Memphis,Tenn.
1959 St.L N C 8 .167
1960 St.L N C 10 .200
1961 St.L N C 22 .239
BLTR 40 .218

McCAULEY, ALLEN B.
b.Mar.4,1863 Indianapolis,Ind.
1884 Ind a P-1 17 {2-7 .189}
1890 Phi N 1 112 .244
1891 Was a 1 57 .283
BLTL 186 {2-7 .262}

McCAULEY, F. F.
1895 Was N S 1 .000

McCAULEY JAMES A.
b.1861 Stanley,N.Y.
1884 St.L a C 1 .000
1885 Buf N C-O 24 .205
1885 Chi N C-O 3 .100
1886 Bro a C 10 .233
BLTR 38 .200

McCAULEY, PATRICK M.
b.June 10,1870 Ware,Mass.
d.Jan.23,1917
1893 St.L N C 5 .067
1896 Was N C 21 .247
1903 NY A C 6 .096
TR 32 .200

McCHESNEY, HARRY VINCENT (Pud)
b.June 1,1880 Pittsburgh,Pa.
1904 Chi N O 22 .261
BRTR

McCLAIN, JOSEPH FRED
b.May 5,1933 Johnson City,Tenn.
1961 Was A P 33 8-18
1961 Was A P 10 0-4
BRTR 43 8-22

McCLANAHAN, PETER
b.Oct.24,1906 Cold Spring,Tex.
1931 Pit N H 7 .500
BRTR

McCLELLAN, HARVEY McDOWELL
b.Dec.22,1896 Maysville,Ky.
d.Nov.6,1925
1919 Chi A S-3 7 .333
1920 Chi A 3 10 .300
1921 Chi A 2-S-O 63 .179
1922 Chi A 3 91 .226
1923 Chi A S 141 .235
1924 Chi A S 32 .176
BRTR 344 .221

McCLELLAN, WILLIAM H.
b.1857 Chicago,Ill.
1878 Chi N 2 46 .221
1881 Pro N 2-S-O 65 .164
1883 Phi N S-O 78 .230
1884 Phi N S 110 .256
1885 Bro a 2-3 113 .251
1886 Bro a 2 142 .262
1887 Bro a 2 136 .350
1888 Bro a 2-O 75 .214
1888 Cle a 2-S-O 22 .222
BLTL 787 .258

McCLESKEY, JEFFERSON LAMAR
b.1892 Winder,Ga.
1913 Bos N 3 2 .000
BLTR

McCLOSKEY, ...
1875 Nat n C 10 NR

Yr Cl Lea Pos G Rec

McCLOSKEY, JAMES ELLWOOD
b.May 26,1912 Dansville,Pa.
1936 Bos N P 4 0-0
BLTL

McCLOSKEY, JOHN J.
b.Cripple Creek,Colo.
1906 Phi N P 9 3-3
1907 Phi N P 2 0-0
11 3-3

McCLOSKEY, JOHN JAMES
(Honest John)
b.Apr.4,1862 Louisville,Ky.
d.Nov.17,1940
Non-playing manager Lou (N) 1895-96 and St.L (N) 1906-08.

McCLOSKEY, WILLIAM GEORGE
b.Philadelphia,Pa.
1884 Wil U C-O 9 .133

McCLURE, HAROLD MURRAY
b.Aug.8,1859 Lewisburg,Pa.
d.Feb.19,1919
1882 Bos N O 2 .333
TR

McCLURE, LAWRENCE LEDWITH
b.Oct.3,1885 Wayne,W.Va.
d.Aug.31,1949
1910 NY A O 1 .000
BR

McCLUSKEY, HARRY ROBERTS
b.Mar.26,1893
1915 Cin N P 3 0-0

McCOLL, ALEXANDER BOYD (Red)
b.Mar.29,1896 Eagleville,O.
1933 Was A P 4 1-0
1934 Was A P 42 3-4
BBTR 46 4-4

McCONNAUGHEY, RALPH J.
b.1889
1914 Ind F P 7 0-2
BRTR

McCONNELL, AMBROSE MOSES
b.Apr.29,1883 N.Pownal,Vt.
d.May 20,1942
1908 Bos A 2 140 .279
1909 Bos A 2 121 .238
1910 Bos A 2 12 .125
1910 Chi A 2 32 .296
1911 Chi A 2 104 .280
BLTR 409 .264

McCONNELL, GEORGE N.
b.Sept.16,1879 Shelbyville,Tenn.
1909 NY A P-1 13 {0-1 .209}
1912 NY A P 42 8-12
1913 NY A P 35 5-15
1914 Chi N P 1 0-1
1915 Chi F P 50 25-10
1916 Chi N P 28 4-12
BRTR 169 {42-51 .182}

McCONNELL, SAMUEL FAULKNER
b.June 8,1895 Philadelphia,Pa.
1915 Phi A 3 6 .191
BLTR

McCORMICK, FRANK ANDREW
(Buck)
b.June 9,1913 New York,N.Y.
1934 Cin N 1 12 .313
1937 Cin N 1-2-O 24 .325
1938 Cin N 1 151 .326
1939 Cin N 1 156 .332
1940 Cin N 1 155 .309
1941 Cin N 1 154 .269
1942 Cin N 1 145 .277
1943 Cin N 1 126 .303
1944 Cin N 1 153 .305

(Continued)
1945 Cin N 1 152 .276
1946 Phi N 1 135 .284
1947 Phi N 1 15 .225
1947 Bos N 1 81 .354
1948 Bos N 1 75 .250
BRTR 1534 .299

McCORMICK, HARRY ELWOOD
(Moose)
b.Feb.28,1881 Philadelphia,Pa.
d.July 9,1962
1904 NY N O 54 .266
1904 Pit N O 66 .290
1908 Phi N O 5 .091
1908 NY N O 65 .302
1909 NY N O 110 .290
1912 NY N O 42 .333
1913 NY N O 57 .275
TL 399 .285

McCORMICK, JAMES
b.1856 Paterson,N.J.
d.Mar.10,1918
1878 Ind N P 15 4-9
1879 Cle N M-P-O 75 {20-40 .219}
1880 Cle N M-P-O 77 {44-29 .250}
1881 Cle N M-P-2-O 69 {26-31 .257}
1882 Cle N P-O 67 {35-29 .216}
1883 Cle N P-1-O 41 {27-13 .235}
1884 Cle N P-O 48 {19-22 .263}
1884 Cin U P-O 28 {22-4 .237}
1885 Pro N P 4 1-3
1885 Chi N P-O 25 {20-4 .231}
1886 Chi N P 42 31-11
1887 Pit N P 36 13-23
BRTR 527 {262-218 .237}

McCORMICK, JAMES AMBROSE
b.Nov.2,1868 Spencer,Mass.
d.Feb.1,1948
1892 St.L N 2 2 .000
BRTR

McCORMICK, JOHN (Jerry)
b.Philadelphia,Pa.
d.Sept.19,1905
1883 Bal a 3 98 .261
1884 Key U 2-S-3-O 66 .296
1884 Was U S-3 42 .237
206 .268

McCORMICK, MICHAEL FRANCIS
b.Sept.29,1938 Pasadena,Cal.
1956 NY N P 3 0-1
1957 NY N P 24 3-1
1958 SF N P 42 11-8
1959 SF N P 47 12-16
1960 SF N P 40 15-12
1961 SF N P 40 13-16
1962 SF N P 29 5-5
BLTL 225 59-59

McCORMICK, MICHAEL J.
(Kid)
b.1883 Jersey City,N.J.
d.Nov.19,1953
1904 Bro N 3 105 .184
BRTR

McCORMICK, MYRON WINTHROP
(Mike)
b.May 6,1917 Angel's Camp,Cal.
1940 Cin N O 110 .300
1941 Cin N O 110 .287
1942 Cin N O 40 .237
1943 Cin N O 4 .133

(Continued)
1946 Cin N O 23 .216
1946 Bos N O 59 .262
1947 Bos N O 92 .285
1948 Bos N O 115 .303
1949 Bro N O 55 .209
1950 NY N H 4 .000
1950 Chi A O 55 .232
1951 Was A O 81 .288
BRTR 748 .275

McCORMICK, PATRICK HENRY
b.Oct.25,1855 Syracuse,N.Y.
d.June 21,1888
1879 Syr N P 55 11-13
1881 Wor N P-O 12 {1-8 .122}
1882 Cin a P-O 26 {13-12 .126}
1883 Cin a P 14 9-5
TR 107 {34-38 .207}

McCORMICK, WILLIAM J.
(Barry)
b.Dec.25,1874 Cincinnati,O.
d.Jan.28,1956
1895 Lou N S 3 .273
1896 Chi N 3 45 .219
1897 Chi N S-3 100 .273
1898 Chi N 3 136 .248
1899 Chi N 2 102 .234
1900 Chi N S-3 110 .215
1901 Chi N S 115 .234
1902 St.L A S-3-O 139 .246
1903 St.L A 2 59 .192
1903 Was A 2-3 62 .225
1904 Was A 2 112 .219
TR 983 .237

McCORRY, WILLIAM CHARLES
b.July 9,1887 Saranac Lake,N.Y.
1909 St.L A P 2 0-2
BLTR

McCOSKY, WILLIAM BARNEY
b.Apr.11,1918 Coal Run,Pa.
1939 Det A O 147 .311
1940 Det A O 143 .340
1941 Det A O 127 .324
1942 Det A O 154 .293
1946 Det A O 25 .198
1946 Phi A O 92 .354
1947 Phi A O 137 .328
1948 Phi A O 135 .326
1950 Phi A O 66 .240
1951 Phi A O 12 .296
1951 Cin N O 25 .320
1951 Cle A O 31 .213
1952 Cle A O 54 .213
1953 Cle A H 22 .190
BLTR 1170 .312

McCOVEY, WILLIE LEE
b.Jan.10,1938 Mobile,Ala.
1959 SF N 1 52 .354
1960 SF N 1 101 .238
1961 SF N 1 106 .271
1962 SF N 1-O 91 .293
BLTL 350 .283

McCOY, A. J.
b.Danville,Pa.
1889 Was N O 2 .000

McCOY, BENJAMIN JENISON
b.Nov.9,1915 Jenison,Mich.
1938 Det A 2-3 7 .200
1939 Det A 2-S 55 .302
1940 Phi A 2-3 134 .257
1941 Phi A 2 141 .271
BLTR 337 .269

Yr Cl Lea Pos G Rec

McCRABB, LESTER WILLIAM
(Buster)
b.Nov.4,1914 Fulton,Pa.
1939 Phi A P 5 1-2
1940 Phi A P 4 0-0
1941 Phi A P 26 9-13
1942 Phi A P 1 0-0
1950 Phi A P 2 0-0
BRTR 38 10-15

McCREA, FRANCIS WILLIAM
b.Sept.6,1898 Jersey City,N.J.
1925 Cle A C 1 .200
BRTR

McCREEDIE, WALTER HENRY (Judge)
b.Nov.29,1876 Manchester,Ia.
d.July 29,1934
1903 Bro N O 56 .324

McCREERY, EDWARD P.
b.1891
1914 Det A P 3 1-0
BRTR

McCREERY, THOMAS LEAVENWORTH
b.Oct.19,1874 Beaver,Pa.
d.July 3,1941
1895 Lou N P-1-O 29 {3-2 .336
1896 Lou N P-O 110 {0-1 .351
1897 Lou N O 89 .283
1897 NY N 2-O 49 .290
1898 NY N O 34 .198
1898 Pit N O 51 .304
1899 Pit N O 113 .325
1900 Pit N O 33 .223
1901 Bro N O 84 .302
1902 Bro N 1-O 111 .246
1903 Bro N O 38 .262
1903 Bos N O 23 .217
BB 764 {3-3 .292

McCRELLIS, MARK
1892 St.L N 3 1 .000

McCROHAN, DENNIS J.
(Played under name of Dennis J. Mack)

McCUE, FRANK ALOYSIUS
b.Oct.4,1900 Chicago,Ill.
1922 Phi A 3 2 .000
BBTR

McCULLOUGH, CHARLES
b.1867 Dublin,Ireland.
1890 Bro a P 24 4-20
1890 Syr a P 5 2-2
29 6-22

McCULLOUGH, CLYDE EDWARD
b.Mar.4,1917 Nashville,Tenn.
1940 Chi N C 9 .154
1941 Chi N C 125 .227
1942 Chi N C 109 .282
1943 Chi N C 87 .237
1946 Chi N C 95 .287
1947 Chi N C 86 .252
1948 Chi N C 69 .209
1949 Pit N C 91 .237
1950 Pit N C 103 .254
1951 Pit N C 92 .297
1952 Pit N C-1 66 .233
1953 Chi N C 77 .258
1954 Chi N C-3 31 .259
1955 Chi N C 44 .198
1956 Chi N C 14 .211
BRTR 1098 .252

McCULLOUGH, PAUL WILLARD
b.July 28,1902 New Castle,Pa.
1929 Was A P 3 0-0
BRTR

Yr Cl Lea Pos G Rec

McCULLOUGH, PHILIP LAMAR
b.July 22,1917 Stockbridge,Ga.
1942 Was A P 1 0-0
BRTR

McCURDY, HARRY HENRY
b.Sept.15,1900 Marseilles,Wis.
1922 St.L N C-1 13 .296
1923 St.L N C 67 .265
1926 Chi A C 44 .326
1927 Chi A C 86 .286
1928 Chi A C 49 .262
1930 Phi N C 80 .331
1931 Phi N C 66 .287
1932 Phi N C 62 .235
1933 Phi N C 73 .278
1934 Cin N 1 3 .000
BLTR 543 .282

McDANIEL, LYNDALL DALE
b.Dec.13,1935 Hollis,Okla.
1955 St.L N P 4 0-0
1956 St.L N P 39 7-6
1957 St.L N P 31 15-9
1958 St.L N P 26 5-7
1959 St.L N P 62 14-12
1960 St.L N P 65 12-4
1961 St.L N P 55 10-6
1962 St.L N P 55 3-10
BRTR 337 66-54

McDANIEL, MAX VON
b.Apr.18,1939 Hollis,Okla.
1957 St.L N P 17 7-5
1958 St.L N P 2 0-0
BRTR 19 7-5

McDERMOTT, FRANK A.
(Red)
b.Nov.12,1889 Philadelphia,Pa.
1912 Det A O 5 .250
BRTR

McDERMOTT, JOSEPH
1871 Kek n O 2 NR
1872 Eck n P 7 0-7
1873 Res n S 1 NR
10 {0-7 NR

McDERMOTT, MAURICE JOSEPH
(Mickey)
b.Aug.29,1928 Poughkeepsie,N.Y.
1948 Bos A P 7 0-0
1949 Bos A P 12 5-4
1950 Bos A P 39 7-3
1951 Bos A P 43 8-8
1952 Bos A P 36 10-9
1953 Bos A P 45 18-10
1954 Was A P 54 7-15
1955 Was A P 70 10-10
1956 NY A P 46 2-6
1957 KC A P-1 58 {1-4 .245
1958 Det A P 4 0-0
1961 St.L N P 22 1-0
1961 KC A P 7 0-0
BLTL 443 {69-69 .252

McDERMOTT, MICHAEL JOSEPH
b.Sept.7,1862 St.Louis,Mo.
d.June 30,1943
1889 Lou a P 9 1-7
1895 Lou N P 26 4-19
1896 Lou N P 12 2-7
1897 Cle N P 9 3-4
1897 St.L N P 7 3-4
TR 63 13-41

McDEVITT, DANIEL EUGENE
b.Nov.18,1932 New York,N.Y.
1957 Bro N P 22 7-4

Yr Cl Lea Pos G Rec

(Continued)
1958 LA N P 13 2-6
1959 LA N P 39 10-8
1960 LA N P 24 0-4
1961 NY A P 8 1-2
1961 Min A P 16 1-0
1962 KC A P 33 0-3
BLTL 155 21-27

McDONALD, ...
1884 Was U C-O 2 .167

McDONALD, CHARLES E.
(Tex) (Real name Charles C. Crabtree)
b.Jan.31,1891 Farmersville,Tex.
d.Mar.31,1943
1912 Cin N S 61 .257
1913 Cin N S 11 .364
1913 Bos N 3 62 .353
1914 Pit F 2-3 67 .318
1914 Buf F O 69 .295
1915 Buf F O 87 .271
BLTR 357 .298

McDONALD, DANIEL
b.1847 Brooklyn,N.Y.
d.Nov.23,1880
1872 Atl n O 4 NR
1872 Eck n S 1 .000
1872 Atl n O 11 NR
16 NR

McDONALD, EDWARD C.
b.Oct.28,1886 Albany,N.Y.
d.Mar.11,1946
1911 Bos N 3 54 .206
1912 Bos N 3 121 .259
1913 Chi N H 1 .000
BRTR 176 .244

McDONALD, HENRY M.
b.Jan.16,1911 Santa Monica,Cal.
1931 Phi A P 19 2-4
1933 Phi A P 4 1-1
1933 St.L A P 25 0-4
BRTR 48 3-9

McDONALD, JAMES
b.Philadelphia,Pa.
1902 NY N O 2 .333

McDONALD, JAMES A.
b.Aug.6,1860 San Francisco.Cal.
d.Sept.14,1914
1884 Pit a 3-O 38 .151
1885 Buf N S-O 5 .000
43 .138

McDONALD, JAMES LeROY
(Hot Rod)
b.May 17,1927 Grants Pass,Ore.
1950 Bos A P 9 1-0
1951 St.L A P 17 4-7
1952 NY A P 26 3-4
1953 NY A P 29 9-7
1954 NY A P 16 4-1
1955 Bal A P 21 3-5
1956 Chi A P 8 0-2
1957 Chi A P 10 0-1
1958 Chi A P 3 0-0
BRTR 139 24-27

McDONALD, JOHN J.
1907 Was A P 1 0-0
TR

McDONALD, JOSEPH MALCOLM
1910 St.L A 3 10 .156

McDONNELL, JAMES WILLIAM
b.Aug.15,1922 Gagetown,Mich.

Yr	Cl	Lea	Pos	G	Rec
1943	Cle	A	C	2	.000
1944	Cle	A	C	20	.233
1945	Cle	A	C	28	.196
		BLTR		50	.211

McDONOUGH, EDWARD
b.Sept.13,1886 Elgin,Ill.
d.Sept.2,1926

Yr	Cl	Lea	Pos	G	Rec
1909	Phi	N	C	1	.000
1910	Phi	N	C	4	.111
		TR		5	.095

McDOOLAN, ...

Yr	Cl	Lea	Pos	G	Rec
1873	Mar	n	P	1	0-1
1875	RS	n	P	1	0-1
				2	0-2

McDOUGAL, JOHN A.

Yr	Cl	Lea	Pos	G	Rec
1895	Bro	N	P	5	0-0

McDOUGAL, JOHN H.
(Dewey)
b.Sept.19,1871 Aledo,Ill.
d.Apr.28,1936

Yr	Cl	Lea	Pos	G	Rec
1895	St.L	N	P	15	4-11
1896	St.L	N	P	3	0-1
				18	4-12

McDOUGALD, GILBERT JAMES
b.May 19,1928 San Francisco,Cal.

Yr	Cl	Lea	Pos	G	Rec
1951	NY	A	2-3	131	.306
1952	NY	A	2-3	152	.263
1953	NY	A	2-3	141	.285
1954	NY	A	2-3	126	.259
1955	NY	A	2-3	141	.285
1956	NY	A	2-S-3	120	.311
1957	NY	A	2-S-3	141	.289
1958	NY	A	2-S	138	.250
1959	NY	A	2-S-3	127	.251
1960	NY	A	2-3	119	.258
		BRTR		1336	.276

McDOUGALL, JAMES A.
(Sandy)
b.Feb.18,1878 Buffalo,N.Y.
d.Oct.4,1910

Yr	Cl	Lea	Pos	G	Rec
1905	St.L	N	P	5	1-4

McDOWELL, SAMUEL EDWARD
b.Sept.21,1942 Pittsburgh,Pa.

Yr	Cl	Lea	Pos	G	Rec
1961	Cle	A	P	1	0-0
1962	Cle	A	P	25	3-7
		BLTL		26	3-7

McELROY, JAMES D.
b.San Francisco,Cal.
d.Feb.24,1889

Yr	Cl	Lea	Pos	G	Rec
1884	Phi	N	P-O	13	1-12 .136
1884	Wil	U	P-O	1	0-1 .000
				14	1-13 .131

McELVEEN, PRYOR MYNATT
(Humpy)
b.Nov.5,1880 Atlanta,Ga.
d.Oct.27,1951

Yr	Cl	Lea	Pos	G	Rec
1909	Bro	N	3	67	.198
1910	Bro	N	3	64	.225
1911	Bro	N	2	16	.193
		TR		147	.209

McELWEE, LELAND STANFORD
b.May 23,1894 San Diego,Cal.

Yr	Cl	Lea	Pos	G	Rec
1916	Phi	A	3	54	.265
		BLTR			

McELYEA, FRANK
b.Aug.4,1918 Carmi,Ill.

Yr	Cl	Lea	Pos	G	Rec
1942	Bos	N	O	7	.000
		BRTR			

McEVOY, LOUIS ANTHONY
b.May 30,1902 Williamsburg,Kan.
d.Dec.16,1953

Yr	Cl	Lea	Pos	G	Rec
1930	NY	A	P	28	1-3
1931	NY	A	P	6	0-0
		BRTR		34	1-3

McFADDEN, BERNARD JOSEPH
(Barney)
b.Feb.22,1874 Eckley,Pa.
d.Apr.28,1924

Yr	Cl	Lea	Pos	G	Rec
1901	Cin	N	P	8	3-4
1902	Phi	N	P	1	0-1
		BRTR		9	3-5

McFADDEN, GUY

Yr	Cl	Lea	Pos	G	Rec
1895	St.L	N	1	4	.200

McFARLAN, ALEXANDER SHEPARD
b.Oct,11,1869 St.Louis,Mo.
d.Mar.1939

Yr	Cl	Lea	Pos	G	Rec
1892	Lou	N	O	14	.162

McFARLAN, ANDERSON DANIEL
(Dan)
b.Nov.26,1874 Gainesville,Tex.
d.Sept.24,1924

Yr	Cl	Lea	Pos	G	Rec
1895	Lou	N	P	7	0-6
1899	Bro	N	P	1	0-0
1899	Was	N	P	29	8-18
				37	8-24

McFARLAND, CHARLES EDWARD
(Chappie)
d.Dec.15,1924

Yr	Cl	Lea	Pos	G	Rec
1902	St.L	N	P	2	0-1
1903	St.L	N	P	28	9-19
1904	St.L	N	P	32	13-18
1905	St.L	N	P	31	9-18
1906	St.L	N	P	7	3-4
1906	Pit	N	P	6	1-3
1906	Bro	N	P	1	0-1
		TR		107	35-64

McFARLAND, CLAUDE

Yr	Cl	Lea	Pos	G	Rec
1884	Bal	U	P-O	3	0-1 .286

McFARLAND, EDWARD WILLIAM
b.Aug.3,1874 Cleveland,O.
d.Nov.28,1959

Yr	Cl	Lea	Pos	G	Rec
1893	Cle	N	O	9	.370
1896	St.L	N	C	80	.239
1897	St.L	N	C-1-2-O	31	.324
1897	Phi	N	C	36	.221
1898	Phi	N	C	118	.274
1899	Phi	N	C	90	.333
1900	Phi	N	C	90	.307
1901	Phi	N	C	72	.278
1902	Chi	A	C-1-O	71	.231
1903	Chi	A	C	61	.210
1904	Chi	A	C	50	.263
1905	Chi	A	C	80	.280
1906	Chi	A	C	12	.181
1907	Chi	A	C	52	.283
1908	Bos	A	C	19	.208
		BRTR		871	.272

McFARLAND, HERMUS W.
b.Mar.11,1870 Des Moines,Ia.
d.Sept.21,1935

Yr	Cl	Lea	Pos	G	Rec
1896	Lou	N	O	25	.198
1898	Cin	N	O	15	.286
1901	Chi	A	O	132	.265
1902	Chi	A	O	7	.185
1902	Bal	A	O	63	.321
1903	NY	A	O	103	.223
		BLTR		345	.257

McFARLAND, HOWARD ALEXANDER
b.Mar.7,1911 El Reno,Okla.

Yr	Cl	Lea	Pos	G	Rec
1945	Was	A	O	6	.091
		BRTR			

McFARLAND, LaMONT A.
(Monte)
b.1871 Illinois.
d.Nov.15,1913

Yr	Cl	Lea	Pos	G	Rec
1895	Chi	N	P	2	2-0
1896	Chi	N	P	3	0-3
				5	2-3

McFARLANE, ORLANDO JESUS
b.June 28,1938 Oriente,Cuba

Yr	Cl	Lea	Pos	G	Rec
1962	Pit	N	C	8	087
		BRTR			

McFETRIDGE, JOHN R.
b.Aug.25,1869 Philadelphia,Pa.
d.Jan.10,1917

Yr	Cl	Lea	Pos	G	Rec
1890	Phi	N	P	1	1-0
1903	Phi	N	P	14	1-11
				15	2-11

McGAFFIGAN, MARTIN A.
(Patsy)
b.Sept.22,1888 Carlyle,Ill.
d.Dec.22,1940

Yr	Cl	Lea	Pos	G	Rec
1917	Phi	N	S	19	.167
1918	Phi	N	2-S	54	.203
		BRTR		73	.194

McGAH, EDWARD JOSEPH
b.Sept.30,1921 Oakland,Cal.

Yr	Cl	Lea	Pos	G	Rec
1946	Bos	A	C	15	.216
1947	Bos	A	C	9	.000
		BRTR		24	.157

McGAHA, FRED MELVIN
b.Sept.26,1926 Bastrop,La.
Non-playing manager Cle(A) 1962

McGAMWELL, EDWARD M.
b.Jan.10.1878 Buffalo.N.Y.
d.Nov.1,1950

Yr	Cl	Lea	Pos	G	Rec
1905	Bro	N	1	4	.267

McGANN, DENNIS L.
(Dan)
b.July 15,1872 Shelbyville,Ky.
d.Dec.13,1910

Yr	Cl	Lea	Pos	G	Rec
1895	Lou	N	S-3	17	.313
1896	Bos	N	2	42	.315
1898	Bal	N	1	145	.298
1899	Bro	N	1	63	.245
1899	Was	N	1	75	.338
1900	St.L	N	1	124	.301
1901	St.L	N	1	113	.265
1902	Bal	A	1	68	.314
1902	NY	N	1	61	.301
1903	NY	N	1	129	.270
1904	NY	N	1	141	.286
1905	NY	N	1	136	.299
1906	NY	N	1	133	.237
1907	NY	N	1	81	.298
1908	Bos	N	1	130	.240
				1458	.283

McGARR, JAMES B.
(Chippy)
b.May 10,1863 Worcester,Mass.
d.June 6,1904

Yr	Cl	Lea	Pos	G	Rec
1884	Chi	U	2	18	.160
1886	Ath	a	S	72	.271
1887	Ath	a	S	127	.331
1888	St.L	a	2	35	.187
1889	KC	a	2-S-3-O	25	.287
1889	Bal	a	S	3	.143
1890	Bos	N	3	121	.236
1893	Cle	N	3	63	.309
1894	Cle	N	3	127	.272
1895	Cle	N	3	112	.270
1896	Cle	N	3	111	.266
		BRTR		814	.273

McGARR, JAMES VINCENT
b.Nov.9,1888 Philadelphia,Pa.

Yr	Cl	Lea	Pos	G	Rec
1912	Det	A	O	1	.000

McGARVEY, DANIEL

Yr	Cl	Lea	Pos	G	Rec
1912	Det	A	O	1	.000

McGEACHY, JOHN CHARLES
b.Jan.23,1861 Clinton,Mass.
d.Apr.5,1930

Yr	Cl	Lea	Pos	G	Rec
1886	Det	N	O	7	.333
1886	St.L	N	O	58	.216
1887	Ind	N	O	99	.278
1888	Ind	N	O	118	.219
1889	Ind	N	O	131	.267
1890	Bro	p	O	104	.253
1891	Ath	a	O	46	.217
1891	Bos	a	O	41	.250
	BR			604	.248

McGEARY, MICHAEL HENRY
b.1851 Philadelphia,Pa.

Yr	Cl	Lea	Pos	G	Rec
1871	Tro	n	C-S	29	.244
1872	Ath	n	C-S-O	48	NR
1873	Ath	n	C-S	51	NR
1874	Ath	n	C-S-O	54	NR
1875	Phi	n	2-S-3-O	68	.294
1876	St.L	N	2	60	.259
1877	St.L	N	2-3	57	.253
1879	Pro	N	2-3	84	.276
1880	Pro	N	2-S-3	17	.129
1880	Cle	N	3-O	31	.233
1881	Cle	N	3	10	.211
1882	Det	N	2-S	33	.149
	BRTR			542	NR

McGEE, DANIEL ALOYSIUS
b.Sept.29,1913 New York,N.Y.

Yr	Cl	Lea	Pos	G	Rec
1934	Bos	N	S	7	.136

BRTR

McGEE, F.

Yr	Cl	Lea	Pos	G	Rec
1874	Atl	n	2-S-O	16	NR
1875	Mut	n	O	22	NR
1875	Atl	n	2-3-O	21	NR
1884	Was	U	C-3-O	4	.188
				63	NR

McGEE, FRANCIS D. (Tubby)
b.Apr.28,1899 Columbus,O.
d.Jan.30,1934

Yr	Cl	Lea	Pos	G	Rec
1925	Was	A	1	2	.000

BRTR

McGEE, WILLIAM HENRY
(Fiddler Bill)
b.Nov.16,1911 Batchtown,Ill.

Yr	Cl	Lea	Pos	G	Rec
1935	St.L	N	P	1	1-0
1936	St.L	N	P	7	1-1
1937	St.L	N	P	4	1-0
1938	St.L	N	P	47	7-12
1939	St.L	N	P	43	12-5
1940	St.L	N	P	38	16-10
1941	St.L	N	P	4	0-1
1941	NY	N	P	22	2-9
1942	NY	N	P	31	6-3
	BRTR			197	46-41

McGEEHAN, CORNELIUS BERNARD
b.Oct.6,1883 Drifton,Pa.
d.July 4,1907

Yr	Cl	Lea	Pos	G	Rec
1903	Phi	A	P	6	1-0

McGEEHAN, DANIEL DeSALES
b.June 7,1885 Drifton,Pa.
d.July 12,1955

Yr	Cl	Lea	Pos	G	Rec
1911	St.L	N	2	3	.222

BRTR

McGEHEE, PATRICK HENRY
b.July 2,1888 Meadville,Miss.
d.Dec.30,1946

Yr	Cl	Lea	Pos	G	Rec
1912	Det	A	P	1	0-1

BLTR

McGHEE, WARREN EDWARD
(Ed)
b.Sept.29,1926 Perry,Ark.

Yr	Cl	Lea	Pos	G	Rec
1950	Chi	A	O	3	.167

(Continued)

Yr	Cl	Lea	Pos	G	Rec
1953	Phi	A	O	104	.263
1954	Phi	A	O	21	.208
1954	Chi	A	O	42	.227
1955	Chi	A	O	26	.077
	BRTR			196	.246

McGHEE, WILLIAM HARRISON
b.Sept.5,1908 Shawmut,Ala.

Yr	Cl	Lea	Pos	G	Rec
1944	Phi	A	1	77	.289
1945	Phi	A	1-O	93	.252
	BLTL			170	.272

McGILL, WILLIAM JOHN
(Parson)
b.June 29,1880 McPherson,Kan.

Yr	Cl	Lea	Pos	G	Rec
1907	St.L	A	P	2	1-0

BRTR

McGILL, WILLIAM VANESS
(Kid)
b.Nov.10,1873 Atlanta,Ga.
d.Aug.29,1944

Yr	Cl	Lea	Pos	G	Rec
1890	Cle	p	P	24	11-9
1891	Cin	a	P	16	2-4
1891	St.L	a	P	28	19-9
1892	Cin	N	P	3	1-1
1893	Chi	N	P	35	17-17
1894	Chi	N	P	26	6-19
1895	Phi	N	P	19	10-8
1896	Phi	N	P	12	4-4
	TL			163	70-71

McGILLEN, JOHN JOSEPH
b.Aug.6,1919 Eddystone,Pa.

Yr	Cl	Lea	Pos	G	Rec
1944	Phi	A	P	2	0-0

BLTL

McGILLICUDDY, CORNELIUS
(Played under name of Connie Mack)

McGILLICUDDY, EARLE
(Played under name of Earle Mack)

McGILVRAY, WILLIAM ALEXANDER
b.Apr.29,1883 Portland,Ore.
d.May 23,1952

Yr	Cl	Lea	Pos	G	Rec
1908	Cin	N	H	2	.000

McGINLEY, JAMES WILLIAM
b.Oct.2,1878 Groveland,Mass.

Yr	Cl	Lea	Pos	G	Rec
1904	St.L	N	P	3	2-1
1905	St.L	N	P	1	0-1
				4	2-2

McGINLEY, TIMOTHY S.
b.Philadelphia,Pa.
d.Nov.2,1899

Yr	Cl	Lea	Pos	G	Rec
1875	Cen	n	C-O	13	NR
1875	NH	n	C	32	NR
1876	Bos	N	C	9	.150
				54	NR

McGINN, FRANK J.
b.Cincinnati,O.
d.Nov.19,1897

Yr	Cl	Lea	Pos	G	Rec
1890	Pit	N	O	1	.000

McGINNIS, AUGUST
b.1870 Painesville,O.

Yr	Cl	Lea	Pos	G	Rec
1893	Chi	N	P	13	2-6
1893	Phi	N	P	5	1-3
				18	3-9

McGINNIS, GEORGE W.
(Jumbo)
b.Feb.22,1864 St.Louis,Mo.
d.May 18,1934

Yr	Cl	Lea	Pos	G	Rec
1882	St.L	a	P-2-O	51	25-21 227
1883	St.L	a	P-O	44	29-15 .211
1884	St.L	a	P	40	24-16
1885	St.L	a	P	13	6-6
1886	St.L	a	P	10	5-2
1886	Bal	a	P	26	11-12

(Continued)

Yr	Cl	Lea	Pos	G	Rec
1887	Cin	a	P	9	3-6
				193	103-78 .215

McGINNITY, JOSEPH JEROME
(Iron Man)
b.Mar.19,1871 Rock Island,Ill.
d.Nov.14,1929

Yr	Cl	Lea	Pos	G	Rec
1899	Bal	N	P	47	27-13
1900	Bro	N	P	41	29-9
1901	Bal	A	P	48	26-19
1902	Bal	A	P-O	27	13-10 .295
1902	NY	N	P-2-O	19	8-8 .123
1903	NY	N	P	55	31-20
1904	NY	N	P	51	35-8
1905	NY	N	P	46	22-16
1906	NY	N	P	45	27-12
1907	NY	N	P	47	18-17
1908	NY	N	P	37	11-7
	BRTR			463	247-139 .193

McGLONE, JOHN T.
b.Baltimore,Md.

Yr	Cl	Lea	Pos	G	Rec
1886	Was	N	3	3	.091
1887	Cle	a	3	21	.329
1888	Cle	a	3	55	.183
				79	.221

McGLOTHIN, EZRA MAC
(Pat)
b.Oct.27,1922 Knoxville,Tenn.

Yr	Cl	Lea	Pos	G	Rec
1949	Bro	N	P	7	1-1
1950	Bro	N	P	1	0-0
	BLTR			8	1-1

McGLYNN, ULYSSES SIMPSON GRANT (Stoney)
b.May 26,1872 Lancaster,Pa.
d.Aug.26,1941

Yr	Cl	Lea	Pos	G	Rec
1906	St.L	N	P	6	4-2
1907	St.I,	N	P	45	14-25
1908	St.L	N	P	16	1-6
				67	19-33

McGOVERN, ARTHUR JOHN
b.Feb.27,1882 St.John,N.B.,Canada.
d.Nov.14,1915

Yr	Cl	Lea	Pos	G	Rec
1905	Bos	A	C	15	.114

TR

McGOWAN, FRANK BERNARD
(Beauty)
b.Nov.8,1901 Branford,Conn.

Yr	Cl	Lea	Pos	G	Rec
1922	Phi	A	O	99	.230
1923	Phi	A	O	95	.254
1928	St.L	A	O	47	.363
1929	St.L	A	O	125	.254
1937	Bos	N	O	9	.083
	BLTR			375	.262

McGOWAN, TULLIS EARL
(Mickey)
b.Nov.26,1921 Waycross,Ga.

Yr	Cl	Lea	Pos	G	Rec
1948	NY	N	P	3	0-0

BLTL

McGRANER, HOWARD
b.Sept.11,1889 Luhrig,O.
d.Oct.22,1952

Yr	Cl	Lea	Pos	G	Rec
1912	Cin	N	P	2	1-0

BLTL

McGRAW, JAMES LEO
b.1890
d.Nov.14,1918

Yr	Cl	Lea	Pos	G	Rec
1914	Bro	F	P	1	0-0

McGRAW, JOHN JOSEPH
(Little Napoleon)
b.Apr.7,1873 Truxton,N.Y.
d.Feb.25,1934

Yr	Cl	Lea	Pos	G	Rec
1891	Bal	a	S	31	.245
1892	Bal	N	2-O	76	.267
1893	Bal	N	S	127	.328
1894	Bal	N	3	123	.340
1895	Bal	N	3	93	.374
1896	Bal	N	3	19	.356
1897	Bal	N	3	105	.326
1898	Bal	N	3	141	.334
1899	Bal	N	M-3	118	.390
1900	St.L	N	3	98	.337
1901	Bal	A	M-3	73	.352
1902	Bal	A	M-3	20	.286
1902	NY	N	M-S	34	.226
1903	NY	N	M-2	12	.273
1904	NY	N	M-2	3	.300
1905	NY	N	M-O	3	.000
1906	NY	N	M-3	4	.000
	BLTR			1080	.334

Non-playing manager NY (N) 1907-32.

McGRAW, ROBERT EMMETT
b.Apr.10,1895 LaVeta,Colo.

Yr	Cl	Lea	Pos	G	Rec
1917	NY	A	P	2	0-1
1918	NY	A	P	1	0-1
1919	NY	A	P	6	0-2
1919	Bos	A	P	10	1-0
1920	NY	A	P	15	0-0
1925	Bro	N	P	2	0-2
1926	Bro	N	P	33	9-13
1927	Bro	N	P	1	0-1
1927	St.L	N	P	18	4-5
1928	Phi	N	P	39	7-8
1929	Phi	N	P	41	5-5
	BRTR			168	26-38

McGREW, WALTER HOWARD
(Slim)
b.Aug.5,1899 Yoakum,Tex.

Yr	Cl	Lea	Pos	G	Rec
1922	Was	A	P	1	0-0
1923	Was	A	P	3	0-1
1924	Was	A	P	6	0-1
	BRTR			10	0-2

McGUCKIN, JOSEPH W.
b.1862 Paterson,N.J.
d.Dec.31,1903

Yr	Cl	Lea	Pos	G	Rec
1890	Bal	a	O	10	.056

McGUINNESS, JOHN J.

Yr	Cl	Lea	Pos	G	Rec
1876	Lou	N	2	1	.000
1879	Syr	N	1	12	.294
1884	Key	U	1	52	.243
				65	.249

McGUIRE, JAMES THOMAS
(Deacon)
b.Nov.18,1863 Youngstown,O.
d.Oct.31,1936

Yr	Cl	Lea	Pos	G	Rec
1884	Tol	a	C	45	.184
1885	Det	N	C-O	34	.190
1886	Phi	N	C	48	.197
1887	Phi	N	C	40	.354
1888	Phi	N	C	12	.333
1888	Det	N	C	3	.000
1888	Cle	a	C	25	.207
1890	Roc	a	C	87	.301
1891	Was	a	C	111	.296
1892	Was	N	C	87	.241
1893	Was	N	C	59	.262
1894	Was	N	C	102	.304
1895	Was	N	C	133	.330
1896	Was	N	C	95	.325
1897	Was	N	C	82	.338
1898	Was	N	M-C-1	128	.273
1899	Was	N	C	56	.277
1899	Bro	N	C	43	.338
1900	Bro	N	C	68	.280
1901	Bro	N	C	84	.293
1902	Det	A	C	72	.229
1903	Det	A	C	71	.241
1904	NY	A	C	100	.211
1905	NY	A	C	71	.219

(Continued)

Yr	Cl	Lea	Pos	G	Rec
1906	NY	A	C	51	.299
1907	NY	A	H	1	.000
1907	Bos	A	M-C	6	.500
1908	Bos	A	M-1	1	.000
1908	Cle	A	C	1	.250
1910	Cle	A	M-C	1	.000
1912	Det	A	C	1	.500
	BRTR			1718	.279

Non-playing manager Cle (A) 1909 and 1911.

McGUIRE, MICKEY C.
b.Jan.18,1941 Dayton,O.

Yr	Cl	Lea	Pos	G	Rec
1962	Bal	A	S	6	.000
	BRTR				

McGUIRE, MURRAY MASON
b.Jan.19,1872 Richmond,Va.
d.Sept.10,1945

Yr	Cl	Lea	Pos	G	Rec
1894	Cin	N	P	1	0-0

McGUIRE, THOMAS PATRICK
b.Feb.1,1892 Chicago,Ill.
d.Dec.8,1959

Yr	Cl	Lea	Pos	G	Rec
1914	Chi	F	P	37	5-6
1919	Chi	A	P	1	0-0
	BRTR			38	5-6

McGUNNIGLE, WILLIAM HENRY
(Gunner)
b.Jan.1,1855 Stoughton,Mass.
d.Mar.9,1899

Yr	Cl	Lea	Pos	G	Rec
1879	Buf	N	M-P-O	46	7-5 / .180
1880	Buf	N	M-P-O	7	2-3 / .174
1880	Wor	N	P	1	0-0 / .000
1882	Cle	N	O	1	.200
	BRTR			55	9-8 / .177

Non-playing manager Bro (a) 1888-89, Bro (N) 1890, Pit (N) 1891 and Lou (N) 1896.

McHALE, JAMES BERNARD
b.Dec.17,1875 Miners Mills,Pa.
d.June 18,1959

Yr	Cl	Lea	Pos	G	Rec
1908	Bos	A	O	21	.224
	BRTR				

McHALE, JOHN JOSEPH
b.Sept.21,1921 Detroit,Mich.

Yr	Cl	Lea	Pos	G	Rec
1943	Det	A	H	4	.000
1944	Det	A	H	1	.000
1945	Det	A	1	19	.143
1947	Det	A	1	39	.211
1948	Det	A	H	1	.000
	BLTR			64	.193

McHALE, MARTIN JOSEPH
b.Oct.30,1888 Stoneham,Mass.

Yr	Cl	Lea	Pos	G	Rec
1910	Bos	A	P	2	0-2
1911	Bos	A	P	4	0-0
1913	NY	A	P	7	2-4
1914	NY	A	P	30	7-16
1915	NY	A	P	13	3-7
1916	Bos	A	P	2	0-1
1916	Cle	A	P	5	0-0
	BRTR			63	12-30

McHALE, ROBERT E.
(Rabbit)
b.Feb.7,1870 Sacramento,Cal.

Yr	Cl	Lea	Pos	G	Rec
1898	Was	N	O	10	.171

McHENRY, AUSTIN BUSH
b.Sept.22,1895 Stout,O.
d.Nov.27,1922

Yr	Cl	Lea	Pos	G	Rec
1918	St.L	N	O	80	.261
1919	St.L	N	2-3-O	110	.286
1920	St.L	N	O	137	.282
1921	St.L	N	O	152	.350
1922	St.L	N	O	64	.303
	BRTR			543	.302

McILREE, VANCE ELMER
b.Oct.14.1897 Riverside.Ia.
d.May 6,1959

Yr	Cl	Lea	Pos	G	Rec
1921	Was	A	P	1	0-0
	BRTR				

McILVEEN, HENRY COOKE
(Irish)
b.July 27,1880 Belfast,Ireland.
d.Oct.19,1960

Yr	Cl	Lea	Pos	G	Rec
1906	Pit	N	P	5	0-1
1908	NY	A	O	44	.213
1909	NY	A	H	4	.000
	TL			53	0-1 / .212

McILWAIN, STOVER WILLIAM
b.Sept.22,1939 Savannah,Ga.

Yr	Cl	Lea	Pos	G	Rec
1957	Chi	A	P	1	0-0
1958	Chi	A	P	1	0-0
	BRTR			2	0-0

McINNIS, JOHN PHAELEN
(Stuffy)
b.Sept.19,1890 Gloucester,Mass.
d.Feb.16,1960

Yr	Cl	Lea	Pos	G	Rec
1909	Phi	A	S	19	.239
1910	Phi	A	S	38	.301
1911	Phi	A	1-S	126	.321
1912	Phi	A	1	153	.327
1913	Phi	A	1	148	.326
1914	Phi	A	1	149	.314
1915	Phi	A	1	119	.314
1916	Phi	A	1	140	.295
1917	Phi	A	1	150	.303
1918	Bos	A	1-3	117	.272
1919	Bos	A	1	120	.305
1920	Bos	A	1	148	.297
1921	Bos	A	1	152	.307
1922	Cle	A	1	142	.305
1923	Bos	N	1	154	.315
1924	Bos	N	1	146	.291
1925	Pit	N	1	59	.368
1926	Pit	N	1	47	.299
1927	Phi	N	M-1	1	.000
	BRTR			2128	.308

McINTIRE, HARRY M.
(Rocks)
b.Jan.11,1879 Detroit,Mich.
d.Jan.9,1949

Yr	Cl	Lea	Pos	G	Rec
1905	Bro	N	P	45	9-27
1906	Bro	N	P	42	13-21
1907	Bro	N	P	28	7-15
1908	Bro	N	P	40	11-20
1909	Bro	N	P	32	7-17
1910	Chi	N	P	28	13-9
1911	Chi	N	P	25	11-7
1912	Chi	N	P	7	1-2
1913	Cin	N	P	1	0-1
	BRTR			248	72-119

McINTYRE, FRANK W.
b.Detroit,Mich.

Yr	Cl	Lea	Pos	G	Rec
1883	Det	N	P	1	1-0
1883	Col	a	P	2	1-1
				3	2-1

McINTYRE, MATTHEW W.
b.June 12,1880 Stonington,Conn.
d.Apr.2,1920

Yr	Cl	Lea	Pos	G	Rec
1901	Phi	A	O	82	.283
1904	Det	A	O	152	.254
1905	Det	A	O	131	.265
1906	Det	A	O	133	.260
1907	Det	A	O	20	.284
1908	Det	A	O	151	.295
1909	Det	A	O	125	.244
1910	Det	A	O	83	.236
1911	Chi	A	O	146	.323
1912	Chi	A	O	45	.167
	BLTL			1068	.270

McIVOR, E. OTTO
b.1885 Greenville,Tex.

Yr	Cl	Lea	Pos	G	Rec
1911	St.L	N	O	17	.226
	BRTL				

McJAMES, JAMES McCUTCHEN
(Real name James McCutchen James)
b.Aug.27,1873 Williamsburg,S.C.
d.Sept.23,1901

(Continued)

Yr	Cl	Lea	Pos	G	Rec
1895	Was	N	P	3	1-1
1896	Was	N	P	34	12-21
1897	Was	N	P	41	14-24
1898	Bal	N	P	42	27-14
1899	Bro	N	P	33	17-11
1901	Bro	N	P	13	4-6
	TR			166	75-77

McKAIN, ARCHIE RICHARD
(Happy)
b.May 12,1911 Delphos,Kan.

Yr	Cl	Lea	Pos	G	Rec
1937	Bos	A	P	38	8-8
1938	Bos	A	P	37	5-4
1939	Det	A	P	32	5-6
1940	Det	A	P	27	5-0
1941	Det	A	P	15	2-1
1941	St.L	A	P	8	0-1
1943	St.L	A	P	10	1-1
	BLTL			167	26-21

McKAIN, HAROLD LeROY
b.July 10,1906 Logan,Ia.

Yr	Cl	Lea	Pos	G	Rec
1927	Cle	A	P	2	0-1
1929	Chi	A	P	34	6-9
1930	Chi	A	P	33	6-4
1931	Chi	A	P	32	6-9
1932	Chi	A	P	8	0-0
	BLTR			109	18-23

McKAY, REEVES H.

Yr	Cl	Lea	Pos	G	Rec
1915	St.L	A	P	1	0-0

McKEAN, EDWIN JOHN
b.June 20,1868 Cleveland,O.
d.Aug.16,1919

Yr	Cl	Lea	Pos	G	Rec
1887	Cle	a	S	132	.364
1888	Cle	a	S-O	130	.297
1889	Cle	N	S	123	.302
1890	Cle	N	S	136	.296
1891	Cle	N	S	141	.280
1892	Cle	N	S	128	.269
1893	Cle	N	S	125	.325
1894	Cle	N	S	130	.354
1895	Cle	N	S	132	.344
1896	Cle	N	S	133	.335
1897	Cle	N	S	127	.273
1898	Cle	N	S	151	.285
1899	StL	N	S	67	.281
	BRTR			1655	.311

McKECHNIE, WILLIAM BOYD
(Deacon)
b.Aug.7,1887 Wilkinsburg,Pa.

Yr	Cl	Lea	Pos	G	Rec
1907	Pit	N	2	3	.125
1910	Pit	N	2	60	.217
1911	Pit	N	1-2	92	.227
1912	Pit	N	2-S	24	.247
1913	Bos	N	O	1	.000
1913	NY	A	2	44	.134
1914	Ind	F	3	149	.305
1915	New	F	M-3	126	.257
1916	NY	N	3	71	.238
1916	Cin	N	3	37	.292
1917	Cin	N	2-S-3	48	.254
1918	Pit	N	3	126	.255
1920	Pit	N	3	40	.218
	BBTR			821	.252

Non-playing manager Pit (N) 1922-26, St.L (N) 1928-29, Bos (N) 1930-37 and Cin (N) 1938-46.

McKEE, ...

Yr	Cl	Lea	Pos	G	Rec
1884	Was	U	C-3-O	4	.188

McKEE, JAMES F.
b.Rockford,Ill.
d.June 26,1912
Non-playing manager Mil (U) 1884.

McKEE, RAYMOND ELLIS
(Red)
b.July 20,1890 Shawnee,O.

Yr	Cl	Lea	Pos	G	Rec
1913	Det	A	C	67	.283
1914	Det	A	C	32	.187
1915	Det	A	C	55	.274

(Continued)

Yr	Cl	Lea	Pos	G	Rec
1916	Det	A	C	32	.211
	BLTR			186	.254

McKEE, ROGERS HORNSBY
b.Sept.16,1926 Shelby,N.C.

Yr	Cl	Lea	Pos	G	Rec
1943	Phi	N	P	4	1-0
1944	Phi	N	P	1	0-0
	BLTL			5	1-0

McKEEVER, JAMES
b.S.Boston,Mass.
d.Aug.19,1897

Yr	Cl	Lea	Pos	G	Rec
1884	Bos	U	C-O	16	.141

McKEITHAN, EMMETT JAMES
(Tim)
b.Nov.2,1908 Bostic,N.C.

Yr	Cl	Lea	Pos	G	Rec
1932	Phi	A	P	4	0-1
1933	Phi	A	P	3	1-0
1934	Phi	A	P	3	0-0
	BRTR			10	1-1

McKELVEY, JOHN WELLINGTON
b.Aug.27,1847 Rochester,N.Y.
d.May 31,1944

Yr	Cl	Lea	Pos	G	Rec
1875	NH	n	3-O	43	NR

McKELVY, RUSSELL ERRETT
b.Sept.8,1856 Meadville,Pa.
d.Oct.30,1915

Yr	Cl	Lea	Pos	G	Rec
1878	Ind	N	P-O	60	0-0 .222
1882	Pit	a	O	1	.000
	TR			61	0-0 .219

McKENNA, EDWARD
b.St.Louis,Mo.

Yr	Cl	Lea	Pos	G	Rec
1874	Phi	n	1	1	.000
1877	St.L	N	O	1	.200
1884	Was	U	C-O	32	.188
				34	.184

McKENNA, JAMES WILLIAM
(Kit)
b.Aug.19,1873 Lynchburg,Va.

Yr	Cl	Lea	Pos	G	Rec
1898	Bro	N	P	14	1-7
1899	Bal	N	P	9	2-4
				23	3-11

McKENRY, FRANK GORDON
(Limb)
b.Aug.13,1888 Piney Flat,Tenn.
d.Nov.1,1956

Yr	Cl	Lea	Pos	G	Rec
1915	Cin	N	P	21	5-5
1916	Cin	N	P	6	1-1
	BRTR			27	6-6

McKEON, LAWRENCE J.
b.Mar.25,1866 Indianapolis,Ind.
d.July 18,1915

Yr	Cl	Lea	Pos	G	Rec
1884	Ind	a	P-1	70	18-41 .215
1885	Cin	a	P-O	33	20-13 .157
1886	Cin	a	P-1-2	18	8-9 .250
1886	KC	N	P	2	0-2
				123	46-65 .203

McKEOUGH, DAVID J.
b.1865 Utica,N.Y.
d.July 10,1901

Yr	Cl	Lea	Pos	G	Rec
1890	Roc	a	C	63	.218
1891	Ath	a	C	15	.278
				78	.231

McKINNEY, BUCK
b.Louisville,Ky.
Non-playing manager Lou (a) 1889.

McKINNEY, ROBERT FRANCIS
b.Oct.4,1875 McSherrystown,Pa.
d.Aug.19,1946

Yr	Cl	Lea	Pos	G	Rec
1901	Phi	A	2	2	.000

McKINNON, ALEXANDER J.
b.Aug.14,1856 Boston,Mass.
d.July 24,1887

Yr	Cl	Lea	Pos	G	Rec
1884	NY	N	1	112	.275
1885	St.L	N	1	100	.270
1886	St.L	N	1	122	.301
1887	Pit	N	1	48	.365
				382	.301

McKNIGHT, HENRY DENNIS
(Denny)
b.1847 Pittsburgh,Pa.
d.May 5,1900
Non-playing manager Pit (a) 1884.

McKNIGHT, JAMES ARTHUR
b.June 1,1936 Bee Branch,Ark.

Yr	Cl	Lea	Pos	G	Rec
1960	Chi	N	2-O	3	.333
1962	Chi	N	2-3-O	60	.224
	BRTR			63	.231

McLANE, EDWARD CAMERON
b.Aug.20,1881 Weston,Mass.

Yr	Cl	Lea	Pos	G	Rec
1907	Bro	N	O	1	.000

McLARNEY, ARTHUR JAMES
b.Dec.20,1908 Ft.Worden,Wash.

Yr	Cl	Lea	Pos	G	Rec
1932	NY	N	S	9	.130
	BBTR				

McLARRY, PAUL HOWARD
(Polly)
b.Mar.25,1892 Leonard,Tex.

Yr	Cl	Lea	Pos	G	Rec
1912	Chi	A	H	2	.000
1915	Chi	N	1-2	68	.197
				70	.194

McLAUGHLIN, BERNARD
b.1857 Ireland.
d.Feb.13,1921

Yr	Cl	Lea	Pos	G	Rec
1882	Wor	N	S-O	15	.207
1884	Was	U	S	10	.189
1884	KC	U	P-2-O	40	0-4 .218
1887	Phi	N	2	50	.259
1890	Syr	a	S	81	.260
				196	0-4 .245

McLAUGHLIN, FRANCIS M.
b.June 19,1856 Lowell,Mass.
d.Apr.5,1917

Yr	Cl	Lea	Pos	G	Rec
1883	Pit	a	P-2-S-O	27	0-0 .200
1884	Cin	U	S	15	.246
1884	Chi	U	2-S	15	.284
1884	KC	U	P-2-S-3-O	33	1-1 .219
	BRTR			90	1-1 .235

McLAUGHLIN, JAMES ANSON
(Kid)
b.Apr.12,1888 Randolph,N.Y.
d.Nov.13,1934

Yr	Cl	Lea	Pos	G	Rec
1914	Cin	N	O	3	.000
	BLTR				

McLAUGHLIN, JAMES C.
b.1860 Cleveland,O.
d.Nov.16,1895

Yr	Cl	Lea	Pos	G	Rec
1884	Was	U	S-3	10	.194
1884	Bal	a	P-O	5	1-2 .227
	TL			15	1-2 .207

McLAUGHLIN, JAMES ROBERT
b.Jan.3,1902 St.Louis,Mo.

Yr	Cl	Lea	Pos	G	Rec
1932	St.L	A	3	1	.000
	BRTR				

McLAUGHLIN, JUSTIN THEODORE
b.Mar.24,1912 Allston,Mass.

Yr	Cl	Lea	Pos	G	Rec
1931	Bos	A	P	9	0-0
1932	Bos	A	P	1	0-0
1933	Bos	A	P	6	0-0
			BLTL	16	0-0

McLAUGHLIN, PATRICK ELMER
b.Aug.17,1910 Taylor,Tex.

Yr	Cl	Lea	Pos	G	Rec
1937	Det	A	P	11	0-2
1940	Phi	A	P	1	0-0
1945	Det	A	P	1	0-0
			BRTR	13	0-2

McLAUGHLIN, THOMAS
b.Louisville,Ky.

Yr	Cl	Lea	Pos	G	Rec
1883	Lou	a	1-2-S-3-O	42	.205
1884	Lou	a	S	100	.191
1885	Lou	a	2	113	.215
1886	Met	a	S	74	.137
1891	Was	a	S	14	.250
				343	.198

McLAUGHLIN, WARREN A.
b.Jan.22,1876 N.Plainfield,N.J.
d.Oct.22,1923

Yr	Cl	Lea	Pos	G	Rec
1900	Phi	N	P	1	0-0
1902	Pit	N	P	3	3-0
1903	Phi	N	P	3	0-2
				7	3-2

McLAURIN, RALPH EDGAR
b.May 23,1885 Kissimmee,Fla.
d.Feb.11,1943

Yr	Cl	Lea	Pos	G	Rec
1908	St.L	N	O	8	.227

McLEAN, ALBERT ELDON
b.Sept.20,1912 Chicago,Ill.

Yr	Cl	Lea	Pos	G	Rec
1935	Was	A	P	4	0-0
	BRTR				

McLEAN, JOHN BANNERMAN
(Larry)
b.July 18,1881 Cambridge,Mass.
d.Mar.24,1921

Yr	Cl	Lea	Pos	G	Rec
1901	Bos	A	1	9	.210
1903	Chi	N	C	1	.000
1904	St.L	N	C	24	.167
1906	Cin	N	C	12	.191
1907	Cin	N	C	101	.289
1908	Cin	N	C-1	88	.217
1909	Cin	N	C	95	.256
1910	Cin	N	C	119	.298
1911	Cin	N	C	98	.287
1912	Cin	N	C	102	.243
1913	St.L	N	C	48	.270
1913	NY	N	C	30	.320
1914	NY	N	C	79	.260
1915	NY	N	C	13	.152
			BRTR	819	.263

McLELAND, WAYNE GAFFNEY
(Nubbin)
b.Aug.29,1924 Milton,Ia.

Yr	Cl	Lea	Pos	G	Rec
1951	Det	A	P	6	0-1
1952	Det	A	P	4	0-0
			BRTR	10	0-1

McLEOD, RALPH ALTON
b.Oct.19,1916 N.Quincy,Mass.

Yr	Cl	Lea	Pos	G	Rec
1938	Bos	N	O	6	.286
	BLTL				

McLEOD, SOULE JAMES
b.Sept.12,1909 Wilmot,Ark.

Yr	Cl	Lea	Pos	G	Rec
1930	Was	A	3	18	.265
1932	Was	A	S	7	.000
1933	Phi	N	3	67	.194
			BRTR	92	.203

McLISH, CALVIN COOLIDGE
(Buster)
b.Dec.1,1925 Anadarko,Okla.

Yr	Cl	Lea	Pos	G	Rec
1944	Bro	N	P	31	3-10
1946	Bro	N	P	1	0-0
1947	Pit	N	P	1	0-0
1948	Pit	N	P	3	0-0
1949	Chi	N	P	9	1-1
1951	Chi	N	P	31	4-10
1956	Cle	A	P	39	2-4
1957	Cle	A	P	44	9-7
1958	Cle	A	P	39	16-8
1959	Cle	A	P	35	19-8
1960	Cin	N	P	37	4-14
1961	Chi	A	P	31	10-13
1962	Phi	N	P	32	11-5
			BBTR	333	79-80

McMACKIN, JOHN WEAVER
b.Mar.6,1878 Spartanburg,S.C.
d.Sept.25,1956

Yr	Cl	Lea	Pos	G	Rec
1902	Bro	N	P	4	2-2

McMACKIN, SAMUEL
b.Cleveland,O.
d.Feb.11,1903

Yr	Cl	Lea	Pos	G	Rec
1902	Chi	A	P	1	0-0
1902	Det	A	P	1	0-0
				2	0-0

McMAHAN, JACK WALLY
b.July 22,1932 Hot Springs,Ark.

Yr	Cl	Lea	Pos	G	Rec
1956	Pit	N	P	11	0-0
1956	KC	A	P	23	0-5
			BRTL	34	0-5

McMAHON, DONALD JOHN
b.Jan.4,1930 Brooklyn,N.Y.

Yr	Cl	Lea	Pos	G	Rec
1957	Mil	N	P	32	2-3
1958	Mil	N	P	38	7-2
1959	Mil	N	P	60	5-3
1960	Mil	N	P	48	3-6
1961	Mil	N	P	53	6-4
1962	Mil	N	P	2	0-1
1962	Hou	N	P	51	5-5
			BRTR	284	28-24

McMAHON, HENRY JOHN
(Doc)
b.Dec.19,1886 Woburn,Mass.
d.Dec.12,1929

Yr	Cl	Lea	Pos	G	Rec
1908	Bos	A	P	1	1-0

McMAHON, JOHN HENRY
b.Oct.15,1869 Waterbury,Conn.
d.Dec.30,1894

Yr	Cl	Lea	Pos	G	Rec
1892	NY	N	1	36	.239
1893	NY	N	C	11	.333
			TL	47	.256

McMAHON, JOHN JOSEPH
(Sadie)
b.Sept.19,1867 Wilmington,Del.
d.Feb.20,1954

Yr	Cl	Lea	Pos	G	Rec
1889	Ath	a	P	30	15-11
1890	Ath	a	P	51	29-17
1890	Bal	a	P	12	7-3
1891	Bal	a	P	60	34-25
1892	Bal	N	P	47	19-28
1893	Bal	N	P	40	23-16
1894	Bal	N	P	34	25-8
1895	Bal	N	P	15	10-4
1896	Bal	N	P	21	12-8
1897	Bro	N	P	9	0-0
			TR	319	174-120

McMANUS, FRANCIS E.
b.Sept.21,1875 Lawrence,Mass.
d.Sept.1,1923

Yr	Cl	Lea	Pos	G	Rec
1899	Was	N	C	7	.400
1903	Bro	N	C	2	.000
1904	Det	A	C	1	.000
1904	NY	A	C	4	.000
			TR	14	.235

McMANUS, GEORGE
b.1846
d.Oct.2,1918

Yr	Cl	Lea	Pos	G	Rec
1879	Tro	N	P	2	0-2

Non-playing manager St.L (N) 1877.

McMANUS, JAMES MICHAEL
b.July 20,1936 Brookline,Mass.

Yr	Cl	Lea	Pos	G	Rec
1960	KC	A	1	5	.308
		BLTL			

McMANUS, JOAB LOGAN
b.Sept.7,1887 Palmyra,Ill.
d.Dec.23,1955

Yr	Cl	Lea	Pos	G	Rec
1913	Cin	N	P	1	0-0
		BRTR			

McMANUS, MARTIN JOSEPH
b.Mar.14,1900 Chicago,Ill.

Yr	Cl	Lea	Pos	G	Rec
1920	St.L	A	3	1	.200
1921	St.L	A	1-2-3	121	.260
1922	St.L	A	2	154	.312
1923	St.L	A	1-2	154	.309
1924	St.L	A	2	123	.333
1925	St.L	A	2	154	.288
1926	St.L	A	2-3	149	.284
1927	Det	A	2-S-3	108	.268
1928	Det	A	1-3	139	.288
1929	Det	A	3	154	.280
1930	Det	A	3	132	.320
1931	Det	A	2-3	107	.273
1931	Bos	A	2-3	17	.276
1932	Bos	A	M-2-3	93	.235
1933	Bos	A	M-1-2-3	106	.284
1934	Bos	N	2-3	119	.276
			BRTR	1831	.289

McMILLAN, GEORGE A.
(Reddy)
b.Evansville,Ind.

Yr	Cl	Lea	Pos	G	Rec
1890	NY	N	O	10	.138

McMILLAN, NORMAN ALEXIS
(Bub)
b.Oct.5,1897 Latta,S.C.

Yr	Cl	Lea	Pos	G	Rec
1922	NY	A	O	33	.256
1923	Bos	A	2-S-3	131	.253
1924	St.L	A	2-3	76	.279
1928	Chi	N	2-3	49	.220
1929	Chi	N	3	124	.271
			BRTR	413	.260

McMILLAN, ROY DAVID
b.July 17,1930 Bonham,Tex.

Yr	Cl	Lea	Pos	G	Rec
1951	Cin	N	2-S-3	85	.211
1952	Cin	N	S	154	.244
1953	Cin	N	S	155	.233
1954	Cin	N	S	154	.250
1955	Cin	N	S	151	.268
1956	Cin	N	S	150	.263
1957	Cin	N	S	151	.272
1958	Cin	N	S	145	.229
1959	Cin	N	S	79	.264
1960	Cin	N	2-S	124	.236
1961	Mil	N	S	154	.220
1962	Mil	N	S	137	.246
			BRTR	1639	.246

McMILLAN, THOMAS LAW
(Rabbit)
b.Apr.17,1887 Pittston,Pa.

Yr	Cl	Lea	Pos	G	Rec
1908	Bro	N	S	43	.238
1909	Bro	N	S	108	.212
1910	Bro	N	S	23	.176
1910	Cin	N	S	82	.185
1912	NY	A	S	41	.228
			BRTR	297	.209

McMULLEN, GEORGE
b.California.

Yr	Cl	Lea	Pos	G	Rec
1887	Met	a	P	3	1-2

McMULLEN, HUGH RAPHAEL
b.Dec.16,1901 LaCygne,Kan.

Yr	Cl	Lea	Pos	G	Rec
1925	NY	N	C	5	.133
1926	NY	N	C	57	.187
1928	Was	A	H	1	.000
1929	Cin	N	C	1	.000
		BBTR		64	.176

McMULLEN, JOHN F.
(Lefty)
b.1849 Philadelphia,Pa.
d.Apr.11,1881

Yr	Cl	Lea	Pos	G	Rec
1871	Tro	n	P	29	13-15
1872	Mut	n	P-O	54	2-0 NR
1873	Ath	n	P-O	51	1-0 NR
1874	Ath	n	C-O	55	.387
1875	Phi	n	P-O	53	0-1 .249
		BLTL		242	16-16 NR

McMULLEN, KENNETH LEE
b.June 1,1942 Oxnard,Cal.

Yr	Cl	Lea	Pos	G	Rec
1962	LA	N	O	6	.273
		BRTR			

McMULLIN, FREDERICK WILLIAM
b.Oct.13,1891 Scammon,Kan.
d.Nov.21,1952

Yr	Cl	Lea	Pos	G	Rec
1914	Det	A	S	1	.000
1916	Chi	A	3	68	.257
1917	Chi	A	3	59	.237
1918	Chi	A	3	70	.276
1919	Chi	A	3	60	.294
1920	Chi	A	3	46	.197
		BRTR		304	.256

McNABB, CARL MAC
(Skinny)
b.Jan.25,1918 Stevenson,Ala.

Yr	Cl	Lea	Pos	G	Rec
1945	Det	A	H	1	.000
		BRTR			

McNABB, EDGAR J. (Texas)
b.Oct.24,1865 Mt.Vernon,O.
d.Feb.28,1894

Yr	Cl	Lea	Pos	G	Rec
1893	Bal	N	P	17	8-8

McNAIR, DONALD ERIC
(Boob)
b.Apr.12,1909 Meridian,Miss.
d.Mar.11,1949

Yr	Cl	Lea	Pos	G	Rec
1929	Phi	A	S	4	.500
1930	Phi	A	S-3	78	.266
1931	Phi	A	2-S-3	79	.271
1932	Phi	A	S	135	.285
1933	Phi	A	2-S	89	.261
1934	Phi	A	S	151	.280
1935	Phi	A	1-S-3	137	.270
1936	Bos	A	2-S-3	128	.285
1937	Bos	A	2	126	.292
1938	Bos	A	2-S	46	.156
1939	Chi	A	2-3	129	.324
1940	Chi	A	2-3	66	.227
1941	Det	A	S-3	23	.186
1942	Det	A	S	26	.162
1942	Phi	A	2-S	34	.243
		BRTR		1251	.274

McNALLY, DAVID ARTHUR
b.Oct.31,1942 Billings,Mont.

Yr	Cl	Lea	Pos	G	Rec
1962	Bal	A	P	1	1-0
		BRTL			

McNALLY, MICHAEL JOSEPH
b.Sept.9,1892 Minooka,Pa.

Yr	Cl	Lea	Pos	G	Rec
1915	Bos	A	3	23	.151
1916	Bos	A	2	87	.171
1917	Bos	A	3	42	.300
1919	Bos	A	3	33	.262
1920	Bos	A	2	93	.256
1921	NY	A	2-3	71	.260
1922	NY	A	3	52	.252
1923	NY	A	2-3	30	.211

(Continued)

Yr	Cl	Lea	Pos	G	Rec
1924	NY	A	2-3	49	.247
1925	Was	A	2-S-3	12	.143
		BRTR		492	.238

McNAMARA, GEORGE FRANCIS
b.Jan.11,1903 Chicago,Ill.

Yr	Cl	Lea	Pos	G	Rec
1922	Was	A	O	3	.272
		BLTR			

McNAMARA, JOHN RAYMOND
(Dinny)
b.Sept.16,1905 Lexington,Mass.

Yr	Cl	Lea	Pos	G	Rec
1927	Bos	N	O	11	.000
1928	Bos	N	O	9	.250
		BLTR		20	.077

McNAMARA, JOSEPH
(Played under name of Joseph Mack)

McNAMARA, ROBERT MAXEY
b.Sept.19,1916 Denver,Colo.

Yr	Cl	Lea	Pos	G	Rec
1939	Phi	A	3	9	.222
		BRTR			

McNAMARA, THOMAS HENRY
b.June 19,1899 Roxbury,Mass.

Yr	Cl	Lea	Pos	G	Rec
1922	Pit	N	H	1	.000
		BR			

McNAMARA, TIMOTHY ALOYSIUS
b.Nov.20,1898 Blackstone,Mass.

Yr	Cl	Lea	Pos	G	Rec
1922	Bos	N	P	24	3-4
1923	Bos	N	P	32	3-13
1924	Bos	N	P	35	8-12
1925	Bos	N	P	1	0-0
1926	NY	N	P	6	0-0
		BRTR		98	14-29

McNAUGHTON, GORDON JOSEPH
b.July 31,1910 Chicago,Ill.
d.Aug.6,1942

Yr	Cl	Lea	Pos	G	Rec
1932	Bos	A	P	6	0-1
		BRTR			

McNEAL, JOHN HARLEY
(Harry)
b.Aug.13,1878 Iberia,O.
d.Jan.11,1945

Yr	Cl	Lea	Pos	G	Rec
1901	Cle	A	P	11	5-6
		BRTR			

McNEELY, GEORGE EARL
b.May 12,1899 Sacramento,Cal.

Yr	Cl	Lea	Pos	G	Rec
1924	Was	A	O	43	.330
1925	Was	A	O	122	.285
1926	Was	A	O	124	.303
1927	Was	A	O	73	.276
1928	St.L	A	O	127	.236
1929	St.L	A	O	69	.243
1930	St.L	A	1-O	76	.272
1931	St.L	A	O	49	.225
		BRTR		683	.272

McNEIL, NORMAN FRANCIS
b.Oct.22,1892 Chicago,Ill.
d.Apr.11,1942

Yr	Cl	Lea	Pos	G	Rec
1919	Bos	A	C	5	.273
		BRTR			

McNICHOL, EDWARD
b.Wheeling,W.Va.

Yr	Cl	Lea	Pos	G	Rec
1904	Bos	N	P	17	2-13

McNULTY, PATRICK HOWARD
b.Mar.1,1900 Cleveland,O.

Yr	Cl	Lea	Pos	G	Rec
1922	Cle	A	O	22	.271
1924	Cle	A	O	101	.268
1925	Cle	A	O	118	.314
1926	Cle	A	O	48	.250
1927	Cle	A	O	19	.317
		BLTR		308	.290

McPARTLIN, FRANK
b.Feb.16,1872 Hoosick Falls,N.Y.

Yr	Cl	Lea	Pos	G	Rec
1899	NY	N	P	1	0-0
		TR			

McPHEE, JOHN ALEXANDER
(Bid)
b.Nov.1,1859 Massena,N.Y.
d.Jan.3,1943

Yr	Cl	Lea	Pos	G	Rec
1882	Cin	a	2	78	.218
1883	Cin	a	C-2	94	.235
1884	Cin	a	2	113	.292
1885	Cin	a	2	110	.275
1886	Cin	a	2	140	.272
1887	Cin	a	2	129	.354
1888	Cin	a	2	110	.230
1889	Cin	a	2-3	135	.269
1890	Cin	N	2	132	.255
1891	Cin	N	2	138	.257
1892	Cin	N	2	144	.294
1893	Cin	N	2	127	.307
1894	Cin	N	2	128	.320
1895	Cin	N	2	114	.295
1896	Cin	N	2	116	.299
1897	Cin	N	2	80	.307
1898	Cin	N	2	131	.246
1899	Cin	N	2	106	.283
		BRTR		2125	.281

Non-playing manager Cin (N) 1901-02.

McPHERSON, JOHN JACOB
b.Mar.9,1869 Easton,Pa.
d.Sept.30,1941

Yr	Cl	Lea	Pos	G	Rec
1901	Phi	A	P	1	0-1
1904	Phi	N	P	15	1-9
				16	1-10

McQUAID, HERBERT GEORGE
b.Mar.29,1899 San Francisco,Cal.

Yr	Cl	Lea	Pos	G	Rec
1923	Cin	N	P	12	1-0
1926	NY	A	P	17	1-0
		BRTR		29	2-0

McQUAID, JAMES H.
b.Chicago,Ill.

Yr	Cl	Lea	Pos	G	Rec
1891	St.L	a	2	4	.333
1898	Was	N	O	1	.000
				5	.333

McQUAIG, GERALD JOSEPH
b.Jan.31,1914 Douglas,Ga.

Yr	Cl	Lea	Pos	G	Rec
1934	Phi	A	O	7	.063
		BRTR			

McQUERY, WILLIAM THOMAS
(Max)
b.June 28,1861 Garrard Co.,Ky.
d.June 12,1900

Yr	Cl	Lea	Pos	G	Rec
1884	Cin	U	1	32	.248
1885	Det	N	1	70	.273
1886	KC	N	1	122	.247
1890	Syr	a	1	120	.295
1891	Was	a	1	68	.256
				412	.266

McQUILLAN, GEORGE WASHINGTON
b.May 1,1885 Brooklyn,N.Y.
d.Mar.30,1940

Yr	Cl	Lea	Pos	G	Rec
1907	Phi	N	P	6	2-0
1908	Phi	N	P	48	23-17
1909	Phi	N	P	41	13-16
1910	Phi	N	P	24	9-6
1911	Cin	N	P	19	2-6
1913	Pit	N	P	25	8-6
1914	Pit	N	P	45	13-17
1915	Pit	N	P	31	8-10
1915	Phi	N	P	9	4-3
1916	Phi	N	P	21	1-7
1918	Cle	A	P	5	0-1
		BRTR		274	83-89

McQUILLAN, HUGH A.
(Handsome Hugh)
b.Sept.15,1897 New York,N.Y.
d.Aug.26,1947

Yr	Cl	Lea	Pos	G	Rec
1918	Bos	N	P	1	1-0
1919	Bos	N	P-O	20	2-3 .222

(Continued)

Yr	Cl	Lea	Pos	G	Rec
1920	Bos	N	P	38	11-15
1921	Bos	N	P	45	13-17
1922	Bos	N	P	32	5-10
1922	NY	N	P	15	6-5
1923	NY	N	P	41	15-14
1924	NY	N	P	35	14-8
1925	NY	N	P	16	2-3
1926	NY	N	P	34	11-10
1927	NY	N	P	11	5-4
1927	Bos	N	P	13	3-5
	BRTR			301	88-94 / .195

McQUILLEN, GLENN RICHARD (Red)
b.Apr.19,1917 Strasburg,Va.

Yr	Cl	Lea	Pos	G	Rec
1938	St.L	A	O	43	.284
1941	St.L	A	O	7	.333
1942	St.L	A	O	100	.283
1946	St.L	A	O	59	.241
1947	St.L	A	H	1	.000
	BRTR			210	.274

McQUINN, GEORGE HARTLEY
b.May 29,1909 Ballston,Va.

Yr	Cl	Lea	Pos	G	Rec
1936	Cin	N	1	38	.201
1938	St.L	A	1	148	.324
1939	StL	A	1	154	.316
1940	StL	A	1	151	.279
1941	StL	A	1	130	.297
1942	St.L	A	1	145	.262
1943	St.L	A	1	125	.243
1944	St.L	A	1	146	.250
1945	St.L	A	1	139	.277
1946	Phi	A	1	136	.225
1947	NY	A	1	144	.304
1948	NY	A	1	94	.248
	BLTL			1550	.276

McREMER, ...

Yr	Cl	Lea	Pos	G	Rec
1884	Was	U	P	1	0-0

McSHANNIC, PETER ROBERT
b.Mar.20,1864 Pittsburgh,Pa.
d.Nov.30,1946

Yr	Cl	Lea	Pos	G	Rec
1888	Pit	N	3	26	.194

McSORLEY, JOHN BERNARD (Trick)
b.Dec.6,1858 St.Louis,Mo.
d.Feb.9,1936

Yr	Cl	Lea	Pos	G	Rec
1875	RS	n	3-O	13	NR
1884	Tol	a	1	21	.249
1885	St.L	N	3	2	.500
1886	St.L	a	S	5	.150
	TR			41	NR

McSWEENEY, PAUL
b.St.Louis,Mo.

Yr	Cl	Lea	Pos	G	Rec
1891	St.L	a	2	3	.250

McTAMANY, JAMES J.
b.July 4,1863 Philadelphia,Pa.

Yr	Cl	Lea	Pos	G	Rec
1885	Bro	a	O	35	.238
1886	Bro	a	O	113	.248
1887	Bro	a	O	134	.354
1888	KC	a	O	116	.251
1889	Col	a	O	139	.279
1890	Col	a	O	125	.256
1891	Col	a	O	77	.266
1891	Ath	a	O	53	.209
	TR			792	.275

McTIGUE, WILLIAM PERCY (Rebel)
b.Jan.3,1891 Nashville,Tenn.
d.May 11,1920

Yr	Cl	Lea	Pos	G	Rec
1911	Bos	N	P	14	0-5
1912	Bos	N	P	10	2-0
1913	Bos	N	P	1	0-0
1916	Det	A	P	3	0-1
	BLTL			28	2-6

McVEY, CALVIN ALEXANDER
b.Aug.30,1850 Montrose,Ia.
d.Aug.20,1926

Yr	Cl	Lea	Pos	G	Rec
1871	Bos	n	C-O	32	.366
1872	Bos	n	C-O	46	.306
1873	Bal	n	C-1-2-S-3-O	36	NR
1874	Bos	n	C-O	70	.385
1875	Bos	n	P-C-1-O	82	1-1 / .352
1876	Chi	N	P-1	63	6-0 / .345
1877	Chi	N	P-C-1-2-3	60	4-8 / .368
1878	Cin	N	M-P-C-3	62	1-0 / .293
1879	Cin	N	M-P-C-1-3-O	80	0-2 / .299
	BRTR			531	12-11 / NR

McVEY, GEORGE W.
b.1863 Columbus,O.
d.May 3,1896

Yr	Cl	Lea	Pos	G	Rec
1885	Bro	a	C-1	6	.143

McWEENEY, DOUGLAS LAWRENCE (Buzz)
b.Aug.17,1896 Chicago,Ill.
d.Jan.1,1953

Yr	Cl	Lea	Pos	G	Rec
1921	Chi	A	P	27	3-6
1922	Chi	A	P	4	0-1
1924	Chi	A	P	13	1-3
1926	Bro	N	P	42	11-13
1927	Bro	N	P	34	4-8
1928	Bro	N	P	42	14-14
1929	Bro	N	P	36	4-10
1930	Cin	N	P	8	0-2
	BRTR			206	37-57

McWILLIAMS, WILLIAM HENRY
b.Nov.28,1910 Dubuque,Ia.

Yr	Cl	Lea	Pos	G	Rec
1931	Bos	A	H	2	.000
	BRTR				

MEAD, CHARLES RICHARD
b.Apr.9,1921 Vermillion,Alta.,Canada.

Yr	Cl	Lea	Pos	G	Rec
1943	NY	N	O	37	.274
1944	NY	N	O	39	.179
1945	NY	N	O	11	.270
	BLTR			87	.245

MEADOR, JOHN DAVIS
b.Dec.4,1896 Madison,N.C.

Yr	Cl	Lea	Pos	G	Rec
1920	Pit	N	P	12	0-2
	BRTR				

MEADOWS, HENRY LEE (Specs)
b.July 12,1894 Oxford,N.C.
d.Jan.29,1963

Yr	Cl	Lea	Pos	G	Rec
1915	St.L	N	P	39	13-11
1916	St.L	N	P	51	12-23
1917	St.L	N	P	43	15-9
1918	St.L	N	P	31	8-14
1919	St.L	N	P	22	4-10
1919	Phi	N	P	21	8-10
1920	Phi	N	P	39	16-14
1921	Phi	N	P	28	11-16
1922	Phi	N	P	33	12-18
1923	Phi	N	P	8	1-3
1923	Pit	N	P	31	16-10
1924	Pit	N	P	36	13-12
1925	Pit	N	P	35	19-10
1926	Pit	N	P	36	20-9
1927	Pit	N	P	40	19-10
1928	Pit	N	P	4	1-1
1929	Pit	N	P	1	0-0
	BBTR			498	188-180

MEADOWS, RUFUS RIVERS
b.Aug.25,1907 Hopewell,Va.

Yr	Cl	Lea	Pos	G	Rec
1926	Cin	N	P	1	0-0
	BLTL				

MEAKIM, GEORGE CLINTON
b.July 11,1865 Brooklyn,N.Y.

Yr	Cl	Lea	Pos	G	Rec
1890	Lou	a	P	30	10-8
1891	Ath	a	P	6	2-3
1892	Chi	N	P	2	0-1

(Continued)

Yr	Cl	Lea	Pos	G	Rec
1892	Cin	N	P	3	1-1
1895	Lou	N	P	1	0-0
				42	13-13

MEANS, HARRY L.
b.June 15,1869 Hopkinsville,Ky.
d.Feb.1,1945
Non-playing manager Lou (a) 1889.

MEANY, PATRICK
b.1892 Philadelphia,Pa.
d.Oct.20,1922

Yr	Cl	Lea	Pos	G	Rec
1912	Det	A	S	1	.000
	TR				

MEARA, CHARLES EDWARD
b.Apr.16,1891 New York,N.Y.

Yr	Cl	Lea	Pos	G	Rec
1914	NY	A	O	4	.286
	BLTR				

MEDDLEBROOK, ...

Yr	Cl	Lea	Pos	G	Rec
1884	Bal	U	O	1	.667

MEDEIROS, RAY ANTON
b.May 9,1926 Oakland,Cal.

Yr	Cl	Lea	Pos	G	Rec
1945	Cin	N	H	1	.000
	BRTR				

MEDLINGER, IRVING JOHN
b.June 18,1927 Chicago,Ill.

Yr	Cl	Lea	Pos	G	Rec
1949	St.L	A	P	3	0-0
1951	St.L	A	P	6	0-0
	BLTL			9	0-0

MEDWICK, JOSEPH MICHAEL (Ducky)
b.Nov.24,1911 Carteret,N.J.

Yr	Cl	Lea	Pos	G	Rec
1932	St.L	N	O	26	.349
1933	St.L	N	O	148	.306
1934	St.L	N	O	149	.319
1935	St.L	N	O	154	.353
1936	St.L	N	O	155	.351
1937	St.L	N	O	156	.374
1938	St.L	N	O	146	.322
1939	St.L	N	O	150	.332
1940	St.L	N	O	37	.304
1940	Bro	N	O	106	.300
1941	Bro	N	O	133	.318
1942	Bro	N	O	142	.300
1943	Bro	N	O	48	.272
1943	NY	N	1-O	78	.281
1944	NY	N	O	128	.337
1945	NY	N	O	26	.304
1945	Bos	N	1-O	66	.284
1946	Bro	N	1-O	41	.312
1947	St.L	N	O	75	.307
1948	St.L	N	O	20	.211
	BRTR			1984	.324

MEE, THOMAS WILLIAM
b.Mar.18,1890 Chicago,Ill.

Yr	Cl	Lea	Pos	G	Rec
1910	St.L	A	S	7	.167
	BRTR				

MEEGAN, PETER J. (Steady Pete)
b.Nov.13,1863 San Francisco,Cal.
d.Mar.15,1905

Yr	Cl	Lea	Pos	G	Rec
1884	Ric	a	P-O	23	7-12 / .156
1885	Pit	a	P	19	7-8
				42	14-20 / .156

MEEHAN, WILLIAM THOMAS
b.Sept.3,1891 Osceola,Pa.

Yr	Cl	Lea	Pos	G	Rec
1915	Phi	A	P	1	0-1

MEEK, FRANK J. (Dad)
b.St.Louis,Mo.
d.Dec.26,1922

Yr	Cl	Lea	Pos	G	Rec
1889	St.L	a	C	2	.500
1890	St.L	a	C	4	.333
				6	.353

MEEKER, CHARLES ROY
b.Sept.15,1900 Leadmines,Mo.
d.Mar.25,1929

Yr	Cl	Lea	Pos	G	Rec
1923	Phi	A	P	5	3-0
1924	Phi	A	P	30	5-12
1926	Cin	N	P	7	0-2
	BLTL			42	8-14

MEEKIN, JOUETT
b.Feb.21,1867 New Albany,Ind.
d.Dec.14,1944

Yr	Cl	Lea	Pos	G	Rec
1891	Lou	a	P	33	10-17
1892	Lou	N	P	25	7-10
1892	Was	N	P	13	2-11
1893	Was	N	P	29	10-17
1894	NY	N	P	48	36-10
1895	NY	N	P	30	16-11
1896	NY	N	P	40	26-13
1897	NY	N	P	38	20-11
1898	NY	N	P	36	16-20
1899	NY	N	P	16	5-11
1899	Bos	N	P	17	7-6
1900	Pit	N	P	2	0-2
				327	155-139

MEEKS, SAMUEL MACK
b.Apr.23,1923 Anderson,S.C.

Yr	Cl	Lea	Pos	G	Rec
1948	Was	A	2-S	24	.121
1949	Cin	N	2-S	16	.306
1950	Cin	N	S-3	39	.284
1951	Cin	N	S-3	23	.229
	BRTR			102	.251

MEERS, RUSSELL HARLAN
b.Nov.27,1919 Tilton,Ill.

Yr	Cl	Lea	Pos	G	Rec
1941	Chi	N	P	1	0-1
1946	Chi	N	P	7	1-2
1947	Chi	N	P	35	2-0
	BLTL			43	3-3

MEIER, ARTHUR ERNST
(Dutch)
b.Mar.30,1879 St.Louis,Mo.

Yr	Cl	Lea	Pos	G	Rec
1906	Pit	N	S-O	68	.256

MEIKLE, ARTHUR FRANCIS
(Played under name of
Arthur Francis Nichols)

MEINE, HENRY WILLIAM
(Heinie)
b.May 1,1896 St.Louis,Mo.

Yr	Cl	Lea	Pos	G	Rec
1922	St.L	A	P	1	0-0
1929	Pit	N	P	22	7-6
1930	Pit	N	P	20	6-8
1931	Pit	N	P	36	19-13
1932	Pit	N	P	28	12-9
1933	Pit	N	P	32	15-8
1934	Pit	N	P	26	7-6
	BRTR			165	66-50

MEINERT, WALTER HENRY
b.Dec.11,1890 New York,N.Y.
d.Nov.9,1958

Yr	Cl	Lea	Pos	G	Rec
1913	St.L	A	O	4	.375

MEINKE, FRANK LOUIS
b.Oct.18,1862 Chicago,Ill.
d.Nov.8,1931

Yr	Cl	Lea	Pos	G	Rec
1884	Det	N	P-2-S-3	90	8-21 / .167
1885	Det	N	P-O	1	0-1 / .000
				91	8-22 / .166

MEINKE, ROBERT BERNARD
b.June 25,1887 Chicago,Ill.

Yr	Cl	Lea	Pos	G	Rec
1910	Cin	N	S	2	.000
	BRTR				

MEISEL, ...

Yr	Cl	Lea	Pos	G	Rec
1915	Bal	F	C	1	.000
	TR				

MEISTER, JOHN F.
b.Altoona,Pa.
d.Jan.28,1923

Yr	Cl	Lea	Pos	G	Rec
1884	Tol	a	3	34	.199
1886	Met	a	2	45	.240
1887	Met	a	O	39	.282
				118	.245

MEISTER, KARL DANIEL
b.May 15,1891 Marietta,Ohio

Yr	Cl	Lea	Pos	G	Rec
1913	Cin	N	O	4	285
	BRTR				

MEIXELL, MERTEN MERRILL
(Moxie)
b.Oct.18,1887 Lake Crystal,Minn.

Yr	Cl	Lea	Pos	G	Rec
1912	Cle	A	O	3	.500
	BLTR				

MEJIAS, ROMAN GOMEZ
b.Aug.9,1932 Rio Damuji,Cuba.

Yr	Cl	Lea	Pos	G	Rec
1955	Pit	N	O	71	.216
1957	Pit	N	O	58	.275
1958	Pit	N	O	76	.268
1959	Pit	N	O	96	.236
1960	Pit	N	H	3	.000
1961	Pit	N	O	4	.000
1962	Hou	N	O	146	.286
	BRTR			454	.263

MELE, ALBERT ERNEST
(Dutch)
b.Jan.11,1915 New York,N.Y.

Yr	Cl	Lea	Pos	G	Rec
1937	Cin	N	O	6	.143
	BLTL				

MELE, SABATH ANTHONY
(Sam)
b.Jan.21,1923 Astoria L.I.,N.Y.

Yr	Cl	Lea	Pos	G	Rec
1947	Bos	A	1-O	123	.302
1948	Bos	A	O	66	.233
1949	Bos	A	O	18	.196
1949	Was	A	1-O	78	.242
1950	Was	A	1-O	126	.274
1951	Was	A	1-O	143	.274
1952	Was	A	O	9	.429
1952	Chi	A	1-O	123	.248
1953	Chi	A	1-O	140	.274
1954	Bal	A	O	72	.239
1954	Bos	A	1-O	42	.318
1955	Bos	A	O	14	.129
1955	Cin	N	1-O	35	.210
1956	Cle	A	1-O	57	.254
	BRTR			1046	.267

Non-playing manager Min(A) 1961-62

MELILLO, OSCAR DONALD
(Ski)
b.Aug.4,1902 Pullman,Ill.

Yr	Cl	Lea	Pos	G	Rec
1926	St.L	A	2-3	99	.255
1927	St.L	A	2	107	.225
1928	St.L	A	2-3	51	.189
1929	St.L	A	2	141	.296
1930	St.L	A	2	149	.256
1931	St.L	A	2	151	.306
1932	St.L	A	2	154	.242
1933	St.L	A	2	132	.292
1934	St.L	A	2	144	.241
1935	St.L	A	2	19	.206
1935	Bos	A	2	106	.261
1936	Bos	A	2	98	.226
1937	Bos	A	2	26	.250
	BRTR			1377	.260

Non-playing manager St.L (A) 1938.

MELLANA, JOSEPH PETER
b.Mar.11,1905 Oakland,Cal.

Yr	Cl	Lea	Pos	G	Rec
1927	Phi	A	3	4	.286
	BRTR				

MELLOR, WILLIAM HARPER
b.June 6,1874 Camden,N.J.
d.Nov.4,1940

Yr	Cl	Lea	Pos	G	Rec
1902	Bal	A	1	10	.361
	TR				

MELOAN, PAUL B.
b.Aug.23,1888 Clarksville,Mo.

Yr	Cl	Lea	Pos	G	Rec
1910	Chi	A	O	65	.243
1911	Chi	A	O	1	.333
1911	St.L	A	O	64	.262
	BRTL			130	.253

MELTER, STEPHEN B.

Yr	Cl	Lea	Pos	G	Rec
1909	St.L	N	P	23	0-1
	TR				

MELTON, CLIFFORD GEORGE
(Mickey Mouse)
b.Jan.3,1913 Brevard,N.C.

Yr	Cl	Lea	Pos	G	Rec
1937	NY	N	P	46	20-9
1938	NY	N	P	36	14-14
1939	NY	N	P	41	12-15
1940	NY	N	P	37	10-11
1941	NY	N	P	42	8-11
1942	NY	N	P	23	11-5
1943	NY	N	P	34	9-13
1944	NY	N	P	13	2-2
	BLTL			272	86-80

MELTON, DAVID OLIN
b.Oct.3,1928 Pampa,Tex.

Yr	Cl	Lea	Pos	G	Rec
1956	KC	A	O	3	.333
1958	KC	A	O	9	.000
	BRTR			12	.111

MELTON, REUBEN FRANKLIN
b.Feb.27,1917 Cramerton,N.C.

Yr	Cl	Lea	Pos	G	Rec
1941	Phi	N	P	25	1-5
1942	Phi	N	P	42	9-20
1943	Bro	N	P	30	5-8
1944	Bro	N	P	37	9-13
1946	Bro	N	P	24	6-3
1947	Bro	N	P	4	0-1
	BRTR			162	30-50

MENEFEE, JOHN (Jock)
b.Jan.21,1868 Augusta Co.,Va.
d.Mar.11,1953

Yr	Cl	Lea	Pos	G	Rec
1892	Pit	N	P	2	0-0
1893	Lou	N	P	21	8-8
1894	Lou	N	P	34	8-15
1894	Pit	N	P	13	3-8
1895	Pit	N	P	2	0-1
1898	NY	N	P	1	0-1
1900	Chi	N	P	17	9-5
1901	Chi	N	P-O	46	8-12 / .251
1902	Chi	N	P-1-2-3-O	64	12-9 / .231
1903	Chi	N	P	22	8-10
				222	56-69 / .223

MENKE, DENIS JOHN
b.July 21,1940 Algona,Ia.

Yr	Cl	Lea	Pos	G	Rec
1962	Mil	N	2-S-3-O	50	192
	BRTR				

MENOSKY, MICHAEL WILLIAM
(Leaping Mike)
b.Oct.16,1894 Flint,Mich.

Yr	Cl	Lea	Pos	G	Rec
1914	Pit	F	O	60	.260
1915	Pit	F	O	16	.100
1916	Was	A	O	11	.162
1917	Was	A	O	114	.258
1919	Was	A	O	116	.287
1920	Bos	A	O	141	.297
1921	Bos	A	O	133	.300
1922	Bos	A	O	126	.283
1923	Bos	A	O	84	.229
	BLTR			801	.278

MENSOR, EDWARD E.
b.Nov.6,1889 Woodville,Ont.,Canada.

Yr	Cl	Lea	Pos	G	Rec
1912	Pit	N	O	39	.263
1913	Pit	N	O	44	.179
1914	Pit	N	O	44	.202
				127	.221

MENZE, THEODORE CHARLES
b.Nov.4,1901 St.Louis,Mo.

Yr	Cl	Lea	Pos	G	Rec
1918	St.L	N	O	2	.000
	BRTR				

MEOLA, EMILE MICHAEL (Mike)
b.Oct.19,1908 New York,N.Y.

Yr	Cl	Lea	Pos	G	Rec
1933	Bos	A	P	3	0-0
1936	St.L	A	P	9	0-1
1936	Bos	A	P	6	0-2
	BRTR			18	0-3

MERCANTELLI, EUGENE RUDOLPH (Played under name of Eugene Rudolph Rye)

MERCER, GEORGE BARCLAY (Win)
b.June 20,1874 Harrisville,O.
d.Jan.13,1903

Yr	Cl	Lea	Pos	G	Rec
1894	Was	N	P	43	16-23
1895	Was	N	P	54	14-24
1896	Was	N	P	44	25-19
1897	Was	N	P	45	24-21
1898	Was	N	P-S-O	73	12-16 .334
1899	Was	N	P-3	98	7-14 .303
1900	NY	N	P-3	72	13-16 .308
1901	Was	A	P	50	9-13
1902	Det	A	P	35	15-18
	TR			514	135-164 .293

MERCER, JOHN LOCKE
b.Jan.22,1890 Taylortown,La.

Yr	Cl	Lea	Pos	G	Rec
1910	Pit	N	P	1	0-0
1912	St.L	N	1	1	.000
				2	0-0 .000

MERCER, JOHN LOUIS (Played under name of John Louis Johnson)

MERENA, JOHN JOSEPH (Spike)
b.Nov.18,1911 Paterson,N.J.

Yr	Cl	Lea	Pos	G	Rec
1934	Bos	A	P	4	1-2
	BLTL				

MEREWETHER, ARTHUR FRANCIS
b.Apr.8,1902 E.Providence,R.I.

Yr	Cl	Lea	Pos	G	Rec
1922	Pit	N	2	1	.000
	BRTR				

MERKLE, FREDERICK CHARLES
b.Dec.20,1888 Watertown,Wis.
d.Mar.2,1956

Yr	Cl	Lea	Pos	G	Rec
1907	NY	N	1	15	.255
1908	NY	N	1	18	.268
1909	NY	N	1	71	.191
1910	NY	N	1	144	.292
1911	NY	N	1	148	.283
1912	NY	N	1	129	.309
1913	NY	N	1	153	.261
1914	NY	N	1	146	.258
1915	NY	N	1-O	140	.299
1916	NY	N	1	112	.241
1916	Bro	N	1	23	.208
1917	Bro	N	1	2	.125
1917	Chi	N	1	146	.266
1918	Chi	N	1	129	.297
1919	Chi	N	1-2	133	.267
1920	Chi	N	1	92	.285
1925	NY	A	1	7	.385
1926	NY	A	1	1	.000
	BRTR			1609	.273

MERRILL, EDWARD S.
b.1860 Chicago,Ill.

Yr	Cl	Lea	Pos	G	Rec
1882	Wor	N	3	2	.125
1884	Ind	a	2	54	.183
				56	.181

MERRIMAN, LLOYD ARCHER
b.Aug.2,1924 Clovis,Cal.

Yr	Cl	Lea	Pos	G	Rec
1949	Cin	N	O	103	.230
1950	Cin	N	O	92	.258
1951	Cin	N	O	114	.242
1954	Cin	N	O	73	.268
1955	Chi	A	H	1	.000
1955	Chi	N	O	72	.214
	BLTL			455	.242

MERRITT, GEORGE WASHINGTON
b.Apr.14,1880 Paterson,N.J.
d.Feb.21,1938

Yr	Cl	Lea	Pos	G	Rec
1901	Pit	N	P	4	3-0
1902	Pit	N	P-O	2	0-0 .333
1903	Pit	N	P	8	0-0
	TR			14	3-0 .214

MERRITT, HERMAN G.
b.Nov.12,1900 Kansas City,Mo.
d.June 26,1927

Yr	Cl	Lea	Pos	G	Rec
1921	Det	A	S	20	.370
	BRTR				

MERRITT, JOHN HOWARD
b.Oct.12,1894 Tupelo,Miss.
d.Nov.3,1955

Yr	Cl	Lea	Pos	G	Rec
1913	NY	N	O	1	.000

MERRITT, LLOYD WESLEY
b.Apr.8,1933 St. Louis,Mo.

Yr	Cl	Lea	Pos	G	Rec
1957	St.L	N	P	44	1-2
	BRTR				

MERRITT, WILLIAM HENRY
b.July 30,1870 Lowell,Mass.
d.Nov.17,1937

Yr	Cl	Lea	Pos	G	Rec
1891	Chi	N	C	11	.218
1892	Lou	N	C	45	.195
1893	Bos	N	C	35	.363
1894	Bos	N	C-O	10	.231
1894	Pit	N	C	26	.300
1894	Cin	N	C-1-3-O	30	.316
1895	Cin	N	C	21	.213
1895	Pit	N	C	66	.273
1896	Pit	N	C	70	.296
1897	Pit	N	C	56	.270
1899	Bos	N	C	1	.000
				371	.274

MERSON, ...

Yr	Cl	Lea	Pos	G	Rec
1914	Bro	F	H	1	.000

MERSON, JOHN WARREN
b.Jan.17,1922 Elkridge,Md.

Yr	Cl	Lea	Pos	G	Rec
1951	Pit	N	2	13	.360
1952	Pit	N	2-3	111	.246
1953	Bos	A	2	1	.000
	BRTR			125	.257

MERTES, SAMUEL BLAIR (Sandow)
b.Aug.6,1872 San Francisco,Cal.
d.Mar.11,1945

Yr	Cl	Lea	Pos	G	Rec
1896	Phi	N	O	35	.248
1898	Chi	N	O	70	.304
1899	Chi	N	O	109	.305
1900	Chi	N	1-O	125	.294
1901	Chi	A	2	137	.280
1902	Chi	A	P-C-1-2-S-3-O	129	0-0 .283
1903	NY	N	O	138	.280
1904	NY	N	O	148	.276
1905	NY	N	O	150	.279
1906	NY	N	O	71	.237
1906	St.L	N	O	53	.246
	BRTR			1165	0-0 .280

MERTZ, JAMES VERLIN
b.Aug.10,1918 Lima,O.

Yr	Cl	Lea	Pos	G	Rec
1943	Was	A	P	33	5-7
	BRTR				

MERULLO, LEONARD RICHARD
b.May 5,1917 E.Boston,Mass.

Yr	Cl	Lea	Pos	G	Rec
1941	Chi	N	S	7	.353
1942	Chi	N	S	143	.256
1943	Chi	N	S	129	.254
1944	Chi	N	1-S	66	.212
1945	Chi	N	S	121	.239
1946	Chi	N	S	65	.151
1947	Chi	N	S	108	.241
	BRTR			639	.240

MESNER, STEPHAN MATHIAS
b.Jan.13,1918 Los Angeles,Cal.

Yr	Cl	Lea	Pos	G	Rec
1938	Chi	N	S	2	.250
1939	Chi	N	S	17	.279
1941	St.L	N	3	24	.145
1943	Cin	N	3	137	.272
1944	Cin	N	3	121	.242
1945	Cin	N	2-3	150	.254
	BRTR			451	.252

MESSENGER, ANDREW WARREN (Bud)
b.Feb.1,1898 Grand Blanc,Mich.

Yr	Cl	Lea	Pos	G	Rec
1924	Cle	A	P	5	2-0
	BRTR				

MESSENGER, CHARLES WALTER (Bobby)
b.Mar.19,1884 Bangor,Me.
d.July 10,1951

Yr	Cl	Lea	Pos	G	Rec
1909	Chi	A	O	31	.170
1910	Chi	A	O	9	.185
1911	Chi	A	O	13	.133
1914	St.L	A	O	1	.000
	BLTR			54	.165

MESSITT, THOMAS JOHN
b.July 27,1874 Philadelphia,Pa.
d.Sept.22,1934

Yr	Cl	Lea	Pos	G	Rec
1899	Lou	N	C	2	.125

METCALF, ROBERT
b.Brooklyn,N.Y.

Yr	Cl	Lea	Pos	G	Rec
1875	Mut	n	S-3-O	7	NR

METEVIER, GEORGE DEWEY
b.May 6,1898 Cambridge,Mass.
d.Mar.2,1947

Yr	Cl	Lea	Pos	G	Rec
1922	Cle	A	P	2	2-0
1923	Cle	A	P	26	4-2
1924	Cle	A	P	26	1-5
	BLTR			54	7-7

METHA, FRANK JOSEPH (Scat)
b.Dec.13,1914 Los Angeles,Cal.

Yr	Cl	Lea	Pos	G	Rec
1940	Det	A	2-3	26	.243
	BRTR				

METHENY, ARTHUR BEAUREGARD (Bud)
b.June 1,1917 St.Louis,Mo.

Yr	Cl	Lea	Pos	G	Rec
1943	NY	A	O	103	.261
1944	NY	A	O	137	.239
1945	NY	A	O	133	.248
1946	NY	A	H	3	.000
	BLTL			376	.247

METKOVICH, GEORGE MICHAEL (Catfish)
b.Oct.8,1921 Angel's Camp,Cal.

Yr	Cl	Lea	Pos	G	Rec
1943	Bos	A	1-O	78	.246
1944	Bos	A	1-O	134	.277
1945	Bos	A	1-O	138	.260
1946	Bos	A	O	86	.246
1947	Cle	A	1-O	126	.254
1949	Chi	A	O	93	.237
1951	Pit	N	1-O	120	.293
1952	Pit	N	1-O	125	.271

(Continued)

Yr	Cl	Lea	Pos	G	Rec
1953	Pit	N	1-O	26	.146
1953	Chi	N	1-O	61	.234
1954	Mil	N	1-O	68	.276
		BLTL		1055	.261

METRO, CHARLES
(Real name Charles Moreskonich)
b.Apr.28,1919 Heilwood,Pa.

Yr	Cl	Lea	Pos	G	Rec
1943	Det	A	O	44	.200
1944	Det	A	O	38	.192
1944	Phi	A	2-3-O	24	.100
1945	Phi	A	O	65	.210
		BRTR		171	..193

METZ, LEONARD RAYMOND
b.July 6,1899 LaFayette,Colo.
d.Feb.24,1953

Yr	Cl	Lea	Pos	G	Rec
1923	Phi	N	2-S	12	.216
1924	Phi	N	S	7	.286
1925	Phi	N	2-S	11	.000
		BRTR		30	.169

METZIG, WILLIAM ANDREW
b.Dec.4,1920 Ft.Dodge,Ia.

Yr	Cl	Lea	Pos	G	Rec
1944	Chi	A	2	5	.125
		BRTR			

METZLER, ALEXANDER
b.Jan.4,1903 Fresno,Cal.

Yr	Cl	Lea	Pos	G	Rec
1925	Chi	N	O	9	.184
1926	Phi	A	O	20	.242
1927	Chi	A	O	134	.319
1928	Chi	A	O	139	.304
1929	Chi	A	O	146	.275
1930	Chi	A	O	56	.176
1930	St.L	A	O	56	.261
		BLTR		560	.285

MEUSEL, EMIL FREDERICK
(Irish)
b.June 9,1893 Oakland,Cal.
d.Mar.1,1963

Yr	Cl	Lea	Pos	G	Rec
1914	Was	A	O	1	.000
1918	Phi	N	2-O	124	.279
1919	Phi	N	O	135	.305
1920	Phi	N	O	138	.309
1921	Phi	N	O	84	.353
1921	NY	N	O	62	.329
1922	NY	N	O	154	.330
1923	NY	N	O	146	.297
1924	NY	N	O	139	.310
1925	NY	N	O	135	.328
1926	NY	N	O	129	.292
1927	Bro	N	O	42	.243
		BRTR		1289	.310

MEUSEL, ROBERT WILLIAM
(Long Bob)
b.July 19,1896 San Jose,Cal.

Yr	Cl	Lea	Pos	G	Rec
1920	NY	A	3-O	119	.328
1921	NY	A	O	149	.318
1922	NY	A	O	121	.319
1923	NY	A	O	132	.313
1924	NY	A	O	143	.325
1925	NY	A	3-O	156	.292
1926	NY	A	O	108	.315
1927	NY	A	O	135	.337
1928	NY	A	O	131	.297
1929	NY	A	O	100	.261
1930	Cin	N	O	113	.289
		BRTR		1407	.309

MEYER, BENJAMIN (Earache)
b.Jan.1,1888 Hematite,Mo.

Yr	Cl	Lea	Pos	G	Rec
1913	Bro	N	O	38	.195
1914	Bal	F	O	141	.302
1915	Bal	F	O	35	.233
1915	Buf	F	O	93	.237
1925	Phi	N	2	1	1.000
		BRTR		308	.265

MEYER, GEORGE FRANCIS
b.Aug.22,1912 Chicago,Ill.

Yr	Cl	Lea	Pos	G	Rec
1938	Chi	A	2	24	.296
		BRTR			

MEYER, JOHN ROBERT
b.Mar.23,1932 Philadelphia,Pa.

Yr	Cl	Lea	Pos	G	Rec
1955	Phi	N	P	50	6-11
1956	Phi	N	P	41	7-11
1957	Phi	N	P	19	0-2
1958	Phi	N	P	37	3-6
1959	Phi	N	P	47	5-3
1960	Phi	N	P	7	3-1
1961	Phi	N	P	1	0-0
		BRTR		202	24-34

MEYER, LAMBERT DALTON
(Dutch)
b.Oct.6,1915 Waco,Tex.

Yr	Cl	Lea	Pos	G	Rec
1937	Chi	N	H	1	.000
1940	Det	A	2	23	.259
1941	Det	A	2	46	.190
1942	Det	A	2	14	.327
1945	Cle	A	2	130	.292
1946	Cle	A	2	72	.232
		BRTR		286	.264

MEYER, LEE

Yr	Cl	Lea	Pos	G	Rec
1909	Bro	N	S	7	.130
		TR			

MEYER, RUSSELL CHARLES
(Rowdy)
b.Oct.25,1923 Peru,Ill.

Yr	Cl	Lea	Pos	G	Rec
1946	Chi	N	P	4	0-0
1947	Chi	N	P	23	3-2
1948	Chi	N	P	29	10-10
1949	Phi	N	P	37	17-8
1950	Phi	N	P	32	9-11
1951	Phi	N	P	28	8-9
1952	Phi	N	P	37	13-14
1953	Bro	N	P	34	15-5
1954	Bro	N	P	36	11-6
1955	Bro	N	P	18	6-2
1956	Chi	N	P	20	1-6
1956	Cin	N	P	1	0-0
1957	Bos	A	P	2	0-0
1959	KC	A	P	18	1-0
		BBTR		319	94-73

MEYER, WILLIAM ADAM
b.Jan.14,1892 Knoxville,Tenn.
d.Mar.31,1957

Yr	Cl	Lea	Pos	G	Rec
1913	Chi	A	C	1	1.000
1916	Phi	A	C	50	.232
1917	Phi	A	C	62	.236
		BRTR		113	.236

Non-playing manager Pit (N) 1948-1952.

MEYERLE, LEVI SAMUEL
(Long Levi)
b.1849 Philadelphia,Pa.
d.Nov.4,1921

Yr	Cl	Lea	Pos	G	Rec
1871	Ath	n	3	26	.448
1872	Ath	n	S-3-O	27	NR
1873	Phi	n	3	47	NR
1874	Chi	n	2-S-3-O	52	NR
1875	Phi	n	1-2-3	67	.314
1876	Ath	N	P-3	55	0-2 / .336
1877	Cin	N	2-S-O	27	.327
1884	Key	U	1-O	3	.091
		BRTR		304	0-2 / NR

MEYERS, J. ALBERT
(Bert)
b.Washington,D.C.

Yr	Cl	Lea	Pos	G	Rec
1896	St.L	N	3	122	.258
1898	Was	N	3	31	.261
1900	Phi	N	3	7	.185
				160	.256

MEYERS, JOHN TORTES
(Chief)
b.July 29,1882 Riverside,Cal.

Yr	Cl	Lea	Pos	G	Rec
1909	NY	N	C	64	.277
1910	NY	N	C	117	.285

(Continued)

Yr	Cl	Lea	Pos	G	Rec
1911	NY	N	C	128	.332
1912	NY	N	C	126	.358
1913	NY	N	C	120	.312
1914	NY	N	C	134	.286
1915	NY	N	C	110	.232
1916	Bro	N	C	80	.247
1917	Bro	N	C	47	.214
1917	Bos	N	C	25	.246
		BRTR		951	.291

MEYERS, LEWIS HENRY
(Crazy Horse)
b.Dec.9,1859 Cincinnati,O.
d.Nov.30,1920

Yr	Cl	Lea	Pos	G	Rec
1884	Cin	U	C-O	1	.000

MICELOTTA, ROBERT PETER
(Mickey)
b.Oct.20,1928 Corona,L.I.,N.Y.

Yr	Cl	Lea	Pos	G	Rec
1954	Phi	N	S	13	.000
1955	Phi	N	S	4	.000
		BRTR		17	.000

MICHAELS, CASIMIR EUGENE
(Cass) (Real name Casimir Eugene Kwietniewski)
b.Mar.4,1926 Detroit,Mich.

Yr	Cl	Lea	Pos	G	Rec
(Casimir Eugene Kwietniewski)					
1943	Chi	A	3	2	.000
(Casimir Eugene Michaels)					
1944	Chi	A	S-3	27	.176
1945	Chi	A	2-S	129	.245
1946	Chi	A	2-S-3	91	.258
1947	Chi	A	2-3	110	.273
1948	Chi	A	2-S-O	145	.248
1949	Chi	A	2	154	.308
1950	Chi	A	2	36	.312
1950	Was	A	2	106	.250
1951	Was	A	2	138	.258
1952	Was	A	2	22	.233
1952	St.L	A	2-3	55	.265
1952	Phi	A	2	55	.250
1953	Phi	A	2	117	.251
1954	Chi	A	2-3	101	.262
		BRTR		1288	.262

MICHAELS, JOHN JOSEPH
b.July 10,1907 Bridgeport,Conn.

Yr	Cl	Lea	Pos	G	Rec
1932	Bos	A	P	29	1-6
		BLTL			

MICHAELS, RALPH JOSEPH
b.May 3,1902 Etna,Pa.

Yr	Cl	Lea	Pos	G	Rec
1924	Chi	N	S	8	.364
1925	Chi	N	1-2-S-3	22	.280
1926	Chi	N	H	2	.000
		BRTR		32	.295

MICHAELSON, JOHN AUGUST
b.Aug.12,1893

Yr	Cl	Lea	Pos	G	Rec
1921	Chi	A	P	2	0-0
		BRTR			

MICKELSON, EDWARD ALLEN
b.Sept.9,1926 Ottawa,Ill.

Yr	Cl	Lea	Pos	G	Rec
1950	St.L	N	1	5	.100
1953	St.L	A	1	7	.133
1957	Chi	N	1	6	.000
		BRTR		18	.081

MICKENS, GLENN ROGER
b.July 26,1930 Wilmar,Cal.

Yr	Cl	Lea	Pos	G	Rec
1953	Bro	N	P	4	0-1
		BRTR			

MIDDLETON, JAMES BLAINE
b.May 28,1889 Argos,Ind.

Yr	Cl	Lea	Pos	G	Rec
1917	NY	N	P	13	1-1
1921	Det	A	P	38	6-11
		BRTR		51	7-12

MIDDLETON, JOHN WAYNE
b.Apr.11,1900 Mt.Calm,Tex.

Yr	Cl	Lea	Pos	G	Rec
1922	Cle	A	P	2	0-1
		BLTL			

MIDKIFF, EZRA MILLINGTON
b.Nov.13,1883 Salt Rock,W.Va.
d.Mar.21,1957

Yr	Cl	Lea	Pos	G	Rec
1909	Cin	N	3	1	.000
1912	NY	A	3	21	.244
1913	NY	A	3	68	.215
		BLTR		90	.222

MIDKIFF, RICHARD JAMES
b.Sept.28,1914 Gonzales,Tex.
d.Oct.30,1956

Yr	Cl	Lea	Pos	G	Rec
1938	Bos	A	P	13	1-1
		BRTR			

MIERKOWICZ, EDWARD FRANK
(Mouse)
b.Mar.6,1924 Wyandotte,Mich.

Yr	Cl	Lea	Pos	G	Rec
1945	Det	A	O	10	.133
1947	Det	A	O	21	.190
1948	Det	A	O	3	.200
1950	St.L	N	H	1	.000
		BRTR		35	.175

MIGGINS, LAWRENCE EDWARD
(Irish)
b.Aug.20,1925 New York,N.Y.

Yr	Cl	Lea	Pos	G	Rec
1948	St.L	N	H	1	.000
1952	St.L	N	1-O	42	.229
		BRTR		43	.227

MIHALIC, JOHN
b.Nov.13,1911 Cleveland,O.

Yr	Cl	Lea	Pos	G	Rec
1935	Was	A	S	6	.227
1936	Was	A	2	25	.239
1937	Was	A	2	38	.252
		BRTR		69	.244

MIKLOS, JOHN JOSEPH
b.Nov.27,1914 Chicago,Ill.

Yr	Cl	Lea	Pos	G	Rec
1944	Chi	N	P	2	0-0
		BLTL			

MIKSIS, EDWARD THOMAS
b.Sept.11,1926 Burlington,N.J.

Yr	Cl	Lea	Pos	G	Rec
1944	Bro	N	S-3	26	.220
1946	Bro	N	2-3	23	.146
1947	Bro	N	2-S-3-O	45	.267
1948	Bro	N	2-S-3	86	.213
1949	Bro	N	1-2-S-3	50	.221
1950	Bro	N	2-S-3	51	.250
1951	Bro	N	2-3	19	.200
1951	Chi	N	2	102	.266
1952	Chi	N	2-S	93	.232
1953	Chi	N	2-S	142	.251
1954	Chi	N	2-3-O	38	.202
1955	Chi	N	3-O	131	.235
1956	Chi	N	2-S-3-	114	.239
1957	St.L	N	O	49	.211
1957	Bal	A	H	1	.000
1958	Bal	A	S	3	.000
1958	Cin	N	1-2-S-3-O	69	.140
		BRTR		1042	.236

MILAN, HORACE ROBERT
b.Apr.7,1894 Linden,Tenn.
d.July 1955

Yr	Cl	Lea	Pos	G	Rec
1915	Was	A	O	10	.375
1917	Was	A	O	31	.288
		BRTR		41	.320

MILAN, JESSE CLYDE
(Deerfoot)
b.Mar.25,1887 Linden,Tenn.
d.Mar.3,1953

Yr	Cl	Lea	Pos	G	Rec
1907	Was	A	O	48	.279
1908	Was	A	O	130	.239
1909	Was	A	O	130	.200
1910	Was	A	O	142	.279
1911	Was	A	O	154	.315
1912	Was	A	O	154	.306
1913	Was	A	O	154	.299
1914	Was	A	O	115	.295

(Continued)

Yr	Cl	Lea	Pos	G	Rec
1915	Was	A	O	153	.288
1916	Was	A	O	150	.273
1917	Was	A	O	155	.294
1918	Was	A	O	128	.290
1919	Was	A	O	88	.287
1920	Was	A	O	126	.322
1921	Was	A	O	112	.288
1922	Was	A	M-O	42	.230
		BLTR		1981	.285

MILES, CARL THOMAS
b.Mar.22,1920 Trenton,Mo.

Yr	Cl	Lea	Pos	G	Rec
1940	Phi	A	P	2	0-0
		BBTL			

MILES, DONALD RAY
b.Mar.13,1936 Indianapolis,Ind.

Yr	Cl	Lea	Pos	G	Rec
1958	LA	N	O	8	.182
		BLTR			

MILES, WILSON DANIEL
(Dee)
b.Feb.15,1909 Kellerman,Ala.

Yr	Cl	Lea	Pos	G	Rec
1935	Was	A	O	60	.264
1936	Was	A	O	25	.237
1939	Phi	A	O	106	.300
1940	Phi	A	O	88	.301
1941	Phi	A	O	80	.312
1942	Phi	A	O	99	.272
1943	Bos	A	O	45	.215
		BLTR		503	.280

MILJUS, JOHN KENNETH
(Jovo)
b.June 30,1895 Pittsburgh,Pa.

Yr	Cl	Lea	Pos	G	Rec
1915	Pit	F	P	1	0-0
1917	Bro	N	P	4	0-1
1920	Bro	N	P	10	1-0
1921	Bro	N	P	28	6-3
1927	Pit	N	P	19	8-3
1928	Pit	N	P	21	5-7
1928	Cle	A	P	11	1-4
1929	Cle	A	P	34	8-8
		BRTR		128	29-26

MILLARD, FRANK E.
b.July 4,1865 E.St.Louis,Ill.
d.July 4,1892

Yr	Cl	Lea	Pos	G	Rec
1890	St.L	a	2	1	.000

MILLER, BERT

Yr	Cl	Lea	Pos	G	Rec
1897	Phi	N	2	3	.200

MILLER, BURT
b.Kalamazoo,Mich.

Yr	Cl	Lea	Pos	G	Rec
1897	Lou	N	P	4	0-0

MILLER, C.

Yr	Cl	Lea	Pos	G	Rec
1912	St.L	A	S	1	.000
		TR			

MILLER, CHARLES BRADLEY
(Dusty)
b.Sept.10,1868 Oil City,Pa.
d.Sept.3,1945

Yr	Cl	Lea	Pos	G	Rec
1889	Bal	a	O	11	.125
1890	St.L	a	O	27	.203
1895	Cin	N	O	132	.329
1896	Cin	N	O	125	.318
1897	Cin	N	O	119	.317
1898	Cin	N	O	152	.299
1899	Cin	N	O	80	.260
1899	St.L	N	O	10	.231
		BLTR		656	.299

MILLER, CHARLES HESS
b.Dec.30,1877 Conestoga Center,Pa.
d.Jan.13,1951

Yr	Cl	Lea	Pos	G	Rec
1915	Bal	F	H	1	.000

MILLER, CHARLES M.
b.1892

Yr	Cl	Lea	Pos	G	Rec
1913	St.L	N	O	4	.091
1914	St.L	N	O	36	.194
		BLTL		40	.170

MILLER, DAKIN E.
b.Kansas.
d.Jan.14,1943

Yr	Cl	Lea	Pos	G	Rec
1902	Chi	N	O	50	.225

MILLER, EDMUND JOHN
(Bing)
b.Aug,30,1894 Vinton,Ia.

Yr	Cl	Lea	Pos	G	Rec
1921	Was	A	O	114	.288
1922	Phi	A	O	143	.336
1923	Phi	A	O	123	.299
1924	Phi	A	O	113	.342
1925	Phi	A	1-O	124	.318
1926	Phi	A	O	38	.291
1926	St.L	A	O	94	.331
1927	St.L	A	O	144	.325
1928	Phi	A	O	139	.329
1929	Phi	A	O	147	.335
1930	Phi	A	O	154	.303
1931	Phi	A	O	137	.281
1932	Phi	A	O	95	.295
1933	Phi	A	1-O	67	.275
1934	Phi	A	O	81	.243
1935	Bos	A	O	78	.304
1936	Bos	A	O	30	.298
		BRTR		1821	.312

MILLER, EDWARD ROBERT
(Eppie)
b.Nov.26,1916 Pittsburgh,Pa.

Yr	Cl	Lea	Pos	G	Rec
1936	Cin	N	S	5	.100
1937	Cin	N	S-3	36	.150
1939	Bos	N	S	77	.267
1940	Bos	N	S	151	.276
1941	Bos	N	S	154	.239
1942	Bos	N	S	142	.244
1943	Cin	N	S	154	.224
1944	Cin	N	S	155	.209
1945	Cin	N	S	115	.238
1946	Cin	N	S	91	.194
1947	Cin	N	S	151	.268
1948	Phi	N	S	130	.246
1949	Phi	N	2-S	85	.207
1950	St.L	N	2-S	64	.227
		BRTR		1510	.238

MILLER, EDWIN (Big Ed)
b.Nov.24,1888 Annville,Pa.

Yr	Cl	Lea	Pos	G	Rec
1912	St.L	A	1-S	12	.155
1914	St.L	A	1	34	.138
1918	Cle	A	1	32	.229
		BRTR		78	.195

MILLER, ELMER
b.July 28,1890 Sandusky,O.
d.Nov.28,1944

Yr	Cl	Lea	Pos	G	Rec
1912	St.L	N	O	12	.189
1915	NY	A	O	26	.145
1916	NY	A	O	43	.224
1917	NY	A	O	114	.251
1918	NY	A	O	67	.243
1921	NY	A	O	56	.298
1922	NY	A	O	51	.286
1922	Bos	A	O	44	.172
		BRTR		413	.243

MILLER, ELMER LeROY
b.Apr.17,1904 Detroit,Mich.

Yr	Cl	Lea	Pos	G	Rec
1929	Phi	N	P	31	0-1
		BLTL			

MILLER, FRANK LEE
(Bullet)
b.May 13,1886 Allegan,Mich.

Yr	Cl	Lea	Pos	G	Rec
1913	Chi	A	P	1	0-1
1916	Pit	N	P	30	7-10
1917	Pit	N	P	39	10-19
1918	Pit	N	P	23	11-8
1919	Pit	N	P	32	13-12
1922	Bos	N	P	31	11-13
1923	Bos	N	P	8	0-3
		BRTR		164	52-66

MILLER, FREDERICK
b.Philadelphia,Pa.

Yr	Cl	Lea	Pos	G	Rec
1892	Was	N	S	1	.000

MILLER, FREDERICK HOLMAN (Speedy)
b.June 28,1886 Fairfield,Ind.
d.May 2,1953

Yr	Cl	Lea	Pos	G	Rec
1910	Bro	N	P	3	1-1

MILLER, GEORGE
b.Feb.19,1853 Newport,Ky.
d.July 25,1929

Yr	Cl	Lea	Pos	G	Rec
1877	Cin	N	C	11	.162
1884	Cin	a	C	6	.250
BRTR				17	.190

MILLER, GEORGE FREDERICK (Foghorn)
b.Aug.15,1864 Brooklyn,N.Y.
d.Apr.6,1909

Yr	Cl	Lea	Pos	G	Rec
1884	Pit	a	C-O	88	.222
1885	Pit	a	C	42	.161
1886	Pit	a	C	83	.258
1887	Pit	N	C-O	87	.313
1888	Pit	N	C-O	103	.277
1889	Pit	N	C-O	102	.267
1890	Pit	N	3-O	138	.273
1891	Pit	N	C-S-3-O	131	.285
1892	Pit	N	C-S-O	147	.268
1893	Pit	N	C	40	.194
1894	St.L	N	M-C-2-3	125	.341
1895	St.L	N	C-3-O	123	.290
1896	Lou	N	C-2	84	.273
BRTR				1293	.274

MILLER, HENRY D.

Yr	Cl	Lea	Pos	G	Rec
1892	Chi	N	P	4	1-2

TL

MILLER, HUGH STANLEY (Cotton)
b.Dec.28,1887 St.Louis,Mo.
d.Dec.24,1945

Yr	Cl	Lea	Pos	G	Rec
1911	Phi	N	H	1	.000
1914	St.L	F	1	132	.225
1915	St.L	F	1	6	.500
BRTR				139	.228

MILLER, JACOB GEORGE
b.Feb.5,1897 Baltimore,Md.

Yr	Cl	Lea	Pos	G	Rec
1922	Pit	N	O	3	.091

BRTR

MILLER, JAMES (Rabbit)
b.Pittsburgh,Pa.
d.Feb.8,1937

Yr	Cl	Lea	Pos	G	Rec
1901	NY	N	2	18	.136

MILLER, JAMES ELDRIDGE
b.Feb.13,1913 Celeste,Tex.

Yr	Cl	Lea	Pos	G	Rec
1944	Det	A	C	5	.200
1945	Det	A	C	2	.750
BRTR				7	.444

MILLER, JOHN ANTHONY (Ox)
b.May 4,1915 Gause,Tex.

Yr	Cl	Lea	Pos	G	Rec
1943	Was	A	P	3	0-0
1943	St.L	A	P	2	0-0
1945	St.L	A	P	6	2-1
1946	St.L	A	P	11	1-3
1947	Chi	N	P	4	1-2
BRTR				26	4-6

MILLER, JOHN BARNEY (Dots)
b.Sept.9,1886 Kearny,N.J.
d.Sept.5,1923

Yr	Cl	Lea	Pos	G	Rec
1909	Pit	N	2	150	.279
1910	Pit	N	2	119	.227
1911	Pit	N	2	129	.268
1912	Pit	N	1	148	.275
1913	Pit	N	1	154	.272
1914	St.L	N	1-S	155	.290
1915	St.L	N	1-2	150	.264
1916	St.L	N	1-2-S	143	.238
1917	St.L	N	1-2	148	.248
1919	St.L	N	1-2	101	.231
1920	Phi	N	2-3	98	.254
1921	Phi	N	1-3	84	.297
BRTR				1579	.263

MILLER, JOHN ERNEST
b.May 30,1941 Baltimore,Md.

Yr	Cl	Lea	Pos	G	Rec
1962	Bal	A	P	2	1-1

BRTR

MILLER, JOSEPH A.
b.1861 Baltimore,Md.
d.1928

Yr	Cl	Lea	Pos	G	Rec
1884	Tol	a	S	105	.236
1885	Lou	a	2-S-3	97	.192
				202	.217

MILLER, JOSEPH H. (Cyclone)
b.Sept.24,1859 Springfield,Mass.
d.Oct.13,1916

Yr	Cl	Lea	Pos	G	Rec
1884	Chi	U	P	1	0-0
1884	Pro	N	P-O	6	2-4 / .045
1884	Phi	N	P	1	0-1
1886	Ath	a	P	21	10-9
				29	12-14 / .259

MILLER, JOSEPH WICK
b.July 24,1850 Germany
d.Aug.30,1891

Yr	Cl	Lea	Pos	G	Rec
1872	Nat	n	M-1	1	NR
1875	Wes	n	2	13	NR
1875	Chi	n	2-O	16	NR
				30	NR

MILLER, KENNETH ALBERT
b.May 2,1916 St.Louis,Mo.

Yr	Cl	Lea	Pos	G	Rec
1944	NY	N	P	5	0-1

BRTR

MILLER, L. EDWARD
b.Tecumseh,Mich.

Yr	Cl	Lea	Pos	G	Rec
1884	Tol	a	O	8	.208

MILLER, LAWRENCE H. (Hack)
b.Jan.1,1894 Chicago,Ill.

Yr	Cl	Lea	Pos	G	Rec
1916	Bro	N	O	3	.333
1918	Bos	A	O	12	.276
1922	Chi	N	O	122	.351
1923	Chi	N	O	135	.301
1924	Chi	N	O	53	.336
1925	Chi	N	O	24	.279
BRTR				349	.323

MILLER, LEO ALPHONSO (Red)
b.Feb.11,1897 Philadelphia,Pa.

Yr	Cl	Lea	Pos	G	Rec
1923	Phi	N	P	1	0-0

BRTR

MILLER, LOWELL OTTO (Moonie)
b.June 1,1889 Minden,Neb.
d.Mar.29,1962

Yr	Cl	Lea	Pos	G	Rec
1910	Bro	N	C	28	.167
1911	Bro	N	C	22	.210
1912	Bro	N	C	98	.278
1913	Bro	N	C	104	.272
1914	Bro	N	C	54	.231
1915	Bro	N	C	84	.224
1916	Bro	N	C	73	.255
1917	Bro	N	C	92	.230
1918	Bro	N	C-1	75	.193
1919	Bro	N	C	51	.226
1920	Bro	N	C	90	.289
1921	Bro	N	C	91	.234
1922	Bro	N	C	59	.261
BRTR				921	.245

MILLER, OTIS LOUIS
b.Feb.2,1901 Belleville,Ill.
d.July 26,1959

Yr	Cl	Lea	Pos	G	Rec
1927	St.L	A	S-3	51	.224
1930	Bos	A	2-3	112	.286
1931	Bos	A	3	107	.272
1932	Bos	A	O	2	.000
BRTR				272	.273

MILLER, RALPH DARWIN
b.Mar.15,1873 Cincinnati,O.

(Continued)

Yr	Cl	Lea	Pos	G	Rec
1898	Bro	N	P	21	5-14
1899	Bal	N	P	6	1-2
BRTR				27	6-16

MILLER, RALPH HENRY (Moose)
b.Jan.24,1896 Vinton,Ia.

Yr	Cl	Lea	Pos	G	Rec
1921	Was	A	P	1	0-0

BRTL

MILLER, RALPH JOSEPH
b.Feb.29,1896 Ft.Wayne,Ind.
d.Mar.18,1939

Yr	Cl	Lea	Pos	G	Rec
1920	Phi	N	3	97	.219
1921	Phi	N	S	57	.304
1924	Was	A	2	9	.133
BRTR				163	.248

MILLER, RAYMOND P.
b.Apr.9,1888 Allegheny,Pa.
d.Apr.7,1927

Yr	Cl	Lea	Pos	G	Rec
1917	Cle	A	1	19	.190
1917	Pit	N	1	6	.148
				25	.188

MILLER, ROBERT GERALD
b.July 15,1935 Chicago,Ill.

Yr	Cl	Lea	Pos	G	Rec
1953	Det	A	P	13	1-2
1954	Det	A	P	34	1-1
1955	Det	A	P	9	2-1
1956	Det	A	P	11	0-2
1962	Cin	N	P	6	0-0
1962	NY	N	P	17	2-2
BRTL				90	6-8

MILLER, ROBERT JOHN
b.June 16,1926 Detroit,Mich.

Yr	Cl	Lea	Pos	G	Rec
1949	Phi	N	P	3	0-0
1950	Phi	N	P	35	11-6
1951	Phi	N	P	17	2-1
1952	Phi	N	P	3	0-1
1953	Phi	N	P	35	8-9
1954	Phi	N	P	30	7-9
1955	Phi	N	P	40	8-4
1956	Phi	N	P	49	3-6
1957	Phi	N	P	32	2-5
1958	Phi	N	P	17	1-1
BRTR				261	42-42

MILLER, ROBERT LANE
b.Feb.18,1939 St. Louis,Mo.

Yr	Cl	Lea	Pos	G	Rec
1957	St.L	N	P	7	0-0
1959	St.L	N	P	11	4-3
1960	St.L	N	P	17	4-3
1961	St.L	N	P	35	1-3
1962	NY	N	P	40	1-12
BRTR				110	10-21

MILLER, ROBERT W.

Yr	Cl	Lea	Pos	G	Rec
1890	Roc	a	P	13	3-8
1891	Was	a	P	7	2-3
				20	5-11

MILLER, RODNEY CARTER
b.Jan.16,1940 Portland,Ore.

Yr	Cl	Lea	Pos	G	Rec
1957	Bro	N	H	1	.000

BLTR

MILLER, ROLLAND ARTHUR (Ronnie)
b.Aug.28,1918 Mason City,Ia.

Yr	Cl	Lea	Pos	G	Rec
1941	Was	A	P	1	0-0

BBTR

MILLER, ROSCOE CLYDE (Rubberlegs)
b.Dec.2,1876 Greenville,Ind.
d.Apr.18,1913

Yr	Cl	Lea	Pos	G	Rec
1901	Det	A	P	39	23-13
1902	Det	A	P	20	6-11
1902	NY	N	P	10	1-8
1903	NY	N	P	15	2-5
1904	Pit	N	P	19	7-9
				103	39-46

MILLER, ROY OSCAR (Doc)
b.1883 San Francisco,Cal.
d.July 30,1938

Yr	Cl	Lea	Pos	G	Rec
1910	Chi	N	O	1	.000
1910	Bos	N	O	130	.286
1911	Bos	N	O	146	.333
1912	Bos	N	O	51	.234
1912	Phi	N	O	67	.288
1913	Phi	N	O	69	.345
1914	Cin	N	O	93	.255
	BLTL			557	.295

MILLER, RUDEL CHARLES
b.July 12,1900 Kalamazoo,Mich.

Yr	Cl	Lea	Pos	G	Rec
1929	Phi	A	3	2	.250
	BRTR				

MILLER, RUSSELL LEWIS
b.Mar.25,1900 Wagram,O.
d.Apr.30,1962

Yr	Cl	Lea	Pos	G	Rec
1927	Phi	N	P	2	1-1
1928	Phi	N	P	36	0-12
	BRTR			38	1-13

MILLER, STUART LEONARD
b.Dec.26,1927 Northampton,Mass.

Yr	Cl	Lea	Pos	G	Rec
1952	St.L	N	P	12	6-3
1953	St.L	N	P	42	7-8
1954	St.L	N	P	20	2-3
1956	St.L	N	P	4	0-1
1956	Phi	N	P	29	5-8
1957	NY	N	P	38	7-9
1958	SF	N	P	42	6-9
1959	SF	N	P	59	8-7
1960	SF	N	P	47	7-6
1961	SF	N	P	64	14-5
1962	SF	N	P	60	5-8
	BRTR			417	67-67

MILLER, THOMAS P. (Reddy)
b.Philadelphia,Pa.
d.May 29,1876

Yr	Cl	Lea	Pos	G	Rec
1875	St.L	n	C-3	52	.166

MILLER, THOMAS ROYALL
b.July 5,1897 Powhatan Court House, Va.

Yr	Cl	Lea	Pos	G	Rec
1918	Bos	N	H	2	.000
1919	Bos	N	O	7	.333
	BLTR			9	.250

MILLER, WALTER J. (Jake)
b.Feb.28,1898 Wagram,O.

Yr	Cl	Lea	Pos	G	Rec
1924	Cle	A	P	2	0-1
1925	Cle	A	P	32	10-13
1926	Cle	A	P	18	7-4
1927	Cle	A	P	34	10-8
1928	Cle	A	P	25	8-9
1929	Cle	A	P	29	14-12
1930	Cle	A	P	24	4-4
1931	Cle	A	P	10	2-1
1933	Chi	A	P	30	5-6
	BLTL			204	60-58

MILLER, WALTER W.
b.Oct.19,1884 Gas City,Ind.
d.Mar.1,1956

Yr	Cl	Lea	Pos	G	Rec
1911	Bro	N	P	3	0-1
	BRTR				

MILLER, WARD TAYLOR (Grump)
b.July 5,1885 Dixon,Ill.
d.Sept.4,1958

Yr	Cl	Lea	Pos	G	Rec
1909	Pit	N	O	14	.143
1909	Cin	N	O	43	.310
1910	Cin	N	O	26	.238
1912	Chi	N	O	86	.307
1913	Chi	N	O	80	.236
1914	St.L	F	O	119	.295
1915	St.L	F	O	155	.307
1916	St.L	A	O	146	.266
1917	St.L	A	O	43	.207
	BLTR			712	.278

MILLER, WARREN W.

Yr	Cl	Lea	Pos	G	Rec
1909	Was	A	O	26	.216
1911	Was	A	O	21	.148
				47	.188

MILLER, WILLIAM
b.Cleveland,O.

Yr	Cl	Lea	Pos	G	Rec
1902	Pit	N	O	1	.200

MILLER, WILLIAM FRANCIS
b.Apr.12,1912 Hannibal,Mo.

Yr	Cl	Lea	Pos	G	Rec
1937	St.L	A	P	1	0-1
	BRTR				

MILLER, WILLIAM PAUL
b.July 26,1927 Minersville,Pa.

Yr	Cl	Lea	Pos	G	Rec
1952	NY	A	P	21	4-6
1953	NY	A	P	13	2-1
1954	NY	A	P	2	0-1
1955	Bal	A	P	5	0-1
	BLTL			41	6-9

MILLIES, WALTER LOUIS
b.Oct.18,1908 Chicago,Ill.

Yr	Cl	Lea	Pos	G	Rec
1934	Bro	N	C	2	.000
1936	Was	A	C	74	.312
1937	Was	A	C	59	.223
1939	Phi	N	C	84	.234
1940	Phi	N	C	26	.070
1941	Phi	N	C	1	.000
	BRTR			246	.243

MILLIGAN, JOHN (Jocko)
b.Aug.8,1861 Philadelphia,Pa.
d.Aug.30,1923

Yr	Cl	Lea	Pos	G	Rec
1884	Ath	a	C	66	.295
1885	Ath	a	C	7	.286
1886	Ath	a	C-1	76	.249
1887	Ath	a	C-1	96	.344
1888	St.L	a	C	63	.252
1889	St.L	a	C	72	.370
1890	Phi	p	C	62	.315
1891	Ath	a	C-1	117	.300
1892	Was	N	C-1	76	.277
1893	Bal	N	C-1	23	.240
1893	NY	N	C	40	.243
	BRTR			698	.293

MILLIGAN, JOHN ALEXANDER
b.Jan.22,1904 Schuylerville,N.Y.

Yr	Cl	Lea	Pos	G	Rec
1928	Phi	N	P	13	2-5
1929	Phi	N	P	8	0-1
1930	Phi	N	P	9	1-2
1931	Phi	N	P	3	0-0
1934	Was	A	P	2	0-0
	BRTL			35	3-8

MILLIGAN, WILLIAM J.
b.1877 Buffalo,N.Y.
d.Sept.3,1928

Yr	Cl	Lea	Pos	G	Rec
1901	Phi	A	P	7	0-3
1904	NY	N	P	5	0-1
	TL			12	0-4

MILLIKEN, ROBERT FOGLE (Bobo)
b.Aug.25,1926 Majorsville,W.Va.

Yr	Cl	Lea	Pos	G	Rec
1953	Bro	N	P	37	8-4
1954	Bro	N	P	24	5-2
	BRTR			61	13-6

MILLS, ABBOTT PAIGE (Jack)
b.Oct.23,1889 S.Williamstown,Mass.

Yr	Cl	Lea	Pos	G	Rec
1911	Cle	A	S	13	.294
	BLTR				

MILLS, ARTHUR GRANT
b.Mar.2,1903 Utica,N.Y.

Yr	Cl	Lea	Pos	G	Rec
1927	Bos	N	P	15	0-1
1928	Bos	N	P	4	0-0
	BRTR			19	0-1

MILLS, CHARLES
b.Brooklyn,N.Y.
d.Apr.10,1874

Yr	Cl	Lea	Pos	G	Rec
1871	Mut	n	C-O	33	NR
1872	Mut	n	C-3-O	8	NR
				41	NR

MILLS, COLONEL BUSTER (Bus)
b.Sept.16,1908 Ranger,Tex.

Yr	Cl	Lea	Pos	G	Rec
1934	St.L	N	O	29	.236
1935	Bro	N	O	17	.214
1937	Bos	A	O	123	.295
1938	St.L	A	O	123	.285
1940	NY	A	O	34	.397
1942	Cle	A	O	80	.277
1946	Cle	A	O	9	.273
	BRTR			415	.287

Non-playing manager Cin (N) 1953.

MILLS, EVERETT
b.1845 Newark,N.J.
d.June 22,1908

Yr	Cl	Lea	Pos	G	Rec
1871	Oly	n	1	31	NR
1872	Bal	n	1	53	.276
1873	Bal	n	1-O	54	NR
1874	Har	n	1	53	NR
1875	Har	n	1	78	NR
1876	Har	N	1	63	.259
				332	NR

MILLS, FRANK LeMOYNE
b.May 13,1895 Knoxville,O.

Yr	Cl	Lea	Pos	G	Rec
1914	Cle	A	C	4	.142
	BLTR				

MILLS, HOWARD ROBINSON (Lefty)
b.May 12,1911 Dedham,Mass.

Yr	Cl	Lea	Pos	G	Rec
1934	St.L	A	P	4	0-0
1937	St.L	A	P	2	1-1
1938	St.L	A	P	30	10-12
1939	St.L	A	P	34	4-11
1940	St.L	A	P	26	0-6
	BLTL			96	15-30

MILLS, RUPERT FRANK
b.Oct.12,1892 Newark,N.J.
d.July 20,1929

Yr	Cl	Lea	Pos	G	Rec
1915	New	F	1	41	.205
	BRTR				

MILLS, WILLIAM GRANT
b.Aug.15,1877 Schenevus,N.Y.
d.July 5,1914

Yr	Cl	Lea	Pos	G	Rec
1901	NY	N	P	2	0-2

MILLS, WILLIAM HENRY
b.Nov.2,1920 Boston,Mass.

Yr	Cl	Lea	Pos	G	Rec
1944	Phi	A	C	5	.250
	BRTR				

MILNAR, ALBERT JOSEPH (Happy)
b.Dec.26,1913 Cleveland,O.

Yr	Cl	Lea	Pos	G	Rec
1936	Cle	A	P	4	1-2
1938	Cle	A	P	24	3-1
1939	Cle	A	P	41	14-12
1940	Cle	A	P	37	18-10
1941	Cle	A	P	35	12-19
1942	Cle	A	P	40	6-8
1943	Cle	A	P	19	1-3
1943	St.L	A	P	3	1-2
1946	St.L	A	P	4	1-1
1946	Phi	N	P	1	0-0
	BLTL			208	57-58

MILNE, WILLIAM JAMES (Pete)
b.Apr.10,1925 Mobile,Ala.

Yr	Cl	Lea	Pos	G	Rec
1948	NY	N	O	12	.222
1949	NY	N	O	31	.241
1950	NY	N	H	4	.250
	BLTR			47	.233

MILOSEVICH, MICHAEL
b.Jan.13,1915 Zeigler,Ill.

Yr	Cl	Lea	Pos	G	Rec
1944	NY	A	S	94	.247
1945	NY	A	2-S	30	.217
	BRTR			124	.242

MILSTEAD, GEORGE EARL (Cowboy)
b.Sept.26,1903 Cleburne,Tex.

Yr	Cl	Lea	Pos	G	Rec
1924	Chi	N	P	13	1-1
1925	Chi	N	P	5	1-1
1926	Chi	N	P	18	1-5
		BLTL		36	3-7

MILTON, S. LAWRENCE
b.Pittsburg,Kan.

Yr	Cl	Lea	Pos	G	Rec
1903	St.L	N	P	1	0-0

MINAHAN, DANIEL JOSEPH
b.Nov.28,1865 Troy,N.Y.
d.Aug.8,1929

Yr	Cl	Lea	Pos	G	Rec
1895	Lou	N	3	8	.361
		BRTR			

MINAHAN, EDMUND JOSEPH (Cotton)
b.Dec.10,1882 Springfield,O.
d.May 20,1958

Yr	Cl	Lea	Pos	G	Rec
1907	Cin	N	P	2	0-2
		BRTR			

MINARCIN, RUDY ANTHONY
b.Mar.25,1930 N. Vandergrift,Pa.

Yr	Cl	Lea	Pos	G	Rec
1955	Cin	N	P	41	5-9
1956	Bos	A	P	3	1-0
1957	Bos	A	P	26	0-0
		BRTR		70	6-9

MINCHER, DONALD RAY
b.June 24,1938 Huntsville,Ala.

Yr	Cl	Lea	Pos	G	Rec
1960	Was	A	1	27	.241
1961	Min	A	1	35	.188
1962	Min	A	1	86	.240
		BLTR		148	.223

MINCHER, EDWARD JOHN
b.Baltimore,Md.

Yr	Cl	Lea	Pos	G	Rec
1871	Kek	n	O	9	NR
1872	Nat	n	O	10	NR
				19	NR

MINER, RAYMOND THEADORE
b.Apr.4,1897 Glens Falls, N.Y.

Yr	Cl	Lea	Pos	G	Rec
1921	Phi	A	P	1	0-0
		BRTL			

MINNER, PAUL EDISON (Lefty)
b.July 30,1923 New Wilmington,Pa.

Yr	Cl	Lea	Pos	G	Rec
1946	Bro	N	P	3	0-1
1948	Bro	N	P	31	4-3
1949	Bro	N	P	27	3-1
1950	Chi	N	P	43	8-13
1951	Chi	N	P	36	6-17
1952	Chi	N	P	29	14-9
1953	Chi	N	P	31	12-15
1954	Chi	N	P	33	11-11
1955	Chi	N	P	22	9-9
1956	Chi	N	P	10	2-5
		BLTL		265	69-84

MINNICK, DONALD ATHEY
b.Apr.14,1931 Lynchburg,Va.

Yr	Cl	Lea	Pos	G	Rec
1957	Was	A	P	2	0-1
		BRTR			

MINOSO, SATURNINO ORESTES ARRIETA ARMAS (Minnie)
b.Nov.29,1922 Perico Matanzas,Cuba.

Yr	Cl	Lea	Pos	G	Rec
1949	Cle	A	O	9	.188
1951	Cle	A	1	8	.429
1951	Chi	A	S-3-O	138	.324
1952	Chi	A	S-3-O	147	.281
1953	Chi	A	3-O	151	.313
1954	Chi	A	3-O	153	.320
1955	Chi	A	3-O	139	.288
1956	Chi	A	1-3-O	151	.316
1957	Chi	A	3-O	153	.310
1958	Cle	A	3-O	149	.302
1959	Cle	A	O	148	.302
1960	Chi	A	O	154	.311
1961	Chi	A	O	152	.280
1962	St.L	N	O	39	.196
		BRTR		1691	.303

MIRANDA, GUILLERMO PEREZ (Willy)
b.May 24,1927 Velasco,Cuba

Yr	Cl	Lea	Pos	G	Rec
1951	Was	A	1-S	7	.444
1952	Chi	A	2-S-3	12	.250
1952	St.L	A	S	7	.091
1952	Chi	A	2-S-3	58	.218
1953	St.L	A	S-3	17	.167
1953	NY	A	S	48	.224
1954	NY	A	2-S-3	92	.250
1955	Bal	A	2-S	153	.255
1956	Bal	A	S	148	.217
1957	Bal	A	S	115	.194
1958	Bal	A	S	102	.201
1959	Bal	A	2-S-3	65	.159
		BBTR		824	.221

MISSE, JOHN B.
b.1890

Yr	Cl	Lea	Pos	G	Rec
1914	St.L	F	2-S	97	.189
		BRTR			

MITCHELL, ALBERT ROY
b.Apr.19,1885 Belton,Tex.
d.Sept.8,1959

Yr	Cl	Lea	Pos	G	Rec
1910	St.L	A	P	6	4-2
1911	St.L	A	P	29	4-8
1912	St.L	A	P	9	3-4
1913	St.L	A	P	33	13-16
1914	St.L	A	P	27	4-5
1918	Chi	A	P	2	0-1
1918	Cin	N	P	5	4-0
1919	Cin	N	P	7	0-1
		BRTR		118	32-37

MITCHELL, CLARENCE ELMER
b.Feb.22,1891 Franklin,Neb.

Yr	Cl	Lea	Pos	G	Rec
1911	Det	A	P	5	1-0
1916	Cin	N	P-1-O	56	11-10 / .239
1917	Cin	N	P-1-O	47	9-15 / .278
1918	Bro	N	P	10	0-1
1919	Bro	N	P	34	7-5
1920	Bro	N	P	55	5-2
1921	Bro	N	P	46	11-9
1922	Bro	N	P-1	56	0-3 / .290
1923	Phi	N	P	53	9-10
1924	Phi	N	P	69	6-13
1925	Phi	N	P-1	52	10-17 / .196
1926	Phi	N	P	39	9-14
1927	Phi	N	P	18	6-3
1928	Phi	N	P	5	0-0
1928	St.L	N	P	19	8-9
1929	St.L	N	P	26	8-11
1930	St.L	N	P	1	1-0
1930	NY	N	P	24	10-3
1931	NY	N	P	27	13-11
1932	NY	N	P	8	1-3
		BLTL		650	125-139 / .252

MITCHELL, FREDERICK FRANCIS
(Real name Frederick Francis Yapp)
b.June 5,1878 Cambridge,Mass.

Yr	Cl	Lea	Pos	G	Rec
1901	Bos	A	P	20	6-9
1902	Bos	A	P	1	0-1
1902	Phi	A	P-O	20	5-8 / .184
1903	Phi	N	P	28	11-14
1904	Phi	N	P	25	4-8
1904	Bro	N	P	8	2-4
1905	Bro	N	P	25	3-7
1910	NY	A	C	68	.230
1913	Bos	N	C	4	.333
		BRTR		199	31-51 / .209

Non-playing manager Chi (N) 1917-20 and Bos (N) 1921-23.

MITCHELL, JOHN FRANKLIN
b.Aug.9,1894 Detroit,Mich.

Yr	Cl	Lea	Pos	G	Rec
1921	NY	A	S	13	.262
1922	NY	A	S	4	.000
1922	Bos	A	S	59	.251
1923	Bos	A	S	92	.225
1924	Bro	N	S	64	.263

(Continued)

Yr	Cl	Lea	Pos	G	Rec
1925	Bro	N	S	97	.250
		BBTR		329	.245

MITCHELL, LOREN DALE
b.Aug.23,1921 Colony,Okla.

Yr	Cl	Lea	Pos	G	Rec
1946	Cle	A	O	11	.432
1947	Cle	A	O	123	.316
1948	Cle	A	O	141	.336
1949	Cle	A	O	149	.317
1950	Cle	A	O	130	.308
1951	Cle	A	O	134	.290
1952	Cle	A	O	134	323
1953	Cle	A	O	134	.300
1954	Cle	A	1-O	53	.283
1955	Cle	A	1-O	61	.259
1956	Cle	A	O	38	.133
1956	Bro	N	O	19	.292
		BLTL		1127	.312

MITCHELL, MICHAEL FRANCIS
b.Dec.12,1883 Springfield,O.
d.July 16,1961

Yr	Cl	Lea	Pos	G	Rec
1907	Cin	N	O	148	.292
1908	Cin	N	O	119	.222
1909	Cin	N	O	145	.310
1910	Cin	N	O	156	.286
1911	Cin	N	O	140	.291
1912	Cin	N	O	147	.283
1913	Chi	N	O	82	.262
1913	Pit	N	O	54	.271
1914	Pit	N	O	76	.234
1914	Was	A	O	55	.285
		BRTR		1122	.278

MITCHELL, MONROE BARR
b.Sept.11,1901 Stark ville,Miss.

Yr	Cl	Lea	Pos	G	Rec
1923	Was	A	P	10	2-4
		BRTL			

MITCHELL, ROBERT McKASHA
b.Feb.6,1856 Cincinnati,O.
d.May 1,1933

Yr	Cl	Lea	Pos	G	Rec
1877	Cin	N	P-O	13	6-5 / .204
1878	Cin	N	P-S-O	14	7-2 / .250
1879	Cle	N	P-O	30	4-13 / .146
1882	St.L	a	P-O	1	0-0 / .000
		BLTL		58	17-20 / .182

MITCHELL, WILLIAM A.
b.Dec.1,1888 Sardis,Miss.

Yr	Cl	Lea	Pos	G	Rec
1909	Cle	A	P	3	1-2
1910	Cle	A	P	35	12-8
1911	Cle	A	P	32	7-14
1912	Cle	A	P	22	5-8
1913	Cle	A	P	29	14-8
1914	Cle	A	P	35	12-17
1915	Cle	A	P	36	11-14
1916	Cle	A	P	11	2-5
1916	Det	A	P	24	8-4
1917	Det	A	P	31	12-8
1918	Det	A	P	1	0-1
1919	Det	A	P	3	1-2
		BRTL		262	85-91

MITTERLING, RALPH
b.Apr.19,1890 Freeburg,Pa.
d.Jan.22,1956

Yr	Cl	Lea	Pos	G	Rec
1916	Phi	A	O	13	.154

MIZE, JOHN ROBERT
b.Jan.7,1913 Demorest,Ga.

Yr	Cl	Lea	Pos	G	Rec
1936	St.L	N	1	126	.329
1937	St.L	N	1	145	.364
1938	St.L	N	1	149	.337
1939	St.L	N	1	153	.349
1940	St.L	N	1	155	.314
1941	St.L	N	1	126	.317
1942	NY	N	1	142	.305
1946	NY	N	1	101	.337
1947	NY	N	1	154	.302
1948	NY	N	1	152	.289
1949	NY	N	1	106	.263
1949	NY	A	1	13	.261
1950	NY	A	1	90	.277
1951	NY	A	1	113	.259

(Continued)

Yr	Cl	Lea	Pos	G	Rec
1952	NY	A	1	78	.263
1953	NY	A	1	81	.250
	BLTR			1884	.313

MIZELL, WILMER DAVID
(Vinegar Bend)
b.Aug.13,1930 Leakesville,Miss.

Yr	Cl	Lea	Pos	G	Rec
1952	St.L	N	P	30	10-8
1953	St.L	N	P	33	13-11
1956	St.L	N	P	33	14-14
1957	St.L	N	P	33	8-10
1958	St.L	N	P	30	10-14
1959	St.L	N	P	31	13-10
1960	St.L	N	P	9	1-3
1960	Pit	N	P	23	13-5
1961	Pit	N	P	25	7-10
1962	Pit	N	P	4	1-1
1962	NY	N	P	17	0-2
	BRTL			268	90-88

MIZEUR, WILLIAM
b.June 22,1900 Pana,Ill.

Yr	Cl	Lea	Pos	G	Rec
1923	St.L	A	O	1	.000
1924	St.L	A	O	1	.000
	BLTR			2	.000

MLCKOVSKY, RAYMOND JAMES
(Played under name of Raymond James Mack)

MODAK, MICHAEL JOSEPH ALOYSIUS
b.May 18,1924 Campbell,O.

Yr	Cl	Lea	Pos	G	Rec
1945	Cin	N	P	20	1-2
	BRTR				

MOELLER, DANIEL EDWARD
b.Mar.23,1885 DeWitt,Ia.
d.Apr.14,1951

Yr	Cl	Lea	Pos	G	Rec
1907	Pit	N	O	11	.285
1908	Pit	N	O	27	.193
1912	Was	A	O	132	.276
1913	Was	A	O	153	.236
1914	Was	A	O	151	.250
1915	Was	A	O	118	.226
1916	Was	A	O	78	.245
1916	Cle	A	O	25	.069
	BBTR			695	.243

MOELLER, JOSEPH DOUGLAS
b.Feb.15,1943 Chicago,Ill.

Yr	Cl	Lea	Pos	G	Rec
1962	LA	N	P	19	6-5
	BRTR				

MOELLER, RONALD RALPH
b.Oct.13,1938 Cincinnati,O.

Yr	Cl	Lea	Pos	G	Rec
1956	Bal	A	P	4	0-1
1958	Bal	A	P	4	0-0
1961	LA	A	P	35	4-8
	BLTL			43	4-9

MOFFET, JOSEPH W.
b.Wheeling,W.Va.

Yr	Cl	Lea	Pos	G	Rec
1884	Tol	a	1-3	56	.207

MOFFET, SAMUEL R.
b.1857 Wheeling,W.Va.
d.1907

Yr	Cl	Lea	Pos	G	Rec
1884	Cle	N	P-1-2-3-O	66	3-19 / .179
1887	Ind	N	P	11	1-5
1888	Ind	N	P-O	10	2-5 / .114
	TR			87	6-29 / .167

MOFORD, HERBERT
b.Aug.6,1928 Brooksville,Ky.

Yr	Cl	Lea	Pos	G	Rec
1955	St.L	N	P	14	1-1
1958	Det	A	P	25	4-9
1959	Bos	A	P	4	0-2
1962	NY	N	P	7	0-1
	BRTR			50	5-13

MOGRIDGE, GEORGE ANTHONY
b.Feb.18,1889 Rochester,N.Y.
d.Mar.4,1962

Yr	Cl	Lea	Pos	G	Rec
1911	Chi	A	P	4	0-2
1912	Chi	A	P	9	3-4
1915	NY	A	P	6	2-3
1916	NY	A	P	31	6-12
1917	NY	A	P	29	9-11
1918	NY	A	P	48	15-13
1919	NY	A	P	36	10-8
1920	NY	A	P	26	5-9
1921	Was	A	P	38	18-14
1922	Was	A	P	34	18-13
1923	Was	A	P	33	13-13
1924	Was	A	P	30	16-11
1925	Was	A	P	10	4-3
1925	St.L	A	P	2	1-1
1926	Bos	N	P	40	6-10
1927	Bos	N	P	20	6-4
	BLTL			396	132-131

MOHARDT, JOHN HENRY
b.Jan.20,1900 Pittsburgh,Pa.

Yr	Cl	Lea	Pos	G	Rec
1922	Det	A	O	5	1.000

MOHART, GEORGE BENJAMIN
b.Mar.6,1894 Buffalo,N.Y.

Yr	Cl	Lea	Pos	G	Rec
1920	Bro	N	P	13	0-1
1921	Bro	N	P	2	0-0
	BRTR			15	0-1

MOHLER, ERNEST FOLLETTE
(Kid)
b.Dec.13,1874 Oneida,Ill.
d.Nov.4,1961

Yr	Cl	Lea	Pos	G	Rec
1894	Was	N	S	3	.125

MOISAN, WILLIAM JOSEPH
b.July 30,1925 Bradford,Mass.

Yr	Cl	Lea	Pos	G	Rec
1953	Chi	N	P	3	0-0
	BLTR				

MOKAN, JOHN LEO
b.Sept.23,1895 Buffalo,N.Y.

Yr	Cl	Lea	Pos	G	Rec
1921	Pit	N	O	19	.269
1922	Pit	N	O	31	.258
1922	Phi	N	3-O	47	.252
1923	Phi	N	3-O	113	.313
1924	Phi	N	O	96	.260
1925	Phi	N	O	75	.330
1926	Phi	N	O	127	.303
1927	Phi	N	O	74	.286
	BRTR			582	.291

MOLE, FENTON LeROY (Muscles)
b.June 14,1925 San Leandro,Cal.

Yr	Cl	Lea	Pos	G	Rec
1949	NY	A	1	10	.185
	BLTL				

MOLESWORTH, CARLTON
b.Feb.15,1876 Frederick,Md.
d.July 25,1961

Yr	Cl	Lea	Pos	G	Rec
1895	Was	N	P	4	0-2
	TL				

MOLLENKAMP, FREDERICK HENRY
b.Mar.15,1890 Cincinnati,O.
d.Nov.1,1948

Yr	Cl	Lea	Pos	G	Rec
1914	Phi	N	1	3	.125

MOLLWITZ, FREDERICK (Fritz)
b.June 6,1891 Kolberg,Germany.

Yr	Cl	Lea	Pos	G	Rec
1913	Chi	N	1	3	.428
1914	Chi	N	1	12	.143
1914	Cin	N	1	33	.164
1915	Cin	N	1	153	.259
1916	Cin	N	1	65	.224
1916	Chi	N	1	33	.268
1917	Pit	N	1	36	.257
1918	Pit	N	1	119	.269
1919	Pit	N	1-O	56	.167
1919	St.L	N	1	25	.241
	BRTR			535	.241

MOLYNEAUX, VINCENT L.
b.Aug.17,1894 Niagara Falls,N.Y.

Yr	Cl	Lea	Pos	G	Rec
1917	St.L	A	P	7	0-0
1918	Bos	A	P	6	1-0
	BRTR			13	1-0

MONACO, BLAS
b.Nov.16,1915 San Antonio,Tex.

Yr	Cl	Lea	Pos	G	Rec
1937	Cle	A	2	5	.286
1946	Cle	A	H	12	.000
	BBTR			17	.154

MONAHAN, EDWARD FRANCIS
(Rinty)
b.Apr.28,1928 Brooklyn,N.Y.

Yr	Cl	Lea	Pos	G	Rec
1953	Phi	A	P	4	0-0
	BRTR				

MONBOUQUETTE, WILLIAM CHARLE
b.Aug.11,1936 Medford,Mass.

Yr	Cl	Lea	Pos	G	Rec
1958	Bos	A	P	10	3-4
1959	Bos	A	P	35	7-7
1960	Bos	A	P	38	14-11
1961	Bos	A	P	33	14-14
1962	Bos	A	P	35	15-13
	BRTR			151	53-49

MONCEWICZ, FREDERICK ALFRED
b.Sept.1,1903 Brockton,Mass.

Yr	Cl	Lea	Pos	G	Rec
1928	Bos	A	S	3	.000
	BRTR				

MONCHAK, ALEX
b.Mar.15,1917 Bayonne,N.J.

Yr	Cl	Lea	Pos	G	Rec
1940	Phi	N	2-S	19	.143
	BRTR				

MONROE, EDWARD OLIVER
b.Feb.22,1894 Louisville,Ky.

Yr	Cl	Lea	Pos	G	Rec
1917	NY	A	P	9	1-0
1918	NY	A	P	1	0-0
	BRTR			10	1-0

MONROE, FRANK
b.Hamilton,O.

Yr	Cl	Lea	Pos	G	Rec
1884	Ind	a	C	1	.000

MONROE, JOHN ALLEN
b.Aug.24,1898 Houston,Tex.
d.June 19,1956

Yr	Cl	Lea	Pos	G	Rec
1921	NY	N	2	19	.143
1921	Phi	N	2	41	.286
	BLTR			60	.266

MONROE, ZACHARY CHARLES
b.July 8,1931 Peoria,Ill.

Yr	Cl	Lea	Pos	G	Rec
1958	NY	A	P	21	4-2
1959	NY	A	P	3	0-0
	BRTR			24	4-2

MONTAGUE, EDWARD FRANCIS
b.July 24,1906 San Francisco,Cal.

Yr	Cl	Lea	Pos	G	Rec
1928	Cle	A	S	32	.235
1930	Cle	A	S-3	58	.263
1931	Cle	A	S	64	.285
1932	Cle	A	S-3	66	.245
	BRTR			220	.262

MONTEAGUDO, RENE MIRANDA
b.Oct.12,1915 Havana,Cuba.

Yr	Cl	Lea	Pos	G	Rec
1938	Was	A	P	5	1-1
1940	Was	A	P	27	2-6
1944	Was	A	O	10	.289
1945	Phi	N	P-O	114	0-0 / .301
	BLTL			156	3-7 / .289

MONTEJO, MANUEL
b.Oct.16,1936 Havana,Cuba

Yr	Cl	Lea	Pos	G	Rec
1961	Det	A	P	12	0-0
	BRTR				

MONTEMAYOR, FELIPE ANGEL
b.Feb.7,1930 Monterrey,Mexico

Yr	Cl	Lea	Pos	G	Rec
1953	Pit	N	O	28	.109
1955	**Pit**	**N**	**O**	**36**	**.211**
		BLTL		64	.173

MONTGOMERY, ALVIN ATLAS
b.July 3,1920 Loving,N.Mex.
d.Apr.26,1942

Yr	Cl	Lea	Pos	G	Rec
1941	Bos	N	C	42	.192
		BRTR			

MONZANT, RAMON SEGUNDO
b.Jan.4,1933 Maracaibo,Venezuela.

Yr	Cl	Lea	Pos	G	Rec
1954	NY	N	P	6	0-0
1955	**NY**	**N**	**P**	**29**	**4-8**
1956	**NY**	**N**	**P**	**6**	**1-0**
1957	**NY**	**N**	**P**	**24**	**3-2**
1958	**SF**	**N**	**P**	**44**	**8-11**
1960	SF	N	P	1	0-0
		BRTR		110	16-21

MOOLIC, GEORGE HENRY
b.1865 Lawrence,Mass.
d.Feb.19,1915

Yr	Cl	Lea	Pos	G	Rec
1886	Chi	N	C	15	.145

MOON, LEO
b.June 22,1899 Graham,N.C.

Yr	Cl	Lea	Pos	G	Rec
1932	Cle	A	P	1	0-0
		BRTL			

MOON, WALLACE WADE
b.Apr.3,1930 Trumann,Ark.

Yr	Cl	Lea	Pos	G	Rec
1954	St.L	N	O	151	.304
1955	**St.L**	**N**	**1-O**	**152**	**.295**
1956	**St.L**	**N**	**1-O**	**149**	**.298**
1957	**St.L**	**N**	**O**	**142**	**.295**
1958	**St.L**	**N**	**O**	**108**	**.238**
1959	LA	N	1-O	145	.302
1960	LA	N	O	138	.299
1961	LA	N	O	134	.328
1962	LA	N	1-O	95	.242
		BLTR		1214	.295

MOONEY, JIM IRVING
b.Sept.4,1906 Mooresburg,Tenn.

Yr	Cl	Lea	Pos	G	Rec
1931	NY	N	P	10	7-1
1932	NY	N	P	29	6-10
1933	St.L	N	P	21	2-5
1934	St.L	N	P	32	2-4
		BRTL		92	17-20

MOORE, ALBERT JAMES
b.Aug.4,1902 Brooklyn,N.Y.

Yr	Cl	Lea	Pos	G	Rec
1925	NY	N	O	2	.125
1926	NY	N	O	28	.222
		BRTR		30	.213

MOORE, ANSELM WINN
b.Sept.22,1917 Delhi,La.

Yr	Cl	Lea	Pos	G	Rec
1946	Det	A	O	51	.209
		BLTR			

MOORE, CARLOS WITMAN
b.Aug.13,1907 Clinton,Tenn.
d.July 2,1958

Yr	Cl	Lea	Pos	G	Rec
1930	Was	A	P	4	0-0
		BRTR			

MOORE, CHARLES WESLEY
b.Dec.1,1884 Jackson Co.,Ind.

Yr	Cl	Lea	Pos	G	Rec
1912	Chi	N	2-3	5	.222

MOORE, DEE CEE
b.Apr.6,1914 Amarillo,Tex.

Yr	Cl	Lea	Pos	G	Rec
1936	Cin	N	P-C	6	0-0 / .400
1937	Cin	N	C	7	.077
1943	Bro	N	C-3	37	.253
1943	Phi	N	C-1-3	37	.239
1946	Phi	N	C-1	11	.077
		BRTR		98	0-0 / .232

MOORE, EARL ALONZO (Crossfire)
b.July 29,1878 Pickerington,O.
d.Nov.28,1961

Yr	Cl	Lea	Pos	G	Rec
1901	Cle	A	P	31	16-14
1902	Cle	A	P	36	**17-18**
1903	Cle	A	P	29	**22-7**
1904	Cle	A	P	26	**13-11**
1905	Cle	A	P	30	**16-14**
1906	Cle	A	P	5	1-1
1907	Cle	A	P	3	0-3
1907	NY	A	P	12	**3-4**
1908	Phi	N	P	3	2-1
1909	Phi	N	P	38	18-12
1910	Phi	N	P	46	22-15
1911	Phi	N	P	42	15-19
1912	Phi	N	P	31	9-14
1913	Phi	N	P	12	**0-0**
1913	Chi	N	P	7	1-1
1914	Buf	F	P	33	11-15
		BRTR		384	**166-149**

MOORE, EUEL WALTON (Chief)
b.May 27,1908 Tishomingo,Okla.

Yr	Cl	Lea	Pos	G	Rec
1934	Phi	N	P	20	5-7
1935	Phi	N	P	15	1-6
1935	NY	N	P	6	1-0
1936	Phi	N	P	20	2-3
		BRTR		61	9-16

MOORE, EUGENE JR.
b.Aug.26,1909 Lancaster,Tex.

Yr	Cl	Lea	Pos	G	Rec
1931	Cin	N	O	4	.143
1933	St.L	N	O	11	.395
1934	St.L	N	O	9	.278
1935	St.L	N	H	3	.000
1936	Bos	N	O	151	.290
1937	Bos	N	O	148	.283
1938	Bos	N	O	54	.272
1939	Bro	N	O	107	.225
1940	Bro	N	O	10	.269
1940	Bos	N	O	103	.292
1941	Bos	N	O	129	.272
1942	Was	A	O	1	.000
1943	Was	A	1-O	92	.268
1944	St.L	A	1-O	110	.238
1945	St.L	A	O	110	.260
		BLTL		1042	.270

MOORE, EUGENE SR.
b.Nov.9,1885 Lancaster,Tex.
d.Aug.31,1938

Yr	Cl	Lea	Pos	G	Rec
1909	Pit	N	P	1	0-0
1910	Pit	N	P	4	2-1
1912	Cin	N	P	5	0-1
		BLTL		10	2-2

MOORE, FERDINAND HENRY
b.Feb.20,1896 Indianapolis,Ind.
d.May 6,1947

Yr	Cl	Lea	Pos	G	Rec
1914	Phi	A	1	2	.250

MOORE, GEORGE RAYMOND
b.Nov.25,1872 Cambridge,Mass.
d.Nov.7,1948

Yr	Cl	Lea	Pos	G	Rec
1905	Pit	N	P	1	0-0

MOORE, GRAHAM EDWARD (Eddie)
b.Jan.18,1899 Barlow,Ky.

Yr	Cl	Lea	Pos	G	Rec
1923	Pit	N	S	6	.269
1924	Pit	N	2-3-O	72	.359
1925	Pit	N	2-3-O	142	.298
1926	Pit	N	2-S-3	43	.227
1926	Bos	N	2-S-3	54	.266
1927	Bos	N	2-3-O	112	.302
1928	Bos	N	O	68	.237
1929	Bro	N	2-S	111	.296
1930	Bro	N	2-S-O	76	.281
1932	NY	N	S	37	.264
1934	Cle	A	2	27	.154
		BRTR		748	.285

MOORE, GUY W.
b.May 29,1899 Pine Grove,Pa.
d.June 14,1957

Yr	Cl	Lea	Pos	G	Rec
1922	St.L	N	O	1	.000
		BLTL			

MOORE, HARRY S

Yr	Cl	Lea	Pos	G	Rec
1884	Was	U	O	107	.337

MOORE, JAMES STANFORD
b.Dec.14,1904 Prescott,Ark.

Yr	Cl	Lea	Pos	G	Rec
1928	Cle	A	P	1	0-1
1929	Cle	A	P	2	0-0
1930	Chi	A	P	9	2-1
1931	Chi	A	P	33	0-2
1932	Chi	A	P	1	0-0
		BRTR		46	2-4

MOORE, JAMES WILLIAM
b.Apr.24,1903 Paris,Tenn.

Yr	Cl	Lea	Pos	G	Rec
1930	Chi	A	O	16	.205
1930	Phi	A	O	15	.380
1931	Phi	A	O	49	.223
		BRTR		80	.254

MOORE, JEREMIAH S.
b.Detroit,Mich.

Yr	Cl	Lea	Pos	G	Rec
1884	Alt	U	C-O	20	.298
1884	Cle	N	C	10	.235
1885	Det	N	C	5	.200
				35	.266

MOORE, JOHN FRANCIS
b.Mar.23,1902 Waterville,Conn.

Yr	Cl	Lea	Pos	G	Rec
1928	Chi	N	H	4	.000
1929	Chi	N	O	37	.286
1931	Chi	N	O	39	.240
1932	Chi	N	O	119	.305
1933	Cin	N	O	135	.263
1934	Cin	N	O	16	.190
1934	Phi	N	O	116	.365
1935	Phi	N	O	153	.323
1936	Phi	N	O	124	.328
1937	Phi	N	O	96	.319
1945	Chi	N	H	7	.167
		BLTR		846	.308

MOORE, JOSEPH GREGG (Jo-Jo)
b.Dec.25,1908 Gause,Tex.

Yr	Cl	Lea	Pos	G	Rec
1930	NY	N	O	3	.200
1931	NY	N	O	4	.250
1932	NY	N	O	86	.305
1933	NY	N	O	132	.292
1934	NY	N	O	139	.331
1935	NY	N	O	155	.295
1936	NY	N	O	152	.316
1937	NY	N	O	142	.310
1938	NY	N	O	125	.302
1939	NY	N	O	138	.269
1940	NY	N	O	138	.276
1941	NY	N	O	121	.273
		BLTR		1335	.298

MOORE, LLOYD ALBERT (Whitey)
b.June 10,1912 Tuscarawas,O.

Yr	Cl	Lea	Pos	G	Rec
1936	Cin	N	P	1	1-0
1937	Cin	N	P	13	0-3
1938	Cin	N	P	19	6-4
1939	Cin	N	P	42	13-12
1940	Cin	N	P	25	8-8
1941	Cin	N	P	23	2-1
1942	Cin	N	P	1	0-0
1942	St.L	N	P	9	0-1
		BRTR		133	30-29

MOORE, MAURICE
d.Feb.22,1881

Yr	Cl	Lea	Pos	G	Rec
1875	Atl	n	1-S-3	21	NR

MOORE, RANDOLPH EDWARD
b.June 21,1905 Naples,Tex.

Yr	Cl	Lea	Pos	G	Rec
1927	Chi	A	O	6	.000
1928	Chi	A	O	24	.213
1930	Bos	N	O	83	.288
1931	Bos	N	3-O	83	.260
1932	Bos	N	1-3-O	107	.293
1933	Bos	N	1-O	135	.302
1934	Bos	N	1-O	123	.284
1935	Bos	N	1-O	125	.275
1936	Bro	N	O	42	.239
1937	Bro	N	C	13	.136
1937	St.L	N	O	8	.000
		BLTR		749	.279

MOORE, RAYMOND LeROY
b.June 1,1926 Upper Marlboro,Md.

Yr	Cl	Lea	Pos	G	Rec
1952	Bro	N	P	14	1-2
1953	Bro	N	P	1	0-1
1955	**Bal**	**A**	**P**	**46**	**10-10**
1956	**Bal**	**A**	**P**	**32**	**12-7**
1957	**Bal**	**A**	**P**	**34**	**11-13**
1958	**Chi**	**A**	**P**	**32**	**9-7**
1959	Chi	A	P	29	3-6
1960	Chi	A	P	14	1-1
1960	Was	A	P	37	3-2
1961	Min	A	P	46	4-4
1962	Min	A	P	49	8-3
	BRTR			334	62-56

MOORE, ROY DANIEL
b.Oct.21,1898 Austin,Tex.

Yr	Cl	Lea	Pos	G	Rec
1920	Phi	A	P	27	1-13
1921	Phi	A	P	31	10-10
1922	Phi	A	P	15	0-3
1922	Det	A	P	9	0-0
1923	Det	A	P	4	0-0
	BBTL			86	11-26

MOORE, TERRY BUFORD
b.May 27,1912 Memphis,Tenn.

Yr	Cl	Lea	Pos	G	Rec
1935	St.L	N	O	119	.287
1936	St.L	N	O	143	.264
1937	St.L	N	O	115	.267
1938	St.L	N	O	94	.272
1939	St.L	N	P-O	130	0-0 / .295
1940	St.L	N	O	136	.304
1941	St.L	N	O	122	.294
1942	St.L	N	3-O	130	.288
1946	St.L	N	O	91	.263
1947	St.L	N	O	127	.283
1948	St.L	N	O	91	.232
	BRTR			1298	0-0 / .281

Non-playing manager Phi (N) 1954.

MOORE, WILLIAM ALLEN (Scrappy)
b.Dec.16,1892 St.Louis,Mo.

Yr	Cl	Lea	Pos	G	Rec
1917	St.L	A	3	4	.125
	BRTR				

MOORE, WILLIAM AUSTIN (Cy)
b.Feb.7,1906 Elberton,Ga.

Yr	Cl	Lea	Pos	G	Rec
1929	Bro	N	P	32	3-3
1930	Bro	N	P	1	0-0
1931	Bro	N	P	23	1-2
1932	Bro	N	P	21	0-3
1933	Phi	N	P	36	8-9
1934	Phi	N	P	35	4-9
	BRTR			148	16-26

MOORE, WILLIAM CHRISTOPHER
b.Sept.3,1902 Corning,N.Y.

Yr	Cl	Lea	Pos	G	Rec
1925	Det	A	P	1	0-0
	BRTR				

MOORE, WILLIAM HENRY
b.Dec.12,1903 Kansas City,Mo.

Yr	Cl	Lea	Pos	G	Rec
1926	Bos	A	C	5	.167
1927	Bos	A	C	44	.217
	BLTR			49	.207

MOORE, WILLIAM WILCY (Cy)
b.May 20,1897 Bonita,Tex.

Yr	Cl	Lea	Pos	G	Rec
1927	NY	A	P	50	19-7
1928	NY	A	P	35	4-4
1929	NY	A	P	41	6-4
1931	Bos	A	P	53	11-13
1932	Bos	A	P	37	4-10
1932	NY	A	P	10	2-0
1933	NY	A	P	35	5-6
	BRTR			261	51-44

MOORHEAD, CHARLES ROBERT
b.Jan.23,1938 Chambersburg,Pa.

Yr	Cl	Lea	Pos	G	Rec
1962	NY	N	P	38	0-2
	BRTR				

MOOTY, JACOB T.
b.Apr.13,1913 Milsap,Tex.

Yr	Cl	Lea	Pos	G	Rec
1936	Cin	N	P	8	0-0
1937	Cin	N	P	15	0-3
1940	Chi	N	P	24	6-6
1941	Chi	N	P	33	8-9
1942	Chi	N	P	19	2-5
1943	Chi	N	P	2	0-0
1944	Det	A	P	15	0-0
	BRTR			116	16-23

MORAN, ALBERT THOMAS (Hiker)
b.June 15,1914 Rochester,N.Y.

Yr	Cl	Lea	Pos	G	Rec
1938	Bos	N	P	1	0-0
1939	Bos	N	P	6	1-1
	BRTR			7	1-1

MORAN, CHARLES BARTHEL (Uncle Charlie)
b.Feb.22,1879 Nashville,Tenn.
d.June 13,1949

Yr	Cl	Lea	Pos	G	Rec
1903	St.L	N	P-S	4	0-1 / .429
1908	St.L	N	C	16	.175
	TR			20	0-1 / .221

MORAN, CHARLES VINCENT
b.Mar.26,1879 Washington,D.C.
d.Apr.11,1934

Yr	Cl	Lea	Pos	G	Rec
1903	Was	A	S	98	.232
1904	Was	A	S	61	.209
1904	St.L	A	3	81	.241
1905	St.L	A	2	28	.195
	TR			268	.210

MORAN, HARRY EDWIN
b.Apr.2,1890 Wyndal,W.Va.
d.Nov.28,1962

Yr	Cl	Lea	Pos	G	Rec
1912	Det	A	P	4	0-2
1914	Buf	F	P	30	10-7
1915	New	F	P	33	13-9
	BLTL			67	23-18

MORAN, JOSEPH HERBERT (Herbie)
b.Feb.16,1886 Costello,Pa.
d.Sept.21,1954

Yr	Cl	Lea	Pos	G	Rec
1908	Phi	A	O	19	.153
1908	Bos	N	O	8	.266
1909	Bos	N	O	8	.233
1910	Bos	N	O	20	.119
1912	Bro	N	O	130	.276
1913	Bro	N	O	132	.266
1914	Cin	N	O	107	.235
1914	Bos	N	O	41	.266
1915	Bos	N	O	130	.200
	BLTR			595	.243

MORAN, PATRICK JOSEPH
b.Feb.7,1876 Fitchburg,Mass.
d.Mar.7,1924

Yr	Cl	Lea	Pos	G	Rec
1901	Bos	N	C	53	.216
1902	Bos	N	C-1-O	72	.250
1903	Bos	N	C	108	.262
1904	Bos	N	C-3	111	.226
1905	Bos	N	C	78	.240
1906	Chi	N	C	61	.250
1907	Chi	N	C	59	.227
1908	Chi	N	C	45	.260
1909	Chi	N	C	74	.219
1910	Phi	N	C	56	.236
1911	Phi	N	C	32	.184
1912	Phi	N	C	13	.115
1913	Phi	N	C	1	.000
1914	Phi	N	C	1	.000
	TR			764	.236

Non-playing manager Phi (N) 1915-18 and Cin (N) 1919-23.

MORAN, ROY ELLIS
b.Sept.17,1884 Vincennes,Ind.

Yr	Cl	Lea	Pos	G	Rec
1912	Was	A	O	7	.077
	BRTR				

MORAN, SAMUEL
b.Sept.16,1870 Rochester,N.Y.
d.Aug.29,1897

Yr	Cl	Lea	Pos	G	Rec
1895	Pit	N	P	10	2-5
	TL				

MORAN, WILLIAM L.
b.Oct.10,1869 Joliet,Ill.
d.Apr.8,1916

Yr	Cl	Lea	Pos	G	Rec
1892	St.L	N	C	22	.153
1895	Chi	N	C	15	.163
				37	.157

MORAN, WILLIAM NELSON
b.Nov.27,1933 Montgomery,Ala.

Yr	Cl	Lea	Pos	G	Rec
1958	Cle	A	2-S	115	.226
1959	Cle	A	2-S	11	.294
1961	LA	A	2-S	54	.260
1962	LA	A	2	160	.282
	BRTR			340	.266

MORE, FOREST T.
b.Sept.30,1883 Hayden,Ind.

Yr	Cl	Lea	Pos	G	Rec
1909	St.L	N	P	15	1-5
1909	Bos	N	P	10	1-5
				25	2-10

MOREHART, RAYMOND ANDERSON
b.Dec.2,1899 Kaufman Co., Tex.

Yr	Cl	Lea	Pos	G	Rec
1924	Chi	A	S	31	.200
1926	Chi	A	2	73	.318
1927	NY	A	2	73	.256
	BLTR			177	.269

MOREHEAD, SETH MARVIN
b.Aug.15,1934 Houston,Tex.

Yr	Cl	Lea	Pos	G	Rec
1957	**Phi**	**N**	**P**	**34**	**1-1**
1958	**Phi**	**N**	**P**	**27**	**1-6**
1959	Phi	N	P	3	0-2
1959	Chi	N	P	11	0-1
1960	Chi	N	P	45	2-9
1961	Mil	N	P	12	1-0
	BLTL			132	5-19

MOREJON, DANIEL TORRES
b.July 21,1930 Havana,Cuba

Yr	Cl	Lea	Pos	G	Rec
1958	**Cin**	**N**	**O**	**12**	**.192**
	BRTR				

MORELOCK, A. HARRY
b.Philadelphia,Pa.

Yr	Cl	Lea	Pos	G	Rec
1891	Phi	N	3	4	.071
1892	Phi	N	3	1	.000
				5	.059

MOREN, LEWIS HOWARD
b.Aug.4,1883 Pittsburgh,Pa.

Yr	Cl	Lea	Pos	G	Rec
1903	Pit	N	P	1	0-1
1904	Pit	N	P	1	0-0
1907	Phi	N	P	37	11-18
1908	Phi	N	P	28	8-9
1909	Phi	N	P	40	16-15
1910	Phi	N	P	34	13-14
	TR			141	48-57

MORENO, JULIO GONZALES
b.Jan.28,1921 Guines,Cuba

Yr	Cl	Lea	Pos	G	Rec
1950	Was	A	P	4	1-1
1951	Was	A	P	31	5-11
1952	Was	A	P	26	9-9
1953	Was	A	P	12	3-1
	BRTR			73	18-22

MORESKONICH, CHARLES
(Played under name of Charles Metro)

MOREY, DAVID BEALE
b.Feb.25,1889 Malden,Mass.

Yr	Cl	Lea	Pos	G	Rec
1913	Phi	A	P	2	0-0

MORGAN, CHESTER COLLINS (Chick)
b.June 6,1910 Skene,Miss.

Yr	Cl	Lea	Pos	G	Rec
1935	Det	A	O	14	.174
1938	Det	A	O	74	.284
	BLTR			88	.277

MORGAN, CYRIL ARLON
b.Dec.11,1896 Lakeville,Mass.
d.Sept.11,1946

Yr	Cl	Lea	Pos	G	Rec
1921	Bos	N	P	17	1-1
1922	Bos	N	P	2	0-0
	BRTR			19	1-1

MORGAN, EDWARD CARRE
b.May 22,1904 Cairo,Ill.

Yr	Cl	Lea	Pos	G	Rec
1928	Cle	A	1-3-O	76	.313
1929	Cle	A	O	93	.318
1930	Cle	A	1-O	150	.350
1931	Cle	A	1	131	.351
1932	Cle	A	1	144	.293
1933	Cle	A	1-O	39	.264
1934	Bos	A	1	138	.267
	BRTR			771	.313

MORGAN, EDWIN WILLIS (Pepper)
b.Nov.19,1914 Brady Lake,O.

Yr	Cl	Lea	Pos	G	Rec
1936	St.L	N	O	8	.278
1937	Bro	N	O	31	.188
	BLTL			39	.212

MORGAN, HARRY RICHARD (Cy)
b.Nov.10,1878 Pomeroy,O.
d.June 28,1962

Yr	Cl	Lea	Pos	G	Rec
1903	St.L	A	P	2	0-2
1904	St.L	A	P	8	0-2
1905	St.L	A	P	13	2-6
1907	St.L	A	P	13	2-5
1907	Bos	A	P	13	6-6
1908	Bos	A	P	30	13-14
1909	Bos	A	P	12	3-9
1909	Phi	A	P	27	15-8
1910	Phi	A	P	36	18-12
1911	Phi	A	P	38	15-7
1912	Phi	A	P	13	3-8
1913	Cin	N	P	1	0-1
	BRTR			206	77-80

MORGAN, HENRY WILLIAM (Bill)
b.Brooklyn,N.Y.

Yr	Cl	Lea	Pos	G	Rec
1875	RS	n	P-3-O	19	1-4 NR
1878	Mil	N	2-3-O	14	.175
1882	Pit	a	C-O	16	.279
1883	Pit	a	C-2-S-O	30	.167
1884	Was	a	C-2-S-O	44	.181
1884	Ric	a	C-2-O	6	.100
1884	Bal	U	C-2-O	2	.250
				131	1-4 NR

MORGAN, JAMES EDWARD (Red)
b.Neola,Ia.

Yr	Cl	Lea	Pos	G	Rec
1906	Bos	A	3	88	.215
	TR				

MORGAN, JOHN P.

Yr	Cl	Lea	Pos	G	Rec
1916	Phi	A	3	1	.250
	TR				

MORGAN, JOSEPH MICHAEL
b.Nov.19,1930 Walpole,Mass.

Yr	Cl	Lea	Pos	G	Rec
1959	Mil	N	2	13	.217
1959	KC	A	3	20	.190
1960	Phi	N	3	26	.133
1960	Cle	A	3-O	22	.298
1961	Cle	A	O	4	.200
	BLTR			85	.196

MORGAN, RAYMOND CARYLL
b.June 14,1891 Baltimore,Md.
d.Feb.15,1940

Yr	Cl	Lea	Pos	G	Rec
1911	Was	A	3	25	.213
1912	Was	A	2	80	.238
1913	Was	A	2	137	.272
1914	Was	A	2	147	.257
1915	Was	A	2	62	.233
1916	Was	A	2	99	.267
1917	Was	A	2	101	.266
1918	Was	A	2	88	.233
	BRTR			739	.254

MORGAN, ROBERT MORRIS
b.June 29,1926 Oklahoma City,Okla.

Yr	Cl	Lea	Pos	G	Rec
1950	Bro	N	S-3	67	.226
1952	Bro	N	2-S-3	67	.236
1953	Bro	N	S-3	69	.260
1954	Phi	N	2-S-3	135	.262
1955	Phi	N	1-2-S-3	136	.232
1956	Phi	N	2-3	8	.200
1956	St.L	N	2-S-3	61	.195
1957	Phi	N	2	2	.000
1957	Chi	N	2-3	125	.207
1958	Chi	N	H	1	.000
	BRTR			671	.233

MORGAN, TOM STEPHEN (Plowboy)
b.May 20,1930 El Monte,Cal.

Yr	Cl	Lea	Pos	G	Rec
1951	NY	A	P	27	9-3
1952	NY	A	P	16	5-4
1954	NY	A	P	32	11-5
1955	NY	A	P	40	7-3
1956	NY	A	P	41	6-7
1957	KC	A	P	46	9-7
1958	Det	A	P	39	2-5
1959	Det	A	P	46	1-4
1960	Det	A	P	22	3-2
1960	Was	A	P	14	1-3
1961	LA	A	P	59	8-2
1962	LA	A	P	48	5-2
	BRTR			430	67-47

MORGAN, VERNON THOMAS
b.Aug.8,1928 Emporia,Va.

Yr	Cl	Lea	Pos	G	Rec
1954	Chi	N	3	24	.234
1955	Chi	N	3	7	.143
	BLTR			31	.225

MORHARDT, MEREDITH GOODWIN
b.Jan.16,1937 Manchester,Conn.

Yr	Cl	Lea	Pos	G	Rec
1961	Chi	N	1	7	.278
1962	Chi	N	H	18	.125
	BLTL			25	.206

MORIARITY, EDWARD JEROME
b.Oct.12,1912 Holyoke,Mass.

Yr	Cl	Lea	Pos	G	Rec
1935	Bos	N	2	8	.324
1936	Bos	N	H	6	.167
	BRTR			14	.300

MORIARITY, EUGENE JOHN
b.Holyoke,Mass.

Yr	Cl	Lea	Pos	G	Rec
1884	Bos	N	O	4	.063
1884	Ind	a	P-3-O	10	0-2 .216
1885	Det	N	P-S-3-O	11	0-0 .026
1892	St.L	N	O	46	.175
				71	0-2 .160

MORIARTY, GEORGE JOSEPH
b.July 7,1884 Chicago,Ill.

Yr	Cl	Lea	Pos	G	Rec
1903	Chi	N	3	1	.000
1904	Chi	N	3-O	5	.000
1906	NY	A	3	65	.234
1907	NY	A	1-3	126	.277
1908	NY	A	1-3	101	.236
1909	Det	A	3	133	.273
1910	Det	A	3	136	.251
1911	Det	A	3	130	.243
1912	Det	A	1-3	105	.248
1913	Det	A	3	102	.239
1914	Det	A	3	130	.254
1915	Det	A	3	31	.211
1916	Chi	A	3	7	.200
	TR			1072	.251

Non-playing manager Det (A) 1927-28.

MORIARTY, WILLIAM JOSEPH
b.1883 Chicago,Ill.

Yr	Cl	Lea	Pos	G	Rec
1909	Cin	N	S	6	.250
	BRTR				

MORLEY, WILLIAM M.
b.1890 Port Richmond,S.I.,N.Y.

Yr	Cl	Lea	Pos	G	Rec
1913	Was	A	2	2	.000
	BRTR				

MORRELL, WILLARD BLACKMER
b.Apr.9,1893 Hyde Park,Mass.

Yr	Cl	Lea	Pos	G	Rec
1926	Was	A	P	26	3-3
1930	NY	N	P	2	0-0
1931	NY	N	P	20	5-3
	BRTR			48	8-6

MORRILL, JOHN FRANCIS
(Honest John)
b.Feb.19,1855 Boston,Mass.
d.Apr.2,1932

Yr	Cl	Lea	Pos	G	Rec
1876	Bos	N	C-2	66	.260
1877	Bos	N	1-2-3-O	61	.302
1878	Bos	N	1	60	.240
1879	Bos	N	1-3	84	.281
1880	Bos	N	P-1-3	84	0-0 .240
1881	Bos	N	P-1-2-3	80	0-1 .289
1882	Bos	N	M-P-1-2-S-3-O	82	0-0 .289
1883	Bos	N	M-P-1-2-S-3-O	97	1-0 .319
1884	Bos	N	M-P-1-2-3	106	0-0 .265
1885	Bos	N	M-1-2-3	111	.225
1886	Bos	N	M-1-2-S	117	.246
1887	Bos	N	M-1	124	.331
1888	Bos	N	M-1	134	.197
1889	Was	N	M-1	44	.185
1890	Bos	p	1-S	2	.143
	BRTR			1252	1-1 .264

MORRIS, DOYT THEODORE
b.July 15,1916 Stanley,N.C.

Yr	Cl	Lea	Pos	G	Rec
1937	Phi	A	H	6	.154
	BRTR				

MORRIS, E.
b.Trenton,N.J.

Yr	Cl	Lea	Pos	G	Rec
1884	Bal	U	P-O	1	0-0 .000

MORRIS, EDWARD (Cannonball)
b.Sept.29,1859 Brooklyn,N.Y.
d.Apr.12,1937

Yr	Cl	Lea	Pos	G	Rec
1884	Col	a	P	57	35-13
1885	Pit	a	P	64	39-24
1886	Pit	a	P	63	41-20
1887	Pit	N	P	37	14-22
1888	Pit	N	P	54	29-24
1889	Pit	N	P	21	7-14
1890	Pit	p	P	18	8-6
	BRTL			314	173-123

MORRIS, EDWARD (Big Ed)
b.Dec.7,1899 Foshee,Ala.
d.Mar.3,1932

Yr	Cl	Lea	Pos	G	Rec
1922	Chi	N	P	5	0-0
1928	Bos	A	P	47	19-15
1929	Bos	A	P	33	14-14
1930	Bos	A	P	18	4-9
1931	Bos	A	P	37	5-7
	BRTR			140	42-45

MORRIS, JOHN WALTER
b.Jan.31,1881 Rockwall,Tex.
d.Aug.2,1961

Yr	Cl	Lea	Pos	G	Rec
1908	St.L	N	S	23	.178
	TR				

MORRIS, JOSEPH (Bugs)
(Played under name of
Joseph Harley Bennett
and Joseph Bennett Morris)

MORRIS, P.
b.Rockford,Ill.

Yr	Cl	Lea	Pos	G	Rec
1884	Was	U	S	1	.000

MORRIS, WILLIAM G.
(Real name John L. Fluhrer)
(Played one game with Chicago (N) 1915 under name of Morris-other 6 games under real name)

MORRISETTE, WILLIAM LEE
b.Jan.17,1893 Baltimore,Md.

Yr	Cl	Lea	Pos	G	Rec
1915	Phi	A	P	4	2-0
1916	Phi	A	P	1	0-0
1920	Det	A	P	8	1-1
	BRTR			13	3-1

MORRISON, JOHN DEWEY
(Jughandle Johnny)
b.Oct.22,1896 Pellville,Ky.

Yr	Cl	Lea	Pos	G	Rec
1920	Pit	N	P	2	1-0
1921	Pit	N	P	21	9-7
1922	Pit	N	P	45	17-11
1923	Pit	N	P	42	25-13
1924	Pit	N	P	41	11-16
1925	Pit	N	P	44	17-14
1926	Pit	N	P	26	6-8
1927	Pit	N	P	21	3-2
1929	Bro	N	P	39	13-7
1930	Bro	N	P	16	1-2
	BRTR			297	103-80

MORRISON, JONATHAN W.
b.1859 Port Huron,Mich.

Yr	Cl	Lea	Pos	G	Rec
1884	Ind	a	O	43	.256
1887	Met	a	O	9	.231
				52	.252

MORRISON, MICHAEL
b.Feb.2,1869 Erie,Pa.
d.June 16,1955

Yr	Cl	Lea	Pos	G	Rec
1887	Cle	a	P	41	15-26
1888	Cle	a	P	4	1-3
1890	Syr	a	P-O	32	7-8 .238
1890	Bal	a	P	4	1-3
	BR			81	24-40 .234

MORRISON, PHILIP MELVIN
b.Oct.18,1894 Owensboro,Ky.
d.Jan.18,1955

Yr	Cl	Lea	Pos	G	Rec
1921	Pit	N	P	1	0-0
	BBTR				

MORRISON, STEPHEN HENRY
(Hank)
b.May 22,1866 Olneyville,R.I.
d.Sept.30,1927

Yr	Cl	Lea	Pos	G	Rec
1887	Ind	N	P	8	3-5
	BRTR				

MORRISON, THOMAS J.
b.1861

Yr	Cl	Lea	Pos	G	Rec
1895	Lou	N	S-3	5	.272
1896	Lou	N	3	8	.107
				13	.208

MORRISON, WALTER GUY
b.Aug.29,1898 Hinton,W.Va.
d.Aug.14,1934

Yr	Cl	Lea	Pos	G	Rec
1927	Bos	N	P	11	1-2
1928	Bos	N	P	1	0-0
	BRTR			12	1-2

MORRISSEY, FRANK FREDERICK
(Deacon)
b.Baltimore,Md.

Yr	Cl	Lea	Pos	G	Rec
1901	Bos	A	P	1	0-0
1902	Chi	N	P-3	7	1-3 .090
				8	1-3 .080

MORRISSEY, JOHN ALBERT (King)
b.May 2,1877 Lansing,Mich.
d.Oct.30,1936

Yr	Cl	Lea	Pos	G	Rec
1902	Cin	N	2-O	12	.289
1903	Cin	N	2-S	27	.247
	BRTR			39	.254

MORRISSEY, JOHN H.
b.Janesville,Wis.
d.Apr.29,1884

Yr	Cl	Lea	Pos	G	Rec
1881	Buf	N	3	12	.191
1882	Det	N	3	2	.286
				14	.204

MORRISSEY, JOSEPH ANSELM
(Jo-Jo)
b.Jan.16,1904 Warren,R.I.
d.May 2,1950

Yr	Cl	Lea	Pos	G	Rec
1932	Cin	N	2-S-3	89	.242
1933	Cin	N	2-S-3	148	.230
1936	Chi	A	2-S-3	17	.184
	BRTR			254	.232

MORRISSEY, THOMAS J.
b.1861 Janesville,Wis.

Yr	Cl	Lea	Pos	G	Rec
1884	Mil	U	3	12	.174

MORROW, ROBERT
b.Sept.27,1838 England
d.Feb.6,1898
Non-playing manager Pro (N) 1881.

MORSE, JACOB CHARLES
b.June 7,1860 Concord,N.H.
d.Apr.12,1937
Non-playing manager Bos (U) 1884.

MORSE, NEWELL OBEDIAH (Bud)
b.Sept.4,1904 Berkeley,Cal.

Yr	Cl	Lea	Pos	G	Rec
1929	Phi	A	2	8	.074
	BLTR				

MORSE, PETER R. (Hap)
b.St.Paul,Minn.

Yr	Cl	Lea	Pos	G	Rec
1911	St.L	N	S-O	4	.000
	TR				

MORTON, CHARLES HAZEN
b.Oct.12,1854 Kingsville,O.
d.Dec.13,1921

Yr	Cl	Lea	Pos	G	Rec
1882	Pit	a	2-S-3-O	23	.278
1882	St.L	a	2-O	9	.059
1884	Tol	a	M-P-O	31	0-1 .188
1885	Det	N	M-S-3	22	.177
	TR			85	0-1 .199

Non-playing manager Tol (a) 1890.

MORTON, GUY JR. (Moose)
b.Nov.4,1930 Tuscaloosa,Ala.

Yr	Cl	Lea	Pos	G	Rec
1954	Bos	A	H	1	.000
	BRTR				

MORTON, GUY SR.
b.June 1,1893 Vernon,Ala.
d.Oct.18,1934

Yr	Cl	Lea	Pos	G	Rec
1914	Cle	A	P	20	1-13
1915	Cle	A	P	34	15-15
1916	Cle	A	P	27	12-8
1917	Cle	A	P	35	10-10
1918	Cle	A	P	30	14-8
1919	Cle	A	P	26	9-9
1920	Cle	A	P	29	8-6
1921	Cle	A	P	30	8-3
1922	Cle	A	P	38	14-9
1923	Cle	A	P	33	6-6
1924	Cle	A	P	9	0-1
	BRTR			311	97-88

MORTON, WILLIAM H. (Sparrow)

Yr	Cl	Lea	Pos	G	Rec
1884	Phi	N	P	2	0-2
	TL				

MORTON, WYCLIFFE NATHAN
b.Dec.13,1931 Washington,D.C.

Yr	Cl	Lea	Pos	G	Rec
1961	Det	A	O	77	.287
1962	Det	A	1-O	90	.262
	BRTR			167	.271

MORYN, WALTER JOSEPH
b.Apr.12,1926 St.Paul,Minn.

Yr	Cl	Lea	Pos	G	Rec
1954	Bro	N	O	48	.275
1955	Bro	N	O	11	.263
1956	Chi	N	O	147	.285
1957	Chi	N	O	149	.289
1958	Chi	N	O	143	.264

(Continued)

Yr	Cl	Lea	Pos	G	Rec
1959	Chi	N	O	117	.234
1960	Chi	N	O	38	.294
1960	St.L	N	O	75	.245
1961	St.L	N	O	17	.125
1961	Pit	N	O	40	.200
	BLTR			785	.266

MOSELEY, EARL VICTOR (Vic)
b.Sept.7,1884 Middlebury,O.

Yr	Cl	Lea	Pos	G	Rec
1913	Bos	A	P	17	9-5
1914	Ind	F	P	43	19-18
1915	New	F	P	36	15-15
1916	Cin	N	P	31	7-10
	BRTR			127	50-48

MOSER, ARNOLD ROBERT
b.Aug.9,1915 Houston,Tex.

Yr	Cl	Lea	Pos	G	Rec
1937	Cin	N	H	5	.000
	BRTR				

MOSER, WALTER F.
b.Feb.27,1886 Concord,N.C.

Yr	Cl	Lea	Pos	G	Rec
1906	Phi	N	P	6	0-3
1911	Bos	A	P	6	0-1
1911	St.L	A	P	2	0-1
	BRTR			14	0-5

MOSES, FELIX I.
b.Richmond,Va.
Non-playing manager Ric (a) 1884.

MOSES, WALLACE
b.Oct.8,1910 Uvalda,Ga.

Yr	Cl	Lea	Pos	G	Rec
1935	Phi	A	O	85	.325
1936	Phi	A	O	146	.345
1937	Phi	A	O	154	.320
1938	Phi	A	O	142	.307
1939	Phi	A	O	115	.307
1940	Phi	A	O	142	.309
1941	Phi	A	O	116	.301
1942	Chi	A	O	146	.270
1943	Chi	A	O	150	.245
1944	Chi	A	O	136	.280
1945	Chi	A	O	140	.295
1946	Chi	A	O	56	.274
1946	Bos	A	O	48	.206
1947	Bos	A	O	90	.275
1948	Bos	A	O	78	.259
1949	Phi	A	O	110	.276
1950	Phi	A	O	88	.264
1951	Phi	A	O	70	.191
	BLTL			2012	.291

MOSKIMAN, WILLIAM BANKHEAD
(Doc)
b.Dec.20,1879 Oakland,Cal.
d.Jan.11,1953

Yr	Cl	Lea	Pos	G	Rec
1910	Bos	A	P-1-O	5	0-0 .111
	BRTR				

MOSOLF, JAMES FREDERICK
b.Aug.21,1907 Puyallup,Wash.

Yr	Cl	Lea	Pos	G	Rec
1929	Pit	N	O	8	.462
1930	Pit	N	P-O	40	0-0 .333
1931	Pit	N	O	39	.250
1933	Chi	N	O	31	.268
	BLTR			118	0-0 .295

MOSS, CHARLES CROSBY
b.Mar.20,1911 Meridian,Miss.

Yr	Cl	Lea	Pos	G	Rec
1934	Phi	A	C	10	.200
1935	Phi	A	C	4	.333
1936	Phi	A	C	33	.250
	BRTR			47	.246

MOSS, CHARLES MALCOLM (Mal)
b.Apr.18,1905 Sullivan,Ind.

Yr	Cl	Lea	Pos	G	Rec
1930	Chi	N	P	12	0-0
	BRTL				

MOSS, HOWARD GLENN
b.Oct.17,1918 Gastonia,N.C.

Yr	Cl	Lea	Pos	G	Rec
1942	NY	N	O	7	.000
1946	Cin	N	O	7	.192
1946	Cle	A	3	8	.063
	BRTR			22	.097

MOSS, JOHN LESTER (Les)
b.May 14,1925 Tulsa,Okla.

Yr	Cl	Lea	Pos	G	Rec
1946	St.L	A	C	12	.371
1947	St.L	A	C	96	.157
1948	St.L.	A	C	107	.257
1949	St.L	A	C	97	.291
1950	St.L	A	C	84	.266
1951	St.L	A	C	16	.170
1951	Bos	A	C	71	.198
1952	St.L	A	C	52	.246
1953	St.L	A	C	78	.276
1954	Bal	A	C	50	.246
1955	**Bal**	**A**	**C**	**29**	**.339**
1955	**Chi**	**A**	**C**	**32**	**.254**
1956	**Chi**	**A**	**C**	**56**	**.244**
1957	**Chi**	**A**	**C**	**42**	**.270**
1958	**Chi**	**A**	**H**	**2**	**.000**
	BRTR			**824**	**.247**

MOSS, RAYMOND EARL
b.Dec.5,1902 Chattanooga,Tenn.

Yr	Cl	Lea	Pos	G	Rec
1926	Bro	N	P	1	0-0
1927	Bro	N	P	1	1-0
1928	Bro	N	P	24	0-3
1929	Bro	N	P	42	11-6
1930	Bro	N	P	36	9-6
1931	Bro	N	P	1	0-0
1931	Bos	N	P	12	1-3
	BRTR			117	22-18

MOSSI, DONALD LOUIS
b.Jan.11,1930 St.Helena,Cal.

Yr	Cl	Lea	Pos	G	Rec
1954	Cle	A	P	40	6-1
1955	**Cle**	**A**	**P**	**57**	**4-3**
1956	**Cle**	**A**	**P**	**48**	**6-5**
1957	**Cle**	**A**	**P**	**36**	**11-10**
1958	**Cle**	**A**	**P**	**43**	**7-8**
1959	Det	A	P	36	17-9
1960	Det	A	P	23	9-8
1961	Det	A	P	35	15-7
1962	Det	A	P	36	11-13
	BLTL			354	86-64

MOSSOR, EARL DALTON
b.July 21,1925 Forbes,Tenn.

Yr	Cl	Lea	Pos	G	Rec
1951	Bro	N	P	3	0-0
	BLTR				

MOSTIL, JOHN ANTHONY
b.June 1,1896 Chicago,Ill.

Yr	Cl	Lea	Pos	G	Rec
1918	Chi	A	2	10	.273
1921	Chi	A	O	100	.301
1922	Chi	A	O	132	.304
1923	Chi	A	O	153	.291
1924	Chi	A	O	118	.325
1925	Chi	A	O	153	.299
1926	Chi	A	O	148	.328
1927	Chi	A	O	13	.125
1928	Chi	A	O	133	.270
1929	Chi	A	O	12	.229
	BRTR			972	.301

MOTA, MANUEL RAFAEL
b.Feb.18,1938 Ciudad Trujillo,D.R.

Yr	Cl	Lea	Pos	G	Rec
1962	SF	N	2-3-O	47	.176
	BRTR				

MOTT, ELISHA MATTHEW (Bitsy)
b.June 12,1920 Arcadia,Fla.

Yr	Cl	Lea	Pos	G	Rec
1945	Phi	N	2-S-3	90	.222
	BRTR				

MOTZ, FRANK H.
b.Oct.1,1869 Freeburg,Pa.

Yr	Cl	Lea	Pos	G	Rec
1890	Phi	N	1	1	.000
1893	Cin	N	1	42	.267
1894	Cin	N	1	18	.204
				61	.244

MOULDER, GLEN HUBERT
b.Sept.28,1917 Cleveland,Okla.

Yr	Cl	Lea	Pos	G	Rec
1946	Bro	N	P	1	0-0
1947	St.L	A	P	32	4-2
1948	Chi	A	P	33	3-6
	BRTR			66	7-8

MOULTON, ALBERT THEODORE (Ollie)
b.Jan.16,1886 Medway,Mass.

Yr	Cl	Lea	Pos	G	Rec
1911	St.L	A	2	4	.067
	BRTR				

MOUNTAIN, FRANK H.
b.May 17,1860 Ft.Edward,N.Y.
d.Nov.19,1939

Yr	Cl	Lea	Pos	G	Rec
1880	Tro	N	P	2	1-1
1881	Det	N	P	7	3-4
1882	Wor	N	P	5	0-5
1882	Ath	a	P-O	9	2-6
					.308
1882	Wor	N	P-1-O	20	2-11
					.264
1883	Col	a	P-O	71	26-33
					.216
1884	Col	a	P-O	58	24-17
					.237
1885	Pit	a	P	5	1-4
1886	Pit	a	P-1	18	0-2
					.148
	TR			195	59-83
					.221

MOUNTJOY, WILLIAM R. (Medicine Bill)
b.Port Huron,Mich.
d.June 28,1894

Yr	Cl	Lea	Pos	G	Rec
1883	Cin	a	P	1	0-1
1884	Cin	a	P-O	34	20-12
					.171
1885	Cin	a	P	17	10-7
1885	Bal	a	P-O	7	2-4
					.063
				59	32-24
					.157

MOWE, RAYMOND BENJAMIN
b.July 12,1894 Rochester,Ind.

Yr	Cl	Lea	Pos	G	Rec
1913	Bro	N	S	5	.111
	BLTR				

MOWREY, HARRY HARLAN (Mike)
b.Mar.24,1883 Chambersburg,Pa.
d.Mar.20,1947

Yr	Cl	Lea	Pos	G	Rec
1905	Cin	N	3	7	.266
1906	Cin	N	3	17	.321
1907	Cin	N	3	138	.252
1908	Cin	N	3	63	.220
1909	Cin	N	3	35	.191
1909	St.L	N	3	8	.241
1910	St.L	N	3	141	.282
1911	St.L	N	3	135	.267
1912	St.L	N	3	114	.255
1913	St.L	N	3	132	.260
1914	Pit	N	3	79	.254
1915	Pit	F	3	151	.282
1916	Bro	N	3	144	.244
1917	Bro	N	3	83	.214
	BRTR			1247	.251

MOWRY, JOSEPH ALOYSIUS
b.Apr.6,1908 St.Louis,Mo.

Yr	Cl	Lea	Pos	G	Rec
1933	Bos	N	O	86	.221
1934	Bos	N	O	25	.215
1935	Bos	N	O	81	.265
	BBTR			192	.233

MOYER, CHARLES EDWARD
b.Aug.15,1885 Andover,O.

Yr	Cl	Lea	Pos	G	Rec
1910	Was	A	P	6	0-3

MOYNAHAN, MICHAEL
b.1860 Chicago,Ill.

Yr	Cl	Lea	Pos	G	Rec
1880	Buf	N	S	27	.296
1881	Cle	N	3-O	33	.225
1881	Det	N	3	2	.333
1883	Ath	a	S	93	.283
1884	Ath	a	S	1	.000
1884	Cle	N	2-S-O	12	.304
	BL			168	.285

MROZINSKI, RONALD FRANK
b.Sept.16,1930 White Haven,Pa.

Yr	Cl	Lea	Pos	G	Rec
1954	**Phi**	**N**	**P**	**15**	**1-1**
1955	**Phi**	**N**	**P**	**22**	**0-2**
	BRTL			**37**	**1-3**

MUELLER, CLARENCE FRANKLIN (Heinie)
b.Sept.16,1899 Creve Coeur,Mo.

Yr	Cl	Lea	Pos	G	Rec
1920	St.L	N	O	4	.318
1921	St.L	N	O	55	.352
1922	St.L	N	O	61	.270
1923	St.L	N	O	78	.343
1924	St.L	N	1-O	92	.264
1925	St.L	N	O	78	.313
1926	St.L	N	O	52	.267
1926	NY	N	O	85	.249
1927	NY	N	O	84	.289
1928	Bos	N	O	42	.225
1929	Bos	N	O	46	.204
1935	St.L	A	1-O	16	.185
	BLTL			693	.282

MUELLER, DONALD FREDERICK
b.Apr.14,1927 Creve Coeur,Mo.

Yr	Cl	Lea	Pos	G	Rec
1948	NY	N	O	36	.358
1949	NY	N	O	51	.232
1950	NY	N	O	132	.291
1951	NY	N	O	122	.277
1952	NY	N	O	126	.281
1953	NY	N	O	131	.333
1954	NY	N	O	153	.342
1955	**NY**	**N**	**O**	**147**	**.306**
1956	**NY**	**N**	**O**	**138**	**.269**
1957	**NY**	**N**	**O**	**135**	**.258**
1958	**Chi**	**A**	**O**	**70**	**.253**
1959	Chi	A	H	4	.500
	BLTR			1245	.296

MUELLER, EMMETT JOSEPH
b.July 20,1912 St.Louis,Mo.

Yr	Cl	Lea	Pos	G	Rec
1938	Phi	N	2-3	136	.250
1939	Phi	N	2-3-O	115	.279
1940	Phi	N	1-2-3-O	97	.247
1941	Phi	N	2-3-O	93	.227
	BBTR			441	.253

MUELLER, JOSEPH GORDON
b.Dec.10,1922 Baltimore,Md.

Yr	Cl	Lea	Pos	G	Rec
1950	Bos	A	P	8	0-0
	BRTR				

MUELLER, LESLIE CLYDE
b.Mar.4,1919 Belleville,Ill.

Yr	Cl	Lea	Pos	G	Rec
1941	Det	A	P	4	0-0
1945	Det	A	P	26	6-8
	BRTR			30	6-8

MUELLER, RAY COLEMAN (Iron Man)
b.Mar.8,1912 Pittsburg,Kan.

Yr	Cl	Lea	Pos	G	Rec
1935	Bos	N	C	42	.227
1936	Bos	N	C	24	.197
1937	Bos	N	C	64	.251
1938	Bos	N	C	83	.237
1939	Pit	N	C	86	.233
1940	Pit	N	C	4	.333
1943	Cin	N	C	141	.260
1944	Cin	N	C	155	.286
1946	Cin	N	C	114	.254
1947	Cin	N	C	71	.250
1948	Cin	N	C	14	.206
1949	Cin	N	C	32	.274
1949	NY	N	C	56	.224
1950	NY	N	C	4	.091
1950	Pit	N	C	67	.269
1951	Bos	N	C	28	.157
	BRTR			985	.252

MUELLER, WALTER JOHN
b.Dec.6,1894 Central,Mo.

Yr	Cl	Lea	Pos	G	Rec
1922	Pit	N	O	32	.270
1923	Pit	N	O	40	.306

(Continued)

Yr	Cl	Lea	Pos	G	Rec
1924	Pit	N	O	30	.260
1926	Pit	N	O	19	.242
			BRTR	121	.275

MUELLER, WILLIAM LAWRENCE
b.Nov.9,1920 Bay City,Mich.

Yr	Cl	Lea	Pos	G	Rec
1942	Chi	A	O	26	.165
1945	Chi	A	O	13	.000
			BRTR	39	.149

MUFFETT, BILLY ARNOLD
b.Sept.21,1930 Hammond,Ind.

Yr	Cl	Lea	Pos	G	Rec
1957	St.L	N	P	23	3-2
1958	St.L	N	P	35	4-6
1959	SF	N	P	5	0-0
1960	Bos	A	P	23	6-4
1961	Bos	A	P	38	3-11
1962	Bos	A	P	1	0-0
			BRTR	125	16-23

MUICH, IGNATIUS ANDREW (Joe)
b.Nov.27,1904 St. Louis,Mo.

Yr	Cl	Lea	Pos	G	Rec
1924	Bos	N	P	3	0-0
			BRTR		

MUIR, JOSEPH ALLEN
b.Nov.26,1922 Oriole,Md.

Yr	Cl	Lea	Pos	G	Rec
1951	Pit	N	P	9	0-2
1952	Pit	N	P	12	2-3
			BLTL	21	2-5

MULCAHY, HUGH NOYES
b.Sept.9,1913 Brighton,Mass.

Yr	Cl	Lea	Pos	G	Rec
1935	Phi	N	P-O	19	1-5 .000
1936	Phi	N	P	3	1-1
1937	Phi	N	P	56	8-18
1938	Phi	N	P	47	10-20
1939	Phi	N	P	38	9-16
1940	Phi	N	P	37	13-22
1945	Phi	N	P	5	1-3
1946	Phi	N	P	16	2-4
1947	Pit	N	P	2	0-0
			BRTR	223	45-89 .165

MULDOON, MICHAEL
b.Hartford,Conn.

Yr	Cl	Lea	Pos	G	Rec
1882	Cle	N	3-O	82	.252
1883	Cle	N	3	95	.224
1884	Cle	N	2-3-O	109	.239
1885	Bal	a	3	103	.250
1886	Bal	a	2-3	101	.205
				490	.235

MULLANE, ANTHONY JOHN (Count)
b.Feb.20,1859 Cork,Ireland.
d.Apr.26,1944

Yr	Cl	Lea	Pos	G	Rec
1881	Det	N	P	5	1-4
1882	Lou	a	P-1-2-O	77	31-23 .255
1883	St.L	a	P-1-2-O	77	35-17 .201
1884	Tol	a	P-1-O	95	36-26 .276
1886	Cin	a	P-1-2-S-O	103	31-27 .228
1887	Cin	a	P-O	61	31-17 .284
1888	Cin	a	P-1-2-O	51	27-16 .251
1889	Cin	a	P-1-3-O	62	11-8 .307
1890	Cin	N	P-3-O	81	12-10 .276
1891	Cin	N	P	61	24-23
1892	Cin	N	P	34	20-14
1893	Cin	N	P	27	7-7
1893	Bal	N	P	27	12-15
1894	Bal	N	P	14	7-6
1894	Cle	N	P	8	2-1
			BRTR	783	287-214 .250

MULLEAVY, GREGORY THOMAS (Moe)
b.Sept.25,1905 Detroit,Mich.

Yr	Cl	Lea	Pos	G	Rec
1930	Chi	A	S	77	.263
1932	Chi	A	2	1	.000
1933	Bos	A	H	1	.000
			BRTR	79	.260

MULLEN, ...

Yr	Cl	Lea	Pos	G	Rec
1872	Cle	n	O	1	NR

MULLEN, CHARLES GEORGE
b.Mar.15,1890 Seattle,Wash.

Yr	Cl	Lea	Pos	G	Rec
1910	Chi	A	1	41	.195
1911	Chi	A	1	20	.203
1914	NY	A	1	93	.260
1915	NY	A	1	40	.267
1916	NY	A	1-2	59	.267
			BRTR	253	.247

MULLEN, FORD PARKER (Moon)
b.Feb.9,1917 Olympia,Wash.

Yr	Cl	Lea	Pos	G	Rec
1944	Phi	N	2-3	118	.267
			BLTR		

MULLEN, WILLIAM JOHN
b.Jan.23,1896 St.Louis,Mo.

Yr	Cl	Lea	Pos	G	Rec
1920	St.L	A	2	2	.000
1921	St.L	A	3	4	.000
1923	Bro	N	3	4	.273
1926	Det	A	3	11	.077
1928	St.L	A	3	15	.389
			BRTR	36	.220

MULLER, ...

Yr	Cl	Lea	Pos	G	Rec
1874	Ath	n	C	4	NR
1876	Ath	N	C	1	.000
			BLTL	5	NR

MULLER, FREDERICK WILLIAM
b.Dec.21,1909 Newark,Cal.

Yr	Cl	Lea	Pos	G	Rec
1933	Bos	A	2	15	.188
1934	Bos	A	2-3	2	.000
			BRTR	17	.184

MULLIGAN, ...

Yr	Cl	Lea	Pos	G	Rec
1884	Was	U	3	1	.000

MULLIGAN, EDWARD JOSEPH
b.Aug.27,1894 St.Louis,Mo.

Yr	Cl	Lea	Pos	G	Rec
1915	Chi	N	S-3	11	.363
1916	Chi	N	S	58	.153
1921	Chi	A	3	152	.251
1922	Chi	A	3	103	.234
1928	Pit	N	2-3	27	.233
			BRTR	351	.232

MULLIGAN, JOSEPH IGNATIUS
b.July 31,1913 E.Weymouth,Mass.

Yr	Cl	Lea	Pos	G	Rec
1934	Bos	A	P	14	1-0
			BRTR		

MULLIGAN, RICHARD CHARLES
b.Mar.18,1918 Wilkes-Barre,Pa.

Yr	Cl	Lea	Pos	G	Rec
1941	Was	A	P	1	0-1
1946	Phi	N	P	19	2-2
1946	Bos	N	P	4	1-0
1947	Bos	N	P	1	0-0
			BLTL	25	3-3

MULLIN, GEORGE JOSEPH (Wabash)
b.July 4,1880 Toledo,O.
d.Jan.7,1944

Yr	Cl	Lea	Pos	G	Rec
1902	Det	A	P-O	37	14-15 .328
1903	Det	A	P	46	19-14
1904	Det	A	P	52	16-24
1905	Det	A	P	47	22-18
1906	Det	A	P	50	21-18
1907	Det	A	P	70	20-20
1908	Det	A	P	55	17-12
1909	Det	A	P	52	29-8

(Continued)

Yr	Cl	Lea	Pos	G	Rec
1910	Det	A	P	50	21-12
1911	Det	A	P	40	18-10
1912	Det	A	P	37	12-17
1913	Det	A	P	12	2-7
1913	Was	A	P	12	2-4
1914	Ind	F	P	40	14-10
1915	New	F	P	6	2-2
			BRTR	606	229-191 .262

MULLIN, HENRY
b.S.Boston,Mass.

Yr	Cl	Lea	Pos	G	Rec
1884	Was	a	O	34	.139
1884	Bos	U	O	2	.000
				36	.131

MULLIN, JAMES HENRY
b.Oct.16,1883 New York,N.Y.
d.Jan.24,1925

Yr	Cl	Lea	Pos	G	Rec
1904	Phi	A	1	26	.415
1904	Was	A	2	26	.168
1904	Phi	A	2	17	.157
1905	Was	A	2	49	.190
			TR	118	.197

MULLIN, PATRICK JOSEPH
b.Nov.1,1917 Trotter,Pa.

Yr	Cl	Lea	Pos	G	Rec
1940	Det	A	O	4	.000
1941	Det	A	O	54	.345
1946	Det	A	O	93	.246
1947	Det	A	O	116	.256
1948	Det	A	O	138	.288
1949	Det	A	O	104	.268
1950	Det	A	O	69	.218
1951	Det	A	O	110	.281
1952	Det	A	O	97	.251
1953	Det	A	O	79	.268
			BLTR	864	.271

MULRENNAN, DOMINICK JOSEPH
b.Dec.18,1894 Woburn,Mass.

Yr	Cl	Lea	Pos	G	Rec
1921	Chi	A	P	12	2-8
			TR		

MULRONEY, FRANCIS JOSEPH
b.Apr.8,1906 Mallard,Ia.

Yr	Cl	Lea	Pos	G	Rec
1930	Bos	A	P	2	0-1
			BRTR		

MULVEY, JOSEPH H.
b.Oct.27,1858 Providence,R.I.
d.Aug.21,1928

Yr	Cl	Lea	Pos	G	Rec
1883	Pro	N	2-S	4	.053
1883	Phi	N	3	3	.500
1884	Phi	N	3	99	.229
1885	Phi	N	3	106	.268
1886	Phi	N	3	105	.267
1887	Phi	N	3	109	.317
1888	Phi	N	3	99	.215
1889	Phi	N	3	129	.288
1890	Phi	p	3	120	.291
1891	Ath	a	3	112	.247
1892	Phi	N	3	25	.142
1893	Was	N	3	55	.242
1895	Bro	N	3	13	.327
			BRTR	979	.266

MUNCE, JOHN (Big John)
b.Philadelphia,Pa.

Yr	Cl	Lea	Pos	G	Rec
1884	Wil	U	O	7	.190

MUNCH, JACOB FERDINAND
b.Nov.18,1890 Morton,Pa.

Yr	Cl	Lea	Pos	G	Rec
1918	Phi	A	1	22	.267
			BLTL		

MUNCRIEF, ROBERT CLEVELAND
b.Jan.28,1916 Madill,Okla.

Yr	Cl	Lea	Pos	G	Rec
1937	St.L	A	P	1	0-0
1939	St.L	A	P	2	0-0
1941	St.L	A	P	36	13-9
1942	St.L	A	P	24	6-8
1943	St.L	A	P	35	13-12
1944	St.L	A	P	33	13-8

Yr Cl Lea Pos G Rec

(Continued)
1945 St.L A P 28 13-4
1946 St.L A P 29 3-12
1947 St.L A P 31 8-14
1948 Cle A P 21 5-4
1949 Pit N P 13 1-5
1949 Chi N P 34 5-6
1951 NY A P 2 0-0
BRTR 289 80-82

MUNDINGER, GEORGE
b.New Orleans,La.
1884 Ind a C 3 .200

MUNDY, WILLIAM EDWARD
b.June 28,1889 Salineville,O.
d.Sept.23,1958
1913 Bos A 1 17 .255
BLTL

MUNGER, GEORGE DAVID (Red)
b.Oct.4,1918 Houston,Tex.
1943 St.L N P 32 9-5
1944 St.L N P 21 11-3
1946 St.L N P 10 2-2
1947 St.L N P 40 16-5
1948 St.L N P 39 10-11
1949 St.L N P 35 15-8
1950 St.L N P 32 7-8
1951 St.L N P 23 4-6
1952 St.L N P 1 0-1
1952 Pit N P 5 0-3
1956 Pit N P 35 3-4
BRTR 273 77-56

MUNGO, VAN LINGLE
b.June 9,1911 Pageland,S.C.
1931 Bro N P 5 3-1
1932 Bro N P 39 13-11
1933 Bro N P 41 16-15
1934 Bro N P 46 18-16
1935 Bro N P 44 16-10
1936 Bro N P 50 18-19
1937 Bro N P 28 9-11
1938 Bro N P 32 4-11
1939 Bro N P 29 4-5
1940 Bro N P 8 1-0
1941 Bro N P 2 0-0
1942 NY N P 9 1-2
1943 NY N P 49 3-7
1945 NY N P 28 14-7
BRTR 410 120-115

MUNN, ...
1875 Atl n 2 1 NR

MUNNS, LESLIE ERNEST (Nemo)
b.Dec.1,1909 Grand Forks,N.Dak.
1934 Bro N P 34 3-7
1935 Bro N P 22 1-3
1936 St.L N P 8 0-3
BRTR 64 4-13

MUNSON, CLARENCE HANFORD (Red)
b.July 31,1883 Cincinnati,O.
1905 Phi N C 9 .222
TR

MUNSON, JOSEPH MARTIN NAPOLEON
(Real name Joseph Martin Napoleon Carlson)
b.Nov.6,1899 Renovo,Pa.
1925 Chi N O 9 .371
1926 Chi N O 33 .257
BLTR 42 .287

MUNYAN, JOHN B.
b.Nov.14,1860 Chester,Pa.
d.Feb.18,1945
1887 Cle a O 16 .276
1890 Col a O 2 .167
1890 St.L a C 94 .270
1891 St.L a C 59 .234
171 .261

MURCH, SIMEON T. (Simmy)
b.Nov.21,1880 Castine,Me.
d.June 6,1939
1904 St.L N 2-3 13 .137
1905 St.L N 2-S 4 .111
1908 Bro N 1 6 .181
TR 23 .143

MURCHISON, THOMAS MALCOM (Tim)
b.Oct.8,1896 Liberty,N.C.
d.Oct.20,1962
1917 St.L N P 1 0-0
1920 Cle A P 2 0-0
BRTL 3 0-0

MURDOCK, WILBUR E.
1908 St.L N O 16 .258

MURFF, JOHN ROBERT
b.Apr.1,1922 Burlington,Tex.
1956 Mil N P 14 0-0
1957 Mil N P 12 2-2
BRTR 26 2-2

MURNANE, TIMOTHY HAYES
b.June 4,1852 Bridgeport,Conn.
d.Feb.13,1917
1872 Man n 1 19 NR
1873 Ath n 1-2-O 42 NR
1874 Ath n 1-2-O 19 NR
1875 Phi n 1-2-O 68 .285
1876 Bos N 1 69 .275
1877 Bos N 1-O 35 .279
1878 Pro N 1-O 48 .245
1884 Bos U M-1-O 76 .235
BLTR 376 NR

MURPHY, ...
1884 Met a C 1 .333

MURPHY, CLARENCE
1886 Lou a O 1 .000

MURPHY, CORNELIUS B. (Monk)
b.Oct.15,1863 Worcester,Mass.
d.Aug.1,1914
1884 Alt U P 14 4-6
1884 Phi N P 3 0-3
1890 Bro p P 20 5-10
1890 Bro a P 15 3-9
1890 Bro p P 2 0-0
54 12-28

MURPHY, CORNELIUS DAVID (Stone Face)
b.Nov.1,1870 Northfield,Mass.
d.Dec.14,1945
1893 Cin N C 3 .000
1894 Cin N C 1 .000
BLTR 4 .000

MURPHY, DANIEL FRANCIS
b.Aug.11,1876 Philadelphia,Pa.
d.Nov.22,1955
1900 NY N 2 21 .250
1901 NY N 2 5 .200
1902 Phi A 2 76 .313
1903 Phi A 2 133 .275
1904 Phi A 2 149 .286
1905 Phi A 2 150 .278
1906 Phi A 2 119 .301
1907 Phi A 2 124 .271
1908 Phi A 2-O 142 .265
1909 Phi A O 149 .281
1910 Phi A O 151 .300
1911 Phi A O 141 .329
1912 Phi A O 36 .323
1913 Phi A O 40 .322
1914 Bro F O 50 .311
1915 Bro F O 5 .166
BRTR 1491 .290

MURPHY, DANIEL FRANCIS
b.Aug.23,1942 Beverly,Mass.
1960 Chi N O 31 .120
1961 Chi N O 4 .385
1962 Chi N O 14 .200
BLTR 49 .171

MURPHY, DANIEL J.
b.1864 Brooklyn,N.Y.
1892 NY N C 8 .115

MURPHY, DAVID F. (Dirty Dave)
b.N.Adams,Mass.
1905 Bos N S-3 3 .167
TR

MURPHY, EDWARD J.
b.Jan.22,1877 Auburn,N.Y.
d.Jan.29,1935
1898 Phi N P 7 1-3
1901 St.L N P 20 10-9
1902 St.L N P 19 10-6
1903 St.L N P 24 4-8
TR 70 25-26

MURPHY, EDWARD JOSEPH
b.Aug.23,1919 Joliet,Ill.
1942 Phi N 1 13 .250
BRTR

MURPHY, FRANK MORTON
b.1880 Hackensack,N.J.
d.Nov.2,1912
1901 Bos N O 45 .271
1901 NY N O 34 .143
79 .218

MURPHY, HERBERT C. (Dummy)
b.1890 Indianapolis,Ind.
1914 Phi N S 9 .160
BRTR

MURPHY, HOWARD
b.1882 Milton,Okla.
d.Sept.5,1926
1909 St.L N O 19 .200

MURPHY, JOHN H.
b.Mar.8,1867 Philadelphia,Pa.
1884 Atl U 2-O 13 .158
1884 Wil U P-2-S-3-O 10 {0-6 / .065}
23 {0-6 / .133}

MURPHY, JOHN JOSEPH (Grandma)
b.July 14,1908 New York,N.Y.
1932 NY A P 2 0-0
1934 NY A P 40 14-10
1935 NY A P 40 10-5
1936 NY A P 27 9-3
1937 NY A P 39 13-4
1938 NY A P 32 8-2
1939 NY A P 38 3-6
1940 NY A P 35 8-4
1941 NY A P 35 8-3
1942 NY A P 31 4-10
1943 NY A P 37 12-4
1946 NY A P 27 4-2
1947 Bos A P 32 0-0
BRTR 415 93-53

MURPHY, JOHN P. (Soldier Boy)
b.1879 New Haven,Conn.
d.June 1,1914
1902 St.L N 3 1 .600
1903 Det A S 5 .182
6 .240

MURPHY, JOSEPH A.
b.Sept.7,1866 St.Louis,Mo.
d.Mar.28,1951
1886 Cin a P 5 2-3
1886 St.L N P 4 0-4
1886 St.L a P 1 1-0
1887 St.L a P 1 1-0
11 4-7

MURPHY, JOSEPH EDWARD (Eddie)
b.Oct.2,1891 Hancock,N.Y.

Yr	Cl	Lea	Pos	G	Rec
1912	Phi	A	O	33	.317
1913	Phi	A	O	136	.295
1914	Phi	A	O	148	.272
1915	Phi	A	O	60	.231
1915	Chi	A	O	78	.315
1916	Chi	A	O	51	.210
1917	Chi	A	O	53	.314
1918	Chi	A	O	91	.297
1919	Chi	A	O	30	.486
1920	Chi	A	O	58	.339
1921	Chi	A	O	6	.200
1926	Pit	N	O	16	.118
BLTR				760	.287

MURPHY, LAWRENCE PATRICK

Yr	Cl	Lea	Pos	G	Rec
1891	Was	a	O	107	.255
BL					

MURPHY, LEO JOSEPH
b.Jan.7,1889 Terre Haute,Ind.
d.Aug.12,1960

Yr	Cl	Lea	Pos	G	Rec
1915	Pit	N	C	31	.098
BRTR					

MURPHY, MICHAEL JEROME
b.Aug.19,1888 Forestville,Pa.
d.Oct.27,1952

Yr	Cl	Lea	Pos	G	Rec
1912	St.L	N	C	1	.000
1916	Phi	A	C	14	.107
BRTR				15	.103

MURPHY, MORGAN EDWARD
b.Feb.14,1867 E.Providence,R.I.
d.Oct.3,1938

Yr	Cl	Lea	Pos	G	Rec
1890	Bos	p	C	60	.258
1891	Bos	a	C	107	.218
1892	Cin	N	C	69	.192
1893	Cin	N	C	56	.234
1894	Cin	N	C	76	.268
1895	Cin	N	C	22	.272
1896	St.L	N	C	48	.251
1897	St.L	N	C	55	.177
1898	Pit	N	C	5	.125
1898	Phi	N	C	25	.202
1900	Phi	N	C	11	.277
1901	Phi	A	C-1	9	.179
BRTR				543	.221

MURPHY, PATRICK J.
b.Jan.2,1857 Auburn,Mass.
d.May 19,1927

Yr	Cl	Lea	Pos	G	Rec
1887	NY	N	C	16	.245
1888	NY	N	C	28	.169
1889	NY	N	C	8	.280
1890	NY	N	C	32	.235
				84	.223

MURPHY, RICHARD LEE
b.Oct.25,1931 Cincinnati,O.

Yr	Cl	Lea	Pos	G	Rec
1954	Cin	N	H	6	.000
BLTL					

MURPHY, ROBERT J.
b.Dec.26,1866 Dutchess Co.,N.Y.

Yr	Cl	Lea	Pos	G	Rec
1890	NY	N	P	3	1-1

MURPHY, ROBERT R. (Buzz)
b.Apr.26,1895 Denver,Colo.
d.May 11,1938

Yr	Cl	Lea	Pos	G	Rec
1918	Bos	N	O	9	.375
1919	Was	A	O	79	.262
BLTL				88	.271

MURPHY, WALTER JOSEPH
b.Sept.27,1907 New York,N.Y.

Yr	Cl	Lea	Pos	G	Rec
1931	Bos	A	P	2	0-0
BRTR					

MURPHY, WILLIAM HENRY (Yale)
b.Nov.11,1869 Southville,Mass.
d.Feb.14,1906

Yr	Cl	Lea	Pos	G	Rec
1894	NY	N	S-O	73	.271
1895	NY	N	O	47	.209
1897	NY	N	S	4	.000
				124	.242

MURPHY, WILLIAM N.
(Gentle Willie)
b.Massachusetts.

Yr	Cl	Lea	Pos	G	Rec
1884	Cle	N	S-O	42	.226
1884	Was	a	3-O	5	.454
1884	Bos	U	C-O	1	.000
				48	.249

MURRAY, ANTHONY JOSEPH
b.Apr.30,1904 Chicago,Ill.

Yr	Cl	Lea	Pos	G	Rec
1923	Chi	N	O	2	.250
BRTR					

MURRAY, EDWARD FRANCIS
b.May 12,1896 Mystic,Conn.

Yr	Cl	Lea	Pos	G	Rec
1917	St.L	A	S	1	.000
BRTR					

MURRAY, GEORGE KING (Smiler)
b.Sept.23,1898 Charlotte,N.C.
d.Oct.18,1955

Yr	Cl	Lea	Pos	G	Rec
1922	NY	A	P	22	3-2
1923	Bos	A	P	39	7-11
1924	Bos	A	P	28	2-9
1926	Was	A	P	12	6-3
1927	Was	A	P	7	1-1
1933	Chi	A	P	2	0-0
BRTR				110	19-26

MURRAY, JAMES FRANCIS
(Big Jim)
b.Dec.31,1898 Scranton,Pa.

Yr	Cl	Lea	Pos	G	Rec
1922	Bro	N	P	4	0-0
BLTL					

MURRAY, JAMES O.
b.Jan.16,1880 Galveston,Tex.
d.Apr.25,1945

Yr	Cl	Lea	Pos	G	Rec
1902	Chi	N	O	11	.166
1911	St.L	A	O	31	.186
1914	Bos	N	O	39	.232
BRTL				81	.195

MURRAY, JEREMIAH J. (Miah)
b.Jan.1,1865 Boston,Mass.
d.Jan.11,1922

Yr	Cl	Lea	Pos	G	Rec
1884	Pro	N	C-1-O	8	.185
1885	Lou	a	C-1	11	.162
1888	Was	N	C	12	.098
1891	Was	a	C	2	.000
BRTR				33	.138

MURRAY, JOHN JOSEPH (Red)
b.Mar.4,1884 Arnot ,Pa.
d.Dec.4,1958

Yr	Cl	Lea	Pos	G	Rec
1906	St.L	N	O	41	.257
1907	St.L	N	O	131	.262
1908	St.L	N	O	154	.282
1909	NY	N	O	149	.263
1910	NY	N	O	148	.277
1911	NY	N	O	131	.291
1912	NY	N	O	143	.277
1913	NY	N	O	147	.267
1914	NY	N	O	86	.223
1915	NY	N	O	45	.220
1915	Chi	N	O	51	.299
1917	NY	N	O	22	.045
BRTR				1248	.270

MURRAY, JOSEPH AMBROSE
b.June 4,1913 Fall River,Mass.

Yr	Cl	Lea	Pos	G	Rec
1936	Bos	N	P	4	0-0
BLTL					

MURRAY, JOSEPH AMBROSE
b.Nov.11,1921 Wilkes-Barre,Pa.

Yr	Cl	Lea	Pos	G	Rec
1950	Phi	A	P	8	0-3
BLTL					

MURRAY, PATRICK JOSEPH
b.July 18,1897 Scottsville,N.Y.

Yr	Cl	Lea	Pos	G	Rec
1919	Phi	N	P	8	0-2
BRTL					

MURRAY, RAYMOND LEE
(Deacon)
b.Oct.12,1919 Spring Hope,N.C.

Yr	Cl	Lea	Pos	G	Rec
1948	Cle	A	H	4	.000
1950	Cle	A	C	55	.273

(Continued)

Yr	Cl	Lea	Pos	G	Rec
1951	Cle	A	C	1	1.000
1951	Phi	A	C	40	.213
1952	Phi	A	C	44	.206
1953	Phi	A	C	84	.284
1954	Bal	A	C	22	.246
BRTR				250	.252

MURRAY, ROBERT HAYES
b.July 4,1898 St.Albans,Vt.

Yr	Cl	Lea	Pos	G	Rec
1923	Was	A	3	10	.162
TR					

MURRAY, THOMAS
b.1866 Savannah,Ga.

Yr	Cl	Lea	Pos	G	Rec
1894	Phi	N	S	1	.000

MURRAY, WILLIAM ALLENWOOD
b.Sept.6,1893 Vinalhaven,Me.
d.Sept.14,1943

Yr	Cl	Lea	Pos	G	Rec
1917	Was	A	2	8	.143
BRTR					

MURRAY, WILLIAM JEREMIAH
b.Apr.13,1864 Peabody,Mass.
d.Mar.25,1937
Non-playing manager Phi (N) 1907-09.

MURTAUGH, DANIEL EDWARD
b.Oct.8,1917 Chester,Pa.

Yr	Cl	Lea	Pos	G	Rec
1941	Phi	N	2-S	85	.219
1942	Phi	N	2-S-3	144	.241
1943	Phi	N	2	113	.273
1946	Phi	N	2	6	.211
1947	Bos	N	2-3	3	.125
1948	Pit	N	2	146	.290
1949	Pit	N	2	75	.203
1950	Pit	N	2	118	.294
1951	Pit	N	2-3	77	.199
BRTR				767	.254

Non-playing manager Pit (N) 1957-62

MUSIAL, STANLEY FRANK
(The Man)
b.Nov.21,1920 Donora,Pa.

Yr	Cl	Lea	Pos	G	Rec
1941	St.L	N	O	12	.426
1942	St.L	N	O	140	.315
1943	St.L	N	O	157	.357
1944	St.L	N	O	146	.347
1946	St.L	N	1-O	156	.365
1947	St.L	N	1	149	.312
1948	St.L	N	1-O	155	.376
1949	St.L	N	1-O	157	.338
1950	St.L	N	1-O	146	.346
1951	St.L	N	1-O	152	.355
1952	St.L	N	P-1-O	154	0-0 .336
1953	St.L	N	O	157	.337
1954	St.L	N	1-O	153	.330
1955	St.L	N	1-O	154	.319
1956	St.L	N	1-O	156	.310
1957	St.L	N	1	134	.351
1958	St.L	N	1-O	135	.337
1959	St.L	N	1-O	115	.255
1960	St.L	N	O	116	.275
1961	St.L	N	O	123	.288
1962	St.L	N	O	135	.330
BLTL				2902	0-0 .333

MUSSER, PAUL
b.June 24,1889 Millheim,Pa.

Yr	Cl	Lea	Pos	G	Rec
1912	Was	A	P	8	1-0
1919	Bos	A	P	5	0-2
BRTR				13	1-2

MUSSER, WILLIAM DANIEL (Danny)
b.Sept.5,1906 Zion,Pa.

Yr	Cl	Lea	Pos	G	Rec
1932	Was	A	3	1	.500
BLTR					

MUSSILL, BERNARD JAMES
b.Oct.1,1920 Woodville,Pa.

Yr	Cl	Lea	Pos	G	Rec
1944	Phi	N	P	16	0-1
BRTL					

MUSTAIKIS, ALEXANDER DOMINICK
b.Mar.26,1911 Chelsea,Mass.

Yr	Cl	Lea	Pos	G	Rec
1940	Bos	A	P	6	0-1
BRTR					

MUTRIE, JAMES J. (Truthful Jim)
b.June 13,1851 Chelsea,Mass.
d.Jan.24,1938
Non-playing manager Met (a) 1883-84 and NY (N) 1885-91.

MYATT, GEORGE EDWARD (Mercury)
b.June 14,1914 Denver Colo.

Yr	Cl	Lea	Pos	G	Rec
1938	NY	N	S-3	43	.306
1939	NY	N	3	22	.189
1943	Was	A	2-S-3	42	.245
1944	Was	A	2-S-O	140	.284
1945	Was	A	2-S-3-O	133	.296
1946	Was	A	2-3	15	.235
1947	Was	A	2	12	.000
			BLTR	407	.283

MYATT, GLENN CALVIN
b.July 9,1897 Little Rock,Ark.

Yr	Cl	Lea	Pos	G	Rec
1920	Phi	A	C-O	70	.250
1921	Phi	A	C	44	.203
1923	Cle	A	C	92	.286
1924	Cle	A	C	105	.342
1925	Cle	A	C-O	106	.271
1926	Cle	A	C	56	.248
1927	Cle	A	C	55	.245
1928	Cle	A	C	58	.288
1929	Cle	A	C	59	.233
1930	Cle	A	C	86	.294
1931	Cle	A	C	65	.247
1932	Cle	A	C	82	.246
1933	Cle	A	C	40	.234
1934	Cle	A	C	36	.318
1935	Cle	A	C	10	.083
1935	NY	N	C	13	.222
1936	Det	A	C	27	.218
			BLTR	1004	.270

MYER, CHARLES SOLOMON (Buddy)
b.Mar.16,1904 Ellisville,Miss.

Yr	Cl	Lea	Pos	G	Rec
1925	Was	A	S	4	.250
1926	Was	A	S	132	.304
1927	Was	A	S	15	.216
1927	Bos	A	S	133	.288
1928	Bos	A	3	147	.313
1929	Was	A	2-3	141	.300
1930	Was	A	2	138	.303
1931	Was	A	2	139	.293
1932	Was	A	2	143	.279
1933	Was	A	2	131	.302
1934	Was	A	2	139	.305
1935	Was	A	2	151	.349
1936	Was	A	2	51	.269
1937	Was	A	2	125	.293
1938	Was	A	2	127	.336
1939	Was	A	2	83	.302
1940	Was	A	2	71	.290
1941	Was	A	2	53	.252
			BLTR	1923	.303

MYERS, ALBERT
b.Oct.22,1863 Danville,Ill.
d.Dec.24,1927

Yr	Cl	Lea	Pos	G	Rec
1884	Mil	U	2	12	.326
1885	Phi	N	2	93	.204
1886	KC	N	2	118	.276
1887	Was	N	2	105	.308
1888	Was	N	2	132	.207
1889	Was	N	2	46	.262
1889	Phi	N	2	75	.269
1890	Phi	N	2	117	.277
1891	Phi	N	2	134	.238
				832	.255

MYERS, ELMER GLEN
b.Mar.2,1894 York Springs,Pa.

Yr	Cl	Lea	Pos	G	Rec
1915	Phi	A	P	1	1-0
1916	Phi	A	P	53	14-23
1917	Phi	A	P	38	9-16
1918	Phi	A	P	18	4-8
1919	Cle	A	P	23	8-7
1920	Cle	A	P	16	2-4
1920	Bos	A	P	12	9-1
1921	Bos	A	P	30	8-12
1922	Bos	A	P	3	0-1
			BRTR	194	55-72

MYERS, GEORGE D.
b.1860 Buffalo,N.Y.
d.Jan.6,1911

Yr	Cl	Lea	Pos	G	Rec
1884	Buf	N	C-O	76	.186
1885	Buf	N	C-O	89	.205
1886	St.L	N	C	78	.189
1887	Ind	N	C	66	.284
1888	Ind	N	C	66	.238
1889	Ind	N	C-O	39	.194
			BR	414	.219

MYERS, HENRY C.
b.May 1858 Philadelphia,Pa.
d.Apr.18,1895

Yr	Cl	Lea	Pos	G	Rec
1881	Pro	N	S	1	.000
1882	Bal	a	M-P-S	69	0-2 .223
1884	Wil	U	2-S	6	.167
				76	0-2 .216

MYERS, HENRY HARRISON (Hi)
b.Apr.27,1889 E.Liverpool,O.

Yr	Cl	Lea	Pos	G	Rec
1909	Bro	N	O	6	.227
1911	Bro	N	O	12	.179
1914	Bro	N	O	70	.286
1915	Bro	N	O	153	.248
1916	Bro	N	O	113	.262
1917	Bro	N	1-2-3-O	120	.268
1918	Bro	N	O	107	.256
1919	Bro	N	O	133	.307
1920	Bro	N	O	154	.304
1921	Bro	N	2-O	144	.288
1922	Bro	N	2-O	153	.317
1923	St.L	N	O	96	.300
1924	St.L	N	2-3-O	43	.210
1925	St.L	N	O	1	.000
1925	Cin	N	O	3	.167
1925	St.L	N	H	1	1.000
			BRTR	1309	.281

MYERS, HENRY L.
b.1860 Philadelphia,Pa.
d.June 28,1898

Yr	Cl	Lea	Pos	G	Rec
1890	Ath	a	1-3	5	.167

MYERS, JOSEPH WILLIAM
b.Mar.18,1882 Wilmington,Del.
d.Feb.11,1952

Yr	Cl	Lea	Pos	G	Rec
1905	Phi	A	P	1	0-0

MYERS, LYNNWOOD LINCOLN
b.Feb.23,1914 Enola,Pa.

Yr	Cl	Lea	Pos	G	Rec
1938	St.L	N	S	70	.242
1939	St.L	N	S-3	74	.239
			BRTR	144	.241

MYERS, RALPH E. (Hap)
b.Aug.18,1888 San Francisco,Cal.

Yr	Cl	Lea	Pos	G	Rec
1910	Bos	A	C	3	.333
1911	St.L	A	1	11	.297
1911	Bos	A	1	13	.368
1913	Bos	N	1	140	.273
1914	Bro	F	1	89	.226
1915	Bro	F	1	115	.282
			BRTR	371	.268

MYERS, RICHARD
b.Apr.7,1930 Sacramento,Cal.

Yr	Cl	Lea	Pos	G	Rec
1956	Chi	N	H	4	.000
			BR		

MYERS, WILLIAM HARRISON
b.Aug.14,1910 Enola,Pa.

Yr	Cl	Lea	Pos	G	Rec
1935	Cin	N	S	117	.267
1936	Cin	N	S	98	.269
1937	Cin	N	2-S	124	.251
1938	Cin	N	2-S	134	.253
1939	Cin	N	S	151	.281
1940	Cin	N	S	90	.202
1941	Chi	N	2-S	24	.222
			BRTR	738	.257

NABORS, JOHN JACKSON
b.Nov.19,1887 Piedmont,Ala.
d.Oct.29,1923

Yr	Cl	Lea	Pos	G	Rec
1915	Phi	A	P	10	0-5
1916	Phi	A	P	40	1-21
1917	Phi	A	P	2	0-0
			BRTR	52	1-26

NAGEL, WILLIAM TAYLOR
b.Aug.19,1915 Memphis,Tenn.

Yr	Cl	Lea	Pos	G	Rec
1939	Phi	A	P-2-3	105	0-0 .252
1941	Phi	N	2-3-O	17	.143
1945	Chi	A	1-3	67	.209
			BRTR	189	0-0 .227

NAGELEISEN, LOUIS M.
(Played under name of Louis M. Nagelson)

NAGELSON, LOUIS M.
(Real name Louis M. Nageleisen)
b.June 29,1887 Piqua,O.

Yr	Cl	Lea	Pos	G	Rec
1912	Cle	A	C	2	.000
			BRTR		

NAGLE, THOMAS G.
b.Nov.1,1865 Milwaukee,Wis.
d.Mar.9,1946

Yr	Cl	Lea	Pos	G	Rec
1890	Chi	N	C	38	.264
1891	Chi	N	C	8	.120
				46	.243

NAGLE, WALTER HAROLD (Judge)
b.Mar.10,1880 Santa Rosa, Calif

Yr	Cl	Lea	Pos	G	Rec
1911	Pit	N	P	8	4-2
1911	Bos	A	P	5	1-1
				13	5-3

NAGY, STEPHEN
b.May 28,1920 Franklin,N.J.

Yr	Cl	Lea	Pos	G	Rec
1947	Pit	N	P	6	1-3
1950	Was	A	P	15	2-5
			BLTL	21	3-8

NAHEM, SAMUEL RALPH
b.Oct.19,1915 New York,N.Y.

Yr	Cl	Lea	Pos	G	Rec
1938	Bro	N	P	1	1-0
1941	St.L	N	P	26	5-2
1942	Phi	N	P	35	1-3
1948	Phi	N	P	28	3-3
			BRTR	90	10-8

NAKTENIS, PETER ERNEST
b.June 12,1914 Aberdeen,Wash.

Yr	Cl	Lea	Pos	G	Rec
1936	Phi	A	P	7	0-1
1939	Cin	N	P	3	0-0
			BLTL	10	0-1

NALEWAY, FRANK (Chick)
b.July 4,1901 Chicago,Ill.

Yr	Cl	Lea	Pos	G	Rec
1924	Chi	A	S	1	.000
			BRTR		

NANCE, WILLIAM G. (Kid)
(Real name Willie G. Cooper)
b.Aug.2,1877 Ft.Worth,Tex.
d.May 28,1958

Yr	Cl	Lea	Pos	G	Rec
1897	Lou	N	O	34	.241
1898	Lou	N	O	22	.329
1901	Det	A	O	133	.290
1904	St.L	A	C	1	.333
			BRTR	190	.286

NAPIER, SAMUEL LeROY (Buddy)
b.Dec.18,1889 Montezuma,Tex.

Yr	Cl	Lea	Pos	G	Rec
1912	St.L	A	P	6	0-2
1918	Chi	N	P	1	0-0
1920	Cin	N	P	9	4-2
1921	Cin	N	P	22	0-2
			BRTR	38	4-6

NAPLES, ALOYSIUS FRANCIS
b.Aug.29,1927 St.George,S.I.,N.Y.

Yr	Cl	Lea	Pos	G	Rec
1949	St.L	A	S	2	.143

BRTR

NARAGON, HAROLD RICHARD
b.Oct.1,1928 Zanesville,O.

Yr	Cl	Lea	Pos	G	Rec
1951	Cle	A	C	3	.250
1954	Cle	A	C	46	.238
1955	Cle	A	C	57	.323
1956	Cle	A	C	53	.287
1957	Cle	A	C	57	.256
1958	Cle	A	H	9	.333
1959	Cle	A	C	14	.278
1959	Was	A	C	71	.241
1960	Was	A	C	33	.207
1961	Min	A	C	57	.302
1962	Min	A	C	24	.229
	BLTR			424	.266

NARANJO, LAZARO RAMON GONZALO
b.Nov.25,1934 Havana, Cuba

Yr	Cl	Lea	Pos	G	Rec
1956	Pit	N	P	17	1-2

BLTR

NARLESKI, RAYMOND EDMOND
b.Nov.25,1928 Camden,N.J.

Yr	Cl	Lea	Pos	G	Rec
1954	Cle	A	P	42	3-3
1955	Cle	A	P	60	9-1
1956	Cle	A	P	32	3-2
1957	Cle	A	P	46	11-5
1958	Cle	A	P	44	13-10
1959	Det	A	P	42	4-12
	BRTR			266	43-33

NARLESKI, WILLIAM EDWARD
(Cap)
b.June 9,1899 Keasbey,N.J.

Yr	Cl	Lea	Pos	G	Rec
1929	Bos	A	2-S	96	.277
1930	Bos	A	S-3	39	.235
	BRTR			135	.265

NARRON, SAMUEL
b.Aug.25,1913 Middlesex,N.C.

Yr	Cl	Lea	Pos	G	Rec
1935	St.L	N	C	4	.429
1942	St.L	N	C	10	.400
1943	St.L	N	C	10	.091
	BRTR			24	.286

NASH, KENNETH LELAND
(also played under name of J. A. Costello)
b.July 14,1888 S.Weymouth,Mass.

Yr	Cl	Lea	Pos	G	Rec
1912	Cle	A	S	9	.190
1914	St.L	N	1-2-S-3	24	.275
	BBTR			33	.247

NASH, WILLIAM MITCHELL
b.June 24,1865 Richmond,Va.
d.Nov.16,1929

Yr	Cl	Lea	Pos	G	Rec
1884	Ric	a	3	44	.188
1885	Bos	N	2-3	26	.255
1886	Bos	N	S-3	109	.280
1887	Bos	N	3	118	.368
1888	Bos	N	2-3	135	.283
1889	Bos	N	3	127	.274
1890	Bos	p	3	129	.284
1891	Bos	N	3	139	.276
1892	Bos	N	3	135	.265
1893	Bos	N	3	128	.304
1894	Bos	N	3	132	.294
1895	Bos	N	3	133	.296
1896	Phi	N	M-3	64	.242
1897	Phi	N	S-3	102	.258
1898	Phi	N	3	20	.232
	BRTR			1541	.286

NATON, PETER ALPHONSUS
b.Sept.9,1931 Flushing,L.I.,N.Y.

Yr	Cl	Lea	Pos	G	Rec
1953	Pit	N	C	6	.167

BRTR

NAVA, VINCENT P.
(Real name Irwin Sandy)
b.Apr.12,1850 San Francisco,Cal.
d.June 15,1906

Yr	Cl	Lea	Pos	G	Rec
1882	Pro	N	C-O	27	.206
1883	Pro	N	C-O	27	.240
1884	Pro	N	C-2-S-O	32	.089
1885	Bal	a	C	8	.148
1886	Bal	a	C-S	2	.200
				96	.176

NAVARRO, JULIO VENTURA
b.Aug.8,1936 Vieques, Puerto Rico

Yr	Cl	Lea	Pos	G	Rec
1962	LA	A	P	9	1-1

BRTR

NAYLOR, EARL EUGENE
b.May 19,1919 Kansas City,Mo.

Yr	Cl	Lea	Pos	G	Rec
1942	Phi	N	P-O	76	0-5 / .196
1943	Phi	N	O	33	.175
1946	Bro	N	H	3	.000
	BRTR			112	0-5 / .186

NAYLOR, ROLEINE CECIL
(Rolly)
b.Feb.4,1892 Denton,Tex.

Yr	Cl	Lea	Pos	G	Rec
1917	Phi	A	P	5	2-2
1919	Phi	A	P	31	5-18
1920	Phi	A	P	42	10-23
1921	Phi	A	P	33	3-13
1922	Phi	A	P	36	10-15
1923	Phi	A	P	26	12-7
1924	Phi	A	P	10	0-5
	BRTR			183	42-83

NAYMICK, WILLIAM MICHAEL
(Mike)
b.Sept.4,1917 Berlin,Pa.

Yr	Cl	Lea	Pos	G	Rec
1939	Cle	A	P	2	0-1
1940	Cle	A	P	13	1-2
1943	Cle	A	P	29	4-4
1944	Cle	A	P	7	0-0
1944	St.L	N	P	1	0-0
	BRTR			52	5-7

NEAGLE, JOHN HENRY
b.Jan.2,1858 Syracuse,N.Y.
d.Sept.20,1904

Yr	Cl	Lea	Pos	G	Rec
1879	Cin	N	P-O	3	0-1 / .167
1883	Phi	N	P-O	18	1-4 / .162
1883	Bal	a	P-O	9	1-4 / .270
1883	Pit	a	P-O	29	3-13 / .168
1884	Pit	a	P	41	11-26
	BRTR			100	16-48 / .169

NEAL, CHARLES
b.Jan.30,1931 Longview, Tex.

Yr	Cl	Lea	Pos	G	Rec
1956	Bro	N	2-S	62	.287
1957	Bro	N	2-S-3	128	.270
1958	LA	N	2-S	140	.254
1959	LA	N	2-S	151	.287
1960	LA	N	2-S	139	.256
1961	LA	N	2	108	.235
1962	NY	N	2-S-3	136	.260
	BRTR			864	264

NEAL, JOSEPH H.
b.1865 Wadsworth,O.

Yr	Cl	Lea	Pos	G	Rec
1886	Lou	a	P-O	2	0-1 / .000
1887	Lou	a	P	5	0-4
1890	St.L	a	P	10	3-3
1891	St.L	a	P	15	6-4
	BRTR			32	9-12 / .119

NEAL, OFFA
b.June 5,1876 Benton,Ill.
d.Apr.12,1950

Yr	Cl	Lea	Pos	G	Rec
1905	NY	N	2-3	4	.077

TR

NEALE, ALFRED EARLE
(Greasy)
b.Nov.5,1893 Parkersburg,W.Va.

Yr	Cl	Lea	Pos	G	Rec
1916	Cin	N	O	138	.262
1817	Cin	N	O	121	.294
1918	Cin	N	O	107	.270
1919	Cin	N	O	139	.242
1920	Cin	N	O	150	.255
1921	Phi	N	O	22	.211
1921	Cin	N	O	63	.241
1922	Cin	N	O	25	.233
1924	Cin	N	O	3	.000
	BLTR			768	.259

NEALON, JAMES JOSEPH
b.Oct.13,1872 Sacramento,Cal.
d.Apr.2,1910

Yr	Cl	Lea	Pos	G	Rec
1906	Pit	N	1	154	.255
1907	Pit	N	1	104	.257
				258	.256

NECCIAI, RONALD ANDREW
b.June 18,1932 Manown,Pa.

Yr	Cl	Lea	Pos	G	Rec
1952	Pit	N	P	12	1-6

BRTR

NEEDHAM, THOMAS J.
(Deerfoot)
b.Apr.7,1879 Ireland.
d.Dec.13,1926

Yr	Cl	Lea	Pos	G	Rec
1904	Bos	N	C	78	.260
1905	Bos	N	C	82	.218
1906	Bos	N	C	81	.190
1907	Bos	N	C	79	.196
1908	NY	N	C	47	.209
1909	Chi	N	C	10	.200
1910	Chi	N	C	28	.184
1911	Chi	N	C	23	.194
1912	Chi	N	C	33	.178
1913	Chi	N	C	20	.238
1914	Chi	N	C	9	.118
	BRTR			490	.209

NEEMAN, CALVIN AMANDUS
b.Feb.18,1929 Valmeyer,Ill.

Yr	Cl	Lea	Pos	G	Rec
1957	Chi	N	C	122	.258
1958	Chi	N	C	76	.259
1959	Chi	N	C	44	.162
1960	Chi	N	C	9	.154
1960	Phi	N	C	59	.181
1961	Phi	N	C	19	.226
1962	Pit	N	C	24	.180
	BRTR			353	.229

NEFF, DOUGLAS WILLIAM
b.Oct.8,1891 Harrisonburg,Va.

Yr	Cl	Lea	Pos	G	Rec
1914	Was	A	S	3	.000
1915	Was	A	2-S-3	30	.167
	BRTR			33	.159

NEGRAY, RONALD ALVIN
b.Feb.26,1930 Akron,O.

Yr	Cl	Lea	Pos	G	Rec
1952	Bro	N	P	4	0-0
1955	Phi	N	P	19	4-3
1956	Phi	N	P	39	2-3
1958	LA	N	P	4	0-0
	BRTR			66	6-6

NEHER, JAMES GILMORE
b.Feb.5,1889 Rochester,N.Y.
d.Nov.11,1951

Yr	Cl	Lea	Pos	G	Rec
1912	Cle	A	P	1	0-0

BRTR

NEHF, ARTHUR NEUKOM
b.Julv 31.1892 Terre Haute,Ind.
d.Dec.18,1960

Yr	Cl	Lea	Pos	G	Rec
1915	Bos	N	P	12	5-4
1916	Bos	N	P	23	7-5
1917	Bos	N	P	38	17-8
1918	Bos	N	P-O	35	15-15 / .168

Yr Cl Lea Pos G Rec

(Continued)
1919 Bos N P-O 22 {8-9 / .197
1919 NY N P 13 9-2
1920 NY N P 40 21-12
1921 NY N P 42 20-10
1922 NY N P 37 19-13
1923 NY N P 34 13-10
1924 NY N P-O 33 {14-4 / .228
1925 NY N P 33 11-9
1926 NY N P 2 0-0
1926 Cin N P 7 0-1
1927 Cin N P 21 3-5
1927 Chi N P 8 1-1
1928 Chi N P 31 13-7
1929 Chi N P 32 8-5
BLTL 463 {184-120 / .211

NEIGER, ALVIN EDWARD
b.Mar.26,1939 Wilmington,Del.
1960 Phi N P 6 0-0
BLTL

NEIGHBORS, ROBERT OTIS
b.Nov.9,1917 Talahina,Okla.
d.Aug.8,1952
1939 St.L A S 7 .182
BRTR

NEILL, THOMAS WHITE
b.Nov.7,1919 Hartselle,Ala.
1946 Bos N O 13 .267
1947 Bos N O 7 .200
BLTR 20 .255

NEIS, BERNARD EDMUND
b.Sept.26,1895 Bloomington,Ill.
1920 Bro N O 95 .253
1921 Bro N O 102 .257
1922 Bro N O 61 .229
1923 Bro N O 126 .274
1924 Bro N O 80 .303
1925 Bos N O 106 .285
1926 Bos N O 30 .215
1927 Cle A O 32 .302
1927 Chi A O 45 .289
BBTR 677 .272

NEITZKE, ERNEST FREDERICK
b.Nov.13,1897 Toledo,O.
1921 Bos A P 11 0-0
BRTR

NEKOLA, FRANCIS JOSEPH
(Bots)
b.Dec.10,1907 New York,N.Y.
1929 NY A P 9 0-0
1933 Det A P 2 0-0
BLTL 11 0-0

NELSON, ALBERT FRANCIS (Red)
(Real name Albert W. Horazdovsky)
b.May 19,1886 Cleveland,O.
d.Oct.26,1956
1910 St.L A P 7 5-1
1911 St.L A P 15 3-9
1912 St.L A P 8 0-3
1912 Phi N P 4 2-0
1913 Phi N P 2 0-0
1913 Cin N P 2 0-0
BRTR 38 10-13

NELSON, ANDREW (Peaches)
1908 Chi A P 3 1-0

NELSON, GEORGE EMMETT
(Ramrod)
b.Feb.26,1908 Viborg,S.Dak.
1935 Cin N P 19 4-4
1936 Cin N P 6 1-0
BRTR 25 5-4

Yr Cl Lea Pos G Rec

NELSON, GLENN RICHARD
(Rocky)
b.Nov.18,1924 Portsmouth,O.
1949 St.L N 1 82 .221
1950 St.L N 1 76 .247
1951 St.L N 1-O 9 .222
1951 Pit N 1-O 71 .267
1951 Chi A H 6 .000
1952 Bro N 1 37 .256
1954 Cle A 1 4 .000
1956 Bro N 1 31 .208
1956 St.L N 1-O 38 .232
1959 Pit N 1-O 98 .291
1960 Pit N 1 93 .300
1961 Pit N 1 75 .197
620 .249

NELSON, JACKSON W.
(Candy)
b.Mar.14,1849 Brooklyn,N.Y.
d.Sept.5,1910
1872 Tro n S-O 5 NR
1872 Eck n 2-3-O 16 NR
1873 Mut n 2-3-O 37 NR
1874 Mut n 2-S 65 NR
1875 Mut n 2-3-O 70 NR
1878 Ind N S 18 .136
1879 Tro N S-O 28 .246
1881 Wor N S 23 .275
1883 Met a S 96 .291
1884 Met a S 111 .259
1885 Met a S 107 .251
1886 Met a S-O 109 .230
1887 Met a S-O 68 .361
1887 NY N 3 1 .000
1890 Bro a S 60 .234
BLTR 814 NR

NELSON, LUTHER M.
b.Dec.4,1894 Cable,Ill.
1919 NY A P 9 3-0
BRTR

NELSON, LYNN BERNARD
(Line Drive)
b.Feb.24,1905 Sheldon,N.Dak.
d.Feb.15,1955
1930 Chi N P 37 3-2
1933 Chi N P 29 5-5
1934 Chi N P 2 0-1
1937 Phi A P 74 4-9
1938 Phi A P 67 10-11
1939 Phi A P 40 10-13
1940 Det A P 19 1-1
BLTR 268 33-42

NELSON, MELVIN FREDERICK
b.May 30,1936 San Diego,Cal.
1960 St.L N P 2 0-1
BRTL

NELSON, RAYMOND N.
(Real name
Raymond Nelson Kellog)
b.Aug.4,1875 Holyoke,Mass.
1901 NY N 2 36 .205

NELSON, ROBERT SIDNEY
b.Aug.7,1936 Dallas,Tex.
1955 Bal A 1-O 25 .194
1956 Bal A O 39 .206
1957 Bal A O 15 .217
79 .205

NELSON, THOMAS COUSINEAU
b.May 1,1917 Chicago,Ill.
1945 Bos N 2-3 40 .165
BRTR

NELSON, WILLIAM F.
b.Sept.28,1863 Terre Haute,Ind.
d.June 23,1941
1884 Pit a P 3 1-2
TR

Yr Cl Lea Pos G Rec

NESS, JOHN CHARLES
b.Nov.11,1885 Chicago,Ill.
d.Dec.3,1957
1911 Det A 1 12 .161
1916 Chi A 1 75 .267
BRTR 87 .248

NETZEL, MILO A.
b.May 12,1887 Olean,N.Y.
d.Mar.30,1938
1909 Cle A 3-O 10 .189
TR

NEUBAUER, HAROLD CHARLES
b.May 13,1902 Hoboken,N.J.
d.Sept.9,1949
1925 Bos A P 7 1-0
BRTR

NEUER, JOHN S. (Tacks)
b.1880 Hazleton,Pa.
1907 NY A P 7 4-2

NEUN, JOHN HENRY
b.Oct.28,1900 Baltimore,Md.
1925 Det A 1 60 .266
1926 Det A 1 97 .298
1927 Det A 1 79 .323
1928 Det A 1 36 .213
1930 Bos N 1 81 .325
1931 Bos N 1 79 .221
BBTL 432 .289
Non-playing manager N.Y. (A) 1946 and Cin (N) 1947-48.

NEVEL, ERNIE WRYE
b.Aug.17,1919 Charleston,Mo.
1950 NY A P 3 0-1
1951 NY A P 1 0-0
1953 Cin N P 10 0-0
BRTR 14 0-1

NEVERS, ERNEST ALONZO
b.June 11,1903 Willow River,Minn.
1926 St.L A P 12 2-4
1927 St.L A P 27 3-8
1928 St.L A P 6 1-0
BRTR 45 6-12

NEVINS, ...
1873 Res n 2-3-O 13 NR

NEWCOMBE, DONALD
b.June 14,1926 Madison,N.J.
1949 Bro N P 39 17-8
1950 Bro N P 40 19-11
1951 Bro N P 40 20-9
1954 Bro N P 31 9-8
1955 Bro N P 57 20-5
1956 Bro N P 52 27-7
1957 Bro N P 34 11-12
1958 LA N P 11 0-6
1958 Cin N P 39 7-7
1959 Cin N P 61 13-8
1960 Cin N P 24 4-6
1960 Cle A P 24 2-3
BLTR 452 149-90

NEWELL, JOHN A.
b.Jan.14,1868 Wilmington,Del.
d.Jan.28,1919
1891 Pit N 3 5 .111

NEWELL, T.E.
b.St.Louis,Mo.
1877 St.L N S 1 .000

NEWHOUSER, HAROLD
b.May 20,1921 Detroit,Mich.
1939 Det A P 1 0-1
1940 Det A P 28 9-9
1941 Det A P 33 9-11
1942 Det A P 39 8-14
1943 Det A P 37 8-17
1944 Det A P 47 29-9
1945 Det A P 40 25-9
1946 Det A P 37 26-9

Yr Cl Lea Pos G Rec

(Continued)
1947 Det A P 40 17-17
1948 Det A P 39 21-12
1949 Det A P 38 18-11
1950 Det A P 35 15-13
1951 Det A P 17 6-6
1952 Det A P 26 9-9
1953 Det A P 7 0-1
1954 Cle A P 26 7-2
1955 Cle A P 2 0-0
BLTL 492 207-150

NEWKIRK, FLOYD ELMO
b.July 16,1908 Norris City,Ill.
1934 NY A P 1 0-0
BRTR

NEWKIRK, JOEL IVAN
b.May 1,1896 Kyana,Ind.
1919 Chi N P 1 0-0
1920 Chi N P 2 0-1
BRTR 3 0-1

NEWLIN, MAURICE MILTON
(Mickey)
b.June 22,1914 Bloomingdale,Ind.
1940 St.L A P 1 1-0
1941 St.L A P 14 0-2
BRTR 15 1-2

NEWMAN, CHARLES C.
b.Indianapolis,Ind.
1891 St.L a C 1 .000
1892 NY N O 2 .375
1892 Chi N O 14 .148
17 .244

NEWMAN, FREDERICK W.
b.Feb.21,1942 Boston,Mass.
1962 LA A P 4 0-1

NEWNAM, PATRICK HENRY
b.Dec.10.1880 Hempstead,Tex.
d.June 20,1938
1910 St.L A 1 103 .216
1911 St.L A 1 20 .194
BRTR 123 .213

NEWSOM, LOUIS NORMAN
(Bobo)
b.Aug.11,1907 Hartsville,S.C.
d.Dec.7,1962
1929 Bro N P 3 0-3
1930 Bro N P 2 0-0
1932 Chi N P 1 0-0
1934 St.L A P 50 16-20
1935 St.L A P 7 0-6
1935 Was A P 28 11-12
1936 Was A P 44 17-15
1937 Was A P 13 3-4
1937 Bos A P 31 13-10
1938 St.L A P 46 20-16
1939 St.L A P 6 3-1
1939 Det A P 35 17-10
1940 Det A P 36 21-5
1941 Det A P 43 12-20
1942 Was A P 30 11-17
1942 Bro N P 6 2-2
1943 Bro N P 22 9-4
1943 St.L A P 10 1-6
1943 Was A P 6 3-3
1944 Phi A P 37 13-15
1945 Phi A P 36 8-20
1946 Phi A P 10 3-5
1946 Was A P 24 11-8
1947 Was A P 14 4-6
1947 NY A P 17 7-5
1948 NY N P 11 0-4
1952 Was A P 10 1-1
1952 Phi A P 14 3-3
1953 Phi A P 17 2-1
BRTR 609 211-222

NEWSOME, ASHBY LAMAR
(Skeeter)
b.Oct.18,1910 Phenix City,Ala.
1935 Phi A 2-S-3-O 59 .207
1936 Phi A S 127 .225
1937 Phi A S 122 .253
1938 Phi A S 17 .271
1939 Phi A S 99 .222
1941 Bos A 2-S 93 .225
1942 Bos A 2-S-3 29 .274
1943 Bos A S-3 114 .265
1944 Bos A 2-S-3 136 .242
1945 Bos A 2-S-3 125 .290
1946 Phi N 2-S-3 112 .232
1947 Phi N 2-S-3 95 .229
BRTR 1128 .245

NEWSOME, HEBER HAMPTON
(Dick)
b.Dec.13,1909 Ahoskie,N.C.
1941 Bos A P 36 19-10
1942 Bos A P 24 8-10
1943 Bos A P 27 8-13
BRTR 87 35-33

NEWTON, EUSTACE JAMES
(Doc)
b.Oct.26,1877 Indianapolis,Ind.
d.May 14,1931
1900 Cin N P 30 9-14
1901 Cin N P 20 4-13
1901 Bro N P 13 7-5
1902 Bro N P-1 32 15-14 / 174
1905 NY A P 12 2-4
1906 NY A P 21 7-5
1907 NY A P 19 7-10
1908 NY A P 23 4-5
1909 NY A P 4 0-3
BLTL 174 55-73 / .172

NIARHOS, CONSTANTINE
GREGORY (Gus)
b.Dec.6,1921 Birmingham,Ala.
1946 NY A C 37 .225
1948 NY A C 83 .268
1949 NY A C 32 .279
1950 NY A H 1 .000
1950 Chi A C 41 .324
1951 Chi A C 66 .256
1952 Bos A C 29 .103
1953 Bos A C 16 .200
1954 Phi N C 3 .200
1955 Phi N C 7 .111
BRTR 315 .252

NICE, CHARLES REIFF
b.July 1,1870 Philadelphia,Pa.
d.May 9,1908
1895 Bos N S 9 .229

NICHOL, SAMUEL ANDERSON
b.Apr.20,1869 Ireland.
d.Apr.19,1937
1888 Pit N O 8 .045
1890 Col a O 14 .188
22 .147

NICHOLAS, DONALD LEIGH
b.Oct.30,1930 Phoenix,Ariz.
1952 Chi A H 3 .000
1954 Chi A H 7 .000
BLTR 10 .000

NICHOLLS, SIMON
BURDETTE
b.July 17,1882 Germantown,Md.
d.Mar.12,1911
1903 Det A S 2 .375
1906 Phi A S 12 .219
1907 Phi A 2-S 124 .302
1908 Phi A 2-S 150 .216
1909 Phi A 3 21 .211
1910 Cle A S 3 .000
BLTR 312 .252

NICHOLS, ALBERT H.
1875 Atl n 3 32 NR
1876 Mut N 3 57 .177
1877 Lou N 1-2-S-3 6 .211
95 NR

NICHOLS, ARTHUR FRANCIS
(Real name Arthur Francis Meikle)
b.July 14,1871 Manchester,N.H.
d.Aug.9,1945
1898 Chi N C 13 .264
1899 Chi N C 17 .277
1900 Chi N C 8 .208
1901 St.L N C-O 82 .247
1902 St.L N C-1-O 69 .272
1903 St.L N 1 33 .192
222 .248

NICHOLS, CHARLES AUGUSTUS
(Kid)
b.Sept,14,1869 Madison,Wis.
d.Apr.11,1953
1890 Bos N P 47 27-19
1891 Bos N P 50 30-17
1892 Bos N P 54 35-16
1893 Bos N P 47 32-14
1894 Bos N P 46 33-13
1895 Bos N P 43 27-16
1896 Bos N P 45 30-14
1897 Bos N P 43 32-11
1898 Bos N P 45 33-12
1899 Bos N P 41 20-18
1900 Bos N P 29 13-14
1901 Bos N P 46 18-15
1904 St.L N M-P 36 20-12
1905 St.L N M-P 8 1-5
1905 Phi N P 18 10-6
1906 Phi N P 4 0-2
BBTR 602 361-204

NICHOLS, CHESTER
RAYMOND JR.
b.Feb.22,1931 Pawtucket,R.I.
1951 Bos N P 33 11-8
1954 Mil N P 35 9-11
1955 Mil N P 34 9-8
1956 Mil N P 2 0-1
1960 Bos A P 6 0-2
1961 Bos A P 26 3-2
1962 Bos A P 29 1-1
BRTL 165 33-28

NICHOLS, CHESTER
RAYMOND SR.
b.July 2,1897 Woonsocket,R.I.
1926 Pit N P 3 0-0
1927 Pit N P 8 0-3
1928 NY N P 3 0-0
1930 Phi N P 26 1-2
1931 Phi N P 3 0-1
1932 Phi N P 11 0-2
BRTR 54 1-8

NICHOLS, DOLAN LEVON
b.Feb.28,1930 Tishomingo,Miss.
1958 Chi N P 24 0-4
BRTR

NICHOLS, FREDERICK C.
(Tricky)
b.Bridgeport,Conn.
1875 NH n P-O 33 4-28 / NR
1876 Bos N P 1 1-0
1877 St.L N P-O 51 18-23 / .168
1878 Pro N P 11 4-7
1880 Wor N P 2 0-2
1882 Bal a P-O 27 1-13 / .154
BRTR 125 28-73 / NR

NICHOLS, ROY
b.Mar.3,1921 N.Little Rock,Ark.
1944 NY N 2-3 11 .222
BRTR

NICHOLSON, DAVID LAWRENCE
b.Aug.29,1939 St. Louis,Mo.

Yr	Cl	Lea	Pos	G	Rec
1960	Bal	A	O	54	.186
1962	Bal	A	O	97	.173
	BRTR			151	.178

NICHOLSON, FRANK COLLINS
b.Aug.29,1889 Berlin,Pa.

Yr	Cl	Lea	Pos	G	Rec
1912	Phi	N	P	2	0-0
	BRTR				

NICHOLSON, FREDERICK
(Shoemaker)
b.Sept.1,1894 Honey Grove,Tex.

Yr	Cl	Lea	Pos	G	Rec
1917	Det	A	O	13	.286
1919	Pit	N	1-O	30	.273
1920	Pit	N	O	99	.360
1921	Bos	N	O	83	.327
1922	Bos	N	O	78	.252
	BRTR			303	.311

NICHOLSON, OVID
b.Aug.18,1892 Salem,Ind.

Yr	Cl	Lea	Pos	G	Rec
1912	Pit	N	O	6	.454
	BLTR				

NICHOLSON, THOMAS C.
(Parson)
b.Apr.14,1862 Pleasant Valley,O.
d.Feb.28,1917

Yr	Cl	Lea	Pos	G	Rec
1888	Det	N	2	24	.259
1890	Tol	a	2	133	.261
1895	Was	N	S	10	.184
				167	.256

NICHOLSON, WILLIAM BECK
(Swish)
b.Dec.11,1914 Chestertown,Md.

Yr	Cl	Lea	Pos	G	Rec
1936	Phi	A	O	11	.000
1939	Chi	N	O	58	.295
1940	Chi	N	O	135	.297
1941	Chi	N	O	147	.254
1942	Chi	N	O	152	.294
1943	Chi	N	O	154	.309
1944	Chi	N	O	156	.287
1945	Chi	N	O	151	.243
1946	Chi	N	O	105	.220
1947	Chi	N	O	148	.244
1948	Chi	N	O	143	.261
1949	Phi	N	O	98	.234
1950	Phi	N	O	41	.224
1951	Phi	N	O	85	.241
1952	Phi	N	O	55	.273
1953	Phi	N	O	38	.210
	BLTR			1677	.268

NICKLIN, SAMUEL STRANG
(Played under name of
Samuel Nicklin Strang)

NICOL, GEORGE EDWARD
b.Oct.17,1870 Barry,Ill.
d.Aug.10,1924

Yr	Cl	Lea	Pos	G	Rec
1890	St.L	a	P	4	2-2
1891	Chi	N	P	3	0-1
1894	Pit	N	P	9	4-2
1894	Lou	N	P-O	28	3-3 / .345
	TL			44	9-8 / .344

NICOL, HUGH N.
b.Jan.1,1858 Ramsey,Scotland.
d.June 27,1921

Yr	Cl	Lea	Pos	G	Rec
1881	Chi	N	S-O	26	.203
1882	Chi	N	S-O	47	.198
1883	St.L	a	2-O	85	.263
1884	St.L	a	2-O	110	.270
1885	St.L	a	O	112	.211
1886	St.L	a	O	67	.204
1887	Cin	a	O	126	.334
1888	Cin	a	2-S-O	134	.236
1889	Cin	a	2-3-O	122	.246
1890	Cin	N	O	50	.209
	BRTR			879	.254

Non-playing manager St.L (N) 1897.

NIEBERGALL, CHARLES ARTHUR (Nig)
b.May 23,1899 New York,N.Y.

Yr	Cl	Lea	Pos	G	Rec
1921	St.L	N	C	5	.167
1923	St.L	N	C	9	.107
1924	St.L	N	C	40	.293
	BRTR			54	.231

NIEHAUS, ALBERT BERNARD
b.June 1,1901 Cincinnati,O.
d.Oct.14,1931

Yr	Cl	Lea	Pos	G	Rec
1925	Pit	N	1	17	.219
1925	Cin	N	1	51	.299
	BRTR			68	.275

NIEHAUS, RICHARD J.
b.Oct.24,1892 Covington,Ky.
d.Mar.12,1957

Yr	Cl	Lea	Pos	G	Rec
1913	St.L	N	P	3	0-2
1914	St.L	N	P	8	1-0
1915	St.L	N	P	15	2-1
1920	Cle	A	P	19	1-2
	BLTL			45	4-5

NIEHOFF, JOHN ALBERT
(Bert)
b.May 13,1884 Louisville,Col.

Yr	Cl	Lea	Pos	G	Rec
1913	Cin	N	3	2	.000
1914	Cin	N	3	142	.242
1915	Phi	N	2	148	.238
1916	Phi	N	2	146	.243
1917	Phi	N	2	114	.255
1918	St.L	N	2	22	.176
1918	NY	N	2	7	.261
	BRTR			581	.240

NIELSEN, MILTON ROBERT
b.Feb.8,1925 Tyler,Minn.

Yr	Cl	Lea	Pos	G	Rec
1949	Cle	A	O	3	.111
1951	Cle	A	H	16	.000
	BLTL			19	.067

NIEMAN, ELMER LeROY
(Butch)
b.Feb.8,1919 Herkimer,Kan.

Yr	Cl	Lea	Pos	G	Rec
1943	Bos	N	O	101	.251
1944	Bos	N	O	134	.265
1945	Bos	N	O	97	.247
	BLTL			332	.256

NIEMAN, ROBERT CHARLES
b.Jan.26,1927 Cincinnati,O.

Yr	Cl	Lea	Pos	G	Rec
1951	St.L	A	O	12	.372
1952	St.L	A	O	131	.289
1953	Det	A	O	142	.281
1954	Det	A	O	91	.263
1955	Chi	A	O	99	.283
1956	Chi	A	O	14	.300
1956	Bal	A	O	114	.322
1957	Bal	A	O	129	.276
1958	Bal	A	O	105	.325
1959	Bal	A	O	118	.292
1960	St.L	N	O	81	.287
1961	St.L	N	O	6	.471
1961	Cle	A	O	39	.354
1962	Cle	A	H	2	.000
1962	SF	N	O	30	.300
	BRTR			1113	.295

NIEMES, JACOB LELAND
b.Oct.19,1919 Cincinnati,O.

Yr	Cl	Lea	Pos	G	Rec
1943	Cin	N	P	3	0-0
	BRTL				

NIEMIEC, ALFRED JOSEPH
b.May 18,1911 Meriden,Conn.

Yr	Cl	Lea	Pos	G	Rec
1934	Bos	A	2	9	.219
1936	Phi	A	2	69	.197
	BRTR			78	.200

NIGGELING, JOHN ARNOLD
b.July 10,1905 Remsen,Ia.

Yr	Cl	Lea	Pos	G	Rec
1938	Bos	N	P	2	1-0
1939	Cin	N	P	10	2-1
1940	St.L	A	P	28	7-11
1941	St.L	A	P	24	7-9
1942	St.L	A	P	28	15-11
1943	St.L	A	P	20	6-8
1943	Was	A	P	6	4-2
1944	Was	A	P	24	10-8
1945	Was	A	P	26	7-12
1946	Was	A	P	8	3-2
1946	Bos	N	P	8	2-5
	BRTR			184	64-69

NILAND, THOMAS JAMES
(Honest Tom)
b.Apr.14,1870 Lynn,Mass.
d.Apr.30,1950

Yr	Cl	Lea	Pos	G	Rec
1896	St.L	N	S-O	18	.162
	BRTR				

NILES, HARRY CLYDE
b.Sept.10,1880 Buchanan,Mich.
d.Apr.18,1953

Yr	Cl	Lea	Pos	G	Rec
1906	St.L	A	3-O	142	.229
1907	St.L	A	2	120	.289
1908	NY	A	2	95	.250
1908	Bos	A	2	18	.235
1909	Bos	A	O	145	.245
1910	Bos	A	O	18	.214
1910	Cle	A	O	70	.212
	BRTR			608	.246

NILES, WILLIAM A.
b.1869 Covington,Ky.
d.June 1,1897

Yr	Cl	Lea	Pos	G	Rec
1895	Pit	N	3	11	.205

NILL, GEORGE CHARLES
(Rabbit)
b.July 14,1881 Ft.Wayne,Ind.
d.May 24,1962

Yr	Cl	Lea	Pos	G	Rec
1904	Was	A	2	15	.167
1905	Was	A	2-3	103	.182
1906	Was	A	2-S-O	89	.235
1907	Was	A	2-S-3	66	.218
1907	Cle	A	2	12	.286
1908	Cle	A	S	11	.215
	BRTR			296	.212

NIPPERT, MERLIN LEE
b.Sept.1,1938 Reed,Okla.

Yr	Cl	Lea	Pos	G	Rec
1962	Bos	A	P	4	0-0
	BRTR				

NISCHWITZ, RONALD LEE
b.July 1,1937 Dayton,O.

Yr	Cl	Lea	Pos	G	Rec
1961	Det	A	P	6	0-1
1962	Det	A	P	48	4-5
	BBTL			54	4-6

NITCHOLAS, OTHO JAMES
b.Sept.13,1911 McKinney,Tex.

Yr	Cl	Lea	Pos	G	Rec
1945	Bro	N	P	7	1-0
	BRTR				

NIXON, ALBERT RICHARD
(Humpty Dumpty)
b.Apr.20,1892 Atlantic City,N.J.
d.Nov.9,1960

Yr	Cl	Lea	Pos	G	Rec
1915	Bro	N	O	14	.231
1916	Bro	N	O	1	1.000
1918	Bro	N	O	6	.454
1921	Bos	N	O	55	.239
1922	Bos	N	O	86	.264
1923	Bos	N	O	88	.274
1926	Phi	N	O	93	.293
1927	Phi	N	O	54	.312
1928	Phi	N	O	25	.234
	BRTL			422	.276

NIXON, RUSSELL EUGENE
b.Feb.19,1935 Harrison,O.

Yr	Cl	Lea	Pos	G	Rec
1957	Cle	A	C	62	.281
1958	Cle	A	C	113	.301

(Continued)

Yr	Cl	Lea	Pos	G	Rec
1959	Cle	A	C	82	.240
1960	Cle	A	C	25	.244
1960	Bos	A	C	80	.298
1961	Bos	A	C	87	.289
1962	Bos	A	C	65	.278
	BLTR			514	.281

NIXON, WILLARD LEE
b.June 17,1928 Lindale,Ga.

Yr	Cl	Lea	Pos	G	Rec
1950	Bos	A	P	22	8-6
1951	Bos	A	P	34	7-4
1952	Bos	A	P	33	5-4
1953	Bos	A	P	23	4-8
1954	Bos	A	P	31	11-12
1955	Bos	A	P	31	12-10
1956	Bos	A	P	23	9-8
1957	Bos	A	P	32	12-13
1958	Bos	A	P	10	1-7
	BLTR			239	69-72

NOBLE, RAFAEL MIGUEL
(Ray)
b.Mar.15,1922 Central Hatillo,Cuba.

Yr	Cl	Lea	Pos	G	Rec
1951	NY	N	C	55	.234
1952	NY	N	C	6	.000
1953	NY	N	C	46	.206
	BRTR			107	.218

NOFTSKER, GEORGE W.

Yr	Cl	Lea	Pos	G	Rec
1884	Alt	U	C-O	7	.042

NOLAN, EDWARD SYLVESTER
(The Only)
b.Nov.7,1858 Paterson,N.J.
d.May 19,1913

Yr	Cl	Lea	Pos	G	Rec
1878	Ind	N	P	35	13-22
1881	Cle	N	P-3-O	40	7-13 .251
1883	Pit	a	P-O	7	0-6 .296
1884	Wil	U	P-O	9	1-4 .242
1885	Phi	N	P-O	8	1-7 .133
	BLTR			99	22-52 .247

NONNENKAMP, LEO WILLIAM
(Red)
b.July 7,1911 St.Louis,Mo.

Yr	Cl	Lea	Pos	G	Rec
1933	Pit	N	H	1	.000
1938	Bos	A	O	87	.283
1939	Bos	A	O	58	.240
1940	Bos	A	H	9	.000
	BLTL			155	.262

NOONAN, PETER JOHN
b.Nov.24,1881 W.Stockbridge,Mass.

Yr	Cl	Lea	Pos	G	Rec
1904	Phi	A	C	38	.202
1906	Chi	N	C	1	.333
1906	St.L	N	C-1	39	.168
1907	St.L	N	C	70	.224
	BRTR			148	.205

NOPS, JEREMIAH H.
b.June 23,1875 Toledo,O.
d.Mar.26,1937

Yr	Cl	Lea	Pos	G	Rec
1896	Phi	N	P	1	1-0
1896	Bal	N	P	3	2-1
1897	Bal	N	P	28	20-7
1898	Bal	N	P	29	19-10
1899	Bal	N	P	32	16-12
1900	Bro	N	P	9	3-4
1901	Bal	A	P	27	11-12
	TL			129	72-46

NORDSTROM, ANDREW ARTHUR
(Played under name of
Andrew Arthur Carey)

NORDYKE, LOUIS E.
b.Geneva,O.

Yr	Cl	Lea	Pos	G	Rec
1906	St.L	A	1	25	.245

NOREN, IRVING ARNOLD
b.Nov.29,1924 Jamestown,N.Y.

Yr	Cl	Lea	Pos	G	Rec
1950	Was	A	1-O	138	.295
1951	Was	A	O	129	.279
1952	Was	A	O	12	.245
1952	NY	A	1-O	93	.235
1953	NY	A	O	109	.267
1954	NY	A	1-O	125	.319
1955	NY	A	O	132	.253
1956	NY	A	1-O	29	.216
1957	KC	A	1-O	81	.213
1957	St.L	N	O	17	.367
1958	St.L	N	O	117	.264
1959	St.L	N	1-O	8	.125
1959	Chi	N	1-O	65	.321
1960	Chi	N	1-O	12	.091
1960	LA	N	H	26	.200
	BLTL			1093	.275

NORMAN, FRED HUBERT
b.Aug.20,1942 San Antonio,Tex.

Yr	Cl	Lea	Pos	G	Rec
1962	KC	A	P	1	0-0
	BLTL				

NORMAN, HENRY WILLIS
PATRICK (Bill)
b.July 16,1910 St.Louis,Mo.
d.Apr.21,1962

Yr	Cl	Lea	Pos	G	Rec
1931	Chi	A	O	24	.182
1932	Chi	A	O	13	.229
	BRTR			37	.204

Non-playing manager Det (A) 1958.

NORRIS, LEO JOHN
b.May 17,1908 New Orleans,La.

Yr	Cl	Lea	Pos	G	Rec
1936	Phi	N	2-S	154	.265
1937	Phi	N	2-S-3	116	.257
	BRTR			270	.262

NORTH, LOUIS ALEXANDER
b.June 15,1891 Elgin,Ill.

Yr	Cl	Lea	Pos	G	Rec
1913	Det	A	P	1	0-1
1917	St.L	N	P	5	0-0
1920	St.L	N	P	26	3-2
1921	St.L	N	P	40	4-4
1922	St.L	N	P	53	10-3
1923	St.L	N	P	34	3-4
1924	St.L	N	P	9	0-0
1924	Bos	N	P	6	1-2
	BRTR			174	21-16

NORTHEN, HUBBARD ELWIN
b.Aug.16,1889 Atlanta,Tex.
d.Oct.1,1947

Yr	Cl	Lea	Pos	G	Rec
1910	St.L	A	O	26	.198
1911	Cin	N	O	1	.000
1911	Bro	N	O	19	.316
1912	Bro	N	O	118	.282
	BLTL			164	.272

NORTHEY, RONALD JAMES
b.Apr.26,1920 Mahanoy City,Pa.

Yr	Cl	Lea	Pos	G	Rec
1942	Phi	N	O	127	.251
1943	Phi	N	O	147	.278
1944	Phi	N	O	152	.288
1946	Phi	N	O	128	.249
1947	Phi	N	O	13	.255
1947	St.L	N	3-O	110	.293
1948	St.L	N	O	96	.321
1949	St.L	N	O	90	.260
1950	Cin	N	O	27	.260
1950	Chi	N	O	53	.281
1952	Chi	N	H	1	.000
1955	Chi	A	O	14	.357
1956	Chi	A	O	53	.354
1957	Chi	A	H	40	.185
1957	Phi	N	H	33	.269
	BLTR			1084	.276

NORTHROP, GEORGE HOWARD
(Jerky)
b.Jan.5,1888 Lewisburg,Pa.
d.Nov.16,1945

Yr	Cl	Lea	Pos	G	Rec
1918	Bos	N	P	7	5-1
1919	Bos	N	P	12	1-5
	BLTR			19	6-6

NORTON, ELISHA S.
b.Aug.17,1873 Conneaut,O.

Yr	Cl	Lea	Pos	G	Rec
1896	Was	N	P	8	3-2
1897	Was	N	P	8	1-1
				16	4-3

NORTON, J. J.
(Played under name of
Thomas John Carey)

NORTON, PETER J.
b.June 19,1850 Wisconsin
d.Feb.8,1923

Yr	Cl	Lea	Pos	G	Rec
1871	Oly	n	O	1	.000

NOTTEBART, DONALD EDWARD
b.Jan.23,1936 W.Newton,Mass.

Yr	Cl	Lea	Pos	G	Rec
1960	Mil	N	P	5	1-0
1961	Mil	N	P	38	6-7
1962	Mil	N	P	39	2-2
	BRTR			82	9-9

NOURSE, CHESTER LINWOOD
b.Aug.7,1887 Ipswich,Mass.
d.Apr.20,1958

Yr	Cl	Lea	Pos	G	Rec
1909	Bos	A	P	3	0-0

NOVIKOFF, LOUIS
(Mad Russian)
b.Oct.12,1915 Glendale,Ariz.

Yr	Cl	Lea	Pos	G	Rec
1941	Chi	N	O	62	.241
1942	Chi	N	O	128	.300
1943	Chi	N	O	78	.279
1944	Chi	N	O	71	.281
1946	Phi	N	O	17	.304
	BRTR			356	.282

NOVOTNEY, RALPH JOSEPH
(Rube)
b.Aug.5,1924 Streator,Ill.

Yr	Cl	Lea	Pos	G	Rec
1949	Chi	N	C	22	.269
	BRTR				

NOYES, WINFIELD CHARLES
b.June 16,1889 Pleasanton,Neb.

Yr	Cl	Lea	Pos	G	Rec
1913	Bos	N	P	11	0-0
1917	Phi	A	P	27	10-10
1919	Phi	A	P	10	1-5
1919	Chi	A	P	1	0-0
	BRTR			49	11-15

NUNAMAKER, LESLIE GRANT
b.Aug.25,1889 Aurora,Neb.
d.Nov.14,1938

Yr	Cl	Lea	Pos	G	Rec
1911	Bos	A	C	62	.257
1912	Bos	A	C	35	.252
1913	Bos	A	C	30	.227
1914	Bos	A	C	5	.200
1914	NY	A	C	86	.265
1915	NY	A	C	87	.225
1916	NY	A	C	91	.296
1917	NY	A	C	104	.261
1918	St.L	A	C	85	.259
1919	Cle	A	C	26	.256
1920	Cle	A	C	34	.333
1921	Cle	A	C	46	.359
1922	Cle	A	C	25	.302
	BRTR			716	.268

NUNN, HOWARD RALPH
b.Oct.18,1935 Westfield,N.C.

Yr	Cl	Lea	Pos	G	Rec
1959	St.L	N	P	16	2-2
1961	Cin	N	P	24	2-1
1962	Cin	N	P	6	0-0
	BRTR			46	4-3

NUSZ, -----

Yr	Cl	Lea	Pos	G	Rec
1884	Was	U	O	1	.000

Yr Cl Lea Pos G Rec

NUTTER, EVERETT CLARENCE
b.1885
1919 Bos N O 18 .212
BLTR

NUXHALL, JOSEPH HENRY
b.July 30,1928 Hamilton,O.
1944 Cin N P 1 0-0
1952 Cin N P 37 1-4
1953 Cin N P 30 9-11
1954 Cin N P 36 12-5
1955 Cin N P 53 17-12
1956 Cin N P 44 13-11
1957 Cin N P 42 10-10
1958 Cin N P 36 12-11
1959 Cin N P 12 5-0
1960 Cin N P 39 1-8
1961 KC A P 56 5-8
1962 LA A P 5 0-0
1962 Cin N P 12 5-0
BLTL 419 94-89

NYE, OTTO ADAM
b.Sept.24,1894 Springfield,O.
d.Sept.19,1932
1917 St.L A H 1 .000

OAKES, ENNIS TALMADGE (Rebel)
b.Dec.17,1886 Homer,La.
d.Feb.28,1948
1909 Cin N O 113 .270
1910 St.L N O 127 .252
1911 St.L N O 151 .263
1912 St.L N O 136 .281
1913 St.L N O 147 .293
1914 Pit F M-O 145 .311
1915 Pit F M-O 153 .281
BLTR 972 .280

OANA, HENRY KAMEHAMEHA (Prince)
b.Jan.22,1910 Waipahu,Hawaii.
1934 Phi N O 6 .238
1943 Det A P 20 3-2
1945 Det A P 4 0-0
BRTR 30 3-2 / .308

OBERLANDER, HARTMAN LOUIS
b.May 12, 1864 Waukegan, Ill.
d.Nov.14,1922
1888 Cle a P 3 1-2

OBERLIN, FRANK RUFUS
b.Mar.26,1876 Elsie,Mich.
d.Jan.6,1952
1906 Bos A P 4 1-3
1907 Bos A P 12 1-5
1907 Was A P 12 2-6
1909 Was A P 10 1-3
1910 Was A P 8 1-6
BRTR 46 6-23

O'BRIEN, EDWARD JOSEPH
b.Dec.11,1930 S.Amboy,N.J.
1953 Pit N S 89 .238
1955 Pit N S-3-O 75 .233
1956 Pit N P-2-S-3-O 63 0-0 / .264
1957 Pit N P 3 1-0
1958 Pit N P 1 0-0
BRTR 231 1-0 / .236

O'BRIEN, FRANK ANDREW (Dink)
b.Sept.13,1898 San Francisco,Cal.
1923 Phi N C 15 .333
BRTR

O'BRIEN, GEORGE JOSEPH
b.Nov.4,1889 Cleveland,O.
1915 St.L A C 3 .222
BRTR

O'BRIEN, JEREMIAH
b.Worcester,Mass.
d.July 5, 1911
1887 Was N 2 1 .000

O'BRIEN, JOHN E.
1884 Bal U O 18 .256

O'BRIEN, JOHN F.
b.Apr.15,1867 W.Troy,N.Y.
d.Mar.11,1892
1888 Cle a P 31 11-19
1889 Cle N P 41 22-17
1890 Cle p P 26 8-16
1891 Bos a P 41 19-13
BRTR 139 60-65

O'BRIEN, JOHN J.
b.July 14,1870 St.John,N.B.,Canada.
d.May 13,1913
1891 Bro N 2 43 .251
1893 Chi N 2 4 .416
1895 Lou N 2 128 .262
1896 Lou N 2 49 .333
1896 Was N 2 69 .270
1897 Was N 2 84 .242
1899 Bal N 2 39 .190
1899 Pit N 2 76 .223
BLTR 492 .256

O'BRIEN, JOHN JOSEPH
b.Feb.5,1873 W.Troy,N.Y.
d.June 11,1933
1899 Was N O 121 .279
1901 Was A O 12 .184
1901 Cle A O 91 .286
1903 Bos A O 96 .212
320 .259

O'BRIEN, JOHN K.
(Real name John K. Bvrne)
b.June 12,1860 Philadelphia,Pa.
d.Nov.2,1910
1882 Ath a C-1-O 62 .304
1883 Ath a C-1-S-3-O 93 .281
1884 Ath a C-O 38 .300
1885 Ath a C 61 .261
1886 Ath a C-1-3 105 .257
1887 Bro a C 30 .269
1888 Bal a C 57 .224
1890 Ath a 1 110 .270
BRTR 556 .276

O'BRIEN, JOHN THOMAS
b.Dec.11,1930 S.Amboy,N.J.
1953 Pit N 2-S 89 .247
1955 Pit N 2 84 .299
1956 Pit N P-2-S 73 1-0 / .173
1957 Pit N P-2-S 34 0-3 / .314
1958 Pit N H 3 .000
1958 St.L N P-2-S 12 0-0 / .000
1959 Mil N 2 44 .198
BRTR 339 1-3 / .250

O'BRIEN, PETER F.
b.June 16,1868 Chicago,Ill.
1890 Chi N 2 27 .275

O'BRIEN, PETER J.
b.1876 Binghamton,N.Y.
d.Jan.31,1917
1901 Cin N 2 15 .208
1906 St.L A 2-3 151 .233
1907 Cle A 3 43 .244
1907 Was A 2 39 .185
BLTR 248 .231

O'BRIEN, RAYMOND JOSEPH
b.Oct.31,1892 St.Louis,Mo.
d.Mar.31,1942
1916 Pit N O 16 .211
BLTL

O'BRIEN, THOMAS EDWARD
b.Dec.19,1918 Anniston,Ala.
1943 Pit N 3-O 89 .310
1944 Pit N 3-O 85 .250
1945 Pit N O 58 .335
1949 Bos A O 49 .224
1950 Bos A O 9 .129
1950 Was A O 3 .111
BRTR 293 .275

O'BRIEN, THOMAS F.
b.Feb.20,1873 Verona,Pa.
d.Feb.4,1901
1897 Bal N 1 38 .268
1898 Bal N O 19 .217
1898 Pit N 1-O 104 .259
1899 NY N 3-O 152 .305
1900 Pit N 1-O 94 .294
407 .284

O'BRIEN, THOMAS H.
b.Salem,Mass.
d.Apr.21,1921
b.Providence,R.I.
1882 Wor N 2-3-O 22 .202
1883 Bal a 2-O 33 .294
1884 Bos U 2 102 .265
1885 Bal a 1-2 8 .182
1887 Met a 1 29 .248
1890 Roc a 1 73 .181
267 .239

O'BRIEN, THOMAS JOSEPH (Buck)
b.May 10,1882 Brockton,Mass.
d.July 25,1959
1911 Bos A P 6 5-1
1912 Bos A P 35 18-13
1913 Bos A P 13 4-9
1913 Chi A P 6 0-3
BRTR 60 27-26

O'BRIEN, WILLIAM D. (Darby)
b.Sept.1,1863 Peoria,Ill.
d.June 15,1893
1887 Met a O 129 .353
1888 Bro a O 136 .275
1889 Bro a O 136 .312
1890 Bro N O 85 .314
1891 Bro N O 102 .260
1892 Bro N O 121 .245
BRTR 709 .292

O'BRIEN, WILLIAM SMITH
b.Apr.16,1860 Albany,N.Y.
d.May 27,1911
1884 St.P U P-3 8 1-1 / .241
1884 KC U 1-3 4 .235
1887 Was N 1 113 .310
1888 Was N 1 133 .225
1889 Was N 1 2 .000
1890 Bro a 1 95 .277
BR 355 1-1 / .266

OCK, HAROLD DAVID (Whitey)
b.Mar.17,1912 Brooklyn,N.Y.
1935 Bro N C 1 .000
BRTR

OCKEY, WALTER ANDREW
(Real name Walter Andrew Okypch)
b.Jan.4,1920 New York,N.Y.
1944 NY N P 2 0-0
BRTR

O'CONNELL, DANIEL FRANCIS
b.Jan.21,1929 Paterson,N.J.
1950 Pit N S-3 79 .292
1953 Pit N 2-3 149 .294
1954 Mil N 1-2-3-3 146 .279
1955 Mil N 2-S-3 124 .225
1956 Mil N 2-S-3 139 .239
1957 Mil N 2 48 .235

(Continued)

Yr	Cl	Lea	Pos	G	Rec
1957	NY	N	2-3	95	.266
1958	SF	N	2-3	107	.232
1959	SF	N	2-3	34	.190
1961	Was	A	2-3	138	.260
1962	Was	A	2-3	84	.263
		BRTR		1143	.260

O'CONNELL, JAMES JOSEPH
b.Feb.11,1901 Sacramento,Cal.

Yr	Cl	Lea	Pos	G	Rec
1923	NY	N	1-O	87	.250
1924	NY	N	2-O	52	.317
		BLTR		139	.270

O'CONNELL, JOHN CHARLES
b.June 13,1905 Pittsburgh,Pa.

Yr	Cl	Lea	Pos	G	Rec
1928	Pit	N	C	1	.000
1929	Pit	N	C	2	.143
		BRTR		3	.125

O'CONNELL, JOHN JOSEPH
b.May 16,1872 Lawrence,Mass.

Yr	Cl	Lea	Pos	G	Rec
1891	Bal	a	2-S	7	.172
1902	Det	A	1-2	8	.136
				15	.157

O'CONNELL, PATRICK H.
b.June 10,1861 Bangor, Me.
d.Jan.24,1943

Yr	Cl	Lea	Pos	G	Rec
1886	Bal	a	O	42	.186
1890	Bro	a	3	11	.237
				53	.192

O'CONNOR, ANDREW JAMES
b.Sept.14,1884 Roxbury,Mass.

Yr	Cl	Lea	Pos	G	Rec
1908	NY	A	P	1	0-1

O'CONNOR, DANIEL C.
b.Guelph,Ont.,Canada.

Yr	Cl	Lea	Pos	G	Rec
1890	Lou	a	1	6	.480

O'CONNOR, FRANK HENRY
b.Sept.15,1870 Keeseville,N.Y.
d.Dec.26,1913

Yr	Cl	Lea	Pos	G	Rec
1893	Phi	N	P	3	0-0
		TL			

O'CONNOR, JAMES MATTHEW
(Played under name of James Matthew Connor)

O'CONNOR, JOHN J.

Yr	Cl	Lea	Pos	G	Rec
1916	Chi	N	C	1	.000
		TR			

O'CONNOR, JOHN JOSEPH
(Rowdy Jack)
b.Mar.3,1867 St.Louis,Mo.
d.Nov.14,1937

Yr	Cl	Lea	Pos	G	Rec
1887	Cin	a	C-O	12	.133
1888	Cin	a	C-O	36	.201
1889	Col	a	C	107	.269
1890	Col	a	C	118	.341
1891	Col	a	C-O	56	.260
1892	Cle	N	C-O	139	.253
1893	Cle	N	C-O	93	.309
1894	Cle	N	C-O	80	.324
1895	Cle	N	C-1	88	.293
1896	Cle	N	C	60	.300
1897	Cle	N	1-O	100	.290
1898	Cle	N	C-1	129	.262
1899	St.L	N	C-1	79	.261
1900	St.L	N	C	10	.219
1900	Pit	N	C	38	.242
1901	Pit	N	C	56	.200
1902	Pit	N	C-1	45	.292
1903	NY	A	C	64	.197
1904	St.L	A	C	13	.178
1906	St.L	A	C	58	.190
1907	St.L	A	C	25	.157
1910	St.L	A	M-C	1	.000
		BRTR		1407	.268

Non-playing manager St.L (A) 1909.

O'CONNOR, PATRICK FRANCIS
b.Aug.4,1879 Windsor Locks,Conn.
d.Aug.17,1950

Yr	Cl	Lea	Pos	G	Rec
1908	Pit	N	C	12	.187
1909	Pit	N	C	9	.312

(Continued)

Yr	Cl	Lea	Pos	G	Rec
1910	Pit	N	C	1	.250
1914	St.L	N	C	10	.000
1915	Pit	F	C	70	.224
1918	NY	A	C	1	.333
		BRTR		103	.222

O'DAY, HENRY F.
b.July 8,1863 Chicago,Ill.
d.July 2,1935.

Yr	Cl	Lea	Pos	G	Rec
1884	Tol	a	P-O	65	10-29 .209
1885	Pit	a	P	14	5-7
1886	Was	N	P	6	2-2
1887	Was	N	P	34	8-19
1888	Was	N	P	47	16-31
1889	Was	N	P	13	4-5
1889	NY	N	P	15	9-6
1890	NY	p	P	43	22-15
		TR		237	76-114 .198

Non-playing manager Cin (N) 1912 and Chi (N) 1914.

O'DEA, JAMES KENNETH (Ken)
b.Mar.16,1913 Lima,N.Y.

Yr	Cl	Lea	Pos	G	Rec
1935	Chi	N	C	76	.257
1936	Chi	N	C	80	.307
1937	Chi	N	C	83	.301
1938	Chi	N	C	86	.263
1939	NY	N	C	52	.175
1940	NY	N	C	48	.240
1941	NY	N	C	59	.213
1942	St.L	N	C	58	.234
1943	St.L	N	C	71	.281
1944	St.L	N	C	85	.249
1945	St.L	N	C	100	.254
1946	St.L	N	C	22	.123
1946	Bos	N	C	12	.219
		BLTR		832	.255

O'DEA, PAUL
b.July 3,1920 Cleveland,O.

Yr	Cl	Lea	Pos	G	Rec
1944	Cle	A	P-1-O	76	0-0 .318
1945	Cle	A	P-O	87	0-0 .235
		BLTL		163	0-0 .272

O'DELL, WILLIAM OLIVER
b.Feb.10,1933 Whitmire,S.C.

Yr	Cl	Lea	Pos	G	Rec
1954	Bal	A	P	7	1-1
1956	Bal	A	P	4	0-0
1957	Bal	A	P	37	4-10
1958	Bal	A	P	42	14-11
1959	Bal	A	P	43	10-12
1960	SF	N	P	49	8-13
1961	SF	N	P	49	7-5
1962	SF	N	P	49	19-14
		BBTL		280	63-66

ODENWALD. THEODORE JOSEPH
b.Jan.4,1902 Hudson,Wis.

Yr	Cl	Lea	Pos	G	Rec
1921	Cle	A	P	10	1-0
1922	Cle	A	P	1	0-0
		BRTL		11	1-0

ODOM, DAVID EVERETT (Blimp)
b.June 5,1918 Dinuba,Cal.

Yr	Cl	Lea	Pos	G	Rec
1943	Bos	N	P	22	0-3
		BRTR			

ODOM, HERMAN BOYD (Heinie)
b.Oct.13,1900 Rusk,Tex.

Yr	Cl	Lea	Pos	G	Rec
1925	NY	A	3	1	1.000
		BBTR			

O'DONNELL, ...

Yr	Cl	Lea	Pos	G	Rec
1884	Key	U	C	1	.250

O'DONNELL, GEORGE DANA
b.May 27,1929 Jacksonville,Ill.

Yr	Cl	Lea	Pos	G	Rec
1954	Pit	N	P	21	3-9
		BRTR			

O'DONNELL, HARRY HERMAN
b.Apr.2,1894 Philadelphia,Pa.
d.Jan.31,1958

Yr	Cl	Lea	Pos	G	Rec
1927	Phi	N	C	16	.063
		BRTR			

O'DOUL, FRANK JOSEPH (Lefty)
b.Mar.4,1897 San Francisco,Cal.

Yr	Cl	Lea	Pos	G	Rec
1919	NY	A	P	19	0-0
1920	NY	A	P	13	0-0
1922	NY	A	P	8	0-0
1923	Bos	A	P	36	1-1
1928	NY	N	O	114	.319
1929	Phi	N	O	154	.398
1930	Phi	N	O	140	.383
1931	Bro	N	O	134	.336
1932	Bro	N	O	148	.368
1933	Bro	N	O	43	.252
1933	NY	N	O	78	.306
1934	NY	N	O	83	.316
		BLTL		970	1-1 .349

O'DOWD, JOHN LEO
b.Jan.3,1891 S.Weymouth,Mass.

Yr	Cl	Lea	Pos	G	Rec
1912	NY	A	S	10	.194
		TR			

ODWELL, FREDERICK WILLIAM
b.Sept.25,1872 Downsville,N.Y.
d.Aug.12,1948

Yr	Cl	Lea	Pos	G	Rec
1904	Cin	N	O	126	.284
1905	Cin	N	O	126	.241
1906	Cin	N	O	57	.223
1907	Cin	N	O	84	.270
		BLTR		393	.258

OERTEL, CHARLES FRANK
b.Mar.12,1931 Coffeyville,Kans.

Yr	Cl	Lea	Pos	G	Rec
1958	Bal	A	O	14	.167
		BLTR			

OESCHGER, JOSEPH CARL
b.May 23,1891 Glendale,Cal.

Yr	Cl	Lea	Pos	G	Rec
1914	Phi	N	P	32	4-8
1915	Phi	N	P	6	1-0
1916	Phi	N	P	14	1-0
1917	Phi	N	P	43	15-14
1918	Phi	N	P	30	6-18
1919	Phi	N	P	5	0-1
1919	NY	N	P	5	0-1
1919	Bos	N	P	7	4-2
1920	Bos	N	P	38	15-13
1921	Bos	N	P	46	20-14
1922	Bos	N	P	46	6-21
1923	Bos	N	P	44	5-15
1924	NY	N	P	10	2-0
1924	Phi	N	P	19	2-7
1925	Bro	N	P	21	1-2
		BRTR		366	82-116

O'FARRELL, ROBERT ARTHUR
b.Oct.19,1896 Waukegan,Ill.

Yr	Cl	Lea	Pos	G	Rec
1915	Chi	N	C	2	.667
1916	Chi	N	C	1	.000
1917	Chi	N	C	3	.375
1918	Chi	N	C	52	.283
1919	Chi	N	C	49	.216
1920	Chi	N	C	94	.248
1921	Chi	N	C	96	.250
1922	Chi	N	C	128	.323
1923	Chi	N	C	131	.319
1924	Chi	N	C	71	.241
1925	Chi	N	C	17	.182
1925	St.L	N	C	94	.278
1926	St.L	N	C	147	.293
1927	St.L	N	M-C	61	.264
1928	St.L	N	C	16	.212
1928	NY	N	C	75	.195
1929	NY	N	C	91	.306
1930	NY	N	C	94	.301
1931	NY	N	C	85	.224
1932	NY	N	C	50	.239

Yr	Cl	Lea	Pos	G	Rec
1933	St.L	N	C	55	.239
1934	Cin	N	M-C	44	.244
1934	Chi	N	C	22	.224
1935	St.L	N	C	14	.000
	BRTR			1492	.273

OGDEN, JOHN MAHLON
b.Nov.5,1897 Ogden,Pa.

Yr	Cl	Lea	Pos	G	Rec
1918	NY	N	P	5	0-0
1928	St.L	A	P	38	15-16
1929	St.L	A	P	34	4-8
1931	Cin	N	P	23	4-8
1932	Cin	N	P	27	2-2
	BRTR			127	25-34

OGDEN, WARREN HARVEY (Curly)
b.Jan.24,1901 Ogden,Pa.

Yr	Cl	Lea	Pos	G	Rec
1922	Phi	A	P	17	1-4
1923	Phi	A	P	19	1-2
1924	Phi	A	P	5	0-3
1924	Was	A	P	14	9-5
1925	Was	A	P	17	3-1
1926	Was	A	P	22	4-4
	BRTR			94	18-19

OGLESBY, JAMES DORN
b.Aug.10,1915 Polk Co.,Mo.
d.Sept.1,1955

Yr	Cl	Lea	Pos	G	Rec
1936	Phi	A	1	3	.182
	BLTL				

OGRODOWSKI, AMBROSE FRANCIS (Bruce)
b.Feb.17,1913 Hoytville,Pa.
d.Mar.5,1956

Yr	Cl	Lea	Pos	G	Rec
1936	St.L	N	C	94	.228
1937	St.L	N	C	90	.233
	BRTR			184	.231

OGRODOWSKI, JOSEPH ANTHONY
b.Nov.20,1906 Morris,W.Va.

Yr	Cl	Lea	Pos	G	Rec
1925	Bos	N	P	1	0-0
	BRTR				

O'HAGAN, HAROLD P.
b.Sept.30,1873 Washington,D.C.
d.Jan.14,1913

Yr	Cl	Lea	Pos	G	Rec
1892	Was	N	C	1	.250
1902	Chi	N	1	33	.188
1902	NY	N	1	24	.138
1902	Cle	A	1	3	.384
				61	.177

O'HARA, JAMES FRANCIS (Kid)
b.Dec.19,1875 Wilkes-Barre,Pa.
d.Dec.1,1954

Yr	Cl	Lea	Pos	G	Rec
1904	Bos	N	O	8	.207

O'HARA, THOMAS F.
b.July 13,1885 Waverly,N.Y.
d.June 8,1954

Yr	Cl	Lea	Pos	G	Rec
1906	St.L	N	O	14	.321
1907	St.L	N	O	47	.237
				61	.257

O'HARA, WILLIAM A.
b.Aug.14,1883 Toronto,Ont.,Canada.

Yr	Cl	Lea	Pos	G	Rec
1909	NY	N	O	111	.236
1910	St.L	N	P-1-O	9	0-0 / .150
	BL			120	0-0 / .231

OHL, JOSEPH EARL
b.Jan.10,1888 Jobstown,N.J.
d.Dec.18,1951

Yr	Cl	Lea	Pos	G	Rec
1909	Was	A	P	4	0-0
	BLTL				

OKRIE, FRANK ANTHONY (Lefty)
b.Oct.28,1896 Detroit,Mich.
d.Oct.16,1959

Yr	Cl	Lea	Pos	G	Rec
1920	Det	A	P	21	1-2
	BLTL				

OKRIE, LEONARD JOSEPH
b.July 16,1924 Detroit,Mich.

Yr	Cl	Lea	Pos	G	Rec
1948	Was	A	C	19	.238
1950	Was	A	C	17	.222
1951	Was	A	C	5	.125
1952	Bos	A	C	1	.000
	BRTR			42	.218

OKYPCH, WALTER ANDREW
(Played under name of Walter Andrew Ockey)

OLDFIELD, DAVID
b.Philadelphia,Pa.

Yr	Cl	Lea	Pos	G	Rec
1883	Bal	a	C	1	.000
1885	Bro	a	C-O	10	.308
1886	Bro	a	C	14	.240
1886	Was	N	C	19	.158
	TR			44	.211

OLDHAM, JOHN CYRUS (Red)
b.July 15,1893 Zion,Md.
d.Jan.28,1961

Yr	Cl	Lea	Pos	G	Rec
1914	Det	A	P	9	2-4
1915	Det	A	P	17	2-0
1920	Det	A	P	39	8-13
1921	Det	A	P	42	11-14
1922	Det	A	P	43	10-13
1925	Pit	N	P	11	3-2
1926	Pit	N	P	17	2-2
	BLTL			178	38-48

OLDHAM, JOHN HARDIN
b.Nov.6,1932 Salinas,Cal.

Yr	Cl	Lea	Pos	G	Rec
1956	Cin	N	H	1	.000
	BL				

OLDIS, ROBERT CARL
b.Jan.5,1928 Preston,Ia.

Yr	Cl	Lea	Pos	G	Rec
1953	Was	A	C	7	.250
1954	Was	A	C-3	11	.333
1955	Was	A	C	6	.000
1960	Pit	N	C	22	.200
1961	Pit	N	C	4	.000
1962	Phi	N	C	38	.263
	BRTR			88	.245

OLDRING, REUBEN NOSHIER
b.May 30,1884 New York,N.Y.
d.Sept.9,1961

Yr	Cl	Lea	Pos	G	Rec
1905	NY	A	S	8	.300
1906	Phi	A	3	59	.241
1907	Phi	A	O	117	.286
1908	Phi	A	O	116	.221
1909	Phi	A	O	90	.230
1910	Phi	A	O	134	.308
1911	Phi	A	O	121	.297
1912	Phi	A	O	98	.301
1913	Phi	A	O	136	.283
1914	Phi	A	O	119	.277
1915	Phi	A	O	107	.248
1916	Phi	A	O	40	.247
1916	NY	A	O	43	.234
1918	Phi	A	O	49	.233
	BRTR			1237	.270

O'LEARY, CHARLES TIMOTHY
b.Oct.15,1881 Chicago,Ill.
d.Jan.6,1941

Yr	Cl	Lea	Pos	G	Rec
1904	Det	A	S	135	.215
1905	Det	A	S	148	.213
1906	Det	A	S	128	.219
1907	Det	A	S	139	.241
1908	Det	A	S	65	.251
1909	Det	A	3	76	.203
1910	Det	A	2-S	65	.242
1911	Det	A	2	74	.266
1912	Det	A	2	3	.200
1913	St.L	N	2-S	121	.217
1934	St.L	A	H	1	1.000
	BRTR			955	.234

O'LEARY, DANIEL (Hustling Dan)
b.Oct.22,1856 Detroit,Mich.
d.June 24,1922

Yr	Cl	Lea	Pos	G	Rec
1879	Pro	N	O	2	.429
1880	Bos	N	O	3	.250
1881	Det	N	O	2	.000
1882	Wor	N	O	6	.167
1884	Cin	U	M-O	27	.252
	BL			40	.235

OLIN, FRANKLIN WALTER
b.Jan.9,1860 Woodford,Vt.
d.May 20,1951

Yr	Cl	Lea	Pos	G	Rec
1884	Was	a	2-O	21	.386
1884	Was	U	O	1	.000
1884	Tol	a	O	26	.271
1885	Det	N	3	1	.500
				49	.306

OLIVA, ANTONIO
b.July 20,1938 Pinar Del Rio,Cuba

Yr	Cl	Lea	Pos	G	Rec
1962	Min	A	O	9	.444
	BLTR				

OLIVARES, EDWARD BALZAC
b.Nov.5,1938 Brooklyn,N.Y.

Yr	Cl	Lea	Pos	G	Rec
1960	St.L	N	3	3	.000
1961	St.L	N	O	21	.167
	BRTR			24	.143

OLIVER, EUGENE GEORGE
b.Mar.22,1935 Moline,Ill.

Yr	Cl	Lea	Pos	G	Rec
1959	St.L	N	C-1-O	68	.244
1961	St.L	N	C-O	22	.269
1962	St.L	N	C-1-O	122	.258
	BRTR			212	.255

OLIVER, RICHARD
(Real name Tracy Souter Barrett)

OLIVER, THOMAS NOBLE (Rebel)
b.Jan.15,1903 Montgomery,Ala.

Yr	Cl	Lea	Pos	G	Rec
1930	Bos	A	O	154	.293
1931	Bos	A	O	148	.276
1932	Bos	A	O	122	.264
1933	Bos	A	O	90	.258
	BRTR			514	.277

OLIVO, DIOMEDES ANTONIO
b.Jan.22,1920 Guayubin,D.R.

Yr	Cl	Lea	Pos	G	Rec
1960	Pit	N	P	4	0-0
1962	Pit	N	P	62	5-1
	BLTL			66	5-1

OLIVO, FREDERICO EMILIO
b.Mar.18,1929 Guayubin,D.R.

Yr	Cl	Lea	Pos	G	Rec
1961	Mil	N	P	3	0-0
	BRTR				

OLMO, LUIS RODRIGUEZ
b.Aug.11,1919 Arecibo,Puerto Rico

Yr	Cl	Lea	Pos	G	Rec
1943	Bro	N	O	57	.303
1944	Bro	N	2-3-O	136	.258
1945	Bro	N	2-3-O	141	.313
1949	Bro	N	O	38	.305
1950	Bos	N	3-O	69	.227
1951	Bos	N	O	21	.196
	BRTR			462	.281

OLMSTEAD, FREDERICK D.
b.1884 Ravenna,Mich.

Yr	Cl	Lea	Pos	G	Rec
1905	Bos	A	P	3	1-2
1908	Chi	A	P	1	1-0
1909	Chi	A	P	8	3-2
1910	Chi	A	P	32	10-12
1911	Chi	A	P	25	6-6
	BRTR			69	20-22

OLSEN, ALBERT WILLIAM
b.Mar.30,1921 San Diego,Cal.

Yr	Cl	Lea	Pos	G	Rec
1943	Bos	A	H	1	.000
BLTL					

OLSEN, ARTHUR OLE
b.Sept.12,1896 S.Norwalk,Conn.

Yr	Cl	Lea	Pos	G	Rec
1922	Det	A	P	39	7-6
1923	Det	A	P	17	1-1
BRTR				56	8-7

OLSEN, BERNARD CHARLES
b.Sept.11,1919 Everett,Mass.

Yr	Cl	Lea	Pos	G	Rec
1941	Chi	N	O	24	.288
BRTR					

OLSEN, VERNON JARL
b.Mar.16,1918 Hillsboro,Ore.

Yr	Cl	Lea	Pos	G	Rec
1939	Chi	N	P	4	1-0
1940	Chi	N	P	35	13-9
1941	Chi	N	P	37	10-8
1942	Chi	N	P	32	6-9
1946	Chi	N	P	5	0-0
BRTL				113	30-26

OLSON, ARTHUR
b.Sept.12,1896 S.Norwalk,Conn.

Yr	Cl	Lea	Pos	G	Rec
1922	Det	A	P	39	7-6
1923	Det	A	P	17	1-1
BRTR				56	8-7

OLSON, IVAN MASSIE (Ivy)
b.Oct.14,1885 Kansas City,Mo.

Yr	Cl	Lea	Pos	G	Rec
1911	Cle	A	S	140	.261
1912	Cle	A	S-3	123	.253
1913	Cle	A	1-3	104	.248
1914	Cle	A	2-S-3	89	.242
1915	Cin	N	1-2-3	63	.232
1915	Bro	N	3	18	.077
1916	Bro	N	3	108	.254
1917	Bro	N	S	139	.269
1918	Bro	N	S	126	.239
1919	Bro	N	S	140	.278
1920	Bro	N	2-S	143	.254
1921	Bro	N	2-S	151	.267
1922	Bro	N	2-S	136	.272
1923	Bro	N	1-2-S-3	82	.260
1924	Bro	N	2-S	10	.222
BRTR				1572	.267

OLSON, KARL ARTHUR
b.July 6,1930 Ross, Cal.

Yr	Cl	Lea	Pos	G	Rec
1951	Bos	A	O	5	.100
1953	Bos	A	O	25	.123
1954	Bos	A	O	101	.260
1955	Bos	A	O	26	.250
1956	Was	A	O	106	.246
1957	Was	A	O	8	.167
1957	Det	A	O	8	.143
BRTR				279	.235

OLSON, MARVIN CLEMENT
b.May 28,1907 Gayville,S.Dak.

Yr	Cl	Lea	Pos	G	Rec
1931	Bos	A	2	15	.189
1932	Bos	A	2	115	.248
1933	Bos	A	2	3	.000
BRTR				133	.241

OLSON, THEODORE OTTO
b.Aug.27,1912 Squantum,Mass.

Yr	Cl	Lea	Pos	G	Rec
1936	Bos	A	P	5	1-1
1937	Bos	A	P	11	0-0
1938	Bos	A	P	2	0-0
BRTR				18	1-1

O'MARA, OLIVER EDWARD
b.Mar.8,1892 St.Louis,Mo.

Yr	Cl	Lea	Pos	G	Rec
1912	Det	A	S	1	.000
1914	Bro	N	S	67	.263
1915	Bro	N	S	149	.244
1916	Bro	N	S	72	.202
1918	Bro	N	3	121	.213
1919	Bro	N	3	2	.000
TR				412	.231

O'MEARA, THOMAS EDWARD
b.Dec.12,1872 Chicago,Ill.
d.Feb.16,1902

Yr	Cl	Lea	Pos	G	Rec
1895	Cle	N	C	1	.000
1896	Cle	N	C	9	.148
				10	.135

O'NEAL, ...

Yr	Cl	Lea	Pos	G	Rec
1874	Har	n	O	1	.000

O'NEAL, ORAN HERBERT
b.May 2,1900 Gatewood,Mo.

Yr	Cl	Lea	Pos	G	Rec
1925	Phi	N	P	11	0-0
1927	Phi	N	P	2	0-0
BRTR				13	0-0

O'NEIL, DENNIS
b.1861 Ireland.

Yr	Cl	Lea	Pos	G	Rec
1893	St.L	N	1	7	.120

O'NEIL, EDWARD J.
b.Mar.11,1859 Fall River,Mass.
d.Sept.30,1892

Yr	Cl	Lea	Pos	G	Rec
1890	Tol	a	P	3	2-1
1890	Ath	a	P-3-O	11	0-8 .176
TR				14	2-9 .136

O'NEIL, GEORGE MICHAEL (Mickey)
b.Apr.12,1898 St.Louis,Mo.

Yr	Cl	Lea	Pos	G	Rec
1919	Bos	N	C	11	.214
1920	Bos	N	C	112	.283
1921	Bos	N	C	98	.249
1922	Bos	N	C	83	.223
1923	Bos	N	C	96	.212
1924	Bos	N	C	106	.246
1925	Bos	N	C	70	.258
1926	Bro	N	C	75	.209
1927	Was	A	C	5	.000
1927	NY	N	C	16	.132
BRTR				672	.239

O'NEIL, JOHN FRANCIS
b.April 19,1921 Shelbiana,Ky.

Yr	Cl	Lea	Pos	G	Rec
1946	Phi	N	S	46	.266
BRTR					

O'NEILL, ...
b.Bedford,Pa.

Yr	Cl	Lea	Pos	G	Rec
1875	Atl	n	P-S-O	6	0-4 NR

O'NEILL, FREDERICK J.
b.1865 London,Ont.,Canada.
d.Mar.7,1892

Yr	Cl	Lea	Pos	G	Rec
1887	Met	a	O	5	.391

O'NEILL, HARRY MINK
b.May 8,1917 Philadelphia,Pa.
d.Mar.6,1945

Yr	Cl	Lea	Pos	G	Rec
1939	Phi	A	C	1	.000
BRTR					

O'NEILL, JAMES EDWARD (Tip)
b.May 25,1858 Woodstock,Ont.,Canada.
d.Dec.31,1915

Yr	Cl	Lea	Pos	G	Rec
1883	NY	N	P-O	23	7-13 .178
1884	St.L	a	P-O	77	10-4 .272
1885	St.L	a	O	51	.342
1886	St.L	a	O	138	.329
1887	St.L	a	O	123	.492
1888	St.L	a	O	130	.332
1889	St.L	a	O	133	.337
1890	Chi	p	O	137	.302
1891	St.L	a	O	127	.321
1892	Cin	N	O	107	.250
BRTR				1046	17-17 .332

O'NEILL, JAMES LEO
b.Feb.23,1895 Minooka,Pa.

Yr	Cl	Lea	Pos	G	Rec
1920	Was	A	S	86	.289
1923	Was	A	2-S	23	.273
BRTR				109	.287

O'NEILL, JOHN J.
b.New York,N.Y.

Yr	Cl	Lea	Pos	G	Rec
1899	NY	N	C	2	.000
1902	NY	N	C	2	.000
TR				4	.000

O'NEILL, JOHN JOSEPH
b.Jan.10,1873 Maam,County Galway, Ireland.
d.June 29,1935

Yr	Cl	Lea	Pos	G	Rec
1902	St.L	N	C	56	.154
1903	St.L	N	C	74	.236
1904	Chi	N	C	49	.214
1905	Chi	N	C	50	.198
1906	Bos	N	C	51	.180
TR				280	.199

O'NEILL, JOSEPH HENRY
b.Feb.1,1897 Ridgetown,Ont.,Canada.

Yr	Cl	Lea	Pos	G	Rec
1922	Phi	A	P	1	0-0
1923	Phi	A	P	3	0-0
BRTR				4	0-0

O'NEILL, MICHAEL JOYCE
(Also played in 1901 under name of Joyce)
b.Sept.7,1877 Maam,County Galway, Ireland.
d.Aug.12,1959

Yr	Cl	Lea	Pos	G	Rec
(Michael Joyce)					
1901	St.L	N	P	6	2-2
(Michael Joyce O'Neill)					
1902	St.L	N	P-O	36	16-15 .318
1903	St.L	N	P	32	4-13
1904	St.L	N	P	28	10-14
1907	Cin	N	O	9	.069
BRTR				111	32-44 .255

O'NEILL, PHILIP BERNARD
(Peaches)
b.Aug.30,1879 Anderson,Ind.
d.Aug.2,1955

Yr	Cl	Lea	Pos	G	Rec
1904	Cin	N	C	8	.267
TR					

O'NEILL, ROBERT EMMETT
(Pinky)
b.Jan.13,1918 San Mateo,Cal.

Yr	Cl	Lea	Pos	G	Rec
1943	Bos	A	P	11	1-4
1944	Bos	A	P	28	6-11
1945	Bos	A	P	24	8-11
1946	Chi	N	P	1	0-0
1946	Chi	A	P	2	0-0
BRTR				66	15-26

O'NEILL, STEPHEN FRANCIS
b.July 6,1891 Minooka,Pa.
d.Jan.26,1962

Yr	Cl	Lea	Pos	G	Rec
1911	Cle	A	C	9	.111
1912	Cle	A	C	68	.228
1913	Cle	A	C	78	.295
1914	Cle	A	C	86	.253
1915	Cle	A	C	121	.236
1916	Cle	A	C	130	.235
1917	Cle	A	C	129	.184
1918	Cle	A	C	114	.242
1919	Cle	A	C	125	.289
1920	Cle	A	C	149	.321
1921	Cle	A	C	106	.322
1922	Cle	A	C	133	.311
1923	Cle	A	C	113	.248
1924	Bos	A	C	106	.238
1925	NY	A	C	35	.286
1927	St.L	A	C	74	.230
1928	St.L	A	C	10	.292
BRTR				1586	.263

Non-playing manager Cle (A) 1935-37, Det (A) 1943-48, Bos (A) 1950-51 and Phi (N) 1952-54.

O'NEILL, WILLIAM JOHN
b.Jan.22,1880 St.John,N.B.,Canada.
d.July 27,1920

Yr	Cl	Lea	Pos	G	Rec
1904	Bos	A	O	18	.192
1904	Was	A	O	94	.277
1906	Chi	A	O	94	.248
				206	.242

Yr Cl Lea Pos G Rec

ONIS, MANUEL RALPH
b.Oct.24,1911 Tampa,Fla.
1935 Bro N C 1 1.000
BRTR

ONSLOW, EDWARD JOSEPH
b.Feb.17,1893 Meadville,Pa.
1912 Det A 1 35 .227
1913 Det A 1 17 .255
1918 Cle A O 2 .200
1927 Was A 1 9 .222
BLTL 63 .232

ONSLOW, JOHN JAMES
b.Oct.13,1888 Scottdale,Pa.
d.Dec.22,1960
1912 Det A C 31 .159
1917 NY N C 9 .250
BRTR 40 .169
Non-playing manager Chi (A) 1949-50.

ORAN, THOMAS
d.Sept.21,1886
1875 RS n O 19 NR

ORAVETZ, ERNEST EUGENE
b.Jan.24,1932 Johnstown,Pa.
1955 Was A O 100 .270
1956 Was A O 88 .248
BBTL 188 .263

ORDENANA, ANTONIO RODRIGUEZ
b.Oct.30,1920 Regla,Cuba.
1943 Pit N S 1 .500
BRTR

ORENGO, JOSEPH CHARLES
b.Nov.29,1916 San Francisco,Cal.
1939 St.L N S 7 .000
1940 St.L N 2-S-3 129 .287
1941 NY N 2-S-3 77 .214
1943 NY N 1 83 .218
1943 Bro N 3 7 .200
1944 Det A 1-2-S-3 46 .201
1945 Chi A 2-3 17 .067
BRTR 366 .238

ORME, GEORGE WILLIAM
b.Sept.16,1891 Lebanon,Ind.
d.Mar.16,1962
1920 Bos A O 4 .323
BRTR

ORNDORFF, JESSE WALWORK THAYER
b.Jan.15,1881 Chicago,Ill.
d.Sept.28,1960
1907 Bos N C 5 .100
BLTR

O'ROURKE, ...
1872 Eck n P 1 0-1

O'ROURKE, FRANCIS JAMES (Blackie)
b.Nov.28,1891 Hamilton,Ont.,Canada.
1912 Bos N S 61 .122
1917 Bro N 3 64 .237
1918 Bro N 2 4 .167
1920 Was A S 14 .277
1921 Was A S 123 .234
1922 Bos A S-3 67 .264
1924 Det A 2 47 .276
1925 Det A 2-3 124 .293
1926 Det A 2-S-3 111 .242
1927 St.L A 2-3 140 .268
1928 St.L A 3 99 .263
1929 St.L A 3 154 .251
1930 St.L A S-3 115 .268
1931 St.L A 1-S 8 .222
BRTR 1131 .254

O'ROURKE, JAMES HENRY (Orator Jim)
b.Aug.24,1852 E.Bridgeport,Conn.
d.Jan.8,1919
1872 Man n S- 18 NR
1873 Bos n C-1-O 57 .347
1874 Bos n 1 69 .349
(Continued)
1875 Bos n 1-3-O 74 .289
1876 Bos N O 70 .312
1877 Bos N O 61 .362
1878 Bos N O 60 .274
1879 Pro N 1-O 80 .351
1880 Bos N C-1-S-3-O 84 .281
1881 Buf N M-C-1-S-3-O 83 .301
1882 Buf N M-C-S-3-O 84 .281
1883 Buf N M-P-C-S-3-O 93 {0-0 .327}
1884 Buf N M-P-C-1-3-O 104 {0-1 .350}
1885 NY N C-O 112 .299
1886 NY N C-O 104 .309
1887 NY N C-3-O 103 .344
1888 NY N O 107 .273
1889 NY N O 128 .320
1890 NY p O 111 .366
1891 NY N O 136 .301
1892 NY N O 112 .297
1893 Was N M-1-O 129 .305
1904 NY N C 1 .250
BRTR 1980 {0-1 NR}

O'ROURKE, JAMES STEPHEN (Queenie)
b.Dec.26,1889 Bridgeport,Conn.
1908 NY A 2-S-3-O 34 .231
TR

O'ROURKE, JOHN
b.Bridgeport,Conn.
d.June 23,1911
1879 Bos N O 70 .341
1880 Bos N O 78 .282
1883 Met a 1-O 79 .256
BL 227 .299

O'ROURKE, JOSEPH LEO
b.Oct.28,1906 Philadelphia,Pa.
1929 Phi N H 3 .000
BLTR

O'ROURKE, JOSEPH PATRICK (Patsy)
b.Apr.13,1884 Philadelphia,Pa.
d.Apr.18,1956
1908 St.L N S 53 .195
TR

O'ROURKE, MICHAEL J.
1890 Bal a P 9 2-2

O'ROURKE, THOMAS JOSEPH
b.1863 New York,N.Y.
d.July 19,1929
1887 Bos N C 21 .223
1888 Bos N C 20 .175
1890 NY N C 2 .000
1890 Syr a C 43 .227
TR 86 .211

O'ROURKE, TIMOTHY PATRICK (Voiceless Tim)
b.May 18,1864 Chicago,Ill.
d.Apr.20,1938
1890 Syr a 3 82 .288
1891 Col a 3 34 .261
1892 Bal N S 62 .317
1893 Bal N S 31 .379
1893 Lou N S 90 .290
1894 Lou N 3 55 .284
1894 St.L N O 18 .274
1894 Was N 1 7 .179
TR 379 .295

ORR, DAVID L.
b.Sept.29,1859 New York,N.Y.
d.June 3,1915
1883 Met a 1 1 .250
1883 NY N O 1 .000
1883 Met a 1 12 .326
1884 Met a 1 110 .352
1885 Met a 1 107 .366
1886 Met a 1 136 .346
1887 Met a M-1 85 .403
1888 Bro a 1 95 .303
1889 Col a 1 134 .325
1890 Bro p 1 107 .387
BRTR 788 .353

ORR, WILLIAM J.
b.Apr.22,1891 San Francisco,Cal.
1913 Phi A S 27 .200
1914 Phi A S 10 .167
BRTR 37 .191

ORRELL, FORREST GORDON (Joe)
b.Oct.6,1918 National City,Cal.
1943 Det A P 10 0-0
1944 Det A P 10 2-1
1945 Det A P 12 2-3
BRTR 32 4-4

ORSATTI, ERNEST RALPH
b.Sept.8,1904 Los Angeles,Cal.
1927 St.L N O 27 .315
1928 St.L N O 27 .304
1929 St.L N 1-O 113 .332
1930 St.L N 1-O 48 .321
1931 St.L N O 70 .291
1932 St.L N O 101 .336
1933 St.L N 1-O 120 .298
1934 St.L N O 105 .300
1935 St.L N O 90 .240
BLTL 701 .306

ORSINO, JOHN JOSEPH
b.Apr.22,1938 Teaneck,N.J.
1961 SF N C 25 .277
1962 SF N C 18 .271
BRTR 43 .275

ORTEGA, FILOMENO CORONADO
b.Oct.7,1939 Gilbert,Ariz.
1960 LA N P 3 0-0
1961 LA N P 4 0-2
1962 LA N P 24 0-2
BRTR 31 0-4

O'ROURKE, JAMES PATRICK
b.June 22,1937 Walla Walla,Wash.
1959 St.L N H 2 .000
BRTR

ORTH, ALBERT LEWIS (Smiling Al)
b.Sept.5,1872 Danville,Ind.
d.Oct.8,1948
1895 Phi N P 11 8-1
1896 Phi N P 24 15-9
1897 Phi N P 42 14-19
1898 Phi N P 32 15-12
1899 Phi N P 17 13-3
1900 Phi N P 35 14-14
1901 Phi N P 35 21-12
1902 Was A P-1-S-O 54 {19-18 .218}
1903 Was A P 54 10-21
1904 Was A P-O 32 {3-4 .236}
1904 NY A P-O 24 {11-5 .365}
1905 NY A P 40 18-18
1906 NY A P 47 27-17
1907 NY A P 43 14-21
1908 NY A P 38 2-13
1909 NY A P 22 1-0
BLTR 550 {205-187 .276}

ORTIZ, OLIVERIO NUNEZ (Baby)
b.Dec.5,1919 Camaguey,Cuba.

Yr	Cl	Lea	Pos	G	Rec
1944	Was	A	P	2	0-2
BRTR					

ORTIZ, ROBERTO GONZALO NUNEZ
b.June 30,1917 Senado,Cuba.

Yr	Cl	Lea	Pos	G	Rec
1941	Was	A	O	22	.329
1942	Was	A	O	20	.167
1943	Was	A	O	1	.250
1944	Was	A	O	85	.253
1949	Was	A	O	40	.279
1950	Was	A	O	39	.227
1950	Phi	A	O	6	.071
BRTR				213	.255

ORWOLL, OSWALD CHRISTIAN
b.Nov.17,1900 Portland,Ore.

Yr	Cl	Lea	Pos	G	Rec
1928	Phi	A	P-1	64	6-5 / .306
1929	Phi	A	P	30	0-2
BLTL				94	6-7 / .294

OSBORN, FRANK ROBERT
b.Apr.17,1903 San Diego,Tex.

Yr	Cl	Lea	Pos	G	Rec
1925	Chi	N	P	1	0-0
1926	Chi	N	P	31	6-5
1927	Chi	N	P	24	5-5
1929	Chi	N	P	3	0-0
1930	Chi	N	P	35	10-6
1931	Pit	N	P	27	6-1
BRTR				121	27-17

OSBORN, WILFRED P. (Green)
b.Nov.28,1883 Sycamore,O.
d.Sept.2,1954

Yr	Cl	Lea	Pos	G	Rec
1907	Phi	N	O	37	.276
1908	Phi	N	O	152	.267
1909	Phi	N	O	54	.185
BLTR				243	.252

OSBORNE, ERNEST PRESTON (Tiny)
b.Apr.9,1896 Covington,Ga.

Yr	Cl	Lea	Pos	G	Rec
1922	Chi	N	P	41	9-5
1923	Chi	N	P	37	8-15
1924	Chi	N	P	2	0-0
1924	Bro	N	P	21	6-5
1925	Bro	N	P	41	8-15
BLTR				142	31-40

OSBORNE, FREDERICK W.
b.Hampton,Ia.

Yr	Cl	Lea	Pos	G	Rec
1890	Pit	N	P-O	41	0-6 / .238

OSBORNE, LAWRENCE SIDNEY
b.Oct.12,1935 Chattahoochee,Ga.

Yr	Cl	Lea	Pos	G	Rec
1957	Det	A	1-O	11	.148
1958	Det	A	H	2	.000
1959	Det	A	1-O	86	.191
1961	Det	A	1-3	71	.215
1962	Det	A	C-1-3	64	.230
BLTR				234	.200

OSBORNE, WAYNE HAROLD (Fish Hook)
b.Oct.11,1912 Watsonville,Cal.

Yr	Cl	Lea	Pos	G	Rec
1935	Pit	N	P	3	0-0
1936	Bos	N	P	5	1-1
BLTR				8	1-1

OSGOOD, CHARLES BENJAMIN
b.Nov.23,1926 Somerville,Mass.

Yr	Cl	Lea	Pos	G	Rec
1944	Bro	N	P	1	0-0
BRTR					

O'SHEA, FRANCIS JOSEPH
(Played under name of Francis Joseph Shea)

OSINSKI, DANIEL
b.Nov.17,1933 Chicago,Ill.

Yr	Cl	Lea	Pos	G	Rec
1962	KC	A	P	4	0-0
1962	LA	A	P	33	6-4
BRTR				37	6-4

OSTDIEK, HENRY GIRARD
b.Apr.12,1881 Ottumwa,Ia.

Yr	Cl	Lea	Pos	G	Rec
1904	Cle	A	C	7	.157
1908	Bos	A	C	1	.000
BRTR				8	.143

OSTEEN, CLAUDE WILSON
b.Aug.9,1939 Lewisburg,Tenn.

Yr	Cl	Lea	Pos	G	Rec
1957	Cin	N	P	3	0-0
1959	Cin	N	P	2	0-0
1960	Cin	N	P	26	0-1
1961	Cin	N	P-O	6	0-0 / 000
1961	Was	A	P	3	1-1
1962	Was	A	P	37	8-13
BLTL				77	9-15 / 171

OSTEEN, JAMES CHAMP
b.Feb.24,1877 Hendersonville,N.C.
d.Dec.14,1962

Yr	Cl	Lea	Pos	G	Rec
1903	Was	A	S	10	.195
1904	NY	A	3	27	.202
1908	St.L	N	S	29	.196
1909	St.L	N	S	16	.199
BLTR				82	.199

OSTENDORF, FREDERICK K.
b.1890 Baltimore,Md.

Yr	Cl	Lea	Pos	G	Rec
1914	Ind	F	P	1	0-0
BBTR					

OSTER, WILLIAM CHARLES
b.Jan.2,1933 New York,N.Y.

Yr	Cl	Lea	Pos	G	Rec
1954	Phi	A	P	8	0-1
BLTL					

OSTERGARD, ROBERT LUND (Red)
b.May 11,1898 Galveston,Tex.

Yr	Cl	Lea	Pos	G	Rec
1921	Chi	A	S	12	.364
BLTR					

OSTERHOUT, CHARLES H.
b.1857 Syracuse,N.Y.
d.May 21,1933

Yr	Cl	Lea	Pos	G	Rec
1879	Syr	N	C-2	2	.000

OSTERMUELLER, FREDERICK RAYMOND (Fritz)
b.Sept.15,1907 Quincy,Ill.
d.Dec.17,1957

Yr	Cl	Lea	Pos	G	Rec
1934	Bos	A	P	33	10-13
1935	Bos	A	P	22	7-8
1936	Bos	A	P	43	10-16
1937	Bos	A	P	25	3-7
1938	Bos	A	P	33	13-5
1939	Bos	A	P	34	11-7
1940	Bos	A	P	33	5-9
1941	St.L	A	P	16	0-3
1942	St.L	A	P	10	3-1
1943	St.L	A	P	11	0-2
1943	Bro	N	P	8	1-1
1944	Bro	N	P	11	2-1
1944	Pit	N	P	29	11-7
1945	Pit	N	P	14	5-4
1946	Pit	N	P	28	13-10
1947	Pit	N	P	26	12-10
1948	Pit	N	P	23	8-11
BLTL				399	114-115

OSTROWSKI, JOHN THEODORE
b.Oct.17,1920 Chicago,Ill.

Yr	Cl	Lea	Pos	G	Rec
1943	Chi	N	3-O	10	.207
1944	Chi	N	O	8	.154
1945	Chi	N	3	7	.300
1946	Chi	N	2-3	64	.213
1948	Bos	A	H	1	.000
1949	Chi	A	3-O	49	.266
1950	Chi	A	O	21	.222
1950	Was	A	O	55	.227
1950	Chi	A	O	1	.500
BRTR				216	.234

OSTROWSKI, JOSEPH PAUL (Specs)
b.Aug.15,1919 W.Wyoming,Pa.

Yr	Cl	Lea	Pos	G	Rec
1948	St.L	A	P	26	4-6
1949	St.L	A	P	40	8-8
1950	St.L	A	P	9	2-4
1950	NY	A	P	21	1-1
1951	NY	A	P	34	6-4
1952	NY	A	P	20	2-2
BLTL				150	23-25

OTERO, REGINO JOSEPH GOMEZ
b.Sept.7,1917 Havana,Cuba.

Yr	Cl	Lea	Pos	G	Rec
1945	Chi	N	1	14	.391
BLTR					

OTEY, WILLIAM TILFORD
b.Dec.16,1886 Dayton,O.
d.Apr.23,1931

Yr	Cl	Lea	Pos	G	Rec
1907	Pit	N	P	3	0-1
1910	Was	A	P	9	0-1
1911	Was	A	P	12	2-4
				24	2-6

OTIS, HARRY GEORGE
b.Oct.5,1886 W.New York,N.J.

Yr	Cl	Lea	Pos	G	Rec
1909	Cle	A	P	5	2-2
TL					

OTIS, PAUL FRANKLIN
b.Dec.24,1889 Scituate,Mass.

Yr	Cl	Lea	Pos	G	Rec
1912	NY	A	O	4	.000

O'TOOLE, JAMES JEROME
b.Jan.10,1937 Chicago,Ill.

Yr	Cl	Lea	Pos	G	Rec
1958	Cin	N	P	1	0-1
1959	Cin	N	P	29	5-8
1960	Cin	N	P	34	12-12
1961	Cin	N	P	39	19-9
1962	Cin	N	P	36	16-13
BBTR				139	52-43

O'TOOLE, MARTIN JAMES
b.Nov.27,1888 Wm.Penn,Pa.
b.Feb.18,1949

Yr	Cl	Lea	Pos	G	Rec
1908	Cin	N	P	3	1-0
1911	Pit	N	P	5	3-2
1912	Pit	N	P	37	15-17
1913	Pit	N	P	26	6-8
1914	Pit	N	P	19	1-8
1914	NY	N	P	10	1-1
BRTR				100	27-36

OTT, MELVIN THOMAS
b.Mar.2,1908 Gretna,La.
d.Nov.21,1958

Yr	Cl	Lea	Pos	G	Rec
1926	NY	N	O	35	.383
1927	NY	N	O	82	.282
1928	NY	N	O	124	.322
1929	NY	N	O	150	.328
1930	NY	N	O	148	.349
1931	NY	N	O	138	.292
1932	NY	N	O	154	.318
1933	NY	N	O	152	.283
1934	NY	N	O	153	.326
1935	NY	N	3-O	152	.322
1936	NY	N	O	150	.328
1937	NY	N	3-O	151	.294
1938	NY	N	3-O	150	.311
1939	NY	N	3-O	125	.308
1940	NY	N	3-O	151	.289
1941	NY	N	O	148	.286
1942	NY	N	M-O	152	.295
1943	NY	N	M-3-O	125	.234
1944	NY	N	M-O	120	.288
1945	NY	N	M-O	135	.308
1946	NY	N	M-O	31	.074
1947	NY	N	M-H	4	.000
BLTR				2730	.304

Non-playing manager NY (N) 1948.

OTT, WILLIAM JOSEPH
b.Nov.23,1940 New York,N.Y.

Yr	Cl	Lea	Pos	G	Rec
1962	Chi	N	O	12	.143
BBTR					

OTTEN, JOSEPH G.
b.Murphysboro,Ill.

Yr	Cl	Lea	Pos	G	Rec
1895	St.L	N	C	24	.233
	TR				

OTTERSON, WILLIAM JOHN
b.May 4,1862 Allegheny,Pa.
d.Sept.24,1940

Yr	Cl	Lea	Pos	G	Rec
1887	Bro	a	S	30	.269
	TR				

OULLIBER, JOHN ANDREW
b.Feb.24,1911 New Orleans,La.

Yr	Cl	Lea	Pos	G	Rec
1933	Cle	A	O	22	.267
	BRTR				

OUTEN, WILLIAM AUSTIN (Chick)
b.June 17,1905 Mt.Holly,N.C.

Yr	Cl	Lea	Pos	G	Rec
1933	Bro	N	C	93	.248
	BLTR				

OUTLAW, JAMES PAULUS
b.Jan.20,1913 Orme,Tenn.

Yr	Cl	Lea	Pos	G	Rec
1937	Cin	N	3	49	.273
1938	Cin	N	H	4	.000
1939	Bos	N	O	65	.263
1943	Det	A	O	20	.269
1944	Det	A	O	139	.273
1945	Det	A	3-O	132	.271
1946	Det	A	3-O	92	.261
1947	Det	A	3-O	70	.228
1948	Det	A	3-O	74	.283
1949	Det	A	H	5	.250
	BRTR			650	.268

OVERALL, ORVAL
b.Feb.2,1881 Visalia,Cal.
d.July 14,1947

Yr	Cl	Lea	Pos	G	Rec
1905	Cin	N	P	42	17-23
1906	Cin	N	P	13	4-5
1906	Chi	N	P	18	12-3
1907	Chi	N	P	36	23-7
1908	Chi	N	P	37	15-11
1909	Chi	N	P	38	20-11
1910	Chi	N	P	24	12-6
1913	Chi	N	P	10	4-5
	BBTR			218	107-71

OVERBECK, HENRY A.
b.St.Louis,Mo.

Yr	Cl	Lea	Pos	G	Rec
1883	Pit	a	1	2	.222
1883	St.L	a	O	4	.000
1884	Bal	U	P-3-O	33	0-0 / .159
1884	KC	U	P-1-3-O	26	0-3 / .174
				65	0-3 / .157

OVERMIRE, FRANK (Stubby)
b.May 16,1919 Moline,Mich.

Yr	Cl	Lea	Pos	G	Rec
1943	Det	A	P	29	7-6
1944	Det	A	P	32	11-11
1945	Det	A	P	31	9-9
1946	Det	A	P	24	5-7
1947	Det	A	P	28	11-5
1948	Det	A	P	37	3-4
1949	Det	A	P	14	1-3
1950	St.L	A	P	31	9-12
1951	St.L	A	P	8	1-6
1951	NY	A	P	15	1-1
1952	St.L	A	P	17	0-3
	BRTL			266	58-67

OVITZ, ERNEST GAYHEART
b.Oct.7,1885 Mineral Point,Wis.

Yr	Cl	Lea	Pos	G	Rec
1911	Chi	N	P	1	0-0

OWEN, ARNOLD MALCOLM (Mickey)
b.Apr.4,1916 Springfield,Mo.

Yr	Cl	Lea	Pos	G	Rec
1937	St.L	N	C	80	.231
1938	St.L	N	C	122	.267
1939	St.L	N	C	131	.259
1940	St.L	N	C	117	.264

(Continued)

Yr	Cl	Lea	Pos	G	Rec
1941	Bro	N	C	128	.231
1942	Bro	N	C	133	.259
1943	Bro	N	C-S	106	.260
1944	Bro	N	C-2	130	.273
1945	Bro	N	C	24	.286
1949	Chi	N	C	62	.273
1950	Chi	N	C	86	.243
1951	Chi	N	C	58	.184
1954	Bos	A	C	32	.235
	BRTR			1209	.255

OWEN, FRANK MALCOLM (Yip)
b.Dec.23,1879 Ypsilanti,Mich.
d.Nov.27,1942

Yr	Cl	Lea	Pos	G	Rec
1901	Det	A	P	9	1-4
1903	Chi	A	P	26	8-11
1904	Chi	A	P	37	21-15
1905	Chi	A	P	42	22-14
1906	Chi	A	P	42	22-13
1907	Chi	A	P	11	2-3
1908	Chi	A	P	25	6-7
1909	Chi	A	P	3	1-1
	TR			195	83-68

OWEN, MARVIN JAMES (Freck)
b.Mar.22,1908 San Jose,Cal.

Yr	Cl	Lea	Pos	G	Rec
1931	Det	A	1-S-3	105	.223
1933	Det	A	3	138	.262
1934	Det	A	3	154	.317
1935	Det	A	3	134	.263
1936	Det	A	3	154	.295
1937	Det	A	3	107	.288
1938	Chi	A	3	141	.281
1939	Chi	A	3	58	.237
1940	Bos	A	1-3	20	.211
	BRTR			1011	.275

OWENS, FRANK WALTER
b.Jan.25,1884 Toronto,Ont.,Canada.
d.July 2,1958

Yr	Cl	Lea	Pos	G	Rec
1905	Bos	A	C	1	.000
1909	Chi	A	C	64	.201
1914	Bro	F	C	55	.274
1915	Bal	F	C	98	.245
	BRTR			218	.241

OWENS, FURMAN LEE
b.June 6,1910 Converse,S.C.

Yr	Cl	Lea	Pos	G	Rec
1935	Phi	A	C	2	.250
	BRTR				

OWENS, JAMES PHILIP
b.Jan.16,1934 Gifford,Pa.

Yr	Cl	Lea	Pos	G	Rec
1955	Phi	N	P	3	0-2
1956	Phi	N	P	10	0-4
1958	Phi	N	P	1	1-0
1959	Phi	N	P	31	12-12
1960	Phi	N	P	31	4-14
1961	Phi	N	P-O	21	5-10 / .074
1962	Phi	N	P	23	2-4
	BRTR			120	24-46 / .101

OWENS, THOMAS LLEWELLYN (Red)
b.Nov.1,1874 Pottsville,Pa.
d.Aug.21,1952

Yr	Cl	Lea	Pos	G	Rec
1899	Phi	N	2	8	.045
1905	Bro	N	2	43	.215
	BRTR			51	.196

OXLEY, HENRY HAVELOCK
b.Charlottetown,P.E.I.,Canada.

Yr	Cl	Lea	Pos	G	Rec
1884	NY	N	C	2	.000
1884	Met	a	C	1	.000
				3	.000

OYLER, ANDREW PAUL
b.May 5,1880 Newville,Pa.

Yr	Cl	Lea	Pos	G	Rec
1902	Bal	A	2-S-3-O	26	.227
	BRTR				

OZMER, HORACE ROBERT
b.May 25,1901 Atlanta,Ga.

Yr	Cl	Lea	Pos	G	Rec
1923	Phi	A	P	1	0-0
	BRTR				

PABOR, CHARLES HENRY
b.Sept.24,1846 Brooklyn,N.Y.
d.Apr.22,1913

Yr	Cl	Lea	Pos	G	Rec
1871	Cle	n	P-O	29	0-1 / NR
1872	Cle	n	P-O	21	1-1 / NR
1873	Atl	n	O	55	NR
1874	Phi	n	O	5	NR
1875	Atl	n	M-O	41	NR
1875	NH	n	O	6	NR
	TL			157	1-2 / NR

PABST, EDWARD D. A.
b.St.Louis,Mo.

Yr	Cl	Lea	Pos	G	Rec
1890	Ath	a	O	8	.345
1890	St.L	a	O	4	.143
				12	.279

PACK, FRANKIE
b.Apr.10,1928 Morristown,Tenn.

Yr	Cl	Lea	Pos	G	Rec
1949	St.L	A	H	1	.000
	BLTR				

PACKARD. EUGENE MILO
b.July 13,1889 Colorado Springs,Colo.

Yr	Cl	Lea	Pos	G	Rec
1912	Cin	N	P	1	1-0
1913	Cin	N	P	43	7-11
1914	KC	F	P	40	20-14
1915	KC	F	P	39	20-12
1916	Chi	N	P	44	10-6
1917	Chi	N	P	2	0-0
1917	St.L	N	P	36	9-6
1918	St.L	N	P	36	12-12
1919	Phi	N	P	27	6-8
	BLTL			268	85-69

PADDEN, RICHARD J. (Brains)
b.Sept.17,1870 Martin's Ferry,O.
d.Oct.31,1922

Yr	Cl	Lea	Pos	G	Rec
1896	Pit	N	2	60	.239
1897	Pit	N	2	135	.281
1898	Pit	N	2	128	.256
1899	Was	N	2-S	131	.272
1901	St.L	N	2	123	.253
1902	St.L	A	2	117	.265
1903	St.L	A	2	29	.202
1904	St.L	A	2	132	.238
1905	St.L	A	2	16	.172
	BRTR			871	.256

PADDEN, THOMAS FRANCIS
b.Oct.6,1908 Manchester,N.H.

Yr	Cl	Lea	Pos	G	Rec
1932	Pit	N	C	47	.263
1933	Pit	N	C	30	.211
1934	Pit	N	C	82	.321
1935	Pit	N	C	97	.272
1936	Pit	N	C	88	.249
1937	Pit	N	C	35	.286
1943	Phi	N	C	17	.293
1943	Was	A	C	3	.000
	BRTR			399	.272

PADDOCK, DELMAR HAROLD
b.June 6,1887 Volga,S.D.
d.Feb.6,1952

Yr	Cl	Lea	Pos	G	Rec
1912	Chi	A	H	1	.000
1912	NY	A	3	45	.287
	BLTR			46	.287

PADGETT, DONALD WILSON
b.Dec.5,1913 Caroleen,N.C.

Yr	Cl	Lea	Pos	G	Rec
1937	St.L	N	O	123	.314
1938	St.L	N	1-O	110	.271
1939	St.L	N	C	92	.399
1940	St.L	N	C-1	93	.242
1941	St.L	N	C-1-O	107	.247
1946	Bro	N	C	19	.167
1946	Bos	N	C	44	.255
1947	Phi	N	C	75	.316
1948	Phi	N	C	36	.230
	BLTR			699	.288

PADGETT, ERNEST KITCHEN
(Red)
b.Mar.1,1899 Philadelphia,Pa.
d.Apr.15,1957

Yr	Cl	Lea	Pos	G	Rec
1923	Bos	N	2-S	4	.182
1924	Bos	N	2-3	138	.255
1925	Bos	N	2-S-3	86	.305
1926	Cle	A	3	36	.210
1927	Cle	A	2	7	.286
BRTR				271	.266

PAFKO, ANDREW
(Handy Andy)
b.Feb.25,1921 Boyceville,Wis.

Yr	Cl	Lea	Pos	G	Rec
1943	Chi	N	O	13	.379
1944	Chi	N	O	128	.269
1945	Chi	N	O	144	.298
1946	Chi	N	O	65	.282
1947	Chi	N	O	129	.302
1948	Chi	N	3	142	.312
1949	Chi	N	3-O	144	.281
1950	Chi	N	O	146	.304
1951	Chi	N	O	49	.264
1951	Bro	N	O	84	.249
1952	Bro	N	3-O	150	.287
1953	Mil	N	O	140	.297
1954	Mil	N	O	138	.286
1955	Mil	N	3-O	86	.266
1956	Mil	N	O	45	.258
1957	Mil	N	O	83	.277
1958	Mil	N	O	95	.238
1959	Mil	N	O	71	.218
BRTR				1852	.285

PAGAN, JOSE ANTONIO
b.May 5,1935 Barceloneta,Porto Rico

Yr	Cl	Lea	Pos	G	Rec
1959	SF	N	2-S-3	31	.174
1960	SF	N	S-3	18	.286
1961	SF	N	S-O	134	.253
1962	SF	N	S	164	.259
BRTR				347	.254

PAGE, JOSEPH FRANCIS
(Fireman)
b.Oct.28,1917 Cherry Valley,Pa.

Yr	Cl	Lea	Pos	G	Rec
1944	NY	A	P	19	5-7
1945	NY	A	P	20	6-3
1946	NY	A	P	32	9-8
1947	NY	A	P	56	14-8
1948	NY	A	P	55	7-8
1949	NY	A	P	60	13-8
1950	NY	A	P	37	3-7
1954	Pit	N	P	7	0-0
BLTL				286	57-49

PAGE, PHILIP RAUSAC
b.Aug.23,1905 Springfield,Mass.
d.June 26,1958

Yr	Cl	Lea	Pos	G	Rec
1928	Det	A	P	3	2-0
1929	Det	A	P	10	0-2
1930	Det	A	P	12	0-1
1934	Bro	N	P	6	1-0
BRTL				31	3-3

PAGE, SAMUEL WALTER
b.Feb.11,1916 Woodruff,S.C.

Yr	Cl	Lea	Pos	G	Rec
1939	Phi	A	P	4	0-3
BLTR					

PAGE, VANCE LINWOOD
b.Sept.15,1905 Elm City,N.C.
d.July 14,1951

Yr	Cl	Lea	Pos	G	Rec
1938	Chi	N	P	13	5-4
1939	Chi	N	P	27	7-7
1940	Chi	N	P	31	1-3
1941	Chi	N	P	25	2-2
BRTR				96	15-16

PAGLIARONI, JAMES VINCENT
b.Dec.8,1937 Dearborn,Mich.

Yr	Cl	Lea	Pos	G	Rec
1955	Bos	A	C	1	.000
1960	Bos	A	C	28	.306
1961	Bos	A	C	120	.242
1962	Bos	A	C	90	.258
BRTR				239	.254

PAIGE, GEORGE L. (Pat)
b.1885 Paw Paw,Mich.

Yr	Cl	Lea	Pos	G	Rec
1911	Cle	A	P	2	1-0
BRTR					

PAIGE, LeROY (Satchel)
b.July 7,1906 Mobile,Ala.

Yr	Cl	Lea	Pos	G	Rec
1948	Cle	A	P	21	6-1
1949	Cle	A	P	31	4-7
1951	St.L	A	P	23	3-4
1952	St.L	A	P	46	12-10
1953	St.L	A	P	57	3-9
BRTR				178	28-31

PAINE, PHILLIPS STEERE
(Flip)
b.June 8,1930 Chepachet,R.I.

Yr	Cl	Lea	Pos	G	Rec
1951	Bos	N	P	21	2-0
1954	Mil	N	P	11	1-0
1955	Mil	N	P	15	2-0
1956	Mil	N	P	1	0-0
1957	Mil	N	P	1	0-0
1958	St.L	N	P	46	5-1
BRTR				95	10-1

PALAGYI, MICHAEL RAYMOND
b.July 4,1917 Conneaut,O.

Yr	Cl	Lea	Pos	G	Rec
1939	Was	A	P	1	0-0
BRTR					

PALICA, ERVIN MARTIN
(Real name Ervin Martin Pavliecivich)
b.Feb.9,1928 Lomita,Cal.

Yr	Cl	Lea	Pos	G	Rec
1945	Bro	N	H	2	.000
1947	Bro	N	P	3	0-1
1948	Bro	N	P	45	6-6
1949	Bro	N	P	49	8-9
1950	Bro	N	P	48	13-8
1951	Bro	N	P	20	2-6
1953	Bro	N	P	4	0-0
1954	Bro	N	P	28	3-3
1955	Bal	A	P	33	5-11
1956	Bal	A	P	30	4-11
BRTR				262	41-55 .198

PALM, RICHARD PAUL
(Mike)
b.Feb.13,1925 Boston,Mass.

Yr	Cl	Lea	Pos	G	Rec
1948	Bos	A	P	3	0-0
BRTR					

PALMER, ...
b.St.Louis,Mo.

Yr	Cl	Lea	Pos	G	Rec
1885	St.L	N	P	4	0-4

PALMER, EDWIN HENRY
(Baldy)
b.June 1,1893 Petty,Tex.

Yr	Cl	Lea	Pos	G	Rec
1917	Phi	A	3	16	.212
BRTR					

PALMERO, EMILIO A.
(Cubie)
b.June 13,1895 Havana,Cuba.

Yr	Cl	Lea	Pos	G	Rec
1915	NY	N	P	3	0-2
1916	NY	N	P	5	0-3
1921	St.L	A	P	29	4-7
1926	Was	A	P	7	2-2
1928	Bos	N	P	3	0-1
BBTL				47	6-15

PALMISANO, JOSEPH A.
b.Nov.19,1902 West Point,Ga.

Yr	Cl	Lea	Pos	G	Rec
1931	Phi	A	C	19	.227
BRTR					

PALMQUIST, EDWIN LEE
b.June 10,1933 Los Angeles,Cal.

Yr	Cl	Lea	Pos	G	Rec
1960	LA	N	P	22	0-1
1961	LA	N	P	5	0-1
1961	Min	A	P	9	1-1
BRTR				36	1-3

PALYS, STANLEY FRANCIS
b.May 1,1930 Blakely,Pa.

Yr	Cl	Lea	Pos	G	Rec
1953	Phi	N	O	2	.000
1954	Phi	N	O	2	.250
1955	Phi	N	O	15	.288
1955	Cin	N	1-O	79	.230
1956	Cin	N	O	40	.226
BRTR				138	.237

PANER, GEORGE WASHINGTON
(Played under name of George Washington Paynter)

PAOLINELLI, RINALDO ANGELO
(Played under name of Ralph Arthur Pinelli)

PAPA, JOHN PAUL
b.Dec.5,1940 Bridgeport,Conn.

Yr	Cl	Lea	Pos	G	Rec
1961	Bal	A	P	2	0-0
1962	Bal	A	P	1	0-0
BRTR				3	0-0

PAPAI, ALFRED THOMAS
b.May 7,1919 Divernon,Ill.

Yr	Cl	Lea	Pos	G	Rec
1948	St.L	N	P	11	0-1
1949	St.L	A	P	42	4-11
1950	Bos	A	P	16	4-2
1950	St.L	N	P	13	1-0
1955	Chi	A	P	7	0-0
BRTR				89	9-14

PAPE, LAWRENCE ALBERT
b.1883 Norwood,O.
d.Aug.3,1918

Yr	Cl	Lea	Pos	G	Rec
1909	Bos	A	P	11	2-0
1911	Bos	A	P	27	10-8
1912	Bos	A	P	10	1-1
BRTR				48	13-9

PAPISH, FRANK RICHARD
b.Oct.21,1917 Pueblo,Colo.

Yr	Cl	Lea	Pos	G	Rec
1945	Chi	A	P	19	4-4
1946	Chi	A	P	31	7-5
1947	Chi	A	P	38	12-12
1948	Chi	A	P	32	2-8
1949	Cle	A	P	25	1-0
1950	Pit	N	P	4	0-0
BRTL				149	26-29

PAPPALAU, JOHN JOSEPH
b.Apr.3,1875 Albany,N.Y.
d.May 12,1944

Yr	Cl	Lea	Pos	G	Rec
1897	Cle	N	P	2	0-0

PAPPAS, MILTON STEPHEN
b.May 11,1939 Detroit,Mich.

Yr	Cl	Lea	Pos	G	Rec
1957	Bal	A	P	4	0-0
1958	Bal	A	P-2	32	10-10 .143
1959	Bal	A	P	33	15-9
1960	Bal	A	P	30	15-11
1961	Bal	A	P	26	13-9
1962	Bal	A	P	35	12-10
BRTR				160	65 49 .143

PARENT, FREDERICK ALFRED
b.Nov.25,1875 Biddeford,Me.

Yr	Cl	Lea	Pos	G	Rec
1899	St.L	N	2	2	.125
1901	Bos	A	S	138	.318
1902	Bos	A	S	139	.288
1903	Bos	A	S	139	.304
1904	Bos	A	S	155	.296
1905	Bos	A	S	153	.234
1906	Bos	A	S	149	.235
1907	Bos	A	S-O	114	.276
1908	Chi	A	S	119	.207
1909	Chi	A	S-O	136	.261
1910	Chi	A	S	81	.178
1911	Chi	A	2	3	.444
BRTR				1328	.265

PARISSE, LOUIS PETER
(Tony)
b.June 25,1911 Philadelphia,Pa.
d.June 2,1956

Yr	Cl	Lea	Pos	G	Rec
1943	Phi	A	C	6	.176
1944	Phi	A	C	4	.000
			BRTR	10	.143

PARK, JAMES
b.Nov.10,1892 Richmond,Ky.

Yr	Cl	Lea	Pos	G	Rec
1915	St.L	A	P	3	2-0
1916	St.L	A	P	26	1-4
1917	St.L	A	P	13	1-1
			BRTR	42	4-5

PARKER, CLARENCE McKAY
(Ace)
b.May 17,1912 Portsmouth,Va.

Yr	Cl	Lea	Pos	G	Rec
1937	Phi	A	S	38	.117
1938	Phi	A	S	56	.230
			BRTR	94	.179

PARKER, CLARENCE PERKINS
b.May 22,1893 Somerville,Mass.

Yr	Cl	Lea	Pos	G	Rec
1915	St.L	A	O	3	.167

PARKER, DOUGLAS WOOLEY
(Dixie)
b.Apr.24,1896 Green Pond,Ala.

Yr	Cl	Lea	Pos	G	Rec
1923	Phi	N	C	4	.200
	BLTR				

PARKER, FRANCIS JAMES
(Salty)
b.July 8,1913 E.St.Louis,Ill.

Yr	Cl	Lea	Pos	G	Rec
1936	Det	A	1-S	11	.280
	BRTR				

PARKER, HARLEY PARK
(Doc)
b.June 14,1874 Theresa,N.Y.
d.Mar.3,1941

Yr	Cl	Lea	Pos	G	Rec
1893	Chi	N	P	1	0-0
1895	Chi	N	P	7	4-3
1896	Chi	N	P	10	1-5
1901	Cin	N	P	1	0-1
			BRTR	19	5-9

PARKER, JAY

Yr	Cl	Lea	Pos	G	Rec
1899	Pit	N	P	1	0-0

PARKER, ROY W.
b.1897

Yr	Cl	Lea	Pos	G	Rec
1919	St.L	N	P	2	0-0
	BRTR				

PARKINSON, FRANK JOSEPH
b.Mar.23,1898 Trenton,N.J.

Yr	Cl	Lea	Pos	G	Rec
1921	Phi	N	S	108	.253
1922	Phi	N	2	141	.275
1923	Phi	N	2-S-3	67	.242
1924	Phi	N	2-S-3	62	.212
			BRTR	378	.256

PARKS, ARTHUR WILLIAM
b.Nov.1,1914 Paris,Ark.

Yr	Cl	Lea	Pos	G	Rec
1937	Bro	N	O	7	.313
1939	Bro	N	O	71	.272
			BLTR	78	.275

PARKS, VERNON HENRY
(Slicker)
b.Nov.10,1897 Fowler,Mich.

Yr	Cl	Lea	Pos	G	Rec
1921	Det	A	P	10	3-2
	BRTR				

PARKS, WILLIAM ROBERT
b.June 4,1849 Easton,Pa.
d.Oct.10,1911

Yr	Cl	Lea	Pos	G	Rec
1875	Nat	n	P-O	25	3-9 / NR
1875	Phi	n	O	2	NR
1876	Bos	N	O	1	.000
				28	3-9 / NR

PARMELEE, LeROY EARL
(Tarzan)
b.Apr.25,1907 Lambertville,Mich.

Yr	Cl	Lea	Pos	G	Rec
1929	NY	N	P	2	1-0
1930	NY	N	P	11	0-1
1931	NY	N	P	13	2-2
1932	NY	N	P	8	0-3
1933	NY	N	P	33	13-8
1934	NY	N	P	22	10-6
1935	NY	N	P	34	14-10
1936	St.L	N	P	37	11-11
1937	Chi	N	P	37	7-8
1939	Phi	A	P	16	1-6
			BRTR	213	59-55

PARNELL, MELVIN LLOYD
(Dusty)
b.June 13,1922 New Orleans,La.

Yr	Cl	Lea	Pos	G	Rec
1947	Bos	A	P	15	2-3
1948	Bos	A	P	35	15-8
1949	Bos	A	P	39	25-7
1950	Bos	A	P	40	18-10
1951	Bos	A	P	37	18-11
1952	Bos	A	P	35	12-12
1953	Bos	A	P	38	21-8
1954	Bos	A	P	19	3-7
1955	Bos	A	P	14	2-3
1956	Bos	A	P	21	7-6
			BLTL	293	123-75

PARNHAM, JAMES ARTHUR
(Rube)
b.Feb.1,1896 Heidelberg,Pa.

Yr	Cl	Lea	Pos	G	Rec
1916	Phi	A	P	4	2-1
1917	Phi	A	P	2	0-1
			BRTR	6	2-2

PARROTT, THOMAS WILLIAM
(Tacks)
b.Apr.10.1868 E.Portland,Ore.
d.Jan.1,1932

Yr	Cl	Lea	Pos	G	Rec
1893	Chi	N	P	12	0-4
1893	Cin	N	P	17	9-8
1894	Cin	N	P	59	19-19
1895	Cin	N	P	47	11-20
1896	St.L	N	P-O	118	1-1 / .288
			BRTR	253	40-52 / .304

PARROT, WALTER E.
(Jiggs)
b.July 14,1871 Portland,Ore.
d.Apr.14,1898

Yr	Cl	Lea	Pos	G	Rec
1892	Chi	N	3	79	.215
1893	Chi	N	3	113	.252
1894	Chi	N	2	126	.244
1895	Chi	N	S	3	.200
				321	.240

PARSON, WILLIAM EDWIN
(Jiggs)
b.Dec.27,1886 Parker,S.Dak.

Yr	Cl	Lea	Pos	G	Rec
1910	Bos	N	P	10	0-2
1911	Bos	N	P	7	0-1
			BRTR	17	0-3

PARSONS, CHARLES J.
b.July 18,1863 Covington,Pa.
d.Apr.1,1936

Yr	Cl	Lea	Pos	G	Rec
1886	Bos	N	P	2	0-2
1887	Met	a	P	4	1-1
1890	Cle	N	P	2	0-1
			TL	8	1-4

PARSONS, EDWARD DIXON
(Dixie)
b.May 12,1916 Talladega,Ala.

Yr	Cl	Lea	Pos	G	Rec
1939	Det	A	C	5	.000
1942	Det	A	C	63	.197
1943	Det	A	C	40	.142
			BRTR	108	.176

PARSONS, JOHN S.
b.Napoleon,O.

Yr	Cl	Lea	Pos	G	Rec
1884	Cin	a	O	1	.000

PARTEE, ROY ROBERT
b.Sept.7,1918 Los Angeles,Cal.

Yr	Cl	Lea	Pos	G	Rec
1943	Bos	A	C	96	.281
1944	Bos	A	C	89	.243
1946	Bos	A	C	40	.315
1947	Bos	A	C	60	.231
1948	St.L	A	C	82	.203
			BRTR	367	.250

PARTENHEIMER, HAROLD PHILIP
b.Aug.30,1891 Greenfield,Mass.

Yr	Cl	Lea	Pos	G	Rec
1913	Det	A	3	1	.000
	TR				

PARTENHEIMER, STANWOOD WENDELL
b.Oct.21,1922 Chicopee Falls,Mass.

Yr	Cl	Lea	Pos	G	Rec
1944	Bos	A	P	1	0-0
1945	St.L	N	P	8	0-0
			BBTL	9	0-0

PARTRIDGE, JAMES BAGG
(Jay)
b.Nov.15,1902 Mountville,Ga.

Yr	Cl	Lea	Pos	G	Rec
1927	Bro	N	2	146	.260
1928	Bro	N	2	37	.247
			BLTR	183	.259

PASCHAL, BENJAMIN EDWIN
b.Oct.13,1895 Enterprise,Ala.

Yr	Cl	Lea	Pos	G	Rec
1915	Cle	A	O	9	.111
1920	Bos	A	O	9	.250
1924	NY	A	O	4	.272
1925	NY	A	O	89	.360
1926	NY	A	O	96	.287
1927	NY	A	O	50	.317
1928	NY	A	O	65	.316
1929	NY	A	O	42	.208
			BRTR	364	.309

PASCUAL, CAMILO ALBERTO
b.Jan.20,1934 Havana,Cuba.

Yr	Cl	Lea	Pos	G	Rec
1954	Was	A	P	48	4-7
1955	Was	A	P	43	2-12
1956	Was	A	P	43	6-18
1957	Was	A	P	32	8-17
1958	Was	A	P	31	8-12
1959	Was	A	P	32	17-10
1960	Was	A	P	27	12-8
1961	Min	A	P	35	15-16
1962	Min	A	P	34	20-11
			BRTR	325	91-111

PASCUAL, CARLOS LUIS
b.Mar.13,1930 Havana,Cuba

Yr	Cl	Lea	Pos	G	Rec
1950	Was	A	P	2	1-1
	BRTR				

PASEK, JOHN PAUL
b.June 26,1906 Niagara Falls,N.Y.

Yr	Cl	Lea	Pos	G	Rec
1933	Det	A	C	28	.246
1934	Chi	A	C	4	.333
			BRTR	32	.257

PASKERT, GEORGE HENRY
(Dode)
b.Aug.28,1881 Cleveland,O.
d.Feb.12,1959

Yr	Cl	Lea	Pos	G	Rec
1907	Cin	N	O	16	.280
1908	Cin	N	O	116	.243
1909	Cin	N	O	88	.251
1910	Cin	N	O	141	.300
1911	Phi	N	O	153	.273
1912	Phi	N	O	145	.315
1913	Phi	N	O	124	.262
1914	Phi	N	O	132	.264
1915	Phi	N	O	109	.244
1916	Phi	N	O	149	.279
1917	Phi	N	O	141	.251
1918	Chi	N	3-O	127	.286
1919	Chi	N	O	88	.196
1920	Chi	N	O	139	.279
1921	Cin	N	O	27	.174
			BRTR	1695	.268

PASQUARIELLO, MICHAEL JOHN
b.Nov.7,1898 Philadelphia,Pa.

Yr	Cl	Lea	Pos	G	Rec
1919	Phi	N	1	1	1.000
1919	St.L	N	H	1	.000
	BRTR			2	.500

PASSEAU, CLAUDE WILLIAM
b.Apr.9,1911 Waynesboro,Miss.

Yr	Cl	Lea	Pos	G	Rec
1935	Pit	N	P	1	0-1
1936	Phi	N	P	50	11-15
1937	Phi	N	P	50	14-18
1938	Phi	N	P	45	11-18
1939	Phi	N	P	8	2-4
1939	Chi	N	P	35	13-9
1940	Chi	N	P	46	20-13
1941	Chi	N	P	34	14-14
1942	Chi	N	P	35	19-14
1943	Chi	N	P	35	15-12
1944	Chi	N	P	34	15-9
1945	Chi	N	P	34	17-9
1946	Chi	N	P	21	9-8
1947	Chi	N	P	19	2-6
	BRTR			447	162-150

PASTORIUS, JAMES W.
(Sunny Jim)
b.July 12,1881 Pittsburgh,Pa.
d.May 10.1941

Yr	Cl	Lea	Pos	G	Rec
1906	Bro	N	P	29	10-14
1907	Bro	N	P	28	16-12
1908	Bro	N	P	28	4-20
1909	Bro	N	P	12	1-9
	BLTL			97	31-55

PATE, JOSEPH WILLIAM
b.June 6,1892 Alice,Tex.
d.Dec.26,1948

Yr	Cl	Lea	Pos	G	Rec
1926	Phi	A	P	47	9-0
1927	Phi	A	P	32	0-3
	BLTL			79	9-3

PATRICK, ROBERT LEE
b.Oct.27,1917 Ft.Smith,Ark.

Yr	Cl	Lea	Pos	G	Rec
1941	Det	A	O	5	.286
1942	Det	A	O	4	.250
	BRTR			9	.267

PATTEE, HARRY ERNEST
b.Jan.17,1882 Charlestown,Mass.

Yr	Cl	Lea	Pos	G	Rec
1908	Bro	N	2	74	.216

BLTR

PATTEN, CASE L.
b.May 7,1876 Westport,N.Y.
d.May 31,1935

Yr	Cl	Lea	Pos	G	Rec
1901	Was	A	P	31	18-10
1902	Was	A	P-O	39	17-17 / .095
1903	Was	A	P	35	10-23
1904	Was	A	P	44	15-21
1905	Was	A	P	43	16-20
1906	Was	A	P	38	19-16
1907	Was	A	P	36	12-17
1908	Was	A	P	5	1-3
1908	Bos	A	P	1	0-0
1909	Bos	A	P	1	0-0
	TL			273	108-127 / .132

PATTERSON, DANIEL THOMAS
b.1846

Yr	Cl	Lea	Pos	G	Rec
1871	Mut	n	O	32	NR
1872	Eck	n	1-O	10	NR
1874	Mut	n	1	1	NR
1875	Atl	n	2-O	10	NR
				53	NR

PATTERSON, GEORGE

Yr	Cl	Lea	Pos	G	Rec
1884	Key	U	O	2	.143

PATTERSON, HAMILTON
b.Oct.13,1877 Belleville,Ill.
d.Nov.25,1945

Yr	Cl	Lea	Pos	G	Rec
1909	St.L	A	1-O	17	.204
1909	Chi	A	O	1	.000
	TR			18	.192

PATTERSON, HENRY JOSEPH
b.July 17,1907 San Francisco,Cal.

Yr	Cl	Lea	Pos	G	Rec
1932	Bos	A	C	1	.000

TR

PATTERSON, LORENZO CLAIRE
b.Oct.5,1887 Arkansas City,Kan.
d.Mar.28,1913

Yr	Cl	Lea	Pos	G	Rec
1909	Cin	N	O	4	.125

BLTR

PATTERSON, ROY LEWIS
(Boy Wonder)
b.Dec.17,1877 Stoddard,Wis.
d.Apr.14,1953

Yr	Cl	Lea	Pos	G	Rec
1901	Chi	A	P	40	20-16
1902	Chi	A	P	34	20-13
1903	Chi	A	P	34	14-16
1904	Chi	A	P	22	7-9
1905	Chi	A	P	13	4-5
1906	Chi	A	P	22	10-7
1907	Chi	A	P	19	4-6
	BRTR			184	79-72

PATTERSON, WILLIAM JENNINGS BRYAN (Pat)
b.Jan.29,1901 Belleville,Ill.

Yr	Cl	Lea	Pos	G	Rec
1921	NY	N	3	23	.400

BRTR

PATTISON, JAMES WELLS
b.Dec.18,1908 New York,N.Y.

Yr	Cl	Lea	Pos	G	Rec
1929	Bro	N	P	6	0-1

BLTL

PATTON, EUGENE TUNNEY
b.July 8,1926 Coatesville,Pa.

Yr	Cl	Lea	Pos	G	Rec
1944	Bos	N	H	1	.000

BLTR

PATTON, GEORGE WILLIAM
b.Oct.7,1912 Cornwall,Pa.

Yr	Cl	Lea	Pos	G	Rec
1935	Phi	A	C	9	.300

BRTR

PATTON, HARRY C.
b.Davenport,Ia.

Yr	Cl	Lea	Pos	G	Rec
1910	St.L	N	P	1	0-0

PATTON, THOMAS ALLEN
b.Sept.5,1935 Honey Brook,Pa.

Yr	Cl	Lea	Pos	G	Rec
1957	Bal	A	C	1	.000

BRTR

PAUL, ...

Yr	Cl	Lea	Pos	G	Rec
1876	Ath	N	C	3	.167

PAULA, CARLOS CONILL
b.Nov.4,1928 Havana,Cuba

Yr	Cl	Lea	Pos	G	Rec
1954	Was	A	O	9	.167
1955	Was	A	O	115	.299
1956	Was	A	O	33	.183
	BRTR			157	.271

PAULETTE, E. EUGENE
(Gene)
b.May 26,1891 Little Rock,Ark.

Yr	Cl	Lea	Pos	G	Rec
1911	NY	N	1	10	.167
1916	St.L	A	H	5	.500
1917	St.L	A	1	12	.182
1917	St.L	N	1	95	.265
1918	St.L	N	P-1-2-S-3-O	125	0-0 / .273
1919	St.L	N	S	43	.215
1919	Phi	N	O	67	.259
1920	Phi	N	1	143	.288
	BRTR			500	0-0 / .268

PAULSON, PAUL GUILFORD
b.Mar.2,1902 Graettinger,Ia.

Yr	Cl	Lea	Pos	G	Rec
1925	St.L	N	P	1	0-0

BRTR

PAUXTIS, SIMON FRANCIS
b.July 20,1885 W.Pittston,Pa.
d.Mar.14,1961

Yr	Cl	Lea	Pos	G	Rec
1909	Cin	N	C	4	.125

BRTR

PAVESKOVICH, JOHN MICHAEL
(Played under name of John Michael Pesky)

PAVLETICH, DONALD STEPHEN
b.July 13,1938 Milwaukee,Wis.

Yr	Cl	Lea	Pos	G	Rec
1957	Cin	N	H	1	.000
1959	Cin	N	H	1	.000
1962	Cin	N	C-1	34	.222
	BRTR			36	.219

PAVLIECIVICH, ERVIN MARTIN
(Played under name of Ervin Martin Palica)

PAWELEK, THEODORE JOHN
b.Aug.15,1920 Chicago Heights,Ill.

Yr	Cl	Lea	Pos	G	Rec
1946	Chi	N	C	4	.250

BLTR

PAWLOSKI, STANLEY WALTER
b.Sept.6,1931 Wanamie,Pa.

Yr	Cl	Lea	Pos	G	Rec
1955	Cle	A	2	2	.125

BRTR

PAYNE, FREDERICK THOMAS
b.Sept.2,1880 Camden,N.Y.
d.Jan.16,1954

Yr	Cl	Lea	Pos	G	Rec
1906	Det	A	C-O	72	.270
1907	Det	A	C	53	.167
1908	Det	A	C	20	.067
1909	Chi	A	C	32	.244
1910	Chi	A	C	91	.222
1911	Chi	A	C	66	.203
	BRTR			334	.215

PAYNE, GEORGE WASHINGTON
b.May 23,1894 Mt.Vernon,Ky.
d.Jan.24,1959

Yr	Cl	Lea	Pos	G	Rec
1920	Chi	A	P	12	1-1

BRTR

PAYNE, HARLEY F. (Lady)
b.Jan.9,1868 Windsor,O.

Yr	Cl	Lea	Pos	G	Rec
1896	Bro	N	P	32	14-13
1897	Bro	N	P	39	13-21
1898	Bro	N	P	1	1-0
1899	Pit	N	P	4	1-3
				76	29-37

PAYNTER, GEORGE WASHINGTON
(Real name George Washington Paner)
b.July 6,1871 Cincinnati,O.
d.Oct.1,1950

Yr	Cl	Lea	Pos	G	Rec
1894	St.L	N	O	1	.000

PEACOCK, JOHN GASTON
b.Jan.10,1910 Fremont,N.C.

Yr	Cl	Lea	Pos	G	Rec
1937	Bos	A	C	9	.313
1938	Bos	A	C	72	.303
1939	Bos	A	C	92	.277
1940	Bos	A	C	63	.282
1941	Bos	A	C	79	.284
1942	Bos	A	C	88	.266
1943	Bos	A	C	48	.202
1944	Bos	A	C	4	.000
1944	Phi	N	C-2	83	.225
1945	Phi	N	C	33	.203
1945	Bro	N	C	48	.255
	BLTR			619	.262

PEAK, ELIAS
b.Philadelphia,Pa.

Yr	Cl	Lea	Pos	G	Rec
1884	Bos	U	O	1	.000
1884	Key	U	2-S-O	54	.199
				55	.196

PEARCE, FRANKLIN THOMAS
b.Aug.31,1905 Middletown,Ky.
d.Sept.3,1950

Yr	Cl	Lea	Pos	G	Rec
1933	Phi	N	P	20	5-4
1934	Phi	N	P	7	0-2
1935	Phi	N	P	5	0-0
	BRTR			32	5-6

PEARCE, GEORGE THOMAS
(Filbert)
b.Jan.10,1888 Aurora,Ill.
d.Oct.11,1935

Yr	Cl	Lea	Pos	G	Rec
1912	Chi	N	P	3	0-0
1913	Chi	N	P	25	13-5
1914	Chi	N	P	30	9-12
1915	Chi	N	P	36	13-9
1916	Chi	N	P	4	0-0
1917	St.L	N	P	5	1-1
	BLTL			103	36-27

PEARCE, GRAYSON S.
(Grace)
b.New York,N.Y.
d.Aug.29,1894

Yr	Cl	Lea	Pos	G	Rec
1876	Lou	N	P	1	0-0
1882	Lou	a	2-O	9	.294
1882	Bal	a	2-S-O	42	.210
1883	Col	a	2-O	11	.220
1883	NY	N	2-O	18	.095
1884	Met	a	2-O	5	.250
	BRTR			86	0-0 .200

PEARCE, HARRY JAMES
b.July 12,1889 Philadelphia,Pa.
d.Jan.8,1942

Yr	Cl	Lea	Pos	G	Rec
1917	Phi	N	S	4	.250
1918	Phi	N	1-2-S	60	.244
1919	Phi	N	2-S-3	68	.180
	BRTR			132	.208

PEARCE, JAMES MADISON
b.June 9,1925 Zebulon,N.C.

Yr	Cl	Lea	Pos	G	Rec
1949	Was	A	P	2	0-1
1950	Was	A	P	20	2-1
1953	Was	A	P	4	0-1
1954	Cin	N	P	2	1-0
1955	Cin	N	P	2	0-1
	BRTR			30	3-4

PEARCE, RICHARD J.
(Dickey)
b.Jan.2,1836 Brooklyn,N.Y.
d.Sept.18,1908

Yr	Cl	Lea	Pos	G	Rec
1871	Mut	n	S	34	NR
1872	Mut	n	M-S-O	44	NR
1873	Atl	n	S	55	NR
1874	Atl	n	S	36	NR
1874	Phi	n	S	1	NR
1874	Atl*	n	S-3	20	NR
1875	St.L	N	S	67	.256
1876	St.L	N	S	25	.200
1877	St.L	N	S	8	.172
	BRTR			290	NR

PEARCE, WILLIAM C.
(Ducky)
b.Mar.17,1885 Corning,O.
d.May 22,1933

Yr	Cl	Lea	Pos	G	Rec
1908	Cin	N	C	2	.000
1909	Cin	N	C	2	.000
	BRTR			4	.000

PEARS, FRANK T.
b.St.Louis,Mo.

Yr	Cl	Lea	Pos	G	Rec
1889	KC	a	P	3	0-2
1893	St.L	N	P	1	0-0
	TR			4	0-2

PEARSON, ALBERT GREGORY
b.Sept.12,1935 Alhambra,Cal.

Yr	Cl	Lea	Pos	G	Rec
1958	Was	A	O	146	.275

(Continued)

Yr	Cl	Lea	Pos	G	Rec
1959	Was	A	O	25	.188
1959	Bal	A	O	80	.232
1960	Bal	A	O	48	.244
1961	LA	A	O	144	.288
1962	LA	A	O	160	.261
	BLTL			603	.248

PEARSON, ALEXANDER F.
b.Homestead,Pa.

Yr	Cl	Lea	Pos	G	Rec
1902	St.L	N	P	11	2-6
1903	Cle	A	P	4	1-2
				15	3-8

PEARSON, DAVID P.
b.Aug.20,1855 Wilkes-Barre,Pa.
d.Nov.11,1922

Yr	Cl	Lea	Pos	G	Rec
1876	Cin	N	P-C-O	56	0-1 .235
	BRTR				

PEARSON, ISAAC OVERTON
b.Mar.1,1918 Grenada,Miss.

Yr	Cl	Lea	Pos	G	Rec
1939	Phi	N	P	27	2-13
1940	Phi	N	P	29	3-14
1941	Phi	N	P	46	4-14
1942	Phi	N	P	35	1-6
1946	Phi	N	P	5	1-0
1948	Chi	A	P	23	2-3
	BRTR			165	13-50

PEARSON, MARCELLUS MONTE
(Hoot)
b.Sept.2,1909 Oakland,Cal.

Yr	Cl	Lea	Pos	G	Rec
1932	Cle	A	P	8	0-0
1933	Cle	A	P	19	10-5
1934	Cle	A	P	39	18-13
1935	Cle	A	P	30	8-13
1936	NY	A	P	33	19-7
1937	NY	A	P	22	9-3
1938	NY	A	P	28	16-7
1939	NY	A	P	22	12-5
1940	NY	A	P	16	7-6
1941	Cin	N	P	8	1-3
	BRTR			225	100-62

PEASLEY, MARVIN WARREN
b.July 16,1889 Jonesport,Me.
d.Dec.27,1948

Yr	Cl	Lea	Pos	G	Rec
1910	Det	A	P	2	0-1
	BLTL				

PECHINEY, GEORGE ADOLPHE
b.Sept.20,1861 Cincinnati,O.
d.July 14,1943

Yr	Cl	Lea	Pos	G	Rec
1885	Cin	a	P	11	7-4
1886	Cin	a	P-O	43	17-21 .221
1887	Cle	a	P	10	1-9
	BRTR			64	25-34 .220

PECHOUS, CHARLES EDWARD
b.Oct.5,1896 Chicago,Ill.

Yr	Cl	Lea	Pos	G	Rec
1915	Chi	F	3	18	.220
1916	Chi	N	3	22	.145
1917	Chi	N	S	13	.244
	BRTR			53	.193

PECK, HAROLD ARTHUR
b.Apr.20,1917 Big Bend,Wis.

Yr	Cl	Lea	Pos	G	Rec
1943	Bro	N	H	1	.000
1944	Phi	A	O	2	.250
1945	Phi	A	O	112	.276
1946	Phi	A	O	48	.247
1947	Cle	A	O	114	.293
1948	Cle	A	O	45	.286
1949	Cle	A	O	33	.310
	BLTL			355	.279

PECKINPAUGH, ROGER THORPE
b.Feb.5,1891 Wooster,O.

Yr	Cl	Lea	Pos	G	Rec
1910	Cle	A	S	15	.200
1912	Cle	A	S	69	.212
1913	Cle	A	S	1	.000
1913	NY	A	S	95	.268
1914	NY	A	M-S	157	.223
1915	NY	A	S	142	.220
1916	NY	A	S	142	.255
1917	NY	A	S	148	.260
1918	NY	A	S	122	.231
1919	NY	A	S	122	.305
1920	NY	A	S	139	.270
1921	NY	A	S	149	.288
1922	Was	A	S	147	.254
1923	Was	A	S	154	.264
1924	Was	A	S	155	.272
1925	Was	A	1-S	126	.294
1926	Was	A	S	57	.238
1927	Chi	A	S	68	.295
	BRTR			2008	.259

Non-playing manager Cle (A) 1928-33 and 1941.

PEDEN, LESLIE EARL
(Gooch)
b.Sept.17,1923 Azle,Tex.

Yr	Cl	Lea	Pos	G	Rec
1953	Was	A	C	9	.250
	BRTR				

PEDROES, CHARLES P.
(Chick)
b.Chicago,Ill.

Yr	Cl	Lea	Pos	G	Rec
1902	Chi	N	O	2	.000

PEEK, STEPHEN GEORGE
b.July 30,1914 Springfield,Mass.

Yr	Cl	Lea	Pos	G	Rec
1941	NY	A	P	17	4-2
	BBTR				

PEEL, HOMER HEFNER
b.Oct.10,1902 Port Sullivan,Tex.

Yr	Cl	Lea	Pos	G	Rec
1927	St.L	N	O	2	.000
1929	Phi	N	O	53	.269
1930	St.L	N	O	26	.164
1933	NY	N	O	84	.257
1934	NY	N	O	21	.195
	BRTR			186	.238

PEERSON, JACK CHILES
b.Aug.28,1910 Brunswick,Ga.

Yr	Cl	Lea	Pos	G	Rec
1935	Phi	A	S	10	.316
1936	Phi	A	2-S	8	.324
	BRTR			18	.321

PEERY, GEORGE A.
(Red)
b.Aug.15,1906 Santaquin,Utah.

Yr	Cl	Lea	Pos	G	Rec
1927	Pit	N	P	1	0-0
1929	Bos	N	P	10	0-1
	BLTL			11	0-1

PEETE, CHARLES
b.Feb.22,1929 Franklin,Va.
d.Nov.27,1956

Yr	Cl	Lea	Pos	G	Rec
1956	St.L	N	O	23	.192
	BLTR				

PEFFER, MONTE
b.1891 New York,N.Y.

Yr	Cl	Lea	Pos	G	Rec
1913	Phi	A	S	1	.000
	BRTR				

PEITZ, HENRY CLEMENT
(Heinie)
b.Nov.28,1870 St.Louis,Mo.
d.Oct.23,1943

Yr	Cl	Lea	Pos	G	Rec
1893	St.L	N	C	94	.266
1894	St.L	N	C-1-3	100	.274
1895	St.L	N	C	90	.288
1896	Cin	N	C	67	.298
1897	Cin	N	C	73	.297
1898	Cin	N	C	100	.281
1899	Cin	N	C	91	.271
1900	Cin	N	C	84	.251
1901	Cin	N	C-2	73	.311
1902	Cin	N	C-1-2-3	104	.313

(Continued)

Yr	Cl	Lea	Pos	G	Rec
1903	Cin	N	C	102	.260
1904	Cin	N	C-1	82	.243
1905	Pit	N	C	88	.223
1906	Pit	N	C	38	.240
1913	St.L	N	C-O	3	.333
			BRTR	1189	.274

PEITZ, JOSEPH

Yr	Cl	Lea	Pos	G	Rec
1892	St.L	N	O	1	.000
1894	St.L	N	O	5	.421
				6	.364

PELLAGRINI, EDWARD CHARLES
b.Mar.13,1919 Boston,Mass.

Yr	Cl	Lea	Pos	G	Rec
1946	Bos	A	S-3	22	.211
1947	Bos	A	S-3	74	.203
1948	St.L	A	S	105	.238
1949	St.L	A	S	79	.238
1951	Phi	N	2-S-3	86	.234
1952	Cin	N	1-2-S-3	46	.170
1953	Pit	N	2-S-3	78	.253
1954	Pit	N	2-S-3	73	.216
			BRTR	563	.226

PELOUZE, ...

Yr	Cl	Lea	Pos	G	Rec
1886	St.L	N	O	1	.000

PELTY, BARNEY
b.Sept.10,1880 Farmington,Mo.
d.May 24,1939

Yr	Cl	Lea	Pos	G	Rec
1903	St.L	A	P	8	4-4
1904	St.L	A	P	40	14-18
1905	St.L	A	P	31	13-14
1906	St.L	A	P	35	17-12
1907	St.L	A	P	36	12-21
1908	St.L	A	P	21	7-14
1909	St.L	A	P	37	11-11
1910	St.L	A	P	27	5-10
1911	St.L	A	P	29	7-15
1912	St.L	A	P	6	0-3
1912	Was	A	P	11	2-6
			BRTR	281	92-118

PELTZ, JOHN
b.Apr.23,1861 New Orleans,La.
d.Feb.27,1906

Yr	Cl	Lea	Pos	G	Rec
1884	Ind	a	O	106	.213
1888	Bal	a	O	1	.250
1890	Bro	a	O	99	.234
1890	Syr	a	O	5	.176
1890	Tol	a	O	18	.227
				229	.223

PENA, ORLANDO GUEVARA
b.Nov.17,1937 Victoria de las Tunas, Cuba

Yr	Cl	Lea	Pos	G	Rec
1958	Cin	N	P	9	1-0
1959	Cin	N	P	46	5-9
1960	Cin	N	P	4	0-1
1962	KC	A	P	13	6-4
			BRTR	72	12-14

PENCE, ELMER CLAIR
b.Aug.17,1900 Valley Springs,Cal.

Yr	Cl	Lea	Pos	G	Rec
1922	Chi	A	O	1	.000
			BRTR		

PENCE, RUSSELL WILLIAM
b.Mar.11,1900 Marine,Ill.

Yr	Cl	Lea	Pos	G	Rec
1921	Chi	A	P	4	0-0
			BRTR		

PENDLETON, JAMES EDWARD
b.Jan.7,1926 St.Charles,Mo.

Yr	Cl	Lea	Pos	G	Rec
1953	Mil	N	S-O	120	.299
1954	Mil	N	O	71	.220
1955	Mil	N	S-3-O	8	.000
1956	Mil	N	1-2-S-3	14	.000
1957	Pit	N	S-3-O	46	.305
1958	Pit	N	H	3	.333

(Continued)

Yr	Cl	Lea	Pos	G	Rec
1959	Cin	N	S-3-O	65	.257
1962	Hou	N	1-S-3-O	117	.246
			BRTR	444	.255

PENNER, WILLIAM KENNETH
(Ken)
b.Apr.24,1896 Florence,Ala.
d.May 28,1959

Yr	Cl	Lea	Pos	G	Rec
1916	Cle	A	P	4	1-0
1929	Chi	N	P	5	0-1
			BLTR	9	1-1

PENNINGTON, GEORGE LOUIS
(Kewpie)
b.Sept.24,1896 New York,N.Y.

Yr	Cl	Lea	Pos	G	Rec
1917	St.L	A	P	1	0-0
			BRTR		

PENNOCK, HERBERT JEFFERIS
b.Feb.19.1894 Kennett Square,Pa.
d.Jan.30,1948

Yr	Cl	Lea	Pos	G	Rec
1912	Phi	A	P	17	1-2
1913	Phi	A	P	6	4-1
1914	Phi	A	P	27	11-4
1915	Phi	A	P	11	3-5
1915	Bos	A	P	5	0-0
1916	Bos	A	P	11	0-2
1917	Bos	A	P	24	5-5
1919	Bos	A	P	32	17-8
1920	Bos	A	P	38	16-13
1921	Bos	A	P	32	12-14
1922	Bos	A	P	32	10-17
1923	NY	A	P	35	19-6
1924	NY	A	P	40	21-9
1925	NY	A	P	47	16-17
1926	NY	A	P	40	23-11
1927	NY	A	P	34	19-8
1928	NY	A	P	28	17-6
1929	NY	A	P	27	9-11
1930	NY	A	P	25	11-7
1931	NY	A	P	25	11-6
1932	NY	A	P	22	9-5
1933	NY	A	P	23	7-4
1934	Bos	A	P	30	2-0
			BBTL	611	243-161

PENSON, PAUL EUGENE
b.July 12,1931 Kansas City,Kan.

Yr	Cl	Lea	Pos	G	Rec
1954	Phi	N	P	5	1-1
			BRTR		

PEOPLES, JAMES E.
b.Oct.7,1863 Utica,N.Y.
d.Aug.30,1920

Yr	Cl	Lea	Pos	G	Rec
1884	Cin	a	C-1-S-3-O	70	.180
1885	Cin	a	P-C-O	7	{0-2 .136
1885	Bro	a	C	40	.205
1886	Bro	a	C	94	.221
1887	Bro	a	C	73	.283
1888	Bro	a	C	33	.198
1889	Col	a	C	28	.223
			TR	345	{0-2 .224

PEPITONE, JOSEPH ANTHONY
b.Oct.9,1940 Brooklyn,N.Y.

Yr	Cl	Lea	Pos	G	Rec
1962	NY	A	1-O	63	.239
			BLTL		

PEPLOSKI, HENRY STEPHEN
b.Sept.15,1907 Wilmington,Del.

Yr	Cl	Lea	Pos	G	Rec
1929	Bos	N	3	6	.200
			BLTR		

PEPLOSKI, JOSEPH ALOYSIUS
(Pepper)
b.Sept.12,1891 Brooklyn,N.Y.

Yr	Cl	Lea	Pos	G	Rec
1913	Det	A	3	2	.500
			BRTR		

PEPPER, HUGH McLAURIN
(Laurin)
b.Jan.18,1931 Vaughn,Miss.

Yr	Cl	Lea	Pos	G	Rec
1954	Pit	N	P	14	1-5
1955	Pit	N	P	14	0-1
1956	Pit	N	P	11	1-1
1957	Pit	N	P	7	0-1
			BRTR	46	2-8

PEPPER, RAYMOND WATSON
b.Aug.5,1905 Decatur,Ala.

Yr	Cl	Lea	Pos	G	Rec
1932	St.L	N	O	21	.246
1933	St.L	N	O	3	.222
1934	St.L	A	O	148	.298
1935	St.L	A	O	92	.253
1936	St.L	A	O	75	.282
			BRTR	339	.281

PEPPER, ROBERT ERNEST
b.May 3,1895 Rosston,Pa.

Yr	Cl	Lea	Pos	G	Rec
1915	Phi	A	P	1	0-0
			BRTR		

PEPPER, WILLIAM HARRISON
b.Webb City,Mo.

Yr	Cl	Lea	Pos	G	Rec
1894	Lou	N	P	2	0-1

PERDUE, HUBBARD E.
b.June 7,1886 Gallatin,Tenn.

Yr	Cl	Lea	Pos	G	Rec
1911	Bos	N	P	24	6-10
1912	Bos	N	P	37	13-16
1913	Bos	N	P	38	16-13
1914	Bos	N	P	9	2-5
1914	St.L	N	P	22	8-8
1915	St.L	N	P	31	6-12
			BRTR	161	51-64

PEREZ, GEORGE THOMAS
b.Dec.29,1937 San Fernando,Cal.

Yr	Cl	Lea	Pos	G	Rec
1958	Pit	N	P	4	0-1
			BRTR		

PERKINS, CHARLES SULLIVAN
(Lefty)
b.Sept.9,1905 Birmingham,Ala.

Yr	Cl	Lea	Pos	G	Rec
1930	Phi	A	P	8	0-0
1934	Bro	N	P	11	0-3
			BLTL	19	0-3

PERKINS, RALPH FOSTER
(Cy)
b.Feb.27,1896 Gloucester,Mass.

Yr	Cl	Lea	Pos	G	Rec
1915	Phi	A	C	7	.190
1917	Phi	A	C	6	.167
1918	Phi	A	C	68	.188
1919	Phi	A	C	101	.252
1920	Phi	A	C	148	.260
1921	Phi	A	C	141	.288
1922	Phi	A	C	148	.267
1923	Phi	A	C	143	.270
1924	Phi	A	C	128	.242
1925	Phi	A	C-3	65	.307
1926	Phi	A	C	63	.291
1927	Phi	A	C	59	.256
1928	Phi	A	C	19	.172
1929	Phi	A	C	38	.211
1930	Phi	A	C	20	.158
1931	NY	A	C	16	.255
1934	Det	A	H	1	.000
			BRTR	1171	.259

PERKOVICH, JOHN JOSEPH
b.Mar.10,1924 Chicago,Ill.

Yr	Cl	Lea	Pos	G	Rec
1950	Chi	A	P	1	0-0
			BRTR		

PERKOWSKI, HARRY WALTER
b.Sept.6,1922 Dante,Va.

Yr	Cl	Lea	Pos	G	Rec
1947	Cin	N	P	3	0-0
1949	Cin	N	P	5	1-1
1950	Cin	N	P	32	0-0
1951	Cin	N	P	37	3-6
1952	Cin	N	P	33	12-10
1953	Cin	N	P	33	12-11
1954	Cin	N	P	28	2-8
1955	Chi	N	P	26	3-4
			BLTL	197	33-40

PERME, LEONARD JOSEPH
b.Nov.25,1918 Cleveland,O.

Yr	Cl	Lea	Pos	G	Rec
1942	Chi	A	P	4	0-1
1946	Chi	A	P	4	0-0
BLTL				8	0-1

PERNOLL, HENRY HUBBARD
(Hub)
b.Mar.14,1888 Applegate,Ore.
d.Feb.18,1944

Yr	Cl	Lea	Pos	G	Rec
1910	Det	A	P	11	4-3
1912	Det	A	P	3	0-0
BRTL				14	4-3

PERRANOSKI, RONALD PETER
b.Apr.1,1937 Paterson,N.J.

Yr	Cl	Lea	Pos	G	Rec
1961	LA	N	P	53	7-5
1962	LA	N	P	70	6-6
BLTL				123	13-11

PERRIN, JOHN STEPHENSON
b.Feb.4,1893 Escanaba,Mich.

Yr	Cl	Lea	Pos	G	Rec
1921	Bos	A	O	4	.231
BLTR					

PERRIN, WILLIAM JOSEPH
b.June 23,1911 New Orleans,La.

Yr	Cl	Lea	Pos	G	Rec
1934	Cle	A	P	1	0-1
BRTL					

PERRINE, JOHN GROVER
(Nig)
b.Jan.14,1885 Clinton,Wis.
d.Aug.13,1948

Yr	Cl	Lea	Pos	G	Rec
1907	Was	A	2-S	44	.171
TR					

PERRING, GEORGE WILSON
b.Aug.13,1884 Sharon,Wis.
d.Aug.20,1960

Yr	Cl	Lea	Pos	G	Rec
1908	Cle	A	S-3	89	.216
1909	Cle	A	3	88	.223
1910	Cle	A	3	39	.221
1914	KC	F	1-3	144	.282
1915	KC	F	1-2-3	153	.257
BRTR				513	.249

PERRITT, WILLIAM DAYTON
(Pol)
b.Aug.30,1892 Arcadia,La.
d.Oct.15,1947

Yr	Cl	Lea	Pos	G	Rec
1912	St.L	N	P	6	1-1
1913	St.L	N	P	36	6-14
1914	St.L	N	P	41	16-13
1915	NY	N	P	35	12-18
1916	NY	N	P	40	18-11
1917	NY	N	P	35	17-7
1918	NY	N	P	36	18-13
1919	NY	N	P	11	1-1
1920	NY	N	P	8	0-0
1921	NY	N	P	5	0-0
1921	Det	A	P	4	1-0
BRTR				257	92-78

PERRY, BOYD GLENN
b.Mar.21,1914 Snow Camp,N.C.

Yr	Cl	Lea	Pos	G	Rec
1941	Det	A	2-S	36	.181
BRTR					

PERRY, CLAYTON SHIELDS
b.Dec.18,1881 Clayton,Wis.
d.Jan.13,1954

Yr	Cl	Lea	Pos	G	Rec
1908	Det	A	3	7	.118
TR					

PERRY, GAYLORD JACKSON
b.Sept.15,1938 Williamston,N.C.

Yr	Cl	Lea	Pos	G	Rec
1962	SF	N	P	13	3-1
BRTR					

PERRY, HERBERT SCOTT
b.Apr.17,1892 Corsicana,Tex.
d.Oct.27,1959

Yr	Cl	Lea	Pos	G	Rec
1915	St.L	A	P	1	0-0
1916	Chi	N	P	4	2-1
1917	Cin	N	P	4	0-0
1918	Phi	A	P	44	21-19
1919	Phi	A	P	25	4-17
1920	Phi	A	P	42	11-25
1921	Phi	A	P	12	3-6
BRTR				132	41-68

PERRY, JAMES EVAN
b.Oct.30,1936 Williamston,N.C.

Yr	Cl	Lea	Pos	G	Rec
1959	Cle	A	P	44	12-10
1960	Cle	A	P	42	18-10
1961	Cle	A	P	35	10-17
1962	Cle	A	P	35	12-12
BBTR				156	52-49

PERRY, WILLIAM HENRY
(Socks)
b.July 28,1886 Howell,Mich.
d.July 18,1956

Yr	Cl	Lea	Pos	G	Rec
1912	Det	A	O	13	.162
BLTR					

PERRYMAN, EMMETT KEY
(Parson)
b.Oct.24,1888 Everett Springs,Ga.

Yr	Cl	Lea	Pos	G	Rec
1915	St.L	A	P	24	2-3
BRTR					

PERSICO, SALVATORE JOSEPH
(Played under name of
Joseph Smith)

PERTICA, WILLIAM ANDREW
b.Aug.17,1899 Santa Barbara,Cal.

Yr	Cl	Lea	Pos	G	Rec
1918	Bos	A	P	1	0-0
1921	St.L	N	P	38	14-10
1922	St.L	N	P-S	35	8-8 / .181
1923	St.L	N	P	1	0-0
BRTR				75	22-18 / .152

PESANO, ALFRED MANUEL
(Played under name of
Alfred Manuel Martin)

PESKY, JOHN MICHAEL
(Real name John Michael
Paveskovich)
b.Sept.27,1919 Portland,Ore.

Yr	Cl	Lea	Pos	G	Rec
1942	Bos	A	S	147	.331
1946	Bos	A	S	153	.335
1947	Bos	A	S-3	155	.324
1948	Bos	A	3	143	.281
1949	Bos	A	3	148	.306
1950	Bos	A	S-3	127	.312
1951	Bos	A	2-S-3	131	.313
1952	Bos	A	S-3	25	.149
1952	Det	A	2-S-3	69	.254
1953	Det	A	2	103	.292
1954	Det	A	H	20	.176
1954	Was	A	2-S	49	.253
BLTR				1270	.307

PETERMAN, WILLIAM DAVID
b.Mar.20,1921 Philadelphia,Pa.

Yr	Cl	Lea	Pos	G	Rec
1942	Phi	N	C	1	1.000
BRTR					

PETERS, GARY CHARLES
b.Apr.21,1937 Grove City,Pa.

Yr	Cl	Lea	Pos	G	Rec
1959	Chi	A	P	2	0-0
1960	Chi	A	P	2	0-0
1961	Chi	A	P	3	0-0
1962	Chi	A	P	5	0-1
BLTL				12	0-1

PETERS, JOHN PAUL
b.Apr.8,1850 Louisana,Mo.
d.Jan.4,1924

Yr	Cl	Lea	Pos	G	Rec
1874	Chi	n	2-S-3	54	NR
1875	Chi	n	2-S	70	NR
1876	Chi	N	S	66	.348
1877	Chi	N	S	60	.317
1878	Mil	N	2-S	54	.311
1879	Chi	N	S	79	.254
1880	Pro	N	S	83	.230
1881	Buf	N	S-O	54	.214
1882	Pit	a	2-S	72	.278
1883	Pit	a	S	8	.107
1884	Pit	a	S	1	.000
BRTR				601	NR

PETERS, JOHN WILLIAM
b.July 14,1893 Kansas City,Kan.
d.Feb.21,1932

Yr	Cl	Lea	Pos	G	Rec
1915	Det	A	C	1	.000
1918	Cle	A	C	1	.000
1921	Phi	N	C	55	.290
1922	Phi	N	C	55	.244
BRTR				112	.265

PETERS, OSCAR C.
(Rube)
b.Mar.15,1886 Grand Fork,Ill.

Yr	Cl	Lea	Pos	G	Rec
1912	Chi	A	P	23	5-6
1914	Bro	F	P	11	1-1
BRTR				34	6-7

PETERS, RUSSELL DIXON
(Rusty)
b.Dec.14,1914 Roanoke,Va.

Yr	Cl	Lea	Pos	G	Rec
1936	Phi	A	S-3	45	.218
1937	Phi	A	2-S-3	116	.260
1938	Phi	A	S	2	.000
1940	Cle	A	1-2-S-3	30	.239
1941	Cle	A	2-S-3	29	.206
1942	Cle	A	2-S-3	34	.224
1943	Cle	A	2-S-3-O	79	.219
1944	Cle	A	2-S-3	88	.223
1946	Cle	A	S	9	.286
1947	St.L	A	2-S	39	.340
BRTR				471	.236

PETERSON, CARL FRANCIS
b.Apr.23,1925 Portland,Ore.

Yr	Cl	Lea	Pos	G	Rec
1955	Chi	A	S	6	.286
1957	Bal	A	S	7	.176
BRTR				13	.237

PETERSON, CHARLES ANDREW
b.Aug.15,1942 Tacoma,Wash.

Yr	Cl	Lea	Pos	G	Rec
1962	SF	N	S	4	.167
BRTR					

PETERSON, HARDING WILLIAM
b.Oct.17,1929 Perth Amboy,N.J.

Yr	Cl	Lea	Pos	G	Rec
1955	Pit	N	C	32	.247
1957	Pit	N	C	30	.301
1958	Pit	N	C	2	.333
1959	Pit	N	C	2	.000
BRTR				66	.273

PETERSON, JAMES NIELS
b.Aug.18,1908 Philadelphia,Pa.

Yr	Cl	Lea	Pos	G	Rec
1931	Phi	A	P	6	0-1
1933	Phi	A	P	32	2-5
1937	Bro	N	P	3	0-0
BRTR				41	2-6

PETERSON, KENT FRANKLIN
(Pete)
b.Dec.21,1925 Goshen,Utah.

Yr	Cl	Lea	Pos	G	Rec
1944	Cin	N	P	1	0-0
1947	Cin	N	P	37	6-13
1948	Cin	N	P	43	2-15
1949	Cin	N	P	30	4-5
1950	Cin	N	P	9	0-3
1951	Cin	N	P	9	1-1
1952	Phi	N	P	3	0-0
1953	Phi	N	P	15	0-1
BRTL				147	13-38

PETERSON, ROBERT A.
b.Philadelphia,Pa.

Yr	Cl	Lea	Pos	G	Rec
1906	Bos	A	C	39	.203
1907	Bos	A	C	4	.000
TR				43	.183

PETERSON, SIDNEY HERBERT
b.Jan.31,1918 Havelock,N.Dak.

Yr	Cl	Lea	Pos	G	Rec
1943	St.L	A	P	3	2-0
BRTR					

PETOSKEY, FREDERICK LEE (Ted)
b.Jan.5,1911 St.Charles,Mich.

Yr	Cl	Lea	Pos	G	Rec
1934	Cin	N	O	6	.000
1935	Cin	N	O	4	.400
	BRTR			10	.167

PETROSKY, JAMES
(Played under name of James Clark)

PETTEE, PATRICK E.
b.Jan.10,1863 Natick,Mass.
d.Oct.9,1934

Yr	Cl	Lea	Pos	G	Rec
1891	Lou	a	2	2	.167
	TR				

PETTIGREW, JIM NED
b.Aug.25,1881 Honey Grove,Tex.
d.Aug.20,1952

Yr	Cl	Lea	Pos	G	Rec
1914	Buf	F	H	2	.000

PETTIT, GEORGE WILLIAM PAUL
b.Nov.29,1931 Los Angeles,Cal.

Yr	Cl	Lea	Pos	G	Rec
1951	Pit	N	P	2	0-0
1953	Pit	N	P	11	1-2
	BLTL			13	1-2

PETTIT, LEON ARTHUR (Lefty)
b.June 23,1902 Waynesburg,Pa.

Yr	Cl	Lea	Pos	G	Rec
1935	Was	A	P	41	8-5
1937	Phi	N	P	3	0-1
	BLTL			44	8-6

PETTIT, ROBERT HENRY
b.July 19,1861 Williamstown,Mass.
d.Nov.1,1910

Yr	Cl	Lea	Pos	G	Rec
1887	Chi	N	O	32	.301
1888	Chi	N	O	43	.254
1891	Mil	a	3	21	.174
				96	.254

PETTY, CHARLES E.
b.June 28,1868 Nashville,Tenn.

Yr	Cl	Lea	Pos	G	Rec
1889	Cin	a	P	5	2-3
1893	NY	N	P	9	5-2
1894	Was	N	P	15	3-8
1894	Cle	N	P	3	0-2
	TR			32	10-15

PETTY, JESSE LEE
b.Nov.23,1894 Orr,Okla.

Yr	Cl	Lea	Pos	G	Rec
1921	Cle	A	P	4	0-0
1925	Bro	N	P	28	9-9
1926	Bro	N	P	38	17-17
1927	Bro	N	P	42	13-18
1928	Bro	N	P	40	15-15
1929	Pit	N	P	36	11-10
1930	Pit	N	P	10	1-6
1930	Chi	N	P	9	1-3
	BRTL			207	67-78

PEZOLD, LORENZ (Larry)
b.1893

Yr	Cl	Lea	Pos	G	Rec
1914	Cle	A	3	23	.226
	BRTR				

PEZZOLO, FRANCESCO STEPHANO (Played under name of Frank L. Bodie)

PEZZULLO, JOHN (Pretzels)
b.Dec.10,1911 Bridgeport,Conn.

Yr	Cl	Lea	Pos	G	Rec
1935	Phi	N	P	41	3-5
1936	Phi	N	P	1	0-0
	BLTL			42	3-5

PFEFFER, EDWARD JOSEPH (Jeff)
b.Mar.4,1889 Seymour,Ill.

Yr	Cl	Lea	Pos	G	Rec
1911	St.L	A	P	2	0-0
1913	Bro	N	P	5	0-1
1914	Bro	N	P	44	23-12
1915	Bro	N	P	40	19-14
1916	Bro	N	P	43	25-11
1917	Bro	N	P	31	11-15
1918	Bro	N	P	1	1-0
1919	Bro	N	P	30	17-13
1920	Bro	N	P	30	16-9
1921	Bro	N	P	6	1-5
1921	St.L	N	P	18	9-3
1922	St.L	N	P	45	19-12
1923	St.L	N	P	26	8-9
1924	St.L	N	P	16	4-5
1924	Pit	N	P	15	5-3
	BRTR			352	158-112

PFEFFER, FRANCIS XAVIER (Big Jeff)
b.Mar.31,1882 Champaign,Ill.
d.Dec.19,1954

Yr	Cl	Lea	Pos	G	Rec
1905	Chi	N	P	15	5-5
1906	Bos	N	P	50	13-22
1907	Bos	N	P	19	6-8
1908	Bos	N	P	4	0-0
1910	Chi	N	P-O	14	1-0 / .158
1911	Bos	N	P	30	7-5
	BRTR			132	32-40 / .203

PFEFFER, NATHANIEL FREDERICK (Dandelion)
b.Mar.17,1860 Louisville,Ky.
d.Apr.10,1932

Yr	Cl	Lea	Pos	G	Rec
1882	Tro	N	S-3	83	.221
1883	Chi	N	1-2-S-O	96	.234
1884	Chi	N	P-2	111	0-0 / .289
1885	Chi	N	P-2-O	112	3-1 / .240
1886	Chi	N	2	119	.263
1887	Chi	N	2	123	.325
1888	Chi	N	2	135	.249
1889	Chi	N	2	134	.241
1890	Chi	p	2	123	.268
1891	Chi	N	2	137	.246
1892	Lou	N	M-2	124	.261
1893	Lou	N	2	124	.269
1894	Lou	N	2-S	104	.297
1895	Lou	N	1-2-S	11	.288
1896	NY	N	2	4	.143
1896	Chi	N	2	95	.244
1897	Chi	N	2	32	.230
	BRTR			1667	3-1 / .262

PFIESTENBERGER, JOHN THEODORE JOSEPH
(Played under name of John Theodore Joseph Pfiester)

PFIESTER, JOHN THEODORE JOSEPH
(Real name John Theodore Joseph Pfiestenberger)
b.May 24,1878 Cincinnati,O.
d.Sept.3,1953

Yr	Cl	Lea	Pos	G	Rec
1903	Pit	N	P	3	0-3
1904	Pit	N	P	3	1-1
1906	Chi	N	P	31	20-8
1907	Chi	N	P	30	14-9
1908	Chi	N	P	33	12-10
1909	Chi	N	P	29	17-6
1910	Chi	N	P	14	6-3
1911	Chi	N	P	6	2-4
	BRTL			149	72-44

PFISTER, DANIEL ALBIN
b.Dec.20,1936 Plainfield,N.J.

Yr	Cl	Lea	Pos	G	Rec
1961	KC	A	P	2	0-0
1962	KC	A	P	52	4-14
	BRTR			54	4-14

PFISTER, GEORGE EDWARD
b.Sept.4,1918 Bound Brook,N.J.

Yr	Cl	Lea	Pos	G	Rec
1941	Bro	N	C	1	.000
	BRTR				

PFLANN, WILLIAM F.
b.Brooklyn,N.Y.

Yr	Cl	Lea	Pos	G	Rec
1894	Cin	N	P	1	0-1

PFUND, LeROY HERBERT
b.Oct.10,1919 Oak Park,Ill.

Yr	Cl	Lea	Pos	G	Rec
1945	Bro	N	P	15	3-2
	BRTR				

PFYL, MEINHARD CHARLES (Monte)
b.May 11,1886 St.Louis,Mo.
d.Oct.1945

Yr	Cl	Lea	Pos	G	Rec
1907	NY	N	1	1	.000

PHEBUS, RAYMOND WILLIAM
b.Aug.2,1910 Cherryvale,Kan.

Yr	Cl	Lea	Pos	G	Rec
1936	Was	A	P	2	0-0
1937	Was	A	P	6	3-2
1938	Was	A	P	5	0-0
	BRTR			13	3-2

PHELAN, ARTHUR EDWARD
b.Aug.14,1889 Macon Co.,Ill.

Yr	Cl	Lea	Pos	G	Rec
1910	Cin	N	3	17	.214
1912	Cin	N	3	130	.243
1913	Chi	N	2-3	91	.249
1914	Chi	N	S	25	.283
1915	Chi	N	2-3	133	.219
	BRTR			396	.236

PHELAN, DANIEL B.
b.Waterbury,Conn.

Yr	Cl	Lea	Pos	G	Rec
1890	Lou	a	1	8	.250

PHELAN, JAMES D. (Dick)
b.Dec.10,1854 Towanda,Pa.
d.Feb.13,1931

Yr	Cl	Lea	Pos	G	Rec
1884	Bal	U	2	97	.254
1885	Buf	N	2	4	.133
1885	St.L	N	3	2	.250
				103	.249

PHELAN, LEWIS G.
Non-playing manager St.L (N) 1895.

PHELPS, CORNELIUS CARMAN (Neal)
b.Nov.19,1840 New York,N.Y.
d.Feb.12,1885

Yr	Cl	Lea	Pos	G	Rec
1871	Kek	n	1	1	.000
1873	Mut	n	O	1	.000
1874	Mut	n	O	4	NR
1875	Mut	n	O	2	NR
1876	Mut	N	O	1	.000
1876	Ath	N	C	1	.000
				10	NR

PHELPS, EDWARD JOSEPH
b.Mar.3,1879 Albany,N.Y.
d.Jan.31,1942

Yr	Cl	Lea	Pos	G	Rec
1902	Pit	N	C-1	18	.197
1903	Pit	N	C	79	.282
1904	Pit	N	C	92	.242
1905	Cin	N	C	44	.231
1906	Cin	N	C	12	.275
1906	Pit	N	C	40	.237
1907	Pit	N	C	36	.212
1908	Pit	N	C	20	.234
1909	St.L	N	C	83	.248
1910	St.L	N	C	80	.263
1912	Bro	N	C	52	.288
1913	Bro	N	C	15	.222
	BRTR			571	.251

PHELPS, ERNEST GORDON (Blimp)
b.Apr.19,1908 Odenton,Md.

Yr	Cl	Lea	Pos	G	Rec
1931	Was	A	H	3	.333
1933	Chi	N	C	3	.286
1934	Chi	N	C	44	.286

Yr	Cl	Lea	Pos	G	Rec
(Continued)					
1935	Bro	N	C	47	.364
1936	Bro	N	C	115	.367
1937	Bro	N	C	121	.313
1938	Bro	N	C	66	.308
1939	Bro	N	C	98	.285
1940	Bro	N	C-1	118	.295
1941	Bro	N	C	16	.233
1942	Pit	N	C	95	.284
	BLTR			726	.310

PHELPS, RAYMOND CLIFFORD
b.Dec.11,1903 Dunlap,Tenn.

Yr	Cl	Lea	Pos	G	Rec
1930	Bro	N	P	36	14-7
1931	Bro	N	P	28	7-9
1932	Bro	N	P	20	4-5
1935	Chi	A	P	27	4-8
1936	Chi	A	P	15	4-6
	BRTR			126	33-35

PHILLEY, DAVID EARL
b.May 16,1920 Paris,Tex.

Yr	Cl	Lea	Pos	G	Rec
1941	Chi	A	O	7	.222
1946	Chi	A	O	17	.353
1947	Chi	A	3-O	143	.258
1948	Chi	A	O	137	.287
1949	Chi	A	O	146	.286
1950	Chi	A	O	156	.242
1951	Chi	A	O	7	.240
1951	Phi	A	3-O	125	.263
1952	Phi	A	3-O	151	.263
1953	Phi	A	3-O	157	.303
1954	Cle	A	O	133	.226
1955	Cle	A	O	44	.306
1955	Bal	A	3-O	82	.296
1956	Bal	A	3-O	32	.205
1956	Chi	A	1-O	86	.265
1957	Chi	A	1-O	22	.324
1957	Det	A	1-3-O	65	.283
1958	Phi	N	1-O	91	.309
1959	Phi	N	1-O	99	.291
1960	Phi	N	1-O	14	.333
1960	SF	N	3-O	39	.164
1960	Bal	A	3-O	14	.265
1961	Bal	A	1-O	99	.250
1962	Bos	A	S-O	38	.143
	BBTR			1904	.270

PHILLIPPE, CHARLES LOUIS
(Deacon)
b.May 23,1872 Rural Retreat,Va.
d.Mar.30,1952

Yr	Cl	Lea	Pos	G	Rec
1899	Lou	N	P	42	20-17
1900	Pit	N	P	32	18-14
1901	Pit	N	P	34	22-12
1902	Pit	N	P	30	20-9
1903	Pit	N	P	37	25-9
1904	Pit	N	P	21	10-10
1905	Pit	N	P	38	22-13
1906	Pit	N	P	33	15-10
1907	Pit	N	P	35	14-11
1908	Pit	N	P	5	0-0
1909	Pit	N	P	22	8-3
1910	Pit	N	P	31	14-2
1911	Pit	N	P	3	0-0
	BRTR			363	188-110

PHILLIPS, ALBERT ABERNATHY (Buzzy)
b.May 25,1904 Newton,N.C.

Yr	Cl	Lea	Pos	G	Rec
1930	Phi	N	P	14	0-0
	BRTR				

PHILLIPS, CLARENCE LEMUEL
(Red)
b.Nov.3,1911 Pauls Valley,Okla.

Yr	Cl	Lea	Pos	G	Rec
1934	Det	A	P	7	2-0
1936	Det	A	P	22	2-4
	BRTR			29	4-4

PHILLIPS, DAMON ROSWELL
b.June 8,1919 Corsicana,Tex.

Yr	Cl	Lea	Pos	G	Rec
1942	Cin	N	S	28	.202
1944	Bos	N	S-3	140	.258
1946	Bos	N	H	2	.500
	BRTR			170	.250

PHILLIPS, EDWARD DAVID
b.Feb.17,1902 Worcester,Mass.

Yr	Cl	Lea	Pos	G	Rec
1924	Bos	N	C	3	.000
1929	Det	A	C	68	.235
1931	Pit	N	C	106	.232
1932	NY	A	C	9	.290
1934	Was	A	C	56	.195
1935	Cle	A	C	70	.273
	BRTR			312	.237

PHILLIPS, HORACE B.
b.May 14,1853 Salem,O.
Non-playing manager Col (a) 1883, Pit (a) 1884-86 and Pit (N) 1887-89.

PHILLIPS, HOWARD EDWARD
(Eddie)
b.July 8,1931 St.Louis,Mo.

Yr	Cl	Lea	Pos	G	Rec
1953	St.L	N	H	9	.000
	BBTR				

PHILLIPS, JACK DORN
(Stretch)
b.Sept.6,1921 Clarence,N.Y.

Yr	Cl	Lea	Pos	G	Rec
1947	NY	A	1	16	.278
1948	NY	A	1	1	.000
1949	NY	A	1	45	.308
1949	Pit	N	1-3	18	.232
1950	Pit	N	P-1-3	69	0-0 / .293
1951	Pit	N	1-3	70	.237
1952	Pit	N	1	1	.000
1955	Det	A	1-3	55	.316
1956	Det	A	1-2-O	67	.295
1957	Det	A	H	1	.000
	BRTR			343	0-0 / .283

PHILLIPS, JOHN MELVIN
(Bubba)
b.Feb.24,1930 West Point,Miss.

Yr	Cl	Lea	Pos	G	Rec
1955	Det	A	3-O	95	.234
1956	Chi	A	3-O	67	.273
1957	Chi	A	3-O	121	.270
1958	Chi	A	3-O	84	.273
1959	Chi	A	3-O	117	.264
1960	Cle	A	3-O	113	.207
1961	Cle	A	3	143	.264
1962	Cle	A	2-3-O	148	.258
	BRTR			888	.256

PHILLIPS, JOHN STEPHEN
b.May 24,1921 St.Louis,Mo.
d.June 9,1958

Yr	Cl	Lea	Pos	G	Rec
1945	NY	N	P	2	0-0
	BRTR				

PHILLIPS, MARR B.
b.June 16,1862 Pittsburgh,Pa.
d.Apr.1928

Yr	Cl	Lea	Pos	G	Rec
1884	Ind	a	S	97	.266
1885	Det	N	S	33	.208
1885	Pit	a	S	2	.375
1890	Roc	a	S	65	.196
				197	.235

PHILLIPS, RICHARD EUGENE
b.Nov.24,1931 Racine,Wis.

Yr	Cl	Lea	Pos	G	Rec
1962	SF	N	2	5	.000
	BLTR				

PHILLIPS, THOMAS GERALD
b.Apr.1,1889 Phillipsburg,Pa.
d.Apr.12,1929

Yr	Cl	Lea	Pos	G	Rec
1915	St.L	A	P	5	1-3
1919	Cle	A	P	22	3-2
1921	Was	A	P	1	1-0
1922	Was	A	P	17	3-7
	BRTR			45	8-12

PHILLIPS, WILLIAM B.
b.1857 St.John,N.B.,Canada.
d.Oct.7,1900

Yr	Cl	Lea	Pos	G	Rec
1879	Cle	N	1	81	.271
1880	Cle	N	1	84	.255
1881	Cle	N	1	84	.270
1882	Cle	N	C-1	76	.266
(Continued)					
1883	Cle	N	1	94	.244
1884	Cle	N	1	110	.272
1885	Bro	a	1	100	.293
1886	Bro	a	1	142	.281
1887	Bro	a	1	132	.322
1888	KC	a	1	129	.235
	BRTR			1032	.273

PHILLIPS, WILLIAM CORCORAN
(Whoa Bill)
b.Nov.9,1868 Allenport,Pa.
d.Oct.25,1941

Yr	Cl	Lea	Pos	G	Rec
1890	Pit	N	P	15	1-9
1895	Cin	N	P	17	5-5
1899	Cin	N	P	31	17-8
1900	Cin	N	P	27	9-11
1901	Cin	N	P	33	14-18
1902	Cin	N	P	33	16-17
1903	Cin	N	P	16	7-6
	TR			172	69-74

Non-playing manager Ind (F) 1914 and New (F) 1915.

PHILLIPS, WILLIAM TAYLOR
b.June 18,1933 Atlanta,Ga.

Yr	Cl	Lea	Pos	G	Rec
1956	Mil	N	P	23	5-3
1957	Mil	N	P	27	3-2
1958	Chi	N	P	39	7-10
1959	Chi	N	P	7	0-2
1959	Phi	N	P	32	1-4
1960	Phi	N	P	10	0-1
	BLTL			138	16-22

PHYLE, WILLIAM JOSEPH
b.June 25,1875 Duluth,Minn.
d.Aug.7,1953

Yr	Cl	Lea	Pos	G	Rec
1898	Chi	N	P	3	2-1
1899	Chi	N	P	10	2-8
1901	NY	N	P	20	7-10
1906	St.L	N	3	21	.178
	TR			54	11-19 / .176

PIATT, WILEY HARLAN
b.July 13,1874 Blue Creek,O.
d.Sept.20,1946

Yr	Cl	Lea	Pos	G	Rec
1898	Phi	N	P	38	24-14
1899	Phi	N	P	39	23-15
1900	Phi	N	P	19	9-9
1901	Phi	A	P	18	7-11
1901	Chi	A	P	8	3-5
1902	Chi	A	P	31	12-13
1903	Bos	N	P	25	9-15
	TL			178	87-82

PICCIUTO, NICHOLAS THOMAS
b.Aug.27,1921 Newark,N.J.

Yr	Cl	Lea	Pos	G	Rec
1945	Phi	N	2-3	36	.135
	BRTR				

PICHE, RONALD JACQUES
b.May 22,1935 Verdun,Que.,Canada

Yr	Cl	Lea	Pos	G	Rec
1960	Mil	N	P	37	3-5
1961	Mil	N	P	12	2-2
1962	Mil	N	P	16	3-2
	BRTR			65	8-9

PICINICH, VALENTINE JOHN
b.Apr.1,1889 New York,N.Y.
d.Dec.5,1942

Yr	Cl	Lea	Pos	G	Rec
1916	Phi	A	C	40	.195
1917	Phi	A	C	2	.333
1918	Was	A	C	47	.230
1919	Was	A	C	80	.274
1920	Was	A	C	48	.203
1921	Was	A	C	45	.277
1922	Was	A	C	76	.229
1923	Bos	A	C	87	.276
1924	Bos	A	C	69	.273
1925	Bos	A	C	90	.255
1926	Cin	N	C	89	.263
1927	Cin	N	C	65	.254
1928	Cin	N	C	96	.302
1929	Bro	N	C	93	.260

Yr Cl Lea Pos G Rec

(Continued)
1930 Bro N C 23 .217
1931 Bro N C 24 .267
1932 Bro N C 41 .257
1933 Bro N C 6 .167
1933 Pit N C 16 .250
BRTR 1037 .258

PICK, CHARLES THOMAS
b.Apr.12,1888 Rustburg,Va.
d.June 26,1954
1914 Was A O 10 .347
1915 Was A H 3 .000
1916 Phi A 3 121 .241
1918 Chi N 2-3 29 .326
1919 Chi N 2-3 75 .231
1919 Bos N 1-2-3- 34 .273
1920 Bos N O 95 .274
BLTR 367 .260

PICK, EDGAR EVERETT
b.May 7,1899 Providence,R.I.
1923 Cin N O 9 .375
1924 Cin N O 3 .000
1927 Chi N 3 54 .171
BBTR 66 .178

PICKERING, OLIVER DAN
b.Apr.9,1870 Olney,Ill.
d.Jan.20,1952
1896 Lou N O 45 .303
1897 Lou N O 62 .258
1897 Cle N 2-O 47 .346
1901 Cle A O 138 .308
1902 Cle A 1-O 60 .259
1903 Phi A O 137 .281
1904 Phi A O 122 .224
1907 St.L A O 151 .276
1908 Was A O 113 .225
BLTR 875 .272

PICKERING, URBANE HUGH
(Brute)
b.June 3,1904 Modesto,Cal.
1931 Bos A 2-3 103 .252
1932 Bos A 3 132 .260
BRTR 235 .257

PICKETT, CHARLES A.
b.Columbus,O.
1910 St.L N P 2 0-0

PICKETT, DAVID T.
b.May 26,1874 Brookline,Mass.
1898 Bos N O 14 .272

PICKETT, JOHN THOMAS
b.Feb.20,1866 Chicago,Ill.
d.July 4,1922
1889 KC a O 41 .223
1890 Phi p 2 100 .281
1892 Bal N 2 36 .208
BRTR 177 .250

PICKREL, CLARENCE DOUGLAS
b.Mar.28,1911 Gretna,Va.
1933 Phi N P 9 1-0
1934 Bos N P 19 0-0
BRTR 19 1-0

PICKUP, CLARENCE WILLIAM
b.Oct.29,1897 Philadelphia,Pa.
1918 Phi N O 1 1.000

PICONE, MARIO PETER
(Babe)
b.July 5,1926 Brooklyn,N.Y.
1947 NY N P 2 0-0
1952 NY N P 2 0-1
1954 NY N P 5 0-0
1954 Cin N P 4 0-1
BRTR 13 0-2

PICUS, JOHN QUINN
(Played under name of
John Picus Quinn)

PIECHOTA, ALOYSIUS EDWARD
(Pie)
b.Jan.19,1915 Chicago,Ill.
1940 Bos N P 21 2-5
1941 Bos N P 1 0-0
BRTR 22 2-5

PIEH, EDWIN JOHN
(Cy)
b.Sept.29,1886 Wannikee,Wis.
d.Sept.12,1945
1913 NY A P 4 1-0
1914 NY A P 13 4-4
1915 NY A P 21 4-5
BRTR 38 9-9

PIERCE, GEORGE T.
(Filbert)
b.Jan.10,1888 Aurora,Ill.
d.Oct.11,1935
1912 Chi N P 3 0-0
1913 Chi N P 25 13-5
1914 Chi N P 30 9-12
1915 Chi N P 36 13-9
1916 Chi N P 4 0-0
1917 St.L N P 5 1-1
BLTL 103 36-27

PIERCE, MAURICE
b.Washington,D.C.
1884 Was U 3 2 .143

PIERCE, RAYMOND LESTER
b.June 6,1900 Emporia,Kan.
1924 Chi N P 6 0-0
1925 Phi N P 23 5-4
1926 Phi N P 39 2-7
BLTL 68 7-11

PIERCE, WALTER WILLIAM
(Bill)
b.Apr.2,1927 Detroit,Mich.
1945 Det A P 5 0-0
1948 Det A P 22 3-0
1949 Chi A P 39 7-15
1950 Chi A P 40 12-16
1951 Chi A P 39 15-14
1952 Chi A P 35 15-12
1953 Chi A P-1 42 {18-12 / .126}
1954 Chi A P 38 9-10
1955 Chi A P 34 15-10
1956 Chi A P 39 20-9
1957 Chi A P 41 20-12
1958 Chi A P 35 17-11
1959 Chi A P 34 14-15
1960 Chi A P 32 14-7
1961 Chi A P 39 10-9
1962 SF N P 30 16-6
BLTL 544 {205-158 / .185}

PIERCY, ANDREW J.
b.Aug.1856 San Jose,Cal.
d.Dec.27,1932
1881 Chi N 2-3 2 .250
TR

PIERCY, WILLIAM BENTON
(Wild Bill)
b.May 2,1896 El Monte,Cal.
d.Aug.28,1951
1917 NY A P 1 0-1
1921 NY A P 14 5-4
1922 Bos A P 29 3-9
1923 Bos A P 30 8-17
1924 Bos A P 23 5-7
1926 Chi N P 19 6-5
BRTR 116 27-43

PIERETTI, MARINO PAUL
(Chick)
b.Sept.23,1921 Marlia,Italy.
1945 Was A P 44 14-13
1946 Was A P 30 2-2
1947 Was A P 23 2-4
1948 Was A P 13 0-2
1948 Chi A P 32 8-10
1949 Chi A P 48 4-6
1950 Cle A P 30 0-1
BRTR 220 30-38

PIEROTTI, ALBERT FELIX
b.Oct.24,1895 Boston,Mass.
1920 Bos N P 6 1-1
1921 Bos N P 2 0-1
BBTR 8 1-2

PIERRE, RICHARD J.
b.Grand Haven,Mich.
1883 Phi N S 5 .158

PIERRO, WILLIAM LEONARD
b.Apr.15,1926 Brooklyn,N.Y.
1950 Pit N P 13 0-2
BRTR

PIERSALL, JAMES ANTHONY
b.Nov.14,1929 Waterbury,Conn.
1950 Bos A O 6 .286
1952 Bos A S-3-O 56 .267
1953 Bos A O 151 .272
1954 Bos A O 133 .285
1955 Bos A O 149 .283
1956 Bos A O 155 .293
1957 Bos A O 151 .261
1958 Bos A O 130 .237
1959 Cle A 3-O 100 .246
1960 Cle A O 138 .282
1961 Cle A O 121 .322
1962 Was A O 135 .244
BRTR 1425 .274

PIERSON, EDWARD DAVID
b.Newark,N.J.
1885 Met a 2 3 .091
TR

PIERSON, WILLIAM MORRIS
b.June 13,1899 Atlantic City,N.J.
d.Feb.20,1959
1918 Phi A P 8 0-1
1919 Phi A P 2 0-0
1924 Phi A P 1 0-0
BLTL 11 0-1

PIET, ANTHONY FRANCIS
(Real name Anthony Francis
Pietruszka)
b.Dec.6,1906 Berwick,Pa.
1931 Pit N 2 44 .299
1932 Pit N 2 154 .282
1933 Pit N 2 107 .323
1934 Cin N 2-3 106 .259
1935 Cin N O 6 .200
1935 Chi A 2-3 77 .298
1936 Chi A 2-3 109 .273
1937 Chi A 2-3 100 .235
1938 Det A 3 41 .213
BRTR 744 .277

PIETRUSZKA, ANTHONY FRANCIS
(Played under name of
Anthony Francis Piet)

PIEZ, CHARLES WILLIAM
(Sandy)
b.Oct.13,1892 New York,N.Y.
d.Dec.29,1930
1914 NY N O 35 .375
BRTR

PIGNATANO, JOSEPH BENJAMIN
b.Aug.4,1929 Brooklyn,N.Y.
1957 Bro N C 8 .214
1958 LA N C 63 .218

Yr Cl Lea Pos G Rec

(Continued)
1959 LA N C 52 .237
1960 LA N C 58 .233
1961 KC A C-3 92 .243
1962 SF N C 7 .200
1962 NY N C 27 .232
BRTR 307 .234

PIKE, J.
b.New York,N.Y.
1877 Har N O 1 .250

PIKE, JESSE WILLARD
b.July 31,1916 Dustin,Okla.
1946 NY N O 16 .171
BLTR

PIKE, LIPMAN E.
b.May 25,1845 New York,N.Y.
d.Oct.10,1893
1871 Tro n M-1-2-O 28 .351
1872 Bal n 2-3-O 55 .267
1873 Bal n 2-O 56 NR
1874 Har n M-2-S-O 52 NR
1875 St.L n 2-O 67 .342
1876 St.L N O 63 .314
1877 Cin N M-2-S-O 58 .297
1878 Cin N O 28 .326
1878 Pro N 2 5 .227
1881 Wor N O 5 .091
1887 Met a O 1 .000
BLTL 418 NR

PIKTUZIS, GEORGE RICHARD
b.Jan.3,1932 Chicago, Ill.
1956 Chi N P 2 0-0
BRTL

PILARCIK, ALFRED JAMES
b.July 3,1930 Whiting,Ind.
1956 KC A O 69 .251
1957 Bal A O 142 .278
1958 Bal A O 141 .243
1959 Bal A O 130 .282
1960 Bal A O 104 .247
1961 KC A O 35 .200
1961 Chi A O 47 .177
BLTL 668 .256

PILLETTE, DUANE XAVIER
(Dee)
b.July 24,1922 Detroit,Mich.
1949 NY A P 12 2-4
1950 NY A P 4 0-0
1950 St.L A P 27 3-5
1951 St.L A P 41 6-14
1952 St.L A P 35 10-13
1953 St.L A P 31 7-13
1954 Bal A P 25 10-14
1955 Bal A P 7 0-3
1956 Phi N P 20 0-0
BRTR 202 38-66

PILLETTE, HERMAN POLYCARP
(Old Folks)
b.Dec.26,1895 St.Paul,Ore.
d.Apr.30,1960
1917 Cin N P 1 0-0
1922 Det A P 40 19-12
1923 Det A P 47 14-19
1924 Det A P 19 1-1.
BRTR 107 34-32

PILLION, CECIL RANDOLPH
(Squiz)
b.Apr.13,1898 Hartford,Conn.
1915 Phi A P 2 0-0
TL

PILNEY, ANDREW JAMES
b.Jan.19.1913 Frontenac,Kan.
1936 Bos N H 3 .000
BRTR

PINCKNEY, GEORGE BURTON
b.Jan.11,1862 Peoria,Ill.
d.Nov.9,1926
1884 Cle N 2-S 35 .309
1885 Bro a 2-3 111 .288
1886 Bro a 3 142 .260
1887 Bro a 3 138 .326
1888 Bro a 3 143 .260
1889 Bro a 3 138 .253
1890 Bro N 3 126 .309
1891 Bro N 3 135 .278
1892 St.L N 3 78 .172
1893 Lou N 3 118 .226
BRTR 1164 .272

PINELLI, RALPH ARTHUR
(Babe) (Real name Rinaldo Angelo Paolinelli)
b.Oct.18,1895 San Francisco,Cal.
1918 Chi A 3 24 .231
1920 Det A S-3 102 .229
1922 Cin N 3 156 .305
1923 Cin N 3 117 .277
1924 Cin N 3 144 .306
1925 Cin N S-3 130 .283
1926 Cin N 2-S-3 71 .222
1927 Cin N 2-S-3 30 .197
BRTR 774 .276

PINKHAM, EDWARD
b.1849 Brooklyn,N.Y.
1871 Chi n P-3-O 24 {1-0 / NR}
TL

PINNANCE, EDWARD D.
(Peanuts)
b.Oct.22,1879 Walpole Island,Ont.
d.Dec.12,1944
1903 Phi A P 2 0-1
BLTR

PINSON, VADA EDWARD
b.Aug.11,1936 Memphis,Tenn.
1958 Cin N O 27 .271
1959 Cin N O 154 .316
1960 Cin N O 154 .287
1961 Cin N O 154 .343
1962 Cin N O 155 .292
BLTL 644 .308

PINTO, WILLIAM LERTON
b.Apr.8,1898 Chillicothe,O.
1922 Phi N P 9 0-1
1924 Phi N P 3 0-0
BLTL 12 0-1

PIPGRAS, EDWARD JOHN
b.June 15,1905 Schleswig,Ia.
1932 Bro N P 5 0-1
BRTR

PIPGRAS, GEORGE WILLIAM
b.Dec.20,1899 Denison,Ia.
1923 NY A P 8 1-3
1924 NY A P 9 0-1
1927 NY A P 29 10-3
1928 NY A P 46 24-13
1929 NY A P 39 18-12
1930 NY A P 44 15-15
1931 NY A P 36 7-6
1932 NY A P 32 16-9
1933 NY A P 4 2-2
1933 Bos A P 22 9-8
1934 Bos A P 2 0-0
1935 Bos A P 5 0-1
BRTR 276 102-73

PIPP, WALTER CLEMENT
b.Feb.17,1893 Chicago,Ill.
1913 Det A 1 11 .178
1915 NY A 1 136 .246
1916 NY A 1 151 .262
1917 NY A 1 155 .244
1918 NY A 1 91 .304
1919 NY A 1 138 .275
1920 NY A 1 153 .280
1921 NY A 1 153 .296
1922 NY A 1 152 .329
1923 NY A 1 144 .304
1924 NY A 1 153 .295
1925 NY A 1 62 .230
1926 Cin N 1 155 .291
1927 Cin N 1 122 .260
1928 Cin N 1 95 .283
BLTL 1871 .281

PIPPEN, HENRY HAROLD
(Cotton)
b.Apr.2,1910 Cisco,Tex.
1936 St.L N P 6 0-2
1939 Phi A P 25 4-11
1939 Det A P 3 0-1
1940 Det A P 4 1-2
BRTR 38 5-16

PISONI, JAMES PETE
b.Aug.14,1929 St.Louis,Mo.
1953 St.L A O 3 .083
1956 KC A O 10 .267
1957 KC A O 44 .237
1959 Mil N O 9 .167
1959 NY A O 17 .176
1960 NY A O 20 .111
BRTR 103 .212

PITKO, ALEXANDER (Spunk)
b.Nov.22,1917 Burlington,N.J.
1938 Phi N O 7 .316
1939 Was A O 4 .125
BRTR 11 .259

PITLER, JACOB ALBERT
b.Apr.22,1894 New York,N.Y.
1917 Pit N 2 109 .233
1918 Pit N 2 3 .000
BRTR 112 .232

PITTINGER, CHARLES RENO
(Togie)
b.1871 Greencastle,Pa.
d.Jan.14,1909
1900 Bos N P 18 2-9
1901 Bos N P 32 15-16
1902 Bos N P 44 27-15
1903 Bos N P 44 18-22
1904 Bos N P 38 14-21
1905 Phi N P 46 23-16
1906 Phi N P 20 8-10
1907 Phi N P 16 9-5
TR 258 116-114

PITTINGER, CLARKE ALONZO
(Pinkie)
b.Feb.24,1899 Hudson,Mich.
1921 Bos A O 40 .198
1922 Bos A S-3 66 .259
1923 Bos A 2 60 .215
1925 Chi N S-3 59 .312
1927 Cin N 2-S-3 31 .274
1928 Cin N 2-S-3 40 .237
1929 Cin N 2-S-3 77 .295
BRTR 373 .252

PITULA, STANLEY
b.Mar.23,1931 Hackensack,N.J.
1957 Cle A P 24 2-2
BRTR

PITZ, HERMAN
b.July 18,1865 Brooklyn,N.Y.
1890 Bro a C 61 .129
1890 Syr a C-S-O 29 .216
90 .155

PIZARRO, JUAN CORDOVA
b.Feb.7,1937 Santurce,Porto Rico

Yr	Cl	Lea	Pos	G	Rec
1957	Mil	N	P	25	5-6
1958	Mil	N	P	16	6-4
1959	Mil	N	P	29	6-2
1960	Mil	N	P	23	6-7
1961	Chi	A	P	40	14-7
1962	Chi	A	P	37	12-14
	BLTL			170	49-40

PLANETA, EMIL JOSEPH
b.Jan.31,1909 Higganum, Conn.
d.Feb.2,1963

Yr	Cl	Lea	Pos	G	Rec
1931	NY	N	P	2	0-0
	BRTR				

PLANK, EDWARD STEWART
b.Aug.31,1875 Gettysburg,Pa.
d.Feb.24,1926

Yr	Cl	Lea	Pos	G	Rec
1901	Phi	A	P	33	16-14
1902	Phi	A	P	36	20-15
1903	Phi	A	P	43	23-16
1904	Phi	A	P	45	26-15
1905	Phi	A	P	41	26-12
1906	Phi	A	P	26	19-6
1907	Phi	A	P	43	24-16
1908	Phi	A	P	36	14-16
1909	Phi	A	P	35	19-10
1910	Phi	A	P	38	16-10
1911	Phi	A	P	40	22-8
1912	Phi	A	P	34	26-6
1913	Phi	A	P	35	17-10
1914	Phi	A	P	30	16-6
1915	St.L	F	P	40	21-11
1916	St.L	A	P	37	16-15
1917	St.L	A	P	20	5-6
	BLTL			612	326-192

PLARSKI, DONALD JOSEPH
b.Nov.9,1929 Chicago,Ill.

Yr	Cl	Lea	Pos	G	Rec
1955	KC	A	O	8	.091
	BRTR				

PLASKETT, ELMO ALEXANDER
b.June 27,1938 Frederiksted,V.I.

Yr	Cl	Lea	Pos	G	Rec
1962	Pit	N	C	7	.286
	BRTR				

PLATT, MIZELL GEORGE (Whitey)
b.Aug.21,1920 W.Palm Beach,Fla.

Yr	Cl	Lea	Pos	G	Rec
1942	Chi	N	O	4	.063
1943	Chi	N	O	19	.171
1946	Chi	A	O	84	.251
1948	St.L	A	O	123	.271
1949	St.L	A	1-O	102	.258
	BRTR			332	.255

PLATTE, ALFRED FREDERICK JOSEPH
b.Apr.13,1890 Grand Rapids,Mich.

Yr	Cl	Lea	Pos	G	Rec
1913	Det	A	O	9	.111
	BLTL				

PLEIS, WILLIAM
b.Aug.5,1938 St.Louis,Mo.

Yr	Cl	Lea	Pos	G	Rec
1961	Min	A	P	37	4-2
1962	Min	A	P	21	2-5
	BLTL			58	6-7

PLESS, RANCE
b.Dec.6,1925 Greenevillé,Tenn.

Yr	Cl	Lea	Pos	G	Rec
1956	KC	A	1-3	48	.271
	BRTR				

PLEWS, HERBERT EUGENE
b.June 14,1928 Helena,Mont.

Yr	Cl	Lea	Pos	G	Rec
1956	Was	A	2-S-3	91	.270
1957	Was	A	2-S-3	104	.271
1958	Was	A	2-3	111	.258
1959	Was	A	2	27	.225
1959	Bos	A	H	13	.083
	BLTR			346	262

PLITT, NORMAN WILLIAM
b.Feb.21,1893 York,Pa.
d.Feb.1,1954

Yr	Cl	Lea	Pos	G	Rec
1918	Bro	N	P	1	0-0
1927	Bro	N	P	19	2-6
1927	NY	N	P	3	1-0
	BRTR			23	3-6

PLOCK, WALTER S.
b.July 2,1869 Philadelphia,Pa.
d.Apr.28,1900

Yr	Cl	Lea	Pos	G	Rec
1891	Phi	N	O	2	.400

POAT, RAYMOND WILLIS
b.Dec.19,1917 Chicago,Ill.

Yr	Cl	Lea	Pos	G	Rec
1942	Cle	A	P	4	1-3
1943	Cle	A	P	17	2-5
1944	Cle	A	P	36	4-8
1947	NY	N	P	7	4-3
1948	NY	N	P	39	11-10
1949	NY	N	P	2	0-0
1949	Pit	N	P	11	0-1
	BRTR			116	22-30

PODBIELAN, CLARENCE ANTHONY (Bud)
b.Mar.6,1924 Curlew,Wash.

Yr	Cl	Lea	Pos	G	Rec
1949	Bro	N	P	7	0-1
1950	Bro	N	P	20	5-4
1951	Bro	N	P	27	2-2
1952	Bro	N	P	4	0-0
1952	Cin	N	P	24	4-5
1953	Cin	N	P	36	6-16
1954	Cin	N	P	27	7-10
1955	Cin	N	P	17	1-2
1957	Cin	N	P	5	0-1
1959	Cle	A	P	6	0-1
	BRTR			173	25-42

PODGAJNY, JOHN SIGMUND (Specs)
b.June 10,1920 Chester,Pa.

Yr	Cl	Lea	Pos	G	Rec
1940	Phi	N	P	4	1-3
1941	Phi	N	P	35	9-12
1942	Phi	N	P	44	6-14
1943	Phi	N	P	13	4-4
1943	Pit	N	P	21	0-4
1946	Cle	A	P	6	0-0
	BRTR			123	20-37

PODRES, JOHN JOSEPH
b.Sept.30,1932 Witherbee,N.Y.

Yr	Cl	Lea	Pos	G	Rec
1953	Bro	N	P	34	9-4
1954	Bro	N	P	38	11-7
1955	Bro	N	P	32	9-10
1957	Bro	N	P	35	12-9
1958	LA	N	P	42	13-15
1959	LA	N	P	34	14-9
1960	LA	N	P	34	14-12
1961	LA	N	P	32	18-5
1962	LA	N	P	40	15-13
	BLTL			321	115-84

POETZ, JOSEPH FRANK
b.June 22,1901 St.Louis,Mo.
d.Feb.7,1942

Yr	Cl	Lea	Pos	G	Rec
1926	NY	N	P	2	0-1
	BRTR				

POFAHL, JAMES WILLARD
b.June 18,1917 Faribault,Minn.

Yr	Cl	Lea	Pos	G	Rec
1940	Was	A	2-S	119	.234
1941	Was	A	S	22	.187
1942	Was	A	2-S-3	84	.208
	BRTR			225	.220

POFFENBERGER, CLETUS ELWOOD (Boots)
b.July 1,1915 Williamsport,Md.

Yr	Cl	Lea	Pos	G	Rec
1937	Det	A	P	29	10-5
1938	Det	A	P	25	6-7
1939	Bro	N	P	3	0-0
	BRTR			57	16-12

POHOLSKY, THOMAS GEORGE
b.Aug.26,1929 Detroit,Mich.

Yr	Cl	Lea	Pos	G	Rec
1950	St.L	N	P	5	0-0
1951	St.L	N	P	38	7-13
1954	St.L	N	P	25	5-7
1955	St.L	N	P-O	30	9-11 / .182
1956	St.L	N	P	33	9-14
1957	Chi	N	P	28	1-7
	BRTR			159	31-52 / .171

POINDEXTER, CHESTER JENNINGS (Jinx)
b.Sept.30,1910 Pauls Valley,Okla.

Yr	Cl	Lea	Pos	G	Rec
1936	Bos	A	P	3	0-2
1939	Phi	N	P	11	0-0
	BLTL			14	0-2

POLACHANIN, NICHOLAS JOSEPH (Played under name of Nicholas Joseph Polly)

POLAND, HUGH REID
b.Jan.19,1913 Tompkinsville,Ky.

Yr	Cl	Lea	Pos	G	Rec
1943	NY	N	C	4	.083
1943	Bos	N	C	44	.191
1944	Bos	N	C	8	.130
1946	Bos	N	C	4	.167
1947	Phi	N	C	4	.000
1947	Cin	N	C	16	.333
1948	Cin	N	H	3	.333
	BLTR			83	.185

POLCHOW, LOUIS WILLIAM
b.Mar.14,1881 Mankato,Minn.
d.Sept.8,1912

Yr	Cl	Lea	Pos	G	Rec
1902	Cle	A	P	1	0-1

POLHEMUS, MARK S.
b.Oct.4,1864 Brooklyn,N.Y.

Yr	Cl	Lea	Pos	G	Rec
1887	Ind	N	O	19	.259

POLIVKA, KENNETH LYLE
b.Jan.21,1921 Chicago,Ill.

Yr	Cl	Lea	Pos	G	Rec
1947	Cin	N	P	2	0-0
	BLTL				

POLLET, HOWARD JOSEPH
b.June 26,1921 New Orleans,La.

Yr	Cl	Lea	Pos	G	Rec
1941	St.L	N	P	9	5-2
1942	St.L	N	P	27	7-5
1943	St.L	N	P	16	8-4
1946	St.L	N	P	40	21-10
1947	St.L	N	P	37	9-11
1948	St.L	N	P	38	13-8
1949	St.L	N	P	39	20-9
1950	St.L	N	P	38	14-13
1951	St.L	N	P	6	0-3
1951	Pit	N	P	21	6-10
1952	Pit	N	P	31	7-16
1953	Pit	N	P	5	1-1
1953	Chi	N	P	25	5-6
1954	Chi	N	P	20	8-10
1955	Chi	N	P	24	4-3
1956	Chi	A	P	12	3-1
1956	Pit	N	P	19	0-4
	BLTL			407	131-116

POLLI, LOUIS AMERICO
b.July 9,1903 Barre,Vt.

Yr	Cl	Lea	Pos	G	Rec
1932	St.L	A	P	5	0-0
1944	NY	N	P	19	0-2
	BRTR			24	0-2

POLLY, NICHOLAS JOSEPH (Real name Nicholas Joseph Polachanin)
b.Apr.18,1917 Chicago,Ill.

Yr	Cl	Lea	Pos	G	Rec
1937	Bro	N	3	10	.222
1945	Bos	A	3	4	.143
	BRTR			14	.200

POMORSKI, JOHN LEON
b.Dec.30,1907 Brooklyn,N.Y.

Yr	Cl	Lea	Pos	G	Rec
1934	Chi	A	P	3	0-0
	BRTR				

POND, ERASMUS ARLINGTON
(Arlie)
b.Jan.19,1872 Rutland,Vt.
d.Sept.19,1930

Yr	Cl	Lea	Pos	G	Rec
1895	Bal	N	P	7	0-1
1896	Bal	N	P	24	15-8
1897	Bal	N	P	31	18-9
1898	Bal	N	P	2	1-1
	TR			64	34-19

POND, RALPH BENJAMIN
b.May 4,1888 Eau Claire,Wis.
d.Sept.8,1947

Yr	Cl	Lea	Pos	G	Rec
1910	Bos	A	O	1	.333

PONDER, CHARLES ELMER
b.June 26,1893 Mangum,Okla.

Yr	Cl	Lea	Pos	G	Rec
1917	Pit	N	P	3	1-1
1919	Pit	N	P	9	0-5
1920	Pit	N	P	33	11-15
1921	Pit	N	P	8	2-0
1921	Chi	N	P	16	3-6
	BRTR			69	17-27

POOL, HARLIN WELTY
(Samson)
b.Mar.13,1908 Lakeport,Cal.
d.Feb.15,1963

Yr	Cl	Lea	Pos	G	Rec
1934	Cin	N	O	99	.327
1935	Cin	N	O	28	.176
	BLTR			127	.303

POOLE, EDWARD I.
b.Sept.7,1877 Wheeling,W.Va.
d.Mar.23,1920

Yr	Cl	Lea	Pos	G	Rec
1900	Pit	N	P	2	1-0
1901	Pit	N	P	23	5-4
1902	Pit	N	P	1	0-0
1902	Cin	N	P	16	12-4
1903	Cin	N	P	25	8-13
1904	Bro	N	P	24	7-14
	TR			91	33-35

POOLE, JAMES RALPH
(Easy)
b.May 12,1895 Stony Point N.C.

Yr	Cl	Lea	Pos	G	Rec
1925	Phi	A	1	133	.298
1926	Phi	A	1	112	.294
1927	Phi	A	1	38	.222
	BLTR			283	.288

POOLE, RAYMOND HERMAN
b.Jan.16,1920 Salisbury,N.C.

Yr	Cl	Lea	Pos	G	Rec
1941	Phi	A	H	2	.000
1947	Phi	A	H	13	.231
	BLTR			15	.200

POORMAN, THOMAS IVERSON
b.Oct.14,1857 Lock Haven,Pa.
d.Feb.18,1905

Yr	Cl	Lea	Pos	G	Rec
1880	Buf	N	P-O	19	1-8 .159
1880	Chi	N	P-O	7	1-0 .200
1884	Tol	a	P-O	93	0-1 .224
1885	Bos	N	O	55	.241
1886	Bos	N	O	88	.261
1887	Ath	a	O	135	.316
1888	Ath	a	O	85	.227
	TR			482	2-9 .260

POPE, DAVID
b.June 17,1925 Talladega,Ala.

Yr	Cl	Lea	Pos	G	Rec
1952	Cle	A	O	12	.294
1954	Cle	A	O	60	.294
1955	Cle	A	O	35	.298
1955	Bal	A	O	86	.248
1956	Bal	A	O	12	.158
1956	Cle	A	O	25	.243
	BLTR			230	.265

POPP, WILLIAM PETER
b.June 7,1877 St.Louis,Mo.
d.Sept.7,1909

Yr	Cl	Lea	Pos	G	Rec
1902	St.L	N	P	9	2-6
	TR				

POPPLEIN, GEORGE J.
b.Baltimore,Md.

Yr	Cl	Lea	Pos	G	Rec
1873	Mar	n	O	1	.000

PORRAY, EDMUND JOSEPH
b.Dec.15,1888 Brooklyn,N.Y.
d.July 13,1954

Yr	Cl	Lea	Pos	G	Rec
1914	Buf	F	P	3	0-1

PORTER, DANIEL EDWARD
b.Oct.17,1931 Decatur,Ill.

Yr	Cl	Lea	Pos	G	Rec
1951	Was	A	O	13	.211
	BLTL				

PORTER, EDWARD S. (Ned)
b.May 6,1906 Appalachicola,Fla.

Yr	Cl	Lea	Pos	G	Rec
1926	NY	N	P	2	0-0
1927	NY	N	P	1	0-0
	BRTR			3	0-0

PORTER, HENRY
b.1857 Vergennes,Vt.
d.Dec.30,1906

Yr	Cl	Lea	Pos	G	Rec
1884	KC	U	O	3	083
1884	Mil	U	P-1-O	10	3-2 .278
1885	Bro	a	P	55	33-21
1886	Bro	a	P	48	28-20
1887	Bro	a	P	40	16-23
1888	KC	a	P	55	17-37
1889	KC	a	P	4	0-3
	BRTR			215	97-106 .189

PORTER, IRVING MARBLE
b.May 17,1888 Lynn,Mass.

Yr	Cl	Lea	Pos	G	Rec
1914	Chi	A	O	1	.000
	BBTR				

PORTER, J. W. (Jay)
b.Jan.17,1933 Shawnee,Okla.

Yr	Cl	Lea	Pos	G	Rec
1952	St.L	A	3-O	33	.250
1955	Det	A	C-1-O	24	.236
1956	Det	A	C-O	14	.095
1957	Det	A	C-1-O	58	.250
1958	Cle	A	C-1-3	40	.200
1959	Was	A	C-1	37	.226
1959	St.L	N	C-1	23	.212
	BRTR			229	.228

PORTER, JAMES
b.Bloomington,Ill.

Yr	Cl	Lea	Pos	G	Rec
1902	Phi	A	P	1	0-1

PORTER, RICHARD TWILLEY
(Wiggles)
b.Dec.30,1901 Princess Anne,Md.

Yr	Cl	Lea	Pos	G	Rec
1929	Cle	A	2-O	71	.328
1930	Cle	A	O	119	.350
1931	Cle	A	O	114	.312
1932	Cle	A	O	146	.308
1933	Cle	A	O	132	.267
1934	Cle	A	O	13	.227
1934	Bos	A	O	80	.302
	BLTR			675	.308

PORTERFIELD, ERWIN COOLIDGE (Bob)
b.Aug.10,1923 Newport,Va.

Yr	Cl	Lea	Pos	G	Rec
1948	NY	A	P	16	5-3
1949	NY	A	P	12	2-5
1950	NY	A	P	11	1-1
1951	NY	A	P	2	0-0
1951	Was	A	P	19	9-8
1952	Was	A	P	31	13-14
1953	Was	A	P	37	22-10
1954	Was	A	P	32	13-15
1955	Was	A	P	30	10-17
1956	Bos	A	P	25	3-12
1957	Bos	A	P	28	4-4
1958	Bos	A	P	2	0-0
1958	Pit	N	P	37	4-6

(Continued)

Yr	Cl	Lea	Pos	G	Rec
1959	Pit	N	P	36	1-2
1959	Chi	N	P	4	0-0
	BRTR			322	87-97

PORTO, ALFRED
b.June 27,1927 Heilwood,Pa.

Yr	Cl	Lea	Pos	G	Rec
1948	Phi	N	P	3	0-0
	BLTL				

PORTOCARRERO, ARNOLD MARIO
b.July 5,1931 New York,N.Y.

Yr	Cl	Lea	Pos	G	Rec
1954	Phi	A	P	34	9-18
1955	KC	A	P	24	5-9
1956	KC	A	P	3	0-1
1957	KC	A	P	33	4-9
1958	Bal	A	P	32	15-11
1959	Bal	A	P	27	2-7
1960	Bal	A	P	13	3-2
	BRTR			166	38-57

POSADA, LEOPOLDO HERNANDEZ
b.Apr.15,1936 Havana,Cuba

Yr	Cl	Lea	Pos	G	Rec
1960	KC	A	O	10	.361
1961	KC	A	O	116	.253
1962	KC	A	O	29	.196
	BRTR			155	.256

POSEDEL, WILLIAM JOHN
(Barnacle Bill)
b.Aug.2,1909 San Francisco,Cal.

Yr	Cl	Lea	Pos	G	Rec
1938	Bro	N	P	33	8-9
1939	Bos	N	P	33	15-13
1940	Bos	N	P	35	12-17
1941	Bos	N	P	18	4-4
1946	Bos	N	P	19	2-0
	BRTR			138	41-43

POSER, JOHN FALK
b.Mar.16,1910 Columbus,Wis.

Yr	Cl	Lea	Pos	G	Rec
1932	Chi	A	P	5	0-0
1935	St.L	A	P	4	1-1
	BLTR			9	1-1

POSSEHL, LOUIS THOMAS
b.Apr.12,1926 Chicago,Ill.

Yr	Cl	Lea	Pos	G	Rec
1946	Phi	N	P	4	1-2
1947	Phi	N	P	2	0-0
1948	Phi	N	P	4	1-1
1951	Phi	N	P	2	0-1
1952	Phi	N	P	4	0-1
	BRTR			16	2-5

POST, SAMUEL GILBERT
b.Nov.17,1896 Richmond,Va.

Yr	Cl	Lea	Pos	G	Rec
1922	Bro	N	1	9	.280
	BLTL				

POST, WALTER CHARLES
b.July 9,1929 St.Wendelin,O.

Yr	Cl	Lea	Pos	G	Rec
1949	Cin	N	O	6	.250
1951	Cin	N	O	15	.220
1952	Cin	N	O	19	.155
1953	Cin	N	O	11	.242
1954	Cin	N	O	130	.255
1955	Cin	N	O	154	.309
1956	Cin	N	O	143	.249
1957	Cin	N	O	134	.244
1958	Phi	N	O	110	.282
1959	Phi	N	O	132	.254
1960	Phi	N	O	34	.286
1960	Cin	N	O	77	.281
1961	Cin	N	O	99	.294
1962	Cin	N	O	109	.263
	BRTR			1173	.267

POSTE, E.

Yr	Cl	Lea	Pos	G	Rec
1902	Det	A	O	3	.083

POTT, NELSON ALEXANDER
b.July 16,1899 Cincinnati,O.

Yr	Cl	Lea	Pos	G	Rec
1922	Cle	A	P	2	0-0
	BBTL				

POTTER, MARYLAND DYKES
b.Sept.7,1910 Ashland,Ky.

Yr	Cl	Lea	Pos	G	Rec
1938	Bro	N	P	2	0-0
	BRTR				

POTTER, NELSON THOMAS
b.Aug.23,1911 Mt.Morris,Ill.

Yr	Cl	Lea	Pos	G	Rec
1936	St.L	N	P	1	0-0
1938	Phi	A	P	38	2-12
1939	Phi	A	P	41	8-12
1940	Phi	A	P	31	9-14
1941	Phi	A	P	10	1-1
1941	Bos	A	P	10	2-0
1943	St.L	A	P	33	10-5
1944	St.L	A	P	32	19-7
1945	St.L	A	P	32	15-11
1946	St.L	A	P	23	8-9
1947	St.L	A	P	32	4-10
1948	St.L	A	P	2	1-1
1948	Phi	A	P	8	2-2
1948	Bos	N	P	18	5-2
1949	Bos	N	P	41	6-11
	BLTR			352	92-97

POTTER, ROBERT H.
b.Mar.18,1902 Flatwoods,Ky.

Yr	Cl	Lea	Pos	G	Rec
1923	Was	A	P	1	0-0
	BRTR				

POTTS, DANIEL
b.Kent,O.

Yr	Cl	Lea	Pos	G	Rec
1892	Was	N	C	1	.333

POTTS, JOHN FREDERICK
b.Feb.6,1887 Troy,O.
d.Sept.5,1962

Yr	Cl	Lea	Pos	G	Rec
1914	KC	F	O	40	.287
	BLTR				

POUNDS, WILLIAM CHARLES
b.Paterson,N.J.

Yr	Cl	Lea	Pos	G	Rec
1903	Cle	A	P	1	0-0
1903	Bro	N	P	1	0-0
				2	0-0

POWELL, ALVIN JACOB
(Jake)
b.July 15,1908 Silver Spring,Md.
d.Nov.4,1948

Yr	Cl	Lea	Pos	G	Rec
1930	Was	A	O	3	.000
1934	Was	A	O	9	.286
1935	Was	A	2-O	139	.312
1936	Was	A	O	53	.290
1936	NY	A	O	87	.306
1937	NY	A	O	97	.263
1938	NY	A	O	45	.256
1939	NY	A	O	31	.244
1940	NY	A	O	12	.185
1943	Was	A	O	37	.265
1944	Was	A	3-O	96	.240
1945	Was	A	O	31	.194
1945	Phi	N	O	48	.231
	BRTR			688	.271

POWELL, CHARLES ABNER
(Ab)
b.Dec.15,1860 Shenandoah,Pa.
d.Aug.7,1953

Yr	Cl	Lea	Pos	G	Rec
1884	Was	U	P-2-3-O	47	4-12 .270
1886	Bal	a	P-O	10	2-5 .147
1886	Cin	a	P-C-S-O	19	0-1 .230
	BRTR			76	6-18 .246

POWELL, JAMES E.
b.1859 Richmond,Va.

Yr	Cl	Lea	Pos	G	Rec
1884	Ric	a	1	40	.243

POWELL, JOHN JOSEPH
(Red)
b.July 9,1874 Bloomington,Ill.
d.Oct.17,1944

Yr	Cl	Lea	Pos	G	Rec
1897	Cle	N	P	28	15-9
1898	Cle	N	P	40	24-15
1899	St.L	N	P	46	23-21
1900	St.L	N	P	37	17-18
1901	St.L	N	P	37	19-18
1902	St.L	A	P-C-1-O	44	22-17 .217
1903	St.L	A	P	39	15-19
1904	NY	A	P	47	23-19
1905	NY	A	P	37	9-11
1905	St.L	A	P	3	2-1
1906	St.L	A	P	29	13-14
1907	St.L	A	P	35	13-16
1908	St.L	A	P	33	16-13
1909	St.L	A	P	34	12-16
1910	St.L	A	P	21	7-11
1911	St.L	A	P	32	8-19
1912	St.L	A	P	31	9-16
	BRTR			573	247-253 .191

POWELL, JOHN WESLEY
b.Aug.17,1941 Lakeland,Fla.

Yr	Cl	Lea	Pos	G	Rec
1961	Bal	A	O	4	.077
1962	Bal	A	1-O	124	.243
	BLTR			128	.237

POWELL, MARTIN J.
b.Mar.25,1856 Fitchburg,Mass.
d.Feb.5,1888

Yr	Cl	Lea	Pos	G	Rec
1881	Det	N	C-1	55	.310
1882	Det	N	1	77	.247
1883	Det	N	1	97	.267
1884	Cin	U	1	45	.314
1885	Ath	a	1	18	.164
	BL			292	.276

POWELL, RAYMOND REATH
(Rabbit)
b.Nov.20,1888 Siloam Springs,Ark.
d.Oct.16,1962

Yr	Cl	Lea	Pos	G	Rec
1913	Det	A	O	2	.000
1917	Bos	N	O	88	.272
1918	Bos	N	O	53	.213
1919	Bos	N	O	123	.236
1920	Bos	N	O	147	.225
1921	Bos	N	O	149	.306
1922	Bos	N	O	142	.296
1923	Bos	N	O	97	.302
1924	Bos	N	O	74	.261
	BLTR			875	.271

POWELL, ROBERT LEROY
b.Oct.17,1933 Flint,Mich.

Yr	Cl	Lea	Pos	G	Rec
1955	Chi	A	H	1	.000
1957	Chi	A	H	1	.000
	BRTR			2	.000

POWELL, SAMUEL

Yr	Cl	Lea	Pos	G	Rec
1913	St.L	A	P	2	0-0

POWELL, WILLIAM BURRUSS
(Big Bill)
b.May 8,1885 Richmond,Va.

Yr	Cl	Lea	Pos	G	Rec
1909	Pit	N	P	3	0-1
1910	Pit	N	P	12	4-6
1912	Chi	N	P	1	0-0
1913	Cin	N	P	1	0-1
	BRTR			17	4-8

POWER, THOMAS E.
b.San Francisco,Cal.
d.Feb.25,1898

Yr	Cl	Lea	Pos	G	Rec
1890	Bal	a	1	38	.211

POWER, VICTOR PELLOT
b.Nov.1,1931 Arecibo,Puerto Rico

Yr	Cl	Lea	Pos	G	Rec
1954	Phi	A	1-S-3-O	127	.255
1955	KC	A	1	147	.319
1956	KC	A	1-2-O	127	.309
1957	KC	A	1-2-O	129	.259

(Continued)

Yr	Cl	Lea	Pos	G	Rec
1958	KC	A	1-2	52	.302
1958	Cle	A	1-2-S-3-O	93	.317
1959	Cle	A	1-2-3	147	.289
1960	Cle	A	1-S-3	147	.288
1961	Cle	A	1-2	147	.268
1962	Min	A	1-2	144	.290
	BRTR			1260	.289

POWERS, ELLIS FOREE
(Mike)
b.Mar.2,1906 Crestwood,Ky.

Yr	Cl	Lea	Pos	G	Rec
1932	Cle	A	O	14	.182
1933	Cle	A	O	24	.277
	BLTL			38	.238

POWERS, JAMES T.
b.1868 New York,N.Y.

Yr	Cl	Lea	Pos	G	Rec
1890	Bro	a	P	4	1-2

POWERS, JOHN CALVIN
b.July 8,1929 Birmingham,Ala.

Yr	Cl	Lea	Pos	G	Rec
1955	Pit	N	O	2	.250
1956	Pit	N	O	11	.048
1957	Pit	N	O	20	.286
1958	Pit	N	O	57	.183
1959	Cin	N	O	43	.256
1960	Bal	A	O	10	.111
1960	Cle	A	O	8	.167
	BLTR			151	.195

POWERS, JOHN LLOYD
(Ike)
b.Mar.13,1906 Hancock,Md.

Yr	Cl	Lea	Pos	G	Rec
1927	Phi	A	P	11	1-1
1928	Phi	A	P	9	1-0
	BRTR			20	2-1

POWERS, LESLIE EDWIN
b.Jan.20,1912 Seattle,Wash.

Yr	Cl	Lea	Pos	G	Rec
1938	NY	N	H	2	.000
1939	Phi	N	1	19	.346
	BLTL			21	.327

POWERS, MICHAEL RILEY
b.Sept.22,1870 Pittsfield,Mass.
d.Apr.26,1909

Yr	Cl	Lea	Pos	G	Rec
1898	Lou	N	C	27	.298
1899	Lou	N	C	41	.211
1899	Was	N	C-1	14	.333
1901	Phi	A	C	116	.248
1902	Phi	A	C-1	71	.271
1903	Phi	A	C	74	.227
1904	Phi	A	C	57	.187
1905	Phi	A	C	22	.183
1905	NY	A	C	11	.083
1905	Phi	A	C	19	.161
1906	Phi	A	C	58	.157
1907	Phi	A	C	59	.182
1908	Phi	A	C	62	.180
1909	Phi	A	C	1	.250
	BRTR			632	.218

POWERS, PATRICK THOMAS
b.June 27,1860. Trenton,N.J.
d.Aug.29,1925
Non-playing manager Roc (a) 1890 and N.Y. (N) 1892.

POWERS, PHILIP J.
(Grandmother)
b.July 26,1853 New York,N.Y.
d.Dec.23,1914

Yr	Cl	Lea	Pos	G	Rec
1878	Chi	N	C-O	9	.140
1880	Bos	N	C-O	35	.148
1881	Cle	N	C-3	6	.143
1882	Cin	a	C-1-O	15	.212
1883	Cin	a	C-O	29	.234
1884	Cin	a	C-1-O	35	.158
1885	Cin	a	C	15	.267
1885	Bal	a	C-O	9	.121
	BRTR			153	.184

Yr	Cl	Lea	Pos	G	Rec
POWIS, CARL EDGAR					
b.Jan.11,1928 Philadelphia,Pa.					
1957	Bal	A	O	15	.195
BRTR					
PRAMESA, JOHN STEVEN					
b.Aug.28,1925 Barton,O.					
1949	Cin	N	C	17	.240
1950	Cin	N	C	74	.307
1951	Cin	N	C	72	.229
1952	Chi	N	C	22	.283
BRTR				185	.268
PRATT, ALBERT G. (Uncle Al)					
b.Nov.19,1847 Allegheny,Pa.					
d.Nov.21,1937					
1871	Cle	n	P-O	29	10-18 NR
1872	Cle	n	P-O	14	3-8 NR
				43	13-26 NR
Non-playing manager Pit (a) 1882-83.					
PRATT, DERRILL BURNHAM (Del)					
b.Jan.10,1888 Walhalla,S.C.					
1912	St.L	A	2-S	151	.302
1913	St.L	A	2	154	.296
1914	St.L	A	2	158	.282
1915	St.L	A	2	159	.291
1916	St.L	A	2	158	.267
1917	St.L	A	2	123	.247
1918	NY	A	2	126	.275
1919	NY	A	2	140	.292
1920	NY	A	2	154	.314
1921	Bos	A	2	135	.324
1922	Bos	A	2	154	.302
1923	Det	A	1-2	101	.310
1924	Det	A	1-2	121	.303
BRTR				1834	.292
PRATT, FRANCIS BRUCE					
b.Aug.24,1897 Blocton,Ala.					
1921	Chi	A	H	1	.000
TR					
PRATT, LESTER JOHN (Larry)					
b.Oct.8,1887 Gibson City,Ill.					
1914	Bos	A	C	5	.000
1915	Bro	F	C	20	.191
1915	New	F	C	5	.500
BRTR				30	.196
PRATT, THOMAS J.					
b.1840 Worcester,Mass.					
d.Sept.29,1908					
1871	Ath	n	1	1	NR
1884	Bal	a	O	1	.250
				17	NR
Non-playing manager Key (U) 1884.					
PREIBISCH, MELVIN ADOLPHUS (Primo)					
b.Nov.23,1915 Sealy,Tex.					
1940	Bos	N	O	11	.225
1941	Bos	N	O	5	.000
BRTR				16	.205
PRENDERGAST, JAMES BARTHOLOMEW					
b.Aug.23,1917 Brooklyn,N.Y.					
1948	Bos	N	P	10	1-1
BLTL					
PRENDERGAST, MICHAEL THOMAS					
b.Sept.15,1890 Arlington,Ill.					
1914	Chi	F	P	23	5-9
1915	Chi	F	P	37	14-12
1916	Chi	N	P	35	6-11
1917	Chi	N	P	35	3-6
1918	Phi	N	P	33	13-14
1919	Phi	N	P	5	0-1
BRTR				168	41-53

Yr	Cl	Lea	Pos	G	Rec
PRENTISS, GEORGE PEPPER (Kitten) (Played under name of George P. Wilson)					
PRESKO, JOSEPH EDWARD					
b.Oct.7,1928 Kansas City,Mo.					
1951	St.L	N	P	15	7-4
1952	St.L	N	P	28	7-10
1953	St.L	N	P	35	6-13
1954	St.L	N	P	38	4-9
1957	Det	A	P	7	1-1
1958	Det	A	P	7	0-0
BRTR				130	25-37
PRESCOTT, GEORGE BERTRAND					
b.Mar.27,1931 Colon,Panama					
1961	KC	A	O	10	.083
BRTR					
PRESSNELL, FOREST CHARLES (Tot)					
b.Aug.8,1907 Findlay,O.					
1938	Bro	N	P	43	11-14
1939	Bro	N	P	31	9-7
1940	Bro	N	P	24	6-5
1941	Chi	N	P	29	5-3
1942	Chi	N	P	27	1-1
BRTR				154	32-30
PRESTON, WALTER B.					
b.1871 Galveston,Tex.					
1895	Lou	N	3-O	49	.292
BLTR					
PRICE, JAMES L.					
Non-playing manager NY (N) 1884.					
PRICE, JOHN THOMAS REID					
b.Nov.13,1913 Winborn,Miss.					
1946	Cle	A	S	7	.231
BLTR					
PRICE, JOSEPH PRESTON					
b.Aug.10,1897 Milligan College,Tenn.					
d.Jan.15,1961					
1928	NY	N	O	1	.000
BRTR					
PRICE, WILLIAM					
b.Philadelphia,Pa.					
1890	Ath	a	P	1	1-0
PRICHARD, ROBERT ALEXANDER					
b.Oct.21,1917 Paris,Tex.					
1939	Was	A	1	26	.235
BLTL					
PRIDDY, GERALD EDWARD					
b.Nov.9,1919 Los Angeles,Cal.					
1941	NY	A	1-2-3	56	.213
1942	NY	A	1-2-S-3	59	.280
1943	Was	A	2-S-3	149	.271
1946	Was	A	2	138	.254
1947	Was	A	2	147	.214
1948	St.L	A	2	151	.296
1949	St.L	A	2	145	.290
1950	Det	A	2	157	.277
1951	Det	A	2-S	154	.260
1952	Det	A	2	75	.283
1953	Det	A	1-2-3	65	.235
BRTR				1296	.265
PRIDDY, ROBERT SIMPSON					
b.Dec.10.1939 Pittsburgh,Pa.					
1962	Pit	N	P	2	1-0
BRTR					
PRIEST, JOHN GOODING					
b.June 23,1891 St.Joseph,Mo.					
1911	NY	A	2	8	.142
1912	NY	A	H	2	.500
BRTR				10	.174
PRIM, RAYMOND LEE (Pop)					
b.Dec.30,1906 Salitpa,Ala.					
1933	Was	A	P	2	0-1
1934	Was	A	P	8	0-2
1935	Phi	N	P	29	3-4
1943	Chi	N	P	29	4-3

Yr	Cl	Lea	Pos	G	Rec
(Continued)					
1945	Chi	N	P	34	13-8
1946	Chi	N	P	14	2-3
BRTL				116	22-21
PRINCE, DONALD MARK					
b.Apr.5,1938 Clarkton,N.C.					
1962	Chi	N	P	1	0-0
BRTR					
PRINCE, WALTER F.					
b.1860 N.Andover,Mass.					
d.Mar.2,1938					
1883	Lou	a	1-S-O	4	.182
1884	Det	N	O	7	.130
1884	Was	a	1	43	.211
1884	Was	U	1	1	.250
				55	.200
PRITCHARD, HAROLD WILLIAM					
b.Jan.25,1936 South Gate,Cal.					
1957	Pit	N	S-O	23	.091
BRTR					
PROCTOR, JAMES ARTHUR					
b.Sept.9,1935 Brandywine,Md.					
1959	Det	A	P	2	0-1
BRTR					
PROCTOR, L.					
1912	St.L	A	H	1	.000
PROCTOR, RICHARD C.					
b.1901					
1923	Chi	A	P	2	0-0
BRTR					
PROESER, GEORGE					
b.May 30,1864 Cincinnati,O.					
d.Oct.14,1941					
1888	Cle	a	P	7	3-4
1890	Syr	a	O	13	.264
				20	3-4 .276
PROPST, WILLIAM JACOB (Jake)					
b.Mar.10,1895 Kennedy,Ala.					
1923	Was	A	H	1	.000
PROTHRO, JAMES THOMSON (Doc)					
b.July 20,1894 Memphis,Tenn.					
1920	Was	A	S	6	.385
1923	Was	A	3	6	.250
1924	Was	A	3	46	.333
1925	Bos	A	S-3	119	.313
1926	Cin	N	3	3	.200
BRTR				180	.319
Non-playing manager Phi (N) 1939-41.					
PROUGH, H. CLINTON (Bill)					
b.Nov.25,1888 Martle,Ind.					
1912	Cin	N	P	1	0-0
BRTR					
PRUDHOMME, JOHN OLGUS					
b.Nov.20,1902 Frierson,La.					
1929	Det	A	P	34	1-6
BRTR					
PRUESS, EARL HENRY					
b.Apr.2,1895 Chicago,Ill.					
1920	St.L	A	O	1	.000
BBTR					

Yr Cl Lea Pos G Rec

PRUETT, HUBERT SHELBY
(Shucks)
b.Sept.1,1900 Higginsville,Ky.
1922 St.L A P 39 7-7
1923 St.L A P 32 4-7
1924 St.L A P 33 3-4
1927 Phi N P 31 7-17
1928 Phi N P 13 2-4
1930 NY N P 45 5-4
1932 Bos N P 18 1-5
BLTL 211 29-48

PRUETT, JAMES CALVIN
b.Dec.16,1918 Nashville,Tenn.
1944 Phi A C 3 .250
1945 Phi A C 6 .222
BRTR 9 .231

PRUIETT, CHARLES LeROY
(Tex)
b.Apr.10,1883 Osgood,Ind.
d.Mar.6,1953
1907 Bos A P 35 3-11
1908 Bos A P 13 1-7
BLTL 48 4-18

PUCCINELLI, GEORGE LAWRENCE (Pooch)
b.June 22,1906 San Francisco,Cal.
d.Apr.16,1956
1930 St.L N O 11 .563
1932 St.L N O 31 .278
1934 St.L A O 10 .231
1936 Phi A O 135 .278
BRTR 187 .283

PUCKETT, TROY LEVI
b.Dec.10,1889 Winchester,Ind.
1911 Phi N P 1 0-0
BLTR

PUHL, JOHN
b.Bayonne,N.J.
d.1900
1898 NY N 3 2 .250
1899 NY N 3 1 .000
3 .200

PUMPELLY, SPENCER ARMSTRONG
b.Apr.11,1893 Owego,N.Y.
1925 Was A P 1 0-0

PURCELL, WILLIAM A.
(Blondy)
b.Paterson,N.J.
d.1905
1879 Syr N P-C-O 62 4-14 .265
1879 Cin N P-O 12 0-2 .231
1880 Cin N P-S-O 76 3-16 .283
1881 Cle N O 20 .165
1881 Buf N P-O 30 4-1 .267
1882 Buf N P-O 84 2-2 .276
1883 Phi N P-S-3-O 96 2-8 .270
1884 Phi N P-O 102 2-5 .244
1885 Ath a P-O 66 0-1 .298
1885 Bos N O 21 .218
1886 Bal a O 27 .224
1887 Bal a O 140 .305
1888 Bal a O 101 .233
1888 Ath a 3-O 18 .167
1889 Ath a O 130 .306
1890 Ath a O 106 .287
1091 17-49 .272

PURDY, EVERETT VIRGIL
(Pid)
b.June 15,1904 Beatrice,Neb.
d.Jan.16,1951
1926 Chi A O 11 .182
1927 Cin N O 18 .355
1928 Cin N O 70 .309
1929 Cin N O 82 .271
BLTR 181 .293

PURKEY, ROBERT THOMAS
b.July 14,1929 Pittsburgh,Pa.
1954 Pit N P 36 3-8
1955 Pit N P 14 2-7
1956 Pit N P 2 0-0
1957 Pit N P 48 11-14
1958 Cin N P 37 17-11
1959 Cin N P 38 13-18
1960 Cin N P 41 17-11
1961 Cin N P 36 16-12
1962 Cin N P 37 23-5
BRTR 289 102-86

PURNELL, JESSE RHOADES
b.May 11,1879 Edge Hill,Pa.
1904 Phi N 3 7 .105
BLTR

PURNER, OSCAR
1895 Was N P 1 0-0

PURTELL, WILLIAM PATRICK
b.Jan.6,1886 Columbus,O.
d.Mar.17.1962
1908 Chi A 3 26 .130
1909 Chi A 2-3 103 .258
1910 Chi A 3 102 .222
1910 Bos A 3 49 .211
1911 Bos A 3 27 .280
1914 Det A 3 26 .171
BRTR 333 .227

PUTNAM, AUGUSTUS
b.Nov.21,1817 Hartford,Conn.
d.Jan.13,1890
Non-playing manager Man (n) 1872.

PUTTMAN, AMBROSE NICHOLAS
b.Sept.9,1880 Cincinnati,O.
d.June 21,1936
1903 NY A P 3 2-0
1904 NY A P 10 2-2
1905 NY A P 17 3-7
1906 St.L N P 4 2-2
TL 34 9-9

PYBURN, JAMES EDWARD
b.Nov.1,1932 Fairfield,Ala.
1955 Bal A 3-O 39 .204
1956 Bal A O 84 .173
1957 Bal A C-O 35 .225
BRTR 158 .190

PYECHA, JOHN NICHOLAS
b.Nov.25,1931 Aliquippa,Pa.
1954 Chi N P 1 0-1
BRTR

PYLE, HARLAN ALBERT
b.Jan.31,1905 Liberty,Neb.
1928 Cin N P 2 0-0
BRTR

PYLE, HARRY THOMAS
(Shadow)
b.Oct.30,1861 Reading,Pa.
d.Nov.26,1908
1884 Phi N P 1 0-1
1887 Chi N P 4 1-3
5 1-4

PYLE, HERBERT EWALD
(Lefty)
b.Aug.27,1913 St.Louis,Mo.
1939 St.L A P 6 0-2
(Continued)
1942 St.L A P 2 0-0
1943 Was A P 18 4-8
1944 NY N P 31 7-10
1945 NY N P 6 0-0
1945 Bos N P 4 0-1
BLTL 67 11-21

PYTLAK, FRANK ANTHONY
b.July 30,1908 Buffalo,N.Y.
1932 Cle A C 12 .241
1933 Cle A C 80 .310
1934 Cle A C 91 .260
1935 Cle A C 55 .295
1936 Cle A C 75 .321
1937 Cle A C 125 .315
1938 Cle A C 113 .308
1939 Cle A C 63 .268
1940 Cle A C-O 62 .141
1941 Bos A C 106 .271
1945 Bos A C 9 .118
1946 Bos A C 4 .143
BRTR 795 .282

QUALTERS, THOMAS FRANCIS
b.Apr.1,1935 McKeesport.Pa.
1953 Phi N P 1 0-0
1957 Phi N P 6 0-0
1958 Phi N P 1 0-0
1958 Chi A P 26 0-0
BRTR 34 0-0

QUARLES, WILLIAM H.
b.1869 Petersburg,Va.
d.Mar.25,1897
1891 Was a P 4 2-2
1893 Bos N P 4 2-2
8 4-4

QUEEN, MELVIN JOSEPH
b.Mar.4,1918 Maxwell,Pa.
1942 NY A P 4 1-0
1944 NY A P 10 6-3
1946 NY A P 14 1-1
1947 NY A P 5 0-0
1947 Pit N P 14 3-7
1948 Pit N P 25 4-4
1950 Pit N P 33 5-14
1951 Pit N P 39 7-9
1952 Pit N P 2 0-2
BRTR 146 27-40

QUEEN, WILLIAM EDDLEMAN
b.Nov.28,1928 Gastonia,N.C.
1954 Mil N O 3 .000
BRTR

QUELLICH, GEORGE WILLIAM
b.Feb.10,1903 Johnsville,Cal.
d.Aug.31,1958
1931 Det A O 13 .222
BRTR

QUEST, JOSEPH L.
b.1852 New Castle,Pa.
1871 Cle n 2-S 3 NR
1878 Ind N 2 59 .213
1879 Chi N 2 79 .220
1880 Chi N 2-S 80 .245
1881 Chi N 2-S 77 .249
1882 Chi N 2 42 .201
1883 Det N 2 36 .204
1883 St.L a 2 20 .253
1884 St.L a 2 81 .200
1884 Pit a 2-S 12 .209
1885 Det N 2-S 55 .195
1886 Ath a S 41 .200
BRTR 585 NR

QUICK, EDWIN S.
b. Baltimore,Md.
1903 NY A P 1 0-1

QUICK, JAMES HAROLD
b.Oct.4,1919 Rome,Ga.
1939 Was A S 12 .244
BRTR

QUILLIN, LEE
b.May 5,1882 North Branch,Minn.

Yr	Cl	Lea	Pos	G	Rec
1906	Chi	A	S	3	.111
1907	Chi	A	3	49	.192
		TR		52	.186

QUINLAN, ...

Yr	Cl	Lea	Pos	G	Rec
1874	Phi	n	S	1	.000

QUINLAN, LAWRENCE A.
b. Marlboro,Mass.

Yr	Cl	Lea	Pos	G	Rec
1891	Bos	a	C	2	.000

QUINLAN, THOMAS FINNERS
b.Oct.21,1887 Scranton,Pa.

Yr	Cl	Lea	Pos	G	Rec
1913	St.L	N	O	13	.160
1915	Chi	A	O	42	.193
		BLTL		55	.183

QUINN, CLARENCE C.

Yr	Cl	Lea	Pos	G	Rec
1902	Phi	A	P	1	0-1
1903	Phi	A	P	2	0-0
				3	0-1

QUINN, FRANK J.
b. Grand Rapids,Mich.
d.Feb.17,1920

Yr	Cl	Lea	Pos	G	Rec
1899	Chi	N	O	12	.181

QUINN, FRANK WILLIAM
b.Nov.27,1927 Springfield,Mass.

Yr	Cl	Lea	Pos	G	Rec
1949	Bos	A	P	8	0-0
1950	Bos	A	P	1	0-0
		BRTR		9	0-0

QUINN, JOHN EDWARD PICK
b.Sept.12,1885 Framingham,Mass.
d.Apr.9,1956

Yr	Cl	Lea	Pos	G	Rec
1911	Phi	N	C	1	.000
		TR			

QUINN, JOHN PICUS
(Real name John Quinn Picus)
b.July 5,1884 Hazleton,Pa.
d.Apr.17,1946

Yr	Cl	Lea	Pos	G	Rec
1909	NY	A	P	22	9-5
1910	NY	A	P	35	18-12
1911	NY	A	P	39	8-9
1912	NY	A	P	16	5-7
1913	Bos	N	P	8	4-3
1914	Bal	F	P	48	26-14
1915	Bal	F	P	54	9-22
1918	Chi	A	P	6	5-1
1919	NY	A	P	38	15-14
1920	NY	A	P	41	18-10
1921	NY	A	P	33	8-7
1922	Bos	A	P	40	13-15
1923	Bos	A	P	42	13-17
1924	Bos	A	P	44	12-13
1925	Bos	A	P	19	7-8
1925	Phi	A	P	18	6-3
1926	Phi	A	P	31	10-11
1927	Phi	A	P	34	15-10
1928	Phi	A	P	31	18-7
1929	Phi	A	P	35	11-9
1930	Phi	A	P	35	9-7
1931	Bro	N	P	39	5-4
1932	Bro	N	P	42	3-7
1933	Cin	N	P	14	0-1
		BRTR		764	247-216

QUINN, JOSEPH C.
b.1851 Chicago,Ill.
d.Jan.2,1909

Yr	Cl	Lea	Pos	G	Rec
1871	Kek	n	C	4	NR
1875	Wes	n	C-O	11	NR
1875	Har	n	C-O	4	NR
1875	Chi	n	C-O	16	NR
1881	Bos	N	1	1	.000
1881	Wor	N	C	2	.125
				38	NR

QUINN, JOSEPH J.
b.Dec.25,1864 Sydney,Australia
d.Nov.12,1940

Yr	Cl	Lea	Pos	G	Rec
1884	St.L	U	1	82	.261
1885	St.L	N	1-3-O	97	.212

(Continued)

Yr	Cl	Lea	Pos	G	Rec
1886	St.L	N	2-O	75	.232
1888	Bos	N	2	38	.301
1889	Bos	N	2-S	111	.261
1890	Bos	p	2	129	.296
1891	Bos	N	2	123	.247
1892	Bos	N	2	142	.219
1893	St.L	N	2	135	.241
1894	St.L	N	2	106	.274
1895	St.L	N	M-2	134	.309
1896	St.L	N	2	48	.231
1896	Bal	N	2	20	.295
1897	Bal	N	S-3	71	.264
1898	Bal	N	2-3-O	11	.281
1898	St.L	N	2	99	.250
1899	Cle	N	M-2	146	.292
1900	St.L	N	2-S-3	22	.259
1900	Cin	N	2	72	.279
1901	Was	A	2	66	.251
		BRTR		1727	.262

QUINN, PATRICK
b. Boston,Mass.
d.Mar.1893

Yr	Cl	Lea	Pos	G	Rec
1873	Res	n	C	1	NR
1875	Atl	n	3-O	2	NR
1877	Chi	N	O	4	.071
				7	NR

QUINN, THOMAS G.
b.Apr.25,1864 Annapolis,Md.
d.July 24,1932

Yr	Cl	Lea	Pos	G	Rec
1886	Pit	a	C	3	.000
1889	Bal	a	C	54	.174
1890	Pit	p	C	56	.207
				113	.181

QUINN, WELLINGTON HUNT (Wimpy)
b.May 14,1918 Birmingham,Ala.
d.Sept.1,1954

Yr	Cl	Lea	Pos	G	Rec
1941	Chi	N	P	3	0-0
		BRTR			

QUINTON, MARSHALL J.
b.Philadelphia,Pa.

Yr	Cl	Lea	Pos	G	Rec
1884	Ric	a	C-O	26	.231
1885	Ath	a	C	7	.207
				33	.226

QUIRK, ARTHUR LINCOLN
b.Apr.11,1938 Providence, R.I.

Yr	Cl	Lea	Pos	G	Rec
1962	Bal	A	P	7	2-2
		BRTL			

RABBITT, JOSEPH PATRICK
b.Jan.15,1901 Frontenac,Kan.

Yr	Cl	Lea	Pos	G	Rec
1922	Cle	A	O	2	.333
		BLTR			

RABE, CHARLES HENRY
b.May 6,1932 Boyce,Tex.

Yr	Cl	Lea	Pos	G	Rec
1957	Cin	N	P	2	0-1
1958	Cin	N	P	9	0-3
		BLTL		11	0-4

RACHUNOK, STEPHEN STEPANOVICH
b.Dec.5,1916 Rittman,O.

Yr	Cl	Lea	Pos	G	Rec
1940	Bro	N	P	2	0-1
		BRTR			

RACKLEY, MARVIN EUGENE
b.July 25,1921 Seneca,S.C.

Yr	Cl	Lea	Pos	G	Rec
1947	Bro	N	O	18	.222
1948	Bro	N	O	88	.327
1949	Bro	N	O	63	.300
1949	Pit	N	O	11	.314
1950	Cin	N	H	5	.500
		BLTL		185	.317

RADATZ, RICHARD RAYMOND
b.Apr.2,1937 Detroit,Mich.

Yr	Cl	Lea	Pos	G	Rec
1962	Bos	A	P	62	9-6
		BRTR			

RADBOURN, CHARLES (Old Hoss)
b.Dec.9,1853 Rochester,N.Y.
d.Feb.5,1897

Yr	Cl	Lea	Pos	G	Rec
1880	Buf	N	2-O	6	.143
1881	Pro	N	P-2-S-O	70	25-12 .221
1882	Pro	N	P-S-O	83	33-19 .239
1883	Pro	N	P-1-O	89	44-23 .283
1884	Pro	N	P-1-2-S-3-O	85	60-12 .233
1885	Pro	N	P-2-O	65	28-21 .232
1886	Bos	N	P	66	27-31
1887	Bos	N	P	48	24-23
1888	Bos	N	P	24	7-16
1889	Bos	N	P	35	20-11
1890	Bos	p	P	43	26-12
1891	Cin	N	P	27	12-12
		BRTR		641	306-192 .241

RADBOURN, GEORGE
b.Apr.8,1856 Bloomington,Ill.
d.Jan.1,1904

Yr	Cl	Lea	Pos	G	Rec
1883	Det	N	P-O	3	1-1 .154

RADCLIFF, JOHN J.
b.1846 Camden,N.J.
d.July 26,1911

Yr	Cl	Lea	Pos	G	Rec
1871	Ath	n	S	28	.333
1872	Bal	n	2-S-3	55	.297
1873	Bal	n	2-S-3-O	45	NR
1874	Phi	n	1-2-S-3-O	22	NR
1875	Cen	n	S	5	NR
				155	NR

RADCLIFF, RAYMOND ALLEN (Rip)
b.Jan.19,1906 Kiowa,Okla.
d.May 23, 1962

Yr	Cl	Lea	Pos	G	Rec
1934	Chi	A	O	14	.268
1935	Chi	A	O	146	.286
1936	Chi	A	O	138	.335
1937	Chi	A	O	144	.325
1938	Chi	A	1-O	129	.330
1939	Chi	A	1-O	113	.264
1940	St.L	A	1-O	150	.342
1941	St.L	A	O	19	.282
1941	Det	A	O	96	.317
1942	Det	A	1-O	62	.250
1943	Det	A	1-O	70	.261
		BLTL		1081	.311

RADEBAUGH, ROY
b.Feb.22,1884 Champaign,Ill.
d.Jan.17,1945

Yr	Cl	Lea	Pos	G	Rec
1911	St.L	N	P	2	0-0
		BRTR			

RADER, DONALD R.
b.Sept.5,1894 Wolcott,Ind.

Yr	Cl	Lea	Pos	G	Rec
1913	Chi	A	3-O	4	.333
1921	Phi	N	S	9	.281
		BLTR		13	.286

RADER, DREW LEON
b.Aug.19,1901 Elmira,N.Y.

Yr	Cl	Lea	Pos	G	Rec
1921	Pit	N	P	1	0-0
		BRTL			

RADFORD, PAUL REVERE (Shorty)
b.Oct.14,1861 Roxbury,Mass.
d.Feb.21,1945

Yr	Cl	Lea	Pos	G	Rec
1883	Bos	N	O	71	.205
1884	Pro	N	P-1-S-O	96	0-0 .202
1885	Pro	N	P-S-O	105	0-1 .242
1886	KC	N	S-O	122	.229
1887	Met	a	S-O	128	.404
1888	Bro	a	O	91	.224
1889	Cle	N	O	136	.238
1890	Cle	p	S-O	122	.292
1891	Bos	a	S	133	.257

(Continued)

Yr	Cl	Lea	Pos	G	Rec
1892	Was	N	S-3-O	134	.254
1893	Was	N	O	124	.228
1894	Was	N	2-S-O	93	.233
	BRTR			1355	{0-1 .259

RADTKE, JACK WILLIAM
b.Apr.14,1913 Denver,Colo.

Yr	Cl	Lea	Pos	G	Rec
1936	Bro	N	2	33	.097
	BBTR				

RAETHER, HAROLD HERMAN
b.Oct.10,1932 Lake Mills,Wis.

Yr	Cl	Lea	Pos	G	Rec
1954	Phi	A	P	1	0-0
1957	KC	A	P	1	0-0
	BRTR			2	0-0

RAFFENSBERGER, KENNETH DAVID
b.Aug.8,1917 York,Pa.

Yr	Cl	Lea	Pos	G	Rec
1939	St.L	N	P	1	0-0
1940	Chi	N	P	43	7-9
1941	Chi	N	P	10	0-1
1943	Phi	N	P	1	0-1
1944	Phi	N	P	38	13-20
1945	Phi	N	P	5	0-3
1946	Phi	N	P	39	8-15
1947	Phi	N	P	10	2-6
1947	Cin	N	P	19	6-5
1948	Cin	N	P	40	11-12
1949	Cin	N	P	41	18-17
1950	Cin	N	P	38	14-19
1951	Cin	N	P	42	16-17
1952	Cin	N	P	38	17-13
1953	Cin	N	P	26	7-14
1954	Cin	N	P	6	0-2
	BRTL			397	119-154

RAFTER, JOHN CORNELIUS
b.Feb.20,1875 Lansingburg,N.Y.
d.Jan.5,1943

Yr	Cl	Lea	Pos	G	Rec
1904	Pit	N	C	1	.000
	TR				

RAFTERY, THOMAS L.
b.Oct.5,1881 Haverhill,Mass.
d.Jan.1,1955

Yr	Cl	Lea	Pos	G	Rec
1909	Cle	A	O	8	.269

RAGAN, DON CARLOS PATRICK (Pat)
b.Nov.15,1888 Blanchard,Ia.
d.Sept.4,1956

Yr	Cl	Lea	Pos	G	Rec
1909	Cin	N	P	2	0-1
1909	Chi	N	P	2	0-0
1911	Bro	N	P	22	4-3
1912	Bro	N	P	36	7-18
1913	Bro.	N	P	44	15-18
1914	Bro	N	P	38	10-15
1915	Bro	N	P	4	1-0
1915	Bos	N	P	34	16-12
1916	Bos	N	P	31	9-9
1917	Bos	N	P	30	6-9
1918	Bos	N	P	30	8-17
1919	Bos	N	P	4	0-2
1919	NY	N	P	7	1-0
1919	Chi	A	P	1	0-0
1923	Phi	N	P	1	0-0
	BRTR			286	77-104

RAGLAND, FRANK ROLAND
b.May 26,1905 Paris,Miss.
d.July 28,1959

Yr	Cl	Lea	Pos	G	Rec
1932	Was	A	P	12	1-0
1933	Phi	N	P	11	0-4
	BRTR			23	1-4

RAINES, LAWRENCE GLENN
b.Mar.2,1930 Cincinnati,O.

Yr	Cl	Lea	Pos	G	Rec
1957	Cle	A	2-S-3-O	96	.262
1958	Cle	A	2	7	.000
	BRTR			103	.253

RAINEY, JOHN PAUL
b.July 26,1864 Birmingham,Mich.
d.Nov.11,1912

Yr	Cl	Lea	Pos	G	Rec
1887	NY	N	3	17	.349
1890	Buf	p	O	42	.248
	BLTR			59	.276

RAKOW, EDWARD CHARLES
b.May 30,1936 Pittsburgh,Pa.

Yr	Cl	Lea	Pos	G	Rec
1960	L.A.	N	P	9	0-1
1961	K.C.	A	P	45	2-8
1962	K.C.	A	P	42	14-17
	BBTR			96	16-26

RALEIGH, JOHN AUSTIN
b.Apr.21,1890 Elkhorn,Wis.
d.Aug.24,1955

Yr	Cl	Lea	Pos	G	Rec
1909	St.L	N	P	15	1-10
1910	St.L	N	P	3	0-0
	BRTL			18	1-10

RALSTON, SAMUEL BERYL
(Doc)
b.Aug.3,1885 Pierpont,O.

Yr	Cl	Lea	Pos	G	Rec
1910	Was	A	O	22	.205
	BRTR				

RAMAZZOTTI, ROBERT LOUIS
b.Jan.16,1919 Elanora,Pa.

Yr	Cl	Lea	Pos	G	Rec
1946	Bro	N	2-3	62	.208
1948	Bro	N	2	4	.000
1949	Bro	N	3	5	.154
1949	Chi	N	2-S-3	65	.179
1950	Chi	N	2-S-3	61	.262
1951	Chi	N	2-S-3	73	.247
1952	Chi	N	2	50	.284
1953	Chi	N	2	26	.154
	BRTR			346	.230

RAMBERT, ELMER DONALD (Pep)
b.Aug.1,1917 Cleveland,O.

Yr	Cl	Lea	Pos	G	Rec
1939	Pit	N	P	2	0-0
1940	Pit	N	P	3	0-1
	BRTR			5	0-1

RAMBO, WARREN DAWSON
b.Nov.1,1906 Thoroughfare,N.J.

Yr	Cl	Lea	Pos	G	Rec
1926	Phi	N	P	1	0-0
	BRTR				

RAMOS, JESUS MANUEL GARCIA (Chucho)
b.Apr.12,1918 Maturin,Venezuela

Yr	Cl	Lea	Pos	G	Rec
1944	Cin	N	O	4	.500
	BRTL				

RAMOS, PEDRO
b.Mar.28,1935 Pinar Del Rio,Cuba

Yr	Cl	Lea	Pos	G	Rec
1955	Was	A	P	59	5-11
1956	Was	A	P	56	12-10
1957	Was	A	P	56	12-16
1958	Was	A	P	53	14-18
1959	Was	A	P	45	13-19
1960	Was	A	P	53	11-18
1961	Min	A	P	53	11-20
1962	Cle	A	P	39	10-12
	BRTR			414	88-124

RAMSDELL, JAMES WILLARD
(Willie)
b.Apr.18,1918 Williamsburg,Kan.

Yr	Cl	Lea	Pos	G	Rec
1947	Bro	N	P	2	1-1
1948	Bro	N	P	27	4-4
1950	Bro	N	P	5	1-2
1950	Cin	N	P	27	7-12
1951	Cin	N	P	31	9-17
1952	Chi	N	P	19	2-3
	BRTR			111	24-39

RAMSEY, THOMAS A. (Toad)
b.Aug.8,1864 Indianapolis,Ind.
d.Mar.27,1906

Yr	Cl	Lea	Pos	G	Rec
1885	Lou	a	P	9	3-4

(Continued)

Yr	Cl	Lea	Pos	G	Rec
1886	Lou	a	P	66	37-27
1887	Lou	a	P	66	39-27
1888	Lou	a	P	41	8-30
1889	Lou	a	P	20	2-18
1889	St.L	a	P	6	4-2
1890	St.L	a	P	44	22-14
	BRTL			252	115-122

RAMSEY, WILLIAM THRACE
b.Feb.20,1921 Osceola,Ark.

Yr	Cl	Lea	Pos	G	Rec
1945	Bos	N	O	78	.292
	BRTR				

RAND, RICHARD HILTON
b.Mar.7,1931 South Gate,Cal.

Yr	Cl	Lea	Pos	G	Rec
1953	St.L	N	C	9	.290
1955	St.L	N	C	3	.300
1957	Pit	N	C	60	.219
	BRTR			72	.240

RANDALL, NEWTON J.
b.Feb.3,1881 New Lowell, Ont., Canada
d.May 3,1955

Yr	Cl	Lea	Pos	G	Rec
1907	Chi	N	O	21	.205
1907	Bos	N	O	73	.213
				94	.211

RANEW, MERRITT THOMAS
b.May 10,1938 Albany,Ga.

Yr	Cl	Lea	Pos	G	Rec
1962	Hou	N	C	71	.234
	BLTR				

RANEY, FRANK ROBERT (Ribs)
(Real name Frank Robert Raniszewski)
b.Feb.16,1923 Detroit,Mich.

Yr	Cl	Lea	Pos	G	Rec
1949	St.L	A	P	3	1-2
1950	St.L	A	P	1	0-1
	BRTR			4	1-3

RANISZEWSKI, FRANK ROBERT
(Played under name of Frank Robert Raney

RAPP, EARL WELLINGTON
b.May 20,1921 Corunna,Mich.

Yr	Cl	Lea	Pos	G	Rec
1949	Det	A	H	1	.000
1949	Chi	A	O	19	.259
1951	NY	N	H	13	.091
1951	St.L	A	O	26	.327
1952	St.L	A	O	30	.143
1952	Was	A	O	46	.284
	BLTR			135	.271

RAPP, JOSEPH ALOYSIUS (Goldie)
b.Feb.6,1892 Cincinnati,O.

Yr	Cl	Lea	Pos	G	Rec
1921	NY	N	3	58	.215
1921	Phi	N	3	52	.277
1922	Phi	N	S-3	119	.253
1923	Phi	N	3	47	.263
	BBTR			276	.253

RARIDEN, WILLIAM ANGEL
b.Feb.5,1888 Bedford,Ind.
d.Aug.28,1942

Yr	Cl	Lea	Pos	G	Rec
1909	Bos	N	C	13	.167
1910	Bos	N	C	49	.226
1911	Bos	N	C	69	.228
1912	Bos	N	C	79	.223
1913	Bos	N	C	95	.236
1914	Ind	F	C	132	.236
1915	New	F	C	142	.278
1916	NY	N	C	120	.222
1917	NY	N	C	101	.271
1918	NY	N	C	69	.224
1919	Cin	N	C	74	.216
1920	Cin	N	C	39	.248
	BRTR			982	.239

RASCHI, VICTOR ANGELO JOHN
b.Mar.28,1919 W.Springfield,Mass.

Yr	Cl	Lea	Pos	G	Rec
1946	NY	A	P	2	2-0
1947	NY	A	P	15	7-2
1948	NY	A	P	36	19-8
1949	NY	A	P	38	21-10
1950	NY	A	P	33	21-8
1951	NY	A	P	35	21-10
1952	NY	A	P	31	16-6
1953	NY	A	P	28	13-6
1954	St.L	N	P	30	8-9
1955	St.L	N	P	1	0-1
1955	KC	A	P	20	4-6
		BRTR		269	132-66

RASMUSSEN, HENRY
b.1893 Chicago,Ill.

Yr	Cl	Lea	Pos	G	Rec
1915	Chi	F	P	2	0-0

RATH, MAURICE CHARLES
b.Dec.25,1887 Mobeetie,Tex.
d.Nov.18,1945

Yr	Cl	Lea	Pos	G	Rec
1909	Phi	A	S-3	7	.269
1910	Phi	A	3	15	.160
1910	Cle	A	3	27	.191
1912	Chi	A	2	157	.272
1913	Chi	A	2	90	.197
1919	Cin	N	2	138	.264
1920	Cin	N	2-3-O	129	.267
		BLTR		563	.254

RAUB, THOMAS JEFFERSON
b.May 7,1875 Paterson,N.J.
d.Feb.16,1949

Yr	Cl	Lea	Pos	G	Rec
1903	Chi	N	C	27	.226
1906	St.L	N	C	22	.282
		TR		49	.253

RAWLINGS, JOHN WILLIAM (Red)
b.Aug.17,1892 Bloomfield,Ia.

Yr	Cl	Lea	Pos	G	Rec
1914	Cin	N	3	33	.217
1914	KC	F	S	61	.209
1915	KC	F	S	120	.213
1917	Bos	N	2-S	122	.256
1918	Bos	N	2-S-O	111	.207
1919	Bos	N	2-S-O	77	.255
1920	Bos	N	2	5	.000
1920	Phi	N	2	98	.234
1921	Phi	N	2	60	.291
1921	NY	N	2	86	.267
1922	NY	N	2-3	88	.282
1923	Pit	N	2	119	.284
1924	Pit	N	H	3	.333
1925	Pit	N	2	36	.282
1926	Pit	N	2	61	.232
		BRTR		1080	.249

RAY, CARL GRADY
b.1893 Greensboro,N.C.

Yr	Cl	Lea	Pos	G	Rec
1915	Phi	A	P	2	0-1
1916	Phi	A	P	3	0-1
		BLTL		5	0-2

RAY, IRVING BURTON (Stubby)
b.Jan.22,1864 Harrington,Me.
d.Mar.21,1947

Yr	Cl	Lea	Pos	G	Rec
1888	Bos	N	S	50	.247
1889	Bos	N	S	9	.312
1889	Bal	a	S	27	.330
1890	Bal	a	S	38	.347
1891	Bal	a	S-O	103	.277
		TL		227	.290

RAY, ROBERT H. (Farmer)
b.1889 Oklahoma City,Okla.

Yr	Cl	Lea	Pos	G	Rec
1910	St.L	A	P	21	4-10
		TR			

RAYDON, CURTIS LOWELL
b.Nov.18,1933 Bloomington,Ill.

Yr	Cl	Lea	Pos	G	Rec
1958	Pit	N	P	31	8-4
		BRTR			

RAYMER, FREDERICK CHARLES
b.Nov.12,1875 Leavenworth,Kan.
d.June 12,1957

Yr	Cl	Lea	Pos	G	Rec
1901	Chi	N	S-3	118	.235
1904	Bos	N	2	114	.210
1905	Bos	N	2	136	.211
		TR		368	.218

RAYMOND, ARTHUR LAWRENCE (Bugs)
b.Feb.24,1882 Chicago,Ill.
d.Sept.7,1912

Yr	Cl	Lea	Pos	G	Rec
1904	Det	A	P	5	0-1
1907	St.L	N	P	10	3-4
1908	St.L	N	P	48	15-25
1909	NY	N	P	39	18-12
1910	NY	N	P	19	4-11
1911	NY	N	P	17	6-4
		BRTR		138	46-57

RAYMOND, HARRY H.
(Real name Harry H. Truman)
b.Feb.20,1866 Utica,N.Y.

Yr	Cl	Lea	Pos	G	Rec
1888	Lou	a	3	32	.208
1889	Lou	a	P-3	130	0-0 .241
1890	Lou	a	3	122	.280
1891	Lou	a	S	14	.207
1892	Pit	N	3	11	.083
1892	Was	N	3	4	.067
				313	0-0 .247

RAYMOND, JOSEPH CLAUDE MARC
b.May 7,1937 St.Jean,Que.,Canada

Yr	Cl	Lea	Pos	G	Rec
1959	Chi	A	P	3	0-0
1961	Mil	N	P	13	1-0
1962	Mil	N	P	26	5-5
		BRTR		42	6-5

RAYMOND, LOUIS A.

Yr	Cl	Lea	Pos	G	Rec
1919	Phi	N	2	1	.500
		TR			

REACH, ALFRED JAMES
b.May 25,1840 London,England.
d.Jan.14,1928

Yr	Cl	Lea	Pos	G	Rec
1871	Ath	n	2	26	.371
1872	Ath	n	1-O	25	NR
1873	Ath	n	2-O	12	NR
1874	Ath	n	O	14	NR
1875	Ath	n	2-O	5	NR
		TL		82	NR

REACH, ROBERT
b.Aug.28,1843 Williamsburg,N.Y.
d.May 19,1922

Yr	Cl	Lea	Pos	G	Rec
1872	Oly	n	S	1	NR
1873	Nat	n	S	1	NR
				2	NR

REAGAN, ARTHUR (Rip)
b.1882 Ft.Scott,Kan.

Yr	Cl	Lea	Pos	G	Rec
1903	Cin	N	P	3	0-2
		BRTR			

REAGAN, J.

Yr	Cl	Lea	Pos	G	Rec
1898	NY	N	O	2	.200

REARDON, JAMES MATTHEW
b.1866 Hoosick Falls,N.Y.
d.Feb.25,1891

Yr	Cl	Lea	Pos	G	Rec
1886	St.L	N	P	1	0-1
1886	Cin	a	P-O	1	0-1 .000
				2	0-2 .143

REARDON, PHILIP MICHAEL
b.Oct.3,1883 Brooklyn,N.Y.
d.Sept.28,1920

Yr	Cl	Lea	Pos	G	Rec
1906	Bro	N	O	5	.071
		BRTR			

REBEL, ARTHUR ANTHONY
b.Mar.4,1915 Cincinnati,O.

Yr	Cl	Lea	Pos	G	Rec
1938	Phi	N	O	7	.222
1945	St.L	N	O	26	.347
		BLTL		33	.333

RECCIUS, J. WILLIAM (Bill)
b.1847 Frankfurt-on-Main,Germany.
d.Jan.25,1911
Non-playing manager Lou (a) 1882-83.

RECCIUS, JOHN
b.June 7,1862 Louisville,Ky.
d.Sept.1,1930

Yr	Cl	Lea	Pos	G	Rec
1882	Lou	a	P-O	73	4-6 .216
1883	Lou	a	P-O	17	0-0 .154
				90	4-6 .205

RECCIUS, PHILIP
b.June 7,1862 Louisville,Ky.
d.Feb.15,1903

Yr	Cl	Lea	Pos	G	Rec
1882	Lou	a	O	3	.091
1883	Lou	a	O	1	.333
1884	Lou	a	P-S-3	75	5-7 .249
1885	Lou	a	P-3	105	0-5 .240
1886	Lou	a	P-O	5	0-1 .267
1887	Lou	a	S-O	11	.341
1887	Cle	a	3	62	.295
1888	Lou	a	3	2	.223
1890	Roc	a	O	1	.000
				265	5-13 .243

REDDING, PHILIP HAYDEN
b.Jan.25,1890
d.Mar.31,1928

Yr	Cl	Lea	Pos	G	Rec
1912	St.L	N	P	3	2-1
1913	St.L	N	P	1	0-0
		BLTR		4	2-1

REDER, JOHN ANTHONY
b.Sept.24,1909 Lublin,Poland.

Yr	Cl	Lea	Pos	G	Rec
1932	Bos	A	1	17	.135
		BRTR			

REDFERN, GEORGE HOWARD (Buck)
b.Apr.7,1902 Asheville,N.C.

Yr	Cl	Lea	Pos	G	Rec
1928	Chi	A	2-S	86	.234
1929	Chi	A	2	21	.130
		BRTR		107	.218

REDMOND, HARRY JOHN
b.Sept.13,1887 Cleveland,O.
d.July 10,1960

Yr	Cl	Lea	Pos	G	Rec
1909	Bro	N	2	6	.100
		TR			

REDMOND, JACKSON McKITTRICK (Red)
b.Sept.3,1910 Florence,Ariz.

Yr	Cl	Lea	Pos	G	Rec
1935	Was	A	C	22	.176
		BLTR			

REDMOND, WILLIAM T.
b.St.Louis,Mo.

Yr	Cl	Lea	Pos	G	Rec
1875	RS	n	S-3	19	NR
1877	Cin	N	S	3	.250
1878	Mil	N	S-O	47	.229
		BLTL		69	NR

Yr Cl Lea Pos G Rec

REED, ...
1874 Bal n O 1 .000

REED, HOWARD DEAN
b.Dec.12,1936 Ft. Worth,Tex.
1958 KC A P 3 1-0
1959 K.C. A P 6 0-3
1960 K.C. A P 1 0-0
BRTR 10 1-3

REED, JOHN BURWELL
b.Feb.2,1933 Silver City,Miss.
1961 N.Y. A O 28 .154
1962 N.Y. A O 88 .302
BRTR 116 .268

REED, MILTON D.
b.July 4,1890 Atlanta,Ga.
1911 St.L N H 1 .000
1913 Phi N 2-S 13 .240
1914 Phi N S 44 .206
1915 Bro F 2 10 .290
BLTR 68 .224

REED, RALPH EDWIN
b.Oct.18,1890 Beaver,Pa.
d.Feb.16,1959
1915 New F 3 20 .247
BRTR

REED, WILLIAM JOSEPH
b.Nov.12,1922 Shawano,Wis.
1952 Bos N 2 15 .250
BLTR

REEDER, JAMES EDWARD (Icicle)
b.1865 Cincinnati,O.
1884 Cin a O 3 .143
1884 Was U O 3 .167
6 .154

REEDER, NICHOLAS
(Real name Nicholas Herchenroeder)
b.Mar.22,1867 Louisville,Ky.
d.Sept.26,1894
1891 Lou a 3 1 .000

REEDER, WILLIAM EDGAR
b.Feb.20,1922 Dike,Tex.
1949 St.L N P 21 1-1
BRTR

REESE, ANDREW JACKSON
b.Feb.7,1904 Tupelo,Miss.
1927 NY N 3-O 97 .265
1928 NY N 2-O 109 .308
1929 NY N 2 58 .263
1930 NY N 3-O 67 .273
BRTR 331 .281

REESE, HAROLD HENRY (Pee Wee)
b.July 23,1919 Ekron,Ky.
1940 Bro N S 84 .272
1941 Bro N S 152 .228
1942 Bro N S 151 .255
1946 Bro N S 152 .284
1947 Bro N S 142 .284
1948 Bro N S 151 .274
1949 Bro N S 155 .279
1950 Bro N S-3 141 .260
1951 Bro N S 154 .286
1952 Bro N S 149 .272
1953 Bro N S 140 .271
1954 Bro N S 141 .309
1955 Bro N S 145 .282
1956 Bro N S-3 147 .257
1957 Bro N S-3 103 .224
1958 LA N S-3 59 .224
BRTR 2166 .269

REESE, JAMES HYMIE
(Real name James Hymie Solomon)
b.Oct.1,1904 Los Angeles,Cal.
1930 NY A 2 77 .346
1931 NY A 2 65 .241
1932 St.L N 2 90 .265
BLTR 232 .278

REESE, STANLEY MILTON
b.Feb.23,1899 Cynthiana,Ky.
d.Aug.29,1937
1918 Was A P 2 1-0
TR

REEVES, ROBERT EDWIN (Gunner)
b.June 24,1904 Chattanooga,Tenn.
1926 Was A 3 20 .224
1927 Was A S-3 112 .255
1928 Was A 2-S 102 .303
1929 Bos A 3 140 .248
1930 Bos A 2-S-3 92 .217
1931 Bos A P-2 36 {0-0 .167}
BRTR 502 {0-0 .252}

REGALADO, RUDOLPH VALENTINO
b.Oct.1,1930 Los Angeles,Cal.
1954 Cle A 2-3 65 .250
1955 Cle A 2-3 10 .240
1956 Cle A 1-3 16 .234
BRTR 91 .246

REGAN, MICHAEL JOSEPH
b.Nov.19,1888 Phoenix,N.Y.
d.May 23,1961
1917 Cin N P 33 11-10
1918 Cin N P 23 5-5
1919 Cin N P 1 0-0
BRTR 57 16-15

REGAN, PHILIP RAYMOND
b.Apr.6,1937 Otsego,Mich.
1960 Det A P 17 0-4
1961 Det A P 33 10-7
1962 Det A P 35 11-9
BRTR 21-20

REGAN, WILLIAM WRIGHT
b.Jan.23,1899 Pittsburgh,Pa.
1926 Bos A 2 108 .263
1927 Bos A 2 129 .274
1928 Bos A 2 138 .264
1929 Bos A 2-3 104 .288
1930 Bos A 2 134 .266
1931 Pit N 2 28 .202
BRTR 641 .267

REGO, ANTHONY J.
(Real name Anthony J. DeRego)
b.Oct.1,1897 Wailuku,Hawaii.
1924 St.L A C 24 .220
1925 St.L A C 20 .406
BRTR 44 .286

REHG, WALTER PHILLIP
b.Aug.31,1888 Summerfield,Ill.
d.Apr.5,1946
1912 Pit N O 7 .000
1913 Bos A O 30 .277
1914 Bos A O 84 .218
1915 Bos A O 5 .200
1917 Bos N O 87 .270
1918 Bos N O 40 .241
1919 Cin N O 5 .167
BRTR 258 .251

REIBER, FRANK BERNARD
bSept.19,1909 Huntington,W.Va.
1933 Det A C 13 .278
1934 Det A H 3 .000
1935 Det A C 8 .273
1936 Det A C 20 .273
BRTR 44 .271

REICH, HERMAN CHARLES
b.Nov.23,1918 Los Angeles,Cal.
1949 Was A H 2 .000
1949 Cle A O 1 .500
1949 Chi N 1-0 108 .280
BRTL 111 .279

REICHLE, RICHARD WENDELL
b.Nov.23,1897 Lincoln,Ill.
1922 Bos A O 6 .250
1923 Bos A O 122 .258
BLTR 128 .257

REID, EARL PERCY
b.June 8,1915 Holly Pond,Ala.
1946 Bos N P 2 1-0
BLTR

REID, WILLIAM A. (Sandy)
b.1857 London,Ont.,Canada.
1883 Bal a 2-S 16 .285
1884 Pit a O 19 .246
35 .269

REIDY, WILLIAM JOSEPH
b.Oct.9,1873 Cleveland,O.
d.Oct.14,1915
1896 NY N P 2 0-1
1899 Bro N P 2 0-0
1901 Mil A P 36 15-18
1902 St.L A P-O 13 3-5 .195
1903 St.L A P 6 1-5
1903 Bro N P 15 6-7
1904 Bro N P-2 11 {0-4 .196}
TR 85 {25-40 .150}

REILLEY, ALEXANDER ALOYSIUS (Duke)
b.Aug.25,1884 Chicago,Ill.
1909 Cle A O 20 .210

REILLEY, CHARLES E.
b.1856 Massachusetts
d.1888
1879 Tro N C-1 61 .232
1880 Cin N C-3-O 29 .204
1881 Det N C-1-S-3-O 18 .179
1881 Wor N C 2 .375
1882 Pro N C 3 .182
TR 113 .214

REILLY, ARCHER E.
b.Feb.18,1893 Huntington,W.Va.
1917 Pit N 3 1 .000
BRTR

REILLY, BERNARD EUGENE (Barney)
b.Feb.7,1884 Brockton,Mass.
d.Nov.15,1934
1909 Chi A 2 12 .120
BRTR

REILLY, CHARLES (Josh)
b.1868 San Francisco,Cal.
d.June 13,1938
1896 Chi N 2 9 .205

REILLY, CHARLES T. (Princeton)
b. New Brunswick,N.J.
1889 Col a 3 6 .478
1890 Col a 3 137 .270
1891 Pit N 3 110 .211
1892 Phi N 3 81 .201
1893 Phi N 3 104 .252
1894 Phi N 3 36 .272
1895 Phi N S 44 .267
1897 Was N 3 101 .275
BBTR 619 .250

REILLY, HAROLD J.
1919 Chi N O 1 .000

REILLY, JOHN GOOD (Long John)
b.Oct.5,1858 Tusculum,O.
d.May 31,1937

Yr	Cl	Lea	Pos	G	Rec
1880	Cin	N	1-O	72	.195
1883	Cin	a	1	97	.289
1884	Cin	a	1-S-O	106	.339
1885	Cin	a	1-O	106	.308
1886	Cin	a	1-O	115	.270
1887	Cin	a	1-O	134	.334
1888	Cin	a	1-O	126	.324
1889	Cin	a	1-O	111	.261
1890	Cin	N	1	133	.300
1891	Cin	N	1-O	133	.200
	BRTR			1133	.284

REILLY, JOSEPH J.
b.New York,N.Y.

Yr	Cl	Lea	Pos	G	Rec
1884	Bos	U	3-O	3	.000
1885	Met	a	2-3	10	.122
				13	.096

REILLY, THOMAS H.
b.Aug.3,1884 St.Louis,Mo.

Yr	Cl	Lea	Pos	G	Rec
1908	St.L	N	S	29	.173
1909	St.L	N	S	4	.167
1914	Cle	A	H	1	.000
	BRTR			34	.170

REINHART, ARTHUR CONRAD
b.May 29,1899 Ackley,Ia.
d.Nov.11,1946

Yr	Cl	Lea	Pos	G	Rec
1919	St.L	N	P	1	0-0
1925	St.L	N	P	28	11-5
1926	St.L	N	P	40	10-5
1927	St.L	N	P	27	5-2
1928	St.L	N	P	27	4-6
	BLTL			123	30-18

REINHOLZ, ARTHUR AUGUST
b.Jan.27,1903 Detroit,Mich.

Yr	Cl	Lea	Pos	G	Rec
1928	Cle	A	3	2	.333
	BRTR				

REINICKER, WALTER
(Real name Walter Smith)

Yr	Cl	Lea	Pos	G	Rec
1915	Bal	F	3	3	.125

REIPSCHLAGER, CHRISTOPHER FREDERICK (Rip)
b.June 11,1862 New York,N.Y.
d.Sept.19,1960

Yr	Cl	Lea	Pos	G	Rec
1883	Met	a	C-O	35	.189
1884	Met	a	C	59	.236
1885	Met	a	C	72	.234
1886	Met	a	C	66	.221
1887	Cle	a	C	63	.248
	BRTR			295	.229

REIS, HARRIE CRANE (Jack)
b.June 14,1890 Cincinnati,O.
d.July 20,1939

Yr	Cl	Lea	Pos	G	Rec
1911	St.L	N	P	3	0-0
	BRTR				

REIS, LAWRENCE P.

Yr	Cl	Lea	Pos	G	Rec
1877	Chi	N	P	4	3-1
1878	Chi	N	P-O	5	1-3 / .150
	BRTR			9	4-4 / .140

REIS, ROBERT JOSEPH THOMAS
b.Jan.2,1910 Woodside,N.Y.

Yr	Cl	Lea	Pos	G	Rec
1931	Bro	N	2-3	6	.294
1932	Bro	N	3	1	.250
1935	Bro	N	P-1-2-3-O	52	3-2 / .247
1936	Bos	N	P	37	6-5
1937	Bos	N	P-O	45	0-0 / .244
1938	Bos	N	P-O	34	1-6 / .184
	BRTR			175	10-13 / .233

REIS, THOMAS EDWARD
b.Aug.6,1915 Newport,Ky.

Yr	Cl	Lea	Pos	G	Rec
1938	Phi	N	P	4	0-1
1938	Bos	N	P	4	0-0
	BRTR			8	0-1

REISER, HAROLD PATRICK (Pete)
b.Mar.17,1919 St.Louis,Mo.

Yr	Cl	Lea	Pos	G	Rec
1940	Bro	N	S-3-O	58	.293
1941	Bro	N	O	137	.343
1942	Bro	N	O	125	.310
1946	Bro	N	3-O	122	.277
1947	Bro	N	O	110	.309
1948	Bro	N	O	64	.236
1949	Bos	N	3-O	84	.272
1950	Bos	N	3-O	53	.205
1951	Pit	N	3-O	74	.271
1952	Cle	A	O	34	.136
	BBTR			861	.295

REISIGI , JACOB (Bugs)
b.Dec.12,1887 Brooklyn,N.Y.

Yr	Cl	Lea	Pos	G	Rec
1911	Cle	A	P	2	0-1
	BRTR				

REISING, CHARLES

Yr	Cl	Lea	Pos	G	Rec
1884	Ind	a	O	1	.000

REISLING, FRANK CARL (Doc)
b.July 25,1874 Martin's Ferry,O.
d.Mar.4,1955

Yr	Cl	Lea	Pos	G	Rec
1904	Bro	N	P	7	3-3
1905	Bro	N	P	2	0-0
1909	Was	A	P	12	2-4
1910	Was	A	P	31	9-10
	BRTR			52	14-17

REISS, ALBERT ALLEN
b.Jan.8,1909 Elizabeth,N.J.

Yr	Cl	Lea	Pos	G	Rec
1932	Phi	A	S	9	.200
	BBTR				

REITZ, HENRY P. (Heinie)
b.June 29,1867 Chicago,Ill.
d.Nov.10,1914

Yr	Cl	Lea	Pos	G	Rec
1893	Bal	N	2	130	.297
1894	Bal	N	2	109	.306
1895	Bal	N	2-3	63	.281
1896	Bal	N	2	119	.283
1897	Bal	N	2	127	.289
1898	Was	N	2	132	.302
1899	Pit	N	2	35	.263
	TR			715	.293

REMENTER, WILLIS J. (Butch)
b.Philadelphia,Pa.

Yr	Cl	Lea	Pos	G	Rec
1904	Phi	N	C	1	.000
	TR				

REMNEAS, ALEXANDER
b.1889

Yr	Cl	Lea	Pos	G	Rec
1912	Det	A	P	1	0-0
1915	St.L	A	P	2	0-0
	BRTR			3	0-0

REMSEN, JOHN JAY
b.1851 Brooklyn,N.Y.

Yr	Cl	Lea	Pos	G	Rec
1872	Atl	n	O	36	NR
1873	Atl	n	O	51	NR
1874	Mut	n	O	64	NR
1875	Har	n	O	85	NR
1876	Har	N	O	69	.274
1877	St.L	N	O	33	.260
1878	Chi	N	O	55	.233
1879	Chi	N	1-O	39	.248
1881	Cle	N	O	48	.174
1884	Phi	N	O	10	.222
1884	Bro	a	O	81	.238
	BR			571	NR

RENFER, ERWIN ARTHUR
b.Dec.11,1895 Elgin,Ill.
d.Oct.2.1957

Yr	Cl	Lea	Pos	G	Rec
1913	Det	A	P	1	0-1
	BRTR				

RENFROE, MARSHALL DANIEL
B.May 25,1936 Century,Fla.

Yr	Cl	Lea	Pos	G	Rec
1959	S.F.	N	P	1	0-0
	BLTL				

RENIFF, HAROLD EUGENE
b.July 2,1938 Warren,O.

Yr	Cl	Lea	Pos	G	Rec
1961	N.Y.	A	P	25	2-0
1962	N.Y.	A	P	2	0-0
	BRTR			27	2-0

RENINGER, JAMES DAVID
b.Mar.7,1916 Aurora,Ill.

Yr	Cl	Lea	Pos	G	Rec
1938	Phi	A	P	4	0-2
1939	Phi	A	P	4	0-2
	BRTR			8	0-4

RENNA, WILLIAM BENEDITTO
b.Oct.14,1924 Hanford,Cal.

Yr	Cl	Lea	Pos	G	Rec
1953	NY	A	O	61	.314
1954	Phi	A	O	123	.232
1955	KC	A	O	100	.213
1956	KC	A	O	33	.271
1958	Bos	A	O	39	.268
1955	K.C.	A	O	100	.213
1956	K.C.	A	O	33	.271
1958	Bos	A	O	39	.268
1959	Bos	A	O	14	.091
	BRTR			370	.239

RENSA, GEORGE ANTHONY (Pug)
b.Sept.29,1901 Parsons,Pa.

Yr	Cl	Lea	Pos	G	Rec
1930	Det	A	C	20	.270
1930	Phi	N	C	54	.285
1931	Phi	N	C	19	.103
1933	NY	A	C	8	.310
1937	Chi	A	C	26	.298
1938	Chi	A	C	59	.248
1939	Chi	A	C	14	.200
	BRTR			200	.280

REPASS, ROBERT WILLIS
b.Nov.6,1917 W.Pittston,Pa.

Yr	Cl	Lea	Pos	G	Rec
1939	St.L	N	2	3	.333
1942	Was	A	2-S-3	81	.239
	BRTR			84	.242

REPULSKI, ELDON JOHN (Rip)
b.Oct.4,1927 Sauk Rapids,Minn.

Yr	Cl	Lea	Pos	G	Rec
1953	St.L	N	O	153	.275
1954	St.L	N	O	152	.283
1955	St.L	N	O	147	.270
1956	St.L	N	O	112	.277
1957	Phi	N	O	134	.260
1958	Phi	N	O	85	.244
1959	L.A.	N	O	53	.255
1960	L.A.	N	O	4	.200
1960	Bos	A	O	73	.243
1961	Bos	A	O	15	.269
	BRTR			928	.269

RESCIGNO, XAVIER FREDERICK (Mr. X)
b.Oct.13,1913 New York,N.Y.

Yr	Cl	Lea	Pos	G	Rec
1943	Pit	N	P	37	6-9
1944	Pit	N	P	48	10-8
1945	Pit	N	P	44	3-5
	BRTR			129	19-22

RESSLER, LAWRENCE P.

Yr	Cl	Lea	Pos	G	Rec
1875	Nat	n	2-O	25	NR

RESTELLI, DINO PAUL (Dingo)
b.Sept.23,1924 St.Louis,Mo.

Yr	Cl	Lea	Pos	G	Rec
1949	Pit	N	1-O	72	.250
1951	Pit	N	O	21	.184
	BRTR			93	.241

RETTGER, GEORGE EDWARD
b.July 29,1868 Cleveland,O.
d.June 5,1921

Yr	Cl	Lea	Pos	G	Rec
1891	St.L	a	P	15	10-3

(Continued)

Yr	Cl	Lea	Pos	G	Rec
1892	Cle	N	P	6	1-4
1892	Cin	N	P-O	2	1-0 .125
			TR	23	12-7 .092

RETTIG, ADOLPH JOHN (Otto)
b.Jan.29,1894 New York,N.Y.

Yr	Cl	Lea	Pos	G	Rec
1922	Phi	A	P	4	1-2
			BRTR		

RETZER, KENNETH LEO
b.Apr.30,1934 Wood River,Ill.

Yr	Cl	Lea	Pos	G	Rec
1961	Was	A	C	16	.340
1962	Was	A	C	109	.285
			BLTR	125	.293

REULBACH, EDWARD MARVIN (Big Ed)
b.Dec.1,1882 Detroit,Mich.
d.July 17,1961

Yr	Cl	Lea	Pos	G	Rec
1905	Chi	N	P	34	17-13
1906	Chi	N	P	34	19-4
1907	Chi	N	P	27	17-4
1908	Chi	N	P	46	24-7
1909	Chi	N	P	35	19-10
1910	Chi	N	P	24	12-8
1911	Chi	N	P	33	16-9
1912	Chi	N	P	39	10-6
1913	Chi	N	P	9	1-3
1913	Bro	N	P	16	7-6
1914	Bro	N	P	44	11-18
1915	New	F	P	33	21-10
1916	Bos	N	P	21	7-6
1917	Bos	N	P	5	0-1
			BRTR	400	181-105

REVELS, ...

Yr	Cl	Lea	Pos	G	Rec
1874	Bal	n	O	1	.000

REXTER, ...

Yr	Cl	Lea	Pos	G	Rec
1875	Atl	n	O	1	.000

REYES, NAPOLEON AGUILERA
b.Nov.24,1919 Oriente Province,Cuba.

Yr	Cl	Lea	Pos	G	Rec
1943	NY	N	1-3	40	.256
1944	NY	N	1-3-O	116	.289
1945	NY	N	1-3	122	.288
1950	NY	N	1	1	.000
			BRTR	279	.284

REYNOLDS, ALLIE PIERCE
b.Feb.10,1915 Bethany,Okla.

Yr	Cl	Lea	Pos	G	Rec
1942	Cle	A	P	2	0-0
1943	Cle	A	P	39	11-12
1944	Cle	A	P	41	11-8
1945	Cle	A	P	44	18-12
1946	Cle	A	P	35	11-15
1947	NY	A	P	38	19-8
1948	NY	A	P	41	16-7
1949	NY	A	P	37	17-6
1950	NY	A	P	36	16-12
1951	NY	A	P	43	17-8
1952	NY	A	P	41	20-8
1953	NY	A	P	42	13-7
1954	NY	A	P	36	13-4
			BRTR	475	182-107

REYNOLDS, CARL NETTLES
b.Feb.1,1903 LaRue,Tex.

Yr	Cl	Lea	Pos	G	Rec
1927	Chi	A	O	14	.214
1928	Chi	A	O	84	.323
1929	Chi	A	O	131	.317
1930	Chi	A	O	138	.359
1931	Chi	A	O	118	.290
1932	Was	A	O	102	.305
1933	St.L	A	O	135	.286
1934	Bos	A	O	113	.303
1935	Bos	A	O	78	.270
1936	Was	A	O	89	.276
1937	Chi	N	O	7	.273
1938	Chi	N	O	125	.302
1939	Chi	N	O	88	.246
			BRTR	1222	.302

REYNOLDS, CHARLES E.
b.July 31,1857 Allegany,N.Y.
d.May 1,1913

Yr	Cl	Lea	Pos	G	Rec
1882	Ath	a	P-O	2	1-1 .125

REYNOLDS, CHARLES L.
b.May 1,1865 Williamsburgh,Ind.

Yr	Cl	Lea	Pos	G	Rec
1889	KC	a	C	1	.250
1889	Bro	a	C	11	.222
				12	.225

REYNOLDS, DANIEL VANCE (Squirrel)
b.Nov.27,1919 Stony Point,N.C.

Yr	Cl	Lea	Pos	G	Rec
1945	Chi	A	2-S	29	.167
			BRTR		

REYNOLDS, E. ROSS
b.Aug.20,1889 Edwards Co.,Tex.

Yr	Cl	Lea	Pos	G	Rec
1914	Det	A	P	20	5-3
1915	Det	A	P	4	0-1
			BRTR	24	5-4

REYNOLDS, WILLIAM D.
b.1888 White Plains,Ga.

Yr	Cl	Lea	Pos	G	Rec
1913	NY	A	C	5	.000
1914	NY	A	C	4	.400
			BRTR	9	.200

RHAWN, ROBERT JOHN (Rocky)
b.Feb.13,1919 Catawissa,Pa.

Yr	Cl	Lea	Pos	G	Rec
1947	NY	N	2-3	13	.311
1948	NY	N	S-3	36	.273
1949	NY	N	2	14	.172
1949	Pit	N	3	3	.143
1949	Chi	A	S-3	24	.205
			BRTR	90	.237

RHEAM, KENNETH JOHNSTON (Cy)
b.Sept.28,1893 Pittsburgh,Pa.
d.Oct.23,1947

Yr	Cl	Lea	Pos	G	Rec
1914	Pit	F	1	72	.209
1915	Pit	F	O	27	.174
			BRTR	99	.201

RHEM, CHARLES FLINT
b.Jan.24,1903 Rhems,S.C.

Yr	Cl	Lea	Pos	G	Rec
1924	St.L	N	P	6	2-2
1925	St.L	N	P	30	8-13
1926	St.L	N	P	34	20-7
1927	St.L	N	P	27	10-12
1928	St.L	N	P	28	11-8
1930	St.L	N	P	26	12-8
1931	St.L	N	P	33	11-10
1932	St.L	N	P	6	4-2
1932	Phi	N	P	26	11-7
1933	Phi	N	P	28	5-14
1934	St.L	N	P	5	1-0
1934	Bos	N	P	25	8-8
1935	Bos	N	P	10	0-5
1936	St.L	N	P	10	2-1
			BRTR	294	105-97

RHIEL, WILLIAM JOSEPH
b.Sept.30,1901 Youngstown,O.
d.Aug.16,1946

Yr	Cl	Lea	Pos	G	Rec
1929	Bro	N	2	76	.278
1930	Bos	N	3	20	.170
1932	Det	A	1-3	84	.280
1933	Det	A	O	19	.176
			BRTR	199	.266

RHINES, WILLIAM PEARL (Bunker)
b.Mar.14,1869 Ridgway,Pa.
d.Jan.30,1922

Yr	Cl	Lea	Pos	G	Rec
1890	Cin	N	P	45	28-17
1891	Cin	N	P	43	16-27
1892	Cin	N	P	12	3-4
1893	Lou	N	P	5	1-3
1895	Cin	N	P	32	20-12

(Continued)

Yr	Cl	Lea	Pos	G	Rec
1896	Cin	N	P	17	10-7
1897	Cin	N	P	36	19-15
1898	Pit	N	P	31	12-15
1899	Pit	N	P	10	4-3
				231	113-103

RHOADES, ROBERT BRUCE (Dusty)
b.Oct.4,1879 Wooster,O.

Yr	Cl	Lea	Pos	G	Rec
1902	Chi	N	P	16	4-7
1903	St.L	N	P	18	5-8
1903	Cle	A	P	5	2-3
1904	Cle	A	P	29	11-9
1905	Cle	A	P	33	17-12
1906	Cle	A	P	38	22-10
1907	Cle	A	P	35	15-14
1908	Cle	A	P	37	18-12
1909	Cle	A	P	20	5-9
			TR	231	99-85

RHODES, CHARLES A. (Dusty)

Yr	Cl	Lea	Pos	G	Rec
1906	St.L	N	P	9	4-5
1908	Cin	N	P	1	0-0
1908	St.L	N	P	4	1-2
1909	St.L	N	P	12	3-5
				26	8-12

RHODES, JAMES LAMAR (Dusty)
b.May 13,1927 Mathews,Ala.

Yr	Cl	Lea	Pos	G	Rec
1952	NY	N	O	67	.250
1953	NY	N	O	76	.233
1954	NY	N	O	82	.341
1955	NY	N	O	94	.305
1956	NY	N	O	111	.217
1957	NY	N	O	92	.205
1959	S.F.	N	H	54	.188
				576	.253

RHODES, JOHN GORDON (Dusty)
b.Aug.11,1907 Salt Lake City,Utah.
d.Mar.22,1960

Yr	Cl	Lea	Pos	G	Rec
1929	NY	A	P	10	0-4
1930	NY	A	P	3	0-0
1931	NY	A	P	18	6-3
1932	NY	A	P	10	1-2
1932	Bos	A	P	12	1-8
1933	Bos	A	P	35	12-15
1934	Bos	A	P	44	12-12
1935	Bos	A	P	36	2-10
1936	Phi	A	P	35	9-20
			BRTR	203	43-74

RHODES, WILLIAM CLARENCE
b.Pottstown,Pa.

Yr	Cl	Lea	Pos	G	Rec
1893	Lou	N	P	17	5-12

RHYNE, HAROLD
b.Mar.30,1899 San Jose,Cal.

Yr	Cl	Lea	Pos	G	Rec
1926	Pit	N	2-S	109	.251
1927	Pit	N	2-3	62	.274
1929	Bos	A	S	120	.252
1930	Bos	A	S	107	.203
1931	Bos	A	S	147	.273
1932	Bos	A	S	71	.227
1933	Chi	A	2-S-3	39	.265
			BRTR	655	.250

RICE, DELBERT W.
b.Oct.27,1922 Portsmouth,O.

Yr	Cl	Lea	Pos	G	Rec
1945	St.L	N	C	83	.261
1946	St.L	N	C	55	.273
1947	St.L	N	C	97	.218
1948	St.L	N	C	100	.197
1949	St.L	N	C	92	.236
1950	St.L	N	C	130	.244
1951	St.L	N	C	122	.251
1952	St.L	N	C	147	.259
1953	St.L	N	C	135	.236
1954	St.L	N	C	56	.252
1955	St.L	N	C	20	.203
1955	Mil	N	C	27	.197
1956	Mil	N	C	71	.213
1957	Mil	N	C	54	.229
1958	Mil	N	C	43	.223
1959	Mil	N	C	13	.207

(Continued)

Yr	Cl	Lea	Pos	G	Rec
1960	Chi	N	C	18	.231
1960	St.L.	N	C	1	.000
1960	Bal	A	C	1	.000
1961	La	A	C	44	.241
	BRTR			1309	.237

RICE, EDGAR CHARLES (Sam)
b.Feb.20,1892 Morocco,Ind.

Yr	Cl	Lea	Pos	G	Rec
1915	Was	A	P	4	1-0
1916	Was	A	P-O	58	0-1 .299
1917	Was	A	O	155	.302
1918	Was	A	O	7	.348
1919	Was	A	O	141	.321
1920	Was	A	O	153	.338
1921	Was	A	O	143	.330
1922	Was	A	O	154	.295
1923	Was	A	O	148	.316
1924	Was	A	O	154	.334
1925	Was	A	O	152	.350
1926	Was	A	O	152	.337
1927	Was	A	O	142	.297
1928	Was	A	O	148	.328
1929	Was	A	O	150	.323
1930	Was	A	O	147	.349
1931	Was	A	O	120	.310
1932	Was	A	O	106	.323
1933	Was	A	O	73	.294
1934	Cle	A	O	97	.293
	BLTR			2404	1-1 .322

RICE, HAROLD HOUSTEN (Hoot)
b.Feb.11,1924 Morganette,W.Va.

Yr	Cl	Lea	Pos	G	Rec
1948	St.L	N	O	8	.323
1949	St.L	N	O	40	.196
1950	St.L	N	O	44	.211
1951	St.L	N	O	69	.254
1952	St.L	N	O	98	.288
1953	St.L	N	H	8	.250
1953	Pit	N	O	78	.311
1954	Pit	N	O	28	.173
1954	Chi	N	O	51	.153
	BLTR			424	.260

RICE, HARRY FRANCIS
b.Nov.22,1901 Anna,Ill.

Yr	Cl	Lea	Pos	G	Rec
1923	St.L	A	H	4	.000
1924	St.L	A	3	44	.279
1925	St.L	A	C-1-2-3-O	103	.359
1926	St.L	A	O	148	.313
1927	St.L	A	O	137	.287
1928	Det	A	O	131	.302
1929	Det	A	O	130	.304
1930	Det	A	O	37	.305
1930	NY	A	O	100	.298
1931	Was	A	O	47	.265
1933	Cin	N	3-O	143	.261
	BLTR			1024	.299

RICE, LEONARD OLIVER
b.Sept.2,1918 Lead,S.Dak.

Yr	Cl	Lea	Pos	G	Rec
1944	Cin	N	C	10	.000
1945	Chi	N	C	32	.232
	BRTR			42	.223

RICE, ROBERT TURNBULL
b.May 28,1900 Philadelphia,Pa.

Yr	Cl	Lea	Pos	G	Rec
1926	Phi	N	3	19	.148
	BRTR				

RICH, WOODROW EARL
b.Mar.9,1917 Morganton,N.C.

Yr	Cl	Lea	Pos	G	Rec
1939	Bos	A	P	21	4-3
1940	Bos	A	P	3	1-0
1941	Bos	A	P	2	0-0
1944	Bos	N	P	7	1-1
	BLTR			33	6-4

RICHARDS, DUANE LEE
b.Dec.16,1936 Randolph Co.,Ind.

Yr	Cl	Lea	Pos	G	Rec
1960	Cin	N	P	2	0-0

RICHARDS, FRED CHARLES
b.Nov.3,1927 Warren,O.

Yr	Cl	Lea	Pos	G	Rec
1951	Chi	N	1	10	.296
	BLTL				

RICHARDS, PAUL RAPIER
b.Nov.21,1908 Waxahachie,Tex.

Yr	Cl	Lea	Pos	G	Rec
1932	Bro	N	C	3	.000
1933	NY	N	C	51	.195
1934	NY	N	C	42	.160
1935	NY	N	C	7	.250
1935	Phi	A	C	85	.245
1943	Det	A	C	100	.220
1944	Det	A	C	95	.237
1945	Det	A	C	83	.256
1946	Det	A	C	57	.201
	BRTR			523	.227

Non-playing manager Chi (A) 1951-54; Bal (A) 1955-58.

RICHARDSON, ----

Yr	Cl	Lea	Pos	G	Rec
1884	Chi	U	2	1	.000

RICHARDSON, ARTHUR HARDING (Hardy)
b.Apr.21,1855 Paulsboro,N.J.
d.Jan.14,1931

Yr	Cl	Lea	Pos	G	Rec
1879	Buf	N	3	78	.278
1880	Buf	N	C-3	80	.252
1881	Buf	N	2-S-O	83	.290
1882	Buf	N	2	83	.271
1883	Buf	N	2	90	.310
1884	Buf	N	1-2-3-O	98	.301
1885	Buf	N	P-2-S-O	96	0-0 .319
1886	Det	N	2-O	125	.351
1887	Det	N	2-O	120	.363
1888	Det	N	2	57	.289
1889	Bos	N	2-O	132	.304
1890	Bos	p	O	130	.332
1891	Bos	a	O	74	.264
1892	Was	N	2	9	.114
1892	NY	N	2-O	61	.223
	BRTR			1316	0-0 .302

RICHARDSON, CLIFFORD NOLEN
b.Jan.18,1903 Chattanooga,Tenn.
d.Sept.25,1951

Yr	Cl	Lea	Pos	G	Rec
1929	Det	A	S	13	.190
1931	Det	A	3	38	.270
1932	Det	A	3	69	.219
1935	NY	A	S	12	.217
1938	Cin	N	S	35	.290
1939	Cin	N	S	1	.000
	BRTR			168	.247

RICHARDSON, DANIEL (Denny)
b.Jan.25,1863 Elmira,N.Y.
d.Sept.15,1926

Yr	Cl	Lea	Pos	G	Rec
1884	NY	N	S-O	70	.259
1885	NY	N	P-3-O	48	5-1 .262
1886	NY	N	P-O	64	0-1 .232
1887	NY	N	2	122	.332
1888	NY	N	2	135	.226
1889	NY	N	2	124	.279
1890	NY	p	2-S	123	.258
1891	NY	N	2	123	.262
1892	Was	N	M-2-S	142	.240
1893	Bro	N	2	51	.246
1894	Lou	N	S	116	.255
	BRTR			1118	5-2 .261

RICHARDSON, JOHN WILLIAM
b.Oct.3,1892 Central City, Ill.

Yr	Cl	Lea	Pos	G	Rec
1915	Phi	A	P	3	0-1
1916	Phi	A	P	1	0-0
	BRTR			4	0-1

RICHARDSON, KENNETH FRANKLIN
b.May 2,1915 Orleans,Ind.

Yr	Cl	Lea	Pos	G	Rec
1942	Phi	A	1-3-O	6	.067
1946	Phi	N	2	6	.150
	BRTR			12	.114

RICHARDSON, ROBERT CLINTON
b.Aug.19,1935 Sumter,S.C.

Yr	Cl	Lea	Pos	G	Rec
1955	NY	A	2-S	11	.154
1956	NY	A	2	5	.143
1957	NY	A	2	97	.256
1958	NY	A	2-S-3	73	.247
1959	NY	A	2-S-3	134	.301
1960	NY	A	2-3	150	.252
1961	NY	A	2	162	.261
1962	NY	A	2	161	.302
	BRTR			793	.274

RICHARDSON, THOMAS MITCHELL
b.Aug.7,1883 Louisville,Ill.
d.Nov.15,1939

Yr	Cl	Lea	Pos	G	Rec
1917	St.L	A	H	1	.000

RICHARDSON, WILLIAM H.
b.Leavenworth,Kan.

Yr	Cl	Lea	Pos	G	Rec
1901	St.L	N	1	15	.211

RICHBOURG, LANCELOT CLAYTON
b.Dec.18,1899 DeFuniak Springs,Fla.

Yr	Cl	Lea	Pos	G	Rec
1921	Phi	N	2	10	.200
1924	Was	A	O	15	.281
1927	Bos	N	O	115	.309
1928	Bos	N	O	148	.337
1929	Bos	N	O	139	.305
1930	Bos	N	O	130	.304
1931	Bos	N	O	97	.287
1932	Chi	N	O	44	.257
	BLTR			698	.308

RICHERT, PETER GERARD
b.Oct.29,1939 Mineola, N.Y.

Yr	Cl	Lea	Pos	G	Rec
1962	LA	N	P	19	5-4
	BLTL				

RICHIE, LEWIS A.
b.Aug.23,1883 Ambler,Pa.
d.Aug.15,1936

Yr	Cl	Lea	Pos	G	Rec
1906	Phi	N	P	33	9-11
1907	Phi	N	P	25	6-6
1908	Phi	N	P	25	7-10
1909	Phi	N	P	11	1-1
1909	Bos	N	P	22	7-7
1910	Bos	N	P	4	0-3
1910	Chi	N	P	28	11-4
1911	Chi	N	P	36	15-11
1912	Chi	N	P	39	16-8
1913	Chi	N	P	16	2-4
	BRTR			242	74-65

RICHMOND, BERYL JUSTICE
b.Aug.24,1908 Glen Easton,W.Va.

Yr	Cl	Lea	Pos	G	Rec
1933	Chi	N	P	5	0-0
1934	Cin	N	P	6	1-2
	BBTL			11	1-2

RICHMOND, DONALD LESTER
b.Oct.27,1919 Gillett,Pa.

Yr	Cl	Lea	Pos	G	Rec
1941	Phi	A	3	9	.200
1946	Phi	A	3	16	.290
1947	Phi	A	2-3	19	.190
1951	St.L	N	3	12	.088
	BLTR			56	.211

RICHMOND, JOHN H.
b.Philadelphia,Pa.

Yr	Cl	Lea	Pos	G	Rec
1875	Ath	n	C-2-O	27	.213
1879	Syr	N	S-O	61	.211
1880	Bos	N	S-O	31	.248
1881	Bos	N	S-O	26	.275
1882	Cle	N	O	39	.154
1882	Ath	a	O	19	.173
1893	Bro	N	2	51	.246
1894	Lou	N	S	116	.255
	BRTR			1118	5-2 .261

RICHMOND, JOHN LEE
b.May 5,1857 Sheffield,O.
d.Sept.30,1929

Yr	Cl	Lea	Pos	G	Rec
1879	Bos	N	P	1	1-0
1880	Wor	N	P-O	75	31-33 .224
1881	Wor	N	P-O	60	25-27 .251
1882	Wor	N	P-O	55	14-33 .280
1883	Pro	N	P-O	48	3-8 .283
1886	Cin	a	P-O	8	0-1 .260
	TL			247	74-102 .258

RICHMOND, RAYMOND S.
b.June 5,1896 Fillmore,Ill.

Yr	Cl	Lea	Pos	G	Rec
1920	St.L	A	P	2	2-0
1921	St.L	A	P	6	0-1
	BRTR			8	2-1

RICHTER, ALLEN GORDON
b.Feb.7,1928 Norfolk,Va.

Yr	Cl	Lea	Pos	G	Rec
1951	Bos	A	S	5	.091
1953	Bos	A	S	1	.000
	BRTR			6	.091

RICHTER, EMIL HENRY (Reggie)
b.Sept.14,1889 Dusseldorf,Germany
d.Aug.3,1934

Yr	Cl	Lea	Pos	G	Rec
1911	Chi	N	P	22	1-3
	BRTR				

RICHTER, JOHN M.
b.Louisville,Ky.

Yr	Cl	Lea	Pos	G	Rec
1898	Lou	N	3	3	.154

RICKERT, JOSEPH FRANCIS
b.Dec.12,1876 London,O.
d.Oct.15,1943

Yr	Cl	Lea	Pos	G	Rec
1898	Pit	N	O	2	.167
1901	Bos	N	O	13	.175
				15	.174

RICKERT, MARVIN AUGUST
b.Jan.8,1921 Long Branch,Wash.

Yr	Cl	Lea	Pos	G	Rec
1942	Chi	N	O	8	.269
1946	Chi	N	O	111	.263
1947	Chi	N	1-O	71	.146
1948	Cin	N	H	8	.167
1948	Bos	N	O	3	.231
1949	Bos	N	1-O	100	.292
1950	Pit	N	O	17	.150
1950	Chi	A	1-O	84	.237
	BLTR			402	.247

RICKETTS, RICHARD JAMES
b.Dec.4,1933 Pottstown,Pa.

Yr	Cl	Lea	Pos	G	Rec
1959	St.L	N	P	12	1-6

RICKEY, WESLEY BRANCH
b.Dec.20,1881 Lucasville,O.

Yr	Cl	Lea	Pos	G	Rec
1905	St.L	A	C	1	.000
1906	St.L	A	C	64	.284
1907	NY	A	C-O	52	.182
1914	St.L	A	M-H	2	.000
	BLTR			119	.239

Non-playing manager St.L (A) 1913-15 and St.L (N) 1919-25.

RICKLEY, CHRISTOPHER
b.Philadelphia,Pa.

Yr	Cl	Lea	Pos	G	Rec
1884	Key	U	S	7	.207

RICKS, JOHN

Yr	Cl	Lea	Pos	G	Rec
1891	St.L	a	3	5	.158
1894	St.L	N	3	1	.000
				6	.150

RICO, ARTHUR RAYMOND
b.July 23,1896 Roxbury,Mass.
d.Jan.3,1919

Yr	Cl	Lea	Pos	G	Rec
1916	Bos	N	C	4	.000
1917	Bos	N	C	13	.286
	BRTR			17	.222

RICONDA, HARRY PAUL
b.Mar.17,1897 New York,N.Y.
d.Nov.15,1958

Yr	Cl	Lea	Pos	G	Rec
1923	Phi	A	3	55	.263
1924	Phi	A	3	83	.253
1926	Bos	N	3	4	.167
1928	Bro	N	2-S-3	92	.224
1929	Pit	N	S	8	.467
1930	Cin	N	H	1	.000
	BRTR			243	.243

RIDDLE, ELMER RAY
b.July 31,1914 Columbus,Ga.

Yr	Cl	Lea	Pos	G	Rec
1939	Cin	N	P	1	0-0
1940	Cin	N	P	15	1-2
1941	Cin	N	P	33	19-4
1942	Cin	N	P	29	7-11
1943	Cin	N	P	36	21-11
1944	Cin	N	P	4	2-2
1945	Cin	N	P	12	1-4
1947	Cin	N	P	16	1-0
1948	Pit	N	P	29	12-10
1949	Pit	N	P	16	1-8
	BRTR			191	65-52

RIDDLE, JOHN H.
b.Philadelphia,Pa.

Yr	Cl	Lea	Pos	G	Rec
1889	Was	N	C	11	.210
1890	Ath	a	C-O	25	.115
				36	.147

RIDDLE, JOHN LUDY (Mutt)
b.Oct.3,1905 Clinton,S.C.

Yr	Cl	Lea	Pos	G	Rec
1930	Chi	A	C	25	.241
1937	Was	A	C	8	.269
1937	Bos	N	C	2	.000
1938	Bos	N	C	19	.281
1941	Cin	N	C	10	.300
1944	Cin	N	C	1	.000
1945	Cin	N	C	23	.178
1948	Pit	N	C	10	.200
	BRTR			98	.238

RIDDLEMOSER, DORSEY LEE
b.Mar.25,1875 Frederick,Md.
d.May 11,1954

Yr	Cl	Lea	Pos	G	Rec
1899	Was	N	P	1	0-0

RIDGEWAY, JOHN A.
b.1891 Philadelphia,Pa.

Yr	Cl	Lea	Pos	G	Rec
1914	Bal	F	P	4	0-0
	BLTR				

RIDZIK, STEPHEN GEORGE
b.Apr.29,1929 Yonkers,N.Y.

Yr	Cl	Lea	Pos	G	Rec
1950	Phi	N	P	1	0-0
1952	Phi	N	P	24	4-2
1953	Phi	N	P	42	9-6
1954	Phi	N	P	35	4-5
1955	Phi	N	P	3	0-1
1955	Cin	N	P	13	0-3
1956	NY	N	P	44	6-2
1957	NY	N	P	16	0-2
1958	Cle	A	P	6	0-2
	BRTR			184	23-23

RIEBE, HARVEY DONALD (Hank)
b.Oct.10,1921 Euclid,O.

Yr	Cl	Lea	Pos	G	Rec
1942	Det	A	C	11	.314
1947	Det	A	C	8	.000
1948	Det	A	C	25	.194
1949	Det	A	C	17	.182
	BRTR			61	.212

RIEGER, ELMER JAY
b.Feb.25,1889 Perris,Cal.
d.Oct.21,1959

Yr	Cl	Lea	Pos	G	Rec
1910	St.L	N	P	13	0-2
	TR				

RIGGERT, JOSEPH ALOYSIUS
b.Dec.11,1886 Janesville,Wis.

Yr	Cl	Lea	Pos	G	Rec
1911	Bos	A	O	50	.212
1914	Bro	N	O	27	.190
1914	St.L	N	O	34	.216
1919	Bos	N	O	63	.283
	BRTR			174	.240

RIGGS, LEWIS SIDNEY
b.Apr.22,1910 Mebane,N.C.

Yr	Cl	Lea	Pos	G	Rec
1934	St.L	N	H	2	.000
1935	Cin	N	3	142	.278
1936	Cin	N	3	141	.257
1937	Cin	N	2-S-3	122	.242
1938	Cin	N	3	142	.252
1939	Cin	N	3	22	.158
1940	Cin	N	3	41	.292
1941	Bro	N	1-2-3	77	.305
1942	Bro	N	1-3	70	.278
1946	Bro	N	3	1	.000
	BLTR			760	.262

RIGNEY, EMORY ELMO (Topper)
b.Jan.7,1897 Groveton,Tex.

Yr	Cl	Lea	Pos	G	Rec
1922	Det	A	S	155	.300
1923	Det	A	S	129	.315
1924	Det	A	S	147	.289
1925	Det	A	S-3	62	.247
1926	Bos	A	S	148	.270
1927	Bos	A	3	7	.118
1927	Was	A	S-3	46	.271
	BRTR			694	.288

RIGNEY, JOHN DUNGAN
b.Oct.28,1914 Oak Park,Ill.

Yr	Cl	Lea	Pos	G	Rec
1937	Chi	A	P	22	2-5
1938	Chi	A	P	38	9-9
1939	Chi	A	P	35	15-8
1940	Chi	A	P	40	15-18
1941	Chi	A	P	30	13-13
1942	Chi	A	P	7	3-3
1946	Chi	A	P	15	5-5
1947	Chi	A	P	11	2-3
	BRTR			198	64-64

RIGNEY, WILLIAM JOSEPH (Specs)
b.Jan.29,1918 Alameda, Cal.

Yr	Cl	Lea	Pos	G	Rec
1946	NY	N	S-3	110	.236
1947	NY	N	2-S-3	130	.267
1948	NY	N	2-S	113	.264
1949	NY	N	2-S-3	122	.278
1950	NY	N	2-3	56	.181
1951	NY	N	2-3	44	.232
1952	NY	N	1-2-S-3	60	.300
1953	NY	N	2-3	19	.250
	BRTR			654	.259

Non-playing manager NY (N) 1956-57, SF (N) 1958-60 and LA (A) 1961-62

RIKARD, CULLEY
b.May 9,1915 Oxford,Miss.

Yr	Cl	Lea	Pos	G	Rec
1941	Pit	N	O	6	.200
1942	Pit	N	O	38	.192
1947	Pit	N	O	109	.287
	BLTR			153	.270

RILEY, JAMES JOSEPH
b.Nov.10,1886 Buffalo,N.Y.
d.Mar.25,1949

Yr	Cl	Lea	Pos	G	Rec
1910	Bos	N	O	1	.000
	TR				

RILEY, JAMES NORMAN
b.May 25,1897 Bayfield,N.B.,Canada.

Yr	Cl	Lea	Pos	G	Rec
1921	St.L	A	3	4	.000
1923	Was	A	1	2	.000
	BLTR			6	.000

RILEY, LEON FRANCIS
b.Aug.20,1906 Princeton,Neb.

Yr	Cl	Lea	Pos	G	Rec
1944	Phi	N	O	4	.083
	BLTR				

RILEY, WILLIAM J. (Pigtail)
b.Nov.1853 Philadelphia,Pa.
d.Nov.9,1887

Yr	Cl	Lea	Pos	G	Rec
1875	Wes	n	O	8	NR
1879	Cle	N	O	43	.142
				51	NR

RING, JAMES JOSEPH
b.Feb.15,1895 Brooklyn,N.Y.

Yr	Cl	Lea	Pos	G	Rec
1917	Cin	N	P	24	3-7
1918	Cin	N	P	21	9-5
1919	Cin	N	P	32	10-9
1920	Cin	N	P	42	17-16
1921	Phi	N	P	34	10-19
1922	Phi	N	P	40	12-18
1923	Phi	N	P	41	18-16
1924	Phi	N	P	32	10-12
1925	Phi	N	P	38	14-16
1926	NY	N	P	39	11-10
1927	St.L	N	P	13	0-4
1928	Phi	N	P	35	4-17
			BRTR	391	118-149

RINGO, FRANK C
b.Oct.12,1861 Liberty,Mo.
d.Apr.12,1889

Yr	Cl	Lea	Pos	G	Rec
1883	Phi	N	C-2-S-3-O	57	.183
1884	Phi	N	C	25	.132
1884	Ath	a	C	2	.000
1885	Det	N	C-3-O	16	.246
1885	Pit	a	C	3	.182
1886	Pit	a	C	16	.241
1886	KC	N	C	16	.232
				135	.193

RINKER, ROBERT JOHN
b.Apr.21,1923 Audenried,Pa.

Yr	Cl	Lea	Pos	G	Rec
1950	Phi	A	C	3	.333
			BRTR		

RIPLEY, WALTER FRANKLIN
b.Nov.26,1916 Worcester,Mass.

Yr	Cl	Lea	Pos	G	Rec
1935	Bos	A	P	2	0-0
			BRTR		

RIPPAY, BENJAMIN WESLEY
(Played under name of Charles Wesley Jones)

RIPPLE, CHARLES DAWSON
b.Dec.1,1921 Bolton,N.C.

Yr	Cl	Lea	Pos	G	Rec
1944	Phi	N	P	1	0-0
1945	Phi	N	P	4	0-1
1946	Phi	N	P	6	1-0
			BLTL	11	1-1

RIPPLE, JAMES ALBERT
b.Oct.14,1909 Export,Pa.
d.July 16,1959

Yr	Cl	Lea	Pos	G	Rec
1936	NY	N	O	96	.305
1937	NY	N	O	121	.317
1938	NY	N	O	134	.261
1939	NY	N	O	66	.228
1939	Bro	N	O	28	.330
1940	Bro	N	O	7	.231
1940	Cin	N	O	32	.307
1941	Cin	N	O	38	.216
1943	Phi	A	O	32	.238
			BBTR	554	.282

RIPPLEMEYER, RAYMOND

Yr	Cl	Lea	Pos	G	Rec
1962	Was	A	P	18	1-2

RISBERG, CHARLES AUGUST (Swede)
b.Oct.13,1894 San Francisco,Cal.

Yr	Cl	Lea	Pos	G	Rec
1917	Chi	A	S	149	.203
1918	Chi	A	2-S-3	82	.256
1919	Chi	A	1-S	119	.256
1920	Chi	A	S	126	.266
			BRTR	476	.243

RISING, PERRY SUMNER (Pop)
b.Industry,Pa.

Yr	Cl	Lea	Pos	G	Rec
1905	Bos	A	O	11	.100

RITCHEY, CLAUDE CASSIUS
b.Oct.5,1873 Emlenton,Pa.
d.Nov.8,1951

Yr	Cl	Lea	Pos	G	Rec
1897	Cin	N	S-O	100	.288
1898	Lou	N	2-S	152	.259
1899	Lou	N	2	147	.309
1900	Pit	N	2	123	.295

(Continued)

Yr	Cl	Lea	Pos	G	Rec
1901	Pit	N	2	140	.298
1902	Pit	N	2-O	114	.275
1903	Pit	N	2	137	.287
1904	Pit	N	2	156	.263
1905	Pit	N	2	153	.255
1906	Pit	N	2	151	.269
1907	Bos	N	2	144	.255
1908	Bos	N	2	120	.273
1909	Bos	N	2	25	.172
			BLTR	1662	.276

RITTER, ...

Yr	Cl	Lea	Pos	G	Rec
1885	Buf	N	2	2	.167

RITTER, ...
b.Columbus,O.

Yr	Cl	Lea	Pos	G	Rec
1890	Tol	a	C	1	.000

RITTER, LOUIS ELMER (Old Dog)
b.Sept.7,1875 Liverpool,Pa.
d.May 27,1952

Yr	Cl	Lea	Pos	G	Rec
1902	Bro	N	C	16	.250
1903	Bro	N	C	75	.236
1904	Bro	N	C	63	.248
1905	Bro	N	C	90	.219
1906	Bro	N	C	67	.208
1907	Bro	N	C	89	.203
1908	Bro	N	C	37	.192
			TR	437	.221

RITTER, WILLIAM HERBERT (Hank)
b.Oct.12,1893 McCoysville,Pa.

Yr	Cl	Lea	Pos	G	Rec
1912	Phi	N	P	3	0-0
1914	NY	N	P	1	1-0
1915	NY	N	P	22	2-1
1916	NY	N	P	3	1-0
			BRTR	29	4-1

RITTERSON, E. W.

Yr	Cl	Lea	Pos	G	Rec
1876	Ath	N	C	15	.250
			BRTR		

RITZ, JAMES L.
b.1874 Pittsburgh,Pa.
d.Nov.10,1896

Yr	Cl	Lea	Pos	G	Rec
1894	Pit	N	3	1	.000

RIVERA, MANUEL JOSEPH (Jim)
b.July 22,1922 Brooklyn,N.Y.

Yr	Cl	Lea	Pos	G	Rec
1952	St.L	A	O	97	.256
1952	Chi	A	O	53	.249
1953	Chi	A	O	156	.259
1954	Chi	A	O	145	.286
1955	Chi	A	O	147	.264
1956	Chi	A	O	139	.255
1957	Chi	A	1-O	125	.256
1958	Chi	A	O	116	.225
1959	Chi	A	O	80	.220
1960	Chi	A	O	48	.294
1961	Chi	A	H	1	.000
1961	KC	A	O	64	.241
			BLTL	1171	.256

RIVIERE, ARTHUR BERNARD (Tink)
b.Aug.2,1899 Liberty,Tex.

Yr	Cl	Lea	Pos	G	Rec
1921	St.L	N	P	18	1-0
1925	Chi	A	P	3	0-0
			BRTR	21	1-0

RIXEY, EPPA (Jeptha)
b.May 3,1891 Culpeper,Va.
d.Feb.28,1963

Yr	Cl	Lea	Pos	G	Rec
1912	Phi	N	P	23	10-10
1913	Phi	N	P	35	9-5
1914	Phi	N	P	24	2-11
1915	Phi	N	P	29	11-12
1916	Phi	N	P	38	22-10
1917	Phi	N	P	39	16-21
1919	Phi	N	P	23	6-12
1920	Phi	N	P	43	11-22
1921	Cin	N	P	40	19-18
1922	Cin	N	P	40	25-13
1923	Cin	N	P	42	20-15
1924	Cin	N	P	35	15-14
1925	Cin	N	P	39	21-11

(Continued)

Yr	Cl	Lea	Pos	G	Rec
1926	Cin	N	P	37	14-8
1927	Cin	N	P	34	12-10
1928	Cin	N	P	43	19-18
1929	Cin	N	P	35	10-13
1930	Cin	N	P	32	9-13
1931	Cin	N	P	22	4-7
1932	Cin	N	P	25	5-5
1933	Cin	N	P	16	6-3
			BRTL	694	266-251

RIZZO, JOHN COSTA
b.July 30,1912 Houston,Tex.

Yr	Cl	Lea	Pos	G	Rec
1938	Pit	N	O	143	.301
1939	Pit	N	O	94	.261
1940	Pit	N	O	9	.179
1940	Cin	N	O	31	.282
1940	Phi	N	O	103	.292
1941	Phi	N	3-O	99	.217
1942	Bro	N	O	78	.230
			BRTR	557	.270

RIZZUTO, PHILIP FRANCIS (Scooter)
b.Sept.25,1918 Glendale,L.I.,N.Y.

Yr	Cl	Lea	Pos	G	Rec
1941	NY	A	S	133	.307
1942	NY	A	S	144	.284
1946	NY	A	S	126	.257
1947	NY	A	S	153	.273
1948	NY	A	S	128	.252
1949	NY	A	S	153	.275
1950	NY	A	S	155	.324
1951	NY	A	S	144	.274
1952	NY	A	S	152	.254
1953	NY	A	S	134	.271
1954	NY	A	2-S	127	.195
1955	NY	A	2-S	81	.259
1956	NY	A	S	31	.231
			BRTR	1661	.273

ROACH, JAMES MICHAEL (Mike)
b.1876 New York,N.Y.
d.Nov.12,1916

Yr	Cl	Lea	Pos	G	Rec
1899	Was	N	C	21	.237

ROACH, JOHN F.
b.Athens,Pa.
d.Mar.1,1915

Yr	Cl	Lea	Pos	G	Rec
1887	NY	N	P	1	0-1
			TL		

ROACH, MELVIN EARL
b.Jan.25,1933 Richmond,Va.

Yr	Cl	Lea	Pos	G	Rec
1953	Mil	N	2	5	.000
1954	Mil	N	1	3	.000
1957	Mil	N	2	7	.167
1958	Mil	N	1-2-O	44	.309
1959	Mil	N	2-3-O	19	.097
1960	Mil	N	1-2-3-O	48	.300
1961	Mil	N	1-O	13	.167
1961	Chi	N	1-2	23	.128
1962	Phi	N	1-2-S-3-O	65	.190
			BRTR	227	.239

ROACH, SKEL
(Real name Rudolph C. Weichbrodt)
b.Oct.20,1871 Chicago,Ill.

Yr	Cl	Lea	Pos	G	Rec
1899	Chi	N	P	1	1-0

ROACH, WILBUR C. (Roxy)
b.Nov.28,1884 Morrisdale Mines,Pa.
d.Dec.25,1947

Yr	Cl	Lea	Pos	G	Rec
1910	NY	A	S	70	.214
1911	NY	A	S	12	.250
1912	Was	A	S	2	.500
1915	Buf	F	S	92	.270
			BRTR	176	.249

ROARKE, MICHAEL THOMAS
b.Nov.8,1930 W.Warwick,R.I.

Yr	Cl	Lea	Pos	G	Rec
1961	Det	A	C	86	.223
1962	Det	A	C	56	.213
			BRTR	142	.219

ROAT, FREDERICK
b.Feb.10,1868 Oregon,Ill.

Yr	Cl	Lea	Pos	G	Rec
1890	Pit	N	3	57	.223
1892	Chi	N	2	8	.200
				65	.220

ROBELLO, THOMAS VARDASCO
b.Feb.9,1913 Oakland,Cal.

Yr	Cl	Lea	Pos	G	Rec
1933	Cin	N	2-3	14	.233
1934	Cin	N	H	2	.000
	BRTR			16	.219

ROBERGE, JOSEPH ALBERT ARMAND (Skippy)
b.May 19,1917 Lowell,Mass.

Yr	Cl	Lea	Pos	G	Rec
1941	Bos	N	2-S-3	55	.216
1942	Bos	N	2-3	74	.215
1946	Bos	N	3	48	.231
	BRTR			177	.220

ROBERTAILLE, ANTHONY F. (Chick)
b.Mar.2,1879 Whitehall,N.Y.
d.July 30,1947

Yr	Cl	Lea	Pos	G	Rec
1904	Pit	N	P	9	5-3
1905	Pit	N	P	17	7-6
				26	12-9

ROBERTS, CHARLES EMORY (Red)
b.Aug.8,1918 Carrollton,Ga.

Yr	Cl	Lea	Pos	G	Rec
1943	Was	A	S-3	9	.261
	BRTR				

ROBERTS, CHESTER A. (Skipper)
b.Jan.11,1888 Kellogg,Ida.

Yr	Cl	Lea	Pos	G	Rec
1913	St.L	N	C	26	.146
1914	Pit	F	C	32	.226
1914	Chi	F	C	4	.333
1914	Pit	F	C	18	.228
	BLTR			80	.210

ROBERTS, CURTIS BENJAMIN
b.Aug.16,1929 Pineland,Tex.

Yr	Cl	Lea	Pos	G	Rec
1954	Pit	N	2	134	.232
1955	Pit	N	2	6	.118
1956	Pit	N	2	31	.177
	BRTR			171	.223

ROBERTS, DAVID LEONARD
b.June 30,1934 Panama City,Panama

Yr	Cl	Lea	Pos	G	Rec
1962	Hou	N	1-O	16	.245

ROBERTS, JAMES NEWSOM
b.Oct.13,1897 Artesia,Miss.

Yr	Cl	Lea	Pos	G	Rec
1924	Bro	N	P	11	0-3
1925	Bro	N	P	1	0-0
	BRTR			12	0-3

ROBERTS, RAYMOND
b.Aug.25,1896 Cruger,Miss.

Yr	Cl	Lea	Pos	G	Rec
1919	Phi	A	P	3	0-2
	BLTR				

ROBERTS, ROBIN EVAN
b.Sept.30,1926 Springfield,Ill.

Yr	Cl	Lea	Pos	G	Rec
1948	Phi	N	P	21	7-9
1949	Phi	N	P	43	15-15
1950	Phi	N	P	40	20-11
1951	Phi	N	P	44	21-15
1952	Phi	N	P	39	28-7
1953	Phi	N	P	44	23-16
1954	Phi	N	P	45	23-15
1955	Phi	N	P	51	23-14
1956	Phi	N	P	43	19-18
1957	Phi	N	P	39	10-22
1958	Phi	N	P	36	17-14
1959	Phi	N	P	35	15-17
1960	Phi	N	P	35	12-16
1961	Phi	N	P	26	1-10
1962	Bal	A	P	27	10-9
	BBTR			568	244-208

ROBERTS, THOMAS
b.Baltimore,Md.

Yr	Cl	Lea	Pos	G	Rec
1874	Atl	n	O	1	.000

ROBERTSON, ALFRED JAMES (Jim)
b.Jan.29,1928 Chicago,Ill.

Yr	Cl	Lea	Pos	G	Rec
1954	Phi	A	C	63	.184
1955	KC	A	C	6	.250
	BRTR			69	.187

ROBERTSON, CHARLES CULBERTSON
b.Jan.31,1897 Sherman,Tex.

Yr	Cl	Lea	Pos	G	Rec
1919	Chi	A	P	1	0-1
1922	Chi	A	P	37	14-15
1923	Chi	A	P	38	13-18
1924	Chi	A	P	17	4-10
1925	Chi	A	P	24	8-12
1926	St.L	A	P	8	1-2
1927	Bos	N	P	28	7-17
1928	Bos	N	P	13	2-5
	BLTR			166	49-80

ROBERTSON, DARYL BERDENE
b.Jan.5,1936 Cripple Creek,Colo.

Yr	Cl	Lea	Pos	G	Rec
1962	Chi	N	S-3	9	.105
	BRTR				

ROBERTSON, DAVIS AYDELOTTE
b.June 10,1889 Norfolk,Va.

Yr	Cl	Lea	Pos	G	Rec
1912	NY	N	1-O	3	.000
1914	NY	N	O	82	.266
1915	NY	N	O	141	.294
1916	NY	N	O	150	.307
1917	NY	N	O	142	.259
1919	NY	N	O	1	.000
1919	Chi	N	O	27	.208
1920	Chi	N	O	134	.300
1921	Chi	N	O	22	.222
1921	Pit	N	O	60	.322
1922	NY	N	O	42	.276
	BLTL			804	.287

ROBERTSON, DONALD ALEXANDER
b.Oct.15,1930 Harvey,Ill.

Yr	Cl	Lea	Pos	G	Rec
1954	Chi	N	O	14	.000
	BLTL				

ROBERTSON, EUGENE EDWARD
b.Dec.25,1899 St.Louis,Mo.

Yr	Cl	Lea	Pos	G	Rec
1922	St.L	A	S-3	18	.296
1923	St.L	A	3	78	.247
1924	St.L	A	3	121	.319
1925	St.L	A	S-3	154	.271
1926	St.L	A	S-3	78	.251
1928	NY	A	3	83	.291
1929	NY	A	3	90	.298
1929	Bos	N	3	8	.286
1930	Bos	N	3	21	.186
	BLTR			651	.280

ROBERTSON, JOHN HENRY
(Played under name of John Henry Robinson)

ROBERTSON, RICHARD J.
b.1891 Washington,D.C.

Yr	Cl	Lea	Pos	G	Rec
1913	Cin	N	P	2	0-1
1918	Bro	N	P	14	3-6
1919	Was	A	P	7	0-2
	BRTR			23	3-9

ROBERTSON, SHERRARD ALEXANDER
b.Jan.1,1919 Montreal,Que.,Canada.

Yr	Cl	Lea	Pos	G	Rec
1940	Was	A	S	10	.212
1941	Was	A	3	1	.000
1943	Was	A	S-3	59	.217
1946	Was	A	2-S-3-O	74	.200
1947	Was	A	2-3-O	95	.233
1948	Was	A	O	71	.246
1949	Was	A	2-3-O	110	.251
1950	Was	A	2-3-O	71	.260
1951	Was	A	O	62	.189
1952	Was	A	H	1	.000
1952	Phi	A	2-3-O	43	.200
	BLTR			597	.230

ROBINSON, AARON ANDREW
b.June 23,1916 Lancaster,S.C.

Yr	Cl	Lea	Pos	G	Rec
1943	NY	A	H	1	.000
1945	NY	A	C	50	.281
1946	NY	A	C	100	.297
1947	NY	A	C	82	.270
1948	Chi	A	C	98	.252
1949	Det	A	C	110	.269
1950	Det	A	C	107	.226
1951	Det	A	C	36	.207
1951	Bos	A	C	26	.203
	BLTR			610	.260

ROBINSON, A. V.

Yr	Cl	Lea	Pos	G	Rec
1872	Oly	n	O	7	NR

ROBINSON, BROOKS CALBERT
b.May 18,1937 Little Rock,Ark.

Yr	Cl	Lea	Pos	G	Rec
1955	Bal	A	3	6	.091
1956	Bal	A	2-3	15	.227
1957	Bal	A	3	50	.239
1958	Bal	A	2-3	145	.238
1959	Bal	A	2-3	88	.284
1960	Bal	A	2-3	152	.294
1961	Bal	A	2-S-3	163	.287
1962	Bal	A	2-S-3	162	.303
	BRTR			781	.279

ROBINSON, CHARLES HENRY
b.July 27,1856 Westerly,R.I.
d.May 18,1913

Yr	Cl	Lea	Pos	G	Rec
1884	Ind	a	C-S-O	19	.286
1885	Bro	a	C	12	.143
				31	.241

ROBINSON, CLYDE (Rabbit)
b.Ashtabula,O.
d.Apr.16,1915

Yr	Cl	Lea	Pos	G	Rec
1903	Was	A	2-S-O	103	.219
1904	Det	A	2-S-3-O	97	.204
1910	Cin	N	3	2	.000
	TR			202	.230

ROBINSON, EARL JOHN
b.Nov.3,1936 New Orleans,La.

Yr	Cl	Lea	Pos	G	Rec
1958	LA	N	3	8	.200
1961	Bal	A	O	96	.266
1962	Bal	A	O	29	.286
	BRTR				

ROBINSON, FLOYD ANDREW
b.May 9,1936 Prescott,Ark.

Yr	Cl	Lea	Pos	G	Rec
1960	Chi	A	O	22	.283
1961	Chi	A	O	132	.310
1962	Chi	A	O	156	.312
	BLTL				

ROBINSON, FRANK
b.Aug.31,1935 Beaumont,Tex.

Yr	Cl	Lea	Pos	G	Rec
1956	Cin	N	O	152	.290
1957	Cin	N	1-O	150	.322
1958	Cin	N	3-O	148	.269
1959	Cin	N	1-O	146	.311
1960	Cin	N	1-3-O	139	.297
1961	Cin	N	3-O	153	.323
1962	Cin	N	O	162	.342
	BRTR			000	.000

ROBINSON, FREDERIC HENRY
b.July 6,1856 South Acton,Mass.
d.Dec.18,1933

Yr	Cl	Lea	Pos	G	Rec
1884	Cin	U	2	3	.231
	BRTR				

ROBINSON, HUMBERTO VALENTINO
b.June 25,1930 Colon,Panama

Yr	Cl	Lea	Pos	G	Rec
1955	Mil	N	P	13	3-1
1956	Mil	N	P	1	0-0
1958	Mil	N	P	19	2-4
1959	Cle	A	P	5	1-0
1959	Phi	N	P	33	0-4
1960	Phi	N	P	33	0-4
	BRTR			102	8-13

ROBINSON, JACK ROOSEVELT
b.Jan.31,1919 Cairo,Ga.

Yr	Cl	Lea	Pos	G	Rec
1947	Bro	N	1	151	.296
1948	Bro	N	1-2	147	.296
1949	Bro	N	2	156	.342
1950	Bro	N	2	144	.328
1951	Bro	N	2	153	.338
1952	Bro	N	2	149	.308
1953	Bro	N	1-2-S-3-O	136	.329
1954	Bro	N	2-3-O	124	.311
1955	Bro	N	1-2-3-O	105	.256
1956	Bro	N	1-2-3-O	117	.275
		BRTR		1382	.311

ROBINSON, JOHN (Bridgeport)
b.E.Greenwich,Conn.

Yr	Cl	Lea	Pos	G	Rec
1902	NY	N	C	4	.000
		TR			

ROBINSON, JOHN EDWARD
b.Feb.20,1921 Orange,N.J.

Yr	Cl	Lea	Pos	G	Rec
1949	Bos	A	P	3	0-0
		BRTR			

ROBINSON, JOHN HENRY (Hank)
(Real name John Henry Robertson)
b.Aug.16,1889 Floyd,Ark.

Yr	Cl	Lea	Pos	G	Rec
1911	Pit	N	P	5	0-1
1912	Pit	N	P	33	12-7
1913	Pit	N	P	43	14-9
1914	St.L	N	P	26	7-8
1915	St.L	N	P	32	7-8
1918	NY	A	P	11	2-4
		BRTL		150	42-37

ROBINSON, WILBERT (Uncle Robbie)
b.June 29,1864 Bolton,Mass.
d.Aug.8,1934

Yr	Cl	Lea	Pos	G	Rec
1886	Ath	a	C-1	87	.205
1887	Ath	a	C	68	.286
1888	Ath	a	C	67	.268
1889	Ath	a	C	69	.242
1890	Ath	a	C	83	.236
1890	Bal	a	C-1	14	.271
1891	Bal	a	C	93	.221
1892	Bal	N	C	83	.270
1893	Bal	N	C	91	.338
1894	Bal	N	C	106	.348
1895	Bal	N	C	74	.264
1896	Bal	N	C	66	.354
1897	Bal	N	C	47	.313
1898	Bal	N	C	77	.276
1899	Bal	N	C	105	.284
1900	St.L	N	C	56	.255
1901	Bal	A	C	71	.298
1902	Bal	A	M-C	90	.292
		BRTR		1347	.286

Non-playing manager Bro (N) 1914-31.

ROBINSON, WILLIAM EDWARD (Eddie)
b.Dec.15,1920 Paris,Tex.

Yr	Cl	Lea	Pos	G	Rec
1942	Cle	A	1	8	.125
1946	Cle	A	1	7	.467
1947	Cle	A	1	95	.245
1948	Cle	A	1	134	.254
1949	Was	A	1	143	.294
1950	Was	A	1	36	.240
1950	Chi	A	1	119	.311
1951	Chi	A	1	151	.282
1952	Chi	A	1	155	.296
1953	Phi	A	1	156	.247
1954	NY	A	1	85	.261
1955	NY	A	1	88	.208
1956	NY	A	1	26	.222
1956	KC	A	1	75	.198
1957	Det	A	H	13	.000
1957	Cle	A	1	19	.222
1957	Bal	A	H	4	.000
		BLTR		1314	.268

ROBINSON, WILLIAM H. (Yank)
b.Sept.19,1859 Philadelphia,Pa.
d.Aug.25,1894

Yr	Cl	Lea	Pos	G	Rec
1882	Det	N	P-S-O	11	0-0 .162
1884	Bal	U	P-C-S-3	98	2-3 .269
1885	St.L	a	C-2-O	78	.259
1886	St.L	a	P-2	133	0-1 .279
1887	St.L	a	2	124	.426
1888	St.L	a	2-S	134	.231
1889	St.L	a	2	132	.210
1890	Pit	p	2	98	.239
1891	Cin	a	2-S	97	.178
1892	Was	N	3	64	.180
		BRTR		969	2-4 .262

ROBISON, MATTHEW STANLEY
b.1857 Dubuque,Ia.
d.Mar.24,1911
Non-playing manager St L (N) 1905.

ROCAP, ADAM
b.1854 Philadelphia,Pa.
d.Mar.29,1892

Yr	Cl	Lea	Pos	G	Rec
1875	Ath	n	2-O	13	.186

ROCCO, MICHAEL DOMINIC
b.Mar.2,1916 St.Paul,Minn.

Yr	Cl	Lea	Pos	G	Rec
1943	Cle	A	1	108	.240
1944	Cle	A	1	155	.266
1945	Cle	A	1	143	.264
1946	Cle	A	1	34	.245
		BLTL		440	.258

ROCHE, ARMANDO BAEZ
b.Dec.7,1926 Havana,Cuba.

Yr	Cl	Lea	Pos	G	Rec
1945	Was	A	P	2	0-0
		BRTR			

ROCHE, JOHN JOSEPH (Red)
b.Nov.22,1890 Los Angeles,Cal.

Yr	Cl	Lea	Pos	G	Rec
1914	St.L	N	C	12	.667
1915	St.L	N	C	46	.205
1917	St.L	N	C	1	.000
		BRTR		59	.286

ROCHEFORT, BENNETT HAROLD
(Real name Bennett Harold Rochefort Gilbert)
b.Aug.15,1896 Camden,N.J.

Yr	Cl	Lea	Pos	G	Rec
1914	Phi	A	1	1	.500
		BLTR			

ROCHELLI, LOUIS JOSEPH
b.Jan.11,1919 Williamson,Ill.

Yr	Cl	Lea	Pos	G	Rec
1944	Bro	N	2	5	.176
		BRTR			

ROCK, LESTER HENRY
(Real name Lester Henry Schwarzrock)
b.Aug.19,1912 Springfield,Minn.

Yr	Cl	Lea	Pos	G	Rec
1936	Chi	A	1	2	.000
		BLTR			

ROCKENFELD, ISAAC B.
b.Nov.3,1878 Omaha,Neb.

Yr	Cl	Lea	Pos	G	Rec
1905	St.L	A	2	95	.217
1906	St.L	A	2	27	.236
		TR		122	.222

RODGERS, KENNETH ANDRE IAN
b.Dec.2,1934 Nassau, Bahamas Islands

Yr	Cl	Lea	Pos	G	Rec
1957	NY	N	S-3	32	.244
1958	SF	N	S	22	.206
1959	SF	N	S	71	.250
1960	SF	N	1-S-3-O	81	.244
1961	Chi	N	1-2-S-O	73	.266
1962	Chi	N	1-S	138	.278
		BRTR		417	.259

RODGERS, ROBERT LEROY
b.Aug.16,1938 Delaware,O.

Yr	Cl	Lea	Pos	G	Rec
1961	LA	A	C	16	.321
1962	LA	A	C	155	.258
		BBTR		171	.264

RODGERS, WILBUR KINCAID (Rawmeat Bill)
b.Apr.18,1887 Amberly Village,O.

Yr	Cl	Lea	Pos	G	Rec
1915	Cle	A	2	16	.298
1915	Bos	A	2	11	.000
1915	Cin	N	2-S-3-O	72	.239
1916	Cin	N	2-S	3	.000
		BLTR		102	.243

RODGERS, WILLIAM SHERMAN
b.Dec.5,1922 Harrisburg,Pa.

Yr	Cl	Lea	Pos	G	Rec
1944	Pit	N	O	2	.250
1945	Pit	N	H	1	1.000
		BLTL		3	.400

RODIN, ERIC CHAPMAN
b.Feb.5,1930 Orange,N.J.

Yr	Cl	Lea	Pos	G	Rec
1954	NY	N	O	5	.000
		BRTR			

RODRIGUEZ, ANTONIO ORDENANA
(Played under name of Antonio Ordenana)

RODRIGUEZ, HECTOR ANTONIO
b.June 13,1921 Alquizar,Cuba.

Yr	Cl	Lea	Pos	G	Rec
1952	Chi	A	3	124	.265
		BRTR			

RODRIGUEZ, FERNANDO PEDRO
b.Apr.29,1920 Havana,Cuba

Yr	Cl	Lea	Pos	G	Rec
1958	Chi	N	P	7	0-0
1959	Phi	N	P	1	0-0
		BRTR		8	0-0

RODRIGUEZ, JOSE
b.July 25,1894 Havana,Cuba.
d.Jan.21,1953

Yr	Cl	Lea	Pos	G	Rec
1916	NY	N	H	1	.000
1917	NY	N	1	7	.200
1918	NY	N	1-2-3	50	.160
		BRTR		58	.166

ROE, ELWIN CHARLES (Preacher)
b.Feb.26,1915 Ash Flat,Ark.

Yr	Cl	Lea	Pos	G	Rec
1938	St.L	N	P	1	0-0
1944	Pit	N	P	39	13-11
1945	Pit	N	P	33	14-13
1946	Pit	N	P	21	3-8
1947	Pit	N	P	38	4-15
1948	Bro	N	P	34	12-8
1949	Bro	N	P	30	15-6
1950	Bro	N	P	36	19-11
1951	Bro	N	P	34	22-3
1952	Bro	N	P	27	11-2
1953	Bro	N	P	25	11-3
1954	Bro	N	P	15	3-4
		BRTL		333	127-84

ROE, FREDERICK CLAY
b.Mar.27,1901 Memphis,Tenn.
d.Apr.3,1956

Yr	Cl	Lea	Pos	G	Rec
1923	Was	A	P	1	0-1
		BLTL			

ROEBUCK, EDWARD JACK
b.July 3,1931 E. Millsboro,Pa.

Yr	Cl	Lea	Pos	G	Rec
1955	Bro	N	P	47	5-6
1956	Bro	N	P	43	5-4
1957	Bro	N	P	44	8-2
1958	LA	N	P	32	0-1
1960	LA	N	P	58	8-3
1961	LA	N	P	5	2-0
1962	LA	N	P	64	10-2
		BRTR		293	38-18

ROETTGER, OSCAR FREDERICK LOUIS (Okkie)
b.Feb.19,1900 St.Louis,Mo.

Yr	Cl	Lea	Pos	G	Rec
1923	NY	A	P	5	0-0
1924	NY	A	P	1	0-0
1927	Bro	N	O	5	.000
1932	Phi	A	1	26	.233
		BRTR		37	0-0 .212

ROETTGER, WALTER HENRY
b.Aug.28,1902 St.Louis,Mo.
d.Sept.14,1951

Yr	Cl	Lea	Pos	G	Rec
1927	St.L	N	O	5	.000
1928	St.L	N	O	68	.341
1929	St.L	N	O	79	.253
1930	NY	N	O	121	.283
1931	Cin	N	O	44	.351
1931	St.L	N	O	45	.285
1932	Cin	N	O	106	.277
1933	Cin	N	O	84	.239
1934	Pit	N	O	47	.245
	BRTR			599	.285

ROETZ, EDWARD BERNARD
b.Sept.6,1905 Philadelphia,Pa.

Yr	Cl	Lea	Pos	G	Rec
1929	St.L	A	1-2-S	16	.244
	BRTR				

ROGALSKI, JOSEPH ANTHONY
b.July 15,1912 Ashland,Wis.
d.Nov.20,1951

Yr	Cl	Lea	Pos	G	Rec
1938	Det	A	P	2	0-0
	BRTR				

ROGELL, WILLIAM GEORGE
b.Nov.24,1904 Springfield,Ill.

Yr	Cl	Lea	Pos	G	Rec
1925	Bos	A	2-S	58	.195
1927	Bos	A	3	82	.266
1928	Bos	A	2-S	102	.233
1930	Det	A	S-3	54	.166
1931	Det	A	S	48	.303
1932	Det	A	S	143	.271
1933	Det	A	S	155	.295
1934	Det	A	S	154	.296
1935	Det	A	S	150	.275
1936	Det	A	S	146	.274
1937	Det	A	S	146	.276
1938	Det	A	S	136	.259
1939	Det	A	S-3	74	.230
1940	Chi	N	2-S-3	33	.136
	BBTR			1481	.267

ROGERS, EMMETT
b.1868 Rome,N.Y.

Yr	Cl	Lea	Pos	G	Rec
1890	Tol	a	C	35	.184

ROGERS, FRALEY W.
b.Brooklyn,N.Y.
d.May 10,1881

Yr	Cl	Lea	Pos	G	Rec
1872	Bos	n	1-O	45	.294

ROGERS, JAMES F.
b.Apr.9,1872 Hartford,Conn.
d.Jan.21,1900

Yr	Cl	Lea	Pos	G	Rec
1896	Was	N	2-3-O	38	.279
1896	Lou	N	2	74	.256
1897	Lou	N	M-2	40	.148
				152	.235

ROGERS, JAY LEWIS
b.Aug.3,1888 Sandusky,N.Y.

Yr	Cl	Lea	Pos	G	Rec
1914	NY	A	C	5	.000
	BRTR				

ROGERS, LEE OTIS (Buck)
b.Oct.8,1913 Tuscaloosa,Ala.

Yr	Cl	Lea	Pos	G	Rec
1938	Bos	A	P	14	1-1
1938	Bro	N	P	14	0-2
	BRTL			28	1-3

ROGERS, ORLIN WOODROW (Buck)
b.Nov.5,1912 Spring Garden,Va.

Yr	Cl	Lea	Pos	G	Rec
1935	Was	A	P	2	0-1
	BRTL				

ROGERS, STANLEY FRANK (Packy)
(Real name Stanley Frank Hazinski)
b.Apr.26,1914 Swoyersville,Pa.

Yr	Cl	Lea	Pos	G	Rec
1938	Bro	N	2-S-3	23	.189
	BRTR				

ROGERS, THOMAS ANDREW (Shotgun)
b.Feb.12,1895 Scottsville,Ky.
d.Mar.7,1936

Yr	Cl	Lea	Pos	G	Rec
1917	St.L	A	P	24	3-6
1918	St.L	A	P	29	8-10
1919	St.L	A	P	2	0-1
1919	Phi	A	P	23	4-12
1921	NY	A	P	6	0-1
	BRTR			84	15-30

ROGGE, F. CLINTON
b.July 19,1889 Memphis,Mich.

Yr	Cl	Lea	Pos	G	Rec
1915	Pit	F	P	34	17-11
1921	Cin	N	P	6	1-2
	BLTR			40	18-13

ROGOVIN, SAUL WALTER
b.Oct.10,1922 Brooklyn,N.Y.

Yr	Cl	Lea	Pos	G	Rec
1949	Det	A	P	5	0-1
1950	Det	A	P	11	2-1
1951	Det	A	P	5	1-1
1951	Chi	A	P	24	11-7
1952	Chi	A	P	33	14-9
1953	Chi	A	P	22	7-12
1955	Bal	A	P	15	1-8
1955	Phi	N	P	13	5-3
1956	Phi	N	P	22	7-6
1957	Phi	N	P	4	0-0
	BRTR			154	48-48

ROHE, GEORGE ANTHONY
b.Sept.15,1875 Cincinnati,O.
d.June 10,1957

Yr	Cl	Lea	Pos	G	Rec
1901	Bal	A	3	14	.294
1905	Chi	A	2-3	34	.212
1906	Chi	A	3	74	.258
1907	Chi	A	2-S-3	144	.213
	BRTR			266	.227

ROHWER, RAY
b.June 5,1895 Dixon,Cal.

Yr	Cl	Lea	Pos	G	Rec
1921	Pit	N	O	30	.250
1922	Pit	N	O	53	.294
	BLTL			83	.284

ROIG, ANTON AMBROSE
b.Dec.23,1928 New Orleans,La.

Yr	Cl	Lea	Pos	G	Rec
1953	Was	A	2	3	.125
1955	Was	A	2-S-3	29	.228
1956	Was	A	2-S	44	.210
	BRTR			76	.212

ROJAS, OCTAVIO RIVAS
b.Mar.6,1939 Havana,Cuba

Yr	Cl	Lea	Pos	G	Rec
1962	Cin	N	2-3	39	.221
	BRTR				

ROJEK, STANLEY ANDREW
b.Apr.21,1919 N.Tonawanda,N.Y.

Yr	Cl	Lea	Pos	G	Rec
1942	Bro	N	H	1	.000
1946	Bro	N	2-S-3	45	.277
1947	Bro	N	2-S-3	32	.263
1948	Pit	N	S	156	.290
1949	Pit	N	S	144	.244
1950	Pit	N	2-S	76	.257
1951	Pit	N	S	8	.188
1951	St.L	N	S	51	.274
1952	St.L	A	2-S	9	.143
	BRTR			522	.266

ROLAND, JAMES IVAN
b.Dec.14,1942 Franklin,N.C.

Yr	Cl	Lea	Pos	G	Rec
1962	Min	A	P	1	0-0
	BLTL				

ROLFE, ROBERT ABIAL
(Red)
b.Oct.17,1908 Penacook,N.H.

Yr	Cl	Lea	Pos	G	Rec
1931	NY	A	S	1	.000
1934	NY	A	S-3	89	.287
1935	NY	A	S-3	149	.300
1936	NY	A	3	135	.319
1937	NY	A	3	154	.276

(Continued)

Yr	Cl	Lea	Pos	G	Rec
1938	NY	A	3	151	.311
1939	NY	A	3	152	.329
1940	NY	A	3	139	.250
1941	NY	A	3	136	.264
1942	NY	A	3	69	.219
	BLTR			1175	.289

Non-playing manager Det (A) 1949-52.

ROLLING, RAYMOND COPELAND
b.Sept.8,1896 St.Louis,Mo.

Yr	Cl	Lea	Pos	G	Rec
1912	St.L	N	2	5	.200
	BRTR				

ROLLINGS, WILLIAM RUSSELL
(Red)
b.Mar.21,1904 Mobile,Ala.

Yr	Cl	Lea	Pos	G	Rec
1927	Bos	A	1-3	82	.266
1928	Bos	A	1-2-3	50	.229
1930	Bos	N	2-3	52	.236
	BLTR			184	.251

ROLLINS, RICHARD JOHN
b.Apr.16,1938 Mt.Pleasant,Pa.

Yr	Cl	Lea	Pos	G	Rec
1961	Min	A	2-3	13	.294
1962	Min	A	S-3	159	.298
	BRTR			172	.298

ROLLINSON, ...

Yr	Cl	Lea	Pos	G	Rec
1884	Was	U	C	1	.000

ROMANO, JAMES KING
b.Apr.6,1927 Brooklyn,N.Y.

Yr	Cl	Lea	Pos	G	Rec
1950	Bro	N	P	3	0-0
	BRTR				

ROMANO, JOHN ANTHONY
(Honey)
b.Aug.23,1934 Hoboken,N.J.

Yr	Cl	Lea	Pos	G	Rec
1958	Chi	A	C	4	.286
1959	Chi	A	C	53	.294
1960	Cle	A	C	108	.272
1961	Cle	A	C	142	.299
1962	Cle	A	C	135	.261
	BRTR			442	.280

ROMBERGER, ALLEN IRVING
(Dutch)
b.May 26,1927 Klingerstown,Pa.

Yr	Cl	Lea	Pos	G	Rec
1954	Phi	A	P	10	1-1
	BRTR				

ROMMEL, EDWIN AMERICUS
b.Sept.13,1897 Baltimore,Md.

Yr	Cl	Lea	Pos	G	Rec
1920	Phi	A	P	34	7-7
1921	Phi	A	P	46	16-23
1922	Phi	A	P	51	27-13
1923	Phi	A	P	56	18-19
1924	Phi	A	P	45	18-15
1925	Phi	A	P	52	21-10
1926	Phi	A	P	37	11-11
1927	Phi	A	P	30	11-3
1928	Phi	A	P	43	13-5
1929	Phi	A	P	32	12-2
1930	Phi	A	P	35	9-4
1931	Phi	A	P	29	7-5
1932	Phi	A	P	17	1-2
	BRTR			507	171-119

ROMONOSKY, JOHN
b.July 7,1929 Harrisburg,Ill.

Yr	Cl	Lea	Pos	G	Rec
1953	St.L	N	P	2	0-0
1958	Was	A	P	27	2-4
1959	Was	A	P	20	1-0
	BRTR			49	3-4

RONDEAU, HENRI JOSEPH
b.May 7,1887 Danielson,Conn.
d.May 28,1943

Yr	Cl	Lea	Pos	G	Rec
1913	Det	A	C-1	35	.186
1915	Was	A	O	14	.154
1916	Was	A	O	50	.222
	BRTR			99	.203

ROOF, PHILLIP ANTHONY
b.Mar.5,1941 Paducah, Ky.

Yr	Cl	Lea	Pos	G	Rec
1961	Mil	N	C	1	.000
	BRTR				

ROOKS, GEORGE BRINTON McCLELLAN (Real name George Brinton McClellan Ruckser)
b.Oct.21,1863 Chicago,Ill.
d.Mar.11,1935

Yr	Cl	Lea	Pos	G	Rec
1891	Bos	N	O	5	.125

ROONEY, FRANK L.

Yr	Cl	Lea	Pos	G	Rec
1914	Ind	F	1	12	.212

ROOT, CHARLES HENRY
b.Mar.17,1899 Middletown,O.

Yr	Cl	Lea	Pos	G	Rec
1923	St.L	A	P	27	0-4
1926	Chi	N	P	42	18-17
1927	Chi	N	P	48	26-15
1928	Chi	N	P	40	14-18
1929	Chi	N	P	43	19-6
1930	Chi	N	P	37	16-14
1931	Chi	N	P	39	17-14
1932	Chi	N	P	39	15-10
1933	Chi	N	P	35	15-10
1934	Chi	N	P	34	4-7
1935	Chi	N	P	38	15-8
1936	Chi	N	P	33	3-6
1937	Chi	N	P	43	13-5
1938	Chi	N	P	44	8-7
1939	Chi	N	P	35	8-8
1940	Chi	N	P	36	2-4
1941	Chi	N	P	19	8-7
	BRTR			632	201-160

ROSAR, WARREN VINCENT (Buddy)
b.July 3,1914 Buffalo,N.Y.

Yr	Cl	Lea	Pos	G	Rec
1939	NY	A	C	43	.276
1940	NY	A	C	73	.298
1941	NY	A	C	67	.287
1942	NY	A	C	69	.230
1943	Cle	A	C	115	.283
1944	Cle	A	C	99	.263
1945	Phi	A	C	92	.210
1946	Phi	A	C	121	.283
1947	Phi	A	C	102	.259
1948	Phi	A	C	90	.255
1949	Phi	A	C	32	.200
1950	Bos	A	C	27	.298
1951	Bos	A	C	58	.229
	BRTR			988	.261

ROSE, CHARLES ALFRED
b.Sept.1,1885 Macon,Mo.

Yr	Cl	Lea	Pos	G	Rec
1909	St.L	A	P	3	1-2
	BLTL				

ROSEBORO, JOHN H.
b.May 13,1933 Ashland,O.

Yr	Cl	Lea	Pos	G	Rec
1957	Bro	N	C-1	35	.145
1958	Bro	N	C-O	114	.271
1959	LA	N	C	118	.232
1960	LA	N	C-1-3	103	.213
1961	LA	N	C	128	.251
1962	LA	N	C	128	.249
	BLTR			626	.241

ROSEBROUGH, E. E. (Zeke)
b.Charleston,Ill.

Yr	Cl	Lea	Pos	G	Rec
1898	Pit	N	P	4	0-2
1899	Pit	N	P	2	0-1
				6	0-3

ROSELLI, ROBERT EDWARD
b.Dec.10,1931 San Francisco,Cal.

Yr	Cl	Lea	Pos	G	Rec
1955	Mil	N	C	6	.222
1956	Mil	N	C	4	.500
1958	Mil	N	H	1	.000
1961	Chi	A	C	22	.263
1962	Chi	A	C	35	.188
	BRTR			68	.219

ROSEMAN, JAMES J. (Chief)
b.1856 New York,N.Y.

Yr	Cl	Lea	Pos	G	Rec
1882	Tro	N	O	80	.236
1883	Met	a	1-O	93	.260
1884	Met	a	O	107	.295
1885	Met	a	P-O	101	0-1 .284
1886	Met	a	O	134	.228
1887	Ath	a	O	21	.325
1887	Met	a	O	59	.281
1887	Bro	a	O	1	.250
1890	St.L	a	M-O	80	.322
1890	Lou	a	O	2	.250
				678	0-1 .271

ROSEN, ALBERT LEONARD (Flip)
b.Feb.29,1924 Spartanburg,S.C.

Yr	Cl	Lea	Pos	G	Rec
1947	Cle	A	3-O	7	.111
1948	Cle	A	3	5	.200
1949	Cle	A	3	23	.159
1950	Cle	A	3	155	.287
1951	Cle	A	3	154	.265
1952	Cle	A	1-S-3	148	.302
1953	Cle	A	1-S-3	155	.336
1954	Cle	A	1-2-S-3	137	.300
1955	Cle	A	1-3	139	.244
1956	Cle	A	3	121	.267
	BRTR			1044	.285

ROSEN, GOODWIN GEORGE
b.Aug.28,1913 Toronto,Ont.,Canada.

Yr	Cl	Lea	Pos	G	Rec
1937	Bro	N	O	22	.312
1938	Bro	N	O	138	.281
1939	Bro	N	O	54	.251
1944	Bro	N	O	89	.261
1945	Bro	N	O	145	.325
1946	Bro	N	O	3	.333
1946	NY	N	O	100	.281
	BLTL			551	.291

ROSENBERG, HARRY
b.June 22,1909 San Francisco,Cal.

Yr	Cl	Lea	Pos	G	Rec
1930	NY	N	O	9	.000
	BRTR				

ROSENBERG, LOUIS
b.Mar.5,1903 San Francisco, Calif.

Yr	Cl	Lea	Pos	G	Rec
1923	Chi	A	2-O	3	.250
	BRTR				

ROSENFELD, MAX
b.Dec.23,1902 New York,N.Y.

Yr	Cl	Lea	Pos	G	Rec
1931	Bro	N	O	3	.222
1932	Bro	N	O	34	.359
1933	Bro	N	O	5	.111
	BRTR			42	.298

ROSENTHAL, LAWRENCE JOHN
b.May 21,1912 St.Paul,Minn.

Yr	Cl	Lea	Pos	G	Rec
1936	Chi	A	O	85	.281
1937	Chi	A	O	58	.289
1938	Chi	A	O	61	.286
1939	Chi	A	O	107	.265
1940	Chi	A	O	107	.301
1941	Chi	A	O	20	.237
1941	Cle	A	1-O	45	.187
1944	NY	A	O	36	.198
1944	Phi	A	O	32	.204
1945	Phi	A	O	28	.200
	BLTL			579	.263

ROSENTHAL, SIMON
b.Nov.13,1903 Boston,Mass.

Yr	Cl	Lea	Pos	G	Rec
1925	Bos	A	O	19	.264
1926	Bos	A	O	104	.267
	BLTL			123	.266

ROSER, EMERSON COREY (Steve)
b.Jan.25,1918 Rome,N.Y.

Yr	Cl	Lea	Pos	G	Rec
1944	NY	A	P	16	4-3
1945	NY	A	P	11	0-0
1946	NY	A	P	4	1-1
1946	Bos	N	P	14	1-1
	BRTR			45	6-5

(Continued)

ROSER, JOHN JOSEPH
b.Nov.15,1901 St.Louis,Mo.

Yr	Cl	Lea	Pos	G	Rec
1922	Bos	N	O	32	.239
	BLTL				

ROSS, CHESTER FRANKLIN (Buster)
b.Mar.11,1904 Mayfield,Ky.

Yr	Cl	Lea	Pos	G	Rec
1924	Bos	A	P	30	4-3
1925	Bos	A	P	33	3-8
1926	Bos	A	P	1	0-1
	BLTL			64	7-12

ROSS, CHESTER JAMES
b.Apr.1,1918 Buffalo,N.Y.

Yr	Cl	Lea	Pos	G	Rec
1939	Bos	N	O	11	.323
1940	Bos	N	O	149	.281
1941	Bos	N	O	29	.120
1942	Bos	N	O	76	.195
1943	Bos	N	O	94	.218
1944	Bos	N	O	54	.227
	BRTR			413	.241

ROSS, CLIFFORD DAVID
b.Aug.3,1928 Philadelphia,Pa.

Yr	Cl	Lea	Pos	G	Rec
1954	Cin	N	P	4	0-0
	BLTL				

ROSS, DONALD RAYMOND
b.July 16,1915 Pasadena,Cal.

Yr	Cl	Lea	Pos	G	Rec
1938	Det	A	3	77	.260
1940	Bro	N	3	10	.289
1942	Det	A	3-O	87	.274
1943	Det	A	2-S-3-O	89	.267
1944	Det	A	1-O	66	.210
1945	Det	A	3	8	.379
1945	Cle	A	3	106	.262
1946	Cle	A	3-O	55	.268
	BRTR			498	.262

ROSS, EBEN B.
b.Gananoque,Ont.,Canada.

Yr	Cl	Lea	Pos	G	Rec
1902	Bal	A	P	2	1-1

ROSS, FLOYD ROBERT
b.Nov.2,1928 Fullerton,Cal.

Yr	Cl	Lea	Pos	G	Rec
1950	Was	A	P	6	0-1
1951	Was	A	P	11	0-1
1956	Phi	N	P	3	0-0
	BRTL			20	0-2

ROSS, GEORGE SIDNEY
b.June 28,1893 San Rafael,Cal.
d.Apr.22,1935

Yr	Cl	Lea	Pos	G	Rec
1918	NY	N	P	1	0-0
	BLTL				

ROSS, LEE RAVEN (Buck)
b.Feb.3,1915 Norwood,N.C.

Yr	Cl	Lea	Pos	G	Rec
1936	Phi	A	P	30	9-14
1937	Phi	A	P	28	5-10
1938	Phi	A	P	29	9-16
1939	Phi	A	P	29	6-14
1940	Phi	A	P	24	5-10
1941	Phi	A	P	1	0-1
1941	Chi	A	P	20	3-8
1942	Chi	A	P	22	5-7
1943	Chi	A	P	21	11-7
1944	Chi	A	P	20	2-7
1945	Chi	A	P	13	1-1
	BRTR			237	56-95

ROSSI, JOSEPH ANTHONY
b.Mar.13,1923 Oakland,Cal.

Yr	Cl	Lea	Pos	G	Rec
1952	Cin	N	C	55	.221
	BRTR				

ROSSMAN, CLAUDE R.
b.June 17, 1881 Philmont,N.Y.
d.Jan.16,1928

Yr	Cl	Lea	Pos	G	Rec
1904	Cle	A	O	18	.190
1906	Cle	A	1	118	.308
1907	Det	A	1	153	.277
1908	Det	A	1	138	.294
1909	Det	A	1	80	.246
1909	St.L	A	1	4	.467
	BLTL			511	.282

ROSSO, FRANCIS JAMES
b.Mar.1,1921 Agawam,Mass.

Yr	Cl	Lea	Pos	G	Rec
1944	NY	N	P	3	0-0
	BRTR				

ROTBLATT, MARVIN JOSEPH
b.Oct.18,1927 Chicago,Ill.

Yr	Cl	Lea	Pos	G	Rec
1948	Chi	A	P	7	0-1
1950	Chi	A	P	2	0-0
1951	Chi	A	P	26	4-2
	BBTL			35	4-3

ROTH, FRANK CHARLES
b.Oct.11,1878 Burlington,Wis.
d.Mar.27,1955

Yr	Cl	Lea	Pos	G	Rec
1903	Phi	N	C	61	.273
1904	Phi	N	C	68	.258
1905	St.L	A	C	35	.262
1906	Chi	A	C	16	.196
1909	Cin	N	C	52	.238
1910	Cin	N	C	27	.200
	BRTR			259	.248

ROTH, ROBERT FRANK
(Braggo)
b.Aug.28,1892 Burlington,Wis.
d.Sept.11,1936

Yr	Cl	Lea	Pos	G	Rec
1914	Chi	A	O	34	.294
1915	Chi	A	3-O	69	.257
1915	Cle	A	O	40	.287
1916	Cle	A	O	125	.286
1917	Cle	A	O	145	.285
1918	Cle	A	O	106	.283
1919	Phi	A	O	48	.323
1919	Bos	A	O	63	.256
1920	Was	A	O	138	.290
1921	NY	A	O	43	.283
	BRTR			811	.284

ROTHEL, ROBERT BURTON
b.Sept.17,1923 Columbia Station,O.

Yr	Cl	Lea	Pos	G	Rec
1945	Cle	A	3	4	.200
	BRTR				

ROTHERMEL, EDWARD HILL
(Bobby)
b.Dec.18,1870 Fleetwood,Pa.

Yr	Cl	Lea	Pos	G	Rec
1899	Bal	N	2	10	.095

ROTHFUSS, JOHN
b.1872 Irvington,N.J.

Yr	Cl	Lea	Pos	G	Rec
1897	Pit	N	1	31	.348

ROTHGEB, CLAUDE JAMES
b.Jan.1,1880 Milford,Ill.
d.July 5,1944

Yr	Cl	Lea	Pos	G	Rec
1905	Was	A	O	6	.133

ROTHROCK, JOHN HUSTON
b.Mar.14,1905 Long Beach,Cal.

Yr	Cl	Lea	Pos	G	Rec
1925	Bos	A	S	22	.345
1926	Bos	A	S	15	.294
1927	Bos	A	1-2-S-3	117	.260
1928	Bos	A	P-1-S-3-O	117	0-0 .267
1929	Bos	A	O	143	.300
1930	Bos	A	3-O	45	.277
1931	Bos	A	2-O	133	.278
1932	Bos	A	O	12	.208
1932	Chi	A	O	39	.188
1934	St.L	N	O	154	.284
1935	St.L	N	O	129	.273
1937	Phi	A	O	88	.267
	BBTR			1014	0-0 .276

ROUSH, EDD J.
b.May 8,1893 Oakland City,Ind.

Yr	Cl	Lea	Pos	G	Rec
1913	Chi	A	O	9	.100
1914	Ind	F	O	74	.333
1915	New	F	O	145	.298
1916	NY	N	O	39	.188
1916	Cin	N	O	69	.287
1917	Cin	N	O	136	.341
1918	Cin	N	O	113	.333
1919	Cin	N	O	133	.321
1920	Cin	N	1-2-O	149	.339
1921	Cin	N	O	112	.352
1922	Cin	N	O	49	.351
1923	Cin	N	O	138	.351
1924	Cin	N	O	121	.348
1925	Cin	N	O	134	.339
1926	Cin	N	1-O	144	.323
1927	NY	N	O	140	.304
1928	NY	N	O	46	.252
1929	NY	N	O	115	.324
1931	Cin	N	O	101	.271
	BLTL			1967	.323

ROUTCLIFFE, PHILIP J.
(Chicken)
b.Oct.24,1870 Oswego,N.Y.
d.Oct.4,1918

Yr	Cl	Lea	Pos	G	Rec
1890	Pit	N	O	1	.250

ROWAN, DAVID
(Real name David Drohan)
b.Dec.6,1883 Eananoque,Ont.,Canada
d.July 30,1955

Yr	Cl	Lea	Pos	G	Rec
1911	St.L	A	1	18	.384

ROWAN, JOHN ARTHUR
b.June 16,1886 New Castle,Pa.

Yr	Cl	Lea	Pos	G	Rec
1906	Det	A	P	1	0-1
1908	Cin	N	P	8	3-3
1909	Cin	N	P	38	11-12
1910	Cin	N	P	42	14-13
1911	Phi	N	P	12	3-4
1911	Chi	N	P	1	0-0
1913	Cin	N	P	5	0-4
1914	Cin	N	P	12	1-3
	BRTR			119	32-40

ROWE, DAVID E.
b.Jacksonville,Ill.
d.Oct.12,1918

Yr	Cl	Lea	Pos	G	Rec
1877	Chi	N	P-O	2	0-1 .286
1882	Cle	N	P-O	23	0-1 .247
1883	Bal	a	P-1-S-O	59	0-0 .297
1884	St.L	U	P-S-O	87	1-0 .292
1885	St.L	N	O	16	.161
1886	KC	N	M-O	105	.240
1888	KC	a	M-O	32	.195
	BR			324	1-2 .257

ROWE, HARLAND STIMSON
b.Apr.20,1896 Springvale,Me.

Yr	Cl	Lea	Pos	G	Rec
1916	Phi	A	3	17	.139
	BLTR				

ROWE, JOHN CHARLES
b.Dec.8,1857 Harrisburg,Pa.
d.Apr.26,1911

Yr	Cl	Lea	Pos	G	Rec
1879	Buf	N	C-O	8	.382
1880	Buf	N	C-3-O	77	.256
1881	Buf	N	C-S-3-O	61	.333
1882	Buf	N	C-S-3-O	75	.266
1883	Buf	N	C-S-3-O	86	.275
1884	Buf	N	C-S-O	91	.310
1885	Buf	N	C-S-O	98	.289
1886	Det	N	S	111	.303
1887	Det	N	S	123	.363
1888	Det	N	S	105	.277
1889	Pit	N	S	74	.258
1890	Buf	p	M-S	125	.250
	BLTR			1034	.292

ROWE, LYNWOOD THOMAS
(Schoolboy)
b.Jan.11,1912 Waco,Tex.
d.Jan.8,1961

Yr	Cl	Lea	Pos	G	Rec
1933	Det	A	P	21	7-4
1934	Det	A	P	51	24-8
1935	Det	A	P	45	19-13
1936	Det	A	P	45	19-10
1937	Det	A	P	10	1-4
1938	Det	A	P	4	0-2
1939	Det	A	P	31	10-12
1940	Det	A	P	27	16-3
1941	Det	A	P	32	8-6
1942	Det	A	P	2	1-0
1942	Bro	N	P	14	1-0
1943	Phi	N	P	82	14-8
1946	Phi	N	P	30	11-4
1947	Phi	N	P	43	14-10
1948	Phi	N	P	31	10-10
1949	Phi	N	P	23	3-7
	BRTR			491	158-101

ROWELL, CARVEL WILLIAM
(Bama)
b.Jan.13,1917 Citronelle,Ala.

Yr	Cl	Lea	Pos	G	Rec
1939	Bos	N	O	21	.186
1940	Bos	N	2-O	130	.305
1941	Bos	N	2-3-O	138	.267
1946	Bos	N	O	95	.280
1947	Bos	N	2-3-O	113	.276
1948	Phi	N	2-3-O	77	.240
	BLTR			574	.275

ROWEN, W. EDWARD (Ed)
b.Oct.22,1857 Bridgeport,Conn.
d.Feb.22,1892

Yr	Cl	Lea	Pos	G	Rec
1882	Bos	N	C-S-3-O	82	.245
1883	Ath	a	C-2-3-O	49	.227
1884	Ath	a	C	4	.400
				135	.243

ROWLAND, CHARLES LELAND
b.July 23,1899 Henderson,N.C.

Yr	Cl	Lea	Pos	G	Rec
1923	Phi	A	C	6	.000
	BRTR				

ROWLAND, CLARENCE HENRY
(Pants)
b.Feb.12,1879 Platteville,Wis.
Non-playing manager Chi (A) 1915-18.

ROXBURGH, JAMES A.
b.San Francisco,Cal.

Yr	Cl	Lea	Pos	G	Rec
1884	Bal	a	C	2	.333
1887	Ath	a	C	2	.125
				4	.214

ROY, CHARLES ROBERT
b.June 22,1884 Beaulieu,Minn.

Yr	Cl	Lea	Pos	G	Rec
1906	Phi	N	P	8	0-1

ROY, EMILE ARTHUR
b.May 26,1907 Brighton,Mass.

Yr	Cl	Lea	Pos	G	Rec
1933	Phi	A	P	1	0-1
	BBTR				

ROY, JEAN PIERRE
b.June 26,1920 Montreal,Que.,Canada.

Yr	Cl	Lea	Pos	G	Rec
1946	Bro	N	P	3	0-0
	BBTR				

ROY, LUTHER FRANKLIN
b.July 29,1902 Oaltenah,Tenn.

Yr	Cl	Lea	Pos	G	Rec
1924	Cle	A	P	16	0-5
1925	Cle	A	P	6	0-0
1927	Chi	N	P	11	3-1
1929	Phi	N	P	21	3-6
1929	Bro	N	P	2	0-0
	BRTR			56	6-12

ROY, NORMAN BROOKS
b.Nov.15,1928 Newton,Mass.

Yr	Cl	Lea	Pos	G	Rec
1950	Bos	N	P	19	4-3
	BRTR				

ROZEK, RICHARD LOUIS
b.Mar.27,1927 Cedar Rapids,Ia.

Yr	Cl	Lea	Pos	G	Rec
1950	Cle	A	P	12	0-0
1951	Cle	A	P	7	0-0
1952	Cle	A	P	10	1-0
1953	Phi	A	P	2	0-0
1954	Phi	A	P	2	0-0
	BLTL			33	1-0

RUBELING, ALBERT WILLIAM
b.May 10,1914 Parkville,Md.

Yr	Cl	Lea	Pos	G	Rec
1940	Phi	A	2-3	108	.245
1941	Phi	A	3	6	.263
1943	Pit	N	2-3	47	.262
1944	Pit	N	2-3-O	92	.245
	BRTR			253	.249

RUBLE, WILLIAM ARTHUR
(Art)
b.Mar.11,1903 Knoxville,Tenn.

Yr	Cl	Lea	Pos	G	Rec
1927	Det	A	O	56	.165
1934	Phi	N	O	19	.278
	BLTR			75	.207

RUCKER, GEORGE NAPOLEON
(Nap)
b.Sept.30,1884 Crabapple,Ga.

Yr	Cl	Lea	Pos	G	Rec
1907	Bro	N	P	37	15-13
1908	Bro	N	P	42	17-19
1909	Bro	N	P	38	13-19
1910	Bro	N	P	41	17-18
1911	Bro	N	P	48	22-18
1912	Bro	N	P	45	18-21
1913	Bro	N	P	41	14-15
1914	Bro	N	P	16	7-6
1915	Bro	N	P	19	9-4
1916	Bro	N	P	9	2-1
	BRTL			336	134-134

RUCKER, JOHN JOEL
b.Jan.15,1917 Crabapple,Ga.

Yr	Cl	Lea	Pos	G	Rec
1940	NY	N	O	86	.296
1941	NY	N	O	143	.288
1943	NY	N	O	132	.273
1944	NY	N	O	144	.244
1945	NY	N	O	105	.273
1946	NY	N	O	95	.264
	BLTR			705	.272

RUCKSER, GEORGE BRINTON McCLELLAN
(Played under name of George Brinton McClellan Rooks)

RUDDERHAM, JOHN EDMUND
b.Aug.30,1863 Quincy,Mass.
d.Apr.3,1942

Yr	Cl	Lea	Pos	G	Rec
1884	Bos	U	O	1	.250
	BRTR				

RUDOLPH, ERNEST WILLIAM
b.Feb.13,1913 Black River Falls,Wis.

Yr	Cl	Lea	Pos	G	Rec
1945	Bro	N	P	7	1-0
	BLTR				

RUDOLPH, FREDERICK DONALD
b.Aug.16,1931 Baltimore,Md.

Yr	Cl	Lea	Pos	G	Rec
1957	Chi	A	P	5	1-0
1958	Chi	A	P	7	1-0
1959	Chi	N	P	4	0-0
1959	Cin	N	P	5	0-0
1962	Cle	A	P	1	0-0
1962	Was	A	P	37	8-10
	BLTL			59	10-10

RUDOLPH, JOHN HERMAN
b.July 10,1882 Natrona,Pa.

Yr	Cl	Lea	Pos	G	Rec
1903	Phi	N	H	1	.000
1904	Chi	N	O	2	.250
				3	.200

RUDOLPH, RICHARD (Baldy)
b.Aug.25,1887 New York,N.Y.
d.Oct.20,1949

Yr	Cl	Lea	Pos	G	Rec
1910	NY	N	P	3	0-1
1911	NY	N	P	1	0-0

(Continued)

Yr	Cl	Lea	Pos	G	Rec
1913	Bos	N	P	35	14-13
1914	Bos	N	P	43	27-10
1915	Bos	N	P	45	22-19
1916	Bos	N	P	41	19-12
1917	Bos	N	P	32	13-13
1918	Bos	N	P	21	9-10
1919	Bos	N	P	37	13-18
1920	Bos	N	P	18	4-8
1922	Bos	N	P	3	0-2
1923	Bos	N	P	4	1-2
1927	Bos	N	P	1	0-0
	BBTR			284	122-108

RUEL, HEROLD DOMINIC
(Muddy)
b.Feb.20,1896 St.Louis,Mo.

Yr	Cl	Lea	Pos	G	Rec
1915	St.L	A	C	10	.000
1917	NY	A	C	6	.118
1918	NY	A	C	3	.333
1919	NY	A	C	81	.240
1920	NY	A	C	82	.268
1921	Bos	A	C	113	.277
1922	Bos	A	C	116	.255
1923	Was	A	C	136	.316
1924	Was	A	C	149	.283
1925	Was	A	C-1	127	.310
1926	Was	A	C	117	.299
1927	Was	A	C	131	.308
1928	Was	A	C	108	.257
1929	Was	A	C	69	.245
1930	Was	A	C	66	.253
1931	Bos	A	C	33	.301
1931	Det	A	C	14	.120
1932	Det	A	C	50	.235
1933	St.L	A	C	36	.190
1934	Chi	A	C	22	.211
	BRTR			1469	.276

Non-playing manager St.L (A) 1947.

RUETHER, WALTER HENRY
(Dutch)
b.Sept.13,1893 Alameda,Cal.

Yr	Cl	Lea	Pos	G	Rec
1917	Chi	N	P	31	2-0
1917	Cin	N	P	19	1-2
1918	Cin	N	P	2	0-1
1919	Cin	N	P	42	19-6
1920	Cin	N	P	45	16-12
1921	Bro	N	P	49	10-13
1922	Bro	N	P	67	21-12
1923	Bro	N	P-1	49	15-14 .274
1924	Bro	N	P	33	8-13
1925	Was	A	P-1	55	18-7 .333
1926	Was	A	P	47	13-6
1926	NY	A	P	13	2-3
1927	NY	A	P	35	13-6
	BLTL			487	138-95 .258

RUFER, RUDOLPH JOSEPH
b.Oct.28,1926 New York,N.Y.

Yr	Cl	Lea	Pos	G	Rec
1949	NY	N	S	7	.067
1950	NY	N	S	15	.091
	BRTR			22	.077

RUFFING, CHARLES HERBERT (Red)
b.May 3,1904 Granville,Ill.

Yr	Cl	Lea	Pos	G	Rec
1924	Bos	A	P	8	0-0
1925	Bos	A	P	37	9-18
1926	Bos	A	P	37	6-15
1927	Bos	A	P	29	5-13
1928	Bos	A	P	60	10-25
1929	Bos	A	P	60	9-22
1930	Bos	A	P	6	0-3
1930	NY	A	P	52	15-5
1931	NY	A	P	48	16-14
1932	NY	A	P	55	18-7
1933	NY	A	P	55	9-14
1934	NY	A	P	45	19-11
1935	NY	A	P	50	16-11
1936	NY	A	P	53	20-12
1937	NY	A	P	54	20-7
1938	NY	A	P	45	21-7
1939	NY	A	P	44	21-7
1940	NY	A	P	33	15-12
1941	NY	A	P	38	15-6
1942	NY	A	P	30	14-7
1945	NY	A	P	21	7-3

(Continued)

Yr	Cl	Lea	Pos	G	Rec
1946	NY	A	P	8	5-1
1947	Chi	A	P	14	3-5
	BRTR			882	273-225

RULLO, JOSEPH VINCENT
b.June 16,1919 New York,N.Y.

Yr	Cl	Lea	Pos	G	Rec
1943	Phi	A	2	16	.291
1944	Phi	A	1-2	35	.167
	BRTR			51	.212

RUMLER, WILLIAM GEORGE
b.Mar.27,1892 Milford,Neb.

Yr	Cl	Lea	Pos	G	Rec
1914	St.L	A	C	33	.174
1916	St.L	A	O	27	.324
1917	St.L	A	O	78	.261
	BRTR			138	.251

RUNNELS, JAMES EDWARD (Pete)
b.Jan.28,1928 Lufkin,Tex.

Yr	Cl	Lea	Pos	G	Rec
1951	Was	A	S	78	.278
1952	Was	A	2-S	152	.285
1953	Was	A	2-S	137	.257
1954	Was	A	2-S-O	139	.268
1955	Was	A	2-S	134	.284
1956	Was	A	1-2-S	147	.310
1957	Was	A	1-2-S	134	.230
1958	Bos	A	1-2	147	.322
1959	Bos	A	1-2-S	147	.314
1960	Bos	A	1-2-3	143	.320
1961	Bos	A	1-2-S-3	143	.317
1962	Bos	A	1	152	.326
	BLTR			1653	.294

RUSH, JESSE HOWARD (Andy)
b.Dec.26,1896 New Haven,W.Va.

Yr	Cl	Lea	Pos	G	Rec
1925	Bro	N	P	4	0-1
	BRTR				

RUSH, ROBERT RANSOM
d.Dec.21,1925 Battle Creek,Mich.

Yr	Cl	Lea	Pos	G	Rec
1948	Chi	N	P	36	5-11
1949	Chi	N	P	35	10-18
1950	Chi	N	P	40	13-20
1951	Chi	N	P	37	11-12
1952	Chi	N	P	34	17-13
1953	Chi	N	P	29	9-14
1954	Chi	N	P	33	13-15
1955	Chi	N	P	33	13-11
1956	Chi	N	P	32	13-10
1957	Chi	N	P	31	6-16
1958	Mil	N	P	28	10-6
1959	Mil	N	P	31	5-6
1960	Mil	N	P	10	2-0
1960	Chi	A	P	9	0-0
	BRTR			420	127-152

RUSIE, AMOS WILSON
b.May 30,1871 Mooresville, Ind.
d.Dec.6,1942

Yr	Cl	Lea	Pos	G	Rec
1889	Ind	N	P	26	11-11
1890	NY	N	P	73	28-33
1891	NY	N	P	56	34-20
1892	NY	N	P	65	32-28
1893	NY	N	P	55	33-21
1894	NY	N	P	50	36-13
1895	NY	N	P	47	23-22
1887	NY	N	P	37	28-8
1898	NY	N	P	36	20-11
1901	Cin	N	P	3	0-1
	BRTR			448	245-168

RUSSELL, ALLEN E. (Rubberarm)
b.July 31,1893 Baltimore,Md.

Yr	Cl	Lea	Pos	G	Rec
1915	NY	A	P	5	1-2
1916	NY	A	P	35	6-10
1917	NY	A	P	30	7-8
1918	NY	A	P	29	8-11
1919	NY	A	P	23	9-4
1919	Bos	A	P	21	8-5
1920	Bos	A	P	17	5-6
1921	Bos	A	P	39	7-11
1922	Bos	A	P	34	6-7
1923	Was	A	P	54	10-7

(Continued)

Yr	Cl	Lea	Pos	G	Rec
1924	Was	A	P	37	5-1
1925	Was	A	P	32	2-4
BBTR				356	74-76

RUSSELL, CLARENCE DICKSON (Lefty)
b.July 18,1890 Baltimore,Md.
d.Jan.22,1962

Yr	Cl	Lea	Pos	G	Rec
1910	Phi	A	P	1	1-0
1911	Phi	A	P	7	0-2
1912	Phi	A	P	3	0-2
BLTL				11	1-4

RUSSELL, EWELL ALBERT (Reb)
b.Apr.12,1889 Jackson,Miss.

Yr	Cl	Lea	Pos	G	Rec
1913	Chi	A	P	44	22-16
1914	Chi	A	P	39	8-12
1915	Chi	A	P	45	11-12
1916	Chi	A	P	56	18-11
1917	Chi	A	P	39	15-5
1918	Chi	A	P	27	6-5
1919	Chi	A	P	1	0-0
1922	Pit	N	O	60	.368
1923	Pit	N	O	94	.289
BLTL				405	80-61 / .269

RUSSELL, GLEN DAVID (Rip)
b.Jan.26,1915 Los Angeles,Cal.

Yr	Cl	Lea	Pos	G	Rec
1939	Chi	N	1	143	.273
1940	Chi	N	1-3	68	.247
1941	Chi	N	1	6	.294
1942	Chi	N	1-2-3-O	102	.242
1946	Bos	A	2-3	80	.208
1947	Bos	A	3	26	.154
BRTR				425	.255

RUSSELL, HARVEY HOLMES
b.Jan.10,1887 Marshall,Va.

Yr	Cl	Lea	Pos	G	Rec
1914	Bal	F	C	79	.247
1915	Bal	F	C	52	.243
BLTR				131	.246

RUSSELL, JACK ERWIN
b.Oct.24,1905 Paris,Tex.

Yr	Cl	Lea	Pos	G	Rec
1926	Bos	A	P	37	0-5
1927	Bos	A	P	35	4-9
1928	Bos	A	P	35	11-14
1929	Bos	A	P	37	6-18
1930	Bos	A	P	41	9-20
1931	Bos	A	P	41	10-18
1932	Bos	A	P	11	1-7
1932	Cle	A	P	20	5-7
1933	Was	A	P	50	12-6
1934	Was	A	P	54	5-10
1935	Was	A	P	43	4-9
1936	Was	A	P	18	3-2
1936	Bos	A	P	23	0-3
1937	Det	A	P	25	2-5
1938	Chi	N	P	42	6-1
1939	Chi	N	P	43	4-3
1940	St.L	N	P	26	3-4
BRTR				581	85-141

RUSSELL, JAMES WILLIAM
b.Oct.1,1919 Fayette City,Pa.

Yr	Cl	Lea	Pos	G	Rec
1942	Pit	N	O	5	.071
1943	Pit	N	1-O	146	.259
1944	Pit	N	O	152	.312
1945	Pit	N	O	146	.284
1946	Pit	N	1-O	146	.277
1947	Pit	N	O	128	.253
1948	Bos	N	O	89	.264
1949	Bos	N	O	130	.231
1950	Bro	N	O	77	.229
1951	Bro	N	O	16	.000
BBTR				1035	.267

RUSSELL, JOHN ALBERT
b.Oct.20,1895 San Mateo,Cal.
d.Nov.20,1930

Yr	Cl	Lea	Pos	G	Rec
1917	Bro	N	P	5	0-1
1918	Bro	N	P	1	0-0
1921	Chi	A	P	11	2-5
1922	Chi	A	P	5	0-1
BLTL				22	2-7

RUSSELL, LLOYD OPAL
b.Apr.10,1915 Ada,Okla.

Yr	Cl	Lea	Pos	G	Rec
1938	Cle	A	H	2	.000
BRTR					

RUSSELL, PAUL
b.Little Rock,Ark.

Yr	Cl	Lea	Pos	G	Rec
1894	St.L	N	O	3	.100

RUSSO, MARIUS UGO (Lefty)
b.July 19,1914 Brooklyn,N.Y.

Yr	Cl	Lea	Pos	G	Rec
1939	NY	A	P	21	8-3
1940	NY	A	P	30	14-8
1941	NY	A	P	28	14-10
1942	NY	A	P	9	4-1
1943	NY	A	P	24	5-10
1946	NY	A	P	10	0-2
BRTL				122	45-34

RUST, ...
b.Louisville,Ky.

Yr	Cl	Lea	Pos	G	Rec
1882	Bal	a	P-O	1	0-0 / .333

RUSZKOWSKI, HENRY ALEXANDER
b.Nov.10,1925 Cleveland,O.

Yr	Cl	Lea	Pos	G	Rec
1944	Cle	A	C	3	.375
1945	Cle	A	C	14	.204
1947	Cle	A	C	23	.259
BRTR				40	.238

RUTH, GEORGE HERMAN (Babe)
b.Feb.6,1895 Baltimore,Md.
d.Aug.16,1948

Yr	Cl	Lea	Pos	G	Rec
1914	Bos	A	P	5	2-1
1915	Bos	A	P-O	42	18-6 / .315
1916	Bos	A	P-O	67	23-12 / .272
1917	Bos	A	P-O	52	24-13 / .325
1918	Bos	A	P-1-O	95	13-7 / .300
1919	Bos	A	P-O	130	8-5 / .322
1920	NY	A	P-O	142	1-0 / .376
1921	NY	A	P-O	152	2-0 / .378
1922	NY	A	O	110	.315
1923	NY	A	O	152	.393
1924	NY	A	O	153	.378
1925	NY	A	O	98	.290
1926	NY	A	O	152	.372
1927	NY	A	O	151	.356
1928	NY	A	O	154	.323
1929	NY	A	O	135	.345
1930	NY	A	P-O	145	1-0 / .359
1931	NY	A	O	145	.373
1932	NY	A	O	132	.341
1933	NY	A	P-O	137	1-0 / .301
1934	NY	A	O	125	.288
1935	Bos	N	O	28	.181
BLTL				2502	93-44 / .342

RUTHERFORD, JAMES HOLLIS
b.Sept.26,1886 Stillwater,Minn.
d.Sept.18,1956

Yr	Cl	Lea	Pos	G	Rec
1910	Cle	A	O	1	.500

RUTHERFORD, JOHN WILLIAM
b.May 5,1926 Belleville,Ont.,Canada.

Yr	Cl	Lea	Pos	G	Rec
1952	Bro	N	P	22	7-7
BLTR					

RUTNER, MILTON MICKEY
b.Mar.18,1920 Hempstead,N.Y.

Yr	Cl	Lea	Pos	G	Rec
1947	Phi	A	3	12	.250
BRTR					

RYAN, CORNELIUS JOSEPH (Connie)
b.Feb.27,1920 New Orleans,La.

Yr	Cl	Lea	Pos	G	Rec
1942	NY	N	2	11	.185
1943	Bos	N	2-3	132	.212
1944	Bos	N	2-3	88	.295
1946	Bos	N	2-3	143	.241
1947	Bos	N	2-S	150	.265
1948	Bos	N	2-3	51	.213
1949	Bos	N	1-2-S-3	85	.250
1950	Bos	N	2	20	.194
1950	Cin	N	2	106	.259
1951	Cin	N	1-2-3-O	136	.237
1952	Phi	N	2	154	.241
1953	Phi	N	1-2	90	.296
1953	Chi	A	3	17	.222
1954	Cin	N	H	1	.000
BRTR				1184	.248

RYAN, DANIEL R. (Cyclone)
b.1866 Erie,Pa.

Yr	Cl	Lea	Pos	G	Rec
1887	Met	a	1	8	.285
1891	Bos	N	P	1	0-0
				9	0-0 / .278

RYAN, J.

Yr	Cl	Lea	Pos	G	Rec
1895	St.L	N	3	2	.000

RYAN, JACK (Gulfport)
b.Sept.19,1884 Lawrenceville,Ill.
d.Oct.16,1949

Yr	Cl	Lea	Pos	G	Rec
1908	Cle	A	P	8	1-0
1909	Bos	A	P	14	4-3
1911	Bro	N	P	3	0-1
TR				25	5-4

RYAN, JAMES E.
b.Feb.11,1863 Clinton,Mass.
d.Oct.26,1923

Yr	Cl	Lea	Pos	G	Rec
1885	Chi	N	S-O	3	.462
1886	Chi	N	O	84	.306
1887	Chi	N	P-O	126	0-0 / .355
1888	Chi	N	P-O	130	3-1 / .331
1889	Chi	N	S-O	135	.324
1890	Chi	p	O	118	.330
1891	Chi	N	O	118	.289
1892	Chi	N	O	127	.289
1893	Chi	N	O	82	.304
1894	Chi	N	O	108	.359
1895	Chi	N	O	108	.322
1896	Chi	N	O	127	.312
1897	Chi	N	O	135	.309
1898	Chi	N	O	143	.322
1899	Chi	N	O	124	.301
1900	Chi	N	O	106	.276
1902	Was	A	O	120	.317
1903	Was	A	O	114	.245
BRTL				2008	3-1 / .314

RYAN, JOHN A.
b.Birmingham,Mich.

Yr	Cl	Lea	Pos	G	Rec
1884	Bal	U	P-O	6	3-2 / .095

RYAN, JOHN BENNETT
b.Nov.12,1868 Haverhill,Mass.

Yr	Cl	Lea	Pos	G	Rec
1889	Lou	a	C	21	.163
1890	Lou	a	C	94	.219
1891	Lou	a	C	75	.212
1894	Bos	N	C	49	.271
1895	Bos	N	C	49	.295
1896	Bos	N	C	8	.094
1898	Bro	N	C	82	.189
1899	Bal	N	C	2	.500
1901	St.L	N	C	80	.196
1902	St.L	N	C-1-2-S-3	74	.177

(Continued)

Yr	Cl	Lea	Pos	G	Rec
1903	St.L	N	C-1	66	.238
1912	Was	A	3	1	.000
1913	Was	A	C	1	.000
	BRTR			602	.216

RYAN, JOHN BUDD (Bud)
b.Oct.6,1885 Denver,Col.
d.July 9,1956

Yr	Cl	Lea	Pos	G	Rec
1912	Cle	A	O	93	.271
1913	Cle	A	O	73	.296
	BLTR			166	.282

RYAN, JOHN COLLINS (Blondy)
b.Jan.4,1906 Lynn,Mass.
d.Nov.28,1959

Yr	Cl	Lea	Pos	G	Rec
1930	Chi	A	3	28	.207
1933	NY	N	S	146	.238
1934	NY	N	2-S-3	110	.242
1935	Phi	N	S	39	.264
1935	NY	A	S	30	.238
1937	NY	N	S	21	.240
1938	NY	N	2-S-3	12	.208
	BRTR			386	.239

RYAN, JOHN FRANCIS
b.May 5,1905 Kansas City,Kan.

Yr	Cl	Lea	Pos	G	Rec
1929	Bos	A	S-O	2	.000
	BRTR				

RYAN, JOHN JOSEPH
b.Philadelphia,Pa.
d.Mar.22,1902

Yr	Cl	Lea	Pos	G	Rec
1873	Phi	n	1	1	NR
1874	Bal	n	O	47	NR
1875	NH	n	P-C-S-3-O	37	1-5 / NR
1876	Lou	N	O	65	.247
1877	Cin	N	O	6	.154
				156	1-5 / NR

RYAN, JOHN M.
b.Hamilton,O.

Yr	Cl	Lea	Pos	G	Rec
1884	Was	U	3-O	7	.143
1884	Wil	U	O	2	.167
				9	.147

RYAN, WILFRED PATRICK DOLAN (Rosy)
b.Mar.15,1898 Worcester,Mass.

Yr	Cl	Lea	Pos	G	Rec
1919	NY	N	P	4	1-2
1920	NY	N	P	3	0-1
1921	NY	N	P	36	7-10
1922	NY	N	P	46	17-12
1923	NY	N	P	45	16-5
1924	NY	N	P	37	8-6
1925	Bos	N	P	38	2-8
1926	Bos	N	P	7	0-2
1928	NY	A	P	3	0-0
1933	Bro	N	P	30	1-1
	BLTR			249	52-47

RYBA, DOMINIC JOSEPH (Mike)
b.June 9,1903 DeLancey,Pa.

Yr	Cl	Lea	Pos	G	Rec
1935	St.L	N	P	2	1-1
1936	St.L	N	P	18	5-1
1937	St.L	N	P	41	9-6
1938	St.L	N	P	3	1-1
1941	Bos	A	P	40	7-3
1942	Bos	A	P-C	21	3-3 / .294
1943	Bos	A	P	40	7-5
1944	Bos	A	P	42	12-7
1945	Bos	A	P	34	7-6
1946	Bos	A	P	9	0-1
	BRTR			250	52-34 / .235

RYDER, THOMAS

Yr	Cl	Lea	Pos	G	Rec
1884	St.L	U	O	8	.214

RYE, EUGENE RUDOLPH (Half-Pint) (Real name Eugene Rudolph Mercantelli)
b.Nov.15,1906 Chicago,Ill.

Yr	Cl	Lea	Pos	G	Rec
1931	Bos	A	O	17	.179
	BLTR				

SABO, ALEXANDER (Giz) (Real name Alexander Szabo)
b.Feb.14,1910 Highland Park,N.J.

Yr	Cl	Lea	Pos	G	Rec
1936	Was	A	C	4	.375
1937	Was	A	C	1	.000
	BRTR			5	.375

SACKA, FRANK
b.Aug.30,1924 Romulus,Mich.

Yr	Cl	Lea	Pos	G	Rec
1951	Was	A	C	7	.250
1953	Was	A	C	7	.278
	BRTR			14	.265

SADECKI, RAYMOND MICHAEL
b.Dec.26,1940 Kansas City,Kan.

Yr	Cl	Lea	Pos	G	Rec
1960	St.L	N	P	29	9-9
1961	St.L	N	P	36	14-10
1962	St.L	N	P	24	6-8
	BLTL			89	29-27

SADOWSKI, EDWARD ROMAN
b.Jan.19,1932 Pittsburgh,Pa.

Yr	Cl	Lea	Pos	G	Rec
1960	Bos	A	C	38	.215
1961	LA	A	C	69	.232
1962	LA	A	C	27	.200
	BRTR			134	.221

SADOWSKI, ROBERT FRANK
b.Jan.15,1937 St.Louis,Mo.

Yr	Cl	Lea	Pos	G	Rec
1960	St.L	N	2	1	.000
1961	Phi	N	3	16	.130
1962	Chi	A	2-3	79	.231
	BLTR			96	.200

SADOWSKI, THEODORE
b.Apr.1,1936 Pittsburgh,Pa.

Yr	Cl	Lea	Pos	G	Rec
1960	Was	A	P	9	1-0
1961	Min	A	P	15	0-2
1962	Min	A	P	19	1-1
	BRTR			43	2-3

SAFFELL, THOMAS JUDSON
b.July 26,1922 Etowah,Tenn.

Yr	Cl	Lea	Pos	G	Rec
1949	Pit	N	O	73	.322
1950	Pit	N	O	67	.203
1951	Pit	N	O	49	.200
1955	Pit	N	O	73	.168
1955	KC	A	O	9	.216
	BLTR			271	.238

SAGE, HENRY
b.Mar.16,1864 Rock Island,Ill.
d.May 27,1947

Yr	Cl	Lea	Pos	G	Rec
1890	Tol	a	P-C	58	0-1 / .139
	BR				

SAGER, SAMUEL B. (Pony)
b.1847 Marshalltown,Ia.

Yr	Cl	Lea	Pos	G	Rec
1871	Rok	n	S-O	8	NR

SAIER, VICTOR SYLVESTER
b.May 4,1891 Lansing,Mich.

Yr	Cl	Lea	Pos	G	Rec
1911	Chi	N	1	73	.259
1912	Chi	N	1	122	.288
1913	Chi	N	1	149	.289
1914	Chi	N	1	153	.240
1915	Chi	N	1	144	.264
1916	Chi	N	1	147	.253
1917	Chi	N	1	6	.238
1919	Pit	N	1	58	.223
	BLTR			852	.262

SAIN, JOHN FRANKLIN
b.Sept.25,1917 Havana,Ark.

Yr	Cl	Lea	Pos	G	Rec
1942	Bos	N	P	40	4-7
1946	Bos	N	P	40	20-14
1947	Bos	N	P	40	21-12
1948	Bos	N	P	43	24-15
1949	Bos	N	P	39	10-17
1950	Bos	N	P	37	20-13

(Continued)

Yr	Cl	Lea	Pos	G	Rec
1951	Bos	N	P	26	5-13
1951	NY	A	P	7	2-1
1952	NY	A	P	47	11-6
1953	NY	A	P	41	14-7
1954	NY	A	P	45	6-6
1955	NY	A	P	3	0-0
1955	KC	A	P	25	2-5
	BRTR			433	139-116

ST.CLAIRE, EDWARD JOSEPH (Ebba)
b.Aug.5,1921 Whitehall,N.Y.

Yr	Cl	Lea	Pos	G	Rec
1951	Bos	N	C	72	.282
1952	Bos	N	C	39	.213
1953	Mil	N	C	33	.200
1954	NY	N	C	20	.262
	BBTR			164	.249

ST.VRAIN, JAMES H.
b.June 6,1883 Monroe Co.,Mo.
d.June 12,1937

Yr	Cl	Lea	Pos	G	Rec
1902	Chi	N	P	12	5-6
	BRTL				

SALE, FREDERICK LINK
b.May 2,1902 Chester,S.C.
d.May 27,1956

Yr	Cl	Lea	Pos	G	Rec
1924	Pit	N	P	1	0-0
	BRTR				

SALES, EDWARD A.
b.1861 Harrisburg,Pa.
d.Aug.10,1912

Yr	Cl	Lea	Pos	G	Rec
1890	Pit	N	S	51	.228
		TR			

SALISBURY, HENRY H.
b.May 15,1855 Providence,R.I.
d.Mar.29,1933

Yr	Cl	Lea	Pos	G	Rec
1879	Tro	N	P-O	10	4-6 / .056
1882	Pit	a	P-O	39	20-19 / .152
				49	24-25 / .143

SALISBURY, WILLIAM A.
b.1876 Iowa.

Yr	Cl	Lea	Pos	G	Rec
1902	Phi	N	P	2	0-0

SALKELD, WILLIAM FRANKLIN
b.Mar.8,1917 Pocatello,Ida.

Yr	Cl	Lea	Pos	G	Rec
1945	Pit	N	C	95	.311
1946	Pit	N	C	69	.294
1947	Pit	N	C	47	.213
1948	Bos	N	C	78	.242
1949	Bos	N	C	66	.255
1950	Chi	A	C	1	.000
	BLTR			356	.273

SALLEE, HARRY FRANKLIN (Slim)
b.Feb.3,1885 Higginsport,O.
d.Mar.22,1950

Yr	Cl	Lea	Pos	G	Rec
1908	St.L	N	P	25	3-8
1909	St.L	N	P	32	10-11
1910	St.L	N	P	18	7-8
1911	St.L	N	P	36	15-9
1912	St.L	N	P	48	16-17
1913	St.L	N	P	50	19-15
1914	St.L	N	P	46	18-17
1915	St.L	N	P	46	13-17
1916	St.L	N	P	16	5-5
1916	NY	N	P	15	9-4
1917	NY	N	P	34	18-7
1918	NY	N	P	18	8-8
1919	Cin	N	P	29	21-7
1920	Cin	N	P	21	5-6
1920	NY	N	P	5	1-0
1921	NY	N	P	37	6-4
	BLTL			476	174-143

SALMON, ROGER ELLIOTT
b.May 11,1891 Newark,N.J.

Yr	Cl	Lea	Pos	G	Rec
1912	Phi	A	P	1	1-0
	BLTL				

SALTZGAVER, OTTO HAMLIN
(Jack)
b.Jan.23,1906 Croton,Ia.

Yr	Cl	Lea	Pos	G	Rec
1932	NY	A	2	20	.128
1934	NY	A	1-3	94	.271
1935	NY	A	1-2-3	61	.262
1936	NY	A	3	34	.211
1937	NY	A	1	17	.182
1945	Pit	N	2-3	52	.325
	BLTR			278	.260

SALVE, AUGUSTUS WILLIAM
b.Dec.29,1885 Boston,Mass.

Yr	Cl	Lea	Pos	G	Rec
1908	Phi	A	P	2	0-1
	TL				

SALVESON, JOHN THEODORE
b.Jan.5,1914 Fullerton,Cal.

Yr	Cl	Lea	Pos	G	Rec
1933	NY	N	P	8	0-2
1934	NY	N	P	13	3-1
1935	Pit	N	P	5	0-1
1935	Chi	A	P	20	1-2
1943	Cle	A	P	23	5-3
1945	Cle	A	P	19	0-0
	BRTR			88	9-9

SALVO, MANUEL (Gyp)
b.June 30,1913 Sacramento,Cal.

Yr	Cl	Lea	Pos	G	Rec
1939	NY	N	P	32	4-10
1940	Bos	N	P	21	10-9
1941	Bos	N	P	35	7-16
1942	Bos	N	P	25	7-8
1943	Bos	N	P	1	0-0
1943	Phi	N	P	1	0-0
1943	Bos	N	P	20	5-7
	BRTR			135	33-50

SAMCOFF, EDWARD WILLIAM
b.Sept.1,1924 Sacramento,Cal.

Yr	Cl	Lea	Pos	G	Rec
1951	Phi	A	2	4	.000
	BRTR				

SAMFORD, RONALD EDWARD
b.Feb.28,1930 Dallas,Tex.

Yr	Cl	Lea	Pos	G	Rec
1954	NY	N	2	12	.000
1955	Det	A	S	1	.000
1957	Det	A	2-S-3	54	.220
1959	Was	A	2-S	54	.224
	BRTR			158	.219

SAMUEL, AMADO RUPERTO
b.Dec.6,1938 San Pedro de Macoris,D.R.

Yr	Cl	Lea	Pos	G	Rec
1962	Mil	N	2-S-3	76	.206
	BRTR				

SAMUELS, JOSEPH JONAS
b.Mar.21,1908 Scranton,Pa.

Yr	Cl	Lea	Pos	G	Rec
1930	Det	A	P	2	0-0
	BRTR				

SAMUELS, SAMUEL EARL
(Ike)
b.Feb.20,1876 Chicago,Ill.

Yr	Cl	Lea	Pos	G	Rec
1895	St.L	N	3	22	.186
	BRTR				

SANBERG, GUSTAVE E.
b.Feb.23,1896 Long Island City,N.Y.
d.Feb.3,1930

Yr	Cl	Lea	Pos	G	Rec
1923	Cin	N	C	7	.176
1924	Cin	N	C	24	.173
	BRTR			31	.174

SANCHEZ, JOSE ZARDON
(Played under name of
Joseph Zardon)

SANCHEZ, RAUL GUADALUPE RODRIGUEZ
b.Dec.12,1930 Marianao,Cuba.

Yr	Cl	Lea	Pos	G	Rec
1952	Was	A	P	3	1-1
1957	Cin	N	P	38	3-2

(Continued)

Yr	Cl	Lea	Pos	G	Rec
1960	Cin	N	P	8	1-0
	BRTR			49	5-3

SAND, JOHN HENRY
(Heinie)
b.July 3,1897 San Francisco,Cal.
d.Nov.3,1958

Yr	Cl	Lea	Pos	G	Rec
1923	Phi	N	S-3	132	.228
1924	Phi	N	S	137	.245
1925	Phi	N	S	148	.278
1926	Phi	N	S	149	.272
1927	Phi	N	S-3	141	.299
1928	Phi	N	S	141	.211
	BRTR			848	.258

SANDERS, ALEXANDER BENJAMIN (Ben)
b.Feb.16,1865 Carpathen,Va.
d.Aug.29,1930

Yr	Cl	Lea	Pos	G	Rec
1888	Phi	N	P-O	57	19-10 / .245
1889	Phi	N	P	41	19-17
1890	Phi	p	P	44	21-19
1891	Ath	a	P-O	41	12-7 / .253
1892	Lou	N	P-1	53	12-17 / .267
	BRTR			236	83-70 / .267

SANDERS, DEE WILMA
b.Apr.8,1921 Quitman,Tex.

Yr	Cl	Lea	Pos	G	Rec
1945	St.L	A	P	2	0-0
	BRTR				

SANDERS, RAYMOND FLOYD
b.Dec.4,1917 Bonne Terre,Mo.

Yr	Cl	Lea	Pos	G	Rec
1942	St.L	N	1	95	.252
1943	St.L	N	1	144	.280
1944	St.L	N	1	154	.295
1945	St.L	N	1	143	.276
1946	Bos	N	1	80	.243
1948	Bos	N	H	5	.250
1949	Bos	N	1	9	.143
	BLTR			630	.275

SANDERS, ROY GARVIN
(Pep)
b.Aug.1,1893 Stafford,Kan.
d.Jan.17,1950

Yr	Cl	Lea	Pos	G	Rec
1917	Cin	N	P	3	0-1
1918	Pit	N	P	28	7-9
	BRTR			31	7-10

SANDERS, ROY L. (Simon)
b.1894

Yr	Cl	Lea	Pos	G	Rec
1918	NY	A	P	6	0-2
1920	St.L	A	P	8	1-1
	BRTR			14	1-3

SANDERS, WARREN WILLIAMS
b.Aug.2,1877 Maynardville,Tenn.
d.Aug.3,1962

Yr	Cl	Lea	Pos	G	Rec
1903	St.L	N	P	8	1-6
1904	St.L	N	P	4	1-2
				•12	2-8

SANDLOCK, MICHAEL JOSEPH
b.Oct.17,1916 Old Greenwich,Conn.

Yr	Cl	Lea	Pos	G	Rec
1942	Bos	N	S	2	1.000
1944	Bos	N	S-3	30	.100
1945	Bro	N	C-2-S-3	80	.282
1946	Bro	N	C-3	19	.147
1953	Pit	N	C	64	.131
	BBTR			195	.240

SANDY, IRWIN
(Played under name of
Vincent Nava)

SANFORD, JOHN DOWARD
b.June 23,1917 Chatham,Va.

Yr	Cl	Lea	Pos	G	Rec
1940	Was	A	1	34	.197
1941	Was	A	1	3	.400
1946	Was	A	1	10	.231
	BRTR			47	.209

SANFORD, JOHN FREDERICK
(Fred)
b.Aug.9,1919 Salt Lake City,Utah.

Yr	Cl	Lea	Pos	G	Rec
1943	St.L	A	P	3	0-0
1946	St.L	A	P	3	2-1
1947	St.L	A	P	34	7-16
1948	St.L	A	P	43	12-21
1949	NY	A	P	29	7-3
1950	NY	A	P	26	5-4
1951	NY	A	P	11	0-3
1951	Was	A	P	7	2-3
1951	St.L	A	P	9	2-4
	BBTR			165	37-55

SANFORD, JOHN STANLEY
b.May 18,1929 Wellesley Hills,Mass.

Yr	Cl	Lea	Pos	G	Rec
1956	Phi	N	P	3	1-0
1957	Phi	N	P	33	19-8
1958	Phi	N	P	38	10-13
1959	SF	N	P	36	15-12
1960	SF	N	P	37	12-14
1961	SF	N	P	39	13-9
1962	SF	N	P	39	24-7
	BRTR			225	94-63

SANICKI, EDWARD ROBERT
(Butch)
b.July 7,1924 Wallington,N.J.

Yr	Cl	Lea	Pos	G	Rec
1949	Phi	N	O	7	.231
1951	Phi	N	O	13	.500
	BRTR			20	.294

SANKEY, BENJAMIN TURNER
b.Sept.2,1907 Nauvoo,Ala.

Yr	Cl	Lea	Pos	G	Rec
1929	Pit	N	S	2	.143
1930	Pit	N	2-S	13	.167
1931	Pit	N	S	57	.227
	BRTR			72	.213

SANTIAGO, JOSE GUILLERMO
b.Apr.9,1929 Coamo, Puerto Rico

Yr	Cl	Lea	Pos	G	Rec
1954	Cle	A	P	1	0-0
1955	Cle	A	P	17	2-0
1956	KC	A	P	9	1-2
	BRTR			27	3-2

SANTO, RONALD EDWARD
b.Feb.25,1940 Seattle,Wash.

Yr	Cl	Lea	Pos	G	Rec
1960	Chi	N	3	95	.251
1961	Chi	N	3	154	.284
1962	Chi	N	S-3	162	.227
	BRTR			000	.000

SANTRY, EDWARD
b.Chicago,Ill.

Yr	Cl	Lea	Pos	G	Rec
1884	Det	N	2-S	6	.174

SARGENT, JOSEPH ALEXANDER
b.Sept.24,1893 Rochester,N.Y.
d.July 5,1950

Yr	Cl	Lea	Pos	G	Rec
1921	Det	A	2-S-3	66	.253
	BRTR				

SARNI, WILLIAM F.
b.Sept.19,1927 Los Angeles,Cal.

Yr	Cl	Lea	Pos	G	Rec
1951	St.L	N	C	36	.174
1952	St.L	N	C	3	.200
1954	St.L	N	C	123	.300
1955	St.L	N	C	107	.256
1956	St.L	N	C	43	.291
1956	NY	N	C	78	.231
	BRTR			390	.263

SATRIANO, THOMAS VICTOR
b.Aug.28,1940 Pittsburgh,Pa.

Yr	Cl	Lea	Pos	G	Rec
1961	LA	A	2-S-3	35	.198
1962	LA	A	3	10	.421
	BLTR			00	.000

SAUCIER, FRANCIS FIELD
b.May 28,1927 Leslie,Mo.

Yr	Cl	Lea	Pos	G	Rec
1951	St.L	A	O	18	.071
	BLTR				

SAUER, EDWARD (Horn)
b.Jan.3,1920 Pittsburgh,Pa.

Yr	Cl	Lea	Pos	G	Rec
1943	Chi	N	O	14	.273
1944	Chi	N	O	23	.220
1945	Chi	N	O	49	.258
1949	St.L	N	H	24	.222
1949	Bos	N	O	79	.266
	BRTR			189	.256

SAUER, HENRY JOHN
b.Mar.17,1919 Pittsburgh,Pa.

Yr	Cl	Lea	Pos	G	Rec
1941	Cin	N	O	9	.303
1942	Cin	N	1	7	.250
1945	Cin	N	1-O	31	.293
1948	Cin	N	1-O	145	.260
1949	Cin	N	1-O	42	.237
1949	Chi	N	O	96	.291
1950	Chi	N	1-O	145	.274
1951	Chi	N	O	141	.263
1952	Chi	N	O	151	.270
1953	Chi	N	O	108	.263
1954	Chi	N	O	142	.288
1955	Chi	N	O	29	.211
1956	St.L	N	O	75	.298
1957	NY	N	O	127	.259
1958	SF	N	O	88	.250
1959	SF	N	O	13	.067
	BRTR			1399	.266

SAUNDERS, RUSSELL COLLIER
b.Mar.12,1906 Trenton,N.J.

Yr	Cl	Lea	Pos	G	Rec
1927	Phi	A	O	5	.133
	BRTR				

SAUTERS, AL.
b.Philadelphia,Pa.

Yr	Cl	Lea	Pos	G	Rec
1890	Ath	a	3	14	.098

SAVAGE, DONALD ANTHONY
b.Mar.5,1919 Bloomfield,N.J.
d.Dec.25,1961

Yr	Cl	Lea	Pos	G	Rec
1944	NY	A	3	71	.264
1945	NY	A	3-O	34	.224
	BRTR			105	.256

SAVAGE, HAROLD JAMES
b.Bridgeport,Conn.

Yr	Cl	Lea	Pos	G	Rec
1912	Phi	N	2	2	.000
1914	Pit	F	3-O	132	.285
1915	Pit	F	O	14	.150
	BLTR			148	.280

SAVAGE, JOHN ROBERT
(Bob)
b.Dec.1,1921 Manchester,N.H.

Yr	Cl	Lea	Pos	G	Rec
1942	Phi	A	P	8	0-1
1946	Phi	A	P	40	3-15
1947	Phi	A	P	44	8-10
1948	Phi	A	P	33	5-1
1949	St.L	A	P	4	0-0
	BRTR			129	16-27

SAVAGE, THEODORE E.
b.Feb.21,1937 E.St.Louis,Ill.

Yr	Cl	Lea	Pos	G	Rec
1962	Phi	N	O	127	.266
	BRTR				

SAVERINE, ROBERT PAUL
b.Jan.2,1941 Norwalk,Conn.

Yr	Cl	Lea	Pos	G	Rec
1959	Bal	A	H	1	.000
1962	Bal	A	2	8	.238
	BBTR			9	.238

SAVIDGE, DONALD SNYDER
b.Aug.28,1908 Berwick,Pa.

Yr	Cl	Lea	Pos	G	Rec
1929	Was	A	P	3	0-0
	BRTR				

SAVIDGE, RALPH AUSTIN
b.Feb.3,1879 Berwick,Pa.
d.July 22,1959

Yr	Cl	Lea	Pos	G	Rec
1908	Cin	N	P	4	0-1
1909	Cin	N	P	1	0-0
	BRTR			5	0-1

SAVRANSKY, MORRIS (Moe)
b.Jan.13,1929 Cleveland,O.

Yr	Cl	Lea	Pos	G	Rec
1954	Cin	N	P	16	0-2
	BLTL				

SAWATSKI, CARL ERNEST
(Swats)
b.Nov.4,1927 Shickshinny,Pa.

Yr	Cl	Lea	Pos	G	Rec
194	Chi	N	H	2	.000
1950	Chi	N	C	38	.175
1953	Chi	N	C	43	.220
1954	Chi	A	C	43	.183
1957	Mil	N	C	58	.238
1958	Mil	N	C	10	.100
1958	Phi	N	C	60	.230
1959	Phi	N	C	74	.293
1960	St.L	N	C	78	.229
1961	St.L	N	C-O	86	.299
1962	St.L	N	C	85	.252
	BLTR			577	.243

SAWYER, CARL EVERETT
(Huck)
b.Oct.19,1890 Seattle,Wash.
d.Jan.17,1957

Yr	Cl	Lea	Pos	G	Rec
1915	Was	A	2	10	.117
1916	Was	A	2	16	.194
	BRTR			26	.190

SAWYER, EDWIN MILBY
b.Sept.10,1910 Westerly,R.I.
Non-playing manager Phi (N) 1948-52, 1958 and 1958-60

SAWYER, WILLARD NEWTON
b.July 29,1863 Kent,O.
d.Jan.5,1936

Yr	Cl	Lea	Pos	G	Rec
1883	Cle	N	P	17	4-10

SAX, ERIK OLIVER (Ollie)
b.Nov.5,1906 Branford,Conn.

Yr	Cl	Lea	Pos	G	Rec
1928	St.L	A	3	16	.176
	BRTR				

SAY, JAMES I.
b.1862 Baltimore,Md.
d.June 23,1894

Yr	Cl	Lea	Pos	G	Rec
1882	Lou	a	3	1	.500
1882	Ath	a	S	1	.500
1884	Wil	U	3	16	.220
1884	KC	U	3	2	.250
1887	Cle	a	3	15	.367
				35	.304

SAY, LEWIS I.
b.Feb.4,1854 Baltimore,Md.
d.June 5,1930

Yr	Cl	Lea	Pos	G	Rec
1873	Mar	n	S-O	2	NR
1874	Bal	n	S	18	NR
1875	Nat	n	2-S-O	9	NR
1880	Cin	N	S	47	.202
1882	Ath	a	S	71	.221
1883	Bal	a	S	84	.260
1884	Bal	U	S	79	.256
1884	KC	U	2-S	17	.217
	BRTR			327	NR

SAYLES, WILLIAM NISBETH
b.July 27,1917 Portland,Ore.

Yr	Cl	Lea	Pos	G	Rec
1939	Bos	A	P	5	0-0
1943	NY	N	P	19	1-3
1943	Bro	N	P	6	0-0
	BRTR			30	1-3

SAYLOR, PHILIP ANDREW
(Lefty)
b.Jan.2,1871 Van Wert Co.,O.
d.July 23,1937

Yr	Cl	Lea	Pos	G	Rec
1891	Phi	N	P	1	0-0
	TL				

SCALA, GERARD DANIEL
b.Sept.27,1926 Bayonne,N.J.

Yr	Cl	Lea	Pos	G	Rec
1948	Chi	A	O	3	.000
1949	Chi	A	O	37	.250
1950	Chi	A	O	40	.194
	BLTR			80	.223

SCALZI, FRANK JOHN
(Skeeter)
b.June 16,1915 Lafferty,O.

Yr	Cl	Lea	Pos	G	Rec
1939	NY	N	S-3	11	.333
	BRTR				

SCALZI, JOHN ANTHONY
b.Mar.22.1907 Stamford,Conn.
d.Sept.27,1962

Yr	Cl	Lea	Pos	G	Rec
1931	Bos	N	H	2	.000
	BRTR				

SCANLAN, FRANK ALOYSIUS
b.Apr.28,1890 Syracuse,N.Y.

Yr	Cl	Lea	Pos	G	Rec
1909	Phi	N	P	6	0-0

SCANLAN, WILLIAM DENNIS
(Doc)
b.Mar.7,1881 Syracuse,N.Y.
d.May 29,1949

Yr	Cl	Lea	Pos	G	Rec
1903	Pit	N	P	1	0-1
1904	Pit	N	P	4	1-2
1904	Bro	N	P	14	7-7
1905	Bro	N	P	33	15-11
1906	Bro	N	P	38	18-13
1907	Bro	N	P	17	6-8
1909	Bro	N	P	19	8-7
1910	Bro	N	P	34	9-11
1911	Bro	N	P	22	3-10
	BLTR			182	67-70

SCANLON, M. J.
b.Chicago,Ill.

Yr	Cl	Lea	Pos	G	Rec
1890	NY	N	1	3	.000

SCANLON, MICHAEL B.
b.1847 Cork,Ireland
d.Jan.18,1929
Non-playing manager Was (U) 1884 and Was (N) 1886.

SCANNELL, JOHN J.

Yr	Cl	Lea	Pos	G	Rec
1884	Bos	U	O	6	.304

SCANTLEBURY, PATRICIO ATHELSTAN
b.Nov.11,1925 Panama City,Panama

Yr	Cl	Lea	Pos	G	Rec
1956	Cin	N	P	8	0-1
	BLTL				

SCARBOROUGH, RAY WILSON
b.July 23,1917 Mt.Gilead,N.C.

Yr	Cl	Lea	Pos	G	Rec
1942	Was	A	P	17	2-1
1943	Was	A	P	24	4-4
1946	Was	A	P	32	7-11
1947	Was	A	P	33	6-13
1948	Was	A	P	31	15-8
1949	Was	A	P	34	13-11
1950	Was	A	P	8	3-5
1950	Chi	A	P	27	10-13
1951	Bos	A	P	37	12-9
1952	Bos	A	P	28	1-5
1952	NY	A	P	9	5-1
1953	NY	A	P	25	2-2
1953	Det	A	P	13	0-2
	BRTR			318	80-85

SCARRITT, RUSSELL MALLORY
b.Jan.14,1903 Pensacola,Fla.

Yr	Cl	Lea	Pos	G	Rec
1929	Bos	A	O	151	.294
1930	Bos	A	O	113	.289
1931	Bos	A	O	10	.154
1932	Phi	N	O	11	.182
	BLTR			285	.285

SCARSELLA, LESLIE GEORGE
b.Nov.23,1913 Santa Cruz,Cal.
d.Dec.17,1958

Yr	Cl	Lea	Pos	G	Rec
1935	Cin	N	1	6	.200
1936	Cin	N	1	115	.313
1937	Cin	N	1-O	110	.246
1939	Cin	N	H	16	.143
1940	Bos	N	1	18	.300
BLTL				265	.285

SCHACHT, ALEXANDER
b.Nov.11,1892 New York,N.Y.

Yr	Cl	Lea	Pos	G	Rec
1919	Was	A	P	2	2-0
1920	Was	A	P	22	6-4
1921	Was	A	P	30	6-6
BRTR				54	14-10

SCHACHT, SIDNEY
b.Feb.3,1924 Bogota,N.J.

Yr	Cl	Lea	Pos	G	Rec
1950	St.L	A	P	9	0-0
1951	St.L	A	P	6	0-0
1951	Bos	N	P	5	0-2
BRTR				20	0-2

SCHACKER, HAROLD
b.Apr.6,1925 Brooklyn,N.Y.

Yr	Cl	Lea	Pos	G	Rec
1945	Bos	N	P	6	0-1
BRTR					

SCHAEFER, HERMAN A.
(Germany)
b.Feb.4,1878 Chicago,Ill.
d.May 16,1919

Yr	Cl	Lea	Pos	G	Rec
1901	Chi	N	2	2	.375
1902	Chi	N	1-3-O	80	.188
1905	Det	A	2	153	.244
1906	Det	A	2	124	.238
1907	Det	A	2-S	109	.258
1908	Det	A	2-S-3	153	.259
1909	Det	A	2	87	.250
1909	Was	A	2	37	.155
1910	Was	A	2-O	74	.275
1911	Was	A	1	125	.334
1912	Was	A	1-2-O	60	.247
1913	Was	A	P-2	52	0-0 .320
1914	Was	A	2	25	.241
1915	New	F	O	58	.214
1916	NY	A	O	1	.000
1918	Cle	A	2	1	.000
BRTR				1141	0-0 .256

SCHAEFFER, HARRY EDWARD
b.June 23,1925 Reading,Pa.

Yr	Cl	Lea	Pos	G	Rec
1952	NY	A	P	5	0-1
BLTL					

SCHAFER, HARRY C.
(Silk Stocking)
b.Aug.14,1846 Philadelphia,Pa.
d.Feb.28,1935

Yr	Cl	Lea	Pos	G	Rec
1871	Bos	n	3	33	NR
1872	Bos	n	3-O	48	.262
1873	Bos	n	3-O	60	.284
1874	Bos	n	3	71	.275
1875	Bos	n	3	51	.295
1876	Bos	N	3	70	.248
1877	Bos	N	S-3-O	33	.277
1878	Bos	N	O	4	.235
1879	Cin	N	S	1	.000
BRTR				371	NR

SCHAFER, JOHN W.
b.Lock Haven,Pa.

Yr	Cl	Lea	Pos	G	Rec
1886	Met	a	P	8	5-3
1887	Met	a	P	13	2-11
				21	7-14

SCHAFFER, GEORGE (Orator)
b.1852 Philadelphia,Pa.

Yr	Cl	Lea	Pos	G	Rec
1874	Har	n	O	9	NR
1874	Mut	n	O	1	NR
1875	Phi	n	1-3-O	16	NR
1877	Lou	N	1-O	61	.285
1878	Ind	N	O	60	.344
1879	Chi	N	O	70	.319
1880	Cle	N	O	82	.265

(Continued)

Yr	Cl	Lea	Pos	G	Rec
1881	Cle	N	O	84	.257
1882	Cle	N	O	82	.218
1883	Buf	N	O	94	.292
1884	St.L	U	O	89	.354
1885	St.L	N	O	69	.194
1885	Ath	a	O	2	.222
1886	Ath	a	O	21	.344
1890	Ath	a	O	106	.286
BLTR				846	NR

SCHAFFER, TAYLOR
b.Philadelphia,Pa.

Yr	Cl	Lea	Pos	G	Rec
1890	Ath	a	2	70	.178

SCHAFFER, JIMMIE RONALD
b.Apr.5,1936 Limeport,Pa.

Yr	Cl	Lea	Pos	G	Rec
1961	St.L	N	C	68	.255
1962	St.L	N	C	70	.242
BRTR				138	.251

SCHAIVE, JOHN EDWARD
b.Feb.25,1934 Springfield,Ill.

Yr	Cl	Lea	Pos	G	Rec
1958	Was	A	2	7	.250
1959	Was	A	2	16	.153
1960	Was	A	6	6	.250
1962	Was	A	2-3	82	.253
BRTR				111	.234

SCHAFFERNOTH, JOSEPH ARTHUR
b.Aug.6,1937 Springfield,N.J.

Yr	Cl	Lea	Pos	G	Rec
1959	Chi	N	P	5	1-0
1960	Chi	N	P	33	2-3
1961	Chi	N	P	21	0-4
1961	Cle	A	P	15	0-1
BRTR				73	3-8

SCHALK, LeROY JOHN
b.Nov.9,1908 Chicago,Ill.

Yr	Cl	Lea	Pos	G	Rec
1932	NY	A	2	3	.250
1944	Chi	A	2-S	146	.220
1945	Chi	A	2	133	.248
BRTR				282	.233

SCHALK, RAYMOND WILLIAM
(Cracker)
b.Aug.12,1892 Harvel,Ill.

Yr	Cl	Lea	Pos	G	Rec
1912	Chi	A	C	23	.286
1913	Chi	A	C	128	.244
1914	Chi	A	C	135	.270
1915	Chi	A	C	135	.266
1916	Chi	A	C	129	.232
1917	Chi	A	C	140	.227
1918	Chi	A	C	108	.219
1919	Chi	A	C	131	.282
1920	Chi	A	C	151	.270
1921	Chi	A	C	128	.252
1922	Chi	A	C	142	.281
1923	Chi	A	C	123	.228
1924	Chi	A	C	57	.196
1925	Chi	A	C	125	.274
1926	Chi	A	C	82	.265
1927	Chi	A	M-C	16	.231
1928	Chi	A	M-C	2	1.000
1929	NY	N	C	5	.000
BRTR				1760	.253

SCHALLER, WALTER (Biff)
b.Sept.23,1889 Chicago,Ill.
d.Oct.9,1939

Yr	Cl	Lea	Pos	G	Rec
1911	Det	A	O	40	.133
1913	Chi	A	O	34	.219
BLTR				74	.186

SCHALLICK, AUGUST
(Played under name of
August Shallix)

SCHALLOCK, ARTHUR LAWRENCE
b.Apr.25,1925 Mill Valley,Cal.

Yr	Cl	Lea	Pos	G	Rec
1951	NY	A	P	11	3-1
1952	NY	A	P	2	0-0
1953	NY	A	P	7	0-0
1954	NY	A	P	6	0-1
1955	NY	A	P	2	0-0
1955	Bal	A	P	30	3-5
BLTL				58	6-7

SCHANG, ROBERT M.
b.Dec.7,1891 S.Wales,N.Y.

Yr	Cl	Lea	Pos	G	Rec
1914	Pit	N	C	10	.250
1915	Pit	N	C	56	.184
1915	NY	N	C	12	.143
1927	St.L	N	C	3	.200
BBTR				81	.188

SCHANG, WALTER HENRY
b.Aug.22,1889 S.Wales,N.Y.

Yr	Cl	Lea	Pos	G	Rec
1913	Phi	A	C	77	.266
1914	Phi	A	C	107	.287
1915	Phi	A	C-3-O	116	.248
1916	Phi	A	C-O	110	.266
1917	Phi	A	C	118	.285
1918	Bos	A	C-O	88	.245
1919	Bos	A	C	113	.306
1920	Bos	A	C-O	122	.305
1921	NY	A	C	134	.316
1922	NY	A	C	124	.319
1923	NY	A	C	84	.276
1924	NY	A	C	114	.292
1925	NY	A	C	73	.240
1926	St.L	A	C	103	.330
1927	St.L	A	C	97	.319
1928	St.L	A	C	91	.285
1929	St.L	A	C	94	.237
1930	Phi	A	C	45	.174
1931	Det	A	C	30	.184
BBTR				1840	.284

SCHANZ, CHARLEY MURRELL
b.June 8,1919 Anacortes,Wash.

Yr	Cl	Lea	Pos	G	Rec
1944	Phi	N	P	40	13-16
1945	Phi	N	P	35	4-15
1946	Phi	N	P	32	6-6
1947	Phi	N	P	34	2-4
1950	Bos	A	P	14	3-2
BRTR				155	28-43

SCHAPPERT, JOHN
b.Brooklyn,N.Y.

Yr	Cl	Lea	Pos	G	Rec
1882	St.L	a	P-O	15	8-7 .173

SCHARDT, WILBURT
b.Jan.20,1886 Cleveland,O.

Yr	Cl	Lea	Pos	G	Rec
1911	Bro	N	P	39	5-15
1912	Bro	N	P	7	0-1
BRTR				46	5-16

SCHAREIN, ARTHUR OTTO
(Scoop)
b.June 30,1905 Decatur,Ill.

Yr	Cl	Lea	Pos	G	Rec
1932	St.L	A	3	81	.304
1933	St.L	A	3	123	.204
1934	St.L	A	H	1	.500
BRTR				205	.244

SCHAREIN, GEORGE ALBERT
(Tom)
b.Nov.21,1914 Decatur,Ill.

Yr	Cl	Lea	Pos	G	Rec
1937	Phi	N	S	146	.241
1938	Phi	N	2-S	117	.238
1939	Phi	N	S	118	.238
1940	Phi	N	S	7	.294
BRTR				388	.240

SCHARF, EDWARD T.
b.Baltimore,Md.
d.May 12,1937

Yr	Cl	Lea	Pos	G	Rec
1882	Bal	a	3-O	10	.243
1883	Bal	a	S	3	.143
				13	.216

SCHAUER, ...

Yr	Cl	Lea	Pos	G	Rec
1890	Col	a	1	1	.500

SCHAUER, ALEXANDER JOHN
(Rube) (Real name Alexander John Dimitrihoff)
b.Mar.19,1892 Odessa, Russia.
d.Apr.15,1957

Yr	Cl	Lea	Pos	G	Rec
1913	NY	N	P	3	0-1
1914	NY	N	P	6	0-0
1915	NY	N	P	32	2-8
1916	NY	N	P	19	1-4
1917	Phi	A	P	33	7-16
	BRTR			93	10-29

SCHEER, ALLEN G.
b.Oct.27,1889 Groveport, O.
d.May 6,1959

Yr	Cl	Lea	Pos	G	Rec
1913	Bro	N	O	6	.272
1914	Ind	F	O	117	.309
1915	New	F	O	155	.269
	BLTR			278	.283

SCHEER, HENRY WILLIAM
(Heinie)
b.June 23,1900 New York, N.Y.

Yr	Cl	Lea	Pos	G	Rec
1922	Phi	A	2-3	51	.171
1923	Phi	A	2	69	.238
	BRTR			120	.212

SCHEEREN, FREDERICK
(Fritz)
b.Sept.8,1891 Ford City, Pa.

Yr	Cl	Lea	Pos	G	Rec
1914	Pit	N	O	11	.267
1915	Pit	N	O	4	.000
	BRTR			15	.243

SCHEETZ, OWEN FRANKLIN
b.Dec.24,1913 New Bedford, O.

Yr	Cl	Lea	Pos	G	Rec
1943	Was	A	P	6	0-0
	BRTR				

SCHEFFING, ROBERT BODEN
b.Aug.11,1915 Overland, Mo.

Yr	Cl	Lea	Pos	G	Rec
1941	Chi	N	C	51	.242
1942	Chi	N	C	44	.196
1946	Chi	N	C	63	.278
1947	Chi	N	C	110	.264
1948	Chi	N	C	102	.300
1949	Chi	N	C	55	.268
1950	Chi	N	C	12	.188
1950	Cin	N	C	21	.277
1951	Cin	N	C	47	.254
1951	St.L	N	C	12	.111
	BRTR			517	.263

Non-playing manager Chi (N) 1957-59 and Detroit (A) 1961-62

SCHEFFLER, THEODORE J.
b.New York, N.Y.

Yr	Cl	Lea	Pos	G	Rec
1888	Det	N	O	27	.202
1890	Roc	a	O	117	.239
				144	.233

SCHEGG (Lefty)

Yr	Cl	Lea	Pos	G	Rec
1912	Was	A	P	2	0-0

SCHEIB, CARL ALVIN
b.Jan.1,1927 Gratz, Pa.

Yr	Cl	Lea	Pos	G	Rec
1943	Phi	A	P	6	0-1
1944	Phi	A	P	15	0-0
1945	Phi	A	P	4	0-0
1947	Phi	A	P	22	4-6
1948	Phi	A	P-O	52	14-8 / .298
1949	Phi	A	P	47	9-12
1950	Phi	A	P	50	3-10
1951	Phi	A	P	48	1-12
1952	Phi	A	P	44	11-7
1953	Phi	A	P	35	3-7
1954	Phi	A	P	1	0-1
1954	St.L	N	P	3	0-1
	BRTR			327	45-65 / .250

SCHEIBECK, FRANK
b.June 28,1865 Detroit, Mich.
d.Oct.22,1956

Yr	Cl	Lea	Pos	G	Rec
1887	Cle	a	P-3	3	0-0 / .364
1888	Det	N	S	1	.000
1890	Tol	a	S	134	.234
1894	Pit	N	2-S-3-O	26	.347
1894	Was	N	S	49	.238
1895	Was	N	S	48	.182
1899	Was	N	S	27	.287
1901	Cle	A	S	93	.217
1906	Det	A	2	3	.125
	BRTR			384	0-0 / .243

SCHEIBLE, JOHN G.
b.Feb.16,1866 Youngstown, O.
d.Aug.9,1897

Yr	Cl	Lea	Pos	G	Rec
1893	Cle	N	P	3	1-1
1894	Phi	N	P	1	0-1
				4	1-2

SCHELL, CLYDE DANIEL
(Danny)
b.Dec.26,1927 Fostoria, Mich.

Yr	Cl	Lea	Pos	G	Rec
1954	Phi	N	O	92	.283
1955	Phi	N	H	2	.000
	BRTR			94	.281

SCHELLE, GERARD ANTHONY
(Jim)
b.Apr.13,1917 Baltimore, Md.

Yr	Cl	Lea	Pos	G	Rec
1939	Phi	A	P	1	0-0
	BRTR				

SCHELLHASSE, ALBERT HERMAN
b.Mar.22,1864 Evansville, Ind.
d.Jan.4,1919

Yr	Cl	Lea	Pos	G	Rec
1890	Bos	N	C	9	.096
1891	Lou	a	C	6	.156
	TR			15	.120

SCHEMANSKE, FREDERICK GEORGE
b.Apr.28,1903 Detroit, Mich.

Yr	Cl	Lea	Pos	G	Rec
1923	Was	A	P	2	0-0
	BRTR				

SCHEMER, MICHAEL
b.Nov.20,1917 Baltimore, Md.

Yr	Cl	Lea	Pos	G	Rec
1945	NY	N	1	31	.333
1946	NY	N	H	1	.000
	BLTL			32	.330

SCHENCK, WILLIAM G.
b.Brooklyn, N.Y.

Yr	Cl	Lea	Pos	G	Rec
1882	Lou	a	P-S-3-O	59	1-0 / .265
1884	Ric	a	2-S	41	.218
1885	Bro	a	3	1	.000
				101	1-0 / .237

SCHENEBERG, JOHN B.
b.Sept.15,1890 Guyandotte, W.Va.
d.Sept.7,1950

Yr	Cl	Lea	Pos	G	Rec
1913	Pit	N	P	1	0-1
1920	St.L	A	P	1	0-0
	BBTR			2	0-1

SCHENZ, HENRY LEONARD
b.Apr.11,1921 New Richmond, O.

Yr	Cl	Lea	Pos	G	Rec
1946	Chi	N	3	6	.182
1947	Chi	N	3	7	.071
1948	Chi	N	2-3	96	.261
1949	Chi	N	3	7	.429
1950	Pit	N	2-S-3	58	.228
1951	Pit	N	2-3	25	.213
1951	NY	N	H	8	.000
	BRTR			207	.247

SCHEPNER, JOSEPH MARTIN
b.Aug.10,1895 Aliquippa, Pa.
d.July 25,1959

Yr	Cl	Lea	Pos	G	Rec
1919	St.L	A	3	14	.212
	BRTR				

SCHERBARTH, ROBERT ELMER
b.Jan.18,1926 Milwaukee, Wis.

Yr	Cl	Lea	Pos	G	Rec
1950	Bos	A	C	1	.000
	BRTR				

SCHERER, HARRY

Yr	Cl	Lea	Pos	G	Rec
1889	Lou	a	O	1	.333

SCHESLER, CHARLES (Dutch)
b.June 1,1900 Frankfort, Germany.
d.Nov.19,1953

Yr	Cl	Lea	Pos	G	Rec
1931	Phi	N	P	17	0-0
	BRTR				

SCHETTLER, LOUIS MARTIN
b.June 12,1886 Pittsburgh, Pa.

Yr	Cl	Lea	Pos	G	Rec
1910	Phi	N	P	27	2-6
	TR				

SCHIAPPACASSE, LOUIS JOSEPH
b.Mar.9,1882 Ann Arbor, Mich.
d.Sept.19,1910

Yr	Cl	Lea	Pos	G	Rec
1902	Det	A	O	2	.000

SCHICK, MAURICE D.
b.Apr.17,1895 Chicago, Ill.

Yr	Cl	Lea	Pos	G	Rec
1917	Chi	N	O	14	.147
	BRTR				

SCHILLING, CHARLES THOMAS
b.Oct. 25,1937 Brooklyn, N.Y.

Yr	Cl	Lea	Pos	G	Rec
1961	Bos	A	2	158	.259
1962	Bos	A	1	119	.230
	BRTR			277	.247

SCHILLINGS, ELBERT ISAIAH (Red)
b.Mar.29,1900 Deport, Tex.
d.Jan.7,1954

Yr	Cl	Lea	Pos	G	Rec
1922	Phi	A	P	4	0-0
	BRTR				

SCHINDLER, WILLIAM GIBBONS
b.July 10,1896 Perryville, Mo.

Yr	Cl	Lea	Pos	G	Rec
1920	St.L	N	C	1	.000
	BRTR				

SCHIRICK, HARRY ERNEST
(Dutch)
b.June 15,1890 Ruby, N.Y.

Yr	Cl	Lea	Pos	G	Rec
1914	St.L	A	H	1	.000
	BRTR				

SCHLAFLY, HARRY LAWRENCE
(Larry)
b.Sept.20,1878 Beach City, O.
d.June 29,1919

Yr	Cl	Lea	Pos	G	Rec
1902	Chi	N	2-S-3-O	10	.333
1906	Was	A	2	123	.246
1907	Was	A	2	24	.135
1914	Buf	F	M-2	52	.254
	BRTR			209	.239

Non-playing manager Buf (F) 1915.

SCHLEI, GEORGE HENRY
(Admiral)
b.Jan.12,1882 Cincinnati, O.
d.Jan.24,1958

Yr	Cl	Lea	Pos	G	Rec
1904	Cin	N	C	88	.237
1905	Cin	N	C	95	.226
1906	Cin	N	C-1	112	.245
1907	Cin	N	C	72	.272
1908	Cin	N	C	88	.220
1909	NY	N	C	89	.244
1910	NY	N	C	49	.192
1911	NY	N	C	1	.000
	BRTR			594	.237

SCHLIEBNER, FREDERICK PAUL (Dutch)
b.May 19,1894 Berlin,Germany.

Yr	Cl	Lea	Pos	G	Rec
1923	Bro	N	1	19	.250
1923	St.L	A	1	127	.275
	BRTR			146	.271

SCHLITZER, VICTOR JOSEPH (Biff)
b.Dec.4,1884 Rochester,N.Y.
d.Jan.4,1948

Yr	Cl	Lea	Pos	G	Rec
1908	Phi	A	P	23	6-8
1909	Phi	A	P	9	2-6
1909	Bos	A	P	9	2-2
1914	Buf	F	P	3	0-0
	BRTR			44	10-16

SCHLUETER, NORMAN JOHN (Duke)
b.Sept.25,1917 Belleville,Ill.

Yr	Cl	Lea	Pos	G	Rec
1938	Chi	A	C	35	.229
1939	Chi	A	C	34	.232
1944	Cle	A	C	49	.123
	BRTR			118	.186

SCHMANDT, RAYMOND HENRY
b.Jan.25,1896 St.Louis,Mo.

Yr	Cl	Lea	Pos	G	Rec
1915	St.L	A	1	2	.000
1918	Bro	N	2	34	.307
1919	Bro	N	1-2-3	47	.165
1920	Bro	N	1	28	.238
1921	Bro	N	1	95	.306
1922	Bro	N	1	110	.267
	BRTR			316	.269

SCHMEES, GEORGE EDWARD
b.Sept.6,1924 Cincinnati,O.

Yr	Cl	Lea	Pos	G	Rec
1952	St.L	A	1-O	34	.131
1952	Bos	A	P-1-O	42	0-0 / .203
	BLTL			76	0-0 / .168

SCHMELZ, GUSTAVUS HEINRICH
b.Sept.26,1850 Columbus,O.
d.Oct.14,1925
Non-playing manager Col (a) 1884, St. L (N) 1886, Cin (a) 1887-89, Cle (N) 1890, Col (a) 1890-91 and Was (N) 1894-97.

SCHMIDT, CHARLES (Boss)
b.Sept.12,1880 London,Ark.
d.Nov.14,1932

Yr	Cl	Lea	Pos	G	Rec
1906	Det	A	C	68	.218
1907	Det	A	C	104	.244
1908	Det	A	C	122	.265
1909	Det	A	C	84	.209
1910	Det	A	C	71	.259
1911	Det	A	C	28	.283
	BBTR			477	.243

SCHMIDT, CHARLES JOHN (Butch)
b.July 19,1887 Baltimore,Md.
d.Sept.4,1952

Yr	Cl	Lea	Pos	G	Rec
1909	NY	A	P	1	0-0
1913	Bos	N	1	22	.308
1914	Bos	N	1	147	.285
1915	Bos	N	1	127	.251
	BLTL			297	0-0 / .272

SCHMIDT, FRANK ELMER
(Played under name of Frank Elmer Smith)

SCHMIDT, FREDERICK (Crazy)
b.Feb.13,1868 Chicago,Ill.
d.Oct.5,1940

Yr	Cl	Lea	Pos	G	Rec
1890	Pit	N	P	11	1-9
1892	Bal	N	P	7	1-4
1893	Bal	N	P	9	3-2
1893	NY	N	P	4	0-2
1899	Cle	N	P	21	2-17
1901	Bal	A	P	4	0-2
	BLTL			56	7-36

SCHMIDT, FREDERICK ALBERT
b.Feb.9,1916 Hartford,Conn.

Yr	Cl	Lea	Pos	G	Rec
1944	St.L	N	P	37	7-3
1946	St.L	N	P	16	1-0
1947	St.L	N	P	2	0-0
1947	Phi	N	P	29	5-8
1947	Chi	N	P	1	0-0
	BRTR			85	13-11

SCHMIDT, HENRY M.
b.June 26,1873 Brownsville,Tex.
d.Apr.23,1926

Yr	Cl	Lea	Pos	G	Rec
1903	Bro	N	P	41	22-13
	TR				

SCHMIDT, HERMAN (Pete)
b.St.Louis,Mo.

Yr	Cl	Lea	Pos	G	Rec
1913	St.L	A	P	1	0-0

SCHMIDT, ROBERT BENJAMIN
b.Apr.22,1933 St. Louis,Mo.

Yr	Cl	Lea	Pos	G	Rec
1958	SF	N	C	127	.244
1959	SF	N	C	71	.243
1960	SF	N	C	110	.267
1961	SF	N	C	2	.167
1962	Cin	N	C	27	.129
1962	Was	A	C	88	.242
	BRTR			425	.243

SCHMIDT, WALTER JOSEPH
b.Mar.20,1887 Coal Hill,Ark.

Yr	Cl	Lea	Pos	G	Rec
1916	Pit	N	C	64	.190
1917	Pit	N	C	72	.246
1918	Pit	N	C	105	.238
1919	Pit	N	C	85	.251
1920	Pit	N	C	94	.277
1921	Pit	N	C	114	.282
1922	Pit	N	C	40	.328
1923	Pit	N	C	97	.248
1924	Pit	N	C	58	.243
1925	St.L	N	C	37	.253
	BRTR			766	.257

SCHMIDT, WILLARD RAYMOND
b.May 29,1929 Hays,Kan.

Yr	Cl	Lea	Pos	G	Rec
1952	St.L	N	P	18	2-3
1953	St.L	N	P	6	0-2
1955	St.L	N	P	20	7-6
1956	St.L	N	P	33	6-8
1957	St.L	N	P	40	10-3
1958	Cin	N	P	41	3-5
1959	Cin	N	P	36	3-2
				194	31-29

SCHMITZ, JOHN ALBERT (Bear Tracks)
b.Nov.27,1920 Wausau,Wis.

Yr	Cl	Lea	Pos	G	Rec
1941	Chi	N	P	6	2-0
1942	Chi	N	P	23	3-7
1946	Chi	N	P	42	11-11
1947	Chi	N	P	38	13-18
1948	Chi	N	P	34	18-13
1949	Chi	N	P	36	11-13
1950	Chi	N	P	39	10-16
1951	Chi	N	P	8	1-2
1951	Bro	N	P	16	1-4
1952	Bro	N	P	10	1-1
1952	NY	A	P	5	1-1
1952	Cin	N	P	3	1-0
1953	NY	A	P	3	0-0
1953	Was	A	P	24	2-7
1954	Was	A	P	29	11-8
1955	Was	A	P	32	7-10
1956	Bos	A	P	2	0-0
1956	Bal	A	P	18	0-3
	BRTL			368	93-114

SCHMULBACH, HENRY ALRIVES
b.Jan.17,1925 E.St.Louis,Ill.-

Yr	Cl	Lea	Pos	G	Rec
1943	St.L	A	H	1	.000
	BLTR				

SCHMUTZ, CHARLES OTTO
b.Jan.1,1891 San Diego,Cal.
d.June 27,1962

Yr	Cl	Lea	Pos	G	Rec
1914	Bro	N	P	18	1-3
1915	Bro	N	P	1	0-0
	BRTR			19	1-3

SCHNEIBERG, FRANK FREDERICK
b.Mar.12,1882 Milwaukee,Wis.
d.May 18,1948

Yr	Cl	Lea	Pos	G	Rec
1910	Bro	N	P	1	0-0

SCHNEIDER, EMANUEL SEBASTIAN (Played under name of Emanuel Sebastian Snyder)

SCHNEIDER, PETER JOSEPH
b.Aug.20,1895 Los Angeles,Cal.
d.June 1,1957

Yr	Cl	Lea	Pos	G	Rec
1914	Cin	N	P	31	5-13
1915	Cin	N	P	48	14-19
1916	Cin	N	P	49	10-19
1917	Cin	N	P	49	20-19
1918	Cin	N	P	36	10-15
1919	NY	A	P	7	0-1
	BRTR			220	59-86

SCHNELL, KARL OTTO
b.Sept.20,1899 Los Angeles,Cal.

Yr	Cl	Lea	Pos	G	Rec
1922	Cin	N	P	10	0-0
1923	Cin	N	P	1	0-0
	BRTR			11	0-0

SCHOCKEOR, URBAIN JACQUES
(Played under name of Urban James Shocker)

SCHOENDIENST, ALBERT FRED (Red)
b.Feb.2,1923 Germantown,Ill.

Yr	Cl	Lea	Pos	G	Rec
1945	St.L	N	2-S-O	137	.278
1946	St.L	N	2-S-3	142	.281
1947	St.L	N	2-3-O	151	.253
1948	St.L	N	2	119	.272
1949	St.L	N	2-S-3-O	151	.297
1950	St.L	N	2-S-3	153	.276
1951	St.L	N	2-S	135	.289
1952	St.L	N	2-S-3	152	.303
1953	St.L	N	2	146	.342
1954	St.L	N	2	148	.315
1955	St.L	N	2	145	.268
1956	St.L	N	2	40	.314
1956	NY	N	2	92	.296
1957	NY	N	2	57	.307
1957	Mil	N	2-O	93	.310
1958	Mil	N	2	106	.262
1959	Mil	N	2	5	.000
1960	Mil	N	2	68	.257
1961	St.L	M	2	72	.300
1962	St.L	N	2-3	98	.301
	BBTR			2210	.289

SCHOFIELD, JOHN RICHARD (Dick)
b.Jan.7,1935 Springfield,Ill.

Yr	Cl	Lea	Pos	G	Rec
1953	St.L	N	S	33	.179
1954	St.L	N	S	43	.143
1955	St.L	N	S	12	.000
1956	St.L	N	S	16	.100
1957	St.L	N	S	65	.161
1958	St.L	N	S	39	.213
1958	Pit	N	S-3	26	.148
1959	Pit	N	2-S-O	81	.234
1960	Pit	N	2-S-3	65	.333
1961	Pit	N	2-S-3-O	60	.192
1962	Pit	N	2-S-3	54	.288
	BBTR			494	.229

SCHOONMAKER, JERALD LEE
b.Dec.14,1933 Seymour,Mo.

Yr	Cl	Lea	Pos	G	Rec
1955	Was	A	O	20	.152
1957	Was	A	O	30	.087
	BRTR			50	.130

SCHORR, EDWARD WALTER
b.Feb.16,1892 Bremen,O.

Yr	Cl	Lea	Pos	G	Rec
1915	Chi	N	P	2	0-0
		BRTR			

SCHOTT, EUGENE ARTHUR
b.July 14,1913 Batavia,O.

Yr	Cl	Lea	Pos	G	Rec
1935	Cin	N	P	36	8-11
1936	Cin	N	P	39	11-11
1937	Cin	N	P	50	4-13
1938	Cin	N	P	31	5-5
1939	Phi	N	P	8	0-1
1939	Bro	N	P	1	0-0
		BRTR		165	28-41

SCHRAMKA, PAUL EDWARD
b.Mar.22,1928 Milwaukee,Wis.

Yr	Cl	Lea	Pos	G	Rec
1953	Chi	N	O	2	.000
		BLTL			

SCHRECKENGOST, OSSEE FREEMAN (Also played under name of Schreck)
b.Apr.11,1875 Fairmount City,Pa.
d.July 9,1914

Yr	Cl	Lea	Pos	G	Rec
1897	Lou	N	C	1	.000
1898	Cle	N	C	5	.367
1899	St.L	N	1-O	6	.000
1899	Cle	N	C-1-S-O	43	.315
1899	St.L	N	C	60	.306
1901	Bos	A	C	83	.320
1902	Cle	A	1	18	.338
1902	Phi	A	C-O	78	.312
1903	Phi	A	C	91	.222
1904	Phi	A	C	94	.189
1905	Phi	A	C	114	.274
1906	Phi	A	C	98	.284
1907	Phi	A	C	101	.272
1908	Phi	A	C	71	.222
1908	Chi	A	C	6	.188
		BRTR		869	.272

SCHREIBER, DAVID BARNEY
b.May 8,1882 Waverly,O.

Yr	Cl	Lea	Pos	G	Rec
1911	Cin	N	P	3	0-1
		BLTL			

SCHREIBER, HENRY WARD
b.July 13,1893 Cleveland,O.

Yr	Cl	Lea	Pos	G	Rec
1914	Chi	A	O	1	.000
1917	Bos	N	S-3	2	.286
1919	Cin	N	S-3	19	.224
1921	NY	N	2-S	4	.167
1926	Chi	N	2-S-3	10	.056
		BRTR		36	.187

SCHREIBER, PAUL FREDERICK
b.Oct.8,1902 Jacksonville,Fla.

Yr	Cl	Lea	Pos	G	Rec
1922	Bro	N	P	1	0-0
1923	Bro	N	P	9	0-0
1945	NY	A	P	2	0-0
		BRTR		12	0-0

SCHRIVER, WILLIAM F. (Pop)
b.June 11,1866 Brooklyn,N.Y.
d.Dec.27,1932

Yr	Cl	Lea	Pos	G	Rec
1886	Bro	a	C	9	.040
1888	Phi	N	C	39	.194
1889	Phi	N	C	55	.265
1890	Phi	N	C	57	.273
1891	Chi	N	C	25	.311
1892	Chi	N	C	89	.222
1893	Chi	N	C	59	.295
1894	Chi	N	C	94	.269
1895	NY	N	C	24	.290
1897	Cin	N	C	52	.310
1898	Pit	N	C	93	.227
1899	Pit	N	C	84	.297
1900	Pit	N	C	23	.317
1901	St.L	N	C-1	44	.286
		BRTR		747	.263

SCHROLL, ALBERT BRINGHURST
b.Mar.22,1932 New Orleans,La.

Yr	Cl	Lea	Pos	G	Rec
1958	Bos	A	P	5	0-0
1959	Phi	N	P	3	1-1
1959	Bos	A	P	14	1-4
1960	Chi	N	P	2	0-0
1961	Min	A	P	11	4-4
		BRTR		35	6-9

SCHUBLE, HENRY GEORGE (Heinie)
b.Nov.1,1906 Houston,Tex.

Yr	Cl	Lea	Pos	G	Rec
1927	St.L	N	S	65	.257
1929	Det	A	S	92	.233
1932	Det	A	S-3	101	.271
1933	Det	A	2-S-3	49	.219
1934	Det	A	1-2-3	11	.267
1935	Det	A	2-3	11	.250
1936	St.L	N	3	2	.000
		BRTR		331	.251

SCHUERHOLZ, FRED PETER (Played under name of Fred Peter Sherry)

SCHULMERICH, EDWARD WESLEY (Wes)
b.Aug.21,1902 Hillsboro,Ore.

Yr	Cl	Lea	Pos	G	Rec
1931	Bos	N	O	95	.309
1932	Bos	N	O	119	.260
1933	Bos	N	O	29	.247
1933	Phi	N	O	97	.334
1934	Phi	N	O	15	.250
1934	Cin	N	O	74	.263
		BRTR		429	.289

SCHULT, ARTHUR WILLIAM (Dutch)
b.June 20,1928 Brooklyn,N.Y.

Yr	Cl	Lea	Pos	G	Rec
1953	NY	A	H	7	.000
1956	Cin	N	O	5	.429
1957	Cin	N	O	21	.265
1957	Was	A	1-O	77	.263
1959	Chi	N	1-O	42	.271
1960	Chi	N	1-O	12	.133
		BRTR		164	.264

SCHULT, FRED WILLIAM (Played under name of Fred William Schulte)

SCHULTE, DAVID
b.Cincinnati,O.

Yr	Cl	Lea	Pos	G	Rec
1906	Bos	N	S	2	.000
		TR			

SCHULTE, FRANK (Wildfire)
b.Sept.17,1882 Cohocton,N.Y.
d.Oct.2,1949

Yr	Cl	Lea	Pos	G	Rec
1904	Chi	N	O	20	.286
1905	Chi	N	O	123	.274
1906	Chi	N	O	146	.281
1907	Chi	N	O	92	.287
1908	Chi	N	O	102	.236
1909	Chi	N	O	140	.264
1910	Chi	N	O	150	.301
1911	Chi	N	O	154	.300
1912	Chi	N	O	139	.264
1913	Chi	N	O	132	.278
1914	Chi	N	O	137	.241
1915	Chi	N	O	151	.249
1916	Chi	N	O	72	.305
1916	Pit	N	O	55	.241
1917	Pit	N	O	30	.216
1917	Phi	N	O	64	.213
1918	Was	A	O	93	.288
		BLTR		1800	.270

SCHULTE, FRED WILLIAM (Real name Fred William Schult)
b.Jan.13,1904 Belvidere,Ill.

Yr	Cl	Lea	Pos	G	Rec
1927	St.L	A	O	60	.317
1928	St.L	A	O	146	.286
1929	St.L	A	O	121	.307
1930	St.L	A	O	113	.278
1931	St.L	A	O	134	.304

(Continued)

Yr	Cl	Lea	Pos	G	Rec
1932	St.L	A	O	146	.294
1933	Was	A	O	144	.295
1934	Was	A	O	136	.298
1935	Was	A	O	75	.268
1936	Pit	N	O	74	.261
1937	Pit	N	O	29	.100
		BRTR		1178	.292

SCHULTE, HERMAN JOSEPH (Ham) (Real name Herman Joseph Schultehenrich)
b.Sept.1,1913 St.Charles,Mo.

Yr	Cl	Lea	Pos	G	Rec
1940	Phi	N	2-S	120	.236
		BRTR			

SCHULTE, JOHN CLEMENT
b.Sept.8,1897 Fredericktown,Mo.

Yr	Cl	Lea	Pos	G	Rec
1923	St.L	A	C	7	.000
1927	St.L	N	C	64	.288
1928	Phi	N	C	65	.248
1929	Chi	N	C	31	.261
1932	St.L	A	C	15	.208
1932	Bos	N	C	10	.222
		BLTR		192	.261

SCHULTE, LEONARD WILLIAM (Real name Leonard William Schultehenrich)
b.Dec.6,1917 St.Charles,Mo.

Yr	Cl	Lea	Pos	G	Rec
1944	St.L	A	H	1	.000
1945	St.L	A	2-S-3	119	.247
1946	St.L	A	2-3	4	.400
		BRTR		124	.248

SCHULTEHENRICH, HERMAN JOSEPH (Played under name of Herman Joseph Schulte)

SCHULTEHENRICH, LEONARD WILLIAM (Played under name of Leonard William Schulte)

SCHULTZ, GEORGE WARREN
b.Aug.15,1926 Beverly,N.J.

Yr	Cl	Lea	Pos	G	Rec
1955	St.L	N	P	19	1-2
1959	Det	A	P	13	1-2
1961	Chi	N	P	41	7-6
1962	Chi	N	P	51	5-5
		BRTR		124	14-15

SCHULTZ, HOWARD HENRY (Stretch)
b.July 3,1922 St.Paul,Minn.

Yr	Cl	Lea	Pos	G	Rec
1943	Bro	N	1	45	.269
1944	Bro	N	1	138	.255
1945	Bro	N	1	39	.239
1946	Bro	N	1	90	.253
1947	Bro	N	1	2	.000
1947	Phi	N	1	114	.223
1948	Phi	N	1	6	.077
1948	Cin	N	1	36	.167
		BRTR		470	.241

SCHULTZ, JOHN
b.St.Louis,Mo.

Yr	Cl	Lea	Pos	G	Rec
1891	St.L	a	C	1	.000

SCHULTZ, JOSEPH CHARLES JR. (Dode)
b.Aug.29,1918 Chicago,Ill.

Yr	Cl	Lea	Pos	G	Rec
1939	Pit	N	C	4	.286
1940	Pit	N	C	16	.194
1941	Pit	N	C	2	.500
1943	St.L	A	C	46	.239
1944	St.L	A	C	3	.250
1945	St.L	A	C	41	.295
1946	St.L	A	C	42	.386
1947	St.L	A	H	43	.184
1948	St.L	A	H	43	.189
		BLTR		240	.259

SCHULTZ, JOSEPH CHARLES SR.
(Germany)
b.July 24,1893 Pittaburgh,Pa.
d.Apr.13,1941

Yr	Cl	Lea	Pos	G	Rec
1912	Bos	N	2	4	.250
1913	Bos	N	O	8	.222
1915	Bro	N	3	56	.292
1915	Chi	N	3	7	.250
1916	Pit	N	2-3	77	.260
1919	St.L	N	O	88	.253
1920	St.L	N	O	99	.263
1921	St.L	N	O	92	.309
1922	St.L	N	O	112	.313
1923	St.L	N	O	2	.286
1924	St.L	N	O	12	.167
1924	Phi	N	O	88	.285
1925	Phi	N	O	24	.344
1925	Cin	N	2-O	33	.323
			BRTR	702	.285

SCHULTZ, ROBERT DUFFY
(Bill)
b.Nov.27,1925 Louisville,Ky.

Yr	Cl	Lea	Pos	G	Rec
1951	Chi	N	P	17	3-6
1952	Chi	N	P	29	6-3
1953	Chi	N	P	7	0-2
1953	Pit	N	P	11	0-2
1955	Det	A	P	1	0-0
			BRTL	65	9-13

SCHULTZ, WALLACE LUTHER
(Toots)
b.Oct.10,1888 McKeesport,Pa.
d.Jan.30,1959

Yr	Cl	Lea	Pos	G	Rec
1911	Phi	N	P	5	0-3
1912	Phi	N	P	23	1-4
			BRTR	28	1-7

SCHULTZ, WEBB CARL
b.Jan.31,1898 Wautoma,Wis.

Yr	Cl	Lea	Pos	G	Rec
1924	Chi	A	P	1	0-0
		BRTR			

SCHULTZ, WILLIAM MICHAEL
(Mike)
b.Dec.17,1920 Syracuse,N.Y.

Yr	Cl	Lea	Pos	G	Rec
1947	Cin	N	P	1	0-0
		BLTL			

SCHULTZE, JOHN F.
b.Burlington,N.J.

Yr	Cl	Lea	Pos	G	Rec
1891	Phi	N	P	6	0-3

SCHULZ, ALBERT C.
(Lefty)
b.May 12,1889 Toledo,O.
d.Dec.14,1931

Yr	Cl	Lea	Pos	G	Rec
1912	NY	A	P	3	1-0
1913	NY	A	P	33	8-14
1914	NY	A	P	4	1-3
1914	Buf	F	P	24	9-12
1915	Buf	F	P	42	21-14
1916	Cin	N	P	44	8-19
			BRTL	150	48-62

SCHULZ, WALTER FREDERICK
b.Apr.16,1900 St.Louis,Mo.
d.Feb.27,1928

Yr	Cl	Lea	Pos	G	Rec
1920	St.L	N	P	2	0-0
		BRTR			

SCHUMACHER, HAROLD HENRY
(Prince Hal)
b.Nov.23,1910 Hinckley,N.Y.

Yr	Cl	Lea	Pos	G	Rec
1931	NY	N	P	8	1-1
1932	NY	N	P	30	5-6
1933	NY	N	P	39	19-12
1934	NY	N	P	44	23-10
1935	NY	N	P	38	19-9
1936	NY	N	P	46	11-13
1937	NY	N	P	45	13-12
1938	NY	N	P	36	13-8
1939	NY	N	P	30	13-10
1940	NY	N	P	35	13-13

(Continued)

Yr	Cl	Lea	Pos	G	Rec
1941	NY	N	P-O	38	12-10 / .152
1942	NY	N	P	37	12-13
1946	NY	N	P	24	4-4
			BRTR	450	158-121 / .202

SCHUMANN, CARL J. (Hack)
b.Aug.13,1884 Buffalo,N.Y.
d.Mar.25,1946

Yr	Cl	Lea	Pos	G	Rec
1906	Phi	A	P	4	0-2
		TR			

SCHUPP, FERDINAND MAURICE
b.Jan.16,1892 Louisville,Ky.

Yr	Cl	Lea	Pos	G	Rec
1913	NY	N	P	5	0-0
1914	NY	N	P	8	0-0
1915	NY	N	P	23	1-0
1916	NY	N	P	30	9-3
1917	NY	N	P	36	21-7
1918	NY	N	P	10	0-1
1919	NY	N	P	9	1-3
1919	St.L	N	P	10	4-4
1920	St.L	N	P	39	16-13
1921	St.L	N	P	9	2-0
1921	Bro	N	P	20	3-4
1922	Chi	A	P	18	4-4
			BBTL	217	61-39

SCHUSTER, WILLIAM CHARLES
(Broadway)
b.Aug.4,1914 Buffalo,N.Y.

Yr	Cl	Lea	Pos	G	Rec
1937	Pit	N	S	3	.500
1939	Bos	N	S-3	2	.000
1943	Chi	N	S	13	.294
1944	Chi	N	2-S	60	.221
1945	Chi	N	2-S-3	45	.191
			BRTR	123	.234

SCHWALL, DONALD BERNARD
b.Mar.2,1938 Wilkes-Barre,Pa.

Yr	Cl	Lea	Pos	G	Rec
1961	Bos	A	P	27	15-7
1962	Bos	A	P	34	9-15
			BRTR	61	24-22

SCHWAMB, RALPH RICHARD
(Blackie)
b.Aug.6,1926 Los Angeles,Cal.

Yr	Cl	Lea	Pos	G	Rec
1948	St.L	A	P	12	1-1
		BRTR			

SCHWARTZ, WILLIAM AUGUST
(Pop)
b.Apr.3,1864 Jamestown,Ky.
d.Dec.22,1940

Yr	Cl	Lea	Pos	G	Rec
1883	Col	a	C-1	2	.250
1884	Cin	U	C	24	.263
			BRTR	26	.262

SCHWARTZ, WILLIAM CHARLES
b.Apr.22,1884 Cleveland,O.
d.Aug.29,1961

Yr	Cl	Lea	Pos	G	Rec
1904	Cle	A	1	24	.151
		TR			

SCHWARTZ, WILLIAM DWIGHT
b.Jan.30,1891 Birmingham,Ala.
d.June 24,1949.

Yr	Cl	Lea	Pos	G	Rec
1914	NY	A	C	1	.000
		TR			

SCHWARZROCK, LESTER HENRY
(Played under name of
Lester Henry Rock)

SCHWEITZER, ALBERT CASPAR
b.Dec.1882 Cleveland,O.

Yr	Cl	Lea	Pos	G	Rec
1908	St.L	A	O	64	.291
1909	St.L	A	O	27	.224
1910	St.L	A	O	113	.230
1911	St.L	A	O	76	.215
			BRTR	280	.238

SCHWENCK, RUDOLPH C.
(Ruby)

Yr	Cl	Lea	Pos	G	Rec
1909	Chi	N	P	3	1-1

SCHWENK, HAROLD EDWARD
b.Aug.23,1890 Schuylkill Haven,Pa.
d.Sept.4.1955.

Yr	Cl	Lea	Pos	G	Rec
1913	St.L	A	P	1	1-0
		BLTL			

SCHWERT, PIUS LOUIS
b.Nov.22,1892 Angola,N.Y.
d.Mar.11,1941

Yr	Cl	Lea	Pos	G	Rec
1914	NY	A	C	2	.000
1915	NY	A	C	9	.278
			BRTR	11	.208

SCHWIND, ARTHUR E.
b.1892 Ottawa,Ont.,Canada.

Yr	Cl	Lea	Pos	G	Rec
1912	Bos	N	3	1	.000
		BBTR			

SCHYPINSKI, GERALD ALBERT
b.Sept.16,1931 Detroit,Mich.

Yr	Cl	Lea	Pos	G	Rec
1955	KC	A	2-S	22	.217
		BLTR			

SCOFFIC, LOUIS (Weaser)
b.May 20,1914 Herrin,Ill.

Yr	Cl	Lea	Pos	G	Rec
1936	St.L	N	O	4	.429
		BRTR			

SCORE, HERBERT JUDE
b.June 7,1933 Rosedale,N.Y.

Yr	Cl	Lea	Pos	G	Rec
1955	Cle	A	P	33	16-10
1956	Cle	A	P	35	20-9
1957	Cle	A	P	5	2-1
1958	Cle	A	P	12	2-3
1959	Cle	A	P	30	9-11
1960	Chi	A	P	23	5-10
1961	Chi	A	P	8	1-2
1962	Chi	A	P	4	0-0
			BLTL	150	55-46

SCOTT, ...

Yr	Cl	Lea	Pos	G	Rec
1884	Bal	U	3-O	13	.226

SCOTT, AMOS RICHARD
(Dick)
b.Feb.5,1882 Bethel,O.
d.Apr.11.1911

Yr	Cl	Lea	Pos	G	Rec
1901	Cin	N	P	3	0-2
		BRTR			

SCOTT, EDWARD
b.Aug.12,1874 Toledo,O.

Yr	Cl	Lea	Pos	G	Rec
1900	Cin	N	P	39	17-20
1901	Cle	A	P	16	7-6
			BRTR	55	24-26

SCOTT, FLOYD JOHN
(Pete)
b.Dec.21,1898 Woodland,Cal.
d.May 3,1953

Yr	Cl	Lea	Pos	G	Rec
1926	Chi	N	O	77	.286
1927	Chi	N	O	71	.314
1928	Pit	N	O	60	.311
			BRTR	208	.303

SCOTT, GEORGE WILLIAM
b.Nov.17,1896 Trenton,Mo.

Yr	Cl	Lea	Pos	G	Rec
1920	St.L	N	P	2	0-0
		BRTR			

SCOTT, JAMES (Death Valley)
b.Apr.23,1888 Deadwood,S.Dak.
d.Apr.7,1957

Yr	Cl	Lea	Pos	G	Rec
1909	Chi	A	P	36	12-12
1910	Chi	A	P	40	8-18
1911	Chi	A	P	39	14-11
1912	Chi	A	P	5	2-2
1913	Chi	A	P	44	20-20
1914	Chi	A	P	41	14-18
1915	Chi	A	P	48	24-11
1916	Chi	A	P	32	7-14
1917	Chi	A	P	24	6-7
			BRTR	309	107-113

SCOTT, JAMES W.
b.1887

Yr	Cl	Lea	Pos	G	Rec
1914	Pit	F	S	8	.250
BRTR					

SCOTT, JOHN WILLIAM
b.Apr.18,1892 Ridgeway,N.C.
d.Nov.30,1959

Yr	Cl	Lea	Pos	G	Rec
1916	Pit	N	P	3	0-0
1917	Bos	N	P	7	1-2
1919	Bos	N	P-O	24	6-6 / .175
1920	Bos	N	P	44	10-21
1921	Bos	N	P	51	15-13
1922	Cin	N	P	1	0-0
1922	NY	N	P	17	8-2
1923	NY	N	P	40	16-7
1925	NY	N	P	41	14-15
1926	NY	N	P	51	13-15
1927	Phi	N	P	83	9-21
1928	NY	N	P	16	4-1
1929	NY	N	P	30	7-6
BLTR				408	103-109 / .275

SCOTT, LEGRANT EDWARD
b.July 25,1911 Cleveland,O.

Yr	Cl	Lea	Pos	G	Rec
1939	Phi	N	O	76	.280
BLTL					

SCOTT, LEWIS EVERETT
(Deacon)
b.Nov.19,1892 Bluffton,Ind.
d.Nov.2,1960

Yr	Cl	Lea	Pos	G	Rec
1914	Bos	A	S	144	.239
1915	Bos	A	S	100	.201
1916	Bos	A	S	123	.232
1917	Bos	A	S	157	.241
1918	Bos	A	S	126	.221
1919	Bos	A	S	138	.278
1920	Bos	A	S	154	.269
1921	Bos	A	S	154	.262
1922	NY	A	S	154	.269
1923	NY	A	S	152	.246
1924	NY	A	S	153	.250
1925	NY	A	S	22	.217
1925	Was	A	S	33	.272
1926	Chi	A	S	40	.252
1926	Cin	N	S	4	.667
BRTR				1654	.249

SCOTT, MARSHALL (Lefty)
b.July 15,1915 Roswell,N.M.

Yr	Cl	Lea	Pos	G	Rec
1945	Phi	N	P	8	0-2
BRTL					

SCOTT, MILTON PARKER
b.Jan.17,1866 Chicago,Ill.
d.Nov.3,1938

Yr	Cl	Lea	Pos	G	Rec
1882	Chi	N	1	1	.400
1884	Det	N	1	108	.249
1885	Det	N	1	38	.263
1885	Pit	a	1	55	.241
1886	Bal	a	1	137	.192
				339	.232

SCROGGINS, JAMES LYNN
b.1893

Yr	Cl	Lea	Pos	G	Rec
1913	Chi	A	P	1	0-0
BLTL					

SCZEPKOWSKI, THEODORE WALTER (Played under name of Theodore Walter Sepkowski)

SEARS, KENNETH EUGENE
(Ziggy)
b.July 6,1917 Streator,Ill.

Yr	Cl	Lea	Pos	G	Rec
1943	NY	A	C	60	.278
1946	St.L	A	C	7	.333
BLTR				67	.282

SEATON, THOMAS GORDON
b.Aug.30,1889 Blair,Neb.
d.Apr.10,1940

Yr	Cl	Lea	Pos	G	Rec
1912	Phi	N	P	44	16-12
1913	Phi	N	P	52	27-12
1914	Bro	F	P	44	25-14
1915	Bro	F	P	26	7-7
1915	New	F	P	18	7-10
1916	Chi	N	P	31	6-6
1917	Chi	N	P	16	5-4
BBTR				231	93-65

SEATS, THOMAS EDWARD
b.Sept.24,1912 Farmington,N.C.

Yr	Cl	Lea	Pos	G	Rec
1940	Det	A	P	26	2-2
1945	Bro	N	P	31	10-7
BBTL				57	12-9

SEBRING, JAMES DENNISON
b.Mar.22,1882 Williamsport,Pa.
d.Dec.22,1909

Yr	Cl	Lea	Pos	G	Rec
1902	Pit	N	O	19	.338
1903	Pit	N	O	124	.277
1904	Pit	N	O	80	.269
1904	Cin	N	O	56	.225
1905	Cin	N	O	56	.286
1909	Bro	N	O	25	.099
1909	Was	A	O	1	.000
BLTL				361	.262

SECHRIST THEODORE O'HARA
(Doc)
b.Feb.10,1876 Williamstown,Ky.
d.Apr.2,1950

Yr	Cl	Lea	Pos	G	Rec
1899	NY	N	P	1	0-0
BRTR					

SECORY, FRANK EDWARD
b.Aug.24,1912 Mason City,Ia.

Yr	Cl	Lea	Pos	G	Rec
1940	Det	A	H	1	.000
1942	Cin	N	O	2	.000
1944	Chi	N	O	22	.321
1945	Chi	N	O	35	.158
1946	Chi	N	O	33	.233
BRTR				93	.228

SEDGWICK, HENRY KENNETH
(Duke)
b.June 1,1899 Martin's Ferry,O.

Yr	Cl	Lea	Pos	G	Rec
1921	Phi	N	P	16	1-3
1923	Was	A	P	5	0-1
BRTR				21	1-4

SEE, CHARLES HENRY (Chad)
b.Oct.13,1897 Pleasantville,N.Y.
d.July 19,1948

Yr	Cl	Lea	Pos	G	Rec
1919	Cin	N	O	8	.286
1920	Cin	N	P-O	47	0-0 / .305
1921	Cin	N	O	37	.245
BLTR				92	0-0 / .267

SEEDS, ROBERT IRA
(Suitcase Bob)
b.Feb.24,1907 Ringgold,Tex.

Yr	Cl	Lea	Pos	G	Rec
1930	Cle	A	O	85	.285
1931	Cle	A	O	48	.306
1932	Cle	A	O	2	.000
1932	Chi	A	O	116	.291
1933	Bos	A	1-O	82	.243
1934	Bos	A	O	8	.167
1934	Cle	A	O	61	.247
1936	NY	A	O	13	.262
1938	NY	N	O	81	.291
1939	NY	N	O	63	.266
1940	NY	N	O	56	.290
BRTR				615	.277

SEEREY, JAMES PATRICK
(Pat)
b.Mar.17,1923 Wilburton,Okla.

Yr	Cl	Lea	Pos	G	Rec
1943	Cle	A	O	26	.222
1944	Cle	A	O	101	.234
1945	Cle	A	O	126	.237
1946	Cle	A	O	117	.225
1947	Cle	A	O	82	.171
1948	Cle	A	O	10	.261
1948	Chi	A	O	95	.229
1949	Chi	A	O	4	.000
BRTR				561	.224

SEERY, JOHN EMMETT
b.Feb.13,1861 Princeville,Ill.

Yr	Cl	Lea	Pos	G	Rec
1884	Bal	U	C-3-O	107	.309
1884	KC	U	O	1	.400
1885	St.L	N	3-O	58	.162
1886	St.L	N	O	126	.238
1887	Ind	N	O	122	.326
(Continued)					
1888	Ind	N	O	133	.220
1889	Ind	N	O	127	.313
1890	Bro	p	O	104	.222
1891	Cin	a	O	97	.282
1892	Lou	N	O	42	.194
BLTR				917	.266

SEGRIST, KAL HILL
b.Apr.14,1931 Greenville,Tex.

Yr	Cl	Lea	Pos	G	Rec
1952	NY	A	2-3	13	.043
1955	Bal	A	1-2-3	7	.333
BRTR				20	.125

SEGUI, DIEGO PABLO
b.Aug.17,1938 Holguin,Cuba

Yr	Cl	Lea	Pos	G	Rec
1962	KC	A	P	37	8-5
BRTR					

SEIBOLD, HARRY (Socks)
b.Apr.3,1896 Philadelphia,Pa.

Yr	Cl	Lea	Pos	G	Rec
1915	Phi	A	S	10	.115
1916	Phi	A	P	5	1-2
1917	Phi	A	P	36	4-16
1919	Phi	A	P	15	2-3
1929	Bos	N	P	33	12-17
1930	Bos	N	P	36	15-16
1931	Bos	N	P	33	10-18
1932	Bos	N	P	28	3-10
1933	Bos	N	P	11	1-4
BRTR				207	48-86 / .196

SELBACH, ALBERT CARL
(Kip)
b.Mar.24,1872 Columbus,O.
d.Feb.17,1956

Yr	Cl	Lea	Pos	G	Rec
1894	Was	N	S-O	96	.300
1895	Was	N	O	129	.324
1896	Was	N	O	121	.316
1897	Was	N	O	126	.317
1898	Was	N	O	131	.302
1899	Cin	N	O	139	.302
1900	NY	N	O	141	.345
1901	NY	N	O	125	.292
1902	Bal	A	O	128	.321
1903	Was	A	O	141	.252
1904	Was	A	O	48	.264
1904	Bos	A	O	98	.369
1905	Bos	A	O	115	.246
1906	Bos	A	O	60	.211
BRTR				1598	.296

SELEE, FRANK GIBSON
b.Oct.26,1859 Amherst,N.H.
d.July 5,1909
Non-playing manager Bos (N) 1890-1901 and Chi (N) 1902-05.

SELKIRK, GEORGE ALEXANDER
(Twinkletoes)
b.Jan.4,1899 Huntsville,Ont.,Canada.

Yr	Cl	Lea	Pos	G	Rec
1934	NY	A	O	46	.313
1935	NY	A	O	128	.312
1936	NY	A	O	137	.308
1937	NY	A	O	78	.328
1938	NY	A	O	99	.254
1939	NY	A	O	128	.306
1940	NY	A	O	118	.269
1941	NY	A	O	70	.220
1942	NY	A	O	42	.192
BLTR				846	.293

SELL, LESTER ELWOOD
(Epp)
b.Apr.26,1897 Llewellyn,Pa.
d.Feb.20,1961

Yr	Cl	Lea	Pos	G	Rec
1922	St.L	N	P	7	4-2
1923	St.L	N	P	5	0-1
BRTR				12	4-3

SELLERS, OLIVER
b.Mar.7,1881 Homeville,Pa.
d.Jan.14,1952

Yr	Cl	Lea	Pos	G	Rec
1910	Bos	N	O	12	.156
BRTR					

SELMAN, FRANK C.
(Also played under name of Frank C. Williams)
b.Baltimore,Md.
d.Oct.14,1890

Yr	Cl	Lea	Pos	G	Rec
1871	Kek	n	C-3	14	NR
1872	Oly	n	C-3	8	NR
1873	Mar	n	P	1	0-1
1874	Bal	n	C-S-O	12	NR
1875	Nat	n	1	1	NR
				36	0-1 / NR

SELPH, CAREY ISOM
b.Dec.5,1902 Donaldson,Ark.

Yr	Cl	Lea	Pos	G	Rec
1929	St.L	N	2	25	.235
1932	Chi	A	3	116	.283
	BRTR			141	.277

SEMINICK, ANDREW WASIL
b.Sept.12,1920 Pierce,W.Va.

Yr	Cl	Lea	Pos	G	Rec
1943	Phi	N	C	22	.181
1944	Phi	N	C-O	22	.222
1945	Phi	N	C-3-O	80	.239
1946	Phi	N	C	124	.264
1947	Phi	N	C	111	.252
1948	Phi	N	C	125	.225
1949	Phi	N	C	109	.243
1950	Phi	N	C	130	.288
1951	Phi	N	C	101	.227
1952	Cin	N	C	108	.256
1953	Cin	N	C	119	.235
1954	Cin	N	C	86	.235
1955	Cin	N	C	6	.133
1955	Phi	N	C	93	.246
1956	Phi	N	C	60	.199
1957	Phi	N	C	8	.091
	BRTR			1304	.243

SEMPROCH, ROMAN ANTHONY
b.Jan.7,1931 Cleveland,O.

Yr	Cl	Lea	Pos	G	Rec
1958	Phi	N	P	36	13-11
1959	Phi	N	P	30	3-10
1960	Det	A	P	17	3-0
1961	LA	A	P	2	0-0
	BRTR			85	19-21

SENERCHIA, EMANUEL ROBERT
(Sonny)
b.Apr.8,1931 Newark,N.J.

Yr	Cl	Lea	Pos	G	Rec
1952	Pit	N	3	29	.220
	BRTR				

SENSENDERFER, JOHN PHILLIPS JENKINS
b.Dec.28,1847 Philadelphia,Pa.
d.May 3,1903

Yr	Cl	Lea	Pos	G	Rec
1871	Ath	n	O	25	.371
1872	Ath	n	O	1	NR
1873	Ath	n	O	19	NR
1874	Ath	n	O	4	NR
				49	NR

SENTELLE, LEOPOLD THEODORE (Paul)
b.Aug.27,1879 New Orleans,La.
d.Apr.27,1923

Yr	Cl	Lea	Pos	G	Rec
1906	Phi	N	2-3	55	.229
1907	Phi	N	S	3	.000
	TR			58	.226

SEPKOWSKI, THEODORE WALTER
(Real name Theodore Walter Sczepkowski)
b.Nov.9,1923 Baltimore,Md.

Yr	Cl	Lea	Pos	G	Rec
1942	Cle	A	2	5	.100
1946	Cle	A	3	2	.500
1947	Cle	A	O	10	.125
1947	NY	A	H	2	.000
	BLTR			19	.231

SERAD, WILLIAM I
b.1863 Philadelphia,Pa.
d.Nov.1,1925

Yr	Cl	Lea	Pos	G	Rec
1884	Buf	N	P-O	38	17-21 / .175
1885	Buf	N	P	29	8-21
1887	Cin	a	P-O	22	11-11 / .278
1888	Cin	a	P	6	1-3
	BRTR			95	37-56 / .183

SERAFIN, JOSEPH STANLEY
(Played under name of Joseph Stanley Cobb)

SERENA, WILLIAM ROBERT
b.Oct.2,1924 Alameda,Cal.

Yr	Cl	Lea	Pos	G	Rec
1949	Chi	N	3	12	.216
1950	Chi	N	3	127	.239
1951	Chi	N	3	13	.333
1952	Chi	N	2-3	122	.274
1953	Chi	N	2-3	93	.251
1954	Chi	N	2-3	41	.159
	BRTR			408	.251

SESSI, WALTER ANTHONY
b.July 23,1918 Finleyville,Pa.

Yr	Cl	Lea	Pos	G	Rec
1941	St.L	N	O	5	.000
1946	St.L	N	H	15	.143
	BLTL			20	.074

SETTLEMIRE, EDGAR MERLE
(Lefty)
b.Jan.19,1903 Santa Fe,O.

Yr	Cl	Lea	Pos	G	Rec
1928	Bos	A	P	33	0-6
	BLTL				

SEVEREID, HENRY LEVAI
b.June 1,1891 Story City,Ia.

Yr	Cl	Lea	Pos	G	Rec
1911	Cin	N	C	22	.304
1912	Cin	N	C	50	.237
1913	Cin	N	C	8	.200
1915	St.L	A	C	80	.222
1916	St.L	A	C	100	.273
1917	St.L	A	C	143	.265
1918	St.L	A	C	51	.256
1919	St.L	A	C	112	.248
1920	St.L	A	C	123	.277
1921	St.L	A	C	143	.324
1922	St.L	A	C	137	.321
1923	St.L	A	C	122	.308
1924	St.L	A	C	137	.308
1925	St.L	A	C	34	.358
1925	Was	A	C	46	.364
1926	Was	A	C	22	.212
1926	NY	A	C	41	.266
	BRTR			1371	.289

SEWARD, EDWARD WILLIAM
(Real name Edward W. Sewer)
b.June 29,1867 Cleveland,O.
d.July 30,1947

Yr	Cl	Lea	Pos	G	Rec
1885	Pro	N	P	1	0-1
1887	Ath	a	P	75	25-24
1888	Ath	a	P	64	34-19
1889	Ath	a	P	45	21-16
1890	Ath	a	P	27	6-13
1891	Cle	N	P	7	1-0
	TR			219	87-73

SEWARD, FRANK MARTIN
b.Apr,7,1922 Pensauken,N.J.

Yr	Cl	Lea	Pos	G	Rec
1943	NY	N	P	1	0-1
1944	NY	N	P	25	3-2
	BRTR			26	3-3

SEWARD, GEORGE E.
b.St.Louis,Mo.

Yr	Cl	Lea	Pos	G	Rec
1875	St.L	n	C-2-O	23	.210
1876	Mut	N	2	1	.000
1882	St.L	a	C-O	38	.195
				62	.198

SEWELL, JAMES LUTHER
(Luke)
b.Jan.15,1901 Titus,Ala.

Yr	Cl	Lea	Pos	G	Rec
1921	Cle	A	C	3	.000
1922	Cle	A	C	41	.264
1923	Cle	A	C	10	.200
1924	Cle	A	C	63	.291
1925	Cle	A	C-O	74	.232
1926	Cle	A	C	126	.238
1927	Cle	A	C	128	.293
1928	Cle	A	C	122	.270
1929	Cle	A	C	124	.236
1930	Cle	A	C	76	.257
1931	Cle	A	C	108	.275
1932	Cle	A	C	87	.253
1933	Was	A	C	141	.264
1934	Was	A	C-1-2-3-O	72	.237
1935	Chi	A	C	118	.285
1936	Chi	A	C	128	.251
1937	Chi	A	C	122	.269
1938	Chi	A	C	65	.213
1939	Cle	A	C	16	.150
1942	St.L	A	M-C	6	.083
	BRTR			1630	.259

Non-playing manager St.L (A) 1941, 1943-46 and Cin (N) 1949-52.

SEWELL, JOSEPH WHEELER
b.Oct.9,1898 Titus,Ala.

Yr	Cl	Lea	Pos	G	Rec
1920	Cle	A	S	22	.329
1921	Cle	A	S	154	.318
1922	Cle	A	2-S	153	.299
1923	Cle	A	S	153	.353
1924	Cle	A	S	153	.316
1925	Cle	A	2-S	155	.335
1926	Cle	A	S	154	.324
1927	Cle	A	S	153	.316
1928	Cle	A	S-3	155	.323
1929	Cle	A	3	152	.315
1930	Cle	A	3	109	.289
1931	NY	A	3	130	.302
1932	NY	A	3	124	.272
1933	NY	A	3	135	.273
	BLTR			1902	.312

SEWELL, THOMAS WESLEY
b.Apr.16,1906 Titus,Ala.
d.July 30,1956

Yr	Cl	Lea	Pos	G	Rec
1927	Chi	N	H	1	.000
	BLTR				

SEWELL, TRUETT BANKS
(Rip)
b.May 11,1908 Decatur,Ala.

Yr	Cl	Lea	Pos	G	Rec
1932	Det	A	P	5	0-0
1938	Pit	N	P	17	0-1
1939	Pit	N	P	52	10-9
1940	Pit	N	P	47	16-5
1941	Pit	N	P	42	14-17
1942	Pit	N	P	41	17-15
1943	Pit	N	P	41	21-9
1944	Pit	N	P	44	21-12
1945	Pit	N	P	35	11-9
1946	Pit	N	P	26	8-12
1947	Pit	N	P	24	6-4
1948	Pit	N	P	21	13-3
1949	Pit	N	P	28	6-1
	BLTR			423	143-97

SEWER, EDWARD W.
(Played under name of Edward W. Seward)

SEXAUER, ELMER GEORGE
b.May 21,1926 St.Louis Co.,Mo.

Yr	Cl	Lea	Pos	G	Rec
1948	Bro	N	P	2	0-0
	BRTR				

SEXTON, FRANK JOSEPH
b.July 8,1872 Brockton,Mass.
d.Jan.4,1938

Yr	Cl	Lea	Pos	G	Rec
1895	Bos	N	P	10	1-4

SEXTON, THOMAS W.
b.Mar.14,1865 Milwaukee,Wis.
d.Feb.8,1934

Yr	Cl	Lea	Pos	G	Rec
1884	Mil	U	S	12	.229

Yr Cl Lea Pos G Rec

SEYBOLD, RALPH ORLANDO
(Socks)
b.Nov.23,1870 Washingtonville,O.
d.Dec.22,1921
1899 Cin N O 22 .221
1901 Phi A 1-O 114 .332
1902 Phi A O 137 .317
1903 Phi A 1-O 137 .299
1904 Phi A O 143 .282
1905 Phi A O 132 .271
1906 Phi A O 116 .316
1907 Phi A O 147 .271
1908 Phi A O 48 .215
BRTR 996 .293

SEYMOUR, JOHN BENTLEY
(Cy)
b.Dec.9,1872 Albany,N.Y.
d.Sept.20,1919
1896 NY N P 12 2-4
1897 NY N P 41 20-14
1898 NY N P-O 78 {25-17 .273
1899 NY N P 45 13-18
1900 NY N P 21 2-2
1901 Bal A O 137 .302
1902 Bal A O 72 .278
1902 Cin N P-3-O 60 {0-0 .349
1903 Cin N O 135 .342
1904 Cin N O 130 .312
1905 Cin N O 149 .377
1906 Cin N O 79 .257
1906 NY N O 72 .320
1907 NY N O 126 .294
1908 NY N O 155 .267
1909 NY N O 73 .310
1910 NY N O 76 .265
1913 Bos N O 39 .178
BLTL 1500 {62-55 .307

SEYMOUR, THOMAS
b.1858 Pittsburgh,Pa.
d.Feb.17,1916
1882 Pit a P 1 0-1

SHAFER, ARTHUR JOSEPH
(Tillie)
b.Mar.22,1889 Los Angeles,Cal.
d.Jan.10,1962
1909 NY N 3 31 .179
1910 NY N 3 27 .182
1912 NY N S 78 .288
1913 NY N 2-S-3-O 138 .287
BLTR 274 .273

SHAFER, RALPH NEWTON
b.Mar.17,1894 Cincinnati,O.
d.Feb.5,1950
1914 Pit N H 1 .000

SHAFFER, ...
1875 Atl n O 1 .000

SHAFFER, FRANK
1884 Alt U C-3-O 19 .284
1884 KC U C-2-S-3-O 43 .172
1884 Bal U O 3 .077
65 .200

SHALLIX, AUGUST
(Real name August Schallick)
b.Mar.29,1858 Bielefeld,Germany.
d.Oct.10,1937
1884 Cin a P 23 11-10
1885 Cin a P-O 13 {7-4 .128
BRTR 36 {18-14 .085

SHAMBRICK, OTTO H.
(Played under name of
Otto H. Shomberg)

Yr Cl Lea Pos G Rec

SHANDLEY, JAMES J.
b.New York
1876 Mut N O 2 .125

SHANER, WALTER DEDAKER
(Skinny)
b.May 24,1901 Lynchburg,Va.
1923 Cle A 3 3 .250
1926 Bos A O 69 .283
1927 Bos A O 122 .273
1929 Cin N 1-O 13 .321
BRTR 207 .278

SHANKS, HOWARD SAMUEL
(Hank)
b.July 21,1890 Chicago,Ill.
d.July 30,1941
1912 Was A O 115 .236
1913 Was A O 109 .254
1914 Was A O 143 .224
1915 Was A 3-O 141 .250
1916 Was A 3-O 140 .253
1917 Was A S-O 126 .202
1918 Was A 2-O 120 .257
1919 Was A 2-S 135 .248
1920 Was A 1-3-O 128 .268
1921 Was A 3 154 .302
1922 Was A 3-O 84 .283
1923 Bos A 2-3 131 .254
1924 Bos A S-3 72 .259
1925 NY A 2-3-O 66 .258
BRTR 1664 .253

SHANLEY, HENRY ROAT
(Doc)
b.Jan.30,1889 Chicago,Ill.
d.Dec.14,1934
1912 St.L A S 5 .000
BRTR

SHANNABROOK, W. H.
b.1885 Massillon,O.
1906 Was A 3 1 .000
TR

SHANNER, W. W.
1920 Phi A P 1 0-0

SHANNON, DANIEL W.
b.Mar.23,1865 Bridgeport,Conn.
d.Oct.25,1913
1889 Lou a M-2 120 .262
1890 Phi p 2 18 .260
1890 NY p 2-S-3 83 .238
1891 Was a M-S 19 .118
240 .238

SHANNON, FRANK E.
(Tod)
b.Dec.3,1873 San Francisco,Cal.
1892 Was N S 1 .200
1895 Was N S 1 .200
1896 Lou N S 31 .161
33 .163

SHANNON, JOSEPH ALOYSIUS
b.Feb.11,1895 Jersey City,N.J.
d.July 28,1955.
1915 Bos N O 5 .200
BRTR

SHANNON, MAURICE JOSEPH
(Red)
b.Feb.11,1895 Jersey City,N.J.
1915 Bos N S 1 .000
1917 Phi A S 11 .257
1918 Phi A 2-S 72 .240
1919 Phi A 2 39 .271
1919 Bos A 2 80 .259
1920 Was A S 63 .288
1920 Phi A S 24 .167
1921 Phi A H 1 .000
1926 Chi N S 19 .333
BBTR 310 .257

Yr Cl Lea Pos G Rec

SHANNON, OWEN DENNIS IGNATIUS
b.Dec.22,1885 Omaha,Neb.
d.Apr.10,1918
1903 St.L A C 8 .200
1907 Was A C 4 .143
BRTR 12 .188

SHANNON, THOMAS MICHAEL
b.July 5,1939 St.Louis,Mo.
1962 St.L N O 10 .133
BRTR

SHANNON, WALTER CHARLES
b.Jan.23,1934 Cleveland,O.
1959 St.L N 2-S 47 .284
1960 St.L N 2-S 18 .174
BLTR 65 .263

SHANNON, WILLIAM PORTER
(Spike)
b.Feb.7,1878 Pittsburgh,Pa.
d.May 16,1940
1904 St.L N O 133 .280
1905 St.L N O 140 .268
1906 St.L N O 80 .258
1906 NY N O 76 .254
1907 NY N O 155 .265
1908 NY N O 74 .224
1908 Pit N O 32 .197
TR 690 .259

SHANTZ, ROBERT CLAYTON
b.Sept.26,1925 Pottstown,Pa.
1949 Phi A P 33 6-8
1950 Phi A P 37 8-14
1951 Phi A P 36 18-10
1952 Phi A P 34 24-7
1953 Phi A P 21 5-9
1954 Phi A P 7 1-0
1955 KC A P 26 5-10
1956 KC A P 51 2-7
1957 NY A P 33 11-5
1958 NY A P-O 33 {7-6 .229
1959 NY A P 40 7-3
1960 NY A P 43 5-4
1961 Pit N P 44 6-3
1962 Hou N P 7 1-1
1962 St.L N P 28 5-3
BRTL 473 {111-90 .198

SHANTZ, WILMER EBERT
(Billy)
b.July 31,1927 Pottstown,Pa.
1954 Phi A C 51 .256
1955 KC A C 79 .258
1960 NY A C 1 .000
BRTR 131 .257

SHARMAN, RALPH EDWARD
b.1895 Norwood,O.
d.May 24,1918
1917 Phi A O 13 .297
BRTR

SHARPE, BAYARD HESTON
(Bud)
b.Aug.6,1881 West Chester,Pa.
d.May 31,1916
1905 Bos N O 45 .182
1910 Bos N 1 113 .239
1910 Pit N 1 4 .188
BLTR 162 .222

SHARROTT, GEORGE OSCAR
b.Nov.2,1869 W.New Brighton,S.I.,N.Y.
d.Jan.6,1932
1893 Bro N P 11 4-7
1894 Bro N P 3 1-1
14 5-8

SHARROTT, JOHN HENRY

b.Aug.13,1869 Bangor,Me.
d.Dec.31,1927

Yr	Cl	Lea	Pos	G	Rec
1890	NY	N	P	29	11-9
1891	NY	N	P	10	4-3
1892	NY	N	P-O	5	0-1 / .000
1893	Phi	N	P-O	30	2-3 / .254
				74	17-16 / .236

SHARSIG, WILLIAM J.

b.1855 Philadelphia,Pa.
d.Feb.1,1902
Non-playing manager Ath (a) 1882-91.

SHAUGHNESSY, FRANCIS JOSEPH (Shag)

b.Apr.8,1885 S.Amboy,Ill.

Yr	Cl	Lea	Pos	G	Rec
1905	Was	A	O	1	.000
1908	Phi	A	O	8	.321
BRTR				9	.290

SHAUTE, JOSEPH BENJAMIN (Lefty)

b.Aug.1,1900 Peckville,Pa.

Yr	Cl	Lea	Pos	G	Rec
1922	Cle	A	P	5	0-0
1923	Cle	A	P	34	10-8
1924	Cle	A	P	46	20-17
1925	Cle	A	P	29	4-12
1926	Cle	A	P	34	14-10
1927	Cle	A	P	45	9-16
1928	Cle	A	P	36	13-17
1929	Cle	A	P	26	8-8
1930	Cle	A	P	4	0-0
1931	Bro	N	P	25	11-8
1932	Bro	N	P	35	7-7
1933	Bro	N	P	41	3-4
1934	Cin	N	P	8	0-2
BLTL				368	99-109

SHAW, ALBERT S.

b.Mar.1,1881 Toledo,Ill.

Yr	Cl	Lea	Pos	G	Rec
1907	St.L	N	O	8	.303
1908	St.L	N	O	96	.264
1909	St.L	N	O	92	.248
1914	Bro	F	O	110	.321
1915	KC	F	O	132	.279
BLTR				438	.279

SHAW, ALFRED L.

b.May 22,1874 Burslem,England
d.Mar.25,1958

Yr	Cl	Lea	Pos	G	Rec
1901	Det	A	C	57	.275
1907	Bos	A	C	76	.192
1908	Chi	A	C	32	.082
1909	Bos	N	C	18	.100
BRTR				183	.207

SHAW, BENJAMIN NATHANIEL

b.Mar.16,1896 La Center,Ky.
d.Mar.16,1959

Yr	Cl	Lea	Pos	G	Rec
1917	Pit	N	O	2	.000
1918	Pit	N	C	21	.194
BRTR				23	.184

SHAW, FREDERICK LANDER (Dupee)

b.May 31,1859 Charlestown,Mass.
d.June 11,1938

Yr	Cl	Lea	Pos	G	Rec
1883	Det	N	P-O	38	11-18 / .189
1884	Det	N	P-O	36	8-18 / .191
1884	Bos	U	P-O	44	22-15 / .235
1885	Pro	N	P-O	49	23-26 / .133
1886	Was	N	P	45	14-31
1887	Was	N	P	21	7-14
1888	Was	N	P	3	0-3
TL				236	85-125 / .174

SHAW, JAMES ALOYSIUS (Grunting Jim)

b.Aug.19,1893 Pittsburgh,Pa.
d.Jan.27,1962

Yr	Cl	Lea	Pos	G	Rec
1913	Was	A	P	2	0-1
1914	Was	A	P	45	15-17
1915	Was	A	P	25	5-12
1916	Was	A	P	26	3-8
1917	Was	A	P	47	15-14
1918	Was	A	P	41	16-12
1919	Was	A	P	45	16-17
1920	Was	A	P	38	11-18
1921	Was	A	P	15	1-0
BRTR				284	82-99

SHAW, ROBERT JOHN

b.June 29,1933 Bronx,N.Y.

Yr	Cl	Lea	Pos	G	Rec
1957	Det	A	P	7	0-1
1958	Det	A	P	12	1-2
1958	Chi	A	P	29	4-2
1959	Chi	A	P	47	18-6
1960	Chi	A	P	36	13-13
1961	Chi	A	P	14	3-4
1961	KC	A	P	28	9-10
1962	Mil	N	P	38	15-9
BRTR				211	63-47

SHAW, ROYAL N. (Hunky)

b.Sept.29,1884 N.Yakima,Wash.

Yr	Cl	Lea	Pos	G	Rec
1908	Pit	N	O	1	.000
1909	Pit	N	H	1	.000
				2	.000

SHAW, SAMUEL E.

b.1863 Baltimore,Md.

Yr	Cl	Lea	Pos	G	Rec
1888	Bal	a	P	6	2-4
1893	Chi	N	P	2	1-0
BRTR				8	3-4

SHAWKEY, JAMES ROBERT (Bob)

b.Dec.4,1890 Brookville,Pa.

Yr	Cl	Lea	Pos	G	Rec
1913	Phi	A	P	17	7-5
1914	Phi	A	P	34	16-8
1915	Phi	A	P	17	6-5
1915	NY	A	P	16	4-8
1916	NY	A	P	53	24-14
1917	NY	A	P	32	13-15
1918	NY	A	P	3	1-1
1919	NY	A	P	41	20-11
1920	NY	A	P	38	20-13
1921	NY	A	P	38	18-12
1922	NY	A	P	39	20-12
1923	NY	A	P	36	16-11
1924	NY	A	P	38	16-11
1925	NY	A	P	32	6-14
1926	NY	A	P	29	8-7
1927	NY	A	P	19	2-3
BRTR				482	197-150

Non-playing manager NY (A) 1930

SHAY, ARTHUR JOSEPH (Marty)

b.Apr.25,1898 Boston,Mass.
d.Feb.20,1951

Yr	Cl	Lea	Pos	G	Rec
1916	Chi	N	2	2	.286
1924	Bos	N	2-S	19	.235
BRTR				21	.240

SHAY, DANIEL C.

b.Nov.8,1876 Kansas CityMO.
d.Dec.1,1927

Yr	Cl	Lea	Pos	G	Rec
1901	Cle	A	S	19	.226
1904	St.L	N	S	98	.256
1905	St.L	N	2-S	78	.238
1907	NY	N	S	24	.190
TR				219	.240

SHEA, FRANCIS JOSEPH (Spec) (Real name Francis Joseph O'Shea)

b.Oct.2,1922 Naugatuck,Conn.

Yr	Cl	Lea	Pos	G	Rec
1947	NY	A	P	27	14-5
1948	NY	A	P	28	9-10
1949	NY	A	P	20	1-1
1951	NY	A	P	25	5-5
1952	Was	A	P	22	11-7

(Continued)

Yr	Cl	Lea	Pos	G	Rec
1953	Was	A	P	23	12-7
1954	Was	A	P	23	2-9
1955	Was	A	P	27	2-2
BRTR				195	56-46

SHEA, GERALD J.

b.St.Louis,Mo.

Yr	Cl	Lea	Pos	G	Rec
1905	St.L	N	C	2	.333

SHEA, JOHN EDWARD (Napoleon)

b.May 23, 1878 Ware,Mass.

Yr	Cl	Lea	Pos	G	Rec
1902	Phi	N	C	3	.111
BRTR					

SHEA, JOHN MICHAEL JOSEPH

b.Dec.27,1904 Everett,Mass.

Yr	Cl	Lea	Pos	G	Rec
1928	Bos	A	P	1	0-0
BLTL					

SHEA, MERVYN DAVID JOHN

b.Sept.5,1900 San Francisco,Cal.
d.Jan.27,1953

Yr	Cl	Lea	Pos	G	Rec
1927	Det	A	C	34	.176
1928	Det	A	C	39	.236
1929	Det	A	C	50	.290
1933	Bos	A	C	16	.143
1933	St.L	A	C	94	.262
1934	Chi	A	C	62	.159
1935	Chi	A	C	46	.230
1936	Chi	A	C	14	.125
1937	Chi	A	C	25	.211
1938	Bro	N	C	48	.183
1939	Det	A	C	4	.000
1944	Phi	N	C	7	.267
BRTR				439	.220

SHEA, MICHAEL J.

b.Mar.10,1867 New Orleans,La.

Yr	Cl	Lea	Pos	G	Rec
1887	Cin	a	P	2	1-1

SHEA, PATRICK HENRY (Red)

b.Nov.29,1898 Ware,Mass.

Yr	Cl	Lea	Pos	G	Rec
1918	Phi	A	P	3	0-0
1921	NY	N	P	9	5-2
1922	NY	N	P	11	0-3
BRTR				23	5-5

SHEALY, ALBERT BERLEY

b.Mar.24,1902 Chapin,S.C.

Yr	Cl	Lea	Pos	G	Rec
1928	NY	A	P	23	8-6
1930	Chi	N	P	24	0-0
BRTR				47	8-6

SHEAN, DAVID WILLIAM

b.July 9,1883 Arlington,Mass.

Yr	Cl	Lea	Pos	G	Rec
1906	Phi	A	2	22	.213
1908	Phi	N	S	14	.106
1909	Phi	N	2	29	.232
1909	Bos	N	2	72	.241
1910	Bos	N	2	148	.239
1911	Chi	N	2-S	43	.193
1912	Bos	N	S	2	.400
1917	Cin	N	2	131	.210
1918	Bos	A	2	115	.264
1919	Bos	A	2	29	.140
BRTR				605	.228

SHEARER, RAY SOLOMON

b.Sept.19,1929 Jacobus,Pa.

Yr	Cl	Lea	Pos	G	Rec
1957	Mil	N	O	2	.500
BRTR					

SHEARON, JOHN M.

b.1870 Pittsburgh,Pa.

Yr	Cl	Lea	Pos	G	Rec
1891	Cle	N	P-O	30	1-4 / .234
1896	Cle	N	O	15	.174
				45	1-4 / .214

SHEARS, GEORGE PENFIELD

b.Apr.13,1890 Marshall,Mo.

Yr	Cl	Lea	Pos	G	Rec
1912	NY	A	P	4	0-0
BRTL					

SHECKARD, SAMUEL JAMES TILDEN (Jimmy)
b.Nov.23,1878 Upper Chanceford,Pa.
d.Jan.15,1947

Yr	Cl	Lea	Pos	G	Rec
1897	Bro	N	S-O	13	.326
1898	Bro	N	O	105	.290
1899	Bal	N	O	147	.298
1900	Bro	N	O	75	.305
1901	Bro	N	O	133	.353
1902	Bal	A	O	4	.266
1902	Bro	N	O	122	.273
1903	Bro	N	O	139	.332
1904	Bro	N	O	143	.239
1905	Bro	N	O	129	.292
1906	Chi	N	O	149	.262
1907	Chi	N	O	142	.267
1908	Chi	N	O	115	.231
1909	Chi	N	O	148	.255
1910	Chi	N	O	143	.256
1911	Chi	N	O	156	.276
1912	Chi	N	O	146	.245
1913	St.L	N	O	52	.199
1913	Cin	N	O	47	.190
	BLTR			2108	.276

SHEEHAN, DANIEL

Yr	Cl	Lea	Pos	G	Rec
1884	Bal	U	O	1	.000

SHEEHAN, DANIEL
b.Glenville,O.

Yr	Cl	Lea	Pos	G	Rec
1900	NY	N	S	1	.000

SHEEHAN, JAMES THOMAS
b.June 3,1915 New Haven,Conn.

Yr	Cl	Lea	Pos	G	Rec
1936	NY	N	C	1	.000
	BRTR				

SHEEHAN, JOHN THOMAS
b.Apr.15,1894 Chicago,Ill.

Yr	Cl	Lea	Pos	G	Rec
1920	Bro	N	3	4	.400
1921	Bro	N	3	5	.000
	BBTR			9	.176

SHEEHAN, THOMAS CLANCY
b.Mar.31,1894 Ottawa,Ill.

Yr	Cl	Lea	Pos	G	Rec
1915	Phi	A	P	15	4-8
1916	Phi	A	P	38	1-15
1921	NY	A	P	12	1-0
1924	Cin	N	P	41	9-11
1925	Cin	N	P	10	1-0
1925	Pit	N	P	24	1-1
1926	Pit	N	P	9	0-2
	BRTR			149	17-37

Non-playing manager SF (N) 1960

SHEEHAN, THOMAS H.
b.Nov.6,1877 Sacramento,Cal.
d.May 22,1959

Yr	Cl	Lea	Pos	G	Rec
1906	Pit	N	3	90	.241
1907	Pit	N	3	67	.274
1908	Bro	N	3	145	.214
	TR			302	.236

SHEEHAN, TIMOTHY JAMES
b.Feb.13,1868 Hartford,Conn.
d.Oct.21,1923

Yr	Cl	Lea	Pos	G	Rec
1895	St.L	N	O	49	.324
1896	St.L	N	O	5	.133
				54	.309

SHEELY, EARL HOMER (Whitey)
b.Feb.12,1893 Bushnell,Ill.
d.Sept.16,1952

Yr	Cl	Lea	Pos	G	Rec
1921	Chi	A	1	154	.304
1922	Chi	A	1	149	.317
1923	Chi	A	1	156	.296
1924	Chi	A	1	146	.320
1925	Chi	A	1	153	.315
1926	Chi	A	1	145	.299
1927	Chi	A	1	45	.209
1929	Pit	N	1	139	.293
1931	Bos	N	1	147	.273
	BRTR			1234	.300

SHEELY, HOLLIS KIMBALL
b.Nov.26,1920 Spokane,Wash.

Yr	Cl	Lea	Pos	G	Rec
1951	Chi	A	C	34	.180
1952	Chi	A	C	36	.240
1953	Chi	A	C	31	.217
	BLTR			101	.210

SHEERIN, CHARLES JOSEPH
b.Apr.17,1911 Brooklyn,N.Y.

Yr	Cl	Lea	Pos	G	Rec
1936	Phi	N	2-3	39	.264
	BRTR				

SHELDON, RONALD FRANK
b.Dec.17,1939 Putnam,Conn.

Yr	Cl	Lea	Pos	G	Rec
1961	NY	A	P	36	11-5
1962	NY	A	P	34	7-8
	BRTR			70	18-13

SHELLENBACK, FRANK VICTOR
b.Dec.16,1898 Joplin,Mo.

Yr	Cl	Lea	Pos	G	Rec
1918	Chi	A	P	29	10-12
1919	Chi	A	P	8	1-3
	BRTR			37	11-15

SHELLEY, HUBERT LENEIRRE (Hugh)
b.Oct.26,1910 Rogers,Tex.

Yr	Cl	Lea	Pos	G	Rec
1935	Det	A	O	7	.250
	BRTR				

SHELTON, ANDREW KEMPER (Skeeter)
b.June 29,1888 Huntington,W.Va.
d.Jan.9,1954

Yr	Cl	Lea	Pos	G	Rec
1915	NY	A	O	10	.025
	BRTR				

SHEMO, STEPHEN STANLEY
b.Apr.9,1917 Swoyersville,Pa.

Yr	Cl	Lea	Pos	G	Rec
1944	Bos	N	2-3	18	.290
1945	Bos	N	2-S-3	17	.239
	BRTR			35	.260

SHEPARD, BERT ROBERT
b.June 28,1920 Dana,Ind.

Yr	Cl	Lea	Pos	G	Rec
1945	Was	A	P	1	0-0
	BLTL				

SHEPARD, JACK LEROY
b.May 13,1932 Clovis,Cal.

Yr	Cl	Lea	Pos	G	Rec
1953	Pit	N	C	2	.250
1954	Pit	N	C	82	.304
1955	Pit	N	C	94	.239
1956	Pit	N	C-1	100	.242
	BRTR			278	.260

SHEPHERDSON, RAYMOND FRANCIS
b.May 3,1897 Little Falls,N.Y.

Yr	Cl	Lea	Pos	G	Rec
1924	St.L	N	C	3	.000
	BRTR				

SHEPPARD, JOHN
b.Baltimore,Md.

Yr	Cl	Lea	Pos	G	Rec
1873	Mar	n	C-O	3	.000

SHERDEL, WILLIAM HENRY (Wee Willie)
b.Aug.15,1896 Hanover,Pa.

Yr	Cl	Lea	Pos	G	Rec
1918	St.L	N	P	35	6-12
1919	St.L	N	P	40	5-9
1920	St.L	N	P	49	11-10
1921	St.L	N	P	39	9-8
1922	St.L	N	P	48	17-13
1923	St.L	N	P	45	15-13
1924	St.L	N	P-O	49	8-9 .200
1925	St.L	N	P	33	15-6

(Continued)

Yr	Cl	Lea	Pos	G	Rec
1926	St.L	N	P	36	16-12
1927	St.L	N	P	39	17-12
1928	St.L	N	P	38	21-10
1929	St.L	N	P	33	10-15
1930	St.L	N	P	13	3-2
1930	Bos	N	P	21	6-5
1931	Bos	N	P	27	6-10
1932	Bos	N	P	1	0-0
1932	St.L	N	P	3	0-0
	BLTL			549	165-146 .223

SHERID, ROY RICHARD
b.Jan.25,1908 Norristown,Pa.

Yr	Cl	Lea	Pos	G	Rec
1929	NY	A	P	33	6-6
1930	NY	A	P	37	12-13
1931	NY	A	P	17	5-5
	BRTR			87	23-24

SHERIDAN, ...

Yr	Cl	Lea	Pos	G	Rec
1875	Atl	n	O	1	.000

SHERIDAN, EUGENE ANTHONY (Red)
b.Nov.14,1896 Brooklyn,N.Y.

Yr	Cl	Lea	Pos	G	Rec
1918	Bro	N	2	2	.250
1920	Bro	N	S	2	.000
	BBTR			4	.167

SHERIDAN, NEILL RAWLINS
b.Nov.20,1921 Sacramento,Cal.

Yr	Cl	Lea	Pos	G	Rec
1948	Bos	A	H	2	.000
	BRTR				

SHERLING, EDWARD CREECH
b.July 18,1897 Coalburg,Ala.

Yr	Cl	Lea	Pos	G	Rec
1924	Phi	A	H	4	.500
	BRTR				

SHERLOCK, JOHN CLINTON (Monk)
b.Oct.26,1904 Buffalo,N.Y.

Yr	Cl	Lea	Pos	G	Rec
1930	Phi	N	1	92	.324
	BRTR				

SHERLOCK, VINCENT THOMAS (Baldy)
b.Mar.27,1909 Buffalo,N.Y.

Yr	Cl	Lea	Pos	G	Rec
1935	Bro	N	2	9	.462
	BRTR				

SHERMAN, DANIEL L. (Babe)
b.1892 Connecticut.

Yr	Cl	Lea	Pos	G	Rec
1914	Chi	F	P	1	0-1
	BRTR				

SHERMAN, JOEL POWERS
b.Nov.14,1890 Yarmouth,Mass.

Yr	Cl	Lea	Pos	G	Rec
1915	Phi	A	P	2	1-0
	BRTR				

SHERRY, FRED PETER (Real name Fred Peter Schuerholz)
b.Jan.13,1889 Honesdale,Pa.

Yr	Cl	Lea	Pos	G	Rec
1911	Was	A	P	10	0-4

SHERRY, LAWRENCE
b.July 25,1935 Los Angeles,Cal.

Yr	Cl	Lea	Pos	G	Rec
1958	LA	N	P	5	0-0
1959	LA	N	P	23	7-2
1960	LA	N	P	57	14-10
1961	LA	N	P	53	4-4
1962	LA	N	P	58	7-3
	BRTR			196	32-19

SHERRY, NORMAN BURT
b.July 16, 1931 New York,N.Y.

Yr	Cl	Lea	Pos	G	Rec
1959	L.A.	N	C	2	.333
1960	L.A.	N	C	47	.283
1961	L.A.	N	C	47	.256
1962	L.A.	N	C	35	.182
	BRTR			131	.249

SHETRONE, BARRY STEVAN
b.July 6,1938 Baltimore,Md.

Yr	Cl	Lea	Pos	G	Rec
1959	Bal	A	O	33	.203
1960	Bal	A	H	1	.000
1961	Bal	A	O	3	.143
1962	Bal	A	O	21	.250
	BLTR			58	.209

SHETTSLINE, WILLIAM JOSEPH
b.Oct.25,1863 Philadelphia,Pa.
d.Feb.22,1933
Non-playing manager Phi (N) 1898-1902.

SHETZLINE, JOHN HENRY
b.1850 Philadelphia,Pa.
d.Dec.15,1892

Yr	Cl	Lea	Pos	G	Rec
1882	Bal	a	2-S-3-O	76	.226

SHEVLIN, JAMES CORNELIUS
b.July 9,1909 Cincinnati,O.

Yr	Cl	Lea	Pos	G	Rec
1930	Det	A	1	28	.143
1932	Cin	N	1	7	.208
1934	Cin	N	1	18	.308
	BLTL			53	.247

SHIELDS, BENJAMIN COWAN
(Lefty)
b.June 17,1903 Huntersville,N.C.

Yr	Cl	Lea	Pos	G	Rec
1924	NY	A	P	2	0-0
1925	NY	A	P	4	3-0
1930	Bos	A	P	3	0-0
1931	Phi	N	P	4	1-0
	BRTL			13	4-0

SHIELDS, CHARLES JESSAMINE
b.Dec.10,1879 Jackson,Tenn.
d.Aug.27,1953

Yr	Cl	Lea	Pos	G	Rec
1902	Bal	A	P-O	23	3-9 / .163
1902	St.L	A	P	4	3-0
1907	St.L	N	P	3	0-3
	BLTL			30	6-12 / .219

SHIELDS, FRANCIS LEROY
(Pete)
b.Sept.21,1891 Swiftwater,Miss.

Yr	Cl	Lea	Pos	G	Rec
1915	Cle	A	1	23	.208
	BRTR				

SHIELDS, VINCENT WILLIAM
b.Nov.18,1902 Fredericton,N.B.,Canada.

Yr	Cl	Lea	Pos	G	Rec
1924	St.L	N	P	3	1-1
	BLTR				

SHIFFLETT, GARLAND J.
b.Mar.28,1935 Elkton,Va.

Yr	Cl	Lea	Pos	G	Rec
1957	Was	A	P	6	0-0
	BRTR				

SHILLING, JAMES ROBERT
b.May 14,1915 Tulsa,Okla.

Yr	Cl	Lea	Pos	G	Rec
1939	Cle	A	2	31	.276
1939	Phi	N	2-S-3	11	.303
	BRTR			42	.282

SHINAULT, ENOCH ERSKINE
(Ginger)
b.Sept.6,1892 Memphis,Tenn.
d.Dec.29,1930

Yr	Cl	Lea	Pos	G	Rec
1921	Cle	A	C	22	.378
1922	Cle	A	C	13	.133
	BRTR			35	.295

SHINDLE, WILLIAM
b.Dec.5,1863 Gloucester,N.J.

Yr	Cl	Lea	Pos	G	Rec
1886	Det	N	S	5	.333
1887	Det	N	3	20	.340
1888	Bal	a	3	135	.216
1889	Bal	a	3	138	.315
1890	Phi	p	S	132	.236
1891	Phi	N	3	103	.210
1892	Bal	N	3	143	.253

(Continued)

Yr	Cl	Lea	Pos	G	Rec
1893	Bal	N	3	125	.259
1894	Bro	N	3	117	.300
1895	Bro	N	3	118	.278
1896	Bro	N	3	131	.281
1897	Bro	N	3	134	.289
1898	Bro	N	3	120	.228
	TR			1421	.271

SHINNERS, RALPH PETER
b.Oct.4.1897 Milwaukee,Wis.
d.July 23,1962

Yr	Cl	Lea	Pos	G	Rec
1922	NY	N	O	56	.251
1923	NY	N	O	33	.154
1925	St.L	N	O	74	.295
	BRTR			163	.276

SHINNICK, TIMOTHY JAMES
(Dandy)
b.Nov.6,1867 Exeter,N.H.
d.May 18,1944

Yr	Cl	Lea	Pos	G	Rec
1890	Lou	a	2	133	.267
1891	Lou	a	2	135	.225
	BBTR			268	.244

SHIPKE, WILLIAM M.
(Tony) (Real name William M. Shipkrethaver)
b.Nov.18,1882 St.Louis,Mo.
d.Sept.10,1940

Yr	Cl	Lea	Pos	G	Rec
1906	Cle	A	3	2	.000
1907	Was	A	3	64	.196
1908	Was	A	3	111	.208
1909	Was	A	3	8	.154
	TR			185	.200

SHIPKRETHAVER, WILLIAM M.
(Played under name of William M. Shipke)

SHIPLEY, JOSEPH CLARK
b.May 9,1935 Morristown,Tenn.

Yr	Cl	Lea	Pos	G	Rec
1958	SF	N	P	1	0-0
1959	S.F.	N	P	10	0-0
1960	S.F.	N	P	15	0-0
	BRTR				

SHIRES, ARTHUR LEE
(The Great)
b.Aug.13,1907 Italy,Tex.

Yr	Cl	Lea	Pos	G	Rec
1928	Chi	A	1	33	.341
1929	Chi	A	1	100	.312
1930	Chi	A	1	37	.260
1930	Was	A	1	38	.365
1932	Bos	N	1	82	.238
	BLTR			290	.291

SHIREY, CLAIR LEE (Duke)
b.1899 Hagerstown,Md.
d.Sept.1,1962

Yr	Cl	Lea	Pos	G	Rec
1920	Was	A	P	2	0-1
	BB				

SHIRLEY, ALVIS NEWMAN
(Tex)
b.Apr.25,1918 Birthright,Tex.

Yr	Cl	Lea	Pos	G	Rec
1941	Phi	A	P	5	0-1
1942	Phi	A	P	15	0-1
1944	St.L	A	P	30	5-4
1945	St.L	A	P	43	8-12
1946	St.L	A	P	35	6-12
	BRTR			128	19-30

SHIRLEY, ERNEST RAEFORD
(Mule)
b.May 24,1901 Snow Hill,N.C.
d.Aug.4,1955.

Yr	Cl	Lea	Pos	G	Rec
1924	Was	A	1	30	.234
1925	Was	A	1	14	.130
	BLTL			44	.210

SHIVER, IVEY MERWIN
(Chick)
b.Jan.22,1906 Sylvester,Ga.

Yr	Cl	Lea	Pos	G	Rec
1931	Det	A	O	2	.111
1934	Cin	N	O	19	.203
	BRTR			21	.191

SHOCH, GEORGE QUINTUS
b.Jan.6,1859 Philadelphia,Pa.
d.Sept.30,1937

Yr	Cl	Lea	Pos	G	Rec
1886	Was	N	O	26	.294
1887	Was	N	O	69	.294
1888	Was	N	S-O	90	.183
1889	Was	N	O	30	.238
1891	Mil	a	2	34	.299
1892	Bal	N	S	75	.279
1893	Bro	N	3-O	93	.276
1894	Bro	N	O	63	.320
1895	Bro	N	O	58	.263
1896	Bro	N	2	75	.278
1897	Bro	N	2	79	.290
	BRTR			692	.271

SHOCKER, URBAN JAMES
(Real name Urbain Jacques Schockeor)
b.Aug.22,1890 Cleveland,O.
d.Sept.9,1928

Yr	Cl	Lea	Pos	G	Rec
1916	NY	A	P	12	4-3
1917	NY	A	P	26	8-4
1918	St.L	A	P	14	6-5
1919	St.L	A	P	30	13-11
1920	St.L	A	P	38	20-10
1921	St.L	A	P	47	27-12
1922	St.L	A	P	48	24-17
1923	St.L	A	P	43	20-12
1924	St.L	A	P	40	16-13
1925	NY	A	P	41	12-12
1926	NY	A	P	41	19-11
1927	NY	A	P	31	18-6
1928	NY	A	P	1	0-0
	BRTR			412	187-117

SHOEMAKER, CHARLES LANDIS
B.Aug.10,1939 Los Angeles,Cal.

Yr	Cl	Lea	Pos	G	Rec
1961	K.C.	A	2	7	.385
1962	K.C.	A	2	5	.182
	BLTR			12	.324

SHOENICK, LEWIS N.
(Jumbo)
b.1862 Chicago,Ill.

Yr	Cl	Lea	Pos	G	Rec
1884	Chi	U	1-O	70	.315
1884	Pit	U	1	18	.276
1884	Bal	U	1	16	.283
1888	Ind	N	1	48	.237
1889	Ind	N	1	16	.242
	TR			168	.280

SHOFFNER, MILBURN JAMES
(Milt)
b.Nov.13,1905 Sherman,Tex.

Yr	Cl	Lea	Pos	G	Rec
1929	Cle	A	P	11	2-3
1930	Cle	A	P	24	3-4
1931	Cle	A	P	12	2-3
1937	Bos	N	P	6	3-1
1938	Bos	N	P	27	8-7
1939	Bos	N	P	25	4-6
1939	Cin	N	P	10	2-2
1940	Cin	N	P	20	1-0
	BLTL			135	25-26

SHOFNER, FRANK STRICKLAND
(Strick)
b.July 23,1920 Crawford,Tex.

Yr	Cl	Lea	Pos	G	Rec
1947	Bos	A	3	5	.154
	BLTR				

SHOKES, EDWARD CHRISTOPHER
b.Jan.27,1920 Charleston,S.C.

Yr	Cl	Lea	Pos	G	Rec
1941	Cin	N	H	1	.000
1946	Cin	N	1	31	.120
	BLTL			32	.119

SHOMBERG, OTTO H.
(Real name Otto H. Shambrick)
b.Nov.14,1864 Milwaukee,Wis.
d.May 3,1927

Yr	Cl	Lea	Pos	G	Rec
1886	Pit	a	1	72	.295
1887	Ind	N	1	112	.389
1888	Ind	N	1	29	.214
	TL			213	.329

SHOOK, RAYMOND CURTIS
b.Nov.18,1890 Perry,Ohio

Yr	Cl	Lea	Pos	G	Rec
1916	Chi	A	H	1	.000
	BRTR				

SHOOP, RONALD LEE
b.Sept.19,1932 Rural Valley, Pa.

Yr	Cl	Lea	Pos	G	Rec
1959	Det	A	C	3	.143
	BRTR				

SHORE, ERNEST GRADY
b.Mar.24,1891 E.Bend,N.C.

Yr	Cl	Lea	Pos	G	Rec
1912	NY	N	P	1	0-0
1914	Bos	A	P	19	10-4
1915	Bos	A	P	38	19-7
1916	Bos	A	P	38	16-10
1917	Bos	A	P	29	13-10
1919	NY	A	P	20	5-8
1920	NY	A	P	14	2-2
	BRTR			159	65-41

SHORE, RAYMOND EVERETT
b.June 9,1921 Cincinnati,O.

Yr	Cl	Lea	Pos	G	Rec
1946	St.L	A	P	1	0-0
1948	St.L	A	P	17	1-2
1949	St.L	A	P	13	0-1
	BRTR			31	1-3

SHORES, WILLIAM DAVID
b.May 26,1904 Abilene,Tex.

Yr	Cl	Lea	Pos	G	Rec
1928	Phi	A	P	3	1-1
1929	Phi	A	P	39	11-6
1930	Phi	A	P	31	12-4
1931	Phi	A	P	6	0-3
1933	NY	N	P	8	2-1
1936	Chi	A	P	9	0-0
	BRTR			96	26-15

SHORT, CHRISTOPHER JOSEPH
b.Sept.19,1937 Milford, Del.

Yr	Cl	Lea	Pos	G	Rec
1959	Phi	N	P	3	0-0
1960	Phi	N	P	42	6-9
1961	Phi	N	P-C	40	6-12 .162
1962	Phi	N	P	48	11-9
	BLTL			133	23-30 .135

SHORT, DAVID ORVIS
b.May 11,1917 Magnolia,Ark.

Yr	Cl	Lea	Pos	G	Rec
1940	Chi	A	H	4	.333
1941	Chi	A	O	3	.000
	BLTR			7	.091

SHORT, WILLIAM ROSS
b.Nov.27,1937 Kingston,N.Y.

Yr	Cl	Lea	Pos	G	Rec
1960	N.Y.	A	P	10	3-5
1962	Bal	A	P	5	0-0
	BLTL			15	3-5

SHORTEN, CHARLES HENRY
(Chuck)
b.Apr.19,1893 Scranton,Pa.

Yr	Cl	Lea	Pos	G	Rec
1915	Bos	A	O	6	.214
1916	Bos	A	O	53	.295
1917	Bos	A	O	69	.179
1919	Det	A	O	95	.315
1920	Det	A	O	116	.288
1921	Det	A	O	92	.272
1922	St.L	A	O	55	.275
1924	Cin	N	O	41	.275
	BLTL			527	.275

SHOTTON, BURTON EDWIN
(Barney)
b.Oct.18,1884 Brownhelm,O.
d.July 29,1962

Yr	Cl	Lea	Pos	G	Rec
1909	St.L	A	O	17	.262
1911	St.L	A	O	139	.255
1912	St.L	A	O	154	.290
1913	St.L	A	O	149	.293
1914	St.L	A	O	154	.269
1915	St.L	A	O	156	.283
1916	St.L	A	O	157	.282
1917	St.L	A	O	118	.224
1918	Was	A	O	126	.261
1919	St.L	N	O	85	.285
1920	St.L	N	O	62	.228
1921	St.L	N	O	38	.250
1922	St.L	N	O	34	.200
1923	St.L	N	O	1	.000
	BLTR			1390	.270

Non-playing manager Phi (N) 1928-33, Cin (N) 1934, Bro (N) 1947 and Bro (N) 1948-50.

SHOUN, CLYDE MITCHELL
(Hardrock)
b.Mar.20,1915 Mountain City,Tenn.

Yr	Cl	Lea	Pos	G	Rec
1935	Chi	N	P	5	1-0
1936	Chi	N	P	4	0-0
1937	Chi	N	P	37	7-7
1938	St.L	N	P	40	6-6
1939	St.L	N	P	53	3-1
1940	St.L	N	P	54	13-11
1941	St.L	N	P	26	3-5
1942	St.L	N	P	2	0-0
1942	Cin	N	P	34	1-3
1943	Cin	N	P	45	14-5
1944	Cin	N	P	38	13-10
1946	Cin	N	P	27	1-6
1947	Cin	N	P	10	0-0
1947	Bos	N	P	26	5-3
1948	Bos	N	P	36	5-1
1949	Bos	N	P	1	0-0
1949	Chi	A	P	16	1-1
	BLTL			454	73-59

SHOUP, JOHN F.
b.Sept.30,1851 Cincinnati,O.
d.Feb.13,1920

Yr	Cl	Lea	Pos	G	Rec
1879	Tro	N	S	10	.097
1882	St.L	a	2	2	.000
1884	Was	U	O	1	.750
	TL			13	.135

SHOVELIN, JOHN J.
b.July 19,1892 Drifton,Pa.

Yr	Cl	Lea	Pos	G	Rec
1911	Pit	N	H	2	.000
1919	St.L	A	2	9	.212
1920	St.L	A	2	7	.286
	BRTR			18	.220

SHREVE, LOUIS LEONARD
(Ledell)
b.Louisville,Ky.

Yr	Cl	Lea	Pos	G	Rec
1887	Bal	a	P	6	2-1
1887	Ind	N	P	15	5-10
1888	Ind	N	P	36	11-24
1889	Ind	N	P	3	0-3
	TR			60	18-38

SHRIVER, HARRY GRAYDON
b.Sept.2,1897 Wadestown,W.Va.

Yr	Cl	Lea	Pos	G	Rec
1922	Bro	N	P	25	4-6
1923	Bro	N	P	1	0-0
	BRTR			26	4-6

SHUBA, GEORGE THOMAS
b.Dec.13,1924 Youngstown,O.

Yr	Cl	Lea	Pos	G	Rec
1948	Bro	N	O	63	.267
1949	Bro	N	H	1	.000
1950	Bro	N	O	34	.207
1952	Bro	N	O	94	.305
1953	Bro	N	O	74	.254
1954	Bro	N	O	45	.154
1955	Bro	N	O	44	.275
	BLTR			355	.259

SHUGART, WILLIAM FRANK
b.1867 Chicago,Ill.

Yr	Cl	Lea	Pos	G	Rec
1890	Chi	p	S	29	.177
1891	Pit	N	S	75	.285
1892	Pit	N	S	137	.276
1893	Pit	N	S-O	52	.274
1893	St.L	N	S-O	57	.297
1894	St.L	N	O	133	.285
1895	Lou	N	S-O	112	.256
1897	Phi	N	S	40	.251
1901	Chi	A	S	107	.251
	BLTR			742	.268

SHULTZ, WALLACE LUTHER
b.Oct.10,1888 McKeesport,Pa.
d.Jan.30,1959

Yr	Cl	Lea	Pos	G	Rec
1911	Phi	N	P	5	0-3
1912	Phi	N	P	23	1-4
	BRTR			28	1-7

SHUMAN, HARRY
b.Mar.5,1916 Philadelphia,Pa.

Yr	Cl	Lea	Pos	G	Rec
1942	Pit	N	P	1	0-0
1943	Pit	N	P	11	0-0
1944	Phi	N	P	18	0-0
	BRTR			30	0-0

SHUPE, VINCENT WILLIAM
b.Sept.5,1921 E.Canton,O.
d.Apr.5,1962

Yr	Cl	Lea	Pos	G	Rec
1945	Bos	N	1	78	.269
	BLTL				

SICKING, EDWARD JOSEPH
b.Mar.30,1897 St.Bernard,O.

Yr	Cl	Lea	Pos	G	Rec
1916	Chi	N	3	1	.000
1918	NY	N	2-S-3	46	.250
1919	NY	N	2-S	6	.333
1919	Phi	N	2-S-3	61	.216
1920	NY	N	3	46	.172
1920	Cin	N	2-S-3	37	.266
1927	Pit	N	2	6	.143
	BRTR			203	.226

SIEBERN, NORMAN LEROY
b.July 26,1933 St. Louis,Mo.

Yr	Cl	Lea	Pos	G	Rec
1956	NY	A	O	54	.204
1958	NY	A	O	134	.300
1959	NY	A	1-O	120	.271
1960	KC	A	1-O	144	.279
1961	KC	A	1-O	153	.296
1962	KC	A	1	162	.308
	BLTR			767	.287

SIEBERT, RICHARD WALTHER
b.Feb.19,1912 Fall River,Mass.

Yr	Cl	Lea	Pos	G	Rec
1932	Bro	N	1	6	.286
1936	Bro	N	O	2	.000
1937	St.L	N	1	22	.184
1938	St.L	N	H	1	1.000
1938	Phi	A	1	48	.284
1939	Phi	A	1	101	.294
1940	Phi	A	1	154	.286
1941	Phi	A	1	123	.334
1942	Phi	A	1	153	.260
1943	Phi	A	1	146	.251
1944	Phi	A	1-O	132	.306
1945	Phi	A	1	147	.267
	BLTL			1035	.282

SIEFKE, FREDERICK EDWIN
b.Mar.27,1870 New York,N.Y.
d.Apr.18,1893

Yr	Cl	Lea	Pos	G	Rec
1890	Br	a	3	16	.137

SIEGEL, JOHN
b.York,Pa.

Yr	Cl	Lea	Pos	G	Rec
1884	Key	U	3	8	.226

SIEGLE, JOHN HERBERT
b.July 8,1874 Urbana,O.

Yr	Cl	Lea	Pos	G	Rec
1905	Cin	N	O	16	.304
1906	Cin	N	O	21	.118
BRTR				37	.202

SIEMER, OSCAR SYLVESTER
b.Aug.14,1902 St.Louis,Mo.
d.Dec.5,1959

Yr	Cl	Lea	Pos	G	Rec
1925	Bos	N	C	16	.304
1926	Bos	N	C	31	.205
BRTR				47	.244

SIEVER, EDWARD T.
b.Apr.2,1878 Lewistown,Ill.
d.Feb.5,1920

Yr	Cl	Lea	Pos	G	Rec
1901	Det	A	P	37	18-11
1902	Det	A	P	25	8-13
1903	St.L	A	P	32	14-15
1904	St.L	A	P	30	11-16
1906	Det	A	P	29	14-10
1907	Det	A	P	38	19-10
1908	Det	A	P	11	2-6
TL				202	86-81

SIEVERS, ROY EDWARD
(Squirrel)
b.Nov.18,1926 St.Louis,Mo.

Yr	Cl	Lea	Pos	G	Rec
1949	St.L	A	3-O	140	.306
1950	St.L	A	3-O	113	.238
1951	St.L	A	O	31	.225
1952	St.L	A	1	11	.200
1953	St.L	A	1	92	.270
1954	Was	A	1-O	145	.232
1955	Was	A	1-3-O	144	.271
1956	Was	A	1-O	• 152	.253
1957	Was	A	1-O	152	.301
1958	Was	A	1-O	148	.295
1959	Was	A	1-O	115	.242
1960	Chi	A	1-O	127	.295
1961	Chi	A	1	141	.295
1962	Phi	N	1-O	144	.262
BRTR				1655	.272

SIFFEL, FRANK
b.Philadelphia,Pa.

Yr	Cl	Lea	Pos	G	Rec
1884	Ath	a	C	7	.143
1885	Ath	a	C-O	3	.100
				10	.129

SIGAFOOS, FRANCIS LEONARD
b.Mar.21,1904 Easton,Pa.

Yr	Cl	Lea	Pos	G	Rec
1926	Phi	A	S	13	.255
1929	Det	A	2-S-3	14	.174
1929	Chi	A	H	7	.333
1931	Cin	N	S-3	21	.169
BRTR				55	.201

SIGLIN, WESLEY PETER
(Paddy)
b.Sept.24,1891 Aurelia,Ia.
d.Aug.5,1956

Yr	Cl	Lea	Pos	G	Rec
1914	Pit	N	2	14	.154
1915	Pit	N	2	6	.285
1916	Pit	N	2	3	.250
BRTR				23	.180

SIGMAN, W. TRIPLETT
(Trip)
b.Jan.17,1905 Mooresville,N.C.

Yr	Cl	Lea	Pos	G	Rec
1929	Phi	N	O	10	.517
1930	Phi	N	O	52	.270
BLTR				62	.325

SIGNER, WALTER DONALD
b.Oct.12,1913 New York,N.Y.

Yr	Cl	Lea	Pos	G	Rec
1943	Chi	N	P	4	2-1
1945	Chi	N	P	6	0-0
BRTR				10	2-1

SIGSBY, SETH DEWITT
b.Troy,N.Y.

Yr	Cl	Lea	Pos	G	Rec
1893	NY	N	P	1	0-0

SILBER, EDWARD JAMES
b.June 8,1915 Philadelphia,Pa.

Yr	Cl	Lea	Pos	G	Rec
1937	St.L	A	O	22	.313
1939	St.L	A	H	1	.000
BRTR				23	.310

SILCH, EDWARD (Baldy)
b.Feb.22,1865 St.Louis,Mo.
d.Jan.15,1895

Yr	Cl	Lea	Pos	G	Rec
1888	Bro	a	O	13	.260
TR					

SILVA, DANIEL JAMES
b.Oct.5,1899 Everett,Mass.

Yr	Cl	Lea	Pos	G	Rec
1919	Was	A	3	1	.250
BRTR					

SILVERA, AARON ALBERT
b.Aug.26,1935 San Diego,Cal.

Yr	Cl	Lea	Pos	G	Rec
1955	Cin	N	O	13	.143
1956	Cin	N	O	1	.000
BRTR				14	.143

SILVERA, CHARLES ANTHONY RYAN (Swede)
b.Oct.13,1924 San Francisco,Cal.

Yr	Cl	Lea	Pos	G	Rec
1948	NY	A	C	4	.571
1949	NY	A	C	58	.315
1950	NY	A	C	18	.160
1951	NY	A	C	18	.275
1952	NY	A	C	20	.327
1953	NY	A	C-3	42	.280
1954	NY	A	C	20	.270
1955	NY	A	C	13	.174
1956	NY	A	C	7	.222
1957	Chi	N	C	26	.208
BRTR				226	.282

SILVERMAN, JESSE
(Played under name of Jesse Baker)

SILVESTRI, KENNETH JOSEPH
(Hatch)
b.May 3,1916 Chicago,Ill.

Yr	Cl	Lea	Pos	G	Rec
1939	Chi	A	C	22	.173
1940	Chi	A	C	28	.250
1941	NY	A	C	17	.250
1946	NY	A	C	13	.286
1947	NY	A	C	3	.200
1949	Phi	N	C-2-S	4	.000
1950	Phi	N	C	11	.250
1951	Phi	N	C-2	4	.222
BBTR				102	.217

SIMA, ALBERT
b.Oct.7,1921 Mahwah,N.J.

Yr	Cl	Lea	Pos	G	Rec
1950	Was	A	P	17	4-5
1951	Was	A	P	18	3-7
1953	Was	A	P	31	2-3
1954	Chi	A	P	5	0-1
1954	Phi	A	P	29	2-5
BRTL				100	11-21

SIMMONS, ALOYSIUS HARRY
(Bucketfoot) (Real name Aloysius Harry Szymanski)
b.May 22,1903 Milwaukee,Wis.
d.May 26,1956

Yr	Cl	Lea	Pos	G	Rec
1924	Phi	A	O	152	.308
1925	Phi	A	O	153	.386
1926	Phi	A	O	147	.343
1927	Phi	A	O	106	.392
1928	Phi	A	O	119	.351
1929	Phi	A	O	143	.365
1930	Phi	A	O	138	.381
1931	Phi	A	O	128	.390
1932	Phi	A	O	154	.322
1933	Chi	A	O	146	.331
1934	Chi	A	O	138	.344
1935	Chi	A	O	128	.267

(Continued)

Yr	Cl	Lea	Pos	G	Rec
1936	Det	A	O	143	.327
1937	Was	A	O	103	.279
1938	Was	A	O	125	.302
1939	Bos	N	O	93	.282
1939	Cin	N	O	9	.143
1940	Phi	A	O	37	.309
1941	Phi	A	O	9	.125
1943	Bos	A	O	40	.203
1944	Phi	A	O	4	.500
BRTR				2215	.334

SIMMONS, CURTIS THOMAS
b.May 19,1929 Egypt,Pa.

Yr	Cl	Lea	Pos	G	Rec
1947	Phi	N	P	1	1-0
1948	Phi	N	P	31	7-13
1949	Phi	N	P	39	4-10
1950	Phi	N	P	34	17-8
1952	Phi	N	P	28	14-8
1953	Phi	N	P	32	16-13
1954	Phi	N	P	38	14-15
1955	Phi	N	P	27	8-8
1956	Phi	N	P	39	15-10
1957	Phi	N	P	38	12-11
1958	Phi	N	P	38	7-14
1959	Phi	N	P	8	0-0
1960	Phi	N	P	4	0-0
1960	St.L	N	P	29	7-4
1961	St.L	N	P	32	9-10
1962	St.L	N	P	31	10-10
BLTL				449	141-134

SIMMONS, GEORGE WASHINGTON
(Hack)
b.Jan.29,1885 Brooklyn,N.Y.
d.Apr.26,1942

Yr	Cl	Lea	Pos	G	Rec
1910	Det	A	1	42	.191
1912	NY	A	2	110	.239
1914	Bal	F	2-O	113	.269
1915	Bal	F	O	39	.205
BRTR				304	.242

SIMMONS, JOHN EARL
b.July 7,1924 Birmingham,Ala.

Yr	Cl	Lea	Pos	G	Rec
1949	Was	A	O	62	.215
BRTR					

SIMMONS, JOSEPH S.
b.June 13,1845 New York,N.Y.
d.Dec.10,1888

Yr	Cl	Lea	Pos	G	Rec
1871	Chi	n	1-O	27	NR
1872	Cle	n	1-O	17	NR
1875	Wes	n	1-O	13	NR
				57	NR

Non-playing manager Wil (U) 1884.

SIMMONS, LEWIS
b.Aug.27,1838 New Castle,Pa.
d.Sept.2,1911
Non-playing manager Ath (a) 1886.

SIMMONS, PATRICK CLEMENT
b.Nov.29,1908 Watervliet,N.Y.

Yr	Cl	Lea	Pos	G	Rec
1928	Bos	A	P	31	0-2
1929	Bos	A	P	2	0-0
BRTR				33	0-2

SIMON, HENRY J.
b.Aug.25,1862 Utica,N.Y.
d.Jan.2,1925

Yr	Cl	Lea	Pos	G	Rec
1887	Cle	a	O	3	.100
1890	Bro	a	O	90	.247
1890	Syr	a	O	37	.294
				130	.257

SIMON, MICHAEL EDWARD
b.Apr.13,1883 North Vernon,Ind.

Yr	Cl	Lea	Pos	G	Rec
1909	Pit	N	C	12	.167
1910	Pit	N	C	20	.213
1911	Pit	N	C	68	.228
1912	Pit	N	C	42	.301
1913	Pit	N	C	92	.247
1914	St.L	F	C	93	.219
1915	Bro	F	C	47	.175
BRTR				374	.229

SIMON, SYLVESTER ADAM (Sammy)
b.Dec.14,1897 Evansville,Ind.

Yr	Cl	Lea	Pos	G	Rec
1923	St.L	A	H	1	.000
1924	St.L	A	S-3	23	.250
BRTR				24	.242

SIMONS, MELBERN ELLIS (Butch)
b.July 1,1902 Carlyle,Ill.

Yr	Cl	Lea	Pos	G	Rec
1931	Chi	A	O	68	.275
1932	Chi	A	O	7	.000
BLTR				75	.268

SIMPSON, HARRY LEON
b.Dec.3,1925 Atlanta,Ga.

Yr	Cl	Lea	Pos	G	Rec
1951	Cle	A	1-O	122	.229
1952	Cle	A	1-O	146	.266
1953	Cle	A	1-O	82	.227
1955	Cle	A	H	3	.000
1955	KC	A	1-O	112	.301
1956	KC	A	1-O	141	.293
1957	KC	A	1-O	50	.296
1957	NY	A	1-O	75	.250
1958	NY	A	O	24	.216
1958	KC	A	1-O	78	.264
1959	KC	A	1	8	.286
1959	Chi	A	1-O	38	.187
1959	Pit	N	O	9	.267
BLTR				888	.266

SIMPSON, MARTIN
b.Baltimore,Md.

Yr	Cl	Lea	Pos	G	Rec
1873	Mar	n	C-2	4	NR

SIMPSON, RICHARD CHARLES
b.July 28,1943 Washington,D.C.

Yr	Cl	Lea	Pos	G	Rec
1962	LA	A	O	6	.250
BRTR					

SIMPSON, THOMAS LEO (Duke)
b.Sept.15,1927 Columbus,O.

Yr	Cl	Lea	Pos	G	Rec
1953	Chi	N	P	30	1-2
BRTR					

SIMS, CLARENCE
b.1892

Yr	Cl	Lea	Pos	G	Rec
1915	St.L	A	P	3	1-0
BRTR					

SINCOCK, HERBERT SYLVESTER
b.Sept,8,1887 Barkerville,B.C.,Canada.

Yr	Cl	Lea	Pos	G	Rec
1908	Cin	N	P	1	0-0

SINER, HOSEA JOHN
b.Mar.20,1885 Shelburn,Ind.
d.June 11,1948

Yr	Cl	Lea	Pos	G	Rec
1909	Bos	N	3	10	.130
TR					

SINGLETON, BERT ELMER (Smoky)
b.June 26,1920 Ogden,Utah.

Yr	Cl	Lea	Pos	G	Rec
1945	Bos	N	P	7	1-4
1946	Bos	N	P	16	0-1
1947	Pit	N	P	41	2-2
1948	Pit	N	P	38	4-6
1950	Was	A	P	21	1-2
1957	Chi	N	P	6	0-1
1958	Chi	N	P	2	1-0
1959	Chi	N	P	21	2-1
BRTR				152	11-17

SINGLETON, JOHN EDWARD (Sheriff)
b.Nov.27,1896 Gallipolis,O.
d.Oct.24,1937

Yr	Cl	Lea	Pos	G	Rec
1922	Phi	N	P	22	1-10
BRTR					

SINGTON, FREDERIC WILLIAM
b.Feb.24,1910 Birmingham,Ala.

Yr	Cl	Lea	Pos	G	Rec
1934	Was	A	O	9	.286

(Continued)

Yr	Cl	Lea	Pos	G	Rec
1935	Was	A	O	20	.182
1936	Was	A	O	25	.319
1937	Was	A	O	78	.237
1938	Bro	N	O	17	.358
1939	Bro	N	O	32	.274
BRTR				181	.273

SIPEK, RICHARD FRANCIS
b.Jan.16,1923 Chicago,Ill.

Yr	Cl	Lea	Pos	G	Rec
1945	Cin	N	O	82	.244
BLTR					

SISK, THOMAS WAYNE
b.Apr.12,1942 Ardmore,Okla.

Yr	Cl	Lea	Pos	G	Rec
1962	Pit	N	P	5	0-2
BRTR					

SISLER, DAVID MICHAEL
b.Oct.16,1931 St. Louis,Mo.

Yr	Cl	Lea	Pos	G	Rec
1956	Bos	A	P	39	9-8
1957	Bos	A	P	22	7-8
1958	Bos	A	P	30	8-9
1959	Bos	A	P	3	0-0
1959	Det	A	P	32	1-3
1960	Det	A	P	41	7-5
1961	Was	A	P	45	2-8
1962	Cin	N	P	35	4-3
BRTR				247	38-44

SISLER, GEORGE HAROLD (Gorgeous George)
b.Mar.24,1893 Manchester,O.

Yr	Cl	Lea	Pos	G	Rec
1915	St.L	A	P-1-O	81	4-5 .285
1916	St.L	A	P-1-3	151	1-3 .305
1917	St.L	A	1-2	135	.353
1918	St.L	A	1	114	341
1919	St.L	A	1	132	.352
1920	St.L	A	P-1	154	0-0 .407
1921	St.L	A	1	138	.371
1922	St.L	A	1	142	.420
1924	St.L	A	M-1	151	.305
1925	St.L	A	M-P-1	150	0-0 .345
1926	St.L	A	M-P-1	150	0-0 .289
1927	St.L	A	1	149	.327
1928	Was	A	1-O	20	.245
1928	Bos	N	P-1	118	0-0 .340
1929	Bos	N	1	154	.326
1930	Bos	N	1	116	.309
BLTL				2055	5-8 .340

SISLER, RICHARD ALLAN
b.Nov.2,1920 St.Louis,Mo.

Yr	Cl	Lea	Pos	G	Rec
1946	St.L	N	1-O	83	.260
1947	St.L	N	1-O	46	.203
1948	Phi	N	1	121	.274
1949	Phi	N	1	121	.289
1950	Phi	N	O	141	.296
1951	Phi	N	O	125	.287
1952	Cin	N	O	11	.185
1952	St.L	N	1	119	.261
1953	St.L	N	1	32	.256
BLTR				799	.276

SISTI, SEBASTIAN DANIEL (Sibby)
b.July 26,1920 Buffalo,N.Y.

Yr	Cl	Lea	Pos	G	Rec
1939	Bos	N	2-S-3	63	.226
1940	Bos	N	2-3	123	.251
1941	Bos	N	2-S-3	140	.259
1942	Bos	N	2-O	129	.211
1946	Bos	N	3	1	.000
1947	Bos	N	2-S	56	.281
1948	Bos	N	2-S	83	.244
1949	Bos	N	2-S-3	101	.257
1950	Bos	N	1-2-S-3-O	69	.171
1951	Bos	N	1-2-S-3-O	114	.279
1952	Bos	N	2-S-3-O	90	.212

(Continued)

Yr	Cl	Lea	Pos	G	Rec
1953	Mil	N	2-S-3	38	.217
1954	Mil	N	H	9	.000
BRTR				1016	.244

SITTON, CARL VEDDER
b.Sept,22,1882 Pendleton,S.C.
d.Sept.11,1931

Yr	Cl	Lea	Pos	G	Rec
1909	Cle	A	P	14	3-2
TR					

SIVESS, PETER
b.Sept.23,1913 South River N.J.

Yr	Cl	Lea	Pos	G	Rec
1936	Phi	N	P	17	3-4
1937	Phi	N	P	6	1-1
1938	Phi	N	P	39	3-6
BRTR				62	7-11

SIXSMITH, EDWARD
b.Franklin,Pa.

Yr	Cl	Lea	Pos	G	Rec
1884	Phi	N	C	1	.000

SKAFF, FRANCIS MICHAEL
b.Sept.30,1913 LaCrosse,Wis.

Yr	Cl	Lea	Pos	G	Rec
1935	Bro	N	3	6	.545
1943	Phi	A	1-S-3	32	.281
BRTR				38	.320

SKAUGSTAD, DAVID WENDELL
b.Jan.10,1940 Algona,Ia.

Yr	Cl	Lea	Pos	G	Rec
1957	Cin	N	P	2	0-0
BLTL					

SKEELS, DAVID
b.Dec.29,1892 Washington
d.Dec.3,1926

Yr	Cl	Lea	Pos	G	Rec
1910	Det	A	P	1	0-0
BLTR					

SKETCHLEY, HARRY CLEMENT
b.Mar.30,1920 Virden,Man.,Canada.

Yr	Cl	Lea	Pos	G	Rec
1942	Chi	A	O	13	.194
BLTL					

SKIFF, WILLIAM FRANKLIN
b.Oct.16,1895 New Rochelle,N.Y.

Yr	Cl	Lea	Pos	G	Rec
1921	Pit	N	C	16	.289
1926	NY	A	C	6	.099
BRTR				22	.250

SKINNER, ...

Yr	Cl	Lea	Pos	G	Rec
1884	Bal	U	O	1	.333
1884	Chi	U	O	1	.333
				2	.333

SKINNER, ELISHA HARRISON CAMP
b.June 25,1900 Douglasville,Ga.
d.Aug.4,1944

Yr	Cl	Lea	Pos	G	Rec
1922	NY	A	O	27	.182
1923	Bos	A	O	7	.230
BLTR				34	.196

SKINNER, ROBERT RALPH
b.Oct.3,1931 La Jolla,Cal.

Yr	Cl	Lea	Pos	G	Rec
1954	Pit	N	1-O	132	.249
1956	Pit	N	1-3-O	113	.202
1957	Pit	N	1-3-O	126	.305
1958	Pit	N	O	144	.321
1959	Pit	N	1-O	143	.280
1960	Pit	N	O	145	.273
1961	Pit	N	O	119	.268
1962	Pit	N	O	144	.302
BLTR				1066	.280

SKIZAS, LOUIS PETER
b.June 2,1932 Chicago, Ill.

Yr	Cl	Lea	Pos	G	Rec
1956	NY	A	H	6	.167
1956	KC	A	O	83	.316
1957	KC	A	3-O	119	.245
1958	Det	A	3-O	23	.242
1959	Chi	A	O	8	.077
BRTR				239	.270

SKOPEC, JOHN (Buckshot)
b.Chicago,Ill.

Yr	Cl	Lea	Pos	G	Rec
1901	Chi	A	P	10	6-4
1903	Det	A	P	6	2-2
			TL	16	8-6

SKOWRON, WILLIAM JOSEPH (Moose)
b.Dec.18,1930 Chicago,Ill.

Yr	Cl	Lea	Pos	G	Rec
1954	NY	A	1-2-3	87	.340
1955	NY	A	1-3	108	.319
1956	NY	A	1-3	134	.308
1957	NY	A	1	122	.304
1958	NY	A	1-3	126	.273
1959	NY	A	1	74	.298
1960	NY	A	1	146	.309
1961	NY	A	1	150	.267
1962	NY	A	1	140	.270
			BRTR	1087	.294

SLADE, GORDON LEIGH (Oskie)
b.Oct.9,1904 Salt Lake City,Utah.

Yr	Cl	Lea	Pos	G	Rec
1930	Bro	N	S	25	.216
1931	Bro	N	S	85	.239
1932	Bro	N	S-3	79	.240
1933	St.L	N	2-S	39	.113
1934	Cin	N	2-S	138	.285
1935	Cin	N	2-S-3-O	71	.281
			BRTR	437	.257

SLADEN, ARTHUR
b.Lowell,Mass.

Yr	Cl	Lea	Pos	G	Rec
1884	Bos	U	O	2	.000

SLAGLE, JAMES FRANKLIN (Shorty)
b.July 11,1873 Worthville,Pa.

Yr	Cl	Lea	Pos	G	Rec
1899	Was	N	O	146	.273
1900	Phi	N	O	141	.299
1901	Phi	N	O	48	.189
1901	Bos	N	O	65	.278
1902	Chi	N	O	114	.313
1903	Chi	N	O	139	.298
1904	Chi	N	O	120	.260
1905	Chi	N	O	155	.269
1906	Chi	N	O	127	.239
1907	Chi	N	O	136	.258
1908	Chi	N	O	101	.222
			BLTR	1292	.269

SLAGLE, JOHN A.
b.Lawrence,Ind.

Yr	Cl	Lea	Pos	G	Rec
1891	Cin	a	P	1	0-0

SLAGLE, WALTER JOHN
b.Dec.15,1878 Kenton,O.

Yr	Cl	Lea	Pos	G	Rec
1910	Cin	N	P	1	0-0

TR

SLAPNICKA, CYRIL CHARLES
b.Mar.23,1886 Cedar Rapids,Ia.

Yr	Cl	Lea	Pos	G	Rec
1911	Chi	N	P	3	0-2
1918	Pit	N	P	7	1-4
			BRTR	10	1-6

SLAPPEY, JOHN HENRY
b.Aug.8,1898 Albany,Ga.
d.June 10,1957

Yr	Cl	Lea	Pos	G	Rec
1920	Phi	A	P	3	0-1

BLTL

SLATTERY, JOHN THOMAS
b.Jan.6,1878 S.Boston,Mass.
d.July 17,1949

Yr	Cl	Lea	Pos	G	Rec
1901	Bos	A	C	1	.500
1903	Cle	A	1	4	.000
1903	Chi	A	C-1	61	.231
1906	St.L	N	C	2	.000
1909	Was	A	C	32	.214
			TR	100	.221

Non-playing manager Bos (N) 1928.

SLATTERY, MICHAEL J.
b.Oct.28,1865 S.Boston,Mass.
d.Oct.16,1904

Yr	Cl	Lea	Pos	G	Rec
1884	Bos	U	O	105	.208
1888	NY	N	O	103	.245
1889	NY	N	O	12	.286
1890	NY	p	O	97	.290
1891	Cin	N	O	41	.221
1891	Was	a	O	15	.283
			BLTL	373	.249

SLATTERY, PHILIP RICHARD
b.Feb.25,1894 Harper,Ia.

Yr	Cl	Lea	Pos	G	Rec
1915	Pit	N	P	3	0-0

BRTL

SLAUGHTER, BYRON ATKINS (Barney)
b.Oct.6,1884 Smyrna,Del.
d.May 17,1961

Yr	Cl	Lea	Pos	G	Rec
1910	Phi	N	P	8	0-1

BRTR

SLAUGHTER, ENOS BRADSHER (Country)
b.Apr.27,1916 Roxboro,N.C.

Yr	Cl	Lea	Pos	G	Rec
1938	St.L	N	O	112	.276
1939	St.L	N	O	149	.320
1940	St.L	N	O	140	.306
1941	St.L	N	O	113	.311
1942	St.L	N	O	152	.318
1946	St.L	N	O	156	.300
1947	St.L	N	O	147	.294
1948	St.L	N	O	146	.321
1949	St.L	N	O	151	.336
1950	St.L	N	O	148	.290
1951	St.L	N	O	123	.281
1952	St.L	N	O	140	.300
1953	St.L	N	O	143	.291
1954	NY	A	O	69	.248
1955	NY	A	H	10	.111
1955	KC	A	O	108	.322
1956	KC	A	O	91	.278
1956	NY	A	O	24	.289
1957	NY	A	O	96	.254
1958	NY	A	O	77	.304
1959	NY	A	O	74	.172
1959	Mil	N	O	11	.167
			BLTR	2380	.300

SLAYBACK, ELBERT
b.May 12,1902 Paducah,Ky.

Yr	Cl	Lea	Pos	G	Rec
1926	NY	N	2	2	.000

BRTR

SLAYTON, FOSTER HERBERT (Steve)
b.Apr.26,1902 Barre,Vt.

Yr	Cl	Lea	Pos	G	Rec
1928	Bos	A	P	3	0-0

BRTR

SLEATER, LOUIS MORTIMER
b.Sept.8,1927 St.Louis,Mo.

Yr	Cl	Lea	Pos	G	Rec
1950	St.L	A	P	1	0-0
1951	St.L	A	P	25	1-9
1952	St.L	A	P	4	0-1
1952	Was	A	P	15	4-2
1955	KC	A	P	21	1-1
1956	Mil	N	P	25	2-2
1957	Det	A	P	41	3-3
1958	Det	A	P	4	0-0
1958	Bal	A	P	9	1-0
			BLTL	145	12-18

SLOAN, BRUCE ADAM
b.Oct.4,1914 McAlester,Okla.

Yr	Cl	Lea	Pos	G	Rec
1944	NY	N	O	59	.269

BLTL

SLOAN, YALE Y.
b.Dec.24,1891 Madisonville,Tenn.
d.Sept.12,1956

Yr	Cl	Lea	Pos	G	Rec
1913	St.L	A	O	7	.269
1917	St.L	A	O	109	.230
1919	St.L	A	O	27	.238
			BLTR	143	.234

SLOAT, DWAIN CLIFFORD (Lefty)
b.Dec.1,1918 Nokomis,Ill.

Yr	Cl	Lea	Pos	G	Rec
1948	Bro	N	P	4	0-1
1949	Chi	N	P	5	0-0
			BRTL	9	0-1

SMADT, JAN
(Played under name of John W. Smith)

SMALL, CHARLES ALBERT
b.Oct.24,1903 Lewiston,Me.
d.Jan.14,1953

Yr	Cl	Lea	Pos	G	Rec
1930	Bos	A	O	25	.167

BLTR

SMALL, JAMES ARTHUR
b.Mar.28,1937 Portland,Ore.

Yr	Cl	Lea	Pos	G	Rec
1955	Det	A	O	12	.000
1956	Det	A	O	58	.319
1957	Det	A	O	36	.214
1958	KC	A	O	2	.000
			BLTL	108	.270

SMALLEY, ROY FREDERICK
b.June 9,1926 Springfield,Mo.

Yr	Cl	Lea	Pos	G	Rec
1948	Chi	N	S	124	.216
1949	Chi	N	S	135	.245
1950	Chi	N	S	154	.230
1951	Chi	N	S	79	.231
1952	Chi	N	S	87	.222
1953	Chi	N	S	82	.249
1954	Mil	N	1-2-S	25	.222
1955	Phi	N	2-S-3	92	.196
1956	Phi	N	S	65	.226
1957	Phi	N	S	28	.161
1958	Phi	N	S	1	.000
			BRTR	872	.227

SMALLEY, WILLIAM D. (Deacon)
b.June 27,1871 Oakland,Cal.
d.Oct.11,1891

Yr	Cl	Lea	Pos	G	Rec
1890	Cle	N	3	136	.213
1891	Was	a	3	9	.171
			BRTR	145	.208

SMALLWOOD, WALTER CLAYTON
b.Apr.24,1895 Brookville,Md.

Yr	Cl	Lea	Pos	G	Rec
1917	NY	A	P	2	0-0
1919	NY	A	P	6	0-0
			BRTR	8	0-0

SMAZA, JOSEPH PAUL
b.July 7,1923 Detroit,Mich.

Yr	Cl	Lea	Pos	G	Rec
1946	Chi	A	O	2	.200

BLTL

SMEJKAL, FRANK JOHN
(Played under name of Frank John Smykal)

SMILEY, WILLIAM B.
b.1856 Baltimore,Md.
d.July 11,1884

Yr	Cl	Lea	Pos	G	Rec
1874	Bal	n	3	2	NR
1882	St.L	a	2-S-O	58	.208
1882	Bal	a	2-S	16	.113
				76	NR

SMITH, ALBERT EDGAR
b.Oct.15,1860 North Haven,Conn.

Yr	Cl	Lea	Pos	G	Rec
1883	Bos	N	O	29	.217

SMITH, ALEXANDER BENJAMIN (Broadway)
b.1871 New York,N.Y.
d.July 9,1919

Yr	Cl	Lea	Pos	G	Rec
1897	Bro	N	C-O	61	.309
1898	Bro	N	C-O	48	.260
1899	Bro	N	C	16	.164
1899	Bal	N	C-1-O	41	.383
1900	Bro	N	C-3	7	.240
1901	NY	N	P-C	29	0-1 / .168

(Continued)

Yr	Cl	Lea	Pos	G	Rec
1902	Bal	A	C-1-2-3-O	40	.234
1903	Bos	A	C	12	.333
1904	Chi	N	C-1	10	.173
1906	NY	N	C-1	14	.185
			TR	278	0-1 / .263

SMITH, ALEXANDER CHARLES
b.Sept.12,1855 Troy,N.Y.
d.Mar.29,1932

Yr	Cl	Lea	Pos	G	Rec
1882	Tro	N	1	34	.236
1882	Wor	N	1	19	.216
				53	.230

SMITH, ALFRED JOHN
b.Oct.12,1908 Belleville,Ill.

Yr	Cl	Lea	Pos	G	Rec
1934	NY	N	P	30	3-5
1935	NY	N	P	40	10-8
1936	NY	N	P	43	14-13
1937	NY	N	P	33	5-4
1938	Phi	N	P	37	1-4
1939	Phi	N	P	5	0-0
1940	Cle	A	P	31	15-7
1941	Cle	A	P	30	12-13
1942	Cle	A	P	30	10-15
1943	Cle	A	P	30	17-7
1944	Cle	A	P	28	7-13
1945	Cle	A	P	22	5-12
			BLTL	359	99-101

SMITH, ALFRED KENDRICKS
b.Dec.13,1903 Norristown,Pa.

Yr	Cl	Lea	Pos	G	Rec
1926	NY	N	P	1	0-0

BRTR

SMITH, ALPHONSE EUGENE (Fuzzy)
b.Feb.7,1928 Kirkwood,Mo.

Yr	Cl	Lea	Pos	G	Rec
1953	Cle	A	3-O	47	.240
1954	Cle	A	S-3-O	131	.281
1955	Cle	A	2-S-3-O	154	.306
1956	Cle	A	2-3-O	141	.274
1957	Cle	A	3-O	135	.247
1958	Chi	A	3-O	139	.252
1959	Chi	A	3-O	129	.237
1960	Chi	A	O	142	.315
1961	Chi	A	3-O	147	.278
1962	Chi	A	3-O	142	.292
			BRTR	1307	.276

SMITH, ANTHONY (Irish)
b.Chicago,Ill.

Yr	Cl	Lea	Pos	G	Rec
1907	Was	A	S	51	.187
1910	Bro	N	S	106	.181
1911	Bro	N	S	12	.138
			TR	169	.180

SMITH, ARTHUR LAIRD
b.June 21,1906 Boston,Mass.

Yr	Cl	Lea	Pos	G	Rec
1932	Chi	A	P	3	0-1

BRTR

SMITH, BOBBY GENE
b.May 28,1934 Hood River,Ore.

Yr	Cl	Lea	Pos	G	Rec
1957	St.L	N	O	93	.211
1958	St.L	N	O	28	.284
1959	St.L	N	O	43	.217
1960	Phi	N	3-O	98	.286
1961	Phi	N	O	79	.253
1962	NY	N	O	8	.136
1962	Chi	N	O	13	.172
1962	St.L	N	O	91	.231
			BRTR	453	.244

SMITH, CARR E.
b.Apr.8,1901 Kernersville,N.C.

Yr	Cl	Lea	Pos	G	Rec
1923	Was	A	O	5	.111
1924	Was	A	O	6	.191
			BRTR	11	.150

SMITH, CHARLES E.
b.Apr.20,1880 Cleveland,O.
d.Jan.3,1929

Yr	Cl	Lea	Pos	G	Rec
1902	Cle	A	P	3	0-1
1906	Was	A	P	33	9-16
1907	Was	A	P	37	11-21
1908	Was	A	P	30	9-13
1909	Was	A	P	21	2-12
1909	Bos	A	P	5	4-0
1910	Bos	A	P	23	11-6
1911	Bos	A	P	1	0-0
1911	Chi	N	P	7	3-2
1912	Chi	N	P	21	7-4
1913	Chi	N	P	20	7-9
1914	Chi	N	P	16	2-4
			BRTR	217	65-88

SMITH, CHARLES HENRY (Pacer)
b.Aug.4,1853 Pendleton,Ind.
d.Nov.29,1895

Yr	Cl	Lea	Pos	G	Rec
1877	Chi	N	2-O	24	.202
1877	Cin	N	C-2-O	9	.281
			BRTR	33	.222

SMITH, CHARLES J.
b.Dec.11,1840 Brooklyn,N.Y.
d.Nov.15,1897

Yr	Cl	Lea	Pos	G	Rec
1871	Mut	n	2-3	15	NR

SMITH, CHARLES MARVIN (Pap)
b.Oct.12,1856 Windsor,N.S.,Canada.
d.Apr.18,1927

Yr	Cl	Lea	Pos	G	Rec
1880	Cin	N	2-O	82	.199
1881	Cle	N	3	10	.118
1881	Wor	N	2-O	11	.068
1881	Buf	N	2	3	.000
1882	Ath	a	2-S-3-O	20	.090
1882	Bal	a	O	1	.000
1882	Lou	a	S	3	.182
1883	Col	a	P-2-3	96	0-0 / .258
1884	Col	a	2	108	.240
1885	Pit	a	2	106	.258
1886	Pit	a	2-S	126	.223
1887	Pit	N	2-S	122	.263
1888	Pit	N	2-S	130	.207
1889	Pit	N	S	72	.210
1889	Bos	N	S	59	.257
1890	Bos	N	2	134	.229
1891	Was	a	2	27	.161
			BRTR	1110	0-0 / .228

SMITH, CHARLES WILLIAM
b.Sept.15,1937 Charleston,S.C.

Yr	Cl	Lea	Pos	G	Rec
1960	LA	N	3	18	.167
1961	LA	N	S-3	9	.250
1961	Phi	N	S-3	112	.248
1962	Chi	A	3	65	.207
			BRTR	204	.231

SMITH, CLARENCE OSSIE (Pop-Box)
b.May 23,1892 Newport,Tenn.
d.Feb.16,1924

Yr	Cl	Lea	Pos	G	Rec
1913	Chi	A	P	15	0-1
1916	Cle	A	P	5	1-3
1917	Cle	A	P	6	0-1
			BRTR	26	1-5

SMITH, CLAY JAMIESON
b.Sept.11,1914 Cambridge,Kan.

Yr	Cl	Lea	Pos	G	Rec
1938	Cle	A	P	4	0-0
1940	Det	A	P	14	1-1
			BRTR	18	1-1

SMITH, DAVID MERWIN
b.Dec.17,1914 Sellers,S.C.

Yr	Cl	Lea	Pos	G	Rec
1938	Phi	A	P	21	2-1
1939	Phi	A	P	1	0-0
			BRTR	22	2-1

SMITH, DOUGLASS WELDON
b.May 25,1893 Miller's Falls,Mass.

Yr	Cl	Lea	Pos	G	Rec
1912	Bos	A	P	1	0-0

BLTL

SMITH, E. J.

Yr	Cl	Lea	Pos	G	Rec
1890	Buf	p	1	1	.000

SMITH, EARL CALVIN
b.Mar.14,1928 Sunnyside,Wash.

Yr	Cl	Lea	Pos	G	Rec
1955	Pit	N	O	5	063

BRTR

SMITH, EARL LEONARD
b.Jan.20,1891 Oak Hill,O.
d.Mar.14,1943

Yr	Cl	Lea	Pos	G	Rec
1916	Chi	N	O	14	.259
1917	St.L	A	O	52	.281
1918	St.L	A	O	89	.269
1919	St.L	A	O	88	.250
1920	St.L	A	3-O	103	.306
1921	St.L	A	3-O	25	.333
1921	Was	A	O	59	.217
1922	Was	A	O	65	.259
			BBTR	495	.271

SMITH, EARL SUTTON
b.Feb.14,1897 Hot Springs,Ark.

Yr	Cl	Lea	Pos	G	Rec
1919	NY	N	C	21	.250
1920	NY	N	C	91	.294
1921	NY	N	C	89	.336
1922	NY	N	C	90	.277
1923	NY	N	C	24	.206
1923	Bos	N	C	72	.288
1924	Bos	N	C	33	.271
1924	Pit	N	C	39	.369
1925	Pit	N	C	109	.313
1926	Pit	N	C	105	.346
1927	Pit	N	C	66	.270
1928	Pit	N	C	32	.247
1928	St.L	N	C	24	.224
1929	St.L	N	C	57	.345
1930	St.L	N	C	8	.000
			BLTR	860	.303

SMITH, EDGAR
b.Dec.14,1913 Columbus,N.J.

Yr	Cl	Lea	Pos	G	Rec
1936	Phi	A	P	2	1-1
1937	Phi	A	P	40	4-17
1938	Phi	A	P	43	3-10
1939	Phi	A	P	3	1-0
1939	Chi	A	P	29	9-11
1940	Chi	A	P	32	14-9
1941	Chi	A	P	34	13-17
1942	Chi	A	P	29	7-20
1943	Chi	A	P	25	11-11
1946	Chi	A	P	24	8-11
1947	Chi	A	P	15	1-3
1947	Bos	A	P	8	1-3
			BBTL	284	73-113

SMITH, EDGAR E
b.1862 Providence,R.I.

Yr	Cl	Lea	Pos	G	Rec
1883	Pro	N	1-O	2	.222
1883	Phi	N	P-O	1	0-1 / .750
1884	Was	a	P-O	14	0-2 / .089
1885	Pro	N	P	1	1-0
1890	Cle	N	P	7	1-4
			BRTR	25	2-7 / .173

SMITH, EDWARD
b.Feb.21,1880 South Bend,Ind.

Yr	Cl	Lea	Pos	G	Rec
1906	St.L	A	P	19	7-10

TL

SMITH, EDWARD MAYO
b.Jan.17,1915 New London,Mo.

Yr	Cl	Lea	Pos	G	Rec
1945	Phi	A	O	73	.212

BLTR

Non-playing Manager Phi (N) 1955-58 and Cin (N) 1959

SMITH, ELMER ELLSWORTH (Mike)
b.Mar.28,1868 Allegheny,Pa.
d.Nov.5,1945

Yr	Cl	Lea	Pos	G	Rec
1886	Cin	a	P-O	9	4-5 / .308
1887	Cin	a	P-O	52	33-18 / .288
1888	Cin	a	P-O	40	22-17 / .220

(Continued)

Yr	Cl	Lea	Pos	G	Rec
1889	Cin	a	P	29	10-12
1892	Pit	N	P-O	136	7-6 .282
1893	Pit	N	O	128	.366
1894	Pit	N	O	125	.352
1895	Pit	N	O	124	.296
1896	Pit	N	O	120	.358
1897	Pit	N	O	122	.311
1898	Cin	N	O	122	.344
1899	Cin	N	O	87	.295
1900	Cin	N	O	29	.270
1900	NY	N	O	87	.274
1901	Pit	N	O	4	.000
1901	Bos	N	O	18	.240
		BLTL		1232	76-58 .314

SMITH, ELMER JOHN
b.Sept.21,1892 Sandusky,O.

Yr	Cl	Lea	Pos	G	Rec
1914	Cle	A	O	13	.333
1915	Cle	A	O	144	.248
1916	Cle	A	O	79	.277
1916	Was	A	O	45	.214
1917	Was	A	O	35	.222
1917	Cle	A	O	64	.261
1919	Cle	A	O	114	.278
1920	Cle	A	O	129	.316
1921	Cle	A	O	129	.290
1922	Bos	A	O	73	.282
1922	NY	A	O	21	.208
1923	NY	A	O	70	.306
1925	Cin	N	O	96	.271
		BLTR		1012	.277

SMITH, ELWOOD HOPE
b.Nov.16,1904 S.Norfolk,Va.

Yr	Cl	Lea	Pos	G	Rec
1926	NY	N	O	4	.143
		BLTR			

SMITH, ERNEST HENRY
b.Oct.11,1901 Paterson,N.J.

Yr	Cl	Lea	Pos	G	Rec
1930	Chi	A	S	24	.241
		BRTR			

SMITH, FRANK ELMER (Nig)
(Real name Frank Elmer Schmidt)
b.Oct.28,1879 Pittsburgh, Pa.
d.Nov.3,1952

Yr	Cl	Lea	Pos	G	Rec
1904	Chi	A	P	26	16-10
1905	Chi	A	P	39	19-12
1906	Chi	A	P	20	5-5
1907	Chi	A	P	42	22-11
1908	Chi	A	P	43	16-17
1909	Chi	A	P	53	25-17
1910	Chi	A	P	24	4-10
1910	Bos	A	P	4	1-1
1911	Bos	A	P	1	0-0
1911	Cin	N	P	34	10-14
1912	Cin	N	P	8	1-1
1914	Bal	F	P	33	10-8
1915	Bal	F	P	17	4-6
1915	Bro	F	P	9	5-0
		BRTR		353	138-112

SMITH, FRANK L.
b.1857 Canandaigua,N.Y.

Yr	Cl	Lea	Pos	G	Rec
1884	Pit	a	C-O	10	.263

SMITH, FRANK THOMAS
b.Apr.4,1928 Pierrepont Manor,N.Y.

Yr	Cl	Lea	Pos	G	Rec
1950	Cin	N	P	38	2-7
1951	Cin	N	P	50	5-5
1952	Cin	N	P	53	12-11
1953	Cin	N	P	50	8-1
1954	Cin	N	P	50	5-8
1955	St.L	N	P	28	3-1
1956	Cin	N	P	2	0-0
		BRTR		271	35-33

SMITH, FREDERICK
b.Nov.24,1879 New Diggins,Wis.

Yr	Cl	Lea	Pos	G	Rec
1907	Cin	N	P	18	2-7
		BRTR			

SMITH, FREDERICK C.
b.1863

Yr	Cl	Lea	Pos	G	Rec
1890	Tol	a	P	37	19-14
		BLTR			

SMITH, FREDERICK H. (Klondike)
b.1889

Yr	Cl	Lea	Pos	G	Rec
1912	NY	A	O	7	.185
		BLTL			

SMITH, FREDERICK VINCENT
b.July 29,1891 Cleveland, O.

Yr	Cl	Lea	Pos	G	Rec
1913	Bos	N	3	92	.228
1914	Buf	F	S-3	146	.222
1915	Buf	F	S	35	.220
1915	Bro	F	S	109	.245
1917	St.L	N	3	56	.182
		BRTR		438	.225

SMITH, GEORGE ALLEN (Columbia George)
b.May 31,1892 E.Port Chester,Conn.

Yr	Cl	Lea	Pos	G	Rec
1916	NY	N	P	9	3-0
1917	NY	N	P	14	0-3
1918	Cin	N	P	10	2-3
1918	NY	N	P	5	2-3
1918	Bro	N	P	8	4-1
1919	NY	N	P	3	0-2
1919	Phi	N	P	31	5-11
1920	Phi	N	P	43	13-18
1921	Phi	N	P	39	4-20
1922	Phi	N	P	42	5-14
1923	Bro	N	P	25	3-6
		BRTR		229	41-81

SMITH, GEORGE HENRY (Heinie)
b.Mar.4,1873 Pittsburgh,Pa.
d.June 25,1939

Yr	Cl	Lea	Pos	G	Rec
1897	Lou	N	2	21	.280
1898	Lou	N	2	31	.207
1899	Pit	N	2	15	.264
1902	NY	N	M-2	140	.248
1903	Det	A	2	93	.222
		BRTR		300	.239

SMITH, GEORGE J. (Germany)
b.Apr.21,1863 Pittsburgh,Pa.
d.Dec.1,1927

Yr	Cl	Lea	Pos	G	Rec
1884	Alt	U	P-S	25	0-0 .307
1884	Cle	N	2-S	71	.258
1885	Bro	a	S	109	.256
1886	Bro	a	S	117	.249
1887	Bro	a	S	104	.307
1888	Bro	a	S	103	.214
1889	Bro	a	S	121	.233
1890	Bro	N	S	129	.191
1891	Cin	N	S	138	.205
1892	Cin	N	S	138	.248
1893	Cin	N	S	130	.244
1894	Cin	N	S	128	.266
1895	Cin	N	S	127	.297
1896	Cin	N	S	119	.282
1897	Bro	N	S	113	.207
1898	St.L	N	S	51	.156
		BRTR		1723	0-0 .245

SMITH, GEORGE L.
Non-playing manager Syr (N) 1879.

SMITH, GEORGE SELBY
b.Oct.27,1901 Louisville,Ky.

Yr	Cl	Lea	Pos	G	Rec
1926	Det	A	P	23	1-2
1927	Det	A	P	30	4-1
1928	Det	A	P	39	1-1
1929	Det	A	P	14	3-2
1930	Bos	A	P	29	1-2
		BRTR		135	10-8

SMITH, HAROLD LAVERNE
b.June 30,1905 Creston,Ia.

Yr	Cl	Lea	Pos	G	Rec
1932	Pit	N	P	2	1-0
1933	Pit	N	P	28	8-7
1934	Pit	N	P	20	3-4
1935	Pit	N	P	1	0-0
		BRTR		51	12-11

SMITH, HAROLD RAYMOND
b.June 1,1931 Barling,Ark.

Yr	Cl	Lea	Pos	G	Rec
1956	St.L	N	C	75	.282
1957	St.L	N	C	100	.279
1958	St.L	N	C	77	.227
1959	St.L	N	C	142	.270
1960	St.L	N	C	127	.228
1961	St.L	N	C	45	.248
		BRTR		566	.258

SMITH, HAROLD WAYNE
b.Dec.30,1930 West Frankfort,Ill.

Yr	Cl	Lea	Pos	G	Rec
1955	Bal	A	C	135	.271
1956	Bal	A	C	78	.262
1956	KC	A	C	36	.275
1957	KC	A	C	107	.303
1958	KC	A	C-1-3	99	.273
1959	KC	A	C-3	108	.288
1960	Pit	N	C	77	.295
1961	Pit	N	C	67	.223
1962	Hou	N	C-1-3	109	.235
		BRTR		816	.271

SMITH, HARRY
b.1889

Yr	Cl	Lea	Pos	G	Rec
1912	Chi	A	P	1	1-0
		BRTR			

SMITH, HARRY N.
b.North Vernon,Ind.

Yr	Cl	Lea	Pos	G	Rec
1889	Lou	a	C	1	1.000

SMITH, HARRY THOMAS
b.Oct.31,1874 Yorkshire,England.
d.Feb.17,1933

Yr	Cl	Lea	Pos	G	Rec
1901	Phi	A	C	11	.318
1902	Pit	N	C	49	.187
1903	Pit	N	C	61	.175
1904	Pit	N	C	47	.248
1905	Pit	N	C	1	.000
1906	Pit	N	C	1	.000
1907	Pit	N	C	18	.263
1908	Bos	N	C	38	.246
1909	Bos	N	M-C	31	.168
1910	Bos	N	C	38	.238
		BRTR		295	.212

SMITH, HARVEY FETTERHOFF
b.July 24,1871 Dauphin Co.,Pa.
d.Nov.12,1962

Yr	Cl	Lea	Pos	G	Rec
1896	Was	N	3	34	.288
		BLTR			

SMITH, HENRY JOSEPH (Happy)
b.July 14,1883 Coquille,Ore.

Yr	Cl	Lea	Pos	G	Rec
1910	Bro	N	O	16	.237
		TR			

SMITH, JACK HATFIELD
b.Nov.15,1935 Pineville,Ky.

Yr	Cl	Lea	Pos	G	Rec
1962	LA	N	P	8	0-0
		BRTR			

SMITH, JACOB G.
b.Dubois,Pa.

Yr	Cl	Lea	Pos	G	Rec
1911	Phi	N	P	2	0-0

SMITH, JAMES A. (Stub)
b.Nov.26,1876 Elmwood,Ill.

Yr	Cl	Lea	Pos	G	Rec
1898	Bos	N	S	3	.100

SMITH, JAMES CARLISLE (Red)
b.Apr.6,1890 Atlanta,Ga.

Yr	Cl	Lea	Pos	G	Rec
1911	Bro	N	3	28	.261
1912	Bro	N	3	128	.286
1913	Bro	N	3	151	.296
1914	Bro	N	3	90	.245
1914	Bos	N	3	60	.314
1915	Bos	N	3	157	.264
1916	Bos	N	3	150	.259
1917	Bos	N	3	147	.295
1918	Bos	N	3	119	.298
1919	Bos	N	3-O	87	.245
		BRTR		1117	.278

SMITH, JAMES HARRY
b.May 15,1890 Baltimore,Md.
d.Apr.1,1922

Yr	Cl	Lea	Pos	G	Rec
1914	NY	N	C	5	.428
1915	NY	N	C	21	.125
1915	Bro	F	C	25	.215
1917	Cin	N	C	8	.118
1918	Cin	N	C	13	.185
		BRTR		72	.189

SMITH, JAMES LAWRENCE
b.May 15,1895 Pittsburgh,Pa.

Yr	Cl	Lea	Pos	G	Rec
1914	Chi	F	S	3	.500
1915	Chi	F	S	94	.217
1915	Bal	F	S	33	.191
1916	Pit	N	S	36	.188
1917	NY	N	2	36	.229
1918	Bos	N	2-S-3-O	34	.225
1919	Cin	N	2-S-3-O	28	.275
1921	Phi	N	2	67	.231
1922	Phi	N	2-S-3	38	.219
		BBTR		369	.221

SMITH, JOHN
b.Baltimore,Md.

Yr	Cl	Lea	Pos	G	Rec
1873	Mar	n	S-O	5	NR
1874	Bal	n	S	5	NR
1875	NH	n	S	1	NR
				11	NR

SMITH, JOHN FRANCIS (Phenomenal)
(Real name John Francis Gammon)
b.Dec.12,1864 Phildadelphia,Pa.
d.Apr.3,1952

Yr	Cl	Lea	Pos	G	Rec
1884	Bal	U	P-O	10	3-5 / .158
1884	Ath	a	P	1	0-1
1884	Pit	a	P	1	0-1
1885	Bro	a	P	1	0-1
1885	Ath	a	P	1	0-1
1886	Det	N	P	3	1-1
1887	Bal	a	P	62	29-29
1888	Bal	a	P	35	15-20
1888	Ath	a	P	3	2-0
1889	Ath	a	P	4	1-3
1890	Phi	N	P	22	7-15
1890	Pit	N	P	6	2-3
1891	Phi	N	P	3	1-2
		BLTL		151	61-82 / .279

SMITH, JOHN MARSHALL
b.Sept.27,1906 Washington,D.C.

Yr	Cl	Lea	Pos	G	Rec
1931	Bos	A	1	4	.133

BBTR

SMITH, JOHN W. (Chick)
(Real name Jan Smadt)
b.Dec.2,1892 Dayton,Ky.
d.Oct.11,1935

Yr	Cl	Lea	Pos	G	Rec
1913	Cin	N	P	5	0-1

BLTL

SMITH, JOHN W.
b.June 23,1895 Chicago,Ill.

Yr	Cl	Lea	Pos	G	Rec
1915	St.L	N	O	4	.187
1916	St.L	N	O	130	.244
1917	St.L	N	O	137	.297
1918	St.L	N	O	42	.211
1919	St.L	N	O	119	.223
1920	St.L	N	O	91	.332
1921	St.L	N	O	116	.328
1922	St.L	N	O	143	.309
1923	St.L	N	O	124	.310
1924	St.L	N	O	124	.283
1925	St.L	N	O	80	.251
1926	St.L	N	O	1	.000
1926	Bos	N	O	96	.311
1927	Bos	N	O	84	.317
1928	Bos	N	O	96	.280
1929	Bos	N	O	19	.250
		BLTL		1406	.287

SMITH, JOSEPH
(Real name Salvatore Joseph Persico)
b.Dec.29,1893 New York, N.Y.

Yr	Cl	Lea	Pos	G	Rec
1913	NY	A	C	14	.161

BRTR

SMITH, JUDSON GRANT
b.Jan.13,1869 Green Oak,Mich.
d.Dec.7,1947

Yr	Cl	Lea	Pos	G	Rec
1893	Cin	N	S-3-O	16	.233
1893	St.L	N	3	4	.067
1896	Pit	N	3	4	.333
1898	Was	N	3	65	.302
1901	Pit	N	3	6	.130
		BRTR		95	.275

SMITH, LAWRENCE PATRICK (Paddy)
b.May 10,1894 New Rochelle,N.Y.

Yr	Cl	Lea	Pos	G	Rec
1920	Bos	A	C	2	.000

BLTR

SMITH, LEO H.
b.May 13,1863 Brooklyn,N.Y.

Yr	Cl	Lea	Pos	G	Rec
1890	Roc	a	S	35	.190

SMITH, LOUIS O. (Bull)

Yr	Cl	Lea	Pos	G	Rec
1904	Pit	N	O	13	.142
1906	Chi	N	H	1	.000
1911	Was	A	H	1	.000
		TR		15	.140

SMITH, MARVIN HAROLD (Red)
b.July 17,1900 Ashley,Ill.
d.Feb.19,1961

Yr	Cl	Lea	Pos	G	Rec
1925	Phi	A	S-3	20	.286

BLTR

SMITH, MILTON
b.Mar.27,1929 Columbus,Ga.

Yr	Cl	Lea	Pos	G	Rec
1955	Cin	N	2-3	36	.196

BRTR

SMITH, NATHANIEL BEVERLY
b.Apr.26,1935 Chicago,Ill.

Yr	Cl	Lea	Pos	G	Rec
1962	Bal	A	C	5	.222

BRTR

SMITH, OLIVER H.
b.1868 Mt. Vernon,O.

Yr	Cl	Lea	Pos	G	Rec
1894	Lou	N	O	89	.288

SMITH, PAUL LESLIE
b.Mar.19,1931 New Castle,Pa.

Yr	Cl	Lea	Pos	G	Rec
1953	Pit	N	1-O	118	.283
1957	Pit	N	1-O	81	.253
1958	Pit	N	H	6	.333
1958	Chi	N	1	18	.150
		BLTL		223	.270

SMITH, PAUL STONER
b.May 7,1888 Mt. Zion,Ill.
d.July 3,1958

Yr	Cl	Lea	Pos	G	Rec
1916	Cin	N	O	10	.227

BBTR

SMITH, PETER LUKE
b.Mar.19,1940 Natick,Mass.

Yr	Cl	Lea	Pos	G	Rec
1962	Bos	A	P	1	0-1

BRTR

SMITH, REGINALD
b.Louisville,Ky.

Yr	Cl	Lea	Pos	G	Rec
1886	Ath	a	P	1	0-1

SMITH, RICHARD HARRISON
b.July 21,1927 Blandburg,Pa.

Yr	Cl	Lea	Pos	G	Rec
1951	Pit	N	3	12	.174
1952	Pit	N	2-S-3	29	.106
1953	Pit	N	S	13	.163
1954	Pit	N	3	12	.097
1955	Pit	N	S	4	.000
		BRTR		70	.134

SMITH, RICHARD PAUL
b.May 18,1904 Brokow,Wis.

Yr	Cl	Lea	Pos	G	Rec
1927	NY	N	C	1	.000

BRTR

SMITH, ROBERT A.
b.1892

Yr	Cl	Lea	Pos	G	Rec
1913	Chi	A	P	1	0-0
1915	Buf	F	P	1	0-0
		BRTR		2	0-0

SMITH, ROBERT ELDRIDGE
b.Apr.22,1898 Rogersville,Tenn.

Yr	Cl	Lea	Pos	G	Rec
1923	Bos	N	2-S	115	.251
1924	Bos	N	S-3	106	.228
1925	Bos	N	P-2-S-O	58	5-3 / .282
1926	Bos	N	P	40	10-13
1927	Bos	N	P	54	10-18
1928	Bos	N	P	39	13-17
1929	Bos	N	P	39	11-17
1930	Bos	N	P	39	10-14
1931	Chi	N	P	36	15-12
1932	Chi	N	P	36	4-3
1933	Cin	N	P-S	23	4-4 / .200
1933	Bos	N	P	14	4-3
1934	Bos	N	P	42	6-9
1935	Bos	N	P	47	8-18
1936	Bos	N	P	35	6-7
1937	Bos	N	P	19	0-1
		BRTR		742	106-139 / .242

SMITH, ROBERT GILCHRIST
b.Feb.1,1931 Woodsville,N.H.

Yr	Cl	Lea	Pos	G	Rec
1955	Bos	A	P	1	0-0
1957	St.L	N	P	6	0-0
1957	Pit	N	P	20	2-4
1958	Pit	N	P	35	2-2
1959	Pit	N	P	20	0-0
1959	Det	A	P	9	0-3
		BRTL		91	4-9

SMITH, ROBERT WALKAY
b.May 13,1928 Clarence,Mo.

Yr	Cl	Lea	Pos	G	Rec
1958	Bos	A	P	17	4-3
1959	Chi	N	P	1	0-0
1959	Cle	A	P	12	0-1
		BLTL		30	4-4

SMITH, RUFUS FRAZIER
b.Jan.24,1905 Guilford College,N.C.

Yr	Cl	Lea	Pos	G	Rec
1927	Det	A	P	1	0-0

BRTL

SMITH, SAMUEL
b.1857 Baltimore,Md.

Yr	Cl	Lea	Pos	G	Rec
1888	Lou	a	1	56	.246

BR

SMITH, SHERROD MALONE
b.Feb.18,1891 Mansfield,Ga.
d.Sept.12,1949

Yr	Cl	Lea	Pos	G	Rec
1911	Pit	N	P	1	0-0
1912	Pit	N	P	3	0-0
1915	Bro	N	P	29	14-8
1916	Bro	N	P	38	14-10
1917	Bro	N	P	43	12-12
1919	Bro	N	P	30	7-12
1920	Bro	N	P	33	11-9
1921	Bro	N	P	35	7-11
1922	Bro	N	P	28	4-8
1922	Cle	A	P	2	1-0
1923	Cle	A	P	30	9-6
1924	Cle	A	P	40	12-14
1925	Cle	A	P	31	11-14
1926	Cle	A	P	27	11-10
1927	Cle	A	P	11	1-4
		BRTL		381	114-118

SMITH, SYDNEY
b.Aug.31,1883 Camden,S.C.
d.June 5,1961

Yr	Cl	Lea	Pos	G	Rec
1908	Phi	A	C	45	.205
1908	St.L	A	C	28	.182

(Continued)

Yr	Cl	Lea	Pos	G	Rec
1910	Cle	A	C	9	.346
1911	Cle	A	C	58	.299
1914	Pit	N	C	4	.300
1915	Pit	N	H	1	.000
	BRTR			145	.247

SMITH, THOMAS E.
b.Dec.5,1871 S.Boston,Mass.
d.Mar.2,1929

Yr	Cl	Lea	Pos	G	Rec
1894	Bos	N	P	2	0-0
1895	Phi	N	P	11	3-3
1896	Lou	N	P	14	1-5
1898	St.L	N	P	1	0-1
				28	4-9

SMITH, THOMAS N.
b.Baltimore,Md.

Yr	Cl	Lea	Pos	G	Rec
1875	Atl	n	2	3	NR

SMITH, VINCENT AMBROSE
b.Dec.7,1916 Richmond,Va.

Yr	Cl	Lea	Pos	G	Rec
1941	Pit	N	C	9	.303
1946	Pit	N	C	7	.190
	BRTR			16	.259

SMITH, WALLACE H.
b.Mar.13,1889 Philadelphia,Pa.

Yr	Cl	Lea	Pos	G	Rec
1911	St.L	N	S-3	60	.216
1912	St.L	N	S-3	75	.256
1914	Was	A	2	45	.196
	BRTR			180	.229

SMITH, WALTER
(Played under name of Walter Reinicker)

SMITH, WILBUR FLOYD (Wib)
b.Aug.30,1886 Evart,Mich.
d.Nov.18,1959

Yr	Cl	Lea	Pos	G	Rec
1909	St.L	A	C	17	.190
	BLTR				

SMITH, WILLARD JEHU
b.Apr.11,1892 Logansport,Ind.

Yr	Cl	Lea	Pos	G	Rec
1917	Pit	N	C	11	.143
1918	Pit	N	C	15	.167
	BRTR			26	.156

SMITH, WILLIAM
d.Oct.28,1897

Yr	Cl	Lea	Pos	G	Rec
1886	Det	N	P	10	5-4

SMITH, WILLIAM E.
b.E.Liverpool,O.

Yr	Cl	Lea	Pos	G	Rec
1884	Cle	N	O	1	.000

SMITH, WILLIAM GARLAND
b.June 8,1934 Washington,D.C.

Yr	Cl	Lea	Pos	G	Rec
1958	St.L	N	P	2	0-1
1959	St.L	N	P	6	0-0
1962	Phi	N	P	24	1-5
	BLTL			32	1-6

SMITH, WILLIAM J.
b.Baltimore,Md.
d.Aug.9,1886

Yr	Cl	Lea	Pos	G	Rec
1873	Mar	n	M-C-2-O	6	NR

SMOLL, CLYDE HETRICK (Lefty)
b.Apr.17,1915 Quakertown,Pa.

Yr	Cl	Lea	Pos	G	Rec
1940	Phi	N	P	33	2-8
	BBTL				

SMOOT, HOMER (Doc)
b.Mar.23,1878 Galestown,Md.
d.Mar.,1928

Yr	Cl	Lea	Pos	G	Rec
1902	St.L	N	O	129	.313
1903	St.L	N	O	129	.296
1904	St.L	N	O	137	.281
1905	St.L	N	O	138	.311

(Continued)

Yr	Cl	Lea	Pos	G	Rec
1906	St.L	N	O	86	.248
1906	Cin	N	O	59	.259
	BLTR			678	.290

SMOWREY, HARRY NEITZ
(Played under name of Henry Neitz Smoyer)

SMOYER, HENRY NEITZ
(Real name Harry Neitz Smowrey)

Yr	Cl	Lea	Pos	G	Rec
1912	St.L	A	S-3	6	.214
	TR				

SMYKAL, FRANK JOHN
b.Oct.13,1889 Chicago,Ill.
d.Aug.11,1950

Yr	Cl	Lea	Pos	G	Rec
1916	Pit	N	S	6	.300
	BRTR				

SMYRES, CLARENCE MELVIN (Clancy)
b.May 24,1922 Culver City,Cal.

Yr	Cl	Lea	Pos	G	Rec
1944	Bro	N	H	5	.000
	BBTR				

SMYTH, JAMES DANIEL (Red)
b.Jan.30,1893 Holly Springs,Miss.
d.Apr.14,1958

Yr	Cl	Lea	Pos	G	Rec
1915	Bro	N	O	19	.136
1916	Bro	N	O	2	.000
1917	Bro	N	O	29	.120
1917	St.L	N	O	38	.211
1918	St.L	N	2-O	40	.212
	BLTR			128	.193

SMYTHE, WILLIAM HARRY
b.Oct.24,1904 Augusta,Ga.

Yr	Cl	Lea	Pos	G	Rec
1929	Phi	N	P	20	4-6
1930	Phi	N	P	25	0-3
1934	NY	A	P	8	0-2
1934	Bro	N	P	10	1-1
	BLTL			63	5-12

SNEED, JOHN L.
b.Columbus,O.
d.Jan.4,1899

Yr	Cl	Lea	Pos	G	Rec
1884	Ind	a	O	27	.105
1890	Tol	a	O	9	.167
1890	Col	a	O	128	.309
1891	Col	a	O	99	.261
				263	.267

SNELL, CHARLES A.
b.Nov.29,1893 Reading,Pa.

Yr	Cl	Lea	Pos	G	Rec
1912	St.L	A	C	8	.222
	BRTR				

SNELL, WALTER HENRY (Doc)
b.May 19,1889 W.Bridgewater,Mass.

Yr	Cl	Lea	Pos	G	Rec
1913	Bos	A	C	6	.250
	BRTR				

SNIDER, EDWIN DONALD (Duke)
b.Sept.19,1926 Los Angeles,Cal.

Yr	Cl	Lea	Pos	G	Rec
1947	Bro	N	O	40	.241
1948	Bro	N	O	53	.244
1949	Bro	N	O	146	.292
1950	Bro	N	O	152	.321
1951	Bro	N	O	150	.277
1952	Bro	N	O	144	.303
1953	Bro	N	O	153	.336
1954	Bro	N	O	149	.341
1955	Bro	N	O	148	.309
1956	Bro	N	O	151	.292
1957	Bro	N	O	139	.274
1958	LA	N	O	106	.312
1959	LA	N	O	126	.308
1960	LA	N	O	101	.243
1961	LA	N	O	85	.296
1962	LA	N	O	80	.278
	BLTR			1923	.300

SNIPES, WYATT EURE (Roxy)
b.Oct.28,1896 Marion S.C.
d.May 1,1941

Yr	Cl	Lea	Pos	G	Rec
1923	Chi	A	H	1	.000
	BLTR				

SNODGRASS, FRED CARLISLE
b.Oct.19,1887 Ventura,Cal.

Yr	Cl	Lea	Pos	G	Rec
1908	NY	N	C	5	.250
1909	NY	N	O	22	.300
1910	NY	N	O	112	.321
1911	NY	N	O	151	.294
1912	NY	N	1-O	146	.269
1913	NY	N	O	141	.291
1914	NY	N	O	113	.263
1915	NY	N	O	80	.151
1915	Bos	N	O	23	.278
1916	Bos	N	O	112	.249
	BRTR			905	.275

SNODGRASS, WALTER AMZI
b.Springfield,O.

Yr	Cl	Lea	Pos	G	Rec
1901	Bal	A	O	2	.100

SNOVER, COLONEL LESTER
b.May 16,1896 Hallstead,Pa.

Yr	Cl	Lea	Pos	G	Rec
1919	NY	N	P	2	0-1
	BLTL				

SNOW, ...
b. Boston,Mass.

Yr	Cl	Lea	Pos	G	Rec
1874	Atl	n	O	1	.000

SNYDER, BERNARD AUSTIN
b.Aug.25,1913 Philadelphia,Pa.

Yr	Cl	Lea	Pos	G	Rec
1935	Phi	A	2-S	10	.344
	BRTR				

SNYDER, CHARLES
b. Camden,N.J.
d.Mar.10,1901

Yr	Cl	Lea	Pos	G	Rec
1890	Ath	a	C-O	9	.419

SNYDER, CHARLES N. (Pop)
b.Oct.6,1854 Washington,D.C.
d.Oct.29,1924

Yr	Cl	Lea	Pos	G	Rec
1873	Nat	n	C-O	28	NR
1874	Bal	n	C	34	NR
1875	Phi	n	C	65	.233
1876	Lou	N	C	56	.195
1877	Lou	N	C-S-O	61	.258
1878	Bos	N	C	60	.212
1879	Bos	N	C	81	.234
1881	Bos	N	C-2-S-O	60	.228
1882	Cin	a	C-1-O	72	.289
1883	Cin	a	M-C-S	58	.245
1884	Cin	a	M-C-1-O	68	.284
1885	Cin	a	C-1	38	.250
1886	Cin	a	C-1-O	52	.195
1887	Cle	a	C	73	.276
1888	Cle	a	C	63	.216
1889	Cle	N	C	21	.192
1890	Cle	p	C	12	.183
1891	Was	a	M-C	8	.179
	BRTR			910	NR

SNYDER, EMANUEL SEBASTIAN (Redleg)
(Real name Emanuel Sebastian Schneider)
b.Dec.12,1853 Camden,N.J.
d.Nov.11,1933

Yr	Cl	Lea	Pos	G	Rec
1876	Cin	N	O	55	.150
1884	Wil	U	1-O	17	.192
	BRTR			72	.159

SNYDER, EUGENE WALTER
b.Mar.31,1931 York,Pa.

Yr	Cl	Lea	Pos	G	Rec
1959	LA	N	P	11	1-1
	BRTL				

SNYDER, FRANK C. (Cooney)
b. London,Ont.,Canada
d.May 9,1917

Yr	Cl	Lea	Pos	G	Rec
1898	Lou	N	C	15	.169

SNYDER, FRANK J. (Pancho)
b.May 27,1893 San Antonio,Tex.

(Continued)
d.Jan.5,1962

Yr	Cl	Lea	Pos	G	Rec
1912	St.L	N	C	11	.111
1913	St.L	N	C	7	.190
1914	St.L	N	C	100	.230
1915	St.L	N	C	144	.298
1916	St.L	N	C-1	132	.259
1917	St.L	N	C	115	.237
1918	St.L	N	C-1	39	.250
1919	St.L	N	C-1	50	.182
1919	NY	N	C	32	.228
1920	NY	N	C	87	.250
1921	NY	N	C	108	.320
1922	NY	N	C	104	.343
1923	NY	N	C	120	.256
1924	NY	N	C	118	.302
1925	NY	N	C	107	.240
1926	NY	N	C	55	.216
1927	St.L	N	C	63	.258
		BRTR		1392	.265

SNYDER, GEORGE T.
b.1849 Philadelphia,Pa.
d.Aug.2,1905.

Yr	Cl	Lea	Pos	G	Rec
1882	Ath	a	P	1	1-0

SNYDER, JAMES
b.1851 New York
d.1881

Yr	Cl	Lea	Pos	G	Rec
1872	Eck	n	C-S-O	22	NR

SNYDER, JAMES ROBERT
b.Aug.15,1932 Dearborn,Mich.

Yr	Cl	Lea	Pos	G	Rec
1961	Min	A	2	3	.100
1962	Min	A	1-2	12	.100
		BRTR		15	.067

SNYDER, JERRY GEORGE
b.July 21,1929 Jenks,Okla.

Yr	Cl	Lea	Pos	G	Rec
1952	Was	A	2-S	36	.158
1953	Was	A	2-S	29	.339
1954	Was	A	2-S	64	.234
1955	Was	A	2-S	46	.224
1956	Was	A	2-S	43	.270
1957	Was	A	2-S-3	42	.151
1958	Was	A	2-S	6	.111
		BRTR		266	.230

SNYDER, JOHN WILLIAM
b.1892 Allegheny Co.,Pa.

Yr	Cl	Lea	Pos	G	Rec
1914	Buf	F	C	1	.000
1917	Bro	N	C	7	.273
		BRTR		8	.273

SNYDER, JOSHUA

Yr	Cl	Lea	Pos	G	Rec
1872	Eck	n	O	7	NR

SNYDER, RUSSELL HENRY
b.June 22,1934 Nelson,Neb.

Yr	Cl	Lea	Pos	G	Rec
1959	KC	A	O	73	.313
1960	KC	A	O	125	.260
1961	Bal	A	O	115	.292
1962	Bal	A	O	139	.305
		BLTR		452	.293

SNYDER, WILLIAM NICHOLS
b.Jan.28,1898 Mansfield,O.
d.Oct.8,1934

Yr	Cl	Lea	Pos	G	Rec
1919	Was	A	P	2	0-1
1920	Was	A	P	16	2-1
		BRTR		18	2-2

SOCKALEXIS, LOUIS FRANCIS (Chief)
b.Oct.24,1873 Old Town,Me.
d.Dec.24,1913

Yr	Cl	Lea	Pos	G	Rec
1897	Cle	N	O	66	.331
1898	Cle	N	O	20	.222
1899	Cle	N	O	7	.252
		BLTR		93	.307

SODD, WILLIAM
b.Sept.18,1914 Ft.Worth,Tex.

Yr	Cl	Lea	Pos	G	Rec
1937	Cle	A	H	1	.000
		BRTR			

SOLIS, MARCELINO
b.July 19,1930 San Luis Potosi,Mex.

Yr	Cl	Lea	Pos	G	Rec
1958	Chi	N	P	15	3-3
		BLTL			

SOLOMON, HYMIE
(Played under name of Hymie Reese)

SOLOMON, MOSES (Hickory)
b.Dec.8,1900 New York,N.Y.

Yr	Cl	Lea	Pos	G	Rec
1923	NY	N	O	2	.375
		BLTL			

SOLTERS, JULIUS JOSEPH (Moose)
(Real name Julius Joseph Soltesz)
b.Mar.22,1908 Pittsburgh,Pa.

Yr	Cl	Lea	Pos	G	Rec
1934	Bos	A	O	101	.299
1935	Bos	A	O	24	.241
1935	St.L	A	O	127	.330
1936	St.L	A	O	152	.291
1937	Cle	A	O	152	.323
1938	Cle	A	O	67	.201
1939	Cle	A	O	41	.275
1939	St.L	A	O	40	.206
1940	Chi	A	O	116	.308
1941	Chi	A	O	76	.259
1943	Chi	A	O	42	.155
		BRTR		938	.289

SOLTESZ, JULIUS JOSEPH
(Played under name of Julius Joseph Solters)

SOMERLOTT, JOHN WESLEY
b.Oct.26,1882 Flint.Ind.

Yr	Cl	Lea	Pos	G	Rec
1910	Was	A	1	16	.222
1911	Was	A	1	13	.175
		TR		29	.204

SOMERVILLE, EDWARD
d.Sept.1877

Yr	Cl	Lea	Pos	G	Rec
1875	Cen	n	2-3	14	NR
1875	NH	n	1-2-S-3	33	NR
1876	Lou	N	2	64	.187
		BRTR		111	NR

SOMMER, JOSEPH JOHN
b.Apr.3,1853 Covington,Ky.
d.Jan.16,1938

Yr	Cl	Lea	Pos	G	Rec
1880	Cin	N	S-3-O	20	.182
1882	Cin	a	O	80	.280
1883	Cin	a	P-3-O	97	0-0 / .281
1884	Bal	a	3-O	107	.272
1885	Bal	a	O	110	.250
1886	Bal	a	2-O	139	.215
1887	Bal	a	O	131	.355
1888	Bal	a	S-O	79	.215
1889	Bal	a	O	106	.224
1890	Cle	N	P-O	9	0-1 / .294
1890	Bal	a	O	38	.239
		BRTR		916	0-1 / .262

SOMMERS, JOSEPH ANDREW (Pete)
b.Oct.26,1866 Cleveland,O.
d.July 22,1908

Yr	Cl	Lea	Pos	G	Rec
1887	Met	a	C	32	.219
1888	Bos	N	C	4	.231
1889	Chi	N	C	12	.239
1889	Ind	N	C	19	.241
1890	NY	N	C-1-O	17	.070
1890	Cle	N	C-O	8	.192
		BR		92	.209

SOMMERS, RUDOLPH
b.Oct.30,1886 Cincinnati,O.
d.Mar.18,1949

Yr	Cl	Lea	Pos	G	Rec
1912	Chi	N	P	1	0-1
1914	Bro	F	P	23	2-7
1926	Bos	A	P	2	0-0
1927	Bos	A	P	7	0-0
		BLTL		33	2-8

SOMMERS, WILLIAM (Kid)
b.Toronto,Ont.,Canada
d.Oct.16,1895

Yr	Cl	Lea	Pos	G	Rec
1889	Cle	N	C	2	.000
1893	St.L	N	C	2	.000
		TR		4	.000

SOMMERS, WILLIAM DUNN
b.Feb.17,1924 Brooklyn,N.Y.

Yr	Cl	Lea	Pos	G	Rec
1950	St.L	A	2-3	65	.255
		BRTR			

SOMMERVILLE, ANDREW
(Real name Henry Travers Summersgill)
b.Feb.6,1876 Brooklyn,N.Y.
d.June 16,1931

Yr	Cl	Lea	Pos	G	Rec
1894	Bro	N	P	1	0-1

SONGER, DONALD C.
b.Jan.31,1900 Walnut,Kan.
d.Oct.3,1962

Yr	Cl	Lea	Pos	G	Rec
1924	Pit	N	P	4	0-0
1925	Pit	N	P	8	0-1
1926	Pit	N	P	35	7-8
1927	Pit	N	P	2	0-0
1927	NY	N	P	22	3-5
		BLTL		71	10-14

SORRELL, VICTOR GARLAND
b.Apr.9,1902 Morrisville,N.C.

Yr	Cl	Lea	Pos	G	Rec
1928	Det	A	P	29	8-11
1929	Det	A	P	36	14-15
1930	Det	A	P	35	16-11
1931	Det	A	P	35	13-14
1932	Det	A	P	33	14-14
1933	Det	A	P	36	11-15
1934	Det	A	P	28	6-9
1935	Det	A	P	12	4-3
1936	Det	A	P	30	6-7
1937	Det	A	P	7	0-2
		BRTR		281	92-101

SORRELLS, RAYMOND EDWIN (Chick
b.July 31,1898 Royse City,Tex.

Yr	Cl	Lea	Pos	G	Rec
1922	Cle	A	S	2	.000
		BRTR			

SOTHERN, DENNIS ELWOOD
b.Jan.20,1904 Washington,D.C.

Yr	Cl	Lea	Pos	G	Rec
1926	Phi	N	O	14	.245
1928	Phi	N	O	141	.285
1929	Phi	N	O	76	.306
1930	Phi	N	O	90	.280
1930	Pit	N	O	17	.176
1931	Bro	N	O	19	.161
		BRTR		357	.280

SOTHORON, ALLEN SUTTON
b.Apr.29,1893 Laura,O.
d.June 17,1939

Yr	Cl	Lea	Pos	G	Rec
1914	St.L	A	P	1	0-0
1915	St.L	A	P	3	0-1
1917	St.L	A	P	49	14-19
1918	St.L	A	P	29	13-12
1919	St.L	A	P	39	20-12
1920	St.L	A	P	36	8-15
1921	St.L	A	P	5	1-2
1921	Bos	A	P	2	0-2
1921	Cle	A	P	22	12-4
1922	Cle	A	P	6	1-3
1924	St.L	N	P	29	10-16
1925	St.L	N	P	28	10-10
1926	St.L	N	P	15	3-3
		BBTR		264	92-99

Non-playing manager St.L (A) 1933.

SOUCHOCK, STEPHEN (Bud)
b.Mar.3,1919 Yatesboro,Pa.

Yr	Cl	Lea	Pos	G	Rec
1946	NY	A	1	47	.302
1948	NY	A	1	44	.203
1949	Chi	A	1-O	84	.234
1951	Det	A	1-2-3-O	91	.245
1952	Det	A	1-3-O	92	.249
1953	Det	A	1-O	89	.302
1954	Det	A	3-O	25	.179
1955	Det	A	H	1	1.000
	BRTR			473	.255

SOUTHWICK, CLYDE AUBRA
b.Nov.3,1886 Maxwell,Ia.
d.Oct.14,1961

Yr	Cl	Lea	Pos	G	Rec
1911	St.L	A	C	4	.250
	BLTR				

SOUTHWORTH, WILLIAM HARRISON
b.Mar.9,1893 Harvard,Neb.

Yr	Cl	Lea	Pos	G	Rec
1913	Cle	A	O	1	.000
1915	Cle	A	O	60	.220
1918	Pit	N	O	64	.341
1919	Pit	N	O	121	.280
1920	Pit	N	O	146	.284
1921	Bos	N	O	141	.308
1922	Bos	N	O	43	.322
1923	Bos	N	2-O	153	.319
1924	NY	N	O	94	.256
1925	NY	N	O	123	.292
1926	NY	N	O	36	.328
1926	St.L	N	O	99	.317
1927	St.L	N	O	92	.301
1929	St.L	N	M-O	19	.188
	BLTR			1192	.298

Non-playing manager St.L (N) 1940-45 and Bos (N) 1946-51.

SOWDERS, JOHN
b.Dec.10,1866 Louisville,Ky.
d.July 29,1908

Yr	Cl	Lea	Pos	G	Rec
1887	Ind	N	P	1	0-0
1889	KC	a	P	28	6-16
1890	Bro	p	P	40	18-16
	BRTL			69	24-32

SOWDERS, LEONARD
b.June 29,1861 Louisville,Ky.
d.Nov.19,1888

Yr	Cl	Lea	Pos	G	Rec
1886	Bal	a	O	23	.267

SOWDERS, WILLIAM JEFFERSON (Little Bill)
b.Nov.29,1864 Louisville,Ky.
d.Feb.2,1951

Yr	Cl	Lea	Pos	G	Rec
1888	Bos	N	P	35	19-15
1889	Bos	N	P	4	2-2
1889	Pit	N	P-O	14	5-4 .256
1890	Pit	N	P	17	3-7
	BRTR			70	29-28 .189

SPADE, ROBERT
b.Jan.4,1877 Akron,O.
d.Sept.7,1924

Yr	Cl	Lea	Pos	G	Rec
1907	Cin	N	P	3	1-1
1908	Cin	N	P	35	17-12
1909	Cin	N	P	14	5-5
1910	Cin	N	P	3	1-2
1910	St.L	A	P	7	1-3
	BRTR			62	25-23

SPAHN, WARREN EDWARD (Hook)
b.Apr.23,1921 Buffalo,N.Y.

Yr	Cl	Lea	Pos	G	Rec
1942	Bos	N	P	4	0-0
1946	Bos	N	P	24	8-5
1947	Bos	N	P	41	21-10
1948	Bos	N	P	36	15-12
1949	Bos	N	P	40	21-14
1950	Bos	N	P	41	21-17
1951	Bos	N	P	42	22-14
1952	Bos	N	P	52	14-19
1953	Mil	N	P	38	23-7
1954	Mil	N	P	41	21-12
1955	Mil	N	P	40	17-14
1956	Mil	N	P	39	20-11
1957	Mil	N	P	39	21-11
1958	Mil	N	P	41	22-11

(Continued)

Yr	Cl	Lea	Pos	G	Rec
1959	Mil	N	P	40	21-15
1960	Mil	N	P	40	21-10
1961	Mil	N	P	39	21-13
1962	Mil	N	P	36	18-14
	BLTL			673	327-209

SPALDING, ALBERT GOODWILL
b.Sept.2,1850 Byron,Ill.
d.Sept.9,1915

Yr	Cl	Lea	Pos	G	Rec
1871	Bos	n	P	33	21-10
1872	Bos	n	P-O	48	36-8 .339
1873	Bos	n	P-O	60	41-15 .359
1874	Bos	n	P	71	52-18
1875	Bos	n	P-1-O	74	56-5 .318
1876	Chi	N	M-P-O	66	46-14 .306
1877	Chi	N	M-P-1-2-3	60	0-0 .256
1878	Chi	N	2	1	.500
	BRTR			413	253-70 NR

SPALDING, CHARLES HARRY (Dick)
b.Oct.13,1897 Philadelphia,Pa.
d.Feb.3,1950

Yr	Cl	Lea	Pos	G	Rec
1927	Phi	N	O	115	.296
1928	Was	A	O	16	.348
	BLTL			131	.299

SPANGLER, ALBERT DONALD
b.July 8,1933 Philadelphia,Pa.

Yr	Cl	Lea	Pos	G	Rec
1959	Mil	N	O	6	.417
1960	Mil	N	O	101	.267
1961	Mil	N	O	68	.268
1962	Hou	N	O	129	.285
	BLTL			000	000

SPARKS, TULLY FRANK
b.Apr.18,1877 Monroe,La.
d.July 15,1937.

Yr	Cl	Lea	Pos	G	Rec
1897	Phi	N	P	1	0-1
1899	Pit	N	P	25	9-7
1901	Mil	A	P	30	6-17
1902	NY	N	P	15	4-11
1902	Bos	A	P	17	7-8
1903	Phi	N	P	28	11-15
1904	Phi	N	P	26	9-16
1905	Phi	N	P	34	13-11
1906	Phi	N	P	42	19-16
1907	Phi	N	P	33	22-8
1908	Phi	N	P	33	16-15
1909	Phi	N	P	24	6-11
1910	Phi	N	P	3	0-2
	BRTR			311	122-138

SPEAKE, ROBERT CHARLES
b.Aug.22,1930 Springfield,Mo.

Yr	Cl	Lea	Pos	G	Rec
1955	Chi	N	1-O	95	.218
1957	Chi	N	1-O	129	.232
1958	SF	N	O	66	.211
1959	SF	N	H	15	.091
	BLTL			305	.223

SPEAKER, TRISTRAM E. (Tris)
b.Apr.4,1888 Hubbard,Tex.
d.Dec.8,1958

Yr	Cl	Lea	Pos	G	Rec
1907	Bos	A	O	7	.158
1908	Bos	A	O	31	.220
1909	Bos	A	O	143	.309
1910	Bos	A	O	141	.340
1911	Bos	A	O	141	.327
1912	Bos	A	O	153	.383
1913	Bos	A	O	141	.366
1914	Bos	A	P-O	158	0-0 .338
1915	Bos	A	O	150	.322
1916	Cle	A	O	151	.386

(Continued)

Yr	Cl	Lea	Pos	G	Rec
1917	Cle	A	O	142	.352
1918	Cle	A	O	127	.319
1919	Cle	A	M-O	134	.296
1920	Cle	A	M-O	150	.388
1921	Cle	A	M-O	132	.362
1922	Cle	A	M-O	131	.378
1923	Cle	A	M-O	150	.380
1924	Cle	A	M-O	135	.344
1925	Cle	A	M-O	117	.389
1926	Cle	A	M-O	150	.304
1927	Was	A	1-O	141	.327
1928	Phi	A	O	64	.267
	BLTL			2789	0-0 .344

SPEECE, BYRON FRANKLIN
b.Jan.6,1897 West Baden,Ind.

Yr	Cl	Lea	Pos	G	Rec
1924	Was	A	P	21	2-1
1925	Cle	A	P	28	3-5
1926	Cle	A	P	2	0-0
1930	Phi	N	P	11	0-0
	BRTR			62	5-6

SPEER, FLOYD VERNIE
b.Jan.27,1914 Booneville,Ark.

Yr	Cl	Lea	Pos	G	Rec
1943	Chi	A	P	1	0-0
1944	Chi	A	P	2	0-0
	BRTR			3	0-0

SPEER, GEORGE NATHAN (Kid)
b.June 16,1886 Corning,Mo.
d.Jan.13,1946

Yr	Cl	Lea	Pos	G	Rec
1909	Det	A	P	13	4-4
	BLTL				

SPENCE, HARRISON L.
b.Feb.22,1856 New York,N.Y.
d.May 19,1908
Non-playing manager Ind (N) 1888.

SPENCE, STANLEY ORVILLE
b.Mar.20,1915 S. Portsmouth,Ky.

Yr	Cl	Lea	Pos	G	Rec
1940	Bos	A	O	51	.279
1941	Bos	A	1-O	86	.232
1942	Was	A	O	149	.323
1943	Was	A	O	149	.267
1944	Was	A	1-O	153	.313
1946	Was	A	O	152	.292
1947	Was	A	O	147	.279
1948	Bos	A	1-O	114	.235
1949	Bos	A	O	7	.150
1949	St.L	A	1-O	104	.245
	BLTL			1112	.282

SPENCER, ...

Yr	Cl	Lea	Pos	G	Rec
1872	Nat	n	S	1	.000

SPENCER, CHESTER ARTHUR
b.Mar.4,1883 Portsmouth,O.
d.Nov.10,1938

Yr	Cl	Lea	Pos	G	Rec
1906	Bos	N	O	7	.148
	BLTR				

SPENCER, DARYL DEAN
b.July 13,1929 Wichita,Kan.

Yr	Cl	Lea	Pos	G	Rec
1952	NY	N	S-3	7	.294
1953	NY	N	2-S-3	118	.208
1956	NY	N	2-S-3	146	.221
1957	NY	N	2-S-3	148	.249
1958	SF	N	2-S	148	.256
1959	SF	N	2-S	152	.265
1960	St.L	N	2-S	148	.258
1961	St.L	N	S	37	.254
1961	LA	N	S-3	60	.243
1962	LA	N	S-3	77	.236
	BRTR			1041	.245

SPENCER, EDWARD RUSSELL (Tubby)
b.Jan.26,1884 Oil City,Pa.
d.Feb.1,1945

Yr	Cl	Lea	Pos	G	Rec
1905	St.L	A	C	35	.235
1906	St.L	A	C	58	.176
1907	St.L	A	C	71	.265
1908	St.L	A	C	91	.210

Yr	Cl	Lea	Pos	G	Rec
(Continued)					
1909	Bos	A	C	28	.162
1911	Phi	N	C	11	.156
1916	Det	A	C	19	.370
1917	Det	A	C	70	.239
1918	Det	A	C	66	.219
	BRTR			449	.225

SPENCER, FRANK G.
b.1886

Yr	Cl	Lea	Pos	G	Rec
1912	St.L	A	P	1	0-0
	BRTR				

SPENCER, GEORGE ELWELL
b.July 7,1926 Columbus,O.

Yr	Cl	Lea	Pos	G	Rec
1950	NY	N	P	10	1-0
1951	NY	N	P	57	10-4
1952	NY	N	P	35	3-5
1953	NY	N	P	1	0-0
1954	NY	N	P	6	1-0
1955	NY	N	P	1	0-0
1958	Det	A	P	7	1-0
1960	Det	A	P	5	0-1
	BRTR			122	16-10

SPENCER, GLENN EDWARD
b.Sept.11,1905 Corning,N.Y.
d.Dec.30 1958

Yr	Cl	Lea	Pos	G	Rec
1928	Pit	N	P	4	0-0
1930	Pit	N	P	41	8-9
1931	Pit	N	P	38	11-12
1932	Pit	N	P	39	4-8
1933	NY	N	P	17	0-2
	BRTR			139	23-31

SPENCER•L. BENJAMIN (Ben)
b.1890

Yr	Cl	Lea	Pos	G	Rec
1913	Was	A	O	8	.300
	BLTL				

SPENCER, ROY HAMPTON
b.Feb.22,1900 Scranton,N.C.

Yr	Cl	Lea	Pos	G	Rec
1925	Pit	N	C	14	.214
1926	Pit	N	C	28	.395
1927	Pit	N	C	38	.283
1929	Was	A	C	50	.155
1930	Was	A	C	93	.255
1931	Was	A	C	145	.275
1932	Was	A	C	102	.246
1933	Cle	A	C	75	.203
1934	Cle	A	C	5	.143
1936	NY	N	C	19	.278
1937	Bro	N	C	51	.205
1938	Bro	N	C	16	.267
	BRTR			636	.247

SPENCER, VERNON MURRAY
b.Feb.23,1896 Wixom,Mich.

Yr	Cl	Lea	Pos	G	Rec
1920	NY	N	O	45	.200
	BLTR				

SPERAW, PAUL BACHMAN
b.Oct.5,1896 Annville,Pa.
d.Feb.22,1962

Yr	Cl	Lea	Pos	G	Rec
1920	St.L	A	3	1	.000
	BRTR				

SPERBER, EDWIN GEORGE
b.Jan.21,1897 Cincinnati,O.

Yr	Cl	Lea	Pos	G	Rec
1924	Bos	N	O	24	.288
1925	Bos	N	O	2	.000
	BLTL			26	.279

SPERRY, STANLEY KENNETH
b.Feb.19,1914 Evansville,Wis.
d.Sept.27,1962

Yr	Cl	Lea	Pos	G	Rec
1936	Phi	N	2	20	.135
1938	Phi	A	2	60	.273
	BLTR			80	.255

SPICER, ROBERT OBERTON
b.Apr.11,1925 Richmond,Va.

Yr	Cl	Lea	Pos	G	Rec
1955	KC	A	P	2	0-0
1956	KC	A	P	2	0-0
	BLTR			4	0-0

SPIES, HENRY (Harry)
b.June 12,1866 New Orleans,La.
d.July 7,1942

Yr	Cl	Lea	Pos	G	Rec
1895	Cin	N	C	14	.200
1895	Lou	N	C	69	.268
				83	.257

SPINDEL, HAROLD STEWART
b.May 27,1913 Chandler,Okla.

Yr	Cl	Lea	Pos	G	Rec
1939	St.L	A	C	48	.269
1945	Phi	N	C	36	.230
1946	Phi	N	C	1	.333
	BRTR			85	.254

SPOGNARDI, ANDREW ETTORE
b.Oct.18,1908 Boston,Mass.

Yr	Cl	Lea	Pos	G	Rec
1932	Bos	A	2-S-3	17	.294
	BRTR				

SPOHRER, ALFRED R.
b.Dec.3,1902 Philadelphia,Pa.

Yr	Cl	Lea	Pos	G	Rec
1928	NY	N	C	2	.000
1928	Bos	N	C	51	.218
1929	Bos	N	C	114	.272
1930	Bos	N	C	112	.317
1931	Bos	N	C	114	.240
1932	Bos	N	C	104	.269
1933	Bos	N	C	67	.250
1934	Bos	N	C	100	.223
1935	Bos	N	C	92	.242
	BRTR			756	.259

SPONSBERG, CARL

Yr	Cl	Lea	Pos	G	Rec
1908	Chi	N	P	1	0-0

SPOONER, KARL BENJAMIN
b.June 23,1931 Oriskany Falls,N.Y.

Yr	Cl	Lea	Pos	G	Rec
1954	Bro	N	P	2	2-0
1955	Bro	N	P	29	8-6
	BRTL			31	10-6

SPOTTS, JAMES RUSSELL
b.Apr.10,1909 Honeybrook,Pa.

Yr	Cl	Lea	Pos	G	Rec
1930	Phi	N	C	3	.000
	BRTR				

SPRAGINS, HOMER FRANKLIN
b.Nov.9,1920 Minter City,Miss.

Yr	Cl	Lea	Pos	G	Rec
1947	Phi	N	P	4	0-0
	BRTR				

SPRAGUE, CHARLES WELLINGTON
b.Oct.10,1864 Cleveland,O.

Yr	Cl	Lea	Pos	G	Rec
1887	Chi	N	P	3	1-1
1889	Cle	N	P	3	0-3
1890	Tol	a	P-O	51	6-7 / .245
	TL			57	7-11 / .236

SPRATT, HENRY LEE
b.July 10,1888 Mason,Va.

Yr	Cl	Lea	Pos	G	Rec
1911	Bos	N	S	41	.240
1912	Bos	N	S	27	.258
	BLTR			68	.247

SPRING, JACK RUSSELL
b.Mar.11,1933 Spokane,Wash.

Yr	Cl	Lea	Pos	G	Rec
1955	Phi	N	P	2	0-1
1957	Bos	A	P	1	0-0
1958	Was	A	P	3	0-0
1961	LA	A	P	18	3-0
1962	LA	A	P	57	4-2
	BRTL			81	7-3

SPRINGER, BRADFORD LOUIS
b.May 9,1904 Detroit,Mich.

Yr	Cl	Lea	Pos	G	Rec
1925	St.L	A	P	2	0-0
1926	Cin	N	P	1	0-0
	BLTL			3	0-0

SPRINGER, EDWARD E.
b.Detroit,Mich.

Yr	Cl	Lea	Pos	G	Rec
1889	Lou	a	P	1	0-1

SPRINZ, JOSEPH CONRAD
b.Aug.3,1902 St.Louis,Mo.

Yr	Cl	Lea	Pos	G	Rec
1930	Cle	A	C	17	.178
1931	Cle	A	C	1	.000
1933	St.L	N	C	3	.200
	BRTR			21	.170

SPROULL, CHARLES WILLIAM
b.Jan.9,1919 Taylorsville,Ga.

Yr	Cl	Lea	Pos	G	Rec
1945	Phi	N	P	34	4-10
	BRTR				

SPROUT, ROBERT SAMUEL
b.Dec.5,1941 Florin,Pa.

Yr	Cl	Lea	Pos	G	Rec
1961	LA	A	P	1	0-0
	BLTL				

SPURGEON, FREDDIE
b.Oct.9,1901 Wabash,Ind.

Yr	Cl	Lea	Pos	G	Rec
1924	Cle	A	2	2	.167
1925	Cle	A	2-S-3	107	.287
1926	Cle	A	2	149	.294
1927	Cle	A	2	57	.252
	BRTR			315	.285

SPURNEY, EDWARD FREDERICK
b.Jan.19,1872 Cleveland,O.
d.Oct.12,1932

Yr	Cl	Lea	Pos	G	Rec
1891	Pit	N	S	3	.285

STACK, WILLIAM EDWARD (Eddie)
b.Oct.24,1887 Chicago,Ill.
d.Aug.28,1958

Yr	Cl	Lea	Pos	G	Rec
1910	Phi	N	P	20	6-7
1911	Phi	N	P	12	5-5
1912	Bro	N	P	28	7-5
1913	Bro	N	P	23	4-4
1913	Chi	N	P	11	4-2
1914	Chi	N	P	6	0-1
	BRTR			100	26-24

STAFFORD, HENRY ALEXANDER (Heinie)
b.Nov.1,1891 Orleans,Vt.

Yr	Cl	Lea	Pos	G	Rec
1916	NY	N	H	1	.000
	TR				

STAFFORD, JAMES JOSEPH (General)
b.Dec.30,1868 Webster,Mass.
d.Sept.11,1923

Yr	Cl	Lea	Pos	G	Rec
1890	Buf	p	P	15	3-9
1893	NY	N	O	67	.301
1894	NY	N	3	11	.229
1895	NY	N	2	123	.293
1896	NY	N	O	59	.282
1897	NY	N	S-O	7	.091
1897	Lou	N	S	112	.280
1898	Lou	N	O	42	.312
1898	Bos	N	1-O	37	.270
1899	Bos	N	O	50	.313
1899	Was	N	2-S-3	30	.243
				553	3-9 / .284

STAFFORD, JOHN HENRY
b.Apr.8,1870 Webster,Mass.
d.July 3,1940

Yr	Cl	Lea	Pos	G	Rec
1893	Cle	N	P	2	0-0

STAFFORD, ROBERT LEE

Yr	Cl	Lea	Pos	G	Rec
1890	Ath	a	O	1	.000

STAFFORD, WILLIAM CHARLES
b.Aug.13,1939 Catskill,N.Y.

Yr	Cl	Lea	Pos	G	Rec
1960	NY	A	P	12	3-1
1961	NY	A	P	36	14-9
1962	NY	A	P	35	14-9
	BRTR			83	31-19

STAHL, CHARLES SYLVESTER (Chick)
b.Jan.10,1873 Ft.Wayne,Ind.
d.Mar.28,1907

Yr	Cl	Lea	Pos	G	Rec
1897	Bos	N	O	111	.359
1898	Bos	N	O	125	.311
1899	Bos	N	O	148	.348
1900	Bos	N	O	134	.293
1901	Bos	A	O	130	.310
1902	Bos	A	O	127	.318
1903	Bos	A	O	78	.279
1904	Bos	A	O	157	.300
1905	Bos	A	O	134	.258
1906	Bos	A	M-O	155	.286
	BLTL			1299	.306

STAHL, GARLAND (Jake)
b.Apr.13,1879 Elkhart,Ill.
d.Sept.18,1922

Yr	Cl	Lea	Pos	G	Rec
1903	Bos	A	C	38	.239
1904	Was	A	1-O	141	.261
1905	Was	A	M-1	140	.250
1906	Was	A	M-1	137	.222
1908	NY	A	1-O	74	.259
1908	Bos	A	1	79	.240
1909	Bos	A	1	127	.294
1910	Bos	A	1	144	.271
1912	Bos	A	M-1	95	.301
1913	Bos	A	M-1	1	.000
	BRTR			976	.260

STAINBACK, GEORGE TUCKER (Tuck)
b.Aug.4,1910 Los Angeles,Cal.

Yr	Cl	Lea	Pos	G	Rec
1934	Chi	N	O	104	.306
1935	Chi	N	O	47	.255
1936	Chi	N	O	44	.173
1937	Chi	N	O	72	.231
1938	St.L	N	O	6	.000
1938	Phi	N	O	30	.259
1938	Bro	N	O	35	.327
1939	Bro	N	O	68	.269
1940	Det	A	O	15	.225
1941	Det	A	O	94	.245
1942	NY	A	O	15	.200
1943	NY	A	O	71	.260
1944	NY	A	O	30	.218
1945	NY	A	O	95	.257
1946	Phi	A	O	91	.244
	BRTR			817	.258

STALBERGER, WILLIAM
b. Detroit,Mich.

Yr	Cl	Lea	Pos	G	Rec
1885	Pro	N	P	1	0-1

STALEY, GALE
b.May 2,1903 Oshkosh,Wis.

Yr	Cl	Lea	Pos	G	Rec
1925	Chi	N	2	7	.423
	BLTR				

STALEY, GERALD LEE
b.Aug.21,1920 Brush Prairie,Wash.

Yr	Cl	Lea	Pos	G	Rec
1947	St.L	N	P	18	1-0
1948	St.L	N	P	31	4-4
1949	St.L	N	P	45	10-10
1950	St.L	N	P	42	13-13
1951	St.L	N	P	42	19-13
1952	St.L	N	P	35	17-14
1953	St.L	N	P	40	18-9
1954	St.L	N	P	48	7-13
1955	Cin	N	P	30	5-8
1955	NY	A	P	2	0-0
1956	NY	A	P	1	0-0
1956	Chi	A	P	26	8-3
1957	Chi	A	P	47	5-1
1958	Chi	A	P	50	4-5
1959	Chi	A	P	67	8-5
1960	Chi	A	P	64	13-8
1961	Chi	A	P	16	0-3
1961	KC	A	P	23	1-1
1961	Det	A	P	13	1-1
	BRTR			640	134-111

STALEY, HENRY E.
b.Nov.3,1866 Jacksonville,Ill.
d.Jan.12,1910

(Continued)

Yr	Cl	Lea	Pos	G	Rec
1888	Pit	N	P	24	12-12
1889	Pit	N	P	49	21-26
1890	Pit	p	P	47	21-23
1891	Pit	N	P	9	2-4
1891	Bos	N	P	27	19-8
1892	Bos	N	P	35	24-11
1893	Bos	N	P	32	19-10
1894	Bos	N	P	25	13-14
1895	St.L	N	P	18	5-13
	BRTR			268	136-121

STALLARD, EVAN TRACY
b.Aug.31,1937 Herald,Va.

Yr	Cl	Lea	Pos	G	Rec
1960	Bos	A	P	4	0-0
1961	Bos	A	P	43	2-7
1962	Bos	A	P	1	0-0
	BRTR			48	2-7

STALLCUP, THOMAS VIRGIL (Red)
b.Jan.3,1922 Ravensford,N.C.

Yr	Cl	Lea	Pos	G	Rec
1947	Cin	N	S	8	.000
1948	Cin	N	S	149	.228
1949	Cin	N	S	141	.254
1950	Cin	N	S	136	.251
1951	Cin	N	S	121	.241
1952	Cin	N	S	2	.000
1952	St.L	N	S	29	.129
1953	St.L	N	H	1	.000
	BRTR			587	.241

STALLER, GEORGE WALBORN
b.Apr.1,1916 Rutherford Heights,Pa.

Yr	Cl	Lea	Pos	G	Rec
1943	Phi	A	O	21	.271
	BLTL				

STALLINGS, GEORGE TWEEDY
b.Nov.17,1867 Augusta,Ga.
d.May 13,1929

Yr	Cl	Lea	Pos	G	Rec
1890	Bro	N	C	4	.000
1897	Phi	N	M-1	1	.400
	BRTR			5	.100

Non-playing manager Phi (N) 1898, Det (A) 1901, NY (A) 1909-10 and Bos (N) 1913-20.

STANAGE, OSCAR HARLAND
b.Mar.17,1883 Tulare,Cal.

Yr	Cl	Lea	Pos	G	Rec
1906	Cin	N	C	1	1.000
1909	Det	A	C	77	.262
1910	Det	A	C	88	.207
1911	Det	A	C	141	.264
1912	Det	A	C	119	.261
1913	Det	A	C	80	.224
1914	Det	A	C	122	.193
1915	Det	A	C	100	.223
1916	Det	A	C	94	.237
1917	Det	A	C	99	.205
1918	Det	A	C	54	.253
1919	Det	A	C	38	.242
1920	Det	A	C	78	.231
1925	Det	A	C	3	.200
	BRTR			1094	.234

STANCEU, CHARLES
b.Jan.9,1916 Canton,O.

Yr	Cl	Lea	Pos	G	Rec
1941	NY	A	P	22	3-3
1946	NY	A	P	3	0-0
1946	Phi	N	P	14	2-4
	BRTR			39	5-7

STANDAERT, JEROME JOHN
b.Nov.2,1902 Chicago,Ill.

Yr	Cl	Lea	Pos	G	Rec
1925	Bro	N	H	1	.000
1926	Bro	N	2-3	66	.345
1929	Bos	A	1	19	.167
	BRTR			86	.318

STANDRIDGE, ALFRED PETER (Pete)
b.Apr.25,1891 Seattle,Wash.

Yr	Cl	Lea	Pos	G	Rec
1911	St.L	N	P	2	0-0
1915	Chi	N	P	30	4-1
	BRTR			32	4-1

STANGE, ALBERT LEE
b.Oct.27,1936 Chicago,Ill.

Yr	Cl	Lea	Pos	G	Rec
1961	Min	A	P	7	1-0
1962	Min	A	P	44	4-3
	BRTR			51	5-3

STANKA, JOE DONALD
b.July 23,1931 Hammon,Okla.

Yr	Cl	Lea	Pos	G	Rec
1959	Chi	A	P	2	1-0
	BRTR				

STANKARD, THOMAS FRANCIS
b.Mar.20,1882 Waltham,Mass.
d.June 13,1958

Yr	Cl	Lea	Pos	G	Rec
1904	Pit	N	3	2	.000
	BRTR				

STANKY, EDWARD RAYMOND (The Brat)
b.Sept.3,1916 Philadelphia,Pa.

Yr	Cl	Lea	Pos	G	Rec
1943	Chi	N	2-S-3	142	.245
1944	Chi	N	2-S-3	13	.240
1944	Bro	N	2-S-3	89	.276
1945	Bro	N	2-S	153	.258
1946	Bro	N	2	144	.273
1947	Bro	N	2	146	.252
1948	Bos	N	2	67	.320
1949	Bos	N	2	138	.285
1950	NY	N	2	152	.300
1951	NY	N	2	145	.247
1952	St.L	N	M-2	53	.229
1953	St.L	N	M-2	17	.267
	BRTR			1259	.268

Non-playing manager St.L (N) 1954-55.

STANLEY, JAMES F.
b.1889

Yr	Cl	Lea	Pos	G	Rec
1914	Chi	F	S	46	.206
	BBTR				

STANLEY, JOHN LEONARD (Buck)
b.Nov.13,1889 Washington,D.C.
d.Aug.13,1940

Yr	Cl	Lea	Pos	G	Rec
1911	Phi	N	P	4	0-1
	BLTL				

STANLEY, JOSEPH
b. New Jersey

Yr	Cl	Lea	Pos	G	Rec
1884	Bal	U	O	5	.217

STANLEY, JOSEPH BERNARD
b.Apr.2,1881 Washington,D.C.

Yr	Cl	Lea	Pos	G	Rec
1897	Was	N	P	1	0-0
1902	Was	A	O	3	.333
1903	Bos	N	P-O	79	{ 0-0 / .250
1904	Bos	N	O	3	.000
1905	Was	A	O	28	.261
1906	Was	A	O	73	.163
1909	Chi	N	O	16	.135
	BBTR			203	{ 0-0 / .213

STANSBURY, JOHN JAMES
b.Dec.6,1886 Phillipsburg,N.J.

Yr	Cl	Lea	Pos	G	Rec
1918	Bos	A	3	20	.128
	BRTR				

STANTON, GEORGE WASHINGTON (Buck)
b.June 19,1906 Stantonsburg,N.C.

Yr	Cl	Lea	Pos	G	Rec
1931	St.L	A	O	13	.200
	BLTL				

STANTON, HARRY ANDREW
b.St.Louis,Mo.

Yr	Cl	Lea	Pos	G	Rec
1900	St.L	N	C	1	.000
1904	Chi	N	C	1	.000
	TR			2	.000

STAPLES, JOSEPH F.
b.Buffalo,N.Y.

Yr	Cl	Lea	Pos	G	Rec
1885	Buf	N	2-O	7	.045

STARGELL, WILVER DORNEL
b.Mar.6,1941 Earlsboro,Okla.

Yr	Cl	Lea	Pos	G	Rec
1962	Pit	N	O	10	.290
	BLTL				

STARK, MONROE RANDOLPH
b.1885 Ripley,Miss.
d.Dec.1,1924

Yr	Cl	Lea	Pos	G	Rec
1909	Cle	A	S	19	.200
1910	Bro	N	S	30	.165
1911	Bro	N	2-S	55	.295
1912	Bro	N	S	8	.182
	BRTR			112	.238

STARKELL, CONARD
b.Nov.16,1880 Tacoma,Wash.
d.Jan.19,1933

Yr	Cl	Lea	Pos	G	Rec
1906	Was	A	P	1	0-0
	TR				

STARNAGLE, GEORGE HENRY (Real name George Henry Steurnagel)
b.Oct.6,1873 Belleville,Ill.
d.Feb.15,1946

Yr	Cl	Lea	Pos	G	Rec
1902	Cle	A	C	1	.000
	BRTR				

STARR, CHARLES WATKIN
b.Aug.30,1878 Pike Co.,O.
d.Oct.18,1937

Yr	Cl	Lea	Pos	G	Rec
1905	St.L	A	2	64	.206
1908	Pit	N	S	19	.186
1909	Bos	N	2	61	.222
1909	Phi	N	2	3	.000
	TR			147	.211

STARR, RAYMOND FRANCIS
b.Apr.23,1906 Nowata,Okla.

Yr	Cl	Lea	Pos	G	Rec
1932	St.L	N	P	3	1-1
1933	NY	N	P	6	0-1
1933	Bos	N	P	9	0-1
1941	Cin	N	P	7	3-2
1942	Cin	N	P	37	15-13
1943	Cin	N	P	36	11-10
1944	Pit	N	P	27	6-5
1945	Pit	N	P	4	0-2
1945	Chi	N	P	9	1-0
	BRTR			138	37-35

STARR, RICHARD EUGENE
b.Mar.2,1921 Kittanning,Pa.

Yr	Cl	Lea	Pos	G	Rec
1947	NY	A	P	4	1-0
1948	NY	A	P	1	0-0
1949	St.L	A	P	30	1-7
1950	St.L	A	P	33	7-5
1951	St.L	A	P	15	2-5
1951	Was	A	P	11	1-7
	BRTR			94	12-24

STARR, WILLIAM (Chick)
b.Feb.16,1911 Brooklyn,N.Y.

Yr	Cl	Lea	Pos	G	Rec
1935	Was	A	C	12	.208
1936	Was	A	C	1	.000
	BRTR			13	.208

START, JOSEPH (Rocks)
b.Oct.14,1843 New York,N.Y.
d.Mar.27,1927

Yr	Cl	Lea	Pos	G	Rec
1871	Mut	n	1	34	NR
1872	Mut	n	1	55	NR
1873	Mut	n	1	54	NR
1874	Mut	n	1	64	NR
1875	Mut	n	1	69	.210
1876	Mut	N	1	56	.276
1877	Har	N	1	60	.332
1878	Chi	N	1	60	.345
1879	Pro	N	1	65	.318
1880	Pro	N	1	79	.280
1881	Pro	N	1	79	.327
1882	Pro	N	1	82	.328
1883	Pro	N	1	87	.283
1884	Pro	N	1	90	.273
1885	Pro	N	1	99	.275
1886	Was	N	1	29	.229
	BLTL			1062	NR

STATZ, ARNOLD JOHN (Jigger)
b.Oct.20,1897 Waukegan,Ill.

Yr	Cl	Lea	Pos	G	Rec
1919	NY	N	2-O	21	.300
1920	NY	N	O	16	.133
1920	Bos	A	O	2	.000
1922	Chi	N	O	110	.297
1923	Chi	N	O	154	.319
1924	Chi	N	2-O	135	.277
1925	Chi	N	O	38	.257
1927	Bro	N	O	130	.274
1928	Bro	N	O	77	.234
	BBTR			683	.285

STAUFFER, CHARLES EDWARD
b.Jan.10,1898 Emsworth,Pa.

Yr	Cl	Lea	Pos	G	Rec
1923	Chi	N	P	1	0-0
1925	St.L	A	P	20	0-1
	BRTR			21	0-1

STEARNS, WILLIAM

Yr	Cl	Lea	Pos	G	Rec
1871	Oly	n	P	2	2-0
1872	Nat	n	P	10	0-10
1873	Nat	n	P	31	7-24
1874	Har	n	P-O	32	2-16 NR
1875	Nat	n	P-O	19	2-12 NR
				94	13-62 NR

STEARNS, DANIEL ECKFORD
b.Oct.18,1861 Buffalo,N.Y.
d.June 28,1944

Yr	Cl	Lea	Pos	G	Rec
1880	Buf	N	C-2-S-3-O	21	.232
1881	Det	N	S	3	.100
1882	Cin	a	1-2-S-O	49	.302
1883	Bal	a	1-O	94	.248
1884	Bal	a	1	101	.241
1885	Bal	a	1	67	.186
1885	Buf	N	C-1-S	30	.200
1889	KC	a	1	139	.288
	BLTR			504	.252

STECHER, CHARLES
b.Bordentown,N.J.

Yr	Cl	Lea	Pos	G	Rec
1890	Ath	a	P	10	0-7

STEDROUSKE, ...
b.Troy,N.Y.

Yr	Cl	Lea	Pos	G	Rec
1879	Chi	N	2-3	4	.083

STEELE, ELMER RAE
b.May 17,1886 Muitezskill,N.Y.

Yr	Cl	Lea	Pos	G	Rec
1907	Bos	A	P	4	0-1
1908	Bos	A	P	16	5-7
1909	Bos	A	P	15	4-2
1910	Pit	N	P	3	0-3
1911	Pit	N	P	31	9-9
1911	Bro	N	P	5	0-0
	BRTR			74	18-22

STEELE, ROBERT WESLEY
b.Jan.5,1895 Vankleek Hill,Ont.,Can.

Yr	Cl	Lea	Pos	G	Rec
1916	St.L	N	P	29	5-15
1917	St.L	N	P	12	1-3
1917	Pit	N	P	33	5-11
1918	Pit	N	P	10	2-3
1918	NY	N	P	12	3-5
1919	NY	N	P	1	0-1
	BBTL			97	16-38

STEELE, WILLIAM MITCHELL (Big Bill)
b.Oct.5,1885 Milford,Pa.
d.Oct.19,1949

Yr	Cl	Lea	Pos	G	Rec
1910	St.L	N	P	9	4-4
1911	St.L	N	P	43	18-19
1912	St.L	N	P	41	9-13
1913	St.L	N	P	12	4-4
1914	St.L	N	P	17	1-2
1914	Bro	N	P	8	1-1
	BRTR			130	37-43

STEELMAN, MORRIS JAMES (Farmer)
b.June 29,1875 Millville,N.J.
d.Sept.16,1944

Yr	Cl	Lea	Pos	G	Rec
1899	Lou	N	C	5	.062
1900	Bro	N	C	1	.000
1901	Bro	N	C	1	.333
1901	Phi	A	C	27	.267
1902	Phi	A	C-O	10	.187
	TR			44	.220

STEEN, WILLIAM JOHN
b.Nov.11,1887 Pittsburgh,Pa.

Yr	Cl	Lea	Pos	G	Rec
1912	Cle	A	P	22	9-8
1913	Cle	A	P	18	4-5
1914	Cle	A	P	29	9-14
1915	Cle	A	P	10	0-4
1915	Det	A	P	20	6-1
	BRTR			99	28-32

STEENGRAFE, MILTON HENRY
b.May 26,1900 San Francisco,Cal.

Yr	Cl	Lea	Pos	G	Rec
1924	Chi	A	P	3	0-0
1926	Chi	A	P	13	1-2
	BRTR			16	1-2

STEERE, FRED EUGENE
b.Aug.16,1872 S.Scituate,R.I.
d.Mar.13,1942

Yr	Cl	Lea	Pos	G	Rec
1894	Pit	N	S	10	.184

STEEVENS, MORRIS DALE
b.Oct.7,1940 Salem,Ill.

Yr	Cl	Lea	Pos	G	Rec
1962	Chi	N	P	12	0-1
	BLTL				

STEIN, EDWARD F.
b.Sept.5,1869 Detroit,Mich.
d.May 10,1928

Yr	Cl	Lea	Pos	G	Rec
1890	Chi	N	P	18	11-6
1891	Chi	N	P	13	6-6
1892	Bro	N	P	45	27-18
1893	Bro	N	P	35	19-14
1894	Bro	N	P	41	26-14
1895	Bro	N	P	28	13-13
1896	Bro	N	P	17	3-7
1898	Bro	N	P	3	0-2
				200	107-80

STEIN, IRVIN MICHAEL
b.May 21,1911 Madisonville,La.

Yr	Cl	Lea	Pos	G	Rec
1932	Phi	A	P	1	0-0
	BRTR				

STEIN, JUSTIN MARION
b.Aug.9,1913 St.Louis,Mo.

Yr	Cl	Lea	Pos	G	Rec
1938	Phi	N	2-3	11	.256
1938	Cin	N	2-S	11	.333
	BRTR			22	.281

STEINBACHER, HENRY JOHN
b.Mar.22,1913 Sacramento,Cal.

Yr	Cl	Lea	Pos	G	Rec
1937	Chi	A	O	26	.260
1938	Chi	A	O	106	.331
1939	Chi	A	O	71	.171
	BLTR			203	.292

STEINBRENNER, EUGENE GASS
b.Nov.16,1892 Pittsburgh,Pa.

Yr	Cl	Lea	Pos	G	Rec
1912	Phi	N	2	3	.100
	TR				

STEINECKE, WILLIAM ROBERT
b.Feb.7,1907 Cincinnati,O.

Yr	Cl	Lea	Pos	G	Rec
1931	Pit	N	C	4	.000
	BRTR				

STEINEDER, RAYMOND J.
b.Feb.25,1897 Vineland,N.J.

Yr	Cl	Lea	Pos	G	Rec
1923	Pit	N	P	15	2-0
1924	Pit	N	P	5	0-1
1924	Phi	N	P	9	1-1
	BRTR			29	3-2

STEINER, BENJAMIN SAUNDERS
b.July 28,1922 Alexandria,Va.

Yr	Cl	Lea	Pos	G	Rec
1945	Bos	A	2	78	.257
1946	Bos	A	3	3	.250
1947	Det	A	H	1	.000
	BLTR			82	.256

STEINER, JAMES HARRY (Red)
b.Jan.7,1917 Los Angeles,Cal.

Yr	Cl	Lea	Pos	G	Rec
1945	Cle	A	C	12	.143
1945	Bos	A	C	26	.207
	BLTR			38	.190

STEINFELDT, HARRY M.
b.Sept.29,1876 St.Louis,Mo.
d.Aug.17,1914

Yr	Cl	Lea	Pos	G	Rec
1898	Cin	N	2-O	83	.289
1899	Cin	N	2-3	107	.242
1900	Cin	N	2-3	136	.247
1901	Cin	N	2-3	105	.250
1902	Cin	N	S-3-O	128	.276
1903	Cin	N	3	118	.312
1904	Cin	N	3	98	.224
1905	Cin	N	3	106	.271
1906	Chi	N	3	151	.327
1907	Chi	N	3	151	.266
1908	Chi	N	3	150	.241
1909	Chi	N	3	151	.252
1910	Chi	N	3	128	.252
1911	Bos	N	3	19	.254
	BRTR			1631	.267

STELLBAUER, WILLIAM JENNINGS
b.Mar.20,1894 Bremond,Tex.

Yr	Cl	Lea	Pos	G	Rec
1916	Phi	A	O	25	.270
	BRTR				

STELZLE, JACOB C.
(Played under name of Jacob C. Stenzel)

STEM, FREDERICK B.

Yr	Cl	Lea	Pos	G	Rec
1908	Bos	N	1	19	.278
1909	Bos	N	1	68	.208
				87	.224

STEMMEYER, WILLIAM (Cannon Ball)
b.May 6,1864 Cleveland,O.
d.May 4,1945

Yr	Cl	Lea	Pos	G	Rec
1885	Bos	N	P	2	1-1
1886	Bos	N	P	41	22-18
1887	Bos	N	P	14	6-8
1888	Cle	a	P	3	0-2
	BRTR			60	29-29

STENGEL, CHARLES DILLON (Casey)
b.July 30,1889 Kansas City,Mo.

Yr	Cl	Lea	Pos	G	Rec
1912	Bro	N	O	17	.316
1913	Bro	N	O	124	.272
1914	Bro	N	O	126	.316
1915	Bro	N	O	132	.237
1916	Bro	N	O	127	.279
1917	Bro	N	O	150	.257
1918	Pit	N	O	39	.246
1919	Pit	N	O	89	.293
1920	Phi	N	O	129	.292
1921	Phi	N	O	24	.305
1921	NY	N	O	18	.227
1922	NY	N	O	84	.368
1923	NY	N	O	75	.339
1924	Bos	N	O	131	.280
1925	Bos	N	O	12	.077
	BLTL			1277	.284

Non-playing manager Bro (N) 1934-36. Bos (N) 1938-43, NY (A) 1949-60, and NY (N) 1962.

STENHOUSE, DAVID ROTCHFORD
b.Sept.12,1933 Westerly,R.I.

Yr	Cl	Lea	Pos	G	Rec
1962	Was	A	P	34	11-12
	BRTR				

STENZEL, JACOB C.
(Real name Jacob C. Stelzle)
b.June 24,1867 Cincinnati,O.
d.Jan.6,1919

Yr	Cl	Lea	Pos	G	Rec
1890	Chi	N	C-O	11	.209
1892	Pit	N	O	2	.000
1893	Pit	N	O	51	.409
1894	Pit	N	O	131	.351
1895	Pit	N	O	131	.384
1896	Pit	N	O	112	.366
1897	Bal	N	O	131	.351
1898	Bal	N	O	35	.254
1898	St.L	N	O	105	.287
1899	St.L	N	O	32	.270
1899	Cin	N	O	9	.321
	BRTR			750	.344

STEPHENS, BRYAN MARIS
b.July 14,1920 Fayetteville,Ark.

Yr	Cl	Lea	Pos	G	Rec
1947	Cle	A	P	31	5-10
1948	St.L	A	P	43	3-6
	BRTR			74	8-16

STEPHENS, CLARENCE WRIGHT
b.Aug.19,1863 Cincinnati,O.
d.Feb.28,1945

Yr	Cl	Lea	Pos	G	Rec
1886	Cin	a	P	1	1-0
1891	Cin	N	P	1	0-1
1892	Cin	N	P	2	0-1
	TR			4	1-2

STEPHENS, GEORGE BENJAMIN
b.Sept.28,1867 Romeo,Mich.
d.Aug.5,1896

Yr	Cl	Lea	Pos	G	Rec
1892	Bal	N	P	5	1-0
1893	Was	N	P	9	1-6
1894	Was	N	P	3	0-3
				17	2-9

STEPHENS, GLEN EUGENE (Gene)
b.Jan.20,1933 Gravette,Ark.

Yr	Cl	Lea	Pos	G	Rec
1952	Bos	A	O	21	.226
1953	Bos	A	O	78	.204
1955	Bos	A	O	109	.293
1956	Bos	A	O	104	.270
1957	Bos	A	O	120	.266
1958	Bos	A	O	134	.219
1959	Bos	A	O	92	.278
1960	Bos	A	O	35	.229
1960	Bal	A	O	84	.238
1961	Bal	A	O	32	.190
1961	KC	A	O	62	.208
1962	KC	A	H	5	.000
	BLTR			876	.239

STEPHENS, JAMES WALTER
b.Dec.10,1883 Salineville,O.

Yr	Cl	Lea	Pos	G	Rec
1907	St.L	A	C	58	.202
1908	St.L	A	C	47	.200
1909	St.L	A	C	79	.220
1910	St.L	A	C	99	.241
1911	St.L	A	C	70	.231
1912	St.L	A	C	74	.249
	BRTR			427	.227

STEPHENS, VERNON DECATUR (Junior)
b.Oct.23,1920 McAlister,N.Mex.

Yr	Cl	Lea	Pos	G	Rec
1941	St.L	A	S	3	.500
1942	St.L	A	S	145	.294
1943	St.L	A	S-O	137	.289
1944	St.L	A	S	145	.293
1945	St.L	A	S-3	149	.289
1946	St.L	A	S	115	.307
1947	St.L	A	S	150	.279
1948	Bos	A	S	155	.269
1949	Bos	A	S	155	.290
1950	Bos	A	S	149	.295
1951	Bos	A	S-3	109	.300
1952	Bos	A	S-3	92	.254
1953	Chi	A	S-3	44	.186
1953	St.L	A	3	46	.321

(Continued)

Yr	Cl	Lea	Pos	G	Rec
1954	Bal	A	3	101	.285
1955	Bal	A	3	3	.167
1955	Chi	A	3	22	.250
	BRTR			1720	.286

STEPHENSON, JACKSON RIGGS (Old Hoss)
b.Jan.5,1898 Akron,Ala.

Yr	Cl	Lea	Pos	G	Rec
1921	Cle	A	2	65	.330
1922	Cle	A	2-3	86	.339
1923	Cle	A	2	91	.319
1924	Cle	A	2	71	.371
1925	Cle	A	O	19	.296
1926	Chi	N	O	82	.338
1927	Chi	N	O	152	.344
1928	Chi	N	O	137	.324
1929	Chi	N	O	136	.362
1930	Chi	N	O	109	.367
1931	Chi	N	O	80	.319
1932	Chi	N	O	147	.324
1933	Chi	N	O	97	.329
1934	Chi	N	O	38	.216
	BRTR			1310	.336

STEPHENSON, JOSEPH CHESTER
b.June 30,1921 Detroit,Mich.

Yr	Cl	Lea	Pos	G	Rec
1943	NY	N	C	9	.250
1944	Chi	N	C	4	.125
1947	Chi	A	C	16	.143
	BRTR			29	.179

STEPHENSON, REUBEN CRANDOL (Dummy)
b.Sept.22,1869 Petersburg,N.J.
d.Dec.1,1924

Yr	Cl	Lea	Pos	G	Rec
1892	Phi	N	O	8	.277

STEPHENSON, ROBERT LOYD
b.Aug.11,1928 Blair,Okla.

Yr	Cl	Lea	Pos	G	Rec
1955	St.L	N	2-S-3	67	.243
	BRTR				

STEPHENSON, WALTER McQUEEN (Tarzan)
b.Mar.27,1913 Saluda,N.C.

Yr	Cl	Lea	Pos	G	Rec
1935	Chi	N	C	16	.385
1936	Chi	N	C	6	.083
1937	Phi	N	C	10	.261
	BRTR			32	.279

STERLING, JOHN A.
b.Philadelphia,Pa.

Yr	Cl	Lea	Pos	G	Rec
1890	Ath	a	P	1	0-1

STERRETT, CHARLES HURLBUT (Dutch)
b.Oct.1,1889 Milroy,Pa.

Yr	Cl	Lea	Pos	G	Rec
1912	NY	A	1-O	66	.265
1913	NY	A	C	21	.171
	BRTR			87	.253

STEURNAGEL, GEORGE HENRY
(Played under name of George Henry Starnagle)

STEVENS, CHARLES AUGUSTUS
b.July 10,1918 Van Houten,N.Mex.

Yr	Cl	Lea	Pos	G	Rec
1941	St.L	A	1	4	.154
1946	St.L	A	1	122	.248
1948	St.L	A	1	85	.260
	BBTL			211	.251

STEVENS, EDWARD LEE
b.Jan.12,1925 Galveston,Tex.

Yr	Cl	Lea	Pos	G	Rec
1945	Bro	N	1	55	.274
1946	Bro	N	1	103	.242
1947	Bro	N	1	5	.154
1948	Pit	N	1	128	.254
1949	Pit	N	1	67	.262
1950	Pit	N	1	17	.196
	BLTL			375	.252

STEVENS, JAMES ARTHUR
b.Aug.25,1889 Williamsburg,Md.

Yr	Cl	Lea	Pos	G	Rec
1914	Was	A	P	2	0-0
	BBTR				

STEVENS, R. C.
b.July 22,1934 Moultrie,Ga.

Yr	Cl	Lea	Pos	G	Rec
1958	Pit	N	1	59	.267
1959	Pit	N	1	3	.286
1960	Pit	N	1	9	.000
1961	Was	A	1	33	.129
				104	.210

STEVENS, ROBERT JORDAN
b.Apr.17,1910 Chevy Chase,Md.

Yr	Cl	Lea	Pos	G	Rec
1931	Phi	N	S	12	.343
BLTR					

STEWART, ASA (Ace)
b.Feb.14,1869 Terre Haute,Ind.
d.Apr.17,1912

Yr	Cl	Lea	Pos	G	Rec
1895	Chi	N	2	97	.244
BRTR					

STEWART, CHARLES EUGENE (Tuffy)
b.July 31,1883 Chicago,Ill.
d.Nov.18,1934

Yr	Cl	Lea	Pos	G	Rec
1913	Chi	N	O	9	.125
1914	Chi	N	H	1	.000
BLTL				10	.111

STEWART, EDWARD PERRY (Bud)
b.June 15,1916 Sacramento,Cal.

Yr	Cl	Lea	Pos	G	Rec
1941	Pit	N	O	73	.267
1942	Pit	N	2-3-O	82	.219
1948	NY	A	H	6	.200
1948	Was	A	O	118	.279
1949	Was	A	O	118	.284
1950	Was	A	O	118	.267
1951	Chi	A	O	95	.276
1952	Chi	A	O	92	.267
1953	Chi	A	O	53	.271
1954	Chi	A	O	18	.077
BLTR				773	.268

STEWART, FRANK
b.Sept.8,1906 Minneapolis,Minn.

Yr	Cl	Lea	Pos	G	Rec
1927	Chi	A	P	1	0-1
BRTR					

STEWART, GLEN WELDON (Gabby)
b.Sept.29,1914 Tullahoma,Tenn.

Yr	Cl	Lea	Pos	G	Rec
1940	NY	N	S-3	15	.138
1943	Phi	N	C-1-2-S	110	.211
1944	Phi	N	2-S-3	118	.220
BRTR				243	.213

STEWART, JOHN FRANKLIN (Stuffy)
b.Jan.31,1896 Lake City,Fla.

Yr	Cl	Lea	Pos	G	Rec
1916	St.L	N	2	9	.176
1917	St.L	N	2	13	.000
1921	St.L	A	H	3	.333
1922	Pit	N	2	3	.154
1923	Bro	N	2	4	.364
1925	Was	A	2-3	7	.353
1926	Was	A	2	62	.270
1927	Was	A	2	56	.240
1929	Was	A	2	22	.000
BRTR				179	.238

STEWART, JOSEPH LAWRENCE
b.Mar.11,1879 Monroe,N.C.
d.Feb.10,1913

Yr	Cl	Lea	Pos	G	Rec
1904	Bos	N	P	2	0-0

STEWART, MARK
b.Oct.11,1889 Paris,Tenn.
d.Jan.17,1932

Yr	Cl	Lea	Pos	G	Rec
1913	Cin	N	C	1	.000
BLTR					

STEWART, VESTON GOFF (Bunky)
b.Jan.7,1931 New Bern,N.C.

Yr	Cl	Lea	Pos	G	Rec
1952	Was	A	P	1	0-0
1953	Was	A	P	2	0-2
1954	Was	A	P	29	0-2
1955	Was	A	P	7	0-0
1956	Was	A	P	34	5-7
BLTL				73	5-11

STEWART, WALTER CLEVELAND (Lefty)
b.Sept.23,1900 Sparta,Tenn.

Yr	Cl	Lea	Pos	G	Rec
1921	Det	A	P	5	0-0
1927	St.L	A	P	28	8-11
1928	St.L	A	P	29	7-9
1929	St.L	A	P	23	9-6
1930	St.L	A	P	35	20-12
1931	St.L	A	P	36	14-17
1932	St.L	A	P	41	15-19
1933	Was	A	P-2	35	15-6 .143
1934	Was	A	P	25	7-11
1935	Was	A	P	1	0-1
1935	Cle	A	P	24	6-6
BRTL				282	101-98 .204

STEWART, WALTER NESBITT (Neb)
b.May 21,1918 S.Charleston,O.

Yr	Cl	Lea	Pos	G	Rec
1940	Phi	N	O	10	.129
BRTR					

STEWART, WILLIAM MACKLIN (Mack)
b.Sept.23,1913 Stevenson,Ala.

Yr	Cl	Lea	Pos	G	Rec
1944	Chi	N	P	8	0-0
1945	Chi	N	P	16	0-1
BRTR				24	0-1

STEWART, WILLIAM WAYNE
b.Apr.15,1929 Bay City,Mich.

Yr	Cl	Lea	Pos	G	Rec
1955	KC	A	O	11	.111
BRTR					

STIELY, FREDERICK WARREN
b.June 1,1901 Valley View,Pa.

Yr	Cl	Lea	Pos	G	Rec
1929	St.L	A	P	1	1-0
1930	St.L	A	P	5	0-1
1931	St.L	A	P	4	0-0
BLTL				10	1-1

STIGMAN, RICHARD LEWIS
b.Jan.24,1936 Nimrod,Minn.

Yr	Cl	Lea	Pos	G	Rec
1960	Cle	A	P	41	5-11
1961	Cle	A	P	22	2-5
1962	Min	A	P	40	12-5
BRTL				103	19-21

STILES, ROLLAND MAYS (Lena)
b.Nov.17,1906 Ratcliff,Ark.

Yr	Cl	Lea	Pos	G	Rec
1930	St.L	A	P	20	3-6
1931	St.L	A	P	34	3-1
1933	St.L	A	P	31	3-7
BRTR				85	9-14

STILLWELL, RONALD ROY
b.Dec.3,1939 Los Angeles,Calif.

Yr	Cl	Lea	Pos	G	Rec
1961	Was	A	S	8	.125
1962	Was	A	2-S	6	.273
BRTR				14	.211

STIMMEL, ARCHIBALD MAY (Lumbago)
b.May 30,1873 Woodsboro,Md.
d.Aug.18,1958

Yr	Cl	Lea	Pos	G	Rec
1900	Cin	N	P	2	1-1
1901	Cin	N	P	20	4-14
1902	Cin	N	P	4	0-4
BRTR				26	5-19

STIMSON, CARL REMUS
b.July 18,1894 Hamburg,Ia.
d.Nov.9,1936

Yr	Cl	Lea	Pos	G	Rec
1923	Bos	A	P	2	0-0
BBTR					

STINE, HARRY C.
b.Feb.20,1864 Shenandoah,Pa.
d.June 5,1924

Yr	Cl	Lea	Pos	G	Rec
1890	Ath	a	P	1	0-1

STINE, LEE ELBERT
b.Nov.17,1913 Stillwater,Okla.

Yr	Cl	Lea	Pos	G	Rec
1934	Chi	A	P	4	0-0
1935	Chi	A	P	1	0-0
1936	Cin	N	P	40	3-8
1938	NY	A	P	4	0-0
BRTR				49	3-8

STIRES, GERRETT
b.Oct.13,1849 Hunterdon Co,N.J.
d.June 13,1933

Yr	Cl	Lea	Pos	G	Rec
1871	Rok	n	O	25	NR

STIRNWEISS, GEORGE HENRY (Snuffy)
b.Oct.26,1919 New York,N.Y.
d.Sept.15,1958

Yr	Cl	Lea	Pos	G	Rec
1943	NY	A	2-S	83	.219
1944	NY	A	2	154	.319
1945	NY	A	2	152	.309
1946	NY	A	2-S-3	129	.251
1947	NY	A	2	148	.256
1948	NY	A	2	141	.252
1949	NY	A	2-3	70	.261
1950	NY	A	2	7	.000
1950	St.L	A	2-S-3	93	.218
1951	Cle	A	2-3	50	.216
1952	Cle	A	3	1	.000
BRTR				1028	.268

STIVETTS, JOHN ELMER (Happy Jack)
b.Mar.31,1868 Ashland,Pa.
d.Apr.19,1930

Yr	Cl	Lea	Pos	G	Rec
1889	St.L	a	P	26	12-7
1890	St.L	a	P	67	31-20
1891	St.L	a	P-O	85	31-21 .305
1892	Bos	N	P-O	64	33-14 .300
1893	Bos	N	P	41	21-12
1894	Bos	N	P	57	25-14
1895	Bos	N	P	38	16-16
1896	Bos	N	P	59	22-13
1897	Bos	N	P-O	49	12-4 .388
1898	Bos	N	P-O	27	0-1 .252
1899	Cle	N	P	18	0-4
				531	203-126 .305

STOBBS, CHARLES KLEIN (Chuck)
b.July 2,1929 Wheeling,W Va.

Yr	Cl	Lea	Pos	G	Rec
1947	Bos	A	P	4	0-1
1948	Bos	A	P	6	0-0
1949	Bos	A	P	26	11-6
1950	Bos	A	P	32	12-7
1951	Bos	A	P	34	10-9
1952	Chi	A	P	38	7-12
1953	Was	A	P	27	11-8
1954	Was	A	P	31	11-11
1955	Was	A	P	41	4-14
1956	Was	A	P	38	15-15
1957	Was	A	P	42	8-20
1958	Was	A	P	19	2-6
1958	St.L	N	P	17	1-3
1959	Was	A	P	41	1-8
1960	Was	A	P	40	12-7
1961	Min	A	P	24	2-3
BLTL				460	107-130

STOCK, MILTON JOSEPH
b.July 11,1893 Chicago,Ill.

Yr	Cl	Lea	Pos	G	Rec
1913	NY	N	S	7	.176
1914	NY	N	3	115	.263
1915	Phi	N	3	69	.260
1916	Phi	N	S-3	132	.281
1917	Phi	N	S-3	150	.264
1918	Phi	N	3	123	.274
1919	St.L	N	2-3	135	.307
1920	St.L	N	3	155	.319
1921	St.L	N	3	149	.307
1922	St.L	N	S-3	151	.304
1923	St.L	N	2-3	151	.289
1924	Bro	N	3	142	.242

(Continued)

Yr	Cl	Lea	Pos	G	Rec
1925	Bro	N	2-3	146	.328
1926	Bro	N	2	3	.000
	BRTR			1628	.289

STOCK, WESLEY GAY
b.Apr.10,1934 Longview,Wash.

Yr	Cl	Lea	Pos	G	Rec
1959	Bal	A	P	7	0-0
1960	Bal	A	P	17	2-2
1961	Bal	A	P	35	5-0
1962	Bal	A	P	53	3-2
	BRTR			112	10-4

STOCKSDALE, OTIS H.
b.Aug.7,1871 Carroll Co.,Md.

Yr	Cl	Lea	Pos	G	Rec
1893	Was	N	P	12	2-8
1894	Was	N	P	19	5-8
1895	Was	N	P	20	5-10
1895	Bos	N	P-1	8	2-2 / .308
1896	Bal	N	P	2	0-0
				61	14-28 / .323

STOCKWELL, LEONARD C.
b.Aug.25,1859 Cordova,Ill.
d.Sept.15,1904

Yr	Cl	Lea	Pos	G	Rec
1879	Cle	N	O	2	.000
1884	Lou	a	C-O	2	.111
1890	Cle	N	C	2	.286
	TR			6	.136

STODDARD, ...

Yr	Cl	Lea	Pos	G	Rec
1875	Atl	n	O	2	NR

STOKES, ALBERT JOHN
b.Jan.1,1900 Chicago,Ill.

Yr	Cl	Lea	Pos	G	Rec
1925	Bos	A	C	17	.212
1926	Bos	A	C	30	.163
	BRTR			47	.181

STOKES, ARTHUR MELTON
b.Sept.13,1897 Emmitsburg,Md.
d.June 3,1962

Yr	Cl	Lea	Pos	G	Rec
1925	Phi	A	P	12	1-1
	BRTR				

STONE, CHARLES RICHARD (Dick)
b.Dec.5,1911 Oklahoma City,Okla.

Yr	Cl	Lea	Pos	G	Rec
1945	Was	A	P	3	0-0
	BLTL				

STONE, DARRAH DEAN
b.Sept.1,1930 Moline,Ill.

Yr	Cl	Lea	Pos	G	Rec
1953	Was	A	P	3	0-1
1954	Was	A	P	31	12-10
1955	Was	A	P	43	6-13
1956	Was	A	P	42	5-7
1957	Was	A	P	3	0-0
1957	Bos	A	P	17	1-3
1959	St.L	N	P	18	0-1
1962	Hou	N	P	15	3-2
1962	Chi	A	P	27	1-0
	BLTL			199	28-37

STONE, DWIGHT ELY
b.Aug.2,1886 Holt Co.,Neb.

Yr	Cl	Lea	Pos	G	Rec
1913	St.L	A	P	17	2-6
1914	KC	F	P	34	7-14
	BRTR			51	9-20

STONE, E. ARNOLD
b.Oct.9,1897 Hudson Falls,N.Y.
d.July 29,1948

Yr	Cl	Lea	Pos	G	Rec
1923	Pit	N	P	9	0-1
1924	Pit	N	P	26	4-2
	BRTL			35	4-3

STONE, GEORGE ROBERT
b.Sept.3,1876 Clinton,Ia.
d.Jan.5,1945

Yr	Cl	Lea	Pos	G	Rec
1903	Bos	A	H	2	.000
1905	St.L	A	O	154	.296

(Continued)

Yr	Cl	Lea	Pos	G	Rec
1906	St.L	A	O	154	.358
1907	St.L	A	O	155	.320
1908	St.L	A	O	148	.281
1909	St.L	A	O	83	.287
1910	St.L	A	O	152	.256
	BLTL			848	.301

STONE, JOHN VERNON (Rocky)
b.Aug.23,1918 Redding,Cal.

Yr	Cl	Lea	Pos	G	Rec
1943	Cin	N	P	13	0-1
	BRTR				

STONE, JONATHAN THOMAS (Rocky)
b.Oct.10,1905 Mulberry,Tenn.
d.Nov.30,1955

Yr	Cl	Lea	Pos	G	Rec
1928	Det	A	O	26	.354
1929	Det	A	O	51	.260
1930	Det	A	O	126	.313
1931	Det	A	O	147	.327
1932	Det	A	O	144	.297
1933	Det	A	O	148	.280
1934	Was	A	O	113	.315
1935	Was	A	O	125	.315
1936	Was	A	O	123	.341
1937	Was	A	O	139	.330
1938	Was	A	O	56	.244
	BLTR			1198	.310

STONE, WILLIAM ARTHUR (Tige)
b.Sept.18,1901 Macon,Ga.

Yr	Cl	Lea	Pos	G	Rec
1923	St.L	N	P-O	5	0-0 / 1.000
	BRTR				

STONEHAM, JOHN ANDREW
b.Nov.8,1908 Wood River,Ill.

Yr	Cl	Lea	Pos	G	Rec
1933	Chi	A	O	10	.120
	BLTR				

STONER, ULYSSES SIMPSON GRANT (Lil)
b.Feb.28,1899 Bowie,Tex.

Yr	Cl	Lea	Pos	G	Rec
1922	Det	A	P	17	4-4
1924	Det	A	P	37	11-11
1925	Det	A	P	34	10-9
1926	Det	A	P	32	7-10
1927	Det	A	P	38	10-13
1928	Det	A	P	36	5-8
1929	Det	A	P	24	3-3
1930	Pit	N	P	5	0-0
1931	Phi	N	P	7	0-0
	BRTR			230	50-58

STORIE, HOWARD EDWARD (Sponge)
b.May 15,1911 Pittsfield,Mass.

Yr	Cl	Lea	Pos	G	Rec
1931	Bos	A	C	6	.118
1932	Bos	A	C	6	.375
	BRTR			12	.200

STORKE, ALAN MARSHALL
b.Sept.27,1884 Auburn,N.Y.
d.Mar.18,1910

Yr	Cl	Lea	Pos	G	Rec
1906	Pit	N	S-3	5	.250
1907	Pit	N	1-3	102	.258
1908	Pit	N	1	56	.252
1909	Pit	N	1	32	.254
1909	St.L	N	S	48	.282
	TR			243	.260

STORTI, LINDO IVAN
b.Dec.5,1906 Santa Monica,Cal.

Yr	Cl	Lea	Pos	G	Rec
1930	St.L	A	2	7	.321
1931	St.L	A	3	86	.220
1932	St.L	A	3	53	.259
1933	St.L	A	2-3	70	.195
	BBTR			216	.227

STOUCH, THOMAS C.
b.Philadelphia,Pa.
d.Oct.7,1956

Yr	Cl	Lea	Pos	G	Rec
1898	Lou	N	2	4	.377

STOUT, ALLYN McCLELLAND (Fish Hook)
b.Oct.31,1904 Peoria,Ill.

Yr	Cl	Lea	Pos	G	Rec
1931	St.L	N	P	30	6-0
1932	St.L	N	P	36	4-5
1933	St.L	N	P	1	0-0
1933	Cin	N	P	23	2-3
1934	Cin	N	P	41	6-8
1935	NY	N	P	40	1-4
1943	Bos	N	P	9	1-0
	BRTR			180	20-20

STOVALL, GEORGE THOMAS (Firebrand)
b.Nov.23,1878 Independence,Mo.
d.Nov.5,1951

Yr	Cl	Lea	Pos	G	Rec
1904	Cle	A	1	51	.297
1905	Cle	A	1-2	111	.272
1906	Cle	A	1-2-3	116	.273
1907	Cle	A	1	124	.236
1908	Cle	A	1	138	.292
1909	Cle	A	1	145	.246
1910	Cle	A	1	142	.261
1911	Cle	A	M-1	126	.271
1912	St.L	A	M-1	115	.254
1913	St.L	A	M-1	89	.287
1914	KC	F	M-1	122	.270
1915	KC	F	M-1	130	.233
	BRTR			1409	.264

STOVALL, JESSE CRANMER (Scout)
b.July 24,1876 Independence,Mo.
d.July12,1955.

Yr	Cl	Lea	Pos	G	Rec
1903	Cle	A	P	6	5-1
1904	Det	A	P	23	2-13
	BLTR			29	7-14

STOVEY, HARRY DUFFIELD
(Real name Harry Duffield Stowe)
b.Dec.26,1856 Philadelphia,Pa.
d.Sept.20,1937

Yr	Cl	Lea	Pos	G	Rec
1880	Wor	N	P-1-O	81	0-0 / .258
1881	Wor	N	1-O	74	.270
1882	Wor	N	1-O	84	.288
1883	Ath	a	P-C-1-O	93	0-0 / .318
1884	Ath	a	1	106	.404
1885	Ath	a	1-O	112	.342
1886	Ath	a	1-O	123	.317
1887	Ath	a	1-O	124	.402
1888	Ath	a	O	130	.318
1889	Ath	a	O	138	.330
1890	Bos	p	O	118	.308
1891	Bos	N	O	133	.279
1892	Bos	N	O	38	.171
1892	Bal	N	O	74	.374
1893	Bal	N	O	8	.167
1893	Bro	N	O	45	.266
	BRTR			1481	0-0 / .320

STOVIAK, RAYMOND THOMAS
b.June 7,1915 Scottdale,Pa.

Yr	Cl	Lea	Pos	G	Rec
1938	Phi	N	O	10	.000
	BLTL				

STOWE, HAROLD RUDOLPH
b.Aug.29,1937 Gastonia,N.C.

Yr	Cl	Lea	Pos	G	Rec
1960	NY	A	P	1	0-0
	BLTL				

STOWE, HARRY DUFFIELD
(Played under name of Harry Duffield Stovey)

STRAHS, RICHARD BERNARD
b.Dec.4,1926 Evanston,Ill.

Yr	Cl	Lea	Pos	G	Rec
1954	Chi	A	P	9	0-0
	BRTR				

STRAND, PAUL EDWARD
b.Dec.19,1894 Carbonado,Wash.

Yr	Cl	Lea	Pos	G	Rec
1913	Bos	N	P	7	0-0
1914	Bos	N	P	18	6-2
1915	Bos	N	P	24	1-1
1924	Phi	A	O	47	.228
	BRTL			96	7-3 / .215

Yr Cl Lea Pos G Rec

STRANDS, JOHN LAWRENCE (Larry)
b.1889 Chicago,Ill.
1915 New F 2-3 34 .187
BRTR

STRANDS, LEWIS
1915 Chi F 2 1 .000

STRANG, SAMUEL NICKLIN
(Real name Samuel Strang Nicklin)
b.Dec.16,1876 Chattanooga,Tenn.
d.Mar.13,1932
1896 Lou N S 14 .222
1900 Chi N 3 25 .276
1901 NY N 2-3 135 .291
1902 Chi A 3 137 .273
1902 Chi N 2-3 3 .363
1903 Bro N 3 135 .272
1904 Bro N 2 76 .192
1905 NY N 2-O 96 .259
1906 NY N 2-O 104 .319
1907 NY N O 95 .252
1908 NY N 3 22 .094
BBTR 842 .266

STRANGE, ALAN COCHRANE (Inky)
b.Nov.7,1909 Philadelphia,Pa.
1934 St.L A S 127 .233
1935 St.L A S 49 .231
1935 Was A S 20 .185
1940 St.L A 2-S 54 .186
1941 St.L A 1-S-3 45 .232
1942 St.L A 2-S-3 19 .270
BRTR 314 .223

STRATTON, ASA EVANS
b.Feb.10,1853 Grafton,Mass.
d.Aug.14,1925
1881 Wor N S 1 .250

STRATTON, C. SCOTT
b.Oct.2,1869 Campbellsburg,Ky.
d.Mar.8,1939
1888 Lou a P-O 65 {10-17 .266}
1889 Lou a P-O 62 {3-14 .280}
1890 Lou a P 54 34-15
1891 Pit N P 3 0-2
1891 Lou a P 33 6-12
1892 Lou N P 60 21-20
1893 Lou N P-O 58 {12-24 .252}
1894 Lou N P-O 13 {1-3 .282}
1894 Chi N P 20 9-6
1895 Chi N P 8 2-3
TR 376 {98-116 .280}

STRATTON, EDWARD
b.Baltimore,Md.
1873 Mar n P-O 4 {0-3 NR}

STRATTON, MONTY FRANKLIN PIERCE
b.May 21,1912 Celeste,Tex.
1934 Chi A P 1 0-0
1935 Chi A P 5 1-2
1936 Chi A P 16 5-7
1937 Chi A P 22 15-5
1938 Chi A P 27 15-9
BRTR 71 36-23

STRAUB, JOSEPH
b.Jan.19,1858 Milwaukee,Wis.
1880 Tro N C 3 .231
1882 Ath a C-O 8 .188
1883 Col a C-1-O 27 .135
38 .152

Yr Cl Lea Pos G Rec

STRAUSS, JOSEPH
b.1844 Hungary
d.June 25,1906
1884 KC U C-2-3-O 15 .208
1885 Lou a C-O 2 .167
1886 Lou a O 77 .210
1886 Bro a C-O 9 .235
TR 103 .213

STREAKER, JOHN A.
(Played under name of John A. Stricker)

STREET, CHARLES EVARD (Gabby)
b.Sept.30,1882 Huntsville,Ala.
d.Feb.6,1951
1904 Cin N C 11 .121
1905 Cin N C 2 .000
1905 Bos N C 3 .167
1905 Cin N C 27 .247
1908 Was A C 131 .206
1909 Was A C 137 .211
1910 Was A C 89 .203
1911 Was A C 72 .222
1912 NY A C 28 .182
1931 St.L N M-C 1 .000
BRTR 501 .208
Non-playing manager St.L (N) 1930, 1932-33 and St.L (A) 1938.

STREIT, OSCAR W.
b.July 7,1873 Florence,Ala.
d.Oct.10,1935
1899 Bos N P 2 1-0
1902 Cle A P 8 0-7
10 1-7

STRELECKI, EDWARD HAROLD
b.Apr.10,1905 Newark,N.J.
1928 St.L A P 22 0-2
1929 St.L A P 7 1-1
1931 Cin N P 13 0-0
BRTR 42 1-3

STREMMEL, PHILIP
b.Apr.16,1880 Zanesville,O.
d.Dec.26,1947
1909 St.L A P 2 0-2
1910 St.L A P 5 0-3
7 0-5

STREULI, WALTER HERBERT
b.Sept.26,1935 Memphis,Tenn.
1954 Det A C 1 .000
1955 Det A C 2 .250
1956 Det A C 3 .250
BRTR 6 .250

STRICKER, JOHN A. (Cub)
(Real name John A. Streaker)
b.June 8,1859 Philadelphia,Pa.
1882 Ath a P-2-O 74 {1-0 .203}
1883 Ath a C-2-O 89 .254
1884 Ath a 2 109 .236
1885 Ath a 2 106 .211
1887 Cle a 2 131 .333
1888 Cle a 2 126 .231
1889 Cle N 2 136 .251
1890 Cle p 2 127 .248
1891 Bos a 2 139 .225
1892 St.L N 2-S 28 .206
1892 Bal N 2 72 .275
1893 Was N 2 59 .181
BRTR 1196 {1-0 .246}

STRICKLAND, GEORGE BEVAN (Bo)
b.Jan.10,1926 New Orleans,La.
1950 Pit N S-3 23 .111
1951 Pit N 2-S 138 .216
1952 Pit N 1-2-S-3 76 .177
1952 Cle A 2-S 31 .216
1953 Cle A 1-S 123 .284
1954 Cle A S 112 .213

Yr Cl Lea Pos G Rec

(Continued)
1955 Cle A S 130 .209
1956 Cle A 2-S-3 85 .211
1957 Cle A 2-S-3 89 .234
1959 Cle A 2-S-3 132 .238
1960 Cle A 2-S-3 32 .167
BRTR 971 .224

STRICKLAND, WILLIAM GOSS
b.Mar.29,1911 Nashville,Ga.
1937 St.L A P 9 0-0
BRTR

STRICKLETT, ELMER G. (Spitball)
b.Aug.29,1876 Glasco,Kan.
1904 Chi A P 1 0-1
1905 Bro N P 33 8-20
1906 Bro N P 41 14-18
1907 Bro N P 30 12-14
TR 105 34-53

STRIEF, GEORGE ANDREW
b.Oct.16,1856 Cincinnati,O.
d.Apr.1,1946
1879 Cle N 2-O 71 .174
1882 Pit a 2-S 73 .202
1883 St.L a 2-O 78 .211
1884 St.L a O 47 .193
1884 KC U 2 14 .094
1884 Pit U 2 15 .182
1884 Cle N 3-O 8 .241
1885 Ath a 2-S-3 44 .270
350 .197

STRIKE, JOHN
b.Philadelphia,Pa.
1882 Lou a C-1-2-S-O 33 .142
1886 Phi N P 2 1-1
35 {1-1 .134}

STRIKER, WILBUR SCOTT
b.Oct.23,1933 Cranberry Twp.,O.
1959 Cle A P 1 1-0
1960 Chi A P 2 0-0
BLTL 3 1-0

STRINCEVICH, NICHOLAS MIHAILOVICH
b.Mar.1,1916 Gary,Ind.
1940 Bos N P 33 4-8
1941 Bos N P 3 0-0
1941 Pit N P 12 1-2
1942 Pit N P 7 0-0
1944 Pit N P 40 14-7
1945 Pit N P 36 16-10
1946 Pit N P 32 10-15
1947 Pit N P 32 1-6
1948 Pit N P 3 0-0
1948 Phi N P 6 0-1
BRTR 204 46-49

STRINGER, LOUIS BERNARD
b.May 13,1917 Grand Rapids,Mich.
1941 Chi N 2 145 .246
1942 Chi N 2-3 121 .236
1946 Chi N 2-S-3 80 .244
1948 Bos A 2 4 .091
1949 Bos A 2 35 .268
1950 Bos A 2-S-3 24 .294
BRTR 409 .242

STRIPP, JOSEPH VALENTINE (Jersey Joe)
b.Feb.3,1903 Harrison,N.J.
1928 Cin N S-3-O 42 .288
1929 Cin N 2-3 64 .214
1930 Cin N 1-3 130 .306
1931 Cin N 1-3 105 .324
1932 Bro N 1-3 138 .303
1933 Bro N 3 141 .277
1934 Bro N 3 104 .315
1935 Bro N 1-3-O 109 .306

(Continued)

Yr	Cl	Lea	Pos	G	Rec
1936	Bro	N	3	110	.317
1937	Bro	N	1-3	90	.243
1938	St.L	N	3	54	.286
1938	Bos	N	3	59	.275
	BRTR			1146	.294

STROBEL, ALBERT IRVING
b.May 11,1884 S.Boston,Mass.
d.Feb.10,1955

Yr	Cl	Lea	Pos	G	Rec
1905	Bos	N	3-O	5	.105
1906	Bos	N	2	99	.202
	TR			104	.196

STROMME, FLOYD MARVIN (Rock)
b.Aug.1,1916 Cooperstown,N.Dak.

Yr	Cl	Lea	Pos	G	Rec
1939	Cle	A	P	5	0-1
	BRTR				

STRONER, JAMES M.
b.May 29,1904 Chicago,Ill.

Yr	Cl	Lea	Pos	G	Rec
1929	Pit	N	3	6	.375
	BRTR				

STROUD, RALPH E. (Sailor)
b.May 15,1885 Ironia,N.J.

Yr	Cl	Lea	Pos	G	Rec
1910	Det	A	P	28	5-9
1915	NY	N	P	32	12-9
1916	NY	N	P	10	3-2
	BRTR			70	20-20

STRUNK, AMOS AARON
b.Nov.22,1889 Philadelphia,Pa.

Yr	Cl	Lea	Pos	G	Rec
1908	Phi	A	O	12	.222
1909	Phi	A	O	11	.114
1910	Phi	A	O	16	.333
1911	Phi	A	O	74	.256
1912	Phi	A	O	120	.289
1913	Phi	A	O	93	.305
1914	Phi	A	O	122	.275
1915	Phi	A	O	132	.297
1916	Phi	A	O	150	.316
1917	Phi	A	O	148	.281
1918	Bos	A	O	114	.256
1919	Bos	A	O	48	.271
1919	Phi	A	O	60	.211
1920	Phi	A	O	57	.307
1920	Chi	A	O	52	.220
1921	Chi	A	O	121	.332
1922	Chi	A	O	92	.289
1923	Chi	A	O	54	.315
1924	Chi	A	O	1	.000
1924	Phi	A	O	30	.143
	BLTL			1507	.283

STRUSS, CLARENCE H. (Steamboat)
b.Feb.24,1912 Chicago,Ill.

Yr	Cl	Lea	Pos	G	Rec
1934	Pit	N	P	1	0-1
	BRTR				

STRYKER, STERLING ALBERT (Dutch)
b.July 29,1896 Atlantic Highlands,N.J.

Yr	Cl	Lea	Pos	G	Rec
1924	Bos	N	P	20	3-8
1926	Bro	N	P	2	0-0
	BRTR			22	3-8

STUART, JOHN DAVIS
b.Apr.27,1901 Clinton,Tenn.

Yr	Cl	Lea	Pos	G	Rec
1922	St.L	N	P	2	0-0
1923	St.L	N	P	37	9-5
1924	St.L	N	P-3	30	9-11 / .204
1925	St.L	N	P	15	2-2
	BRTR			84	20-18 / .228

STUART, LUTHER LANE (Luke)
b.May 23,1892 Alamance Co.,N.C.
d.June 15,1947

Yr	Cl	Lea	Pos	G	Rec
1921	St.L	A	2	3	.333
	BRTR				

STUART, MARLIN HENRY
b.Aug.8,1918 Paragould,Ark.

Yr	Cl	Lea	Pos	G	Rec
1949	Det	A	P	15	0-2
1950	Det	A	P	19	3-1
1951	Det	A	P	29	4-6
1952	Det	A	P	30	3-2
1952	St.L	A	P	12	1-2
1953	St.L	A	P	60	8-2
1954	Bal	A	P	22	1-2
1954	NY	A	P	10	3-0
	BLTR			197	23-17

STUART, RICHARD LEE
b.Nov.7,1932 San Francisco,Cal.

Yr	Cl	Lea	Pos	G	Rec
1958	Pit	N	1	67	.268
1959	Pit	N	1-O	118	.297
1960	Pit	N	1	122	.260
1961	Pit	N	1-O	138	.301
1962	Pit	N	1	114	.228
	BRTR			559	.273

STUART, WILLIAM ALEXANDER (Chauncey)
b.Donora,Pa.

Yr	Cl	Lea	Pos	G	Rec
1895	Pit	N	S	19	.259
1899	NY	N	2	1	.000
				20	.250

STUDLEY, SEYMOUR L. (Warhorse)
b.Washington,D.C.

Yr	Cl	Lea	Pos	G	Rec
1872	Nat	n	O	5	NR

STUELAND, GEORGE ANTON
b.Mar.2,1899 Renwick,Ia.

Yr	Cl	Lea	Pos	G	Rec
1921	Chi	N	P	2	0-1
1922	Chi	N	P	35	9-4
1923	Chi	N	P	6	0-1
1925	Chi	N	P	2	0-0
	BBTR			45	9-6

STUFFEL, PAUL HARRINGTON
b.Mar.22,1927 Canton,O.

Yr	Cl	Lea	Pos	G	Rec
1950	Phi	N	P	3	0-0
1952	Phi	N	P	2	1-0
1953	Phi	N	P	2	0-0
	BRTR			7	1-0

STULTZ, GEORGE IRVIN
b.June 30,1873 Louisville,Ky.

Yr	Cl	Lea	Pos	G	Rec
1894	Bos	N	P	1	1-0

STUMP, JAMES GILBERT
b.Feb.10,1932 Lansing,Mich.

Yr	Cl	Lea	Pos	G	Rec
1957	Det	A	P	6	1-0
1959	Det	A	P	5	0-0
	BRTR			11	1-0

STUMPF, GEORGE FREDERICK
b.Dec.15,1910 New Orleans,La.

Yr	Cl	Lea	Pos	G	Rec
1931	Bos	A	O	7	.250
1932	Bos	A	O	79	.201
1933	Bos	A	O	22	.341
1936	Chi	A	O	10	.273
	BLTL			118	.235

STUMPF, WILLIAM FREDERICK
b.Mar.21,1892 Baltimore,Md.

Yr	Cl	Lea	Pos	G	Rec
1912	NY	A	S	40	.240
1913	NY	A	S	12	.207
	BRTR			52	.236

STURDIVANT, THOMAS VIRGIL
b.Apr.28,1930 Gordon,Kan.

Yr	Cl	Lea	Pos	G	Rec
1955	NY	A	P	33	1-3
1956	NY	A	P	32	16-8
1957	NY	A	P	28	16-6
1958	NY	A	P	15	3-6
1959	NY	A	P	7	0-2
1959	KC	A	P	37	2-6
1960	Bos	A	P	40	3-3
1961	Was	A	P	15	2-6
1961	Pit	N	P	13	5-2

(Continued)

Yr	Cl	Lea	Pos	G	Rec
1962	Pit	N	P	49	9-5
	BLTR			269	57-47

STURDY, GUY A.
b.Aug.7,1899 Sherman,Tex.

Yr	Cl	Lea	Pos	G	Rec
1927	St.L	A	1	5	.429
1928	St.L	A	1	54	.222
	BLTL			59	.288

STURGEON, ROBERT HARWOOD
b.Aug.6,1920 Clinton,Ind.

Yr	Cl	Lea	Pos	G	Rec
1940	Chi	N	S	7	.190
1941	Chi	N	2-S-3	129	.245
1942	Chi	N	2-S-3	63	.247
1946	Chi	N	2-S	100	.296
1947	Chi	N	2-S-3	87	.254
1948	Bos	N	2-S-3	34	.218
	BRTR			420	.257

STURGIS, DEAN DONNELL
b.Dec.1,1893 Uniontown,Pa.
d.June 4,1950

Yr	Cl	Lea	Pos	G	Rec
1914	Phi	A	C	4	.250
	BRTR				

STURM, JOHN PETER JOSEPH
b.Jan.23,1916 St.Louis,Mo.

Yr	Cl	Lea	Pos	G	Rec
1941	NY	A	1	124	.239
	BLTL				

STUTZ, GEORGE (Satan)
b.Feb.12,1893 Philadelphia,Pa.
d.Dec.29,1930

Yr	Cl	Lea	Pos	G	Rec
1926	Phi	N	S	6	.000
	BLTR				

STYLES, WILLIAM GRAVES (Lena)
b.Nov.27,1897 Gurley,Ala.
d.Mar.14,1956

Yr	Cl	Lea	Pos	G	Rec
1919	Phi	A	C	8	.273
1920	Phi	A	C	24	.260
1921	Phi	A	C	4	.200
1930	Cin	N	C-1	7	.250
1931	Cin	N	C	34	.241
	BRTR			77	.249

STYNES, CORNELIUS W.
b.1869 Arlington,Mass.
d.Mar.26,1944

Yr	Cl	Lea	Pos	G	Rec
1890	Cle	p	C	2	.000

SUAREZ, LUIS ABELARDO
b.Aug.24,1916 Alto Songo,Cuba.

Yr	Cl	Lea	Pos	G	Rec
1944	Was	A	3	1	.000
	BRTR				

SUCHE, CHARLES MORRIS
b.Aug.5,1915 San Antonio,Tex.

Yr	Cl	Lea	Pos	G	Rec
1938	Cle	A	P	1	0-0
	BRTL				

SUCHECKI, JAMES JOSEPH
b.Aug.25,1926 Chicago,Ill.

Yr	Cl	Lea	Pos	G	Rec
1950	Bos	A	P	4	0-0
1951	St.L	A	P	29	0-6
1952	Pit	N	P	5	0-0
	BRTR			38	0-6

SUCK, ANTHONY
b.June 11,1858 Chicago,Ill.
d.Jan.29,1895

Yr	Cl	Lea	Pos	G	Rec
1883	Buf	N	C-O	2	.000
1884	Chi	U	C-S-3-O	43	.149
1884	Pit	U	C	10	.182
1884	Bal	U	C	3	.300
				58	.156

SUDER, PETER (Pecky)
b.Apr.16,1916 Aliquippa,Pa.

Yr	Cl	Lea	Pos	G	Rec
1941	Phi	A	S-3	139	.245
1942	Phi	A	2-S-3	128	.256
1943	Phi	A	2-S-3	131	.221
1946	Phi	A	1-2-S-3-O	128	.281
1947	Phi	A	2-S-3	145	.241
1948	Phi	A	2	148	.241
1949	Phi	A	2-S-3	118	.267
1950	Phi	A	1-2-S-3	77	.246
1951	Phi	A	2-S-3	123	.245
1952	Phi	A	2-S-3	74	.241
1953	Phi	A	2-S-3	115	.286
1954	Phi	A	2-S-3	69	.200
1955	KC	A	2	26	.210
	BRTR			1421	.249

SUDHOFF, JOHN WILLIAM (Wee Willie)
b.Sept.17,1874 St.Louis,Mo.
d.May 25,1917

Yr	Cl	Lea	Pos	G	Rec
1897	St.L	N	P	11	1-8
1898	St.L	N	P	38	11-26
1899	Cle	N	P	22	3-8
1899	St.L	N	P	22	12-10
1900	St.L	N	P	32	6-8
1901	St.L	N	P	33	17-11
1902	St.L	A	P-O	31	11-13 .171
1903	St.L	A	P	41	21-16
1904	St.L	A	P	29	7-14
1905	St.L	A	P	32	10-20
1906	Was	A	P	8	0-2
	TR			299	99-136 .180

SUGDEN, JOSEPH
b.July 31,1870 Philadelphia,Pa.
d.June 28,1959

Yr	Cl	Lea	Pos	G	Rec
1893	Pit	N	C	25	.273
1894	Pit	N	C	39	.333
1895	Pit	N	C	45	.310
1896	Pit	N	C	77	.298
1897	Pit	N	C	63	.219
1898	St.L	N	C	80	.259
1899	Cle	N	C	78	.281
1901	Chi	A	C	48	.283
1902	St.L	A	P-C-1-O	69	0-0 .231
1903	St.L	A	C	79	.214
1904	St.L	A	C-1	104	.262
1905	St.L	A	P-C	91	0-1 .173
1912	Det	A	1	1	.333
	BBTR			819	0-1 .255

SUGGS, GEORGE FRANKLIN
b.July 7,1883 Kinston,N.C.
d.Apr.4,1949

Yr	Cl	Lea	Pos	G	Rec
1908	Det	A	P	6	1-0
1909	Det	A	P	9	1-3
1910	Cin	N	P	35	20-12
1911	Cin	N	P	36	15-13
1912	Cin	N	P	42	19-16
1913	Cin	N	P	36	8-15
1914	Bal	F	P	43	24-14
1915	Bal	F	P	32	11-17
	BRTR			239	99-90

SUHR, AUGUST RICHARD
b.Jan.3,1907 San Francisco,Cal.

Yr	Cl	Lea	Pos	G	Rec
1930	Pit	N	1	151	.286
1931	Pit	N	1	87	.211
1932	Pit	N	1	154	.263
1933	Pit	N	1	154	.267
1934	Pit	N	1	151	.283
1935	Pit	N	1-O	153	.272
1936	Pit	N	1	156	.312
1937	Pit	N	1	151	.278
1938	Pit	N	1	145	.294
1939	Pit	N	1	63	.289
1939	Phi	N	1	60	.318
1940	Phi	N	1	10	.160
	BLTR			1435	.281

SUKEFORTH, CLYDE LEROY
b.Nov.30,1901 Washington,Me.

Yr	Cl	Lea	Pos	G	Rec
1926	Cin	N	H	1	.000
1927	Cin	N	C	38	.190
1928	Cin	N	C	33	.132
1929	Cin	N	C	84	.354
1930	Cin	N	C	94	.284
1931	Cin	N	C	112	.256
1932	Bro	N	C	59	.234
1933	Bro	N	C	20	.056
1934	Bro	N	C	27	.163
1945	Bro	N	C	18	.294
	BLTR			486	.264

Non-playing manager Bro (N) 1947.

SULIK, ERNEST RICHARD (Dave)
b.July 7,1910 San Francisco,Cal.

Yr	Cl	Lea	Pos	G	Rec
1936	Phi	N	O	122	.287
	BLTL				

SULLIVAN, ...

Yr	Cl	Lea	Pos	G	Rec
1875	NH	n	O	2	NR

SULLIVAN, ANDREW R.
b.Aug.30,1884 Southborough,Mass.
d.Feb.14,1920

Yr	Cl	Lea	Pos	G	Rec
1904	Bos	N	S	1	.000
	TR				

SULLIVAN, CARL MANCEL (Jack)
b.Feb.22,1918 McKinney,Tex.

Yr	Cl	Lea	Pos	G	Rec
1944	Det	A	2	1	.000
	BRTR				

SULLIVAN, CHARLES EDWARD
b.May 23,1905 Yadkin Valley,N.C.
d.May 28,1935

Yr	Cl	Lea	Pos	G	Rec
1928	Det	A	P	3	0-2
1930	Det	A	P	40	1-5
1931	Det	A	P	31	3-2
	BLTR			74	4-9

SULLIVAN, DANIEL C. (Link)
b.May 9,1857 Providence,R.I.
d.Oct.26,1893

Yr	Cl	Lea	Pos	G	Rec
1882	Lou	a	C-S-3-O	67	.284
1883	Lou	a	C-S-3-O	36	.225
1884	Lou	a	C	64	.245
1885	Lou	a	C	13	.156
1885	St.L	a	C	17	.138
1886	Pit	a	C	1	.000
	TR			198	.242

SULLIVAN, DENNIS J.
b.1854 S.Boston,Mass.

Yr	Cl	Lea	Pos	G	Rec
1879	Pro	N	3	5	.250
1880	Bos	N	C	1	.250
				6	.250

SULLIVAN, DENNIS WILLIAM
b.Vermillion,S.D.

Yr	Cl	Lea	Pos	G	Rec
1905	Was	A	O	3	.000
1907	Bos	A	O	144	.245
1908	Bos	A	O	100	.241
1908	Cle	A	O	4	.000
1909	Cle	A	O	3	.667
	BLTR			254	.239

SULLIVAN, EDWARD TROWBRIDGE
(Also played under real name of Edward Trowbridge Collins Sr.)

SULLIVAN, FLORENCE P.
b.1862 E.St.Louis,Ill.
d.Feb.15,1897

Yr	Cl	Lea	Pos	G	Rec
1884	Pit	a	P	54	16-35

SULLIVAN, FRANKLIN LEAL
b.Jan.23,1930 Hollywood,Cal.

Yr	Cl	Lea	Pos	G	Rec
1953	Bos	A	P	14	1-1
1954	Bos	A	P	36	15-12
1955	Bos	A	P	35	18-13
1956	Bos	A	P	34	14-7
1957	Bos	A	P	31	14-11
1958	Bos	A	P	32	13-9
1959	Bos	A	P	30	9-11
1960	Bos	A	P	40	6-16
1961	Phi	N	P	49	3-16
1962	Phi	N	P	19	0-2
1962	Min	A	P	21	4-1
	BRTR			341	97-99

SULLIVAN, HARRY ANDREW
b.Apr.12,1888 Rockford,Ill.
d.Sept.22,1919

Yr	Cl	Lea	Pos	G	Rec
1909	St.L	N	P	2	0-0
	BLTL				

SULLIVAN, HAYWOOD COOPER
b.Dec.15,1930 Donalsonville,Ga.

Yr	Cl	Lea	Pos	G	Rec
1955	Bos	A	C	2	.000
1957	Bos	A	C	2	.000
1959	Bos	A	C	4	.000
1960	Bos	A	C	52	.161
1961	KC	A	C-1-O	117	.242
1962	KC	A	C-1	95	.248
	BRTR			272	.241

SULLIVAN, JAMES E.
b.Apr.25,1869 Charlestown,Mass.
d.Dec.2,1901

Yr	Cl	Lea	Pos	G	Rec
1891	Bos	N	P	1	0-0
1891	Col	a	P	1	0-1
1895	Bos	N	P	26	11-9
1896	Bos	N	P	24	11-13
1897	Bos	N	P	13	4-4
				65	26-27

SULLIVAN, JAMES P.
d.May 22,1898
Non-playing manager Col (a) 1890.
1890.

SULLIVAN, JAMES RICHARD
b.Apr.5,1896 Mine Run,Va.

Yr	Cl	Lea	Pos	G	Rec
1921	Phi	A	P	2	0-2
1922	Phi	A	P	20	0-2
1923	Cle	A	P	3	0-1
	BRTR			25	0-5

SULLIVAN, JOHN EUGENE
b.Feb.16,1873 Illinois.
d.June 5,1924

Yr	Cl	Lea	Pos	G	Rec
1905	Det	A	C	13	.176
1908	Pit	N	C	1	.000
	TR			14	.171

SULLIVAN, JOHN FRANK (Chubb)
b.Jan.12,1859 Boston,Mass.
d.Sept.12,1881

Yr	Cl	Lea	Pos	G	Rec
1877	Cin	N	1	8	.250
1878	Cin	N	1	62	.255
1880	Wor	N	1	42	.267
	BRTR			112	.262

SULLIVAN, JOHN JEREMIAH
b.May 31,1896 Chicago,Ill.
d.July 7,1958

Yr	Cl	Lea	Pos	G	Rec
1919	Chi	A	P	4	0-1
	BLTL				

SULLIVAN, JOHN LAWRENCE
b.Mar.21,1893 Williamsport,Pa.

Yr	Cl	Lea	Pos	G	Rec
1920	Bos	N	O	81	.296
1921	Bos	N	O	5	.000
1921	Chi	N	O	76	.329
	BRTR			162	.309

SULLIVAN, JOHN PATRICK
b.Nov.2,1920 Chicago,Ill.

Yr	Cl	Lea	Pos	G	Rec
1942	Was	A	S	94	.235
1943	Was	A	S	134	.208
1944	Was	A	S	138	.251
1947	Was	A	2-S	49	.256
1948	Was	A	2-S	85	.208
1949	St.L	A	2-S-3	105	.226
			BRTR	605	.230

SULLIVAN, JOSEPH
b.Sept.26,1910 MasonCity,Ill.

Yr	Cl	Lea	Pos	G	Rec
1935	Det	A	P	25	6-6
1936	Det	A	P	26	2-5
1939	Bos	N	P	33	6-9
1940	Bos	N	P	36	10-14
1941	Bos	N	P	16	2-2
1941	Pit	N	P	16	4-1
			BLTL	152	30-37

SULLIVAN, JOSEPH DANIEL
b.Jan.6,1870 Charlestown,Mass.
d.Nov.2,1897

Yr	Cl	Lea	Pos	G	Rec
1893	Was	N	S	127	.271
1894	Was	N	2-S-3	17	.239
1894	Phi	N	S	76	.358
1895	Phi	N	3-O	91	.340
1896	Phi	N	O	38	.269
1896	St.L	N	O	60	.287
				409	.304

SULLIVAN, MARTIN J.
b.Oct.20,1862 Lowell,Mass.
d.Jan.5,1894

Yr	Cl	Lea	Pos	G	Rec
1887	Chi	N	O	115	.334
1888	Chi	N	O	75	.235
1889	Ind	N	O	69	.285
1890	Bos	N	O	121	.285
1891	Bos	N	O	17	.224
1891	Cle	N	O	1	.250
			BRTR	398	.288

SULLIVAN, MICHAEL J.
b.1866 Philadelphia,Pa.

Yr	Cl	Lea	Pos	G	Rec
1888	Ath	a	3-O	28	.277

SULLIVAN, MICHAEL J. (Big Mike)
b.Oct.23,1866 S.Boston,Mass.
d.June 14,1906

Yr	Cl	Lea	Pos	G	Rec
1889	Was	N	P	9	0-3
1890	Chi	N	P	12	5-6
1891	Ath	a	P	2	0-2
1891	NY	N	P	3	1-2
1892	Cin	N	P	18	12-6
1893	Cin	N	P	22	7-13
1894	Was	N	P	14	2-10
1894	Cle	N	P	12	6-4
1895	Cle	N	P	5	1-4
1896	NY	N	P	23	10-12
1897	NY	N	P	21	8-7
1898	Bos	N	P	3	0-2
1899	Bos	N	P	1	1-0
			BL	145	53-71

SULLIVAN, PATRICK
b.Dec.22,1862 Milwaukee,Wis.
d.Mar.29,1886

Yr	Cl	Lea	Pos	G	Rec
1884	KC	U	P-C-3-O	31	0-1 .193
			TR		

SULLIVAN, PAUL THOMAS (Lefty)
b.Sept.7,1916 Nashville,Tenn.

Yr	Cl	Lea	Pos	G	Rec
1939	Cle	A	P	7	0-1
			BLTL		

SULLIVAN, RUSSELL GUY H.
b.Feb.19,1923 Fredericksburg,Va.

Yr	Cl	Lea	Pos	G	Rec
1951	Det	A	O	7	.192
1952	Det	A	O	15	.327
1953	Det	A	O	23	.250
			BLTR	45	.267

SULLIVAN, SUTER G.
b.1872 Baltimore,Md.

Yr	Cl	Lea	Pos	G	Rec
1898	St.L	N	S	40	.225
1899	Cle	N	3-O	126	.250
				166	.245

SULLIVAN, THEODORE PAUL
b.1852 County Clare,Ireland.
d.July 5,1929

Yr	Cl	Lea	Pos	G	Rec
1884	KC	U	M-S-O	3	.333

Non-playing manager St.L (a) 1882-83, St.L (U) 1884 and Was (N) 1888.

SULLIVAN, THOMAS
b.Mar.1,1860 New York,N.Y.
d.Apr.12,1947

Yr	Cl	Lea	Pos	G	Rec
1884	Col	a	P	4	2-2
1886	Lou	a	P	9	2-7
1888	KC	a	P-O	28	8-16 .109
1889	KC	a	P	10	2-8
				51	14-33 .116

SULLIVAN, THOMAS A.
b.Oct.18,1897 Boston,Mass.

Yr	Cl	Lea	Pos	G	Rec
1922	Phi	N	P	3	0-0
			BLTL		

SULLIVAN, THOMAS BRANDON
b.Dec.19,1906 Nome,Alaska
d.Aug.16,1944

Yr	Cl	Lea	Pos	G	Rec
1925	Cin	N	C	1	.000
			BRTR		

SULLIVAN, THOMAS JEFFERSON (Sleeper)
b.St.Louis,Mo.
d.Sept.25,1899

Yr	Cl	Lea	Pos	G	Rec
1881	Buf	N	C-O	31	.190
1882	St.L	a	C	51	.182
1883	St.L	a	C-O	8	.148
1884	St.L	U	P-C	2	1-0 .167
			TR	92	1-0 .185

SULLIVAN, WILLIAM
b.July 4,1854 Ireland
d.Nov.13,1884

Yr	Cl	Lea	Pos	G	Rec
1878	Chi	N	O	2	.000

SULLIVAN, WILLIAM JOSEPH JR.
b.Oct.23,1910 Chicago,Ill.

Yr	Cl	Lea	Pos	G	Rec
1931	Chi	A	3	92	.275
1932	Chi	A	1-3	93	.316
1933	Chi	A	C-1	54	.192
1935	Cin	N	1-2-3	85	.266
1936	Cle	A	C	93	.351
1937	Cle	A	C	72	.286
1938	St.L	A	C	111	.277
1939	St.L	A	C-O	118	.289
1940	Det	A	C-3	78	.309
1941	Det	A	C	85	.282
1942	Bro	N	C	43	.267
1947	Pit	N	C	38	.255
			BLTR	962	.289

SULLIVAN, WILLIAM JOSEPH SR.
b.Feb.1,1875 Oakland,Wis.

Yr	Cl	Lea	Pos	G	Rec
1899	Bos	N	C	22	.284
1900	Bos	N	C	66	.267
1910	Chi	A	C	98	.245
1902	Chi	A	C-1-O	78	.151
1903	Chi	A	C	32	.188
1904	Chi	A	C	108	.235
1905	Chi	A	C	98	.201
1906	Chi	A	C	118	.214
1907	Chi	A	C	112	.179
1908	Chi	A	C	137	.191
1909	Chi	A	M-C	97	.162
1910	Chi	A	C	45	.183
1911	Chi	A	C	89	.215
1912	Chi	A	C	39	.209
1914	Chi	A	C	1	.000
1916	Det	A	C	1	.000
			BRTR	1141	.213

SULLIVAN, WILLIAM T.

Yr	Cl	Lea	Pos	G	Rec
1890	Syr	a	P	6	2-4

SUMMA, HOMER WAYNE
b.Nov.3,1899 Gentry,Mo.

Yr	Cl	Lea	Pos	G	Rec
1920	Pit	N	O	10	.318
1922	Cle	A	O	12	.348
1923	Cle	A	O	137	.328
1924	Cle	A	O	111	.290

(Continued)

Yr	Cl	Lea	Pos	G	Rec
1925	Cle	A	3-O	75	.330
1926	Cle	A	O	154	.308
1927	Cle	A	O	145	.286
1928	Cle	A	O	134	.284
1929	Phi	A	O	37	.272
1930	Phi	A	O	25	.278
			BLTR	840	.301

SUMMERS, OREN EDGAR (Kickapoo Ed)
b.Dec.5,1884 Ladoga,Ind.
d.May 12,1953

Yr	Cl	Lea	Pos	G	Rec
1908	Det	A	P	40	24-12
1909	Det	A	P	35	19-9
1910	Det	A	P	30	13-12
1911	Det	A	P	30	11-11
1912	Det	A	P	3	2-1
			BLTR	138	69-45

SUMMERSGILL, HENRY TRAVERS
(Played under name of Andrew Sommerville)

SUMNER, CARL RINEDAHL
b.Sept.28,1908 Cambridge,Mass.

Yr	Cl	Lea	Pos	G	Rec
1928	Bos	A	O	16	.276
			BLTL		

SUNDAY, ARTHUR
(Real name August Wacher)
b.Jan.21,1862 Springfield, O.

Yr	Cl	Lea	Pos	G	Rec
1890	Bro	p	O	24	.292

SUNDAY, WILLIAM ASHLEY (Parson)
b.Nov.19,1862 Ames,Ia.
d.Nov.6,1935

Yr	Cl	Lea	Pos	G	Rec
1883	Chi	N	O	15	.259
1884	Chi	N	O	43	.221
1885	Chi	N	O	42	.255
1886	Chi	N	O	25	.242
1887	Chi	N	O	48	.359
1888	Pit	N	O	119	.233
1889	Pit	N	O	80	.239
1890	Pit	N	O	85	.268
1890	Phi	N	O	31	.256
			BL	488	.258

SUNDIN, GORDON VINCENT
b.Oct.10,1937 Minneapolis,Minn.

Yr	Cl	Lea	Pos	G	Rec
1956	Bal	A	P	1	0-0
			BRTR		

SUNDRA, STEPHEN RICHARD (Smokey)
b.Mar.27,1910 Luxor,Pa.
d.Mar.23,1952

Yr	Cl	Lea	Pos	G	Rec
1936	NY	A	P	1	0-0
1938	NY	A	P	25	6-4
1939	NY	A	P	24	11-1
1940	NY	A	P	27	4-6
1941	Was	A	P	28	9-13
1942	Was	A	P	6	1-3
1942	St.L	A	P	20	8-3
1943	St.L	A	P	32	15-11
1944	St.L	A	P	3	2-0
1946	St.L	A	P	2	0-0
			BBTR	168	56-41

SUNKEL, THOMAS JACOB (Lefty)
b.Aug.9,1912 Paris,Ill.

Yr	Cl	Lea	Pos	G	Rec
1937	St.L	N	P	9	0-0
1939	St.L	N	P	20	4-4
1941	NY	N	P	2	1-1
1942	NY	N	P	19	3-6
1943	NY	N	P	1	0-1
1944	Bro	N	P	12	1-3
			BLTL	63	9-15

SURKONT, MAXIM CONSTANTINE
b.June 16,1922 Central Falls,R.I.

Yr	Cl	Lea	Pos	G	Rec
1949	Chi	A	P	44	3-5
1950	Bos	N	P	9	5-2
1951	Bos	N	P	37	12-16
1952	Bos	N	P	31	12-13
1953	Mil	N	P	28	11-5

(Continued)

Yr	Cl	Lea	Pos	G	Rec
1954	Pit	N	P	33	9-18
1955	Pit	N	P	35	7-14
1956	Pit	N	P	1	0-0
1956	St.L	N	P	5	0-0
1956	NY	N	P	8	2-2
1957	NY	N	P	5	0-1
	BRTR			236	61-76

SUSCE, GEORGE CYRIL METHODIUS (Good Kid)
b.Aug.13,1908 Pittsburgh, Pa.

Yr	Cl	Lea	Pos	G	Rec
1929	Phi	N	C	17	.294
1932	Det	A	C	2	.000
1939	Pit	N	C	31	.227
1940	St.L	A	C	61	.212
1941	Cle	A	C	1	.000
1942	Cle	A	C	2	1.000
1943	Cle	A	C	3	.000
1944	Cle	A	C	29	.230
	BRTR			146	.228

SUSCE, GEORGE DANIEL JR.
b.Sept.13,1931 Pittsburgh,Pa.

Yr	Cl	Lea	Pos	G	Rec
1955	Bos	A	P	29	9-7
1956	Bos	A	P	21	2-4
1957	Bos	A	P	29	7-3
1958	Bos	A	P	2	0-0
1958	Det	A	P	27	4-3
1959	Det	A	P	9	0-0
	BRTR			117	22-17

SUSKO, PETER JOHN
b.July 20,1904 Laura,O.

Yr	Cl	Lea	Pos	G	Rec
1934	Was	A	1	58	.286
	BLTL				

SUTCLIFFE, CHARLES I. (Butch)
b.July 22,1915 Fall River,Mass.

Yr	Cl	Lea	Pos	G	Rec
1938	Bos	N	C	4	.250
	BRTR				

SUTCLIFFE, EDWARD ELMER (Sy)
b.Apr.15,1863 Wheaton,Ill.
d.Feb.13,1893

Yr	Cl	Lea	Pos	G	Rec
1884	Chi	N	C	4	.200
1885	Chi	N	C-O	11	.195
1885	St.L	N	C-O	15	.140
1888	Det	N	S	49	.257
1889	Cle	N	C	65	.248
1890	Cle	p	C-O	99	.329
1891	Was	a	C-O	51	.365
1892	Bal	N	1	66	.275
	BL			360	.273

SUTHERLAND, HARVEY S. (Suds)
b.Feb.20,1896 Coburg,Ore.

Yr	Cl	Lea	Pos	G	Rec
1921	Det	A	P	17	6-2
	BRTR				

SUTHERLAND, HOWARD ALVIN (Dizzy)
b.Apr.9,1923 Washington,D.C.

Yr	Cl	Lea	Pos	G	Rec
1949	Was	A	P	1	0-1
	BLTL				

SUTOR, HARRY G. (Rube)
b.Portland,Ore.

Yr	Cl	Lea	Pos	G	Rec
1909	Chi	A	P	18	2-3
	TL				

SUTTHOFF, JOHN GERHARD (Sunny Jack)
b.June 29,1873 Cincinnati,O.
d.Aug.3,1942

Yr	Cl	Lea	Pos	G	Rec
1898	Was	N	P	2	0-2
1899	St.L	N	P	2	1-1
1901	Cin	N	P-O	11	1-6 .121
1903	Cin	N	P	30	16-11
1904	Cin	N	P	12	3-3
1904	Phi	N	P	19	4-13
1905	Phi	N	P	13	3-3
	BLTR			89	28-39 .149

SUTTON, EZRA BALLOU
b.Sept.17,1850 Seneca,N.Y.
d.June 20,1907

Yr	Cl	Lea	Pos	G	Rec
1871	Cle	n	3	29	NR
1872	Cle	n	3	21	NR
1873	Ath	n	2-S-3	50	NR
1874	Ath	n	S-3	55	NR
1875	Ath	n	1-3-O	75	.328
1876	Ath	N	1-2-3	54	.293
1877	Bos	N	S-3	58	.292
1878	Bos	N	3	60	.226
1879	Bos	N	S-3	84	.248
1880	Bos	N	S-3	74	.250
1881	Bos	N	S-3	83	.291
1882	Bos	N	S-3	80	.255
1883	Bos	N	S-3-O	94	.323
1884	Bos	N	3	106	.349
1885	Bos	N	1-S-3	108	.312
1886	Bos	N	2-S-3-O	116	.276
1887	Bos	N	S-O	74	.327
1888	Bos	N	3	28	.218
	BRTR			1249	NR

SWABACH, WILLIAM

Yr	Cl	Lea	Pos	G	Rec
1887	NY	N	P	2	0-1

SWACINA, HARRY J. (Swats)
b.1881 St.Louis,Mo.

Yr	Cl	Lea	Pos	G	Rec
1907	Pit	N	1	26	.200
1908	Pit	N	1	50	.216
1914	Bal	F	1	158	.276
1915	Bal	F	1	85	.247
	BRTR			319	.254

SWAIM, JOHN HILLARY (Cy)
b.Mar.11,1874 Cadwalader,O.
d.Nov.8,1918

Yr	Cl	Lea	Pos	G	Rec
1897	Was	N	P	24	5-12
1898	Was	N	P	15	3-11
				39	8-23

SWAN, ALBERT D.
b.May 11,1845 Tewksbury,Mass.
d.Aug.27,1885

Yr	Cl	Lea	Pos	G	Rec
1884	Was	a	1-3	5	.143
1884	Ric	a	1	3	.500
				8	.258

SWANDELL, JOHN MARTIN (Marty)
b.1845 New York

Yr	Cl	Lea	Pos	G	Rec
1872	Eck	n	1-2-3-O	12	NR
1873	Res	n	1	2	NR
				14	NR

SWANDER, EDWARD O. (Pinky)
b.July 4,1880 Portsmouth,O.
d.Oct.24,1944

Yr	Cl	Lea	Pos	G	Rec
1903	St.L	A	O	14	.250
1904	St.L	A	O	1	.000
				15	.245

SWANN, HENRY (Ducky)
b.1892

Yr	Cl	Lea	Pos	G	Rec
1914	KC	F	P	1	0-1
	BRTR				

SWANSON, ARTHUR LEONARD
b.Oct.15,1936 Baton Rouge,La.

Yr	Cl	Lea	Pos	G	Rec
1955	Pit	N	P	1	0-0
1956	Pit	N	P	10	0-0
1957	Pit	N	P	32	3-3
	BRTR			43	3-3

SWANSON, ERNEST EVAR
b.Oct.15,1902 DeKalb,Ill.

Yr	Cl	Lea	Pos	G	Rec
1929	Cin	N	O	148	.300
1930	Cin	N	O	95	.309
1932	Chi	A	O	14	.308
1933	Chi	A	O	144	.306
1934	Chi	A	O	117	.298
	BRTR			518	.303

SWANSON, KARL EDWARD
b.Dec.17,1903 Moline,Ill.

Yr	Cl	Lea	Pos	G	Rec
1928	Chi	A	2	22	.141
1929	Chi	A	H	2	.000
	BLTR			24	.138

SWANSON, WILLIAM ANDREW
b.Oct.4,1894 New York,N.Y.

Yr	Cl	Lea	Pos	G	Rec
1914	Bos	A	2	11	.211
	BBTR				

SWARTWOOD, CYRUS EDWARD
b.Jan.12,1859 Rockford,Ill.
d.May 10,1924

Yr	Cl	Lea	Pos	G	Rec
1881	Buf	N	O	1	.250
1882	Pit	a	1-O	71	.319
1883	Pit	a	C-1-O	95	.369
1884	Pit	a	1-O	102	.330
1885	Bro	a	O	100	.242
1886	Bro	a	O	123	.262
1887	Bro	a	O	91	.344
1890	Tol	a	O	126	.309
1892	Pit	N	O	12	.263
	TR			721	.309

SWARTZ, MONROE
b.Jan.1,1897 Farmersville,O.

Yr	Cl	Lea	Pos	G	Rec
1920	Cin	N	P	1	0-1
	BRTR				

SWARTZ, SHERWIN MERLE (Bud)
b.June 13,1929 Tulsa,Okla.

Yr	Cl	Lea	Pos	G	Rec
1947	St.L	A	P	5	0-0
	BLTL				

SWARTZEL, PARKE B.
b.Nov.21,1864 Knightstown,Ind.
d.Jan.3,1940

Yr	Cl	Lea	Pos	G	Rec
1889	KC	a	P	52	19-26
	BRTR				

SWASEY, CHARLES JAMES
(Played under name of Charles James Sweazy)

SWEAZY, CHARLES JAMES
(Real name Charles James Swasey)
b.Sept.3,1847 Haverhill,N.H.
d.Mar.30,1908

Yr	Cl	Lea	Pos	G	Rec
1871	Oly	n	2	4	NR
1872	Cle	n	2-O	12	NR
1873	Bos	n	2	1	NR
1874	Bal	n	2-O	8	NR
1874	Atl	n	2	10	NR
1875	RS	n	M-2	19	NR
1876	Cin	N	2-O	56	.203
1878	Pro	N	2	54	.178
	BRTR			164	NR

SWEENEY, ...

Yr	Cl	Lea	Pos	G	Rec
1914	Phi	A	O	1	.000

SWEENEY, CHARLES J.
b.Apr.13,1863 San Francisco,Cal.
d.Apr.4,1902

Yr	Cl	Lea	Pos	G	Rec
1882	Ath	a	P-O	24	8-11 .175
1882	Pro	N	O	1	.000
1883	Pro	N	P-1-O	21	11-9 .218
1884	Pro	N	P-1-O	40	17-7 .302
1884	St.L	U	P-1-O	46	24-8 .307
1885	St.L	N	P-O	73	12-20 .207
1886	St.L	N	P	17	5-6
1887	Cle	a	P-1	36	0-3 .329
				258	77-64 .259

SWEENEY, DANIEL J.
b.Jan.28,1868 Philadelphia,Pa.
d.July13,1913.

Yr	Cl	Lea	Pos	G	Rec
1895	Lou	N	O	21	.279

SWEENEY, EDWARD FRANCIS (Big Ed)
b.July 19,1888 Chicago,Ill.
d.July 4,1947

Yr	Cl	Lea	Pos	G	Rec
1908	NY	A	C	32	.146
1909	NY	A	C	67	.267
1910	NY	A	C	78	.200
1911	NY	A	C	83	.231
1912	NY	A	C	110	.268
1913	NY	A	C	117	.265
1914	NY	A	C	87	.213
1915	NY	A	C	53	.190
1919	Pit	N	C	17	.095
	BRTR			644	.232

SWEENEY, HENRY LEON
b.Dec.28,1917 Franklin,Tenn.

Yr	Cl	Lea	Pos	G	Rec
1944	Pit	N	1	1	.000
	BLTL				

SWEENEY, JEREMIAH H.
b.1860 Boston,Mass.
d.Aug.25,1891

Yr	Cl	Lea	Pos	G	Rec
1884	KC	U	1	30	.260

SWEENEY, JOHN J. (Rooney)
b.1860
d.Aug.10,1886

Yr	Cl	Lea	Pos	G	Rec
1883	Bal	a	C-2-O	25	.232
1884	Bal	U	C-O	43	.239
1885	St.L	N	C-O	3	.091
				71	.231

SWEENEY, PETER JAY
b.Dec.31,1863 California
d.Aug.22,1901

Yr	Cl	Lea	Pos	G	Rec
1888	Was	N	3	11	.181
1889	Was	N	3	49	.228
1889	St.L	a	3	9	.310
1890	St.L	a	3	49	.162
1890	Lou	a	2	2	.143
1890	Ath	a	2	14	.157
	BRTR			134	.202

SWEENEY, WILLIAM J.
b.1858 Philadelphia,Pa.
d.Aug.2,1903

Yr	Cl	Lea	Pos	G	Rec
1884	Bal	U	P	83	40-21

SWEENEY, WILLIAM JOHN
b.Mar.6,1886 Covington,Ky.
d.May 26,1948

Yr	Cl	Lea	Pos	G	Rec
1907	Chi	N	3	3	.100
1907	Bos	N	3	57	.262
1908	Bos	N	3	127	.244
1909	Bos	N	S-3	138	.243
1910	Bos	N	1-S-3	147	.267
1911	Bos	N	2	136	.314
1912	Bos	N	2	153	.344
1913	Bos	N	2	139	.257
1914	Chi	N	2	134	.218
	BRTR			1034	.272

SWEENEY, WILLIAM JOSEPH
b.Dec.29,1904 Cleveland,O.
d.Apr.18,1957

Yr	Cl	Lea	Pos	G	Rec
1928	Det	A	1	89	.252
1930	Bos	A	1	88	.309
1931	Bos	A	1	131	.295
	BRTR			308	.286

SWEETLAND, LESTER LEO
b.Aug.14,1902 St.Ignace,Mich.

Yr	Cl	Lea	Pos	G	Rec
1927	Phi	N	P	25	2-10
1928	Phi	N	P	41	3-15
1929	Phi	N	P	53	13-11
1930	Phi	N	P	35	7-15
1931	Chi	N	P	29	8-7
	BRTL			183	33-58

SWEIGERT,.....

Yr	Cl	Lea	Pos	G	Rec
1890	Ath	a	O	1	.000

SWENTOR, AUGUST WALTER
b.Dec.13,1902 Rockford,Ill.

Yr	Cl	Lea	Pos	G	Rec
1922	Chi	A	3	1	.000
	BRTR				

SWETONIC, STEPHEN ALBERT
b.Aug.13,1904 Mt.Pleasant,Pa.

Yr	Cl	Lea	Pos	G	Rec
1929	Pit	N	P	42	8-10
1930	Pit	N	P	23	6-6
1931	Pit	N	P	14	0-2
1932	Pit	N	P	24	11-6
1933	Pit	N	P	31	12-12
1935	Pit	N	P	1	0-0
	BRTR			135	37-36

SWETT, CHARLES A. (Pop)
b.Apr.15,1868 San Francisco,Cal.

Yr	Cl	Lea	Pos	G	Rec
1890	Bos	p	C	37	.193

SWIFT, ROBERT VIRGIL
b.Mar.6,1915 Salina,Kan.

Yr	Cl	Lea	Pos	G	Rec
1940	St.L	A	C	130	.244
1941	St.L	A	C	63	.259
1942	St.L	A	C	29	.197
1942	Phi	A	C	60	.229
1943	Phi	A	C	77	.192
1944	Det	A	C	80	.255
1945	Det	A	C	95	.233
1946	Det	A	C	42	.234
1947	Det	A	C	97	.251
1948	Det	A	C	113	.223
1949	Det	A	C	74	.238
1950	Det	A	C	67	.227
1951	Det	A	C	44	.192
1952	Det	A	C	28	.138
1953	Det	A	C	2	.333
	BRTR			1001	.231

SWIFT, WILLIAM
b.Jan.10,1908 Elmira,N.Y.

Yr	Cl	Lea	Pos	G	Rec
1932	Pit	N	P	39	14-10
1933	Pit	N	P	37	14-10
1934	Pit	N	P	37	11-13
1935	Pit	N	P	39	15-8
1936	Pit	N	P	45	16-16
1937	Pit	N	P	36	9-10
1938	Pit	N	P	36	7-5
1939	Pit	N	P	36	5-7
1940	Bos	N	P	4	1-1
1941	Bro	N	P	9	3-0
1943	Chi	A	P	18	0-2
	BRTR			336	95-82

SWIGART, OADIS VAUGHN
b.Feb.13,1916 Archie,Mo.

Yr	Cl	Lea	Pos	G	Rec
1939	Pit	N	P	3	1-1
1940	Pit	N	P	7	0-2
	BLTR			10	1-3

SWIGLER, ADAM WILLIAM
b.Sept.21,1895 Philadelphia,Pa.

Yr	Cl	Lea	Pos	G	Rec
1917	NY	N	P	1	0-1

SWINDELL, CHARLES JAY
b.Oct.26,1877 Rockford,Ill.
d.July 22,1940

Yr	Cl	Lea	Pos	G	Rec
1904	St.L	N	C	3	.125
	TR				

SWINDELL, JOEL ERNEST
b.July 5,1885 Rose Hill,Kan.

Yr	Cl	Lea	Pos	G	Rec
1911	Cle	A	P	4	0-1
1913	Cle	A	H	1	.000
	TR			5	0-1 .200

SWORMSTEDT, LEONARD JORDAN
b.Cincinnati,O.

Yr	Cl	Lea	Pos	G	Rec
1901	Cin	N	P	4	2-1
1902	Cin	N	P	2	0-1
1906	Bos	A	P	3	1-1
	BRTR			9	3-3

SYLVESTER, LOUIS J.
b.Feb.14,1855 Springfield,Ill.

Yr	Cl	Lea	Pos	G	Rec
1884	Cin	U	P-O	70	0-2 .264
1886	Lou	a	O	54	.227

(Continued)

Yr	Cl	Lea	Pos	G	Rec
1886	Cin	a	O	14	.156
1887	St.L	a	O	28	.298
	BRTR			166	0-2 .253

SZABO, ALEXANDER
(Played under name of Alexander Sabo)

SZEKELY, JOSEPH
b.Feb.2,1926 Cleveland,O.

Yr	Cl	Lea	Pos	G	Rec
1953	Cin	N	O	5	.077
	BRTR				

SZYMANSKI, ALOYSIUS HARRY
(Played under name of Aloysius Harry Simmons)

TABER, EDWARD TIMOTHY (Lefty)
b.Jan.11,1902 Rock Island,Ill.

Yr	Cl	Lea	Pos	G	Rec
1926	Phi	N	P	6	0-0
1927	Phi	N	P	3	0-1
	BLTL			9	0-1

TABER, JOHN PARDON
b.June 28,1868 Acushnet,Mass.
d.Feb.21,1940

Yr	Cl	Lea	Pos	G	Rec
1890	Bos	N	P	2	0-1

TABOR, JAMES REUBIN
b.Nov.5,1916 Owens Crossroads,Ala.
d.Aug.22,1953

Yr	Cl	Lea	Pos	G	Rec
1938	Bos	A	3	19	.316
1939	Bos	A	3	149	.289
1940	Bos	A	3	120	.285
1941	Bos	A	3	126	.279
1942	Bos	A	3	139	.252
1943	Bos	A	3-O	137	.242
1944	Bos	A	3	116	.285
1946	Phi	N	3	124	.268
1947	Phi	N	3	75	.235
	BRTR			1005	.270

TAFF, JOHN G.
b.1890

Yr	Cl	Lea	Pos	G	Rec
1913	Phi	A	P	5	0-1
	BRTR				

TAGGART, ROBERT JOHN
(Also played under name of James Kelly)
b.Feb.1,1890 Bloomfield,N.J.

Yr	Cl	Lea	Pos	G	Rec
(James Kelly)					
1914	Pit	N	O	32	.227
1915	Pit	F	O	148	.290
(Robert John Taggart)					
1918	Bos	N	O	35	.329
	BLTR			215	.294

TAITT, DOUGLAS JOHN (Poco)
b.Aug.3,1903 Bay City,Mich.

Yr	Cl	Lea	Pos	G	Rec
1928	Bos	A	P-O	143	0-0 .299
1929	Bos	A	O	26	.281
1929	Chi	A	O	47	.168
1931	Phi	N	O	38	.225
1932	Phi	N	H	4	.000
	BLTR			258	0-0 .263

TALBOT, ROBERT DALE
b.June 6,1927 Visalia,Cal.

Yr	Cl	Lea	Pos	G	Rec
1953	Chi	N	O	8	.333
1954	Chi	N	O	114	.241
	BRTR			122	.247

TALCOTT, LeROY EVERETT
b.Jan.16,1921 Boston,Mass.

Yr	Cl	Lea	Pos	G	Rec
1943	Bos	N	P	1	0-0
	BRTR				

TAMULIS, VITAUTAS CASIMIRUS (Vito)
b.July 11,1911 Cambridge,Mass.

Yr	Cl	Lea	Pos	G	Rec
1934	NY	A	P	1	1-0
1935	NY	A	P	30	10-5
1938	St.L	A	P	3	0-3
1938	Bro	N	P	39	12-6
1939	Bro	N	P	39	9-8
1940	Bro	N	P-1	42	8-5 .130
1941	Phi	N	P	6	0-1
1941	Bro	N	P	12	0-0
BLTL				172	40-28 .175

TANKERSLEY, LAWRENCE WILLIAM (Leo)
b.June 8,1901 Terrell,Tex.

Yr	Cl	Lea	Pos	G	Rec
1925	Chi	A	C	1	.000
BRTR					

TANNEHILL, JESSE NILES (Powder)
b.July 14,1874 Dayton,Ky.
d.Sept.22,1956

Yr	Cl	Lea	Pos	G	Rec
1894	Cin	N	P	5	1-1
1897	Pit	N	P-O	53	8-8 .266
1898	Pit	N	P	45	24-14
1899	Pit	N	P	40	23-14
1900	Pit	N	P	32	20-7
1901	Pit	N	P	40	18-10
1902	Pit	N	P-O	41	20-6 .289
1903	NY	A	P	39	15-15
1904	Bos	A	P	45	20-10
1905	Bos	A	P	37	23-10
1906	Bos	A	P	31	13-11
1907	Bos	A	P	21	6-7
1908	Bos	A	P	1	1-0
1908	Was	A	P	26	1-4
1909	Was	A	P	16	1-1
1911	Cin	N	P	1	0-0
BLTL				473	194-118 .261

TANNEHILL, LEE FORD
b.Oct.26,1880 Dayton,Ky.
d.Feb.16,1938

Yr	Cl	Lea	Pos	G	Rec
1903	Chi	A	S	136	.220
1904	Chi	A	3	153	.226
1905	Chi	A	3	142	.200
1906	Chi	A	S-3	112	.175
1907	Chi	A	3	33	.241
1908	Chi	A	3	141	.216
1909	Chi	A	S-3	155	.222
1910	Chi	A	1-S	67	.222
1911	Chi	A	2-S	141	.254
1912	Chi	A	3	2	.000
BRTR				1082	.219

TANNER, CHARLES WILLIAM
b.July 4,1929 New Castle,Pa.

Yr	Cl	Lea	Pos	G	Rec
1955	Mil	N	O	97	.247
1956	Mil	N	O	60	.238
1957	Mil	N	O	22	.246
1957	Chi	N	O	95	.286
1958	Chi	N	O	73	.262
1959	Cle	A	O	14	.150
1960	Cle	A	O	21	.280
1961	LA	A	O	7	.125
1962	LA	A	O	7	.125
BLTL				396	.261

TAPPE, ELVIN WALTER
b.May 21,1929 Quincy,Ill.

Yr	Cl	Lea	Pos	G	Rec
1954	Chi	N	C	46	.185
1955	Chi	N	C	2	.000
1956	Chi	N	C	3	.000
1958	Chi	N	C	17	.214
1960	Chi	N	C	51	.233
1962	Chi	N	M-C	26	.208
BRTR				145	.207

Non-playing manager Chi (N) 1961-62.

TAPPE, THEODORE NASH
b.Feb.2,1931 Seattle,Wash.

Yr	Cl	Lea	Pos	G	Rec
1950	Cin	N	H	7	.200
1951	Cin	N	H	4	.333
1955	Chi	N	O	23	.260
BLTR				34	.259

TARBERT, WILBUR ARLINGTON (Arlie)
b.Sept.10,1904 Cleveland,O.
d.Nov.27,1946

Yr	Cl	Lea	Pos	G	Rec
1927	Bos	A	O	33	.189
1928	Bos	A	O	6	.176
BRTR				39	.186

TARTABULL, JOSE
b.Nov.27,1939 Cienfuegos,Cuba

Yr	Cl	Lea	Pos	G	Rec
1962	KC	A	O	107	.277
BLTL					

TASBY, WILLIE
b.Jan.8,1933 Shreveport,La.

Yr	Cl	Lea	Pos	G	Rec
1958	Bal	A	O	18	.200
1959	Bal	A	O	142	.250
1960	Bal	A	O	39	.212
1960	Bos	A	O	105	.281
1961	Was	A	O	141	.251
1962	Was	A	O	11	.206
1962	Cle	A	3-O	75	.241
BRTR				531	.252

TATE, ALVIN WALTER
b.July 1,1919 Coleman,Okla.

Yr	Cl	Lea	Pos	G	Rec
1946	Pit	N	P	2	0-1
BRTR					

TATE, EDWARD CHRISTOPHER (Pop)
b.Dec.22,1861 Richmond,Va.
d.June 1932

Yr	Cl	Lea	Pos	G	Rec
1885	Bos	N	C	4	.167
1886	Bos	N	C	31	.226
1887	Bos	N	C	55	.271
1888	Bos	N	C	40	.229
1889	Bal	a	C	72	.178
1890	Bal	a	C	20	.219
BRTL				222	.225

TATE, HENRY BENNETT (Bennie)
b.Dec.3,1901 Whitwell,Tenn.

Yr	Cl	Lea	Pos	G	Rec
1924	Was	A	C	21	.302
1925	Was	A	C	16	.481
1926	Was	A	C	59	.267
1927	Was	A	C	61	.313
1928	Was	A	C	57	.246
1929	Was	A	C	81	.294
1930	Was	A	C	14	.231
1930	Chi	A	C	72	.326
1931	Chi	A	C	89	.267
1932	Chi	A	C	4	.100
1932	Bos	A	C	81	.245
1934	Chi	N	O	11	.125
BLTR				566	.279

TATE, HUGH HENRY
b.May 19,1880 Everett,Pa.
d.Aug.7,1956

Yr	Cl	Lea	Pos	G	Rec
1905	Was	A	O	4	.230
BRTR					

TATE, LEE WILLIE
b.Mar.18,1932 Black Rock,Ark.

Yr	Cl	Lea	Pos	G	Rec
1958	St.L	N	S	10	.200
1959	St.L	N	2-S-3	41	.140
BRTR				51	.165

TATUM, THOMAS VEE TEE
b.July 16,1919 Boyd,Tex.

Yr	Cl	Lea	Pos	G	Rec
1941	Bro	N	O	8	.167
1947	Bro	N	O	4	.000

(Continued)

Yr	Cl	Lea	Pos	G	Rec
1947	Cin	N	2-O	69	.273
BRTR				81	.258

TAUBENSEE, FRED JOSEPH
(Played under name of Fred Joseph Tauby)

TAUBY, FRED JOSEPH
(Real name Fred Joseph Taubensee)
b.Mar.27,1906 Canton,O.
d.Nov.23,1955

Yr	Cl	Lea	Pos	G	Rec
1935	Chi	A	O	13	.125
1937	Phi	N	O	11	.000
BRTR				24	.077

TAUSCHER, WALTER EDWARD
b.Nov.22,1903 La Salle,Ill.

Yr	Cl	Lea	Pos	G	Rec
1928	Pit	N	P	17	0-0
1931	Was	A	P	6	1-0
BRTR				23	1-0

TAUSSIG, DONALD FRANKLIN
b.Feb.19,1932 New York,N.Y.

Yr	Cl	Lea	Pos	G	Rec
1958	SF	N	O	39	.200
1961	St.L	N	O	98	.287
1962	Hou	N	O	16	.200
BRTR				153	.262

TAVENER, JOHN ADAM (Rabbit)
b.Dec.27,1898 Celina,O.

Yr	Cl	Lea	Pos	G	Rec
1921	Det	A	S	2	.000
1925	Det	A	S	134	.245
1926	Det	A	S	156	.265
1927	Det	A	S	116	.274
1928	Det	A	S	132	.260
1929	Cle	A	S	92	.212
BLTR				632	.255

TAYLOR, ANTONIO SANCHEZ
b.Dec.19,1935 Central Alava,Cuba

Yr	Cl	Lea	Pos	G	Rec
1958	Chi	N	2-3	140	.235
1959	Chi	N	2-S	150	.280
1960	Chi	N	2	19	.263
1960	Phi	N	2-3	127	.287
1961	Phi	N	2-3	106	.250
1962	Phi	N	2-S	152	.259
BRTR				694	.264

TAYLOR, ARLISS W.

Yr	Cl	Lea	Pos	G	Rec
1921	Phi	A	P	1	0-1

TAYLOR, BENJAMIN

Yr	Cl	Lea	Pos	G	Rec
1912	Cin	N	P	2	0-0
TR					

TAYLOR, C.L. (Chink)
b.Feb.9,1898 Burnet,Tex.

Yr	Cl	Lea	Pos	G	Rec
1925	Chi	N	O	8	.000
BRTR					

TAYLOR, DANIEL TURNEY
b.Dec.23,1901 Lash,Pa.

Yr	Cl	Lea	Pos	G	Rec
1926	Was	A	O	21	.300
1929	Chi	N	O	2	.000
1930	Chi	N	O	74	.283
1931	Chi	N	O	88	.300
1932	Chi	N	O	6	.227
1932	Bro	N	O	105	.324
1933	Bro	N	O	103	.285
1934	Bro	N	O	120	.299
1935	Bro	N	O	112	.290
1936	Bro	N	O	43	.293
BRTR				674	.297

TAYLOR, EDWARD

Yr	Cl	Lea	Pos	G	Rec
1903	St.L	N	P	1	0-0

TAYLOR, EDWARD JAMES
b.Nov.17,1902 Chicago,Ill.

Yr	Cl	Lea	Pos	G	Rec
1926	Bos	N	S-3	92	.268
BRTR					

TAYLOR, EUGENE BENJAMIN
b.Sept.30,1924 Metropolis,Ill.

Yr	Cl	Lea	Pos	G	Rec
1951	St.L	A	1	33	.258
1952	Det	A	1	7	.167
1955	Mil	N	1	12	.100
	BLTL			52	.231

TAYLOR, FREDERICK RANKIN
b.Dec.3,1926 Zanesville,O.

Yr	Cl	Lea	Pos	G	Rec
1950	Was	A	1	6	.125
1951	Was	A	1	6	.167
1952	Was	A	1	10	.263
	BLTR			22	.191

TAYLOR, GEORGE EDWARD
b.Feb.3,1855 Belfast,Me.
d.Feb.19,1888

Yr	Cl	Lea	Pos	G	Rec
1884	Pit	a	O	41	.202

TAYLOR, GEORGE J.
b.Nov.22,1853 New York
Non-playing manager Bro (a) 1884.

TAYLOR, HARRY EVANS
b.Dec.2,1935 San Angelo,Tex.

Yr	Cl	Lea	Pos	G	Rec
1957	KC	A	P	2	0-0
	BRTR				

TAYLOR, HARRY LEONARD
b.Apr.14,1866 Halsey Valley,N.Y.
d.July 12,1955

Yr	Cl	Lea	Pos	G	Rec
1890	Lou	a	1	134	.279
1891	Lou	a	1	91	.289
1892	Lou	N	1-O	123	.274
1893	Bal	N	1	88	.294
	BL			436	.283

TAYLOR, HARRY WARREN
b.Dec.26,1908 McKeesport,Pa.

Yr	Cl	Lea	Pos	G	Rec
1932	Chi	N	1	10	.125
	BLTL				

TAYLOR, JAMES HARRY
b.May 20,1919 E.Glenn,Ind.

Yr	Cl	Lea	Pos	G	Rec
1946	Bro	N	P	4	0-0
1947	Bro	N	P	33	10-5
1948	Bro	N	P	17	2-7
1950	Bos	A	P	3	2-0
1951	Bos	A	P	31	4-9
1952	Bos	A	P	2	1-0
	BRTR			90	19-21

TAYLOR, JAMES WREN (Zack)
b.July 27,1898 Yulee,Fla.

Yr	Cl	Lea	Pos	G	Rec
1920	Bro	N	C	5	.167
1921	Bro	N	C	30	.196
1922	Bro	N	C	7	.214
1923	Bro	N	C	96	.288
1924	Bro	N	C	99	.290
1925	Bro	N	C	109	.310
1926	Bos	N	C	125	.255
1927	Bos	N	C	30	.240
1927	NY	N	C	83	.233
1928	Bos	N	C	125	.251
1929	Bos	N	C	34	.248
1929	Chi	N	C	64	.274
1930	Chi	N	C	32	.232
1931	Chi	N	C	8	.250
1932	Chi	N	C	21	.200
1933	Chi	N	C	16	.000
1934	NY	A	C	4	.143
1935	Bro	N	C	26	.130
	BRTR			914	.261

Non-playing manager St.L (A) 1946 and 1948-51.

TAYLOR, JOE CEPHUS
b.Mar.2,1926 Chapman,Ala.

Yr	Cl	Lea	Pos	G	Rec
1954	Phi	A	O	18	.224
1957	Cin	N	O	33	.262
1958	St.L	N	O	18	.304
1958	Bal	A	O	36	.273
1959	Bal	A	O	14	.156
	BRTR			119	.249

TAYLOR, JOHN BUDD (Brewery)
b.May 27,1873 W.New Brighton,S.I., N.Y.
d.Feb.7,1900

Yr	Cl	Lea	Pos	G	Rec
1891	NY	N	P	1	0-1
1892	Phi	N	P	3	2-0
1893	Phi	N	P	19	8-8
1894	Phi	N	P	34	24-10
1895	Phi	N	P	40	26-13
1896	Phi	N	P	44	21-20
1897	Phi	N	P	37	18-18
1898	St.L	N	P	49	16-31
1899	Cin	N	P	24	8-10
				251	123-111

TAYLOR, JOHN W.
b.Sept.13,1873 Straightsville,O.
d.Mar.4,1938

Yr	Cl	Lea	Pos	G	Rec
1898	Chi	N	P	5	5-0
1899	Chi	N	P	42	18-22
1900	Chi	N	P	27	9-17
1901	Chi	N	P	33	13-19
1902	Chi	N	P-1-2-3-O	53	22-11 .239
1903	Chi	N	P	39	21-14
1904	St.L	N	P	41	22-19
1905	St.L	N	P	39	15-20
1906	St.L	N	P	17	8-9
1906	Chi	N	P	17	12-3
1907	Chi	N	P	18	7-5
	BRTR			331	152-139 .222

TAYLOR, LEO THOMAS
b.May 13,1903 Walla Walla,Wash.

Yr	Cl	Lea	Pos	G	Rec
1923	Chi	A	H	1	.000
	BRTR				

TAYLOR, LUTHER HADEN (Dummy)
b.Feb.21,1876 Olathe,Kan.
d.Aug.22,1958

Yr	Cl	Lea	Pos	G	Rec
1900	NY	N	P	11	4-3
1901	NY	N	P	45	18-27
1902	Cle	A	P	4	1-3
1902	NY	N	P	23	8-15
1903	NY	N	P	33	13-13
1904	NY	N	P	37	21-15
1905	NY	N	P	32	16-9
1906	NY	N	P	31	17-9
1907	NY	N	P	29	11-7
1908	NY	N	P	27	8-5
	BRTR			272	117-106

TAYLOR, ROBERT DALE
b.Apr.3,1939 Metropolis,Ill.

Yr	Cl	Lea	Pos	G	Rec
1957	Mil	N	C	7	.000
1958	Mil	N	O	4	.125
1961	Mil	N	C-O	20	.192
1962	Mil	N	O	20	.255
	BRTR			51	.220

TAYLOR, RONALD WESLEY
b.Dec.13,1937 Toronto,Ont.,Canada

Yr	Cl	Lea	Pos	G	Rec
1962	Cle	A	P	8	2-2
	BRTR				

TAYLOR, SAMUEL DOUGLAS
b.Feb.27,1933 Woodruff,S.C.

Yr	Cl	Lea	Pos	G	Rec
1958	Chi	N	C	96	.259
1959	Chi	N	C	110	.269
1960	Chi	N	C	74	.207
1961	Chi	N	C	89	.238
1962	Chi	N	C	7	.133
1962	NY	N	C	68	.222
	BLTR			444	.245

TAYLOR, THOMAS LIVINGSTONE CARLTON
b.Sept.17,1895 Mexia, Tex.
d.Apr.5,1956

Yr	Cl	Lea	Pos	G	Rec
1924	Was	A	3	26	.260
	BRTR				

TAYLOR, VERNON CHARLES (Pete)
b.Nov.26,1927 Severn,Md.

Yr	Cl	Lea	Pos	G	Rec
1952	St.L	A	P	1	0-0
	BRTR				

TAYLOR, WALLACE NAPOLEON
b.1872 Pittsburgh,Pa.
d.Sept.13,1905

Yr	Cl	Lea	Pos	G	Rec
1898	Lou	N	3	9	.200

TAYLOR, WILEY
b.Mar.18,1888 Wamego,Kan.
d.July 9,1954

Yr	Cl	Lea	Pos	G	Rec
1911	Det	A	P	3	0-2
1912	Chi	A	P	3	0-1
1913	St.L	A	P	5	0-2
1914	St.L	A	P	9	2-5
	BRTR			20	2-10

TAYLOR, WILLIAM HENRY (Bollicky Bill)
b.1855 Washington,D.C.
d.May 14,1900

Yr	Cl	Lea	Pos	G	Rec
1874	Bal	n	1	12	NR
1877	Har	N	O	2	.375
1879	Tro	N	O	24	.214
1881	Wor	N	P-O	6	0-1 .111
1881	Det	N	3	1	.500
1881	Cle	N	P-3-O	25	0-0 .222
1882	Pit	a	P-C-1-3-O	65	0-0 .286
1883	Pit	a	P-C-1-O	83	3-8 .259
1884	St.L	U	P-1-O	42	24-2 .371
1884	Ath	a	P	32	18-12
1885	Ath	a	P	6	1-5
1886	Bal	a	P-O	10	1-6 .333
1887	Ath	a	P	1	1-0
	TR			309	48-34 NR

TAYLOR, WILLIAM MICHAEL
b.Dec.30,1929 Alhambra,Cal.

Yr	Cl	Lea	Pos	G	Rec
1954	NY	N	O	55	.185
1955	NY	N	O	65	.266
1956	NY	N	O	1	.250
1957	NY	N	H	11	.000
1957	Det	A	O	9	.348
1958	Det	A	O	8	.375
	BLTR			149	.237

TEACHOUT, ARTHUR JOHN (Bud)
b.Feb.27,1904 Los Angeles,Cal.

Yr	Cl	Lea	Pos	G	Rec
1930	Chi	N	P	42	11-4
1931	Chi	N	P	37	1-2
1932	St.L	N	P	1	0-0
	BRTL			80	12-6

TEBBETTS, GEORGE ROBERT (Birdie)
b.Nov.10,1909 Burlington,Vt.

Yr	Cl	Lea	Pos	G	Rec
1936	Det	A	C	10	.303
1937	Det	A	C	50	.191
1938	Det	A	C	53	.294
1939	Det	A	C	106	.261
1940	Det	A	C	111	.296
1941	Det	A	C	110	.284
1942	Det	A	C	99	.247
1946	Det	A	C	87	.243
1947	Det	A	C	20	.094
1947	Bos	A	C	90	.299
1948	Bos	A	C	128	.280
1949	Bos	A	C	122	.270
1950	Bos	A	C	79	.310
1951	Cle	A	C	55	.263
1952	Cle	A	C	42	.248
	BRTR			1162	.270

Non-playing manager Cin (N) 1954-58, and Mil (N) 1961-62.

TEBEAU, GEORGE E. (White Wings)
b.Dec.26,1862 St.Louis,Mo.
d.Feb.4,1923

Yr	Cl	Lea	Pos	G	Rec
1887	Cin	a	P-O	88	0-0 .361
1888	Cin	a	O	121	.228
1889	Cin	a	1-O	135	.255
1890	Tol	a	O	96	.261

(Continued)

Yr	Cl	Lea	Pos	G	Rec
1894	Was	N	O	60	.226
1894	Cle	N	O	45	.316
1895	Cle	N	1-O	87	.323
BRTR				632	0-0 / .284

TEBEAU, OLIVER WENDELL
(Pat)
b.Dec.5,1864 St.Louis,Mo.
d.May 15,1918

Yr	Cl	Lea	Pos	G	Rec
1887	Chi	N	3	20	.208
1889	Cle	N	3	136	.282
1890	Cle	P	M-3	108	.292
1891	Cle	N	M-3	61	.261
1892	Cle	N	M-3	84	.246
1893	Cle	N	M-1-3	115	.359
1894	Cle	N	M-1	110	.305
1895	Cle	N	M-1	66	.329
1896	Cle	N	M-1	132	.271
1897	Cle	N	M-1-2	111	.267
1898	Cle	N	M-1-2	130	.254
1899	St.L	N	M-1	76	.253
1900	St.L	N	M-1	1	.000
BRTR				1150	.284

TEDROW, ALLEN SEYMOUR
b.Dec.14,1891 Westerville,O.
d.Jan.23,1958

Yr	Cl	Lea	Pos	G	Rec
1914	Cle	A	P	4	1-2
BRTL					

TEED, RICHARD LEROY
b.Mar.8,1926 Springfield,Mass.

Yr	Cl	Lea	Pos	G	Rec
1953	Bro	N	H	1	.000
BRTR					

TEMPLE, JOHN ELLIS
b.Aug.8,1929 Lexington,N.C.

Yr	Cl	Lea	Pos	G	Rec
1952	Cin	N	2	30	.196
1953	Cin	N	2	63	.264
1954	Cin	N	2	146	.307
1955	Cin	N	2-S	150	.281
1956	Cin	N	2-O	154	.285
1957	Cin	N	2	145	.284
1958	Cin	N	1-2	141	.306
1959	Cin	N	2	149	.311
1960	Cle	A	2-3	98	.268
1961	Cle	A	2	129	.276
1962	Bal	A	2	78	.263
1962	Hou	N	2-3	31	.263
BRTR				1314	.286

TEMPLETON, CHARLES SHERMAN
b.June 1,1932 Detroit,Mich.

Yr	Cl	Lea	Pos	G	Rec
1955	Bro	N	P	4	0-1
1956	Bro	N	P	6	0-1
BRTL				10	0-2

TENER, JOHN KINLEY
b.July 25,1863 Tyrone Co.,Ireland.
d.May 19,1946

Yr	Cl	Lea	Pos	G	Rec
1885	Bal	a	O	1	.000
1888	Chi	N	P	14	7-5
1889	Chi	N	P	38	14-15
1890	Pit	p	P	19	3-13
BRTR				72	24-33 / .235

TENNANT, JAMES McDONNELL
b.Mar.3,1907 Shepherdstown,W.Va.

Yr	Cl	Lea	Pos	G	Rec
1929	NY	N	P	1	0-0
BRTR					

TENNANT, THOMAS FRANCIS
b.July 3,1882 Monroe,Wis.
d.Feb.16,1955

Yr	Cl	Lea	Pos	G	Rec
1912	St.L	A	H	2	.000
BLTL					

TENNEY, FREDERICK
b.Nov.26,1871 Georgetown,Mass.
d.July 3,1952

Yr	Cl	Lea	Pos	G	Rec
1894	Bos	N	C	24	.387
1895	Bos	N	C-O	42	.276
1896	Bos	N	C-O	86	.342
1897	Bos	N	1	131	.325
1898	Bos	N	1	117	.335

(Continued)

Yr	Cl	Lea	Pos	G	Rec
1899	Bos	N	1	150	.350
1900	Bos	N	1	111	.284
1901	Bos	N	1	113	.278
1902	Bos	N	1	134	.314
1903	Bos	N	1	122	.313
1904	Bos	N	1	147	.270
1905	Bos	N	M-1	148	.288
1906	Bos	N	M-1	143	.283
1907	Bos	N	M-1	149	.273
1908	NY	N	1	156	.256
1909	NY	N	1	98	.235
1911	Bos	N	M-1	98	.263
BLTL				1969	.295

TENNEY, FREDERICK CLAY
b.June 9,1859 Marlboro,N.H.

Yr	Cl	Lea	Pos	G	Rec
1884	Was	U	1-O	30	.236
1884	Bos	U	P	5	4-1
1884	Wil	U	P	1	0-1
				36	4-2 / .217

TEPSIC, JOSEPH JOHN
b.Sept.18,1923 Solvan,Pa.

Yr	Cl	Lea	Pos	G	Rec
1946	Bro	N	O	15	.000
BRTR					

TERRELL, THOMAS
b.Louisville,Ky.
d.July,1893

Yr	Cl	Lea	Pos	G	Rec
1886	Lou	a	C	1	.250

TERRY, ...

Yr	Cl	Lea	Pos	G	Rec
1875	Nat	n	1-O	5	NR

TERRY, JOHN
b.St.Louis,Mo.

Yr	Cl	Lea	Pos	G	Rec
1902	Det	A	P	1	0-1
1903	St.L	A	P	3	1-0
				4	1-1

TERRY, LANCELOT YANK
b.Feb.11,1911 Bedford,Ind.

Yr	Cl	Lea	Pos	G	Rec
1940	Bos	A	P	4	1-0
1942	Bos	A	P	20	6-5
1943	Bos	A	P	30	7-9
1944	Bos	A	P	27	6-10
1945	Bos	A	P	12	0-4
BRTR				93	20-28

TERRY, WILLIAM HAROLD
(Memphis Bill)
b.Oct.30,1898 Atlanta,Ga.

Yr	Cl	Lea	Pos	G	Rec
1923	NY	N	1	3	.143
1924	NY	N	1	77	.239
1925	NY	N	1	133	.319
1926	NY	N	1-O	98	.289
1927	NY	N	1	150	.326
1928	NY	N	1	149	.326
1929	NY	N	1	150	.372
1930	NY	N	1	154	.401
1931	NY	N	1	153	.349
1932	NY	N	M-1	154	.350
1933	NY	N	M-1	123	.322
1934	NY	N	M-1	153	.354
1935	NY	N	M-1	145	.341
1936	NY	N	M-1	79	.310
BLTL				1721	.341

Non-playing manager N.Y. (N) 1937-41.

TERRY, RALPH WILLARD
b.Jan.9,1936 Big Cabin,Okla.

Yr	Cl	Lea	Pos	G	Rec
1956	NY	A	P	3	1-2
1957	NY	A	P	7	1-1
1957	KC	A	P	22	4-11
1958	KC	A	P	40	11-13
1959	KC	A	P	9	2-4
1959	NY	A	P	24	3-7
1960	NY	A	P	35	10-8
1961	NY	A	P	31	16-3
1962	NY	A	P	43	23-12
BRTR				214	71-16

TERRY, WILLIAM J.
(Adonis)
b.Aug.7,1864 Westfield,Mass.
d.Feb.24,1915

Yr	Cl	Lea	Pos	G	Rec
1884	Bro	a	P-O	67	19-35 / .235
1885	Bro	a	P-O	70	6-16 / .162
1886	Bro	a	P-O	75	18-15 / .250
1887	Bro	a	P-O	86	17-16 / .335
1888	Bro	a	P	30	13-8
1889	Bro	a	P	48	21-16
1890	Bro	N	P-O	99	26-15 / .278
1891	Bro	N	P	25	6-15
1892	Bal	N	P	6	1-1
1892	Pit	N	P	27	20-7
1893	Pit	N	P	21	12-7
1894	Pit	N	P	6	0-1
1894	Chi	N	P	24	4-12
1895	Chi	N	P	39	21-14
1896	Chi	N	P	29	14-15
1897	Chi	N	P	1	0-0
BRTR				653	198-193 / .271

TERRY, ZEBULON ALEXANDER
b.June 17,1891 Denison,Tex.

Yr	Cl	Lea	Pos	G	Rec
1916	Chi	A	S	94	.190
1917	Chi	A	S	2	.100
1918	Bos	N	S	28	.305
1919	Pit	N	S	129	.227
1920	Chi	N	2-S	133	.280
1921	Chi	N	2	123	.275
1922	Chi	N	2-S-3	131	.286
BRTR				640	.260

TERWILLIGER, RICHARD MARTIN
b.June 27,1906 Sand Lake,Mich.

Yr	Cl	Lea	Pos	G	Rec
1932	St.L	N	P	1	0-0
BRTR					

TERWILLIGER, WILLARD WAYNE
(Twig)
b.June 27,1925 Clare,Mich.

Yr	Cl	Lea	Pos	G	Rec
1949	Chi	N	2	36	.223
1950	Chi	N	1-2-3-O	133	.242
1951	Chi	N	2	50	.214
1951	Bro	N	2-3	37	.280
1953	Was	A	2	134	.252
1954	Was	A	2-S-3	106	.208
1955	NY	N	2-S-3	80	.257
1956	NY	N	2	14	.222
1959	KC	A	2-S-3	74	.267
1960	KC	A	2	2	.000
BRTR				666	.240

TESCH, ALBERT JOHN
b.Jan.27,1891 Jersey City,N.J.
d.Aug.3,1947

Yr	Cl	Lea	Pos	G	Rec
1915	Bro	F	2	7	.286
TR					

TESREAU, CHARLES MONROE
(Jeff)
b.Mar.5,1889 Ironton,Mo.
d.Sept.24,1946

Yr	Cl	Lea	Pos	G	Rec
1912	NY	N	P	36	17-7
1913	NY	N	P	41	22-13
1914	NY	N	P	42	26-10
1915	NY	N	P	43	19-16
1916	NY	N	P	41	14-14
1917	NY	N	P	33	13-8
1918	NY	N	P	12	4-4
BRTR				248	115-72

TESTA, NICHOLAS
b.June 29,1928 New York,N.Y.

Yr	Cl	Lea	Pos	G	Rec
1958	SF	N	C	1	.000
BRTR					

TETTELBACH, RICHARD MORLEY
b.June 26,1929 New Haven,Conn.

Yr	Cl	Lea	Pos	G	Rec
1955	NY	A	O	2	.000
1956	Was	A	O	18	.156
1957	Was	A	O	9	.182
		BRTR		29	.150

TEXTOR, GEORGE B.
b.Dec.27,1889 Newport,Ky.
d.Mar.11,1954

Yr	Cl	Lea	Pos	G	Rec
1914	Ind	F	C	20	.179
1915	New	F	C	3	.333
		BRTR		23	.194

THACKER, MORRIS BENTON
b.May 21,1934 Louisville,Ky.

Yr	Cl	Lea	Pos	G	Rec
1958	Chi	N	C	11	.250
1960	Chi	N	C	54	.156
1961	Chi	N	C	25	.171
1962	Chi	N	C	65	.187
		BRTR		155	.180

THAKE, ALBERT
b.1847 New York,N.Y.
d.Sept.1,1872

Yr	Cl	Lea	Pos	G	Rec
1872	Atl	n	2-O	18	NR

THATCHER, ULYSSES GRANT
b.Feb.23,1877 Maytown,Pa.
d.Mar.17,1936

Yr	Cl	Lea	Pos	G	Rec
1903	Bro	N	P	4	3-1
1904	Bro	N	P	1	1-0
		TR		5	4-1

THAYER, EDWARD L.
b.Mechanic Falls,Me.

Yr	Cl	Lea	Pos	G	Rec
1876	Mut	N	2	1	.000

THEIS, JOHN LOUIS
b.July 23,1891 Georgetown,O.
d.July 6,1941

Yr	Cl	Lea	Pos	G	Rec
1920	Cin	N	P	1	0-0

THESENGA, ARNOLD JOSEPH (Jug)
b.Apr.27,1914 Jefferson,S.Dak.

Yr	Cl	Lea	Pos	G	Rec
1944	Was	A	P	5	0-0
		BRTR			

THEVENOW, THOMAS JOSEPH
b.Sept.6,1903 Madison,Ind.
d.July 28,1957

Yr	Cl	Lea	Pos	G	Rec
1924	St.L	N	S	23	.202
1925	St.L	N	S	50	.269
1926	St.L	N	S	156	.256
1927	St.L	N	S	59	.194
1928	St.L	N	S	69	.205
1929	Phi	N	S	90	.227
1930	Phi	N	S	156	.286
1931	Pit	N	S	120	.213
1932	Pit	N	S-3	59	.237
1933	Pit	N	2-S-3	73	.312
1934	Pit	N	2-3	122	.271
1935	Pit	N	2-S-3	110	.238
1936	Cin	N	2-S-3	106	.234
1937	Bos	N	S	21	.118
1938	Pit	N	2-S-3	15	.200
		BRTR		1229	.248

THIEL, MAYNARD BERT
b.May 4,1926 Marion,Wis.

Yr	Cl	Lea	Pos	G	Rec
1952	Bos	N	P	4	1-1
		BRTR			

THIELMAN, HENRY JOSEPH
b.Oct.30,1880 St.Cloud,Minn.
d.Sept.2,1942

Yr	Cl	Lea	Pos	G	Rec
1902	NY	N	P-O	6	0-1 .111
1902	Cin	N	P	29	9-15
1903	Bro	N	P	8	0-3
		BRTR		43	9-19 .121

THIELMAN, JOHN PETER (Jake)
b.Mar.20,1879 St.Cloud,Minn.
d.Jan.28,1928

Yr	Cl	Lea	Pos	G	Rec
1905	St.L	N	P	33	15-16
1906	St.L	N	P	3	0-3
1907	Cle	A	P	21	11-8
1908	Cle	A	P	11	3-3
1908	Bos	A	P	1	1-0
				69	30-30

THIES, VERNON ARTHUR
b.Apr.1,1928 St.Louis,Mo.

Yr	Cl	Lea	Pos	G	Rec
1954	Pit	N	P	33	3-9
1955	Pit	N	P	1	0-1
		BRTR		34	3-10

THOENY, JOHN
(Played under name of John Thoney)

THOMAS, ALPHONSE THOMAS (Tommy)
b.Dec.23,1899 Baltimore,Md.

Yr	Cl	Lea	Pos	G	Rec
1926	Chi	A	P	44	15-12
1927	Chi	A	P	40	19-16
1928	Chi	A	P	36	17-16
1929	Chi	A	P	37	14-18
1930	Chi	A	P	34	5-13
1931	Chi	A	P	43	10-14
1932	Chi	A	P	12	3-3
1932	Was	A	P	18	8-7
1933	Was	A	P	35	7-7
1934	Was	A	P	33	8-9
1935	Was	A	P	1	0-0
1935	Phi	N	P	4	0-1
1936	St.L	A	P	36	11-9
1937	St.L	A	P	17	0-1
1937	Bos	A	P	9	0-2
		BRTR		399	117-128

THOMAS, BLAINE M.
b.1888 Payson,Ariz.
d.Aug.21,1915

Yr	Cl	Lea	Pos	G	Rec
1911	Bos	A	P	2	0-0
		BRTR			

THOMAS, CARL LESLIE
b.May 28,1932 Minneapolis,Minn.

Yr	Cl	Lea	Pos	G	Rec
1960	Cle	A	P	5	1-0
		BRTR			

THOMAS, CHESTER D. (Pinch)
b.Jan.24,1888 Camp Point,Ill.
d.Dec.24,1953

Yr	Cl	Lea	Pos	G	Rec
1912	Bos	A	C	13	.194
1913	Bos	A	C	37	.286
1914	Bos	A	C	63	.192
1915	Bos	A	C	86	.236
1916	Bos	A	C	99	.264
1917	Bos	A	C	83	.238
1918	Cle	A	C	32	.247
1919	Cle	A	C	34	.109
1920	Cle	A	C	7	.333
1921	Cle	A	C	21	.257
		BLTR		475	.237

THOMAS, CLARENCE FRANKLIN (Lefty)
b.Oct.4,1903 Abingdon,Va.
d.Mar.21,1952

Yr	Cl	Lea	Pos	G	Rec
1925	Was	A	P	2	0-2
1926	Was	A	P	6	0-0
		BRTL		8	0-2

THOMAS, CLAUDE ALFRED
b.May 15,1890 Stanberry,Mo.
d.Mar.6,1946

Yr	Cl	Lea	Pos	G	Rec
1916	Was	A	P	7	0-3
		BLTl			

THOMAS, FAY WESLEY (Scow)
b.Oct.10,1904 Wichita,Kan.

Yr	Cl	Lea	Pos	G	Rec
1927	NY	N	P	9	0-0
1931	Cle	A	P	16	2-4
1932	Bro	N	P	7	0-1
1935	St.L	A	P	49	7-15
		BRTR		81	9-20

THOMAS, FORREST (Frosty)
b.May 23,1883 Buchanan Co.,Mo.

Yr	Cl	Lea	Pos	G	Rec
1905	Det	A	P	2	0-2
		BRTR			

THOMAS, FRANK JOSEPH
b.June 11,1929 Pittsburgh,Pa.

Yr	Cl	Lea	Pos	G	Rec
1951	Pit	N	O	39	.264
1952	Pit	N	O	6	.095
1953	Pit	N	O	128	.255
1954	Pit	N	O	153	.298
1955	Pit	N	O	142	.245
1956	Pit	N	2-3-O	157	.282
1957	Pit	N	1-3-O	151	.290
1958	Pit	N	1-3-O	149	.281
1959	Cin	N	1-3-O	108	.225
1960	Chi	N	1-3-O	135	.238
1961	Chi	N	1-O	15	.260
1961	Mil	N	1-O	124	.284
1962	NY	N	1-3-O	156	.266
		BRTR		1463	.268

THOMAS, FREDERICK HARVEY
b.Dec.19,1892 Milwaukee,Wis.

Yr	Cl	Lea	Pos	G	Rec
1918	Bos	A	3	44	.257
1919	Phi	A	3	124	.212
1920	Phi	A	3	77	.233
1920	Was	A	3	2	.000
		BRTR		247	.225

THOMAS, FREDERICK L.
b.Indiana
Non-playing manager Ind (N) 1887.

THOMAS, GEORGE EDWARD
b.Nov.29,1937 Minneapolis,Minn.

Yr	Cl	Lea	Pos	G	Rec
1957	Det	A	3	1	.000
1958	Det	A	O	1	.000
1961	Det	A	S-O	17	.000
1961	LA	A	3-O	79	.280
1962	LA	A	O	56	.238
		BRTR		154	.260

THOMAS, HERBERT MARK
b.May 26,1902 Sampson City,Fla.

Yr	Cl	Lea	Pos	G	Rec
1924	Bos	N	O	32	.220
1925	Bos	N	2	5	.235
1927	Bos	N	2	24	.230
1927	NY	N	O	13	.176
		BRTR		74	.221

THOMAS, IRA FELIX
b.Jan.22,1881 Ballston Spa,N.Y.
d.Oct.11,1958

Yr	Cl	Lea	Pos	G	Rec
1906	NY	A	C	44	.200
1907	NY	A	C	80	.192
1908	Det	A	C	40	.307
1909	Phi	A	C	84	.223
1910	Phi	A	C	60	.277
1911	Phi	A	C	103	.273
1912	Phi	A	C	46	.216
1913	Phi	A	C	21	.283
1914	Phi	A	C	2	.000
1915	Phi	A	C	1	.000
		BRTR		481	.242

THOMAS, JAMES LEROY
b.Feb.5,1936 St.Louis,Mo.

Yr	Cl	Lea	Pos	G	Rec
1961	NY	A	H	2	.500
1961	LA	A	1-O	130	.284
1962	LA	A	1-O	160	.290
		BLTR		292	.288

THOMAS, JOHN TILLMAN
b.Mar.10,1929 Sedalia,Mo.

Yr	Cl	Lea	Pos	G	Rec
1951	St.L	A	S	14	.350
		BRTR			

THOMAS, KEITH MARSHALL
(Kite)
b.Apr.27,1924 Kansas City,Kan.

Yr	Cl	Lea	Pos	G	Rec
1952	Phi	A	O	75	.250
1953	Phi	A	O	24	.122
1953	Was	A	C-O	38	.293
		BRTR		137	.233

THOMAS, LEO RAYMOND
b.July 26,1924 Turlock,Cal.

Yr	Cl	Lea	Pos	G	Rec
1950	St.L	A	3	35	.198
1952	St.L	A	2-S-3	41	.234
1952	Chi	A	3	19	.167
		BRTR		95	.212

THOMAS, LUTHER BAXTER (Bud)
b.Sept.6,1910 N.Garden,Va.

Yr	Cl	Lea	Pos	G	Rec
1932	Was	A	P	2	0-0
1933	Was	A	P	2	0-0
1937	Phi	A	P	35	8-15
1938	Phi	A	P	42	9-14
1939	Phi	A	P	2	0-1
1939	Was	A	P	4	0-0
1939	Det	A	P	27	7-0
1940	Det	A	P	3	0-1
1941	Det	A	P	26	1-3
		BRTR		143	25-34

THOMAS, MYLES LEWIS
b.Oct.22,1899 State College,Pa.

Yr	Cl	Lea	Pos	G	Rec
1926	NY	A	P	33	6-6
1927	NY	A	P	21	7-4
1928	NY	A	P	13	1-0
1929	NY	A	P	5	0-2
1929	Was	A	P	22	7-8
1930	Was	A	P	14	2-2
		BRTR		108	23-22

THOMAS, RAYMOND JOSEPH
b.July 8,1912 Dover,N.H.

Yr	Cl	Lea	Pos	G	Rec
1938	Bro	N	C	1	.333
		BRTR			

THOMAS, ROBERT WILLIAM
(Red)
b.Apr.25,1899 Hargrove,Ala.
d.Mar.29,1962

Yr	Cl	Lea	Pos	G	Rec
1921	Chi	N	O	8	.267
		BRTR			

THOMAS, ROY ALLEN
b.Mar.24,1874 Norristown,Pa.
d.Nov.20,1959

Yr	Cl	Lea	Pos	G	Rec
1899	Phi	N	O	148	.324
1900	Phi	N	P-O	139	0-0 / .325
1901	Phi	N	O	128	.305
1902	Phi	N	O	138	.292
1903	Phi	N	O	130	.327
1904	Phi	N	O	139	.290
1905	Phi	N	O	147	.317
1906	Phi	N	O	142	.254
1907	Phi	N	O	121	.243
1908	Phi	N	O	6	.167
1908	Pit	N	O	101	.256
1909	Bos	N	O	77	.263
1910	Phi	N	O	20	.183
1911	Phi	N	O	21	.133
		BLTL		1457	0-0 / .291

THOMAS, THOMAS W.
b.Dec.27,1873 Shawnee,O.
d.Sept.22,1942

Yr	Cl	Lea	Pos	G	Rec
1899	St.L	N	P	4	1-1
1900	St.L	N	P	5	1-0
				9	2-1

THOMAS, VALMY
b.Oct.21,1929 Christiansted,St.Croix, V.I.

Yr	Cl	Lea	Pos	G	Rec
1957	NY	N	C	88	.249
1958	SF	N	C	63	.259

(Continued)

Yr	Cl	Lea	Pos	G	Rec
1959	Phi	N	C-3	66	.200
1960	Bal	A	C	8	.063
1961	Cle	A	C	27	.209
		BRTR		252	.230

THOMAS, WALTER W.

Yr	Cl	Lea	Pos	G	Rec
1908	Bos	N	S	5	.154
		TR			

THOMAS, WILLIAM MISKEY
b.Dec.8,1877 Norristown,Pa.
d.Jan.14,1950

Yr	Cl	Lea	Pos	G	Rec
1902	Phi	N	1-2-O	6	.176
		TR			

THOMASEN, ARTHUR WILSON
b.Sept.9,1884 Liberty,Mo.
d.May 2,1944

Yr	Cl	Lea	Pos	G	Rec
1910	Cle	A	O	17	.158

THOMPSON, A. M.
b.St.Paul,Minn.

Yr	Cl	Lea	Pos	G	Rec
1875	Nat	n	C-O	10	NR
1875	Atl	n	O	1	NR
				11	NR

Non-playing manager St. P (U) 1884.

THOMPSON, ARTHUR J.

Yr	Cl	Lea	Pos	G	Rec
1884	Was	U	P	1	0-1

THOMPSON, CHARLES LEMOINE
b.Mar.1,1926 Coalport,Pa.

Yr	Cl	Lea	Pos	G	Rec
1954	Bro	N	C	10	.154
1956	KC	A	C	92	.272
1957	KC	A	C	81	.204
1958	Det	A	C	4	.167
		BLTR		187	.238

THOMPSON, DAVID FORREST
b.Mar.3,1918 Mooresville,N.C.

Yr	Cl	Lea	Pos	G	Rec
1948	Was	A	P	46	6-10
1949	Was	A	P	10	1-3
		BLTL		56	7-13

THOMPSON, DONALD NEWLIN
b.Dec.28,1923 Swepsonville,N.C.

Yr	Cl	Lea	Pos	G	Rec
1949	Bos	N	O	7	.182
1951	Bro	N	O	80	.229
1953	Bro	N	O	96	.242
1954	Bro	N	O	34	.040
		BLTL		217	.218

THOMPSON, EUGENE EARL
(Junior)
b.June 7,1917 Latham,Ill.

Yr	Cl	Lea	Pos	G	Rec
1939	Cin	N	P	42	13-5
1940	Cin	N	P	33	16-9
1941	Cin	N	P	27	6-6
1942	Cin	N	P	29	4-7
1946	NY	N	P	39	4-6
1947	NY	N	P	15	4-2
		BRTR		185	47-35

THOMPSON, FRANK E.
b.July 4,1893 Springfield,Mo.
d.June 27,1940

Yr	Cl	Lea	Pos	G	Rec
1920	St.L	A	3	22	.170
		BRTR			

THOMPSON, FULLER WEIDNER
b.May 1,1889 Los Angeles,Cal.

Yr	Cl	Lea	Pos	G	Rec
1911	Bos	N	P	3	0-0
		BRTR			

THOMPSON, HARRY
b.Mar.25,1893 Nanticoke,Pa.
d.Feb.14,1951

Yr	Cl	Lea	Pos	G	Rec
1919	Was	A	P	18	0-3
1919	Phi	A	P	5	0-1
		BLTL		23	0-4

THOMPSON, HENRY CURTIS
b.Dec.8,1925 Oklahoma City,Okla.

Yr	Cl	Lea	Pos	G	Rec
1947	St.L	A	2	27	.256
1949	NY	N	2-3	75	.280
1950	NY	N	3-O	148	.289
1951	NY	N	3	87	.235
1952	NY	N	2-3-O	128	.260
1953	NY	N	2-3-O	114	.302
1954	NY	N	2-3-O	136	.263
1955	NY	N	2-S-3	135	.245
1956	NY	N	S-3-O	83	.235
		BLTR		933	.267

THOMPSON, HOMER
b.June 1,1892 Spring City,Tenn.

Yr	Cl	Lea	Pos	G	Rec
1912	NY	A	C	1	.000
		BRTR			

THOMPSON, JAMES ALFRED
(Shag)
b.Apr.29,1893 Haw River,N.C.

Yr	Cl	Lea	Pos	G	Rec
1914	Phi	A	O	16	.172
1915	Phi	A	O	17	.333
1916	Phi	A	O	15	.000
		BLTR		48	.203

THOMPSON, JOHN DUDLEY (Lee)
b.Feb.26,1898 Smithfield,Utah

Yr	Cl	Lea	Pos	G	Rec
1921	Chi	A	P	4	0-3
		BLTL			

THOMPSON, JOHN GUS
b.June 22,1877 Humboldt,Ia.
d.Mar.28,1958

Yr	Cl	Lea	Pos	G	Rec
1903	Pit	N	P	5	2-2
1906	St.L	N	P	17	2-11
				22	4-13

THOMPSON, JOHN P. F. (Tug)
b.Indianapolis,Ind.

Yr	Cl	Lea	Pos	G	Rec
1882	Cin	a	O	1	.200
1884	Ind	a	C-O	24	.204
				25	.204

THOMPSON, JOHN SAMUEL
(Jocko)
b.Jan.17,1920 Beverly,Mass.

Yr	Cl	Lea	Pos	G	Rec
1948	Phi	N	P	2	1-0
1949	Phi	N	P	9	1-3
1950	Phi	N	P	2	0-0
1951	Phi	N	P	30	4-8
		BLTL		43	6-11

THOMPSON, LAFAYETTE FRESCO
b.June 6,1903 Centerville,Ala.

Yr	Cl	Lea	Pos	G	Rec
1925	Pit	N	2	14	.243
1926	NY	N	2	2	.625
1927	Phi	N	2	153	.303
1928	Phi	N	2	152	.287
1929	Phi	N	2	148	.324
1930	Phi	N	2	122	.282
1931	Bro	N	2-S	74	.265
1932	Bro	N	H	3	.000
1934	NY	N	H	1	.000
		BRTR		669	.298

THOMPSON, RUPERT LUCKHART
(Tommy)
b.May 19,1910 Lincoln,Ill.

Yr	Cl	Lea	Pos	G	Rec
1933	Bos	N	O	24	.186
1934	Bos	N	O	105	.265
1935	Bos	N	O	112	.273
1936	Bos	N	1-O	106	.286
1938	Chi	A	1	19	.111
1939	Chi	A	O	1	.000
1939	St.L	A	O	30	.302
		BLTR		397	.266

THOMPSON, SAMUEL L. (Big Sam)
b.Mar.5,1860 Danville,Ind.
d.Nov.7,1922

Yr	Cl	Lea	Pos	G	Rec
1885	Det	N	O	63	.303
1886	Det	N	O	122	.310
1887	Det	N	O	127	.406
1888	Det	N	O	55	.281
1889	Phi	N	O	128	.296
1890	Phi	N	O	132	.313
1891	Phi	N	O	133	.295
1892	Phi	N	O	151	.303
1893	Phi	N	O	130	.377
1894	Phi	N	O	102	.403
1895	Phi	N	O	118	.394
1896	Phi	N	O	119	.305
1897	Phi	N	O	3	.250
1898	Phi	N	O	14	.365
1906	Det	A	O	8	.225
			BL	1405	.336

THOMPSON, THOMAS CARL
b.Nov.7,1889 Spring City,Tenn.
d.Jan.16,1963

Yr	Cl	Lea	Pos	G	Rec
1912	NY	A	P	8	0-2
			BRTR		

THOMPSON, WILL McLAIN
b.Aug.30,1870 Pittsburgh,Pa.

Yr	Cl	Lea	Pos	G	Rec
1892	Pit	N	P	1	0-1

THOMSON, ROBERT BROWN
b.Oct.25,1923 Glasgow,Scotland.

Yr	Cl	Lea	Pos	G	Rec
1946	NY	N	3	18	.315
1947	NY	N	2-O	138	.283
1948	NY	N	O	138	.248
1949	NY	N	O	156	.309
1950	NY	N	O	149	.252
1951	NY	N	3-O	148	.294
1952	NY	N	3-O	153	.270
1953	NY	N	O	154	.288
1954	Mil	N	O	43	.232
1955	Mil	N	O	101	.257
1956	Mil	N	3-O	142	.235
1957	Mil	N	O	41	.236
1957	NY	N	3-O	81	.242
1958	Chi	N	3-O	152	.283
1959	Chi	N	O	122	.259
1960	Bos	A	1-O	40	.263
1960	Bal	A	O	3	.000
			BRTR	1779	.270

THONEY, JOHN (Bullet John)
(Real name John Thoeny)
b.Dec.8,1880 Ft.Thomas,Ky.
d.Oct.24,1948

Yr	Cl	Lea	Pos	G	Rec
1902	Cle	A	2-S-O	28	.291
1902	Bal	A	3	3	.000
1903	Cle	A	O	32	.213
1904	Was	A	O	17	.300
1904	NY	A	3-O	35	.231
1908	Bos	A	O	109	.255
1909	Bos	A	O	14	.184
1911	Bos	A	O	26	.250
			BRTR	264	.235

THORMAHLEN, HERBERT EHLER
(Lefty)
b.July 5,1896 Jersey City,N.J.
d.Feb.6,1955

Yr	Cl	Lea	Pos	G	Rec
1917	NY	A	P	1	0-1
1918	NY	A	P	16	7-3
1919	NY	A	P	30	13-9
1920	NY	A	P	29	9-6
1921	Bos	A	P	23	1-7
1925	Bro	N	P	5	0-3
			BLTL	104	30-29

THORNTON, JOHN
b.1870 Washington,D.C.
d.1893

Yr	Cl	Lea	Pos	G	Rec
1889	Was	N	P	1	0-1
1891	Phi	N	P	30	15-11
1892	Phi	N	P-O	5	0-1 .385
1892	St.L	N	O	1	.000
				37	15-12 .157

THORNTON, WALTER MILLER
b.Feb.28,1875 Peoria,Ill.
d.July 14,1960

Yr	Cl	Lea	Pos	G	Rec
1895	Chi	N	P	9	3-2
1896	Chi	N	P	9	2-1
1897	Chi	N	P-O	71	6-9 .329
1898	Chi	N	P-O	56	12-9 .283
				145	23-21 .313

THORPE, BENJAMIN ROBERT
b.Nov.19,1926 Caryville,Fla.

Yr	Cl	Lea	Pos	G	Rec
1951	Bos	N	H	2	.500
1952	Bos	N	O	81	.260
1953	Mil	N	O	27	.162
			BRTR	110	.251

THORPE, JAMES FRANCIS
b.May 28,1886 Prague,Okla.
d.Mar.28,1953

Yr	Cl	Lea	Pos	G	Rec
1913	NY	N	O	19	.143
1914	NY	N	O	30	.194
1915	NY	N	O	17	.231
1917	Cin	N	O	77	.247
1917	NY	N	O	26	.200
1918	NY	N	O	58	.248
1919	NY	N	O	2	.333
1919	Bos	N	1-O	60	.327
			BBTR	289	.252

THORPE, ROBERT JOSEPH
b.Jan.12,1935 San Diego,Cal.
d.Mar.17,1960

Yr	Cl	Lea	Pos	G	Rec
1955	Chi	N	P	2	0-0
			BRTR		

THRASHER, FRANK EDWARD
(Buck)
b.Aug.9,1889 Watkinsville,Ga.
d.June 12,1938

Yr	Cl	Lea	Pos	G	Rec
1916	Phi	A	O	7	.310
1917	Phi	A	O	23	.234
			BLTR	30	.255

THRONEBERRY, MARVIN EUGENE
b.Sept.2,1933 Shelby Co.,Tenn.

Yr	Cl	Lea	Pos	G	Rec
1955	NY	A	1	1	1.000
1958	NY	A	1-O	60	.227
1959	NY	A	1-O	80	.240
1960	KC	A	1	104	.250
1961	KC	A	1-O	40	.238
1961	Bal	A	1-O	56	.208
1962	Bal	A	O	9	.000
1962	NY	N	1	116	.244
			BLTL	466	.238

THRONEBERRY, MAYNARD FAYE
b.June 22,1931 Memphis,Tenn.

Yr	Cl	Lea	Pos	G	Rec
1952	Bos	A	O	98	.258
1955	Bos	A	O	60	.257
1956	Bos	A	O	24	.220
1957	Bos	A	H	1	.000
1957	Was	A	O	68	.185
1958	Was	A	O	44	.184
1959	Was	A	O	117	.251
1960	Was	A	O	85	.248
1961	LA	A	O	24	.194
			BLTR	521	.236

THUMAN, LOUIS CHARLES FRANK
b.Dec.13,1916 Baltimore,Md.

Yr	Cl	Lea	Pos	G	Rec
1939	Was	A	P	3	0-0
1940	Was	A	P	2	0-1
			BRTR	5	0-1

THURMAN, ROBERT BURNS
b.May 14,1923 Wichita,Kan.

Yr	Cl	Lea	Pos	G	Rec
1955	Cin	N	O	82	.217
1956	Cin	N	O	80	.295
1957	Cin	N	O	74	.247
1958	Cin	N	O	94	.230
1959	Cin	N	H	4	.250
			BLTL	334	.246

THURSTON, HOLLIS JOHN
(Sloppy)
b.June 2,1899 Fremont,Neb.

Yr	Cl	Lea	Pos	G	Rec
1923	St.L	A	P	2	0-0
1923	Chi	A	P	45	7-8
1924	Chi	A	P	51	20-14
1925	Chi	A	P	44	10-14
1926	Chi	A	P	38	6-8
1927	Was	A	P	42	13-13
1930	Bro	N	P	36	6-4
1931	Bro	N	P	24	9-9
1932	Bro	N	P	29	12-8
1933	Bro	N	P	32	6-8
			BRTR	343	89-86

TIEFENAUER, BOBBY GENE
b.Oct.10,1929 Desloge,Mo.

Yr	Cl	Lea	Pos	G	Rec
1952	St.L	N	P	6	0-0
1955	St.L	N	P	18	1-4
1960	Cle	A	P	6	0-1
1961	St.L	N	P	3	0-0
1962	Hou	N	P	43	2-4
			BRTR	76	3-9

TIEFENTHALER, VERLE MATHEW
b.July 11,1937 Breda,Ia.

Yr	Cl	Lea	Pos	G	Rec
1962	Chi	A	P	2	0-0
			BLTR		

TIEMEYER, EDWARD CARL
b.May 9,1885 Cincinnati,O.
d.Sept.26,1946

Yr	Cl	Lea	Pos	G	Rec
1906	Cin	N	P	5	0-0
1907	Cin	N	H	1	.000
1909	NY	A	1	4	.363
			BRTR	10	0-0 .273

TIERNAN, MICHAEL JOSEPH
(Silent Mike)
b.Jan.21,1867 Trenton,N.J.
d.Nov.9,1918

Yr	Cl	Lea	Pos	G	Rec
1887	NY	N	O	103	.340
1888	NY	N	O	113	.293
1889	NY	N	O	122	.334
1890	NY	N	O	133	.303
1891	NY	N	O	133	.303
1892	NY	N	O	114	.297
1893	NY	N	O	124	.327
1894	NY	N	O	112	.282
1895	NY	N	O	119	.354
1896	NY	N	O	133	.361
1897	NY	N	O	129	.331
1898	NY	N	O	103	.286
1899	NY	N	O	36	.250
			BLTL	1474	.318

TIERNAY, WILLIAM J.
b.May 14,1858 Washington,D.C.
d.Sept.21,1898

Yr	Cl	Lea	Pos	G	Rec
1882	Cin	a	1	1	.000
1884	Bal	U	O	1	.333
				2	.125

TIERNEY, JAMES ARTHUR
(Cotton)
b.Feb.10,1894 Kansas City,Kan.
d.Apr.18,1953

Yr	Cl	Lea	Pos	G	Rec
1920	Pit	N	2	12	.260
1921	Pit	N	2-3	117	.299

Yr	Cl	Lea	Pos	G	Rec
1922	Pit	N	2-S-3-O	122	.345
1923	Pit	N	2	29	.292
1923	Phi	N	2-3-O	121	.317
1924	Bos	N	2-3	136	.259
1925	Bro	N	1-2-3	93	.257
	BRTR			630	.296

TIETJE, LESLIE WILLIAM (Toots)
b.Sept.11,1911 Sumner,Ia.

Yr	Cl	Lea	Pos	G	Rec
1933	Chi	A	P	3	2-0
1934	Chi	A	P	34	5-14
1935	Chi	A	P	30	9-15
1936	Chi	A	P	2	0-0
1936	St.L	A	P	16	3-5
1937	St.L	A	P	5	1-2
1938	St.L	A	P	18	2-5
	BRTR			108	22-41

TIFT, RAYMOND FRANK
b.June 21,1884 Fitchburg,Mass.
d.Mar.29,1945

Yr	Cl	Lea	Pos	G	Rec
1907	NY	A	P	4	0-0
	TR				

TIGHE, JOHN THOMAS
b.Aug.9,1913 Kearny,N.J.
Non-playing manager Det (A) 1957-58.

TILLEY, JOHN C.
b.1856 New York,N.Y.

Yr	Cl	Lea	Pos	G	Rec
1882	Cle	N	O	15	.089
1884	Tol	a	O	17	.182
1884	St.P	U	O	9	.148
				41	.138

TILLMAN, JOHN L. (Ducky)
b.Oct.6,1898 Bridgeport,Conn.

Yr	Cl	Lea	Pos	G	Rec
1915	St.L	A	P	2	0-0
	BBTR				

TILLMAN, JOHN ROBERT
b.Mar.24,1937 Nashville,Tenn.

Yr	Cl	Lea	Pos	G	Rec
1962	Bos	A	C	81	.229
	BRTR				

TINCUP, AUSTIN BEN
b.Dec.14,1890 Sherman,Tex.

Yr	Cl	Lea	Pos	G	Rec
1914	Phi	N	P	31	8-10
1915	Phi	N	P	11	0-0
1916	Phi	N	P	1	0-0
1918	Phi	N	P	11	0-1
1928	Chi	N	P	2	0-0
	BLTR			56	8-11

TINKER, JOSEPH BERT
b.July 27,1880 Muscotah,Kan.
d.July 27,1948

Yr	Cl	Lea	Pos	G	Rec
1902	Chi	N	S-3	133	.273
1903	Chi	N	S-3	124	.296
1904	Chi	N	S	141	.221
1905	Chi	N	S	149	.247
1906	Chi	N	S	148	.233
1907	Chi	N	S	113	.221
1908	Chi	N	S	157	.266
1909	Chi	N	S	143	.256
1910	Chi	N	S	132	.288
1911	Chi	N	S	143	.278
1912	Chi	N	S	142	.282
1913	Cin	N	M-S	110	.317
1914	Chi	F	M-S	127	.259
1915	Chi	F	M-S	30	.275
1916	Chi	N	M-2	7	.100
	BRTR			1799	.263

TINNING, LYLE FORREST (Bud)
b.Mar.12,1907 Pilger,Neb.
d.Jan.17,1961

Yr	Cl	Lea	Pos	G	Rec
1932	Chi	N	P	24	5-3
1933	Chi	N	P	32	13-6
1934	Chi	N	P	39	4-6
1935	St.L	N	P	4	0-0
	BBTR			99	22-15

TIPPER, JAMES
b.June 18,1849 Middletown,Conn.
d.Apr.19,1895

Yr	Cl	Lea	Pos	G	Rec
1872	Man	n	3-O	19	NR
1874	Har	n	O	45	NR
1875	NH	n	O	41	NR
				105	NR

TIPPLE, DANIEL SLAUGHTER
(Big Dan)
b.Feb.13,1892 Rockford,Ill.
d.Mar.26,1960

Yr	Cl	Lea	Pos	G	Rec
1915	NY	A	P	3	1-1
	BRTR				

TIPTON, ERIC GORDON (The Red)
b.Apr.20,1915 Petersburg,Va.

Yr	Cl	Lea	Pos	G	Rec
1939	Phi	A	O	47	.231
1940	Phi	A	O	2	.125
1941	Phi	A	O	1	.500
1942	Cin	N	O	63	.222
1943	Cin	N	O	140	.288
1944	Cin	N	O	140	.301
1945	Cin	N	O	108	.242
	BRTR			501	.270

TIPTON, JOSEPH JOHN
b.Feb.18,1923 Copperhill,Tenn.

Yr	Cl	Lea	Pos	G	Rec
1948	Cle	A	C	47	.289
1949	Chi	A	C	67	.204
1950	Phi	A	C	64	.266
1951	Phi	A	C	72	.239
1952	Phi	A	C	23	.191
1952	Cle	A	C	43	.248
1953	Cle	A	C	47	.229
1954	Was	A	C	54	.223
	BRTR			417	.236

TISING, JOHN JOSEPH
b.Oct.9,1903 High Point,Mo.

Yr	Cl	Lea	Pos	G	Rec
1936	Pit	N	P	10	1-3
	BLTR				

TITCOMB, LEDELL (Cannonball)
b.Aug.21,1865 W.Baldwin,Me.
d.June 9,1950

Yr	Cl	Lea	Pos	G	Rec
1886	Phi	N	P	5	0-5
1887	Ath	a	P	3	1-2
1887	NY	N	P	9	4-3
1888	NY	N	P	23	14-8
1889	NY	N	P	4	2-2
1890	Roc	a	P	21	9-8
	BLTL			65	30-28

TITUS, JOHN FRANKLIN
(Silent John)
b.Feb.21,1876 St.Clair,Pa.
d.Jan.8,1943

Yr	Cl	Lea	Pos	G	Rec
1903	Phi	N	O	72	.286
1904	Phi	N	O	140	.294
1905	Phi	N	O	147	.308
1906	Phi	N	O	142	.267
1907	Phi	N	O	142	.275
1908	Phi	N	O	149	.286
1909	Phi	N	O	149	.270
1910	Phi	N	O	142	.241
1911	Phi	N	O	60	.284
1912	Phi	N	O	45	.274
1912	Bos	N	O	96	.325
1913	Bos	N	O	87	.297
	BLTL			1371	.282

TKACZUK, EDWARD TERRANCE
(Played under name of
Edward Terrance Kazak)

TOBIN, JAMES ANTHONY
(Abba Dabba)
b.Dec.27,1912 Oakland,Cal.

Yr	Cl	Lea	Pos	G	Rec
1937	Pit	N	P	21	6-3
1938	Pit	N	P	56	14-12
1939	Pit	N	P	43	9-9
1940	Bos	N	P	20	7-3

(Continued)

Yr	Cl	Lea	Pos	G	Rec
1941	Bos	N	P	43	12-12
1942	Bos	N	P	47	12-21
1943	Bos	N	P-1	46	14-14 .280
1944	Bos	N	P	62	18-19
1945	Bos	N	P	41	9-14
1945	Det	A	P	17	4-5
	BRTR			396	105-112 .230

TOBIN, JOHN MARTIN
b.Sept.15,1908 Jamaica Plain,Mass.

Yr	Cl	Lea	Pos	G	Rec
1932	NY	N	H	1	.000
	BRTR				

TOBIN, JOHN PATRICK
b.Jan.8,1921 Oakland,Cal.

Yr	Cl	Lea	Pos	G	Rec
1945	Bos	A	2-3-O	84	.252
	BLTR				

TOBIN, JOHN THOMAS
b.May 4,1892 St.Louis,Mo.

Yr	Cl	Lea	Pos	G	Rec
1914	St.L	F	O	135	.270
1915	St.L	F	O	158	.299
1916	St.L	A	O	77	.213
1918	St.L	A	O	122	.277
1919	St.L	A	O	127	.327
1920	St.L	A	O	147	.340
1921	St.L	A	O	150	.352
1922	St.L	A	O	146	.331
1923	St.L	A	O	151	.317
1924	St.L	A	O	136	.299
1925	St.L	A	1-O	77	.301
1926	Was	A	O	27	.212
1926	Bos	A	O	51	.273
1927	Bos	A	O	111	.310
	BLTL			1615	.309

TOBIN, MARION BROOKS (Pat)
b.Jan.28,1916 Hermitage,Ark.

Yr	Cl	Lea	Pos	G	Rec
1941	Phi	A	P	1	0-0
	BRTR				

TOBIN, WILLIAM
b.Feb.6,1859 Hartford,Conn.

Yr	Cl	Lea	Pos	G	Rec
1880	Wor	N	1	5	.125
1880	Tro	N	1	32	.152
				37	.142

TODD, ALFRED CHESTER
b.Jan.7,1902 Troy,N.Y.

Yr	Cl	Lea	Pos	G	Rec
1932	Phi	N	C	33	.229
1933	Phi	N	C-O	73	.206
1934	Phi	N	C	91	.318
1935	Phi	N	C	107	.290
1936	Pit	N	C	76	.273
1937	Pit	N	C	133	.307
1938	Pit	N	C	133	.265
1939	Bro	N	C	86	.277
1940	Chi	N	C	104	.255
1941	Chi	N	H	6	.167
1943	Chi	N	C	21	.133
	BRTR			863	.276

TODD, FRANK
b.Aberdeen,Md.

Yr	Cl	Lea	Pos	G	Rec
1898	Lou	N	P	3	0-3
		TL			

TODT, PHILIP JULIUS (Hook)
b.Aug.9,1902 St.Louis,Mo.

Yr	Cl	Lea	Pos	G	Rec
1924	Bos	A	1	52	.262
1925	Bos	A	1	141	.278
1926	Bos	A	1	154	.255
1927	Bos	A	1	140	.236
1928	Bos	A	1	144	.252
1929	Bos	A	1	153	.262
1930	Bos	A	1	111	.269
1931	Phi	A	1	62	.244
	BLTL			957	.258

TOENES, WILLIAM HARRELL
(Hal)
b.Oct.8,1917 Mobile,Ala.

Yr	Cl	Lea	Pos	G	Rec
1947	Was	A	P	3	0-1
	BRTR				

TOLSON, CHARLES JULIUS (Chick)
b.Nov.6,1901 Washington,D.C.

Yr	Cl	Lea	Pos	G	Rec
1925	Cle	A	1	3	.250
1926	Chi	N	1	57	.313
1927	Chi	N	1	39	.296
1929	Chi	N	1	32	.257
1930	Chi	N	1	13	.300
	BRTR			144	.284

TOMANEK, RICHARD CARL (Bones)
b.Jan.6,1931 Avon Lake,O.

Yr	Cl	Lea	Pos	G	Rec
1953	Cle	A	P	1	1-0
1954	Cle	A	P	1	0-0
1957	Cle	A	P	34	2-1
1958	Cle	A	P	20	2-3
1958	KC	A	P	36	5-5
1959	KC	A	P	16	0-1
	BLTL			108	10-10

TOMASIC, ANDREW JOHN
b.Dec.10,1919 Hokendauqua,Pa.

Yr	Cl	Lea	Pos	G	Rec
1949	NY	N	P	2	0-1
	BRTR				

TOMER, GEORGE

Yr	Cl	Lea	Pos	G	Rec
1913	St.L	A	H	1	.000
	BLTR				

TOMNEY, PHILIP H.
b.July 17,1863 Reading,Pa.
d.Mar.18,1892

Yr	Cl	Lea	Pos	G	Rec
1888	Lou	a	S	34	.149
1889	Lou	a	S	112	.215
1890	Lou	a	S	110	.264
	BRTR			256	.229

TOMPKINS, CHARLES HERBERT
b.Sept.1,1889 Prescott,Ark.

Yr	Cl	Lea	Pos	G	Rec
1912	Cin	N	P	1	0-0
	BRTR				

TONEY, FREDERICK ARTHUR
b.Dec.11,1887 Nashville,Tenn.
d.Mar.11,1953

Yr	Cl	Lea	Pos	G	Rec
1911	Chi	N	P	18	1-1
1912	Chi	N	P	9	1-2
1913	Chi	N	P	7	2-2
1915	Cin	N	P	36	17-6
1916	Cin	N	P	41	14-17
1917	Cin	N	P	43	24-16
1918	Cin	N	P	22	6-10
1918	NY	N	P	11	6-2
1919	NY	N	P	24	13-6
1920	NY	N	P	42	21-11
1921	NY	N	P	42	18-11
1922	NY	N	P	13	5-6
1923	St.L	N	P	29	11-12
	BRTR			337	139-102

TONKIN, HARRY GLENVILLE (Doc)
b.Aug.11,1881 Concord,N.H.
d.May 30,1959

Yr	Cl	Lea	Pos	G	Rec
1907	Was	A	P	1	0-0
	BLTL				

TONNEMAN. CHARLES RICHARD
b.Sept.10,1881 Chicago,Ill.
d.Aug.7,1951

Yr	Cl	Lea	Pos	G	Rec
1911	Bos	A	C	2	.200
	BRTR				

TOOLE, STEPHEN J.
b.1862 New Orleans,La.

Yr	Cl	Lea	Pos	G	Rec
1886	Bro	a	P	13	6-6
1887	Bro	a	P	26	13-10
1888	KC	a	P	13	4-6
1890	Bro	a	P	6	2-4
	BRTL			58	25-26

TOOLEY, ALBERT R. (Bert)
b.1887

Yr	Cl	Lea	Pos	G	Rec
1911	Bro	N	S	114	.206
1912	Bro	N	S	77	.234
	BRTR			191	.216

TOPORCER, GEORGE (Specs)
b.Feb.9,1899 New York,N.Y.

Yr	Cl	Lea	Pos	G	Rec
1921	St.L	N	2	22	.264
1922	St.L	N	2-S-3-O	116	.323
1923	St.L	N	1-2-S-3	97	.254
1924	St.L	N	2-S-3	70	.313
1925	St.L	N	2-S	83	.284
1926	St.L	N	2	64	.250
1927	St.L	N	S-3	86	.248
1928	St.L	N	1-2	8	.000
	BLTR			546	.279

TOPPIN, RUPERTO
b.Dec.7,1941 Panama City,Panama

Yr	Cl	Lea	Pos	G	Rec
1962	KC	A	P	2	0-0
	BRTR				

TORGESON, CLIFFORD EARL
b.Jan.1,1924 Snohomish,Wash.

Yr	Cl	Lea	Pos	G	Rec
1947	Bos	N	1	128	.281
1948	Bos	N	1	134	.253
1949	Bos	N	1	25	.260
1950	Bos	N	1	156	.290
1951	Bos	N	1	155	.263
1952	Bos	N	1-O	122	.230
1953	Phi	N	1	111	.274
1954	Phi	N	1	135	.271
1955	Phi	N	1	47	.267
1955	Det	A	1	89	.283
1956	Det	A	1	117	.264
1957	Det	A	1	30	.240
1957	Chi	A	1-O	86	.295
1958	Chi	A	1	96	.266
1959	Chi	A	1	127	.220
1960	Chi	A	1	68	.263
1961	Chi	A	1	20	.067
1961	NY	A	1	22	.111
	BLTL			1668	.265

TORKELSON, CHESTER LEROY (Red)
b.Mar.19,1894 Chicago,Ill.

Yr	Cl	Lea	Pos	G	Rec
1917	Cle	A	P	4	2-1
	BRTR				

TORPHY, WALTER ANTHONY (Red)
b.Nov.6,1898 Fall River,Mass.

Yr	Cl	Lea	Pos	G	Rec
1920	Bos	N	1	3	.200
	BRTR				

TORRE, FRANK JOSEPH
b.Dec.30,1931 Brooklyn,N.Y.

Yr	Cl	Lea	Pos	G	Rec
1956	Mil	N	1	111	.258
1957	Mil	N	1	129	.272
1958	Mil	N	1	138	.309
1959	Mil	N	1	115	.228
1960	Mil	N	1	21	.205
1962	Phi	N	1	108	.310
	BLTL			622	.283

TORRE, JOSEPH PAUL
b.July 18,1940 Brooklyn,N.Y.

Yr	Cl	Lea	Pos	G	Rec
1960	Mil	N	H	2	.500
1961	Mil	N	C	113	.278
1962	Mil	N	C	80	.282
	BRTR			195	.280

TORRES, FELIX
b.May 1,1932 Ponce,Porto Rico

Yr	Cl	Lea	Pos	G	Rec
1962	LA	A	3	127	.259
	BRTR				

TORRES, DON GILBERTO NUNEZ (Gil)
b.Aug.23,1915 Regla,Cuba.

Yr	Cl	Lea	Pos	G	Rec
1940	Was	A	P	2	0-0
1944	Was	A	1-2-3	134	.267
1945	Was	A	S-3	147	.237
1946	Was	A	P-2-S-3	63	0-0 .254
	BRTR			346	0-0 .252

TORRES, RICARDO J.
b.1894 Cuba.

Yr	Cl	Lea	Pos	G	Rec
1920	Was	A	C-1	16	.333
1921	Was	A	C	2	.333
1922	Was	A	C	4	.000
	BRTR			22	.297

TOST, LOUIS EUGENE
b.Dec.1,1914 Enumclaw,Wash.

Yr	Cl	Lea	Pos	G	Rec
1942	Bos	N	P	35	10-10
1943	Bos	N	P	3	0-1
1947	Pit	N	P	1	0-0
	BLTL			39	10-11

TOUCHSTONE, CLAYLAND MAFFITT
b.Jan.24,1903 Moore,Pa.
d.Apr.28,1949

Yr	Cl	Lea	Pos	G	Rec
1928	Bos	N	P	5	0-0
1929	Bos	N	P	1	0-0
1945	Chi	A	P	6	0-0
	BRTR			12	0-0

TOWNE, JAY KING (Babe)
b.Mar.12,1880 Coon Rapids,Ia.
d.Oct.29,1938

Yr	Cl	Lea	Pos	G	Rec
1906	Chi	A	C	13	.290
	BLTR				

TOWNSEND, GEORGE H. (Sleepy)
b.June 4,1868 Hartsdale,N.Y.
d.Mar.15,1930

Yr	Cl	Lea	Pos	G	Rec
1887	Ath	a	C	34	.217
1888	Ath	a	C	43	.150
1890	Bal	a	C	19	.214
1891	Bal	a	C	59	.178
	BRTR			155	.186

TOWNSEND, IRA DANCE
b.Jan.9,1897 Weimar,Tex.

Yr	Cl	Lea	Pos	G	Rec
1920	Bos	N	P	4	0-0
1921	Bos	N	P	4	0-0
	BRTR			8	0-0

TOWNSEND, JOHN (Happy)
b.Apr.9,1883 Townsend,Del.

Yr	Cl	Lea	Pos	G	Rec
1901	Phi	N	P	18	9-6
1902	Was	A	P	27	9-16
1903	Was	A	P	20	2-11
1904	Was	A	P	38	5-27
1905	Was	A	P	34	6-17
1906	Cle	A	P	16	3-7
	BRTR			153	34-84

TOWNSEND, LEO ALPHONSE
b.Jan.15,1891 Mobile,Ala.

Yr	Cl	Lea	Pos	G	Rec
1920	Bos	N	P	7	2-2
1921	Bos	N	P	1	0-1
	BLTL			8	2-3

TOY, JAMES MADISON
b.Feb.20,1858 Beaver Falls,Pa.
d.Mar.13,1919

Yr	Cl	Lea	Pos	G	Rec
1887	Cle	a	1	109	.239
1890	Bro	a	C	43	.172
				152	.218

TOTH, PAUL LOUIS
b.June 30,1935 McRoberts,Ky.

Yr	Cl	Lea	Pos	G	Rec
1962	St.L	N	P	6	1-0
1962	Chi	N	P	6	3-1
	BRTR			12	4-1

TOZIER, WILLIAM RALPH
b.July 3,1882 St.Louis,Mo.

Yr	Cl	Lea	Pos	G	Rec
1908	Cin	N	P	4	0-0
	BRTR				

TRACEWSKI, RICHARD JOSEPH
b.Feb.3,1935 Eynon,Pa.

Yr	Cl	Lea	Pos	G	Rec
1962	LA	N	S	15	.000
	BRTR				

TRAFFLEY, JOHN
b.Baltimore,Md.

Yr	Cl	Lea	Pos	G	Rec
1889	Lou	a	O	1	.500

TRAFFLEY, WILLIAM F.
b.Dec.21,1859 Staten Island,N.Y.
d.June 24,1908

Yr	Cl	Lea	Pos	G	Rec
1878	Chi	N	C	2	.111
1883	Cin	a	C-2-S	29	.200
1884	Bal	a	C-O	54	.186
1885	Bal	a	C	70	.156
1886	Bal	a	C	25	.224
	BRTR			180	.226

TRAGESSER, WALTER JOSEPH
b.June 14,1887 Lafayette,Ind.

Yr	Cl	Lea	Pos	G	Rec
1913	Bos	N	C	1	.000
1915	Bos	N	C	7	.000
1916	Bos	N	C	41	.204
1917	Bos	N	C	98	.222
1918	Bos	N	C	7	.000
1919	Bos	N	C	20	.272
1919	Phi	N	C	35	.164
1920	Phi	N	C	62	.210
	BRTR			271	.215

TRAMBACK, STEPHEN JOSEPH
(Red)
b.Oct.1,1918 Iselin,Pa.

Yr	Cl	Lea	Pos	G	Rec
1940	NY	N	O	2	.250
	BLTL				

TRAUTMAN, FREDERICK ORLANDO
b.Mar.24,1892 Bucyrus,O.

Yr	Cl	Lea	Pos	G	Rec
1915	New	F	P	1	0-0
	BRTR				

TRAVERS, ALOYSIUS JOSEPH
(Joe)
b.May 7,1892 Philadelphia,Pa.

Yr	Cl	Lea	Pos	G	Rec
1912	Det	A	P	1	0-1

TRAVIS, CECIL HOWEL
b.Aug.8,1913 Riverdale,Ga.

Yr	Cl	Lea	Pos	G	Rec
1933	Was	A	3	18	.302
1934	Was	A	3	109	.319
1935	Was	A	3-O	138	.318
1936	Was	A	S-O	138	.317
1937	Was	A	S	135	.344
1938	Was	A	S	146	.335
1939	Was	A	S	130	.292
1940	Was	A	S-3	136	.322
1941	Was	A	S-3	152	.359
1945	Was	A	3	15	.241
1946	Was	A	S-3	137	.252
1947	Was	A	S-3	74	.216
	BLTR			1328	.313

TRAY, JAMES
b.1860 Jackson,Mich.

Yr	Cl	Lea	Pos	G	Rec
1884	Ind	a	C	6	.261

TRAYNOR, HAROLD JOSEPH (Pie)
b.Nov.11,1899 Framingham,Mass.

Yr	Cl	Lea	Pos	G	Rec
1920	Pit	N	S	17	.212
1921	Pit	N	3	7	.263
1922	Pit	N	S-3	142	.281
1923	Pit	N	3	153	.338
1924	Pit	N	3	142	.294

(Continued)

Yr	Cl	Lea	Pos	G	Rec
1925	Pit	N	S-3	150	.320
1926	Pit	N	3	152	.317
1927	Pit	N	3	149	.342
1928	Pit	N	3	144	.337
1929	Pit	N	3	130	.356
1930	Pit	N	3	130	.366
1931	Pit	N	3	155	.298
1932	Pit	N	3	135	.329
1933	Pit	N	3	154	.304
1934	Pit	N	M-3	119	.309
1935	Pit	N	M-1-3	57	.279
1937	Pit	N	M-3	5	.167
	BRTR			1941	.320

Non-playing manager Pit (N) 1936, 1938-39.

TREACEY, FREDERICK
b.1847 Brooklyn,N.Y.

Yr	Cl	Lea	Pos	G	Rec
1871	Chi	n	O	25	NR
1872	Ath	n	O	48	NR
1873	Phi	n	O	51	NR
1874	Chi	n	O	35	NR
1875	Cen	n	O	11	NR
1875	Phi	n	O	42	NR
1876	Mut	N	O	57	.210
				269	NR

TREACEY, P.
b.1852 Brooklyn,N.Y.

Yr	Cl	Lea	Pos	G	Rec
1876	Mut	N	S	2	.167

TREADAWAY, EDGAR RAYMOND
(Ray)
b.Oct.31,1907 Ragland,Ala.
d.Oct.12,1935

Yr	Cl	Lea	Pos	G	Rec
1930	Was	A	3	6	.211
	BLTR				

TREADWAY, GEORGE B.
b.Nov.11,1866 Greenup Co.,Ky.
d.Nov.17,1928

Yr	Cl	Lea	Pos	G	Rec
1893	Bal	N	O	114	.268
1894	Bro	N	O	122	.336
1895	Bro	N	O	85	.262
1896	Lou	N	O	2	.143
	BL			323	.292

TREADWAY, THADFORD LEON
(Red)
b.Apr.28,1920 Athalon,N.C.

Yr	Cl	Lea	Pos	G	Rec
1944	NY	N	O	50	.300
1945	NY	N	O	88	.241
	BLTR			138	.267

TRECHOCK, FRANK ADAM
b.Dec.24,1915 Windber,Pa.

Yr	Cl	Lea	Pos	G	Rec
1937	Was	A	S	1	.500
	BRTR				

TREKELL, HARRY R.
b.1893

Yr	Cl	Lea	Pos	G	Rec
1913	St.L	N	P	7	0-1
	BRTR				

TREMARK, NICHOLAS JOSEPH
b.Oct.15,1912 Yonkers,N.Y.

Yr	Cl	Lea	Pos	G	Rec
1934	Bro	N	O	17	.250
1935	Bro	N	O	10	.231
1936	Bro	N	O	8	.250
	BLTL			35	.247

TREMBLY, EDWARD J.
(Played under name of Edward J. Trumbull)

TREMEL, WILLIAM LEONARD
b.July 4,1929 Lilly,Pa.

Yr	Cl	Lea	Pos	G	Rec
1954	Chi	N	P	33	1-2
1955	Chi	N	P	23	3-0
1956	Chi	N	P	1	0-0
	BRTR			57	4-2

TREMPER, CARLTON OVERTON
b.Mar.22,1906 Brooklyn,N.Y.

Yr	Cl	Lea	Pos	G	Rec
1927	Bro	N	O	26	.233
1928	Bro	N	O	10	.194
	BRTR			36	.220

TRENWITH, GEORGE
d.Feb.1,1890

Yr	Cl	Lea	Pos	G	Rec
1875	Cen	n	3	10	NR
1875	NH	n	3	6	NR
				16	NR

TRESH, MICHAEL
b.Feb.23,1914 Hazleton,Pa.

Yr	Cl	Lea	Pos	G	Rec
1938	Chi	A	C	10	.241
1939	Chi	A	C	119	.259
1940	Chi	A	C	135	.281
1941	Chi	A	C	115	.251
1942	Chi	A	C	72	.232
1943	Chi	A	C	86	.215
1944	Chi	A	C	93	.260
1945	Chi	A	C	150	.249
1946	Chi	A	C	80	.217
1947	Chi	A	C	90	.241
1948	Chi	A	C	39	.250
1949	Cle	A	C	38	.216
	BRTR			1027	.249

TRESH, THOMAS MICHAEL
b.Sept.20,1938 Detroit,Mich.

Yr	Cl	Lea	Pos	G	Rec
1961	NY	A	S	9	.250
1962	NY	A	S-O	157	.286
	BBTR			166	.286

TRIANDOS, GUS
b.July 30,1930 San Francisco,Cal.

Yr	Cl	Lea	Pos	G	Rec
1953	NY	A	C-1	18	.157
1954	NY	A	C	2	.000
1955	Bal	A	C-1-3	140	.277
1956	Bal	A	C-1	131	.279
1957	Bal	A	C	129	.254
1958	Bal	A	C	137	.245
1959	Bal	A	C	126	.216
1960	Bal	A	C	109	.269
1961	Bal	A	C	115	.244
1962	Bal	A	C	66	.159
	BRTR			973	.248

TRICE, ROBERT LEE
b.Aug.28,1928 Newton,Ga.

Yr	Cl	Lea	Pos	G	Rec
1953	Phi	A	P	3	2-1
1954	Phi	A	P	20	7-8
1955	KC	A	P	4	0-0
	BRTR			27	9-9

TRIEBEL, GEORGE W.
(Played under name of George W. Creamer)

TRIMBLE, JOSEPH GERARD
b.Oct.12,1930 Providence,R.I.

Yr	Cl	Lea	Pos	G	Rec
1955	Bos	A	P	2	0-0
1957	Pit	N	P	5	0-2
	BRTR			7	0-2

TRIMBLE, W.
Non-playing manager Wes (n) 1875.

TRINKLE, KENNETH WAYNE
b.Dec.15,1919 Paoli,Ind.

Yr	Cl	Lea	Pos	G	Rec
1943	NY	N	P	11	1-5
1946	NY	N	P	48	7-14
1947	NY	N	P	62	8-4
1948	NY	N	P	53	4-5
1949	Phi	N	P	42	1-1
	BRTR			216	21-29

TRIPLETT, HERMAN COAKER
b.Dec.18,1914 Boone,N.C.

Yr	Cl	Lea	Pos	G	Rec
1938	Chi	N	O	12	.250
1941	St.L	N	O	76	.286
1942	St.L	N	O	64	.273
1943	St.L	N	O	9	.080
1943	Phi	N	O	105	.272
1944	Phi	N	O	84	.234
1945	Phi	N	O	120	.240
	BRTR			470	.256

TROSKY, HAROLD ARTHUR JR.
(Real Name
Harold Arthur Troyavesky Jr.)
b.Sept.29,1936 Cleveland,Ohio

Yr	Cl	Lea	Pos	G	Rec
1958	Chi	A	P	2	1-0
BRTR					

TROSKY, HAROLD ARTHUR SR.
(Real name
Harold Arthur Troyavesky Sr.)
b.Nov.11,1912 Norway,Ia.

Yr	Cl	Lea	Pos	G	Rec
1933	Cle	A	1	11	.295
1934	Cle	A	1	154	.330
1935	Cle	A	1	154	.271
1936	Cle	A	1	151	.343
1937	Cle	A	1	153	.298
1938	Cle	A	1	150	.334
1939	Cle	A	1	122	.335
1940	Cle	A	1	140	.295
1941	Cle	A	1	89	.294
1944	Chi	A	1	135	.241
1946	Chi	A	1	88	.254
BLTR				1347	.302

TROST, MICHAEL J.
b.1866 Philadelphia,Pa.
d.Mar.24,1901

Yr	Cl	Lea	Pos	G	Rec
1890	St.L	a	C	17	.250
1895	Lou	N	1	2	.111
				19	.217

TROTT, SAMUEL W.
b.1858 Washington,D.C.
d.June 5,1925

Yr	Cl	Lea	Pos	G	Rec
1880	Bos	N	C-O	38	.197
1881	Det	N	C	6	.192
1882	Det	N	C-1-2-S-O	30	.246
1883	Det	N	C-1-2-O	73	.233
1884	Bal	a	C	72	.254
1885	Bal	a	C	20	.289
1887	Bal	a	C	85	.302
1888	Bal	a	C	31	.275
BLTR				355	.258

Non-playing manager Was (a) 1891.

TROTTER, WILLIAM FELIX
b.Aug.10,1908 Cisne,Ill.

Yr	Cl	Lea	Pos	G	Rec
1937	St.L	A	P	34	2-9
1938	St.L	A	P	1	0-1
1939	St.L	A	P	41	6-13
1940	St.L	A	P	36	7-6
1941	St.L	A	P	29	4-2
1942	St.L	A	P	3	0-1
1942	Was	A	P	17	3-1
1944	St.L	N	P	2	0-1
BRTR				163	22-34

TROUPE, QUINCY THOMAS
b.Dec.25,1922 St.Louis,Mo.

Yr	Cl	Lea	Pos	G	Rec
1952	Cle	A	C	6	.100
BBTR					

TROUT, PAUL HOWARD (Dizzy)
b.June 29,1915 Sandcut,Ind.

Yr	Cl	Lea	Pos	G	Rec
1939	Det	A	P	35	9-10
1940	Det	A	P	33	3-7
1941	Det	A	P	40	9-9
1942	Det	A	P	36	12-18
1943	Det	A	P	45	20-12
1944	Det	A	P	51	27-14
1945	Det	A	P	42	18-15
1946	Det	A	P	40	17-13
1947	Det	A	P	34	10-11
1948	Det	A	P	32	10-14
1949	Det	A	P	33	3-6
1950	Det	A	P	34	13-5
1951	Det	A	P	42	9-14
1952	Det	A	P	10	1-5
1952	Bos	A	P	26	9-8
1957	Bal	A	P	2	0-0
BRTR				535	170-161

TROWBRIDGE, ROBERT
b.June 27,1930 Hudson,N.Y.

Yr	Cl	Lea	Pos	G	Rec
1956	Mil	N	P	19	3-2
1957	Mil	N	P	32	7-5
1958	Mil	N	P	27	1-3
1959	Mil	N	P	16	1-0
1960	KC	A	P	22	1-3
BRTR				116	13-13

TROY, JOHN JOSEPH (Dasher)
b.May 8,1856 New York,N.Y.
d.Mar.30,1938

Yr	Cl	Lea	Pos	G	Rec
1881	Det	N	2-3	11	.304
1882	Det	N	2-S	39	.232
1882	Pro	N	S	4	.235
1883	NY	N	2-S	82	.216
1884	Met	a	2	107	.264
1885	Met	a	2	46	.225
BRTR				289	.242

TROY, ROBERT
b.Aug.22,1888 Germany
d.Oct.7,1918

Yr	Cl	Lea	Pos	G	Rec
1912	Det	A	P	1	0-1
BRTR					

TROYAVESKY, HAROLD ARTHUR JR.
(Played under name of
Harold Arthur Trosky Jr.)

TROYAVESKY, HAROLD ARTHUR SR.
(Played under name of
Harold Arthur Trosky Sr.)

TRUAX, FREDERICK W.

Yr	Cl	Lea	Pos	G	Rec
1890	Pit	N	O	1	.333

TRUBY, HARRY GARVIN
(Bird Eye)
b.May 12,1870 Ironton,O.
d.Mar.21,1953

Yr	Cl	Lea	Pos	G	Rec
1895	Chi	N	2	33	.339
1896	Chi	N	2	27	.266
1896	Pit	N	2	8	.156
TR				68	.286

TRUCKS, VIRGIL OLIVER (Fire)
b.Apr.26,1919 Birmingham,Ala.

Yr	Cl	Lea	Pos	G	Rec
1941	Det	A	P	1	0-0
1942	Det	A	P	28	14-8
1943	Det	A	P	33	16-10
1945	Det	A	P	1	0-0
1946	Det	A	P	32	14-9
1947	Det	A	P	36	10-12
1948	Det	A	P	43	14-13
1949	Det	A	P	41	19-11
1950	Det	A	P	7	3-1
1951	Det	A	P	37	13-8
1952	Det	A	P	35	5-19
1953	St.L	A	P	16	5-4
1953	Chi	A	P	24	15-6
1954	Chi	A	P	40	19-12
1955	Chi	A	P	32	13-8
1956	Det	A	P	22	6-5
1957	KC	A	P	48	9-7
1958	KC	A	P	16	0-1
1958	NY	A	P	25	2-1
BRTR				517	177-135

TRUESDALE, FRANK D.
b.Dec.12,1885 Kirkwood,Mo.

Yr	Cl	Lea	Pos	G	Rec
1910	St.L	A	2	123	.219
1911	St.L	A	2	1	.000
1914	NY	A	2	77	.212
1918	Bos	A	2	15	.278
BBTR				216	.220

TRUMAN, HARRY H.
(Played under name of
Harry H. Raymond)

TRUMBULL, EDWARD J.
(Real name Edward J. Trembly)
b.Nov.3,1860 Chicopee Falls,Mass.

Yr	Cl	Lea	Pos	G	Rec
1884	Was	a	P-O	24	1-9 .109

TSITOURIS, JOHN PHILIP
b.May 4,1936 Monroe,N.C.

Yr	Cl	Lea	Pos	G	Rec
1957	Det	A	P	2	1-0
1958	KC	A	P	1	0-0
1959	KC	A	P	24	4-3
1960	KC	A	P	14	0-2
1962	Cin	N	P	4	1-0
BRTR				45	6-5

TUCKER, OLIVER DINWIDDIE
b.Jan.27,1902 Radiant,Va.
d.July 13,1940

Yr	Cl	Lea	Pos	G	Rec
1927	Was	A	O	20	.208
1928	Cle	A	O	14	.128
BLTR				34	.155

TUCKER, THOMAS J. (Foghorn)
b.Oct.28,1863 Holyoke,Mass.
d.Oct.22,1935

Yr	Cl	Lea	Pos	G	Rec
1887	Bal	a	1	136	.315
1888	Bal	a	1	136	.291
1889	Bal	a	1	134	.375
1890	Bos	N	1	132	.295
1891	Bos	N	1	140	.272
1892	Bos	N	1	148	.281
1893	Bos	N	1	121	.299
1894	Bos	N	1	122	.328
1895	Bos	N	1	126	.254
1896	Bos	N	1	122	.304
1897	Bos	N	1	2	.143
1897	Was	N	1	96	.333
1898	Bro	N	1	73	.278
1898	St.L	N	1	72	.238
1899	Cle	N	1	126	.237
BBTR				1686	.295

TUCKER, THURMAN LOWELL
(Joe E.)
b.Sept.26,1917 Gordon,Tex.

Yr	Cl	Lea	Pos	G	Rec
1942	Chi	A	O	7	.125
1943	Chi	A	O	139	.235
1944	Chi	A	O	124	.287
1946	Chi	A	O	121	.288
1947	Chi	A	O	89	.236
1948	Cle	A	O	83	.260
1949	Cle	A	O	80	.244
1950	Cle	A	O	57	.178
1951	Cle	A	H	1	.000
BLTR				701	.255

TUCKEY, THOMAS H.
b.Birmingham,England.

Yr	Cl	Lea	Pos	G	Rec
1908	Bos	N	P	8	3-3
1909	Bos	N	P	17	0-9
TL				25	3-12

TUERO, OSCAR MONZON
b.Dec.17,1892 Havana,Cuba.

Yr	Cl	Lea	Pos	G	Rec
1918	St.L	N	P	12	1-2
1919	St.L	N	P	45	5-7
1920	St.L	N	P	2	0-0
BRTR				59	6-9

TURBEVILLE, GEORGE EDWARD
b.Aug.24,1916 Turbeville,S.C.

Yr	Cl	Lea	Pos	G	Rec
1935	Phi	A	P	19	0-3
1936	Phi	A	P	12	2-5
1937	Phi	A	P	31	0-4
BBTL				62	2-12

TURBIDY, JEREMIAH
b.July 4,1852 Dudley,Mass.
d.Sept.5,1920

Yr	Cl	Lea	Pos	G	Rec
1884	KC	U	S	12	.279

Yr Cl Lea Pos G Rec

TURCHIN, EDWARD LAWRENCE
b.Feb.10,1917 New York,N.Y.

Yr	Cl	Lea	Pos	G	Rec
1943	Cle	A	S-3	11	.231
	BRTR				

TURGEON, EUGENE JOSEPH (Pete)
b.Jan.3,1898 Minneapolis,Minn.

Yr	Cl	Lea	Pos	G	Rec
1923	Chi	N	S	3	.167
	BRTR				

TURK, LUCAS NEWTON (Harlem)
b.May 2,1898 Homer,Ga.

Yr	Cl	Lea	Pos	G	Rec
1922	Was	A	P	5	0-0
	BRTR				

TURLEY, ROBERT LEE
b.Sept.19,1930 Troy,Ill.

Yr	Cl	Lea	Pos	G	Rec
1951	St.L	A	P	1	0-1
1953	St.L	A	P	10	2-6
1954	Bal	A	P	35	14-15
1955	NY	A	P	36	17-13
1956	NY	A	P	27	8-4
1957	NY	A	P	32	13-6
1958	NY	A	P	33	21-7
1959	NY	A	P	33	8-11
1960	NY	A	P	34	9-3
1961	NY	A	P	15	3-5
1962	NY	A	P	24	3-3
	BRTR			256	98-74

TURNER, EARL EDWIN
b.May 6,1923 Pittsfield,Mass.

Yr	Cl	Lea	Pos	G	Rec
1948	Pit	N	C	2	.000
1950	Pit	N	C	40	.243
	BRTR			42	.240

TURNER, GEORGE A. (Tuck)
b.1870 W.New Brighton,S.I.,N.Y.

Yr	Cl	Lea	Pos	G	Rec
1893	Phi	N	O	35	.324
1894	Phi	N	O	77	.423
1895	Phi	N	O	48	.388
1896	Phi	N	O	11	.231
1896	St.L	N	O	48	.255
1897	St.L	N	O	102	.289
1898	St.L	N	O	34	.210
	BL			355	.325

TURNER, JAMES RILEY (Milkman)
b.Aug.6,1904 Antioch,Tenn.

Yr	Cl	Lea	Pos	G	Rec
1937	Bos	N	P	39	20-11
1938	Bos	N	P	35	14-18
1939	Bos	N	P	25	4-11
1940	Cin	N	P	25	14-7
1941	Cin	N	P	23	6-4
1942	Cin	N	P	3	0-0
1942	NY	A	P	5	1-1
1943	NY	A	P	18	3-0
1944	NY	A	P	35	4-4
1945	NY	A	P	30	3-4
	BLTR			238	69-60

TURNER, TERRENCE LAMONT (Cotton)
b.Feb.28,1881 Sandy Lake,Pa.
d.July 18,1960

Yr	Cl	Lea	Pos	G	Rec
1901	Pit	N	3	2	.428
1904	Cle	A	S	111	.236
1905	Cle	A	S	154	.263
1906	Cle	A	S	147	.291
1907	Cle	A	S	142	.242
1908	Cle	A	S-O	60	.239
1909	Cle	A	2-S	53	.250
1910	Cle	A	S-3	150	.230
1911	Cle	A	3	117	.252
1912	Cle	A	3	103	.308
1913	Cle	A	2-S-3	120	.248
1914	Cle	A	2-3	120	.245
1915	Cle	A	2-3	75	.252
1916	Cle	A	2-3	124	.262
1917	Cle	A	2-3	69	.205
1918	Cle	A	2-3	74	.249
1919	Phi	A	S	38	.189
	BRTR			1659	.256

TURNER, THEODORE HOLTOP
b.May 4,1892 Louisville,Ky.
d.Feb.4.1958

Yr	Cl	Lea	Pos	G	Rec
1920	Chi	N	P	1	0-0
	BRTR				

TURNER, THOMAS LOVATT (Tink)
b.Feb.20.1890 Philadelphia,Pa.
d.Feb.25,1962

Yr	Cl	Lea	Pos	G	Rec
1915	Phi	A	P	1	0-1
	BRTR				

TURNER, THOMAS RICHARD
b.Sept.8,1916 Custer,Okla.

Yr	Cl	Lea	Pos	G	Rec
1940	Chi	A	C	37	.208
1941	Chi	A	C	38	.238
1942	Chi	A	C	56	.242
1943	Chi	A	C	51	.240
1944	Chi	A	C	36	.230
1944	St.L	A	C	15	.320
	BRTR			233	.237

TUTTLE, WILLIAM ROBERT
b.July 4,1929 Elmwood,Ill.

Yr	Cl	Lea	Pos	G	Rec
1952	Det	A	O	7	.240
1954	Det	A	O	147	.266
1955	Det	A	O	154	.279
1956	Det	A	O	140	.253
1957	Det	A	O	133	.251
1958	KC	A	O	148	.231
1959	KC	A	O	126	.300
1960	KC	A	O	151	.256
1961	KC	A	O	25	.262
1961	Min	A	2-3-O	113	.246
1962	Min	A	O	110	.210
	BRTR			1254	.259

TUTWEILER, ELMER S.
b.Nov.19,1905 Carbon Hill,Ala.

Yr	Cl	Lea	Pos	G	Rec
1928	Pit	N	P	2	0-0
	BRTR				

TUTWEILER, GUY ISBELL
b.July 17,1889 Coalburg,Ala.

Yr	Cl	Lea	Pos	G	Rec
1911	Det	A	2-O	13	.186
1913	Det	A	1	14	.191
	BLTR			27	.190

TWINEHAM, ARTHUR W. (Old Hoss)
b.Nov.26,1866 Galesburg,Ill.

Yr	Cl	Lea	Pos	G	Rec
1893	St.L	N	C	14	.325
1894	St.L	N	C	31	.314
	BLTR			45	.317

TWINING, HOWARD EARLE (Doc)
b.May 30,1894 Horsham,Pa.

Yr	Cl	Lea	Pos	G	Rec
1916	Cin	N	P	1	0-0
	BRTR				

TWITCHELL, LAWRENCE GRANT
b.Feb.18,1864 Cleveland,O.
d.Aug.23,1930

Yr	Cl	Lea	Pos	G	Rec
1886	Det	N	P	4	2-2
1887	Det	N	P-O	63	10-1 .352
1888	Det	N	O	130	.244
1889	Cle	N	O	134	.275
1890	Cle	p	P-O	56	0-0 .224
1890	Buf	p	P-O	44	5-7 .216
1891	Col	a	P-O	57	1-1 .275
1892	Was	N	O	51	.221
1893	Lou	N	O	45	.331
1894	Lou	N	O	51	.265
	BRTR			635	18-11 .266

TWOMBLY, CLARENCE EDWARD
b.Jan.18,1896 Jamaica Plain,Mass.

Yr	Cl	Lea	Pos	G	Rec
1920	Chi	N	O	78	.235
1921	Chi	N	O	87	.377
	BLTR			165	.304

TWOMBLY, EDWIN PARKER (Cy)
b.June 14,1897 Groveland,Mass.

Yr	Cl	Lea	Pos	G	Rec
1921	Chi	A	P	7	1-2
	BLTL				

TWOMBLY, GEORGE FREDERICK
b.June 4,1892 Boston,Mass.

Yr	Cl	Lea	Pos	G	Rec
1914	Cin	N	O	68	.233
1915	Cin	N	O	46	.197
1916	Cin	N	O	3	.000
1917	Bos	N	O	32	.186
1919	Was	A	O	1	.000
	BRTR			150	.211

TYACK, JAMES FREDERICK
b.Jan.9,1911 Florence,Mont.

Yr	Cl	Lea	Pos	G	Rec
1943	Phi	A	O	54	.258
	BLTR				

TYLER, FREDERICK FRANKLIN
b.Dec.16,1891 Derry,N.H.
d.Oct.14,1945

Yr	Cl	Lea	Pos	G	Rec
1914	Bos	N	C	6	.105
	TR				

TYLER, GEORGE ALBERT (Lefty)
b.Dec.14,1889 Derry,N.H.
d.Sept.29,1953

Yr	Cl	Lea	Pos	G	Rec
1910	Bos	N	P	4	0-0
1911	Bos	N	P	28	7-10
1912	Bos	N	P	42	12-22
1913	Bos	N	P	43	16-17
1914	Bos	N	P	38	16-14
1915	Bos	N	P	45	10-9
1916	Bos	N	P	39	17-10
1917	Bos	N	P	61	14-12
1918	Chi	N	P	38	19-8
1919	Chi	N	P	6	2-2
1920	Chi	N	P	29	11-12
1921	Chi	N	P	19	3-2
	BLTL			392	127-118

TYLER, JOHN ANTHONY (Ty-Ty)
b.July 30,1909 Mt.Pleasant,Pa.

Yr	Cl	Lea	Pos	G	Rec
1934	Bos	N	O	3	.167
1935	Bos	N	O	13	.340
	BBTR			16	.321

TYNG, JAMES ALEXANDER
b.Mar.27,1856 Philadelphia,Pa.
d.Oct.30,1931

Yr	Cl	Lea	Pos	G	Rec
1879	Bos	N	P	3	1-2
1888	Phi	N	P	1	0-0
				4	1-2

TYREE, EARL CARLTON (Ty)
b.Mar.4,1890 Rushville,Ill.
d.May 17,1954

Yr	Cl	Lea	Pos	G	Rec
1914	Chi	N	C	1	.000
	BRTR				

TYRIVER, DAVID BURTON
b.Oct.31,1937 Oshkosh,Wis.

Yr	Cl	Lea	Pos	G	Rec
1962	Cle	A	P	4	0-0
	BRTR				

TYSON, ALBERT THOMAS (Ty)
b.June 1,1897 Wilkes-Barre,Pa.
d.Aug.16,1953

Yr	Cl	Lea	Pos	G	Rec
1926	NY	N	O	97	.293
1927	NY	N	O	43	.264
1928	Bro	N	O	59	.271
	BRTR			199	.280

TYSON, CECIL WASHINGTON (Slim)
b.Dec.6,1914 Elm City,N.C.

Yr	Cl	Lea	Pos	G	Rec
1944	Phi	N	H	1	.000
	BLTR				

UCHRINSCKO, JAMES EMERSON
b.Oct.20,1902 W.Newton,Pa.

Yr	Cl	Lea	Pos	G	Rec
1926	Was	A	P	3	0-0
	BLTR				

UECKER, ROBERT GEORGE
b.Jan.26,1935 Milwaukee,Wis.

Yr	Cl	Lea	Pos	G	Rec
1962	Mil	N	C	33	.250
	BRTR				

UHALT, BERNARD BARTHOLOMEW (Frenchy)
b.Apr.27,1910 Bakersfield,Cal.

Yr	Cl	Lea	Pos	G	Rec
1934	Chi	A	O	57	.242
	BLTR				

UHLE, GEORGE ERNEST (The Bull)
b.Sept.18,1898 Cleveland,O.

Yr	Cl	Lea	Pos	G	Rec
1919	Cle	A	P	26	10-5
1920	Cle	A	P	27	4-5
1921	Cle	A	P	48	16-13
1922	Cle	A	P	56	22-16
1923	Cle	A	P	58	26-16
1924	Cle	A	P	59	9-15
1925	Cle	A	P	55	13-11
1926	Cle	A	P	50	27-11
1927	Cle	A	P	43	8-9
1928	Cle	A	P	55	12-17
1929	Det	A	P	40	15-11
1930	Det	A	P	59	12-12
1931	Det	A	P	53	11-12
1932	Det	A	P	38	6-6
1933	Det	A	P	1	0-0
1933	NY	N	P	8	1-1
1933	NY	A	P	12	6-1
1934	NY	A	P	10	2-4
1936	Cle	A	P	24	0-1
	BRTR			722	200-166

UHLE, ROBERT ELWOOD
b.Sept.17,1914 San Francisco,Cal.

Yr	Cl	Lea	Pos	G	Rec
1938	Chi	A	P	1	0-0
1940	Det	A	P	1	0-0
	BBTL			2	0-0

UHLER, MAURICE W.
b.Dec.14,1886 Pikesville,Md.
d.May 4,1918

Yr	Cl	Lea	Pos	G	Rec
1914	Cin	N	O	46	.214
	BRTR				

UHLIR, CHARLES
b.July 30,1912 Chicago,Ill.

Yr	Cl	Lea	Pos	G	Rec
1934	Chi	A	O	14	.148
	BLTL				

ULATOWSKI, CLEMENT LAMBERT (Played under name of Clement Lambert Clemens)

ULISNEY, MICHAEL EDWARD
b.Sept.28,1917 Greenwall,Pa.

Yr	Cl	Lea	Pos	G	Rec
1945	Bos	N	C	11	.389
	BRTR				

ULLRICH, CARLOS SANTIAGO CASTELLO (Sandy)
b.July 25,1922 Havana,Cuba.

Yr	Cl	Lea	Pos	G	Rec
1944	Was	A	P	3	0-0
1945	Was	A	P	28	3-3
	BRTR			31	3-3

ULRICH, FRANK W. (Dutch)
b.Nov.18,1899 Baltimore,Md.
d.Feb.12,1929

Yr	Cl	Lea	Pos	G	Rec
1925	Phi	N	P	21	3-3
1926	Phi	N	P	45	8-13
1927	Phi	N	P	32	8-11
	BRTR			98	19-27

ULRICH, GEORGE F.
b.Philadelphia,Pa.

Yr	Cl	Lea	Pos	G	Rec
1892	Was	N	S	6	.291
1893	Cin	N	O	1	.000
1896	NY	N	O	14	.178
				21	.180

UMBRICHT, JAMES
b.Sept.17,1930 Chicago,Ill.

Yr	Cl	Lea	Pos	G	Rec
1959	Pit	N	P	1	0-0
1960	Pit	N	P	17	1-2
1961	Pit	N	P	1	0-0
1962	Hou	N	P	34	4-0
	BRTR			53	5-2

UMPHLETT, THOMAS MULLEN
b.May 12,1930 Scotland Neck,N.C.

Yr	Cl	Lea	Pos	G	Rec
1953	Bos	A	O	137	.283
1954	Was	A	1-O	114	.219
1955	Was	A	O	110	.217
	BRTR			361	.246

UNDERHILL, WILLIE VERN
b.Sept.6,1904 Yowell,Tex.

Yr	Cl	Lea	Pos	G	Rec
1927	Cle	A	P	4	0-2
1928	Cle	A	P	11	1-2
	BRTR			15	1-4

UNDERWOOD, FRED G.
b.1869 Kansas
d.Jan.26,1906

Yr	Cl	Lea	Pos	G	Rec
1894	Bro	N	P	7	2-3

UNGLAUB, ROBERT ALEXANDER
b.July 31,1881 Baltimore,Md.
d.Nov.29,1916

Yr	Cl	Lea	Pos	G	Rec
1904	NY	A	3	6	.211
1904	Bos	A	3	7	.182
1905	Bos	A	3	43	.223
1907	Bos	A	M-1	139	.255
1908	Bos	A	1	72	.262
1908	Was	A	3	72	.307
1909	Was	A	1-2-O	130	.264
1910	Was	A	1	124	.234
	BRTR			593	.258

UNSER, ALBERT BERNARD
b.Oct.21,1914 Morrisville,Ill.

Yr	Cl	Lea	Pos	G	Rec
1942	Det	A	C	4	.375
1943	Det	A	C	38	.248
1944	Det	A	C-2	11	.120
1945	Cin	N	C	67	.265
	BRTR			120	.252

UPCHURCH, JEFFERSON WOODROW (Woody)
b.Apr.13,1911 Buies Creek,N.C.

Yr	Cl	Lea	Pos	G	Rec
1935	Phi	A	P	3	0-2
1936	Phi	A	P	7	0-2
	BRTL			10	0-4

UPHAM, WILLIAM LAWRENCE
b.Apr.4,1888 Akron,O.

Yr	Cl	Lea	Pos	G	Rec
1915	Bro	F	P	26	6-8
1918	Bos	N	P	3	1-1
	BBTR			29	7-9

UPP, GEORGE HENRY (Jerry)
b.Dec.10,1883 Sandusky,O.
d.June 30,1937

Yr	Cl	Lea	Pos	G	Rec
1909	Cle	A	P	7	2-1
	TL				

UPRIGHT, R. T. (Dixie)
b.May 30,1926 Cabarrus Co.,N.C.

Yr	Cl	Lea	Pos	G	Rec
1953	St.L	A	H	9	.250
	BLTL				

UPTON, THOMAS HERBERT (Muscles)
b.Dec.29,1926 Esther,Mo.

Yr	Cl	Lea	Pos	G	Rec
1950	St.L	A	2-S-3	124	.237
1951	St.L	A	S	52	.198
1952	Was	A	S	5	.000
	BRTR			181	.225

UPTON, WILLIAM RAY
b.July 18,1929 Esther,Mo.

Yr	Cl	Lea	Pos	G	Rec
1954	Phi	A	P	2	0-0
	BRTR				

URBAN, JACK ELMER
b.Dec.5,1928 Omaha,Neb.

Yr	Cl	Lea	Pos	G	Rec
1957	KC	A	P	37	7-4
1958	KC	A	P	31	8-11
1959	St.L	N	P	8	0-0
	BRTR			76	15-15

URBAN, LOUIS JOHN (Luke)
b.Mar.20,1898 Fall River,Mass.

Yr	Cl	Lea	Pos	G	Rec
1927	Bos	N	C	35	.288
1928	Bos	N	C	15	.176
	BRTR			50	.273

URBANSKI, WILLIAM MICHAEL
b.June 15,1904 Linoleumville,S.I.,N.Y.

Yr	Cl	Lea	Pos	G	Rec
1931	Bos	N	S-3	82	.238
1932	Bos	N	S	136	.272
1933	Bos	N	S	144	.251
1934	Bos	N	S	146	.293
1935	Bos	N	S	132	.229
1936	Bos	N	S-3	122	.261
1937	Bos	N	H	1	.000
	BRTR			763	.260

URY, LOUIS
b.Ft.Smith,Ark.

Yr	Cl	Lea	Pos	G	Rec
1903	St.L	N	1	2	.142
	TR				

USHER, ROBERT ROYCE
b.Mar.1,1925 San Diego,Cal.

Yr	Cl	Lea	Pos	G	Rec
1946	Cin	N	3-O	92	.204
1947	Cin	N	O	9	.182
1950	Cin	N	O	106	.259
1951	Cin	N	O	114	.208
1952	Chi	N	H	1	.000
1957	Cle	A	3-O	10	.125
1957	Was	A	O	96	.261
	BRTR			428	.235

USSAT, WILLIAM AUGUST
b.Apr.11,1904 Dayton,O.
d.May 29,1959

Yr	Cl	Lea	Pos	G	Rec
1925	Cle	A	2	1	.000
1927	Cle	A	3	4	.187
	BRTR			5	.187

VACHE, ERNEST LEWIS (Tex)
b.Nov.17,1895 Santa Monica,Cal.
d.June 11,1953

Yr	Cl	Lea	Pos	G	Rec
1925	Bos	A	O	110	.313
	BRTR				

VADEBONCOEUR, EUGENE F.
b.Syracuse,N.Y.
d.Oct.16,1935

Yr	Cl	Lea	Pos	G	Rec
1884	Phi	N	C	4	.214

VAIL, ROBERT GARFIELD (Doc)
b.1882 Hodgdon,Me.

Yr	Cl	Lea	Pos	G	Rec
1908	Pit	N	P	4	1-2

VALDES, ARMANDO VIERA
b.May 2,1922 Cardenas,Cuba.

Yr	Cl	Lea	Pos	G	Rec
1944	Was	A	H	1	.000
	BRTR				

VALDES, RENE GUTIERREZ (Real name Rene Valdes Gutierrez)
b.June 2,1929 Guanabacoa,Cuba

Yr	Cl	Lea	Pos	G	Rec
1957	Bro	N	P	5	1-1
	BRTR				

VALDIVIELSO, JOSE LOPEZ
b.May 22,1934 Matanzas,Cuba

Yr	Cl	Lea	Pos	G	Rec
1955	Was	A	S	94	.221
1956	Was	A	S	90	.236
1959	Was	A	S	24	.286
1960	Was	A	S-3	117	.213
1961	Min	A	2-S-3	76	.195
	BRTR			401	.219

VALENTINE, FRED LEE
b.Jan.19,1935 Clarkside,Miss.

Yr	Cl	Lea	Pos	G	Rec
1959	Bal	A	O	12	.316
	BBTR				

VALENTINE, HAROLD LEWIS
(Corky)
b.Jan.4,1930 Troy,O.

Yr	Cl	Lea	Pos	G	Rec
1954	Cin	N	P	36	12-11
1955	Cin	N	P	10	2-1
	BRTR			46	14-12

VALENTINE, JOHN G.
b.Nov.21,1855 Brooklyn,N.Y.

Yr	Cl	Lea	Pos	G	Rec
1883	Col	a	P-O	15	{2-9 .294

VALENTINE, ROBERT

Yr	Cl	Lea	Pos	G	Rec
1876	Mut	N	C	1	.000

VALENTINETTI, VITO JOHN
b.Sept.16,1929 W.New York,N.J.

Yr	Cl	Lea	Pos	G	Rec
1954	Chi	A	P	1	0-0
1956	Chi	N	P	42	6-4
1957	Chi	N	P	9	0-0
1957	Cle	A	P	11	2-2
1958	Det	A	P	15	1-0
1958	Was	A	P	23	4-6
1959	Was	A	P	7	0-2
	BRTR			108	13-14

VALENZUELA, BENJAMIN BELTRAN
b.June 2,1933 Los Mochis,Mexico

Yr	Cl	Lea	Pos	G	Rec
1958	St.L	N	3	10	.214
	BRTR				

VALO, ELMER WILLIAM
b.Mar.5,1921 Ribnik,Czecho-Slovakia.

Yr	Cl	Lea	Pos	G	Rec
1940	Phi	A	O	6	.348
1941	Phi	A	O	15	.420
1942	Phi	A	O	133	.251
1943	Phi	A	O	77	.221
1946	Phi	A	O	108	.307
1947	Phi	A	O	112	.300
1948	Phi	A	O	113	.305
1949	Phi	A	O	150	.283
1950	Phi	A	O	129	.280
1951	Phi	A	O	123	.302
1952	Phi	A	O	129	.281
1953	Phi	A	O	50	.224
1954	Phi	A	O	95	.214
1955	KC	A	O	112	.364
1956	KC	A	O	9	.222
1956	Phi	N	O	98	.289
1957	Bro	N	O	81	.273
1958	LA	N	O	65	.248
1959	Cle	A	O	34	.292
1960	NY	A	O	8	.000
1960	Was	A	O	76	.281
1961	Min	A	O	33	.156
1961	Phi	N	O	50	.186
	BLTR			1806	.282

VAN ALSTYNE, CLAYTON EMORY (Spike)
b.May 24,1900 Stuyvesant,N.Y.
d.Jan.5,1960

Yr	Cl	Lea	Pos	G	Rec
1927	Was	A	P	2	0-0
1928	Was	A	P	4	0-0
	BRTR			6	0-0

VAN ATTA, RUSSELL
(Sheriff)
b.June 21,1906 Augusta,N.J.

Yr	Cl	Lea	Pos	G	Rec
1933	NY	A	P	26	12-4
1934	NY	A	P	28	3-5
1935	NY	A	P	5	0-0
1935	St.L	A	P	53	9-16
1936	St.L	A	P	53	4-7
1937	St.L	A	P	16	1-2
1938	St.L	A	P	25	4-7
1939	St.L	A	P	2	0-0
	BLTL			208	33-41

VAN BRABANT, CAMILLE OSCAR (Ossie)
b.Sept.28,1928 Berkley,Mich.

Yr	Cl	Lea	Pos	G	Rec
1954	Phi	A	P	9	0-2
1955	KC	A	P	2	0-0
	BRTR			11	0-2

VAN BUREN, EDWARD EUGENE
(Deacon)
b.Dec.14,1870 La Salle,Co.,Ill.
d.June 29.1957

Yr	Cl	Lea	Pos	G	Rec
1904	Bro	N	O	1	1.000
1904	Phi	N	O	12	.233
				13	.250

VAN CAMP, ALBERT JOSEPH
b.Sept.7,1904 Moline,Ill.

Yr	Cl	Lea	Pos	G	Rec
1928	Cle	A	1	5	.235
1931	Bos	A	1-O	101	.275
1932	Bos	A	1	34	.223
	BRTR			140	.261

VANCE, CLARENCE ARTHUR
(Dazzy)
b.Mar.4,1891 Orient,Ia.
d.Feb 16,1961

Yr	Cl	Lea	Pos	G	Rec
1915	Pit	N	P	1	0-1
1915	NY	A	P	8	0-3
1918	NY	A	P	2	0-0
1922	Bro	N	P	36	18-12
1923	Bro	N	P	37	18-15
1924	Bro	N	P	35	28-6
1925	Bro	N	P	31	22-9
1926	Bro	N	P	22	9-10
1927	Bro	N	P	34	16-15
1928	Bro	N	P	38	22-10
1929	Bro	N	P	31	14-13
1930	Bro	N	P	35	17-15
1931	Bro	N	P	30	11-13
1932	Bro	N	P	27	12-11
1933	St.L	N	P	28	6-2
1934	Cin	N	P	6	0-2
1934	St.L	N	P	19	1-1
1935	Bro	N	P	20	3-2
	BRTR			440	197-140

VANCE, JOSEPH ALBERT
(Sandy)
b.Sept.16,1905 Devine,Tex.

Yr	Cl	Lea	Pos	G	Rec
1935	Chi	A	P	10	2-2
1937	NY	A	P	2	1-0
1938	NY	A	P	4	0-0
	BRTR			16	3-2

VAN CUYK, CHRISTIAN GERALD
b.Mar.1,1927 Kimberly,Wis.

Yr	Cl	Lea	Pos	G	Rec
1950	Bro	N	P	12	1-3
1951	Bro	N	P	9	1-2
1952	Bro	N	P	23	5-6
	BLTL			44	7-11

VAN CUYK, JOHN HENRY
b.July 7,1921 Little Chute,Wis.

Yr	Cl	Lea	Pos	G	Rec
1947	Bro	N	P	2	0-0
1948	Bro	N	P	3	0-0
1949	Bro	N	P	2	0-0
	BLTL			7	0-0

VANDAGRIFT, CARL WILLIAM
b.Apr.22,1884 Centralia,Ill.
d.Oct.9,1920

Yr	Cl	Lea	Pos	G	Rec
1914	Ind	F	2	42	.246
	BRTR				

VANDEMANN, FREDERICK H.
(Played under name of
Frederick H. Abbott)

VANDENBERG, HAROLD HARRIS
(Hy)
b.Mar.17,1909 Abilene,Kan.

Yr	Cl	Lea	Pos	G	Rec
1935	Bos	A	P	3	0-0

(Continued)

Yr	Cl	Lea	Pos	G	Rec
1937	NY	N	P	1	0-1
1938	NY	N	P	6	0-1
1939	NY	N	P	2	0-0
1940	NY	N	P	13	1-1
1944	Chi	N	P	35	7-4
1945	Chi	N	P	30	7-3
	BRTR			90	15-10

VANDER MEER, JOHN SAMUEL
b.Nov.2,1914 Prospect Park,N.J.

Yr	Cl	Lea	Pos	G	Rec
1937	Cin	N	P	21	3-5
1938	Cin	N	P	33	15-10
1939	Cin	N	P	30	5-9
1940	Cin	N	P	12	3-1
1941	Cin	N	P	35	16-13
1942	Cin	N	P	37	18-12
1943	Cin	N	P	40	15-16
1946	Cin	N	P	33	10-12
1947	Cin	N	P	31	9-14
1948	Cin	N	P	41	17-14
1949	Cin	N	P	33	5-10
1950	Chi	N	P	35	3-4
1951	Cle	A	P	1	0-1
	BRTL			382	119-121

VAN DUSEN, FREDERICK WILLIAM
b.July 31,1937 Jackson Heights,N.Y.

Yr	Cl	Lea	Pos	G	Rec
1955	Phi	N	H	1	.000
	BL				

VAN DYKE, BENJAMIN HARRISON
b.1888 Harrisville,Pa.

Yr	Cl	Lea	Pos	G	Rec
1909	Phi	N	P	2	0-0
1912	Bos	A	P	3	1-0
	BRTL			5	1-0

VAN DYKE, WILLIAM JENNINGS
b.Dec.15,1863 Paris,Ill.
d.May 5,1933

Yr	Cl	Lea	Pos	G	Rec
1890	Tol	a	O	128	.266
1892	St.L	N	O	3	.000
1893	Bos	N	O	3	.250
	BRTR			134	.262

VANGILDER, ELAM RUSSELL
b.Apr.23,1896 Cape Girardeau,Mo.

Yr	Cl	Lea	Pos	G	Rec
1919	St.L	A	P	3	1-0
1920	St.L	A	P	24	3-8
1921	St.L	A	P	31	11-12
1922	St.L	A	P	45	19-13
1923	St.L	A	P	45	16-17
1924	St.L	A	P	43	5-10
1925	St.L	A	P	51	14-8
1926	St.L	A	P	42	9-11
1927	St.L	A	P	44	10-12
1928	Det	A	P	38	11-10
1929	Det	A	P	6	0-1
	BRTR			372	99-102

VAN HALTREN, GEORGE E.
(Rip)
b.Mar.30,1866 St.Louis,Mo.
d.Oct.1,1945

Yr	Cl	Lea	Pos	G	Rec
1887	Chi	N	P-O	44	{12-7 .278
1888	Chi	N	P-O	81	{13-11 .283
1889	Chi	N	O	134	.322
1890	Bro	p	P-O	92	{15-10 .346
1891	Bal	a	M-P-S-O	136	{0-1 .316
1892	Bal	N	M-O	135	.304
1892	Pit	N	O	13	.212
1893	Pit	N	O	123	.350
1894	NY	N	O	139	.333
1895	NY	N	O	131	.338
1896	NY	N	P-O	133	{1-0 .353
1897	NY	N	O	131	.332
1898	NY	N	O	155	.315
1899	NY	N	O	153	.301
1900	NY	N	O	141	.319
1901	NY	N	P-O	133	{0-1 .342

Yr	Cl	Lea	Pos	G	Rec
(Continued)					
1902	NY	N	O	26	.250
1903	NY	N	O	75	.257
	BLTL			1975	41-30 .322

VANN, JOHN SILAS
b.June 7,1893 Fairland,Okla.
d.June 10,1958

Yr	Cl	Lea	Pos	G	Rec
1913	St.L	N	H	1	.000
	BRTR				

VAN NOY, JAY LOWELL
b.Nov.4,1928 Garland,Utah

Yr	Cl	Lea	Pos	G	Rec
1951	St.L	N	O	6	.000
	BLTR				

VAN ROBAYS, MAURICE RENE
(Bomber)
b.Nov.15,1914 Detroit,Mich.

Yr	Cl	Lea	Pos	G	Rec
1939	Pit	N	O	27	.314
1940	Pit	N	1-O	145	.273
1941	Pit	N	O	129	.282
1942	Pit	N	O	100	.232
1943	Pit	N	O	69	.288
1946	Pit	N	1-O	59	.212
	BRTR			529	.267

VAN TAPPEN, W.
b.1891

Yr	Cl	Lea	Pos	G	Rec
1914	KC	F	3	18	.200
	BRTR				

VAN ZANDT, CHARLES ISAAC
(Ike)
b.1877 Brooklyn,N.Y.
d.Sept.14,1908

Yr	Cl	Lea	Pos	G	Rec
1901	NY	N	P	3	0-0
1904	Chi	N	O	3	.000
1905	St.L	A	O	94	.233
				100	0-0 .224

VAN ZANT, RICHARD

Yr	Cl	Lea	Pos	G	Rec
1888	Cle	a	3	10	.187

VARENHORST, H.
b.St.Louis,Mo.

Yr	Cl	Lea	Pos	G	Rec
1904	St.L	A	H	1	.000

VARGA, ANDREW WILLIAM
b.Dec.11,1930 Chicago,Ill.

Yr	Cl	Lea	Pos	G	Rec
1950	Chi	N	P	1	0-0
1951	Chi	N	P	2	0-0
	BRTL			3	0-0

VARGAS, ROBERTO ENRIQUE
b.May 29,1929 Santurce, Puerto Rico

Yr	Cl	Lea	Pos	G	Rec
1955	Mil	N	P	25	0-0
	BLTL				

VARGUS, WILLIAM FAY
b.Nov.11,1900 N.Scituate,Mass.

Yr	Cl	Lea	Pos	G	Rec
1925	Bos	N	P	11	1-1
1926	Bos	N	P	4	0-0
	BLTL			15	1-1

VARNER, GLEN GANN (Buck)
b.Aug.17,1930 Hixon,Tenn.

Yr	Cl	Lea	Pos	G	Rec
1952	Was	A	O	2	.000
	BLTR				

VARNEY, LAWRENCE DELANO
(Dike)
b.Aug.9,1880 Dover,N.H.

Yr	Cl	Lea	Pos	G	Rec
1902	Cle	A	P	3	2-1
	TL				

VASBINDER, MOSES CALHOUN
b.July 19,1880 Scio,O.
d.Dec.22,1950

Yr	Cl	Lea	Pos	G	Rec
1902	Cle	A	P	2	0-0
	BRTR				

VAUGHAN, CECIL PORTER
b.May 11,1919 Stevensville,Va.

Yr	Cl	Lea	Pos	G	Rec
1940	Phi	A	P	18	2-9
1941	Phi	A	P	5	0-2
1946	Phi	A	P	1	0-0
	BRTL			24	2-11

VAUGHAN, JOSEPH FLOYD
(Arky)
b.Mar.9,1912 Clifty,Ark.
d.Aug.30,1952

Yr	Cl	Lea	Pos	G	Rec
1932	Pit	N	S	129	.318
1933	Pit	N	S	152	.314
1934	Pit	N	S	149	.333
1935	Pit	N	S	137	.385
1936	Pit	N	S	156	.335
1937	Pit	N	S-O	126	.322
1938	Pit	N	S	148	.322
1939	Pit	N	S	152	.306
1940	Pit	N	S-3	156	.300
1941	Pit	N	S-3	106	.316
1942	Bro	N	2-S-3	128	.277
1943	Bro	N	S-3	149	.305
1947	Bro	N	3-O	64	.325
1948	Bro	N	3-O	65	.244
	BLTR			1817	.318

VAUGHN, CLARENCE LEROY
b.Sept.4,1911 Sedalia,Mo.
d.Mar.1,1937

Yr	Cl	Lea	Pos	G	Rec
1934	Phi	A	P	2	0-0
	BBTR				

VAUGHN, FREDERICK THOMAS
(Muscles)
b.Oct.18,1918 Coalinga,Cal.

Yr	Cl	Lea	Pos	G	Rec
1944	Was	A	2-3	30	.257
1945	Was	A	2-S	80	.235
	BRTR			110	.242

VAUGHN, HARRY FRANCIS
(Farmer)
b.Mar.1,1864 Rural,O.
d.Feb.21,1914

Yr	Cl	Lea	Pos	G	Rec
1886	Cin	a	C	1	.000
1888	Lou	a	C-O	49	.203
1889	Lou	a	C	90	.233
1890	NY	p	C	45	.248
1891	Cin	a	P-C-1-3-O	45	0-0 .255
1891	Mil	a	C-1	24	.330
1892	Cin	N	C	85	.257
1893	Cin	N	C-1-O	119	.299
1894	Cin	N	C-1	67	.309
1895	Cin	N	C	88	.305
1896	Cin	N	C-1	113	.297
1897	Cin	N	1	50	.305
1898	Cin	N	C-1	73	.303
1899	Cin	N	1	28	.178
	BRTR			877	0-0 .276

VAUGHN, JAMES LESLIE
(Hippo)
b.Apr.9,1888 Weatherford,Tex.

Yr	Cl	Lea	Pos	G	Rec
1908	NY	A	P	2	0-0
1910	NY	A	P	29	13-11
1911	NY	A	P	26	8-10
1912	NY	A	P	13	2-8
1912	Was	A	P	9	4-3
1913	Chi	N	P	7	5-1
1914	Chi	N	P	42	21-13
1915	Chi	N	P	43	20-12
1916	Chi	N	P	44	17-15
1917	Chi	N	P	41	23-13
1918	Chi	N	P	35	22-10
1919	Chi	N	P	38	21-14
1920	Chi	N	P	40	19-16
1921	Chi	N	P	17	3-11
	BLTL			386	178-137

VAUGHN, ROBERT
b.June 4,1885 Stamford,N.Y.

Yr	Cl	Lea	Pos	G	Rec
1909	NY	A	2	5	.143
1915	St.L	F	2	144	.274
	BRTR			149	.271

VEACH, ALVIS LINDELL
b.Aug.6,1911 Maylene,Ala.

Yr	Cl	Lea	Pos	G	Rec
1935	Phi	A	P	2	0-2
	BRTR				

VEACH, ROBERT HENRY
b.June 29,1888 St.Charles,Ky.
d.Aug.7,1945

Yr	Cl	Lea	Pos	G	Rec
1912	Det	A	O	23	.342
1913	Det	A	O	138	.269
1914	Det	A	O	149	.275
1915	Det	A	O	152	.313
1916	Det	A	O	150	.306
1917	Det	A	O	154	.319
1918	Det	A	P-O	127	0-0 .279
1919	Det	A	O	139	.355
1920	Det	A	O	154	.307
1921	Det	A	O	150	.338
1922	Det	A	O	155	.327
1923	Det	A	O	114	.321
1924	Bos	A	O	142	.295
1925	Bos	A	O	1	.200
1925	NY	A	O	56	.353
1925	Was	A	O	18	.243
	BLTR			1822	0-0 .310

VEACH, WILLIAM WALTER
(Peek-A-Boo)
b.June 15,1863 Indianapolis,Ind.
d.Nov.12,1937

Yr	Cl	Lea	Pos	G	Rec
1884	KC	U	P-O	27	2-9 .127
1887	Lou	a	P	1	0-1
1890	Cle	N	1	62	.237
1890	Pit	N	1	8	.300
				98	2-10 .216

VEAL, ORVILLE INMAN
(Coot)
b.July 9,1932 Sandersville,Ga.

Yr	Cl	Lea	Pos	G	Rec
1958	Det	A	S	58	.256
1959	Det	A	S	77	.202
1960	Det	A	2-S-3	27	.297
1961	Was	A	S	69	.202
1962	Pit	N	H	1	.000
	BRTR			232	.231

VEALE, ROBERT ANDREW
b.Oct.28,1935 Birmingham,Ala.

Yr	Cl	Lea	Pos	G	Rec
1962	Pit	N	P	11	2-2
	BBTL				

VEDDER, LOUIS EDWARD
b.Apr.20,1897 Oakville,Mich.

Yr	Cl	Lea	Pos	G	Rec
1920	Det	A	P	1	0-0
	BRTR				

VEIGEL, ALLEN FRANCIS
b.Jan.30,1917 Tuscarawas,O.

Yr	Cl	Lea	Pos	G	Rec
1939	Bos	N	P	2	0-1
	BRTR				

VEIL, FREDERICK WILLIAM
(Bucky)
b.1881 Williamsport,Pa.
d.Apr.16,1931

Yr	Cl	Lea	Pos	G	Rec
1903	Pit	N	P	12	5-3
1904	Pit	N	P	1	0-0
	TR			13	5-3

VELTMAN, ARTHUR PATRICK
(Pat)
b.Mar.24,1906 Mobile,Ala.

Yr	Cl	Lea	Pos	G	Rec
1926	Chi	A	O	4	.000
1928	NY	N	O	1	.333
1929	NY	N	C	2	.000
1931	Bos	N	H	1	.000
1932	NY	N	H	2	.000
1934	Pit	N	C	12	.107
	BRTR			22	.132

VENTURA, VINCENT
b.Apr.18,1917 New York,N.Y.

Yr	Cl	Lea	Pos	G	Rec
1945	Was	A	O	18	.207
	BBTR				

VERBAN, EMIL MATTHEW
(Antelope)
b.Aug.27,1915 Lincoln,Ill.

Yr	Cl	Lea	Pos	G	Rec
1944	St.L	N	2	146	.257
1945	St.L	N	2	155	.278
1946	St.L	N	2	1	.000
1946	Phi	N	2	138	.275
1947	Phi	N	2	155	.285
1948	Phi	N	2	55	.231
1948	Chi	N	2	56	.295
1949	Chi	N	2	98	.289
1950	Chi	N	2-S-3-O	45	.108
1950	Bos	N	2	4	.000
	BRTR			853	.272

VERBLE, GENE KERMIT
b.June 29,1928 Concord,N.C.

Yr	Cl	Lea	Pos	G	Rec
1951	Was	A	2-S-3	68	.203
1953	Was	A	S	13	.190
	BRTR			81	.202

VERDEL, ALFRED ALBERT
b.June 10,1921 Punxsutawney,Pa.

Yr	Cl	Lea	Pos	G	Rec
1944	Phi	N	P	1	0-0
	BRTR				

VERDI, FRANK MICHAEL
b.June 2,1926 Brooklyn,N.Y.

Yr	Cl	Lea	Pos	G	Rec
1953	NY	A	S	1	.000
	BRTR				

VEREKER, THOMAS

Yr	Cl	Lea	Pos	G	Rec
1915	Bal	F	P	2	0-0

VERGEZ, JOHN LOUIS
b.July 9,1906 Oakland,Cal.

Yr	Cl	Lea	Pos	G	Rec
1931	NY	N	3	152	.278
1932	NY	N	3	118	.261
1933	NY	N	3	123	.271
1934	NY	N	3	108	.200
1935	Phi	N	S-3	148	.249
1936	Phi	N	3	15	.275
1936	St.L	N	3	8	.167
	BRTR			672	.255

VERNON, JAMES BARTON
(Mickey)
b.Apr.22,1918 Marcus Hook,Pa.

Yr	Cl	Lea	Pos	G	Rec
1939	Was	A	1	76	.257
1940	Was	A	1	5	.158
1941	Was	A	1	138	.299
1942	Was	A	1	151	.271
1943	Was	A	1	145	.268
1946	Was	A	1	148	.353
1947	Was	A	1	154	.265
1948	Was	A	1	150	.242
1949	Cle	A	1	153	.291
1950	Cle	A	1	28	.189
1950	Was	A	1	90	.306
1951	Was	A	1	141	.293
1952	Was	A	1	154	.251
1953	Was	A	1	152	.337
1954	Was	A	1	151	.290
1955	Was	A	1	150	.301
1956	Bos	A	1	119	.310
1957	Bos	A	1	102	.241
1958	Cle	A	1	119	.293
1959	Mil	N	1-O	74	.220
1960	Pit	N	H	9	.125
	BLTL			2409	286

Non-playing manager Was(A) 1961-62

VERNON, JOSEPH HENRY
b.Nov.25,1889 Mansfield,Mass.

Yr	Cl	Lea	Pos	G	Rec
1912	Chi	N	P	1	0-0
1914	Bro	F	P	1	0-0
	BRTR			2	0-0

VERSALLES, ZOILO
b.Dec.18,1939 Havana,Cuba

Yr	Cl	Lea	Pos	G	Rec
1959	Was	A	S	29	.153
1960	Was	A	S	15	.133
1961	Min	A	S	129	.280
1962	Min	A	S	160	.241
	BRTR			333	.250

VIAU, LEON
b.July 5,1866 Corinth,Vt.
d.Dec.31,1947

Yr	Cl	Lea	Pos	G	Rec
1888	Cin	a	P-O	41	27-14 .085
1889	Cin	a	P	47	21-19
1890	Cin	N	P	12	7-3
1890	Cle	N	P	14	4-10
1891	Cle	N	P	39	18-20
1892	Cle	N	P	1	1-0
1892	Lou	N	P	20	4-11
1892	Bos	N	P	2	1-0
	BRTR			176	83-77 .141

VICK, HENRY ARTHUR
(Ernie)
b.July 2,1900 Toledo,O.

Yr	Cl	Lea	Pos	G	Rec
1922	St.L	N	C	3	.333
1924	St.L	N	C	16	.348
1925	St.L	N	C	14	.188
1926	St.L	N	C	24	.196
	BRTR			57	.232

VICK, SAMUEL BRUCE
b.Apr.12,1895 Central Academy,Miss.

Yr	Cl	Lea	Pos	G	Rec
1917	NY	A	O	10	.278
1918	NY	A	O	2	.667
1919	NY	A	O	106	.248
1920	NY	A	O	51	.220
1921	Bos	A	O	44	.260
	BRTR			213	.248

VICKERS, HARRY PORTER
(Rube)
b.May 17,1878 Pittsford,Mich.
d.Dec.9,1958

Yr	Cl	Lea	Pos	G	Rec
1902	Cin	N	P-C	4	0-3 .363
1903	Bro	N	P-O	3	0-1 .000
1907	Phi	A	P	10	2-2
1908	Phi	A	P	53	18-19
1909	Phi	A	P	18	2-2
	BLTR			88	22-27 .167

VICKERY, THOMAS GILL
(Vinegar Tom)
b.May 5,1867 Milford,Mass.
d.Mar.21,1921

Yr	Cl	Lea	Pos	G	Rec
1890	Phi	N	P	45	24-18
1891	Chi	N	P	14	6-5
1892	Bal	N	P	19	8-11
1893	Phi	N	P	14	5-5
				92	43-39

VICO, GEORGE STEVE
(Sam)
b.Aug.9,1923 San Fernando,Cal.

Yr	Cl	Lea	Pos	G	Rec
1948	Det	A	1	144	.267
1949	Det	A	1	67	.190
	BLTR			211	.250

VINES, ROBERT EARL
b.Feb.25,1898 Waxahachie,Tex.

Yr	Cl	Lea	Pos	G	Rec
1924	St.L	N	P	2	0-0
1925	Phi	N	P	3	0-0
	BRTR			5	0-0

VINSON, ERNEST AUGUSTUS
(Rube)
b.Mar.20,1879 Dover,Del.
d.Oct.12,1951

Yr	Cl	Lea	Pos	G	Rec
1904	Cle	A	O	15	.269
1905	Cle	A	O	38	.195
1906	Chi	A	O	10	.250
				63	.220

VINTON, WILLIAM M.
b.Apr.27,1865 Winthrop,Mass.
d.Sept.2,1893

Yr	Cl	Lea	Pos	G	Rec
1884	Phi	N	P	21	9-8

(Continued)

Yr	Cl	Lea	Pos	G	Rec
1885	Phi	N	P	9	3-6
1885	Ath	a	P-O	7	4-3 .192
	BRTR			37	16-17 .119

VIOX, JAMES HARRY
b.Dec.30,1891 Lockland,O.

Yr	Cl	Lea	Pos	G	Rec
1912	Pit	N	3	33	.186
1913	Pit	N	2	137	.317
1914	Pit	N	2	143	.265
1915	Pit	N	2	150	.256
1916	Pit	N	2	43	.250
	BRTR			506	.272

VIRDON, WILLIAM CHARLES
b.June 9,1931 Hazel Park,Mich.

Yr	Cl	Lea	Pos	G	Rec
1955	St.L	N	O	144	.281
1956	St.L	N	O	24	.211
1956	Pit	N	O	133	.334
1957	Pit	N	O	144	.251
1958	Pit	N	O	144	.267
1959	Pit	N	O	144	.254
1960	Pit	N	O	120	.264
1961	Pit	N	O	146	.260
1962	Pit	N	O	156	.247
	BLTR			1155	.268

VIRGIL, OSVALDO JOSE (Ossie)
b.May 17,1933 Corpus Christi,D.R.

Yr	Cl	Lea	Pos	G	Rec
1956	NY	N	3	3	.417
1957	NY	N	S-3-O	96	.235
1958	Det	A	3	49	.244
1960	Det	A	C-2-S-3	62	.227
1961	Det	A	C-2-S-3	20	.133
1961	KC	A	C-3	11	.143
1962	Bal	A	H	1	.000
	BRTR			242	.231

VIRTUE, JACOB KITCHLINE
b.Mar.2,1865 Philadelphia,Pa.
d.Feb.3,1943

Yr	Cl	Lea	Pos	G	Rec
1890	Cle	N	1	62	.305
1891	Cle	N	1	139	.262
1892	Cle	N	1	147	.282
1893	Cle	N	1	95	.287
1894	Cle	N	O	23	.270
	BL			466	.282

VISNER, JOSEPH P.
b.Sept.27,1862 Minneapolis,Minn.

Yr	Cl	Lea	Pos	G	Rec
1885	Bal	a	O	4	.214
1889	Bro	a	C-O	80	.249
1890	Pit	p	O	127	.265
1891	Was	a	O	13	.229
1891	St.L	a	O	5	.136
	BLTR			229	.258

VITELLI, JOSEPH ANTHONY
b.Apr.12,1911 McKee's Rocks,Pa.

Yr	Cl	Lea	Pos	G	Rec
1944	Pit	N	P	4	0-0
1945	Pit	N	H	1	.000
	BRTR			5	0-0 .000

VITT, OSCAR JOSEPH
b.Jan.4,1890 San Francisco,Cal.
d.Jan.31,1963

Yr	Cl	Lea	Pos	G	Rec
1912	Det	A	2-3-O	73	.245
1913	Det	A	2-3	99	.240
1914	Det	A	2-3	66	.251
1915	Det	A	3	152	.250
1916	Det	A	3	153	.226
1917	Det	A	3	140	.254
1918	Det	A	3	81	.239
1919	Bos	A	3	133	.243
1920	Bos	A	3	87	.220
1921	Bos	A	3	78	.190
	BRTR			1062	.240

Non-playing manager Cle (A) 1938-40.

Yr Cl Lea Pos G Rec

VOGEL, OTTO HENRY
b.Oct.26,1899 Davenport,Ia.
1923 Chi N 3-O 41 .210
1924 Chi N O 70 .267
BRTR 111 .249

VOIGT, OLEN EDWARD
b.Jan.21,1899 Wheaton,Ill.
1924 St.L A P 8 1-0
BBTR

VOISELLE, WILLIAM SYMMES
(Big Bill)
b.Jan.29,1919 Greenwood,S.C.
1942 NY N P 2 0-1
1943 NY N P 4 1-2
1944 NY N P 44 21-16
1945 NY N P 41 14-14
1946 NY N P 36 9-15
1947 NY N P 11 1-4
1947 Bos N P 22 8-7
1948 Bos N P 37 13-13
1949 Bos N P 30 7-8
1950 Chi N P 19 0-4
BRTR 246 74-84

VOLLMER, CLYDE FREDERICK
b.Sept.24,1921 Cincinnati,O.
1942 Cin N O 12 .093
1946 Cin N O 9 .182
1947 Cin N O 78 .219
1948 Cin N O 7 .111
1948 Was A O 1 .400
1949 Was A O 129 .253
1950 Was A O 6 .286
1950 Bos A O 57 .284
1951 Bos A O 115 .251
1952 Bos A O 90 .264
1953 Bos A H 1 .000
1953 Was A O 118 .260
1954 Was A O 62 .256
BRTR 685 .251

VOLZ, JACOB PHILLIP
b.Apr.4,1878 San Antonio,Tex.
d.Aug.11,1962
1901 Bos A P 1 1-0
1905 Bos N P 3 0-2
1908 Cin N P 7 1-2
TR 11 2-4

VON DER AHE, CHRISTIAN FREDERICK WILHELM
b.Nov.7,1851 Hille,Germany.
d.June 7,1913
Non-playing manager St.L (a) 1884, St.L (N) 1892, 1895 and 1897.

VON KOLNITZ, ALFRED HOLMES
(Fritz)
b.May 20,1893 Charleston,S.C.
d.Mar.18,1948
1914 Cin N 3 41 .221
1915 Cin N C-1-S-3-O 50 .192
1916 Chi A 3 24 .227
BRTR 115 .212

VORHEES, HENRY BERT
(Cy)
b.Sept.30,1874 Lodi,O.
d.Feb.9,1910
1902 Phi N P 10 3-2
1902 Was A P 1 0-1
11 3-3

VOSMIK, JOSEPH FRANKLIN
b.Apr.4,1910 Cleveland,O.
1930 Cle A O 9 .231
1931 Cle A O 149 .320
1932 Cle A O 153 .312
1933 Cle A O 119 .263
1934 Cle A O 104 .341
1935 Cle A O 152 .348
1936 Cle A O 138 .287
1937 St.L A O 144 .325
1938 Bos A O 146 .324
1939 Bos A O 145 .276

Yr Cl Lea Pos G Rec

(Continued)
1940 Bro N O 116 .282
1941 Bro N O 25 .196
1944 Was A O 14 .194
BRTR 1414 .307

VOSS, ALEXANDER
b.1855 Atlanta,Ga.
d.Aug.31,1906
1884 Was U P-1-S-3-O 63 {7-14 .190}
1884 KC U P-O 14 {1-7 .089}
BRTR 77 {8-21 .173}

VOWINKEL, JOHN HENRY
(Rip)
b.Nov.18,1884 Oswego,N.Y.
1905 Cin N P 6 3-3
BRTR

VOYLES, PHILIP VANCE
b.May 12,1900 Murphy,N.Car.
1929 Bos N O 20 .235
BLTR

WACHER, AUGUST
(Played under name of Arthur Sunday)

WACHTEL, PAUL HORINE
b.Apr.30,1893 Myersville,Md.
1917 Bro N P 2 0-0
BRTR

WACKER, CHARLES
b.New Albany,Ind.
1909 Pit N P 1 0-0
BRTR

WADDELL, GEORGE EDWARD
(Rube)
b.Oct.13,1876 Bradford,Pa.
d.Apr.1,1914
1897 Lou N P 2 0-1
1899 Lou N P 10 7-2
1900 Pit N P 22 10-10
1901 Pit N P 2 0-2
1901 Chi N P 31 14-14
1902 Phi A P 33 24-7
1903 Phi A P 38 22-16
1904 Phi A P 46 26-17
1905 Phi A P 46 26-11
1906 Phi A P 41 16-16
1907 Phi A P 43 19-13
1908 St.L A P 43 19-14
1909 St.L A P 31 11-14
1910 St.L A P 10 3-1
BRTL 398 197-138

WADDEY, FRANK ORUM
b.Aug.21,1905 Memphis,Tenn.
1931 St.L A O 14 .273
BLTL

WADE, ABRAHAM LINCOLN
b.Dec.20,1880 Spring City,Pa.
1907 NY N O 1 .000
BRTR

WADE, BENJAMIN STYRON
b.Nov.26,1922 Morehead City,N.C.
1948 Chi N P 2 0-1
1952 Bro N P 37 11-9
1953 Bro N P 32 7-5
1954 Bro N P 23 1-1
1954 St.L N P 13 0-0
1955 Pit N P 11 0-1
BRTR 118 19-17

Yr Cl Lea Pos G Rec

WADE, GALEARD LEE
b.Jan.20,1929 Hollister,Mo.
1955 Chi N O 9 .182
1956 Chi N O 10 .000
BLTR 19 .133

WADE, JACOB FIELDS
(Whistling Jake)
b.Apr.1,1912 Morehead City,N.C.
1936 Det A P 13 4-5
1937 Det A P 33 7-10
1938 Det A P 27 3-2
1939 Bos A P 20 1-4
1939 St.L A P 4 0-2
1942 Chi A P 15 5-5
1943 Chi A P 21 3-7
1944 Chi A P 19 2-4
1946 NY A P 13 2-1
1946 Was A P 6 0-0
BLTL 171 27-40

WADE, RICHARD FRANK
(Rip)
b.Jan.12,1899 Duluth,Minn.
d.June 16,1957
1923 Was A O 33 .232
BLTR

WADSWORTH, WILLIAM JOHN
(Jack)
b.Dec.16,1868 Wellington,O.
d.July 8,1941
1890 Cle N P 20 2-15
1893 Bal N P 3 0-2
1894 Lou N P 23 4-17
1895 Lou N P 2 0-1
BLTR 48 6-35

WAGENHURST, ELWOOD OTTO
b.June 3,1863 Kutztown,Pa.
d.Feb.12,1946
1888 Phi N 3 2 .125

WAGNER, ALBERT (Butz)
b.Sept.17,1869 Carnegie,Pa.
d.Nov.26,1928
1898 Was N 3 57 .232
1898 Bro N 3 11 .237
68 .233

WAGNER, CHARLES F.
(Heinie)
b.Sept.23,1881 New York,N.Y.
d.Mar.20,1943
1902 NY N S 17 .214
1906 Bos A 2 9 .250
1907 Bos A S 111 .213
1908 Bos A S 153 .247
1909 Bos A S 124 .256
1910 Bos A S 142 .273
1911 Bos A 2 80 .257
1912 Bos A S 144 .274
1913 Bos A S 109 .226
1915 Bos A 2 84 .239
1916 Bos A S 4 .500
1918 Bos A 2 3 .125
BRTR 980 .249
Non-playing manager Bos (A) 1930.

WAGNER, CHARLES THOMAS
(Broadway)
b.Dec.3,1915 Reading,Pa.
1938 Bos A P 13 1-3
1939 Bos A P 11 3-1
1940 Bos A P 13 1-0
1941 Bos A P 29 12-8
1942 Bos A P 29 14-11
1946 Bos A P 8 1-0
BRTR 103 32-23

WAGNER, HAROLD EDWARD
b.July 2,1915 Riverton,N.J.

Yr	Cl	Lea	Pos	G	Rec
1937	Phi	A	C	1	.000
1938	Phi	A	C	33	.227
1939	Phi	A	C	5	.125
1940	Phi	A	C	34	.253
1941	Phi	A	C	46	.221
1942	Phi	A	C	104	.236
1943	Phi	A	C	111	.239
1944	Phi	A	C	5	.250
1944	Bos	A	C	66	.332
1946	Bos	A	C	117	.230
1947	Bos	A	C	21	.231
1947	Det	A	C	71	.288
1948	Det	A	C	54	.202
1948	Phi	N	C	3	.000
1949	Phi	N	C	1	.000
	BLTR			672	.248

WAGNER, JACOB EARLE
b.Nov.6,1861 York, Pa.
d.Nov.10,1943
Non-playing manager Was (N)1892-93.

WAGNER, JOHN PETER
(Honus)
b.Feb.24,1874 Carnegie, Pa.
d.Dec.6,1955

Yr	Cl	Lea	Pos	G	Rec
1897	Lou	N	O	61	.344
1898	Lou	N	1-3	148	.305
1899	Lou	N	3-O	144	.359
1900	Pit	N	O	134	.381
1901	Pit	N	S-3-O	141	.352
1902	Pit	N	P-1-2-S-O	137	0-0 .329
1903	Pit	N	S	129	.355
1904	Pit	N	S	132	.349
1905	Pit	N	S	147	.363
1906	Pit	N	S	140	.339
1907	Pit	N	S	142	.350
1908	Pit	N	S	151	.354
1909	Pit	N	S	137	.339
1910	Pit	N	S	150	.320
1911	Pit	N	1-S	130	.334
1912	Pit	N	S	145	.324
1913	Pit	N	S	114	.300
1914	Pit	N	S-3	150	.252
1915	Pit	N	S	156	.274
1916	Pit	N	1-S	123	.287
1917	Pit	N	M-1-3	74	.265
	BRTR			2785	0-0 .329

WAGNER, JOSEPH BERNARD
b.Apr.24,1889 New York,N.Y.

Yr	Cl	Lea	Pos	G	Rec
1915	Cin	N	2-S-3-O	75	.178
	BRTR				

WAGNER, LEON LAMAR
b.May 13,1934 Chattanooga,Tenn.

Yr	Cl	Lea	Pos	G	Rec
1958	SF	N	O	74	.317
1959	SF	N	O	87	.225
1960	St.L	N	O	39	.214
1961	LA	A	O	133	.280
1962	LA	A	O	160	.268
	BLTR			493	.272

WAGNER, WILLIAM GEORGE
(Bull)
b.Jan.1,1887 Lillie,Mich.

Yr	Cl	Lea	Pos	G	Rec
1913	Bro	N	P	18	4-2
1914	Bro	N	P	6	0-1
	BRTR			24	4-3

WAGNER, WILLIAM JOSEPH
b.Jan.2,1894 Jessup,Ia.
d.Jan.11,1951

Yr	Cl	Lea	Pos	G	Rec
1914	Pit	N	C	3	.000
1915	Pit	N	C	5	.000
1916	Pit	N	C	19	.237
1917	Pit	N	C	53	.205
1918	Bos	N	C	13	.213
	BRTR			93	.207

WAHL, KERMIT EMERSON
b.Nov.18,1922 Columbia,S.Dak.

Yr	Cl	Lea	Pos	G	Rec
1944	Cin	N	3	4	.000
1945	Cin	N	2-S-3	71	.201
1947	Cin	N	2-S-3	39	.173
1950	Phi	A	2-S-3	89	.257
1951	Phi	A	3	20	.186
1951	St.L	A	3	8	.333
	BRTR			231	.226

WAITKUS, EDWARD STEPHEN
b.Sept.4,1919 Cambridge,Mass.

Yr	Cl	Lea	Pos	G	Rec
1941	Chi	N	1	12	.179
1946	Chi	N	1	113	.304
1947	Chi	N	1	130	.292
1948	Chi	N	1-O	139	.296
1949	Phi	N	1	54	.306
1950	Phi	N	1	154	.284
1951	Phi	N	1	145	.257
1952	Phi	N	1	146	.289
1953	Phi	N	1	81	.291
1954	Bal	A	1	95	.283
1955	Bal	A	1	38	.259
1955	Phi	N	1	33	.280
	BLTL			1140	.285

WAITT, CHARLES C.
b.Oct.14,1853 Hallowell,Me.

Yr	Cl	Lea	Pos	G	Rec
1875	St.L	n	O	30	.211
1877	Chi	N	O	10	.098
1882	Bal	a	O	72	.154
1883	Phi	N	O	1	.333
				113	.167

WAKEFIELD, HOWARD JOHN
b.Apr.2,1884 Bucyrus,O.
d.Apr.16,1941

Yr	Cl	Lea	Pos	G	Rec
1905	Cle	A	C	10	.111
1906	Was	A	C	77	.280
1907	Cle	A	C	26	.135
	BRTR			113	.248

WAKEFIELD, RICHARD CUMMINGS
b.May 6,1921 Chicago,Ill.

Yr	Cl	Lea	Pos	G	Rec
1941	Det	A	O	7	.143
1943	Det	A	O	155	.316
1944	Det	A	O	78	.355
1946	Det	A	O	111	.268
1947	Det	A	O	112	.283
1948	Det	A	O	110	.276
1949	Det	A	O	59	.206
1950	NY	A	H	3	.500
1952	NY	N	H	3	.000
	BLTR			638	.293

WALBERG, GEORGE ELVIN
(Rube)
b.July 27,1899 Seattle,Wash.

Yr	Cl	Lea	Pos	G	Rec
1923	NY	N	P	2	0-0
1923	Phi	A	P	26	4-8
1924	Phi	A	P	6	0-0
1925	Phi	A	P	53	8-14
1926	Phi	A	P	40	12-10
1927	Phi	A	P	47	16-12
1928	Phi	A	P	38	17-12
1929	Phi	A	P	40	18-11
1930	Phi	A	P	38	13-12
1931	Phi	A	P	45	20-12
1932	Phi	A	P	41	17-10
1933	Phi	A	P	41	9-13
1934	Bos	A	P	30	6-7
1935	Bos	A	P	44	5-9
1936	Bos	A	P	24	5-4
1937	Bos	A	P	32	5-7
	BLTL			547	155-141

WALCZAK, EDWIN JOSEPH
b.Sept.21,1918 Jewett City,Conn.

Yr	Cl	Lea	Pos	G	Rec
1945	Phi	N	2-S	20	.211
	BRTR				

WALDBAUER, ALBERT CHARLES
(Doc)
b.1897

Yr	Cl	Lea	Pos	G	Rec
1917	Was	A	P	2	0-0
	BBTR				

WALDEN, FREDERICK THOMAS
b.June 25,1890 Fayette,Mo.
d.Sept.27,1955

Yr	Cl	Lea	Pos	G	Rec
1912	St.L	A	C	1	.000
	BRTR				

WALDO, HIRAM HUNGERFORD
b.Nov.23,1827 Elba,N.Y.
d.Apr.26,1912
Non-playing manager Roc (n) 1871.

WALDRON, IRVING
b.Jan.21,1876 Hillside,N.Y.
d.July 22,1944

Yr	Cl	Lea	Pos	G	Rec
1901	Mil	A	O	62	.288
1901	Was	A	O	79	.321
	BRTR			141	.306

WALENTOSKI, NORMAN EDWARD
(Played under name of
Norman Edward Wallen)

WALKER, ALBERT BLUFORD
(Rube)
b.May 16,1926 Lenoir,N.C.

Yr	Cl	Lea	Pos	G	Rec
1948	Chi	N	C	79	.275
1949	Chi	N	C	56	.244
1950	Chi	N	C	74	.230
1951	Chi	N	C	37	.234
1951	Bro	N	C	36	.243
1952	Bro	N	C	46	.259
1953	Bro	N	C	43	.242
1954	Bro	N	C	50	.181
1955	Bro	N	C	48	.252
1956	Bro	N	C	54	.212
1957	Bro	N	C	60	.181
1958	LA	N	C	25	.114
	BLTR			608	.227

WALKER, CHARLES FRANKLIN
(Frank)
b.Sept.22,1894 Enoree,S.C.

Yr	Cl	Lea	Pos	G	Rec
1917	Det	A	O	2	.000
1918	Det	A	O	55	.198
1920	Phi	A	O	24	.231
1921	Phi	A	O	19	.227
1925	NY	N	O	39	.222
	BRTR			139	.214

WALKER, CLARENCE WILLIAM
(Tilly)
b.Sept.4,1889 Telford,Tenn.
d.Sept.20,1959

Yr	Cl	Lea	Pos	G	Rec
1911	Was	A	O	98	.278
1912	Was	A	O	36	.273
1913	St.L	A	O	23	.294
1914	St.L	A	O	151	.298
1915	St.L	A	O	144	.269
1916	Bos	A	O	128	.265
1917	Bos	A	O	106	.246
1918	Phi	A	O	114	.294
1919	Phi	A	O	125	.292
1920	Phi	A	O	149	.268
1921	Phi	A	O	142	.304
1922	Phi	A	O	153	.283
1923	Phi	A	O	52	.275
	BRTR			1421	.281

WALKER, EDWARD HARRISON
b.Aug.11,1874 Cambois,England
d.Sept.30,1947

Yr	Cl	Lea	Pos	G	Rec
1902	Cle	A	P	1	0-1
1903	Cle	A	P	3	0-0
	TL			4	0-1

WALKER, ERNEST ROBERT
b.Sept.15,1890 Blossburg,Ala.

Yr	Cl	Lea	Pos	G	Rec
1913	St.L	A	O	7	.214
1914	St.L	A	O	71	.298
1915	St.L	A	O	50	.211
	BLTR			128	.256

WALKER, EWART GLADSTONE (Dixie)
b.June 1,1887 Brownsville,Pa.

Yr	Cl	Lea	Pos	G	Rec
1909	Was	A	P	4	3-1
1910	Was	A	P	29	11-11
1911	Was	A	P	34	8-13
1912	Was	A	P	9	3-6
	BLTR			76	25-31

WALKER, FRED (Dixie)
b.Sept.24,1910 Villa Rica,Ga.

Yr	Cl	Lea	Pos	G	Rec
1931	NY	A	O	2	.300
1933	NY	A	O	98	.274
1934	NY	A	O	17	.118
1935	NY	A	O	8	.154
1936	NY	A	O	6	.350
1936	Chi	A	O	26	.271
1937	Chi	A	O	154	.302
1938	Det	A	O	127	.308
1939	Det	A	O	43	.305
1939	Bro	N	O	61	.280
1940	Bro	N	O	143	.308
1941	Bro	N	O	148	.311
1942	Bro	N	O	118	.290
1943	Bro	N	O	138	.302
1944	Bro	N	O	147	.357
1945	Bro	N	O	154	.300
1946	Bro	N	O	150	.319
1947	Bro	N	O	148	.306
1948	Pit	N	O	129	.316
1949	Pit	N	1-O	88	.282
	BLTR			1905	.306

WALKER, FREDERICK MITCHELL (Mysterious)
b.Mar.21,1884 Utica.Neb.
d.Feb.1,1958

Yr	Cl	Lea	Pos	G	Rec
1910	Cin	N	P	1	0-0
1913	Bro	N	P	10	1-3
1914	Pit	F	P	31	4-16
1915	Bro	F	P	13	2-4
	BRTR			55	7-23

WALKER, GEORGE A.
b.Hamilton,Ont.,Canada

Yr	Cl	Lea	Pos	G	Rec
1888	Bal	a	P	4	1-3

WALKER, GERALD HOLMES (Gee)
b.Mar.19,1908 Gulfport,Miss.

Yr	Cl	Lea	Pos	G	Rec
1931	Det	A	O	59	.296
1932	Det	A	O	126	.323
1933	Det	A	O	127	.280
1934	Det	A	O	98	.300
1935	Det	A	O	98	.301
1936	Det	A	O	134	.353
1937	Det	A	O	151	.335
1938	Chi	A	O	120	.305
1939	Chi	A	O	149	.291
1940	Was	A	O	140	.294
1941	Cle	A	O	121	.283
1942	Cin	N	O	119	.230
1943	Cin	N	O	114	.245
1944	Cin	N	O	121	.278
1945	Cin	N	3-O	106	.253
	BRTR			1783	.294

WALKER, HARRY WILLIAM (The Hat)
b.Oct.22,1918 Pascagoula,Miss.

Yr	Cl	Lea	Pos	G	Rec
1940	St.L	N	O	7	.185
1941	St.L	N	O	7	.267
1942	St.L	N	2-O	74	.314
1943	St.L	N	2-O	148	.295
1946	St.L	N	1-O	112	.237
1947	St.L	N	O	10	.200
1947	Phi	N	1-O	130	.371
1948	Phi	N	1-3-O	112	.292
1949	Chi	N	O	42	.264

(Continued)

Yr	Cl	Lea	Pos	G	Rec
1949	Cin	N	1-O	86	.318
1950	St.L	N	1-O	60	.207
1951	St.L	N	1-O	8	.308
1955	St.L	N	M-O	11	.357
	BLTR			807	.296

WALKER, HARVEY WILLOS (Hub)
b.Aug.17,1906 Gulfport,Miss.

Yr	Cl	Lea	Pos	G	Rec
1931	Det	A	O	90	.286
1935	Det	A	O	9	.160
1936	Cin	N	C-1-O	92	.275
1937	Cin	N	2-O	78	.249
1945	Det	A	O	28	.130
	BLTR			297	.263

WALKER, JAMES ROY
b.Mar.12,1893 Lawrenceburg,Tenn.

Yr	Cl	Lea	Pos	G	Rec
1912	Cle	A	P	2	0-0
1915	Cle	A	P	25	5-9
1917	Chi	N	P	2	0-1
1918	Chi	N	P	13	1-3
1921	St.L	N	P	38	11-12
1922	St.L	N	P	12	1-2
	BBTR			92	18-27

WALKER, JERRY ALLEN
b.Feb.12,1939 Byng,Okla.

Yr	Cl	Lea	Pos	G	Rec
1957	Bal	A	P	13	1-0
1958	Bal	A	P	6	0-0
1959	Bal	A	P	31	11-10
1960	Bal	A	P	35	3-4
1961	KC	A	P	45	8-14
1962	KC	A	P	36	8-9
	BBTR			166	31-37

WALKER, JOHN MILES
b.Dec.4,1896 Toulon,Ill.

Yr	Cl	Lea	Pos	G	Rec
1919	Phi	A	C	3	.000
1920	Phi	A	C	6	.235
1921	Phi	A	1	113	.258
1922	Phi	A	C	2	.000
	BRTR			124	.252

WALKER, JOSEPH RICHARD
b.Jan.23,1901 Munhall,Pa.

Yr	Cl	Lea	Pos	G	Rec
1923	St.L	N	1	2	.286
	BRTR				

WALKER, MARTIN VAN BUREN
b.Mar.27,1903 Philadelphia,Pa.

Yr	Cl	Lea	Pos	G	Rec
1928	Phi	N	P	1	0-1
	BLTL				

WALKER, MOSES FLEETWOOD (Fleet)
b.Oct.7,1857 Mt.Pleasant,O.
d.May 11,1924

Yr	Cl	Lea	Pos	G	Rec
1884	Tol	a	C	41	.251
	BRTR				

WALKER, OSCAR
b.Mar.18,1854 Brooklyn,N.Y.
d.May 20,1889

Yr	Cl	Lea	Pos	G	Rec
1875	Atl	n	O	1	.000
1879	Buf	N	1	70	.266
1880	Buf	N	1	33	.230
1882	St.L	a	1-2-O	76	.233
1884	Bro	a	1-O	95	.268
	BL			275	.253

WALKER, THOMAS WILLIAM
b.Aug.1,1878 Philadelphia,Pa.
d.July 10,1944

Yr	Cl	Lea	Pos	G	Rec
1902	Phi	A	P	1	0-1
1904	Cin	N	P	25	15-10
1905	Cin	N	P	23	10-6
	BRTR			49	25-17

WALKER, WALTER S.
b.Ionia,Mich.

Yr	Cl	Lea	Pos	G	Rec
1884	Det	N	C	1	.250
1885	Bal	a	O	3	.000
				4	.077

WALKER, WELDAY WILBERFORCE
b.July 27,1860 Steubenville,O.
d.Nov.23,1937

Yr	Cl	Lea	Pos	G	Rec
1884	Tol	a	O	6	.222

WALKER, WILLIAM CURTIS (Curt)
b.July 3,1896 Beeville,Tex.
d.Dec.9,1955

Yr	Cl	Lea	Pos	G	Rec
1919	NY	A	H	1	.000
1920	NY	N	O	8	.000
1921	NY	N	O	64	.286
1921	Phi	N	O	21	.338
1922	Phi	N	O	148	.337
1923	Phi	N	1-O	140	.281
1924	Phi	N	O	24	.296
1924	Cin	N	O	109	.300
1925	Cin	N	O	145	.318
1926	Cin	N	O	155	.306
1927	Cin	N	O	146	.292
1928	Cin	N	O	123	.279
1929	Cin	N	O	141	.313
1930	Cin	N	O	134	.307
	BLTR			1359	.304

WALKER, WILLIAM HENRY
b.Oct.7,1903 E.St.Louis,Ill.

Yr	Cl	Lea	Pos	G	Rec
1927	NY	N	P	3	0-0
1928	NY	N	P	22	3-6
1929	NY	N	P	29	14-7
1930	NY	N	P	40	17-15
1931	NY	N	P	37	16-9
1932	NY	N	P	31	8-12
1933	St.L	N	P	29	9-10
1934	St.L	N	P	24	12-4
1935	St.L	N	P	38	13-8
1936	St.L	N	P	22	5-6
	BRTL			275	97-77

WALKUP, JAMES ELTON
b.Dec.14,1911 Havana,Ark.

Yr	Cl	Lea	Pos	G	Rec
1934	St.L	A	P	3	0-0
1935	St.L	A	P	55	6-9
1936	St.L	A	P	5	0-3
1937	St.L	A	P	27	9-12
1938	St.L	A	P	18	1-12
1939	St.L	A	P	1	0-1
1939	Det	A	P	7	0-1
	BRTR			116	16-38

WALKUP, JAMES HUEY
b.Nov.3,1895 Havana,Ark.

Yr	Cl	Lea	Pos	G	Rec
1927	Det	A	P	2	0-0
	BRTL				

WALL, ...

Yr	Cl	Lea	Pos	G	Rec
1873	Nat	n	S	1	NR

WALL, JOSEPH FRANCIS (Gummy)
b.July 24,1873 Brooklyn,N.Y.
d.July 17,1936

Yr	Cl	Lea	Pos	G	Rec
1901	NY	N	C	3	.286
1902	NY	N	O	6	.357
1902	Bro	N	C	5	.176
	BLTL			14	.282

WALL, MURRAY WESLEY
b.Sept.19,1926 Dallas,Tex.

Yr	Cl	Lea	Pos	G	Rec
1950	Bos	N	P	1	0-0
1957	Bos	A	P	11	3-0
1958	Bos	A	P	52	8-9
1959	Bos	A	P	26	2-5
1959	Was	A	P	1	0-0
	BRTR			91	13-14

WALLACE, C. E. (Jack)
b.1891

Yr	Cl	Lea	Pos	G	Rec
1915	Chi	N	C	2	.285
	BRTR				

WALLACE, FREDERICK RENSHAW (Jesse)
b.Sept.20,1893 Church Hill,Md.

Yr	Cl	Lea	Pos	G	Rec
1919	Phi	N	S	2	.200
	TR				

WALLACE, HARRY CLINTON
(Lefty)
b.July 23,1882 Richmond,Ind.
d.July 9,1951

Yr	Cl	Lea	Pos	G	Rec
1912	Phi	N	P	4	0-0
	BLTL				

WALLACE, JAMES HAROLD
(Lefty)
b.Aug.12,1921 Evansville,Ind.

Yr	Cl	Lea	Pos	G	Rec
1942	Bos	N	P	19	1-3
1945	Bos	N	P	6	1-0
1946	Bos	N	P	27	3-3
	BLTL			52	5-6

WALLACE, JAMES L.
b.Nov.14,1881 S.Boston,Mass.
d.May 16,1953

Yr	Cl	Lea	Pos	G	Rec
1905	Pit	N	O	7	.214
	BLTL				

WALLACE, RHODERICK JOHN (Bobby)
b.Nov.4,1873 Pittsburgh,Pa.
d.Nov.3,1960

Yr	Cl	Lea	Pos	G	Rec
1894	Cle	N	P	4	2-2
1895	Cle	N	P	27	14-10
1896	Cle	N	P	33	9-6
1897	Cle	N	3	131	.339
1898	Cle	N	3	153	.269
1899	St.L	N	S-3	151	.302
1900	St.L	N	S	129	.272
1901	St.L	N	S	135	.322
1902	St.L	A	P-S-O	133	0-0 / .287
1903	St.L	A	S	136	.245
1904	St.L	A	S	139	.273
1905	St.L	A	S	156	.271
1906	St.L	A	S	139	.258
1907	St.L	A	S	147	.257
1908	St.L	A	S	137	.253
1909	St.L	A	S-3	116	.238
1910	St.L	A	S-3	138	.258
1911	St.L	A	M-S	125	.232
1912	St.L	A	M-S	99	.241
1913	St.L	A	S	52	.211
1914	St.L	A	S	26	.219
1915	St.L	A	S	9	.231
1916	St.L	A	S-3	14	.278
1917	St.L	N	S-3	8	.100
1918	St.L	N	2-S-3	32	.153
	BRTR			2369	25-18 / .268

Non-playing manager Cin (N) 1937.

WALLAESA, JOHN
b.Aug.31,1919 Easton,Pa.

Yr	Cl	Lea	Pos	G	Rec
1940	Phi	A	S	6	.150
1942	Phi	A	S	36	.256
1946	Phi	A	S	63	.196
1947	Chi	A	S-3-O	81	.195
1948	Chi	A	S-O	33	.188
	BBTR			219	.205

WALLEN, NORMAN EDWARD
(Real name Norman Edward Walentoski)
b.Feb.13,1917 Milwaukee,Wis.

Yr	Cl	Lea	Pos	G	Rec
1945	Bos	N	3	4	.133
	BRTR				

WALLER, JOHN FRANCIS
(Red)
b.1883 Washington,D.C.
d.Feb.9,1915

Yr	Cl	Lea	Pos	G	Rec
1909	NY	N	P	1	0-0

WALLS, RAY LEE
b.Jan.6,1933 San Diego,Cal.

Yr	Cl	Lea	Pos	G	Rec
1952	Pit	N	O	32	.188
1956	Pit	N	3-O	143	.274
1957	Pit	N	O	8	.182
1957	Chi	N	3-O	117	.240
1958	Chi	N	O	136	.304

(Continued)

Yr	Cl	Lea	Pos	G	Rec
1959	Chi	N	O	120	.257
1960	Cin	N	1-O	29	.274
1960	Phi	N	1-3-O	65	.199
1961	Phi	N	1-3-O	91	.280
1962	LA	N	1-3-O	60	.266
	BRTR			801	.264

WALSH, AUGUST S.
b.Aug.9,1904 Wilmington,Del.

Yr	Cl	Lea	Pos	G	Rec
1927	Phi	N	P	1	0-1
1928	Phi	N	P	39	4-9
	BRTR			40	4-10

WALSH, AUSTIN
b.1892

Yr	Cl	Lea	Pos	G	Rec
1914	Chi	F	O	52	.235
	BLTL				

WALSH, CORNELIUS
b.Apr.23,1885 St.Louis,Mo.
d.Apr.5,1953

Yr	Cl	Lea	Pos	G	Rec
1907	Pit	N	P	1	0-0

WALSH, EDWARD ARTHUR
b.Feb.11,1905 Meriden,Conn.
d.Oct.31,1937

Yr	Cl	Lea	Pos	G	Rec
1928	Chi	A	P	14	4-7
1929	Chi	A	P	25	6-11
1930	Chi	A	P	39	1-4
1932	Chi	A	P	4	0-2
	BRTR			82	11-24

WALSH, EDWARD AUGUSTIN
(Big Ed)
b.May 14,1881 Plains, Pa.
d.May 26,1959

Yr	Cl	Lea	Pos	G	Rec
1904	Chi	A	P	18	5-5
1905	Chi	A	P	29	8-5
1906	Chi	A	P	42	17-13
1907	Chi	A	P	57	24-18
1908	Chi	A	P	66	40-15
1909	Chi	A	P	32	15-11
1910	Chi	A	P	52	18-20
1911	Chi	A	P	62	27-18
1912	Chi	A	P	61	27-17
1913	Chi	A	P	16	8-3
1914	Chi	A	P	11	2-3
1915	Chi	A	P	5	3-0
1916	Chi	A	P	2	0-1
1917	Bos	N	P	4	0-1
	BRTR			457	194-130

WALSH, JAMES CHARLES
b.Sept.22,1885 Conneaught,Ireland.
d.July 3,1962

Yr	Cl	Lea	Pos	G	Rec
1912	Phi	A	O	31	.252
1913	Phi	A	O	94	.255
1914	NY	A	O	43	.207
1914	Phi	A	O	67	.226
1915	Phi	A	O	117	.206
1916	Phi	A	O	112	.222
1916	Bos	A	O	15	.348
1917	Bos	A	O	57	.265
	BRTR			536	.231

WALSH, JAMES GERALD
(Junior)
b.Mar.7,1920 Newark,N.J.

Yr	Cl	Lea	Pos	G	Rec
1946	Pit	N	P	4	0-1
1948	Pit	N	P	2	1-0
1949	Pit	N	P	9	1-4
1950	Pit	N	P	38	1-1
1951	Pit	N	P	36	1-4
	BRTR			89	4-10

WALSH, JAMES THOMAS
b.July 10,1894 Boston,Mass.

Yr	Cl	Lea	Pos	G	Rec
1921	Det	A	P	3	0-0
	TL				

WALSH, JOHN
b.Wilkes-Barre,Pa.

Yr	Cl	Lea	Pos	G	Rec
1903	Phi	N	3	1	.000
	TR				

WALSH, JOSEPH A. (Reddy)
b.Nov.1865 Chicago,Ill.

Yr	Cl	Lea	Pos	G	Rec
1891	Bal	a	S	25	.189

WALSH, JOSEPH FRANCIS
b.Oct.14,1887 Waterbury,Conn.

Yr	Cl	Lea	Pos	G	Rec
1910	NY	A	C	2	.333
1911	NY	A	C	4	.222
	BRTR			6	.267

WALSH, JOSEPH PATRICK
(Tweet)
b.Mar.13,1917 Roxbury,Mass.

Yr	Cl	Lea	Pos	G	Rec
1938	Bos	N	S	4	.000
	BRTR				

WALSH, MICHAEL F.
b.1852 Covington,Ky.
Non-playing manager Lou (a) 1884.

WALSH, MICHAEL TIMOTHY
(Runt)
b.Mar.25,1887 Lima,O.
d.Jan.21,1947

Yr	Cl	Lea	Pos	G	Rec
1910	Phi	N	2-O	67	.248
1911	Phi	N	P-C-1-2-S-3	84	0-0 / .270

WALSH, THOMAS JOSEPH
b.Feb.28,1886 Davenport,Ia.

Yr	Cl	Lea	Pos	G	Rec
1906	Chi	N	C	2	.000
	TR				

WALSH, THOMAS L. (Dee)
b.1892 St.Louis,Mo.

Yr	Cl	Lea	Pos	G	Rec
1913	St.L	A	S	23	.170
1914	St.L	A	S	7	.087
1915	St.L	A	P-O	59	0-0 / .220
	BBTR			89	0-0 / .195

WALSH, WALTER WILLIAM
b.Apr.30,1897 Newark,N.J.

Yr	Cl	Lea	Pos	G	Rec
1920	Phi	N	H	1	.000
	BRTR				

WALTER, JAMES BERNARD
b.Aug.15,1908 Dover,Tenn.

Yr	Cl	Lea	Pos	G	Rec
1930	Pit	N	P	1	0-0
	BRTR				

WALTERS, ALFRED JOHN
(Roxy)
b.Nov.5,1892 San Francisco,Cal.
d.June 3,1956

Yr	Cl	Lea	Pos	G	Rec
1915	NY	A	C	2	.333
1916	NY	A	C	66	.266
1917	NY	A	C	61	.263
1918	NY	A	C	64	.199
1919	Bos	A	C	48	.193
1920	Bos	A	C	88	.198
1921	Bos	A	C	54	.201
1922	Bos	A	C	38	.194
1923	Bos	A	C	40	.250
1924	Cle	A	C	32	.257
1925	Cle	A	C	5	.200
	BRTR			498	.222

WALTERS, JAMES FREDERICK
b.Sept.4,1912 Laurel,Miss.

Yr	Cl	Lea	Pos	G	Rec
1945	Bos	A	C	40	.172
	BRTR				

WALTERS, KENNETH ROGERS
b.Nov.11,1933 Fresno,Cal

Yr	Cl	Lea	Pos	G	Rec
1960	Phi	N	O	24	.239
1961	Phi	N	1-3-O	86	.228
	BRTR			210	.236

WALTERS, WILLIAM HENRY
(Bucky)
b.Apr.19,1909 Philadelphia,Pa.

Yr	Cl	Lea	Pos	G	Rec
1931	Bos	N	2-3	9	.211
1932	Bos	N	3	22	.187
1933	Bos	A	2-3	52	.256
1934	Bos	A	3	23	.216
1934	Phi	N	P-3	83	0-0 .260
1935	Phi	N	P-2-3-O	49	9-9 .250
1936	Phi	N	P	64	11-21
1937	Phi	N	P	56	14-15
1938	Phi	N	P	15	4-8
1938	Cin	N	P	36	11-6
1939	Cin	N	P	40	27-11
1940	Cin	N	P	37	22-10
1941	Cin	N	P	39	19-15
1942	Cin	N	P-O	40	15-14 .242
1943	Cin	N	P	37	15-15
1944	Cin	N	P	37	23-8
1945	Cin	N	P	24	10-10
1946	Cin	N	P	24	10-7
1947	Cin	N	P	20	8-8
1948	Cin	N	M-P	7	0-3
1950	Bos	N	P	1	0-0
	BRTR			715	198-160 .243

Non-playing manager Cin (N) 1949.

WALTON, ZACH
(Also played under real name of Jonathan Thompson Walton Zachary)

WALTZ, JOHN J.
Non-playing manager Bal (N) 1892

WAMBSGANSS, WILLIAM ADOLPH
b.Mar.19,1894 Cleveland,O.

Yr	Cl	Lea	Pos	G	Rec
1914	Cle	A	S	43	.217
1915	Cle	A	2-3	121	.195
1916	Cle	A	2-S	136	.246
1917	Cle	A	2	141	.255
1918	Cle	A	2	87	.295
1919	Cle	A	2	139	.278
1920	Cle	A	2	153	.244
1921	Cle	A	2	107	.285
1922	Cle	A	2-S	143	.262
1923	Cle	A	2	101	.290
1924	Bos	A	2	155	.275
1925	Bos	A	1-2	111	.231
1926	Phi	A	S	54	.352
	BRTR			1491	.259

WANER, LLOYD JAMES
(Little Poison)
b.Mar.16,1906 Harrah,Okla.

Yr	Cl	Lea	Pos	G	Rec
1927	Pit	N	O	150	.355
1928	Pit	N	O	152	.335
1929	Pit	N	O	151	.353
1930	Pit	N	O	68	.362
1931	Pit	N	O	154	.314
1932	Pit	N	O	134	.333
1933	Pit	N	O	121	.276
1934	Pit	N	O	140	.283
1935	Pit	N	O	122	.309
1936	Pit	N	O	106	.321
1937	Pit	N	O	129	.330
1938	Pit	N	O	147	.313
1939	Pit	N	O	112	.285
1940	Pit	N	O	72	.259
1941	Pit	N	O	3	.250
1941	Bos	N	O	19	.412
1941	Cin	N	O	55	.256
1942	Phi	N	O	101	.261
1944	Bro	N	O	15	.286
1944	Pit	N	O	19	.357
1945	Pit	N	O	23	.263
	BLTR			1993	.316

WANER, PAUL GLEE
(Big Poison)
b.Apr.16,1903 Harrah,Okla.

Yr	Cl	Lea	Pos	G	Rec
1926	Pit	N	O	144	.336
1927	Pit	N	1-O	155	.380
1928	Pit	N	1-O	152	.370
1929	Pit	N	O	151	.336
1930	Pit	N	O	145	.368
1931	Pit	N	1-O	150	.322

(Continued)

Yr	Cl	Lea	Pos	G	Rec
1932	Pit	N	O	154	.341
1933	Pit	N	O	154	.309
1934	Pit	N	O	146	.362
1935	Pit	N	O	139	.321
1936	Pit	N	O	148	.373
1937	Pit	N	O	154	.354
1938	Pit	N	O	148	.280
1939	Pit	N	O	125	.328
1940	Pit	N	1-O	89	.290
1941	Bro	N	O	11	.171
1941	Bos	N	O	95	.279
1942	Bos	N	O	114	.258
1943	Bro	N	O	82	.311
1944	Bro	N	O	83	.287
1944	NY	A	H	9	.143
1945	NY	A	H	1	.000
	BLTL			2549	.333

WANNER, CLARENCE MELLERT
(Jack)
b.May 14,1884 Reading,Pa.

Yr	Cl	Lea	Pos	G	Rec
1909	NY	A	S	3	.125

BRTR

WANNINGER, PAUL LOUIS
(Pee-Wee)
b.Dec.12,1904 Birmingham,Ala.

Yr	Cl	Lea	Pos	G	Rec
1925	NY	A	2-S-3	117	.236
1927	Bos	A	S	18	.200
1927	Cin	N	S	28	.247
	BLTR			163	.234

WARD, ...
(Hap)

Yr	Cl	Lea	Pos	G	Rec
1912	Det	A	O	1	.000

WARD, AARON LEE
b.Aug.28,1896 Booneville,Ark.
d.Jan.30,1961

Yr	Cl	Lea	Pos	G	Rec
1917	NY	A	S	8	.115
1918	NY	A	S	20	.125
1919	NY	A	1-S	27	.205
1920	NY	A	3	127	.256
1921	NY	A	2-3	153	.306
1922	NY	A	2	154	.267
1923	NY	A	2	152	.284
1924	NY	A	2	120	.253
1925	NY	A	2-3	125	.246
1926	NY	A	1	22	.323
1927	Chi	A	2	145	.270
1928	Cle	A	2-S-3	6	.111
	BRTR			1059	.268

WARD, CHARLES WILLIAM
b.July 31,1894 St.Louis,Mo.

Yr	Cl	Lea	Pos	G	Rec
1917	Pit	N	S	125	.236
1918	Bro	N	S	2	.333
1919	Bro	N	3	45	.233
1920	Bro	N	S	19	.155
1921	Bro	N	S	12	.071
1922	Bro	N	S	33	.274
	BRTR			236	.228

WARD, E. JOHN
b.Washington,D.C.

Yr	Cl	Lea	Pos	G	Rec
1884	Was	U	O	1	.250
1885	Pro	N	P	1	0-1
				2	0-1 .143

WARD, FRANK GRAY
(Piggy)
b.Apr.16,1867 Chambersburg,Pa.
d.Oct.24,1912

Yr	Cl	Lea	Pos	G	Rec
1883	Phi	N	3	1	.000
1889	Phi	N	2	7	.160
1891	Pit	N	O	5	.333
1892	Bal	N	O	53	.282
1893	Bal	N	O	11	.250
1893	Cin	N	O	38	.281
1894	Was	N	2	89	.303
				204	.286

WARD, JAMES H. H.
b.Mar.1855 Boston,Mass.
d.June 4,1886

Yr	Cl	Lea	Pos	G	Rec
1876	Ath	N	C	1	.500

WARD, JOHN A. (Rube)
b.Washington Court House,O.

Yr	Cl	Lea	Pos	G	Rec
1902	Bro	N	O	13	.290

WARD, JOHN MONTGOMERY
b.Mar.3,1860 Bellefonte,Pa.
d.Mar.4,1925

Yr	Cl	Lea	Pos	G	Rec
1878	Pro	N	P	35	22-13
1879	Pro	N	P-3	82	44-18 .287
1880	Pro	N	P-3-O	82	40-23 .226
1881	Pro	N	P-S-O	83	18-18 .241
1882	Pro	N	P-S-O	83	19-13 .245
1883	NY	N	P-2-S-3-O	88	12-14 .258
1884	NY	N	P-2-O	109	3-3 .249
1885	NY	N	S	111	.226
1886	NY	N	S	122	.273
1887	NY	N	S	129	.371
1888	NY	N	S	122	.251
1889	NY	N	S	114	.298
1890	Bro	p	M-S	128	.371
1891	Bro	N	M-2-S	104	.287
1892	Bro	N	M-2	148	.273
1893	NY	N	M-2	134	.348
1894	NY	N	M-2	136	.262
	BLTR			1810	158-102 .284

WARD, JOSEPH A.
b.Sept.2,1884 Philadelphia,Pa.
d.Aug.11,1934

Yr	Cl	Lea	Pos	G	Rec
1906	Phi	N	3	30	.295
1909	NY	A	2	9	.179
1909	Phi	N	2	63	.266
1910	Phi	N	1	33	.145
	TR			135	.237

WARD, PETER THOMAS
b.July 26,1939 Montreal,Que.,Canada

Yr	Cl	Lea	Pos	G	Rec
1962	Bal	A	O	8	.143

BLTR

WARD, PRESTON MEYER
b.July 24,1927 Columbia,Mo.

Yr	Cl	Lea	Pos	G	Rec
1948	Bro	N	1	42	.260
1950	Chi	N	1	80	.253
1953	Chi	N	1-O	33	.230
1953	Pit	N	1	88	.210
1954	Pit	N	1-3-O	117	.269
1955	Pit	N	1-O	84	.212
1956	Pit	N	3-O	16	.333
1956	Cle	A	1-O	87	.253
1957	Cle	A	1	10	.182
1958	Cle	A	1-3-O	48	.338
1958	KC	A	1-3-O	81	.254
1959	KC	A	1-O	58	.248
	BLTR			744	.253

WARD, RICHARD O.
b.May 21,1911 Kennebec,S.Dak.

Yr	Cl	Lea	Pos	G	Rec
1934	Chi	N	P	3	0-0
1935	St.L	N	P	1	0-0
	BRTR			4	0-0

WARE, GEORGE
Non-playing manager Pro (N) 1878.

WARES, CLYDE ELLSWORTH
(Buzzy)
b.Mar.23,1886 Newburg Township Mich.

Yr	Cl	Lea	Pos	G	Rec
1913	St.L	A	S	10	.286
1914	St.L	A	S	81	.209
	BRTR			91	.220

WARHOP, JOHN MILTON
(Chief) (Real name John Milton Wauhop)
b.July 4,1884 Hinton,W.Va.
d.Oct.4,1960

Yr	Cl	Lea	Pos	G	Rec
1908	NY	A	P	5	1-3
1909	NY	A	P	36	13-15
1910	NY	A	P	37	14-14
1911	NY	A	P	32	12-13
1912	NY	A	P	37	10-19
1913	NY	A	P	14	4-4
1914	NY	A	P	35	8-15
1915	NY	A	P	21	7-9
	BRTR			217	69-92

WARMOTH, WALLACE WALTER
(Cy)
b.Feb.2,1893 Mt.Carmel,Ill.
d.June 20,1957

Yr	Cl	Lea	Pos	G	Rec
1916	St.L	N	P	3	0-0
1922	Was	A	P	5	1-0
1923	Was	A	P	21	7-4
	BLTL			29	8-4

WARNEKE, LONNIE
b.Mar.28,1909 Mt.Ida,Ark.

Yr	Cl	Lea	Pos	G	Rec
1930	Chi	N	P	1	0-0
1931	Chi	N	P	20	2-4
1932	Chi	N	P	35	22-6
1933	Chi	N	P	39	18-13
1934	Chi	N	P	52	22-10
1935	Chi	N	P	44	20-13
1936	Chi	N	P	40	16-13
1937	St.L	N	P	36	18-11
1938	St.L	N	P	31	13-8
1939	St.L	N	P	34	13-7
1940	St.L	N	P	33	16-10
1941	St.L	N	P	37	17-9
1942	St.L	N	P	12	6-4
1942	Chi	N	P	15	5-7
1943	Chi	N	P	21	4-5
1945	Chi	N	P	9	0-1
	BRTR			459	192-121

WARNER, EDWARD EMORY
b.Dec.29,1888 Fitchburg,Mass.
d.Feb.2,1954

Yr	Cl	Lea	Pos	G	Rec
1912	Pit	N	P	11	1-1
	BRTL				

WARNER, FREDERICK JOHN RODNEY
b.1855 Philadelphia,Pa.
d.Feb.13,1886

Yr	Cl	Lea	Pos	G	Rec
1875	Cen	n	O	14	NR
1876	Ath	N	O	1	.000
1878	Ind	N	S	41	.243
1879	Cle	N	3-O	76	.243
1883	Phi	N	3	38	.233
1884	Bro	a	3	85	.212
				255	NR

WARNER, GEORGE HOKE
(Hooks)
b.May 22,1894 Pittsburgh,Pa.
d.Feb.19,1947

Yr	Cl	Lea	Pos	G	Rec
1916	Pit	N	3	44	.238
1917	Pit	N	3	3	.200
1919	Pit	N	3	6	.125
1921	Chi	N	3	14	.211
	BLTR			67	.228

WARNER, JACK DYER
b.July 12,1940 Brandywine,W.Va.

Yr	Cl	Lea	Pos	G	Rec
1962	Chi	N	P	7	0-0
	BRTR				

WARNER, JOHN JOSEPH
b.Aug.15,1872 New York,N.Y.
d.Dec.21,1943

Yr	Cl	Lea	Pos	G	Rec
1895	Bos	N	C	3	.143
1895	Lou	N	C	60	.263
1896	Lou	N	C-1	33	.209
1896	NY	N	C	16	.264
1897	NY	N	C	110	.274
1898	NY	N	C	108	.259

(Continued)

Yr	Cl	Lea	Pos	G	Rec
1899	NY	N	C	83	.271
1900	NY	N	C	31	.269
1901	NY	N	C	77	.239
1902	Bos	A	C	64	.234
1903	NY	N	C	85	.284
1904	NY	N	C	86	.199
1905	St.L	N	C	41	.255
1905	Det	A	C	36	.202
1906	Det	A	C	49	.242
1906	Was	A	C	33	.204
1907	Was	A	C	72	.256
1908	Was	A	C	51	.241
	TR			1038	.250

WARNER, JOHN RALPH
b.Aug.29,1903 Evansville,Ind.

Yr	Cl	Lea	Pos	G	Rec
1925	Det	A	3	10	.333
1926	Det	A	3	100	.251
1927	Det	A	3	139	.267
1928	Det	A	3	75	.214
1929	Bro	N	S	17	.274
1930	Bro	N	3	21	.320
1931	Bro	N	S-3	9	.500
1933	Phi	N	2-S-3	107	.224
	BRTR			478	.250

WARNOCK, HAROLD CHARLES
b.Jan.6,1912 New York,N.Y.

Yr	Cl	Lea	Pos	G	Rec
1935	St.L	A	O	6	.286
	BLTR				

WARREN, BENJAMIN LOUIS
b.Mar.1,1913 Elk City,Okla.

Yr	Cl	Lea	Pos	G	Rec
1939	Phi	N	C	18	.232
1940	Phi	N	C-1	106	.246
1941	Phi	N	C	121	.215
1942	Phi	N	C-1	90	.209
1946	NY	N	C	39	.159
1947	NY	N	C	3	.200
	BRTR			377	.219

WARREN, THOMAS GENTRY
b.July 5,1920 Tulsa,Okla.

Yr	Cl	Lea	Pos	G	Rec
1944	Bro	N	P	41	1-4
	BLTR				

WARREN, WILLIAM
(Real name William Warren White)

WARREN, WILLIAM H.
b.Feb.11,1887 Cairo,Ill.

Yr	Cl	Lea	Pos	G	Rec
1914	Ind	F	C	23	.239
1915	New	F	C	5	.333
	BLTR			28	.245

WARSTLER, HAROLD BURTON
(Rabbit)
b.Sept.13,1904 N.Canton,O.

Yr	Cl	Lea	Pos	G	Rec
1930	Bos	A	S	54	.185
1931	Bos	A	2-S	66	.243
1932	Bos	A	S	115	.211
1933	Bos	A	S	92	.217
1934	Phi	A	2	117	.236
1935	Phi	A	2-3	138	.250
1936	Phi	A	2	66	.250
1936	Bos	N	S	74	.211
1937	Bos	N	S	149	.223
1938	Bos	N	S	142	.231
1939	Bos	N	2-S-3	114	.243
1940	Bos	N	2	33	.211
1940	Chi	N	2-S	45	.226
	BRTR			1205	.229

WARWICK, CARL WAYNE
b.Feb.27,1937 Dallas,Tex.

Yr	Cl	Lea	Pos	G	Rec
1961	LA	N	O	19	.091
1961	St.L	N	O	55	.250
1962	St.L	N	O	13	.348
1962	Hou	N	O	130	.260
	BRTL			217	.304

WARWICK, FIRMIN NEWTON
(Bill)
b.Nov.26,1898 Philadelphia,Pa.

Yr	Cl	Lea	Pos	G	Rec
1921	Pit	N	C	1	.000
1925	St.L	N	C	13	.293
1926	St.L	N	C	9	.357
	BRTR			23	.286

WASDELL, JAMES CHARLES
b.May 15,1915 Cleveland,O.

Yr	Cl	Lea	Pos	G	Rec
1937	Was	A	1	32	.255
1938	Was	A	1	53	.236
1939	Was	A	1	29	.303
1940	Was	A	1	10	.086
1940	Bro	N	1-O	77	.278
1941	Bro	N	O	94	.299
1942	Pit	N	1-O	122	.259
1943	Pit	N	H	4	.500
1943	Phi	N	1-O	141	.261
1944	Phi	N	1-O	133	.277
1945	Phi	N	1-O	134	.300
1946	Phi	N	1-O	26	.255
1946	Cle	A	1-O	32	.268
1947	Cle	A	H	1	.000
	BLTL			888	.273

WASEM, LINCOLN WILLIAM
b.Jan.30,1911 Birmingham,O.

Yr	Cl	Lea	Pos	G	Rec
1937	Bos	N	C	2	.000
	BRTR				

WASHBURN, GEORGE EDWARD
b.Oct.6,1914 Solon,Me.

Yr	Cl	Lea	Pos	G	Rec
1941	NY	A	P	1	0-1
	BLTR				

WASHBURN, LIBE
b.June 16,1874 Lynn,N.H.
d.Mar.22,1940

Yr	Cl	Lea	Pos	G	Rec
1902	NY	N	O	6	.444
1903	Phi	N	P	8	0-4
				14	{ 0-4 / .286

WASHBURN, RAY CLARK
b.May 31,1938 Pasco,Wash.

Yr	Cl	Lea	Pos	G	Rec
1961	St.L	N	P	3	1-1
1962	St.L	N	P	34	12-9
	BRTR			37	13-10

WASHER, WILLIS (Buck)
b.1882 Akron,O.

Yr	Cl	Lea	Pos	G	Rec
1905	Phi	N	P	1	0-0
	TR				

WASHINGTON, SLOANE VERNON
(Vern)
b.June 4,1908 Linden,Tex.

Yr	Cl	Lea	Pos	G	Rec
1935	Chi	A	O	108	.288
1936	Chi	A	O	20	.163
	BLTR			128	.268

WATERMAN, FREDERICK A.
b.1846 New York,N.Y.
d.Dec.16,1899

Yr	Cl	Lea	Pos	G	Rec
1871	Oly	n	C-3	32	NR
1872	Oly	n	C-3	9	NR
1873	Nat	n	S-3-O	15	NR
1875	Chi	n	2-3	4	NR
				60	NR

WATERS, FRED WARREN
b.Jan.2,1928 Benton,Miss.

Yr	Cl	Lea	Pos	G	Rec
1955	Pit	N	P	2	0-0
1956	Pit	N	P	23	2-2
	BLTL			25	2-2

WATKINS, EDWARD

Yr	Cl	Lea	Pos	G	Rec
1902	Phi	N	O	1	.000

WATKINS, GEORGE ARCHIBALD
b.June 4,1902 Palestine,Tex.

Yr	Cl	Lea	Pos	G	Rec
1930	St.L	N	1-O	119	.373
1931	St.L	N	O	131	.288
1932	St.L	N	O	127	.312
1933	St.L	N	O	138	.278
1934	NY	N	O	105	.247
1935	Phi	N	O	150	.270
1936	Phi	N	O	19	.243
1936	Bro	N	O	105	.256
		BLTR		894	.288

WATKINS, HARVEY L.
Non-playing manager N.Y.(N) 1895.

WATKINS, WILLIAM HENRY
b.May 5,1859 Brantford,Ont.,Canada.
d.June 9,1937

Yr	Cl	Lea	Pos	G	Rec
1884	Ind	a	M-2-3	34	.211

Non-playing manager Det (N) 1885-88, KC (a) 1888-89, St.L (N) 1893, and Pit (N) 1898-99.

WATLINGTON, JULIUS NEAL
b.Dec.25,1925 Yanceyville,N.C.

Yr	Cl	Lea	Pos	G	Rec
1953	Phi	A	C	21	.159
		BLTR			

WATSON, ARTHUR (Doc)
b.1886 Louisville,Ky.

Yr	Cl	Lea	Pos	G	Rec
1914	Bro	F	C	19	.289
1915	Bro	F	C	8	.294
1915	Buf	F	C	21	.452
		BLTR		48	.344

WATSON, CHARLES J.
b.1889

Yr	Cl	Lea	Pos	G	Rec
1913	Chi	N	P	1	1-0
1914	Chi	F	P	26	9-8
1914	St.L	F	P	9	3-4
1915	St.L	F	P	25	9-9
		BRTL		61	22-21

WATSON, JOHN REEVES
(Mule)
b.Oct.15,1896 Homer,La.
d.Aug.25,1949

Yr	Cl	Lea	Pos	G	Rec
1918	Phi	A	P	21	6-10
1919	Phi	A	P	4	0-1
1920	Bos	N	P	13	5-4
1920	Pit	N	P	5	0-0
1921	Bos	N	P	44	14-13
1922	Bos	N	P	41	8-14
1923	Bos	N	P	11	1-2
1923	NY	N	P	17	8-5
1924	NY	N	P	22	7-4
		BRTR		178	49-53

WATSON, JOHN THOMAS
b.Jan.16,1909 Tazewell,Va.

Yr	Cl	Lea	Pos	G	Rec
1930	Det	A	S	4	.250
		BLTR			

WATSON, MILTON W.
b.1893 Texas

Yr	Cl	Lea	Pos	G	Rec
1916	St.L	N	P	18	4-6
1917	St.L	N	P	41	10-13
1918	Phi	N	P	23	5-7
1919	Phi	N	P	8	2-4
		BRTR		90	21-30

WATSON, WALTER L.
(Mother)
b.Jan.27,1865 Middleport,O.
d.Nov.23,1898

Yr	Cl	Lea	Pos	G	Rec
1887	Cin	a	P-O	2	1-1 / .222

WATT, ALBERT BAILEY
b.Dec.12,1899 Washington,D.C.

Yr	Cl	Lea	Pos	G	Rec
1920	Was	A	2	1	1.000
		BRTR			

WATT, FRANK MARION (Kilo)
b.Dec.15,1902 Washington,D.C.

Yr	Cl	Lea	Pos	G	Rec
1931	Phi	N	P	38	5-5
		BRTR			

WATWOOD, JOHN CLIFFORD
b.Aug.17,1906 Alexander City,Ala.

Yr	Cl	Lea	Pos	G	Rec
1929	Chi	A	O	85	.302
1930	Chi	A	1-O	133	.302
1931	Chi	A	O	128	.283
1932	Chi	A	O	15	.296
1932	Bos	A	1-O	95	.249
1933	Bos	A	O	13	.133
1939	Phi	N	1	2	.167
		BLTL		471	.283

WAUGH, JAMES ELDEN
b.Nov.25,1933 Lancaster,O.

Yr	Cl	Lea	Pos	G	Rec
1952	Pit	N	P	17	1-6
1953	Pit	N	P	29	4-5
		BRTR		46	5-11

WAUHOP, JOHN MILTON
(Played under name of John Milton Warhop)

WAY, ROBERT CLINTON
b.Apr.2,1906 Emlenton,Pa.

Yr	Cl	Lea	Pos	G	Rec
1927	Chi	A	2	5	.333
		BRTR			

WAYENBURG, FRANK
b.Aug.27,1900 Fleming,Kan.

Yr	Cl	Lea	Pos	G	Rec
1924	Cle	A	P	2	0-0
		BRTR			

WEAFER, KENNETH ALBERT
(Al)
b.Feb.6,1914 Woburn,Mass.

Yr	Cl	Lea	Pos	G	Rec
1936	Bos	N	P	1	0-0
		BRTR			

WEATHERLY, CYRIL ROY
(Stormy)
b.Feb.25,1915 Warren,Tex.

Yr	Cl	Lea	Pos	G	Rec
1936	Cle	A	O	84	.335
1937	Cle	A	O	53	.201
1938	Cle	A	O	83	.262
1939	Cle	A	O	95	.310
1940	Cle	A	O	135	.303
1941	Cle	A	O	102	.289
1942	Cle	A	O	128	.258
1943	NY	A	O	77	.264
1946	NY	A	H	2	.500
1950	NY	N	O	52	.261
		BLTL		811	.286

WEAVER, ARTHUR COGGSHALL
(Six O'Clock)
b.Apr.7,1879 Wichita,Kan.
d.Mar.23,1917

Yr	Cl	Lea	Pos	G	Rec
1902	St.L	N	C	11	.171
1903	St.L	N	C	16	.245
1903	Pit	N	C	15	.239
1905	St.L	A	C	28	.120
1908	Chi	A	C	15	.200
		TR		85	.184

WEAVER, DAVID FLOYD
b.May 12,1941 Ben Franklin,Tex.

Yr	Cl	Lea	Pos	G	Rec
1962	Cle	A	P	1	1-0
		BRTR			

WEAVER, GEORGE DAVIS
(Buck)
b.Aug.18,1890 Stowe,Pa.
d.Jan.31,1956

Yr	Cl	Lea	Pos	G	Rec
1912	Chi	A	S	147	.224
1913	Chi	A	S	151	.272
1914	Chi	A	S	136	.246
1915	Chi	A	S	148	.268
1916	Chi	A	S-3	151	.227
1917	Chi	A	S-3	118	.284
1918	Chi	A	S-3	112	.300
1919	Chi	A	S-3	140	.296
1920	Chi	A	S-3	151	.333
		BBTR		1254	.272

WEAVER, HARRY A.
b.Feb.26,1895 Clarendon,Pa.

Yr	Cl	Lea	Pos	G	Rec
1915	Phi	A	P	2	0-2
1916	Phi	A	P	3	0-0
1917	Chi	N	P	4	1-1
1918	Chi	N	P	8	2-2
1919	Chi	N	P	2	0-1
		BRTR		19	3-6

WEAVER, JAMES DEMENT
(Big Jim)
b.Nov.25,1904 Fulton,Ky.

Yr	Cl	Lea	Pos	G	Rec
1928	Was	A	P	3	0-0
1931	NY	A	P	17	2-1
1934	St.L	A	P	5	2-0
1934	Chi	N	P	27	11-9
1935	Pit	N	P	33	14-8
1936	Pit	N	P	38	14-8
1937	Pit	N	P	32	8-5
1938	St.L	A	P	1	0-1
1938	Cin	N	P	30	6-4
1939	Cin	N	P	3	0-0
		BRTR		189	57-36

WEAVER, MONTGOMERY MORTON (Prof)
b.June 15,1906 Helton,N.C.

Yr	Cl	Lea	Pos	G	Rec
1931	Was	A	P	3	1-0
1932	Was	A	P	44	22-10
1933	Was	A	P	23	10-5
1934	Was	A	P	31	11-15
1935	Was	A	P	5	1-1
1936	Was	A	P	26	6-4
1937	Was	A	P	30	12-9
1938	Was	A	P	31	7-6
1939	Bos	A	P	9	1-0
		BLTR		202	71-50

WEAVER, ORVILLE F. (Orlie)
b.June 4,1888 Newport,Ky.

Yr	Cl	Lea	Pos	G	Rec
1910	Chi	N	P	7	1-1
1911	Chi	N	P	6	2-2
1911	Bos	N	P	27	3-12
		BRTR		40	6-15

WEAVER, SAMUEL H.
b.July 20,1855 Philadelphia,Pa.
d.Feb.1,1914

Yr	Cl	Lea	Pos	G	Rec
1875	Phi	n	P	1	1-0
1878	Mil	N	P	47	12-30
1882	Ath	a	P-O	42	26-15 / .240
1883	Lou	a	P-1-O	50	24-20 / .195
1884	Key	U	P	20	5-12
1886	Ath	a	P	2	0-2
		BRTR		162	68-79 / .211

WEAVER, WILLIAM B. (Farmer)
b.Mar.23,1865 Parkersburg,W.Va.
d.Jan.25,1943

Yr	Cl	Lea	Pos	G	Rec
1886	Bro	a	C	1	.000
1888	Lou	a	O	26	.274
1889	Lou	a	O	124	.290
1890	Lou	a	O	130	.292
1891	Lou	a	O	133	.284
1892	Lou	N	O	136	.268
1893	Lou	N	C-O	104	.309
1894	Lou	N	C	60	.206
1894	Pit	N	C-S-3-O	30	.352
				744	.285

WEBB, CLEON EARL
b.Mar.1,1885 Mt.Gilead,O.
d.Jan.12,1958

Yr	Cl	Lea	Pos	G	Rec
1910	Pit	N	P	7	2-1
		BBTL			

WEBB, EARL WILLIAM
b.Sept.17,1899 Ravenscroft,Tenn.

Yr	Cl	Lea	Pos	G	Rec
1925	NY	N	O	4	.000
1927	Chi	N	O	102	.301
1928	Chi	N	O	62	.250
1930	Bos	A	O	127	.323
1931	Bos	A	O	151	.333

Yr Cl Lea Pos G Rec

(Continued)
1932 Bos A O 52 .281
1932 Det A O 87 .287
1933 Det A O 6 .273
1933 Chi A O 58 .308
BLTR 649 .306

WEBB, JAMES LEVERNE (Skeeter)
b.Nov.4,1911 Meridian,Miss.
1932 St.L N S 1 .000
1938 Cle A S 20 .276
1939 Cle A S 81 .264
1940 Chi A 2-S-3 84 .237
1941 Chi A 2-S-3 29 .190
1942 Chi A 2 32 .170
1943 Chi A 2 58 .235
1944 Chi A 2-S 139 .211
1945 Det A 2-S 118 .199
1946 Det A 2-S 64 .219
1947 Det A 2-S 50 .203
1948 Phi A 2-S 23 .148
BRTR 699 .219

WEBB, SAMUEL HENRY (Red)
b.Sept.25,1924 Washington,D.C.
1948 NY N P 5 2-1
1949 NY N P 20 1-1
BLTR 25 3-2

WEBB, WILLIAM FREDERICK
b.Dec.12,1917 Atlanta,Ga.
1943 Phi N P 1 0-0
BRTR

WEBB, WILLIAM JOSEPH
b.June 25,1896 Chicago,Ill.
d.Jan.12,1943
1917 Pit N 2-S 5 .200
BRTR

WEBBER, ...
1884 Ind a C 3 .000

WEBBER, LESTER ELMER
b.May 6,1917 Santa Maria,Cal.
1942 Bro N P 19 3-2
1943 Bro N P 54 2-2
1944 Bro N P 48 7-8
1945 Bro N P 17 7-3
1946 Bro N P 11 3-3
1946 Cle A P 4 1-1
1948 Cle A P 1 0-0
BRTR 154 23-19

WEBER, CHARLES P. (Count)
b.Oct.22,1868 Cincinnati,O.
d.June 13,1914
1898 Was N P 1 0-1

WEBER, HARRY
b.Indianapolis,Ind.
1884 Det N O 2 .000

WEBSTER, RAYMOND GEORGE
b.Nov.15,1937 Grass Valley,Cal.
1959 Cle A 2-3 40 .203
1960 Bos A 2 7 .000
BRTR 47 .195

WECKBECKER, PETER
b.Aug.30,1866 Harmony,Pa.
1889 Ind N C 1 .000
1890 Lou a C 30 .234
31 .232

WEEDEN, CHARLES ALBERT
b.Dec.21,1882 Northwood,N.H.
d.Jan.7,1939
1911 Bos N H 1 .000
TR

WEEKLY, JOHN
b.June 14,1937 New Orleans,La.
1962 Hou N O 13 .192
BRTR

WEHDE, WILBUR (Biggs)
b.Nov.23,1906 Holstein,Ia.
1930 Chi A P 4 0-0
1931 Chi A P 8 1-0
BRTR 12 1-0

WEHMEIER, HERMAN RALPH
b.Feb.18,1927 Cincinnati,O.
1945 Cin N P 3 0-1
1947 Cin N P 1 0-0
1948 Cin N P 36 11-8
1949 Cin N P 36 11-12
1950 Cin N P 54 10-18
1951 Cin N P 46 7-10
1952 Cin N P 41 9-11
1953 Cin N P 29 1-6
1954 Cin N P 13 0-3
1954 Phi N P 25 10-8
1955 Phi N P 34 10-12
1956 Phi N P 3 0-2
1956 St.L N P 42 12-9
1957 St.L N P 40 10-7
1958 St.L N P 3 0-1
1958 Det A P 7 1-0
BRTR 413 92-108

WEICHBRODT, RUDOLPH C.
(Played under name of Skel Roach)

WEIDMAN, GEORGE E. (Stump)
b.Feb.17,1861 Rochester,NY.
d.Mar,3,1905
1880 Buf N P-O 23 {0-10 .100}
1881 Det N P 13 8-5
1882 Det N P-S-O 50 {26-20 .217}
1883 Det N P-2-O 76 {19-23 .173}
1884 Det N P-2-S-O 79 {5-22 .162}
1885 Det N P-O 43 {14-23 .156}
1886 KC N P 51 12-37
1887 Det N P 21 13-6
1887 Met a P-O 12 {4-8 .229}
1887 NY N P 2 0-2
1888 NY N P 2 1-1
BRTR 374 {102-157 .177}

WEIGEL, RALPH RICHARD
b.Oct.2,1921 Mercer Co.,O.
1946 Cle A C 6 .167
1948 Chi A C-O 66 .233
1949 Was A C 34 .233
BRTR 106 .230

WEIHE, JOHN GARIBALDI (Podge)
b.Nov.13,1862 Cincinnati,O.
d.Apr.15,1914
1883 Cin a O 1 .250
1884 Ind a O 64 .261
BRTR 65 .260

WEIK, RICHARD HENRY (Legs)
b.Nov.17,1927 Waterloo,Ia.
1948 Was A P 3 1-2
1949 Was A P 28 3-12
1950 Was A P 14 1-3
1950 Cle A P 11 1-3
1953 Cle A H 1 .000
1953 Det A P 12 0-1
1954 Det A P 9 0-1
BRTR 78 {6-22 .226}

WEILAND, EDWIN NICHOLAS
b.Nov.26,1915 Evanston,Ill.
1940 Chi A P 5 0-0
1942 Chi A P 5 0-0
BLTR 10 0-0

WEILAND, ROBERT GEORGE (Lefty)
b.Dec.14,1905 Chicago,Ill.
1928 Chi A P 1 1-0
1929 Chi A P 15 2-4
1930 Chi A P 14 0-4
1931 Chi A P 15 2-7
1932 Bos A P 43 6-16
1933 Bos A P 39 8-14
1934 Bos A P 11 1-5
1934 Cle A P 16 1-5
1935 St.L A P 14 0-2
1937 St.L N P 41 15-14
1938 St.L N P 35 16-11
1939 St.L N P 32 10-12
1940 St.L N P 1 0-0
BLTL 277 62-94

WEILENMANN, CARL WOOLWORTH
(Played under name of Carl Woolworth Weilman)

WEILMAN, CARL WOOLWORTH (Zeke)
(Real name Carl Woolworth Weilenmann)
b.Nov.29,1889 Hamilton,O.
d.May 26,1924
1912 St.L A P 9 2-4
1913 St.L A P 39 10-20
1914 St.L A P 39 19-13
1915 St.L A P 47 18-18
1916 St.L A P 46 17-18
1917 St.L A P 5 1-2
1919 St.L A P 20 10-6
1920 St.L A P 30 9-13
BLTL 235 86-94

WEIMER, JOHN WILLIAM (Jake)
b.Nov.13,1883 Reading,Pa.
d.Nov.30,1944
1903 Chi N P 35 20-8
1904 Chi N P 37 20-13
1905 Chi N P 33 18-13
1906 Cin N P 41 20-14
1907 Cin N P 29 11-14
1908 Cin N P 15 8-7
1909 NY N P 1 0-0
BRTL 191 97-69

WEINERT, PHILLIP WALTER (Lefty)
b.Apr.21,1901 Philadelphia,Pa.
1919 Phi N P 1 0-0
1920 Phi N P 10 1-1
1921 Phi N P 8 1-0
1922 Phi N P 34 8-11
1923 Phi N P 39 4-17
1924 Phi N P 8 0-1
1927 Chi N P 5 1-1
1928 Chi N P 10 1-0
1931 NY A P 17 2-2
BLTL 132 18-33

WEINGARTNER, ELMER WILLIAM
b.Aug.13,1918 Cleveland,O.
1945 Cle A S 20 .231
BRTR

WEINTRAUB, PHILIP (Mickey)
b.Oct.12,1907 Chicago,Ill.
1933 NY N O 8 .200
1934 NY N O 37 .351
1935 NY N 1-O 64 .241
1937 Cin N O 49 .271
1937 NY N O 6 .333
1938 Phi N 1 100 .311
1944 NY N 1 104 .316
1945 NY N 1 82 .272
BLTL 450 .295

WEIR, WILLIAM FRANKLIN
Feb.25,1913 Portland,Me.
936 Bos N P 13 4-3
937 Bos N P 10 1-1

(Continued)

Yr	Cl	Lea	Pos	G	Rec
1938	Bos	N	P	5	1-0
1939	Bos	N	P	2	0-0
	BLTL			30	6-4

WEIS, ALBERT JOHN

b.Apr.2,1938 Franklin Square,N.Y.

Yr	Cl	Lea	Pos	G	Rec
1962	Chi	A	2-S-3	7	.083
	BBTR				

WEIS, ARTHUR JOHN (Butch)

b.Mar.2,1903 St.Louis,Mo.

Yr	Cl	Lea	Pos	G	Rec
1922	Chi	N	O	2	.500
1923	Chi	N	O	22	.231
1924	Chi	N	O	37	.278
1925	Chi	N	O	67	.267
	BLTL			128	.270

WEISER, HARRY BUDSON (Bud)

b.Jan.8,1891 Shamokin,Pa.

d.July 31,1961

Yr	Cl	Lea	Pos	G	Rec
1915	Phi	N	O	37	.141
1916	Phi	N	O	4	.300
	BRTR			41	.162

WEISS, JOSEPH HAROLD

b.Jan.27,1894 Chicago,Ill.

Yr	Cl	Lea	Pos	G	Rec
1915	Chi	F	1	29	.239
	BRTR				

WELAJ, JOHN LUDWIG

b.May 27,1915 Moss Creek,Pa.

Yr	Cl	Lea	Pos	G	Rec
1939	Was	A	O	63	.274
1940	Was	A	O	88	.256
1941	Was	A	O	49	.208
1943	Phi	A	O	93	.242
	BRTR			293	.250

WELCH, CURTIS BENTON

b.Feb.11,1862 E.Liverpool,O.

d.Aug.29,1896

Yr	Cl	Lea	Pos	G	Rec
1884	Tol	a	O	109	.224
1885	St.L	a	O	112	.266
1886	St.L	a	O	138	.285
1887	St.L	a	O	131	.307
1888	Ath	a	O	136	.291
1889	Ath	a	O	125	.273
1890	Ath	a	O	106	.283
1890	Bal	a	1-O	19	.122
1891	Bal	a	O	130	.278
1892	Bal	N	O	63	.233
1892	Cin	N	O	24	.220
1893	Lou	N	O	14	.181
	BR			1107	.269

WELCH, FRANK (Booger)

b.Aug.10,1897 Birmingham,Ala.

d.July 25,1957

Yr	Cl	Lea	Pos	G	Rec
1919	Phi	A	O	15	.167
1920	Phi	A	O	100	.258
1921	Phi	A	O	115	.285
1922	Phi	A	O	114	.259
1923	Phi	A	O	125	.297
1924	Phi	A	O	94	.290
1925	Phi	A	O	85	.277
1926	Phi	A	O	75	.281
1927	Bos	A	O	15	.179
	BRTR			738	.287

WELCH, HERBERT M. (Dutch)

b.Oct.19,1900 Dyersburg,Tenn.

Yr	Cl	Lea	Pos	G	Rec
1925	Bos	A	S	13	.289
	BLTR				

WELCH, JOHN VERNON

b.Dec.2,1906 Washington,D.C.

d.Sept.2,1940

Yr	Cl	Lea	Pos	G	Rec
1926	Chi	N	P	3	0-0
1927	Chi	N	P	1	0-0
1928	Chi	N	P	3	0-0
1931	Chi	N	P	8	2-1
1932	Bos	A	P	23	4-6
1933	Bos	A	P	47	4-9
1934	Bos	A	P	41	13-15
1935	Bos	A	P	31	10-9

(Continued)

Yr	Cl	Lea	Pos	G	Rec
1936	Bos	A	P	9	2-1
1936	Pit	N	P	9	0-0
	BLTR			175	35-41

WELCH, MICHAEL F.
(Smiling Mickey)

b.July 4,1859 Brooklyn,N.Y.

d.July 30,1941

Yr	Cl	Lea	Pos	G	Rec
1880	Tro	N	P-O	66	34-30 .286
1881	Tro	N	P	39	20-18
1882	Tro	N	P-O	37	14-16 .248
1883	NY	N	P-O	81	27-21 .239
1884	NY	N	P-O	67	39-21 .256
1885	NY	N	P-O	58	47-11 .206
1886	NY	N	P	59	33-23
1887	NY	N	P	40	23-15
1888	NY	N	P	47	26-19
1889	NY	N	P	41	28-12
1890	NY	N	P	35	18-13
1891	NY	N	P	19	5-11
1892	NY	N	P	2	1-1
	BRTR			591	315-211 .229

WELCH, MILTON EDWARD

b.July 26,1924 Farmersville,Ill.

Yr	Cl	Lea	Pos	G	Rec
1945	Det	A	C	1	.000
	BRTR				

WELCH, THEODORE

b.1893

Yr	Cl	Lea	Pos	G	Rec
1914	St.L	F	P	3	0-0
	BLTR				

WELCHONCE, HARRY M.

b.Steubenville,O.

Yr	Cl	Lea	Pos	G	Rec
1911	Phi	N	O	17	.212
	BLTR				

WELDAY, LYNDON EARL (Mike)

b.Dec.19,1879 Conway,Ia.

d.May 28,1942

Yr	Cl	Lea	Pos	G	Rec
1907	Chi	A	O	24	.229
1909	Chi	A	O	29	.189
	BLTL			53	.202

WELF, OLIVER HENRY

b.Jan.17,1889 Cleveland,O.

Yr	Cl	Lea	Pos	G	Rec
1916	Cle	A	H	1	.000

WELLMAN, ROBERT JOSEPH

b.July 15,1925 Cincinnati,O.

Yr	Cl	Lea	Pos	G	Rec
1948	Phi	A	1-O	4	.200
1950	Phi	A	O	11	.333
	BRTR			15	.280

WELLS, EDWIN LEE
(Satchelfoot)

b.June 7,1900 Ashland,O.

Yr	Cl	Lea	Pos	G	Rec
1923	Det	A	P	7	1-0
1924	Det	A	P	29	6-8
1925	Det	A	P	35	6-9
1926	Det	A	P	36	12-10
1927	Det	A	P	8	0-1
1929	NY	A	P	31	13-9
1930	NY	A	P	29	12-3
1931	NY	A	P	28	9-5
1932	NY	A	P	24	3-3
1933	St.L	A	P	38	6-14
1934	St.L	A	P	33	1-7
	BLTL			298	69-69

WELLS, JACOB

b.Aug.9,1863 Memphis,Tenn.

d.Mar.16,1927

Yr	Cl	Lea	Pos	G	Rec
1888	Det	N	C	16	.157
1890	St.L	a	C	28	.238
	BRTR			44	.210

WELLS, JOHN FREDERICK

b.Nov.25,1923 Junction City,Kan.

Yr	Cl	Lea	Pos	G	Rec
1944	Bro	N	P	4	0-2
	BRTR				

WELLS, LEO DONALD

b.July 18,1917 Kansas City,Kan.

Yr	Cl	Lea	Pos	G	Rec
1942	Chi	A	S	35	.194
1946	Chi	A	S-3	45	.189
	BRTR			80	.190

WELSH, JAMES D.

b.Oct.9,1903 Denver,Colo.

Yr	Cl	Lea	Pos	G	Rec
1925	Bos	N	2-O	122	.312
1926	Bos	N	O	134	.278
1927	Bos	N	O	131	.288
1928	NY	N	O	124	.307
1929	NY	N	O	38	.248
1929	Bos	N	O	53	.290
1930	Bos	N	O	113	.275
	BLTR			715	.290

WELSH, JAMES J. (Tub)

b.July 3,1866 St.Louis,Mo.

Yr	Cl	Lea	Pos	G	Rec
1890	Tol	a	C	33	.263
1895	Lou	N	C-1	39	.224
				72	.241

WELTEROTH, RICHARD JOHN

b.Aug.3,1927 Williamsport,Pa.

Yr	Cl	Lea	Pos	G	Rec
1948	Was	A	P	33	2-1
1949	Was	A	P	52	2-5
1950	Was	A	P	5	0-0
	BRTR			90	4-6

WELZER, ANTON FRANK

b.Apr.5,1901 Milwaukee,Wis.

Yr	Cl	Lea	Pos	G	Rec
1926	Bos	A	P	39	4-2
1927	Bos	A	P	37	6-11
	BRTR			76	10-13

WENDELL, LEWIS CHARLES

b.Mar.22,1892 New York,N.Y.

d.July 11,1953

Yr	Cl	Lea	Pos	G	Rec
1915	NY	N	C	20	.222
1916	NY	N	C	2	.000
1924	Phi	N	C	21	.250
1925	Phi	N	C	18	.077
1926	Phi	N	C	1	.000
	BRTR			62	.180

WENSLOFF, CHAS. WILLIAM
(Butch)

b.Dec.3,1915 Sausalito,Cal.

Yr	Cl	Lea	Pos	G	Rec
1943	NY	A	P	29	13-11
1947	NY	A	P	11	3-1
1948	Cle	A	P	1	0-1
	BRTR			41	16-13

WENTZ, JOHN S.

b.Mar.4,1866 Louisville,Ky.

d.Sept.1907

Yr	Cl	Lea	Pos	G	Rec
1891	Lou	a	2	1	.250

WENTZEL, STANLEY AARON

b.Jan.13,1917 Exeter Township,Pa.

Yr	Cl	Lea	Pos	G	Rec
1945	Bos	N	O	4	.211
	BRTR				

WERA, JULIAN VALENTINE
(Jules)

b.Feb.9,1904 Winona,Minn.

Yr	Cl	Lea	Pos	G	Rec
1927	NY	A	3	38	.239
1929	NY	A	3	5	.417
	BRTR			43	.259

WERBER, WILLIAM MURRAY

b.June 20,1908 Berwyn,Md.

Yr	Cl	Lea	Pos	G	Rec
1930	NY	A	S-3	4	.286
1933	NY	A	H	3	.000
1933	Bos	A	S-3	108	.258
1934	Bos	A	S-3	152	.321
1935	Bos	A	3	124	.255
1936	Bos	A	3-O	145	.275

(Continued)

Yr	Cl	Lea	Pos	G	Rec
1937	Phi	A	3	128	.292
1938	Phi	A	3	134	.259
1939	Cin	N	3	147	.289
1940	Cin	N	3	143	.277
1941	Cin	N	3	109	.239
1942	NY	N	3	98	.205
	BRTR			1295	.271

WERDEN, PERCIVAL WHERITT (Perry)
b.July 21,1865 St.Louis,Mo.
d.Jan.9,1934

Yr	Cl	Lea	Pos	G	Rec
1884	St.L	U	P-O	18	{11-1 .237
1888	Was	N	O	3	.300
1890	Tol	a	1	129	.283
1891	Bal	a	1	137	.292
1892	St.L	N	1	148	.255
1893	St.L	N	1	124	.284
1897	Lou	N	1	134	.301
	BRTR			693	{11-1 .283

WERLE, WILLIAM GEORGE (Bugs)
b.Dec.21,1920 Oakland,Cal.

Yr	Cl	Lea	Pos	G	Rec
1949	Pit	N	P	35	12-13
1950	Pit	N	P	48	8-16
1951	Pit	N	P	59	8-6
1952	Pit	N	P	5	0-0
1952	St.L	N	P	19	1-2
1953	Bos	A	P	5	0-1
1954	Bos	A	P	14	0-1
	BLTL			185	29-39

WERLEY, GEORGE WILLIAM
b.Sept.8,1938 St. Louis,Mo.

Yr	Cl	Lea	Pos	G	Rec
1956	Bal	A	P	1	0-0
	BRTR				

WERRICK, JOSEPH ABRAHAM
b.Oct.25,1858 St.Paul,Minn.
d.May 10,1943

Yr	Cl	Lea	Pos	G	Rec
1884	St.P	U	S	9	.071
1886	Lou	a	3	136	.250
1887	Lou	a	3	136	.333
1888	Lou	a	3	109	.210
	TR			390	.266

WERTZ, DWIGHT LEWIS (Del)
b.1891

Yr	Cl	Lea	Pos	G	Rec
1914	Buf	F	S	3	.000
	BRTR				

WERTZ, HENRY LEVI
b.Apr.20,1901 Pomaria,S.C.

Yr	Cl	Lea	Pos	G	Rec
1926	Bos	N	P	32	11-9
1927	Bos	N	P	42	4-10
1928	Bos	N	P	10	0-2
1929	Bos	N	P	4	0-0
	BRTR			88	15-21

WERTZ, VICTOR WOODROW
b.Feb.9,1925 York,Pa.

Yr	Cl	Lea	Pos	G	Rec
1947	Det	A	O	102	.288
1948	Det	A	O	119	.248
1949	Det	A	O	155	.304
1950	Det	A	O	149	.308
1951	Det	A	O	138	.285
1952	Det	A	O	85	.246
1952	St.L	A	O	37	.346
1953	St.L	A	O	128	.268
1954	Bal	A	O	29	.202
1954	Cle	A	1-O	94	.275
1955	Cle	A	1-O	74	.253
1956	Cle	A	1	136	.264
1957	Cle	A	1	144	.282
1958	Cle	A	1	25	.279
1959	Bos	A	1	94	.275
1960	Bos	A	1	131	.282
1961	Bos	A	1	99	.262
1961	Det	A	H	8	.167
1962	Det	A	1	74	.324
	BLTR			1821	.279

WESNER, ...
b.Washington,D.C.

Yr	Cl	Lea	Pos	G	Rec
1895	Was	N	S	1	.000
	TR				

WEST, FRANK
b.1873 Wilmerding,Pa.

Yr	Cl	Lea	Pos	G	Rec
1894	Bos	N	P	1	0-0

WEST, JAMES (Hi)
b.Aug.8,1884 Roseville,Ill.

Yr	Cl	Lea	Pos	G	Rec
1905	Cle	A	P	6	2-2
1911	Cle	A	P	13	2-4
	BRTR			19	4-6

WEST, MAX EDWARD
b.Nov.28,1916 Dexter,Mo.

Yr	Cl	Lea	Pos	G	Rec
1938	Bos	N	O	123	.234
1939	Bos	N	O	130	.285
1940	Bos	N	1-O	139	.261
1941	Bos	N	O	138	.277
1942	Bos	N	1-O	134	.255
1946	Bos	N	1	1	.000
1946	Cin	N	O	72	.213
1948	Pit	N	1-O	87	.178
	BLTR			824	.254

WEST, MILTON DOUGLASS (Buck)
b.Aug.29,1860 Spring Mill,O.
d.Jan.14,1929

Yr	Cl	Lea	Pos	G	Rec
1884	Cin	a	O	33	.292
1890	Cle	N	O	37	.245
	BRTR			70	.265

WEST, RICHARD THOMAS
b.Nov.24,1917 Louisville,Ky.

Yr	Cl	Lea	Pos	G	Rec
1938	Cin	N	H	1	.000
1939	Cin	N	C-O	8	.211
1940	Cin	N	C	7	.393
1941	Cin	N	C	67	.215
1942	Cin	N	C-O	33	.177
1943	Cin	N	H	3	.000
	BRTR			119	.221

WEST, SAMUEL FILMORE
b.Oct.5,1904 Longview,Tex.

Yr	Cl	Lea	Pos	G	Rec
1927	Was	A	O	38	.239
1928	Was	A	O	125	.301
1929	Was	A	O	142	.267
1930	Was	A	O	120	.328
1931	Was	A	O	132	.333
1932	Was	A	O	146	.287
1933	St.L	A	O	133	.300
1934	St.L	A	O	122	.326
1935	St.L	A	O	138	.300
1936	St.L	A	O	152	.278
1937	St.L	A	O	122	.328
1938	St.L	A	O	44	.309
1938	Was	A	O	92	.302
1939	Was	A	1-O	115	.282
1940	Was	A	1-O	57	.253
1941	Was	A	O	26	.270
1942	Chi	A	O	49	.232
	BLTL			1753	.283

WEST, WALTER MAXWELL (Max)
b.July 14,1904 Sunset,Tex.

Yr	Cl	Lea	Pos	G	Rec
1928	Bro	N	O	7	.286
1929	Bro	N	O	5	.250
	BRTR			12	.276

WEST, WELDON EDISON
b.Sept.3,1915 Gibsonville,N.C.

Yr	Cl	Lea	Pos	G	Rec
1944	St.L	A	P	11	0-0
1945	St.L	A	P	24	3-4
	BRTL			35	3-4

WEST, WILLIAM NELSON
b.Aug.21,1840 Philadelphia,Pa.
d.Aug.18,1891

Yr	Cl	Lea	Pos	G	Rec
1874	Atl	n	2	10	NR
1876	Mut	N	2	1	.000
				11	NR

WESTERBERG, OSCAR
d.Apr.18,1910

Yr	Cl	Lea	Pos	G	Rec
1907	Bos	N	S	3	.222
	TR				

WESTERVELT, HUYLER
b.Oct.1,1870 Piermont,N.Y.

Yr	Cl	Lea	Pos	G	Rec
1894	NY	N	P	18	7-9

WESTERZIL, GEORGE J. (Tex)
b.Mar.7,1891 Detroit,Mich.

Yr	Cl	Lea	Pos	G	Rec
1914	Bro	F	3	149	.253
1915	Bro	F	3	36	.311
1915	Chi	F	3	7	.250
1915	St.L	F	*3	50	.240
	BRTR			242	.258

WESTLAKE, JAMES PATRICK
b.July 30,1930 Sacramento,Cal.

Yr	Cl	Lea	Pos	G	Rec
1955	Phi	N	H	1	.000
	BLTL				

WESTLAKE, WALDON THOMAS (Wally)
b.Nov.8,1920 Gridley,Cal.

Yr	Cl	Lea	Pos	G	Rec
1947	Pit	N	O	112	.273
1948	Pit	N	O	132	.285
1949	Pit	N	O	147	.282
1950	Pit	N	O	139	.285
1951	Pit	N	3-O	50	.282
1951	St.L	N	O	73	.255
1952	St.L	N	O	21	.216
1952	Cin	N	O	59	.202
1952	Cle	A	O	29	.232
1953	Cle	A	O	82	.330
1954	Cle	A	O	85	.263
1955	Cle	A	O	16	.250
1955	Bal	A	O	8	.125
1956	Phi	N	H	5	.000
	BRTR			958	.272

WESTON, ALFRED JOHN
b.Dec.17,1905 Lynn,Mass.

Yr	Cl	Lea	Pos	G	Rec
1929	Bos	N	H	3	.000
	BRTR				

WESTRUM, WESLEY NOREEN
b.Nov.28,1922 Clearbrook,Minn.

Yr	Cl	Lea	Pos	G	Rec
1947	NY	N	C	6	.417
1948	NY	N	C	66	.160
1949	NY	N	C	64	.243
1950	NY	N	C	140	.236
1951	NY	N	C	124	.219
1952	NY	N	C	114	.221
1953	NY	N	C-3	107	.224
1954	NY	N	C	98	.187
1955	NY	N	C	69	.212
1956	NY	N	C	68	.220
1957	NY	N	C	63	.165
	BRTR			919	.217

WETZEL, CHARLES EDWARD (Buzz)
b.Aug.25,1894 Jay,Okla.
d.Mar.7,1941

Yr	Cl	Lea	Pos	G	Rec
1927	Phi	A	P	2	0-0
	BRTR				

WETZEL, FRANKLIN BURTON (Buzz)
b.July 7,1893 Columbus,Ind.
d.Mar.5,1942

Yr	Cl	Lea	Pos	G	Rec
1920	St.L	A	O	7	.428
1921	St.L	A	O	61	.210
	BRTR			68	.243

WETZEL, GEORGE WILLIAM (Shorty)
b.1868 Philadelphia,Pa.
d.Feb.25,1899

Yr	Cl	Lea	Pos	G	Rec
1885	Bal	a	P	2	0-2

WEYHING, AUGUST (Cannonball)
b.Sept.29,1866 Louisville,Ky.
d.Sept.3,1955

Yr	Cl	Lea	Pos	G	Rec
1887	Ath	a	P	55	27-27
1888	Ath	a	P	49	29-18
1889	Ath	a	P	53	30-20
1890	Bro	p	P	49	31-15
1891	Ath	a	P	54	31-20
1892	Phi	N	P	54	28-23
1893	Phi	N	P	41	24-16
1894	Phi	N	P	36	17-14
1895	Phi	N	P	2	0-2
1895	Pit	N	P	3	1-0
1895	Lou	N	P	27	8-19
1896	Lou	N	P	6	2-3
1898	Was	N	P	43	15-26
1899	Was	N	P	40	16-21
1900	St.L	N	P	7	3-4
1900	Bro	N	P	8	3-2
1901	Cle	A	P	2	0-0
1901	Cin	N	P	1	0-1
BRTR				530	265-231

WEYHING, JOHN
b.June 24,1869 Louisville,Ky.
d.June 20,1890

Yr	Cl	Lea	Pos	G	Rec
1888	Cin	a	P	8	3-4
1889	Col	a	P	1	0-0
BLTL				9	3-4

WHALEY, WILLIAM CARL
b.Feb.10,1899 Indianapolis,Ind.
d.Mar.3,1943

Yr	Cl	Lea	Pos	G	Rec
1923	St.L	A	O	23	.240

BRTR

WHALING, ALBERT (Bert)
b.June 25,1890 Los Angeles,Cal.

Yr	Cl	Lea	Pos	G	Rec
1913	Bos	N	C	79	.242
1914	Bos	N	C	60	.209
1915	Bos	N	C	72	.221
BRTR				211	.225

WHEAT, LEROY WILLIAM (Lee)
b.Sept.15,1929 Edwardsville,Ill.

Yr	Cl	Lea	Pos	G	Rec
1954	Phi	A	P	8	0-2
1955	KC	A	P	3	0-0
BRTR				11	0-2

WHEAT, McKINLEY DAVIS (Mack)
b.June 9,1893 Polo,Mo.

Yr	Cl	Lea	Pos	G	Rec
1915	Bro	N	C	8	.071
1916	Bro	N	C	2	.000
1917	Bro	N	C	29	.133
1918	Bro	N	C-O	57	.217
1919	Bro	N	C	41	.205
1920	Phi	N	C	78	.226
1921	Phi	N	C	10	.185
BRTR				225	.204

WHEAT, ZACHARY DAVIS (Zack)
b.May 23,1888 Hamilton,Mo.

Yr	Cl	Lea	Pos	G	Rec
1909	Bro	N	O	26	.304
1910	Bro	N	O	156	.284
1911	Bro	N	O	136	.287
1912	Bro	N	O	123	.305
1913	Bro	N	O	138	.301
1914	Bro	N	O	145	.319
1915	Bro	N	O	146	.258
1916	Bro	N	O	149	.312
1917	Bro	N	O	109	.312
1918	Bro	N	O	105	.335
1919	Bro	N	O	137	.297
1920	Bro	N	O	148	.328
1921	Bro	N	O	148	.320
1922	Bro	N	O	152	.335
1923	Bro	N	O	98	.375
1924	Bro	N	O	141	.375
1925	Bro	N	O	150	.359
1926	Bro	N	O	111	.290
1927	Phi	A	O	88	.324
BLTR				2406	.317

WHEATLEY, CHARLES
b.1893 Kansas City,Mo.

Yr	Cl	Lea	Pos	G	Rec
1912	Det	A	P	5	0-4

BRTR

WHEATON, ELWOOD PIERCE
(Woody)
b.Oct.3,1915 Philadelphia,Pa.

Yr	Cl	Lea	Pos	G	Rec
1943	Phi	A	O	7	.200
1944	Phi	A	P-O	30	0-1 / .186
BLTL				37	0-1 / .191

WHEELER, DONALD WESLEY
b.Sept.29,1922 Minneapolis,Minn.

Yr	Cl	Lea	Pos	G	Rec
1949	Chi	A	C	67	.240

BRTR

WHEELER, EDWARD RAYMOND
b.May 24,1917 Los Angeles,Cal.

Yr	Cl	Lea	Pos	G	Rec
1945	Cle	A	2-S-3	46	.194

BRTR

WHEELER, EDWARD W.
b.June 15,1879 Sherman,Mich.

Yr	Cl	Lea	Pos	G	Rec
1902	Bro	N	2-S-3	24	.128

TR

WHEELER, FLOYD C. (Rip)
b.Mar.2,1898 Marion,Ky.

Yr	Cl	Lea	Pos	G	Rec
1921	Pit	N	P	1	0-0
1922	Pit	N	P	1	0-0
1923	Chi	N	P	3	1-2
1924	Chi	N	P	29	3-6
BRTR				34	4-8

WHEELER, GEORGE HARRISON
(Heavy)
b.Nov.10,1881 Shelburn,Ind.
d.June 14,1918

Yr	Cl	Lea	Pos	G	Rec
1910	Cin	N	O	3	.000

BLTR

WHEELER, GEORGE L.
(Real name George L. Heroux)
b.Aug.3,1869 Methuen,Mass.
d.Mar.23,1946

Yr	Cl	Lea	Pos	G	Rec
1896	Phi	N	P	3	1-1
1897	Phi	N	P	25	10-10
1898	Phi	N	P	15	6-9
1899	Phi	N	P	5	3-2
				48	20-22

WHEELER, HARRY EUGENE
b.Mar.3,1858 Versailles,Ind.
d.Oct.9,1900

Yr	Cl	Lea	Pos	G	Rec
1878	Pro	N	P	7	6-1
1879	Cin	N	P-O	1	0-1 / .000
1880	Cle	N	O	1	.250
1880	Cin	N	3-O	17	.108
1882	Cin	a	P-1-O	75	1-2 / .250
1883	Col	a	P-O	83	0-1 / .225
1884	St.L	a	O	5	.200
1884	KC	U	P-O	14	0-1 / .246
1884	Chi	U	O	19	.241
1884	Pit	U	O	17	.236
1884	Bal	U	O	17	.254
BRTR				256	7-6 / .225

WHEELER, RICHARD
(Real name
Richard Wheeler Maynard)

Yr	Cl	Lea	Pos	G	Rec
1918	St.L	N	O	5	.000

WHEELOCK, WARREN H. (Bobby)
b.Aug.6,1864 Charlestown,Mass.
d.Mar.13,1928

Yr	Cl	Lea	Pos	G	Rec
1887	Bos	N	S-O	44	.314
1890	Col	a	S	59	.267
1891	Col	a	S	136	.230
BRTR				239	.257

WHELAN, JAMES FRANK
b.1890

Yr	Cl	Lea	Pos	G	Rec
1913	St.L	N	O	1	.000

BRTR

WHELAN, THOMAS JOSEPH
b.Jan.3,1894 Lynn,Mass.
d.June 26,1957

Yr	Cl	Lea	Pos	G	Rec
1920	Bos	N	1	1	.000

BRTR

WHICKER, KEMP CASWELL
(Played under name of
Kemp Caswell Wicker)

WHISENANT, THOMAS PETER
(Pete)
b.Dec.14,1929 Asheville,N.C.

Yr	Cl	Lea	Pos	G	Rec
1952	Bos	N	O	24	.192
1955	St.L	N	O	58	.191
1956	Chi	N	O	103	.239
1957	Cin	N	O	67	.211
1958	Cin	N	2-O	85	.236
1959	Cin	N	O	36	.239
1960	Cin	N	H	1	.000
1960	Cle	A	O	7	.167
1960	Was	A	O	58	.226
1961	Min	A	O	10	.000
1961	Cin	N	C-3-O	26	.200
BRTR				475	.224

WHISTLER, LEWIS
(Real Name Lewis Wissler)
b.Mar.10,1868 St.Louis,Mo.
d.Dec.30,1959

Yr	Cl	Lea	Pos	G	Rec
1890	NY	N	1	45	.288
1891	NY	N	S-O	71	.245
1892	Bal	N	1	52	.227
1892	Lou	N	1	80	.252
1893	Lou	N	1	13	.222
1893	St.L	N	1	10	.243
				271	.250

WHITAKER, WALTER ELTON
b.June 27,1884 Chelsea,Mass.

Yr	Cl	Lea	Pos	G	Rec
1916	Phi	A	P	1	0-0

WHITAKER, WILLIAM H.
b.1865 St.Louis,Mo.

Yr	Cl	Lea	Pos	G	Rec
1888	Bal	a	P	2	1-1
1889	Bal	a	P	1	1-0
TR				3	2-1

WHITCHER, ROBERT ARTHUR
b.Apr.29,1919 Berlin,N.H.

Yr	Cl	Lea	Pos	G	Rec
1945	Bos	N	P	9	0-2

BLTL

WHITE, ADELL ABE
b.May 16,1906 Braseltons,Ga.

Yr	Cl	Lea	Pos	G	Rec
1937	St.L	N	P	5	0-1

BRTL

WHITE, ALBERT EUGENE (Fuzz)
b.June 27,1919 Springfield,Mo.

Yr	Cl	Lea	Pos	G	Rec
1940	St.L	A	H	2	.000
1947	NY	N	H	7	.231
BLTR				9	.200

WHITE, C. B.
b.Wakeman,O.

Yr	Cl	Lea	Pos	G	Rec
1883	Phi	N	3	1	.000

WHITE, CHARLES
b.Aug.12,1928 Kinston,N.C.

Yr	Cl	Lea	Pos	G	Rec
1954	Mil	N	C	50	.237
1955	Mil	N	C	12	.233
BLTR				62	.236

WHITE, DONALD WILLIAM
b.Jan.8,1919 Everett,Wash.

Yr	Cl	Lea	Pos	G	Rec
1948	Phi	A	3-O	86	.245
1949	Phi	A	3-O	57	.213
BRTR				143	.232

WHITE, EDWARD PERRY
b.Apr.6,1926 Anniston,Ala.

Yr	Cl	Lea	Pos	G	Rec
1955	Chi	A	O	3	.500

BRTR

Yr Cl Lea Pos G Rec

WHITE, ELDER LAFAYETTE
b.Dec.23,1934 Colerain,N.C.
1962 Chi N 2-S 23 .151
BRTR

WHITE, ELMER
b.May 23,1850 Caton,N.Y.
d.July 19,1938
1871 Cle n C-O 16 NR

WHITE, ERNEST DANIEL
b.Sept.5,1916 Pacolet Mills,S.C.
1940 St.L N P 9 1-1
1941 St.L N P 33 17-7
1942 St.L N P 27 7-5
1943 St.L N P 21 5-5
1946 Bos N P 14 0-1
1947 Bos N P 1 0-0
1948 Bos N P 16 0-2
BRTL 121 30-21

WHITE, GEORGE FREDERICK
(Deke)
b.Sept.8,1872 Albany,N.Y.
d.Nov.27,1957
1895 Phi N P 3 1-0
BBTL

WHITE, GUY HARRIS (Doc)
b.Apr.9,1879 Washington,D.C.
1901 Phi N P 28 14-13
1902 Phi N P-O 50 {16-20 .274}
1903 Chi A P 38 17-16
1904 Chi A P 30 16-10
1905 Chi A P 34 18-14
1906 Chi A P 28 18-6
1907 Chi A P 48 27-13
1908 Chi A P 51 19-13
1909 Chi A P-O 71 {10-9 .238}
1910 Chi A P 56 15-13
1911 Chi A P 39 10-14
1912 Chi A P 28 8-10
1913 Chi A P 17 2-4
BLTL 518 {190-155 .217}

WHITE, HAROLD GEORGE
b.Mar.18,1919 Utica,N.Y.
1941 Det A P 4 0-0
1942 Det A P 34 12-12
1943 Det A P 32 7-12
1946 Det A P 11 1-1
1947 Det A P 35 4-5
1948 Det A P 27 2-1
1949 Det A P 10 1-0
1950 Det A P 42 9-6
1951 Det A P 38 3-4
1952 Det A P 41 1-8
1953 St.L A P 10 0-0
1953 St.L N P 49 6-5
1954 St.L N P 4 0-0
BRTR 337 46-54

WHITE, JAMES LAURIE (Deacon)
b.Dec.2,1847 Caton,N.Y.
d.July 7,1939
1871 Cle n C-2-O 29 NR
1872 Cle n C-2-O 21 NR
1873 Bos n C-O 60 .389
1874 Bos n C-1-O 68 .326
1875 Bos n C-1-O 80 .355
1876 Chi N C 66 .335
1877 Bos N C-1-O 59 .387
1878 Cin N C-3-O 60 .313
1879 Cin N M-C-1-O 77 .330
1880 Cin N 1-2-O 34 .302
1881 Buf N C-1-2-3-O 78 .310
1882 Buf N C-3 83 .281
1883 Buf N C-3 93 .289
1884 Buf N C-3 106 .325
1885 Buf N 3 98 .292
1886 Det N 3 124 .289
1887 Det N 3 111 .341

(Continued))
1888 Det N 3 125 .298
1889 Pit N 3 55 .253
1890 Buf p P-1-3 122 {0-1 .264}
BLTR 1549 {0-1 NR}

WHITE, JOHN F.
b.Indianapolis,Ind.
1904 Bos N O 1 .000
BL

WHITE, JOHN PETER
b.Aug.31,1905 New York,N.Y.
1927 Cin N 2-S 5 .000
1928 Cin N 2 1 .000
BBTR 6 .000

WHITE, JOYNER CLIFFORD (Jo-Jo)
b.June 1,1909 Red Oak,Ga.
1932 Det A O 79 .260
1933 Det A O 91 .252
1934 Det A O 115 .313
1935 Det A O 114 .240
1936 Det A O 58 .275
1937 Det A O 94 .246
1938 Det A O 78 .262
1943 Phi A O 139 .248
1944 Phi A S-O 85 .221
1944 Cin N O 24 .235
BLTR 877 .256
Non-playing manager Cle(A) 1960

WHITE, KIRBY (Red)
b.Jan.3,1884 Hillsboro,O.
d.Apr.22,1943
1909 Bos N P 23 6-13
1910 Bos N P 3 1-2
1910 Pit N P 30 10-9
1911 Pit N P 2 0-1
TR 58 17-25

WHITE, SAMUEL
b.1895
1919 Bos N C 1 .000
BRTR

WHITE, SAMUEL CHARLES
b.July 7,1928 Wenatchee,Wash.
1951 Bos A C 4 .182
1952 Bos A C 115 .281
1953 Bos A C 136 .273
1954 Bos A C 137 .282
1955 Bos A C 143 .261
1956 Bos A C 114 .245
1957 Bos A C 111 .215
1958 Bos A C 102 .259
1959 Bos A C 119 .284
1961 Mil N C 21 .222
1962 Phi N C 41 .216
BRTR 1043 .262

WHITE, STEPHEN VINCENT
b.Dec.21,1884 Dorchester,Mass.
1912 Was A P 1 0-0
1912 Bos N P 3 0-0
BRTR 4 0-0

WHITE, WILLIAM BARNEY
b.June 25,1924 Paris,Tex.
1945 Bro N S-3 4 .000
BRTR

WHITE, WILLIAM DEKOVA
b.Jan.28,1934 Lakewood,O.
1956 NY N 1-O 138 .256
1958 SF N 1-O 26 .241
1959 St.L N 1-O 138 .302
1960 St.L N 1-O 144 .283
1961 St.L N 1 153 .286
1962 St.L N 1-O 159 .324
BLTL 758 .291

WHITE, WILLIAM DIGHTON
b.May 1,1860 Bellaire,O.
d.Dec.31,1924
1884 Pit a S-3 74 .219
1886 Lou a S 135 .262
1887 Lou a S 132 .311
1888 Lou a S-3 49 .283
1888 St.L a S 60 .176
450 .259

WHITE, WILLIAM EDWARD
b.Milner,Ga.
1879 Pro N 1 1 .250

WHITE, WILLIAM HENRY
b.Oct.11,1854 Caton,N.Y.
d.Aug.31,1911
1877 Bos N P 3 2-1
1878 Cin N P-O 51 {29-21 .132}
1879 Cin N P 75 38-30
1880 Cin N P-O 61 {18-43 .165}
1881 Det N P 2 0-2
1882 Cin a P-1-O 54 {40-12 .264}
1883 Cin a P 65 43-22
1884 Cin a M-P 54 34-18
1885 Cin a P 35 17-15
1886 Cin a P 3 1-2
BBTR 403 {222-166 .185}

WHITE, WILLIAM WARREN
(Also played under name of William Warren)
d.Mar.3,1898
1871 Oly n 2 1 .000
1872 Nat n S-3 9 NR
1873 Nat n S-3 39 NR
1874 Bal n 3 45 NR
1875 Chi n 2-S-3-O 70 NR
1884 Was U 2-3 2 .000
166 NR

WHITEHEAD,
BURGESS URQUHART
b.June 29,1910 Tarboro,N.C.
1933 St.L N 2-S 12 .286
1934 St.L N 2-S-3 100 .277
1935 St.L N 2-S-3 107 .263
1936 NY N 2 154 .278
1937 NY N 2 152 .286
1939 NY N 2 95 .239
1940 NY N 2-S-3 133 .282
1941 NY N 2-3 116 .228
1946 Pit N 2-S-3 55 .220
BRTR 924 .263

WHITEHEAD, JOHN HENDERSON
(Silent John)
b.Apr.27,1909 Coleman,Tex.
1935 Chi A P 28 13-13
1936 Chi A P 34 13-13
1937 Chi A P 26 11-8
1938 Chi A P 32 10-11
1939 Chi A P 7 0-3
1939 St.L A P 26 1-3
1940 St.L A P 15 1-3
1942 St.L A P 4 0-0
BRTR 172 49-54

WHITEHEAD, MILTON P.
1884 St.L U P-2-S-3-O 100 {0-1 .225}
1884 KC U 2-S-3 5 .150
105 {0-1 .222}

WHITEHILL, EARL OLIVER
b.Feb.7,1899 Cedar Rapids,Ia.
d.Oct.22,1954
1923 Det A P 8 2-0
1924 Det A P 37 17-9
1925 Det A P 36 11-11
1926 Det A P 36 16-13

(Continued)

Yr	Cl	Lea	Pos	G	Rec
1927	Det	A	P	41	16-14
1928	Det	A	P	31	11-16
1929	Det	A	P	38	14-15
1930	Det	A	P	34	17-13
1931	Det	A	P	34	13-16
1932	Det	A	P	32	16-12
1933	Was	A	P-O	40	22-8 .222
1934	Was	A	P	35	14-11
1935	Was	A	P	34	14-13
1936	Was	A	P	28	14-11
1937	Cle	A	P	33	8-8
1938	Cle	A	P	26	9-8
1939	Chi	N	P	24	4-7
	BLTL			547	218-186 .204

WHITEHOUSE, CHARLES EVIS
b.July 9,1894 Mattoon,Ill.
d.July 19,1960

Yr	Cl	Lea	Pos	G	Rec
1914	Ind.	F	P	8	2-0
1915	New	F	P	11	2-2
1919	Was	A	P	6	0-1
	BBTL			25	4-3

WHITEHOUSE, GILBERT A.
b.Oct.15,1893 Somerville,Mass.

Yr	Cl	Lea	Pos	G	Rec
1912	Bos	N	C	1	.000
1915	New	F	O	35	.217
	TR			36	.211

WHITEHORN, LEE
(Played under name of Arthur Lee Daney)

WHITELY, GURDON
b.Oct.5,1859 Ashaway,R.I.
d.Nov.24,1924

Yr	Cl	Lea	Pos	G	Rec
1884	Cle	N	O	8	.147
1885	Bos	N	C-O	33	.185
				41	.178

WHITEMAN, GEORGE (Lucky)
b.Dec.23,1882 Peoria,Ill.
d.Feb.10,1947

Yr	Cl	Lea	Pos	G	Rec
1907	Bos	A	O	4	.167
1913	NY	A	O	11	.343
1918	Bos	A	O	71	.267
	BRTR			86	.271

WHITFIELD, FRED DWIGHT
b.Jan.7,1938 Vandiver,Ala.

Yr	Cl	Lea	Pos	G	Rec
1962	St.L	N	1	73	.266
	BLTL				

WHITING, EDWARD C.
(Also played under name of Harry Zieber)
b.Philadelphia,Pa.

Yr	Cl	Lea	Pos	G	Rec
1882	Bal	a	C-1-O	73	.267
1883	Lou	a	C-1-3-O	55	.295
1884	Lou	a	C	42	.220
1886	Was	N	C	6	.000
	BLTR			176	.254

WHITING, JESSE W.

Yr	Cl	Lea	Pos	G	Rec
1902	Phi	N	P	1	0-1
1906	Bro	N	P	3	1-1
1907	Bro	N	P	2	0-0
				6	1-2

WHITMAN, DICK CORWIN
b.Nov.9,1920 Woodburn,Ore.

Yr	Cl	Lea	Pos	G	Rec
1946	Bro	N	O	104	.260
1947	Bro	N	O	4	.400
1948	Bro	N	O	60	.291
1949	Bro	N	O	23	.184
1950	Phi	N	O	75	.250
1951	Phi	N	O	19	.118
	BLTR			285	.259

WHITMAN, WALTER FRANKLIN
(Hooker)
b.Aug.15,1924 Marengo,Ind.

Yr	Cl	Lea	Pos	G	Rec
1946	Chi	A	1-2-S	17	.063
1948	Chi	A	S	3	.000
	BRTR			20	.045

WHITNER, EDWARD CLARENCE
(Played under name of Edward Clarence Levy)

WHITNEY, ARTHUR CARTER
(Pinkey)
b.Jan.2,1906 San Antonio,Tex.

Yr	Cl	Lea	Pos	G	Rec
1928	Phi	N	3	151	.301
1929	Phi	N	3	154	.327
1930	Phi	N	3	149	.342
1931	Phi	N	3	130	.287
1932	Phi	N	3	154	.298
1933	Phi	N	3	31	.264
1933	Bos	N	2-3	100	.246
1934	Bos	N	2-3	146	.259
1935	Bos	N	2-3	126	.273
1936	Bos	N	3	10	.175
1936	Phi	N	3	114	.294
1937	Phi	N	3	138	.341
1938	Phi	N	3	102	.277
1939	Phi	N	3	34	.187
	BRTR			1539	.295

WHITNEY, ARTHUR WILSON
b.Jan.16,1858 Brockton,Mass.
d.Aug.17,1943

Yr	Cl	Lea	Pos	G	Rec
1880	Wor	N	3	75	.222
1881	Det	N	3	58	.182
1882	Pro	N	S	11	.071
1882	Det	N	P-S-3	30	0-1 .177
1884	Pit	a	3	22	.299
1885	Pit	a	S	90	.227
1886	Pit	a	S-3	136	.225
1887	Pit	N	3	119	.343
1888	NY	N	3	90	.219
1889	NY	N	3	129	.217
1890	NY	p	S-3	119	.212
1891	Cin	a	3	86	.200
1891	St.L	a	3	2	.000
	BRTR			967	0-1 .235

WHITNEY, FRANK THOMAS
b.Feb.18,1856 Brockton,Mass.

Yr	Cl	Lea	Pos	G	Rec
1876	Bos	N	O	34	.236
	BRTR				

WHITNEY, JAMES E.
(Grasshopper)
b.1856 Binghamton,N.Y.
d.May 21,1891

Yr	Cl	Lea	Pos	G	Rec
1881	Bos	N	P-1-O	74	31-33 .255
1882	Bos	N	P-1-O	60	24-22 .325
1883	Bos	N	P-1-O	96	38-22 .282
1884	Bos	N	P-1-3-O	62	31-17 .260
1885	Bos	N	P-1-O	72	17-32 .234
1886	KC	N	P-O	67	12-32 .239
1887	Was	N	P	52	24-21
1888	Was	N	M-P	42	19-21
1889	Ind	N	P	10	2-7
1890	Ath	a	P	7	2-3
	BLTR			542	200-210 .266

WHITROCK, WILLIAM FRANKLIN
b.Mar.4,1870 Cincinnati,O.
d.July 26,1935

Yr	Cl	Lea	Pos	G	Rec
1890	St.L	a	P	13	6-7
1893	Lou	N	P	8	2-4
1894	Lou	N	P	2	0-1
1894	Cin	N	P	17	2-5
1896	Phi	N	P	2	0-1
	TR			42	10-18

WHITTED, GEORGE BOSTIC
(Possum)
b.Feb.4,1891 Durham,N.C.
d.Oct.16,1962

Yr	Cl	Lea	Pos	G	Rec
1912	St.L	N	3	12	.282
1913	St.L	N	S-3-O	123	.220
1914	St.L	N	O	20	.129
1914	Bos	N	O	66	.216
1915	Phi	N	O	128	.281
1916	Phi	N	1-O	147	.281
1917	Phi	N	O	149	.280
1918	Phi	N	O	24	.244
1919	Phi	N	2	78	.249
1919	Pit	N	3-O	35	.398
1920	Pit	N	3	134	.261
1921	Pit	N	O	108	.280
1922	Bro	N	O	1	.000
	BRTR			1025	.270

WICKER, KEMP CASWELL
(Real name Kemp Caswell Whicker)
b.Aug.13,1906 Kernersville,N.C.

Yr	Cl	Lea	Pos	G	Rec
1936	NY	A	P	7	1-2
1937	NY	A	P	16	7-3
1938	NY	A	P	1	1-0
1941	Bro	N	P	16	1-2
	BRTL			40	10-7

WICKER, ROBERT KITRIDGE
b.May 25,1878 Lawrence Co.,Ind.
d.Jan.22,1955

Yr	Cl	Lea	Pos	G	Rec
1901	St.L	N	P	3	0-0
1902	St.L	N	P-O	22	5-11 .234
1903	St.L	N	P	1	0-0
1903	Chi	N	P	32	20-9
1904	Chi	N	P-O	50	17-10 .219
1905	Chi	N	P	25	13-7
1906	Chi	N	P	10	3-5
1906	Cin	N	P	20	6-11
	BRTR			163	64-53 .206

WICKERSHAM, DAVID CLIFFORD
b.Sept.27,1935 E.Springfield,Pa.

Yr	Cl	Lea	Pos	G	Rec
1960	KC	A	P	5	0-0
1961	KC	A	P	17	2-1
1962	KC	A	P	30	11-4
	BRTR			52	13-5

WICKLAND, ALBERT
b.Jan.27,1890 Chicago,Ill.

Yr	Cl	Lea	Pos	G	Rec
1913	Cin	N	O	26	.215
1914	Chi	F	O	158	.288
1915	Chi	F	O	30	.235
1915	Pit	F	O	110	.303
1918	Bos	N	O	95	.262
1919	NY	A	O	26	.152
	BLTL			445	.275

WIDMAR, ALBERT JOSEPH
b.Mar.20,1925 Cleveland,O.

Yr	Cl	Lea	Pos	G	Rec
1947	Bos	A	P	2	0-0
1948	St.L	A	P	49	2-6
1950	St.L	A	P	36	7-15
1951	St.L	A	P	26	4-9
1952	Chi	A	P	1	0-0
	BRTR			114	13-30

WIDNER, WILLIAM WATERFIELD
(Wild Bill)
b.June 3,1867 Cumminsville,O.
d.Dec.10,1908

Yr	Cl	Lea	Pos	G	Rec
1887	Cin	a	P	1	1-0
1888	Was	N	P	15	4-7
1889	Col	a	P	40	13-22
1890	Col	a	P	13	4-8
1891	Cin	a	P	1	0-1
	BRTR			70	22-38

WIEAND, FRANKLIN DELANO ROOSEVELT
b.Apr.4,1933 Walnutport,Pa.

Yr	Cl	Lea	Pos	G	Rec
1958	Cin	N	P	1	0-0
1960	Cin	N	P	5	0-1
	BRTR			6	0-1

WIEDEMEYER, CHARLES JOHN
b.Jan.31,1915 Chicago,Ill.

Yr	Cl	Lea	Pos	G	Rec
1934	Chi	N	P	4	0-0
	BRTL				

WIENECKE, JOHN
b.Mar.10,1894 Saltzburg,Pa.
d.Mar.16,1933

Yr	Cl	Lea	Pos	G	Rec
1921	Chi	A	P	10	0-1
	BRTL				

WIESLER, ROBERT GEORGE
b.Aug.13,1930 St.Louis,Mo.

Yr	Cl	Lea	Pos	G	Rec
1951	NY	A	P	4	0-2
1954	NY	A	P	6	3-2
1955	NY	A	P	16	0-2
1956	Was	A	P	38	3-12
1957	Was	A	P	3	1-1
1958	Was	A	P	4	0-0
	BBTL			71	7-19

WIETELMANN, WILLIAM FREDERICK (Whitey)
b.Mar.15,1920 Zanesville,O.

Yr	Cl	Lea	Pos	G	Rec
1939	Bos	N	S	23	.203
1940	Bos	N	2-S-3	35	.195
1941	Bos	N	2-S-3	16	.091
1942	Bos	N	2-S	13	.206
1943	Bos	N	S	153	.215
1944	Bos	N	2-S-3	125	.240
1945	Bos	N	P-2-S-3	123	{0-0 .271
1946	Bos	N	P-2-S-3	44	{0-0 .205
1947	Pit	N	1-2-S-3	48	.234
	BBTR			580	{0-0 .232

WIGGS, JAMES ALVIN
b.Sept.1,1879 Trondheim,Norway
d.Jan.20,1963

Yr	Cl	Lea	Pos	G	Rec
1903	Cin	N	P	2	0-1
1905	Det	A	P	6	3-3
1906	Det	A	P	4	1-1
	BRTR			12	4-5

WIGHT, WILLIAM ROBERT (Lefty)
b.Apr.12,1922 Rio Vista,Cal.

Yr	Cl	Lea	Pos	G	Rec
1946	NY	A	P	14	2-2
1947	NY	A	P	1	1-0
1948	Chi	A	P	34	9-20
1949	Chi	A	P	35	15-13
1950	Chi	A	P	30	10-16
1951	Bos	A	P	34	7-7
1952	Bos	A	P	10	2-1
1952	Det	A	P	23	5-9
1953	Det	A	P	13	0-3
1953	Cle	A	P	20	2-1
1955	Cle	A	P	17	0-0
1955	Bal	A	P-1	19	{6-8 .083
1956	Bal	A	P	35	9-12
1957	Bal	A	P	27	6-6
1958	Cin	N	P	7	0-1
1958	St.L	N	P	28	3-0
	BLTL			347	{77-99 .115

WIGINTON, FREDERICK THOMAS
b.Dec.16,1899 Schuyler,Neb.

Yr	Cl	Lea	Pos	G	Rec
1923	St.L	N	P	4	0-0
	BRTR				

WILBER, DELBERT QUENTIN (Babe)
b.Feb.24,1919 Lincoln Park,Mich.

Yr	Cl	Lea	Pos	G	Rec
1946	St.L	N	C	4	.000

(Continued)

Yr	Cl	Lea	Pos	G	Rec
1947	St.L	N	C	51	.232
1948	St.L	N	C	27	.190
1949	St.L	N	H	2	.250
1951	Phi	N	C	84	.278
1952	Phi	N	H	2	.000
1952	Bos	A	C	47	.267
1953	Bos	A	C-1	58	.241
1954	Bos	A	C	23	.123
	BRTR			298	.242

WILBORN, CLAUDE EDWARD
b.Sept.1,1912 Denniston,Va.

Yr	Cl	Lea	Pos	G	Rec
1940	Bos	N	O	5	.000
	BLTR				

WILEY, ...

Yr	Cl	Lea	Pos	G	Rec
1884	Was	U	3-O	1	.000

WILHELM, CHARLES ERNEST
b.May 23,1929 Baltimore,Md.

Yr	Cl	Lea	Pos	G	Rec
1953	Phi	A	S	7	.286
	BRTR				

WILHELM, HARRY L.
b.1875
d.Feb.20,1944

Yr	Cl	Lea	Pos	G	Rec
1899	Lou	N	P	4	1-1

WILHELM, IRVING KEY (Kaiser)
b.Jan.26,1878 Wooster,O.
d.May 21,1936

Yr	Cl	Lea	Pos	G	Rec
1903	Pit	N	P	13	5-3.
1904	Bos	N	P	39	15-21
1905	Bos	N	P	38	4-25
1908	Bro	N	P	42	16-22
1909	Bro	N	P	22	3-13
1910	Bro	N	P	15	3-7
1914	Bal	F	P	42	12-17
1915	Bal	F	P	1	0-0
1921	Phi	N	M-P	4	0-0
	BRTR			216	58-108

Non-playing manager Phi (N) 1922.

WILHELM, JAMES HOYT
b.July 26,1923 Huntersville,N.C.

Yr	Cl	Lea	Pos	G	Rec
1952	NY	N	P	71	15-3
1953	NY	N	P	68	7-8
1954	NY	N	P	57	12-4
1955	NY	N	P	59	4-1
1956	NY	N	P	64	4-9
1957	St.L	N	P	40	1-4
1957	Cle	A	P	2	1-0
1958	Cle	A	P	30	2-7
1958	Bal	A	P	9	1-3
1959	Bal	A	P	32	15-11
1960	Bal	A	P	41	11-8
1961	Bal	A	P	51	9-7
1962	Bal	A	P	52	7-10
	BRTR			576	89-75

WILHOIT, JOSEPH WILLIAM
b.Dec.20,1891 Hiawatha,Kan.
d.Sept.25,1930

Yr	Cl	Lea	Pos	G	Rec
1916	Bos	N	O	116	.230
1917	Bos	N	O	54	.280
1917	Pit	N	O	9	.200
1917	NY	N	O	34	.320
1918	NY	N	O	64	.274
1919	Bos	A	O	6	.333
	BBTR			283	.257

WILIE, DENNIS ERNEST
b.Sept.22,1890 Waco,Tex.

Yr	Cl	Lea	Pos	G	Rec
1911	St.L	N	O	15	.235
1912	St.L	N	O	30	.229
1915	Cle	A	O	45	.252
	BLTL			90	.243

WILKE, HARRY JOSEPH
b.Dec.14,1901 Cincinnati,O.

Yr	Cl	Lea	Pos	G	Rec
1927	Chi	N	3	3	.000
	BRTR				

WILKIE, ALDON JAY
b.Oct.30,1915 Zealandia,Sask.,Canada.

Yr	Cl	Lea	Pos	G	Rec
1941	Pit	N	P	26	2-4
1942	Pit	N	P	36	6-7
1946	Pit	N	P	7	0-0
	BLTL			69	8-11

WILKINS, ROBERT LINWOOD
b.Aug.11,1922 Norfolk,Va.

Yr	Cl	Lea	Pos	G	Rec
1944	Phi	A	S	24	.240
1945	Phi	A	S-O	62	.260
	BRTR			86	.257

WILKINSON, EDWARD E.
b.1890 San Francisco,Cal.

Yr	Cl	Lea	Pos	G	Rec
1911	NY	A	O	10	.231
	BRTR				

WILKINSON, ROY HAMILTON
b.May 8,1894 Canandaigua,N.Y.

Yr	Cl	Lea	Pos	G	Rec
1918	Cle	A	P	1	0-0
1919	Chi	A	P	4	1-1
1920	Chi	A	P	34	7-9
1921	Chi	A	P	36	4-19
1922	Chi	A	P	4	0-1
	BRTR			79	12-30

WILKS, THEODORE (Cork)
b.Nov.13,1915 Fulton,N.Y.

Yr	Cl	Lea	Pos	G	Rec
1944	St.L	N	P	36	17-4
1945	St.L	N	P	18	4-7
1946	St.L	N	P	40	8-0
1947	St.L	N	P	37	4-0
1948	St.L	N	P	57	6-6
1949	St.L	N	P	59	10-3
1950	St.L	N	P	18	2-0
1951	St.L	N	P	17	0-0
1951	Pit	N	P	48	3-5
1952	Pit	N	P	44	5-5
1952	Cle	A	P	7	0-0
1953	Cle	A	P	4	0-0
	BRTR			385	59-30

WILL, ROBERT LEE
b.July 15,1931 Berwyn,Ill.

Yr	Cl	Lea	Pos	G	Rec
1957	Chi	N	O	70	.223
1958	Chi	N	O	6	.250
1960	Chi	N	O	138	.255
1961	Chi	N	1-O	86	.257
1962	Chi	N	O	87	.239
	BLTL			387	.249

WILLETT, ROBERT EDGAR (Ed)
b.Mar.7,1884 Norfolk,Va.
d.May 10,1934

Yr	Cl	Lea	Pos	G	Rec
1906	Det	A	P	4	0-3
1907	Det	A	P	9	1-5
1908	Det	A	P	30	15-9
1909	Det	A	P	41	22-9
1910	Det	A	P	38	16-11
1911	Det	A	P	39	13-14
1912	Det	A	P	37	17-15
1913	Det	A	P	34	13-14
1914	St.L	F	P	27	4-16
1915	St.L	F	P	17	2-3
	BRTR			276	103-99

WILLEY, CARLTON FRANCIS
b.June 6,1931 Cherryfield,Me.

Yr	Cl	Lea	Pos	G	Rec
1958	Mil	N	P	23	9-7
1959	Mil	N	P	26	5-9
1960	Mil	N	P	28	6-7
1961	Mil	N	P	35	6-12
1962	Mil	N	P	30	2-5
	BRTR			142	28-40

WILLIAMS, ALMON EDWARD
b.May 11,1915 Hartselle,Ala.

Yr	Cl	Lea	Pos	G	Rec
1937	Phi	A	P	16	4-1
1938	Phi	A	P	30	0-7
	BRTR			46	4-8

Yr	Cl	Lea	Pos	G	Rec

WILLIAMS, ALVA MITCHEL (Rip)
b.Jan.31,1882 Carthage,Ill.
d.July 23,1933

Yr	Cl	Lea	Pos	G	Rec
1911	Bos	A	C-1	95	.239
1912	Was	A	C	56	.318
1913	Was	A	C	64	.283
1914	Was	A	C	81	.278
1915	Was	A	C-1	91	.244
1916	Was	A	C-1	76	.267
1918	Cle	A	1	28	.239
	BRTR			491	.265

WILLIAMS, ARTHUR FRANK
b.Aug.26,1877 Somerville,Mass.
d.1935

Yr	Cl	Lea	Pos	G	Rec
1902	Chi	N	P-1-0	49	0-2 / .232
		TR			

WILLIAMS, AUGUST RAY
(Gloomy Gus)
b.Mar.20,1887 New Jersey
d.Jan.20,1959

Yr	Cl	Lea	Pos	G	Rec
1911	St.L	A	O	9	.269
1912	St.L	A	O	64	.290
1913	St.L	A	O	149	.273
1914	St.L	A	O	143	.253
1915	St.L	A	O	45	.202
	BLTL			410	.263

WILLIAMS, AUGUSTINE H.
b.1870 New York,N.Y.
d.Oct.14,1890

Yr	Cl	Lea	Pos	G	Rec
1890	Bro	a	P	2	1-1

WILLIAMS, BILLY LEO
b.June 15,1938 Whistler,Ala.

Yr	Cl	Lea	Pos	G	Rec
1959	Chi	N	O	18	.152
1960	Chi	N	O	12	.277
1961	Chi	N	O	146	.278
1962	Chi	N	O	159	.298
	BLTR			335	.284

WILLIAMS, CLAUDE PRESTON
(Lefty)
b.Mar.9,1893 Aurora,Mo.

Yr	Cl	Lea	Pos	G	Rec
1913	Det	A	P	4	0-1
1914	Det	A	P	3	0-0
1916	Chi	A	P	43	13-7
1917	Chi	A	P	45	17-8
1918	Chi	A	P	15	6-4
1919	Chi	A	P	41	23-11
1920	Chi	A	P	39	22-14
	BRTL			190	81-45

WILLIAMS, DAVID CARLOUS
b.Nov.2,1928 Dallas,Tex.

Yr	Cl	Lea	Pos	G	Rec
1949	NY	N	2	13	.240
1951	NY	N	2	30	.266
1952	NY	N	2	138	.254
1953	NY	N	2	112	.297
1954	NY	N	2	142	.222
1955	NY	N	2	82	.251
	BRTR			517	.252

WILLIAMS, DAVID CARTER (Mutt)
b.July 31,1891 Ozark,Ark.
d.Mar.30,1962

Yr	Cl	Lea	Pos	G	Rec
1913	Was	A	P	1	1-0
1914	Was	A	P	5	0-0
	BRTR			6	1-0

WILLIAMS, DAVID O.
b.Scranton,Pa.

Yr	Cl	Lea	Pos	G	Rec
1902	Bos	A	P	3	0-0
		TL			

WILLIAMS, DEWEY EDGAR (Dee)
b.Feb.5,1916 Durham,N.C.

Yr	Cl	Lea	Pos	G	Rec
1944	Chi	N	C	79	.240
1945	Chi	N	C	59	.280
1946	Chi	N	C	4	.200
1947	Chi	N	C	3	.000
1948	Cin	N	C	48	.168
	BRTR			193	.233

WILLIAMS, DONALD FRED
b.Sept.14,1931 Floyd,Va.

Yr	Cl	Lea	Pos	G	Rec
1958	Pit	N	P	2	0-0
1959	Pit	N	P	6	0-0
1962	KC	A	P	3	0-0
	BRTR			11	0-0

WILLIAMS, EARL BAXTER
b.Jan.27,1903 Cumberland Gap,Tenn.
d.Mar.10,1958

Yr	Cl	Lea	Pos	G	Rec
1928	Bos	N	C	3	.000
	BRTR				

WILLIAMS, EDWIN DIBRELL (Dib)
b.Jan.19,1910 Greenbrier,Ark.

Yr	Cl	Lea	Pos	G	Rec
1930	Phi	A	2-S	67	.262
1931	Phi	A	2-S	86	.269
1932	Phi	A	2	62	.251
1933	Phi	A	2-S	115	.289
1934	Phi	A	2	66	.273
1935	Phi	A	2-S	4	.100
1935	Bos	A	2-S-3	75	.211
	BRTR			475	.267

WILLIAMS, ELISHA ALPHONSO
(Dale)
b.Oct.6,1855 Ludlow,Ky.
d.Oct.22,1939

Yr	Cl	Lea	Pos	G	Rec
1876	Cin	N	P	9	1-8
	BRTR				

WILLIAMS, EVON DANIEL (Denny)
b.Dec.13,1899 Portland,Ore.
d.Mar.24,1929

Yr	Cl	Lea	Pos	G	Rec
1921	Cin	N	O	10	.000
1924	Bos	A	O	25	.365
1925	Bos	A	O	68	.229
1928	Bos	A	O	16	.222
	BLTR			119	.259

WILLIAMS, FRANK C.
(Real name Frank C. Selman)

WILLIAMS, FREDERICK (Cy)
b.Dec.21,1888 Wadena,Ind.

Yr	Cl	Lea	Pos	G	Rec
1912	Chi	N	O	28	.242
1913	Chi	N	O	49	.224
1914	Chi	N	O	55	.202
1915	Chi	N	O	151	.257
1916	Chi	N	O	118	.279
1917	Chi	N	O	138	.241
1918	Phi	N	O	94	.276
1919	Phi	N	O	109	.278
1920	Phi	N	O	148	.325
1921	Phi	N	O	146	.320
1922	Phi	N	O	151	.308
1923	Phi	N	O	136	.293
1924	Phi	N	O	148	.328
1925	Phi	N	O	107	.331
1926	Phi	N	O	107	.345
1927	Phi	N	O	131	.274
1928	Phi	N	O	99	.256
1929	Phi	N	O	66	.292
1930	Phi	N	O	21	.471
	BLTL			2002	.292

WILLIAMS, FREDERICK (Pap)
b.July 17,1913 Meridian,Miss.

Yr	Cl	Lea	Pos	G	Rec
1945	Cle	A	1	16	.211
	BRTR				

WILLIAMS, GEORGE
b.Oct.23,1939 Detroit,Mich.

Yr	Cl	Lea	Pos	G	Rec
1961	Phi	N	2	17	.250
1962	Hou	N	2	5	.375
	BRTR			22	.273

WILLIAMS, HARRY P.
b.1891 Galveston,Tex.

Yr	Cl	Lea	Pos	G	Rec
1913	NY	A	1	27	.256
	BRTR				

WILLIAMS, JAMES A.
b.1848 Columbus,O.
d.Oct.24,1918
Non-playing manager St.L (a) 1884 and Cle (a) 1887-88.

WILLIAMS,
JAMES THOMAS WILLIAMS
b.Dec.20,1876 St.Louis,Mo.

Yr	Cl	Lea	Pos	G	Rec
1899	Pit	N	3	153	.352
1900	Pit	N	3	106	.266
1901	Bal	A	2	131	.321
1902	Bal	A	1-2-3	125	.311
1903	NY	A	2	132	.281
1904	NY	A	2	146	.259
1905	NY	A	2	129	.228
1906	NY	A	2	139	.277
1907	NY	A	2	139	.270
1908	St.L	A	2	148	.236
1909	St.L	A	2	110	.195
	BRTR			1458	.276

WILLIAMS, JOHN BRODIE
b.1890 Honolulu,Hawaii.

Yr	Cl	Lea	Pos	G	Rec
1914	Det	A	P	4	0-3
	BRTR				

WILLIAMS, KENNETH ROY
b.June 28,1890 Grant's Pass,Ore.
d.Jan.22,1959

Yr	Cl	Lea	Pos	G	Rec
1915	Cin	N	O	71	.242
1916	Cin	N	O	10	.111
1918	St.L	A	O	2	.000
1919	St.L	A	O	65	.300
1920	St.L	A	O	141	.307
1921	St.L	A	O	146	.347
1922	St.L	A	O	153	.332
1923	St.L	A	O	147	.357
1924	St.L	A	O	114	.324
1925	St.L	A	O	102	.331
1926	St.L	A	O	108	.280
1927	St.L	A	O	131	.323
1928	Bos	A	O	133	.303
1929	Bos	A	O	74	.346
	BLTR			1397	.319

WILLIAMS, LEON THEO
b.Dec.2,1905 Macon,Ga.

Yr	Cl	Lea	Pos	G	Rec
1926	Bro	N	P	12	0-0
	BLTL				

WILLIAMS, MARSHALL McDIARMID
b.Feb.21,1893 Faison,N.C.
d.Feb.22,1935

Yr	Cl	Lea	Pos	G	Rec
1916	Phi	A	P	10	0-6
	BRTR				

WILLIAMS, OTTO GEORGE
b.Nov.2,1877 Newark,N.J.
d.Mar.19,1937

Yr	Cl	Lea	Pos	G	Rec
1902	St.L	N	S	2	.400
1903	St.L	N	S	53	.203
1903	Chi	N	S	37	.223
1904	Chi	N	O	54	.200
1906	Was	A	2	20	.137
	BRTR			166	.202

WILLIAMS, REES GEPPERT
(Steamboat)
b.Jan.31,1892 Cascade,Mont.

Yr	Cl	Lea	Pos	G	Rec
1914	St.L	N	P	6	0-1
1916	St.L	N	P	36	6-7
	BLTR			42	6-8

WILLIAMS, RICHARD HIRSHFELD
b.May 7,1929 St.Louis,Mo.

Yr	Cl	Lea	Pos	G	Rec
1951	Bro	N	O	23	.200
1952	Bro	N	1-3-O	36	.309
1953	Bro	N	O	30	.218
1954	Bro	N	O	16	.147
1956	Bro	N	H	7	.286
1956	Bal	A	1-2-3-O	87	.286
1957	Bal	A	1-3-O	47	.234
1957	Cle	A	3-O	67	.283
1958	Bal	A	1-2-3-O	128	.276

(Continued)

Yr	Cl	Lea	Pos	G	Rec
1959	KC	A	1-2-3-O	130	.266
1960	KC	A	1-3-O	127	.288
1961	Bal	A	1-3-O	103	.206
1962	Bal	A	1-3-O	82	.247
			BRTR	883	.262

WILLIAMS, RINALDO LEWIS
b.Dec.18,1893 Santa Cruz,Cal.

Yr	Cl	Lea	Pos	G	Rec
1914	Bro	F	3	4	.207
			BLTR		

WILLIAMS, ROBERT ELIAS
b.Apr.27,1884 Monday,O.
d.Aug.6,1962

Yr	Cl	Lea	Pos	G	Rec
1911	NY	A	C	20	.191
1912	NY	A	C	20	.136
1913	NY	A	C	6	.158
1914	NY	A	1	59	.163
			BRTR	105	.163

WILLIAMS, ROBERT FULTON
(Ace)
b.Mar.18,1918 Montclair,N.J.

Yr	Cl	Lea	Pos	G	Rec
1940	Bos	N	P	5	0-0
1946	Bos	N	P	1	0-0
			BRTL	6	0-0

WILLIAMS, STANLEY WILSON
b.Sept.14,1936 Enfield,N.H.

Yr	Cl	Lea	Pos	G	Rec
1958	LA	N	P	27	9-7
1959	LA	N	P	35	5-5
1960	LA	N	P	38	14-10
1961	LA	N	P	41	15-12
1962	LA	N	P	40	14-12
			BRTR	181	57-46

WILLIAMS, THEODORE SAMUEL
(The Kid)
b.Aug.30,1918 San Diego,Cal.

Yr	Cl	Lea	Pos	G	Rec
1939	Bos	A	O	149	.327
1940	Bos	A	P-O	144	0-0 .344
1941	Bos	A	O	143	.406
1942	Bos	A	O	150	.356
1946	Bos	A	O	150	.342
1947	Bos	A	O	156	.343
1948	Bos	A	O	137	.369
1949	Bos	A	O	155	.343
1950	Bos	A	O	89	.317
1951	Bos	A	O	148	.318
1952	Bos	A	O	6	.400
1953	Bos	A	O	37	.407
1954	Bos	A	O	117	.345
1955	Bos	A	O	98	.356
1956	Bos	A	O	136	.345
1957	Bos	A	O	132	.388
1958	Bos	A	O	129	.328
1959	Bos	A	O	103	.254
1960	Bos	A	O	113	.316
			BLTR	2292	.344

WILLIAMS, THOMAS C.
b.Aug.19,1870 Pomeroy,O.

Yr	Cl	Lea	Pos	G	Rec
1892	Cle	N	P	3	1-0
1893	Cle	N	P	8	1-1
				11	2-1

WILLIAMS, WALTER MERRILL
(Pop)
b.May 19,1874 Bowdoinham.Me.
d.Aug.4,1959

Yr	Cl	Lea	Pos	G	Rec
1898	Was	N	P	2	0-2
1902	Chi	N	P-O	32	11-15 .194
1903	Chi	N	P	2	0-1
1903	Phi	N	P	3	1-2
1903	Bos	N	P	14	4-5
				53	16-25 .217

WILLIAMS, WASHINGTON J.
b.Philadelphia,Pa.
d.Aug.9,1892

Yr	Cl	Lea	Pos	G	Rec
1884	Ric	a	O	2	.250
1885	Chi	N	P-O	1	0-0 .250
				3	0-0 .250

WILLIAMS, WOODROW WILSON
b.Aug.22,1912 Pamplin,Va.

Yr	Cl	Lea	Pos	G	Rec
1938	Bro	N	S	20	.333
1943	Cin	N	2-S-3	30	.377
1944	Cin	N	2	155	.240
1945	Cin	N	2	133	.237
			BRTR	338	.250

WILLIAMSON, EDWARD NAGLE
(Ned)
b.Oct.24,1857 Philadelphia,Pa.
d.Mar.3,1894

Yr	Cl	Lea	Pos	G	Rec
1878	Ind	N	3	60	.223
1879	Chi	N	3	77	.299
1880	Chi	N	C-2-3	74	.255
1881	Chi	N	P-2-S-3	82	0-1 .268
1882	Chi	N	P-3	82	0-0 .281
1883	Chi	N	P-C-3	98	0-0 .276
1884	Chi	N	P-C-3	106	0-0 .278
1885	Chi	N	P-C-3	112	0-0 .238
1886	Chi	N	S	121	.216
1887	Chi	N	S	127	.371
1888	Chi	N	S	132	.250
1889	Chi	N	S	47	.237
1890	Chi	p	S-3	73	.204
			BRTR	1191	0-1 .267

WILLIAMSON, NATHANIEL HOWARD (Howie)
b.Dec.23,1904 Little Rock,Ark.

Yr	Cl	Lea	Pos	G	Rec
1928	St.L	N	H	10	.222
			BLTL		

WILLIAMSON, SILAS ALBERT
b.Feb.20,1903 Buckville,Ark.

Yr	Cl	Lea	Pos	G	Rec
1928	Chi	A	P	1	0-0
			BRTR		

WILLIGROD, JULIUS
b.California

Yr	Cl	Lea	Pos	G	Rec
1882	Det	N	S-O	2	.286
1882	Cle	N	O	8	.114
				10	.143

WILLINGHAM, THOMAS HUGH
b.May 30,1908 Dalhart,Tex.

Yr	Cl	Lea	Pos	G	Rec
1930	Chi	A	2	3	.250
1931	Phi	N	1-S-3	23	.257
1932	Phi	N	H	4	.000
1933	Phi	N	H	1	.000
			BRTR	31	.233

WILLIS, CHARLES WILLIAM
(Lefty)
b.Nov.4.1905 Leetown,W.Va.
d.May 10,1962

Yr	Cl	Lea	Pos	G	Rec
1925	Phi	A	P	3	0-0
1926	Phi	A	P	13	0-0
1927	Phi	A	P	14	3-1
			BBTL	30	3-1

WILLIS, JAMES GLADDEN
b.Mar.20,1927 Doyline,La.

Yr	Cl	Lea	Pos	G	Rec
1953	Chi	N	P	13	2-1
1954	Chi	N	P	14	0-1
			BLTR	27	2-2

WILLIS, JOSEPH
b.Apr.9,1891 Ironton,O.

Yr	Cl	Lea	Pos	G	Rec
1911	St.L	A	P	1	0-0
1911	St.L	N	P	2	0-1
1912	St.L	N	P	31	4-9
1913	St.L	N	P	2	0-0
			BRTL	36	4-10

WILLIS, LESTER EVANS
(Wimpy)
b.Jan.17,1911 Nacogdoches,Tex.

Yr	Cl	Lea	Pos	G	Rec
1947	Cle	A	P	22	0-2
			BLTL		

WILLIS, VICTOR GAZAWAY
b.Apr.12,1876 Wilmington,Del.
d.Aug.3,1947

Yr	Cl	Lea	Pos	G	Rec
1898	Bos	N	P	38	23-12
1899	Bos	N	P	40	27-9
1900	Bos	N	P	28	9-16
1901	Bos	N	P	36	18-17
1902	Bos	N	P	46	27-19
1903	Bos	N	P	39	12-19
1904	Bos	N	P	49	18-25
1905	Bos	N	P	41	10-29
1906	Pit	N	P	41	23-13
1907	Pit	N	P	39	21-11
1908	Pit	N	P	41	23-11
1909	Pit	N	P	39	22-11
1910	St.L	N	P	33	9-12
			BRTR	510	242-204

WILLOUGHBY, CLAUDE WILLIAM (Weeping Willie)
b.Nov.14,1898 Fredonia,Kan.

Yr	Cl	Lea	Pos	G	Rec
1925	Phi	N	P	3	2-1
1926	Phi	N	P	47	8-12
1927	Phi	N	P	35	3-7
1928	Phi	N	P	35	6-5
1929	Phi	N	P	49	15-14
1930	Phi	N	P	41	4-17
1931	Pit	N	P	9	0-2
			BRTR	219	38-58

WILLS, ...

Yr	Cl	Lea	Pos	G	Rec
1884	Was	a	O	4	.133
1884	KC	U	O	5	.150
				9	.143

WILLS, DAVIS BOWLES
b.Jan.26,1877 Charlottesville,Va.
d.Oct.12,1959

Yr	Cl	Lea	Pos	G	Rec
1899	Lou	N	1	24	.255

WILLS, MAURICE MORNING
b.Oct.2,1932 Washington,D.C.

Yr	Cl	Lea	Pos	G	Rec
1959	LA	N	S	83	.260
1960	LA	N	S	148	.295
1961	LA	N	S	148	.282
1962	LA	N	S	165	.299
			BBTR	544	.288

WILLS, THEODORE CARL
b.Feb.9,1934 Fresno,Cal.

Yr	Cl	Lea	Pos	G	Rec
1959	Bos	A	P	9	2-6
1960	Bos	A	P	16	1-1
1961	Bos	A	P	17	3-2
1962	Bos	A	P	1	0-0
1962	Cin	N	P	26	0-2
			BLTL	69	6-11

WILLSON, FRANK HOXIE
b.Nov.3,1898 Bloomington,Neb.

Yr	Cl	Lea	Pos	G	Rec
1918	Chi	A	H	4	.000
1927	Chi	A	O	7	.100
			BLTL	11	.091

WILMOT, WALTER R.
b.Oct.18,1863 Stevens Point,Wis.
d.Feb.1,1929

Yr	Cl	Lea	Pos	G	Rec
1888	Was	N	O	119	.224
1889	Was	N	O	107	.301
1890	Chi	N	O	139	.278

(Continued)

Yr	Cl	Lea	Pos	G	Rec
1891	Chi	N	O	120	.285
1892	Chi	N	O	92	.220
1893	Chi	N	O	93	.318
1894	Chi	N	O	135	.331
1895	Chi	N	O	108	.299
1897	NY	N	O	13	.242
1898	NY	N	O	34	.246
	BBTL			960	.282

WILSHERE, VERNON SPRAGUE
(Whitey)
b.Aug.3,1912 Skaneateles,N.Y.

Yr	Cl	Lea	Pos	G	Rec
1934	Phi	A	P	9	0-1
1935	Phi	A	P	27	9-9
1936	Phi	A	P	5	1-2
	BLTL			41	10-12

WILSON, ARCHIE CLIFTON
b.Nov.25,1923 Los Angeles,Cal.

Yr	Cl	Lea	Pos	G	Rec
1951	NY	A	O	4	.000
1952	NY	A	H	3	.500
1952	Was	A	O	26	.208
1952	Bos	A	O	18	.263
	BRTR			51	.221

WILSON, ARTHUR EARL
b.Dec.11,1885 Macon,Ill.
d.June 12,1960

Yr	Cl	Lea	Pos	G	Rec
1908	NY	N	C	1	.000
1909	NY	N	C	17	.238
1910	NY	N	C	26	.269
1911	NY	N	C	64	.302
1912	NY	N	C	65	.289
1913	NY	N	C	54	.190
1914	Chi	F	C	138	.287
1915	Chi	F	C	96	.309
1916	Pit	N	C	53	.258
1916	Chi	N	C	36	.193
1917	Chi	N	C	81	.213
1918	Bos	N	C	89	.211
1919	Bos	N	C-1	71	.257
1920	Bos	N	C	16	.053
1921	Cle	A	C	2	.000
	BRTR			809	.258

WILSON, ARTHUR LEE
b.Oct.28,1920 Springville,Ala.

Yr	Cl	Lea	Pos	G	Rec
1951	NY	N	1-2-S	19	.182
	BLTR				

WILSON, A. PARKE
b.Oct.26,1867 Keithsburg,Ill.
d.Dec.20,1934

Yr	Cl	Lea	Pos	G	Rec
1893	NY	N	C	29	.280
1894	NY	N	C	45	.329
1895	NY	N	C	62	.243
1896	NY	N	C	69	.230
1897	NY	N	C	44	.310
1898	NY	N	C	1	.000
1899	NY	N	C-1	93	.268
				343	.270

WILSON, A. PETER
(Pete)

Yr	Cl	Lea	Pos	G	Rec
1908	NY	A	P	7	3-3
1909	NY	A	P	14	5-6
	TL			21	8-9

WILSON, CHARLES MAX
(Maxie)
b.June 3,1916 Haw River,N.C.

Yr	Cl	Lea	Pos	G	Rec
1940	Phi	N	P	3	0-0
1946	Was	A	P	9	0-1
	BLTL			12	0-1

WILSON, CHARLES WOODROW
b.Jan.13,1906 Clinton,S.C.

Yr	Cl	Lea	Pos	G	Rec
1931	Bos	N	3	16	.190
1932	St.L	N	S	24	.198
1933	St.L	N	S	1	.000
1935	St.L	N	3	16	.323
	BBTR			57	.215

WILSON, DUANE LEWIS
b.June 29,1934 Wichita,Kans.

Yr	Cl	Lea	Pos	G	Rec
1958	Bos	A	P	2	0-0
	BLTL				

WILSON, EARL LAWRENCE
b.Oct.2,1935 Ponchatoula,La.

Yr	Cl	Lea	Pos	G	Rec
1959	Bos	A	P	9	1-1
1960	Bos	A	P	15	3-2
1962	Bos	A	P	35	12-8
	BRTR			59	16-11

WILSON, EDWARD FRANCIS
b.Sept.7,1910 New Haven,Conn.

Yr	Cl	Lea	Pos	G	Rec
1936	Bro	N	O	52	.347
1937	Bro	N	O	36	.222
	BLTL			88	.317

WILSON, FINIS E.
b.1891

Yr	Cl	Lea	Pos	G	Rec
1914	Bro	F	P	2	0-1
1915	Bro	F	P	18	1-8
	BLTL			20	1-9

WILSON, FRANCIS EDWARD
(Squash)
b.Apr.20,1902 Medford,Mass.

Yr	Cl	Lea	Pos	G	Rec
1924	Bos	N	O	61	.237
1925	Bos	N	O	12	.419
1926	Bos	N	O	87	.237
1928	Cle	A	H	2	.000
1928	St.L	A	O	6	.000
	BLTR			168	.246

WILSON, FRANK EALTON
(Zeke)
b.Dec.24,1869 Benton,Ala.
d.Apr.26,1928

Yr	Cl	Lea	Pos	G	Rec
1895	Bos	N	P	6	2-4
1895	Cle	N	P	11	5-2
1896	Cle	N	P	29	17-10
1897	Cle	N	P	35	14-14
1898	Cle	N	P	34	13-18
1899	St.L	N	P	5	1-1
				120	52-49

WILSON, GEORGE ARCHIBALD W. (Hickie)
b.Brooklyn,N.Y.

Yr	Cl	Lea	Pos	G	Rec
1884	Bro	a	C-O	24	.214

WILSON, GEORGE FRANK
(Squanto)
b.Mar.29,1889 Old Town,Me.

Yr	Cl	Lea	Pos	G	Rec
1911	Det	A	C	5	.187
1914	Bos	A	1	1	.000
	BBTR			6	.187

WILSON, GEORGE PEACOCK
(Ice House)
b.Sept.14,1912 Maricopa,Calif.

Yr	Cl	Lea	Pos	G	Rec
1934	Det	A	H	1	.000
	BR				

WILSON, GEORGE PEPPER
(Garry) (Also played under name of George P. Prentiss)
b.June 10,1876 Wilmington,Del.
d.Sept.8,1902

Yr	Cl	Lea	Pos	G	Rec
	(George P. Wilson)				
1901	Bos	A	P	2	1-0
	(George P. Prentiss)				
1902	Bos	A	P	6	2-2
1902	Bal	A	P	6	3-3
				14	6-5

WILSON, GEORGE WASHINGTON
(Teddy)
b.Aug.30,1925 Cherryville,N.C.

Yr	Cl	Lea	Pos	G	Rec
1952	Chi	A	O	8	.111
1952	NY	N	1-O	62	.241
1953	NY	N	H	11	.125
1956	NY	N	O	53	.132
1956	NY	A	O	11	.167
	BLTR			145	.191

WILSON, GOMER RUSSELL
(Tex)
b.July 8,1902 Trenton,Tex.
d.Sept.15,1946

Yr	Cl	Lea	Pos	G	Rec
1924	Bro	N	P	2	0-0
	BRTL				

WILSON, GRADY HERBERT
b.Nov.23,1922 Columbus,Ga.

Yr	Cl	Lea	Pos	G	Rec
1948	Pit	N	S	12	.100
	BRTR				

WILSON, HENRY C.
b.Baltimore,Md.

Yr	Cl	Lea	Pos	G	Rec
1898	Bal	N	C	1	.000

WILSON, HOWARD P.
(Highball)
b.Philadelphia,Pa.

Yr	Cl	Lea	Pos	G	Rec
1899	Cle	N	P	1	0-1
1902	Phi	A	P	13	7-4
1903	Was	A	P	32	8-18
1904	Was	A	P	4	0-3
				50	15-26

WILSON, HOWARD WILLIAM
(Chink)

Yr	Cl	Lea	Pos	G	Rec
1906	Was	A	P	1	0-1

WILSON, JAMES
b.July 23,1900 Philadelphia,Pa.
d.June 1,1947

Yr	Cl	Lea	Pos	G	Rec
1923	Phi	N	C-O	85	.262
1924	Phi	N	C-1	95	.279
1925	Phi	N	C-O	108	.328
1926	Phi	N	C	90	.305
1927	Phi	N	C	128	.275
1928	Phi	N	C	21	.300
1928	St.L	N	C	120	.258
1929	St.L	N	C	120	.325
1930	St.L	N	C	107	.318
1931	St.L	N	C	115	.274
1932	St.L	N	C	92	.248
1933	St.L	N	C	113	.255
1934	Phi	N	M-C	91	.292
1935	Phi	N	M-C-2	93	.279
1936	Phi	N	M-C	85	.278
1937	Phi	N	M-C	39	.276
1938	Phi	N	M-C	3	.000
1939	Cin	N	C	4	.333
1940	Cin	N	C	16	.243
	BRTR			1525	.284

Non-playing manager Chicago (N) 1941-44.

WILSON, JAMES ALGER
b.Feb.20,1922 San Diego,Cal.

Yr	Cl	Lea	Pos	G	Rec
1945	Bos	A	P	25	6-8
1946	Bos	A	P	1	0-0
1948	St.L	A	P	4	0-0
1949	Phi	A	P	2	0-0
1951	Bos	N	P	20	7-7
1952	Bos	N	P	33	12-14
1953	Mil	N	P	20	4-9
1954	Mil	N	P	27	8-2
1955	Bal	A	P	34	12-18
1956	Bal	A	P	7	4-2
1956	Chi	A	P	28	9-12
1957	Chi	A	P	31	15-8
1958	Chi	A	P	28	9-9
	BRTR			260	86-89

WILSON, JAMES GARRETT
(Gary)
b.Baltimore,Md.

Yr	Cl	Lea	Pos	G	Rec
1902	Bos	A	2	3	.181
	TR				

WILSON, JOHN FRANCIS
(Black Jack)
b.Apr.12,1912 Portland,Ore.

Yr	Cl	Lea	Pos	G	Rec
1934	Phi	A	P	2	0-1
1935	Bos	A	P	23	3-4
1936	Bos	A	P	44	6-8
1937	Bos	A	P	51	16-10
1938	Bos	A	P	37	15-15
1939	Bos	A	P	37	11-11
1940	Bos	A	P	41	12-6

(Continued)

Yr	Cl	Lea	Pos	G	Rec
1941	Bos	A	P	27	4-13
1942	Was	A	P	12	1-4
1942	Det	A	P	9	0-0
	BRTR			283	68-72

WILSON, JOHN NICODEMUS
b.June 15,1890 Boonsboro,Md.
d.Sept.24,1954

Yr	Cl	Lea	Pos	G	Rec
1913	Was	A	P	3	0-0

WILSON, JOHN OWEN
(Chief)
b.Aug.21,1883 Austin,Tex.
d.Feb.22,1954

Yr	Cl	Lea	Pos	G	Rec
1908	Pit	N	O	144	.227
1909	Pit	N	O	154	.273
1910	Pit	N	O	146	.276
1911	Pit	N	O	146	.300
1912	Pit	N	O	152	.300
1913	Pit	N	O	155	.266
1914	St.L	N	O	154	.259
1915	St.L	N	O	107	.276
1916	St.L	N	O	120	.239
	BLTR			1278	.268

WILSON, JOHN SAMUEL
b.Apr.25,1905 Coal City,Ala.

Yr	Cl	Lea	Pos	G	Rec
1927	Bos	A	P	5	0-2
1928	Bos	A	P	2	0-0
	BRTR			7	0-2

WILSON, LESTER WILBUR
b.July 15,1885 Edmonds,Wash.

Yr	Cl	Lea	Pos	G	Rec
1911	Bos	A	O	4	.000
	BLTR				

WILSON, LEWIS ROBERT
(Hack)
b.Apr.26,1900 Ellwood City,Pa.
d.Nov.23,1948

Yr	Cl	Lea	Pos	G	Rec
1923	NY	N	O	3	.200
1924	NY	N	O	107	.295
1925	NY	N	O	62	.239
1926	Chi	N	O	142	.321
1927	Chi	N	O	146	.318
1928	Chi	N	O	145	.313
1929	Chi	N	O	150	.345
1930	Chi	N	O	155	.356
1931	Chi	N	O	112	.261
1932	Bro	N	O	135	.297
1933	Bro	N	2-O	117	.267
1934	Bro	N	O	67	.262
1934	Phi	N	O	7	.100
	BRTR			1348	.307

WILSON, ROBERT
b.Feb.22,1928 Mexia,Tex.

Yr	Cl	Lea	Pos	G	Rec
1958	LA	N	O	3	.200
	BRTR				

WILSON, ROBERT JAMES
(Red)
b.Mar.7,1929 Milwaukee,Wis.

Yr	Cl	Lea	Pos	G	Rec
1951	Chi	A	C	4	.273
1952	Chi	A	C	2	.000
1953	Chi	A	C	71	.250
1954	Chi	A	C	8	.200
1954	Det	A	C	54	.282
1955	Det	A	C	78	.220
1956	Det	A	C	78	.289
1957	Det	A	C	59	.242
1958	Det	A	C	103	.299
1959	Det	A	C	67	.263
1960	Det	A	C	45	.216
1960	Cle	A	C	32	.216
	BRTR			601	.258

WILSON, ROY EDWARD
b.Sept.13,1896 Foster,Ia.

Yr	Cl	Lea	Pos	G	Rec
1928	Chi	A	P	1	0-0
	BLTL				

WILSON, SAMUEL MARSHALL
(Mike)
b.Dec.2,1896 Glenside,Pa.

Yr	Cl	Lea	Pos	G	Rec
1921	Pit	N	C	5	.000
	BRTR				

WILSON, SAMUEL O'NEIL
b.June 14,1935 Lexington,Tenn.

Yr	Cl	Lea	Pos	G	Rec
1960	SF	N	C	6	.000
	BLTR				

WILSON, THOMAS C.
b.1889

Yr	Cl	Lea	Pos	G	Rec
1914	Was	A	C	1	.000
	BRTR				

WILSON, WALTER WOOD
b.Nov.24,1913 Glenn,Ga.

Yr	Cl	Lea	Pos	G	Rec
1945	Det	A	P	25	1-3
	BLTR				

WILSON, WILLIAM
b.Oct.28,1867 Hannibal,Mo.

Yr	Cl	Lea	Pos	G	Rec
1890	Pit	N	C-1-O	83	.213
1897	Lou	N	C	106	.218
1898	Lou	N	C	30	.182
				219	.211

WILSON, WILLIAM CLARENCE
(Lank)
b.July 20,1896 Kiser,N.C.
d.Aug.31,1962

Yr	Cl	Lea	Pos	G	Rec
1920	Det	A	P	3	1-1
	BRTR				

WILSON, WILLIAM DONALD
b.Nov.6,1928 Central City,Neb.

Yr	Cl	Lea	Pos	G	Rec
1950	Chi	A	O	3	.000
1953	Chi	A	O	9	.059
1954	Chi	A	O	20	.171
1954	Phi	A	O	94	.238
1955	KC	A	P-O	98	0-0 .223
	BRTR			224	0-0 .222

WILSONHOLM, ...

Yr	Cl	Lea	Pos	G	Rec
1883	Phi	N	C-O	3	.091

WILTSE, GEORGE LEROY
(Hooks)
b.Sept.8,1880 Hamilton,N.Y.
d.Jan.21,1959

Yr	Cl	Lea	Pos	G	Rec
1904	NY	N	P	25	13-3
1905	NY	N	P	33	14-7
1906	NY	N	P	40	16-11
1907	NY	N	P	34	13-12
1908	NY	N	P	44	23-14
1909	NY	N	P	37	20-11
1910	NY	N	P	36	14-12
1911	NY	N	P	30	12-9
1912	NY	N	P	28	9-6
1913	NY	N	P	20	0-0
1914	NY	N	P	21	1-1
1915	Bro	F	P	19	3-5
	BRTL			367	138-91

WILTSE, HAROLD JAMES
(Whitey)
b.Aug.6,1903 Clay City,Ill.

Yr	Cl	Lea	Pos	G	Rec
1926	Bos	A	P	37	8-15
1927	Bos	A	P	36	10-18
1928	Bos	A	P	2	0-2
1928	St.L	A	P	26	2-5
1931	Phi	N	P	1	0-0
	BLTL			102	20-40

WILTSE, LEWIS DeWITT
(Snake)
b.Dec.5,1871 Bouckville,N.Y.
d.Aug.25,1928

Yr	Cl	Lea	Pos	G	Rec
1901	Pit	N	P	7	1-4
1901	Phi	A	P	19	14-5
1902	Phi	A	P	20	8-8
1902	Bal	A	P-1-2-O	35	7-9 .296
1903	NY	A	P	4	0-3
	BRTL			85	30-29 .276

WINCENIAK, EDWARD JOSEPH
b.Apr.16,1929 Chicago,Ill.

Yr	Cl	Lea	Pos	G	Rec
1956	Chi	N	2-3	15	.118
1957	Chi	N	2-S-3	17	.240
	BRTR			32	.209

WINCHELL, FREDERICK RUSSELL (Real name Frederick Cook)
b.Jan.23,1882 Arlington,Mass.

Yr	Cl	Lea	Pos	G	Rec
1909	Cle	A	P	4	0-3

WINDHORN, GORDON RAY
b.Dec.19,1933 Watseka,Ill.

Yr	Cl	Lea	Pos	G	Rec
1959	NY	A	O	7	.000
1961	LA	N	O	34	.242
1962	KC	A	O	14	.158
1962	LA	A	O	40	.178
	BRTR			95	.176

WINDLE, WILLIS BREWER
b.Dec.13,1905 Galena,Kan.

Yr	Cl	Lea	Pos	G	Rec
1928	Pit	N	1	1	1.000
1929	Pit	N	1	2	.000
	BLTL			3	.500

WINE, ROBERT PAUL
b.Sept.17,1938 New York,N.Y.

Yr	Cl	Lea	Pos	G	Rec
1960	Phi	N	S	4	.143
1962	Phi	N	S-3	112	.244
	BRTR			116	.240

WINEAPPLE, EDWARD (Lefty)
b.Aug.10,1906 Salem,Mass.

Yr	Cl	Lea	Pos	G	Rec
1929	Was	A	P	1	0-0
	BLTL				

WINEGARNER, RALPH LEE
b.Oct.29,1909 Benton,Kan.

Yr	Cl	Lea	Pos	G	Rec
1930	Cle	A	3	5	.455
1932	Cle	A	P	7	1-0
1934	Cle	A	P-O	32	5-4 .196
1935	Cle	A	P-1-3-O	65	2-2 .310
1936	Cle	A	P	18	0-0
1949	St.L	A	P	9	0-0
	BRTR			136	8-6 .276

WINFORD, JAMES HAROLD
(Cowboy)
b.Oct.9,1909 Shelbyville,Tenn.

Yr	Cl	Lea	Pos	G	Rec
1932	St.L	N	P	4	1-1
1934	St.L	N	P	5	0-2
1935	St.L	N	P	2	0-0
1936	St.L	N	P	39	11-10
1937	St.L	N	P	16	2-4
1938	Bro	N	P	2	0-1
	BRTR			68	14-18

WINGARD, ERNEST JAMES
(Jim)
b.Oct.17,1900 Prattville,Ala.

Yr	Cl	Lea	Pos	G	Rec
1924	St.L	A	P	37	13-12
1925	St.L	A	P-O	34	9-10 .288
1926	St.L	A	P	42	5-8
1927	St.L	A	P	42	2-13
	BLTL			155	29-43 .232

WINGFIELD, FREDERICK DAVIS (Ted)
b.Aug.7,1899 Bedford,Va.

Yr	Cl	Lea	Pos	G	Rec
1923	Was	A	P	1	0-0
1924	Was	A	P	4	0-0
1924	Bos	A	P	4	0-2
1925	Bos	A	P	41	12-19
1926	Bos	A	P	43	11-16
1927	Bos	A	P	22	1-7
BRTR				115	24-44

WINGO, ABSALOM HOLBROOK (Red)
b.May 6,1898 Norcross,Ga.

Yr	Cl	Lea	Pos	G	Rec
1919	Phi	A	O	15	.305
1924	Det	A	O	78	.287
1925	Det	A	O	130	.370
1926	Det	A	O	108	.282
1927	Det	A	O	75	.234
1928	Det	A	O	87	.285
BLTR				493	.308

WINGO, EDMUND (Real name Edmond LaRiviere)
b.Oct.8,1895 St. Anne de Bellevue, Que.,Can.

Yr	Cl	Lea	Pos	G	Rec
1920	Phi	A	C	1	.250
BRTR					

WINGO, IVY BROWN
b.July 8,1890 Norcross,Ga.
d.Mar.1,1941

Yr	Cl	Lea	Pos	G	Rec
1911	St.L	N	C	18	.211
1912	St.L	N	C	100	.265
1913	St.L	N	C	112	.254
1914	St.L	N	C	80	.300
1915	Cin	N	C-O	119	.221
1916	Cin	N	M-C	119	.245
1917	Cin	N	C	121	.266
1918	Cin	N	C-O	100	.254
1919	Cin	N	C	76	.273
1920	Cin	N	C-2	108	.264
1921	Cin	N	C	97	.268
1922	Cin	N	C	80	.284
1923	Cin	N	C	61	.263
1924	Cin	N	C-1	66	.286
1925	Cin	N	C	55	.205
1926	Cin	N	C	7	.200
1929	Cin	N	C	1	.000
BLTR				1320	.260

WINHAM, LAFAYETTE SYLVESTER (Lave)
b.1881 Brooklyn,N.Y.

Yr	Cl	Lea	Pos	G	Rec
1902	Bro	N	P	1	0-0
1903	Pit	N	P	5	3-1
TL				6	3-1

WINKELMAN, GEORGE EDWARD
b.June 14,1865 Philadelphia,Pa.
d.May 19,1960

Yr	Cl	Lea	Pos	G	Rec
1883	Lou	a	O	4	.000
1886	Was	N	P	1	0-1
				5	0-1 / .053

WINN, GEORGE BENJAMIN
b.Oct.26,1897 Perry,Ga.

Yr	Cl	Lea	Pos	G	Rec
1919	Bos	A	P	3	0-0
1922	Cle	A	P	8	1-2
1923	Cle	A	P	1	0-0
BLTL				12	1-2

WINSETT, JOHN THOMAS (Long Tom)
b.Nov.24,1909 McKenzie,Tenn.

Yr	Cl	Lea	Pos	G	Rec
1930	Bos	A	H	1	.000
1931	Bos	A	O	64	.198
1933	Bos	A	O	6	.083
1935	St.L	N	O	7	.500
1936	Bro	N	O	22	.235
1937	Bro	N	P-O	118	0-0 / .237
1938	Bro	N	O	12	.300
BLTR				230	0-0 / .237

WINSTON, HENRY RUDOLPH
b.June 15,1909 Youngsville,N.C.

Yr	Cl	Lea	Pos	G	Rec
1933	Phi	A	P	1	0-0
1936	Bro	N	P	14	1-3
BBTR				15	1-3

WINTER, GEORGE LOVINGTON (Sassafras)
b.Apr.27,1878 New Providence,Pa.
d.May 26,1951

Yr	Cl	Lea	Pos	G	Rec
1901	Bos	A	P	28	17-10
1902	Bos	A	P	20	11-9
1903	Bos	A	P	23	10-8
1904	Bos	A	P	20	8-4
1905	Bos	A	P	34	14-16
1906	Bos	A	P	29	6-18
1907	Bos	A	P	35	12-15
1908	Bos	A	P	22	3-14
1908	Det	A	P	7	2-5
TR				218	83-99

WINTERS, CLARENCE JESSE
b.Sept.7,1900 Detroit,Mich.

Yr	Cl	Lea	Pos	G	Rec
1924	Bos	A	P	4	0-1

WINTERS, JESSE FRANKLIN (Buck)
b.Dec.22,1895 Abilene,Tex.

Yr	Cl	Lea	Pos	G	Rec
1919	NY	N	P	16	1-2
1920	NY	N	P	21	0-0
1921	Phi	N	P	18	5-10
1922	Phi	N	P	34	6-6
1923	Phi	N	P	21	1-6
BRTR				110	13-24

WIRTS, ELWOOD VERNON (Kettle)
b.Oct.30,1897 Sacramento,Cal.

Yr	Cl	Lea	Pos	G	Rec
1921	Chi	N	C	7	.182
1922	Chi	N	C	31	.172
1923	Chi	N	C	5	.200
1924	Chi	A	C	5	.083
BRTR				48	.165

WISE, ARCHIBALD EDWIN
b.July 31,1912 Waxahachie,Tex.

Yr	Cl	Lea	Pos	G	Rec
1932	Chi	A	P	3	0-0
BRTR					

WISE, HUGH EDWARD
b.Mar.9,1906 Campbellsville,Ky.

Yr	Cl	Lea	Pos	G	Rec
1930	Det	A	C	2	.333
BBTR					

WISE, KENDALL COLE (Casey)
b.Sept.8,1932 Lafayette,Ind.

Yr	Cl	Lea	Pos	G	Rec
1957	Chi	N	2-S	43	.179
1958	Mil	N	2-S-3	31	.197
1959	Mil	N	2-S	22	.171
1960	Det	A	2-S-3	30	.147
BBTR				126	.175

WISE, NICHOLAS JOSEPH
b.June 15,1867 Boston,Mass.
d.Jan.15,1923

Yr	Cl	Lea	Pos	G	Rec
1888	Bos	N	C	1	.000
BRTR					

WISE, ROY OGDEN
b.Nov.18,1924 Springfield,Ill.

Yr	Cl	Lea	Pos	G	Rec
1944	Pit	N	P	2	0-0
BRTR					

WISE, SAMUEL WASHINGTON (Modoc)
b.Aug.18,1857 Akron,O.
d.Jan.23,1910

Yr	Cl	Lea	Pos	G	Rec
1881	Det	N	3	1	.500
1882	Bos	N	S-3	77	.225
1883	Bos	N	S	95	.270
1884	Bos	N	2-S	109	.220
1885	Bos	N	2-S-O	107	.283
1886	Bos	N	1-2-S	96	.289

(Continued)

Yr	Cl	Lea	Pos	G	Rec
1887	Bos	N	S-O	110	.380
1888	Bos	N	S	104	.239
1889	Was	N	2-S	120	.250
1890	Buf	p	2	119	.295
1891	Bal	a	2	103	.250
1893	Was	N	2-3	121	.317
TR				1162	.285

WISE, WILLIAM E.
b.Washington,D.C.

Yr	Cl	Lea	Pos	G	Rec
1882	Bal	a	P-O	5	1-1 / .150
1884	Was	U	P-O	78	23-20 / .233
1886	Was	N	P	1	0-1
				84	24-22 / .224

WISNER, JOHN HENRY
b.Nov.5,1899 Grand Rapids,Mich.

Yr	Cl	Lea	Pos	G	Rec
1919	Pit	N	P	4	1-0
1920	Pit	N	P	17	1-3
1925	NY	N	P	24	0-0
1926	NY	N	P	5	2-2
BRTR				50	4-5

WISSLER, LOUIS
(Played under name of Lewis Whistler)

WISTERT, FRANCIS MICHAEL (Whitey)
b.Feb.2,1912 Chicago,Ill.

Yr	Cl	Lea	Pos	G	Rec
1934	Cin	N	P	3	0-1
BRTR					

WITEK, NICHOLAS JOSEPH (Mickey)
b.Dec.19,1915 Luzerne,Pa.

Yr	Cl	Lea	Pos	G	Rec
1940	NY	N	2-S	119	.256
1941	NY	N	2	26	.362
1942	NY	N	2	148	.260
1943	NY	N	2	153	.314
1946	NY	N	2-3	82	.264
1947	NY	N	2	51	.219
1949	NY	A	H	1	1.000
BRTR				580	.277

WITHERUP, LeROY FOSTER
b.July 26,1887 N.Washington,Pa.
d.Dec.23,1941

Yr	Cl	Lea	Pos	G	Rec
1906	Bos	N	P	8	0-3
1908	Was	A	P	6	2-4
1909	Was	A	P	12	2-6
				26	4-13

WITHROW, FRANK BLAINE
b.June 14,1892 Greenwood,Mo.

Yr	Cl	Lea	Pos	G	Rec
1920	Phi	N	C	48	.182
1922	Phi	N	C	10	.333
BRTR				58	.208

WITT, GEORGE ADRIAN
b.Nov.9,1933 Long Beach,Cal.

Yr	Cl	Lea	Pos	G	Rec
1957	Pit	N	P	1	0-1
1958	Pit	N	P	18	9-2
1959	Pit	N	P	15	0-7
1960	Pit	N	P	10	1-2
1961	Pit	N	P	9	0-1
1962	LA	A	P	5	1-1
1962	Hou	N	P	8	0-2
BRTR				66	11-16

WITT, LAWTON WALTER (Whitey) (Real name Ladislaw Waldemar Wittkowski)
b.Sept.28,1895 Orange,Mass.

Yr	Cl	Lea	Pos	G	Rec
1916	Phi	A	S	143	.245
1917	Phi	A	S	128	.252
1919	Phi	A	2-O	122	.267
1920	Phi	A	O	65	.321
1921	Phi	A	O	154	.315

Yr Cl Lea Pos G Rec

(Continued)
1922 NY A O 140 .297
1923 NY A O 146 .314
1924 NY A O 147 .297
1925 NY A O 31 .200
1926 Bro N O 63 .259

BLTR 1139 .287

WITTE, JEROME CHARLES
b.July 30,1917 St.Louis,Mo.
1946 St.L A 1 18 .192
1947 St.L A 1 34 .141

BRTR 52 .159

WITTIG, JOHN CARL
b.June 16,1914 Baltimore,Md.
1938 NY N P 13 2-3
1939 NY N P 5 0-2
1941 NY N P 25 3-5
1943 NY N P 40 5-15
1949 Bos A P 1 0-0

BRTR 84 10-25

WITTKOWSKI, LADISLAW WALDEMAR (Played under name of Lawton Walter Witt)

WOEHR, ANDREW EMIL
b.Feb.4,1898 Ft.Wayne,Ind.
1923 Phi N 3 13 .341
1924 Phi N 2-3 50 .217

BRTR 63 .244

WOERLIN, ...
b.St.Louis,Mo.
1895 Was N S 1 .333

WOJEY, PETER PAUL
b.Dec.1,1922 Stowe,Pa.
1954 Bro N P 14 1-1
1956 Det A P 2 0-0
1957 Det A P 2 0-0

BRTR 18 1-1

WOJCIK, JOHN JOSEPH
b.Apr.6,1942 Olean,N.Y.
1962 KC A O 16 .302
BLTR

WOLF, EMIL
b.1890
1912 Cle A P 1 0-0
BRTR

WOLF, RAYMOND BERNARD (Grandpa)
b.July 15,1904 Chicago,Ill.
1927 Cin N 1 1 .000
BRTR

WOLF, WALTER FRANCIS
b.June 10,1900 Hartford,Conn.
1921 Phi A P 9 0-0
BRTL

WOLF, WILLIAM V. (Chicken)
b.May 12,1862 Louisville,Ky.
d.May 16,1903
1882 Lou a P-1-S-3-O 78 0-0 / .294
1883 Lou a C-2-S-O 88 .250
1884 Lou a C-O 112 .303
1885 Lou a O 113 .288
1886 Lou a O 129 .274
1887 Lou a O 137 .324
1888 Lou a S-O 127 .298
1889 Lou a M-O 130 .291
1890 Lou a O 134 .366
1891 Lou a O 136 .250
1892 St.L N O 4 .220

BR 1188 0-0 / .296

Yr Cl Lea Pos G Rec

WOLFE, CHARLES HUNT
b.Feb.15,1899 Wolfsburg,Pa.
d.Nov.27,1957
1923 Phi A P 3 0-0
BLTR

WOLFE, EDWARD ANTHONY
b.Jan.2,1929 Los Angeles,Cal.
1952 Pit N P 3 0-0
BRTR

WOLFE, HARRY
b.July 7,1893 Cleveland,O.
1917 Chi N S 5 .333
1917 Pit N 2 2 .000

BRTR 7 .200

WOLFE, ROY CHAMBERLAIN (Polly)
b.Sept.1,1888 Knoxville,Ill.
d.Nov.21,1938
1912 Chi A O 1 .000
1914 Chi A O 8 .214

BLTR 9 .207

WOLFE, WILLIAM
b.Jersey City,N.J.
1902 Phi N P 1 0-1

WOLFE, WILLIAM O.
b.Jan.7,1876 Independence,Pa.
d.Feb.27,1953
1903 NY A P 20 6-9
1904 NY A P 7 0-3
1904 Was A P 18 6-9
1905 Was A P 27 9-14
1906 Was A P 4 0-3

BRTR 76 21-38

WOLFF, ROGER FRANCIS
b.Apr.10,1911 Evansville,Ill.
1941 Phi A P 2 0-2
1942 Phi A P 32 12-15
1943 Phi A P 41 10-15
1944 Was A P 33 4-15
1945 Was A P 33 20-10
1946 Was A P 21 5-8
1947 Cle A P 7 0-0
1947 Pit N P 13 1-4

BRTR 182 52-69

WOLFGANG, MELDON JOHN
b.Mar.20,1890 Albany,N.Y.
d.June 30,1947
1914 Chi A P 19 9-5
1915 Chi A P 17 2-2
1916 Chi A P 28 4-6
1917 Chi A P 5 0-0
1918 Chi A P 5 0-1

BRTR 74 15-14

WOLTER, HARRY MEIGS
b.July 11,1884 Monterey,Cal.
1907 Cin N O 4 .133
1907 Pit N P 1 0-0
1907 St.L N P 12 0-0
1909 Bos A P-1 54 4-3 / .244
1910 NY A O 135 .267
1911 NY A O 122 .304
1912 NY A O 11 .393
1913 NY A O 127 .256
1917 Chi N O 117 .249

BLTL 583 4-3 / .270

WOLTERS, REINDER ALBERTIS (Rinie)
b.Dec.18,1842 Schaantz,Holland
d.Jan.3,1917
1871 Mut n P 32 15-16
1872 Cle n P-O 15 2-6 / NR

Yr Cl Lea Pos G Rec

(Continued)
1873 Res n P 1 0-1

48 17-23 / NR

WOLVERTON, HARRY STERLING (Fighting Harry)
b.Dec.6,1873 Mt.Vernon,O.
d.Feb.4,1937
1898 Chi N 3 13 .327
1899 Chi N 3 99 .295
1900 Chi N 3 3 .182
1900 Phi N 3 98 .280
1901 Phi N 3 92 .308
1902 Was A 3 59 .257
1902 Phi N 3 34 .284
1903 Phi N 3 123 .308
1904 Phi N 3 102 .266
1905 Bos N 3 122 .225
1912 NY A M-O 33 .300

TR 778 .279

WOMACK, SIDNEY KIRK
b.Oct.2,1897 Greensburg,La.
d.Aug.8,1958
1926 Bos N C 1 .000
BRTR

WOOD, ...
b.Indiana
1914 Ind F P 2 0-0

WOOD, CHARLES ASHER (Spades)
b.Jan.13,1909 Spartanburg,S.C.
1930 Pit N P 9 4-3
1931 Pit N P 15 2-6

BLTL 24 6-9

WOOD, CHARLES SPENCER
b.Feb.28,1900 Batesville,Miss.
1923 Phi A S 3 .333
BRTR

WOOD, FRED S.
b.1863 Hamilton,Ont.,Canada
d.Aug.28,1933
1884 Det N P-C-S-O 28 0-1 / .221
1885 Buf N C 1 .250

29 0-1 / .222

WOOD, GEORGE A. (Dandy)
b.Nov.9,1858 Boston,Mass.
d.Apr.4,1924
1880 Wor N 1-O 79 .243
1881 Det N O 80 .296
1882 Det N O 81 .263
1883 Det N P-O 96 0-0 / .295
1884 Det N 3-O 112 .251
1885 Det N P-S-3-O 82 0-0 / .290
1886 Phi N O 106 .273
1887 Phi N O 113 .342
1888 Phi N O 105 .230
1889 Phi N O 97 .251
1889 Bal a O 3 .200
1890 Phi p O 132 .304
1891 Ath a M-O 131 .302
1892 Bal N O 20 .183
1892 Cin N O 30 .210

BLTR 1267 0-0 / .278

WOOD, HARRY
b.Baltimore,Md.
1903 Cin N O 2 .000
BLTR

WOOD, JACOB
b.June 22,1937 Elizabeth,N.J.
1961 Det A 2 162 .258
1962 Det A 2 111 .226

BRTR 273 .247

WOOD, JAMES BURR
b.Dec.1,1844 Brooklyn,N.Y.
d.Nov.30,1886

Yr	Cl	Lea	Pos	G	Rec
1871	Chi	n	2	28	NR
1872	Tro	n	M-2	25	NR
1872	Eck	n	M-2	7	NR
1873	Phi	n	2	41	NR
1874	Bal	n	2	1	.000
				102	NR

Non-playing manager Chi (n) 1875.

WOOD, JOHN B.

Yr	Cl	Lea	Pos	G	Rec
1896	St.L	N	P	1	0-0

WOOD, JOSEPH
(Smokey Joe)
b.Oct.25,1889 Kansas City,Mo.

Yr	Cl	Lea	Pos	G	Rec
1908	Bos	A	P	6	1-1
1909	Bos	A	P	24	11-7
1910	Bos	A	P	35	12-13
1911	Bos	A	P	44	23-17
1912	Bos	A	P	43	34-5
1913	Bos	A	P	21	11-5
1914	Bos	A	P	20	9-3
1915	Bos	A	P	29	14-5
1917	Cle	A	P	10	0-1
1918	Cle	A	2-O	119	.296
1919	Cle	A	P-O	72	0-0 / .255
1920	Cle	A	P-O	61	0-0 / .270
1921	Cle	A	O	66	.366
1922	Cle	A	O	142	.297
			BRTR	692	115-57 / .284

WOOD, JOSEPH FRANK
b.May 20,1916 Pike Co.,Pa.

Yr	Cl	Lea	Pos	G	Rec
1944	Bos	A	P	3	0-1
			BRTR		

WOOD, JOSEPH PERRY
b.Oct.3,1919 Houston,Tex.

Yr	Cl	Lea	Pos	G	Rec
1943	Det	A	2-3	60	.323
			BRTR		

WOOD, KENNETH LANIER
b.July 1,1924 Lincolnton,N.C.

Yr	Cl	Lea	Pos	G	Rec
1948	St.L	A	O	10	.083
1949	St.L	A	O	7	.000
1950	St.L	A	O	128	.225
1951	St.L	A	O	109	.237
1952	Bos	A	O	15	.100
1952	Was	A	O	61	.238
1953	Was	A	O	12	.212
			BRTR	342	.224

WOOD, PETER BURKE
b.Feb.1,1857 Hamilton,Ont.,Canada
d.Mar.15,1923

Yr	Cl	Lea	Pos	G	Rec
1885	Buf	N	P-1-O	28	8-15 / .212
1889	Phi	N	P	3	1-1
			TR	31	9-16 / .205

WOOD, ROBERT LYNN
b.July 28,1865 Thorn Hill,O.
d.May 22,1943

Yr	Cl	Lea	Pos	G	Rec
1898	Cin	N	C	30	.280
1899	Cin	N	C	58	.317
1900	Cin	N	C-3	34	.264
1901	Cle	A	C	96	.289
1902	Cle	A	C-1-2-3-O	81	.286
1904	Det	A	C	49	.244
1905	Det	A	C	8	.125
			BRTR	356	.280

WOOD, ROY WINTON
b.May 5,1893 Little Rock,Ark.

Yr	Cl	Lea	Pos	G	Rec
1913	Pit	N	O	14	.285
1914	Cle	A	1-O	72	.236
1915	Cle	A	1	33	.193
			BRTR	119	.231

WOOD, WILBUR FORRESTER
b.Sept.22,1941 Cambridge,Mass.

Yr	Cl	Lea	Pos	G	Rec
1961	Bos	A	P	6	0-0
1962	Bos	A	P	1	0-0
			BRTL	7	0-0

WOODALL, CHARLES LAWRENCE (Larry)
b.July 26,1894 Staunton,Va.

Yr	Cl	Lea	Pos	G	Rec
1920	Det	A	C	18	.245
1921	Det	A	C	46	.363
1922	Det	A	C	50	.344
1923	Det	A	C	71	.277
1924	Det	A	C	67	.309
1925	Det	A	C	75	.205
1926	Det	A	C	67	.233
1927	Det	A	C	88	.280
1928	Det	A	C	65	.210
1929	Det	A	H	1	.000
			BRTR	548	.268

WOODBURN, EUGENE S.
b.Aug.20,1886 Blair,O.

Yr	Cl	Lea	Pos	G	Rec
1911	St.L	N	P	11	1-5
1912	St.L	N	P	20	1-4
			BRTR	31	2-9

WOODCOCK, FRED WAYLAND
b.May 17,1868 Winchendon,Mass.
d.Aug.11,1943

Yr	Cl	Lea	Pos	G	Rec
1892	Pit	N	P	7	1-3

WOODEND, GEORGE ANTHONY
b.Dec.9,1917 Hartford,Conn.

Yr	Cl	Lea	Pos	G	Rec
1944	Bos	N	P	3	0-0
			BRTR		

WOODENSHICK, HAROLD JOSEPH
b.Aug.24,1932 Monaca,Pa.

Yr	Cl	Lea	Pos	G	Rec
1956	Det	A	P	2	0-2
1958	Cle	A	P	14	6-6
1959	Was	A	P	32	2-4
1960	Was	A	P	41	4-5
1961	Was	A	P	7	3-2
1961	Det	A	P	12	1-1
1962	Hou	N	P	31	5-16
			BRTL	139	21-36

WOODHEAD, JAMES (Red)
b.1851,England.
d.1881

Yr	Cl	Lea	Pos	G	Rec
1873	Mar	n	S	1	NR
1879	Syr	N	3	34	.169
				35	NR

WOODLING, EUGENE RICHARD
b.Aug.16,1922 Akron,O.

Yr	Cl	Lea	Pos	G	Rec
1943	Cle	A	O	8	.320
1946	Cle	A	O	61	.188
1947	Pit	N	O	22	.266
1949	NY	A	O	112	.270
1950	NY	A	O	122	.283
1951	NY	A	O	120	.281
1952	NY	A	O	122	.309
1953	NY	A	O	125	.306
1954	NY	A	O	97	.250
1955	Bal	A	O	47	.221
1955	Cle	A	O	79	.278
1956	Cle	A	O	100	.262
1957	Cle	A	O	133	.321
1958	Bal	A	O	133	.276
1959	Bal	A	O	140	.300
1960	Bal	A	O	140	.283
1961	Was	A	O	110	.313
1962	Was	A	O	44	.280
1962	NY	N	O	81	.274
			BLTR	1796	.284

WOODMAN, DANIEL COURTNEY
(Cocoa)
b.July 8,1893 Danvers,Mass.

Yr	Cl	Lea	Pos	G	Rec
1914	Buf	F	P	13	0-0

(Continued)

Yr	Cl	Lea	Pos	G	Rec
1915	Buf	F	P	6	0-0
			BRTR	19	0-0

WOODRUFF, ORVILLE FRANCIS
(Sam)
b.Dec.27,1876 Chilo,O.
d.July 22,1937

Yr	Cl	Lea	Pos	G	Rec
1899	NY	N	O	20	.246
1901	Cle	A	O	1	.250
1904	Cin	N	2-3	87	.190
1910	Cin	N	3	21	.148
			BRTR	129	.192

WOODS, GEORGE ROWLAND
(Pinky)
b.May 22,1920 Waterbury,Conn.

Yr	Cl	Lea	Pos	G	Rec
1943	Bos	A	P	23	5-6
1944	Bos	A	P	38	4-8
1945	Bos	A	P	24	4-7
			BRTR	85	13-21

WOODS, JAMES JEROME
b.Sept.17,1939 Chicago,Ill.

Yr	Cl	Lea	Pos	G	Rec
1957	Chi	N	H	2	.000
1960	Phi	N	3	11	.176
1961	Phi	N	3	23	.229
			BRTR	36	.207

WOODS, JOHN FULTON
b.Jan.18,1901 Princeton,W.Va.
d.Oct.4,1946

Yr	Cl	Lea	Pos	G	Rec
1924	Bos	A	P	1	0-0
			BRTR		

WOODS, WALTER SYDNEY
b.Apr.28,1875 Rye,N.H.
d.Oct.30,1951

Yr	Cl	Lea	Pos	G	Rec
1898	Chi	N	P	41	9-13
1899	Lou	N	P	40	8-13
1900	Pit	N	P	1	0-0
				82	17-26

WOODWARD, FRANK RUSSELL
b.May 17,1896 New Haven,Conn.
d.June 11,1961

Yr	Cl	Lea	Pos	G	Rec
1918	Phi	N	P	2	0-0
1919	Phi	N	P	17	6-9
1919	St.L	N	P	17	3-5
1921	Was	A	P	3	0-0
1922	Was	A	P	1	0-0
1923	Chi	A	P	2	0-1
			BRTR	42	9-15

WOOLDRIDGE, FLOYD LEWIS
b.Aug.25,1928 Jerico Springs,Mo.

Yr	Cl	Lea	Pos	G	Rec
1955	St.L	N	P	18	2-4
			BRTR		

WOOTEN, EARL HAZELL
(Junior)
b.Jan.16,1924 Pelzer,S.C.

Yr	Cl	Lea	Pos	G	Rec
1947	Was	A	O	6	.083
1948	Was	A	P-1-O	88	0-0 / .256
			BRTL	94	0-0 / .241

WORDEN, ...

Yr	Cl	Lea	Pos	G	Rec
1914	Phi	A	P	1	0-0

WORDSWORTH, FAVEL PERRY
b.Jan.1851 New York,N.Y.
d.Aug.12,1888

Yr	Cl	Lea	Pos	G	Rec
1873	Res	n	S	10	NR

WORKMAN, CHARLES THOMAS
b.Jan.6,1915 Leeton,Mo.
d.Jan.3,1953

Yr	Cl	Lea	Pos	G	Rec
1938	Cle	A	O	2	.400
1941	Cle	A	H	9	.000
1943	Bos	N	1-3-O	153	.249
1944	Bos	N	3-O	140	.208

(Continued)

Yr	Cl	Lea	Pos	G	Rec
1945	Bos	N	3-O	139	.274
1946	Bos	N	O	25	.167
1946	Pit	N	3-O	58	.221
	BLTR			526	.242

WORKMAN, HARRY HALL
(Hub)
b.Sept.25,1899 Huntington,W.Va.

Yr	Cl	Lea	Pos	G	Rec
1924	Bos	A	P	11	0-0
	BRTR				

WORKMAN, HENRY KILGARIFF
b.Feb.5,1926 Los Angeles,Cal.

Yr	Cl	Lea	Pos	G	Rec
1950	NY	A	1	2	.200
	BLTR				

WORKS, RALPH TALMADGE
(Judge)
b.Mar.16,1888 Payson,Ill.
d.Aug.10,1941

Yr	Cl	Lea	Pos	G	Rec
1909	Det	A	P	16	3-1
1910	Det	A	P	18	3-6
1911	Det	A	P	31	11-5
1912	Det	A	P	22	5-10
1912	Cin	N	P	3	1-1
1913	Cin	N	P	4	0-1
	BRTR			94	23-24

WORTH, ...

Yr	Cl	Lea	Pos	G	Rec
1872	Atl	n	O	1	NR

WORTHINGTON, ALLAN FULTON
b.Feb.5,1930 Birmingham,Ala.

Yr	Cl	Lea	Pos	G	Rec
1953	NY	N	P	20	4-8
1954	NY	N	P	10	0-2
1956	NY	N	P	28	7-14
1957	NY	N	P	55	8-11
1958	SF	N	P	54	11-7
1959	SF	N	P	42	2-3
1960	Bos	A	P	6	0-1
1960	Chi	A	P	4	1-1
	BRTR			219	33-47

WORTHINGTON, ROBERT LEE
(Red)
b.Apr.24,1906 Alhambra,Cal.

Yr	Cl	Lea	Pos	G	Rec
1931	Bos	N	O	128	.291
1932	Bos	N	O	105	.303
1933	Bos	N	O	17	.156
1934	Bos	N	O	41	.246
1934	St.L	N	H	1	.000
	BRTR			292	.287

WORTMAN, WILLIAM LEWIS
(Chuck)
b.Jan.5,1892 Baltimore,Md.

Yr	Cl	Lea	Pos	G	Rec
1916	Chi	N	S	69	.201
1917	Chi	N	S	75	.174
1918	Chi	N	2-S	17	.118
	BRTR			161	.163

WOULFFE, JAMES JOSEPH
b.Nov.25,1856 New Orleans,La.
d.Dec.19,1924

Yr	Cl	Lea	Pos	G	Rec
1884	Cin	a	3-O	8	.118
1884	Pit	a	O	16	.127
	TR			24	.124

WRIGHT, ALBERT E.
b.Nov.11,1912 San Francisco,Cal.

Yr	Cl	Lea	Pos	G	Rec
1933	Bos	N	2	4	1.000
	BRTR				

WRIGHT, ALBERT OWEN
(Ab)
b.Nov.16,1905 Terlton,Okla.

Yr	Cl	Lea	Pos	G	Rec
1935	Cle	A	O	67	.238
1944	Bos	N	O	71	.256
	BRTR			138	.248

WRIGHT, ALFRED L. H.
b.Mar.30,1842 Cedar Grove,N.J.
d.April 20,1905
Non-playing manager Ath (N) 1876.

WRIGHT, CLARENCE EUGENE
b.Dec.11,1878 Cleveland,O.
d.Oct.29,1930

Yr	Cl	Lea	Pos	G	Rec
1901	Bro	N	P	1	1-0
1902	Cle	A	P-1	24	7-9 / .143
1903	Cle	A	P	15	2-7
1903	St.L	A	P	8	2-4
1904	St.L	A	P	1	0-1
	BRTR			49	12-21 / .165

WRIGHT, DAVID WILLIAM
b.Aug.27,1875 Dennison,O.
d.Jan.18,1946

Yr	Cl	Lea	Pos	G	Rec
1895	Pit	N	P	1	0-0
1897	Chi	N	P	1	1-0
	BRTR			2	1-0

WRIGHT, EDWARD YATMAN

Yr	Cl	Lea	Pos	G	Rec
1916	Chi	A	S	8	.000
	BLTR				

WRIGHT, FOREST GLENN
(Buckshot)
b.Feb.6,1901 Archie,Mo.

Yr	Cl	Lea	Pos	G	Rec
1924	Pit	N	S	153	.287
1925	Pit	N	S-3	153	.308
1926	Pit	N	S	119	.308
1927	Pit	N	S	143	.281
1928	Pit	N	S	108	.310
1929	Bro	N	S	24	.200
1930	Bro	N	S	135	.321
1931	Bro	N	S	77	.284
1932	Bro	N	S	127	.274
1933	Bro	N	1-S-3	71	.255
1935	Chi	A	2	9	.120
	BRTR			1119	.294

WRIGHT, GEORGE
b.Jan.28,1847 New York,N.Y.
d.Aug.21,1937

Yr	Cl	Lea	Pos	G	Rec
1871	Bos	n	1-S	17	.387
1872	Bos	n	S	48	.296
1873	Bos	n	S	59	.378
1874	Bos	n	S	60	.344
1875	Bos	n	S	79	.337
1876	Bos	N	S	70	.292
1877	Bos	N	2-S	61	.276
1878	Bos	N	S	59	.224
1879	Pro	N	M-S	84	.281
1880	Bos	N	S	1	.250
1881	Bos	N	S	7	.179
1882	Pro	N	S	45	.162
	BRTR			590	.302

WRIGHT, HENDERSON EDWARD
(Ed)
b.May 15,1919 Dyersburg,Tenn.

Yr	Cl	Lea	Pos	G	Rec
1945	Bos	N	P	15	8-3
1946	Bos	N	P	36	12-9
1947	Bos	N	P	23	3-3
1948	Bos	N	P	3	0-0
1952	Phi	A	P	24	2-1
	BRTR			101	25-16

WRIGHT, JAMES
b.Sept.19,1900 Hyde,England.

Yr	Cl	Lea	Pos	G	Rec
1927	St.L	A	P	2	1-0
1928	St.L	A	P	2	0-0
	BRTR			4	1-0

WRIGHT, JOSEPH
b.Pittsburgh,Pa.

Yr	Cl	Lea	Pos	G	Rec
1895	Lou	N	O	59	.289
1896	Lou	N	O	2	.143
1896	Pit	N	O	15	.308
				76	.279

WRIGHT, MELVIN JAMES
b.May 11,1929 Manila,Ark.

Yr	Cl	Lea	Pos	G	Rec
1954	St.L	N	P	9	0-0
1955	St.L	N	P	29	2-2
1960	Chi	N	P	9	0-1
1961	Chi	N	P	11	0-1
	BRTR			58	2-4

WRIGHT, PATRICK W.
b.July 5,1868 Pottsville,Pa.

Yr	Cl	Lea	Pos	G	Rec
1890	Chi	N	2	1	.000
1893	Bal	N	2	1	.500
				2	.250

WRIGHT, ROBERT C.
b.1893

Yr	Cl	Lea	Pos	G	Rec
1915	Chi	N	P	2	0-0
	BRTR				

WRIGHT, ROY EARL
Sept.26,1933 Buchtel,O.

Yr	Cl	Lea	Pos	G	Rec
1956	NY	N	P	1	0-1
	BRTR				

WRIGHT, SAMUEL
b.Nov.25,1848 Boston,Mass.
d.May 6,1928

Yr	Cl	Lea	Pos	G	Rec
1875	NH	n	S	33	NR
1876	Bos	N	S	2	.125
1880	Cin	N	S	9	.058
1881	Bos	N	S	1	.250
				45	NR

WRIGHT, TAFT SHEDRON
(Taffy)
b.Aug.10,1913 Tabor City,N.C.

Yr	Cl	Lea	Pos	G	Rec
1938	Was	A	O	100	.350
1939	Was	A	O	129	.309
1940	Chi	A	O	147	.337
1941	Chi	A	O	136	.322
1942	Chi	A	O	85	.333
1946	Chi	A	O	115	.275
1947	Chi	A	O	124	.324
1948	Chi	A	O	134	.279
1949	Phi	A	O	59	.235
	BLTR			1029	.311

WRIGHT, THOMAS EVERETT
b.Sept.22,1923 Rutherford Co.,N.C.

Yr	Cl	Lea	Pos	G	Rec
1948	Bos	A	H	3	.500
1949	Bos	A	H	5	.250
1950	Bos	A	O	54	.318
1951	Bos	A	O	28	.222
1952	St.L	A	O	29	.242
1952	Chi	A	O	60	.258
1953	Chi	A	O	77	.250
1954	Was	A	O	76	.246
1955	Was	A	H	7	.000
1956	Was	A	H	2	.000
	BLTR			341	.255

WRIGHT, WAYNE BROMLEY
(Rasty)
b.Nov.5,1895 Caredo,W.Va.
d.June 12,1948

Yr	Cl	Lea	Pos	G	Rec
1917	St.L	A	P	16	0-0
1918	St.L	A	P	18	8-2
1919	St.L	A	P	24	0-5
1922	St.L	A	P	31	9-7
1923	St.L	A	P	20	7-4
	BRTR			109	24-18

WRIGHT, WILLARD JAMES (Dick)
b.May 5,1890 Worcester,N.Y.
d.Jan.25,1952

Yr	Cl	Lea	Pos	G	Rec
1915	Bro	F	C	4	.000
	TR				

WRIGHT, WILLIAM H.

Yr	Cl	Lea	Pos	G	Rec
1887	Was	N	C	1	.667

WRIGHT, WILLIAM HENRY
(Harry)
b.Jan.10,1835 Sheffield,England.
d.Oct.3,1895

Yr	Cl	Lea	Pos	G	Rec
1871	Bos	n	M-S-O	33	.300

(Continued)

Yr	Cl	Lea	Pos	G	Rec
1872	Bos	n	M-P-O	48	2-0 .271
1873	Bos	n	M-P-O	58	2-1 .260
1874	Bos	n	M-C-O	41	.310
1875	Bos	n	M-O	1	.250
1876	Bos	N	M-O	1	.000
1877	Bos	N	M-O	1	.000
1878	Bos	N	M-O	1	.000
	BRTR			184	4-1 .278

Non-playing manager Bos (N) 1879-81, Prov (N) 1882-83 and Phi (N) 1884-93.

WRIGHT, WILLIAM S. (Rasty)
b.Jan.31,1863 Birmingham,Mich.
d.Oct.1922

Yr	Cl	Lea	Pos	G	Rec
1890	Syr	a	O	89	.285
1890	Cle	N	O	13	.106
				102	.265

WRIGHT, WILLIAM SIMMONS (Lucky)
b.Feb.21,1880 Tontogany,O.
d.July 8,1941

Yr	Cl	Lea	Pos	G	Rec
1909	Cle	A	P	5	0-5

WRIGHTSTONE, RUSSELL GUY
b.Mar.18,1893 Bowmansdale,Pa.

Yr	Cl	Lea	Pos	G	Rec
1920	Phi	N	3	76	.262
1921	Phi	N	3-O	109	.296
1922	Phi	N	1-S-3	99	.305
1923	Phi	N	2-S-3	119	.273
1924	Phi	N	2-S-3-O	118	.307
1925	Phi	N	1-2-S-3-O	92	.346
1926	Phi	N	1-2-3	112	.307
1927	Phi	N	1	141	.306
1928	Phi	N	O	33	.209
1928	NY	N	H	30	.160
	BLTR			929	.297

WRIGLEY, GEORGE WATSON (Zeke)
b.Jan.18,1873 Philadelphia,Pa.
d.Sept.28,1952

Yr	Cl	Lea	Pos	G	Rec
1896	Was	N	2	5	.100
1897	Was	N	S-3-O	102	.284
1898	Was	N	S	111	.245
1899	NY	N	3	4	.133
1899	Bro	N	S	15	.229
				237	.258

WUESTLING, GEORGE (Yats)
b.Oct.18,1905 St.Louis,Mo.

Yr	Cl	Lea	Pos	G	Rec
1929	Det	A	S	54	.200
1930	Det	A	S	4	.000
1930	NY	A	S	25	.190
	BRTR			83	.189

WURM, FRANK JAMES
b.Apr.27,1924 Salem,N.Y.

Yr	Cl	Lea	Pos	G	Rec
1944	Bro	N	P	1	0-0
	BRTL				

WYATT, JOHN
b.Apr.19,1935 Chicago,Ill.

Yr	Cl	Lea	Pos	G	Rec
1961	KC	A	P	5	0-0
1962	KC	A	P	59	10-7
	BRTR			64	10-7

WYATT, JOHN WHITLOW (Whit)
b.Sept.27,1907 Kensington,Ga.

Yr	Cl	Lea	Pos	G	Rec
1929	Det	A	P	4	0-1
1930	Det	A	P	22	4-5
1931	Det	A	P	4	0-2
1932	Det	A	P	42	9-13
1933	Det	A	P	10	0-1
1933	Chi	A	P	26	3-4
1934	Chi	A	P	23	4-11

(Continued)

Yr	Cl	Lea	Pos	G	Rec
1935	Chi	A	P	30	4-3
1936	Chi	A	P	3	0-0
1937	Cle	A	P	29	2-3
1939	Bro	N	P	16	8-3
1940	Bro	N	P	37	15-14
1941	Bro	N	P	40	22-10
1942	Bro	N	P	31	19-7
1943	Bro	N	P	26	14-5
1944	Bro	N	P	11	2-6
1945	Phi	N	P	10	0-7
	BRTR			364	106-95

WYATT, LORAL JOSEPH
b.Apr.6,1901 Petersburg,Ind.

Yr	Cl	Lea	Pos	G	Rec
1924	Cle	A	O	4	.166
	BRTR				

WYCKOFF, JOHN WELDON
b.Feb.19,1892 Williamsport,Pa.

Yr	Cl	Lea	Pos	G	Rec
1913	Phi	A	P	10	3-4
1914	Phi	A	P	32	11-8
1915	Phi	A	P	45	10-22
1916	Phi	A	P	8	0-1
1916	Bos	A	P	8	0-0
1917	Bos	A	P	1	0-0
1918	Bos	A	P	1	0-0
	BRTR			105	24-35

WYLIE, ...
b.Pittsburgh,Pa.

Yr	Cl	Lea	Pos	G	Rec
1882	Pit	a	O	1	.000

WYMAN, FRANK C.
b.May 10,1862 Haverhill,Mass.

Yr	Cl	Lea	Pos	G	Rec
1884	KC	U	P-1-3-O	30	0-2 .203
1884	Chi	U	1	2	.375
				32	0-2 .214

WYNN, EARLY (Gus)
b.Jan.6,1920 Hartford,Ala.

Yr	Cl	Lea	Pos	G	Rec
1939	Was	A	P	3	0-2
1941	Was	A	P	5	3-1
1942	Was	A	P	30	10-16
1943	Was	A	P	38	18-12
1944	Was	A	P	43	8-17
1946	Was	A	P	25	8-5
1947	Was	A	P	54	17-15
1948	Was	A	P	73	8-19
1949	Cle	A	P	35	11-7
1950	Cle	A	P	39	18-8
1951	Cle	A	P	41	20-13
1952	Cle	A	P	44	23-12
1953	Cle	A	P	37	17-12
1954	Cle	A	P	40	23-11
1955	Cle	A	P	34	17-11
1956	Cle	A	P	38	20-9
1957	Cle	A	P	40	14-17
1958	Chi	A	P	40	14-16
1959	Chi	A	P	37	22-10
1960	Chi	A	P	36	13-12
1961	Chi	A	P	17	8-2
1962	Chi	A	P	27	7-15
	BBTR			776	299-242

WYNNE, WILLIAM AVERY
b.Mar.27,1869 Neuse,N.C.
d.Aug.7,1951

Yr	Cl	Lea	Pos	G	Rec
1894	Was	N	P	1	0-1

WYROSTEK, JOHN BARNEY
b.July 12,1919 Fairmont City,Ill.

Yr	Cl	Lea	Pos	G	Rec
1942	Pit	N	O	9	.114
1943	Pit	N	1-2-3-O	51	.152
1946	Phi	N	O	145	.281
1947	Phi	N	O	128	.273
1948	Cin	N	O	136	.273
1949	Cin	N	O	134	.249
1950	Cin	N	1-O	131	.285
1951	Cin	N	O	142	.311
1952	Cin	N	1-O	30	.236
1952	Phi	N	O	98	.274

(Continued)

Yr	Cl	Lea	Pos	G	Rec
1953	Phi	N	O	125	.271
1954	Phi	N	1-O	92	.239
	BLTR			1221	271

WYSE, HENRY WASHINGTON
b.Mar.1,1918 Lunsford,Ark.

Yr	Cl	Lea	Pos	G	Rec
1942	Chi	N	P	4	2-1
1943	Chi	N	P	40	9-7
1944	Chi	N	P	41	16-15
1945	Chi	N	P	38	22-10
1946	Chi	N	P	40	14-12
1947	Chi	N	P	37	6-9
1950	Phi	A	P	41	9-14
1951	Phi	A	P	9	1-2
1951	Was	A	P	3	0-0
	BRTR			253	79-70

WYSHNER, PETER
(Played under name of Peter Gray)

WYSONG, HARLAN (Biff)
b.Apr.13,1905 Clarksville,O.
d.Aug.8,1951

Yr	Cl	Lea	Pos	G	Rec
1930	Cin	N	P	1	0-1
1931	Cin	N	P	12	0-2
1932	Cin	N	P	7	1-0
	BLTL			20	1-3

YAIK, HENRY
b.Detroit,Mich.

Yr	Cl	Lea	Pos	G	Rec
1888	Pit	N	C	2	.333

YALE, WILLIAM M. (Ad)
b.Apr.17,1870 Bristol,Conn.
d.Apr.27,1948

Yr	Cl	Lea	Pos	G	Rec
1905	Bro	N	1	4	.076

YANKOWSKI, GEORGE EDWARD
b.Nov.19,1922 Cambridge,Mass.

Yr	Cl	Lea	Pos	G	Rec
1942	Phi	A	C	6	.154
1949	Chi	A	C	12	.167
	BRTR			18	.161

YANTZ, GEORGE WEBB
b.July 27,1886 Louisville,Ky.

Yr	Cl	Lea	Pos	G	Rec
1912	Chi	N	C	1	1.000
	BRTR				

YAPP, FREDERICK FRANCIS
(Played under name of Frederick Francis Mitchell)

YARNELL, WALDO WILLIAM (Rusty)
b.Oct.22,1902 Maysville,Ky.
d.Mar.22,1934

Yr	Cl	Lea	Pos	G	Rec
1926	Phi	N	P	1	0-1
	BRTR				

YARRISON, BYRON WORDSWORTH (Rube)
b.Mar.9,1896 Montgomery,Pa.

Yr	Cl	Lea	Pos	G	Rec
1922	Phi	A	P	18	1-2
1924	Bro	N	P	3	0-2
	BRTR			21	1-4

YARYAN, CLARENCE EVERETT (Yam)
b.Nov.5,1893 Knowlton,Ia.

Yr	Cl	Lea	Pos	G	Rec
1921	Chi	A	C	45	.304
1922	Chi	A	C	36	.197
	BRTR			81	.260

YASTRZEMSKI, CARL MICHAEL
b.Aug.22,1939 Southampton,N.Y.

Yr	Cl	Lea	Pos	G	Rec
1961	Bos	A	O	148	.266
1962	Bos	A	O	160	.296
	BLTR			308	.282

YDE, EMIL OGDEN
b.Jan.28,1900 Great Lakes,Ill.

Yr	Cl	Lea	Pos	G	Rec
1924	Pit	N	P	50	16-3
1925	Pit	N	P	47	17-9
1926	Pit	N	P	43	8-7
1927	Pit	N	P	23	1-3
1929	Det	A	P	46	7-3
		BBTL		209	49-25

YEABSLEY, ROBERT WATSON
(Bert)
b.Dec.17,1894 Philadelphia,Pa.
d.Feb.8,1961

Yr	Cl	Lea	Pos	G	Rec
1919	Phi	N	H	2	.000
		TR			

YEAGER, GEORGE E. (Abe)
b.June 4,1873 Cincinnati,O.

Yr	Cl	Lea	Pos	G	Rec
1896	Bos	N	1	2	.167
1897	Bos	N	C	26	.239
1898	Bos	N	C	57	.263
1899	Bos	N	C	2	.000
1901	Cle	A	C	39	.226
1901	Pit	N	C	24	.267
1902	NY	N	C-1-O	29	.194
1902	Bal	A	C	11	.184
		TR		190	.236

YEAGER, JOSEPH F. (Little Joe)
b.Aug.28,1875 Philadelphia,Pa.
d.Juiy 2,1937

Yr	Cl	Lea	Pos	G	Rec
1898	Bro	N	P	36	13-20
1899	Bro	N	P	15	3-2
1900	Bro	N	P-3	3	1-1 / .333
1901	Det	A	P	37	12-12
1902	Det	A	P-2-S-3-O	48	5-12 / .231
1903	Det	A	3	109	.259
1905	NY	A	S-3	115	.267
1906	NY	A	S	57	.301
1907	St.L	A	2-3	123	.239
1908	St.L	A	2	10	.352
		TR		553	34-47 / .254

YEARGIN, JAMES ALMOND
(Grapefruit)
b.Oct.16,1902 Mauldin,S.C.
d.May 8,1937

Yr	Cl	Lea	Pos	G	Rec
1922	Bos	N	P	1	0-1
1924	Bos	N	P	32	1-11
		BRTR		33	1-12

YEATMAN, ...

Yr	Cl	Lea	Pos	G	Rec
1872	Nat	n	O	1	.000

YELLE, ARCHIE JOSEPH
b.June 11,1892 Saginaw,Mich.

Yr	Cl	Lea	Pos	G	Rec
1917	Det	A	C	25	.137
1918	Det	A	C	56	.174
1919	Det	A	C	6	.000
		BRTR		87	.166

YELLOWHORSE, MOSES J. (Chief)
b.Mar.28,1900 Pawnee,Okla.

Yr	Cl	Lea	Pos	G	Rec
1921	Pit	N	P	10	5-3
1922	Pit	N	P	28	3-1
		BRTR		38	8-4

YERKES, CHARLES CARROLL
b.June 13,1903 McSherrystown,Pa.
d.Dec.20,1950

Yr	Cl	Lea	Pos	G	Rec
1927	Phi	A	P	1	0-0
1928	Phi	A	P	2	0-1
1929	Phi	A	P	19	1-0
1932	Chi	N	P	2	0-0
1933	Chi	N	P	1	0-0
		BRTL		25	1-1

YERKES, STANLEY (Yank)
b.Boston,Mass.

Yr	Cl	Lea	Pos	G	Rec
1901	Bal	A	P	1	0-1
1901	St.L	N	P	4	3-1
1902	St.L	N	P	36	12-21
1903	St.L	N	P	1	0-1
				42	15-24

YERKES, STEPHEN DOUGLAS
b.Feb.19,1888 Hatboro,Pa.

Yr	Cl	Lea	Pos	G	Rec
1909	Bos	A	S	5	.286
1911	Bos	A	S	142	.279
1912	Bos	A	2	131	.252
1913	Bos	A	2	137	.267
1914	Bos	A	2	92	.218
1914	Pit	F	S	39	.333
1915	Pit	F	2	121	.286
1916	Chi	N	2	44	.263
		BRTR		711	.267

YERRICK, WILLIAM J.
(Played under name of
William J. Banks)

YEWCIC, THOMAS
b.May 9,1932 Conemaugh,Pa.

Yr	Cl	Lea	Pos	G	Rec
1957	Det	A	C	1	.000
		BRTR			

YEWELL, EDWIN LEONARD
b.Washington,D.C.

Yr	Cl	Lea	Pos	G	Rec
1884	Was	a	2-3	35	.258
1884	Was	U	3	1	.000
				36	.247

YINGLING, EARL HERSHEY
(Chink)
b.Oct.29,1888 Chillicothe,O.
d.Oct.2,1962

Yr	Cl	Lea	Pos	G	Rec
1911	Cle	A	P	6	2-1
1912	Bro	N	P	25	6-11
1913	Bro	N	P	40	8-8
1914	Cin	N	P	61	9-13
1918	Was	A	P	8	1-2
		BLTL		140	26-35

YINGLING, JOSEPH
b.1864 Baltimore,Md.

Yr	Cl	Lea	Pos	G	Rec
1886	Was	N	P	1	0-1
1894	Phi	N	S	1	.333
				2	0-1 / .200

YOCHIM, LEONARD JOSEPH
b.Oct.16,1928 New Orleans,La.

Yr	Cl	Lea	Pos	G	Rec
1951	Pit	N	P	2	1-1
1954	Pit	N	P	10	0-1
		BLTL		12	1-2

YOCHIM, RAYMOND AUSTIN ALOYSIUS
b.July 19,1922 New Orleans,La.

Yr	Cl	Lea	Pos	G	Rec
1948	St.L	N	P	1	0-0
1949	St.L	N	P	3	0-0
		BRTR		4	0-0

YOHE, WILLIAM F.
b.Sept.2,1879 Mattoon,Ill.

Yr	Cl	Lea	Pos	G	Rec
1909	Was	A	3	21	.208
		TR			

YORK, ANTHONY BATTON
b.Nov.27,1912 Irene,Tex.

Yr	Cl	Lea	Pos	G	Rec
1944	Chi	N	S-3	28	.235
		BRTR			

YORK, JAMES E. (Lefty)
b.Nov.1,1895 Tuskegee,Ala.

Yr	Cl	Lea	Pos	G	Rec
1919	Phi	A	P	2	0-2
1921	Chi	N	P	40	5-9
		BRTL		42	5-11

YORK, RUDOLPH PRESTON
b.Aug.17,1913 Ragland,Ala.

Yr	Cl	Lea	Pos	G	Rec
1934	Det	A	C	3	.167
1937	Det	A	C-3	104	.307
1938	Det	A	C-O	135	.298
1939	Det	A	C-1	102	.307
1940	Det	A	1	155	.316
1941	Det	A	1	155	.259
1942	Det	A	1	153	.260

(Continued)

Yr	Cl	Lea	Pos	G	Rec
1943	Det	A	1	155	.271
1944	Det	A	1	151	.276
1945	Det	A	1	155	.264
1946	Bos	A	1	154	.276
1947	Bos	A	1	48	.212
1947	Chi	A	1	102	.243
1948	Phi	A	1	31	.157
		BRTR		1603	.275

Non-playing manager Bos (A) 1959

YORK, THOMAS J.
b.July 13,1850 Brooklyn,N.Y.
d.Feb.17,1936

Yr	Cl	Lea	Pos	G	Rec
1871	Tro	n	O	30	NR
1872	Bal	n	O	49	.269
1873	Bal	n	P-O	57	1-0 / NR
1874	Phi	n	O	50	NR
1875	Har	n	O	85	NR
1876	Har	N	O	67	.249
1877	Har	N	O	56	.283
1878	Pro	N	O	60	.302
1879	Pro	N	O	80	.307
1880	Pro	N	O	50	.211
1881	Pro	N	O	84	.304
1882	Pro	N	O	81	.267
1883	Cle	N	O	97	.255
1884	Bal	a	O	84	.228
1885	Bal	a	O	22	.271
		BL		952	1-0 / NR

YOST, EDWARD FREDERICK
b.Oct.13,1926 Brooklyn,N.Y.

Yr	Cl	Lea	Pos	G	Rec
1944	Was	A	S-3	7	.143
1946	Was	A	3	8	.080
1947	Was	A	3	115	.238
1948	Was	A	3	145	.249
1949	Was	A	3	124	.253
1950	Was	A	3	155	.295
1951	Was	A	3-O	154	.283
1952	Was	A	3	157	.233
1953	Was	A	3	152	.272
1954	Was	A	3	155	.256
1955	Was	A	3	122	.243
1956	Was	A	3-O	152	.231
1957	Was	A	3	110	.251
1958	Was	A	1-2-3-O	134	.224
1959	Det	A	2-3	148	.278
1960	Det	A	3	143	.260
1961	LA	A	3	76	.202
1962	LA	A	1-3	52	.240
		BRTR		2109	.254

YOST, GUS

Yr	Cl	Lea	Pos	G	Rec
1893	Chi	N	P	1	1-0

YOTER, ELMER ELSWORTH
b.June 26,1900 Carlisle,Pa.

Yr	Cl	Lea	Pos	G	Rec
1921	Phi	A	H	2	.000
1924	Cle	A	3	19	.273
1927	Chi	N	3	13	.222
1928	Chi	N	3	1	.000
		BRTR		35	.245

YOUNG, CHARLES V.
b.1894 Trenton,N.J.

Yr	Cl	Lea	Pos	G	Rec
1915	Bal	F	P	9	2-3
		BBTR			

YOUNG, DAVID
b.Oct.6,1872 Philadelphia,Pa.
d.Oct.25,1924

Yr	Cl	Lea	Pos	G	Rec
1895	St.L	N	3	1	.400

YOUNG, DELMAR EDWARD
b.Mar.11,1913 Nashville,Tenn.

Yr	Cl	Lea	Pos	G	Rec
1937	Phi	N	2	109	.194
1938	Phi	N	2-S	108	.229
1939	Phi	N	2-S	77	.263
1940	Phi	N	2-S	15	.242
		BBTR		309	.224

YOUNG, DELMAR JOHN
b.Oct.24,1888 Macon,Mo.
d.Dec.17,1959

Yr	Cl	Lea	Pos	G	Rec
1909	Cin	N	O	2	.286
1914	Buf	F	O	79	.278
1915	Buf	F	O	12	.133
			BLTR	93	.268

YOUNG, DENTON TRUE (Cy)
b.Mar.29,1867 Gilmore,O.
d.Nov.4,1955

Yr	Cl	Lea	Pos	G	Rec
1890	Cle	N	P	17	9-7
1891	Cle	N	P	50	28-20
1892	Cle	N	P	49	36-11
1893	Cle	N	P	51	34-17
1894	Cle	N	P	48	25-21
1895	Cle	N	P	46	33-10
1896	Cle	N	P	48	29-14
1897	Cle	N	P	45	21-18
1898	Cle	N	P	44	24-14
1899	St.L	N	P	43	26-14
1900	St.L	N	P	39	20-16
1901	Bos	A	P	45	31-10
1902	Bos	A	P	45	32-11
1903	Bos	A	P	41	28-9
1904	Bos	A	P	43	26-16
1905	Bos	A	P	38	16-18
1906	Bos	A	P	40	13-21
1907	Bos	A	M-P	45	22-15
1908	Bos	A	P	36	21-11
1909	Cle	A	P	34	19-15
1910	Cle	A	P	21	7-10
1911	Cle	A	P	7	3-4
1911	Bos	N	P	11	4-5
			BRTR	886	507-307

YOUNG, GEORGE J.
b.1890

Yr	Cl	Lea	Pos	G	Rec
1913	Cle	A	H	2	.000
			BLTR		

YOUNG, GEORGE W.
Non-playing manager Phi (n) 1873 and 1875.

YOUNG, HARLEY E.
b.Kansas.

Yr	Cl	Lea	Pos	G	Rec
1908	Pit	N	P	8	0-2
1908	Bos	N	P	6	0-1
			TL	14	0-3

YOUNG, HERMAN JOHN
b.Apr.14,1886 Boston,Mass.

Yr	Cl	Lea	Pos	G	Rec
1911	Bos	N	S-3	9	.230
			BRTR		

YOUNG, IRVING MELROSE (Young Cy)
b.July 21,1876 Columbia Falls,Me.
d.Jan.14,1935

Yr	Cl	Lea	Pos	G	Rec
1905	Bos	N	P	43	20-21
1906	Bos	N	P	43	16-25
1907	Bos	N	P	40	10-23
1908	Bos	N	P	16	4-9
1908	Pit	N	P	16	4-3
1910	Chi	A	P	27	4-8
1911	Chi	A	P	24	5-6
			BRTL	209	63-95

YOUNG, J.D.
b.Mt.Carmel,Pa.

Yr	Cl	Lea	Pos	G	Rec
1892	St.L	N	P	1	0-0

YOUNG, LEMUEL FLOYD (Pep)
b.Aug.29,1907 Jamestown,N.C.
d.Jan.14,1962

Yr	Cl	Lea	Pos	G	Rec
1933	Pit	N	2-S	25	.300
1934	Pit	N	2-S	19	.235
1935	Pit	N	2-S-3-O	128	.265
1936	Pit	N	2	125	.248
1937	Pit	N	2-S-3	113	.260
1938	Pit	N	2	149	.278
1939	Pit	N	2	84	.276
1940	Pit	N	2-S-3	54	.250
1941	Cin	N	3	4	.167
1941	St.L	N	H	2	.000
1945	St.L	N	2-S-3	27	.149
			BRTR	730	.262

YOUNG, NICHOLAS EPHRAIM
b.Sept.12,1840 Amsterdam,N.Y.
d.Oct.31,1916
Non-playing manager Oly (n) 1871-72, Nat (n) 1873 and Chi (n) 1874.

YOUNG, NORMAN ROBERT (Babe)
b.July 1,1915 Astoria,N.Y.

Yr	Cl	Lea	Pos	G	Rec
1936	NY	N	1	1	.000
1939	NY	N	1	22	.307
1940	NY	N	1	149	.286
1941	NY	N	1	152	.265
1942	NY	N	1-O	101	.279
1946	NY	N	1-O	104	.278
1947	NY	N	H	14	.071
1947	Cin	N	1	95	.283
1948	Cin	N	1-O	49	.231
1948	St.L	N	1	41	.243
			BLTL	728	.274

YOUNG, RALPH STUART
b.Sept.19,1890 Philadelphia,Pa.

Yr	Cl	Lea	Pos	G	Rec
1913	NY	A	S	7	.067
1915	Det	A	2	123	.244
1916	Det	A	2	153	.263
1917	Det	A	2	141	.231
1918	Det	A	2	91	.188
1919	Det	A	2	125	.210
1920	Det	A	2	150	.291
1921	Det	A	2	107	.299
1922	Phi	A	2	125	.223
			BBTR	1022	.247

YOUNG, RICHARD ENNIS
b.June 3,1928 Seattle,Wash.

Yr	Cl	Lea	Pos	G	Rec
1951	Phi	N	2	15	.235
1952	Phi	N	2	5	.222
			BBTR	20	.234

YOUNG, ROBERT GEORGE
b.Jan.22,1925 Granite,Md.

Yr	Cl	Lea	Pos	G	Rec
1948	St.L	N	3	3	.000
1951	St.L	A	2	147	.260
1952	St.L	A	2	149	.247
1953	St.L	A	2	148	.255
1954	Bal	A	2	130	.245
1955	Bal	A	2	59	.199
1955	Cle	A	2-3	18	.311
1956	Cle	A	H	1	.000
1958	Phi	N	2	32	.233
			BLTR	687	.249

YOUNGS, ROSS MIDDLEBROOK
(Real name Royce Youngs)
b.Apr.10,1897 Shiner,Tex.
d.Oct.22,1927

Yr	Cl	Lea	Pos	G	Rec
1917	NY	N	O	7	.346
1918	NY	N	2-O	121	.302
1919	NY	N	O	130	.311
1920	NY	N	O	153	.351
1921	NY	N	O	141	.327
1922	NY	N	O	149	.330
1923	NY	N	O	152	.336
1924	NY	N	2-O	133	.355
1925	NY	N	2-O	130	.264
1926	NY	N	O	95	.306
			BBTR	1211	.322

YOUNG, RUSSELL CHARLES
b.Sept.15,1903 Bryan,O.

Yr	Cl	Lea	Pos	G	Rec
1931	St.L	A	C	16	.118
			BBTR		

YOUNGBLOOD, ALBERT CLYDE (Chief)
b.June 13,1900 Hillsboro,Tex.

Yr	Cl	Lea	Pos	G	Rec
1922	Was	A	P	2	0-0
			BRTR		

YOUNGMAN, HENRY
b.1865 Indiana,Pa.
d.Jan.24,1936

Yr	Cl	Lea	Pos	G	Rec
1890	Pit	N	2	13	.167

YOUNGS, ROYCE
(Played under name of Ross Young)

YOUNT, FLOYD EDWIN (Eddie)
b.Dec.19,1916 Newton,N.C.

Yr	Cl	Lea	Pos	G	Rec
1937	Phi	A	H	4	.286
1939	Pit	N	O	2	.000
			BRTR	6	.222

YOUNT, HERBERT M.
b.1889

Yr	Cl	Lea	Pos	G	Rec
1914	Bal	F	P	14	1-1
			BRTR		

YOWELL, CARL COLUMBUS
b.Dec.20,1903 Madison,Va.

Yr	Cl	Lea	Pos	G	Rec
1924	Cle	A	P	4	1-1
1925	Cle	A	P	12	2-3
			BLTL	16	3-4

YUHAS, JOHN EDWARD (Eddie)
b.Aug.5,1924 Youngstown,O.

Yr	Cl	Lea	Pos	G	Rec
1952	St.L	N	P	54	12-2
1953	St.L	N	P	2	0-0
			BRTR	56	12-2

YVARS, SALVADOR ANTHONY
b.Feb.20,1924 New York,N.Y.

Yr	Cl	Lea	Pos	G	Rec
1947	NY	N	C	1	.200
1948	NY	N	C	15	.211
1949	NY	N	C	3	.000
1950	NY	N	C	9	.143
1951	NY	N	C	25	.317
1952	NY	N	C	66	.245
1953	NY	N	C	23	.277
1953	St.L	N	C	30	.246
1954	St.L	N	C	38	.246
			BRTR	210	.244

ZABALA, ADRIAN RODRIGUEZ
b.Aug.26,1916 San Antonio de Los Banos,Cuba.

Yr	Cl	Lea	Pos	G	Rec
1945	NY	N	P	11	2-4
1949	NY	N	P	15	2-3
			BLTL	26	4-7

ZABEL, GEORGE WASHINGTON (Zip)
b.Feb.18,1891 Wetmore,Kan.

Yr	Cl	Lea	Pos	G	Rec
1913	Chi	N	P	1	1-0
1914	Chi	N	P	29	4-4
1915	Chi	N	P	37	7-10
			BRTR	67	12-14

ZACHARY, ALBERT MYRON (Chink)
b.Oct.19,1917 Brooklyn,N.Y.

Yr	Cl	Lea	Pos	G	Rec
1944	Bro	N	P	4	0-2
			BRTR		

ZACHARY, JONATHAN THOMPSON WALTON (Tom)
b.May 7,1897 Graham,N.C.
(Zach Walton)

Yr	Cl	Lea	Pos	G	Rec
1918	Phi	A	P	2	2-0

(Jonathan Thompson Walton Zachary)

Yr	Cl	Lea	Pos	G	Rec
1919	Was	A	P	17	1-5
1920	Was	A	P	51	15-16
1921	Was	A	P	38	18-16
1922	Was	A	P	32	15-10
1923	Was	A	P	35	10-16
1924	Was	A	P	32	15-9
1925	Was	A	P	38	12-15
1926	St.L	A	P	34	14-15
1927	St.L	A	P	13	4-6
1927	Was	A	P	15	4-7
1928	Was	A	P	20	6-9
1928	NY	A	P	7	3-3
1929	NY	A	P	26	12-0
1930	NY	A	P	3	1-1
1930	Bos	N	P	25	11-5
1931	Bos	N	P	33	11-15
1932	Bos	N	P	33	12-11
1933	Bos	N	P	27	7-9
1934	Bos	N	P	5	1-2
1934	Bro	N	P	24	5-6
1935	Bro	N	P	25	7-12
1936	Bro	N	P	1	0-0
1936	Phi	N	P	8	0-3
			BLTL	544	186-191

ZACHER, ELMER HENRY
(Silver)
b.Sept.17,1883 Buffalo,N.Y.
d.Dec.20,1944

Yr	Cl	Lea	Pos	G	Rec
1910	NY	N	O	1	.000
1910	St.L	N	O	38	.212
		BRTR		39	.212

ZACHERT, GEORGE
b.1885 Missouri

Yr	Cl	Lea	Pos	G	Rec
1911	St.L	N	P	4	0-2
1912	St.L	N	P	1	0-0
		BLTL		5	0-2

ZAHNER, FREDERICK JOSEPH
b.June 5,1870 Louisville,Ky.
d.July 24,1900

Yr	Cl	Lea	Pos	G	Rec
1894	Lou	N	C	14	.204
1895	Lou	N	C	18	.234
				32	.208

ZAHNISER, PAUL VERNON
b.Sept.6,1896 Sac City,Ia.

Yr	Cl	Lea	Pos	G	Rec
1923	Was	A	P	33	9-10
1924	Was	A	P	23	5-7
1925	Bos	A	P	38	5-12
1926	Bos	A	P	30	6-18
1929	Cin	N	P	1	0-0
		BRTR		125	25-47

ZAK, FRANK TOM
b.Feb.23,1923 Passaic,N.J.

Yr	Cl	Lea	Pos	G	Rec
1944	Pit	N	S	87	.300
1945	Pit	N	2-S	15	.143
1946	Pit	N	S	21	.200
		BRTR		123	.269

ZALUSKY, JOHN FRANCIS
b.June 22,1879 Minneapolis,Minn.
d.Aug.11,1935

Yr	Cl	Lea	Pos	G	Rec
1903	NY	A	C	6	.267
		BRTR			

ZAMLOCH, CARL EUGENE
b.Oct.6,1890 Oakland,Cal.

Yr	Cl	Lea	Pos	G	Rec
1913	Det	A	P	14	1-6
		BRTR			

ZANNI, DOMINICK THOMAS
b.Mar.1,1932 New York,N.Y.

Yr	Cl	Lea	Pos	G	Rec
1958	SF	N	P	1	1-0
1959	SF	N	P	9	0-0
1961	SF	N	P	8	1-0
1962	Chi	A	P	44	6-5
		BRTR		62	8-5

ZAPUSTAS, JOSEPH JOHN
b.July 25,1911 S.Boston,Mass.

Yr	Cl	Lea	Pos	G	Rec
1933	Phi	A	O	2	.200
		BRTR			

ZARDON, JOSE ANTONIO SANCHEZ
b.May 20,1923 Havana,Cuba.

Yr	Cl	Lea	Pos	G	Rec
1945	Was	A	O	54	.290
		BRTR			

ZARILLA, ALLEN LEE
(Zeke)
b.May 1,1919 Los Angeles,Cal.

Yr	Cl	Lea	Pos	G	Rec
1943	St.L	A	O	70	.254
1944	St.L	A	O	100	.299
1946	St.L	A	O	125	.259
1947	St.L	A	O	127	.224
1948	St.L	A	O	144	.329
1949	St.L	A	O	15	.250
1949	Bos	A	O	124	.285
1950	Bos	A	O	130	.325
1951	Chi	A	O	120	.257
1952	Chi	A	O	39	.232
1952	St.L	A	O	48	.238
1952	Bos	A	O	21	.183
1953	Bos	A	O	57	.194
		BLTR		1120	.277

ZAUCHIN, NORBERT HENRY
b.Nov.17,1929 Detroit,Mich.

Yr	Cl	Lea	Pos	G	Rec
1951	Bos	A	1	5	.167
1955	Bos	A	1	130	.239
1956	Bos	A	1	44	.214
1957	Bos	A	1	52	.264
1958	Was	A	1	96	.228
1959	Was	A	1	19	.211
		BRTR		346	.233

ZAY, ...

Yr	Cl	Lea	Pos	G	Rec
1886	Bal	a	P	1	0-1

ZEARFOSS, DAVID WILLIAM TILDEN
b.Jan.1,1868 Schenectady,N.Y.
d.Sept.12,1945

Yr	Cl	Lea	Pos	G	Rec
1896	NY	N	C	16	.220
1897	NY	N	C	5	.363
1898	NY	N	C	1	1.000
1904	St.L	N	C	25	.213
1905	St.L	N	C	19	.157
		TR		66	.208

ZEIDER, ROLLIE HUBERT
(Bunions)
b.Nov.16,1883 Auburn,Ind.

Yr	Cl	Lea	Pos	G	Rec
1910	Chi	A	2-S	136	.217
1911	Chi	A	1-S	73	.254
1912	Chi	A	1-3	129	.245
1913	Chi	A	2	15	.438
1913	NY	A	S	46	.227
1914	Chi	F	3	120	.263
1915	Chi	F	2-S-3	130	.233
1916	Chi	N	2-3	98	.235
1917	Chi	N	2-S-3	108	.243
1918	Chi	N	1-2-3	82	.223
		BRTR		937	.239

ZEISER, MATTHEW J.
b.Sept.25,1888 Chicago,Ill.

Yr	Cl	Lea	Pos	G	Rec
1914	Bos	A	P	2	0-0
		BRTR			

ZERNIAL, GUS EDWARD
(Ozark Ike)
b.June 27,1923 Beaumont,Tex.

Yr	Cl	Lea	Pos	G	Rec
1949	Chi	A	O	73	.318
1950	Chi	A	O	143	.280
1951	Chi	A	O	4	.105
1951	Phi	A	O	139	.274
1952	Phi	A	O	145	.262
1953	Phi	A	O	147	.284
1954	Phi	A	1-O	97	.250
1955	KC	A	O	120	.254
1956	KC	A	O	109	.224
1957	KC	A	1-O	131	.236
1958	Det	A	O	66	.323
1959	Det	A	1-O	60	.227
		BRTR		1234	.265

ZETTLEIN, GEORGE (Charmer)
b.July 18,1844 Brooklyn,N.Y.
d.May 23,1905

Yr	Cl	Lea	Pos	G	Rec
1871	Chi	n	P-O	25	17-7 .400
1871	Mut	n	P	1	0-1
1871	Chi	n	P	3	1-2
1872	Tro	n	P-O	25	14-8 NR
1872	Eck	n	P-O	9	1-7 NR
1873	Phi	n	P	49	35-14
1874	Chi	n	P	57	27-30
1875	Chi	n	P	33	18-15
1875	Phi	n	P	21	11-9
1876	Ath	N	P-1	32	4-19 .211
		BRTR		255	128-112 NR

ZICK, ROBERT GEORGE
b.Apr.26,1927 Chicago,Ill.

Yr	Cl	Lea	Pos	G	Rec
1954	Chi	N	P	10	0-0
		BLTR			

ZIEBER, HARRY
(Also played under real name of Edward C. Whiting)

ZIEGLER, CHARLES W.
b.Feb.2,1875 Canton,O.
d.Mar.16,1904

Yr	Cl	Lea	Pos	G	Rec
1899	Cle	N	2-S	2	.250
1900	Phi	N	3	3	.273
				5	.263

ZIEGLER, GEORGE J.
b.1872 Chicago,Ill.
d.July 22,1916

Yr	Cl	Lea	Pos	G	Rec
1890	Pit	N	P	1	0-0

ZIENTARA, BENEDICT JOSEPH
b.Feb.14,1920 Chicago,Ill.

Yr	Cl	Lea	Pos	G	Rec
1941	Cin	N	2	9	.286
1946	Cin	N	2-3	78	.289
1947	Cin	N	2-3	117	.258
1948	Cin	N	2-S-3	74	.187
		BRTR		278	.254

ZIES, WILLIAM

Yr	Cl	Lea	Pos	G	Rec
1891	St.L	a	C	1	.000

ZIMMER, CHARLES LOUIS
(Chief)
b.Nov.23,1860 Marietta,O.
d.Aug.22,1949

Yr	Cl	Lea	Pos	G	Rec
1884	Det	N	C-O	8	.071
1886	Met	a	C	5	.187
1887	Cle	a	C	14	.321
1888	Cle	a	C	63	.250
1889	Cle	N	C	80	.258
1890	Cle	N	C	125	.214
1891	Cle	N	C	116	.261
1892	Cle	N	C	111	.268
1893	Cle	N	C	55	.309
1894	Cle	N	C	88	.285
1895	Cle	N	C	83	.336
1896	Cle	N	C	89	.273
1897	Cle	N	C	81	.314
1898	Cle	N	C	18	.250
1899	Cle	N	C	20	.342
1899	Lou	N	C	74	.299
1900	Pit	N	C	80	.298
1901	Pit	N	C	67	.222
1902	Pit	N	C-1	40	.268
1903	Phi	N	M-C	35	.220
		BRTR		1252	.272

ZIMMER, DONALD WILLIAM
b.Jan.17,1931 Cincinnati,O.

Yr	Cl	Lea	Pos	G	Rec
1954	Bro	N	S	24	.182
1955	Bro	N	2-S-3	88	.239
1956	Bro	N	2-S-3	17	.300
1957	Bro	N	2-S-3	84	.219
1958	LA	N	2-S-3-O	127	.262
1959	LA	N	2-S-3	97	.165
1960	Chi	N	2-S-3-O	132	.258
1961	Chi	N	2-3-O	128	.252
1962	NY	N	3	14	.077
1962	Cin	N	2-3	63	.250
		BRTR		774	.236

ZIMMERMAN, EDWARD DESMOND
b.Jan.4,1883 Oceanic,N.J.
d.May 6,1945

Yr	Cl	Lea	Pos	G	Rec
1906	St.L	N	3	5	.213
1911	Bro	N	3	122	.185
		BRTR		127	.186

ZIMMERMAN, GERALD ROBERT
b.Sept.21,1934 Omaha,Neb.

Yr	Cl	Lea	Pos	G	Rec
1961	Cin	N	C	76	.206
1962	Min	A	C	34	.274
		BRTR		110	.222

ZIMMERMAN, HENRY (Heinie)
b.Feb.9,1887 New York,N.Y.

Yr	Cl	Lea	Pos	G	Rec
1907	Chi	N	2	3	.142
1908	Chi	N	2	30	.292
1909	Chi	N	2	47	.273
1910	Chi	N	2-S-3	86	.284
1911	Chi	N	2-3	139	.307
1912	Chi	N	1-3	145	.372
1913	Chi	N	3	127	.313
1914	Chi	N	S-3	146	.296
1915	Chi	N	2-3	139	.265
1916	Chi	N	2-3	107	.294
1916	NY	N	2	40	.265
1917	NY	N	3	150	.297
1918	NY	N	1-3	121	.272
1919	NY	N	3	123	.255
	BRTR			1403	.295

ZIMMERMAN, ROY FRANKLIN
b.Sept.13,1916 Pine Grove,Pa.

Yr	Cl	Lea	Pos	G	Rec
1945	NY	N	1-O	27	.276
	BLTL				

ZIMMERMAN, WILLIAM H.
b.Jan.20,1889 Kengen,Germany.

Yr	Cl	Lea	Pos	G	Rec
1915	Bro	N	O	22	.281
	BRTR				

ZINK, WALTER CYRUS
b.Nov.21,1898 Pittsfield,Mass.

Yr	Cl	Lea	Pos	G	Rec
1921	NY	N	P	2	0-0
	BRTR				

ZINN, FRANK
b.1865 Philadelphia,Pa.

Yr	Cl	Lea	Pos	G	Rec
1888	Ath	a	C	2	.000

ZINN, GUY
b.Feb.13,1887 Richie Co.,W.Va.

Yr	Cl	Lea	Pos	G	Rec
1911	NY	A	O	9	.148
1912	NY	A	O	106	.264
1913	Bos	N	O	36	.297
1914	Bal	F	O	61	.277
1915	Bal	F	O	100	.269
	BLTR			312	.270

ZINN, JAMES EDWARD
b.Jan.31,1897 Benton,Ark.

Yr	Cl	Lea	Pos	G	Rec
1919	Phi	A	P	10	1-3
1920	Pit	N	P	8	1-1
1921	Pit	N	P	33	7-6
1922	Pit	N	P	5	0-0
1929	Cle	A	P	20	4-6
	BLTR			76	13-16

ZINSER, WILLIAM FRANCIS
b.Jan.6,1918 Astoria,N.Y.

Yr	Cl	Lea	Pos	G	Rec
1944	Was	A	P	2	0-0
	BRTR				

ZIPFEL, MARION SYLVESTER
b.Nov.18,1938 Belleville,Ill.

Yr	Cl	Lea	Pos	G	Rec
1961	Was	A	1	50	.200
1962	Was	A	1-O	68	.239
	BLTR			118	.220

ZITZMANN, WILLIAM ARTHUR
b.Nov.19,1897 Long Island City,N.Y.

Yr	Cl	Lea	Pos	G	Rec
1919	Pit	N	O	11	.192
1919	Cin	N	O	2	.000
1925	Cin	N	S-O	104	.252
1926	Cin	N	O	53	.245
1927	Cin	N	S-3-O	88	.284
1928	Cin	N	3-O	101	.297
1929	Cin	N	1-O	47	.226
	BRTR			406	.267

ZMICH, EDWARD A.
b.1882

Yr	Cl	Lea	Pos	G	Rec
1910	St.L	N	P	9	0-5
1911	St.L	N	P	4	1-0
	BLTL			13	1-5

ZOLDAK, SAMUEL WALTER (Sad Sam)
b.Dec.8,1919 Brooklyn,N.Y.

Yr	Cl	Lea	Pos	G	Rec
1944	St.L	A	P	18	0-0
1945	St.L	A	P	27	3-2
1946	St.L	A	P	35	9-11
1947	St.L	A	P	35	9-10
1948	St.L	A	P	11	2-4
1948	Cle	A	P	23	9-6
1949	Cle	A	P	27	1-2
1950	Cle	A	P	33	4-2
1951	Phi	A	P	26	6-10
1952	Phi	A	P	16	0-6
	BLTL			251	43-53

ZUBER, WILLIAM HENRY (Goober)
b.Mar.26,1913 Amana,Ia.

Yr	Cl	Lea	Pos	G	Rec
1936	Cle	A	P	2	1-1
1938	Cle	A	P	15	0-3
1939	Cle	A	P	16	2-0
1940	Cle	A	P	17	1-1
1941	Was	A	P	36	6-4
1942	Was	A	P	37	9-9
1943	NY	A	P	20	8-4
1944	NY	A	P	22	5-7
1945	NY	A	P	21	5-11
1946	NY	A	P	3	0-1
1946	Bos	A	P	15	5-1
1947	Bos	A	P	20	1-0
	BRTR			224	43-42

ZUPO, FRANK JOSEPH
b.Aug.29,1939 San Francisco,Cal.

Yr	Cl	Lea	Pos	G	Rec
1957	Bal	A	C	10	.083
1958	Bal	A	C	1	.000
1961	Bal	A	C	5	.500
	BLTR			16	.167

ZUVERINK, GEORGE
b.Aug.20,1924 Holland,Mich.

Yr	Cl	Lea	Pos	G	Rec
1951	Cle	A	P	16	0-0
1952	Cle	A	P	2	0-0
1954	Cin	N	P	2	0-0
1954	Det	A	P	35	9-13
1955	Det	A	P	14	0-5
1955	Bal	A	P	28	4-3
1956	Bal	A	P	62	7-6
1957	Bal	A	P	56	10-6
1958	Bal	A	P	45	2-2
1959	Bal	A	P	6	0-1
	BRTR			266	32-36

ZWILLING, EDWARD HARRISON (Dutch)
b.Nov.2,1888 St.Louis,Mo.

Yr	Cl	Lea	Pos	G	Rec
1910	Chi	A	O	27	.184
1914	Chi	F	O	155	.308
1915	Chi	F	O	150	.291
1916	Chi	N	O	35	.113
	BLTL			367	.284

THE LAST OF HIS KIND

Connie Mack, baseball's most revered figure, died February 8, 1956, in Germantown, Pa., at the age of 93. His career spanned two centuries as player, manager and clubowner, and for the first 50 years of the American League he was the Philadelphia Athletics' only manager. In 1886 (left) the thin New England shoe factory hand started as a catcher with Washington of the National League. This is how he looked (right), 70 years later, only three months before he was to die.

IV WORLD SERIES

America's most discussed and popular sporting event is the World Series which annually pits the championship teams of the two major leagues against each other.

The Series is a logical, lucrative and legendary climax to every baseball season. After five months of campaigning, each club strictly within its own league, two teams survive as the fittest. What better than a post-season playoff to determine a single undisputed champion? Yet the World Series did not always extend in an unbroken skein through professional baseball history. League snobbishness of one sort or another has kept pennant winners apart in certain years rather than let the question of league superiority be settled on the ball field.

In those seasons when the majors consisted of only one league, no World Series was necessary. Still, it is interesting to note that the craving for some sort of post-season playoff was so strong that for several years there was an artificial "championship" set played each Autumn between the first and second place finishers for the Temple Cup.

Herewith arc the highlights, scoring summary, winning and losing pitchers, homers and attendance figures of all past World Series games:

1882

At the end of the American Association's first season, the champion Cincinnati club challenged Chicago's NL winners. Bespectacled Will White blanked Chicago in the opener. Larry Corcoran retaliated in the next game. With honors all even, the series came to an untimely end. AA president Denny McKnight, enraged at player raids and other shabby treatment during the season from the NL, wired the Reds that they would be expelled if they continued the series. Cincinnati was ready to defy McKnight, but Chicago player-manager Cap Anson decided to abandon further play for the best interest of all concerned.

Result: Chicago NL won 1; Cincinnati AA, 1.

1st Game, at Cincinnati, Oct 6					R.	H.	E.
Chicago (NL)	000	000	000	---	0	7	3
Cincinnati (AA)	000	004	00x	---	4	10	2

Pitchers--GOLDSMITH vs. WHITE. Attendance--2,700.

2nd Game, at Cincinnati, Oct. 7							
Chicago (NL)	200	000	000	---	2	4	0
Cincinnati (AA)	000	000	000	---	0	3	3

Pitchers--CORCORAN vs. WHITE. Attendançe--4,500.

1884

With league quarrels ironed out by now, the pennant winners met in a fully sanctioned playoff. Hardly tired after pitching 60 victories for Providence in NL competition, Old Hoss Radbourn went on to conquer New York's Mets, pride of the AA, three times in as many days. He topped Tim Keefe's fine flinging the first two games. Keefe turned umpire for the third game, and when it began to turn into a rout he mercifully called a halt because of alleged darkness at the end of six innings.

Result: Providence NL won 3; Mets AA, 0.

1st Game, at New York, Oct. 23					R.	H.	E.
Metropolitan(AA)	000	000	000	---	0	2	1
Providence (NL)	201	000	30x	---	6	5	3

Pitchers--KEEFE vs. RADBOURN. Attend.--1,800.

2nd Game, at New York, Oct. 24							
Providence (NL)	000	030	0	---	3	5	3
Metropolitan(AA)	000	010	0	---	1	3	0

(called, end of seventh: darkness)

Pitchers -- RADBOURN vs. KEEFE. Homer -- Denny (Pro.). Attendance--1,000.

3rd Game, at New York, Oct. 25						
Providence (NL)	120	144	---	12	13	4
Metropolitan(AA)	000	011	---	2	5	2

(called, end of sixth: darkness)

Pitchers--RADBOURN vs. BECANNON. Att.--300.

1885

In the sixth inning of the second game of this bitter rivalry, manager-captain-first baseman Charlie Comiskey pulled his St. Louis AA club off the field in protest against a decision by umpire Dan Sullivan. The game was declared forfeit to Chicago NL, but the Browns won a moral victory since Sullivan did not officiate thereafter. Animosity lingered long after the series, which ended in a tie. St. Louis counted itself the champion, insisting that the forfeited second game should not count in the records. Most people agreed with Cap Anson that his White Stockings were co-champions. Anson hit safely in every game, batting .423. Comiskey, first to field his position away from first base, was outstanding on defense during an erratic series which totaled more errors than hits.

Result: Chicago NL won 3; St. Louis AA, 3; 1 tie.

1st Game, at Chicago, Oct. 14					R.	H.	E.
St. Louis (AA)	010	400	00	---	5	7	4
Chicago (NL)	000	100	04	---	5	6	11

(called, end of 8th: darkness)

Pitchers -- Caruthers vs. Clarkson. Homer -- Pfeffer (Chi.). Attendance -- 3,000.

2nd Game, at St. Louis, Oct. 15					R.	H.	E.
Chicago (NL)	110	003		---	5	6	5
St. Louis (AA)	300	10x		---	4	2	4

(Game forfeited to Chicago, 9-0)

Pitchers--McCORMICK vs. FOUTZ. Attendance--2,000.

3rd Game, at St. Louis, Oct. 16					R.	H.	E.
Chicago (NL)	111	000	001	---	4	8	12
St. Louis (AA)	500	002	00x	---	7	8	4

Pitchers--CLARKSON vs. CARUTHERS. Att.--3,000.

4th Game, at St. Louis, Oct. 17					R.	H.	E.
Chicago (NL)	000	020	000	---	2	8	3
St. Louis (AA)	001	000	02x	---	3	6	7

Pitchers--McCORMICK vs. FOUTZ. Homer--Dalrymple (Chi.). Attendance--3,000.

5th Game, at Pittsburgh, Oct. 22					R.	H.	E.
Chicago (NL)	400	110	3	---	9	7	1
St. Louis (AA)	010	000	1	---	2	4	7

(called, end of 7th: darkness)

Pitchers--CLARKSON vs. FOUTZ. Attendance--500.

6th Game, at Cincinnati, Oct. 23					R.	H.	E.
Chicago (NL)	200	111	040	---	9	11	10
St. Louis (AA)	002	000	000	---	2	2	7

Pitchers--McCORMICK vs. CARUTHERS. Att.--1,500.

7th Game, at Cincinnati, Oct. 24					R.	H.	E.
Chicago (NL)	200	020	00	---	4	9	17
St. Louis (AA)	004	621	0x	---	13	12	10

(called in 8th: darkness)

Pitchers--McCORMICK vs. FOUTZ. Attend.--1,200.

1886

Renewing their feud of the previous Fall, the Browns and White Stockings met on a winner-take-all basis. St. Louis won only one of the first three games in Chicago, but swept all three at home to make their colorful club-owner, Chris Von der Ahe, gloat over "my poys, champeens of the world." The series ended on a dramatic note. Curt Welch, Brown centerfielder, was on third base in the 10th inning of the last game when King Kelly signaled for a pitchout. Welch daringly streaked for home and made it when Kelly momentarily bobbled the pitch in his mitt. This play was dubbed "Welch's fifteen thousand dollar slide," as a rough estimate of how much it meant to the winners.

Result: St. Louis AA won 4; Chicago NL, 2.

1st Game, at Chicago, Oct. 18					R.	H.	E.
St. Louis (AA)	000	000	000	---	0	5	7
Chicago (NL)	200	001	03x	---	6	10	5

Pitchers--FOUTZ vs. CLARKSON. Attend.--6,000.

2nd Game, at Chicago, Oct. 19					R.	H.	E.
St. Louis (AA)	200	230	50	---	12	13	5
Chicago (NL)	000	000	00	---	0	2	13

(called, end of 8th: darkness)

Pitchers--CARUTHERS vs. McCORMICK. Homers -- O'Neill (St. L.) 2. Attendance--5,000.

3rd Game, at Chicago, Oct. 20					R.	H.	E.
Chicago (NL)	200	112	32	---	11	11	7
St. Louis (AA)	010	002	01	---	4	9	7

(called, end of 8th: darkness)

Pitchers--CLARKSON, Williamson (8) vs. CARUTHERS. Homers--Kelly (Chi.), Gore (Chi.). Attendance--6,000.

4th Game, at St. Louis, Oct. 21					R.	H.	E.
Chicago (NL)	300	002	0	---	5	6	4
St. Louis (AA)	011	033	x	---	8	7	4

(called in 7th: darkness)

Pitchers--CLARKSON vs. FOUTZ. Attendance--8,000.

5th Game, at St. Louis, Oct. 22					R.	H.	E.
Chicago (NL)	011	100	00	---	3	3	3
St. Louis (AA)	214	003	0x	---	10	11	3

(called in 8th: darkness)

Pitchers--WILLIAMSON, Ryan (2) vs. HUDSON. Attendance--10,000.

6th Game, at St. Louis, Oct. 23						R.	H.	E.
Chicago (NL)	010	101	000	0	---	3	6	2
St. Louis (AA)	000	000	030	1	---	4	5	3

Pitchers--CLARKSON vs. CARUTHERS. Homer--Pfeffer (Chi.). Attendance--8,000.

1887

Behind its famed "Big Four" of Dan Brouthers, Deacon White, Hardy Richardson and Jack Rowe, Detroit NL trounced St. Louis AA in a 15-game traveling circus played in 10 different cities. Pitchers Charles Getzein and Lady Baldwin each won four for the new champions, while Ned Hanlon gained a reputation for his fine field direction from centerfield. Arlie Latham stole a dozen bases for the losers, acted as pivotman in a triple play and hit .333.

Result: Detroit NL won 10; St. Louis AA, 5.

1st Game, at St. Louis, Oct. 10					R.	H.	E.
St. Louis (AA)	200	040	000	---	6	16	0
Detroit (NL)	000	000	001	---	1	5	5

Pitchers--CARUTHERS vs. GETZEIN. Attend.--4,208.

2nd Game, at St. Louis, Oct. 11							
Detroit (NL)	022	000	100	---	5	12	2
St. Louis (AA)	000	000	120	---	3	10	7

Pitchers--CONWAY vs. FOUTZ. Attendance--6,408.

3rd Game, at Detroit, Oct. 12									
St. Louis (AA)	010	000	000	000	0	---	1	13	7
Detroit (NL)	000	000	010	000	1	---	2	7	1

Pitchers--CARUTHERS vs. GETZEIN. Attend.--4,509.

4th Game, at Pittsburgh, Oct. 13							
Detroit (NL)	410	012	000	---	8	12	1
St. Louis (AA)	000	000	000	---	0	5	6

Pitchers--BALDWIN vs. KING. Attendance--2,447.

5th Game, at Brooklyn, Oct. 14							
St. Louis (AA)	200	002	100	---	5	7	4
Detroit (NL)	000	020	000	---	2	8	5

Pitchers--CARUTHERS vs. CONWAY. Att.--6,796.

6th Game, at New York, Oct. 15							
Detroit (NL)	330	000	003	---	9	15	1
St. Louis (AA)	000	000	000	---	0	5	8

Pitchers--GETZEIN vs. FOUTZ. Attendance--5,797.

7th Game, at Philadelphia, Oct. 17							
St. Louis (AA)	000	000	001	---	1	10	1
Detroit (NL)	030	000	00x	---	3	7	2

Pitchers--CARUTHERS vs. BALDWIN. Homer--O'Neill (St. L.). Attendance--6,478.

8th Game, at Boston, Oct. 18							
Detroit (NL)	031	003	200	---	9	17	2
St. Louis (AA)	100	001	000	---	2	12	5

Pitchers -- GETZEIN vs. CARUTHERS. Homers -- Thompson (Det.) 2. Attendance--2,891.

9th Game, at Philadelphia, Oct. 19							
St. Louis (AA)	000	101	000	---	2	9	2
Detroit (NL)	000	100	21x	---	4	6	3

Pitchers--KING vs. CONWAY. Attendance--2,389.

10th Game, at Washington, Oct. 21 (AM)							
Detroit (NL)	200	010	001	---	4	9	3
St. Louis (AA)	200	031	41x	---	11	19	5

Pitchers--GETZEIN vs. CARUTHERS. Homers--Latham (St. L.), Welch (St. L.), Richardson (Det.). Attendance--1,261.

11th Game, at Baltimore, Oct. 21 (PM)							
St. Louis (AA)	110	010	000	---	3	13	7
Detroit (NL)	100	344	10x	---	13	18	7

Pitchers -- FOUTZ vs. BALDWIN. Homer -- Twitchell (Det.). Attendance--2,707.

12th Game, at Brooklyn, Oct. 22							
Detroit (NL)	000	010	0	---	1	5	3
St. Louis (AA)	410	000	x	---	5	10	2

(called in 7th: darkness)

Pitchers--CONWAY vs. KING. Attendance--1,138.

13th Game, at Detroit, Oct. 24							
Detroit (NL)	020	100	120	---	6	14	3
St. Louis (AA)	100	010	001	---	3	5	5

Pitchers--BALDWIN vs. CARUTHERS. Attend.--3,389.

14th Game, at Chicago, Oct. 25							
St. Louis (AA)	000	002	100	---	3	10	5
Detroit (NL)	300	010	00x	---	4	4	4

Pitchers--KING vs. GETZEIN. Attendance--378.

15th Game, at St. Louis, Oct. 26						
St. Louis (AA)	340	110	---	9	11	4
Detroit (NL)	011	000	---	2	10	7

(called, end of 6th: cold)

Pitchers--CARUTHERS vs. BALDWIN. Att.--659.

1888

Though St. Louis sold five regulars after losing the previous series, the Browns won the AA pennant for the fourth straight year... only to lose to their NL rivals again. It was decided to play a best-six-out-of-ten series. The New York Giants clinched it in eight games, then tossed away the last two by sending home their big stars: Tim Keefe, Buck Ewing and John Montgomery Ward. Keefe fastballed four victories. Ewing hit hard and, in an era of stolen bases and passed balls galore, stood out as the colossus of catchers. Ward was such a superb all-around player that one newspaperman wrote that the Browns would have won the series if Ward had shortstopped for them instead.

Result: New York NL won 6; St. Louis AA, 4.

1st Game, at New York, Oct. 16					R.	H.	E.
St. Louis (AA)	001	000	000	---	1	3	5
New York (NL)	011	000	00x	---	2	3	4

Pitchers--KING vs. KEEFE. Attendance--4,876.

2nd Game, at New York, Oct. 17							
St. Louis (AA)	010	000	002	---	3	7	4
New York (NL)	000	000	000	---	0	6	1

Pitchers--CHAMBERLAIN vs. WELCH. Att.--5,575.

3rd Game, at New York, Oct. 18							
St. Louis (AA)	000	000	011	---	2	5	5
New York (NL)	200	100	10x	---	4	5	2

Pitchers--KING vs. KEEFE. Attendance--5,780.

4th Game, at Brooklyn, Oct. 19							
New York (NL)	104	010	000	---	6	8	2
St. Louis (AA)	001	000	020	---	3	6	4

Pitchers--CRANE vs. CHAMBERLAIN. Att.--3,062.

5th Game, at New York, Oct. 20							
St. Louis (AA)	003	001	00	---	4	5	5
New York (NL)	100	000	05	---	6	9	2

(called, end of 8th: darkness)

Pitchers--KING vs. KEEFE. Attendance--9,124.

6th Game, at Philadelphia, Oct. 22							
New York (NL)	000	103	35	---	12	13	5
St. Louis (AA)	301	000	01	---	5	3	7

(called, end of 8th: darkness)

Pitchers--WELCH vs. CHAMBERLAIN. Att.--3,281.

7th Game, at St. Louis, Oct. 24							
New York (NL)	030	002	00	---	5	11	3
St. Louis (AA)	000	300	04	---	7	8	3

(called, end of 8th: darkness)

Pitchers--CRANE vs. KING. Attendance--4,624.

8th Game, at St. Louis, Oct. 25							
New York (NL)	103	100	006	---	11	12	2
St. Louis (AA)	000	100	110	---	3	5	6

Pitchers--KEEFE vs. CHAMBERLAIN. Homers--Ewing (N.Y.), Tiernan (N.Y.). Attendance--4,865.

9th Game, at St. Louis, Oct. 26								
St. Louis (AA)	140	020	202	3	---	14	15	4
New York (NL)	035	000	120	0	---	11	14	5

Pitchers--King, DEVLIN (4) vs. GEORGE. Homer--O'Neill (St. L.). Attendance--711.

10th Game, at St. Louis, Oct. 27							
St. Louis (AA)	010	505	421	---	18	17	3
New York (NL)	310	000	021	---	7	13	8

Pitchers--CHAMBERLAIN vs. TITCOMB, Hatfield (5). Homers--George (N.Y.), O'Neill (St. L.), McCarthy (St. L.). Attendance--412.

1889

Manager Jim Mutrie wore his stovepipe hat with regal pride when his Giants repeated as world champions. Cannonball Ed Crane won four games and Hank O'Day, later a famous umpire, won two others. John Ward hit .417 and shortstopped wonderfully. Brooklyn won three of the first four games, only to lose the next five straight.

Result: New York NL won 6; Brooklyn AA, 3.

1st Game, at New York, Oct. 18					R.	H.	E.
New York (NL)	020	210	50	---	10	11	3
Brooklyn (AA)	510	000	24	---	12	14	6

(called, end of 8th: darkness)

Pitchers--KEEFE vs. TERRY. Homer--Collins (Bklyn.). Attendance--8,848.

2nd Game, at Brooklyn, Oct. 19							
New York (NL)	111	120	000	---	6	9	4
Brooklyn (AA)	110	000	000	---	2	3	8

Pitchers--CRANE vs. CARUTHERS. Attend.--16,172.

3rd Game, at New York, Oct. 22							
New York (NL)	200	032	00	---	7	15	2
Brooklyn (AA)	023	120	00	---	8	11	3

(called, end of 8th: darkness)

Pitchers--WELCH, O'Day (6) vs. HUGHES, Caruthers (8). Homers--Corkhill (Bklyn.), O'Rourke (N.Y.). Attendance--5,181.

4th Game, at Brooklyn, Oct. 23							
New York (NL)	001	105		---	7	9	8
Brooklyn (AA)	202	033		---	10	7	1

(called end of sixth: darkness)

Pitchers--CRANE vs. TERRY. Homer--Burns (Bklyn.). Attendance--3,045.

5th Game, at Brooklyn, Oct. 24							
New York (NL)	004	040	021	---	11	12	2
Brooklyn (AA)	000	111	000	---	3	8	2

Pitchers--CRANE vs. CARUTHERS. Homers--Brown (N.Y.), Richardson (N.Y.), Crane (N.Y.). Attendance--2,901.

6th Game, at New York, Oct. 25								
Brooklyn (AA)	010	000	000	00	---	1	6	4
New York (NL)	000	000	001	01	---	2	6	1

Pitchers--TERRY vs O'DAY. Attendance--2,556.

7th Game, at New York, Oct. 26							
Brooklyn (AA)	004	030	000	---	7	5	3
New York (NL)	180	001	10x	---	11	14	4

Pitchers--LOVETT, Caruthers (4) vs. CRANE, Keefe (5). Homers--Richardson (N.Y.), O'Rourke (N.Y.). Attendance--3,312.

8th Game, at Brooklyn, Oct. 28							
New York (NL)	541	203	001	---	16	15	4
Brooklyn (AA)	200	000	023	---	7	5	4

Pitchers--CRANE vs. TERRY, Foutz (5). Homers--Foutz (Bklyn.), Tiernan (N.Y.). Attendance--2,584.

9th Game, at New York, Oct. 29							
Brooklyn (AA)	200	000	000	---	2	4	2
New York (NL)	100	001	10x	---	3	8	5

Pitchers--TERRY vs. O'DAY. Attendance--3,067.

1890

Brooklyn's AA kingpins of 1889 jumped to the NL in 1890 and won the pennant. In the AA, Louisville rose from last to first in one season. However, much of the top talent had switched to the Players League, so the public couldn't cotton to the alleged "world championship" playoff between the NL and AA leaders. Miserable weather further plagued the series. After seven games, the whole thing was called off. By then, each team had won three and one was tied, so, appropriately enough, there was no clear-cut champion.

Result: Brooklyn NL won 3; Louisville AA, 3; 1 tie.

1st Game, at Louisville, Oct. 17					R.	H.	E.
Brooklyn (NL)	300	030	30	---	9	11	1
Louisville (AA)	000	000	00	---	0	2	6

(called, end of 8th: darkness)

Pitchers--TERRY vs. STRATTON. Attendance--5,600.

2nd Game, at Louisville, Oct. 18							
Brooklyn (NL)	020	201	000	---	5	5	3
Louisville (AA)	101	000	001	---	3	6	5

Pitchers--LOVETT vs. DAILY. Attendance--2,860.

3rd Game, at Louisville, Oct. 20							
Brooklyn (NL)	020	130	10	---	7	10	2
Louisville (AA)	001	102	03	---	7	11	3

(called, end of 8th: darkness)

Pitchers--Terry vs Stratton, Meakim (4). Attendance--2,500.

4th Game, at Louisville, Oct. 21							
Brooklyn (NL)	031	000	000	---	4	7	2
Louisville (AA)	301	000	10x	---	5	9	2

Pitchers--LOVETT vs. EHRET. Attendance--1,050.

5th Game, at Brooklyn, Oct. 25							
Louisville (AA)	010	010	000	---	2	5	6
Brooklyn (NL)	210	200	20x	---	7	7	0

Pitchers--DAILY vs. LOVETT. Homer--Burns (Bklyn.). Attendance--1,000.

6th Game, at Brooklyn, Oct. 27							
Louisville (AA)	012	101	220	---	9	13	3
Brooklyn (NL)	100	004	030	---	8	12	3

Pitchers--STRATTON, Ehret (7) vs. TERRY. Attendance--600.

7th Game, at Brooklyn, Oct. 28							
Louisville (AA)	103	000	020	---	6	8	3
Brooklyn (NL)	200	000	000	---	2	4	1

Pitchers--EHRET vs. LOVETT. Attendance--300.

1892

Interleague bitterness over player raids prevented an AA-NL playoff in 1891. By the next year, the majors had amalgamated into one league, the 12-club NL. They used an artificial "split season" to create a "world series," but the experiment was dropped after one trial. Cleveland's Spiders won the first-half pennant.

Boston won the second-half, and also had the best full-season record. The opening playoff game was a memorable 11-inning scoreless tie between two pitchers now in the Hall of Fame, Cy Young and Kid Nichols. Boston won the next five straight. No line scores are listed for this spurious World Series, nor for the similar Temple Cup games of the '90s.

Result: Boston NL won 5, Cleveland NL, 0; 1 tie.

1894

William C. Temple, a Pittsburgh sportsman, donated an expensive cup as prize for a post-season series between the NL champion and runner-up. Ned Hanlon's colorful, scrappy Baltimore Orioles refused to take this series seriously after winning the pennant. They didn't bother keeping in shape, and fell easy prey to the second place Giants.

Result: New York NL won 4; Baltimore NL, 0.

1895

Ned Hanlon's Orioles, still regarding the Temple Cub play as post-season exhibition games, bowed again as the runnerup Spiders cleaned up in five games.

Result: Cleveland NL won 4; Baltimore NL, 1.

1896

Stung by taunts of fans who wouldn't let them forget two straight playoff beatings, the Orioles captured their third straight pennant and then entered the Temple Cup set with calculated fury. Third baseman John McGraw and the rest of Baltimore's champions worked into tiptop shape for the October series. They perfected new strategy, including the notable cutoff play. Then they tore into Cleveland for vengeful 7-1, 7-2, 6-2 and 5-0 trouncings.

Result: Baltimore NL won 4; Cleveland NL, 0.

1897

Baltimore barely lost to Boston in the regular season, but the Orioles proved too strong in post-season play, with 54 runs in five games. Since the Temple Cup was one-sided for the fourth straight year, the event lost its flavor, so the league returned the cup to its donor with thanks and ended the unprofitable playoffs.

Result: Baltimore NL won 4; Boston NL, 1.

1903

Marking the end of AL-NL warfare, presidents of the pennant-winning clubs arranged a best five-out-of nine Series. Pittsburgh had just won its third straight NL flag, but untimely injuries reduced the Pirate pitching staff to one effective operator, Deacon Phillippe. The Deacon pitched 44 innings and won three games, but couldn't carry the load alone. Boston lost three of the first four games, then won four straight to bring the crown to the new league. Bill Dinneen pitched three victories and Cy Young two for Boston.

Result: Boston AL won 5; Pittsburgh NL, 3.

1st Game, at Boston, Oct. 1					R.	H.	E.
Pittsburgh (NL)	401	100	100	---	7	12	2
Boston (AL)	000	000	201	---	3	6	4

Pitchers -- PHILLIPPE vs. YOUNG. Homer -- Sebring (Pitt.). Attendance--16,242.

2nd Game, at Boston, Oct. 2							
Pittsburgh (NL)	000	000	000	---	0	3	2
Boston (AL)	200	001	00x	---	3	9	0

Pitchers--LEEVER, Vail (2) vs. DINNEEN. Homers--Dougherty (Bos.) 2. Attendance--9,415.

3rd Game, at Boston, Oct. 3							
Pittsburgh (NL)	012	000	010	---	4	7	0
Boston (AL)	000	100	010	---	2	4	2

Pitchers--PHILLIPPE vs. HUGHES, Young (3). Attendance--18,801.

4th Game, at Pittsburgh, Oct. 6							
Boston (AL)	000	010	003	---	4	9	1
Pittsburgh (NL)	100	010	30x	---	5	12	1

Pitchers--DINNEEN vs. PHILLIPPE. Attend.--7,600.

5th Game, at Pittsburgh, Oct. 7							
Boston (AL)	000	006	410	---	11	14	2
Pittsburgh (NL)	000	000	020	---	2	6	4

Pitchers--YOUNG vs. KENNEDY, Thompson (8). Attendance--12,322.

6th Game, at Pittsburgh, Oct. 8

					R.	H.	E.
Boston (AL)	003	020	100	---	6	10	1
Pittsburgh (NL)	000	000	300	---	3	10	3

Pitchers--DINEEN vs. LEEVER. Attendance--11,556.

7th Game, at Pittsburgh, Oct. 10

					R.	H.	E.
Boston (AL)	200	202	010	---	7	11	4
Pittsburgh (NL)	000	101	001	---	3	10	3

Pitchers--YOUNG vs. PHILLIPPE. Attend.--17,038.

8th Game, at Boston, Oct. 13

					R.	H.	E.
Pittsburgh (NL)	000	000	000	---	0	4	3
Boston (AL)	000	201	00x	---	3	8	0

Pitchers--PHILLIPPE vs. DINEEN. Attend.--7,455.

1905

Owner John T. Brush and manager John J. McGraw of the Giants felt such personal bitterness toward the "upstart" American League that they refused to let their 1904 NL champions meet Boston's repeating AL winners. Giant players petitioned in vain to have the series played. However, fans and writers criticized Brush so severely that he later drew up the Brush Rules to govern annual post-season playoffs. These regulations are the same ones that are used today, with few exceptions. Brush's Giants happened to repeat in 1905, so they became the first NL team to play under the modern code. Connie Mack's Athletics furnished poor opposition, since Rube Waddell was sidelined with a lame arm. All five games ended in shutouts, with young Christy Mathewson wielding three of them.

Result: New York NL won 4; Philadelphia AL, 1.

1st Game, at Philadelphia, Oct. 9

					R.	H.	E.
New York (NL)	000	020	001	---	3	10	1
Philadelphia(AL)	000	000	000	---	0	4	0

Pitchers--MATHEWSON vs. PLANK. Attend.--17,955.

2nd Game, at New York, Oct. 10

					R.	H.	E.
Philadelphia(AL)	001	000	020	---	3	6	2
New York (NL)	000	000	000	---	0	4	2

Pitchers--BENDER vs. McGINNITY, Ames (9). Attendance--24,922.

3rd Game, at Philadelphia, Oct. 12

					R.	H.	E.
New York (NL)	200	050	002	---	9	9	1
Philadelphia(AL)	000	000	000	---	0	4	5

Pitchers--MATHEWSON vs. COAKLEY. Att.--10,991.

4th Game, at New York, Oct. 13

					R.	H.	E.
Philadelphia(AL)	000	000	000	---	0	5	2
New York (NL)	000	100	00x	---	1	4	1

Pitchers--PLANK vs. McGINNITY. Att.--13,598.

5th Game, at New York, Oct. 14

					R.	H.	E.
Philadelphia (AL)	000	000	000	---	0	6	0
New York (NL)	000	010	01x	---	2	5	1

Pitchers--BENDER vs. MATHEWSON. Attend.--24,187.

1906

No upset in World Series history ever matched the one in this first intracity battle. The Cubs were favored after having won a record number of 116 games that gave them the NL flag by a margin of 20 games. The White Sox, mired in the second division at midseason, finished first only by virtue of a 19-game winning streak in the last month. The "Hitless Wonders" owned a season batting average of .228, ranking next to last in the majors. Yet outfielder-manager Fielder Jones' White Sox won the series in six games. A lowly substitute named George Rohe decided two games for them with triples, and hit .333. Ed Reulbach pitched a one-hitter and Three-Fingered Brown a two-hitter for the only Cub victories.

Result: Chicago AL won 4; Chicago NL, 2.

1st Game, at West Side Park, Chi., Oct. 9

					R.	H.	E.
Chicago (AL)	000	011	000	---	2	4	1
Chicago (NL)	000	001	000	---	1	4	2

Pitchers--ALTROCK vs. BROWN. Attendance--12,693.

2nd Game, at Comiskey Park, Chi., Oct. 10

					R.	H.	E.
Chicago (NL)	031	001	020	---	7	10	2
Chicago (AL)	000	010	000	---	1	1	2

Pitchers--REULBACH vs. WHITE, OWEN. Att.--12,595.

3rd Game, at West Side Park, Chi., Oct. 11

					R.	H.	E.
Chicago (AL)	000	003	000	---	3	4	1
Chicago (NL)	000	000	000	---	0	2	2

Pitchers--WALSH vs. PFEISTER. Attendance--13,750.

4th Game, at Comiskey Park, Chi., Oct. 12

					R.	H.	E.
Chicago (NL)	000	000	100	---	1	7	1
Chicago (AL)	000	000	000	---	0	2	1

Pitchers--BROWN vs. ALTROCK. Attendance--18,385.

5th Game, at West Side Park, Chi., Oct. 13

					R.	H.	E.
Chicago (AL)	102	401	000	---	8	12	6
Chicago (NL)	300	102	000	---	6	6	0

Pitchers--WALSH, White (7) vs. Reulbach, PFEISTER (3), Overall (4). Attendance--23,257.

6th Game, at Comiskey Park, Chi., Oct. 14

					R.	H.	E.
Chicago (NL)	100	010	001	---	3	7	0
Chicago (AL)	340	000	01x	---	8	14	3

Pitchers--BROWN, Overall (2) vs. WHITE. Att.--19,249.

1907

Though a 20-year-old thunderbolt named Ty Cobb had just won his first of a dozen batting crowns, he was a .200 bust in the series, and his Tiger teammates collapsed with him. Hitting hero with a .470 average was Harry Steinfeldt, underrated third baseman of the Cubs' legendary Tinker-Evers-Chance double play combination. Detroit would have won the opener if catcher Charley Schmidt hadn't muffed a third strike with two out in the ninth. Chicago capitalized with the two tying runs, and the game ended in a 12-inning deadlock. The Cubs easily bagged the next four games.

Result: Chicago NL won 4; Detroit AL, 0; 1 tie.

1st Game, at Chicago, Oct. 8						R.	H.	E.
Detroit (AL)	000	000	030	000	---	3	9	3
Chicago (NL)	000	100	002	000	---	3	10	5

(called, end of 12th: darkness)

Pitchers--Donovan vs. Overall, Reulbach (10). Attendance--24,377.

2nd Game, at Chicago, Oct. 9							
Detroit (AL)	010	000	000	---	1	9	1
Chicago (NL)	010	200	00x	---	3	9	1

Pitchers--MULLIN vs. PFEISTER. Attend.--21,901.

3rd Game, at Chicago, Oct. 10							
Detroit (AL)	000	001	000	---	1	6	1
Chicago (NL)	010	310	00x	---	5	10	1

Pitchers--SIEVER, Killian (5) vs. REULBACH. Attendance--13,114.

4th Game, at Detroit, Oct. 11							
Chicago (NL)	000	020	301	---	6	7	2
Detroit (AL)	000	100	000	---	1	5	2

Pitchers--OVERALL vs. DONOVAN. Attend.--11,306.

5th Game, at Detroit, Oct. 12							
Chicago (NL)	110	000	000	---	2	7	1
Detroit (AL)	000	000	000	---	0	7	2

Pitchers--BROWN vs. MULLIN. Attendance--7,370.

1908

After winning the pennant on the last day of the season, the Tigers ran into their series nemesis and lost again in five games. Manager-first baseman Frank Chance, whose Cubs clinched the pennant in a playoff of the "Merkle Boner" game with the Giants, led his team with a .421 batting average and five stolen bases. Orvie Overall and Three-Fingered Brown each pitched a shutout and won one other decision.

Result: Chicago NL won 4; Detroit AL, 1.

1st Game, at Detroit, Oct. 10					R.	H.	E.
Chicago (NL)	004	000	105	---	10	14	2
Detroit (AL)	100	000	320	---	6	10	4

Pitchers--Reulbach, Overall (7), BROWN (8) vs. Killian, SUMMERS (3). Attendance--10,812.

2nd Game, at Chicago, Oct. 11							
Detroit (AL)	000	000	001	---	1	4	1
Chicago (NL)	000	000	06x	---	6	7	1

Pitchers--DONOVAN vs. OVERALL. Homer--Tinker (Chi.). Attendance--17,760.

3rd Game, at Chicago, Oct. 12							
Detroit (AL)	100	005	020	---	8	11	4
Chicago (NL)	000	300	000	---	3	7	2

Pitchers--MULLIN vs. PFEISTER, Reulbach (9). Attendance--14,543.

4th Game, at Detroit, Oct. 13							
Chicago (NL)	002	000	001	---	3	10	0
Detroit (AL)	000	000	000	---	0	4	1

Pitchers--BROWN vs. SUMMERS, Winter (9). Attendance--12,907.

5th Game, at Detroit, Oct. 14							
Chicago (NL)	100	010	000	---	2	10	0
Detroit (AL)	000	000	000	---	0	3	0

Pitchers--OVERALL vs. DONOVAN. Attend.--6,210.

1909

After winning 66 games for Pittsburgh in the regular season, Howie Camnitz, Vic Willis and Lefty Leifield failed to take a series game. But freshman righthander Charles (Babe) Adams whipped the Tigers three times. In the only direct offensive duel between those diamond immortals, Honus Wagner of Pittsburgn surpassed Ty Cobb. Wagner hit .333 stole six bases. Cobb hit only .231 and stole one base, a daring dash home which helped win the second game.

Result: Pittsburgh NL won 4; Detroit AL, 3.

1st Game, at Pittsburgh, Oct. 8					R.	H.	E.
Detroit (AL)	100	000	000	---	1	6	4
Pittsburgh (NL)	000	121	00x	---	4	5	0

Pitchers--MULLIN vs. ADAMS. Homer--Clarke (Pitt.). Attendance--29,264.

2nd Game, at Pittsburgh, Oct. 9							
Detroit (AL)	023	020	000	---	7	9	3
Pittsburgh (NL)	200	000	000	---	2	5	1

Pitchers--DONOVAN vs. CAMNITZ, Willis (3). Attendance--30,915.

3rd Game, at Detroit, Oct. 11							
Pittsburgh (NL)	510	000	002	---	8	10	3
Detroit (AL)	000	000	402	---	6	10	5

Pitchers--MADDOX vs. SUMMERS, Willett (1), Works (8). Attendance--18,277.

4th Game, at Detroit, Oct. 12							
Pittsburgh (NL)	000	000	000	---	0	5	6
Detroit (AL)	020	300	00x	---	5	8	0

Pitchers--LEIFIELD, Phillippe (5) vs. MULLIN. Attendance--17,036.

5th Game, at Pittsburgh, Oct 13							
Detroit (AL)	100	002	010	---	4	6	1
Pittsburgh (NL)	111	000	41x	---	8	10	2

Pitchers--SUMMERS, Willett (8) vs. ADAMS. Homers--D. Jones (Det.), Crawford (Det.), Clarke (Pitts.). Attendance--21,706.

6th Game, at Detroit, Oct. 14							
Pittsburgh (NL)	300	000	001	---	4	7	3
Detroit (AL)	100	211	00x	---	5	10	3

Pitchers--WILLIS, Camnitz (6), Phillippe (7) vs. MULLIN. Attendance--10,535.

7th Game, at Detroit, Oct. 16							
Pittsburgh (NL)	020	203	010	---	8	7	0
Detroit (AL)	000	000	000	---	0	6	3

Pitchers--ADAMS vs. DONOVAN, Mullin (4). Attendance--17,562.

1910

After winning the pennant for the fourth time in five years, the veteran Cubs ran into a series ambush by the young Athletics and were thrashed in five games. Philadelphia averaged seven runs a game and feasted on Cub hurling for a .317 average. Jack Coombs posted three victories and Eddie Collins hit .429.

Result: Philadelphia AL won 4; Chicago NL, 1.

1st Game, at Philadelphia, Oct. 17 R. H. E.
Chicago (NL) 000 000 001 --- 1 3 1
Philadelphia(AL) 021 000 01x --- 4 7 2
Pitchers--OVERALL, McIntire (4) vs. BENDER. Attendance--26,891.

2nd Game, at Philadelphia, Oct. 18
Chicago (NL) 100 000 101 --- 3 8 3
Philadelphia(AL) 002 010 60x --- 9 14 4
Pitchers--BROWN, Richie (8) vs. COOMBS. Attendance --24,597.

3rd Game, at Chicago, Oct. 20
Philadelphia(AL) 125 000 400 --- 12 15 1
Chicago (NL) 120 000 020 --- 5 6 5
Pitchers -- COOMBS vs. Reulbach, McINTIRE (3), Pfeister (3). Homer -- Murphy (Phila.). Attend.--26,210.

4th Game, at Chicago, Oct. 22
Philadelphia(AL) 001 200 000 0 --- 3 11 3
Chicago (NL) 100 100 001 1 --- 4 9 1
Pitchers--BENDER vs. Cole, BROWN (9). Attendance--19,150.

5th Game, at Chicago, Oct. 23
Philadelphia(AL) 100 010 050 --- 7 9 1
Chicago (NL) 010 000 010 --- 2 9 2
Pitchers--COOMBS vs. BROWN. Attendance--27,374.

1911

John Franklin Baker, third baseman for the A's, earned the nickname "Home Run" in this series. His four-base blasts beat Rube Marquard in the second game and Christy Mathewson in the third. Though the Giants had stolen 347 bases from NL rivals, they took no such liberties against A's catching. Every game was a pitching duel till the finale, when the A's hammered three hurlers for 13 hits and 13 runs that brought Chief Bender an easy decision. Giant cleanup hitter Jack Murray went 21-for-0 at the plate.

Result: Philadelphia AL won 4; New York NL, 2.

1st Game, at New York, Oct. 14 R. H. E.
Philadelphia(AL) 010 000 000 --- 1 6 2
New York (NL) 000 100 10x --- 2 5 0
Pitchers--BENDER vs. MATHEWSON. Att.--38,281.

2nd Game, at Philadelphia, Oct. 16
New York (NL) 010 000 000 --- 1 5 3
Philadelphia(AL) 100 002 00x --- 3 4 0
Pitchers--MARQUARD, Crandall (8) vs. PLANK. Homer --Baker (Phil.). Attendance--26,286.

3rd Game, at New York, Oct. 17
Philadelphia(AL) 000 000 001 02 --- 3 9 2
New York (NL) 001 000 000 01 --- 2 3 5
Pitchers--COOMBS vs. MATHEWSON. Homer--Baker (Phil.). Attendance--37,216.

4th Game, at Philadelphia, Oct. 24
New York (NL) 200 000 000 --- 2 7 3
Philadelphia(AL) 000 310 00x --- 4 11 1
Pitchers--MATHEWSON, Wiltse (8) vs. BENDER. Attendance--24,355.

5th Game, at New York, Oct. 25
Philadelphia(AL) 003 000 000 0 --- 3 7 1
New York (NL) 000 000 102 1 --- 4 9 2
Pitchers--Coombs, PLANK (10) vs. Marquard, Ames (4), CRANDALL (8). Homer--Oldring (Phil.). Attendance--33,228.

6th Game, at Philadelphia, Oct. 26
New York (NL) 100 000 001 --- 2 4 3
Philadelphia(AL) 001 401 70x --- 13 13 5
Pitchers--AMES, Wiltse (5), Marquard (7) vs. BENDER. Attendance--20,485.

1912

Behind, three games to one, the Giants rallied to win the next two and practically clinched the title with a 2-1 lead behind Matty in the 10th inning of the last game. In the fateful last half, outfielder Fred Snodgrass muffed a lazy fly by Clyde Engle, Red Sox pinch hitter. On the next play, Snodgrass speared Harry Hooper's deep drive. Steve Yerkes walked. Tris Speaker's simple foul fell between Chief Meyers and Fred Merkle, though either could have caught the ball while shaking hands with the other. Speaker then lined a single to score Engle with the tying run. Duffy Lewis was passed intentionally, and Larry Gardner flied to Josh Devore in deep right, Yerkes scoring after the catch for the winning tally. This marked the third victory of the series for Smoky Joe Wood, who had posted a phenomenal 34-5 season mark for the Sox.

Result: Boston AL won 4; New York NL, 3; 1 tie.

1st Game, at New York, Oct. 8 R. H. E.
Boston (AL) 000 001 300 --- 4 6 1
New York (NL) 002 000 001 --- 3 8 1
Pitchers--WOOD vs. TESREAU, Crandall (8). Attendance--35,730.

2nd Game, at Boston, Oct. 9

New York (NL)	010	100	030	10	---	6	11	5
Boston (AL)	300	010	010	10	---	6	10	1

(called, end of 11th: darkness)

Pitchers--Mathewson vs. Collins, Hall (8). Bedient (11). Attendance--30,148.

3rd Game, at Boston, Oct. 10

New York (NL)	010	010	000	---	2	7	1
Boston (AL)	000	000	001	---	1	7	0

Pitchers--MARQUARD vs. O'BRIEN, Bedient (9). Attendance--36,624.

4th Game, at New York, Oct. 11

Boston (AL)	010	100	001	---	3	8	1
New York (NL)	000	000	100	---	1	9	1

Pitchers--WOOD vs. TESREAU, Ames (8). Attendance--36,502.

5th Game, at Boston, Oct. 12

New York (NL)	000	000	100	---	1	3	1
Boston (AL)	002	000	00x	---	2	5	1

Pitchers--MATHEWSON vs. BEDIENT. Att.--34,683.

6th Game, at New York, Oct. 14

Boston (AL)	020	000	000	---	2	7	2
New York (NL)	500	000	00x	---	5	11	2

Pitchers--O'BRIEN, Collins (2) vs. MARQUARD. Attendance--30,622.

7th Game, at Boston, Oct. 15

New York (NL)	610	002	101	---	11	16	4
Boston (AL)	010	000	210	---	4	9	3

Pitchers--TESREAU vs. WOOD, Hall (2). Homers--Doyle (N. Y.), Gardner (Bos.). Attendance--32,694.

8th Game, at Boston, Oct. 16

New York (NL)	001	000	000	1	---	2	9	2
Boston (AL)	000	000	100	2	---	3	8	5

Pitchers--MATHEWSON vs. Bedient, WOOD (8). Attendance--17,034.

1913

A series of injuries ruined Giant chances. Their only victory was a 10-inning shutout by Mathewson. The A's really romped, with another home run for Baker, who hit .450, plus a .421 average for Eddie Collins. Chief Bender won two; Eddie Plank pitched a two-hitter to top his rival of college days, Matty, and 20-year-old Bullet Joe Bush won his only start handily.

Result: Philadelphia AL won 4; New York NL, 1.

1st Game, at New York, Oct. 7

					R.	H.	E.
Philadelphia(AL)	000	320	010	---	6	11	1
New York (NL)	001	030	000	---	4	11	0

Pitchers--BENDER vs. MARQUARD, Crandall (6), Tesreau (8). Homer--Baker (Phil.). Attend.--36,291.

2nd Game, at Philadelphia, Oct. 8

New York (NL)	000	000	000	3	---	3	7	2
Philadelphia(AL)	000	000	000	0	---	0	8	2

Pitchers--MATHEWSON vs. PLANK. Attend.--20,563.

3rd Game, at New York, Oct. 9

Philadelphia(AL)	320	000	210	---	8	12	1
New York (NL)	000	010	100	---	2	5	1

Pitchers--BUSH vs. TESREAU, Crandall (7). Homer--Schang (Phil.). Attendance--36,896.

4th Game, at Philadelphia, Oct. 10

New York (NL)	000	000	320	---	5	8	2
Philadelphia(AL)	010	320	00x	---	6	9	0

Pitchers--MARQUARD vs. BENDER. Homer--Merkle (N. Y.). Attendance--20,568.

5th Game, at New York, Oct. 11

Philadelphia(AL)	102	000	000	---	3	6	1
New York (NL)	000	010	000	---	1	2	2

Pitchers--PLANK vs. MATHEWSON. Attend.--36,682.

1914

Rising from the cellar in mid-July to the pennant in September, the Boston Braves "Miracle Team" kept their magic touch through the Fall classic. They swept the vaunted A's, $100,000 infield and all. Connie Mack was so shocked that he broke up his star-studded squad the next season. Boston's dependable mound trio of Dick Rudolph, Bill James and George Tyler held the A's to a collective BA of .172. Hank Gowdy went on a .545 hitting rampage for Boston with five walks, a single, three doubles, a triple and homer.

Result: Boston NL won 4; Philadelphia AL, 0.

1st Game, at Philadelphia, Oct. 9

					R.	H.	E.
Boston (NL)	020	013	010	---	7	11	2
Philadelphia(AL)	010	000	000	---	1	5	0

Pitchers--RUDOLPH vs. BENDER, Wyckoff (6). Attendance--20,562.

2nd Game, at Philadelphia, Oct. 10

Boston (NL)	000	000	001	---	1	7	1
Philadelphia(AL)	000	000	000	---	0	2	1

Pitchers--JAMES vs. PLANK. Attendance--20,562.

3rd Game, at Boston, Oct. 12

Philadelphia(AL)	100	100	000	200	---	4	8	2
Boston (NL)	010	100	000	201	---	5	9	1

Pitchers--BUSH vs. Tyler, JAMES (11). Homer--Gowdy (Bos.). Attendance--35,520.

4th Game, at Boston, Oct. 13

Philadelphia(AL)	000	010	000	---	1	7	0
Boston (NL)	000	120	.00x	---	3	6	0

Pitchers--SHAWKEY, Pennock (6) vs. RUDOLPH. Attend.--34,365.

1915

Grover Alexander's 31 victories earned the Phils their first pennant. Alex proceeded to shade Ernie Shore of the Red Sox in the series opener. But Boston bounced back to win the next four, each by one run. Woodrow Wilson, first U. S. President to attend a World Series, threw out the first ball in the second game. A rookie named George Herman Ruth had led the AL with a won-lost of 18-6, but manager Bill Carrigan wouldn't risk him in series competition beyond one unsuccessful pinch-hitting appearance.

Result: Boston AL won 4; Philadelphia NL, 1.

1st Game, at Philadelphia, Oct. 8					R.	H.	E.
Boston (AL)	000	000	010	---	1	8	1
Philadelphia(NL)	000	100	02x	---	3	5	1

Pitchers--SHORE vs. ALEXANDER. Attend.--19,343.

2nd Game at Philadelphia, Oct. 9							
Boston (AL)	100	000	001	---	2	10	0
Philadelphia(NL)	000	010	000	---	1	3	1

Pitchers--FOSTER vs. MAYER. Attendance--20,306.

3rd Game, at Boston, Oct. 11							
Philadelphia(NL)	001	000	000	---	1	3	0
Boston (AL)	000	100	001	---	2	6	1

Pitchers--ALEXANDER vs. LEONARD. Att.--42,300.

4th Game, at Boston, Oct. 12							
Philadelphia(NL)	000	000	010	---	1	7	0
Boston (AL)	001	001	00x	---	2	8	1

Pitchers--CHALMERS vs. SHORE. Attendance--41,096.

5th Game, at Philadelphia, Oct. 13							
Boston (AL)	011	000	021	---	5	10	1
Philadelphia(NL)	200	200	000	---	4	9	1

Pitchers--FOSTER vs. Mayer, RIXEY (3). Homers--Hooper (Bos.) 2, Lewis (Bos.), Luderus (Phil.). At.--20,306.

1916

Brooklyn's plan to beat the Red Sox with southpaws failed. The only Dodger victory was notched by Jack Coombs, the old AL castoff, who thereby won his fifth series game while never being beaten. Duffy Lewis led the Boston batters and Casey Stengel was Brooklyn's hardest hitter. The second game turned out to be the longest in series history, 14 innings, with Babe Ruth blanking the Brooks after a first-inning homer by Hi Myers. Babe drove in the tying run two innings later. Boston won in the 14th when pinch-runner Mike McNally scored from first on a pinch double by Del Gainer.

Result: Boston AL won 4; Brooklyn NL, 1.

1st Game, at Boston, Oct. 7					R.	H.	E.
Brooklyn (NL)	000	100	004	---	5	10	4
Boston (AL)	001	010	31x	---	6	8	1

Pitchers--MARQUARD, Pfeffer (8) vs. SHORE, Mays (9). Attendance--36,117.

2nd Game, at Boston, Oct. 9									
Brooklyn (NL)	100	000	000	000	00	--	1	6	2
Boston (AL)	001	000	000	000	01	--	2	7	1

Pitchers--SMITH vs. RUTH. Homer--H. Myers (Bklyn.). Attendance--41,373.

3rd Game, at Brooklyn, Oct. 10							
Boston (AL)	000	002	100	---	3	7	1
Brooklyn (NL)	001	120	00x	---	4	10	0

Pitchers--MAYS, Foster (6) vs. COOMBS, Pfeffer (7). Homer--Gardner (Bos.). Attendance--21,087.

4th Game, at Brooklyn, Oct. 11							
Boston (AL)	030	110	100	---	6	10	1
Brooklyn (NL)	200	000	000	---	2	5	4

Pitchers--LEONARD vs. MARQUARD, Cheney (5), Rucker (8). Homer--Gardner (Bos.). Attendance--21,662.

5th Game, at Boston, Oct. 12							
Brooklyn (NL)	010	000	000	---	1	3	3
Boston (AL)	012	010	00x	---	4	7	2

Pitchers--PFEFFER, Dell (8) vs. SHORE. Attendance--42,620.

1917

This was a series of heroes and goats. Sometimes the same man was cheered and jeered. Urban Faber tried to steal second base with the bag already occupied, yet more than compensated for the boner by beating the Giants three times. Dave Robertson made a costly muff in the last game, yet the Giant right fielder led both teams with 11 for 22, or an even .500 batting average. Ferdie Schupp, knocked out of the box by the White Sox in less than two innings of the second game, came back to hurl a shutout in the fourth. Third baseman Heinie Zimmerman of the Giants was unjustly ridiculed for chasing Eddie Collins home with the deciding run of the last game, but the real goats were the catcher and first baseman, who had left the plate uncovered in the rundown play. Collins led the victorious Sox with a BA of .409.

Result: Chicago AL won 4; New York NL, 2.

1st Game, at Chicago, Oct. 6					R.	H.	E.
New York (NL)	000	010	000	---	1	7	1
Chicago (AL)	001	100	00x	---	2	7	1

Pitchers -- SALLEE vs. CICOTTE. Homer -- Felsch (Chi.). Attendance--32,000.

2nd Game, at Chicago, Oct. 7							
New York (NL)	020	000	000	---	2	8	1
Chicago (AL)	020	500	00x	---	7	14	1

Pitchers--Schupp, ANDERSON (2), Perritt (4), Tesreau (8) vs. FABER. Attendance--32,000.

3rd Game, at New York, Oct. 10							
Chicago (AL)	000	000	000	---	0	5	3
New York (NL)	000	200	00x	---	2	8	2

Pitchers--CICOTTE vs. BENTON. Attendance--33,616.

4th Game, at New York, Oct. 11							
Chicago (AL)	000	000	000	---	0	7	0
New York (NL)	000	110	12x	---	5	10	1

Pitchers--FABER, Danforth (8) vs. SCHUPP. Homers--Kauff (N.Y.) 2. Attendance--27,746.

5th Game, at Chicago, Oct. 13							
New York (NL)	200	200	100	---	5	12	3
Chicago (AL)	001	001	33x	---	8	14	6

Pitchers--SALLEE, Perritt (8) vs. Russell, Cicotte (1), Williams (7), FABER (8). Attendance--27,323.

6th Game, at New York, Oct. 15							
Chicago (AL)	000	300	001	---	4	7	1
New York (NL)	000	020	000	---	2	6	3

Pitchers--FABER vs. BENTON, Perritt (6). Attendance--33,969.

1918

In this war-curtailed season, the World Series continued only through special permission from the government. Many topnotch stars were in the Service. George Whiteman, a wartime replacement, helped the Red Sox beat Chicago with five timely hits and several crucial catches. Babe Ruth and Carl Mays each won twice, with Babe extending his streak to an all-time record that still stands—29 consecutive scoreless innings. Ruth was held to only one hit in the series, but it was a triple that drove in two runs of a 3-2 decision in the fourth game. The start of the fifth game was delayed an hour by an unsuccessful player "strike" for a higher share of the receipts.

Result: Boston AL won 4; Chicago NL, 2.

1st Game, at Chicago, Sept. 5					R.	H.	E.
Boston (AL)	000	100	000	---	1	5	0
Chicago (NL)	000	000	000	---	0	6	0

Pitchers--RUTH vs. VAUGHN. Attendance--19,274.

2nd Game, at Chicago, Sept. 6							
Boston (AL)	000	000	001	---	1	6	1
Chicago (NL)	030	000	00x	---	3	7	1

Pitchers--BUSH vs. TYLER. Attendance--20,040.

3rd Game, at Chicago, Sept. 7							
Boston (AL)	000	200	000	---	2	7	0
Chicago (NL)	000	010	000	---	1	7	1

Pitchers--MAYS vs. VAUGHN. Attendance--27,054.

4th Game, at Boston, Sept. 9							
Chicago (NL)	000	000	020	---	2	7	1
Boston (AL)	000	200	01x	---	3	4	0

Pitchers--Tyler, DOUGLASS (8) vs. RUTH, Bush (9). Attendance--22,183.

5th Game, at Boston, Sept. 10							
Chicago (NL)	001	000	002	---	3	7	0
Boston (AL)	000	000	000	---	0	5	0

Pitchers--VAUGHN vs. JONES. Attendance--24,694.

6th Game, at Boston, Sept. 11							
Chicago (NL)	000	100	000	---	1	3	2
Boston (AL)	002	000	00x	---	2	5	0

Pitchers--TYLER, Hendrix (8) vs. MAYS. Attendance--15,238.

1919

Post-war interest in baseball was so high that the series was stretched to best-five-out-of-nine. Chicago's White Sox and the Cincinnati Reds had outclassed their league rivals completely. What should have been a memorable struggle between champions turned out to be one of the most shameful events in sports history, because eight players of the favored Sox "sold out" to gamblers. Ed Cicotte, one of the notorious "Black Sox" later dropped by organized baseball, was knocked out of the box in the opening game. Little Dickie Kerr bravely tried to hold off the Reds and won twice. But Chicago was ruined by the conspirators and lost in eight games. Strangely, Shoeless Joe Jackson led his team with a .375 average even though he was in on the shady deal. Earle (Greasy) Neale, later a famous football coach, led the Reds with .357.

Result: Cincinnati NL won 5; Chicago AL, 3.

1st Game, at Cincinnati, Oct. 1					R.	H.	E.
Chicago (AL)	010	000	000	---	1	6	1
Cincinnati (NL)	100	500	21x	---	9	14	1

Pitchers--CICOTTE, Wilkinson (4), Lowdermilk (8) vs. RUETHER. Attendance--30,511.

2nd Game, at Cincinnati, Oct. 2							
Chicago (AL)	000	000	200	---	2	10	1
Cincinnati (NL)	000	301	00x	---	4	4	2

Pitchers--WILLIAMS vs. SALLEE. Attend.--29,690.

3rd Game, at Chicago, Oct. 3							
Cincinnati (NL)	000	000	000	---	0	3	1
Chicago (AL)	020	100	00x	---	3	7	0

Pitchers--FISHER, Luque (8) vs. KERR. Att.--29,126.

4th Game, at Chicago, Oct. 4							
Cincinnati (NL)	000	020	000	---	2	5	2
Chicago (AL)	000	000	000	---	0	3	2

Pitchers--RING vs. CICOTTE. Attendance--34,363.

5th Game, at Chicago, Oct. 6							
Cincinnati (NL)	000	004	001	---	5	4	0
Chicago (AL)	000	000	000	---	0	3	3

Pitchers--ELLER vs. WILLIAMS, Mayer (9). Attendance--34,379.

6th Game, at Cincinnati, Oct. 7								
Chicago (AL)	000	013	000	1	---	5	10	3
Cincinnati (NL)	002	200	000	0	---	4	11	0

Pitchers--KERR vs. Ruether, RING (6). Att.--32,006.

7th Game, at Cincinnati, Oct. 8							
Chicago (AL)	101	020	000	---	4	10	1
Cincinnati (NL)	000	001	000	---	1	7	4

Pitchers--CICOTTE vs. SALLEE, Fisher (5), Luque (6). Attendance--13,923.

8th Game, at Chicago, Oct. 9							
Cincinnati (NL)	410	013	010	---	10	16	2
Chicago (AL)	001	000	040	---	5	10	1

Pitchers--ELLER vs. WILLIAMS, James (1), Wilkinson (6). Homer--Jackson (Chi.). Attendance--32,930.

1920

Player-manager Tris Speaker reached his greatest glory by leading the Indians to the world championship over the Dodgers. Cleveland's conquest was featured by that sturdy battery of former coal miners from Pennsylvania: spitball pitcher Stanley Coveleski, who pitched three complete-game victories and allowed exactly five hits each time, and catcher Steve O'Neill, who hit .333. Walter Mails, a Dodger castoff, hurled a three-hitter to shade Brooklyn's ace, Sherry Smith, 1-0. In the weird fifth game, Brooklyn outhit Cleveland, yet lost, 8-1; Elmer Smith hit a grand slam homer, and Indian second baseman Bill Wambsganns executed an unassisted triple play.

Result: Cleveland AL won 5; Brooklyn NL, 2.

1st Game, at Brooklyn, Oct. 5					R.	H.	E.
Cleveland (AL)	020	100	000	---	3	5	0
Brooklyn (NL)	000	000	100	---	1	5	1

Pitchers--COVELESKI vs. MARQUARD, Mamaux (7). Cadore (9). Attendance--23,573.

2nd Game, at Brooklyn, Oct. 6							
Cleveland (AL)	000	000	000	---	0	7	1
Brooklyn (NL)	101	010	00x	---	3	7	0

Pitchers--BAGBY, Uhle (7) vs. GRIMES. Att.--22,559.

3rd Game, at Brooklyn, Oct. 7							
Cleveland (AL)	000	100	000	---	1	3	1
Brooklyn (NL)	200	000	00x	---	2	6	1

Pitchers--CALDWELL, Mails (1), Uhle (8) vs. SMITH. Attendance--25,088.

4th Game, at Cleveland, Oct. 9							
Brooklyn (NL)	000	100	000	---	1	5	1
Cleveland (AL)	202	001	00x	---	5	12	2

Pitchers--CADORE, Mamaux (2), Marquard (3), Pfeffer (6) vs. COVELESKI. Attendance--25,734.

5th Game, at Cleveland, Oct. 10							
Brooklyn (NL)	000	000	001	---	1	13	1
Cleveland (AL)	400	310	00x	---	8	12	2

Pitchers--GRIMES, Mitchell (4) vs BAGBY. Homers--E. Smith (Clev.), Bagby (Clev.). Attendance--26,884.

6th Game, at Cleveland, Oct. 11							
Brooklyn (NL)	000	000	000	---	0	3	0
Cleveland (AL)	000	001	00x	---	1	7	3

Pitchers--SMITH vs. MAILS. Attendance--27,194.

7th Game, at Cleveland, Oct. 12							
Brooklyn (NL)	000	000	000	---	0	5	2
Cleveland (AL)	000	110	10x	---	3	7	3

Pitchers--GRIMES, Mamaux (8) vs. COVELESKI. Attendance--27,525.

1921

The Yankees, later to dominate the World Series scene, won their first league title but failed to beat the Giants in an all-New York series. Successive shutouts by Carl Mays and Waite Hoyt gave the Yankees a two-game edge. Then the Giants found their batting eye and evened up the series. Hoyt won the fifth game, too, but Babe Ruth wrenched his knee and was lost to the Yanks. The Giants rallied to capture the next three games and the title. Hoyt, who hurled 27 innings in this series without an earned run, lost a 1-0 duel with Art Nehf in the finale.

Result: New York NL won 5; New York AL, 3.

1st Game, at Polo Grounds, N. Y., Oct. 5					R.	H.	E.
New York (AL)	100	011	000	---	3	7	0
New York (NL)	000	000	000	---	0	5	0

Pitchers--MAYS vs. DOUGLAS, Barnes (9). Attendance--30,202.

2nd Game, at Polo Grounds, N. Y., Oct. 6							
New York (NL)	000	000	000	---	0	2	3
New York (AL)	000	100	02x	---	3	3	0

Pitchers--NEHF vs. HOYT. Attendance--34,939.

3rd Game, at Polo Grounds, N. Y., Oct. 7							
New York (AL)	004	000	010	---	5	8	0
New York (NL)	004	000	81x	---	13	20	0

Pitchers--Shawkey, QUINN (3), Collins (7), Rogers (8) vs. Toney, BARNES (3). Attendance--36,509.

4th Game, at Polo Grounds, N. Y., Oct. 9							
New York (NL)	000	000	031	---	4	9	1
New York (AL)	000	010	001	---	2	7	1

Pitchers--DOUGLAS vs. MAYS. Homer--Ruth (AL). Attendance--36,372.

5th Game, at Polo Grounds, N. Y., Oct. 10							
New York (AL)	001	200	000	---	3	6	1
New York (NL)	100	000	000	---	1	10	1

Pitchers--HOYT vs. NEHF. Attendance--35,758.

6th Game, at Polo Grounds, N. Y., Oct. 11							
New York (NL)	030	401	000	---	8	13	0
New York (AL)	320	000	000	---	5	7	2

Pitchers--Toney, BARNES (1) vs. Harper, SHAWKEY (2), Piercy (9). Homers--E. Meusel (NL), Snyder (NL), Fewster (AL). Attendance--34,283.

7th Game, at Polo Grounds, N. Y., Oct. 12							
New York (AL)	010	000	000	---	1	8	1
New York (NL)	000	100	10x	---	2	6	0

Pitchers--MAYS vs. DOUGLAS. Attendance--36,503.

8th Game, at Polo Grounds, N. Y., Oct. 13							
New York (NL)	100	000	000	---	1	6	0
New York (AL)	000	000	000	---	0	4	1

Pitchers--NEHF vs. HOYT. Attendance--25,410.

1922

Giant pitchers held the Yankees to a .203 batting average, Babe Ruth himself being shackled at .118. Poor baserunning further hampered the Yanks, and the best they could do was tie one game. The second match was called at 3-3 after 10 innings because of "darkness." Since there was still half an hour of daylight left, fans booed the game's untimely ending so heavily that Commissioner Landis ordered the gate receipts that day, about $120,000, turned over to charity. Heavy Giant hitting was paced by Heinie Groh's .474 and Frankie Frisch's .471.

Result: New York NL won 4; New York AL, 0; 1 tie.

1st Game, at Polo Grounds, N. Y., Oct. 4					R.	H.	E.
New York (AL)	000	001	100	---	2	7	0
New York (NL)	000	000	03x	---	3	11	3

Pitchers--BUSH, Hoyt (8) vs. Nehf, RYAN (8). Attendance--36,514.

2nd Game, at Polo Grounds, N. Y., Oct. 5								
New York (NL)	300	000	000	0	---	3	8	1
New York (AL)	100	100	010	0	---	3	8	0

(called, end of 10th: darkness)

Pitchers--Barnes vs. Shawkey. Homers--E. Meusel (NL), Ward (AL). Attendance--37,020.

3rd Game, at Polo Grounds, N. Y., Oct. 6							
New York (AL)	000	000	000	---	0	4	1
New York (NL)	002	000	10x	---	3	12	1

Pitchers--HOYT, Jones (8) vs. J. SCOTT. Att.--37,620.

4th Game, at Polo Grounds, N. Y., Oct. 7

New York (NL)	000	040	000	---	4	9	1
New York (AL)	200	000	100	---	3	8	0

Pitchers--McQUILLAN vs. MAYS, Jones (9). Homer--Ward (AL). Attendance--36,242.

5th Game, at Polo Grounds, N. Y., Oct. 8

New York (AL)	100	010	100	---	3	5	0
New York (NL)	020	000	03x	---	5	10	0

Pitchers--BUSH vs. NEHF. Attendance--38,551.

1923

The same rivals met for the third straight Fall, but this time there was a new setting and a different result. The Yankees now had their own Stadium and proceeded to bring it their first world championship banner. Outfielder Casey Stengel of the Giants, destined for fame as manager of Yankee champions more than a quarter century later, accounted for the only two NL victories with timely homers. Herb Pennock pitched two complete game victories and saved another for the Yanks in relief. Babe Ruth featured this first million-dollar Series with three homers, a triple, a double, three singles and eight walks.

Result: New York AL won 4; New York NL, 2.

1st Game, at Yankee Stadium, N. Y., Oct. 10

					R.	H.	E.
New York (NL)	004	000	001	---	5	8	0
New York (AL)	120	000	100	---	4	12	1

Pitchers--Watson, RYAN (3) vs. Hoyt, BUSH (3). Homer--Stengel (NL). Attendance--55,307.

2nd Game, at Polo Grounds, N. Y., Oct. 11

New York (AL)	010	210	000	---	4	10	0
New York (NL)	010	001	000	---	2	9	2

Pitchers -- PENNOCK vs. McQUILLAN, Bentley (4). Homers--Ward (AL), E. Meusel (NL), Ruth (AL) 2. Attendance--40,402.

3rd Game, at Yankee Stadium, N. Y., Oct. 12

New York (NL)	000	000	100	---	1	4	0
New York (AL)	000	000	000	---	0	6	1

Pitchers--NEHF vs. JONES, Bush (8). Homer--Stengel (NL). Attendance--62,430.

4th Game, at Polo Grounds, N. Y., Oct. 13

New York (AL)	061	100	000	---	8	13	1
New York (NL)	000	000	031	---	4	13	1

Pitchers--SHAWKEY, Pennock (8) vs. J. SCOTT, Ryan (2), McQuillan (3), Jonnard (8), Barnes (9). Homer--Youngs (NL). Attendance--46,302.

5th Game, at Yankee Stadium, N. Y., Oct. 14

New York (NL)	010	000	000	---	1	3	2
New York (AL)	340	100	00x	---	8	14	0

Pitchers--BENTLEY, J. Scott (2), Barnes (4), Jonnard (8) vs. BUSH. Homer--Dugan (AL). Attendance--62,817.

6th Game, at Polo Grounds, N. Y., Oct. 15

New York (AL)	100	000	050	---	6	5	0
New York (NL)	100	111	000	---	4	10	1

Pitchers--PENNOCK, Jones (8) vs. NEHF, Ryan (8). Homers--Ruth (AL), Snyder (NL). Attendance--34,172.

1924

Second baseman Bucky Harris was only 27, and in his first year as manager, when he brought Washington its first flag. In the Series he conquered John McGraw's last pennant club by the barest margin. The opener went to the Giants, 4-3, with old Walter Johnson bowing to Art Nehf in 12 innings. The seventh and deciding game also was a 12-inning, 4-3 affair, but this time Johnson, appearing in his first World Series after 18 seasons with the Senators, was the winner. The last game saw the Giants suffer three bad breaks: in the eighth, Harris' grounder took a sudden hop over the head of the substitute third baseman Fred Lindstrom, allowing the two tying runs to score; in the 12th, Giant catcher Hank Gowdy dropped a foul fly when he accidentally stepped on his mask, and on the last play of the series Earl McNeely's grounder took a sharp bounce over Lindstrom's head to send in the winning run.

Result: Washington AL won 4; New York NL, 3.

1st Game, at Washington, Oct. 4

						R.	H.	E.
New York (NL)	010	100	000	002	---	4	14	1
Washington (AL)	000	001	001	001	---	3	10	1

Pitchers--NEHF vs. JOHNSON. Homers--Kelly (N.Y.), Terry (N.Y.). Attendance--35,760.

2nd Game, at Washington, Oct. 5

New York (NL)	000	000	102	---	3	6	0
Washington (AL)	200	010	001	---	4	6	1

Pitchers--BENTLEY vs. ZACHARY, Marberry (9). Homers--Goslin (Wash.), Harris (Wash.). Attend.--35,922.

3rd Game, at New York, Oct. 6

Washington (AL)	000	200	011	---	4	9	2
New York (NL)	021	101	01x	---	6	12	0

Pitchers--MARBERRY, Russell (4), Martina (7), Speece (8) vs. McQUILLAN, Ryan (4), Jonnard (9), Watson (9). Homer--Ryan (N.Y.). Attendance--47,608.

4th Game, at New York, Oct. 7

Washington (AL)	003	020	020	---	7	13	3
New York (NL)	100	001	011	---	4	6	1

Pitchers--MOGRIDGE, Marberry (8) vs. BARNES, Baldwin (6), Dean (8). Homer--Goslin (Wash.). Att.--49,243.

5th Game, at New York, Oct. 8

Washington (AL)	000	100	010	---	2	9	1
New York (NL)	001	020	03x	---	6	13	0

Pitchers--JOHNSON vs. BENTLEY, McQuillan (8). Homers--Bentley (N.Y.), Goslin (Wash.). Attend.--49,211.

6th Game, at Washington, Oct. 9

New York (NL)	100	000	000	---	1	7	1
Washington (AL)	000	020	00x	---	2	4	0

Pitchers--NEHF, Ryan (8) vs. ZACHARY. Attendance--34,254.

7th Game, at Washington, Oct. 10

New York (NL)	000	003	000	000	---	3	8	3
Washington (AL)	000	100	020	001	---	4	10	4

Pitchers--Barnes, McQuillan (8), Nehf (10), BENTLEY (11) vs. Ogden, Mogridge (1), Marberry (6), JOHNSON (9). Homer--Harris (Wash.). Attendance--31,667.

1925

On the verge of extinction several times, Pittsburgh rallied to upset Washington in seven games. Walter Johnson won the opener. His shutout in the fourth gave the Senators a 3-1 edge. But Pittsburgh swept the next three, with Johnson the subject of a sad form reversal in the finale. The gallant righthander couldn't put his usual stuff on the wet ball, this final rainy afternoon, so that the seven Senator runs were not enough. Kiki Cuyler doubled off him with bases loaded in the eighth to drive in the tying and winning runs. Roger Peckinpaugh was the Washington "goat" with eight errors.

Result: Pittsburgh NL won 4; Washington AL, 3.

1st Game, at Pittsburgh, Oct. 7					R.	H.	E.
Washington (AL)	010	020	001	---	4	8	1
Pittsburgh (NL)	000	010	000	---	1	5	0

Pitchers--JOHNSON vs. MEADOWS, Morrison (9). Homers--J. Harris (Wash.), Traynor (Pitt.). Att.--41,723.

2nd Game, at Pittsburgh, Oct. 8					R.	H.	E.
Washington (AL)	010	000	001	---	2	8	2
Pittsburgh (NL)	000	100	02x	---	3	7	0

Pitchers -- COVELESKIE vs. ALDRIDGE. Homers -- Judge (Wash.), Wright (Pitt.), Cuyler (Pitt.). Att.--43,364.

3rd Game, at Washington, Oct. 10					R.	H.	E.
Pittsburgh (NL)	010	101	000	---	3	8	3
Washington (AL)	001	001	20x	---	4	10	1

Pitchers -- KREMER vs. FERGUSON, Marberry (8). Homer--Goslin (Wash.). Attendance--36,495.

4th Game, at Washington, Oct. 11					R.	H.	E.
Pittsburgh (NL)	000	000	000	---	0	6	1
Washington (AL)	004	000	00x	---	4	12	0

Pitchers--YDE, Morrison (3) Adams (8) vs. JOHNSON. Homers--Goslin (Wash.), J. Harris (Wash.). Att.--38,701.

5th Game, at Washington, Oct. 12					R.	H.	E.
Pittsburgh (NL)	002	000	211	---	6	13	0
Washington (AL)	100	100	100	---	3	8	1

Pitchers--ALDRIDGE vs. COVELESKIE, Ballou (7), Zachary (8), Marberry (9). Homer--J. Harris (Wash.). Attendance--35,899.

6th Game, at Pittsburgh, Oct. 13					R.	H.	E.
Washington (AL)	110	000	000	---	2	6	2
Pittsburgh (NL)	002	010	00x	---	3	7	1

Pitchers--FERGUSON, Ballou (8) vs. KREMER. Homers--Goslin (Wash.), Moore (Pitt.). Attendance--43,810.

7th Game, at Pittsburgh, Oct. 15					R.	H.	E.
Washington (AL)	400	200	010	---	7	7	2
Pittsburgh (NL)	003	010	23x	---	9	15	2

Pitchers--JOHNSON vs. Aldridge, Morrison (1) KREMER (5), Oldham (9). Homer--Peckinpaugh (Wash.). Attendance--42,856.

1926

Led by Rogers Hornsby, St. Louis won its first NL pennant and upset the Yankees in the Series. Babe Ruth blasted four homers, three of them in one game, but 39-year-old Grover Alexander emerged as the legendary hero of this battle. Alex won the second and sixth games, then ambled out of the bullpen in the seventh inning of the seventh game to strike out Tony Lazzeri with bases loaded. He added two more hitless innings to seal the triumph.

Result: St. Louis NL won 4; New York AL, 3.

1st Game, at New York, Oct. 2					R.	H.	E.
St. Louis (NL)	100	000	000	---	1	3	1
New York (AL)	100	001	00x	---	2	6	0

Pitchers--SHERDEL, Haines (8) vs. PENNOCK. Attendance--61,658.

2nd Game, at New York, Oct. 3					R.	H.	E.
St. Louis (NL)	002	000	301	---	6	12	1
New York (AL)	020	000	000	---	2	4	0

Pitchers--ALEXANDER vs. SHOCKER, Shawkey (8), Jones (9). Homers--Southworth (St. L.), Thevenow (St. L.). Attendance--63,600.

3rd Game, at St. Louis, Oct. 5					R.	H.	E.
New York (AL)	000	000	000	---	0	5	1
St. Louis (NL)	000	310	00x	---	4	8	0

Pitchers--RUETHER, Shawkey (5), Thomas (8) vs. HAINES. Homer--Haines (St. L.). Attendance--37,708.

4th Game, at St. Louis, Oct. 6					R.	H.	E.
New York (AL)	101	142	100	---	10	14	1
St. Louis (NL)	100	300	001	---	5	14	0

Pitchers--HOYT vs. Rhem, REINHART (5), H. Bell (5), Hallahan (7), Keen (9). Homers--Ruth (N.Y.) 3. Attendance--38,825.

5th Game, at St. Louis, Oct. 7						R.	H.	E.
New York (AL)	000	001	001	1	---	3	9	1
St. Louis (NL)	000	100	100	0	---	2	7	1

Pitchers--PENNOCK vs. SHERDEL. Att.--39,552.

6th Game, at New York, Oct. 9					R.	H.	E.
St. Louis (NL)	300	010	501	---	10	13	2
New York (AL)	000	100	100	---	2	8	1

Pitchers--ALEXANDER vs. SHAWKEY, Shocker (7), Thomas (8). Homer--L. Bell (St. L.). Attend.--48,615.

7th Game, at New York, Oct. 10					R.	H.	E.
St. Louis (NL)	000	300	000	---	3	8	0
New York (AL)	001	001	000	---	2	8	3

Pitchers--HAINES, Alexander (7) vs. HOYT, Pennock (7). Homer--Ruth (N.Y.). Attendance--38,093.

1927

Regarded by many experts as the greatest team of all time, the 1927 Yankees set a league record with 110 victories and went on to sink the Pirates in four straight. Ruth added two Series homers to his season's bag of 60. Relief specialist Cy Moore started the last game for the Yanks and won when John Miljus wild-pitched home the winning run with two out in the ninth. Though he had hit .309 in the regular season, Kiki Cuyler, hero of the 1925 series, was kept on the Pirate bench throughout these four games because of a grudge held by manager Donie Bush.

Result: New York AL won 4; Pittsburgh NL, 0.

1st Game, at Pittsburgh, Oct 5					R.	H.	E.
New York (AL)	103	010	000	---	5	6	1
Pittsburgh (NL)	101	010	010	---	4	9	2

Pitchers--HOYT, Moore (8) vs. KREMER, Miljus (6). Attendance--41,567.

2nd Game, at Pittsburgh, Oct. 6					R.	H.	E.
New York (AL)	003	000	030	---	6	11	0
Pittsburgh (NL)	100	000	010	---	2	7	2

Pitchers--PIPGRAS vs. ALDRIDGE, Cvengros (8), Dawson (9). Attendance--41,634.

3rd Game, at New York, Oct. 7					R.	H.	E.
Pittsburgh (NL)	000	000	010	---	1	3	1
New York (AL)	200	000	60x	---	8	9	0

Pitchers -- MEADOWS, Cvengros (7) vs. PENNOCK. Homer--Ruth (N.Y.). Attendance--60,695.

4th Game, at New York, Oct. 8					R.	H.	E.
Pittsburgh (NL)	100	000	200	---	3	10	1
New York (AL)	100	020	001	---	4	12	2

Pitchers--Hill, MILJUS (7) vs. MOORE. Homer--Ruth (N.Y.). Attendance--57,909.

1928

Though riddled by injuries to four regulars, the Yankees revenged their 1926 upset by mowing down the Cardinals in four straight. Ruth, lame ankle and all, murdered St. Louis pitching for a .625 average, highest in series history. He topped off the fourth game with three homers. Waite Hoyt won the first and last games. Lou Gehrig, middle man in the Yankee "Murderers' Row", had six passes and six hits for the four games, including four homers.

Result: New York AL won 4; St. Louis NL, 0.

1st Game, at New York, Oct. 4					R.	H.	E.
St. Louis (NL)	000	000	100	---	1	3	1
New York (AL)	100	200	01x	---	4	7	0

Pitchers--SHERDEL, Johnson (8) vs. HOYT. Homers--Meusel (N.Y.), Bottomley (St. L.). Attendance--61,425.

2nd Game, at New York, Oct. 5					R.	H.	E.
St. Louis (NL)	030	000	000	---	3	4	1
New york (AL)	314	000	10x	---	9	8	2

Pitchers--ALEXANDER, Mitchell (3) vs. PIPGRAS. Homer--Gehrig (N.Y.). Attendance--60,714.

3rd Game, at St. Louis, Oct. 7					R.	H.	E.
New York (AL)	010	203	100	---	7	7	2
St. Louis (NL)	200	010	000	---	3	9	3

Pitchers--ZACHARY vs. HAINES, Johnson (7), Rhem (8). Homers--Gehrig (N.Y.) 2. Attendance--39,602.

4th Game, at St. Louis, Oct. 9					R.	H.	E.
New York (AL)	000	100	420	---	7	15	2
St. Louis (NL)	001	100	001	---	3	11	0

Pitchers--HOYT vs. SHERDEL, Alexander (7). Homers--Ruth (NY.) 3, Durst (N.Y.), Gehrig (N.Y.). Att.--37,331.

1929

The A's trounced the Cubs by unleashing two of the greatest surprises in World Series history. Connie Mack's pitching choice in the opener was aged Howard Ehmke, who had worked only 55 innings in the regular season. The sidearmer struck out 13, a new Series record, to trim Cub ace Charlie Root. The next thunderbolt came in the seventh inning of the fourth game. With Chicago leading, 8-0, Philadelphia suddenly tore into four pitchers with a record 10-run rally. The ill-starred Cubs had a 2-0 lead in the last inning of the fifth game, with one out and bases empty, when the A's exploded for three runs that wound up the Series.

Result: Philadelphia AL won 4; Chicago NL, 1.

1st Game, at Chicago, Oct. 8					R.	H.	E.
Philadelphia(AL)	000	000	102	---	3	6	1
Chicago (NL)	000	000	001	---	1	8	2

Pitchers--EHMKE vs. ROOT, Bush (8). Homer--Foxx (Phil.). Attendance--50,740.

2nd Game, at Chicago, Oct. 9					R.	H.	E.
Philadelphia(AL)	003	300	120	---	9	12	0
Chicago (NL)	000	030	000	---	3	11	1

Pitchers--EARNSHAW, Grove (5) vs. MALONE, Blake (4), Carlson (6), Nehf (9). Homers--Simmons (Phil.), Foxx (Phil.). Attendance--49,987.

3rd Game, at Philadelphia, Oct. 11					R.	H.	E.
Chicago (NL)	000	003	000	---	3	6	1
Philadelphia(AL)	000	010	000	---	1	9	1

Pitchers--BUSH vs. EARNSHAW. Attendance--29,991.

4th Game, at Philadelphia, Oct. 12					R.	H.	E.
Chicago (NL)	000	205	100	---	8	10	2
Philadelphia(AL)	000	000	(10)0x	---	10	15	2

Pitchers--Root, Nehf (7), BLAKE (7), Malone (7), Carlson (8) vs. Quinn, Walberg (6), ROMMEL (7), Grove (8). Homers--Grimm (Chi.), Haas (Phil.), Simmons (Phil.). Attandance--29,991.

5th Game, at Philadelphia, Oct. 14					R.	H.	E.
Chicago (NL)	002	000	000	---	2	8	1
Philadelphia(AL)	000	000	003	---	3	6	0

Pitchers--MALONE vs. Ehmke, WALBERG (4). Homer--Haas (Phil.). Attendance--29,991.

1930

Connie Mack piloted his fifth world championship team, his A's trumping the Cards in a well-pitched Series. Philadelphia won the first two at home and lost the next two in St. Louis. The fifth game was a scoreless tie until the ninth inning, when Jimmy Foxx cracked a two-run homer off Burleigh Grimes. George Earnshaw notched his second complete-game victory in the sixth game to end the struggle.

Result: Philadelphia AL won 4; St. Louis NL, 2.

1st Game, at Philadelphia, Oct. 1					R.	H.	E.
St. Louis (NL)	002	000	000	---	2	9	0
Philadelphia(AL)	010	101	11x	---	5	5	0

Pitchers -- GRIMES vs. GROVE. Homers -- Cochrane (Phil.), Simmons (Phil.). Attendance--32,295.

2nd Game, at Philadelphia, Oct. 2							
St. Louis (NL)	010	000	000	---	1	6	2
Philadelphia(AL)	202	200	00x	---	6	7	2

Pitchers--RHEM, Lindsey (4), Johnson (7) vs. EARNSHAW. Homers--Cochrane (Phil.), Watkins (St. L.). Attendance--32,295.

3rd Game, at St. Louis, Oct. 4							
Philadelphia(AL)	000	000	000	---	0	7	0
St. Louis (NL)	000	110	21x	---	5	10	0

Pitchers--WALBERG, Shores (5), Quinn (7) vs. HALLAHAN. Homer--Douthit (St. L.). Attendance--36,944.

4th Game, at St. Louis, Oct. 5							
Philadelphia(AL)	100	000	000	---	1	4	1
St. Louis (NL)	001	200	00x	---	3	5	1

Pitchers--GROVE vs. HAINES. Attendance--39,946.

5th Game, at St. Louis, Oct. 6							
Philadelphia(AL)	000	000	002	---	2	5	0
St. Louis (NL)	000	000	000	---	0	3	1

Pitchers--Earnshaw, GROVE (8) vs. GRIMES. Homer--Foxx (Phil.). Attendance--38,844.

6th Game, at Philadelphia, Oct. 8							
St. Louis (NL)	000	000	001	---	1	5	1
Philadelphia(AL)	201	211	00x	---	7	7	0

Pitchers--HALLAHAN, Johnson (3), Lindsey (6), Bell (8) vs. EARNSHAW. Homers -- Dykes (Phil.), Simmons (Phil.). Attendance--32,295.

1931

Pepper Martin, a brash rookie, ran wild for the Cardinals to thwart a star-studded A's team. Martin batted .500, with a homer, four doubles, seven singles, five runs scored and five runs batted in. Hardboiled Burleigh Grimes and lefthander Bill Hallahan each won a pair. Hallahan beat Earnshaw with a shutout in the second game, yielded only one run while beating Waite Hoyt in the fifth and came back in the seventh and last game to save Grimes' victory by stifling a ninth-inning rally.

Result: St. Louis NL won 4; Philadelphia AL, 3.

1st Game, at St. Louis, Oct. 1					R.	H.	E.
Philadelphia(AL)	004	000	200	---	6	11	0
St. Louis (NL)	200	000	000	---	2	12	0

Pitchers--GROVE vs. DERRINGER, Johnson (8). Homer--Simmons (Phil.). Attendance--38,529.

2nd Game, at St. Louis, Oct. 2							
Philadelphia(AL)	000	000	000	---	0	3	0
St. Louis (NL)	010	000	10x	---	2	6	1

Pitchers--EARNSHAW vs. HALLAHAN. Att.--35,947.

3rd Game, at Philadelphia, Oct. 5							
St. Louis (NL)	020	200	001	---	5	12	0
Philadelphia(AL)	000	000	002	---	2	2	0

Pitchers--GRIMES vs. GROVE, Mahaffey (9). Homer--Simmons (Phil.). Attendance--32,295.

4th Game, at Philadelphia, Oct. 6							
St. Louis (NL)	000	000	000	---	0	2	1
Philadelphia(AL)	100	002	00x	---	3	10	0

Pitchers--JOHNSON, Lindsey (6) vs. EARNSHAW. Homer--Foxx (Phil.). Attendance--32,295.

5th Game, at Philadelphia, Oct. 7							
St. Louis (NL)	100	002	011	---	5	12	0
Philadelphia(AL)	000	000	100	---	1	9	0

Pitchers--HALLAHAN vs. HOYT, Walberg (7), Rommel (9). Homers--Martin (St. L.), Watkins (St. L.). Attendance--32,295.

6th Game, at St. Louis, Oct. 9							
Philadelphia(AL)	000	040	400	---	8	8	1
St. Louis (NL)	000	001	000	---	1	5	2

Pitchers--GROVE vs. DERRINGER, Johnson (5), Lindsey (7), Rhem (9). Attendance--39,401.

7th Game, at St. Louis, Oct. 10							
Philadelphia(AL)	000	000	002	---	2	7	1
St. Louis (NL)	202	000	00x	---	4	5	0

Pitchers--EARNSHAW, Walberg (8) vs. GRIMES, Hallahan (9). Attendance--20,805.

1932

The old Yankee habit of winning in four straight victimized the Cubs this time. It was sweet revenge for Yank manager Joe McCarthy, who had been fired as Cub manager two years earlier. Playing in his last World Series, Ruth poled two homers, including his blast into the bleachers right after fabulously pointing there. Though less dramatic than Babe, Gehrig was even more effective with three homers, a double, five singles, two passes, nine runs scored and eight runs batted in.

Result: New York AL won 4; Chicago NL, 0.

1st Game, at New York, Sept. 28					R.	H.	E.
Chicago (NL)	200	000	220	---	6	10	1
New York (AL)	000	305	31x	---	12	8	2

Pitchers--BUSH, Grimes (6), Smith (8) vs. RUFFING. Homer--Gehrig (N.Y.). Attendance--41,459.

2nd Game, at New York, Sept. 29							
Chicago (NL)	101	000	000	---	2	9	0
New York (AL)	202	010	00x	---	5	10	1

Pitchers--WARNEKE vs. GOMEZ. Attendance--50,709.

3rd Game, at Chicago, Oct. 1							
New York (AL)	301	020	001	---	7	8	1
Chicago (NL)	102	100	001	---	5	9	4

Pitchers--PIPGRAS, Pennock (9) vs. ROOT, Malone (5), May (7), Tinning (9). Homers--Ruth (N.Y.) 2, Gehrig (N.Y.) 2, Cuyler (Chi.), Hartnett (Chi.). Attendance--49,986.

4th Game, at Chicago, Oct. 2							
New York (AL)	102	002	404	---	13	19	4
Chicago (NL)	400	001	001	---	6	9	1

Pitchers--Allen, MOORE (1), Pennock (7) vs. Bush, Warneke (1), MAY (4), Tinning (7), Grimes (9). Homers--Demaree (Chi.), Lazzeri (N.Y.) 2, Combs (N.Y.). Attendance--49,844.

1933

Player-manager Bill Terry's strategy, sterling Giant pitching and strong stickwork by Mel Ott repulsed the Senators in five games. Earl

Whitehill prevented a sweep by blanking the Giants in the third game. Carl Hubbell won twice, including an 11-inning struggle in the fourth game. The fifth game also went into extra innings. Ott homered in the 10th, and Dolph Luque stemmed a Senator surge in the last half to end the Series.

Result: New York NL won 4; Washington AL, 1.

1st Game, at New York, Oct. 3					R.	H.	E.
Washington (AL)	000	100	001	---	2	5	3
New York (NL)	202	000	00x	---	4	10	2

Pitchers--STEWART, Russell (3), Thomas (8) vs. HUBBELL. Homer--Ott (N.Y.). Attendance--46,672.

2nd Game, at New York, Oct. 4							
Washington (AL)	001	000	000	---	1	5	0
New York (NL)	000	006	00x	---	6	10	0

Pitchers--CROWDER, Thomas (6), McColl (7) vs. SCHUMACHER. Homer--Goslin (Wash.). Attend.--35,461.

3rd Game, at Washington, Oct. 5							
New York (NL)	000	000	000	---	0	5	0
Washington (AL)	210	000	10x	---	4	9	1

Pitchers--FITZSIMMONS, Bell (8) vs. WHITEHILL. Attendance--25,727.

4th Game, at Washington, Oct. 6								
New York (NL)	000	100	000	01	---	2	11	1
Washington (AL)	000	000	100	00	---	1	8	0

Pitchers--HUBBELL vs. WEAVER, Russell (11). Homer--Terry (N.Y.). Attendance--27,762.

5th Game, at Washington, Oct. 7								
New York (NL)	020	001	000	1	---	4	11	1
Washington (AL)	000	003	000	0	---	3	10	0

Pitchers--Schumacher, LUQUE (6) vs. Crowder, RUSSELL (6). Homers--Schulte (Wash.), Ott (N.Y.). Attendance--28,454.

1934

Coming from behind to capture the NL flag on the last day of the season, the swashbuckling Gashouse Gang then tamed the Tigers. Dizzy Dean, with 30 victories in the regular season, stole the spotlight with two more against Detroit. Brother Paul (nicknamed Daffy) also won a pair. Dizzy was beaned while pinch running in the fourth game, and had to be carried off the field, yet returned to pitch the next day. The roisterous seventh game was an 11-0 triumph for Dizzy, who contributed two of the 17 hits off half a dozen Detroit pitchers. St. Louis slugging star Ducky Medwick bowled over third baseman Owen with a slashing slide in the seventh inning of the finale. When Medwick went to his position in left field, the fans showered him with fruit, vegetables and assorted missiles, so Commissioner Landis ordered Medwick benched to end the ruckus.

Result: St. Louis NL won 4; Detroit AL, 3.

1st Game, at Detroit, Oct. 3					R.	H.	E.
St. Louis (NL)	021	014	000	---	8	13	2
Detroit (AL)	001	001	010	---	3	8	5

Pitchers--J. DEAN vs. CROWDER, Marberry (6) Hogsett (6). Homers--Medwick (St. L.), Greenberg (Det.). Attendance--42,505.

2nd Game, at Detroit, Oct. 4								
St. Louis (NL)	011	000	000	000	---	2	7	3
Detroit (AL)	000	100	001	001	---	3	7	0

Pitchers--Hallahan, W. WALKER (9) vs. ROWE. Attendance--43,451.

3rd Game, at St. Louis, Oct. 5							
Detroit (AL)	000	000	001	---	1	8	2
St. Louis (NL)	110	020	00x	---	4	9	1

Pitchers--BRIDGES, Hogsett (5) vs. P. DEAN. Attendance--34,073.

4th Game, at St. Louis, Oct. 6							
Detroit (AL)	003	100	150	---	10	13	1
St. Louis (NL)	011	200	000	---	4	10	5

Pitchers--AUKER vs. Carleton, Vance (3), W. WALKER (5), Haines (8), Mooney (9). Attendance--37,492.

5th Game, at St. Louis, Oct. 7							
Detroit (AL)	010	002	000	---	3	7	0
St. Louis (NL)	000	000	100	---	1	7	1

Pitchers--BRIDGES vs. J. DEAN, Carleton (9). Homers--Gehringer (Det.), Delancey (St. L.). Attendance--38,536.

6th Game, at Detroit, Oct. 8							
St. Louis (NL)	100	020	100	---	4	10	2
Detroit (AL)	001	002	000	---	3	7	1

Pitchers--P. DEAN vs. ROWE. Attendance--44,551.

7th Game, at Detroit, Oct. 9							
St. Louis (NL)	007	002	200	---	11	17	1
Detroit (AL)	000	000	000	---	0	6	3

Pitchers--J. DEAN vs. AUKER, Rowe (3), Hogsett (3), Bridges (4), Marberry (8), Crowder (9). Attendance--40,902.

1935

Detroit lost its heavy hitting first baseman, Hank Greenberg, with a broken wrist in the third game, but still managed to stop the Cubs in six games. Tommy Bridges curve-balled two decisions for Detroit and Lon Warneke won Chicago's pair. With the score tied in the last inning of the sixth game, and the Cubs needing a victory to square the series, Stan Hack led off for them with a triple. However, he was stranded as Bridges retired the next three batters. In the Tiger half, catcher-manager Mickey Cochrane singled, advanced on an infield out and scored the deciding run on Goose Goslin's single.

Result: Detroit AL won 4; Chicago NL, 2.

1st Game, at Detroit, Oct. 2					R.	H.	E.
Chicago (NL)	200	000	001	---	3	7	0
Detroit (AL)	000	000	000	---	0	4	3

Pitchers -- WARNEKE vs. ROWE. Homer -- Demaree (Chi.). Attendance--47,391.

2nd Game, at Detroit, Oct. 3

Chicago (NL)	000	010	200	---	3	6	1
Detroit (AL)	400	300	10x	---	8	9	2

Pitchers--ROOT, Henshaw (1) Kowalik (4) vs. BRIDGES. Homer--Greenberg (Det.). Attendance--46,742.

3rd Game, at Chicago, Oct. 4

Detroit (AL)	000	001	040	01	---	6	12	2
Chicago (NL)	020	010	002	00	---	5	10	3

Pitchers--Auker, Hogsett (7), ROWE (8) vs. Lee, Warneke (8), FRENCH (10). Homer--Demaree. Attendance--45,532.

4th Game, at Chicago, Oct. 5

Detroit (AL)	001	001	000	---	2	7	0
Chicago (NL)	010	000	000	---	1	5	2

Pitchers--CROWDER vs. CARLETON, Root (8). Homer--Hartnett (Chi.). Attendance--49,350.

5th Game, at Chicago, Oct. 6

Detroit (AL)	000	000	001	---	1	7	1
Chicago (NL)	002	000	10x	---	3	8	0

Pitchers--ROWE vs. WARNEKE, Lee (7). Homer--Klein (Chi.). Attendance--49,237.

6th Game, at Detroit, Oct. 7

Chicago (NL)	001	020	000	---	3	12	0
Detroit (AL)	100	101	001	---	4	12	1

Pitchers -- FRENCH vs. BRIDGES. Homer -- Herman (Chi.). Attendance--48,420.

1936

Carl Hubbell closed the NL season with 16 straight victories and opened the Series with a 6-1 triumph for the Giants. But the Yanks bounced back to bag four of the next five. Lefty Gomez was winning pitcher in a record 18-4 drubbing and a 13-5 whipping that each featured a seven-run inning. Contrasted with his ignoble bases-loaded strikeout of 1926, Tony Lazzeri cleaned the sacks with a homer in the second game. Leading Yank sluggers included Jake Powell (.455), Red Rolfe and rookie Joe DiMaggio.

Result: New York AL won 4; New York NL, 2.

1st Game, at Polo Grounds, N. Y., Sept. 30					R.	H.	E.
New York (AL)	001	000	000	---	1	7	2
New York (NL)	000	011	04x	---	6	9	1

Pitchers--RUFFING vs. HUBBELL. Homers--Bartell (NL), Selkirk (AL). Attendance--39,419.

2nd Game, at Polo Grounds, N. Y., Oct. 2

New York (AL)	207	001	206	---	18	17	0
New York (NL)	010	300	000	---	4	6	1

Pitchers--GOMEZ vs. SCHUMACHER, Smith (3), Coffman (3), Gabler (5), Gumbert (9). Homers--Dickey (AL), Lazzeri (AL). Attendance--43,543.

3rd Game, at Yankee Stadium, N. Y., Oct. 3

New York (NL)	000	010	000	---	1	11	0
New York (AL)	010	000	01x	---	2	4	0

Pitchers--FITZSIMMONS vs. HADLEY, Malone (9). Homers--Gehrig (AL), Ripple (NL). Attendance--64,842.

4th Game, at Yankee Stadium, N. Y., Oct. 4

New York (NL)	000	100	010	---	2	7	1
New York (AL)	013	000	01x	---	5	10	1

Pitchers--HUBBELL, Gabler (8) vs. PEARSON. Homer--Gehrig (AL). Attendance--66,669.

5th Game, at Yankee Stadium, N. Y., Oct. 5

New York (NL)	300	001	000	1	---	5	8	3
New York (AL)	011	002	000	0	---	4	10	1

Pitchers--SCHUMACHER vs. Ruffing, MALONE (7). Homer--Selkirk (AL). Attendance--50,024.

6th Game, at Polo Grounds, N. Y., Oct. 6

New York (AL)	021	200	017	---	13	17	2
New York (NL)	200	010	110	---	5	9	1

Pitchers--GOMEZ, Murphy (7) vs. FITZSIMMONS, Castleman (4), Coffman (9), Gumbert (9). Homers--Moore (NL), Ott (NL), Powell (AL). Attendance--38,427.

1937

Interrupted only by Hubbell's victory in the fourth game, the Yanks easily drove through the Giants. Hubbell was the opening-game victim of a typical Yank "big inning" as the AL sluggers scored seven runs in the sixth inning. Lazzeri hit safely in every game and led the batters with .400. Gomez again won twice.

Result: New York AL won 4; New York NL, 1.

1st Game, at Yankee Stadium, N. Y., Oct. 6					R.	H.	E.
New York (NL)	000	010	000	---	1	6	2
New York (AL)	000	007	01x	---	8	7	0

Pitchers--HUBBELL, Gumbert (6), Coffman (6), Smith (8) vs. GOMEZ. Homer--Lazzeri (AL). Attend.--60,573.

2nd Game, at Yankee Stadium, N. Y., Oct. 7

New York (NL)	100	000	000	---	1	7	0
New York (AL)	000	024	20x	---	8	12	0

Pitchers--MELTON, Gumbert (5), Coffman (6) vs. RUFFING. Attendance--57,675.

3rd Game, at Polo Grounds, N. Y., Oct. 8

New York (AL)	012	110	000	---	5	9	0
New York (NL)	000	000	100	---	1	5	4

Pitchers--PEARSON, Murphy (9) vs. SCHUMACHER, Melton (7), Brennan (9). Attendance--37,395.

4th Game, at Polo Grounds, N. Y., Oct. 9

New York (AL)	101	000	001	---	3	6	0
New York (NL)	060	000	10x	---	7	12	3

Pitchers--HADLEY, Andrews (2), Wicker (8) vs. HUBBELL. Homer--Gehrig (AL). Attendance--44,293.

5th Game, at Polo Grounds, N. Y., Oct. 10

New York (AL)	011	020	000	---	4	8	0
New York (NL)	002	000	000	---	2	10	0

Pitchers--GOMEZ vs. MELTON, Smith (6), Brennan (8). Homers--DiMaggio (AL), Hoag (AL), Ott (NL). Att.--38,216.

1938

Manager Joe McCarthy again beat his former Cub club in four straight games. Big Bill Lee, who won 22 while leading Chicago to the pennant, lost both his starts to the Yanks. Dizzy Dean's fireball was gone, but his slick sidearm stuff stopped the Bombers for seven innings. Diz lost when Frank Crosetti and Joe DiMaggio poked two-run homers in the last two innings. Veteran catcher Bill Dickey and rookie infielder Joe Gordon each hit .400 for the Yanks.

Result: New York AL won 4; Chicago NL, 0.

1st Game, at Chicago, Oct. 5					R.	H.	E.
New York (AL)	020	000	100	---	3	12	1
Chicago (NL)	001	000	000	---	1	9	1

Pitchers--RUFFING vs. LEE, Russell (9). Attendance --43,642.

2nd Game, at Chicago, Oct. 6							
New York (AL)	020	000	022	---	6	7	2
Chicago (NL)	102	000	000	---	3	11	0

Pitchers--GOMEZ, Murphy (8) vs. J. DEAN, French (9). Homers--Crosetti (N.Y.), DiMaggio (N.Y.). Att.--42,108.

3rd Game, at New York, Oct. 8							
Chicago (NL)	000	010	010	---	2	5	1
New York (AL)	000	022	01x	---	5	7	2

Pitchers--BRYANT, Russell (6), French (7) vs. PEARSON. Homers--Dickey (N.Y.), Gordon (N.Y.), Marty (Chi.). Attendance--55,236.

4th Game, at New York, Oct. 9							
Chicago (NL)	000	100	020	---	3	8	1
New York (AL)	030	001	04x	---	8	11	1

Pitchers--LEE, Root (4), Page (7), French (8), Carleton (8), Dean (8) vs. RUFFING. Homers--Henrich (N.Y.), O'Dea (Chi.). Attendance--59,847.

1939

Alert and able to cash in on every break, the Yankees snuffed out the Reds in four straight games to become the first team to win four straight world championships. Monte Pearson's two-hitter in the second game was backed by the timely hitting of Babe Dahlgren, who filled in at first base for non-playing captain Lou Gehrig. Yankee rookie Charlie Keller hit hardest in the Series. Enjoying a 4-2 lead in the ninth inning of the fourth game, the Reds suddenly snapped their Series streak of errorless ball with four costly bobbles in two innings, including catcher Ernie Lombardi's famous "snooze" at home plate (when he was understandably stunned in a collision with King Kong Keller).

Result: New York AL won 4; Cincinnati NL, 0.

1st Game, at New York, Oct. 4					R.	H.	E.
Cincinnati (NL)	000	100	000	---	1	4	0
New York (AL)	000	010	001	---	2	6	0

Pitchers--DERRINGER vs. RUFFING. Attend.--58,541.

2nd Game, at New York, Oct. 5							
Cincinnati (NL)	000	000	000	---	0	2	0
New York (AL)	003	100	00x	---	4	9	0

Pitchers--WALTERS vs. PEARSON. Homer--Dahlgren (N.Y.). Attendance--59,791.

3rd Game, at Cincinnati, Oct. 7							
New York (AL)	202	030	000	---	7	5	1
Cincinnati (NL)	120	000	000	---	3	10	0

Pitchers--Gomez, HADLEY (2) vs. THOMPSON, Grissom (5), Moore (7). Homers--Keller (N.Y.) 2, DiMaggio (N.Y.), Dickey (N.Y.). Attendance--32,723.

4th Game, at Cincinnati, Oct. 8								
New York (AL)	000	000	202	3	---	7	7	1
Cincinnati (NL)	000	000	310	0	---	4	11	4

Pitchers--Hildebrand, Sundra (5), MURPHY (7) vs. Derringer, WALTERS (8). Homers--Keller (N.Y.), Dickey (N.Y.). Attendance--32,794.

1940

No longer having to face the terrifying Yankees, the NL returned to the peak. Cincinnati nipped Detroit's team of oldsters in an airtight series. Bobo Newsom won the opener, but his father, up from South Carolina to watch him, died of a heart attack several hours after the game. Newsom pitched a shutout "for dad" in his next start. Newsom's two decisions were matched by each of two Reds, Bucky Walters and Paul Derringer. Derringer beat Newsom in the finale, when each yielded only seven hits, as slow fielding by Detroit enabled Cincy to score an extra run. Forty-year-old Jimmy Wilson, filling in behind the bat for lame Ernie Lombardi in six games, hit .353 and stole the only base of the Series.

Result: Cincinnati NL won 4; Detroit AL, 3.

1st Game, at Cincinnati, Oct. 2					R.	H	E.
Detroit (AL)	050	020	000	---	7	10	1
Cincinnati (NL)	000	100	010	---	2	8	3

Pitchers--NEWSOM vs. DERRINGER, Moore (2), Riddle (9). Homer--Campbell (Det.). Attendance--31,793.

2nd Game, at Cincinnati, Oct. 3							
Detroit (AL)	200	001	000	---	3	3	1
Cincinnati (NL)	022	100	00x	---	5	9	0

Pitchers--ROWE, Gorsica (4) vs. WALTERS. Homer--Ripple (Cin.). Attendance--30,640.

3rd Game, at Detroit, Oct. 4							
Cincinnati (NL)	100	000	012	---	4	10	1
Detroit (AL)	000	100	42x	---	7	13	1

Pitchers--TURNER, Moore (7), Beggs (8) vs. BRIDGES. Homers--York (Det.), Higgins (Det.). Attend.--52,877.

4th Game, at Detroit, Oct. 5							
Cincinnati (NL)	201	100	010	---	5	11	1
Detroit (AL)	001	001	000	---	2	5	1

Pitchers--DERRINGER vs. TROUT, Smith (3), McKain (7). Attendance--54,093.

5th Game, at Detroit, Oct. 6							
Cincinnati (NL)	000	000	000	---	0	3	0
Detroit (AL)	003	400	01x	---	8	13	0

Pitchers--THOMPSON, Moore (4), Vander Meer (5), Hutchings (8), vs. NEWSOM. Homer--Greenberg (Det.). Attendance--55,189.

6th Game, at Cincinnati, Oct. 7							
Detroit (AL)	000	000	000	---	0	5	0
Cincinnati (NL)	200	001	01x	---	4	10	2

Pitchers--ROWE, Gorsica (1), Hutchinson (8) vs. WALTERS. Homer--Walters (Cin.). Attendance--30,481.

7th Game, at Cincinnati, Oct. 8							
Detroit (AL)	001	000	000	---	1	7	0
Cincinnati (NL)	000	000	20x	---	2	7	1

Pitchers--NEWSOM vs. DERRINGER. Att.--26,854.

1941

Brooklyn bowed to the Yankees in five games that had some bizarre highlights. Joe Gordon, who hit an even .500, backed Red Ruffing's pitching with the deciding runs in the opener. This marked 10 consecutive Series games won by the Bronx Bombers. Whitlow Wyatt severed the proud streak the next day. Fred Fitzsimmon was locked in a scoreless hill duel with Marius Russo in the third game when Russo lined a seventh-inning drive off Fitz kneecap, sending him to the hospital. Sloppy fielding by relief pitcher Hugh Casey opened the gate for the two crucial Yank runs in the eighth. Next day, Casey struck out Tom Henrich for what should have been the last out of the game. But catcher Mickey Owen muffed the pitch too. Henrich raced to first to ignite a four-run rally that won for the Yanks, 7-4.

Result: New York AL won 4; Brooklyn NL, 1.

1st Game, at New York, Oct. 1					R.	H.	E.
Brooklyn (NL)	000	010	100	---	2	6	0
New York (AL)	010	101	00x	---	3	6	1

Pitchers--DAVIS, Casey (6), Allen (7) vs. RUFFING. Homer--Gordon (N.Y.). Attendance--68,540.

2nd Game, at New York, Oct. 2							
Brooklyn (NL)	000	021	000	---	3	6	2
New York (AL)	011	000	000	---	2	9	1

Pitchers--WYATT vs. CHANDLER, Murphy (6). Attendance--66,248.

3rd Game, at Brooklyn, Oct. 4							
New York (AL)	000	000	020	---	2	8	0
Brooklyn (NL)	000	000	010	---	1	4	0

Pitchers--RUSSO vs. Fitzsimmons, CASEY (8), French (8), Allen (9). Attendance--33,100.

4th Game, at Brooklyn, Oct. 5							
New York (AL)	100	200	004	---	7	12	0
Brooklyn (NL)	000	220	000	---	4	9	1

Pitchers--Donald, Breuer (5), MURPHY (8) vs. Higbe, French (4), Allen (5), CASEY (5). Homer--Reiser (Bklyn.). Attendance--33,813.

5th Game, Brooklyn, Oct. 6							
New York (AL)	020	010	000	---	3	6	0
Brooklyn (NL)	001	000	000	---	1	4	1

Pitchers -- BONHAM vs. WYATT. Homer -- Henrich (N.Y.). Attendance--34,072.

1942

A youthful, speedy and nervy Cardinal crew exploded a baseball bombshell by winning the pennant after trailing the Dodgers by 10 1/2 games in August. The Redbirds followed with even a more astounding assault, beating the awesome Yankees four straight after dropping the Series opener to Red Ruffing. St. Louis went winging with such freshman phenoms as third baseman Whitey Kurowski, pitcher John Beazley and outfielder Stan Musial. Kurowski's triple in the eighth inning of the second game and last-inning homer in the finale brought victory to Beazley each time. Rival centerfielders Terry Moore and Joe DiMaggio dazzled on defense.

Result: St. Louis NL won 4; New York AL, 1.

1st Game, at St. Louis, Sept. 30					R.	H.	E.
New York (AL)	000	110	032	---	7	11	0
St. Louis (NL)	000	000	004	---	4	7	4

Pitchers--RUFFING, Chandler (9) vs. M. COOPER, Gumbert (8), Lanier (9). Attendance--34,385.

2nd Game, at St. Louis, Oct. 1							
New York (AL)	000	000	030	---	3	10	2
St. Louis (NL)	200	000	110	---	4	6	0

Pitchers -- BONHAM vs. BEAZLEY. Homer -- Keller (N.Y.). Attendance--34,255.

3rd Game, at New York, Oct. 2							
St. Louis (NL)	001	000	001	---	2	5	1
New York (AL)	000	000	000	---	0	6	1

Pitchers--WHITE vs. CHANDLER, Breuer (9), Turner (9). Attendance--69,123.

4th Game, at New York, Oct. 4							
St. Louis (NL)	000	600	201	---	9	12	1
New York (AL)	100	005	000	---	6	10	1

Pitchers--M. Cooper, Gumbert (6), Pollet (6), LANIER (7) vs. Borowy, DONALD (4), Bonham (7). Homer--Keller (N.Y.). Attendance--69,902.

5th Game, at New York, Oct. 5							
St. Louis (NL)	000	101	002	---	4	9	4
New York (AL)	100	100	000	---	2	7	1

Pitchers--BEAZLEY vs. RUFFING. Homers--Rizzuto (N.Y.), Slaughter (St. L.), Kurowski (St. L.). Att.--69,052.

1943

This one was a reverse of 1942, with the Yanks whipping the Cards in five games. Spud Chandler won the opener and closer. Though his father died the morning of the second game, Morton Cooper pitched to brother Walker, and they brought St. Louis its only decision. Two Card errors in the eighth inning of the third game opened the gates for the winning four-run rally. Marius Russo pitched and batted his way to a 2-1 victory in the next game. Bill Dickey's homer with one aboard accounted for all the runs in the finale, which also saw Cooper strike out the first five Yank batters.

Result: New York AL won 4; St. Louis NL, 1.

1st Game, at New York, Oct. 5					R.	H.	E.
St. Louis (NL)	010	010	000	---	2	7	2
New York (AL)	000	202	00x	---	4	8	2

Pitchers--LANIER vs. CHANDLER. Homer--Gordon (N.Y.). Attendance--68,676.

2nd Game, at New York, Oct. 6

					R.	H.	E.
St. Louis (NL)	001	300	000	---	4	7	2
New York (AL)	000	100	002	---	3	6	0

Pitchers--M. COOPER vs. BONHAM, Murphy (9). Homers--Marion (St. L.), Sanders (St. L.). Att.--68,578.

3rd Game, at New York, Oct. 7

					R.	H.	E.
St. Louis (NL)	000	200	000	---	2	6	4
New York (AL)	000	001	05x	---	6	8	0

Pitchers--BRAZLE, Krist (8), Brecheen (8) vs. BOROWY, Murphy (9). Attendance--69,990.

4th Game, at St. Louis, Oct. 10

					R.	H.	E.
New York (AL)	000	100	010	---	2	6	2
St. Louis (NL)	000	000	100	---	1	7	1

Pitchers--RUSSO vs. Lanier, BRECHEEN (8). Attendance--36,196.

5th Game, at St. Louis, Oct. 11

					R.	H.	E.
New York (AL)	000	002	000	---	2	7	1
St. Louis (NL)	000	000	000	---	0	10	1

Pitchers--CHANDLER vs. M. COOPER, Lanier (8), Dickson (9). Homer--Dickey (N.Y.). Attendance--33,872.

1944

The city of St. Louis enjoyed a "Trolley Series," with the NL entry twice coming from behind to beat the only Brownie team ever to win the AL flag. Of 10 Brown errors, seven came in scoring innings. Mort Cooper lost the opener despite a two-hitter, as George McQuinn blasted a two-run homer. Ken O'Dea's pinch single in the 10th won the next for the Cards. Jack Kramer tamed the Cards the next day, but they snapped back with three straight pitching gems to capture the crown.

Result: St. Louis NL won 4; St. Louis AL, 2.

1st Game, at Sportsman's Park, Oct. 4

					R.	H.	E.
St. Louis (AL)	000	200	000	---	2	2	0
St. Louis (NL)	000	000	001	---	1	7	0

Pitchers--GALEHOUSE vs. M. COOPER, Donnelly (8). Homer--McQuinn (AL). Attendance--33,242.

2nd Game, at Sportsman's Park, Oct. 5

						R.	H.	E.
St. Louis (AL)	000	002	000	0	---	2	7	4
St. Louis (NL)	001	100	000	1	---	3	7	0

Pitchers--Potter, MUNCRIEF (7) vs. Lanier, DONNELLY (8). Attendance--35,076.

3rd Game, at Sportsman's Park, Oct. 6

					R.	H.	E.
St. Louis (NL)	100	000	100	---	2	7	0
St. Louis (AL)	004	000	20x	---	6	8	2

Pitchers--WILKS, Schmidt (3), Jurisich (7), Byerly (7) vs. KRAMER. Attendance--34,737.

4th Game, at Sportsman's Park, Oct. 7

					R.	H.	E.
St. Louis (NL)	202	001	000	---	5	12	0
St. Louis (AL)	000	000	010	---	1	9	1

Pitchers--BRECHEEN vs. JAKUCKI, Hollingsworth (4), Shirley (8). Homer--Musial (NL). Attendance--35,455.

5th Game, at Sportsman's Park, Oct. 8

					R.	H.	E.
St. Louis (NL)	000	001	010	---	2	6	1
St. Louis (AL)	000	000	000	---	0	7	1

Pitchers--M. COOPER vs. GALEHOUSE. Homers--Sanders (NL), Litwhiler (NL). Attendance--36,568.

6th Game, at Sportsman's Park, Oct. 9

					R.	H.	E.
St. Louis (AL)	010	000	000	---	1	3	2
St. Louis (NL)	000	300	00x	---	3	10	0

Pitchers--POTTER, Muncrief (4), Kramer (7) vs. LANIER, Wilks (6). Attendance--31,630.

1945

Returned from war service in midseason, Hank Greenberg hit a grand-slam homer on the last day of the season to put Detroit into the Series. He continued his timely hitting to help beat the Cubs, though he couldn't match the 11 hits each by Doc Cramer, Stan Hack and Phil Cavarretta. Hank Borowy, waived out of the AL in midseason, blanked Detroit in the opener. Only 10 days out of the Navy, Virgil Trucks cuffed the Cubs in the next. Then came Claude Passeau's historic one-hitter, fine flinging jobs by Detroit's Dizzy Trout and Hal Newhouser and a weird overtime Cub victory. That put it up to Newhouser vs. Borowy in the finale, and lefty Hal won decisively as he extended his strikeout total for the Series to 22, a new record.

Result: Detroit AL won 4; Chicago NL, 3.

1st Game, at Detroit, Oct. 3

					R.	H.	E.
Chicago (NL)	403	000	200	---	9	13	0
Detroit (AL)	000	000	000	---	0	6	0

Pitchers--BOROWY vs. NEWHOUSER, Benton (3), Tobin (5), Mueller (8). Homer--Cavarretta (Chi.). Attendance --54,637.

2nd Game, at Detroit, Oct. 4

					R.	H.	E.
Chicago (NL)	000	100	000	---	1	7	0
Detroit (AL)	000	040	00x	---	4	7	0

Pitchers--WYSE, Erickson (7) vs. TRUCKS. Homer--Greenberg (Det.). Attendance--53,636.

3rd Game, at Detroit, Oct. 5

					R.	H.	E.
Chicago (NL)	000	200	100	---	3	8	0
Detroit (AL)	000	000	000	---	0	1	2

Pitchers--PASSEAU vs. OVERMIRE, Benton (7). Attendance--55,500.

4th Game, at Chicago, Oct. 6

					R.	H.	E.
Detroit (AL)	000	400	000	---	4	7	1
Chicago (NL)	000	001	000	---	1	5	1

Pitchers--TROUT vs. PRIM, Derringer (4), Vandenberg (6), Erickson (8). Attendance--42,923.

5th Game, at Chicago, Oct. 7

					R.	H.	E.
Detroit (AL)	001	004	102	---	8	11	0
Chicago (NL)	001	000	201	---	4	7	2

Pitchers--NEWHOUSER vs. BOROWY, Vandenberg (6), Chipman (6), Derringer (7), Erickson (9). Attend.--43,463.

6th Game, at Chicago, Oct. 8

						R.	H.	E.
Detroit (AL)	010	000	240	000	---	7	13	1
Chicago (NL)	000	041	200	001	---	8	15	3

Pitchers--Trucks, Caster (5), Bridges (6), Benton (7), TROUT (8) vs. Passeau, Wyse (7), Prim (8), BOROWY (9). Homer--Greenberg (Det.). Attendance--41,708.

7th Game, at Chicago, Oct. 10

					R.	H.	E.
Detroit (AL)	510	000	120	---	9	9	1
Chicago (NL)	100	100	010	---	3	10	0

Pitchers--NEWHOUSER vs. BOROWY, Derringer (1), Vandenberg (2), Erickson (6), Passeau (8), Wyse (9). Attendance--41,590.

1946

Freshman manager Eddie Dyer guided the Cards to victory in the first pennant playoff in major league history, to break a tie with Brooklyn. Then his underdog team went on to topple the mighty Red Sox in the Series. Hero laurels went to Harry Brecheen for his three victories. Ted Williams earned the "goat horns" for figuratively beating his head against the stonewall "Boudreau defense" throughout the Series. Only once did he deliberately slice a bunt against the overshifted defense, and he reached base easily. Otherwise he pulled as hard as ever and collected only four other hits, all singles, for a .200 average. With two out and the score tied in the eighth inning of the last game, Enos Slaughter scored all the way from first on Harry Walker's hit over the shortstop's head.

Result: St. Louis NL won 4; Boston AL, 3.

1st Game, at St. Louis, Oct. 6						R.	H.	E.
Boston (AL)	010	000	001	1	---	3	9	2
St. Louis (NL)	000	001	010	0	---	2	7	0

Pitchers--Hughson, JOHNSON (9) vs. POLLET. Homer--York (Bos.). Attendance--36,218.

2nd Game, at St. Louis, Oct. 7							
Boston (AL)	000	000	000	---	0	4	1
St. Louis (NL)	001	020	00x	---	3	6	0

Pitchers--HARRIS, Dobson (8) vs. BRECHEEN. Attendance--35,815.

3rd Game, at Boston, Oct. 9							
St. Louis (NL)	000	000	000	---	0	6	1
Boston (AL)	300	000	01x	---	4	8	0

Pitchers--DICKSON, Wilks (8) vs. FERRISS. Homer--York (Bos.). Attendance--34,500.

4th Game, at Boston, Oct. 10							
St. Louis (NL)	033	010	104	---	12	20	1
Boston (AL)	000	100	020	---	3	9	4

Pitchers--MUNGER vs. HUGHSON, Bagby (3), Zuber (6), Brown (8), Ryba (9), Dreisewerd (9). Homers--Slaughter (St. L.), Doerr (Bos.). Attendance--35,645.

5th Game, at Boston, Oct. 11							
St. Louis (NL)	010	000	002	---	3	4	1
Boston (AL)	110	001	30x	---	6	11	3

Pitchers--Pollet, BRAZLE (1), Beazley (8) vs DOBSON. Homer--Culberson (Bos.). Attendance--35,982.

6th Game, at St. Louis, Oct. 13							
Boston (AL)	000	000	100	---	1	7	0
St. Louis (NL)	003	000	01x	---	4	8	0

Pitchers--HARRIS, Hughson (3), Johnson (8) vs. BRECHEEN. Attendance--35,768.

7th Game, at St. Louis, Oct. 15							
Boston (AL)	100	000	020	---	3	8	0
St. Louis (NL)	010	020	01x	---	4	9	1

Pitchers--Ferriss, Dobson (5), KLINGER (8), Johnson (8) vs. Dickson, BRECHEEN (8). Attendance--36,143.

1947

Despite the lack of a single route-going pitcher, the Dodgers forced the Yanks to the full seven games before bowing. This two-million-dollar series was a duel between two of the greatest relief artists in history, with Joe Page surpassing Hugh Casey. In the memorable fourth game, Bill Bevens was one out away from an unprecedented no-hitter when pinch hitter Cookie Lavagetto suddenly doubled home the tying and winning runs for Brooklyn. The sixth game was a three-hour, 19-minute marathon highlighted by Al Gionfriddo's miraculous stab of Joe DiMaggio's 415-foot drive to the bullpen gate. Page pitched five scoreless innings of relief to sew up the finale.

Result: New York AL won 4; Brooklyn NL, 3.

1st Game, at New York, Sept. 30					R.	H.	E.
Brooklyn (NL)	100	001	100	---	3	6	0
New York (AL)	000	050	00x	---	5	4	0

Pitchers--BRANCA, Behrman (5), Casey (7) vs. SHEA, Page (6). Attendance--73,365.

2nd Game, at New York, Oct. 1							
Brooklyn (NL)	001	100	001	---	3	9	2
New York (AL)	101	121	40x	---	10	15	1

Pitchers--LOMBARDI, Gregg (5), Behrman (7), Barney (7) vs. REYNOLDS. Homers--Walker (Bklyn.), Henrich (N.Y.). Attendance--69,865.

3rd Game, at Brooklyn, Oct. 2							
New York (AL)	002	221	100	---	8	13	0
Brooklyn (NL)	061	200	00x	---	9	13	1

Pitchers--NEWSOM, Raschi (2), Drews (3), Chandler (4), Page (6), vs. Hatten, Branca (5), CASEY (7), Homers--DiMaggio (N.Y.), Berra (N.Y.). Attendance--33,098.

4th Game, at Brooklyn, Oct. 3							
New York (AL)	100	100	000	---	2	8	1
Brooklyn (NL)	000	010	002	---	3	1	3

Pitchers--BEVENS vs. Taylor, Gregg (1), Behrman (8), CASEY (9). Attendance--33,443

5th Game, at Brooklyn, Oct. 4							
New York (AL)	000	110	000	---	2	5	0
Brooklyn (NL)	000	001	000	---	1	4	1

Pitchers--SHEA vs. BARNEY, Hatten (5), Behrman (7), Casey (8). Homer--DiMaggio (N.Y.). Attendance--34,379.

6th Game, at New York, Oct. 5							
Brooklyn (NL)	202	004	000	---	8	12	1
New York (AL)	004	100	001	---	6	15	2

Pitchers--Lombardi, BRANCA (3), Hatten (6), Casey (9) vs. Reynolds, Drews (3), PAGE (5), Newsom (6), Raschi (7), Wensloff (8). Attendance--74,065.

7th Game, at New York, Oct. 6							
Brooklyn (NL)	020	000	000	---	2	7	0
New York (AL)	010	201	10x	---	5	7	0

Pitchers--GREGG, Behrman (4), Hatten (6), Barney (6), Casey (7) vs. Shea, Bevens (2), PAGE (5). Att.--71,548.

1948

Player-manager Lou Boudreau cracked four-for-four to beat Boston for Cleveland in the first playoff in AL annals. But Gene Bearden, a wounded war veteran, was the hurling hero of that extra game, and the rookie southpaw proved the main difference in the Series, too. Bob Feller lost the opener to the Braves despite a two-hitter. Bob Lemon, a converted outfielder; Bearden, via shutout, and second-stringer Steve Gromek pitched the Indians to victory in the next three games. Boston won an 11-5 slugfest before the largest crowd in baseball history: 86,288 paid. Lemon started folding late in the sixth game, so tireless Bearden came out of the bullpen for a relief job that clinched the championship.

Result: Cleveland AL won 4; Boston NL, 2.

1st Game, at Boston, Oct. 6					R.	H.	E.
Cleveland (AL)	000	000	000	---	0	4	0
Boston (NL)	000	000	01x	---	1	2	2

Pitchers--FELLER vs. SAIN. Attendance--40,135.

2nd Game, at Boston, Oct. 7							
Cleveland (AL)	000	210	001	---	4	8	1
Boston (NL)	100	000	000	---	1	8	3

Pitchers--LEMON vs. SPAHN, Barrett (5), Potter (8). Attendance--39,633.

3rd Game, at Cleveland, Oct. 8							
Boston (NL)	000	000	000	---	0	5	1
Cleveland (AL)	001	100	00x	---	2	5	0

Pitchers--BICKFORD, Voiselle (4), Barrett (8) vs. BEARDEN. Attendance--70,306.

4th Game, at Cleveland, Oct. 9							
Boston (NL)	000	000	100	---	1	7	0
Cleveland (AL)	101	000	00x	---	2	5	0

Pitchers--SAIN vs. GROMEK. Homers--Doby (Cle.), Rickert (Bost.). Attendance--81,897.

5th Game, at Cleveland, Oct. 10							
Boston (NL)	301	001	600	---	11	12	0
Cleveland (AL)	100	400	000	---	5	6	2

Pitchers--Potter, SPAHN (4) vs. FELLER, Klieman (7), Christopher (7), Paige (7), Muncrief (8). Homers--Elliott (Bost.) 2, Mitchell (Cle.), Hegan (Cle.), Salkeld (Bost.). Attendance--86,288.

6th Game, at Boston, Oct. 11							
Cleveland (AL)	001	002	010	---	4	10	0
Boston (NL)	000	100	020	---	3	9	0

Pitchers--LEMON, Bearden (8) vs. VOISELLE, Spahn (8). Homer--Gordon (Cle.). Attendance--40,103.

1949

Conquering the Dodgers for the third time in less than a decade, the Yankees kept coming up with the right man in the right spot to win in five games. Don Newcombe struck out 11 Yanks in eight innings, only to lose his first game scoreless duel with Allie Reynolds as Tom Henrich opened the home ninth with a homer. Preacher Roe evened it up with a 1-0 job the next day. However, Brooklyn was ruined in the three remaining games by an old nemesis, Bobby Brown, a part-time third baseman and medical student. Brown blasted six hits in those three games and accounted for the deciding margin in all three. Fireman Joe Page contributed more of his incomparable relief to seal the Yankee triumph.

Result: New York AL won 4; Brooklyn NL, 1.

1st Game, at New York, Oct. 5					R.	H.	E.
Brooklyn (NL)	000	000	000	---	0	2	0
New York (AL)	000	000	001	---	1	5	1

Pitchers -- NEWCOMBE vs. REYNOLDS. Homer -- Henrich (N.Y.). Attendance--66,224.

2nd Game, at New York, Oct. 6							
Brooklyn (NL)	010	000	000	---	1	7	2
New York (AL)	000	000	000	---	0	6	1

Pitchers--ROE vs. RASCHI. Attendance--70,053.

3rd Game, at Brooklyn, Oct. 7							
New York (AL)	001	000	003	---	4	5	0
Brooklyn (NL)	000	100	002	---	3	5	0

Pitchers--Byrne, PAGE (4) vs. BRANCA, Banta (9). Homers -- Reese (Bklyn.), Olmo (Bklyn.), Campanella (Bklyn.). Attendance--32,788.

4th Game, at Brooklyn, Oct. 8							
New York (AL)	000	330	000	---	6	10	0
Brooklyn (NL)	000	004	000	---	4	9	1

Pitchers--LOPAT, Reynolds (6) vs. NEWCOMBE, Hatten (4), Erskine (6), Banta (7). Attendance--33,934.

5th Game, at Brooklyn, Oct. 9							
New York (AL)	203	113	000	---	10	11	1
Brooklyn (NL)	001	001	400	---	6	11	2

Pitchers--RASCHI, Page (7) vs. BARNEY, Banta (3), Erskine (6), Hatten (6), Palica (7), Minner (9). Homers--DiMaggio (N.Y.), Hodges (Bklyn.). Attendance--33,711.

1950

After winning the pennant in the 10th inning of the last day of the season, the Philadelphia "Whiz Kids" suffered a severe letdown in the World Series, losing four straight to the Yankees. A daring gamble almost paid off for the NL entry. Manager Ed Sawyer named Jim Konstanty to open the Series, though the bullpen denizen had broken the all-time season record with 74 relief appearances (and no starts!). Konstanty dropped a 1-0 duel to Vic Raschi, who spun a two-hitter. Locked in a .222 batting slump, the Yankees relied on further fine pitching by Allie Reynolds, Ed Lopat, Tom Ferrick and rookie Ed Ford to sweep the rest of the series for their 13th title. Joe DiMaggio blasted a 10th-inning homer into the upper deck of Shibe Park to win the second game.

Result: New York AL won 4; Philadelphia NL, 0.

1st Game, at Philadelphia, Oct. 4					R.	H.	E.
New York (AL)	000	100	000	---	1	5	0
Philadelphia(NL)	000	000	000	---	0	2	1

Pitchers--RASCHI vs. KONSTANTY, Meyer (9). Attendance--30,746.

2nd Game, at Philadelphia, Oct. 5								
New York (AL)	010	000	000	1	---	2	10	0
Philadelphia(NL)	000	010	000	0	---	1	7	0

Pitchers--REYNOLDS vs. ROBERTS. Homer--DiMaggio (N.Y.). Attendance--32,660.

3rd Game, at New York, Oct. 6							
Philadelphia(NL)	000	001	100	---	2	10	2
New York (AL)	001	000	011	---	3	7	0

Pitchers--Heintzelman, Konstanty (8), MEYER (9) vs. Lopat, FERRICK (9). Attendance--64,505.

4th Game, at NewYork, Oct. 7							
Philadelphia(NL)	000	000	002	---	2	7	1
New York (AL)	200	003	00x	---	5	8	2

Pitchers--MILLER, Konstanty (1), Roberts (8) vs. FORD, Reynolds (9). Homer--Berra (N.Y.). Att.--68,098.

1951

The red-hot New York Giants, who had made a sensational late season drive to haul in the NL pennant, were cooled off in the series by a rainy day and resurgent Yankee bats. The Giants had taken a 2-1 lead in games when rain postponed the fourth contest and gave Yankee pitching ace Allie Reynolds an additional day of rest. The Giants were unable to win a game after play resumed. Monte Irvin's theft of home—first in fall competition since 1928—and lefty Dave Koslo's strong hurling job got the Giants off in front in the opener. After Lopat whipped the Giants in the second clash Jim Hearn put the NL one-up the following day. Then came the rain which washed out the Giant chances. McDougald's bases-loaded homer in the fourth battle, Lopat's second win in the fifth and Bob Kuzava's strong relief bit and Hank Bauer's game-saving catch in the sixth game featured the Yankees' next three victories. Irvin slammed 11 hits to tie a record for most safeties in a six-game set, and paced all series hitters with a .458 figure. The series also was marked by the famous "drop kick" incident when Ed Stanky kicked the ball from Phil Rizzuto's hand as the Yankee shortstop was about to tag out the fiery Giant infielder who was attempting to slide into second base on a hit and run play which backfired. Rizzuto dropped the ball and the Giants went on to score five runs in the inning, a vital factor in their third game triumph.

Result: New York AL won 4; New York NL, 2.

1st Game, at Yankee Stadium, N.Y., Oct. 4					R.	H.	E.
New York (NL)	200	003	000	---	5	10	1
New York (AL)	010	000	000	---	1	7	1

Pitchers--KOSLO vs. REYNOLDS, Hogue (7), Morgan (8). Homer--Dark (NL). Attendance--65,673.

2nd Game, at Yankee Stadium, N.Y., Oct. 5							
New York (NL)	000	000	100	---	1	5	1
New York (AL)	110	000	01x	---	3	6	0

Pitchers--JANSEN, Spencer (7) vs. LOPAT. Homer--Collins (AL). Attendance--66,018.

3rd Game, at Polo Grounds, N.Y., Oct. 6							
New York (AL)	000	000	011	---	2	5	2
New York (NL)	010	050	00x	---	6	7	2

Pitchers--RASCHI, Hogue (5), Ostrowski (7) vs. HEARN, Jones (8). Homers--Lockman (NL), Woodling (AL). Attendance--52,035.

4th Game, at Polo Grounds, N.Y., Oct. 8							
New York (AL)	010	120	200	---	6	12	0
New York (NL)	100	000	001	---	2	8	2

Pitchers--REYNOLDS vs. MAGLIE, Jones (6), Kennedy (9). Homer--DiMaggio (AL). Attendance--49,010.

5th Game, at Polo Grounds, N.Y., Oct. 9							
New York (AL)	005	202	400	---	13	12	1
New York (NL)	100	000	000	---	1	5	3

Pitchers--LOPAT vs. JANSEN, Kennedy (4), Spencer (6), Corwin (7), Konikowski (9). Homers--McDougald (AL), Rizzuto (AL). Attendance--47,530.

6th Game, at Yankee Stadium, N.Y., Oct. 10							
New York (NL)	000	010	002	---	3	11	1
New York (AL)	100	003	00x	---	4	7	0

Pitchers--KOSLO, Hearn (7), Jansen (8) vs. RASCHI, Sain (7), Kuzava (9). Attendance--61,711.

1952

Casey Stengel tied the world's championship record of four straight titles as he guided the Yankees through a successful seven-game set against the Brooklyn Dodgers. It equaled the mark established by the Bombers of Joe McCarthy vintage who nailed down titles in 1936, '37, '38 and '39. The Yankees did it the hard way, coming from behind to defeat the Dodgers in the last two games played at the National Leaguers' park. Dodger manager Charley Dressen started ace relief artist Joe Black in the opening game and the big right hander responded with a 4-2 victory. It was the first series pitching triumph ever turned in by a Negro. The teams alternated in winning the next four games before the Yankees thundered back to take the last two. Perhaps the most exciting game of the set was the 11-inning thriller won by Brooklyn, 6-5, which gave the Dodgers their three-two edge. Carl Erskine pitched the distance for the Dodgers, allowing all Yankee runs in the fifth inning. The most dramatic moment of the series was reserved for the seventh inning of the final game. Jackie Robinson popped up a wind-blown fly ball with two out and bases-loaded. With all the runners dashing plate-ward, second baseman Billy Martin circled for the catch. When it appeared as if the ball would drop safely, he just managed to grab it with a last second lunge. Duke Snider slammed four homers for the Dodgers.

Result: New York AL won 4; Brooklyn NL, 3.

1st Game, at Brooklyn, Oct. 1					R.	H.	E.
New York (AL)	010	000	010	---	2	6	2
Broklyn (NL)	010	002	01x	---	4	6	0

Pitchers--REYNOLDS, Scarborough (8) vs. BLACK. Homers--Robinson (Bklyn.), Snider (Bklyn.), Reese (Bklyn.), McDougald (N.Y.). Attendance--34,861.

2nd Game, at Brooklyn, Oct. 2							
New York (AL)	000	115	000	---	7	10	0
Brooklyn (NL)	001	000	000	---	1	3	1

Pitchers--RASCHI vs. ERSKINE, Loes (6), Lehman (8). Homer--Martin (N.Y.). Attendance--33,792.

3rd Game, at New York, Oct. 3							
Brooklyn (NL)	001	010	012	---	5	11	0
New York (AL)	010	000	011	---	3	6	2

Pitchers--ROE vs. LOPAT, Gorman (9). Homers--Berra (N.Y.), Mize (N.Y.). Attendance--66,698.

4th Game, at New York, Oct. 4							
Brooklyn (NL)	000	000	000	---	0	4	1
New York (AL)	000	100	01x	---	2	4	1

Pitchers -- BLACK, Rutherford (8) vs. REYNOLDS. Homer--Mize (N.Y.). Attendance--71,787.

5th Game, at New York, Oct. 5								
Brooklyn (NL)	010	030	100	01	---	6	10	0
New York (AL)	000	050	000	00	---	5	5	1

Pitchers--ERSKINE vs. Blackwell, SAIN (6). Homers--Snider (Bklyn.), Mize (N.Y.). Attendance--70,536.

6th Game, at Brooklyn, Oct. 6							
New York (AL)	000	000	210	---	3	9	0
Brooklyn (NL)	000	001	010	---	2	8	1

Pitchers--RASCHI, Reynolds (8) vs. LOES, Roe (9). Homers--Snider (Bklyn.) 2, Berra (N.Y.), Mantle (N.Y.). Attendance--30,037.

7th Game, at Brooklyn, Oct. 7							
New York (AL)	000	111	100	---	4	10	4
Brooklyn (NL)	000	110	000	---	2	8	1

Pitchers--Lopat, REYNOLDS (4), Raschi (7), Kuzava (7) vs. BLACK, Roe (6), Erskine (8). Homers--Woodling (N.Y.), Mantle (N.Y.). Attendance--33,195.

1953

The Yankees became the first team in history to win five straight world championships as they again tamed Brooklyn, this time in six games. The Yankees won the first two games; the Dodgers rallied to cop the next two but the Yankees, with Mickey Mantle driving a grandslammer in the third inning of game No. 5, took the next two clashes. Erskine established an all-time series mark by striking out 14 batters to give Brooklyn its first victory, a brilliant 3-2 effort which wasn't decided until catcher Roy Campanella clouted an eighth inning home run. Billy Loes got Brooklyn even the following day with a nine-hit triumph before the Yankees recovered to sail through the next two games. Carl Furillo's two-on ninth-inning homer tied the score in the sixth game but Billy Martin, brilliant at bat and in the field throughout, delivered the payoff poke, a game-winning single in the Bombers' half. It was Martin's 12th hit—a new record for a six game series—and he wound up with a .500 batting average.

Result: New York AL won 4; Brooklyn NL, 2.

1st Game, at New York, Sept. 30					R.	H.	E.
Brooklyn (NL)	000	013	100	---	5	12	2
New York (AL)	400	010	13x	---	9	12	0

Pitchers--Erskine, Hughes (2), LABINE (6), Wade (8) vs. Reynolds, SAIN (6). Homers--Gilliam (Bklyn.), Hodges (Bklyn.), Shuba (Bklyn.), Berra (N.Y.), Collins (N.Y.). Attendance--69,374.

2nd Game, at New York, Oct. 1							
Brooklyn (NL)	000	200	000	---	2	9	1
New York (AL)	100	000	12x	---	4	5	0

Pitchers--ROE vs. LOPAT. Homers--Martin (N.Y.), Mantle (N.Y.). Attendance--66,786.

3rd Game, at Brooklyn, Oct. 2							
New York (AL)	000	010	010	---	2	6	0
Brooklyn (NL)	000	011	01x	---	3	9	0

Pitchers--RASCHI vs. ERSKINE. Homer--Campanella (Bklyn.). Attendance--35,270.

4th Game, at Brooklyn, Oct. 3							
New York (AL)	000	020	001	---	3	9	0
Brooklyn (NL)	300	102	10x	---	7	12	0

Pitchers--FORD, Gorman (2), Sain (5), Schallock (7) vs. LOES, Labine (9). Homers--McDougald (N.Y.), Snider (Bklyn.). Attendance--36,775.

5th Game, at Brooklyn, Oct. 4							
New York (AL)	105	000	311	---	11	11	1
Brooklyn (NL)	010	010	041	---	7	14	1

Pitchers--MCDONALD, Kuzava (8), Reynolds (9), vs. PODRES, Meyer (3), Wade (8), Black (9). Homers--Woodling (N.Y.), Mantle (N.Y.), Martin (N.Y.), McDougald (N.Y.), Cox (Bklyn.), Gilliam (Bklyn.). Attendance--36,665.

6th Game, at New York, Oct. 5							
Brooklyn (NL)	000	001	002	---	3	8	3
New York (AL)	210	000	001	---	4	13	0

Pitchers--Erskine, Milliken (5), LABINE (7) vs. Ford, REYNOLDS (8). Homer--Furillo (Bklyn.). Attendance--62,370.

1954

The irrepressible Giants waved their magic wand known as Dusty Rhodes to blot out Cleveland four straight times and smash a seven-year monopoly held by the AL in post-season conflict. It was the first time since 1946 that the AL had lost a series and only the second time in the history of the classic that the NL had swept a series, the miracle Boston Braves first performing the trick on the Philadelphia Athletics in 1914. A Cleveland team which had established a new standard for league victories with 111 was no match for Leo Durocher's surprises after the first two games. The Indians seemed on their way to victory in the eighth inning of the opener only to see outfielder Willie Mays snatch it from their grasp at the base of the centerfield wall. His incredible catch of Vic Wertz' long bid for a triple with two aboard will remain as one of the series' most historic fielding plays. It prevented the Tribe from nailing down the verdict and allowed Rhodes, pinch hitter extraordinary, to drive a three-run, game-winning homer which barely reached the right field stands in the 10th inning. Pitcher Early Wynn failed the following day, as his opponent, Johnny Antonelli, drove in what proved to be the winning tally and Rhodes once again belted a home run. Cleveland's famed hurling staff came apart in the third and fourth frays and the Giants didn't have to resort to heroics to clinch victories in both of them. Rhodes, in six official times at bat, drove in seven runs; Al Dark hit .412 to top the New York batters; Giant third baseman Hank Thompson coaxed seven bases on balls, a new record for a four-game series. But Wertz, the bald-headed outfielder-first baseman, hit for a .500 average to lead both clubs.

Result: New York NL won 4; Cleveland AL, 0.

1st Game, at New York, Sept. 29						R.	H.	E.
Cleveland (AL)	200	000	000	0	---	2	8	0
New York (NL)	002	000	000	3	---	5	9	0

Pitchers--LEMON vs. Maglie, Liddle (8), GRISSOM (8). Homer--Rhodes (N.Y.). Attendance--52,751

2nd Game, at New York, Sept. 30							
Cleveland (AL)	100	000	000	---	1	8	0
New York (NL)	000	020	10x	---	3	4	0

Pitchers--WYNN, Mossi (8) vs. ANTONELLI. Homers--Smith (Cleve), Rhodes (N.Y.). Attendance--49,099.

3rd Game, at Cleveland, Oct. 1							
New York (NL)	103	011	000	---	6	10	1
Cleveland (AL)	000	000	110	---	2	4	2

Pitchers--GOMEZ, Wilhelm (7) vs. GARCIA, Houtteman (4), Narleski (6), Mossi (9). Homer--Wertz (Cleve). Attendance--71,555.

4th Game, at Cleveland, Oct. 2							
New York (NL)	021	040	000	---	7	10	3
Cleveland (AL)	000	030	100	---	4	6	2

Pitchers -- LIDDLE, Wilhelm (7), Antonelli (8) vs. LEMON, Newhouser (5), Narleski (5), Mossi (6), Garcia (8). Homer--Majeski (Cleve.). Attendance--78,102.

1955

This became the "next year" Brooklyn fans had waited for since their American Association champs of 1889 began the habit of losing post-season series. Fittingly enough, the Dodgers, who made a complete shambles of the NL race, victimized the Yankees, a team which had thwarted their last five series bids. Moreover, Walter Alston's boys broke an old series jinx by becoming the first club to take a seven-game set after losing the first two games. Hero of the victory was a 23-year old southpaw, Johnny Podres, who twice befuddled the Yankee sluggers with his tantalizing change-up, winning the third game, 8-3, and then taking the decisive seventh contest, 2-0. In that last one, Gil Hodges, goat of so many past Dodger series setbacks, batted in both runs with a single and a sacrifice fly, while Sandy Amoros made a game-saving catch on Yogi Berra's slice down the left field line and turned it into a double play to kill the Yanks' sixth inning rally. Casey Stengel had defied the "no-southpaws-against-Brooklyn" tradition to win the first two games at Yankee Stadium behind Whitey Ford and Tommy Byrne, the pitchers who had enabled New York to win a close AL pennant race from Cleveland, Chicago and Boston. But the Dodgers came back to take three at Ebbets Field on the pitching of Podres and Clem Labine and the home runs of Duke Snider and Roy Campanella. Alston passed up 20-game winner Don Newcombe to start rookie Karl Spooner in the sixth game, but he was blasted in a five-run first inning, featuring Bill Skowron's three-run homer, and Ford had his first complete game series win. This left it to Podres and Byrne in the finale, with the young southpaw from up-

state New York edging the hero of 1955's biggest baseball comeback story. Snider's four homers raised his NL series record to nine, one back of Lou Gehrig, six behind Babe Ruth.

Result: Brooklyn NL won 4; New York AL, 3.

1st game, at New York, Sept. 28

					R.	H.	E.
Brooklyn (NL)	021	000	020	---	5	10	0
New York (AL)	021	102	00x	---	6	9	1

Pitchers--NEWCOMBE, Bessent (6), Labine (8) vs. FORD, Grim (9). Homers--Furillo (Bklyn), Snider (Bklyn), Howard (N.Y.), Collins (N.Y.) 2. Attendance--63,869.

2nd game, at New York, Sept. 29

					R.	H.	E.
Brooklyn (NL)	000	110	000	---	2	5	2
New York (AL)	000	400	00x	---	4	8	0

Pitchers--LOES, Bessent (4), Spooner (5), Labine (8) vs BYRNE. Attendance--64,707.

3rd game, at Brooklyn, Sept. 30

					R.	H.	E.
New York (AL)	020	000	100	---	3	7	0
Brooklyn (NL)	220	200	20x	---	8	11	1

Pitchers--TURLEY, Morgan (2), Kucks (5), Sturdivant (7) vs PODRES. Homers--Campanella (Bklyn), Mantle (N.Y.). Attendance--34,209.

4th game, at Brooklyn, Oct. 1

					R.	H.	E.
New York (AL)	110	102	000	---	5	9	0
Brooklyn (NL)	001	330	10x	---	8	14	0

Pitchers--LARSEN, Kucks (5), R. Coleman (6), Morgan (7), Sturdivant (8) vs Erskine, Bessent (4), LABINE (5). Homers--McDougald (N.Y.), Campanella (Bklyn), Hodges (Bklyn), Snider (Bklyn). Attendance--36,242.

5th game, at Brooklyn, Oct. 2

					R.	H.	E.
New York (AL)	000	100	110	---	3	6	0
Brooklyn (NL)	021	010	01x	---	5	9	2

Pitchers--GRIM, Turley (7) vs CRAIG, Labine (7). Homers--Cerv (N.Y.), Berra (N.Y.), Amoros (Bklyn), Snider (Bklyn) 2. Attendance--36,796.

6th game, at New York, Oct. 3

					R.	H.	E.
Brooklyn (NL)	000	100	000	---	1	4	1
New York (AL)	500	000	00x	---	5	8	0

Pitchers--SPOONER, Meyer (1), Roebuck (7) vs FORD. Homer--Skowron (N.Y.). Attendance--64,022.

7th game, at New York, Oct. 4

					R.	H.	E.
Brooklyn (NL)	000	101	000	---	2	5	0
New York (AL)	000	000	000	---	0	8	1

Pitchers--PODRES vs BYRNE, Grim (6), Turley (8). Attendance--62,465.

Pitcher Don Larsen is greeted jubilantly by Catcher Yogi Berra after final out of the fifth game in the 1956 World Series. Larsen retired 27 Dodgers in order for the first perfectly pitched game in Series history. (Wide World Photo)

1956

Don Larsen, who in 1954 had lost 21 games while pitching for Baltimore, made history by pitching the only perfect game (27 batters retired consecutively) in Series history when he turned back the Dodgers in the fifth game, 2-0. Form took a complete reversal of the Series played between these two clubs the previous year. This time the Dodgers started fast with victories in the first two games, only to see the Yankees sweep the next three. Clem Labine then outdueled Bob Turley in a 10-inning, 1-0 duel to tie the set at three games apiece before the Yankees blasted Don Newcombe in the decisive contest, 9-0, behind the three-hit pitching of Johnny Kucks. Yogi Berra slammed two homers in the finale and his .360 average was tops for the classic. The Yankee catcher established a new Series mark when he drove in ten runs. Duke Snider's tenth homer put him in a second-place tie with Lou Gehrig for most homers in Series competition. The Yankees established two undistinguished records for futility in the second game when they (1) paraded seven pitchers to the mound (2) who issued a total of 11 bases on balls. But the next five Yankee starters went the distance as the American Leaguers won their 17th title and sixth over their most persistent post-season challengers. Larsen's perfect game, in which Mickey Mantle's homer and Hank Bauer's sacrifice fly accounted for both Yank runs, and Labine's sixth game shutout were the top pitching performances of the Series. Jackie Robinson's left field single tied up the Series in game No. 6.

Result: New York AL won 4; Brooklyn NL, 3.

1st Game, at Brooklyn, Oct. 3

					R.	H.	E.
New York (AL)	200	100	000	---	3	9	1
Brooklyn (NL)	023	100	00x	---	6	9	0

Pitchers--FORD, Kucks (4), Morgan (6) vs. MAGLIE. Homers--Mantle (N.Y.), Robinson (Bklyn.), Hodges (Bklyn.). Martin (N.Y.). Attendance--34,479.

2nd Game, at Brooklyn, Oct. 5

New York (AL)	150	100	001	---	8	12	2
Brooklyn (NL)	061	220	02x	---	13	12	0

Pitchers--Larsen, Kucks (2), Byrne (2), Sturdivant (3), MORGAN (3), Turley (5), McDermott (6) vs. Newcombe, Roebuck (2), BESSENT (3). Homers--Berra (N.Y.), Snider (Bklyn.). Attendance--36,217.

3rd Game, at New York, Oct. 6

Brooklyn (NL)	010	001	100	---	3	8	1
New York (AL)	010	003	01x	---	5	8	1

Pitchers-- CRAIG, Labine (7) vs. FORD Homers--Martin (N.Y.), Slaughter (N.Y.). Attendance--73,977.

4th Game, at New York, Oct. 7

Brooklyn (NL)	000	100	001	---	2	6	0
New York (AL)	100	201	20x	---	6	7	2

Pitchers--ERSKINE, Roebuck (5), Drysdale (7) vs. STURDIVANT. Homers--Mantle (N.Y.), Bauer (N.Y.). Attendance--69,705.

5th Game, at New York, Oct. 8

Brooklyn (NL)	000	000	000	---	0	0	0
New York (AL)	000	101	00x	---	2	5	0

Pitchers--MAGLIE vs. LARSEN. Homer--Mantle (N.Y.). Attendance--64,519.

6th Game, at Brooklyn, Oct. 9

New York (AL)	000	000	000	0----	0	7	0
Brooklyn (NL)	000	000	000	1----	1	4	0

Pitchers--TURLEY vs. LABINE. Attendance--33,224.

7th Game, at Brooklyn, Oct. 10

New York (AL)	202	100	400	---	9	10	0
Brooklyn (NL)	000	000	000	---	0	3	1

Pitchers--KUCKS vs. NEWCOMBE, Bessent (4), Craig (7), Roebuck (7), Erskine (9). Homers--Berra (N.Y.) 2, Howard (N.Y.), Skowron (N.Y.). Attendance--33,782.

1957

Lew Burdette, who was brought up to the big leagues by the Yankees, turned on his old mates with the most superb one-man pitching performance since Christy Mathewson of the Giants shut out the Philadelphia Athletics three times in the 1905 Series. The tall righthander who had been suspected—but never convicted—of firing the outlawed spit ball during the season, turned in three complete game triumphs as Milwaukee won its first post-season classic. Warren Spahn, the lefthander who hooked up with Burdette to pace the Braves to the pennant, was the other winner—a 10-inning, 7—5 thriller which Eddie Mathews decided with a one-on homer. Burdette began his mastery of the Yankees in the second game, and concluded the Series with a second shutout, 5-0, at Yankee Stadium. Whitey Ford, Don Larsen and Bob Turley were the winning Yankee hurlers. Milwaukee's Hank Aaron hit safely in every game and his .393 average led both clubs. The Yankees were below par physically due to Mickey Mantle's leg injury and Bill Skowron's back injury. The Braves played without Bill Bruton, their regular center-fielder. The Series established two historic records—most attendance (394,712) and total receipts ($5,475,-978.94). The net gate receipts were $2,475,978.94 but an additional three million dollars from a new TV-radio contract was added to the kitty to help establish a new financial high.

Result: Milwaukee NL won 4; New York AL, 3.

1st Game, at New York, Oct. 2					R.	H.	E.
Milwaukee (NL)	000	000	100	---	1	5	0
New York (AL)	000	012	00x	---	3	9	1

Pitchers--SPAHN, Johnson (6), McMahon (7) vs. FORD. Attendance--69,476.

2nd Game, at New York, Oct. 3							
Milwaukee (NL)	011	200	000	---	4	8	0
New York (AL)	011	000	000	---	2	7	2

Pitchers--BURDETTE vs. SHANTZ, Ditmar (4), Grim (8). Homers -- Logan (Mil.), Bauer (N.Y.). Attendance--65,202.

3rd Game, at Milwaukee, Oct. 5							
New York (AL)	302	200	500	---	12	9	0
Milwaukee (NL)	010	020	000	---	3	8	1

Pitchers--Turley, LARSEN (2) vs. BUHL, Pizarro (1), Conley (3), Johnson (5), Trowbridge (7), McMahon (8). Homers -- Kubek (N.Y.) 2, Mantle (N.Y.), Aaron (Mil.). Attendance--45,804.

4th Game, at Milwaukee, Oct. 6								
New York (AL)	100	000	003	1	---	5	11	0
Milwaukee (NL)	000	400	000	3	---	7	7	0

Pitchers -- Sturdivant, Shantz (5), Kucks (8), Byrne (8), GRIM (10) vs. SPAHN. Homers--Aaron (Mil.), Torre (Mil.), Howard (N.Y.), Mathews (Mil.). Attendance--45,804.

5th Game, at Milwaukee, Oct. 7							
New York (AL)	000	000	000	---	0	7	0
Milwaukee (NL)	000	001	00x	---	1	6	1

Pitchers -- FORD, Turley (8) vs. BURDETTE. Attendance--45,811.

6th Game, at New York, Oct. 9							
Milwaukee (NL)	000	010	100	---	2	4	0
New York (AL)	002	000	10x	---	3	7	0

Pitchers -- Buhl, JOHNSON (3), McMahon (8) vs. TURLEY. Homers -- Berra (N.Y.), Torre (Mil.), Aaron (Mil.), Bauer (N.Y.). Attendance--61,408.

7th Game, at New York, Oct. 10							
Milwaukee (NL)	004	000	010	---	5	9	1
New York (AL)	000	000	000	---	0	7	3

Pitchers--BURDETTE vs. LARSEN, Shantz (3), Ditmar (4), Sturdivant (6), Byrne (8). Homer--Crandall (Mil.). Attendance--61,207.

1958

The New York Yankees, down three games to one, staged a magnificent comeback to whip the Milwaukee Braves in the fourth straight Series to go the legal limit of seven games. Only once before—when Pittsburgh upset Washington in 1925—had a team come from so far behind to take the classic. It was the 18th championship for the Yankees in 24 attempts and their seventh in nine tries under the guidance of Casey Stengel who settled his personal score with Milwaukee manager Fred Haney. The Braves, behind Warren Spahn and Lew Burdette, took the first two games at Milwaukee. Don Larsen and Ryne Duren combined to halt the Braves in the third contest but Spahn's sparkling two-hit shutout in the fourth game gave the National Leaguers a commanding 3-1 lead and almost assured them of their second straight title. However, the Yankees, with brilliant pitching, refused to fold. Bob Turley hurled a five-hit shutout in the fifth game and stout relief pitching by Art Ditmar, Duren and Turley overcame Spahn's heroic effort in the 4-3 sixth contest which went ten innings. Larsen and Burdette started the decisive battle but big Don left in the third inning after the Yanks had taken a 2-1 lead. Del Crandall's sixth-inning homer tied the game and it was 2-2 as the eighth inning started. After Burdette retired the first two batters, the American Leaguers exploded. Yogi Berra doubled to right and scored on Elston Howard's single through the middle. Andy Carey then beat out an infield hit and Bill Skowron delivered the clincher with a three-run homer. It was the end of the road for Burdette and the Braves. Hank Bauer tied a Series record with four home runs. Milwaukee's Ed Mathews established a new individual mark for futility with eleven strikeouts.

Result: New York AL won 4; Milwaukee NL, 3.

1st Game, at Milwaukee, Oct. 1						R.	H.	E.
New York (AL)	000	120	000	0	---	3	8	1
Milwaukee (NL)	000	200	010	1	---	4	10	0

Pitchers -- Ford, DUREN (8) vs. SPAHN. Homers--Skowron (N.Y.), Bauer (N.Y.). Attendance--46,367.

2nd Game, at Milwaukee, Oct. 2							
New York (AL)	100	100	003	---	5	7	0
Milwaukee (NL)	710	000	23x	---	13	15	1

Pitchers -- TURLEY, Maas (1), Kucks (1), Dickson (5), Monroe (8) vs. BURDETTE. Homers--Bruton (Mil.), Burdette (Mil.), Mantle (N.Y.) 2, Bauer (N.Y.). Attendance--46,367.

3rd Game, at New York, Oct. 4

Milwaukee (NL)	000	000	000	---	0	6	0
New York (AL)	000	020	20x	---	4	4	0

Pitchers--RUSH, McMahon (7) vs. LARSEN, Duren (8). Homer--Bauer (N.Y.). Attendance--71,599.

4th Game, at New York, Oct. 5

Milwaukee (NL)	000	001	110	---	3	9	0
New York (AL)	000	000	000	---	0	2	0

Pitchers--SPAHN vs. FORD, Kucks (8), Dickson (9). Attendance--71,563.

5th Game, at New York, Oct. 6

Milwaukee (NL)	000	000	000	---	0	5	0
New York (AL)	001	006	00x	---	7	10	0

Pitchers--BURDETTE, Pizarro (6), Willey (8) vs. TURLEY. Homer--McDougald (N.Y.). Attendance--65,279.

6th Game, at Milwaukee, Oct. 8

New York (AL)	100	001	000	2	---	4	10	1
Milwaukee (NL)	110	000	000	1	---	3	10	4

Pitchers--Ford, Ditmar (2), DUREN (6), Turley (10) vs. SPAHN, McMahon (10). Homers--Bauer (N.Y.), McDougald (N.Y.). Attendance--46,367.

7th Game, at Milwaukee, Oct. 9

New York (AL)	020	000	040	---	6	8	0
Milwaukee (NL)	100	001	000	---	2	5	2

Pitchers--Larsen, TURLEY (3) vs. BURDETTE, McMahon (8). Homers--Crandall (Mil.), Skowron (N.Y.). Attendance--46,367.

1959

After eight failures in nine attempts, the rejuvenated Dodgers, now transplanted to the West Coast, beat Al Lopez' Chicago White Sox, in six games in the fifty-sixth fall classic. For attendance, receipts and size of players' shares, the series broke all existing records thanks to the enormous seating capacity of the Los Angeles Memorial Coliseum. The three games at Los Angeles drew 92,394; 92,650, and 92,706 respectively. Including the TV and radio rights the receipts totaled $5,628,809.44. Each winning Dodger received $11,231.18 while the losing White Sox each received $7,275.17, also a record. Opening the Series in Chicago Early Wynn, mainstay of the White Sox staff, had little trouble in white-washing the Dodgers 11-0. The Dodgers played badly with Duke Snider booting two chances in the same inning for a Series record. In the third inning the Dodgers collapsed completely when the Go-Go Sox scored seven runs climaxed by Ted Kluszewski's first homer with two aboard. Big Klu repeated with another powerful clout with Landis aboard in the fourth. The Dodgers eked out a victory in the second game on two homers by Charley Neal and another by pinch-hitter Chuck Essegian. Larry Sherry, coming to the aid of Johnny Podres, did a masterful relief job. In the third game the Sox lacked the punch and scored only one run although they got 12 hits, 4 walks, and Billy Goodman was hit by a pitched ball. Don Drysdale gained the victory, although Larry Sherry again had to be called in from the bull pen. The fourth game was a different story to Wynn who gave up 8 hits in 2-2/3 innings and had to give way to Turk Lown when the Dodgers jumped on him in the third for five hits and four runs. The Sox came to life in the seventh and tied the score when Sherm Lollar hammered one over the left field screen scoring Fox and Big Klu, who had singled. Gil Hodges homer in the eighth was the deciding blow as the Dodgers picked up the marbles 5-4. The fifth game was a thriller as Shaw and Donovan stifled the Dodger bats and allowed only one extra-base hit, a triple, by Hodges. In the seventh inning Rivera went to right field and made a sensational running catch of Neal's hard drive with runners on second and third. Fox scored the only run of the game when he led off the fourth inning with a single, advanced to third on Landis' one-bagger, and scored when Lollar hit into a double play. The Dodgers made 13 hits including homers by Snider, Moon, and Essegian to smother the Sox 9-3 in the sixth and deciding game. Wynn, making his third start, was the victim of the savage Dodger attack and left the game in the fourth when the Dodgers scored six runs to put the game and the series on ice.

Result: Los Angeles NL won 4; Chicago AL, 2.

1959

1st Game, at Chicago, Oct. 1st					R	H	E
Los Angeles (NL)	000	000	000	---	0	8	3
Chicago (AL)	207	200	00X	---	11	11	0

Pitchers—CRAIG, Churn (3), Labine (4), Koufax (5), Klippstein (2) vs. WYNN, Staley (8). Homers—Kluszewski (Chi.) 2. Attendance—48,013.

2nd Game, at Chicago, Oct. 2nd					R	H	E
Los Angeles (NL)	000	010	300	---	4	9	1
Chicago (AL)	200	000	010	---	3	8	0

Pitchers—PODRES, Sherry (7) vs. SHAW, Lown (7). Homers—Neal (LA) 2, Essegian (LA). Attendance—47,368.

3rd Game, at Los Angeles, Oct. 4th					R	H	E
Chicago (AL)	000	000	010	---	1	12	0
Los Angeles (NL)	000	000	21X	---	3	5	0

Pitchers—DONOVAN, Staley (7) vs. DRYSDALE, Sherry (8). Attendance—92,394.

4th Game, at Los Angeles, Oct. 5th					R	H	E
Chicago, (AL)	000	000	400	---	4	10	3
Los Angeles (NL)	004	000	01X	---	5	9	0

Pitchers—Wynn, Lown (3), Pierce (4), STALEY (7) vs. Craig, SHERRY (8). Homers—Lollar, (Chi), Hodges (LA). Attendance—92,650.

5th Game, at Los Angeles, Oct. 6th					R	H	E
Chicago (AL)	000	100	000	---	1	5	0
Los Angeles (NL)	000	000	000	---	0	9	0

Pitchers—SHAW, Pierce (7), Donovan (8) vs. KOUFAX, Williams (8). Attendance—92,706.

6th Game, at Chicago, Oct. 8th					R	H	E
Los Angeles (NL)	002	600	001	---	9	13	0
Chicago (AL)	000	300	000	---	3	6	1

Pitchers—Podres, SHERRY (4) vs. WYNN, Donovan (4), Staley (5), Pierce (8), Moore (9). Homers—Snider (LA), Moon (LA), Kluszewski (Chi), Essegian (LA). Attendance—47,653.

1960

The 57th World Series was most peculiar due to the fact that the New York Yankees set many amazing records but were defeated by the Pirates four games to three. Among the World Series records set by the Yanks were: highest batting average (.338), most runs (55), most hits (91), most total bases (142) and most runs batted in (54). The Pirates' ability to come from behind was demonstrated in the first game when Maris homered with two out in the first inning. In their half, the Pirates bounced back with three runs and managed to stay ahead for the rest of the game with Bill Mazeroski, who later clouted the homer that beat the Yanks in the final game, weighing in with his first four-bagger. The second game was a breeze for the Yanks who belted six Pirate pitchers for 16 runs on 19 hits including two homers by Mickey Mantle for a 16-3 win behind Bullet Bob Turley. Resuming the series in Yankee Stadium on Oct. 8th, the Yanks again powdered the ball, winning 10-0 on 16 hits and Whitey Ford's fine four-hit pitching performance. In this game, Bobby Richardson, Yank second-sacker who hit only one home run during the entire season, hit a grand-slam homer in the first inning and batted in a record-breaking six runs during the game. In the fourth game Vern Law and Elroy Face combined to stifle the Yankee bats aided by a remarkable circus catch by Bill Virdon of a liner off Bob Cerv's bat. From that point Face went on to save a 3-2 decision for Law. The Yankee drouth continued into the fifth game despite Maris' second home run of the series. They could do little with Harvey Haddix and when they did threaten the Pirate's lead in the seventh, Face again put out the fire in his accustomed fashion. The sixth game was almost a repetition of the fourth with Whitey Ford returning to the mound. He allowed only seven hits and one walk, shutting out the Pirates by a 12-0 score. In this game the Yank bats again exploded for 17 hits including two triples by Richardson. With the series all even at three games apiece the do-or-die Pirates went to work on Turley and Stafford by scoring four times in the first two innings. Skowron's homer in the fifth gave the Yanks their first run. They scored four more in the sixth which was featured by Yogi Berra's three-run homer. They went ahead 7-4 by continuing the assault on reliefer Elroy Face. Coming to bat in their half of the eighth with their backs to the wall, the Pirates found themselves in familiar surroundings and proceeded to blast out five runs capped by catcher Hal Smith's mighty three-run homer over the left field wall giving them a 9-7 lead. Murtaugh then sent Friend in to protect the 2-run lead but the Yanks tied it all up at 9-9 on three singles and a force. Mazeroski, the lead-off batter for the Pirates in the bottom of the ninth, clobbered Ralph Terry's second pitch over the left field wall and the Corsairs wrapped up their first World Championship since 1925.

Result: Pittsburgh NL won 4; New York AL, 3.

1960

1st Game, at Pittsburgh, Oct. 5th					R	H	E
New York (AL)	100	100	002	---	4	13	2
Pittsburgh (NL)	300	201	00X	---	6	8	0

Pitchers—DITMAR, Coates (1), Maas (5), Duren (7) vs. LAW, Face (8). Homers—Maris (NY), Mazeroski (Pit), Howard (NY). Attendance—36,676.

2nd Game, at Pittsburgh, Oct. 6th					R	H	E
New York (AL)	002	127	301	---	16	19	1
Pittsburgh (NL)	000	100	002	---	3	13	1

Pitchers—TURLEY, Shantz (9) vs. FRIEND, Green (5), Labine (6), Witt (6), Biggon (7), Cheney (9). Homers—Mantle (NY) 2. Attendance—37,308.

3rd Game, at New York, Oct. 8th					R	H	E
Pittsburgh (NL)	000	000	000	---	0	4	0
New York (AL)	600	400	00X	---	10	16	1

Pitchers—MIZELL, Labine (1), Green (1), Witt (4), Cheney (6), Gibbon (8) vs. FORD. Homers—Richardson (NY), Mantle (NY). Attendance—70,001.

4th Game, at New York, Oct. 9th					R	H	E
Pittsburgh (NL)	000	030	000	---	3	7	0
New York (AL)	000	100	100	---	2	8	0

Pitchers—LAW, Face (7), vs. TERRY, Shantz (7), Coates (8). Homers—Skowron (NY). Attendance—67,812.

5th Game, at New York, Oct. 10th					R	H	E
Pittsburgh (NL)	031	000	001	---	5	10	2
New York (AL)	011	000	000	---	2	5	2

Pitchers—HADDIX, Face (7), vs. DITMAR, Arroyo (2), Stafford (3), Duren (8). Homers—Maris (NY). Attendance—62,753.

6th Game, at Pittsburgh, Oct. 12th					R	H	E
New York (AL)	015	002	220	---	12	17	1
Pittsburgh (NL)	000	000	000	---	0	7	1

Pitchers—FORD vs. FRIEND, Cheney (3), Mizell (4), Green (6), Labine (6), Witt (9). Attendance--38,580.

7th Game, at Pittsburgh, Oct. 13th					R	H	E
New York (AL)	000	014	022	---	9	13	1
Pittsburgh (NL)	220	000	051	---	10	11	0

Pitchers—Turley, Stafford (2), Shantz (3), Coates (8), TERRY (8) vs. Law, Face (6), Friend (9), HADDIX (9). Homers—Nelson (Pit), Skowron (NY), Berra (NY), Smith (Pit), Mazeroski (Pit). Attendance—36,683.

1961

The Yankees returned to their winning ways in the 1961 series, having no trouble in disposing of the jittery Cincinnati Reds in five games. In the first game, the peerless Whitey Ford set the Reds down on two measley singles for a 2-0 shutout, striking out six and allowing only one base on balls. Elston Howard and Bill Skowron supplied the punch—each with a homer. Bobby Richardson, batting star of the 1960 series, smacked three singles in four trips to the plate. The Reds turned the tables in the second game, thanks to Joey Jay's 4-hit pitching, and beat the Yanks by a score of 6-2. Scoring two runs in the fourth on an error by Boyer followed by Gordon Coleman's homer, they scored one in each the fifth and sixth and added a couple more in the eighth for good measure. The third game in Cincinnati was a thriller featured by a Yankee attack in the last three innings which overcame a two-run deficit. Roger Maris, who had gone hitless until he came up in the ninth, supplied the clincher when he homered off Bob Purkey. It was all Whitey Ford in the fourth game when he handed out another string of goose-eggs to the Reds allowing only five singles until he retired in the sixth with an ankle injury suffered earlier in the game. In pitching five scoreless frames Ford broke Babe Ruth's record of 29-2/3 consecutive scoreless inning which had stood since 1918. Richardson was again a thorn in the Reds side as he made three more hits. The fifth game resulted in a complete rout of the Reds, the Yanks scoring 13 runs of eight Red pitchers. It set a new record for the number of pitchers used in one World Series game. The Yanks lost no time when nine batters paraded to the plate in the first inning—five of them scoring. Another 5-run blast in the fourth topped by Hector Lopez' homer over the center field fence put the game entirely out of reach of the hapless Reds.

Result: New York AL won 4; Cincinnati NL, 1.

1st Game, at New York, Oct. 4th					R	H	E
Cincinnati (NL)	000	000	000	---	0	2	0
New York (AL)	000	101	00X	---	2	6	0

Pitchers—O'TOOLE, Brosnan (8), vs. FORD. Homers—Howard (NY), Skowron (NY). Attendance—62,397.

2nd Game, at New York, Oct. 5th					R	H	E
Cincinnati (NL)	000	211	020	---	6	9	0
New York (AL)	000	200	000	---	2	4	3

Pitchers—JAY vs. TERRY, Arroyo (8). Homers—Coleman (Cin.), Berra (NY). Attendance—63,083.

3rd Game, at Cincinnati, Oct. 7th					R	H	E
New York (AL)	000	000	111	---	3	6	1
Cincinnati (NL)	001	000	100	---	2	8	0

Pitchers—Stafford, Daley (7), ARROYO (8) vs. PURKEY. Homers—Blanchard (NY), Maris (NY). Attendance—32,589.

4th Game, at Cincinnati, Oct. 8th					R	H	E
New York (AL)	000	112	300	---	7	11	0
Cincinnati (NL)	000	000	000	---	0	5	1

Pitchers—FORD, Coates (6), vs. O'TOOLE, Brosnan (6), Henry (9). Attendance—32,589.

5th Game, at Cincinnati, Oct. 9th					R	H	E
New York (AL)	510	502	000	---	13	15	1
Cincinnati (NL)	003	020	000	---	5	11	3

Pitchers—Terry, DALEY (3), vs. JAY, Maloney (1), K. Johnson (2), Henry (3), Jones (4), Purkey (5), Brosnan (7), Hunt (9). Homers—Blanchard (NY), Robinson (Cin.), Lopez (NY), Post (Cin.). Attendance—32,589.

1962

Rainstorms, first in New York and then in San Francisco, produced the most elongated World Series in history. Beginning in New York, the first game was played on October 4th and the final or 7th game finally was completed on October 16th. As usual, the Yankee ace, Whitey Ford, got the Yanks off to a flying start by setting the Giants down by a score of 6 to 2. It was his fifth consecutive victory in World Series play and his 10th World Series win. The game was even at 2-2 until the Yanks finally broke through with one run in the 7th, two in the 8th and another one for good measure in the ninth. Clete Boyer really iced the game in the 7th when he clouted a homer over the left field fence. The Giants evened it up in the second game with a classy 3-hit performance by Jack Sanford who throttled the Yanks completely, shutting them out by a score of 2-0. Sanford allowed only one extra base hit to Mickey Mantle in pitching his masterpiece. Willie McCovey hit a tremendous homer over the right field barrier for the insurance run. The see-saw action continued in the third game when Roger Maris singled sharply to right-center driving in Tresh and Mantle who had singles before him. Ed Bailey's two-run homer in the ninth was the Giants only scoring threat. The game was well pitched on both sides with Stafford and Pierce in a scoreless duel until the 7th. Pierce allowed the Yanks 5 hits to Stafford's 4 for the Giants. The Giants evened it up again in game Number 4. The go-ahead runs were produced by Chuck Hiller's grand slam homer in the seventh inning. It was the first grand-slammer ever hit by a National League player in a World Series. The Giants used four pitchers in this game and the Yanks three. Whitey Ford was going along with a 2-2 tie when he was lifted for Jim Coates in the seventh. Coates had walked Jim Davenport and Haller had struck out when Matty Alou, batting for Pagan doubled to left. Houk then sent in Bridges and with two down, Hiller lined his homer into the right field seats. As in the previous game, game Number 5 was all tied up at 2-2 in the eighth when Rookie Tom Tresh connected with one of Jack Sanford's serves and the Yankees went ahead to stay. Moving to San

Francisco after the 5th game, the series was delayed five days by rain and it was not until October 15th that the sixth game was played. This time it was all Billy Pierce. Bouncing back after his loss in game Number 3, Billy was master of the situation all the way allowing the powerful Yanks only 3 hits and winning by a score of 5-2. With the Giants ahead 3-0, Roger Maris hammered one over the right field fence. The only other extra base blow was Clete Boyer's double in the eighth. However the Yanks were not to be denied and in the final game they rallied behind Ralph Terry's 4-hit shutout to eke out a narrow 1-0 victory and the series. It was a heart-breaker for Jack Sanford who allowed the Yanks only 7 hits. The lone run was scored in the 5th when Bill Skowron and Clete Boyer singled, Terry walked when Sanford temporarily lost control and Skowron scored as Kubek bounced into a double play. The pitching in the series on the part of both clubs was outstanding especially the Giants corps which held the vaunted power of the Yanks to a meager team average of .199.

Result: New York AL won 4; San Francisco NL, 3.

1962

1st Game, at San Francisco, Oct. 4th					R	H	E
New York (AL)	200	000	121	---	6	11	0
San Francisco (NL)	011	000	000	---	2	10	0

Pitchers—FORD vs. O'DELL, Larson (7), Miller (1). Homer—Boyer (NY). Attendance—43,852.

2nd Game, at San Francisco, Oct. 5th					R	H	E
New York (AL)	000	000	000	---	0	3	1
San Francisco (NL)	100	000	10X	---	2	6	0

Pitchers—TERRY, Daley (8) vs. SANFORD. Homer—McCovey (SF). Attendance—43,910.

3rd Game, at New York, Oct. 7th					R	H	E
San Francisco (NL)	000	000	002	---	2	4	3
New York (AL)	000	000	30X	---	3	5	1

Pitchers—PIERCE, Larsen (7), Bolin (8) vs. STAFFORD. Homer—Bailey (SF). Attendance—71,434.

4th Game, at New York, Oct. 8th					R	H	E
San Francisco (NL)	020	000	401	---	7	9	1
New York (AL)	000	002	001	---	3	9	1

Pitchers—Marichal, Bolin (5), LARSEN (6), O'Dell (7) vs. Ford, COATES (7), Bridges (7). Homers—Haller (SF), Hiller (SF). Attendance—66,607.

5th Game, at New York, Oct. 10th					R	H	E
San Francisco (NL)	001	010	001	---	3	8	2
New York (AL)	000	101	03X	---	5	6	0

Pitchers—SANFORD, Miller (8) vs. TERRY. Homers—Pagan (SF), Tresh (NY). Attendance—63,165.

6th Game, at San Francisco, Oct. 15th					R	H	E
New York (AL)	000	010	010	---	2	3	2
San Francisco (NL)	000	320	00X	---	5	10	1

Pitchers—FORD, Coates (5), Bridges (8) vs. PIERCE. Homer—Maris (NY). Attendance—43,948.

7th Game, at San Francisco, Oct. 16th					R	H	E
New York (AL)	000	010	000	---	1	7	0
San Francisco (NL)	000	000	000	---	0	4	1

Pitchers—TERRY vs. SANFORD, O'Dell (8). Attendance—43,948.

Year	National League	American League (or AA).	Games W-L	Attendance	Receipts	Winning Player's Share	Losing Player's Share
1882	Chicago	Cincinnati(AA)	1-1	7,200	$ 2,000.00	$ 0	$ 0
1884	*Providence	Metropolitans(AA)	3-0	3,100	850.00	100.00	0
1885	Chicago	St. Louis(AA)	3-3a	14,200	3,000.00	0	0
1886	Chicago	*St. Louis(AA)	2-4	43,000	14,000.00	855.00	0
1887	*Detroit	St. Louis(AA)	10-5	51,455	41,050.00	500.00	0
1888	*New York	St. Louis(AA)	6-4	42,270	24,362.10	450.00	0
1889	*New York	Brooklyn (AA)	6-3	47,256	24,262.10	380.15	389.29
1890	Brooklyn	Louisville (AA)	3-3a	13,910	6,000.00	100.00	100.00
1903	Pittsburgh	*Boston	3-5	100,429	55,500.00	1,182.00	1,316.25
1905	*New York	Philadelphia	4-1	91,723	68,437.00	1,142.00	833.75
1906	Chicago	*Chicago	2-4	99,845	106,550.00	1,874.63	439.50
1907	*Chicago	Detroit	4-0a	78,068	101,728.50	2,142.85	1,945.96
1908	*Chicago	Detroit	4-1	62,232	94,975.50	1,317.58	870.00
1909	*Pittsburgh	Detroit	4-3	145,295	188,302.50	1,825.22	1,274.76
1910	Chicago	*Philadelphia	1-4	124,222	173,980.00	2,062.79	1,375.16
1911	New York	*Philadelphia	2-4	179,851	342,164.50	3,654.58	2,436.39
1912	New York	*Boston	3-4a	252,037	490,449.00	4,024.68	2,566.47
1913	New York	*Philadelphia	1-4	151,000	325,980.00	3,246.36	2,164.22
1914	*Boston	Philadelphia	4-0	111,009	225,739.00	2,812.28	2,031.65
1915	Philadelphia	*Boston	1-4	143,351	320,361.50	3,780.25	2,520.17
1916	Brooklyn	*Boston	1-4	162,859	385,590.50	3,910.26	2,834.82
1917	New York	*Chicago	2-4	186,654	425,878.00	3,669.32	2,442.61
1918	Chicago	*Boston	2-4	128,483	179,619.00	1,102.51	671.09
1919	*Cincinnati	Chicago	5-3	236,928	722,414.00	5,207.01	3,254.36
1920	Brooklyn	*Cleveland	2-5	178,737	564,800.00	4,168.00	2,419.60
1921	*New York	New York	5-3	269,976	900,233.00	5,265.00	3,510.00
1922	*New York	New York	4-0a	185,947	605,475.00	4,470.00	3,225.00
1923	New York	*New York	2-4	301,430	1,063,815.00	6,143.49	4,112.89
1924	New York	*Washington	3-4	283,665	1,093,104.00	5,969.64	3,820.29
1925	*Pittsburgh	Washington	4-3	282,848	1,182,854.00	5,332.72	3,734.60
1926	*St. Louis	New York	4-3	328,051	1,207,864.00	5,584.51	3,417.75
1927	Pittsburgh	*New York	0-4	201,705	783,217.00	5,592.17	3,728.10
1928	St. Louis	*New York	0-4	199,072	777,290.00	5,531.91	4,197.37
1929	Chicago	*Philadelphia	1-4	190,490	859,494.00	5,620.57	3,782.01
1930	St. Louis	*Philadelphia	2-4	212,619	953,772.00	5,785.00	3,875.00
1931	*St. Louis	Philadelphia	4-3	231,567	1,030,723.00	4,467.59	3,032.09
1932	Chicago	*New York	0-4	191,998	713,377.00	5,231.77	4,244.60
1933	*New York	Washington	4-1	163,076	679,365.00	4,256.72	3,019.86
1934	*St. Louis	Detroit	4-3	281,510	1,128,995.27b	5,389.57b	3,354.57b
1935	Chicago	*Detroit	2-4	286,672	1,173,794.00b	6,544.76b	4,198.53b
1936	New York	*New York	2-4	302,924	1,304,399.00b	6,430.55b	4,655.58b
1937	New York	*New York	1-4	238,142	1,085,994.00b	6,471.10b	4,489.05b
1938	Chicago	*New York	0-4	200,833	851,166.00	5,782.76	4,674.87
1939	Cincinnati	*New York	0-4	183,849	845,329.00b	5,614.26b	4,282.58b
1940	*Cincinnati	Detroit	4-3	281,927	1,322,328.21b	5,803.62b	3,531.81b
1941	Brooklyn	*New York	1-4	235,773	1,107,762.00b	5,943.31b	4,829.40b
1942	*St. Louis	New York	4-1	277,101	1,205,249.00b	5,573.78	3,018.77
1943	St. Louis	*New York	1-4	277,312	1,205,784.00b	6,139.46	4,321.96
1944	*St. Louis	St. Louis	4-2	206,708	1,006,122.00b	4,626.01	2,743.79
1945	Chicago	*Detroit	3-4	333,457	1,592,454.00b	6,443.34b	3,930.22b
1946	*St. Louis	Boston	4-3	250,071	1,227,900.00c	3,742.34	2,140.89
1947	Brooklyn	*New York	3-4	389,763	2,021,348.92d	5,830.03	4,081.19
1948	Boston	*Cleveland	2-4	358,362	1,948,685.56e	6,772.05	4,651.51
1949	Brooklyn	*New York	1-4	236,710	1,436,527.82f	5,665.54	4,272.73
1950	Philadelphia	*New York	0-4	196,009	1,928,669.03g	5,737.95	4,081.34
1951	New York	*New York	2-4	341,977	2,708,457.47h	6,446.09	4,951.03
1952	Brooklyn	*New York	3-4	340,906	2,747,753.01i	5,982.65	4,200.64
1953	Brooklyn	*New York	2-4	307,350	2,979,269.44j	8,280.68	6,178.42
1954	*New York	Cleveland	4-0	251,507	2,741,203.38k	11,147.90	6,712.50
1955	*Brooklyn	New York	4-3	362,310	3,512,515.34l	9,768.00	5,598.00
1956	Brooklyn	*New York	4-3	345,903	3,333,254.59m	8,714.76	6,934.34
1957	*Milwaukee	New York	4-3	394,712	5,475,978.94n	8,924.36	5,606.06
1958	Milwaukee	*New York	4-3	393,909	5,397,223.03o	8,759.10	5,896.09

1959	*Los Angeles	Chicago		4-2		420,784	5,628,809.440	11,231.18	7,275.17
1960	*Pittsburgh	New York		4-3		349,813	5,480,627.88p	8,417.94	5,214.64
1961	Cincinnati	*New York		4-1		223,247	4,730,059.95p	7,389.13	5,356.37
1962	*New York	San Francisco		4-3		376,864	2,878,891.11	9,882.74	7,291.49

***-Indicates winning team.**
a-Indicates one game tied.
b-Including $100,000 radio receipts.
c-Including $175,000 radio receipts.
d-Including $175,000 radio and $65,000 TV receipts.
e-Including $175,000 radio and $140,000 TV receipts.
f -Including $175,000 radio, $200,000 TV and $31,900 movie-TV receipts.
g-Including $175,000 radio and $800,000 TV receipts.
h-Including $150,000 radio and $925,000 TV receipts.
i -Including $200,000 radio and $925,000 TV receipts.
j -Including $175,000 radio and $1,025,000 TV receipts.
k-Including $150,000 radio and $1,025,000 TV receipts.
l -Including $150,000 radio and $1,025,000 TV receipts.
m-Including $125,000 radio and $1,025,000 TV receipts.
n-Including $3,000,000 radio and TV receipts.
o-Including $3,000,000 radio and TV receipts.
p-Including $3,250,000 Radio and TV receipts.

TEAM RECAPITULATION (1903-1962)

(Figure after team indicates number of Series participated in; figures in parentheses indicate number of Series won and lost; figures following parentheses indicate number of Series games won and lost.)

NATIONAL LEAGUE

Boston, 2 (1-1) 6-4

Brooklyn, 9 (1-8) 20-36

Chicago, 10 (2-8) 19-33

Cincinnati, 4 (2-2) 10-14

Los Angeles, 1 (1-0) 4-2

Milwaukee, 2 (1-1) 7-7

Philadelphia, 2 (0-2) 1-8

Pittsburgh, 5 (3-2) 15-18

New York, 14 (5-9) 39-41

St. Louis, 9 (6-3) 27-27

AMERICAN LEAGUE

Boston, 6 (5-1) 24-14

Chicago, 4 (2-2) 13-13

Cleveland, 3 (2-1) 9-8

Detroit, 7 (2-5) 18-25

New York, 26 (19-7) 89-50

Philadelphia, 8 (5-3) 24-19

St. Louis, 1 (0-1) 2-4

San Francisco, 1 (0-1) 3-4

Washington, 3 (1-2) 8-11

ALL-TIME REGISTER OF WORLD SERIES PLAYERS (1903-1962)

Yr	Cl	Lea	Pos	G	Rec
AARON, HENRY LOUIS					
1957	Mil	N	O	7	.393
1958	Mil	N	O	7	.333
				14	.364
ABBATICCHIO, EDWARD JAMES					
1909	Pit	N	H	1	.000
ABSTEIN, WILLIAM HENRY					
1909	Pit	N	1	7	.231
ADAMS, CHARLES BENJAMIN					
1909	Pit	N	P	3	3-0
1925	Pit	N	P	1	0-0
				4	3-0
ADAMS, EARL JOHN					
1930	St.L	N	3	6	.143
1931	St.L	N	3	2	.250
				8	.160
ADAMS, SPENCER DEWEY					
1925	Was	A	2	2	.000
1926	NY	A	H	2	.000
				4	.000
ADCOCK, JOSEPH WILBUR					
1957	Mil	N	1	5	.200
1958	Mil	N	1	4	.308
				9	.250
AGNEW, SAMUEL LESTER					
1918	Bos	A	C	9	.000
ALDRIDGE, VICTOR E.					
1925	Pit	N	P	3	2-0
1927	Pit	N	P	1	0-1
				4	2-1
ALEXANDER, GROVER CLEVELAND					
1915	Phi	N	P	2	1-1
1926	St.L	N	P	3	2-0
1928	St.L	N	P	2	0-1
				7	3-2
ALLEN, JOHN THOMAS					
1932	NY	A	P	1	0-0
1941	Bro	N	P	3	0-0
				4	0-0
ALOU, FELIPE ROJAS					
1962	SF	N	O	7	.269
ALOU, MATEO ROJAS					
1962	SF	N	O	6	.333
ALTROCK, NICHOLAS					
1906	Chi	A	P	2	1-1
AMES, LEON KESSLING					
1905	NY	N	P	1	0-0
1911	NY	N	P	2	0-1
1912	NY	N	P	1	0-0
				4	0-1
AMOROS, EDMUNDO ISASI					
1952	Bro	N	H	1	.000
1955	Bro	N	O	5	.333
1956	Bro	N	O	6	.053
				12	.161
ANDERSON, JOHN FREDERICK					
1917	NY	N	P	1	0-1
ANDREWS, IVY PAUL					
1937	NY	A	P	1	0-0

Yr	Cl	Lea	Pos	G	Rec
ANTONELLI, JOHN AUGUST					
1954	NY	N	P	2	1-0
APARICIO, LUIS ERNESTO					
1959	Chi	A	S	6	.308
ARCHER, JAMES PATRICK					
1907	Det	A	C	1	.000
1910	Chi	N	C-1	3	.182
				4	.143
ARNOVICH, MORRIS					
1940	Cin	N	O	1	.000
ARROYO, LUIS ENRIQUE					
1960	NY	A	P	1	0-0
1961	NY	A	P	2	1-0
				3	1-0
ASHBURN, RICHIE					
1950	Phi	N	O	4	.176
AUKER, ELDON LEROY					
1934	Det	A	P	2	1-1
1935	Det	A	P	1	0-0
				3	1-1
AVERILL, HOWARD EARL					
1940	Det	A	H	3	.000
AVILA, ROBERTO FRANCISCO GONZALEZ					
1954	Cle	A	2	4	.133
BAGBY, JAMES CHARLES JR.					
1946	Bos	A	P	1	0-0
BAGBY, JAMES CHARLES SR.					
1920	Cle	A	P	2	1-1
BAILEY, LONAS EDGAR					
1962	SF	N	C	6	.071
BAKER, EUGENE WALTER					
1960	Pit	N	H	3	.000
BAKER, FLOYD WILSON					
1944	St.L	A	2	2	.000
BAKER, JOHN FRANKLIN					
1910	Phi	A	3	5	.409
1911	Phi	A	3	6	.375
1913	Phi	A	3	5	.450
1914	Phi	A	3	4	.250
1921	NY	A	3	4	.250
1922	NY	A	H	1	.000
				25	.363
BAKER, WILLIAM PRESLEY					
1940	Cin	N	C	3	.250
BALDWIN, HOWARD EDWARD					
1924	NY	N	P	1	0-0
BALL, NEAL					
1912	Bos	A	H	1	.000
BALLOU, NOBLE WINFRED					
1925	Was	A	P	2	0-0
BANCROFT, DAVID JAMES					
1915	Phi	N	S	5	.294
1921	NY	N	S	8	.152
1922	NY	N	S	5	.211
1923	NY	N	S	6	.083
				24	.172

Yr	Cl	Lea	Pos	G	Rec
BANKHEAD, DANIEL ROBERT					
1947	Bro	N	H	1	.000
BANTA, JOHN KAY					
1949	Bro	N	P	3	0-0
BARBER, SAMUEL TURNER					
1918	Chi	N	H	3	.000
BARNES, JESSE LAWRENCE					
1921	NY	N	P	3	2-0
1922	NY	N	P	1	0-0
				4	2-0
BARNES, VIRGIL JENNINGS					
1923	NY	N	P	2	0-0
1924	NY	N	P	2	0-1
				4	0-1
BARNEY, REX EDWARD					
1947	Bro	N	P	3	0-1
1949	Bro	N	P	1	0-1
				4	0-2
BARNHART, CLYDE LEE					
1925	Pit	N	O	7	.250
1927	Pit	N	O	4	.313
				11	.273
BARRETT, CHARLES HENRY					
1948	Bos	N	P	2	0-0
BARRY, JOHN JOSEPH					
1910	Phi	A	S	5	.235
1911	Phi	A	S	6	.368
1913	Phi	A	S	5	.300
1914	Phi	A	S	4	.071
1915	Bos	A	2	5	.176
				25	.241
BARTELL, RICHARD WILLIAM					
1936	NY	N	S	6	.381
1937	NY	N	S	5	.238
1940	Det	A	S	7	.269
				18	.294
BAUER, HENRY ALBERT					
1949	NY	A	O	3	.167
1950	NY	A	O	4	.133
1951	NY	A	O	6	.167
1952	NY	A	O	7	.056
1953	NY	A	O	6	.261
1955	NY	A	O	6	.429
1956	NY	A	O	7	.281
1957	NY	A	O	7	.258
1958	NY	A	O	7	.323
				53	.245
BEARDEN, HENRY EUGENE					
1948	Cle	A	P	2	1-0
BEAUMONT, CLARENCE HOWETH					
1903	Pit	N	O	8	.265
1910	Chi	N	H	3	.000
				11	.250
BEAZLEY, JOHN ANDREW					
1942	St.L	N	P	2	2-0
1946	St.L	N	P	1	0-0
				3	2-0
BECKER, BEALS					
1911	NY	N	H	3	.000
1912	NY	N	O	2	.000
1915	Phi	N	O	2	.000
				7	.000

Yr	Cl	Lea	Pos	G	Rec
BECKER, HEINZ REINHARD					
1945	Chi	N	H	2	.500
BEDIENT, HUGH CARPENTER					
1912	Bos	A	P	4	1-0
BEGGS, JOSEPH STANLEY					
1940	Cin	N	P	1	0-0
BEHRMAN, HENRY BERNARD					
1947	Bro	N	P	5	0-0
BELARDI, CARROLL WAYNE					
1953	Bro	N	H	2	.000
BELL, DAVID RUSSELL					
1961	Cin	N	H	3	.000
BELL, HERMAN S.					
1926	St.L	N	P	1	0-0
1930	St.L	N	P	1	0-0
1933	NY	N	P	1	0-0
				3	0-0
BELL, LESTER ROWLAND					
1926	St.L	N	3	7	.259
BENDER, CHARLES ALBERT					
1905	Phi	A	P	2	1-1
1910	Phi	A	P	2	1-1
1911	Phi	A	P	3	2-1
1913	Phi	A	P	2	2-0
1914	Phi	A	P	1	0-1
				10	6-4
BENGOUGH, BERNARD OLIVER					
1927	NY	A	C	2	.000
1928	NY	A	C	4	.231
				6	.176
BENTLEY, JOHN NEEDLES					
1923	NY	N	H-P	5	0-1 .600
1924	NY	N	H-P	5	1-2 .286
				10	1-3 .417
BENTON, JOHN ALTON					
1945	Det	A	P	3	0-0
BENTON, JOHN CLEVELAND					
1917	NY	N	P	2	1-1
BERGAMO, AUGUST SAMUEL					
1944	St.L	N	O	3	.000
BERGER, WALTER ANTON					
1937	NY	N	H	3	.000
1939	Cin	N	O	4	.000
				7	.000
BERRA, LAWRENCE PETER					
1947	NY	A	C-O	6	.158
1949	NY	A	C	4	.063
1950	NY	A	C	4	.200
1951	NY	A	C	6	.261
1952	NY	A	C	7	.214
1953	NY	A	C	6	.429
1955	NY	A	C	7	.417
1956	NY	A	C	7	.360
1957	NY	A	C	7	.320
1958	NY	A	C	7	.222
1960	NY	A	C-O	7	.318
1961	NY	A	O	4	.273
1962	NY	A	C	2	.000
				74	.276
BESSENT, FRED DONALD					
1955	Bro	N	P	3	0-0
1956	Bro	N	P	2	1-0
				5	1-0
BEVENS, FLOYD CLIFFORD					
1947	NY	A	P	2	0-1
BICKFORD, VERNON EDGELL					
1948	Bos	N	P	1	0-1
BIGBEE, CARSON LEE					
1925	Pit	N	O	4	.250
BISHOP, MAX FREDERICK					
1929	Phi	A	2	5	.190
1930	Phi	A	2	6	.222
1931	Phi	A	2	7	.148
				18	.182
BLACK, JOSEPH					
1952	Bro	N	P	3	1-2
1953	Bro	N	P	1	0-0
				4	1-2
BLACKWELL, EWELL					
1952	NY	A	P	1	0-0
BLADES, FRANCIS RAYMOND					
1928	St.L	N	H	1	.000
1930	St.L	N	O	5	.111
1931	St.L	N	H	2	.000
				8	.083
BLAIR, CLARENCE VICK					
1929	Chi	N	H	1	.000
BLAKE, JOHN FREDERICK					
1929	Chi	N	P	2	0-1
BLANCHARD, JOHN EDWIN					
1960	NY	A	C	5	.455
1961	NY	A	O	4	.400
1962	NY	A	H	1	.000
				10	.409
BLASINGAME, DONALD LEE					
1961	Cin	N	2	3	.143
BLOCK, SEYMOUR					
1945	Chi	N	H	1	.000
BLOODWORTH, JAMES HENRY					
1950	Phi	N	2	1	.000
BLUEGE, OSWALD LOUIS					
1924	Was	A	S-3	7	.192
1925	Was	A	3	5	.278
1933	Was	A	3	5	.125
				17	.200
BOLEY, JOHN PETER					
1929	Phi	A	S	5	.235
1930	Phi	A	S	6	.095
1931	Phi	A	H	1	.000
				12	.154
BOLIN, BOBBY DONALD					
1962	SF	N	P	2	0-0
BOLLWEG, DONALD RAYMOND					
1953	NY	A	1	3	.000
BOLTON, WILLIAM CLIFTON					
1933	Was	A	H	2	.000
BONGIOVANNI, ANTHONY THOMAS					
1939	Cin	N	H	1	.000
BONHAM, ERNEST EDWARD					
1941	NY	A	P	1	1-0
1942	NY	A	P	2	0-1
1943	NY	A	P	1	0-1
				4	1-2
BOONE, RAYMOND OTIS					
1948	Cle	A	H	1	.000
BORDAGARAY, STANLEY GEORGE					
1939	Cin	N	H	2	.000
1941	NY	A	H	1	.000
				3	.000
BOROM, EDWARD JONES					
1945	Det	A	H	2	.000
BOROWY, HENRY LUDWIG					
1942	NY	A	P	1	0-0
1943	NY	A	P	1	1-0
1945	Chi	N	P	4	2-2
				6	3-2
BOTTOMLEY, JAMES LEROY					
1926	St.L	N	1	7	.345
1928	St.L	N	1	4	.214
1930	St.L	N	1	6	.045
1931	St.L	N	1	7	.160
				24	.200
BOUDREAU, LOUIS					
1948	Cle	A	S	6	.273
BOWMAN, ERNEST FERRELL					
1962	SF	N	S	2	.000
BOYER, CLETIS LEROY					
1960	NY	A	3	4	.250
1961	NY	A	3	5	.267
1962	NY	A	3	7	.318
				16	.286
BRAGAN, ROBERT RANDALL					
1947	Bro	N	H	1	1.000
BRANCA, RALPH THEODORE JOSEPH					
1947	Bro	N	P	3	1-1
1949	Bro	N	P	1	0-1
				4	1-2
BRANSFIELD, WILLIAM EDWARD					
1903	Pit	N	1	8	.206
BRAZLE, ALPHA EUGENE					
1943	St.L	N	P	1	0-1
1946	St.L	N	P	1	0-1
				2	0-2
BRECHEEN, HARRY DAVID					
1943	St.L	N	P	3	0-1
1944	St.L	N	P	1	1-0
1946	St.L	N	P	3	3-0
				7	4-1
BRENNAN, JAMES DONALD					
1937	NY	N	P	2	0-0
BRESNAHAN, ROGER PATRICK					
1905	NY	N	C	5	.313
BREUER, MARVIN HOWARD					
1941	NY	A	P	1	0-0
1942	NY	A	P	1	0-0
				2	0-0
BRICKELL, FREDERICK B.					
1927	Pit	N	H	2	.000
BRIDGES, MARSHALL					
1962	NY	A	P	2	0-0
BRIDGES, THOMAS JEFFERSON DAVIS					
1934	Det	A	P	3	1-1
1935	Det	A	P	2	2-0
1940	Det	A	P	1	1-0
1945	Det	A	P	1	0-0
				7	4-1
BROSNAN, JAMES PATRICK					
1961	Cin	N	P	2	0-0

Yr	Cl	Lea	Pos	G	Rec
BROWN, JAMES ROBERSON					
1942	St.L	N	2	5	.300
BROWN, MACE STANLEY					
1946	Bos	A	P	1	0-0
BROWN, MORDECAI PETER CENTENNIAL					
1906	Chi	N	P	3	1-2
1907	Chi	N	P	1	1-0
1908	Chi	N	P	2	2-0
1910	Chi	N	P	3	1-2
				9	5-4
BROWN, ROBERT WILLIAM					
1947	NY	A	H	4	1.000
1949	NY	A	3	4	.500
1950	NY	A	3	4	.333
1951	NY	A	3	5	.357
				17	.439
BROWN, THOMAS MICHAEL					
1949	Bro	N	H	2	.000
BROWNE, GEORGE E.					
1905	NY	N	0	5	.182
BRUTON, WILLIAM HARON					
1958	Mil	N	0	7	.412
BRYANT, CLAIBORNE HENRY					
1938	Chi	N	P	1	0-1
BUHL, ROBERT RAY					
1957	Mil	N	P	2	0-1
BURDETTE, SELVA LEWIS					
1957	Mil	N	P	3	3-0
1958	Mil	N	P	3	1-2
				6	4-2
BURGESS, FORREST HARRILL					
1960	Pit	N	C	5	.333
BURNS, EDWARD JAMES					
1915	Phi	N	C	5	.188
BURNS, GEORGE HENRY					
1920	Cle	A	1	5	.300
1929	Phi	A	H	1	.000
				6	.250
BURNS, GEORGE JOSEPH					
1913	NY	N	O	5	.158
1917	NY	N	O	6	.227
1921	NY	N	O	8	.333
				19	.257
BUSH, GUY TERRELL					
1929	Chi	N	P	2	1-0
1932	Chi	N	P	2	0-1
				4	1-1
BUSH, LESLIE AMBROSE					
1913	Phi	A	P	1	1-0
1914	Phi	A	P	1	0-1
1918	Bos	A	P	2	0-1
1922	NY	A	P	2	0-2
1923	NY	A	P	3	1-1
				9	2-5
BUSH, OWEN JOSEPH					
1909	Det	A	S	7	.261
BYERLY, ELDRED WILLIAM					
1944	St.L	N	P	1	0-0
BYRD, SAMUEL DEWEY					
1932	NY	A	O	1	.000
BYRNES, MILTON JOHN					
1944	St.L	A	H	3	.000
BYRNE, ROBERT MATHEW					
1909	Pit	N	3	7	.250
1915	Phi	N	H	1	.000
				8	.240
BYRNE, THOMAS JOSEPH					
1949	NY	A	P	1	0-0
1955	NY	A	P	2	1-1
1956	NY	A	P	1	0-0
1957	NY	A	P	2	0-0
				6	1-1
CABALLERO, RALPH JOSEPH					
1950	Phi	N	H	3	.000
CADORE, LEON JOSEPH					
1920	Bro	N	P	2	0-1
CADY, FORREST LEROY					
1912	Bos	A	C	7	.136
1915	Bos	A	C	4	.333
1916	Bos	A	C	2	.250
				13	.188
CALDWELL, RAYMOND BENJAMIN					
1920	Cle	A	P	1	0-1
CAMILLI, ADOLPH LOUIS					
1941	Bro	N	1	5	.167
CAMNITZ, SAMUEL HOWARD					
1909	Pit	N	P	2	0-1
CAMPANELLA, ROY					
1949	Bro	N	C	5	.267
1952	Bro	N	C	7	.214
1953	Bro	N	C	6	.273
1955	Bro	N	C	7	.259
1956	Bro	N	C	7	.182
				32	.237
CAMPBELL, BRUCE DOUGLAS					
1940	Det	A	O	7	.360
CAMPBELL, PAUL McLAUGHLIN					
1946	Bos	A	H	1	.000
CARDENAS, LEONARDO ALFONSO LAZARO					
1961	Cin	N	H	3	.333
CAREY, ANDREW ARTHUR					
1955	NY	A	H	2	.500
1956	NY	A	3	7	.158
1957	NY	A	3	2	.286
1958	NY	A	3	5	.083
				16	.175
CAREY, MAX GEORGE					
1925	Pit	N	O	7	.458
CARLETON, JAMES OTTO					
1934	St.L	N	P	2	0-0
1935	Chi	N	P	1	0-1
1938	Chi	N	P	1	0-0
				4	0-1
CARLSON, HAROLD GUST					
1929	Chi	N	P	2	0-0
CARRIGAN, WILLIAM FRANCIS					
1912	Bos	A	C	2	.000
1915	Bos	A	C	1	.000
1916	Bos	A	C	1	.667
				4	.167
CARROLL, THOMAS EDWARD					
1955	NY	A	H	2	.000
CASEY, HUGH THOMAS					
1941	Bro	N	P	3	0-2
1947	Bro	N	P	6	2-0
				9	2-2
CASH, NORMAN DALTON					
1959	Chi	A	N	4	.000
CASTER, GEORGE JASPER					
1945	Det	A	P	1	0-0
CASTLEMAN, CLYDELL					
1936	NY	N	P	1	0-0
CATHER, THEODORE P.					
1914	Bos	N	O	1	.000
CAVARRETTA, PHILIP JOSEPH					
1935	Chi	N	1	6	.125
1938	Chi	N	O	4	.462
1945	Chi	N	1	7	.423
				17	.317
CEPEDA, ORLANDO MANUEL					
1962	SF	N	1	5	.158
CERV, ROBERT HENRY					
1955	NY	A	O	5	.125
1956	NY	A	H	1	1.000
1960	NY	A	O	4	.357
				10	.258
CHACON, ELIO RODRIGUEZ					
1961	Cin	N	2	4	.250
CHALMERS, GEORGE W.					
1915	Phi	N	P	1	0-1
CHANCE, FRANK LEROY					
1906	Chi	N	1	6	.238
1907	Chi	N	1	4	.214
1908	Chi	N	1	5	.421
1910	Chi	N	1	5	.353
				20	.310
CHANDLER, SPURGEON FERDINAND					
1941	NY	A	P	1	0-1
1942	NY	A	P	2	0-1
1943	NY	A	P	2	2-0
1947	NY	A	P	1	0-0
				6	2-2
CHAPMAN, WILLIAM BENJAMIN					
1932	NY	A	O	4	.294
CHARTAK, MICHAEL GEORGE					
1944	St.L	A	H	2	.000
CHENEY, LAWRENCE RUSSELL					
1916	Bro	N	P	1	0-0
CHENEY, THOMAS EDGAR					
1960	Pit	N	P	3	0-0
CHIOZZA, LOUIS PEO					
1937	NY	N	O	2	.286
CHIPMAN, ROBERT HOWARD					
1945	Chi	N	P	1	0-0
CHRISTMAN, MARQUETTE JOSEPH					
1944	St.L	A	3	6	.091
CHRISTOPHER, JOSEPH O'NEAL					
1960	Pit	N	H	3	.000
CHRISTOPHER, RUSSELL ORMAND					
1948	Cle	A	P	1	0-0

Yr Cl Lea Pos G Rec

CHURN, CLARENCE NOTTINGHAM
1959 LA N P 1 0-0

CICOTTE, EDWARD VICTOR
1917 Chi A P 3 1-1
1919 Chi A P 3 1-2
6 2-3

CIMOLI, GINO NICHOLAS
1956 Bro N O 1 .000
1960 Pit N O 7 .250
8 .250

CLARK, ALFRED ALOYSIUS
1947 NY A O 3 .500
1948 Cle A O 1 .000
4 .200

CLARKE, FREDERICK CLIFFORD
1903 Pit N O 8 .265
1909 Pit N O 7 .211
15 .245

CLARY, ELLIS
1944 St.L A H 1 .000

CLEMENTE, ROBERTO WALKER
1960 Pit N O 7 .310

CLIFTON, HERMAN EARL
1935 Det A 3 4 .000

COAKLEY, ANDREW JAMES
1905 Phi A P 1 0-1

COBB, TYRUS RAYMOND
1907 Det A O 5 .200
1908 Det A O 5 .368
1909 Det A O 7 .231
17 .262

COCHRANE, GORDON STANLEY
1929 Phi A C 5 .400
1930 Phi A C 6 .222
1931 Phi A C 7 .160
1934 Det A C 7 .214
1935 Det A C 6 .292
31 .245

COFFMAN, SAMUEL RICHARD
1936 NY N P 2 0-0
1937 NY N P 2 0-0
4 0-0

COLE, LEONARD LESLIE
1910 Chi N P 1 0-0

COLEMAN, GERALD FRANCIS
1949 NY A 2 5 .250
1950 NY A 2 4 .286
1951 NY A 2 5 .250
1955 NY A S 3 .000
1956 NY A 2 2 .000
1957 NY A 2 7 .364
26 .275

COLEMAN, GORDON CALVIN
1961 Cin N 1 5 .250

COLEMAN, WALTER GARY
1955 NY A P 1 0-0

COLLINS, EDWARD TROWBRIDGE
1910 Phi A 2 5 .429
1911 Phi A 2 6 .286
1913 Phi A 2 5 .421
1914 Phi A 2 4 .214
1917 Chi A 2 6 .409
1919 Chi A 2 8 .226
34 .328

COLLINS, HARRY WARREN
1921 NY A P 1 0-0

Yr Cl Lea Pos G Rec

COLLINS, JAMES ANTHONY
1931 St.L N H 2 .000
1934 St.L N 1 7 .367
1938 Chi N 1 4 .133
13 .277

COLLINS, JAMES JOSEPH
1903 Bos A 3 8 .250

COLLINS, JOHN FRANCIS
1917 Chi A O 6 .286
1919 Chi A O 4 .250
10 .270

COLLINS, JOSEPH EDWARD
1950 NY A 1 1 .000
1951 NY A 1-O 6 .222
1952 NY A 1 6 .000
1953 NY A 1 6 .167
1955 NY A 1-O 5 .167
1956 NY A 1 6 .238
1957 NY A 1 6 .000
36 .163

COLLINS, RAYMOND WILLISTON
1912 Bos A P 2 0-0

COLLINS, THARON PATRICK
1926 NY A C 3 .000
1927 NY A C 2 .000
1928 NY A C 1 1.000
6 .500

COMBS, EARLE BRYAN
1926 NY A O 7 .357
1927 NY A O 4 .313
1928 NY A H 1 .000
1932 NY A O 4 .375
16 .350

CONATSER, CLINTON ASTOR
1948 Bos N O 2 .000

CONLEY, DONALD EUGENE
1957 Mil N P 1 0-0

CONNOLLY, JOSEPH ALOYSIUS
1914 Bos N O 3 .111

COOMBS, JOHN WESLEY
1910 Phi A P 3 3-0
1911 Phi A P 2 1-0
1916 Bro N P 1 1-0
6 5-0

COOPER, CLAUDE
1913 NY N H 2 .000

COOPER, MORTON CECIL
1942 St.L N P 2 0-1
1943 St.L N P 2 1-1
1944 St.L N P 2 1-1
6 2-3

COOPER, WILLIAM WALKER
1942 St.L N C 5 .286
1943 St.L N C 5 .294
1944 St.L N C 6 .318
16 .300

CORWIN, ELMER NATHAN
1951 NY N P 1 0-0

COSCARART, PETER JOSEPH
1941 Bro N 2 3 .000

COUGHLIN, WILLIAM PAUL
1907 Det A 3 5 .250
1908 Det A 3 3 .125
8 .214

COVELESKI, STANLEY
1920 Cle A P 3 3-0
1925 Was A P 2 0-2
5 3-2

Yr Cl Lea Pos G Rec

COVINGTON, JOHN WESLEY
1957 Mil N O 7 .208
1958 Mil N O 7 .269
14 .240

COX, WILLIAM RICHARD
1949 Bro N 3 2 .333
1952 Bro N 3 7 .296
1953 Bro N 3 6 .304
15 .302

CRAFT, HARRY FRANCIS
1939 Cin N O 4 .091
1940 Cin N H 1 .000
5 .083

CRAIG, ROGER LEE
1955 Bro N P 1 1-0
1956 Bro N P 2 0-1
1959 LA N P 2 0-1
5 1-2

CRAMER, ROGER MAXWELL
1931 Phi A H 2 .500
1945 Det A O 7 .379
9 .387

CRANDALL, DELMAR WESLEY
1957 Mil N C 6 .211
1958 Mil N C 7 .240
13 .227

CRANDALL, JAMES OTIS
1911 NY N P 2 1-0
1912 NY N P 1 0-0
1913 NY N P 2 0-0
5 1-0

CRAVATH, CLIFFORD CARLTON
1915 Phi N O 5 .125

CRAWFORD, CLIFFORD RANKIN
1934 St.L N H 2 .000

CRAWFORD, SAMUEL EARL
1907 Det A O 5 .238
1908 Det A O 5 .238
1909 Det A O 7 .250
17 .243

CRESPI, FRANK ANGELO JOSEPH
1942 St.L N H 1 .000

CRIGER, LOUIS
1903 Bos A C 8 .231

CRITZ, HUGH MELVILLE
1933 NY N 2 5 .136

CRONIN, JOSEPH EDWARD
1933 Was A S 5 .318

CROSETTI, FRANK PETER JOSEPH
1932 NY A S 4 .133
1936 NY A S 6 .269
1937 NY A S 5 .048
1938 NY A S 4 .250
1939 NY A S 4 .063
1942 NY A 3 1 .000
1943 NY A S 5 .278
29 .174

CROSS, LAFAYETTE NAPOLEON
1905 Phi A 3 5 .105

CROSS, MONTFORD MONTGOMERY
1905 Phi A S 5 .176

CROUCHER, FRANK DONALD
1940 Det A S 1 .000

CROWDER, ALVIN FLOYD
1933 Was A P 2 0-1
1934 Det A P 2 0-1
1935 Det A P 1 1-0
5 1-2

CULBERSON, DELBERT LEON

Yr	Cl	Lea	Pos	G	Rec
1946	Bos	A	O	5	.222

CULLENBINE, ROY JOSEPH

Yr	Cl	Lea	Pos	G	Rec
1942	NY	A	O	5	.263
1945	Det	A	O	7	.227
				12	.244

CUNNINGHAM, WILLIAM ALOYSIUS

Yr	Cl	Lea	Pos	G	Rec
1922	NY	N	O	4	.200
1923	NY	N	O	4	.143
				8	.176

CUTSHAW, GEORGE WILLIAM

Yr	Cl	Lea	Pos	G	Rec
1916	Bro	N	2	5	.105

CUYLER, HAZEN SHIRLEY

Yr	Cl	Lea	Pos	G	Rec
1925	Pit	N	O	7	.269
1929	Chi	N	O	5	.300
1932	Chi	N	O	4	.278
				16	.281

CVENGROS, MICHAEL JOHN

Yr	Cl	Lea	Pos	G	Rec
1927	Pit	N	P	2	0-0

DAHLEN, WILLIAM FREDERICK

Yr	Cl	Lea	Pos	G	Rec
1905	NY	N	S	5	.000

DAHLGREN, ELLSWORTH TENNEY

Yr	Cl	Lea	Pos	G	Rec
1939	NY	A	1	4	.214

DALEY, BUDDY LEO

Yr	Cl	Lea	Pos	G	Rec
1961	NY	A	P	2	1-0
1962	NY	A	P	1	0-0
				3	1-0

DANFORTH, DAVID CHARLES

Yr	Cl	Lea	Pos	G	Rec
1917	Chi	A	P	1	0-0

DANNING, HARRY

Yr	Cl	Lea	Pos	G	Rec
1936	NY	N	C	2	.000
1937	NY	N	C	3	.250
				5	.214

DARK, ALVIN RALPH

Yr	Cl	Lea	Pos	G	Rec
1948	Bos	N	S	6	.167
1951	NY	N	S	6	.417
1954	NY	N	S	4	.412
				16	.323

DAUBERT, JACOB ELLSWORTH

Yr	Cl	Lea	Pos	G	Rec
1916	Bro	N	1	4	.176
1919	Cin	N	1	8	.241
				12	.217

DAVENPORT, JAMES HOUSTON

Yr	Cl	Lea	Pos	G	Rec
1962	SF	N	3	7	.136

DAVIS, CURTIS BENTON

Yr	Cl	Lea	Pos	G	Rec
1941	Bro	N	P	1	0-1

DAVIS, GEORGE STACEY

Yr	Cl	Lea	Pos	G	Rec
1906	Chi	A	S	3	.308

DAVIS, GEORGE WILLIS

Yr	Cl	Lea	Pos	G	Rec
1933	NY	N	O	5	.368
1936	NY	N	H	4	.500
				9	.381

DAVIS, HARRY H.

Yr	Cl	Lea	Pos	G	Rec
1905	Phi	A	1	5	.200
1910	Phi	A	1	5	.353
1911	Phi	A	1	6	.208
				16	.246

DAVIS, VIRGIL LAWRENCE

Yr	Cl	Lea	Pos	G	Rec
1934	St.L	N	H	2	1.000

DAWSON, RALPH FENTON

Yr	Cl	Lea	Pos	G	Rec
1927	Pit	N	P	1	0-0

DEAL, CHARLES ALBERT

Yr	Cl	Lea	Pos	G	Rec
1914	Bos	N	3	4	.125
1918	Chi	N	3	6	.176
				10	.152

DEAN, JAY HANNA

Yr	Cl	Lea	Pos	G	Rec
1934	St.L	N	P	3	2-1
1938	Chi	N	P	2	0-1
				5	2-2

DEAN, PAUL DEE

Yr	Cl	Lea	Pos	G	Rec
1934	St.L	N	P	2	2-0

DEAN, WAYLAND OGDEN

Yr	Cl	Lea	Pos	G	Rec
1924	NY	N	P	1	0-0

DELAHANTY, JAMES CHRISTOPHER

Yr	Cl	Lea	Pos	G	Rec
1909	Det	A	2	7	.346

DeLANCEY, WILLIAM PINKNEY

Yr	Cl	Lea	Pos	G	Rec
1934	St.L	N	C	7	.172

DELL, WEISER GEORGE

Yr	Cl	Lea	Pos	G	Rec
1916	Bro	N	P	1	0-0

DEMAESTRI, JOSEPH PAUL

Yr	Cl	Lea	Pos	G	Rec
1960	NY	A	S	4	.500

DEMAREE, ALBERT WENTWORTH

Yr	Cl	Lea	Pos	G	Rec
1913	NY	N	P	1	0-1

DEMAREE, JOSEPH FRANKLIN

Yr	Cl	Lea	Pos	G	Rec
1932	Chi	N	O	2	.286
1935	Chi	N	O	6	.250
1938	Chi	N	O	3	.100
1943	St.L	N	H	1	.000
				12	.214

DEMERIT, JOHN STEPHEN

Yr	Cl	Lea	Pos	G	Rec
1957	Mil	N	H	1	.000

DEMETER, DONALD LEE

Yr	Cl	Lea	Pos	G	Rec
1959	LA	N	O	6	.250

DENTE, SAMUEL JOSEPH

Yr	Cl	Lea	Pos	G	Rec
1954	Cle	A	S	3	.000

DERRINGER, SAMUEL PAUL

Yr	Cl	Lea	Pos	G	Rec
1931	St.L	N	P	3	0-2
1939	Cin	N	P	2	0-1
1940	Cin	N	P	3	2-1
1945	Chi	N	P	3	0-0
				11	2-4

DEVLIN, ARTHUR McARTHUR

Yr	Cl	Lea	Pos	G	Rec
1905	NY	N	3	5	.250

DEVORE, JOSHUA

Yr	Cl	Lea	Pos	G	Rec
1911	NY	N	O	6	.167
1912	NY	N	O	7	.250
1914	Bos	N	H	1	.000
				14	.204

DeVORMER, ALBERT E.

Yr	Cl	Lea	Pos	G	Rec
1921	NY	A	C	2	.000

DICKEY, WILLIAM MALCOLM

Yr	Cl	Lea	Pos	G	Rec
1932	NY	A	C	4	.438
1936	NY	A	C	6	.120
1937	NY	A	C	5	.211
1938	NY	A	C	4	.400
1939	NY	A	C	4	.267
1941	NY	A	C	5	.167
1942	NY	A	C	5	.263
1943	NY	A	C	5	.278
				38	.255

DICKSON, MURRY MONROE

Yr	Cl	Lea	Pos	G	Rec
1943	St.L	N	P	1	0-0
1946	St.L	N	P	2	0-1
1958	NY	A	P	2	0-0
				5	0-1

DiMAGGIO, DOMINIC PAUL

Yr	Cl	Lea	Pos	G	Rec
1946	Bos	A	O	7	.259

DiMAGGIO, JOSEPH PAUL

Yr	Cl	Lea	Pos	G	Rec
1936	NY	A	O	6	.346
1937	NY	A	O	5	.273
1938	NY	A	O	4	.267
1939	NY	A	O	4	.313
1941	NY	A	O	5	.263
1942	NY	A	O	5	.333
1947	NY	A	O	7	.231
1949	NY	A	O	5	.111
1950	NY	A	O	4	.308
1951	NY	A	O	6	.261
				51	.271

DINNEEN, WILLIAM HENRY

Yr	Cl	Lea	Pos	G	Rec
1903	Bos	A	P	4	3-1

DITMAR, ARTHUR JOHN

Yr	Cl	Lea	Pos	G	Rec
1957	NY	A	P	2	0-0
1958	NY	A	P	1	0-0
1960	NY	A	P	2	0-2
				5	0-2

DOBSON, JOSEPH GORDON

Yr	Cl	Lea	Pos	G	Rec
1946	Bos	A	P	3	1-0

DOBY, LAWRENCE EUGENE

Yr	Cl	Lea	Pos	G	Rec
1948	Cle	A	O	6	.318
1954	Cle	A	O	4	.125
				10	.237

DOERR, ROBERT PERSHING

Yr	Cl	Lea	Pos	G	Rec
1946	Bos	A	2	6	.409

DOLJACK, FRANK JOSEPH

Yr	Cl	Lea	Pos	G	Rec
1934	Det	A	0	2	.000

DONAHUE, JOHN AUGUSTUS

Yr	Cl	Lea	Pos	G	Rec
1906	Chi	A	1	6	.333

DONALD, RICHARD ATLEY

Yr	Cl	Lea	Pos	G	Rec
1941	NY	A	P	1	0-0
1942	NY	A	P	1	0-1
				2	0-1

DONLIN, MICHAEL JOSEPH

Yr	Cl	Lea	Pos	G	Rec
1905	NY	N	O	5	.316

DONNELLY, SYLVESTER URBAN

Yr	Cl	Lea	Pos	G	Rec
1944	St.L	N	P	2	1-0

DONOVAN, RICHARD EDWARD

Yr	Cl	Lea	Pos	G	Rec
1959	Chi	A	P	3	0-1

DONOVAN, WILLIAM EDWARD

Yr	Cl	Lea	Pos	G	Rec
1907	Det	A	P	2	0-1
1908	Det	A	P	2	0-2
1909	Det	A	P	2	1-1
				6	1-4

DOUGHERTY, PATRICK HENRY

Yr	Cl	Lea	Pos	G	Rec
1903	Bos	A	O	8	.235
1906	Chi	A	O	6	.100
				14	.185

DOUGLAS, PHILIP BROOKS

Yr	Cl	Lea	Pos	G	Rec
1918	Chi	N	P	1	0-1
1921	NY	N	P	3	2-1
				4	2-2

DOUTHIT, TAYLOR LEE

Yr	Cl	Lea	Pos	G	Rec
1926	St.L	N	O	4	.267
1928	St.L	N	O	3	.091
1930	St.L	N	O	6	.083
				13	.140

Yr	Cl	Lea	Pos	G	Rec
DOWNS, JEROME WILLIS					
1908	Det	A	2	2	.168
DOYLE, LAWRENCE JOSEPH					
1911	NY	N	2	6	.304
1912	NY	N	2	8	.242
1913	NY	N	2	5	.150
				19	.237
DREISEWERD, CLEMENT JOHN					
1946	Bos	A	P	1	0-0
DREWS, KARL AUGUST					
1947	NY	A	P	2	0-0
DRYSDALE, DONALD SCOTT					
1956	Bro	N	P	1	0-0
1959	LA	N	P	1	1-0
				2	1-0
DUBUC, JEAN ARTHUR					
1918	Bos	A	H	1	.000
DUGAN, JOSEPH ANTHONY					
1922	NY	A	3	5	.250
1923	NY	A	3	6	.280
1926	NY	A	3	7	.333
1927	NY	A	3	4	.200
1928	NY	A	3	3	.167
				25	.267
DUGEY, OSCAR JOSEPH					
1915	Phi	N	H	2	.000
DUNCAN, LOUIS BAIRD					
1919	Cin	N	O	8	.269
DUREN, RINOLD GEORGE					
1958	NY	A	P	3	1-1
1960	NY	A	P	2	0-0
				5	1-1
DUROCHER, LEO ERNEST					
1928	NY	A	2	4	.000
1934	St.L	N	S	7	.259
				11	.241
DURST, CEDRIC MONTGOMERY					
1927	NY	A	H	1	.000
1928	NY	A	O	4	.375
				5	.333
DUSAK, ERVIN FRANK					
1946	St.L	N	O	4	.250
DYKES, JAMES JOSEPH					
1929	Phi	A	3	5	.421
1930	Phi	A	3	6	.222
1931	Phi	A	3	7	.227
				18	.288
EARNSHAW, GEORGE LIVINGSTON					
1929	Phi	A	P	2	1-1
1930	Phi	A	P	3	2-0
1931	Phi	A	P	3	1-2
				8	4-3
EATON, ZEBULON VANCE					
1945	Det	A	H	1	.000
EDWARDS, CHARLES BRUCE					
1947	Bro	N	C	7	.222
1949	Bro	N	H	2	.500
				9	.241
EDWARDS, JOHN ALBAN					
1961	Cin	N	C	3	.364
EHMKE, HOWARD JOHN					
1929	Phi	A	P	2	1-0

Yr	Cl	Lea	Pos	G	Rec
ELLER, HORACE OWEN					
1919	Cin	N	P	2	2-0
ELLIOTT, ROBERT IRVING					
1948	Bos	N	3	6	.333
ENGLE, ARTHUR CLYDE					
1912	Bos	A	H	3	.333
ENGLISH, ELWOOD GEORGE					
1929	Chi	N	S	5	.190
1932	Chi	N	3	4	.176
				9	.184
ENNIS, DELMER					
1950	Phi	N	O	4	.143
ERICKSON, PAUL WAKEFIELD					
1945	Chi	N	P	4	0-0
ERSKINE, CARL DANIEL					
1949	Bro	N	P	2	0-0
1952	Bro	N	P	3	1-1
1953	Bro	N	P	3	1-0
1955	Bro	N	P	1	0-0
1956	Bro	N	P	2	0-1
				11	2-2
ESPOSITO, SAMUEL					
1959	Chi	A	3	2	.000
ESSEGIAN, CHARLES ABRAHAM					
1959	LA	N	H	4	.667
ETTEN, NICHOLAS RAYMOND THOMAS					
1943	NY	A	1	5	.105
EVANS, JOSEPH PATTON					
1920	Cle	A	O	4	.308
EVERS, JOHN JOSEPH					
1906	Chi	N	2	6	.150
1907	Chi	N	2	5	.350
1908	Chi	N	2	5	.350
1914	Bos	N	2	4	.438
				20	.316
FABER, URBAN CHARLES					
1917	Chi	A	P	4	3-1
FACE, ELROY LEON					
1960	Pit	N	P	4	0-0
FAIRLY, RONALD RAY					
1959	LA	N	O	6	.000
FALLON, GEORGE DECATUR					
1944	St.L	N	2	2	.000
FARRELL, CHARLES A.					
1903	Bos	A	H	2	.000
FELLER, ROBERT WILLIAM ANDREW					
1948	Cle	A	P	2	0-2
FELSCH, OSCAR EMIL					
1917	Chi	A	O	6	.273
1919	Chi	A	O	8	.192
				14	.229
FERGUSON, JAMES ALEXANDER					
1925	Was	A	P	2	1-1
FERRICK, THOMAS JEROME					
1950	NY	A	P	1	1-0
FERRIS, ALBERT SAYLES					
1903	Bos	A	2	8	.290
FERRISS, DAVID MEADOW					
1946	Bos	A	P	2	1-0

Yr	Cl	Lea	Pos	G	Rec
FEWSTER, WILSON LLOYD					
1921	NY	A	O	4	.200
FISHER, GEORGE ALOYS					
1930	St.L	N	H	2	.500
FISHER, RAYMOND LYLE					
1919	Cin	N	P	2	0-1
FITZSIMMONS, FREDERICK LANDIS					
1933	NY	N	P	1	0-1
1936	NY	N	P	2	0-2
1941	Bro	N	P	1	0-0
				4	0-3
FLACK, MAX JOHN					
1918	Chi	N	O	6	.263
FLETCHER, ARTHUR					
1911	NY	N	S	6	.130
1912	NY	N	S	8	.179
1913	NY	N	S	5	.278
1917	NY	N	S	6	.200
				25	.191
FLOWERS, D'ARCY RAYMOND					
1926	St.L	N	H	3	.000
1931	St.L	N	3	5	.091
				8	.071
FORD, EDWARD CHARLES					
1950	NY	A	P	1	1-0
1953	NY	A	P	2	0-1
1955	NY	A	P	2	2-0
1956	NY	A	P	2	1-1
1957	NY	A	P	2	1-1
1958	NY	A	P	3	0-1
1960	NY	A	P	2	2-0
1961	NY	A	P	2	2-0
1962	NY	A	P	3	1-1
				19	10-5
FOSTER, GEORGE					
1915	Bos	A	P	2	2-0
1916	Bos	A	P	1	0-0
				3	2-0
FOX, ERVIN					
1934	Det	A	O	7	.286
1935	Det	A	O	6	.385
1940	Det	A	H	1	.000
				14	.327
FOX, JACOB NELSON					
1959	Chi	A	2	6	.375
FOXX, JAMES EMORY					
1929	Phi	A	1	5	.350
1930	Phi	A	1	6	.333
1931	Phi	A	1	7	.348
				18	.344
FRANKS, HERMAN LOUIS					
1941	Bro	N	C	1	.000
FREEMAN, JOHN F.					
1903	Bos	A	O	8	.391
FREESE, EUGENE LEWIS					
1961	Cin	N	3	5	.063
FRENCH, LAWRENCE HERBERT					
1935	Chi	N	P	2	0-2
1938	Chi	N	P	3	0-0
1941	Bro	N	P	2	0-0
				7	0-2
FRENCH, WALTER EDWARD					
1929	Phi	A	H	1	.000

Yr	Cl	Lea	Pos	G	Rec
FREY, LINUS REINHARD					
1939	Cin	N	2	4	.000
1940	Cin	N	2	3	.000
1947	NY	A	H	1	.000
				8	.000
FRIEND, ROBERT BARTMESS					
1960	Pit	N	P	3	0-2
FRISCH, FRANK FRANCIS					
1921	NY	N	3	8	.300
1922	NY	N	2	5	.471
1923	NY	N	2	6	.400
1924	NY	N	2-3	7	.333
1928	St.L	N	2	4	.231
1930	St.L	N	2	6	.208
1931	St.L	N	2	7	.259
1934	St.L	N	2	7	.194
				50	.294
FULLIS, CHARLES PHILIP					
1934	St.L	N	O	3	.400
FURILLO, CARL ANTHONY					
1947	Bro	N	O	6	.353
1949	Bro	N	O	3	.125
1952	Bro	N	O	7	.174
1953	Bro	N	O	6	.333
1955	Bro	N	O	7	.296
1956	Bro	N	O	7	.240
1959	LA	N	O	4	.250
				40	.266
GABLER, FRANK HAROLD					
1936	NY	N	P	2	0-0
GAINOR, DELOS CHARLES					
1915	Bos	A	1	1	.333
1916	Bos	A	H	1	1.000
				2	.500
GALAN, AUGUST JOHN					
1935	Chi	N	O	6	.160
1938	Chi	N	H	2	.000
1941	Bro	N	H	2	.000
				10	.138
GALEHOUSE, DENNIS WARD					
1944	St.L	A	P	2	1-1
GAMBLE, LEE JESSE					
1939	Cin	N	H	1	.000
GANDIL, CHARLES ARNOLD					
1917	Chi	A	1	6	.261
1919	Chi	A	1	8	.233
				14	.245
GARAGIOLA, JOSEPH HENRY					
1946	St.L	N	C	5	.316
GARCIA, EDWARD MIGUEL					
1954	Cle	A	P	2	0-1
GARDNER, WILLIAM FREDERICK					
1961	NY	A	H	1	.000
GARDNER, WILLIAM LAWRENCE					
1912	Bos	A	3	8	.179
1915	Bos	A	3	5	.235
1916	Bos	A	3	5	.176
1920	Cle	A	3	7	.208
				25	.198
GARMS, DEBS C.					
1943	St.L	N	O	2	.000
1944	St.L	N	H	2	.000
				4	.000
GAZELLA, MICHAEL					
1926	NY	A	3	1	.000
GEARIN, DENNIS JOHN					
1923	NY	N	H	1	.000
GEHRIG, HENRY LOUIS					
1926	NY	A	1	7	.348
1927	NY	A	1	4	.308
1928	NY	A	1	4	.545
1932	NY	A	1	4	.529
1936	NY	A	1	6	.292
1937	NY	A	1	5	.294
1938	NY	A	1	4	.286
				34	.361
GEHRINGER, CHARLES LEONARD					
1934	Det	A	2	7	.379
1935	Det	A	2	6	.375
1940	Det	A	2	7	.214
				20	.321
GELBERT, CHARLES MAGNUS					
1930	St.L	N	S	6	.353
1931	St.L	N	S	7	.261
				13	.300
GERNERT, RICHARD EDWARD					
1961	Cin	N	H	4	.000
GESSLER, HARRY HOMER					
1906	Chi	N	H	2	.000
GETZ, GUSTAVE					
1916	Bro	N	H	1	.000
GIBBON, JOSEPH CHARLES					
1960	Pit	N	P	2	0-0
GIBSON, GEORGE					
1909	Pit	N	C	7	.240
GILBERT, LAWRENCE WILLIAM					
1914	Bos	N	H	1	.000
GILBERT, WILLIAM OLIVER					
1905	NY	N	2	5	.235
GILLESPIE, PAUL ALLEN					
1945	Chi	N	C	3	.000
GILLIAM, JAMES WILLIAM					
1953	Bro	N	2	6	.296
1955	Bro	N	2-0	7	.292
1956	Bro	N	2	7	.083
1959	LA	N	3	6	.240
				26	.230
GIONFRIDDO, ALBERT FRANCIS					
1947	Bro	N	O	4	.000
GLYNN, WILLIAM VINCENT					
1954	Cle	A	1	2	.500
GOLIAT, MIKE MITCHEL					
1950	Phi	N	2	4	.214
GOMEZ, RUBEN COLON					
1954	NY	N	P	1	1-0
GOMEZ, VERNON LOUIS					
1932	NY	A	P	1	1-0
1936	NY	A	P	2	2-0
1937	NY	A	P	2	2-0
1938	NY	A	P	1	1-0
1939	NY	A	P	1	0-0
				7	6-0
GONZALEZ, MIGUEL ANGEL CORDERO					
1929	Chi	N	C	2	.000
GOOCH, JOHN BEVERLY					
1925	Pit	N	C	3	.000
1927	Pit	N	C	3	.000
				6	.000
GOODMAN, IVAL RICHARD					
1939	Cin	N	O	4	.333
1940	Cin	N	O	7	.276
				11	.295
GOODMAN, WILLIAM DALE					
1959	Chi	A	3	5	.231
GORDON, JOSEPH LOWELL					
1938	NY	A	2	4	.400
1939	NY	A	2	4	.143
1941	NY	A	2	5	.500
1942	NY	A	2	5	.095
1943	NY	A	2	5	.235
1948	Cle	A	2	6	.182
				29	.243
GORMAN, THOMAS ALOYSIUS					
1952	NY	A	P	1	0-0
1953	NY	A	P	1	0-0
				2	0-0
GORSICA, JOHN JOSEPH PERRY					
1940	Det	A	P	2	0-0
GOSLIN, LEON ALLEN					
1924	Was	A	O	7	.344
1925	Was	A	O	7	.308
1933	Was	A	O	5	.250
1934	Det	A	O	7	.241
1935	Det	A	O	6	.273
				32	.287
GOWDY, HENRY					
1914	Bos	N	C	4	.545
1923	NY	N	C	3	.000
1924	NY	N	C	7	.259
				14	.310
GRABOWSKI, JOHN PATRICK					
1927	NY	A	C	1	.000
GRANEY, JOHN GLADSTONE					
1920	Cle	A	O	3	.000
GRANT, EDWARD LESLIE					
1913	NY	N	H	2	.000
GRANTHAM, GEORGE FARLEY					
1925	Pit	N	1	5	.133
1927	Pit	N	2	3	.364
				8	.231
GRASSO, NEWTON MICHAEL					
1954	Cle	A	C	1	.000
GRBA, ELI					
1960	NY	A	H	1	.000
GREEN, FRED ALLEN					
1960	Pit	N	P	3	0-0
GREENBERG, HENRY BENJAMIN					
1934	Det	A	1	7	.321
1935	Det	A	1	2	.167
1940	Det	A	O	7	.357
1945	Det	A	O	7	.304
				23	.318
GREGG, HAROLD DANA					
1947	Bro	N	P	3	0-1
GRIFFITH, THOMAS HERMAN					
1920	Bro	N	O	7	.190
GRIM, ROBERT ANTON					
1955	NY	A	P	3	0-1
1957	NY	A	P	2	0-1
				5	0-2
GRIMES, BURLEIGH ARLAND					
1920	Bro	N	P	3	1-2
1930	St.L	N	P	2	0-2
1931	St.L	N	P	2	2-0
1932	Chi	N	P	2	0-0
				9	3-4
GRIMM, CHARLES JOHN					
1929	Chi	N	1	5	.389
1932	Chi	N	1	4	.333
				9	.364

Yr	Cl	Lea	Pos	G	Rec
GRISSOM, LEO THEO					
1939	Cin	N	P	1	0-0
GRISSOM, MARVIN EDWARD					
1954	NY	N	P	1	1-0
GROAT, RICHARD MORROW					
1960	Pit	N	S	7	.214
GROH, HENRY KNIGHT					
1919	Cin	N	3	8	.172
1922	NY	N	3	5	.474
1923	NY	N	3	6	.182
1924	NY	N	H	1	1.000
1927	Pit	N	H	1	.000
				21	.264
GROMEK, STEPHEN JOSEPH					
1948	Cle	A	P	1	1-0
GROVE, ROBERT MOSES					
1929	Phi	A	P	2	0-0
1930	Phi	A	P	3	2-1
1931	Phi	A	P	3	2-1
				8	4-2
GUDAT, MARVIN JOHN					
1932	Chi	N	H	2	.000
GUMBERT, HARRY EDWARD					
1936	NY	N	P	2	0-0
1937	NY	N	P	2	0-0
1942	St.L	N	P	2	0-0
				6	0-0
GUTTERIDGE, DONALD JOSEPH					
1944	St.L	A	2	6	.143
1946	Bos	A	2	3	.400
				9	.192
HAAS, GEORGE WILLIAM					
1929	Phi	A	O	5	.238
1930	Phi	A	O	6	.111
1931	Phi	A	O	7	.130
				18	.161
HACK, STANLEY CAMFIELD					
1932	Chi	N	H	1	.000
1935	Chi	N	S-3	6	.227
1938	Chi	N	3	4	.471
1945	Chi	N	3	7	.367
				18	.348
HADDIX, HARVEY					
1960	Pit	N	P	2	2-0
HADLEY, IRVING DARIUS					
1936	NY	A	P	1	1-0
1937	NY	A	P	1	0-1
1939	NY	A	P	1	1-0
				3	2-1
HAFEY, CHARLES JAMES					
1926	St.L	N	O	7	.185
1928	St.L	N	O	4	.200
1930	St.L	N	O	6	.273
1931	St.L	N	O	6	.167
				23	.205
HAHN, EDGAR WILLIAM					
1906	Chi	A	O	6	.273
HAINES, HENRY LUTHER					
1923	NY	A	O	2	.000
HAINES, JESSE JOSEPH					
1926	St.L	N	P	3	2-0
1928	St.L	N	P	1	0-1
1930	St.L	N	P	1	1-0
1934	St.L	N	P	1	0-0
				6	3-1
HALL, CHARLES LOUIS					
1912	Bos	A	P	2	0-0

Yr	Cl	Lea	Pos	G	Rec
HALLAHAN, WILLIAM ANTHONY					
1926	St.L	N	P	1	0-0
1930	St.L	N	P	2	1-1
1931	St.L	N	P	3	2-0
1934	St.L	N	P	1	0-0
				7	3-1
HALLER, THOMAS FRANK					
1962	SF	N	C	4	.286
HAMNER, GRANVILLE WILBUR					
1950	Phi	N	S	4	.429
HANEBRINK, HARRY ALOYSIUS					
1958	Mil	N	H	2	.000
HARPER, GEORGE WASHINGTON					
1928	St.L	N	O	3	.111
HARPER, HARRY CLAYTON					
1921	NY	A	P	1	0-0
HARRIS, DAVID STANLEY					
1933	Was	A	O	3	.000
HARRIS, JOSEPH					
1925	Was	A	O	7	.440
1927	Pit	N	1	4	.200
				11	.350
HARRIS, MAURICE CHARLES					
1946	Bos	A	P	2	0-2
HARRIS, STANLEY RAYMOND					
1924	Was	A	2	7	.333
1925	Was	A	2	7	.087
				14	.232
HARTNETT, CHARLES LEO					
1929	Chi	N	H	3	.000
1932	Chi	N	C	4	.313
1935	Chi	N	C	6	.292
1938	Chi	N	C	3	.091
				16	.241
HARTSEL, TULLOS FREDERICK					
1905	Phi	A	O	5	.294
1910	Phi	A	O	1	.200
				6	.273
HARTUNG, CLINTON CLARENCE					
1951	NY	N	O	2	.000
HASSETT, JOHN ALOYSIUS					
1942	NY	A	1	3	.333
HATTEN, JOSEPH HILARIAN					
1947	Bro	N	P	4	0-0
1949	Bro	N	P	2	0-0
				6	0-0
HAYWORTH, MYRON CLAUDE					
1944	St.L	A	C	6	.118
HAYWORTH, RAYMOND HALL					
1934	Det	A	C	1	.000
HAZLE, ROBERT SIDNEY					
1957	Mil	N	O	4	.154
HEARN, JAMES TOLBERT					
1951	NY	N	P	2	1-0
HEATHCOTE, CLIFTON EARL					
1929	Chi	N	H	2	.000
HEGAN, JAMES EDWARD					
1948	Cle	A	C	6	.211
1954	Cle	A	C	4	.154
				10	.188

Yr	Cl	Lea	Pos	G	Rec
HEINTZELMAN, KENNETH ALPHONSE					
1950	Phi	N	P	1	0-0
HEMSLEY, RALSTON BURDETT					
1932	Chi	N	C	3	.000
HENDRICK, HARVEY					
1923	NY	A	H	1	.000
HENDRIX, CLAUDE RAYMOND					
1918	Chi	N	H-P	2	0-0 1.000
HENRICH, THOMAS DAVID					
1938	NY	A	O	4	.250
1941	NY	A	O	5	.167
1947	NY	A	O	7	.323
1949	NY	A	1	5	.263
				21	.262
HENRICKSEN, OLAF					
1912	Bos	A	H	2	1.000
1915	Bos	A	H	2	.000
1916	Bos	A	H	1	.000
				5	.333
HENRY, WILLIAM RODMAN					
1961	Cin	N	P	2	0-0
HENSHAW, ROY JOHN					
1935	Chi	N	P	1	0-0
HERMAN, WILLIAM JENNINGS BRYAN					
1932	Chi	N	2	4	.222
1935	Chi	N	2	6	.333
1938	Chi	N	2	4	.188
1941	Bro	N	2	4	.125
				18	.242
HERMANSKI, EUGENE VICTOR					
1947	Bro	N	O	7	.158
1949	Bro	N	O	4	.308
				11	.219
HERSHBERGER, WILLARD McKEE					
1939	Cin	N	C	3	.500
HERZOG, CHARLES LINCOLN					
1911	NY	N	3	6	.190
1912	NY	N	3	8	.400
1913	NY	N	3	5	.053
1917	NY	N	2	6	.250
				25	.245
HEVING, JOHN ALOYSIUS					
1931	Phi	A	H	1	.000
HIGBE, WALTER KIRBY					
1941	Bro	N	P	1	0-0
HIGGINS, MICHAEL FRANKLIN					
1940	Det	A	3	7	.333
1946	Bos	A	3	7	.208
				14	.271
HIGH, ANDREW AIRD					
1928	St.L	N	3	4	.294
1930	St.L	N	3	1	.500
1931	St.L	N	3	4	.267
				9	.294
HILDEBRAND, ORAL CLYDE					
1939	NY	A	P	1	0-0
HILL, CARMEN PROCTOR					
1927	Pit	N	P	1	0-0

Yr	Cl	Lea	Pos	G	Rec
HILLER, CHARLES JOSEPH					
1962	SF	N	2	7	.269
HOAG, MYRIL OLIVER					
1932	NY	A	H	1	.000
1937	NY	A	O	5	.300
1938	NY	A	O	2	.400
				8	.320
HOAK, DONALD ALBERT					
1955	Bro	N	3	3	.333
1960	Pit	N	3	7	.227
				10	.240
HOBLITZEL, RICHARD CARLETON					
1915	Bos	A	1	5	.313
1916	Bos	A	1	5	.235
				10	.273
HODGES, GILBERT RAYMOND					
1947	Bro	N	H	1	.000
1949	Bro	N	1	5	.235
1952	Bro	N	1	7	.000
1953	Bro	N	1	6	.364
1955	Bro	N	1	7	.292
1956	Bro	N	1	7	.304
1959	LA	N	1	6	.391
				39	.267
HOFFMAN, DANIEL JOHN					
1905	Phi	A	H	1	.000
HOFMAN, ARTHUR F.					
1906	Chi	N	O	6	.304
1908	Chi	N	O	5	.316
1910	Chi	N	O	5	.267
				16	.298
HOFMANN, FRED					
1923	NY	A	H	2	.000
HOGSETT, ELON CHESTER					
1934	Det	A	P	3	0-0
1935	Det	A	P	1	0-0
				4	0-0
HOGUE, ROBERT CLINTON					
1951	NY	A	P	2	0-0
HOLKE, WALTER HENRY					
1917	NY	N	1	6	.286
HOLLINGSWORTH, ALBERT WAYNE					
1944	St.L	A	P	1	0-0
HOLLOCHER, CHARLES JACOB					
1918	Chi	N	S	6	.190
HOLM, ROSCOE ALBERT					
1926	St.L	N	O	5	.125
1928	St.L	N	O	3	.167
				8	.136
HOLMES, THOMAS FRANCIS					
1948	Bos	N	O	6	.192
1952	Bro	N	O	3	.000
				9	.185
HOOPER, HARRY BARTHOLOMEW					
1912	Bos	A	O	8	.290
1915	Bos	A	O	5	.350
1916	Bos	A	O	5	.333
1918	Bos	A	O	6	.200
				24	.293
HOOVER, ROBERT JOSEPH					
1945	Det	A	S	1	.333

Yr	Cl	Lea	Pos	G	Rec
HOPP, JOHN LEONARD					
1942	St.L	N	1	5	.176
1943	St.L	N	O	1	.000
1944	St.L	N	O	6	.185
1950	NY	A	1	3	.000
1951	NY	A	H	1	.000
				16	.160
HORNSBY, ROGERS					
1926	St.L	N	2	7	.250
1929	Chi	N	2	5	.238
				12	.245
HOSTETLER, CHARLES CLOYD					
1945	Det	A	H	3	.000
HOUK, RALPH GEORGE					
1947	NY	A	H	1	1.000
1952	NY	A	H	1	.000
				2	.500
HOUTTEMAN, ARTHUR JOSEPH					
1954	Cle	A	P	1	0-0
HOWARD, ELSTON GENE					
1955	NY	A	O	7	.192
1956	NY	A	O	1	.400
1957	NY	A	1	6	.273
1958	NY	A	O	6	.222
1960	NY	A	C	5	.462
1961	NY	A	C	5	.250
1962	NY	A	C	6	.143
				36	.246
HOWARD, GEORGE ELMER					
1907	Chi	N	1	2	.200
1908	Chi	N	H	1	.000
				3	.167
HOYT, WAITE CHARLES					
1921	NY	A	P	3	2-1
1922	NY	A	P	2	0-1
1923	NY	A	P	1	0-0
1926	NY	A	P	2	1-1
1927	NY	A	P	1	1-0
1928	NY	A	P	2	2-0
1931	Phi	A	P	1	0-1
				12	6-4
HUBBELL, CARL OWEN					
1933	NY	N	P	2	2-0
1936	NY	N	P	2	1-1
1937	NY	N	P	2	1-1
				6	4-2
HUGHES, JAMES ROBERT					
1953	Bro	N	P	1	0-0
HUGHES, ROY JOHN					
1945	Chi	N	S	6	.294
HUGHES, THOMAS J.					
1903	Bos	A	P	1	0-1
HUGHSON, CECIL CARLTON					
1946	Bos	A	P	3	0-1
HUNT, KENNETH RAYMOND					
1961	Cin	N	P	1	0-0
HUTCHINGS, JOHN RICHARD JOSEPH					
1940	Cin	N	P	1	0-0
HUTCHINSON, FREDERICK CHARLES					
1940	Det	A	P	1	0-0
HYATT, ROBERT HAMILTON					
1909	Pit	N	O	2	.000
IRVIN, MONFORD MERRILL					
1951	NY	N	O	6	.458
1954	NY	N	O	4	.222
				10	.394

Yr	Cl	Lea	Pos	G	Rec
ISBELL, WILLIAM FRANK					
1906	Chi	A	2	6	.308
JACKSON, JOSEPH JEFFERSON					
1917	Chi	A	O	6	.304
1919	Chi	A	O	8	.375
				14	.345
JACKSON, RANSOM JOSEPH					
1956	Bro	N	H	3	.000
JACKSON, TRAVIS CALVIN					
1923	NY	N	H	1	.000
1924	NY	N	S	7	.074
1933	NY	N	3	5	.222
1936	NY	N	3	6	.190
				19	.149
JAKUCKI, SIGMUND JACK					
1944	St.L	A	P	1	0-1
JAMES, WILLIAM HENRY					
1919	Chi	A	P	1	0-0
JAMES, WILLIAM LAWRENCE					
1914	Bos	N	P	2	2-0
JAMIESON, CHARLES DEVINE					
1920	Cle	A	O	6	.333
JANSEN, LAWRENCE JOSEPH					
1951	NY	N	P	3	0-2
JANVRIN, HAROLD CHANDLER					
1915	Bos	A	S	1	.000
1916	Bos	A	2	5	.217
				6	.208
JAY, JOSEPH RICHARD					
1961	Cin	N	P	2	1-1
JENSEN, JACK EUGENE					
1950	NY	A	H	1	.000
JOHNSON, DARRELL DEAN					
1961	Cin	N	C	2	.500
JOHNSON, DONALD SPORI					
1945	Chi	N	2	7	.172
JOHNSON, EARL DOUGLASS					
1946	Bos	A	P	3	1-0
JOHNSON, ERNEST RUDOLPH					
1923	NY	A	S	2	.000
JOHNSON, ERNEST THORWALD					
1957	Mil	N	P	3	0-1
JOHNSON, KENNETH CARSTENSEN					
1950	Phi	N	H	1	.000
JOHNSON, KENNETH TRAVIS					
1961	Cin	N	P	1	0-0
JOHNSON, ROY CLEVELAND					
1936	NY	A	H	2	.000
JOHNSON, SYLVESTER W.					
1928	St.L	N	P	2	0-0
1930	St.L	N	P	2	0-0
1931	St.L	N	P	3	0-1
				7	0-1
JOHNSON, WALTER PERRY					
1924	Was	A	P	3	1-2
1925	Was	A	P	3	2-1
				6	3-3
JOHNSON, WILLIAM RUSSELL					
1943	NY	A	3	5	.300
1947	NY	A	3	7	.269
1949	NY	A	3	2	.143
1950	NY	A	3	4	.000
				18	.237

Yr	Cl	Lea	Pos	G	Rec
JOHNSTON, JAMES HARLE					
1916	Bro	N	O	3	.300
1920	Bro	N	3	4	.214
				7	.250
JOHNSTON, WHEELER ROGERS					
1920	Cle	A	1	5	.273
JONES, DAVID JEFFERSON					
1907	Det	A	O	5	.353
1908	Det	A	H	3	.000
1909	Det	A	O	7	.233
				15	.265
JONES, FIELDER ALLISON					
1906	Chi	A	O	6	.095
JONES, SAMUEL POND					
1918	Bos	A	P	1	0-1
1922	NY	A	P	2	0-0
1923	NY	A	P	2	0-1
1926	NY	A	P	1	0-0
				6	0-2
JONES, SHELDON LESLIE					
1951	NY	N	P	2	0-0
JONES, SHERMAN JARVIS					
1961	Cin	N	P	1	0-0
JONES, THOMAS					
1909	Det	A	1	7	.250
JONES, VERNAL LEROY					
1946	St.L	N	H	1	.000
1957	Mil	N	H	3	.000
				4	.000
JONES, WILLIE EDWARD					
1950	Phi	N	3	4	.286
JONNARD, CLAUDE ALFRED					
1923	NY	N	P	2	0-0
1924	NY	N	P	1	0-0
				3	0-0
JOOST, EDWIN DAVID					
1940	Cin	N	2	7	.200
JORGENSEN, JOHN DONALD					
1947	Bro	N	3	7	.200
1949	Bro	N	3	4	.182
				11	.194
JUDGE, JOSEPH IGNATIUS					
1924	Was	A	1	7	.385
1925	Was	A	1	7	.174
				14	.286
JUDNICH, WALTER FRANKLIN					
1948	Cle	A	O	4	.077
JURGES, WILLIAM FREDERICK					
1932	Chi	N	S	3	.364
1935	Chi	N	S	6	.250
1938	Chi	N	S	4	.231
				13	.275
JURISICH, ALVIN JOSEPH					
1944	St.L	N	P	1	0-0
KANE, JOHN FRANCIS					
1910	Chi	N	H	1	.000
KASKO, EDWARD MICHAEL					
1961	Cin	N	S	5	.318
KAUFF, BENJAMIN MICHAEL					
1917	NY	N	O	6	.160
KEEN, HOWARD VICTOR					
1926	St.L	N	P	1	0-0

Yr	Cl	Lea	Pos	G	Rec
KELLER, CHARLES ERNEST					
1939	NY	A	O	4	.438
1941	NY	A	O	5	.389
1942	NY	A	O	5	.200
1943	NY	A	O	5	.222
				19	.306
KELLERT, FRANK WILLIAM					
1955	Bro	N	H	3	.333
KELLY, GEORGE LANGE					
1921	NY	N	1	8	.233
1922	NY	N	1	5	.278
1923	NY	N	1	6	.182
1924	NY	N	1-2-O	7	.290
				26	.248
KELTNER, KENNETH FREDERICK					
1948	Cle	A	3	6	.095
KENNEDY, MONTIA CALVIN					
1951	NY	N	P	2	0-0
KENNEDY, ROBERT DANIEL					
1948	Cle	A	O	3	.500
KENNEDY, WILLIAM V.					
1903	Pit	N	P	1	0-1
KERR, JOHN FRANCIS					
1933	Was	A	H	1	.000
KERR, RICHARD HENRY					
1919	Chi	A	P	2	2-0
KILDUFF, PETER JOHN					
1920	Bro	N	2	7	.095
KILLEFER, WILLIAM LAVIER					
1915	Phi	N	H	1	.000
1918	Chi	N	C	6	.118
				7	.111
KILLIAN, EDWIN HENRY					
1907	Det	A	P	1	0-0
1908	Det	A	P	1	0-0
				2	0-0
KING, LEE					
1922	NY	N	O	1	1.000
KLEIN, CHARLES HERBERT					
1935	Chi	N	O	5	.333
KLEIN, LOUIS FRANK					
1943	St.L	N	2	5	.136
KLIEMAN, EDWARD FREDERICK					
1948	Cle	A	P	1	0-0
KLING, JOHN G.					
1906	Chi	N	C	6	.176
1907	Chi	N	C	5	.211
1908	Chi	N	C	5	.250
1910	Chi	N	C	5	.077
				21	.185
KLINGER, ROBERT HAROLD					
1946	Bos	A	P	1	0-1
KLIPPSTEIN, JOHN CALVIN					
1959	LA	N	P	1	0-0
KLUSZEWSKI, THEODORE BERNARD					
1959	Chi	A	1	6	.391
KOENIG, MARK ANTHONY					
1926	NY	A	S	7	.125
1927	NY	A	S	4	.500
1928	NY	A	S	4	.158
1932	Chi	N	S	2	.250
1936	NY	N	2	3	.333
				20	.237

Yr	Cl	Lea	Pos	G	Rec
KONETCHY, EDWARD JOSEPH					
1920	Bro	N	1	7	.174
KONIKOWSKI, ALEXANDER JAMES					
1951	NY	N	P	1	0-0
KONSTANTY, CASIMER JAMES					
1950	Phi	N	P	3	0-1
KOPF, WILLIAM LORENZ					
1919	Cin	N	S	8	.222
KOSLO, GEORGE BERNARD					
1951	NY	N	P	2	1-1
KOUFAX, SANFORD					
1959	LA	N	P	2	0-1
KOWALIK, FABIAN LORENZ					
1935	Chi	N	P	1	0-0
KRAMER, JOHN HENRY					
1944	St.L	A	P	2	1-0
KREEVICH, MICHAEL ANDREAS					
1944	St.L	A	O	6	.231
KREMER, REMY					
1925	Pit	N	P	3	2-1
1927	Pit	N	P	1	0-1
				4	2-2
KRIST, HOWARD WILBUR					
1943	St.L	N	P	1	0-0
KRUEGER, ERNEST GEORGE					
1920	Bro	N	C	4	.167
KUBEK, ANTHONY CHRISTOPHER					
1957	NY	A	3-O	7	.286
1958	NY	A	S	7	.047
1960	NY	A	S-O	7	.383
1961	NY	A	S	5	.227
1962	NY	A	S	7	.276
				33	.238
KUCKS, JOHN CHARLES					
1955	NY	A	P	2	0-0
1956	NY	A	P	3	1-0
1957	NY	A	P	1	0-0
1958	NY	A	P	2	0-0
				8	1-0
KUENN, HARVEY EDWARD					
1962	SF	N	O	4	.083
KUHEL, JOSEPH ANTHONY					
1933	Was	A	1	5	.150
KUROWSKI, GEORGE JOHN					
1942	St.L	N	3	5	.267
1943	St.L	N	3	5	.222
1944	St.L	N	3	6	.217
1946	St.L	N	3	7	.296
				23	.253
KUZAVA, ROBERT LEROY					
1951	NY	A	P	1	0-0
1952	NY	A	P	1	0-0
1953	NY	A	P	1	0-0
				3	0-0
LAABS, CHESTER PETER					
1944	St.L	A	O	5	.200
LABINE, CLEMENT WALTER					
1953	Bro	N	P	3	0-2
1955	Bro	N	P	4	1-0
1956	Bro	N	P	2	1-0
1959	LA	N	P	1	0-0
1960	Pit	N	P	3	0-0
				13	2-2

Yr	Cl	Lea	Pos	G	Rec
LaCHANCE, GEORGE					
1903	Bos	A	1	8	.207
LAMAR, WILLIAM HARMONG					
1920	Bro	N	H	3	.000
LANDIS, JAMES HENRY					
1959	Chi	A	O	6	.292
LANIER, HUBERT MAX					
1942	St.L	N	P	2	1-0
1943	St.L	N	P	3	0-1
1944	St.L	N	P	2	1-0
				7	2-1
LAPP, JOHN WALKER					
1910	Phi	A	C	1	.250
1911	Phi	A	C	2	.250
1913	Phi	A	C	1	.250
1914	Phi	A	C	1	.000
				5	.235
LARKER, NORMAN HOWARD					
1959	LA	N	O	6	.188
LARSEN, DONALD JAMES					
1955	NY	A	P	1	0-1
1956	NY	A	P	2	1-0
1957	NY	A	P	2	1-1
1958	NY	A	P	2	1-0
1958	NY	A	P	2	1-0
1962	SF	N	P	3	1-0
				10	4-2
LAVAGETTO, HARRY ARTHUR					
1941	Bro	N	3	3	.100
1947	Bro	N	3	5	.143
				8	.118
LAW, VERNON SANDERS					
1960	Pit	N	P	3	2-0
LAZZERI, ANTHONY MICHAEL					
1926	NY	A	2	7	.192
1927	NY	A	2	4	.267
1928	NY	A	2	4	.250
1932	NY	A	2	4	.294
1936	NY	A	2	6	.200
1937	NY	A	2	5	.400
1938	Chi	N	H	2	.000
				32	.250
LEACH, THOMAS WILLIAM					
1903	Pit	N	3	8	.273
1909	Pit	N	3-0	6	.273
				14	.273
LEE, WILLIAM CRUTCHER					
1935	Chi	N	P	2	0-0
1938	Chi	N	P	2	0-2
				4	0-2
LEEVER, SAMUEL W.					
1903	Pit	N	P	2	0-2
LEHMAN, KENNETH KARL					
1952	Bro	N	P	1	0-0
LEIBER, HENRY EDWARD					
1936	NY	N	O	2	.000
1937	NY	N	O	3	.364
				5	.235
LEIBOLD, HARRY LORAN					
1917	Chi	A	O	2	.400
1919	Chi	A	O	5	.065
1924	Was	A	O	3	.167
1925	Was	A	H	3	.500
				13	.161
LEIFIELD, ALBERT PETER					
1909	Pit	N	P	1	0-1

Yr	Cl	Lea	Pos	G	Rec
LEMON, ROBERT GRANVILLE					
1948	Cle	A	P	2	2-0
1954	Cle	A	P	2	0-2
				4	2-2
LEONARD, HUBERT BENJAMIN					
1915	Bos	A	P	1	1-0
1916	Bos	A	P	1	1-0
				2	2-0
LESLIE, SAMUEL ANDREW					
1936	NY	N	H	3	.667
1937	NY	N	H	2	.000
				5	.500
LEWIS, GEORGE EDWARD					
1912	Bos	A	O	8	.156
1915	Bos	A	O	5	.444
1916	Bos	A	O	5	.353
				18	.284
LIDDLE, DONALD EUGENE					
1954	NY	N	P	2	1-0
LINDELL, JOHN HARLAN					
1943	NY	A	O	4	.111
1947	NY	A	O	6	.500
1949	NY	A	O	2	.143
				12	.324
LINDSEY, JAMES KENDRICK					
1930	St.L	N	P	2	0-0
1931	St.L	N	P	2	0-0
				4	0-0
LINDSTROM, FREDERICK CHARLES					
1924	NY	N	3	7	.333
1935	Chi	N	3-0	4	.200
				11	.289
LITWHILER, DANIEL WEBSTER					
1943	St.L	N	O	5	.267
1944	St.L	N	O	5	.200
				10	.229
LIVINGSTON, THOMPSON ORVILLE					
1945	Chi	N	C	6	.364
LOCKMAN, CARROLL WALTER					
1951	NY	N	1	6	.240
1954	NY	N	1	4	.111
				10	.186
LOES, WILLIAM					
1952	Bro	N	P	2	0-1
1953	Bro	N	P	1	1-0
1955	Bro	N	P	1	0-1
				4	1-2
LOGAN, JOHN					
1957	Mil	N	S	7	.185
1958	Mil	N	S	7	.120
				14	.154
LOHRKE, JACK WAYNE					
1951	NY	N	H	2	.000
LOLLAR, JOHN SHERMAN					
1947	NY	A	C	2	.750
1959	Chi	A	C	6	.227
				8	.308
LOMBARDI, ERNESTO NATALI					
1939	Cin	N	C	4	.214
1940	Cin	N	C	2	.333
				6	.235
LOMBARDI, VICTOR ALVIN					
1947	Bro	N	P	2	0-1
LONE, RICHARD DALE					
1960	NY	A	H	3	.333
1962	NY	A	1	2	.200
				5	.250

Yr	Cl	Lea	Pos	G	Rec
LOPAT, EDMUND WALTER					
1949	NY	A	P	1	1-0
1950	NY	A	P	1	0-0
1951	NY	A	P	2	2-0
1952	NY	A	P	2	0-1
1953	NY	A	P	1	1-0
				7	4-1
LOPATA, STANLEY EDWARD					
1950	Phi	N	C	2	.000
LOPEZ, HECTOR HEADLEY					
1960	NY	A	O	3	.429
1961	NY	A	O	4	.333
1962	NY	A	H	2	.000
				9	.333
LORD, BRISTOL ROBOTHAM					
1905	Phi	A	O	5	.100
1910	Phi	A	O	5	.182
1911	Phi	A	O	6	.185
				16	.159
LOWDERMILK, GROVER CLEVELAND					
1919	Chi	A	P	1	0-0
LOWN, OMAR JOSEPH					
1959	Chi	A	P	3	0-0
LOWREY, HARRY LEE					
1945	Chi	N	O	7	.310
LUDERUS, FREDERICK W.					
1915	Phi	N	1	5	.438
LUMPE, JERRY DEAN					
1957	NY	A	3	6	.286
1958	NY	A	S-3	6	.167
				12	.231
LUNTE, HARRY AUGUST					
1920	Cle	A	2	1	.000
LUQUE, ADOLFO					
1919	Cin	N	P	2	0-0
1933	NY	N	P	1	1-0
				3	1-0
LYNCH, GERALD THOMAS					
1961	Cin	N	H	4	.000
LYNN, BYRD					
1917	Chi	A	H	1	.000
1919	Chi	A	C	1	.000
				2	.000
MAAS, DUANE FREDERICK					
1958	NY	A	P	1	0-0
1960	NY	A	P	1	0-0
MADDOX, NICHOLAS					
1909	Pit	N	P	1	1-0
MAGEE, SHERWOOD ROBERT					
1919	Cin	N	H	2	.500
MAGLIE, SALVATORE ANTHONY					
1951	NY	N	P	1	0-1
1954	NY	N	P	1	0-0
1956	Bro	N	P	2	1-1
				4	1-2
MAGUIRE, FREDERICK EDWARD					
1923	NY	N	H	2	.000
MAHAFFEY, LEE ROY					
1931	Phi	A	P	1	0-0
MAIER, ROBERT PHILIP					
1945	Det	A	H	1	1.000

Yr	Cl	Lea	Pos	G	Rec
MAILS, JOHN WALTER					
1920	Cle	A	P	2	1-0
MAJESKI, HENRY					
1954	Cle	A	3	4	.167
MALONE, PERCE LEIGH					
1929	Chi	N	P	3	0-2
1932	Chi	N	P	1	0-0
1936	NY	A	P	2	0-1
				6	0-3
MALONEY, JAMES WILLIAM					
1961	Cin	N	P	1	0-0
MAMAUX, ALBERT LEON					
1920	Bro	N	P	3	0-0
MANCUSO, AUGUST RODNEY					
1930	St.L	N	C	2	.286
1931	St.L	N	C	2	.000
1933	NY	N	C	5	.118
1936	NY	N	C	6	.263
1937	NY	N	C	3	.000
				18	.173
MANCUSO, FRANK OCTAVIUS					
1944	St.L	A	C	2	.667
MANN, LESLIE					
1914	Bos	N	O	3	.286
1918	Chi	N	O	6	.227
				9	.241
MANTILLA, FELIX LAMELA					
1957	Mil	N	2	4	.000
1958	Mil	N	S	4	.000
				8	.000
MANTLE, MICKEY CHARLES					
1951	NY	A	O	2	.200
1952	NY	A	O	7	.345
1953	NY	A	O	6	.208
1955	NY	A	O	3	.200
1956	NY	A	O	7	.250
1957	NY	A	O	6	.263
1958	NY	A	O	7	.250
1960	NY	A	O	7	.250
1961	NY	A	O	2	.167
1962	NY	A	O	7	.120
				54	.257
MANUSH, HENRY EMMETT					
1933	Was	A	O	5	.111
MAPES, CLIFFORD FRANKLIN					
1949	NY	A	O	4	.100
1950	NY	A	O	1	.000
				5	.071
MARANVILLE, WALTER JAMES VINCENT					
1914	Bos	N	S	4	.308
1928	St.L	N	S	4	.308
				8	.308
MARBERRY, FREDERICK					
1924	Was	A	P	4	0-1
1925	Was	A	P	2	0-0
1934	Det	A	P	2	0-1
				8	0-2
MARICHAL, JUAN ANTONIO SANCHEZ					
1962	SF	N	P	1	0-0
MARION, MARTIN WHITFORD					
1942	St.L	N	S	5	.111
1943	St.L	N	S	5	.357
1944	St.L	N	S	6	.227
1946	St.L	N	S	7	.250
				23	.231

Yr	Cl	Lea	Pos	G	Rec
MARIS, ROGER EUGENE					
1960	NY	A	O	7	.267
1961	NY	A	O	5	.105
1962	NY	A	O	7	.174
				19	.194
MARQUARD, RICHARD WILLIAM					
1911	NY	N	P	3	0-1
1912	NY	N	P	2	2-0
1913	NY	N	P	2	0-1
1916	Bro	N	P	2	0-2
1920	Bro	N	P	2	0-1
				11	2-5
MARTIN, ALFRED MANUEL					
1951	NY	A	H	1	.000
1952	NY	A	2	7	.217
1953	NY	A	2	6	.500
1955	NY	A	2	7	.320
1956	NY	A	2-3	7	.296
				28	.283
MARTIN, JOHN LEONARD					
1928	St.L	N	H	1	.000
1931	St.L	N	O	7	.500
1934	St.L	N	3	7	.355
				15	.418
MARTINA, JOSEPH JOHN					
1924	Was	A	P	1	0-0
MARTY, JOSEPH ANTON					
1938	Chi	N	O	3	.500
MASI, PHILIP SAMUEL					
1948	Bos	N	C	5	.125
MATHEWS, EDWIN LEE					
1957	Mil	N	3	7	.227
1958	Mil	N	3	7	.160
				14	.191
MATHEWSON, CHRISTOPHER					
1905	NY	N	P	3	3-0
1911	NY	N	P	3	1-2
1912	NY	N	P	3	0-2
1913	NY	N	P	2	1-1
				11	5-5
MAY, FRANK SPRUELL					
1932	Chi	N	P	2	0-1
MAYER, JAMES ERSKINE					
1915	Phi	N	P	2	0-1
1919	Chi	A	P	1	0-0
				3	0-1
MAYO, EDWARD JOSEPH					
1936	NY	N	3	1	.000
1945	Det	A	2	7	.250
				8	.241
MAYO, JOHN LEWIS					
1950	Phi	N	O	3	.000
MAYS, CARL WILLIAM					
1916	Bos	A	P	2	0-1
1918	Bos	A	P	2	2-0
1921	NY	A	P	3	1-2
1922	NY	A	P	1	0-1
				8	3-4
MAYS, WILLIE HOWARD					
1951	NY	N	O	6	.182
1954	NY	N	O	4	.286
1962	SF	N	O	7	.250
				17	.234
MAZEROSKI, WILLIAM STANLEY					
1960	Pit	N	2	7	.308
McANANY, JAMES					
1959	Chi	A	O	3	.000

Yr	Cl	Lea	Pos	G	Rec
McBRIDE, THOMAS RAYMOND					
1946	Bos	A	O	5	.167
McCABE, WILLIAM FRANCIS					
1918	Chi	N	H	3	.000
1920	Bro	N	H	1	.000
				4	.000
McCARTHY, JOHN JOSEPH					
1937	NY	N	1	5	.211
McCARTY, GEORGE LEWIS					
1917	NY	N	C	3	.400
McCOLL, ALEXANDER BOYD					
1933	Was	A	P	1	0-0
McCORMICK, FRANK ANDREW					
1939	Cin	N	1	4	.400
1940	Cin	N	1	7	.214
1948	Bos	N	1	3	.200
				14	.271
McCORMICK, HARRY ELWOOD					
1912	NY	N	H	5	.250
1913	NY	N	H	2	.500
				7	.333
McCORMICK, MYRON WINTHROP					
1940	Cin	N	O	7	.310
1948	Bos	N	O	6	.261
1949	Bro	N	O	1	.000
				14	.288
McCOSKY, WILLIAM BARNEY					
1940	Det	A	O	7	.304
McCOVEY, WILLIE LEE					
1962	SF	N	1-O	4	.200
McCULLOUGH, CLYDE EDWARD					
1945	Chi	N	H	1	.000
McDERMOTT, MAURICE JOSEPH					
1956	NY	A	P	1	0-0
McDONALD, JAMES LeROY					
1953	NY	A	P	1	1-0
McDOUGALD, GILBERT JAMES					
1951	NY	A	2-3	6	.261
1952	NY	A	3	7	.200
1953	NY	A	3	6	.167
1955	NY	A	3	7	.259
1956	NY	A	S	7	.143
1957	NY	A	S	7	.250
1958	NY	A	2	7	.321
1960	NY	A	3	6	.278
				53	.237
McFARLAND, EDWARD WILLIAM					
1906	Chi	A	H	1	.000
McGANN, DENNIS L.					
1905	NY	N	1	5	.235
McGINNITY, JOSEPH JEROME					
1905	NY	N	P	2	1-1
McHALE, JOHN JOSEPH					
1945	Det	A	H	3	.000
McINNIS, JOHN PHAELEN					
1911	Phi	A	1	1	.000
1913	Phi	A	1	5	.118
1914	Phi	A	1	4	.143
1918	Bos	A	1	6	.250
1925	Pit	N	1	4	.286
				20	.200

Yr Cl Lea Pos G Rec

McINTIRE, HARRY M.
1910 Chi N P 2 0-1

McINTYRE, MATTHEW W.
1908 Det A O 5 .225
1909 Det A O 4 .000
9 .190

McKAIN, ARCHIE RICHARD
1940 Det A P 1 0-0

McLEAN, JOHN BANNERMAN
1913 NY N C 5 .500

McMAHON, DONALD JOHN
1957 Mil N P 3 0-0
1958 Mil N P 3 0-0
6 0-0

McMILLAN, NORMAN ALEXIS
1922 NY A O 1 .000
1929 Chi N 3 5 .100
6 .091

McMULLIN, FREDERICK WILLIAM
1917 Chi A 3 6 .125
1919 Chi A H 2 .500
8 .154

McNAIR, DONALD ERIC
1930 Phi A H 1 .000
1931 Phi A 2 2 .000
3 .000

McNALLY, MICHAEL JOSEPH
1916 Bos A H 1 .000
1921 NY A 3 7 .250
1922 NY A 2 1 .000
9 .250

McNEELY, GEORGE EARL
1924 Was A O 7 .222
1925 Was A O 4 .000
11 .222

McQUILLAN, HUGH A.
1922 NY N P 1 1-0
1923 NY N P 2 0-1
1924 NY N P 3 0-0
6 1-1

McQUINN, GEORGE HARTLEY
1944 St.L A 1 6 .438
1947 NY A 1 7 .130
13 .256

MEADOWS, HENRY LEE
1925 Pit N P 1 0-1
1927 Pit N P 1 0-1
2 0-2

MEDWICK, JOSEPH MICHAEL
1934 St.L N O 7 .379
1941 Bro N O 5 .235
12 .326

MELTON, CLIFFORD GEORGE
1937 NY N P 3 0-2

MERKLE, FREDERICK CHARLES
1911 NY N 1 6 .150
1912 NY N 1 8 .273
1913 NY N 1 4 .231
1916 Bro N 1 3 .250
1918 Chi N 1 6 .278
27 .239

MERTES, SAMUEL BLAIR
1905 NY N O 5 .188

MERULLO, LEONARD RICHARD
1945 Chi N S 3 .000

Yr Cl Lea Pos G Rec

METHENY, ARTHUR BEAUREGARD
1943 NY A O 2 .125

METKOVICH, GEORGE MICHAEL
1946 Bos A H 2 .500

MEUSEL, EMIL FREDERICK
1921 NY N O 8 .345
1922 NY N O 5 .250
1923 NY N O 6 .280
1924 NY N O 4 .154
23 .276

MEUSEL, ROBERT WILLIAM
1921 NY A O 8 .200
1922 NY A O 5 .300
1923 NY A O 6 .269
1926 NY A O 7 .238
1927 NY A O 4 .118
1928 NY A O 4 .200
34 .225

MEYER, RUSSELL CHARLES
1950 Phi N P 2 0-1
1953 Bro N P 1 0-0
1955 Bro N P 1 0-0
4 0-1

MEYERS, JOHN TORTES
1911 NY N C 6 .300
1912 NY N C 8 .357
1913 NY N C 1 .000
1916 Bro N C 3 .200
18 .290

MIERKOWICZ, EDWARD FRANK
1945 Det A O 1 .000

MIKSIS, EDWARD THOMAS
1947 Bro N 2-0 5 .250
1949 Bro N 3 3 .286
8 .273

MILJUS, JOHN KENNETH
1927 Pit N P 2 0-1

MILLER, EDMUND JOHN
1929 Phi A O 5 .368
1930 Phi A O 6 .143
1931 Phi A O 7 .269
18 .258

MILLER, ELMER
1921 NY A O 8 .161

MILLER, JOHN BARNEY
1909 Pit N 2 7 .250

MILLER, LAWRENCE H.
1918 Bos A H 1 .000

MILLER, LOWELL OTTO
1916 Bro N C 2 .125
1920 Bro N C 6 .143
8 .136

MILLER, RALPH JOSEPH
1924 Was A 3 4 .182

MILLER, ROBERT JOHN
1950 Phi N P 1 0-1

MILLER, STUART LEONARD
1962 SF N P 2 0-0

MILLIKEN, ROBERT FOGLE
1953 Bro N P 1 0-0

MINNER, PAUL EDISON
1949 Bro N P 1 0-0

MITCHELL, CLARENCE ELMER
1920 Bro N P 1 0-0
1928 St.L N P 1 0-0
2 0-0

Yr Cl Lea Pos G Rec

MITCHELL, LOREN DALE
1948 Cle A O 6 .174
1954 Cle A H 3 .000
1956 Bro N H 4 .000
13 .138

MIZE, JOHN ROBERT
1949 NY A H 2 1.000
1950 NY A 1 4 .133
1951 NY A 1 4 .286
1952 NY A 1 5 .400
1953 NY A H 3 .000
18 .286

MIZELL, WILMER DAVID
1960 Pit N P 2 0-1

MOGRIDGE, GEORGE ANTHONY
1924 Was A P 2 1-0

MONROE, ZACHARY CHARLES
1958 NY A P 1 0-0

MOON, WALLACE WADE
1959 LA N O 6 .261

MOONEY, JIM IRVING
1934 St.L N P 1 0-0

MOORE, EUGENE JR.
1944 St.L A O 6 .182

MOORE, GRAHAM EDWARD
1925 Pit N 2 7 .231

MOORE, JAMES WILLIAM
1930 Phi A O 3 .333
1931 Phi A O 2 .333
5 .333

MOORE, JOHN FRANCIS
1932 Chi N O 2 .000

MOORE, JOSEPH GREGG
1933 NY N O 5 .227
1936 NY N O 6 .214
1937 NY N O 5 .391
16 .274

MOORE, LLOYD ALBERT
1939 Cin N P 1 0-0
1940 Cin N P 3 0-0
4 0-0

MOORE, RAYMOND LEROY
1959 Chi A P 1 0-0

MOORE, TERRY BUFORD
1942 St.L N O 5 .294
1946 St.L N O 7 .148
12 .205

MOORE, WILLIAM WILCY
1927 NY A P 2 1-0
1932 NY A P 1 1-0
3 2-0

MORAN, JOSEPH HERBERT
1914 Bos N O 3 .077

MORAN, PATRICK JOSEPH
1906 Chi N H 2 .000
1907 Chi N H 1 .000
3 .000

MORGAN, ROBERT MORRIS
1952 Bro N 3 2 .000
1953 Bro N H 1 .000
3 .000

Yr	Cl	Lea	Pos	G	Rec
MORGAN, TOM STEPHEN					
1951	NY	A	P	1	0-0
1955	NY	A	P	2	0-0
1956	NY	A	P	2	0-1
				5	0-1
MORIARTY, GEORGE JOSEPH					
1909	Det	A	3	7	.261
MORRISON, JOHN DEWEY					
1925	Pit	N	P	3	0-0
MOSES, WALLACE					
1946	Bos	A	O	4	.417
MOSSI, DONALD LOUIS					
1954	Cle	A	P	3	0-0
MOWREY, HARRY HARLAN					
1916	Bro	N	3	5	.176
MUELLER, DONALD FREDERICK					
1954	NY	N	O	4	.389
MUELLER, LESLIE CLYDE					
1945	Det	A	P	1	0-0
MULLIN, GEORGE JOSEPH					
1907	Det	A	P	2	0-2
1908	Det	A	P	1	1-0
1909	Det	A	P	4	2-1
				7	3-3
MUNCRIEF, ROBERT CLEVELAND					
1944	St.L	A	P	2	0-1
1948	Cle	A	P	1	0-0
				3	0-1
MUNGER, GEORGE DAVID					
1946	St.L	N	P	1	1-0
MURPHY, DANIEL FRANCIS					
1905	Phi	A	2	5	.188
1910	Phi	A	O	5	.350
1911	Phi	A	O	6	.304
				16	.288
MURPHY, JOHN JOSEPH					
1936	NY	A	P	1	0-0
1937	NY	A	P	1	0-0
1938	NY	A	P	1	0-0
1939	NY	A	P	1	1-0
1941	NY	A	P	2	1-0
1943	NY	A	P	2	0-0
				8	2-0
MURPHY, JOSEPH EDWARD					
1913	Phi	A	O	5	.227
1914	Phi	A	O	4	.188
1919	Chi	A	H	3	.000
				12	.200
MURRAY, JOHN JOSEPH					
1911	NY	N	O	6	.000
1912	NY	N	O	8	.323
1913	NY	N	O	5	.250
				19	.206
MUSIAL, STANLEY FRANK					
1942	St.L	N	O	5	.222
1943	St.L	N	O	5	.278
1944	St.L	N	O	6	.304
1946	St.L	N	1	7	.222
				23	.256
MYER, CHARLES SOLOMON					
1925	Was	A	3	3	.250
1933	Was	A	2	5	.300
				8	.286
MYERS, HENRY HARRISON					
1916	Bro	N	O	5	.182
1920	Bro	N	O	7	.231
				12	.208

Yr	Cl	Lea	Pos	G	Rec
MYERS, WILLIAM HARRISON					
1939	Cin	N	S	4	.333
1940	Cin	N	S	7	.130
				11	.200
NARAGON, HAROLD RICHARD					
1954	Cle	A	C	1	.000
NARLESKI, RAYMOND EDMOND					
1954	Cle	A	P	2	0-0
NARRON, SAMUEL					
1943	St.L	N	H	1	.000
NEAL, CHARLES LENARD					
1956	Bro	N	2	1	.000
1959	LA	N	2	6	.370
				7	.323
NEALE, ALFRED EARLE					
1919	Cin	N	O	8	.357
NEEDHAM, THOMAS J.					
1910	Chi	N	H	1	.000
NEHF, ARTHUR NEUKOM					
1921	NY	N	P	3	1-2
1922	NY	N	P	2	1-0
1923	NY	N	P	2	1-1
1924	NY	N	P	3	1-1
1929	Chi	N	P	2	0-0
				12	4-4
NEIS, BERNARD EDMUND					
1920	Bro	N	O	4	.000
NELSON, GLENN RICHARD					
1952	Bro	N	H	4	.000
1960	Pit	N	1	4	.333
				8	.250
NEWCOMBE, DONALD					
1949	Bro	N	P	2	0-2
1955	Bro	N	P	1	0-1
1956	Bro	N	P	2	0-1
				5	0-4
NEWHOUSER, HAROLD					
1945	Det	A	P	3	2-1
1954	Cle	A	P	1	0-0
				4	2-1
NEWSOM, LOUIS NORMAN					
1940	Det	A	P	3	2-1
1947	NY	A	P	2	0-1
				5	2-2
NIARHOS, CONSTANTINE GREGORY					
1949	NY	A	C	1	.000
NICHOLSON, WILLIAM BECK					
1945	Chi	N	O	7	.214
NIEHOFF, JOHN ALBERT					
1915	Phi	N	2	5	.063
NIEMAN, ROBERT CHARLES					
1962	SF	N	H	1	.000
NOBLE, RAFAEL MIGUEL					
1951	NY	N	C	2	.000
NOREN, IRVING ARNOLD					
1952	NY	A	O	4	.300
1953	NY	A	H	2	.000
1955	NY	A	O	5	.063
				11	.148
NUNAMAKER, LESLIE GRANT					
1920	Cle	A	C	2	.500
O'BRIEN, JOHN JOSEPH					
1903	Bos	A	H	2	.000

Yr	Cl	Lea	Pos	G	Rec
O'BRIEN, THOMAS J.					
1912	Bos	A	P	2	0-2
O'CONNELL, JAMES JOSEPH					
1923	NY	N	H	2	.000
O'CONNOR, PATRICK FRANCIS					
1909	Pit	N	H	1	.000
O'DEA, JAMES KENNETH					
1935	Chi	N	H	1	1.000
1938	Chi	N	C	3	.200
1942	St.L	N	H	1	1.000
1943	St.L	N	C	2	.667
1944	St.L	N	H	3	.333
				10	.462
O'DELL, WILLIAM OLIVER					
1962	SF	N	P	3	0-1
O'DOUL, FRANK JOSEPH					
1933	NY	N	H	1	1.000
O'FARRELL, ROBERT ARTHUR					
1918	Chi	N	C	3	.000
1926	St.L	N	C	7	.304
				10	.269
OGDEN, WARREN HARVEY					
1924	Was	A	P	1	0-0
OLDHAM, JOHN CYRUS					
1925	Pit	N	P	1	0-0
OLDIS, ROBERT CARL					
1960	Pit	N	C	2	.000
OLDRING, REUBEN NOSHIER					
1911	Phi	A	O	6	.200
1913	Phi	A	O	5	.273
1914	Phi	A	O	4	.067
				15	.194
O'LEARY, CHARLES TIMOTHY					
1907	Det	A	S	5	.055
1908	Det	A	S	5	.216
1909	Det	A	3	1	.000
				11	.100
OLMO, LUIS RODRIGUEZ					
1949	Bro	N	O	4	.273
OLSON, IVAN MASSIE					
1916	Bro	N	S	5	.250
1920	Bro	N	S	7	.320
				12	.293
O'MARA, OLIVER EDWARD					
1916	Bro	N	H	1	.000
O'NEILL, STEPHEN FRANCIS					
1920	Cle	A	C	7	.333
O'NEILL, WILLIAM JOHN					
1906	Chi	A	O	1	.000
ORSATTI, ERNEST RALPH					
1928	St.L	N	O	4	.286
1930	St.L	N	H	1	.000
1931	St.L	N	O	1	.000
1934	St.L	N	O	7	.318
				13	.273
ORSINO, JOHN JOSEPH					
1962	SF	N	C	1	.000
OSTROWSKI, JOSEPH PAUL					
1951	NY	A	P	1	0-0
O'TOOLE, JAMES JEROME					
1961	Cin	N	P	2	0-2

Yr	*Cl*	*Lea*	*Pos*	*G*	*Rec*
OTT, MELVIN THOMAS					
1933	NY	N	O	5	.389
1936	NY	N	O	6	.304
1937	NY	N	3	5	.200
				16	.295
OUTLAW, JAMES PAULUS					
1945	Det	A	3	7	.179
OVERALL, ORVAL					
1906	Chi	N	P	2	0-0
1907	Chi	N	P	2	1-0
1908	Chi	N	P	3	2-0
1910	Chi	N	P	1	0-1
				8	3-1
OVERMIRE, FRANK					
1945	Det	A	P	1	0-1
OWEN, ARNOLD MALCOLM					
1941	Bro	N	C	5	.167
OWEN, FRANK MALCOLM					
1906	Chi	A	P	1	0-0
OWEN, MARVIN JAMES					
1934	Det	A	3	7	.069
1935	Det	A	1-3	6	.050
				13	.061
PAFKO, ANDREW					
1945	Chi	N	O	7	.214
1952	Bro	N	O	7	.190
1957	Mil	N	O	6	.200
1958	Mil	N	O	4	.333
				24	.222
PAGAN, JOSE ANTONIO					
1962	SF	N	S	7	.368
PAGE, JOSEPH FRANCIS					
1947	NY	A	P	4	1-1
1949	NY	A	P	3	1-0
				7	2-1
PAGE, VANCE LINWOOD					
1938	Chi	N	P	1	0-0
PAIGE, LeROY					
1948	Cle	A	P	1	0-0
PALICA, ERVIN MARTIN					
1949	Bro	N	P	1	0-0
PARENT, FREDERICK ALFRED					
1903	Bos	A	S	8	.281
PARTEE, ROY ROBERT					
1946	Bos	A	C	5	.100
PASCHAL, BENJAMIN EDWIN					
1926	NY	A	H	5	.250
1928	NY	A	O	3	.200
				8	.214
PASKERT, GEORGE HENRY					
1915	Phi	N	O	5	.158
1918	Chi	N	O	6	.190
				11	.175
PASSEAU, CLAUDE WILLIAM					
1945	Chi	N	P	3	1-0
PAYNE, FREDERICK THOMAS					
1907	Det	A	C	2	.250
PEARSON, MARCELLUS MONTE					
1936	NY	A	P	1	1-0
1937	NY	A	P	1	1-0
1938	NY	A	P	1	1-0
1939	NY	A	P	1	1-0
				4	4-0
PECK, HAROLD ARTHUR					
1948	Cle	A	O	1	.000
PECKINPAUGH, ROGER THORPE					
1921	NY	A	S	8	.179
1924	Was	A	S	4	.417
1925	Was	A	S	7	.250
				19	.250
PEEL, HOMER HEFNER					
1933	NY	N	O	2	.500
PENNOCK, HERBERT JEFFERIS					
1914	Phi	A	P	1	0-0
1923	NY	A	P	3	2-0
1926	NY	A	P	3	2-0
1927	NY	A	P	1	1-0
1932	NY	A	P	2	0-0
				10	5-0
PERRITT, WILLIAM DAYTON					
1917	NY	N	P	3	0-0
PESKY, JOHN MICHAEL					
1946	Bos	A	S	7	.233
PFEFFER, EDWARD JOSEPH					
1916	Bro	N	P	3	0-1
1920	Bro	N	P	1	0-0
				4	0-1
PFIESTER, JOHN THEODORE JOSEPH					
1906	Chi	N	P	2	0-2
1907	Chi	N	P	1	1-0
1908	Chi	N	P	1	0-1
1910	Chi	N	P	1	0-0
				5	1-3
PHELPS, EDWARD JOSEPH					
1903	Pit	N	C	8	.233
PHILLEY, DAVID EARL					
1954	Cle	A	O	4	.125
PHILLIPPE, CHARLES LOUIS					
1903	Pit	N	P	5	3-2
1909	Pit	N	P	2	0-0
				7	3-2
PHILLIPS, JACK DORN					
1947	NY	A	1	2	.000
PHILLIPS, JOHN MELVIN					
1959	Chi	A	3-O	3	.300
PICK, CHARLES THOMAS					
1918	Chi	N	2	6	.389
PIERCE, WALTER WILLIAM					
1959	Chi	A	P	3	0-0
1962	SF	N	P	2	1-1
				5	1-1
PIERCY, WILLIAM BENTON					
1921	NY	A	P	1	0-0
PIGNATANO, JOSEPH BENJAMIN					
1959	LA	N	C	1	.000
PINSON, VADA EDWARD					
1961	Cin	N	O	5	.091
PIPGRAS, GEORGE WILLIAM					
1927	NY	A	P	1	1-0
1928	NY	A	P	1	1-0
1932	NY	A	P	1	1-0
				3	3-0
PIPP, WALTER CLEMENT					
1921	NY	A	1	8	.154
1922	NY	A	1	5	.286
1923	NY	A	1	6	.250
				19	.224
PIZARRO, JUAN CORDOVA					
1957	Mil	N	P	1	0-0
1958	Mil	N	P	1	0-0
				2	0-0
PLANK, EDWARD STEWART					
1905	Phi	A	P	2	0-2
1911	Phi	A	P	2	1-1
1913	Phi	A	P	2	1-1
1914	Phi	A	P	1	0-1
				7	2-5
PODRES, JOHN JOSEPH					
1953	Bro	N	P	1	0-1
1955	Bro	N	P	2	2-0
1959	LA	N	P	2	1-0
				5	3-1
POLLET, HOWARD JOSEPH					
1942	St.L	N	P	1	0-0
1946	St.L	N	P	2	0-1
				3	0-1
POPE, DAVID					
1954	Cle	A	O	3	.000
POST, WALTER CHARLES					
1961	Cin	N	O	5	.333
POTTER, NELSON THOMAS					
1944	St.L	A	P	2	0-1
1948	Bos	N	P	2	0-0
				4	0-1
POWELL, ALVIN JACOB					
1936	NY	A	O	6	.455
1937	NY	A	H	1	.000
1938	NY	A	O	1	.000
				8	.435
POWERS, MICHAEL RILEY					
1905	Phi	A	C	3	.143
PRIDDY, GERALD EDWARD					
1942	NY	A	1-3	3	.100
PRIM, RAYMOND LEE					
1945	Chi	N	P	2	0-1
PUCCINELLI, GEORGE LAWRENCE					
1930	St.L	N	H	1	.000
PURKEY, ROBERT THOMAS					
1961	Cin	N	P	2	0-1
QUINN, JOHN PICUS					
1921	NY	A	P	1	0-1
1929	Phi	A	P	1	0-0
1930	Phi	A	P	1	0-0
				3	0-1
RACKLEY, MARVIN EUGENE					
1949	Bro	N	O	2	.000
RARIDEN, WILLIAM ANGEL					
1917	NY	N	C	5	.385
1919	Cin	N	C	5	.211
				10	.281
RASCHI, VICTOR ANGELO JOHN					
1947	NY	A	P	2	0-0
1949	NY	A	P	2	1-1
1950	NY	A	P	1	1-0
1951	NY	A	P	2	1-1
1952	NY	A	P	3	2-0
1953	NY	A	P	1	0-1
				11	5-3

Yr Cl Lea Pos G Rec

RATH, MAURICE SHARLES
1919 Cin N 2 8 .226

RAWLINGS, JOHN WILLIAM
1921 NY N 2 8 .333

REED, JOHN BURWELL
1961 NY A O 3 .000

REESE, HAROLD HENRY
1941 Bro N S 5 .200
1947 Bro N S 7 .304
1949 Bro N S 5 .316
1952 Bro N S 7 .345
1953 Bro N S 6 .208
1955 Bro N S 7 .296
1956 Bro N S 7 .222
44 .272

REGALADO, RUDOLPH VALENTINO
1954 Cle A H 4 .333

REINHART, ARTHUR CONRAD
1926 St.L N P 1 0-1

REISER, HAROLD PATRICK
1941 Bro N O 5 .200
1947 Bro N O 5 .250
10 .214

REPULSKI, ELDON JOHN
1959 LA N O 1 .000

REULBACH, EDWARD MARVIN
1906 Chi N P 2 1-0
1907 Chi N P 2 1-0
1908 Chi N P 2 0-0
1910 Chi N P 1 0-0
7 2-0

REYNOLDS, ALLIE PIERCE
1947 NY A P 2 1-0
1949 NY A P 2 1-0
1950 NY A P 2 1-0
1951 NY A P 2 1-1
1952 NY A P 4 2-1
1953 NY A P 3 1-0
15 7-2

REYNOLDS, CARL NETTLES
1938 Chi N O 4 .000

RHEM, CHARLES FLINT
1926 St.L N P 1 0-0
1928 St.L N P 1 0-0
1930 St.L N P 1 0-1
1931 St.L N P 1 0-0
4 0-1

RHODES, JAMES LAMAR
1954 NY N O 3 .667

RHYNE, HAROLD
1927 Pit N 2 1 .000

RICE, DELBERT W.
1946 St.L N C 3 .500
1957 Mil N C 2 .167
5 .333

RICE, EDGAR CHARLES
1924 Was A O 7 .207
1925 Was A O 7 .364
1933 Was A H 1 1.000
15 .302

RICHARDS, PAUL RAPIER
1945 Det A C 7 .211

RICHARDSON, ROBERT CLINTON
1957 NY A 2 2 .000
1958 NY A 3 4 .000
1960 NY A 2 7 .367
1961 NY A 2 5 .391
1962 NY A 2 7 .148
25 .282

RICHIE, LEWIS A.
1910 Chi N P 1 0-0

RICKERT, MARVIN AUGUST
1948 Bos N O 5 .211

RIDDLE, ELMER RAY
1940 Cin N P 1 0-0

RIGGS, LEWIS SIDNEY
1940 Cin N H 3 .000
1941 Bro N 3 3 .250
6 .182

RIGNEY, WILLIAM JOSEPH
1951 NY N H 4 .250

RING, JAMES JOSEPH
1919 Cin N P 2 1-1

RIPPLE, JAMES ALBERT
1936 NY N O 5 .333
1937 NY N O 5 .294
1940 Cin N O 7 .333
17 .320

RISBERG, CHARLES AUGUST
1917 Chi A H 2 .500
1919 Chi A S 8 .080
10 .111

RITCHEY, CLAUDE CASSIUS
1903 Pit N 2 8 .148

RIVERA, MANUEL JOSEPH
1959 Chi A O 5 .000

RIXEY, EPPA
1915 Phi N P 1 0-1

RIZZUTO, PHILIP FRANCIS
1941 NY A S 5 .111
1942 NY A S 5 .381
1947 NY A S 7 .308
1949 NY A S 5 .167
1950 NY A S 4 .143
1951 NY A S 6 .320
1952 NY A S 7 .148
1953 NY A S 6 .316
1955 NY A S 7 .267
52 .246

ROBERTS, ROBIN EVAN
1950 Phi N P 2 0-1

ROBERTSON, DAVIS AYDELOTTE
1917 NY N O 6 .500

ROBERTSON, EUGENE EDWARD
1928 NY A 3 3 .125

ROBINSON, AARON ANDREW
1947 NY A C 3 .200

ROBINSON, FRANK
1961 Cin N O 5 .200

ROBINSON, JACK ROOSEVELT
1947 Bro N 1 7 .259
1949 Bro N 2 5 .188
1952 Bro N 2 7 .174
1953 Bro N O 6 .320
1955 Bro N 3 6 .182
1956 Bro N 3 7 .250
38 .234

ROBINSON, WILLIAM EDWARD
1948 Cle A 1 6 .300
1955 NY A 1 4 .667
10 .348

ROE, ELWIN CHARLES
1949 Bro N P 1 1-0
1952 Bro N P 3 1-0
1953 Bro N P 1 0-1
5 2-1

ROEBUCK, EDWARD JACK
1955 Bro N P 1 0-0
1956 Bro N P 3 0-0
4 0-0

ROETTGER, WALTER HENRY
1931 St.L N O 3 .286

ROGELL, WILLIAM GEORGE
1934 Det A S 7 .276
1935 Det A S 6 .292
13 .283

ROGERS, THOMAS ANDREW
1921 NY A P 1 0-0

ROHE, GEORGE ANTHONY
1906 Chi A 3 6 .333

ROLFE, ROBERT ABIAL
1936 NY A 3 6 .400
1937 NY A 3 5 .300
1938 NY A 3 4 .167
1939 NY A 3 4 .125
1941 NY A 3 5 .300
1942 NY A 3 4 .353
28 .284

ROMANO, JOHN ANTHONY
1959 Chi A H 1 .000

ROMMEL, EDWIN AMERICUS
1929 Phi A P 1 1-0
1931 Phi A P 1 0-0
2 1-0

ROOT, CHARLES HENRY
1929 Chi N P 2 0-1
1932 Chi N P 1 0-1
1935 Chi N P 2 0-1
1938 Chi N P 1 0-0
6 0-3

ROSAR, WARREN VINCENT
1941 NY A C 1 .000
1942 NY A H 1 1.000
2 1.000

ROSEBORO, JOHN H.
1959 LA N C 6 .095

ROSEN, ALBERT LEONARD
1948 Cle A H 1 .000
1954 Cle A 3 3 .250
4 .231

ROSSMAN, CLAUDE R.
1907 Det A 1 5 .400
1908 Det A 1 5 .159
10 .282

ROTHROCK, JOHN HUSTON
1934 St.L N O 7 .233

ROUSH, EDD J.
1919 Cin N O 8 .214

Yr	Cl	Lea	Pos	G	Rec
ROWE, LYNWOOD THOMAS					
1934	Det	A	P	3	1-1
1935	Det	A	P	3	1-2
1940	Det	A	P	2	0-2
				8	2-5
RUCKER, GEORGE NAPOLEON					
1916	Bro	N	P	1	0-0
RUDOLPH, RICHARD					
1914	Bos	N	P	2	2-0
RUEL, HEROLD DOMINIC					
1924	Was	A	C	7	.095
1925	Was	A	C	7	.316
				14	.200
RUETHER, WALTER HENRY					
1919	Cin	N	P-H	3	1-0 / .667
1925	Was	A	H	1	.000
1926	NY	A	P-H	3	0-0 / .000
				7	1-1 / .364
RUFFING, CHARLES HERBERT					
1932	NY	A	P	1	1-0
1936	NY	A	P	2	0-1
1937	NY	A	P	1	1-0
1938	NY	A	P	2	2-0
1939	NY	A	P	1	1-0
1941	NY	A	P	1	1-0
1942	NY	A	P	2	1-1
				10	7-2
RUSH, ROBERT RANSOM					
1958	Mil	N	P	1	0-1
RUSSELL, ALLEN E.					
1924	Was	A	P	1	0-0
RUSSELL, EWELL ALBERT					
1917	Chi	A	P	1	0-0
RUSSELL, GLEN DAVID					
1946	Bos	A	3	2	1.000
RUSSELL, JACK ERWIN					
1933	Was	A	P	3	0-1
1938	Chi	N	P	2	0-0
				5	0-1
RUSSO, MARIUS UGO					
1941	NY	A	P	1	1-0
1943	NY	A	P	1	1-0
				2	2-0
RUTH, GEORGE HERMAN					
1915	Bos	A	H	1	.000
1916	Bos	A	P	1	1-0
1918	Bos	A	P-O	3	2-0 / .200
1921	NY	A	O	6	.313
1922	NY	A	O	5	.118
1923	NY	A	1-O	6	.368
1926	NY	A	O	7	.300
1927	NY	A	O	4	.400
1928	NY	A	O	4	.625
1932	NY	A	O	4	.333
				41	3-0 / .325
RUTHERFORD, JOHN WILLIAM					
1952	Bro	N	P	1	0-0
RYAN, CORNELIUS JOSEPH					
1948	Bos	N	H	2	.000
RYAN, JOHN COLLINS					
1933	NY	N	S	5	.278
1937	NY	N	H	1	.000
				6	.263

Yr	Cl	Lea	Pos	G	Rec
RYAN, WILFRED PATRICK DOLAN					
1922	NY	N	P	1	1-0
1923	NY	N	P	3	1-0
1924	NY	N	P	2	1-0
				6	3-0
RYBA, DOMINIC JOSEPH					
1946	Bos	A	P	1	0-0
SAIN, JOHN FRANKLIN					
1948	Bos	N	P	2	1-1
1951	NY	A	P	1	0-0
1952	NY	A	P	1	0-1
1953	NY	A	P	2	1-0
				6	2-2
SALKELD, WILLIAM FRANKLIN					
1948	Bos	N	C	5	.222
SALLEE, HARRY FRANKLIN					
1917	NY	N	P	2	0-2
1919	Cin	N	P	2	1-1
				4	1-3
SANDERS, RAYMOND FLOYD					
1942	St.L	N	H	2	.000
1943	St.L	N	1	5	.294
1944	St.L	N	1	6	.286
1948	Bos	N	H	1	.000
				14	.275
SANFORD, JOHN STANLEY					
1962	SF	N	P	3	1-2
SAUER, EDWARD					
1945	Chi	N	H	2	.000
SAWATSKI, CARL ERNEST					
1957	Mil	N	H	2	.000
SCARBOROUGH, RAY WILSON					
1952	NY	A	P	1	0-0
SCHAEFER, HERMAN A.					
1907	Det	A	2	5	.143
1908	Det	A	2-3	5	.110
				10	.135
SCHALK, RAYMOND WILLIAM					
1917	Chi	A	C	6	.263
1919	Chi	A	C	8	.304
				14	.286
SCHALLOCK, ARTHUR LAWRENCE					
1953	NY	A	P	1	0-0
SCHANG, WALTER HENRY					
1913	Phi	A	C	4	.357
1914	Phi	A	C	4	.167
1918	Bos	A	C	5	.444
1921	NY	A	C	8	.286
1922	NY	A	C	5	.188
1923	NY	A	C	6	.318
				32	.287
SCHENZ, HENRY LEONARD					
1951	NY	N	H	1	.000
SCHMANDT, RAYMOND HENRY					
1920	Bro	N	H	1	.000
SCHMIDT, CHARLES					
1907	Det	A	C	3	.166
1908	Det	A	C	4	.071
1909	Det	A	C	6	.222
				13	.159
SCHMIDT, CHARLES JOHN					
1914	Bos	N	1	4	.294
SCHMIDT, FREDERICK ALBERT					
1944	St.L	N	P	1	0-0

Yr	Cl	Lea	Pos	G	Rec
SCHOENDIENST, ALBERT FRED					
1946	St.L	N	2	7	.233
1957	Mil	N	2	5	.278
1958	Mil	N	2	7	.300
				19	.269
SCHOFIELD, JOHN RICHARD					
1960	Pit	N	S	3	.333
SCHRECKENGOST, OSSEE FREEMAN					
1905	Phi	A	C	3	.222
SCHULTE, FRANK					
1906	Chi	N	O	6	.269
1907	Chi	N	O	5	.250
1908	Chi	N	O	5	.389
1910	Chi	N	O	5	.353
				21	.309
SCHULTE, FRED WILLIAM					
1933	Was	A	O	5	.333
SCHUMACHER, HAROLD HENRY					
1933	NY	N	P	2	1-0
1936	NY	N	P	2	1-1
1937	NY	N	P	1	0-1
				5	2-2
SCHUPP, FERDINAND MAURICE					
1917	NY	N	P	2	1-0
SCHUSTER, WILLIAM CHARLES					
1945	Chi	N	S	2	.000
SCOTT, JOHN WILLIAM					
1922	NY	N	P	1	1-0
1923	NY	N	P	2	0-1
				3	1-1
SCOTT, LEWIS EVERETT					
1915	Bos	A	S	5	.055
1916	Bos	A	S	5	.125
1918	Bos	A	S	6	.095
1922	NY	A	S	5	.143
1923	NY	A	S	6	.318
				27	.156
SEBRING, JAMES DENNISON					
1903	Pit	N	O	8	.366
SECORY, FRANK EDWARD					
1945	Chi	N	H	5	.400
SEEDS, ROBERT IRA					
1936	NY	A	H	1	.000
SELKIRK, GEORGE ALEXANDER					
1936	NY	A	O	6	.333
1937	NY	A	O	5	.263
1938	NY	A	O	3	.200
1939	NY	A	O	4	.167
1941	NY	A	H	2	.500
1942	NY	A	H	1	.000
				21	.265
SEMINICK, ANDREW WASIL					
1950	Phi	N	C	4	.182
SEVEREID, HENRY LEVAI					
1925	Was	A	C	1	.333
1926	NY	A	C	7	.273
				8	.280
SEWELL, JAMES LUTHER					
1933	Was	A	C	5	.176
SEWELL, JOSEPH WHEELER					
1920	Cle	A	S	7	.174
1932	NY	A	3	4	.333
				11	.237
SEYBOLD, RALPH ORLANDO					
1905	Phi	A	O	5	.125

Yr Cl Lea Pos G Rec

SHAFER, ARTHUR JOSEPH
1912 NY N S 3 .000
1913 NY N 3-O 5 .158
8 .158

SHANTZ, ROBERT CLAYTON
1957 NY A P 3 0-1

SHAW, ROBERT JOHN
1959 Chi A P 2 1-1

SHAWKEY, JAMES ROBERT
1914 Phi A P 1 0-1
1921 NY A P 2 0-1
1922 NY A P 1 0-0
1923 NY A P 1 1-0
1926 NY A P 3 0-1
8 1-3

SHEA, FRANCIS JOSEPH
1947 NY A P 3 2-0

SHEAN, DAVID WILLIAM
1918 Bos A 2 6 .211

SHECKARD, SAMUEL JAMES TILDEN
1906 Chi N O 6 .000
1907 Chi N O 5 .238
1908 Chi N O 5 .238
1910 Chi N O 5 .286
21 .195

SHEEHAN, JOHN THOMAS
1920 Bro N 3 3 .182

SHERDEL, WILLIAM HENRY
1926 St.L N P 2 0-2
1928 St.L N P 2 0-2
4 0-4

SHERRY, LAWRENCE
1959 LA N P 4 2-0

SHIRLEY, ALVIS NEWMAN
1944 St.L A P 1 0-0

SHIRLEY, ERNEST RAEFORD
1924 Was A H 3 .500

SHOCKER, URBAN JAMES
1926 NY A P 2 0-1

SHORE, ERNEST GRADY
1915 Bos A P 2 1-1
1916 Bos A P 2 2-0
4 3-1

SHORES, WILLIAM DAVID
1930 Phi A P 1 0-0

SHORTEN, CHARLES HENRY
1916 Bos A O 2 .571

SHUBA, GEORGE THOMAS
1952 Bro N O 4 .300
1953 Bro N H 2 1.000
1955 Bro N H 1 .000
7 .333

SIEBERN, NORMAN LEROY
1956 NY A H 1 .000
1958 NY A O 3 .125
4 .111

SIEVER, EDWARD T.
1907 Det A P 1 0-1

SILVERA, CHARLES ANTHONY RYAN
1949 NY A C 1 .000

SILVESTRI, KENNETH JOSEPH
1950 Phi N C 1 .000

SIMMONS, ALOYSIUS HARRY
1929 Phi A O 5 .300
1930 Phi A O 6 .364
1931 Phi A O 7 .333
1939 Cin N O 1 .250
19 .329

SIMPSON, HARRY LEON
1957 NY A 1 5 .083

SISLER, RICHARD ALLAN
1946 St.L N H 2 .000
1950 Phi N O 4 .059
6 .053

SISTI, SEBASTIAN DANIEL
1948 Bos N 2 2 .000

SKINNER, ROBERT RALPH
1960 Pit N O 2 .200

SKOWRON, WILLIAM JOSEPH
1955 NY A 1 5 .333
1956 NY A 1 3 .100
1957 NY A 1 2 .000
1958 NY A 1 7 .259
1960 NY A 1 7 .375
1961 NY A 1 5 .353
1962 NY A 1 6 .222
35 .283

SLAGLE, JAMES JULIUS
1907 Chi N O 5 .273

SLAUGHTER, ENOS BRADSHER
1942 St.L N O 5 .263
1946 St.L N O 7 .320
1956 NY A O 6 .350
1957 NY A O 5 .250
1958 NY A H 4 .000
27 .291

SMITH, ALFRED JOHN
1936 NY N P 1 0-0
1937 NY N P 2 0-0
3 0-0

SMITH, ALPHONSE EUGENE
1954 Cle A O 4 .214
1959 Chi A O 6 .250
10 .235

SMITH, CLAY JAMIESON
1940 Det A P 1 0-0

SMITH, EARL SUTTON
1921 NY N C 3 .000
1922 NY N C 2 .143
1925 Pit N C 6 .350
1927 Pit N C 3 .000
1928 St.L N C 1 .750
15 .239

SMITH, ELMER JOHN
1920 Cle A O 5 .308
1922 NY A H 2 .000
7 .267

SMITH, HAROLD WAYNE
1960 Pit N C 3 .375

SMITH, HARRY THOMAS
1903 Pit N C 1 .000

SMITH, JAMES LAWRENCE
1919 Cin N H 1 .000

SMITH, ROBERT ELDRIDGE
1932 Chi N P 1 0-0

SMITH, SHERROD MALONE
1916 Bro N P 1 0-1
1920 Bro N P 2 1-1
3 1-2

SNIDER, EDWIN DONALD
1949 Bro N O 5 .143
1952 Bro N O 7 .345
1953 Bro N O 6 .320
1955 Bro N O 7 .320
1956 Bro N O 7 .304
1959 LA N O 4 .200
36 .286

SNODGRASS, FRED CARLISLE
1911 NY N O 6 .105
1912 NY N O 8 .212
1913 NY N O 2 .333
16 .182

SNYDER, FRANK J.
1921 NY N C 7 .364
1922 NY N C 4 .333
1923 NY N C 5 .118
1924 NY N H 1 .000
17 .273

SOUTHWORTH, WILLIAM HARRISON
1924 NY N O 5 .000
1926 St.L N O 7 .345
12 .333

SPAHN, WARREN EDWARD
1948 Bos N P 3 1-1
1957 Mil N P 2 1-1
1958 Mil N P 3 2-1
8 4-3

SPEAKER, TRISTRAM E.
1912 Bos A O 8 .300
1915 Bos A O 5 .294
1920 Cle A O 7 .320
20 .306

SPEECE, BYRON FRANKLIN
1924 Was A P 1 0-0

SPENCER, GEORGE ELWELL
1951 NY N P 2 0-0

SPENCER, ROY HAMPTON
1927 Pit N C 1 .000

SPOONER, KARL BENJAMIN
1955 Bro N P 2 0-1

STAHL, CHARLES SYLVESTER
1903 Bos A O 8 .309

STAHL, GARLAND
1912 Bos A 1 8 .281

STAFFORD, WILLIAM CHARLES
1960 NY A P 2 0-0
1961 NY A P 1 0-0
1962 NY A P 1 1-0
4 1-0

STAINBACK, GEORGE TUCKER
1942 NY A H 2 .000
1943 NY A O 5 .176
7 .176

STALEY, GERALD LEE
1959 Chi A P 4 0-1

STANAGE, OSCAR HARLAND
1909 Det A C 2 .200

STANKY, EDWARD RAYMOND

Yr	Cl	Lea	Pos	G	Rec
1947	Bro	N	2	7	.240
1948	Bos	N	2	6	.286
1951	NY	N	2	6	.136
				19	.213

STEINFELDT, HARRY M.

Yr	Cl	Lea	Pos	G	Rec
1906	Chi	N	3	6	.250
1907	Chi	N	3	5	.470
1908	Chi	N	3	5	.250
1910	Chi	N	3	5	.100
				21	.260

STENGEL, CHARLES DILLON

Yr	Cl	Lea	Pos	G	Rec
1916	Bro	N	O	4	.364
1922	NY	N	O	2	.400
1923	NY	N	O	6	.417
				12	.393

STEPHENS, VERNON DECATUR

Yr	Cl	Lea	Pos	G	Rec
1944	St.L	A	S	6	.227

STEPHENSON, JACKSON RIGGS

Yr	Cl	Lea	Pos	G	Rec
1929	Chi	N	O	5	.316
1932	Chi	N	O	4	.444
				9	.378

STEPHENSON, WALTER McQUEEN

Yr	Cl	Lea	Pos	G	Rec
1935	Chi	N	H	1	.000

STEWART, WALTER CLEVELAND

Yr	Cl	Lea	Pos	G	Rec
1933	Was	A	P	1	0-1

STIRNWEISS, GEORGE HENRY

Yr	Cl	Lea	Pos	G	Rec
1943	NY	A	H	1	.000
1947	NY	A	2	7	.259
1949	NY	A	H	1	.000
				9	.250

STOCK, MILTON JOSEPH

Yr	Cl	Lea	Pos	G	Rec
1915	Phi	N	3	5	.118

STRANG, SAMUEL NICKLIN

Yr	Cl	Lea	Pos	G	Rec
1905	NY	N	H	1	.000

STRICKLAND, GEORGE BEVAN

Yr	Cl	Lea	Pos	G	Rec
1954	Cle	A	S	3	.000

STRUNK, AMOS AARON

Yr	Cl	Lea	Pos	G	Rec
1910	Phi	A	O	4	.278
1911	Phi	A	H	1	.000
1913	Phi	A	O	5	.118
1914	Phi	A	O	2	.286
1918	Bos	A	O	6	.174
				18	.200

STUART, RICHARD LEE

Yr	Cl	Lea	Pos	G	Rec
1960	Pit	N	1	5	.150

STURDIVANT, THOMAS VIRGIL

Yr	Cl	Lea	Pos	G	Rec
1955	NY	A	P	2	0-0
1956	NY	A	P	2	1-0
1957	NY	A	P	2	0-0
				6	1-0

STURM, JOHN PETER JOSEPH

Yr	Cl	Lea	Pos	G	Rec
1941	NY	A	1	5	.286

SULLIVAN, WILLIAM JOSEPH JR.

Yr	Cl	Lea	Pos	G	Rec
1940	Det	A	C	5	.154

SULLIVAN, WILLIAM JOSEPH SR.

Yr	Cl	Lea	Pos	G	Rec
1906	Chi	A	C	6	.000

SUMMA, HOMER WAYNE

Yr	Cl	Lea	Pos	G	Rec
1929	Phi	A	H	1	.000

SUMMERS, OREN EDGAR

Yr	Cl	Lea	Pos	G	Rec
1908	Det	A	P	2	0-2
1909	Det	A	P	2	0-2
				4	0-4

SUNDRA, STEPHEN RICHARD

Yr	Cl	Lea	Pos	G	Rec
1939	NY	A	P	1	0-0

SWIFT, ROBERT VIRGIL

Yr	Cl	Lea	Pos	G	Rec
1945	Det	A	C	3	.250

TANNEHILL, LEE FORD

Yr	Cl	Lea	Pos	G	Rec
1906	Chi	A	S	3	.111

TATE, HENRY BENNETT

Yr	Cl	Lea	Pos	G	Rec
1924	Was	A	H	3	.000

TAYLOR, JAMES HARRY

Yr	Cl	Lea	Pos	G	Rec
1947	Bro	N	P	1	0-0

TAYLOR, JAMES WREN

Yr	Cl	Lea	Pos	G	Rec
1929	Chi	N	C	5	.177

TAYLOR, THOMAS LIVINGSTONE CARLTON

Yr	Cl	Lea	Pos	G	Rec
1924	Was	A	3	3	.000

TEBBETTS, GEORGE ROBERT

Yr	Cl	Lea	Pos	G	Rec
1940	Det	A	C	4	.000

TERRY, RALPH WILLARD

Yr	Cl	Lea	Pos	G	Rec
1960	NY	A	P	2	0-2
1961	NY	A	P	2	0-1
1962	NY	A	P	3	2-1
				7	2-4

TERRY, WILLIAM HAROLD

Yr	Cl	Lea	Pos	G	Rec
1924	NY	N	1	5	.429
1933	NY	N	1	5	.273
1936	NY	N	1	6	.240
				16	.295

TESREAU, CHARLES MONROE

Yr	Cl	Lea	Pos	G	Rec
1912	NY	N	P	3	1-2
1913	NY	N	P	2	0-1
1917	NY	N	P	1	0-0
				6	1-3

THEVENOW, THOMAS JOSEPH

Yr	Cl	Lea	Pos	G	Rec
1926	St.L	N	S	7	.417
1928	St.L	N	S	1	.000
				8	.417

THOMAS, ALPHONSE THOMAS

Yr	Cl	Lea	Pos	G	Rec
1933	Was	A	P	2	0-0

THOMAS, CHESTER D.

Yr	Cl	Lea	Pos	G	Rec
1915	Bos	A	C	2	.200
1916	Bos	A	C	3	.143
1920	Cle	A	C	1	.000
				6	.167

THOMAS, FREDERICK HARVEY

Yr	Cl	Lea	Pos	G	Rec
1918	Bos	A	3	6	.117

THOMAS, IRA FELIX

Yr	Cl	Lea	Pos	G	Rec
1908	Det	A	C	2	.500
1910	Phi	A	C	4	.250
1911	Phi	A	C	4	.083
				10	.214

THOMAS, MYLES LEWIS

Yr	Cl	Lea	Pos	G	Rec
1926	NY	A	P	2	0-0

THOMPSON, DONALD NEWLIN

Yr	Cl	Lea	Pos	G	Rec
1953	Bro	N	O	2	.000

THOMPSON, EUGENE EARL

Yr	Cl	Lea	Pos	G	Rec
1939	Cin	N	P	1	0-1
1940	Cin	N	P	1	0-1
				2	0-2

THOMPSON, HENRY CURTIS

Yr	Cl	Lea	Pos	G	Rec
1951	NY	N	O	5	.143
1954	NY	N	3	4	.364
				9	.240

THOMPSON, JOHN GUS

Yr	Cl	Lea	Pos	G	Rec
1903	Pit	N	P	1	0-0

THOMSON, ROBERT BROWN

Yr	Cl	Lea	Pos	G	Rec
1951	NY	N	3	6	.238

THORPE, JAMES FRANCIS

Yr	Cl	Lea	Pos	G	Rec
1917	NY	N	O	1	.000

THRONEBERRY, MARVIN EUGENE

Yr	Cl	Lea	Pos	G	Rec
1958	NY	A	H	1	.000

TINKER, JOSEPH BERT

Yr	Cl	Lea	Pos	G	Rec
1906	Chi	N	S	6	.167
1907	Chi	N	S	5	.154
1908	Chi	N	S	5	.263
1910	Chi	N	S	5	.333
				21	.235

TINNING, LYLE FORREST

Yr	Cl	Lea	Pos	G	Rec
1932	Chi	N	P	2	0-0

TIPTON, JOSEPH JOHN

Yr	Cl	Lea	Pos	G	Rec
1948	Cle	A	H	1	.000

TOBIN, JAMES ANTHONY

Yr	Cl	Lea	Pos	G	Rec
1945	Det	A	P	1	0-0

TODT, PHILIP JULIUS

Yr	Cl	Lea	Pos	G	Rec
1931	Phi	A	H	1	.000

TOLSON, CHARLES JULIUS

Yr	Cl	Lea	Pos	G	Rec
1929	Chi	N	H	1	.000

TONEY, FREDERICK ARTHUR

Yr	Cl	Lea	Pos	G	Rec
1921	NY	N	P	2	0-0

TOPORCER, GEORGE

Yr	Cl	Lea	Pos	G	Rec
1926	St.L	N	H	1	.000

TORGESON, CLIFFORD EARL

Yr	Cl	Lea	Pos	G	Rec
1948	Bos	N	1	5	.389
1959	Chi	A	1	3	.000
				8	.368

TORRE, FRANK JOSEPH

Yr	Cl	Lea	Pos	G	Rec
1957	Mil	N	1	7	.300
1958	Mil	N	1	7	.176
				14	.222

TOWNE, JAY KING

Yr	Cl	Lea	Pos	G	Rec
1906	Chi	A	H	1	.000

TRAYNOR, HAROLD JOSEPH

Yr	Cl	Lea	Pos	G	Rec
1925	Pit	N	3	7	.346
1927	Pit	N	3	4	.200.
				11	.293

TRESH, THOMAS MICHAEL

Yr	Cl	Lea	Pos	G	Rec
1962	NY	A	O	7	.321

TROUT, PAUL HOWARD

Yr	Cl	Lea	Pos	G	Rec
1940	Det	A	P	1	0-1
1945	Det	A	P	2	1-1
				3	1-2

TROWBRIDGE, ROBERT

Yr	Cl	Lea	Pos	G	Rec
1957	Mil	N	P	1	0-0

TRUCKS, VIRGIL OLIVER

Yr	Cl	Lea	Pos	G	Rec
1945	Det	A	P	2	1-0

TUCKER, THURMAN LOWELL

Yr	Cl	Lea	Pos	G	Rec
1948	Cle	A	O	1	.333

TURLEY, ROBERT LEE

Yr	Cl	Lea	Pos	G	Rec
1955	NY	A	P	3	0-1
1956	NY	A	P	3	0-1
1957	NY	A	P	3	1-0
1958	NY	A	P	4	2-1
1960	NY	A	P	2	1-0
				15	4-3

Yr	Cl	Lea	Pos	G	Rec
TURNER, JAMES RILEY					
1940	Cin	N	P	1	0-1
1942	NY	A	P	1	0-0
				2	0-1
TURNER, THOMAS RICHARD					
1944	St.L	A	H	1	.000
TYLER, GEORGE ALBERT					
1914	Bos	N	P	1	0-0
1918	Chi	N	P	3	1-1
				4	1-1
UHLE, GEORGE ERNEST					
1920	Cle	A	P	2	0-0
VANCE, CLARENCE ARTHUR					
1934	St.L	N	P	1	0-0
VANDENBERG, HAROLD HARRIS					
1945	Chi	N	P	3	0-0
VANDER MEER, JOHN SAMUEL					
1940	Cin	N	P	1	0-0
VAUGHAN, JOSEPH FLOYD					
1947	Bro	N	H	3	.500
VAUGHN, JAMES LESLIE					
1918	Chi	N	P	3	1-2
VEACH, ROBERT HENRY					
1925	Was	A	H	2	.000
VEIL, FREDERICK WILLIAM					
1903	Pit	N	P	1	0-0
VERBAN, EMIL MATTHEW					
1944	St.L	N	2	6	.412
VIRDON, WILLIAM CHARLES					
1960	Pit	N	O	7	.241
VOISELLE, WILLIAM SYMMES					
1948	Bos	N	P	2	0-1
WADE, BENJAMIN STYRON					
1953	Bro	N	P	2	0-0
WAGNER, CHARLES F.					
1912	Bos	A	S	8	.167
WAGNER, HAROLD EDWARD					
1946	Bos	A	C	5	.000
WAGNER, JOHN PETER					
1903	Pit	N	S	8	.214
1909	Pit	N	S	7	.333
				15	.269
WAITKUS, EDWARD STEPHEN					
1950	Phi	N	1	4	.267
WALBERG, GEORGE ELVIN					
1929	Phi	A	P	2	1-0
1930	Phi	A	P	1	0-1
1931	Phi	A	P	2	0-0
				5	1-1
WALKER, ALBERT BLUFORD					
1956	Bro	N	H	2	.000
WALKER, CLARENCE WILLIAM					
1916	Bos	A	O	3	.231
WALKER, FRED					
1941	Bro	N	O	5	.222
1947	Bro	N	O	7	.222
				12	.222
WALKER, GERALD HOLMES					
1934	Det	A	H	3	.333
1935	Det	A	O	3	.250
				6	.286
WALKER, HARRY WILLIAM					
1942	St.L	N	H	1	.000
1943	St.L	N	O	5	.167
1946	St.L	N	O	7	.412
				13	.278
WALKER, HARVEY WILLOS					
1945	Det	A	H	2	.500
WALKER, WILLIAM HENRY					
1934	St.L	N	P	2	0-2
WALSH, EDWARD AUGUSTIN					
1906	Chi	A	P	2	2-0
WALSH, JAMES CHARLES					
1914	Phi	A	O	3	.333
1916	Bos	A	O	1	.000
				4	.222
WALTERS, WILLIAM HENRY					
1939	Cin	N	P	2	0-2
1940	Cin	N	P	2	2-0
				4	2-2
WAMBSGANSS, WILLIAM ADOLPH					
1920	Cle	A	2	7	.154
WANER, LLOYD JAMES					
1927	Pit	N	O	4	.400
WANER, PAUL GLEE					
1927	Pit	N	O	4	.333
WARD, AARON LEE					
1921	NY	A	2	8	.192
1922	NY	A	2	5	.154
1923	NY	A	2	6	.417
				19	.270
WARNEKE, LONNIE					
1932	Chi	N	P	2	0-1
1935	Chi	N	P	3	2-0
				5	2-1
WASDELL, JAMES CHARLES					
1941	Bro	N	O	3	.200
WATKINS, GEORGE ARCHIBALD					
1930	St.L	N	O	4	.167
1931	St.L	N	O	5	.286
				9	.231
WATSON, JOHN REEVES					
1923	NY	N	P	1	0-0
1924	NY	N	P	1	0-0
				2	0-0
WEATHERLY, CYRIL ROY					
1943	NY	A	H	1	.000
WEAVER, GEORGE DAVIS					
1917	Chi	A	S	6	.333
1919	Chi	A	3	8	.324
				14	.327
WEAVER, MONTGOMERY MORTON					
1933	Was	A	P	1	0-1
WEBB, JAMES LEVERNE					
1945	Det	A	S	7	.185
WENSLOFF, CHARLES WILLIAM					
1947	NY	A	P	1	0-0
WERBER, WILLIAM MURRAY					
1939	Cin	N	3	4	.250
1940	Cin	N	3	7	.370
				11	.326
WERTZ, VICTOR WOODROW					
1954	Cle	A	1	4	.500
WESTLAKE, WALDON THOMAS					
1954	Cle	A	O	2	.143
WESTRUM, WESLEY NOREEN					
1951	NY	N	C	6	.235
1954	NY	N	C	4	.273
				10	.250
WHEAT, ZACHARY DAVIS					
1916	Bro	N	O	5	.210
1920	Bro	N	O	7	.333
				12	.283
WHITE, ERNEST DANIEL					
1942	St.L	N	P	1	1-0
1943	St.L	N	H	1	.000
				2	1-0 / .000
WHITE, GUY HARRIS					
1906	Chi	A	P	3	1-1
WHITE, JOYNER CLIFFORD					
1934	Det	A	O	7	.130
1935	Det	A	O	5	.263
				12	.194
WHITEHEAD, BURGESS URQUHART					
1934	St.L	N	S	1	.000
1936	NY	N	2	6	.048
1937	NY	N	2	5	.250
				12	.135
WHITEHILL, EARL OLIVER					
1933	Was	A	P	1	1-0
WHITEMAN, GEORGE					
1918	Bos	A	O	6	.250
WHITMAN, DICK CORWIN					
1949	Bro	N	H	1	.000
WHITTED, GEORGE BOSTIC					
1914	Bos	N	O	4	.214
1915	Phi	N	O	5	.066
				9	.138
WICKER, KEMP CASWELL					
1937	NY	A	P	1	0-0
WILHELM, JAMES HOYT					
1954	NY	N	P	2	0-0
WILHOIT, JOSEPH WILLIAM					
1917	NY	N	H	2	.000
WILKINSON, ROY HAMILTON					
1919	Chi	A	P	2	0-0
WILKS, THEODORE					
1944	St.L	N	P	2	0-1
1946	St.L	N	P	1	0-0
				3	0-1
WILLETT, ROBERT EDGAR					
1909	Det	A	P	2	0-0
WILLEY, CARLTON FRANCIS					
1958	Mil	N	P	1	0-0
WILLIAMS, CLAUDE PRESTON					
1917	Chi	A	P	1	0-0
1919	Chi	A	P	3	0-3
				4	0-3
WILLIAMS, DAVID CARLOUS					
1951	NY	N	H	2	.000
1954	NY	N	2	4	.000
				6	.000
WILLIAMS, DEWEY EDGAR					
1945	Chi	N	C	2	.000
WILLIAMS, EDWIN DIBRELL					
1931	Phi	A	S	7	.320
WILLIAMS, RICHARD HIRSHFELD					
1953	Bro	N	H	3	.500

Yr	*Cl*	*Lea*	*Pos*	*G*	*Rec*
WILLIAMS, STANLEY WILSON					
1959	LA	N	P	1	0-0
WILLIAMS, THEODORE SAMUEL					
1946	Bos	A	O	7	.200
WILLS, MAURICE MORNING					
1959	LA	N	S	6	.250
WILLIS, VICTOR GAZAWAY					
1909	Pit	N	P	2	0-1
WILSON, ARTHUR EARL					
1911	NY	N	C	1	.000
1912	NY	N	C	2	1.000
1913	NY	N	C	3	.000
				6	.200
WILSON, GEORGE WASHINGTON					
1956	NY	A	H	1	.000
WILSON, JAMES					
1928	St.L	N	C	3	.091
1930	St.L	N	C	4	.267
1931	St.L	N	C	7	.217
1940	Cin	N	C	6	.353
				20	.242
WILSON, JOHN OWEN					
1909	Pit	N	O	7	.154
WILSON, LEWIS ROBERT					
1924	NY	N	O	7	.233
1929	Chi	N	O	5	.471
				12	.319
WILTSE, GEORGE LeROY					
1911	NY	N	P	2	0-0
1913	NY	N	1	2	.000
				4	0-0 .000
WINGO, IVY BROWN					
1919	Cin	N	C	3	.571
WINTER, GEORGE LOVINGTON					
1908	Det	A	P	1	0-0
WISE, KENDALL COLE					
1958	Mil	N.	H	2	.000
WITT, GEORGE ADRIAN					
1960	Pit	N	P	3	0-0
WITT, LAWTON WALTER					
1922	NY	A	O	5	.222
1923	NY	A	O	6	.240
				11	.233
WOOD, JOSEPH					
1912	Bos	A	P	4	3-1
1920	Cle	A	O	4	.200
				8	3-1 .235
WOODLING, EUGENE RICHARD					
1949	NY	A	O	3	.400
1950	NY	A	O	4	.429
1951	NY	A	O	6	.167
1952	NY	A	O	7	.348
1953	NY	A	O	6	.300
				26	.318
WORKS, RALPH TALMADGE					
1909	Det	A	P	1	0-0
WORTMAN, WILLIAM LEWIS					
1918	Chi	N	2	1	.000

Yr	*Cl*	*Lea*	*Pos*	*G*	*Rec*
WRIGHT, FOREST GLENN					
1925	Pit	N	S	7	.185
1927	Pit	N	S	4	.154
				11	.175
WYATT, JOHN WHITLOW					
1941	Bro	N	P	2	1-1
WYCKOFF, JOHN WELDON					
1914	Phi	A	P	1	0-0
WYNN, EARLY					
1954	Cle	A	P	1	0-1
1959	Chi	A	P	3	1-1
				4	1-2
WYSE, HENRY WASHINGTON					
1945	Chi	N	P	3	0-1
YDE, EMIL OGDEN					
1925	Pit	N	H-P	2	0-1 .000
1927	Pit	N	H	1	.000
				3	0-1 .000
YERKES, STEPHEN DOUGLAS					
1912	Bos	A	2	8	.250
YORK, RUDOLPH PRESTON					
1940	Det	A	1	7	.231
1945	Det	A	1	7	.179
1946	Bos	A	1	7	.261
				21	.221
YOUNG, DENTON TRUE					
1903	Bos	A	P	4	2-1
YOUNG, ROSS					
1921	NY	N	O	8	.280
1922	NY	N	O	5	.375
1923	NY	N	O	6	.348
1924	NY	N	O	7	.185
				26	.285
YVARS, SALVADOR ANTHONY					
1951	NY	N	H	1	.000
ZACHARY, JONATHAN THOMPSON WALTON					
1924	Was	A	P	2	2-0
1925	Was	A	P	1	0-0
1928	NY	A	P	1	1-0
				4	3-0
ZARILLA, ALLEN LEE					
1944	St.L	A	O	4	.100
ZEIDER, ROLLA HUBERT					
1918	Chi	N	3	2	.000
ZIMMER, DONALD WILLIAM					
1955	Bro	N	2	4	.222
1959	LA	N	S	1	.000
				5	.200
ZIMMERMAN, GERALD ROBERT					
1961	Cin	N	C	2	.000
ZIMMERMAN, HENRY					
1907	Chi	N	2	1	.000
1910	Chi	N	2	5	.235
1917	NY	N	3	6	.120
				12	.171
ZUBER, WILLIAM HENRY					
1946	Bos	A	P	1	0-0

V BEST LIFETIME MARKS

(Through 1962 season. All records after 1961 in the American League and after 1962 in the National League were made in a 162 game season.)

MANAGERIAL LEADERS
(Top Five in Each Classification)

SEASONS MANAGED -- Connie Mack 53, John McGraw 34, Bucky Harris 29, Bill McKechnie 25, Joe McCarthy 24, Harry Wright 23, Casey Stengel 22.

PENNANTS WON -- McGraw 10, Casey Stengel 10, Mack 9, Miller Huggins 6, Wright 6, Cap Anson 5, Ned Hanlon 5, Frank Selee 5.

WORLD SERIES WON -- McCarthy 7, Stengel 7, Mack 5, McGraw 3, Huggins 3.

THREE THOUSAND HITTERS
(Players Who Have Amassed 3,000 or More Hits in the Majors)

	YEARS	GAMES	HITS		YEARS	GAMES	HITS
Ty Cobb	24	3,033	4,191	Honus Wagner	21	2,785	3,430
Stan Musial	21	2,902	3,544	Eddie Collins	25	2,826	3,313
Cap Anson	27	2,509	3,516	Nap Lajoie	21	2,475	3,251
Tris Speaker	22	2,789	3,515	Paul Waner	20	2,549	3,152

THREE HUNDRED VICTORIES
(Pitchers Who Have Won 300 or More Games in the Majors)

	YEARS	GAMES	WON		YEARS	GAMES	WON
Cy Young	22	886	507	Tim Keefe	14	604	345
Walter Johnson	21	930	414	Warren Spahn	18	673	327
Grover Alexander	20	701	373	John Clarkson	12	529	327
Christy Mathewson	17	639	373	Ed Plank	17	612	326
Kid Nichols	15	602	361	Mike Welch	13	591	315
Jim Galvin	15	716	362	Hoss Radbourn	12	641	306
				Lefty Grove	17	619	300

FIFTY HOMERS A SEASON
(Players Who Have Hit 50 Or More Homers In A Season)

	YEAR	HOMERS		YEAR	HOMERS
Roger Maris	1961	61	Babe Ruth	1928	54
Babe Ruth	1927	60	Mickey Mantle	1961	54
Babe Ruth	1921	59	Ralph Kiner	1949	54
Hank Greenberg	1938	58	Mickey Mantle	1956	52
Jimmy Foxx	1932	58	Ralph Kiner	1947	51
Hack Wilson	1930	56	Willie Mays	1955	51
Babe Ruth	1920	54	Johnny Mize	1947	51
			Jimmy Foxx	1938	50

THREE HUNDRED HOMER HITTERS
(Players Who Have Hit 300 more More Homers in the Majors)

	YEARS	HOMERS		YEARS	HOMERS
Babe Ruth	22	714	Ralph Kiner	10	369
Jimmy Foxx	20	534	Willie Mays	11	368
Ted Williams	19	521	Joe DiMaggio	13	361
Mel Ott	22	511	Johnny Mize	15	359
Lou Gehrig	17	493	Yogi Berra	17	350
Stan Musial	21	464	Ernie Banks	10	335
Mickey Mantle	12	404	Hank Greenberg	13	331
Ed Mathews	11	399	Al Simmons	20	307
Duke Snider	16	389	Rogers Hornsby	23	302
Gil Hodges	17	370	Chuck Klein	17	300

TRIPLE PLAY UNASSISTED

Neal Ball (shortstop), Cleveland AL vs. Boston, July 19, 1909.
George H. Burns (first base), Boston AL vs. Cleveland, Sept. 14, 1923.

Ernest K. Padgett (shortstop), Boston NL vs. Philadelphia, Oct. 6, 1923.
Forest Glenn Wright (shortstop), Pittsburgh NL vs. St. Louis, May 7, 1925.
James E. Cooney (shortstop), Chicago NL at Pittsburgh, May 30, 1927.
John H. Neun (first base), Detroit AL vs. Cleveland, May 31, 1927.
NOTE: William A. Wambsganss (second base), Cleveland AL vs. Brooklyn NL, Oct. 10, 1920 (World Series).

FOUR HUNDRED BATTERS

(Players Who Have Hit .400 Or More Per Season, At Least 100 Games)
(Note—In 1887, Walks Counted As Hits)

	YEAR	B.A.		YEAR	B.A.
Tip O'Neill	1887	.492	George Sisler	1920	.407
Pete Browning	1887	.471	Sam Thompson	1887	.406
Denny Lyons	1887	.469	Fred Clarke	1897	.406
Hugh Duffy	1894	.438	Ted Williams	1941	.406
Willie Keeler	1897	.432	Harry Stovey	1884	.404
Yank Robinson	1887	.426	Paul Radford	1887	.404
Rogers Hornsby	1924	.424	Sam Thompson	1894	.403
Jesse Burkett	1895	.423	Harry Heilmann	1923	.403
Nap Lajoie	1901	.422	Rogers Hornsby	1925	.403
Cap Anson	1887	.421	Harry Stovey	1887	.402
Ty Cobb	1911	.420	Jesse Burkett	1899	.402
George Sisler	1922	.420	Tom Burns	1887	.401
Dan Brouthers	1887	.419	Ty Cobb	1922	.401
Reddy Mack	1887	.410	Rogers Hornsby	1922	.401
Jesse Burkett	1896	.410	Bill Terry	1930	.401
Ty Cobb	1912	.410	Ed Delahanty	1894	.400
Dude Esterbrook	1884	.408			
Ed Delahanty	1899	.408			
Joe Jackson	1911	.408			

HIGHEST LIFETIME BATTERS

(Players Whose Lifetime Average Is .340 or Better)

	YEAR	B.A.		YEAR	B.A.
Ty Cobb	24	.367	Tris Speaker	22	.344
Rogers Hornsby	23	.358	Ted Williams	19	.344
Joe Jackson	13	.356	Babe Ruth	22	.342
Pete Browing	13	.355	Jesse Burkett	16	.342
Lefty O'Doul	11	.349	Harry Heilmann	17	.342
Dan Brouthers	19	.348	Bill Terry	14	.341
Ed Delahanty	16	.346	George Sisler	15	.340
Billy Hamilton	14	.345	Lou Gehrig	17	.340
Willie Keeler	19	.345			

CONSECUTIVE RECORD STREAKS

(1) CLUB CONSECUTIVE MARKS

World Series Won—
5, New York AL (1949-53)
4, New York AL (1936-39)

Pennants Won—
5, New York AL (1949-53)
4, Boston NA (1872-75)
4, St. Louis AA (1885-88)
4, New York NL (1921-24)
4, New York AL (1936-39)
4, New York AL (1955-58)

Games Won—
26, New York NL (1916)
26, Boston NA (1875)
21, Chicago NL (1880)
21, Chicago NL (1935)
20, St. Louis UA (1884)
20, Providence NL (1884)

Games Lost—
26, Louisville AA (1889)
24, Cleveland NL (1899)
23, Philadelphia NL (1961
23, Pittsburgh NL (1890)

Games without being shut out—
308, New York AL (1931-33)
196, Athletics AA (1886-88)
185, Philadelphia NL (1893-95)

Innings shut out opponents—
56, Pittsburgh NL (1903)
47, Cleveland AL (1948)

Innings shut out by opponents—
48, Philadelphia AL (1906)
45, Cincinnati NL (1931)

CONSECUTIVE RECORD STREAKS (Cont.)

Games in which homers were hit—
25, New York AL (1941).
24, Brooklyn NL (1953).

Errorless games—
11, Cincinnati NL (1953)
10, Brooklyn NL (1942)

(2) BATTING STREAKS:
Games played—
2,130 H. L. Gehrig AL (1925-39
895 S. F. Musial NL (1952-57)

Games scoring runs—
24, W. R. Hamilton NL (1894)
19, J. N. Fox AL (1954)

Games hit safely—
56, J. P. DiMaggio, AL (1941)
44, W. H. Keeler, NL (1897)
37, T. F. Holmes, NL (1945)

Games hit homer—
8, R. D. Long NL (1956)

Hits—
12, M. F. Higgins, AL (1938)
12, W. Dropo, AL (1952)

Bases on balls—
7, W. G. Rogell, AL (1938)
7, M. T. Ott, NL (1943)
7, E. Stanky, NL (1950)

Strikeouts—
6, C. W. Weilman, AL (1913). (15 innings).
6, D. A. Hoak, NL (1956). (17 innings).

(3) FIELDING STREAKS
Games caught—
312, F. W. Hayes, AL (1943-46)
233, R.C. Mueller, NL (1943-45).

Catcher's chances without error—
950, L. P. Berra AL (1957-59)
755, W. V. Rosar AL (1945-47)
511, A. M. Owen NL (1940-41)

Catcher's games without error—
148, L. P. Berra AL (1957-59)
147, W. V. Rosar AL (1945-47)
121, J. F. Hogan NL (1933-34)

Pitcher's chances without error—
273, C. W. Passeau NL (1941-46)
159, T. A. Lyons AL (1934-38)

Pitcher's games without error—
219, M. E. Grissom NL (1954-59)
163, L. Warneke NL (1938-45)
156, J. G. Dobson AL (1939-43)

First Baseman's chances without error—
1,625, J. P. McInnis, AL (1921-22)
1,337, F. A. McCormick, NL (1945-46)

First Baseman's games without error—
163, J. P. McInnis, AL (1921-22)
138, F. A. McCormick, NL (1945-46)

Second Baseman's chances without error—
418, K. D. Hubbs NL (1962)
414, R. P. Doerr AL (1948)

Second Baseman's games without error—
78, K. D. Hubbs NL (1962)
73, R. P. Doerr AL (1948)

Shortstop's chances without error—
383, J. J. Kerr, NL (1946-47)
297, A. C. Carresquel, AL (1951)

Shortstop's games without error—
68, J. J. Kerr, NL (1946-47)
58, P. F. Rizzuto, AL (1949-50)

Third Baseman's games without error—
75, W. E. Kamm, AL (1928)
54, S. C. Hack, NL (1942)

Outfielder's games without error—
199, D. R. Bell NL (1958-59)
194, C. R. Maxwell AL (1957-58)

(4) PITCHING STREAKS:

Innings without relief—
352, J. W. Taylor NL (1904)
337, W. H. Dinneen AL (1904)

Games won—
24, A. C. Spalding NA (1875)
24, C. O. Hubbell NL (1936-37)
22, A. C. Spalding NA (1875)
19, T. J. Keefe NL (1888)
19, R. W. Marquard NL (1912)

Games lost—
23, C. G. Curtis NL (1910-11)
20, J. J. Nabors AL (1916)

Shutout games—
5, G. H. White AL (1904)
4, Many, NL

Shutout innings—
56, W. P. Johnson AL (1913)
46-1/3, C. O. Hubbell NL (1933)

Strikeouts—
9, M. F. Welch NL (1884)
8, C. G. Buffinton NL (1885)
8, E. L. Cushman AA (1885)
8, M. C. Surkont NL (1953)

Bases on balls—
8, W. D. Gray AL (1909)
7, A. J. Mullane NL (1894)
7, G. L. Ewing NL (1902)

Innings without walks—
23, D. T. Young AL (1904)
21-2/3, J. S. Vander Meer NL (1938)

LIFETIME MARKS
Season, Game, Inning

"Many" shows that the record is held jointly by more than two players or teams.

Number in parenthesis, following apostrophe, shows year in which record was made.

INDIVIDUAL BATTING RECORDS

	LIFETIME	SEASON	GAME	INNING
Seasons	Anson, A. C. 27 McGuire, J. T. 26 Collins, E. T. Wallace, R. J. 25 Cobb, T. R. 24			
Games	Cobb, R. R. 3,033 Musial, S. F. 2,902 Collins, E. T. 2,826 Speaker, T. E. 2,789 Wagner, J. P. 2,785 Ott, M. T. 2,730	Wills, M. M. 165 ('62) Davis, H. T. 163 ('62) Colavito, R. D. 163 ('61) Robinson, B. C. 163 ('61)		
At Bats	Cobb, T. R. 11,429 Musial, S. F. 10,635 Wagner, J. P. 10,427 Speaker, T. E. 10,208 Maranville, W. J. 10,078	Jensen, F. D. 696 ('36) Wills, M. M. 695 ('62) Richardson, R. C. 692 ('62) Kuenn, H. E. 679 ('53)	Many 8	Many 3
Runs	Cobb, T. R. 2,244 Ruth, G. H. 2,174 Anson, A. C. 1,969 Gehrig, H. L. 1,888 Speaker, T. E. 1,881	Hamilton, W. R. 196 ('94) Ruth, G. H. 177 ('21) Klein, C. H. 158 ('30)	Hecker, G. J. 7 ('86)	Burns, T. E. 3 ('83) White, S. 3 ('53) Williamson, E. N. 3 ('83)
Hits	Cobb, T. R. 4,191 Musial, S. F. 3,544 Speaker, T. E. 3,515 Anson, A. C. 3,509 Wagner, J. P. 3,430 Collins, E. T. 3,313	Sisler, G. H. 257 ('20) O'Doul, F. J. 254 ('29) Terry, W. H. 254 ('30)	Burnett, J. H. 9 ('32) Robinson, W. 7 ('92)	Burns, T. E. 3 ('83) Williamson, E. N. 3 ('83) Stephens, G. E. 3 ('53) Pfeffer, N. F 3 ('83)

	LIFETIME	SEASON	GAME	INNING
Singles	Cobb, T. R. 3,052 Wagner, J. P. 2,426 Waner, P. G. 2,246	Keeler, W. H. 199 ('97) Waner, L. J. 198 ('27) Rice, E. C. 182 ('25)	Burnett, J. H. 7 ('32)	Many 2
Doubles	Speaker, T. E. 793 Musial, S. F. 715 Wagner, J. P. 651 Waner, P. G. 603	Webb, E. W. 67 ('31) Medwick, J. M. 64 ('36)	Many 4	Many 2
Triples	Crawford, S. E. 312 Cobb, T. R. 297 Wagner, J. P. 252	Wilson, J. O. 36 ('12) Jackson, J. J. 26 ('12) Crawford, S. E. 26 ('14)	Strief, G. A. 4 ('85) Joyce, W. M. 4 ('97)	Many 2
Homers	Ruth, G. H. 714 Foxx, J. E. 534 Ott, M. T. 511	Maris, R. E. 61 ('61) Ruth, G. H. 60 ('27) Foxx, J. E. 58 ('32) Greenberg, H. B. 58 ('38) Wilson, L. R. 56 ('30)	Many 4	Many 2
Total Bases	Musial, S. F. 5,998 Cobb, T. R. 5,863	Ruth, G. H. 457 ('21) Hornsby, R. 450 ('22)	Adcock, J. W. 18 ('54) Delehanty, E. J. 17 ('96) Hodges, G. R. 17 ('50) Lowe, R. L. 17 ('94)	Many 8
Runs Batted In	Ruth, G. H. 2,209 Foxx, J. E. 1,921 Gehrig, H. L. 1,991 Cobb, T. R. 1,901	Wilson, L. R. 190 ('30) Gehrig, H. L. 184 ('31)	A. M. Lazzeri 11 ('36) Bottomley, J. L. 12 ('24)	Cartwright, E. H. 7 ('90)
Batting Average	Cobb, T. R. .367 Hornsby, R. .358	O'Neill, J. F. .492 ('87) Browning, L. R. .471 ('87) Lyons, D. P. .469 ('87) Duffy, H. .438 ('94) Keeler, W. H. .432 ('97)		
Bases on Balls	Ruth, G. H. 2,056 Ott, M. T. 1,708	Ruth, G. H. 170 ('23) Stanky, E. R. 148 ('45)	Wilmot, W. R. 6 ('91) Foxx, J. E. 6 ('38)	Many 2
Strikeouts	Ruth, G. H. 1,330 Foxx, J. E. 1,311	Lemon, J. R. 138 ('56) Wood, Jr. 141 ('62)	Weilman, C. W. 6 ('13) Hoak, D. A. 6 ('56)	Many 2

	LIFETIME	SEASON	GAME	INNING
Hit by Pitcher	No Record	Jennings, H. A. 49 ('96) Evans, L. R. 31 ('10) Minoso, S. O. 23 ('56)	Many 3	Many 1
Sacrifices	Collins, E. T. 509 Daubert, J. E. 392	Richardson, A. H. 68 ('91) Chapman, R. J. 67 ('17) Beckley, J. P. 64 ('93)	Many 4	Many 3
Grounded Into Double Play	No Record	Jensen, J. E. 32 ('54) Lombardi, E. N. 30 ('38)	Goslin, L. A. 4 ('34) Kreevich, M. A. 4 ('39)	
Stolen Bases	Hamilton, W. R. 937	Stovey, H. D. 156 ('88)	Gore, G. F. 7 ('81) Hamilton, W. R. 7 ('94)	Devore, J. 4 ('12)
	Cobb, T. R. 892 Collins, E. T. 744 Carey, M. G. 738	Hamilton, W. R. 115 ('91) Cobb, T. R. 96 ('15) Bescher, R. H. 80 ('11)	Wills, M. M. 104 ('62) Collins, E. T. 6 ('12, twice) McGann, D. L. 5 ('04)	
Pinch Hits	Lucas, C. F. 107 Fothergill, R. R. 76	Leslie, S. A. 22 ('32) Coleman, P. E. 20 ('36) Philley, D. E. 24 ('61)	Many 2	Many 2

INDIVIDUAL FIELDING RECORDS

	LIFETIME	SEASON	GAME	INNING
Total Chances	Vernon, J. B. 19,819 Grimm, C. J. 22,079 Beckley, J. P. 25,462 Vernon, J. B. 21,479 Beckley, J. P. 23,696	Donahue, J. A. 1,998 Kelly, G. L. 1,873	Holke, W. L. 44 ('20) York, R. P. 35 ('45)	Many 5
Putouts	Beckley, J. P. 23,696 Grimm, C. J. 20,702 Vernon, J. B. 19,819	Donahue, J. A. 1,846 ('07) Kelly, G. L. 1,759 ('20)	Holke, W. L. 43 ('20) Unglaub, R. A. 31 ('05) Siebert, R. W. 31 ('45)	Many 3
Assists	Maranville, W. J. 8,953 Collins, E. T. 7,629	Frisch, F. F. 641 ('27) Wright, F. G. 601 ('24)	Cross, L. N. 15 ('07) Corcoran, T. W. 14 ('03)	Many 3
Errors	Long, H. C. 1,040 Wagner, J. P. 720 Appling, L. B. 670	Shindle, W. 115 ('90) Sullivan, J. D. 106 ('93)	Corcoran, L. J. 10 ('84) Leonard, A. J. 9 ('76)	Smith, C. M. 5 ('80)

	LIFETIME	SEASON	GAME	INNING
Double Plays	No Record	Fain, F. R. 194 ('49) Hodges, G. R. 171 ('51)	Many 6	

INDIVIDUAL PITCHING RECORDS

	LIFETIME	SEASON	GAME	INNING
Seasons	Quinn, J. P. 23 Pennock, H. J. 22 Jones, S. P. 22 Ruffing, C. H. 22 Young, D. T. 22			
Games	Young, D. T. 886 Johnson, W. P. 930 Quinn, J. P. 764	White, W. H. 75 ('79) Konstanty, C. J. 74 ('50) Adams, A. T. 70 ('43) Fornieles, J. M. 70 ('60)		
Innings	Young, D. T. 7,377 Johnson, W. P. 5,925 Alexander, G. C. 5,189	White, W. H. 683 ('79) Radbourn, C. G. 672 ('84) Walsh, E. A. 464 ('08)	Oeschger, J. 26 ('20) Cadore, L. L. 26 ('20) Coombs, J. W. 24 ('06) Harris, J. W. 24 ('06)	
Complete Games	Young, D. T. 751 Galvin, J. F. 560 Johnson, W. P. 531 Alexander, G. C. 437	McCormick, J. 74 ('80) White, W. H. 74 ('79) Chesbro, J. D. 48 ('04) Willis, V. G. 45 ('02)		
Won	Young, D. T. 507 Johnson, W. P. 414 Alexander, G. C. 373 Mathewson, C. 373	Radbourn, C. G. 60 ('84) Keefe, T. J. 42 ('86) Spalding, A. G. 56 ('75) Chesbro, J. D. 38 ('04) Walsh, E. A. 40 ('08)		
Lost	Young, D. T. 307 Johnson, W. P. 281 Rixey, E. 251	Coleman, J. F. 48 ('83) Willis, V. G. 29 ('05) Townsend, J. 27 ('04) Groom, R. B. 26 ('09)		

	LIFETIME	SEASON	GAME	INNING
Shutouts	Johnson, W. P. 113	Alexander, G. C. 16 ('16)		
	Alexander, G. C. 90	Coombs, J. W. 13 ('10)		
Runs	No Record	Coleman, J. F. 544 ('83)	Rowe, D. E. 35 ('82)	Mullane, A. J. 16 ('94)
		McGinnity, J. J. 211 ('01)	Derby, G. H. 31 ('83)	O'Doul, F. J. 13 ('23)
		Pittenger, C. R. 196 ('03)	Travers, A. J. 24 ('12)	Kelleher, H. J. 12 ('38)
			Parker, H. P. 21 ('10)	
Hits	No Record	Coleman, J. F. 807 ('83)	Wadsworth, W. J. 36 ('94)	Weidman, G. E. 13 ('83)
		McGinnity, J. J. 401 ('01)	Lisenbee, H. M. 26 ('36)	Adkins, M. T. 12 ('02)
		Pittinger, C. R. 394 ('03)	Parker, H. P. 26 ('01)	Grabowski, R. J. 11 ('34)
Homers Allowed	No Record	Roberts, R. E. 46 ('56)	Sweeney, C. J. 7 ('86)	Many 4
		Ramos, P. 43 ('57)		
Strikeouts	Johnson, W. P. 3,497	Kilroy, M. A. 505 ('86)	Sweeney, C. J. 19 ('84)	Many 4
	Young, D. T. 2,836	Radbourn, C. 411 ('84)	Daly, H. I. 19 ('84)	
	Mathewson, C. 2,499	Feller, R. W. A. 348 ('46)	Feller, R. W. A. 18 ('38)	
		Waddell, G. E. 343 ('04)	Porter, H. 18 ('84)	
			Shaw, F. L. 18 ('84)	
Bases on Balls	Feller, R. W. A. 1,764	Rusie, A. W. 276 ('90)	Haas, B. P. 16 ('15)	Gray, W. D. 8 ('09)
	Rusie, A. W. 1,713	Feller, R. W. A. 208 ('38)	Byrne, T. J. 16 ('51)	Ewing, G.L, 7 ('02)
	Grimes, B. A. 1,295	Jones, S. 185 ('55)	George, W. M. 16 ('87)	Mullane A. J. 7 ('94)
			Van Haltren, G. E. 16 ('87)	
			Gruber, H. J. 16 ('90)	
Hit Batsmen	Johnson, W. P. 204	McGinnity, J. J. 41 ('00)	Knouff, E. 6 ('87)	Many 3
	McGinnity, J. J. 152	Warhop, J. M. 26 ('09)	Bates, F. C. 5 ('99)	
		Weimer, J. W. 23 ('07)	Hawley, E. P. 5 ('96)	
			Healey, J. J. 5 ('87)	
Wild Pitches	No Record	Stemmeyer, W. 64 ('86)	Ryan, J. J. 10 ('76)	Johnson, W. P. 4 ('14)
		Ames, L. K. 30 ('05)	Wheatley, C. 5 ('12)	
		Johnson, W. P. 21 ('10)	Cheney, L. D. 5 ('18)	

	LIFETIME	SEASON	GAME	INNING
Balks	No Record	Boehling, J. J. 6 ('15) Raschi, V. A. 6 ('50) Lanier, H. M. 5 ('50)	Raschi, V. A. 4 ('50)	Shoffner, M. J. 3 ('30)

TEAM BATTING RECORDS

	LIFETIME	SEASON	GAME	INNING
At Bats	No Record	Philadelphia (N) 5,667 ('30) Cleveland (A) 5,646 ('36)	Brooklyn (N) 85 ('20) Philadelphia (A) 84 ('45)	Chicago (N) 23 ('83) Boston (A) 23 ('53) Brooklyn (N) 21 ('52)
Runs	No Record	Boston (N) 1,221 ('94) New York (A) 1,067 ('31) St. Louis (N) 1,004 ('30)	Athletics (NA) 49 ('71) Chicago (N) 36 ('97) Boston (A) 29 ('50) Chicago (A) 29 ('55) St. Louis (N) 28 ('29)	Boston (NA) 21 ('73) Chicago (N) 18 ('83) Boston (A) 17 ('53) Brooklyn (N) 15 ('52)
Hits	No Record	Philadelphia (N) 1,783 ('30) Detroit (A) 1,724 ('21)	Cleveland (A) 33 ('32) Philadelphia (N) 36 ('94) New York (N) 31 ('01)	Chicago (N) 18 ('83) Boston (A) 14 ('53) Kansas City (A) 13 ('56) St. Louis (N) 12 ('25)
Singles	No Record	Philadelphia (N) 1,338 ('94) Detroit (A) 1,298 ('21) Pittsburgh (N) 1,297 ('22)	Philadelphia (N) 28 ('94) Boston (N) 28 ('96) Cleveland (A) 24 ('28) Boston (A) 24 ('53)	St. Louis (N) 11 ('25) Boston (A) 11 ('53)
Doubles	No Record	St. Louis (N) 373 ('30) Cleveland (A) 358 ('30)	Chicago (N) 14 ('83) St. Louis (N) 13 ('31) Detroit (A) 11 ('34)	Boston (N) 7 ('36) Washington (A) 6 ('34)
Triples	No Record	Baltimore (N) 153 ('94) Philadelphia (N) 148 ('94) Pittsburgh (N) 129 ('12) Baltimore (A) 112 ('01) Boston (A) 112 ('03)	Baltimore (N) 9 ('94) Pittsburgh (N) 8 ('25) Chicago (A) 6 ('20) Detroit (A) 6 ('22)	Chicago (A) 5 ('01)

	LIFETIME	SEASON	GAME	INNING
Homers	No Record	New York (N) 221 ('47) Cincinnati (N) 221 ('56) New York (A) 193 ('60)	New York (A) 8 ('39) Milwaukee (N) 8 ('53) Cincinnati (N) 8 ('56)	New York (N) 5 ('39) Philadelphia (N) 5 ('49) Boston (A) 4 ('40) Detroit (A) 4 ('50) Boston (A) 4 ('57)
Total Bases	No Record	New York (A) 2,703 ('36) Chicago (N) 2,684 ('30)	Boston (A) 60 ('50) Cincinnati (N) 55 ('93) San Francisco (N) 50 ('58)	Chicago (N) 29 ('83) Philadelphia (N) 26 ('49) Boston (A) 25 ('40)
Batting Average	No Record	Detroit (N) .347 ('87) Philadelphia (N) .343 ('94) New York (N) .319 ('30) Detroit (A) .316 ('21)	Philadelphia (N) .563 ('94) Chicago (N) .556 ('22) New York (A) .556 ('23)	Chicago (N) .818 ('83) St. Louis (N) .800 ('25) Philadelphia (A) .800 ('02) Chicago (N) .800 ('31)
Sacrifices	No Record	Boston (AA) 392 ('91) Philadelphia (N) 376 ('90) Boston (A) 310 ('17) Chicago (N) 270 ('08)	New York (A) 8 ('18) Cincinnati (N) 8 ('26) Chicago (A) 8 ('27) St. Louis (A) 8 ('28)	Many 2
Hit Batsmen	No Record	Chicago (A) 75 ('56) New York (N) 52 ('17)	Brooklyn (AA) 6 ('87) New York (A) 6 ('13) Detroit (N) 5 ('87) Pittsburgh (N) 5 ('90) Washington (N) 5 ('96)	Boston (N) 4 ('93)
Bases on Balls	No Record	Boston (A) 835 ('49) Brooklyn (N) 732 ('47)	Detroit (A) 18 ('16) Cleveland (A) 18 ('48) Brooklyn (N) 17 ('03) New York (N) 17 ('44)	New York (A) 11 ('49) Cincinnati (N) 9 ('57)
Strikeouts	No Record	Philadelphia (N) 1,054 ('60) Chicago (N) 989 ('57) Washington (A) 883 ('60)	Boston (N) 19 ('84) Boston (UA) 19 ('84) St. Louis (UA) 19 ('84) Pittsburgh (N) 21 ('58)	Many 4

	LIFETIME	SEASON	GAME	INNING
Stolen Bases	No Record	Philadelphia (AA) 638 ('87) New York (N) 426 ('93) New York (N) 347 ('11) Washington (A) 288 ('13)	Philadelphia (AA) 19 ('90) New York (N) 17 ('90) New York (A) 15 ('11) New York (N) 11 ('12) St. Louis (N) 11 ('16)	Washington (A) 8 ('15) Philadelphia (N) 8 ('13)
Left on Base	No Record	St. Louis (A) 1,334 ('41) Brooklyn (N) 1,278 ('47)	Detroit (A) 21 ('21) New York (N) 20 ('29) Pittsburgh (N) 20 ('31) New York (A) 20 ('56)	
Players Used	No Record	Philadelphia (A) 56 ('15) Baltimore (A) 54 ('55) Brooklyn (N) 53 ('44)	New York (A) 26 ('56) New York (N) 25 ('56) St. Louis (N) 25 ('59)	Chicago (N) 23 ('83) Chicago (N) 19 ('22) Boston (A) 19 ('48)

TEAM FIELDING RECORDS

	LIFETIME	SEASON	GAME	INNING
Putouts	No Record	Cleveland (A) 4,396 ('10) Philadelphia (N) 4,359 ('13)	Brooklyn (N) 78 ('20) Boston (N) 78 ('20)	
Assists	No Record	Chicago (A) 2,446 ('07) St. Louis (N) 2,293 ('17)	Detroit (A) 38 ('45) Boston (N) 42 ('20)	Boston (N) 8 ('11)
Errors	No Record	Detroit (A) 425 ('01) Washington (N) 867 ('86) Brooklyn (N) 408 ('05)	Detroit (A) 12 ('01) Chicago (A) 12 ('03) Boston (N) 24 ('76)	Cleveland (A) 6 ('02) New York (A) 6 ('21) Pittsburgh (N) 6 ('03)
Total Chances	No Record	Chicago (A) 6,655 New York (N) 6,472	Boston (N) 122 ('20) Detroit (A) 113 ('45)	Boston (N) 11 ('11)
Fielding Percentage	No Record	Cincinnati (N) .9831 ('58) Cleveland (A) .9829 ('47) Cleveland (A) .9830 ('49)	Many 1.000	

	LIFETIME	SEASON	GAME	INNING
Double Plays	No Record	Philadelphia (A) 217 ('49) Los Angeles (N) 198 ('58)	New York (A) 7 ('42)	
Triple Plays	No Record	Detroit (A) 3 ('11) Boston (A) 3 ('24) Cincinnati (AA) 3 ('82)	(A) Many 1 (N) Many 1	

GENERAL TEAM RECORDS

	LIFETIME	SEASON	GAME	INNING
World Series Won	New York (A) 19 St. Louis (N) 6	Pennants Won: New York (A) 26 New York (N) 17 Chicago (N) 16		
Games Won		Cleveland (A) 111 ('54) Chicago (N) 116 ('06)		
Games Lost		Philadelphia (A) 117 ('16) Cleveland (N) 134 ('99) Boston (N) 115 ('35)		
Pitchers Used		Philadelphia (A) 27 ('15) Kansas City (A) 26 ('55)	St. Louis (A) 9 ('49) Many 8	Many 5
Shutout Games Won		Chicago (A) 30 ('06) Chicago (N) 32 ('07, '09)		
Shutout Games Lost		Washington (A) 29 ('09) St. Louis (N) 33 ('08)		
Longest Game 9 ings. (time)	Bos. vs. N.Y. (A) 3:52 ('53) SF vs. Mil. (N) 3:52 ('60)		Longest Game by Innings	Bro. vs. Bos. (N) 26 ('20) Phi. vs. Bos. (A) 24 ('06) Det. vs. Phi. (A) 24 ('45)
Shortest Game 9 ings. (time)	St. L. vs. N.Y. (A) 0:55 ('26) N.Y. vs. Phi. (N) 0:51 ('19)			

Four of the plaques in baseball's Hall of Fame memorializing the game's greatest players.

VI LEAGUE LEADERS

YEAR	LEA.	BATTING		RUNS		HITS		DOUBLES		TRIPLES	
1876	NL	Barnes Chi.	.404	Barnes Chi.	126	Barnes Chi.	138	Barnes Chi.	23	Hall, Ath. Pike, St. L.	12 12
1877	NL	J. White Bos.	.387	J. White Bos.	39	O'Rourke Bos.	89	Anson Chi.	20	Jones Cin.	10
1878	NL	Dalrymple Mil.	.356	Higham, Pro. Start, Chi.	58 58	Start Chi.	97	Burdock Bos.	17	Higham Pro.	16
1879	NL	Anson Chi.	.407	Jones Bos.	85	Hines Pro.	145	Eden Cle.	26	Dickerson Cin.	14
1880	NL	Gore Chi.	.365	Dalrymple Chi.	90	Dalrymple Chi.	123	Williamson Chi.	29	Stovey Wor.	13
1881	NL	Anson Chi.	.399	Gore Chi.	86	Anson Chi.	137	Kelly Chi.	27	Rowe Buf.	11
1882	NL	Brouthers Buf.	.367	Gore Chi.	99	Brouthers Buf.	129	Kelly Chi.	34	Connor Tro.	17
	AA	Browning Lou.	.382	Swartwood Pit.	93	Carpenter Cin.	125	Browning Lou.	18	Taylor Pit.	12
1883	NL	Brouthers Buf.	.371	Hornung Bos.	106	Brouthers Buf.	156	Williamson Chi.	50	Brouthers Buf.	11
	AA	Swartwood Pit.	.369	Stovey Ath.	110	Swartwood Pit.	149	Stovey Ath.	30	Smith Col.	18
1884	NL	O'Rourke Buf.	.350	Kelly Chi.	120	Dalrymple Chi.	160	Hines Pro.	34	Ewing N. Y.	18
	AA	Esterbrook Met.	.408	Stovey Ath.	126	Esterbrook Met.	185	Barkley Tol.	39	Stovey Ath.	25
	UA	Dunlap St. L.	.420	Dunlap St. L.	157	Dunlap St.L.	178	Schaffer St. L.	38	Rowe St. L.	13
1885	NL	Connor N. Y.	.371	Kelly Chi.	124	Connor N. Y.	169	Anson Chi.	35	O'Rourke N. Y.	16
	AA	Browning Lou.	.367	Stovey Ath.	128	Browning Lou.	176	Larkin Ath.	40	Kuehne Pit.	20
1886	NL	Kelly Chi.	.388	Kelly Chi.	155	Richardson Det.	189	Brouthers Det.	38	Connor N. Y.	20
	AA	Orr Met.	.346	Latham St. L.	153	Orr Met.	196	Larkin Ath.	34	Orr Met.	33
1887	NL	Anson Chi.	.421	Brouthers Det.	153	Brouthers Det.	239	Brouthers Det.	33	Connor N. Y.	24
	AA	O'Neill St. L.	.492	O'Neill St. L.	170	Lyons Ath.	284	O'Neill St L.	46	O'Neill St. L.	24
1888	NL	Anson Chi.	.343	Brouthers Det.	118	Ryan Chi.	182	Ryan Chi.	36	Connor N.Y.	17
	AA	O'Neill St. L.	.332	Pinckney Bro.	133	O'Neill St. L.	176	Reilly Cin.	33	Stovey Ath.	21
1889	NL	Brouthers Bos.	.373	Tiernan N. Y.	146	Glasscock Ind.	209	Kelly Bos.	40	Wilmot Was.	18
	AA	Tucker Bal.	.375	Stovey Ath.	154	Tucker Bal.	198	Welch Ath.	38	Hamilton K. C.	15
1890	NL	Glasscock N. Y.	.336	Collins Bro.	148	Glasscock, N. Y. Thompson, Phi.	172 172	Thompson Phi.	38	Reilly Cin.	26
	AA	Wolf Lou.	.366	McCarthy St. L.	134	Wolf Lou.	200	Childs Syr.	32	Johnson, Col. Werden, Tol.	19 19
	PL	Browning Cle.	.391	Duffy Chi.	161	Duffy Chi.	194	Beckley, Pit. Browning, Cle.	41 41	Shindle Phi.	25

LEAGUE LEADERS

HOME RUNS		RUNS BATTED IN		STOLEN BASES		STRIKEOUTS		WON-LOST		EARNED RUN AVERAGE	
Hall Ath.	5	(No records kept until 1907)		(No records kept until 1886)		Spalding Chi.	115	Spalding Chi.	46-14	(No records kept until 1912)	
Pike Cin.	4	---------	---	---------	---	Bond Bos.	123	Bond Bos.	40-17	---------	---
McKelvy Ind.	9	---------	---	---------	---	Bond Bos.	177	Bond Bos.	40-19	---------	---
Jones Bos.	9	---------	---	---------	---	Ward Pro.	271	Ward Pro.	44-18	---------	---
O'Rourke, Bos. Stovey, Wor.	6 6	---------	---	---------	---	Goldsmith Chi.	178	Goldsmith Chi.	22-3	---------	---
Brouthers Buf.	8	---------	---	---------	---	Corcoran Chi.	252	Corcoran Chi.	31-14	---------	---
Wood Det.	7	---------	---	---------	---	Keefe Tro.	289	Corcoran Chi.	27-13	---------	---
Walker St. L.	7	---------	---	---------	---	Mullane Lou.	281	White Cin.	40-12	---------	---
Ewing N. Y.	9	---------	---	---------	---	Whitney Bos.	308	McCormick Cle.	27-13	---------	---
Stovey Ath.	14	---------	---	---------	---	Keefe Met.	360	Mathews Ath.	30-14	---------	---
Williamson Chi.	27	---------	---	---------	---	Radbourne Pro.	411	Radbourne Pro.	60-12	---------	---
Stovey Cin.	11	---------	---	---------	---	Hecker Lou.	368	Lynch Met.	39-14	---------	---
Reilly Cin. Dunlap, St. L. Crane, Bos.	11 13 13	---------	---	---------	---	Daly Chi.-Pit.	464	Taylor St. L.	24-2	---------	---
Dalrymple Chi.	11	---------	---	---------	---	Clarkson Chi.	333	McCormick Chi.	20-4	---------	---
Stovey Ath.	13	---------	---	---------	---	Morris Pit.	303	Caruthers St. L.	40-13	---------	---
Richardson Det.	11	---------	---	Andrews Phi.	56	Baldwin Det.	340	Flynn Chi.	24-6	---------	---
McPhee Cin.	8	---------	---	Stovey Ath.	96	Kilroy Bal.	505	Foutz St. L.	41-16	---------	---
W. O'Brien Was.	19	---------	---	Ward N. Y.	111	Clarkson Chi.	227	Getzein Det.	29-13	---------	---
O'Neill St. L.	13	---------	---	Stovey Ath.	143	Ramsey Lou.	348	Caruthers St.L.	29-9	---------	---
Ryan Chi.	36	---------	---	Hoy Was.	82	Keefe N. Y.	334	Keefe N. Y.	35-12	---------	---
Reilly Cin.	12	---------	---	Stovey Ath.	156	Seward Ath.	219	Hudson St.L.	26-10	---------	---
Denny, Ind. Thompson, Phi.	17 17	---------	---	Fogarty Phi.	99	Clarkson Bos.	292	Clarkson Bos.	48-19	---------	---
Holliday, Cin. Stovey, Ath.	19 19	---------	---	Hamilton K. C.	117	Baldwin Col.	368	Caruthers Bro.	40-12	---------	---
Tiernan, N. Y.	14	---------	---	Hamilton Phi.	102	Rusie N. Y.	345	Lovett	31-11	---------	---
Campau St.L.	9	---------	---	Welch Ath.-Bal.	95	Ramsey St. L.	234	Stratton	34-15	---------	---
Connor, N. Y. Richardson, Bos.	13 13	---------	---	Brown Bos.	87	Baldwin Chi.	200	Gumbert Bos.	22-9	---------	---

YEAR	LEA.	BATTING		RUNS		HITS		DOUBLES		TRIPLES	
1891	NL	Hamilton Phi.	.338	Hamilton Phi.	142	Hamilton Phi.	179	Griffin Bro.	44	Stovey Bos.	22
	AA	Brouthers Bos.	.352	Brown Bos.	170	Brouthers Bos.	160	Brown Ath	35	Brown, Bos.	22
1892	NL	Childs Cle.	.335	Childs Cle.	135	Brouthers Bro.	197	Connor Phi.	29	Shindle Bal.	14
1893	NL	Duffy Bos.	.378	Long, Bos. Duffy, Bos.	149 149	Thompson Phi.	220	Thompson Phi.	38	Werden St. L.	28
1894	NL	Duffy Bos.	.438	Hamilton Phi.	196	Duffy Bos.	236	Duffy Bos.	46	Reitz, Bal. Thompson, Phi.	28 28
1895	NL	Burkett Cle.	.423	Hamilton Phi.	166	Burkett Cle.	235	Delahanty Phi.	49	Cooley, St. L. Thompson, Phi.	21 21
1896	NL	Burkett Cle.	.410	Burkett Cle.	159	Burkett Cle.	240	Miller Cin.	35	Dahlen Chi.	21
1897	NL	Keeler Bal.	.432	Hamilton Bos.	153	Keeler Bal.	243	Beckley Cin.	38	Davis Pit.	28
1898	NL	Keeler Bal.	.379	McGraw Bal.	142	Burkett Cle.	215	Lajoie Phi.	43	Anderson Bro.	20
1899	NL	Delahanty Phi.	.408	Keeler Bro.	141	Delahanty Phi.	234	Delahanty Phi.	56	Williams Pit.	27
1900	NL	Wagner Pit.	.381	Thomas Phi.	131	Van Haltren N. Y.	181	Wagner Pit.	45	Wagner Pit.	22
1901	NL	Burkett St. L.	.382	Burkett St. L.	139	Burkett St. L.	228	Beckley Cin.	39	Sheckard Bro.	21
	AL	Lajoie Phi.	.422	Lajoie Phi.	145	Lajoie Phi.	229	Lajoie Phi.	48	Williams Bal.	22
1902	NL	Beaumont Pit.	.357	Wagner Pit.	105	Beaumont Pit.	194	Wagner Pit.	32	Crawford Cin.	23
	AL	Delahanty Was.	.376	Fultz Phi.	110	Hickman Cle.	194	Davis Phi.	43	Williams Bal.	23
1903	NL	Wagner Pit.	.355	Beaumont Pit.	137	Beaumont Pit.	209	Clarke, Pit. Mertes, N. Y. Steinfeldt, Cin.	32 32 32	Wagner Pit.	19
	AL	Lajoie Cle.	.355	Dougherty Bos.	108	Dougherty Bos.	195	Seybold Phi.	43	Crawford Det.	25
1904	NL	Wagner Pit.	.349	Browne N. Y.	99	Beckley St. L.	179	Wagner Pit.	44	Lumley Bro.	18
	AL	Lajoie Cle.	.381	Dougherty Bos.-N. Y.	113	Lajoie Cle.	211	Lajoie Cle.	50	Stahl Bos.	22
1905	NL	Seymour Cin.	.377	Donlin N. Y.	124	Seymour Cin.	219	Seymour Cin.	40	Seymour Cin.	21
	AL	Flick Cle.	.306	Davis Phi.	92	Stone St. L.	187	Davis Phi.	47	Flick Cle.	19
1906	NL	Wagner Pit.	.339	Wagner, Pit. Chance, Chi.	103 103	Steinfeldt Chi.	176	Wagne Pit.	38	Clarke, Pit. Schulte, Chi.	13 13
	AL	Stone St. L.	.358	Flick Cle.	98	Lajoie Cle.	214	Lajoie Cle.	49	Flick Cle.	22
1907	NL	Wagner Pit.	.350	Shannon N. Y.	104	Beaumont Bos.	187	Wagner Pit.	38	Alperman, Bro. Ganzel, Cin.	16 16
	AL	Cobb Det.	.350	Crawford Det.	102	Cobb Det.	212	Davis Phi.	37	Flick Cle.	18
1908	NL	Wagner Pit.	.354	Tenney N. Y.	101	Wagner Pit.	201	Wagner Pit.	39	Wagner Pit.	19
	AL	Cobb Det.	.324	McIntyre Det.	105	Cobb Det.	188	Cobb Det.	36	Cobb Det.	20
1909	NL	Wagner Pit.	.339	Leach Pit.	126	Doyle N. Y.	172	Wagner Pit.	39	Mitchell Cin.	17
	AL	Cobb Det.	.377	Cobb Det.	116	Cobb Det.	216	Crawford Det.	35	Baker Phi.	19

HOME RUNS		RUNS BATTED IN		STOLEN BASES		STRIKEOUTS		WON-LOST		EARNED RUN AVERAGE	
Stovey, Bos. Tiernan, N. Y.	16 16	---------	---	Hamilton Phi.	115	Rusie N. Y.	321	Staley Bos.	19-8	---------	---
Farrell Bos.	12	---------	---	Brown Bos.	110	Stivetts St. L.	232	Buffinton Bos. Haddock Bos.	27-9 33-11	---------	---
Holliday Cin.	9	---------	---	Ward Bro.	94	Rusie N. Y.	303	Young Cle.	36-11	---------	---
Delahanty Phi.	19	---------	---	Ward N. Y.	72	Rusie N. Y.	208	Gastright Bos.	12-4	---------	---
Duffy Bos.	18	---------	---	Hamilton Phi.	99	Rusie N. Y.	204	Meekin N.Y.	36-10	---------	---
Thompson Phi.	18	---------	---	Hamilton Phi.	95	Rusie N. Y.	199	Hoffer Bal.	29-8	---------	---
Delahanty Phi.	13	---------	---	Lange Chi.	100	Young Cle.	137	Hoffer Bal.	26-7	---------	---
Delahanty Phi.	19	---------	---	Lange Chi.	83	McJames Was.	161	Rusie N. Y.	28-8	---------	---
Collins Bos.	15	---------	---	F. Clarke Lou.	66	Seymour N. Y.	249	Lewis Bos.	25-8	---------	---
Freeman Was.	25	---------	---	Sheckard Bal.	78	Hahn Cin.	147	Hughes Bro.	25-5	---------	---
Long Bos.	12	---------	---	Barrett Cin.	46	Waddell Pit.	133	McGinnity Bro.	29-9	---------	---
Crawford Cin.	16	---------	---	Wagner Pit.	48	Hahn Cin.	237	Leever Pit.	14-5	---------	---
Lajoie Phi.	13	---------	---	Isbell Chi.	48	Young Bos.	163	Young Bos.	31-10	---------	---
Leach Pit.	6	---------	---	Wagner Pit.	43	Willis Bos.	219	Chesbro Pit.	27-6	---------	---
Seybold Phi.	16	---------	---	Hartsel Phi.	54	Waddell Phi.	210	Waddell Phi	24-7	---------	---
Sheckard Bro.	9	---------	---	Chance, Chi. Sheckard, Bro.	67 67	Mathewson N. Y.	267	Leever Pit.	25-7	---------	---
Freeman Bos.	13	---------	---	Bay Cle.	46	Waddell Phi.	301	Moore Cle.	22-7	---------	---
Lumley Bro.	9	---------	---	Wagner Pit.	53	Mathewson N. Y.	212	McGinnity N. Y.	35-8	---------	---
Davis Phi.	10	---------	---	Flick Cle.	42	Waddell Phi.	343	Chesbro N. Y.	41-13	---------	---
Odwell Cin.	9	---------	---	Devlin, N. Y. Maloney, Chi.	59 59	Mathewson N. Y.	206	Mathewson N.Y.	32-8	---------	---
Davis Phi.	8	---------	---	Hoffman Phi.	46	Waddell Phi.	286	Coakley Phi.	20-8	---------	---
Jordan Bro.	12	---------	---	Chance Chi.	57	Beebe Chi.-St. L.	171	Reulbach Chi.	19-4	---------	---
Davis Phi.	12	---------	---	Anderson, Was. Flick, Cle.	39 39	Waddell Phi.	203	Plank Phi.	19-6	---------	---
Brain Bos.	10	Wagner Pit.	91	Wagner Pit.	61	Mathewson N. Y.	178	Reulbach Chi.	17-4	---------	---
Davis Phi.	8	Cobb Det.	116	Cobb Det.	49	Waddell Phi.	226	Donovan Det.	25-4	---------	---
Jordan Bro.	12	Wagner Pit.	106	Wagner Pit.	53	Mathewson N. Y.	259	Reulbach - Chi.	24-7	---------	---
Crawford Det.	7	Cobb Det.	101	Dougherty Chi.	47	Walsh Chi.	269	Walsh Chi.	40-15	---------	---
Murray N. Y.	7	Wagner Pit.	102	Bescher Cin.	54	Overall Chi.	205	S. Camnitz, Pit. Mathewson, N. Y.	25-6 25-6	---------	---
Cobb Det.	9	Cobb Det.	115	Cobb Det.	76	Smith Chi.	177	Mullin Det.	29-8	---------	---

YEAR	LEA.	BATTING		RUNS		HITS		DOUBLES		TRIPLES	
1910	NL	Magee Phi.	.331	Magee Phi.	110	Byrne, Pit. Wagner, Pit.	178 178	Byrne Pit.	43	Mitchell Cin.	18
	AL	Cobb Det.	.385	Cobb Det.	106	Lajoie Cle.	227	Lajoie Cle.	51	Crawford Det.	19
1911	NL	Wagner Pit.	.334	Sheckard Chi.	121	Miller Bos.	192	Konetchy St. L.	38	Doyle N. Y.	25
	AL	Cobb Det.	.420	Cobb Det.	147	Cobb Det.	248	Cobb Det.	47	Cobb Det.	24
1912	NL	Zimmerman Chi.	.372	Bescher Cin.	120	Zimmerman Chi.	207	Zimmerman Chi.	41	Wilson Pit.	36
	AL	Cobb Det.	.410	Collins Phi.	137	Cobb Det.	227	Speaker Bos.	53	Jackson Cle.	26
1913	NL	Daubert Bro.	.350	Carey, Pit. Leach, Chi.	99 99	Cravath Phi.	179	Smith Bro.	40	Saier Chi.	21
	AL	Cobb Det.	.390	Collins Phi.	125	Jackson Cle.	197	Jackson Cle.	39	Crawford Det.	23
1914	NL	Daubert Bro.	.329	Burns N. Y.	100	Magee Phi.	171	Magee Phi.	39	Carey Pit.	17
	AL	Cobb Det.	.368	Collins Phi.	122	Speaker Bos.	193	Speaker Bos.	46	Crawford Det.	26
	FL	Kauff Ind.	.366	Kauff Ind.	118	Kauff Ind.	210	Kauff Ind.	45	Evans Bro.	15
1915	NL	Doyle N. Y.	.320	Cravath Phi.	89	Doyle N. Y.	189	Doyle N. Y.	40	Long St. L.	25
	AL	Cobb Det.	.370	Cobb Det.	144	Cobb Det.	208	Veach Det.	40	Crawford Det.	19
	FL	Kauff Bro.	.344	Borton St. L.	99	Tobin St. L.	186	Chase Buf.	33	Kelly, Pit. Mann, Chi.	19 19
1916	NL	Chase Cin.	.339	Burns N. Y.	105	Chase Cin.	184	Niehoff Phi.	42	Hinchman Pit.	16
	AL	Speaker Cle.	.386	Cobb Det.	113	Speaker Cle.	211	Graney, Cle. Speaker, Cle.	41 41	Jackson Chi.	21
1917	NL	Roush Cin.	.341	Burns N. Y.	103	Groh Cin.	182	Groh Cin.	39	Hornsby St. L.	17
	AL	Cobb Det.	.383	Bush Det.	112	Cobb Det.	225	Cobb Det.	44	Cobb Det.	23
1918	NL	Z. Wheat Bro.	.335	Groh Cin.	88	Hollocher Chi.	161	Groh Cin.	28	Daubert Bro.	15
	AL	Cobb Det.	.382	Chapman Cle.	84	Burns Phi.	178	Speaker Cle.	33	Cobb Det.	14
1919	NL	Roush Cin.	.321	Burns N. Y.	86	Hornsby St. L.	163	Young N. Y.	31	Southworth, Pit. Myers, Bro.	14 14
	AL	Cobb Det.	.384	Ruth Bos.	103	Cobb, Det. Veach, Det.	191 191	Veach Det.	45	Veach Det.	17
1920	NL	Hornsby St. L.	.370	Burns N. Y.	115	Hornsby St. L.	218	Hornsby St. L.	44	Myers Bro.	22
	AL	Sisler St. L.	.407	Ruth N. Y.	158	Sisler St. L.	257	Speaker Cle.	50	Jackson Chi.	20
1921	NL	Hornsby St. L.	.397	Hornsby St. L.	131	Hornsby St. L.	235	Hornsby St. L.	44	Hornsby, St. L. Powell, Bos.	18 18
	AL	Heilmann Det.	.394	Ruth N. Y.	177	Heilmann Det.	237	Speaker Cle.	52	Shanks Was.	19
1922	NL	Hornsby St. L.	.401	Hornsby St. L.	141	Hornsby St. L.	250	Hornsby St. L.	46	Daubert Cin.	22
	AL	Sisler St. L.	.420	Sisler St. L.	134	Sisler St. L.	246	Speaker Cle.	48	Sisler St. L.	18

HOME RUNS		RUNS BATTED IN		STOLEN BASES		STRIKEOUTS		WON-LOST		EARNED RUN AVERAGE	
Schulte, Chi. Beck, Bos.	10 10	Magee Phi.	116	Bescher Cin.	70	Moore Phi.	185	Phillippe Pit.	14-2	---------	---
Stahl Bos.	10	Crawford Det.	115	Collins Phi.	81	Johnson Was.	313	Bender Phi.	23-5	---------	---
Schulte Chi.	21	Schulte Chi.	121	Bescher Cin.	80	Marquard N. Y.	237	Marquard N. Y.	24-7	---------	---
Baker Phi.	9	Cobb Det.	144	Cobb Det.	83	Walsh Chi.	255	Bender Phi.	17-5	---------	---
Zimmerman Chi.	14	Zimmerman Chi.	106	Bescher Cin.	67	Alexander Phi.	195	Hendrix Pit.	24-9	Tesreau N. Y.	1.96
Baker Phi.	10	Baker Phi.	133	Milan Was.	88	Johnson Was.	303	Wood Bos.	34-5	Not re- corded	
Cravath Phi.	19	Cravath Phi.	129	Carey Pit.	61	Seaton Phi.	168	Humpheries Chi.	16-4	Mathewson N. Y.	2.06
Baker Phi.	12	Baker Phi.	126	Milan Was.	74	Johnson Was.	243	Johnson Was.	36-7	Johnson Was.	1.09
Cravath Phi.	19	Magee Phi.	101	Burns N. Y.	62	Alexander Phi.	214	James Bos.	26-7	Doak St. L.	1.72
Baker, Phi. Crawford, Det.	8 8	Crawford Det.	112	Maisel N. Y.	74	Johnson Was.	225	Bender Phi.	17-3	Leonard Bos.	1.01
Zwilling Chi.	16	---------	---	Kauff Ind.	75	Falkenberg Ind.	245	Ford Buf.	21-6	Krapp Buf.	1.19
Cravath Phi.	24	Cravath Phi.	118	Carey Pit.	36	Alexander Phi.	241	Alexander Phi.	31-10	Alexander Phi.	1.22
Roth Chi.-Cle.	7	Crawford Det.	116	Cobb Det.	96	Johnson Was.	203	Ruth Bos.	18-6	Wood Bos.	1.49
Chase Buf.	17	---------	---	Kauff Bro.	54	Davenport St. L.	228	McConnell Chi.	25-10	Plank St. L.	2.01
Robertson, N. Y. Williams, Chi.	12 12	Chase Cin.	84	Carey Pit.	63	Alexander Phi.	167	Hughes Bos.	16-3	Schupp N. Y.	0.90
Pipp, N. Y.	12	Pipp N. Y.	99	Cobb Det.	68	Johnson Was.	228	Cullop N.Y.	13-6	Ruth Bos.	1.75
Cravath, Phi. Robertson, N. Y.	12 12	Zimmerman N. Y.	100	Carey Pit.	46	Alexander Phi.	201	Schupp N. Y.	21-7	Alexander Phi.	1.85
Pipp N. Y.	9	Veach Det.	115	Cobb Det.	55	Johnson Was.	185	Klepfer Cle.	14-4	Cicotte Chi.	1.53
Cravath Phi.	8	Merkle Chi.	71	Carey Pit.	58	Vaughn Chi.	148	Hendrix Chi.	20-7	Vaughn Chi.	1.74
Ruth, Bos. Walker, Phi.	11 11	Burns, Phi. Veach, Det.	74 74	Sisler St. L.	45	Johnson Was.	162	Jones Bos.	16-5	Johnson Was.	1.28
Cravath Phi.	12	Myers Bro.	72	Burns N. Y.	40	Vaughn Chi.	141	Ruether Cin.	19-6	Alexander Chi.	1.72
Ruth Bos.	29	Ruth Bos.	112	E. Collins Chi.	33	Johnson Was.	147	Cicotte Chi.	29-7	Johnson Was.	1.49
Williams Phi.	15	Hornsby, St. L. Kelly, N. Y.	94 94	Carey Pit.	52	Alexander Chi.	173	Grimes Bro.	23-11	Alexander Chi.	1.91
Ruth N. Y.	54	Ruth N. Y.	137	Rice Was.	62	Coveleskie Cle.	133	Bagby Cle.	31-12	Shawkey N. Y.	2.46
Kelly N. Y.	23	Hornsby St. L.	126	Frisch N. Y.	49	Grimes Bro.	136	Adams, Pit. Glazner, Pit.	14-5 14-5	Doak St. L.	2.58
Ruth N. Y.	59	Ruth N. Y.	170	Sisler St. L.	35	Johnson Was.	143	Mays N.Y. Sothoron Cle	27-9 12-4	Faber Chi.	2.48
Hornsby St. L.	42	Hornsby St. L.	152	Carey Pit.	51	Vance Bro.	134	Douglas N. Y.	11-4	Ryan N. Y.	3.00
Williams St. L.	39	Williams St. L.	155	Sisler St. L.	51	Shocker St. L.	149	Bush N. Y.	26-7	Faber Chi.	2.81

YEAR	LEA.	BATTING		RUNS		HITS		DOUBLES		TRIPLES	
1923	NL	Hornsby St. L.	.384	Young N. Y.	121	Frisch N. Y.	223	Roush Cin.	41	Carey, Pit. Traynor, Pit.	19 19
	AL	Heilmann Det.	.403	Ruth N. Y.	151	Jamieson Cle.	222	Speaker Cle.	59	Goslin, Was. Rice, Was.	18 18
1924	NL	Hornsby St. L.	.424	Hornsby, St. L. Frisch, N. Y.	121 121	Hornsby St. L.	227	Hornsby St. L.	43	Roush Cin.	21
	AL	Ruth N. Y.	.378	Ruth N. Y.	143	Rice Was.	216	Heilmann, Det. J. Sewell, Cle.	45 45	Pipp N. Y.	19
1925	NL	Hornsby St. L.	.403	Cuyler Pit.	144	Bottomley St. L.	227	Bottomley St. L.	44	Cuyler Pit.	26
	AL	Heilmann Det.	.393	Mostil Chi.	135	Simmons Phi.	253	McManus St. L.	44	Goslin Was.	20
1926	NL	Hargrave Cin.	.353	Cuyler Pit.	113	Brown Bos.	201	Bottomley St. L.	40	Waner Pit.	22
	AL	Manush Det.	.378	Ruth N. Y.	139	Burns, Cle. Rice, Was.	216 216	Burns Cle.	64	Gehrig N. Y.	20
1927	NL	P. Waner Pit.	.380	Hornsby, N. Y. L. Waner, Pit.	133 133	P. Waner Pit.	237	Stephenson Chi.	46	P. Waner Pit.	17
	AL	Heilmann Det.	.398	Ruth N. Y.	158	Combs N. Y.	231	Gehrig N. Y.	52	Combs N. Y.	23
1928	NL	Hornsby Bos.	.387	P. Waner Pit.	142	Lindstrom N. Y.	231	P. Waner Pit.	50	Bottomley St. L.	20
	AL	Goslin Was.	.379	Ruth N. Y.	163	Manush St. L.	241	Gehrig, N. Y. Manush, St. L.	47 47	Combs N. Y.	21
1929	NL	O'Doul Phi.	.398	Hornsby Chi.	156	O'Doul Phi.	254	Frederick Bro.	52	L. Waner Pit.	20
	AL	Fonseca Cle.	.369	Gehringer Det.	131	Alexander, Det. Gehringer, Det.	215 215	Gehringer, Det. Johnson, Det. Manush, St. L.	45 45 45	Gehringer Det.	19
1930	NL	Terry N. Y.	.401	Klein Phi.	158	Terry N. Y.	254	Klein Phi.	59	Comorosky Pit.	23
	AL	Simmons Phi.	.381	Simmons Phi.	152	Hodapp Cle.	225	Hodapp Cle.	51	Combs N. Y.	22
1931	NL	Hafey St. L.	.349	Klein, Phi. Terry, N. Y.	121 121	L. Waner Pit.	214	Adams St. L.	46	Terry N. Y.	20
	AL	Simmons Phi.	.390	Gehrig N. Y.	163	Gehrig N. Y.	211	Webb Bos.	67	Johnson Det.	19
1932	NL	O'Doul Bro.	.368	Klein Phi.	152	Klein Phi.	226	P. Waner Pit.	62	Herman Cin.	19
	AL	Alexander Det.-Bos.	.367	Foxx Phi.	151	Simmons Phi.	216	McNair Phi.	47	Cronin Was.	18
1933	NL	Klein Phi.	.368	Martin St. L.	122	Klein Phi.	223	Klein Phi.	44	Vaughan Pit.	19
	AL	Foxx Phi.	.356	Gehrig N. Y.	138	Manush Was.	221	Cronin Was.	45	Manush Was.	17
1934	NL	P. Waner Pit.	.362	P. Waner Pit.	122	P. Waner Pit.	217	Allen, Phi. Cuyler, Chi.	42 42	Medwick St. L.	18
	AL	Gehrig N. Y.	.363	Gehringer Det.	134	Gehringer Det.	214	Greenberg Det.	63	Chapman N. Y.	13
1935	NL	Vaughan Pit.	.385	Galan Chi.	133	Herman Chi.	227	Herman Chi.	57	Goodman Cin.	18
	AL	Myer Was.	.349	Gehrig N. Y.	125	Vosmik Cle.	216	Vosmik Cle.	47	Vosmik Cle.	20
1936	NL	P. Waner Pit.	.373	Vaughan Pit.	122	Medwick St. L.	223	Medwick St. L.	64	Goodman Cin.	14
	AL	Appling Chi.	.388	Gehrig N. Y.	167	Averill Cle.	232	Gehringer Det.	60	Averill, Cle. DiMaggio, N. Y. Rolfe, N. Y.	15 15 15

HOME RUNS		RUNS BATTED IN		STOLEN BASES		STRIKEOUTS		WON-LOST		EARNED RUN AVERAGE	
Williams Phi.	41	Meusel N. Y.	125	Carey Pit.	51	Vance Bro.	197	Luque Cin.	27-8	Luque Cin.	1.93
Ruth N. Y.	41	Ruth, N. Y. Speaker, Cle.	130 130	Collins Chi.	49	Johnson Was.	126	Pennock N. Y.	19-6	Coveleskie Cle.	2.76
Fournier Bro.	27	Kelly N. Y.	136	Carey Pit.	49	Vance Bro.	262	Yde Pit.	16-3	Vance Bro.	2.16
Ruth N. Y.	46	Goslin Was.	129	Collins Chi.	42	Johnson Was.	158	Johnson Was.	23-7	Johnson Was.	2.72
Hornsby St. L.	39	Hornsby St. L.	143	Carey Pit.	46	Vance Bro.	221	Sherdel St. L.	15-6	Luque Cin.	2.63
Meusel N. Y.	33	Meusel N. Y.	138	Mostil Chi.	43	Grove Phi.	116	Coveleskie Was.	20-5	Coveleskie Was.	2.84
Wilson Chi.	21	Bottomley St. L.	120	Cuyler Pit.	35	Vance Bro.	140	Kremer Pit.	20-6	Kremer Pit.	2.61
Ruth N. Y.	47	Ruth N. Y.	155	Mostil Chi.	35	Grove Phi.	194	Uhle Cle	27-11	Grove Phi.	2.51
Williams, Phi. Wilson, Chi.	30 30	P. Waner Pit.	131	Frisch St. L.	48	Vance Bro.	184	Benton N. Y.	13-5	Kremer Pit.	2.47
Ruth N. Y.	60	Gehrig N. Y.	175	Sisler St. L.	27	Grove Phi.	174	Hoyt N. Y.	22-7	Moore N. Y.	2.28
Bottomley, St. L. Wilson, Chi.	31 31	Bottomley St. L.	136	Cuyler Chi.	37	Vance Bro.	200	Benton N. Y.	25-9	Vance Bro.	2.09
Ruth N. Y.	54	Gehrig, N. Y. Ruth, N. Y.	142 142	Myer Bos.	30	Grove Phi.	183	Crowder St. L.	21-5	Braxton Was.	2.52
Klein Phi.	43	Wilson Chi.	159	Cuyler Chi.	43	Malone Chi.	166	Root Chi.	19-6	Walker N. Y.	3.08
Ruth N. Y.	46	Simmons Phi.	157	Gehringer Det.	27	Grove Phi.	170	Grove Phi.	20-6	Zachary N. Y.	2.47
Wilson Chi.	56	Wilson Chi.	190	Cuyler Chi.	37	Hallahan St. L.	177	Teachout Chi.	11-4	Vance Bro.	2.61
Ruth N. Y.	49	Gehrig N. Y.	174	McManus Det.	23	Grove Phi.	214	Grove Phi.	28-5	Grove Phi.	3,00
Klein Phi.	31	Klein Phi.	121	Frisch St. L.	28	Hallahan St. L.	159	Haines St. L.	12-3	Walker N. Y.	2.26
Gehrig, N. Y. Ruth, N. Y.	46 46	Gehrig N. Y.	184	Chapman N. Y.	61	Grove Phi.	175	Grove Phi.	31-4	Grove Phi.	2.05
Klein, Phi. Ott, N. Y.	38 38	Hurst Phi.	143	Klein Phi.	20	Dean St. L.	191	Warneke Chi.	22-6	Warneke Chi.	2.37
Foxx Phi.	58	Foxx Phi.	169	Chapman N. Y.	38	Ruffing N. Y.	190	Allen N. Y.	17-4	Grove Phi.	2.84
Klein Phi.	28	Klein Phi.	120	Martin St. L.	26	Dean St. L.	199	Tinning Chi.	13-6	Hubbell N. Y.	1.66
Foxx Phi.	48	Foxx Phi.	163	Chapman N. Y.	27	Gomez N. Y.	163	Grove, Phi. Van Atta, N. Y.	24-8 12-4	Pearson Cle	2.35
Collins, St. L. Ott, N. Y.	35 35	Ott N. Y.	135	Martin St. L.	23	J. Dean St. L.	195	J. Dean St. L.	30-7	Hubbell N. Y.	2.30
Gehrig N. Y.	49	Gehrig N. Y.	165	Werber Bos.	40	Gomez N. Y.	158	Gomez N. Y.	26-5	Gomez N. Y.	2.33
Berger Bos.	34	Berger Bos.	130	Galan Chi.	22	J. Dean St. L.	182	Lee Chi.	20-6	Blanton Pit.	2.59
Foxx, Phi. Greenberg, Det.	36 36	Greenberg Det.	170	Werber Bos.	29	Bridges Det.	163	Auker Det.	18-7	Grove Bos.	2.70
Ott N. Y.	33	Medwick St. L.	138	J. Martin St. L.	23	Mungo Bro.	238	Hubbell N. Y.	26-6	Hubbell N. Y.	2.31
Gehrig N. Y.	49	Trosky Cle.	162	Lary St. L.	37	Bridges Det.	175	Hadley N. Y.	14-4	Grove Bos.	2.81

YEAR	LEA.	BATTING		RUNS		HITS		DOUBLES		TRIPLES	
1937	NL	Medwick St. L.	.374	Medwick St. L.	111	Medwick St. L.	237	Medwick St. L.	56	Vaughan Pit.	17
	AL	Gehringer Det.	.371	DiMaggio N. Y.	151	Bell St. L.	218	Bell St. L.	51	Kreevich, Chi. Walker, Chi.	16 16
1938	NL	Lombardi Cin.	.342	Ott N. Y.	116	McCormick Cin.	209	Medwick St. L.	47	Mize St. L.	16
	AL	Foxx Bos.	.349	Greenberg Det.	144	Vosmik Bos.	201	Cronin Bos.	51	Heath Cle.	18
1939	NL	Mize St. L.	.349	Werber Cin.	115	McCormick Cin.	209	Slaughter St. L.	52	Herman Chi.	18
	AL	DiMaggio N. Y.	.381	Rolfe N. Y.	139	Rolfe N. Y.	213	Rolfe N. Y.	46	Lewis Was.	16
1940	NL	Garms Pit.	.355	Vaughan Pit.	113	Hack, Chi. F. McC'mick, Cin.	191 191	F. McCormick Cin.	44	Vaughan Pit.	15
	AL	DiMaggio N. Y.	.352	Williams Bos.	134	Cramer, Bos. McCosky, Det. Radcliff, St. L.	200 200 200	Greenberg Det.	50	McCosky Det.	19
1941	NL	Reiser Bro.	.343	Reiser Bro.	117	Hack Chi.	186	Mize, St. L. Reiser, Bro.	39 39	Reiser Bro.	17
	AL	Williams Bos.	.406	Williams Bos.	135	Travis Was.	218	Boudreau Cle.	45	Heath Cle.	20
1942	NL	Lombardi Bos.	.330	Ott N. Y.	118	Slaughter St. L.	188	Marion St. L.	38	Slaughter St. L.	17
	AL	Williams Bos.	.356	Williams Bos.	141	Pesky Bos.	205	Kolloway Chi.	40	Spence Was.	15
1943	NL	Musial St. L.	.357	Vaughan Bro.	112	Musial St. L.	220	Musial St. L.	48	Musial St. L.	20
	AL	Appling Chi.	.328	Case Was.	102	Wakefield Det.	200	Wakefield Det.	38	Lindell, N. Y. Moses, Chi.	12 12
1944	NL	Walker Bro.	.357	Nicholson Chi.	116	Cavarretta, Chi. Musial, St. L.	197 197	Musial St. L.	51	Barrett Pit.	19
	AL	Boudreau Cle.	.327	Stirnweiss N. Y.	125	Stirnweiss N. Y.	205	Boudreau Cle.	45	Lindell, N. Y. Stirnweiss, N. Y.	16 16
1945	NL	Cavarretta Chi.	.355	Stanky Bro.	128	Holmes Bos.	224	Holmes Bos.	47	Olmo Bro.	13
	AL	Stirnweiss N. Y.	.309	Stirnweiss N. Y.	107	Stirnweiss N. Y.	195	Moses Chi.	35	Stirnweiss N. Y.	22
1946	NL	Musial St. L.	.365	Musial St. L.	124	Musial St. L.	228	Musial St. L.	50	Musial St. L.	20
	AL	Vernon Was.	.353	Williams Bos.	142	Pesky Bos.	208	Vernon Was.	51	Edwards Cle.	16
1947	NL	Walker St. L.-Phi.	.363	Mize N. Y.	137	Holmes Bos.	191	Miller Cin.	38	Walker St. L.-Phi.	16
	AL	Williams Bos.	.343	Williams Bos.	125	Pesky Bos.	207	Boudreau Cle.	45	Henrich N. Y.	13
1948	NL	Musial St. L.	.376	Musial St. L.	135	Musial St. L.	230	Musial St. L.	46	Musial St. L.	18
	AL	Williams Bos.	.369	Henrich N. Y.	138	Dillinger St. L.	207	Williams Bos.	44	Henrich N. Y.	14
1949	NL	Robinson Bro.	.342	Reese Bro.	132	Musial St. L.	207	Musial St. L.	41	Musial, St. L. Slaughter, St. L.	13 13
	AL	Kell Det.	.343	Williams Bos.	150	Mitchell Cle.	203	Williams Bos.	39	Mitchell Cle.	23
1950	NL	Musial St. L.	.346	Torgeson Bos.	120	Snider Bro.	199	Schoendienst St. L.	43	Ashburn Phi.	14
	AL	Goodman Bos.	.354	DiMaggio Bos.	131	Kell Det.	218	Kell Det.	56	DiMaggio, Bos. Doerr, Bos. Evers, Det.	11 11 11

HOME RUNS		RUNS BATTED IN		STOLEN BASES		STRIKEOUTS		WON-LOST		EARNED RUN AVERAGE	
Medwick, St. L. Ott, N. Y.	31 31	Medwick St. L.	154	Galan Chi.	23	Hubbell N. Y.	159	Hubbell N. Y.	22-8	Turner Bos.	2.38
DiMaggio N. Y.	46	Greenberg Det.	183	Chapman, Was.-Bos. Werber, Phi.	35 35	Gomez N. Y.	194	Allen Cle.	15-1	Gomez N. Y.	2.33
Ott N. Y.	36	Medwick St. L.	122	Hack Chi.	16	Bryant Chi.	135	Lee Chi.	22-9	Lee Chi.	2.66
Greenberg Det.	58	Foxx Bos.	175	Crosetti N. Y.	27	Feller Cle.	240	Grove Bos.	14-4	Grove Bos.	3.07
Mize St. L.	28	McCormick Cin.	128	Hack, Chi. Handley, Pit.	17 17	Passeau, Phi.-Chi. Walters, Cin.	137 137	Derringer Cin.	25-7	Walters Cin.	2.29
Foxx Bos.	35	Williams Bos.	145	Case Was.	51	Feller Cle.	246	Donald N. Y.	13-3	Grove Bos.	2.54
Mize St. L.	43	Mize St. L.	137	Frey Cin.	22	Higbe Phi.	137	Fitzsimmons Bro.	16-2	Walters Cin.	2.48
Greenberg Det.	41	Greenberg Det.	150	Case Was.	35	Feller Cle.	261	Rowe Det.	16-3	Feller Cle.	2.62
Camilli Bro.	34	Camilli Bro.	120	Murtaugh Phi.	18	Vander Meer Cin.	202	E. Riddle Cin.	19-4	E. Riddle Cin.	2.24
Williams Bos.	37	DiMaggio N. Y.	125	Case Was.	33	Feller Cle.	260	Gomez N. Y.	15-5	Lee Chi.	2.37
Ott N. Y.	30	Mize N. Y.	110	Reiser Bro.	20	Vander Meer Cin.	186	Krist St. L.	13-3	M. Cooper St. L.	1.77
Williams Bos.	36	Williams Bos.	137	Case Was.	44	Hughson, Bos. Newsom, Was.	113 113	Bonham N. Y.	21-5	Lyons Chi.	2.10
Nicholson Chi.	29	Nicholson Chi.	128	Vaughan Bro.	20	Vander Meer Cin.	174	Shoun, Cin. Wyatt, Bro.	14-5 14-5	Pollet St. L.	1.75
York Det.	34	York Det.	118	Case Was.	61	Reynolds Cle.	151	Chandler N. Y.	20-4	Chandler N. Y.	1.64
Nicholson Chi.	33	Nicholson Chi.	122	Barrett Pit.	28	Voiselle N. Y.	161	Wilks St. L.	17-4	Heusser Cin.	2.38
Etten N. Y.	22	Stephens St. L.	109	Stirnweiss N. Y.	55	Newhouser Det.	187	Hughson Bos.	18-5	Trout Det.	2.12
Holmes Bos.	28	Walker Bro.	124	Schoendienst St. L.	26	Roe Pit.	148	Brecheen St. L.	15-4	Borowy Chi.	2.14
Stephens St. L.	24	Etten N. Y.	111	Stirnweiss N. Y.	33	Newhouser Det.	212	Muncrief St. L.	13-4	Newhouser Det.	1.81
Kiner Pit.	23	Slaughter St. L.	130	Reiser Bro.	34	Schmitz Chi.	135	Rowe Phi.	11-4	Pollet St. L.	2.10
Greenberg Det.	44	Greenberg Det.	127	Case Cle.	28	Feller Cle.	348	Ferriss Bos.	25-6	Newhouser Det.	1.94
Kiner, Pit. Mize, N. Y.	51 51	Mize N. Y.	138	Robinson Bro.	29	Blackwell Cin.	193	Jansen N. Y.	21-5	Spahn Bos.	2.33
Williams Bos.	32	Williams Bos.	114	Dillinger St. L.	34	Feller Cle.	196	Shea N. Y.	14-5	Haynes Chi.	2.42
Kiner, Pit. Mize, N. Y.	40 40	Musial St. L.	131	Ashburn Phi.	32	Brecheen St. L.	149	Sewell Pit.	13-3	Brecheen St. L.	2.24
DiMaggio N. Y.	39	DiMaggio N. Y.	155	Dillinger St. L.	28	Feller Cle.	164	Kramer Bos.	18-5	Bearden Cle.	2.43
Kiner Pit.	54	Kiner Pit.	127	Robinson Bro.	37	Spahn Bos.	151	Branca Bro.	13-5	Koslo N. Y.	2.50
Williams Bos.	43	Williams, Bos. Stephens, Bos.	159 159	Dillinger St. L.	20	Trucks Det.	153	Kinder Bos.	23-6	Parnell Bos.	2.78
Kiner Pit.	47	Ennis Phi.	126	Jethroe Bos.	35	Spahn Bos.	191	Maglie N. Y.	18-4	Hearn St. L.-N. Y.	2.49
Rosen Cle.	37	Dropo, Bos. Stephens, Bos.	144 144	DiMaggio Bos.	15	Lemon Cle.	170	Raschi N. Y.	21-8	Wynn Cle.	3.20

YEAR	LEA.	BATTING		RUNS		HITS		DOUBLES		TRIPLES	
1951	NL	Musial St. L.	.355	Kiner, Pit. Musial, St. L.	124 124	Ashburn Phi.	221	Dark N. Y.	41	Bell, Pit. Musial, St. L.	12 12
	AL	Fain Phi.	.344	DiMaggio Bos.	113	Kell Det.	191	Kell, Det. Mele, Was. Yost, Was.	36 36 36	Minoso Cle.-Chi.	14
1952	NL	Musial St. L.	.336	Hemus, St. L. Musial, St. L.	105 105	Musial St. L.	194	Musial St. L.	42	Thomson N. Y.	14
	AL	Fain Phi.	.327	Doby Cle.	104	Fox Chi.	192	Fain Phi.	43	Avila Cle.	11
1953	NL	Furillo Bro.	.344	Snider Bro.	132	Ashburn Phi.	205	Musial St. L.	53	Gilliam Bro.	17
	AL	Vernon Was.	.337	Rosen Cle.	115	Kuenn Det.	209	Vernon Was.	43	Rivera Chi.	16
1954	NL	Mays N. Y.	.345	Musial, St. L. Snider, Bro.	120 120	Mueller N. Y.	212	Musial St. L.	41	Mays N. Y.	13
	AL	Avila Cle.	.341	Mantle N. Y.	129	Fox, Chi. Kuenn, Det.	201 201	Vernon Was.	33	Minoso Chi.	18
1955	NL	Ashburn Phi.	.338	Snider Bro.	126	Kluszewski Cin.	192	Logan, Mil. Aaron, Mil.	37 37	Mays, N. Y. Long, Pit.	13 13
	AL	Kaline Det.	.340	Smith Cle.	123	Kaline Det.	200	Kuenn Det.	38	Mantle, N. Y. Carey, N. Y.	11 11
1956	NL	Aaron Mil.	.328	Robinson Cin.	122	Aaron Mil.	200	Aaron Mil.	34	Bruton Mil.	15
	AL	Mantle N. Y.	.353	Mantle N. Y.	132	Kuenn Det.	196	Piersall Bos.	40	Minoso, Chi. Jensen, Bos. Simpson, K. C. Lemon, Was.	11 11 11 11
1957	NL	Musial St.L.	.351	Aaron Mil.	118	Schoendienst N. Y. - Mil.	200	Hoak Cin.	39	Mays N. Y.	20
	AL	Williams Bos.	.388	Mantle N. Y.	121	Fox Chi.	196	Gardner Bal. Minoso Chi.	36 36	Bauer N. Y. McDougald N. Y. Simpson K. C. - N. Y.	9 9 9
1958	NL	Ashburn Phi.	.350	Mays S. F.	121	Ashburn Phi.	215	Cepeda S. F.	38	Ashburn Phi.	13
	AL	Williams Bos.	.328	Mantle N. Y.	127	Fox Chi.	187	Kuenn Det.	39	Power K. C. - Cle.	10
1959	NL	Aaron Mil.	.355	Pinson Cin.	131	Aaron Mil.	223	Pinson Cin.	47	Moon, L.A. Neal, L.A.	11 11
	AL	Kuenn Det.	.353	Yost Det.	115	Kuenn Det.	198	Kuenn Det.	42	Allison Was.	9
1960	NL	Groat Pit.	.325	Bruton Mil.	112	Mays SF	190	Pinson Cin.	37	Bruton Mil.	13
	AL	Runnels Bos.	.320	Mantle N.Y.	119	Minoso Chi.	184	Francona Cle.	36	Fox Chi.	10
1961	NL	Clemente Pit.	.351	Mays SF	129	Pinson Cin.	208	Aaron Mil.	39	Altman Chi.	12
	AL	Cash Det.	.361	Mantle, NY Maris, NY	132 132	Cash Det.	193	Kaline Det.	41	Wood Det.	14
1962	NL	Davis, H. L.A.	.346	Robinson Cin.	134	Davis, H. L.A.	230	Robinson, F. Cin.	51	Callison, Phi. W.Davis, L.A. Virdon, Pit. Wills, L.A.	10 10 10 10
	AL	Runnels Bos.	.326	Pearson L.A.	115	Richardson N.Y.	209	Robinson, F. Chi.	45	Cimoli K.C.	15

HOME RUNS	RUNS BATTED IN	STOLEN BASES	STRIKEOUTS	WON-LOST	EARNED RUN AVERAGE
Kiner Pit. 42	Irvin N. Y. 121	Jethroe Bos. 35	Newcombe, Bro. 164 Spahn, Bos. 164	Roe Bro. 22-3	Nichols Bos. 2.88
Zernial Chi.-Phi. 33	Zernial Chi.-Phi. 129	Minoso Cle.-Chi. 31	Raschi N. Y. 164	Feller Cle. 22-8	Rogovin Det.-Chi. 2.78
Kiner, Pit. 37 Sauer, Chi. 37	Sauer Chi. 121	Reese Bro. 30	Spahn Bos. 183	Wilhelm N. Y. 15-3	Wilhelm N. Y. 2.43
Doby Cle. 32	Rosen Cle. 105	Minoso Chi. 22	Reynolds N. Y. 160	Shantz Phi. 24-7	Reynolds N. Y. 2.07
Mathews Mil. 47	Campanella Bro. 142	Bruton Mil. 26	Roberts Phi. 198	Erskine Bro. 20-6	Spahn Mil. 2.10
Rosen Cle. 43	Rosen Cle. 145	Minoso Chi. 25	Pierce Chi. 186	Lopat N. Y. 16-4	Lopat N. Y. 2.43
Kluszewski Cin. 49	Kluszewski Cin. 141	Bruton Mil. 34	Roberts Phi. 185	Antonelli N. Y. 21-7	Antonelli N. Y. 2.29
Doby Cle. 32	Doby Cle. 126	Jensen Bos. 22	Turley Bal. 185	Consuegra Chi. 16-3	Garcia Cle. 2.64
Mays N. Y. 51	Snider Bro. 136	Bruton Mil. 25	Jones Chi. 198	Newcombe Bro. 20-5	Friend Pit. 2.84
Mantle N. Y. 37	Jensen, Bos. 116 Boone, Det. 116	Rivera Chi. 25	Score Cle. 245	Byrne N. Y. 16-5	Pierce Chi. 1.97
Snider Bro. 43	Musial St.L. 109	Mays N. Y. 40	Jones Chi. 176	Newcombe Bro. 27-7	Burdette Mil. 2.71
Mantle N. Y. 52	Mantle N. Y. 130	Aparicio Chi. 21	Score Cle. 263	Ford N. Y. 19-6	Ford N. Y. 2.47
Aaron Mil. 44	Aaron Mil. 132	Mays N. Y. 38	Sanford Phi. 188	Buhl Mil. 18-7	Podres Bro. 2.66
Sievers Was. 42	Sievers Was. 114	Aparicio Chi. 28	Wynn Cle. 184	Donovan Chi. 16-6 Sturdivant N. Y. 16-6	Shantz N. Y. 2.45
Banks Chi. 47	Banks Chi. 129	Mays S. F. 31	Jones St.L. 225	Burdette Mil. 20-10 Spahn Mil. 22-11	Miller S. F. 2.47
Mantle N. Y. 42	Jensen Bos. 122	Aparicio Chi. 29	Wynn Chi. 179	Turley N. Y. 21-7	Ford N. Y. 2.01
Mathews Mil. 46	Banks Chi. 143	Mays S.F. 27	Drysdale L.A. 242	Burdette Mil. 21-15 Jones,SF 21-15 Spahn,Mil. 21-15	Jones S.F. 2.82
Colavito,Cle. 42 Killebrew Was. 42	Jensen Bos. 112	Aparicio Chi. 56	Bunning Det. 201	Wynn Chi. 22-10	Wilhelm Bal. 2.19
Banks Chi. 41	Aaron Mil. 126	Wills L.A. 50	Drysdale L.A. 246	Broglio St.L. 21-9	McCormick S.F. 2.70
Mantle N.Y. 40	Maris N.Y. 112	Aparicio Chi. 51	Bunning Det. 201	Perry Cle. 18-10	Baumann Chi 2.68
Cepeda S.F. 46	Cepeda S.F. 142	Wills L.A. 35	Koufax L.A. 269	Podres L.A. 18-5	Spahn Mil. 3.01
Maris N.Y. 61	Maris N.Y. 142	Aparicio Chi. 53	Pascual Min. 221	Ford N.Y. 25-4	Donovan Was. 2.40
Mays S.F. 49	Davis, H. L.A. 153	Wills L.A. 104	Drysdale L.A. 232	Purkey Cin. 23-5	Koufax L.A. 2.54
Killebrew Min. 48	Killebrew Min. 126	Aparicio Chi. 31	Pascual Min. 206	Herbert Chi 20-9	Aguirre Det. 2.21

CLUB LEADERS—INDIVIDUAL LIFETIME

AMERICAN ASSOCIATION

CLUB	BATTING	REC.	PITCHING	W-L	REC.
Athletics	Dennis Lyons (1887)	.469	Bob Mathews (1883)	30-14	.682
Baltimore	Tommy Burns (1887)	.401	Mat Kilroy (1887)	46-20	.697
Boston	Dan Brouthers (1891)	.352	Charles Buffinton (1891)	27-9	.750
			George Haddock (1891)	33-11	.750
Brooklyn	Jim McTamany (1887)	.354	Bob Caruthers (1889)	40-12	.769
Cincinnati	Frank Fennelly (1887)	.368	Will White (1882)	40-12	.769
Cleveland	Pete Hotaling (1887)	.367	Ed Bakely (1888)	25-33	.417
Columbus	John Johnson (1890)	.354	Ed Morris (1884)	35-13	.729
Indianapolis	Jim Keenan (1884)	.305	Larry McKeon (1884)	18-41	.305
Kansas City	Jim Burns (1889)	.303	Jim Conway (1889)	18-19	.486
Louisville	Pete Browning (1887)	.471	Guy Hecker (1884)	52-20	.722
Metropolitans	Dude Esterbrook (1884)	.408	John Lynch (1884)	39-14	.736
Milwaukee	Harry Vaughn (1891)	.330	Frank Killen (1891)	8-3	.727
Pittsburgh	Cy Swartwood (1883)	.369	Ed Morris (1886)	41-20	.672
Richmond	Mike Mansell (1884)	.301	Pete Meegan (1884)	7-12	.368
Rochester	Sandy Griffin (1890)	.305	Bill Calihan (1890)	18-13	.581
St. Louis	Tip O'Neill (1887)	.492	Silver King (1887)	34-11	.756
Syracuse	Cupid Childs (1890)	.344	Ed Mars (1890)	9-6	.600
Toledo	Cy Swartwood (1890)	.309	Tony Mullane (1884)	36-26	.581
Washington	Jim McGuire (1891)	.296	Frank Foreman (1891)	22-22	.500

AMERICAN LEAGUE

CLUB	BATTING	REC.	PITCHING	W-L	REC.
Baltimore	John McGraw (1901)	.352	Hal Brown (1960)	12-5	.706
Boston	Ted Williams (1941)	.406	Joe Wood (1912)	34-5	.872
Chicago	Luke Appling (1936)	.388	Sandy Consuegra (1954)	16-3	.842
Cleveland	Joe Jackson (1911)	.408	Johnny Allen (1937)	15-1	.938
Detroit	Ty Cobb (1911)	.420	Bill Donovan (1907)	25-4	.862
Kansas City	Vic Power (1955)	.319	Dave Wickersham (1962)	11-4	.733
Los Angeles	Lee Thomas (1962)	.290	Ken McBride (1962)	11-5	.688
Milwaukee	John Anderson (1901)	.339	Bill Reidy (1901)	15-18	.455
Minnesota	Jesse Battey (1961)	.302	Camilo Pascual (1962)	20-11	.645
New York	Babe Ruth (1923)	.393	Whitey Ford (1961)	25-4	.862
Philadelphia	Nap Lajoie (1901)	.422	Lefty Grove (1931)	31-4	.886
St. Louis	George Sisler (1922)	.420	General Crowder (1928)	21-5	.808
Washington	Goose Goslin (1928)	.379	Walter Johnson (1913)	36-7	.837

FEDERAL LEAGUE

CLUB	BATTING	REC.	PITCHING	W-L	REC.
Baltimore	Steve Evans (1915)	.319	Jack Quinn (1914)	26-14	.650
Brooklyn	Steve Evans (1914)	.355	Tom Seaton (1914)	25-14	.641
Buffalo	Hal Chase (1914)	.354	Russ Ford (1914)	21-6	.778
Chicago	Bill Fischer (1915)	.326	Claude Hendrix (1914)	29-10	.744
Indianapolis	Bennie Kauff (1914)	.366	George Kaiserling (1914)	17-10	.630
Kansas City	Ted Easterly (1914)	.331	Nick Cullop (1915)	22-11	.667
Newark	Vin Campbell (1915)	.314	Ed Reulbach (1915)	21-10	.677
Pittsburgh	Eggie Lennox (1914)	.317	Frank Allen (1915)	23-13	.639
St. Louis	Doc Crandall (1914)	.312	Mordecai Brown (1914)	11-5	.684

NATIONAL ASSOCIATION

Due to the fact that the records of this first major league are largely incomplete and that some box scores are missing, it is therefore impossible to compute the club leaders in batting and pitching for the National Association.

NATIONAL LEAGUE (1876-1899)

CLUB	BATTING	REC.	PITCHING	W-L	REC.
Athletics	George Hall (1876)	.355	Lon Knight (1876)	10-23	.303
Baltimore	Willie Keeler (1897)	.432	Bill Hoffer (1896)	26-7	.788
Boston	Hugh Duffy (1894)	.438	Fred Klobedanz (1897)	25-8	.758
			Parson Lewis (1898)	25-8	.758
Brooklyn	Willie Keeler (1899)	.376	Jim Hughes (1899)	25-5	.833
Buffalo	Dan Brouthers (1883)	.371	Jim Galvin (1884)	46-21	.687
Chicago	Cap Anson (1887)	.421	Fred Goldsmith (1880)	22-3	.880
Cincinnati	Bug Holliday (1894)	.383	Noodles Hahn (1899)	23-8	.742
Cleveland	Jess Burkett (1895)	.423	Cy Young (1895)	33-10	.767
Detroit	Dan Brouthers (1887)	.419	Lady Baldwin (1886)	31-11	.764
Hartford	John Cassidy (1877)	.378	Tommy Bond (1876)	32-13	.711
Indianapolis	Otto Shomberg (1887)	.389	Bill Burdick (1888)	10-10	.500
			Amos Rusie (1889)	11-11	.500
Kansas City	Al Myers (1886)	.276	Grasshopper Whitney (1886)	12-32	.273
Louisville	Fred Clarke (1897)	.406	Ellsworth Cunningham (1898)	28-15	.651
Milwaukee	Abner Dalrymple (1878)	.356	Sam Weaver (1878)	12-30	.286
Mutuals	Jim Hallinan (1876)	.277	Bob Mathews (1876)	21-34	.382
New York	Roger Connor (1887)	.382	Mickey Welch (1885)	47-11	.810
Philadelphia	Ed Delahanty (1899)	.408	Al Orth (1899)	13-3	.813
Pittsburgh	Jake Stenzel (1895)	.384	Adonis Terry (1892)	20-7	.741
Providence	Paul Hines (1879)	.357	Hoss Radbourn (1884)	60-12	.833
St. Louis	Jess Burkett (1899)	.402	George Bradley (1876)	45-19	.703
Syracuse	John Farrell (1879)	.304	Pat McCormick (1879)	11-13	.458
Troy	Roger Connor (1880)	.332	Mickey Welch (1880)	34-30	.531
Washington	Paul Hines (1887)	.370	Al Maul (1895)	11-6	.647
Worcester	Lewis Dickerson (1881)	.316	Fred Corey (1880)	9-8	.529

NATIONAL LEAGUE (1900-1962)

CLUB	BATTING	REC	PITCHING	W-L	REC.
Boston	Rogers Hornsby (1928)	.387	Tom Hughes (1916)	16-3	.842
Brooklyn	Babe Herman (1930)	.393	Fred Fitzsimmons (1940)	16-2	.889
Chicago	Rogers Hornsby (1929)	.380	King Cole (1910)	20-4	.833
Cincinnati	Cy Seymour (1905)	.377	Elmer Riddle (1941)	19-4	.826
Houston	Roman Mejias (1962)	.286	Bob Bruce (1962)	10-9	.526
Los Angeles	Tommy Davis (1962)	.346	Johnny Podres (1961)	18-5	.783
Milwaukee	Hank Aaron (1959)	.355	Warren Spahn (1953)	23-7	.767
New York	Bill Terry (1930)	.401	Hoyt Wilhelm (1952)	15-3	.833
Philadelphia	Frank O'Doul (1929)	.398	Robin Roberts (1952)	28-7	.800
Pittsburgh	Arky Vaughan (1935)	.385	Elroy Face (1959)	18-1	.947
St. Louis	Rogers Hornsby (1924)	.424	Dizzy Dean (1934)	30-7	.811
San Francisco	Willie Mays (1958)	.347	Jack Sanford (1962)	24-7	.774

PLAYER'S LEAGUE

CLUB	BATTING	REC.	PITCHING	W-L	REC.
Boston	Dan Brouthers (1890)	.345	Ad Gumbert (1890)	22-9	.710
Brooklyn	Dave Orr (1890)	.387	Gus Weyhing (1890)	31-15	.674
Buffalo	Ed Beecher (1890)	.357	Bert Cunningham (1890)	10-15	.400
Chicago	Jimmy Ryan (1890)	.330	Silver King (1890)	33-20	.623
Cleveland	Pete Browning (1890)	.391	Billy McGill (1890)	11-9	.550
New York	Roger Connor (1890)	.372	Tim Keefe (1890)	17-8	.680
Philadelphia	George Wood (1890)	.304	Philip Knell (1890)	20-11	.645
Pittsburgh	Jake Beckley (1890)	.325	Al Maul (1890)	17-11	.607

UNION ASSOCIATION

CLUB	BATTING	REC.	PITCHING	W-L	REC.
Altoona	Germany Smith (1884)	.307	Connie Murphy (1884)	4-6	.400
Baltimore	John Seery (1884)	.309	Bill Sweeney (1884)	40-21	.656
Boston	Ed Crane (1884)	.304	Dupee Shaw (1884)	22-15	.595
Chicago	Lew Shoenick (1884)	.315	One-Arm Daly (1884)	22-25	.468
Cincinnati	Dick Burns (1884)	.315	Jim McCormick (1884)	22-4	.846
Kansas City	Jack Gorman (1884)	.275	Ernest Hickman (1884)	3-13	.188
Keystone	Bill Hoover (1884)	.355	Enoch Bakely (1884)	14-24	.368
Milwaukee	Al Myers (1884)	.326	Ed Cushman (1884)	4-0	1.000
Pittsburgh	Lew Shoenick (1884)	.276	One-Arm Daly (1884)	5-4	.556
St. Louis	Fred Dunlap (1884)	.420	Charles Hodnet (1884)	12-1	.923
			Bill Taylor (1884)	24-2	.923
St. Paul	Jimmy Brown (1884)	.313	Bill O'Brien (1884)	1-1	.500
Washington	Harry Moore (1884)	.337	Charles Gagus (1884)	11-9	.550
Wilmington	Tom Lynch (1884)	.281	Dan Casey (1884)	1-1	.500

VII SPECIAL RECORDS

VANDY'S DOUBLE NO-HITTER

In 1938 a 23-year-old Cincinnati lefthander put together baseball's most unusual pitching feat—no-hit, no-run games back-to-back.

Johnny Vander Meer earned the distinction of being called "Double No-Hitter" by pitching 18 consecutive hitless inning in two complete games, perhaps the most phenomenal of all single season pitching records.

Vandy was in his second season in the National League when lightning struck twice for him. It started on June 11 at Cincinnati where the southpaw whipped the Boston Bees, 3-0. Losing pitcher Danny MacFayden allowed only six hits but gave up a run in the fourth inning and a one-on home run to Ernie Lombardi in the sixth. Vandy's initial no-hitter was fashioned in one hour and 48 minutes, and only his three passes prevented a perfect performance.

On June 15, four days after he became a national figure, Vandy turned in his second successive no-hit, no-run job under more dramatic circumstances. The game marked the first night contest at Brooklyn's Ebbets Field and a capacity crowd watched the Reds' lefty blank the Dodgers, 6-0. Losing pitcher Max Butcher, Tot Pressnell, Luke Hamlin and Vito Tamulis were the Brooklyn hurlers but the center of attraction was the visitors' moundsman.

Four runs in the third inning all but assured Cincinnati of victory but the fans stayed to watch Vander Meer's bid for his double no-hitter. When he recorded the 27th out—his 54th straight without a hit—he had established a personal pitching record which may never be equaled in baseball history.

GIANTS' RECORD STREAKS

The New York Giants of 1916 ran off a remarkable winning streak of 26 games, modern baseball's longest victory string. However, unlike other teams which used long winning runs to make their push for a pennant a bit easier, the Giants of that year finished no higher than fourth.

The streaky Giants actually played that 1916 season in two parts: the first one being another victory string of 17 straight, the second a run of 26. Of the 86 games won by the New Yorkers that season, 43 were accomplished in unusual fashion. The 17 straight victories were all made while the Giants were the visiting club; the streak of 26 was compiled in the last month of the season, all at the Polo Grounds, home grounds for the Giants.

Here are the dates and scores of the two streaks:

ABROAD (17 straight)

May 9: 13—Pittsburgh 5.
May 10: 7—Pittsburgh 1.
May 11: 3—Pittsburgh 2.
May 12: 3—Pittsburgh 2.
May 14: 6—Chicago 4.
May 15: 3—Chicago 2.
May 17: 9—St. Louis 3.
May 18: 3—St. Louis 0.
May 19: 5—St. Louis 4.
May 20: 4—St. Louis 1.
May 21: 11—Cincinnati 1.
May 23: 4—Cincinnati 3.
May 24: 6—Cincinnati 1.
May 26: 12—Boston 1.
May 27: 4—Boston 3.
May 27: 2—Boston 1.
May 29: 3—Boston 0.

HOME (26 straight)

September 7: 4—Brooklyn 1.
September 8: 9—Philadelphia 3.
September 9: 3—Philadelphia 1.
September 9: 3—Philadelphia 0.
September 10: 9—Philadelphia 4.
September 12: 3—Cincinnati 2.
September 13: 3—Cincinnati 0.
September 13: 6—Cincinnati 4.
September 14: 3—Cincinnati 1.
September 16: 8—Pittsburgh 2.
September 16: 4—Pittsburgh 3.
September 18: 2—Pittsburgh 0.
September 18: 1—Pittsburgh 1 (tie)
September 19: 9—Pittsburgh 2.
September 19: 5—Pittsburgh 1.
September 20: 4—Chicago 2.
September 21: 4—Chicago 0.
September 22: 5—Chicago 0.
September 23: 6—St. Louis 1.
September 23: 3—St. Louis 0.
September 25: 1—St. Louis 0.
September 25: 6—St. Louis 2.
September 26: 6—St. Louis 1.
September 27: 3—St. Louis 2.
September 28: 2—Boston 0.
September 28: 6—Boston 0.
September 30: 4—Boston 0.

DIMAGGIO'S 56

Baseball's most amazing single season hitting streak is the one performed by Joe DiMaggio in 1941 when he hit safely in 56 straight games. The graceful New York Yankee outfielder started his incredible string on May 15 and continued it through July 16, a two-month period during which he hit for a .408 average.

On his way to this all-time standard DiMag early passed the National League mark of 33 made by Rogers Hornsby and eclipsed the then existing American League record of 41 set by George Sisler. Three games later, the previous record run of 44 established by Willie Keeler in 1897 was by the boards.

Here is the statistical story of the DiMaggio streak, from start to finish:

Date	Club—Pitchers	AB	R	H	2B	3B	HR	RBI
May 15	Chi—Smith	4	—	1	—	-	—	1
16	Chi—Lee	4	2	2	—	1	1	1
17	Chi—Rigney	3	1	1	—	-	—	—
18	St. L—Harris (2 hits), Niggeling (1)	3	3	3	1	-	—	1
19	St. L—Galehouse	3	—	1	1	-	—	—
20	St. L—Auker	5	1	1	—	-	—	1
21	Det—Rowe (1), Benton (1)	5	—	2	—	-	—	1
22	Det—McKain	4	—	1	—	-	—	1
23	Bos—Newsom	5	—	1	—	-	—	2
24	Bos—Johnson	4	2	1	—	-	—	2
25	Bos—Grove	4	—	1	—	-	—	—
27	Was—Chase (1), Anderson (2), Carrasquel (1)	5	3	4	—	-	1	3
(Night) 28	Was—Hudson	4	1	1	—	1	—	—
29	Was—Sundra	3	1	1	—	-	—	—
30	Bos—Johnson	2	1	1	—	-	—	—
30	Bos—Harris	3	—	1	1	-	—	—
June 1	Cle—Milnar	4	1	1	—	-	—	—
1	Cle—Harder	4	—	1	—	-	—	—
2	Cle—Feller	4	2	2	1	-	—	—
3	Det—Trout	4	1	1	—	-	1	1
5	Det—Newhouser	5	1	1	—	1	—	1
7	St. L—Muncrief (1), Allen (1), Caster (1)	5	2	3	—	-	—	1
8	St. L—Auker	4	3	2	—	-	2	4
8	St. L—Caster (1), Kramer (1)	4	1	2	1	-	1	3
10	Chi—Rigney	5	1	1	—	-	—	—
(Night) 12	Chi—Lee	4	1	2	—	-	1	1
14	Cle—Feller	2	—	1	1	-	—	1
15	Cle—Bagby	3	1	1	—	-	1	1
16	Cle—Milnar	5	—	1	1	-	—	—
17	Chi—Rigney	4	1	1	—	-	—	—
18	Chi—Lee	3	—	1	—	-	—	—
19	Chi—Smith (1), Ross (2)	3	2	3	—	-	1	2
20	Det—Newsom (2), McKain (2)	5	3	4	1	-	—	1
21	Det—Trout	4	—	1	—	-	—	1
22	Det—Newhouser (1), Newsom (1)	5	1	2	1	-	1	2
24	St. L—Muncrief	4	1	1	—	-	—	—
25	St. L—Galehouse	4	1	1	—	-	1	3
26	St. L—Auker	4	—	1	1	-	—	1
27	Phi—Dean	3	1	2	—	-	1	2
28	Phi—Babich (1), Harris (1)	5	1	2	1	-	—	—
29	Was—Leonard	4	1	1	1	-	—	—
29	Was—Anderson	5	1	1	—	-	—	1
July 1	Bos—Harris (1), Ryba (1)	4	—	2	—	-	—	1
1	Bos—Wilson	3	1	1	—	-	—	1
2	Bos—Newsom	5	1	1	—	-	1	3
5	Phi—Marchildon	4	2	1	—	-	1	2
6	Phi—Babich (1), Hadley (3)	5	2	4	1	-	—	2
6	Phi—Knott	4	—	2	—	1	—	2
(Night) 10	St. L—Niggeling	2	—	1	—	-	—	—
11	St. L—Harris (3), Kramer (1)	5	1	4	—	-	1	2
12	St. L—Auker (1), Muncrief (1)	5	1	2	1	-	—	1
13	Chi—Lyons (2), Hallett (1)	4	2	3	—	-	—	—
13	Chi—Lee	4	—	1	—	-	—	—
14	Chi—Rigney	3	—	1	—	-	—	—
15	Chi—Smith	4	1	2	1	-	—	2
16	Cle—Milnar (2), Krakauskas (1)	4	3	3	1	-	—	—
	Totals for 56 games	223	56	91	16	4	15	55

Streak stopped in Cleveland night game, July 17, by Smith and Bagby. Batting average for this streak, .408.

Numbers in parenthesis indicate number of hits off each pitcher if there was more than one in game.

RUTH'S 60

Quick, now! Which is baseball's most remembered number? Why 60, of course, the total number of home runs hit by Babe Ruth in 1927.

It's true that when Ruth reached the magic figure of 60 in 1927 a ball which bounced from the field into the stands was scored as a home run. Under today's rules, this is scored as a two base hit. However, those fortunate enough to see Ruth in all his majesty cannot recall when any of the home runs he drove in his record-making year first struck the playing field before bouncing into the stands.

The Babe, who was the creator of all the home run standards in the ledgers of baseball, hit his 60th homer in the last game of the season. Previous record-holder? Babe Ruth, with 59 in 1921.

The Significant Sixty smashed by Ruth, only 28 of which were hit at his home grounds, the Yankee Stadium.

HR No.	Game No.	Date	Opposing Pitcher and Club	Where Made
		April		
1.	4	15	Ehmke, (R), Phi	N.Y.
2.	11	23	Walberg, (L), Phi	Phi.
3.	12	24	Thurston, (R), Was	Was.
4.	14	29	Harriss, (R), Bos	Bos.
		May		
5.	16	1	Quinn, (R), Phi	N.Y.
6.	16	1	Walberg, (L), Phi	N.Y.
7.	24	10	Gaston, (R), St. L	St.L.
8.	25	11	Nevers, (R), St.L	St.L.
9.	29	17	Collins, (R), Det.	Det.
10.	33	22	Karr, (R), Cle	Cle.
11.	34	23	Thurston, (R), Was	Was.
12.	37	28	Thurston, (R), Was	N.Y.
13.	39	29	MacFayden, (R), Bos	N.Y.
14.	41	30	Walberg, (L), Phi	Phi.
15.	42	31	Ehmke,.(R), Phi	Phi.
16.	43	31	Quinn, (R), Phi	Phi.
		June		
17.	47	5	Whitehill, (L), Det	N.Y.
18.	48	7	Thomas, (R), Chi	N.Y.
19.	52	11	Buckeye, (L), Cle	N.Y.
20.	52	11	Buckeye, (L), Cle	N.Y.
21.	53	12	Uhle, (R), Cle	N.Y.
22.	55	16	Zachary, (L), St.L	N.Y.
23.	60	22	Wiltse, (L), Bos	Bos.
24.	60	22	Wiltse, (L), Bos	Bos.
25.	70	30	Harriss, (R), Bos	N.Y.
		July		
26.	73	3	Lisenbee, (R), Was	Was.
27.	78	8	Whitehill, (L), Det	Det.
28.	79	9	Holloway, (R), Det	Det.
29.	79	9	Holloway, (R), Det	Det.
30.	83	12	Shaute, (L), Cle	Cle.
31.	94	24	Thomas, (R), Chi	Chi.
32.	95	26	Gaston, (R), St. L.	N.Y.
33.	95	26	Gaston, (R), St. L.	N.Y.
34.	98	28	Stewart, (L), St. L	N.Y.
		August		
35.	106	5	G. Smith, (R), Det	N.Y.
36.	110	10	Zachary, (L), Was	Was.
37.	114	16	Thomas, (R), Chi	Chi.
38.	115	17	Connally, (R), Chi.	Chi.
39.	118	20	Miller, (L), Cle	Cle.
40.	120	22	Shaute, (L), Cle	Cle.
41.	124	27	Nevers, (R), St. L.	St.L.
42.	125	28	Wingard, (L), St. L	St.L.
43.	127	31	Welzer, (R), Bos	N.Y.
		September		
44.	128	2	Walberg, (L), Phi	Phi.
45.	132	6	Welzer, (R), Bos	Bos.
46.	132	6	Welzer, (R), Bos	Bos.
47.	133	6	Russell, (R), Bos	Bos.
48.	134	7	MacFayden, (R), Bos.	Bos.
49.	134	7	Harriss, (R), Bos	Bos.
50.	138	11	Gaston, (R), St. L.	N.Y.
51.	139	13	Hudlin, (R), Cle	N.Y.
52.	140	13	Shaute, (L), Cle	N.Y.
53.	143	16	Blankenship, (R), Chi	N.Y.
54.	147	18	Lyons, (R)	N.Y.
55.	148	21	Gibson, (R), Det.	N.Y.
56.	149	22	Holloway, (R), Det	N.Y.
57.	152	27	Grove, (L), Phi	N.Y.
58.	153	29	Lisenbee, (R), Was	N.Y.
59.	153	29	Hopkins, (R), Was	N.Y.
60.	154	30	Zachary, (L), Was	N.Y.

MARIS' 61 Ever since Babe Ruth hit his 60 home runs in 1927 fans have argued about the chances of his record being broken. These arguments were revived in 1930 when Hack Wilson of the Chicago Cubs walloped 56, and again in 1932 and 1938 when first Jimmy Foxx and then Hammerin' Hank Greenberg smacked 58. It took an elongated season of 162 games and Roger Maris' booming bat to best the Babe's record. Like the Babe, Roger socked his record-breaking homer in the last game of the season. Maris, however, hit 30 homers at the Yankee Stadium whereas Babe hit only 28 on his home grounds.

HR No.	Game No.	Date	Opposing Pitcher and Club	Where Made
		April		
1.	10	26	Foytack, (R), Det	Det.
		May		
2.	16	3	Ramos, (R), Min.	Min.
3.	19	6	Grba, (R), L.A.	L.A.
4.	28	17	Burnside (L), Was	N.Y.
5.	29	19	Perry (R), Cle	Cle.
6.	30	20	Bell, (R), Cle	Cle.
7.	31	21	Estrada, (R), Bal	N.Y.
8.	34	24	Conley (R), Bos	N.Y.
9.	37	28	McLish, (R), Chi	N.Y.
10.	39	30	Conley (R), Bos	Bos.
11.	39	30	Fornieles (R), Bos	Bos.
12.	40	31	Muffett (R), Bos	Bos.
		June		
13.	42	2	McLish (R), Chi	Chi.
14.	43	3	Shaw (R), Chi	Chi.
15.	44	4	Kemmerer (R), Chi.	Chi.
16.	47	6	Palmquist, (R), Min	N.Y.
17.	48	7	Ramos, (R), Min.	N.Y.
18.	51	9	Herbert, (R), K.C	N.Y.
19.	54	11	Grba, (R), L.A.	N.Y.
20.	54	11	James, (R), L.A.	N.Y.
21.	56	13	Perry, (R), Cle	Cle.
22.	57	14	Bell, (R), Cle	Cle.
23.	60	17	Mossi, (L), Det	Det.
24.	61	18	Casale, (R), Det	Det.
25.	62	19	Archer, (L), K.C	K.C.
26.	63	20	Nuxhall, (L), K.C	K.C.
27.	65	22	Bass, (R), K.C	K.C.
		July		
28.	73	1	Sisler, (R), Was	N.Y.
29.	74	2	Burnside, (L), Was	N.Y.
30.	74	2	Klippstein, (R), Was	N.Y.
31.	76	4	Lary, (R), Det	N.Y.
32.	77	5	Funk, (R), Cle	N.Y.
33.	81	9	Monbouquette, (R), Bos	N.Y.
34.	83	13	Wynn, (R), Chi.	Chi.
		July		
35.	85	15	Herbert, (R), Chi	Chi.
36.	91	21	Monbouquette, (R), Bos.	Bos.
37.	94	25	Baumann, (L), Chi	N.Y.
38.	94	25	Larsen, (R), Chi.	N.Y.
39.	95	25	Kemmerer, (R), Chi	N.Y.
40.	95	25	Hacker, (R), Chi.	N.Y.
		August		
41.	105	4	Pascual, (R), Min.	N.Y.
42.	113	11	Burnside, (L), Was	Was.
43.	114	12	Donovan, (R), Was	Was.
44.	115	13	Daniels, (R), Was	Was.
45.	116	13	Kutyna, (R), Was	Was.
46.	117	15	Pizarro, (L), Chi	N.Y.
47.	118	16	Pierce, (L), Chi.	N.Y.
48.	118	16	Pierce, (L), Chi.	N.Y.
49.	122	20	Perry, (R), Cle	Cle.
50.	124	22	McBride, (R), L.A	L.A.
51.	128	26	Walker, (R), K.C	K.C.
		September		
52.	134	2	Lary, (R), Det	N.Y.
53.	134	2	Aguirre, (L), Det	N.Y.
54.	139	6	Cheney, (R), Was	N.Y.
55.	140	7	Stigman, (L), Cle	N.Y.
56.	142	9	Grant, (R), Cle.	N.Y.
57.	150	16	Lary, (R), Det	Det.
58.	151	17	Fox, (R), Det	Det.
59.	154	20	Pappas, (R), Bal.	Bal.
60.	158	26	Fisher, (R), Bal	N.Y.
		October		
61.	162	1	Stallard, (R), Bos	N.Y.

19 STRAIGHT WINS

Two more remarkable pitching performances were those recorded by two New York Giants under different pitching standards. Tim Keefe and Rube Marquard each pitched 19 straight victories, Keefe's coming in 1888 when the pitching distance to the plate was a mere 50 feet. Lefthander Marquard managed his record in 1912 under present day pitching requirements.

The victory-by-victory tables of baseball's best season winning streaks:

TIM KEEFE, NEW YORK, N. L., 1888

50 feet; $5\frac{1}{2} \times 4$ Box. High or Low Ball abolished.

DATE	OPPOSING CLUB	DATE	OPPOSING CLUB
June 23 -- Keefe, 7;	Philadelphia, 6	July 20 -- Keefe, 7;	Philadelphia, 6
June 26 -- Keefe, 4;	Philadelphia, 1	July 23 -- Keefe, 2;	Boston, 0
June 29 -- Keefe, 8;	Washington, 3	July 25 -- Keefe, 5;	Boston, 1
July 2 -- Keefe, 6;	Washington, 2	July 28 -- Keefe, 4;	Philadelphia, 2
July 4 -- Keefe, 4;	Detroit, 1	Aug. 1 -- Keefe, 5;	Washington, 4
July 7 -- Keefe, 6;	Pittsburgh, 4	Aug. 3 -- Keefe, 9;	Boston, 6
July 11 -- Keefe, 5;	Indianapolis, 2	Aug. 6 -- Keefe, 3;	Indianapolis, 2
July 13 -- Keefe, 4;	Indianapolis, 0	Aug. 8 -- Keefe, 4;	Indianapolis, 1
July 16 -- Keefe, 12;	Chicago, 4	Aug. 10 -- Keefe, 2;	Pittsburgh, 1
July 17 -- Keefe, 7;	Chicago, 4		

RUBE MARQUARD, NEW YORK, N. L., 1912

60 feet, 5 inches: 24-inch Slab; One Step.

DATE	OPPOSING CLUB	DATE	OPPOSING CLUB
April 11 -- Marquard, 18;	Brooklyn, 3	June 3 -- Marquard, 8;	St. Louis, 3
April 16 -- Marquard, 8;	Boston, 2	June 8 -- Marquard, 6;	Cincinnati, 2
April 24 -- Marquard, 11;	Philadelphia, 4	June 12 -- Marquard, 3;	Chicago, 2
May 1 -- Marquard, 11;	Philadelphia, 4	June 17 -- Marquard, 5;	Pittsburgh, 4
May 7 -- Marquard, 6;	St. Louis, 2	June 19 -- Marquard, 6;	Boston, 5
May 11 -- Marquard, 10;	Chicago, 3	June 21 -- Marquard, 5;	Boston, 2
May 16 -- Marquard, 4;	Pittsburgh, 1	June 25 -- Marquard, 2;	Philadelphia, 1
May 20 -- Marquard, 3;	Cincinnati, 0	June 29 -- Marquard, 8;	Boston, 6
May 24 -- Marquard, 6;	Brooklyn, 3	July 3 — Marquard, 2;	Brooklyn, 1
May 30 -- Marquard, 7;	Philadelphia, 1		

VIII HONORED PLAYERS

HALL OF FAME

Baseball has produced giants in all departments of play since the National Association was born in 1871, and it was inevitable that the deeds of these greats would someday be enshrined in a permanent vault which would make imperishable their all-time credentials.

Thirty-two years before the National Baseball Hall of Fame was established in Cooperstown, New York, on June 12, 1939 the administrators of baseball had set into motion the machinery which was to result in the recognition of this small central New York State village as the cradle of the game.

A special investigating committee appointed by Albert G. Spalding was entrusted with the historical task of discovering the original spot on which baseball was played in America. This committee, headed by A. G. Mills, a former National League president, reported on December 30, 1907 that "the first scheme for playing baseball, according to best obtainable evidence, was devised by Abner Doubleday at Cooperstown, New York, in 1839."

No committee was ever so far from the facts. Doubleday, who may have played at some form of baseball, and in the very village which borders picturesque Lake Otsego, was a student at West Point in the very year he was supposed to have "devised his scheme." Evidently Mills and his committee never bothered to investigate the authenticity of a report which in later years was proved to be without any circumstantial foundation by recognized historians.

But baseball deserves a shrine, and since the natives of Cooperstown have provided a mecca worthy of the pastime just where and when the game was started no longer is an issue of bitter and major controversy. Now at last the game was granted its own permanent museum and display case and dedication came on June 12, 1939. The Museum, Hall of Fame and Doubleday Field, which used to be Farmer Phinney's pasture when Doubleday, later to become a Union Major General in the Civil War, romped as a schoolboy, were all officially launched in impressive ceremonies, the most dramatic of which was the spectacle of the game's greatest heroes taking their appointed places with immortality.

In the National Baseball Museum is housed the world's most complete collection of the game's memorabilia: the largest baseball library in the world; priceless relics such as the first catcher's mitt and the bat with which Ruth clouted his 60th homer in 1927; sculptures, paintings, photographs and drawings that form a classic and graphic history of the colorful long-ago.

Enshrined in The Hall of Fame wing of the Museum are the bronze plaques of the pastime's immortals, placed there by a vote of outstanding experts who have been selected to choose the greats of the diamond. The method of selection is simple: A special committee of baseball officials, picked because of their deep knowledge and service to the game, is entrusted with the honor of choosing players who performed more than a quarter of century ago. All players whose careers began 30 years before and ended five years prior to the election are eligible to gain entrance into the Hall of Fame by a ballot system. Only members of the Baseball Writers' Association of America for at least ten years are eligible to vote, and the successful player must receive at least 75 percent of all votes cast to gain admission.

Since the first group was chosen in 1936 the annual balloting system has been frequently under attack by those who claim sectional and personal favoritism occasionally is the basis for a writer's ballot. However few will deny the qualities of the giants who have been so honored. Their selection has met with an almost unanimous approval from the fans.

A special committee also votes on candidates for Veterans Hall of Fame plaque awards. To be eligible for admission an oldtime player must be retired for at least 30 years prior to election; managers and umpires, retired from their capacities for at least five years, are also eligible.

THE SELECT FIVE

To start its huge family in 1936 the baseball writers of that era chose five players whose performances have stamped them as the greatest of them all by more people than any others. The Select Five to acquire more than 75 percent on the first balloting for Hall of Fame entrance consisted of Ty Cobb, Babe Ruth, Christy Mathewson, Honus Wagner and Walter Johnson, all selected in that order.

It's only fitting that the man to establish more records than any other spiked hero would receive the greatest number of votes. That would be Cobb, the Georgia Peach, son of an educator, who in 24 years in the American League played 3,033 games as if each one was the final clash of a World Series.

What qualities did Cobb possess which made him the first of a heroic group? What abilities did this comet from the South bring to the diamond which enabled him to create records which will forever withstand assault?

TY COBB

First, and always, in the trigger-mind of Cobb was the idea that in competition there must be a loser, and he wanted to be in that role as seldom as possible. Cobb made himself learn to beat his opponent through the simple method of studying his every move and habit. He punished himself to the point of perfection, creating new tricks and ideas which would always keep him far removed, and above, from the rest. He knew the habits of every player he faced, their weaknesses and strengths, and he learned to strike at their most vulnerable points with a fiery spirit, constant study and an unquenchable desire for victory. His education paid off handsomely. He stole 892 bases, compiled 4,191 hits, scored 2,244 runs and amassed a batting average of .367—the most imposing individual lifetime marks ever established in the majors.

Cobb just didn't play at baseball, he lived it—on and off the field. For 12 seasons he paced the league in batting, nine of them in a row. He batted .400 or better three times, and belted .420 in 1911 and .410 the following season.

A lefthanded hitter who gripped his bat with his left hand four inches above his right, Cobb subscribed to the theory that this was the best method with which to strike at a pitched ball. Although the unorthodox grip nullified some of his power, Ty could belt them long when the situation called for it. However, he proved that this grip was adaptable to the drag bunt, at which he was a master, and perfect to pull a pitch to right field, slice it to left or smash straight through the middle of the diamond.

A centerfielder by choice Ty also played the other outfield positions, filled in at second and first base and even pitched. For 24 years he was baseball's dominant figure, the scourge of rival pitchers and opponents' stratagems. Just once did he fail to reach the .300 level—in his freshman season in 1905 when he was an 18-year-old stripling.

Ty was the game's fiercest competitor. He baited rivals, umpires and teammates—but always for a purpose. He claimed, and the records bear him out, that all of this was calculated psychology designed to upset the opposition and inspire his teammates. Cobb's methods must have been successful, his name leads all others in the Hall of Fame.

Cobb helped the Tigers to three pennants; he managed Detroit from 1921 to 1926 and closed out his career with the Philadelphia Athletics, batting .323 in his final season when he was 41 years old. He was truly the game's most dynamic competitor.

BABE RUTH

If Ty Cobb was the most dynamic figure in the history of baseball then George Herman Ruth must have been the most fabulous.

Babe Ruth, a snub-nosed, moon-faced man captured the imagination of a nation with a mincing walk, a pair of pipe-stem legs and the most explosive bat ever carried. For 20 years he held the interest of millions merely by swinging a 42-ounce bat which propelled 714 home runs, more than any player in history.

No other sports figure fired the emotion as did the Babe. Whatever he did—slam a home run or strike out—was accomplished with dramatic overtones. He was a giant of a figure who did everything with gargantuan effects.

Ruth's early boyhood was passed in a Baltimore orphanage while his father eked out a livelihood as a bartender in one of the city's less swanky districts. It was in such a setting that one of America's most legendary sports figures began an education which would elevate him to a position befitting presidents, kings and emperors.

It was as a pitcher that Ruth started his diamond career, and in that role he made his first entrance into the record books. The Boston Red Sox purchased his contract from the Baltimore Orioles of the International League and baseball's most amazing Odyssey was about to be written.

Babe became an outstanding hurler with the Sox, leading the league on two occasions in earned run averages. He also established a World Series record for consecutive scoreless innings by stringing together 29 in the 1916 and 1918 classics. Ruth was quite a pitcher but he was already evidencing prowess at the plate and his manager, Ed Barrow, decided that Ruth as an everyday performer would be more valuable than as an occasional pitcher.

In 1919, playing the outfield when he wasn't occupied on the mound, Ruth shattered all previous home run marks with an insignificant total of 29. The following winter he was sold to the New York Yankees in baseball's biggest deal, the Red Sox receiving $125,000 for their slugging pitcher-outfielder, and an additional $350,000 loan to pay off debts. Ruth's pitching days were now at an end, except for an occasional chore at season's end.

Recognizing the gate attraction of the Bambino's homeric slams, the magnates quickly agreed to introduce the lively ball. It brought fame and fortune to Ruth who crashed 59 homers in 1921 and bettered this standard with an output of 60 in 1927.

His booming bat brought showmanship and busy turnstiles to the game and helped the Yankees erect the Yankee Stadium in 1923, referred to as The House That Ruth Built. The Babe was baseball and he demanded, and received, top dollar for his achievements which included record salaries of

$85,000 in 1930 and 1931, years which will be recalled as the peak of a severe depression.

Ruth was more than just a home run slugger. It was said that he never made a bad play. As a pitcher, he constantly kept the hitters guessing; as an outfielder, he was invariably in the proper position and runners seldom dared to take liberties with one of the game's most powerful and accurate throwing arms; as a base runner, he knew exactly when to try for an extra base.

The Babe retired in 1935 but, like the true showman, reserved one of his most spectacular hitting performances for his last appearance. He slammed three homers in this farewell to baseball at Pittsburgh's spacious Forbes Field, one of which is still regarded as the longest blow ever struck in that city. So closed 22 years by the game's greatest power hitter.

Everything the Babe did was majestic. He commanded the largest tax-free baseball salary, hit the most homers, drew the biggest fine ($5,000) and brought baseball its most lush period. Even in death the Bambino played to an SRO crowd. Thousands filed past to view the idol of millions as his body lay in kingly state in, appropriately enough, The House that He Had Built.

There will always be controversy as to who was better, Cobb or Ruth. Each was superb in his field—Cobb for hitting and base running and aggressive play, Ruth for power, pitching and crowd appeal.

CHRISTY MATHEWSON

Perhaps the first prototype of the All-American boy to enter the majors was Christopher Mathewson, Bucknell University football hero who pitched 373 victories in the National League from 1900 to 1916, a 20th century all-time yearly high average of 23 triumphs.

Matty was cut from a slightly different mold than most of the players of his era and this quality plus his amazing World Series performance in 1905 was to make him the idol of the sports world. Although a member of the New York Giants, one of baseball's most truculent teams of the time, Matty managed to remain above the rest of a hurly-burly cast. His gentle manner and casual aloofness stamped him as an individual who definitely didn't fit in with the pattern of his era.

Mathewson was a model of perfection in all departments. He was more than a pitcher, and frequently served as a fill-in in the outfield and first base replacement, and occasionally was called upon as a pinch-hitter. But Matty was essentially a pitcher, perhaps the finest in the modern annals of the National League and certainly a champion performer in crucial contests.

Perhaps his most sensational stint was the World Series of 1905 when he hurled three victories, all shutouts. He helped the Giants defeat the Philadelphia Athletics by yielding a total of 14 hits in his three shutout triumphs, an unparalleled performance. This was Matty's greatest pitching hour.

Before he concluded his career as manager of the Cincinnati Reds, Matty was to win 30 or more games for three seasons and 20 or more for 12 straight years. He was the greatest exponent of control in the game, and in 1908 walked but 42 batters in 416 innings with a pitch known as the fadeaway. today's version of the screwball. He didn't require the normal four days' rest between assignments and was always ready to pitch an important contest.

Matty was anathema to most of the hitters in the league, but to the weak-hitting Joe Tinker he was just another pitcher. It was the Chicago shortstop who assaulted Matty for the game-winning blows in the memorable 1908 "playoff" contest which gave the pennant to the Cubs.

The loosely-written amateur rules of Matty's day enabled him to embark on a major league career almost immediately after leaving college. While at Bucknell he pitched in the New England League, and was soon moved to the Virginia League where he won 21 games for Norfolk. This earned him a chance with the Giants in 1900 but, after losing three games, he was sent back to the minors. Cincinnati drafted him for the 1901 season, but traded him to the Giants before the opening game. Matty's freshman year was a success and he won 20 games, one of which was a no-hitter. He was to lead New York to four pennants and strike out 2,499, an all-time league standard, in 17 seasons.

Big Six, as he was called, after a famous New York fire engine, had his career—and life—curtailed as a result of World War I. He was gassed while on active duty and fought a losing battle with tuberculosis. When he died in 1925, Matty was president of the Boston Braves.

Beneath the centerfield stands of New York's Polo Grounds a bronze tablet was erected to the memory of Christopher Mathewson. The walk which leads to the campus of Bucknell University also reveres Matty's memory. Baseball, too, hasn't forgotten --and justifiably so. Matty was touched with immortality, enough of it to qualify for The Select Five.

HONUS WAGNER

John McGraw, the famed New York Giant manager, and Ed Barrow, who helped create the New York Yankee dynasty, were regarded as the shrewdest judges of diamond talent of their day. Whenever they were asked to name the best all-around player either ever saw, the answer would always be the same: Honus Wagner.

John Peter Wagner was more than a myth, he was baseball's best shortstop, his league's best hitter, one of its fleetest runners and his league's top record maker. An ungainly man who carried most of his 200 pounds on a ponderous chest and in his gorilla-like arms, Wagner had sheer power and an eagerness for competition which clearly placed him in a class by himself.

His brute strength also lay in a huge pair of hands which were as deft and certain as any that ever pounced on a ground ball. Wagner just didn't scoop up ground balls, he excavated them, digging up large portions of loose dirt and stones. His throws were swift and powerful, and somehow the first baseman could always pluck the ball from the hail of debris aimed at him by Wagner. Very few hits skipped by Honus, and very few runners took their time getting down to first base when he cocked his muscular arm to throw.

Honus' first hero was his brother Al who was something of a semipro star, but it was young John who got to the majors first. However, Honus couldn't quite make up his mind as to whether he was a pitcher, outfielder or infielder, and it wasn't until 1901, his fifth National League season, that he was shifted to shortstop on a permanent basis. It didn't make too much difference where he played, as long as he was allowed to get up to the plate. Honus was at home immediately in his freshman year at Louisville where he carved out a .344 figure. He was to hit better than .300 for the next 16 seasons, play every position but catcher, and finish a brilliant 21-year career with a .329 lifetime average, most of it compiled against a ball as lively as a spool of cotton. After three seasons at Louisville, Wagner was to spend the rest of a remarkable span in Pittsburgh.

Ed Barrow was chiefly responsible for getting Honus started on his baseball career, but only because Ed was out scouting brother Al. Barrow was told he could find the elder Wagner around the railroad tracks outside of Mansfield, Ohio, "throwing stones." So Barrow headed for the tracks. A bowlegged, broad-shouldered youngster was tossing stones faster—and farther—than the others and Barrow was immediately impressed by the boy's marksmanship and strength. It was the wrong Wagner, but Barrow made no mistake. Two seasons of minor league ball and the Flying Dutchman was ready for a career which would see him lead the league eight times in batting, appear in 2,785 games, get 3,430 hits and establish all-time marks for the greatest number of doubles and triples, records second only to those set by the maker of marks, Ty Cobb.

In death as in the record-making department, Wagner has proved to be second best and about as imperishable. Matty, Walter Johnson and Babe Ruth preceded the Flying Dutchman to Valhalla. Cobb remained the last stubborn holdout to the inevitable.

WALTER JOHNSON

Of all the nicknames bestowed upon ball players since Adrian Constantine (Cap) Anson came down the pike, perhaps none was more appropriate than the tag placed on Walter Perry (Barney) Johnson. The Big Train he was called, and he was the fastest express of them all.

Johnson was a man, and a pitcher, completely without guile. Born on a farm in Humboldt, Kansas, he never attempted to act the part of a sophisticated cavalier. On the mound, he remained in character. Speed was his forte, and he never resorted to other artful devices to deceive the batter. Johnson was completely honest at all times—a simple, sincere man; a pitcher of enormous strength who made the ball whistle past the plate like bird shot. It is said that his announced appearance on the mound created more sick cases than the common cold, batters suddenly becoming indisposed when Johnson began his pregame warmup session. But he never took advantage of his exalted position, and none who ever batted against him can recall Johnson deliberately using his tremendous speed to drive batters away from the plate.

From the day he began a fabled career with Washington in 1907, until 1927, when he pitched the last of his 414 victories for the Senators, Walter wasn't heavily blessed with diamond fortune. During his finest years when his arm was strong and his fast ball resembled a blue darter, Washington bore slight resemblance to a baseball team. But in the mid-twenties, when the Senators were chronic challengers and two-time pennant winners, The Big Train was about to be shunted on to a siding.

Johnson's total victories are more than any ever put together in the modern era. His strikeouts (3,497), innings pitched (5,925), complete games (531) and shutouts (113) are other all-time modern marks which are far beyond the grasp of any current competitor. And all of these incredible figures were achieved while he was surrounded by mediocrity and lack of talent. Yet Barney never complained of his lot. He was happy in Washington, and Washington was more than pleased with Walter.

Johnson may never have scaled the peak of pitching pinnacles if it wasn't for the persistence of a cigar salesman who saw him pitch a semipro game in 1906 in Weiser, Idaho. The salesman saw in Walter a potential star, but Joe Cantillon, Washington manager, paid no heed when the salesman wrote him of his Idaho discovery. More letters came to Cantillon, so detailed, that Cantillon no longer could ignore them. Finally Cantillon dispatched an aide to look over Johnson, who reported that everything the salesman said was true.

After three mediocre seasons, Johnson finally caught fire, but not before he blanked the New York Highlanders three times in four days in 1908. Walter's first big season was 1910 when he won 25 games; he was to win 20 or more 11 more times, and twice went over the 30-won mark. During this span he averaged fewer than 2.00 earned runs per season 6 times; won 16 straight in 1912; 14 straight in 1913 and 13 in 1914. In 1913 he pitched 56 consecutive scoreless innings, another all-time statistic.

Walter, so rich in talent as a pitcher, closed his major league career as an unsuccessful manager. He led his beloved Senators from 1929 through '32 and piloted Cleveland from 1933 to '35. However, these lack-lustre campaigns as a field leader never dulled his brilliant playing record, the finest ever assembled by a pitcher, after the turn of the century.

Gentle in spirit, indomitable in competition, Walter Perry Johnson made baseball much richer by his performances.

HALL OF FAME MEMBERS

Pilgrimages to Cooperstown always reach the Hall of Fame wing of the Museum. Here are enshrined the real immortals of the game, titans all. With an eminently qualified Hall of Fame Committee selecting a core of oldtimers, and baseball writers of at least 10 years' standing choosing the modern players (by 75% vote), a true cross-section of the sport's greats has been elected. Plaques with suitable inscriptions hang in the Hall of Fame honoring the following:

Members	Year Elected	Members	Year Elected
GROVER CLEVELAND ALEXANDER	1938	CARL HUBBELL	1947
ADRIAN CONSTANTINE ANSON	1939	HUGHIE JENNINGS	1945
J. FRANKLIN (HOME RUN) BAKER	**1955**	BYRON BANCROFT JOHNSON	1937
EDWARD G. BARROW	**1953**	WALTER PERRY JOHNSON	1936
CHARLES (CHIEF) BENDER	**1953**	WILLIE KEELER	1939
ROGER BRESNAHAN	1945	**MIKE J. (KING) KELLY**	**1945**
DAN BROUTHERS	1945	**WILLIAM J. KLEM**	**1953**
MORDECAI PETER BROWN	1949	**NAPOLEON (LARRY) LAJOIE**	**1937**
HON. MORGAN G. BULKELEY	1937	KENESAW MOUNTAIN LANDIS	1944
JESSE C. BURKETT	1946	THEODORE LYONS	1955
ALEXANDER JOY CARTWRIGHT, JR.	1938	CONNIE MACK	1937
HENRY CHADWICK	1938	WALTER (RABBIT) MARANVILLE	1954
FRANK LEROY CHANCE	1946	CHRISTY MATHEWSON	1936
JOHN DWIGHT CHESBRO	1946	**JOSEPH V. McCARTHY**	**1957**
FRED CLARKE	1945	THOMAS F. McCARTHY	1946
TYRUS RAYMOND COBB	1936	JOSEPH JEROME McGINNITY	1946
GORDON (MICKEY) COCHRANE	1947	JOHN J. McGRAW	1937
EDWARD TROWBRIDGE COLLINS	1939	CHARLES A. (KID) NICHOLS	1949
JAMES COLLINS	1945	JAMES H. O'ROURKE	1945
CHARLES A. COMISKEY	**1939**	MELVIN T. OTT	1951
THOMAS H. CONNOLLY	**1953**	HERBERT J. PENNOCK	1948
SAM CRAWFORD	**1957**	EDWARD S. PLANK	1946
JOSEPH CRONIN	**1956**	CHARLIE RADBOURN	1939
W. A. (CANDY) CUMMINGS	1939	WILBERT ROBINSON	1945
JAY HANNA (DIZZY) DEAN	1953	JACK ROBINSON	1962
ED. DELAHANTY	1945	EDD J. ROUSH	1962
WILLIAM DICKEY	1954	GEORGE HERMAN (BABE) RUTH	1936
JOSEPH P. DiMAGGIO	1955	RAY SCHALK	1955
HUGH DUFFY	1945	AL SIMMONS	1953
JOHN JOSEPH EVERS	1946	GEORGE HAROLD SISLER	1939
WM. B. (BUCK) EWING	1939	ALBERT GOODWILL SPALDING	1939
ROBERT W. FELLER	1962	TRISTRAM E. (TRIS) SPEAKER	1937
JAMES E. FOXX	1951	WILLIAM H. TERRY	1954
FRANK FRISCH	1947	JOSEPH B. TINKER	1946
HENRY LOUIS GEHRIG	1939	HAROLD J. (PIE) TRAYNOR	1948
CHARLES GEHRINGER	1949	C. ARTHUR (DAZZY) VANCE	1955
HENRY GREENBERG	1956	GEORGE EDWARD WADDELL	1946
CLARK C. GRIFFITH	1946	HONUS WAGNER	1936
ROBERT MOSES GROVE	1947	RODERICK (BOBBY) WALLACE	1953
CHARLES LEO (GABBY) HARTNETT	1955	EDWARD ARTHUR WALSH	1946
HARRY HEILMANN	1952	PAUL WANER	1952
ROGERS HORNSBY	1942	**ZACK WHEAT**	**1959**
		GEORGE WRIGHT	**1937**

(Continued)

Members	Year Elected	Members	Year Elected
HARRY WRIGHT	1953	DENTON T. (CY) YOUNG	1937

In addition to the men immortalized on Cooperstown's plaques, there are many who have been enshrined on a special Honor Roll of Baseball in the museum. This Honor Roll was created to honor men for outstanding contributions to baseball other than by active playing. It includes:

BASEBALL WRITERS—Walter Barnes, Boston; Harry E. Cross, New York; William Hanna, New York; Frank Hough, Philadelphia; Sid Mercer, New York; T. H. Murnane, Boston; Francis C. Richter, Philadelphia; Irving E. "Cy" Sanborn, Chicago; John B. Sheridan, St. Louis; William Slocum, New York; George Tidden, New York; Joe Vila, New York.

BASEBALL UMPIRES--William Dinneen, Robert D. Emslie, William Evans, John H. Gaffney, Timothy Hurst, Honest John Kelly, Thomas J. Lynch, Francis "Silk" O'Loughlin, Jack Sheridan.

BASEBALL MANAGERS--William Carrigan, Edward Hanlon, Miller James Huggins, William B. McKechnie Frank G. Selee, John Montgomery Ward.

BASEBALL EXECUTIVES--Ernest S. Barnard, John E. Bruce, John T. Brush, Barney Dreyfuss, Charles H. Ebbets, August Herrmann, John A. Heydler, J. A. "Bob" Quinn, Arthur H. Soden, Nicholas E. Young.

NO-HIT GAMES

Quite distinct from baseball's Hall of Fame is its "hall of fame." The capital difference comes down to this—meritorious service for a long period of years leads to candidacy for an actual plaque in Cooperstown's honored corridors, whereas anybody can make the lower-case "hall of fame" simply by pitching a no-hit game.

Many mediocrities have found the magic formula for one unhittable afternoon, pitchers who landed back in the minors a scant year or two after their headline-making masterpiece. "It's like catching lightning in a bottle," says one veteran manager. Though this simile exaggerates the factor of luck involved, still it can't be a matter of sheer skill, speed and stamina, because fully half the pitchers in the upper-strata, upper-case Hall of Fame never notched no-hitters.

When no batter can reach base—whether by hit, walk, error, hit-by-pitched-ball or plain black magic—then the pitcher has earned a "perfect game." Seven such paragons adorn the no-hit roster, though some statistical purists still challenge Ernie Shore's right to rank up there.

On June 23, 1917, Shore shuffled out of the Red Sox bullpen to relieve Babe Ruth, who had just been ordered out of the game for squawking too boisterously after pitching a fourth ball to the first Washington batter, Ray Morgan. With Shore on the mound, Morgan was thrown out trying to steal second base. Shore proceeded to retire the remaining 26 batters in order.

Far more controversial than Shore's game are two other entries on the all-time no-hit honor roll, which made the grade only when the official scorer changed his mind after having announced a "hit" earlier in the game. Some record books also omit the early no-hitters, because all pitching was underhand until 1884, while the pitching distance was only 45 feet until 1881, 50 feet until 1893 and 60½ feet thereafter.

Here is the complete chronological collection of major league no-hit performances over the first nine innings of a game. An asterisk (*) marks "perfect game." Each line shows the date, pitcher, his club and league, opposing club and final score. All games were played in the home park of the no-hit hurler, except when "at" appears just before the name of the victimized club.

July 28, 1875 - Joseph E. Borden, Philadelphia NA vs. Chicago........ 4-0
July 15, 1876 - George W. Bradley, St. Louis NL vs. Hartford.......... 2-0
June 12, 1880 - John L. Richmond, Worcester NL vs. Cleveland........ 1-0*
June 17, 1880 - John M. Ward, Providence NL vs. Buffalo (AM)........ 5-0*
Aug. 19, 1880 - Lawrence J. Corcoran, Chicago NL vs. Boston......... 6-0
Aug. 20, 1880 - James F. Galvin, Buffalo NL at Worcester.............. 1-0
Sept. 11, 1882 - Antoine J. Mullane, Louisville AA at Cincinnati........ 2-0
Sept. 19, 1882 - Guy J. Hecker, Louisville AA at Pittsburgh............. 3-1
Sept. 20, 1882 - Lawrence J. Corcoran, Chicago NL vs. Worcester.... 5-0
July 25, 1883 - Charles G. Radbourn, Providence NL at Cleveland.... 8-0
Sept. 13, 1883 - Hugh I. Daly, Cleveland NL at Philadelphia............. 1-0
May 24, 1884 - Albert W. Atkisson, Philadelphia AA at Pittsburgh.... 10-1
May 29, 1884 - Edward Morris, Columbus AA at Pittsburgh 5-0
June 5, 1884 - Frank H. Mountain, Columbus AA at Washington....... 12-0
June 27, 1884 - Lawrence J. Corcoran, Chicago NL vs. Providence... 6-0
Aug. 4, 1884 - James F. Galvin, Buffalo NL at Detroit.................. 18-0
Aug. 26, 1884 - Richard S. Burns, Cincinnati UA at Kansas City........ 3-1
Sept. 28, 1884 - Edward L. Cushman, Milwaukee UA vs. Washington... 5-0
Oct. 4, 1884 - Samuel J. Kimber, Brooklyn AA at Toledo (10 innings).. 0-0
July 27, 1885 - John G. Clarkson, Chicago NL at Providence........... 4-0
Aug. 29, 1885 - Charles J. Ferguson, Philadelphia NL vs. Providence 1-0
May 1, 1886 - Albert W. Atkisson, Philadelphia AA vs. New York ... 3-2
July 24, 1886 - William J. Terry, Brooklyn AA vs. St. Louis............ 1-0
Oct. 6, 1886 - Matthew A. Kilroy, Baltimore AA at Pittsburgh........ 6-0
May 27, 1888 - William J. Terry, Brooklyn AA vs. Louisville.......... 4-0
June 6, 1888 - Henry Porter, Kansas City AA at Baltimore............ 4-0
July 26, 1888 - Edward W. Seward, Philadelphia AA vs. Cincinnati ... 12-2
July 31, 1888 - August P. Weyhing, Philadelphia AA vs. Kansas City 4-0
Sept. 15, 1890 - Ledell Titcomb, Rochester AA vs. Syracuse............ 7-0
June 22, 1891 - Thomas J. Lovett, Brooklyn NL vs. New York.......... 4-0
July 31, 1891 - Amos W. Rusie, New York NL vs. Brooklyn............ 6-0
Oct. 4, 1891 - Theodore P. Breitenstein, St. Louis AA vs. Louisville 8-0
Aug. 6, 1892 - John C. Stivetts, Boston NL at Brooklyn................. 11-0
Aug. 22, 1892 - Alexander B. Sanders, Louisville NL vs. Baltimore... 6-2
Oct. 15, 1892 - Charles L. Jones, Cincinnati NL vs. Pittsburgh........ 7-1
Aug. 16, 1893 - William V. Hawke, Baltimore NL at Washington........ 5-0
Sept. 18, 1897 - Denton T. Young, Cleveland NL vs. Cincinnati.......... 6-0
Apr. 22, 1898 - Theodore P. Breitenstein, Cincinnati NL vs. Pittsburgh.. 11-0
Apr. 22, 1898 - James J. Hughes, Baltimore NL vs. Boston............. 8-0
July 8, 1898 - Francis R. Donahue, Philadelphia NL vs. Boston....... 5-0
Aug. 21, 1898 - Walter M. Thornton, Chicago NL vs. Brooklyn.......... 2-0
May 25, 1899 - Charles L. Phillippe, Louisville NL vs. New York..... 7-0
Aug. 7, 1899 - Victor G. Willis, Boston NL vs. Washington............ 7-1
July 12, 1900 - Frank G. Hahn, Cincinnati NL vs. Philadelphia......... 4-0
May 9, 1901 - Earl L. Moore, Cleveland AL vs. Chicago (9 innings, lost 10th).. 2-4
July 15, 1901 - Christopher Mathewson, New York NL at St. Louis.... 5-0
Sept. 20, 1902 - James J. Callahan, Chicago AL vs. Detroit (1st game) 3-0
Sept. 18, 1903 - Charles C. Fraser, Philadelphia NL at Chicago....... 10-0
May 5, 1904 - Denton T. Young, Boston AL vs. Philadelphia.......... 3-0*

June 11, 1904 - Robert K. Wicker, Chicago NL vs. New York (9 innings, won in 12th).. 1-0
Aug. 17, 1904 - Jesse N. Tannehill, Boston AL at Chicago............... 6-0
June 13, 1905 - Christopher Mathewson, New York NL at Chicago..... 1-0
July 22, 1905 - Weldon Henley, Philadelphia AL at St. Louis (1st game) 6-0
Sept. 6, 1905 - Frank E. Smith, Chicago AL at Detroit (2nd game).... 15-0
Sept. 27, 1905 - William H. Dinneen, Boston AL vs. Chicago (1st game) 2-0
May 1, 1906 - John C. Lush, Philadelphia NL at Brooklyn............. 1-0
July 20, 1906 - Malcolm W. Eason, Brooklyn NL at St. Louis........... 2-0
Aug. 1, 1906 - Harry M. McIntire, Brooklyn NL vs. Pittsburgh (10 innings, lost in 13th).. 0-1
May 8, 1907 - Francis X. Pfeffer, Boston NL vs. Cincinnati.......... 6-0
Sept. 20, 1907 - Nicholas Maddox, Pittsburgh NL vs. Brooklyn.......... 2-1
June 30, 1908 - Denton T. Young, Boston AL at New York 8-0
July 4, 1908 - George L. Wiltse, New York NL vs. Philadelphia (10 innings) (AM).. 1-0
Sept. 5, 1908 - George N. Rucker, Brooklyn NL vs. Boston (2nd game).. 6-0
Sept. 18, 1908 - Robert B. Rhoades, Cleveland AL vs. Boston............ 2-1
Sept. 20, 1908 - Frank E. Smith, Chicago AL vs. Philadelphia........... 1-0
Oct. 2, 1908 - Adrian C. Joss, Cleveland AL vs. Chicago.............. 1-0*
Apr. 15, 1909 - Leon K. Ames, New York NL vs. Brooklyn (9 innings, lost in 13th).. 0-3
Apr. 20, 1910 - Adrian C. Joss, Cleveland AL at Chicago................ 1-0
May 12, 1910 - Charles A. Bender, Philadelphia AL vs. Cleveland.... 4-0
Aug. 30, 1910 - Thomas L. Hughes, New York AL vs. Cleveland (9 innings, lost in 11th).. 0-5
July 29, 1911 - Joe Wood, Boston AL vs. St. Louis (1st game).......... 5-0
Aug. 27, 1911 - Edward A. Walsh, Chicago AL vs. Boston................ 5-0
July 4, 1912 - George E. Mullin, Detroit AL vs. St. Louis (PM)....... 7-0
Aug. 30, 1912 - Earl A. Hamilton, St. Louis AL at Detroit............... 5-1
Sept. 6, 1912 - Charles M. Tesreau, New York NL at Philadelphia (1st game).. 3-0
May 14, 1914 - James Scott, Chicago AL at Washington (9 innings, lost in 10th).. 0-1
May 31, 1914 - Joseph L. Benz, Chicago AL vs. Cleveland 6-1
Sept. 9, 1914 - George A. Davis, Boston NL vs. Philadelphia (2nd game).. 7-0
Sept. 19, 1914 - Edward F. LaFitte, Brooklyn FL vs. Kansas City (1st game).. 6-2
Apr. 15, 1915 - Richard W. Marquard, New York NL vs. Brooklyn 2-0
Apr. 24, 1915 - Frank L. Allen, Pittsburgh FL at St. Louis.............. 2-0
May 15, 1915 - Claude R. Hendrix, Chicago FL at Pittsburgh........... 10-0
Aug. 16, 1915 - Miles G. Main, Kansas City FL at Buffalo................ 5-0
Aug. 31, 1915 - James S. Lavender, Chicago NL at New York (1st game).. 2-0
Sept. 7, 1915 - Arthur D. Davenport, St. Louis FL vs. Chicago (1st game).. 3-0
June 16, 1916 - Thomas L. Hughes, Boston NL vs. Pittsburgh........... 2-0
June 21, 1916 - George Foster, Boston AL vs. New York................ 2-0
Aug. 26, 1916 - Leslie J. Bush, Philadelphia AL vs. Cleveland......... 5-0
Aug. 30, 1916 - Hubert B. Leonard, Boston AL vs. St. Louis............ 4-0
Apr. 14, 1917 - Edward V. Cicotte, Chicago AL at St. Louis............ 11-0
Apr. 24, 1917 - George A. Mogridge, New York AL at Boston........... 2-1
May 2, 1917 - Frederick A. Toney, Cincinnati NL at Chicago (10 innings).. 1-0

May 2, 1917 - James L. Vaughn, Chicago NL vs. Cincinnati (9 innings, lost in 10th) 0-1
May 5, 1917 - Ernest G. Koob, St. Louis AL vs. Chicago.......... 1-0
May 6, 1917 - Robert Groom, St. Louis AL vs. Chicago (2nd game).. 3-0
June 23, 1917 - Ernest G. Shore, Boston AL vs. Washington (1st game).......... 4-0*
June 3, 1918 - Hubert B. Leonard, Boston AL at Detroit 5-0
May 11, 1919 - Horace O. Eller, Cincinnati NL vs. St. Louis.......... 6-0
Sept. 10, 1919 - Raymond B. Caldwell, Cleveland AL at New York (1st game).......... 3-0
July 1, 1920 - Walter P. Johnson, Washington AL at Boston.......... 1-0
Apr. 30, 1922 - Charles C. Robertson, Chicago AL at Detroit.......... 2-0*
May 7, 1922 - Jesse L. Barnes, New York NL vs. Philadelphia....... 6-0
Sept. 4, 1923 - Samuel P. Jones, New York AL at Philadelphia......... 2-0
Sept. 7, 1923 - Howard J. Ehmke, Boston AL at Philadelphia.......... 4-0
July 17, 1924 - Jesse J. Haines, St. Louis NL vs. Boston 5-0
Sept. 13, 1925 - Arthur C. Vance, Brooklyn NL vs. Philadelphia (1st game).......... 10-1
Aug. 21, 1926 - Theodore A. Lyons, Chicago AL at Boston.......... 6-0
May 8, 1929 - Carl O. Hubbell, New York NL vs. Pittsburgh.......... 11-0
Apr. 29, 1931 - Wesley C. Ferrell, Cleveland AL vs. St. Louis......... 9-0
Aug. 8, 1931 - Robert J. Burke, Washington AL vs. Boston.......... 5-0
Sept. 18, 1934 - Louis N. Newsom, St. Louis AL vs. Boston (9 innings, lost 10th).......... 1-2
Sept. 21, 1934 - Paul D. Dean, St. Louis NL at Brooklyn (2nd game)... 3-0
Aug. 31, 1935 - Lloyd V. Kennedy, Chicago AL vs. Cleveland.......... 5-0
June 1, 1937 - William J. Dietrich, Chicago AL vs. St. Louis.......... 8-0
June 11, 1938 - John S. Vander Meer, Cincinnati NL vs. Boston........ 3-0
June 15, 1938 - John S. Vander Meer, Cincinnati NL vs. Brooklyn (night).......... 6-0
Aug. 27, 1938 - Marcellus M. Pearson, New York AL vs. Cleveland (2nd game).......... 13-0
Apr. 16, 1940 - Robert W. Feller, Cleveland AL at Chicago.......... 1-0
Apr. 30, 1940 - James O. Carleton, Brooklyn NL at Cincinnati.......... 3-0
Aug. 30, 1941 - Lonnie Warneke, St. Louis NL at Cincinnati.......... 2-0
Apr. 27, 1944 - James A. Tobin, Boston NL vs. Brooklyn 2-0
May 15, 1944 - Clyde M. Shoun, Cincinnati NL vs. Boston 1-0
Sept. 9, 1945 - Richard J. Fowler, Philadelphia AL vs. St. Louis (2nd game).......... 1-0
Apr. 23, 1946 - Edward M. Head, Brooklyn NL vs. Boston.......... 5-0
Apr. 30, 1946 - Robert W. Feller, Cleveland AL at New York.......... 1-0
June 18, 1947 - Ewell Blackwell, Cincinnati NL vs. Boston (night)..... 6-0
July 10, 1947 - Donald P. Black, Cleveland AL vs. Philadelphia (twilight) 3-0
Sept. 3, 1947 - William G. McCahan, Philadelphia AL vs. Washington 3-0
June 30, 1948 - Robert G. Lemon, Cleveland AL at Detroit (night)..... 2-0
Sept. 9, 1948 - Rex E. Barney, Brooklyn NL at New York (night)...... 2-0
Aug. 11, 1950 - Vernon E. Bickford, Boston NL vs. Brooklyn (night).. 7-0
May 6, 1951 - Clifford D. Chambers, Pittsburgh NL at Boston (2nd game).......... 3-0
July 1, 1951 - Robert W. Feller, Cleveland AL vs. Detroit (1st game).......... 2-1
July 12, 1951 - Allie P. Reynolds, New York AL at Cleveland (night) 1-0
Sept. 28, 1951 - Allie P. Reynolds, New York AL vs. Boston (1st game).......... 8-0

May 15, 1952 - Virgil O. Trucks, Detroit AL vs. Washington............ 1-0
June 19, 1952 - Carl D. Erskine, Brooklyn NL vs. Chicago............... 5-0
Aug. 25, 1952 - Virgil O. Trucks, Detroit AL at New York............... 1-0
May 6, 1953 - Alva L. Holloman, St. Louis AL vs. Philadelphia (night).. 6-0
June 12, 1954 - James A. Wilson, Milwaukee NL vs. Philadelphia...... 2-0
May 12, 1955 - Sam Jones, Chicago NL vs. Pittsburgh.................... 4-0
May 12, 1956 - Carl D. Erskine, Brooklyn NL vs. New York............ 3-0
July 14, 1956 - Melvin L. Parnell, Boston AL vs. Chicago............... 4-0
Sept. 25, 1956 - Salvatore A. Maglie, Brooklyn NL vs. Philadelphia..... 5-0
Oct. 8, 1956 - Donald J. Larsen, New York AL vs. Brooklyn NL (World Series)... 2-0*
Aug. 20, 1957 - Robert C. Keegan, Chicago AL vs. Washington........... 6-0
July 20, 1958 - James Bunning, Detroit AL vs. Boston....................... 3-0
Sept. 20, 1958 - Hoyt Wilhelm, Baltimore AL vs. New York.............. 1-0
May 26, 1959 - Harvey Haddiz, Pittsburgh NL vs. Milwaukee................. 0-1

May 15, 1960 - Donald Cardwell, Chicago NL vs. St. Louis..................... 4-0

Aug. 18, 1960 - Lew Burdette, Milwaukee NL vs. Philadelphia................. 1-0

Sept. 16, 1960 - Warren E. Spahn, Milwaukee NL vs. Philadelphia............. 4-0

Apr. 28, 1961 - Warren E. Spahn, Milwaukee NL vs. San Francisco.......... 1-0

May 5, 1962 - Robert Belinsky, Los Angeles AL vs. Baltimore............. 2-0

June 26, 1962 - Earl L. Wilson, Boston AL vs. Los Angeles................... 2-0

June 30, 1962 - Sanford Koufax, Los Angeles NL vs. New York............... 5-0

Aug. 1, 1962 - William Monbouquette, Boston AL vs. Chicago................. 1-0

Aug. 26, 1962 - Jack Kralick, Minnesota AL vs. Kansas City..................... 1-0

ALL-STAR GAMES

For sheer spectacle, the All-Star Game is perhaps baseball's greatest one-day show for the fans. The idea, conceived by the late Arch Ward, sports editor of the *Chicago Tribune*, was originally planned to add a baseball flavor to the Chicago Century of Progress exposition in 1933. However, the success of the initial contest made Ward envision an annual affair between the two leagues in which the best players from each circuit would play.

For a time the fans selected the makeup of the two teams through the use of ballots. However, baseball decided that it would be the best judge of playing talent, and the squads were chosen by the rival managers. When the fans expressed nation-wide dissatisfaction with this system, the game was placed back into their hands. Only the pitchers are now chosen by the rival managers, who qualify for their posts by virtue of winning the pennant in the previous season.

HIGHLIGHTS, THROUGH THE YEARS: 1933, Babe Ruth's line drive homer with one aboard brought the AL triumph. Two of baseball's most famous managers were selected to guide their respective leagues, Connie Mack and John McGraw....1934, Carl Hubbell, although pitching for the losing NL, gained immortality by striking out Babe Ruth, Lou Gehrig, Jimmy Foxx, Al Simmons and Joe Cronin in succession with his incredible screwball... 1935, Lefty Gomez and Mel Harder hurled flawlessly for the winning AL . . . 1936, Joe DiMaggio, baseball's highly-touted rookie, played poorly as Augie Galan's foul-pole homer gave NL its first triumph . . . 1937, President Roosevelt watched Dizzy Dean receive a broken toe which was to hasten the end of his meteoric career . . . 1938, Double no-hit hero Johnny Vander Meer hurled NL to victory . . . 1939, Bob Feller, in relief role, helped Yankee-dominated AL . . . 1940, Max West's first inning homer with two aboard clinched triumph for NL . . . 1941, Ted Williams drove circuit over right field roof with two on and two out in ninth inning to give AL dramatic come-from-behind verdict . . . 1942, Twilight game marked by pair of first inning AL homers . . . 1943, Bobby Doerr drove in three runs for victorious AL . . . 1944, NL coasted as Phil Cavarretta reached base five times . . . 1945, Game suspended in order to comply with wartime restrictions on travel curtailment . . . 1946, Two homers by Ted Williams gave AL its most one-sided triumph . . . 1947, Pitching dominated in slickly-played AL verdict . . . 1948, Underdog AL, riddled by injuries, prevailed . . . 1949, Hitters held sway as AL won slugfest . . . 1950, Red Schoendienst's 14th inning homer gave NL victory behind brilliant pitching... 1951, Four homers helped NL... 1952, Rain-curtailed contest decided by NL circuit clouts . . . 1953, Strong NL pitching kept AL hitters at bay... 1954, Nellie Fox's eighth-inning bloop single gave AL decision in homer-punctuated thriller . . . 1955, Stan Musial cracked game-winning homer in 12th inning as NL overcame five-run deficit . . . 1956, Timely hitting and sparkling third-base play by Ken Boyer helped NL to victory . . . 1957, Early AL lead barely held off late NL rally . . . 1958, Superb relief hurling by Billy O'Dell featured AL triumph.

....1959, Increased to two games to increase player's pension fund. A pitching duel climaxed by Willie Mays' triple enabled the Nationals to win 5-4. The A L. won the second tilt 5-3. The big blows were a homer by Berra, two errors and a single by Nellie Fox.... 1960, Again a double feature with N. L. winning both games Mays' triple and Banks' homer featured the N. L. attack in the first game. The second game featured four home runs by Mathews, Mays, Musial and Boyer; the Nationals winning 6-0....

1961, Two games again featured the 1961 All-Star games. The Nationals won the first game and the second ended in a 1-1 tie. Most of the action in the first game was concentrated in the 9th and 10th innings when the Giants relief artist, little Stu Miller was almost blown off the mound for a costly balk from the gales blowing in Candlestick Park. The gale was also responsible for the 7 errors committed in the game. George Altman of the Cubs entered the game as a pinch hitter in the 8th inning and slammed a home run. The second game marked the first tie game in All-Star history when the rains washed it out after nine innings of play. Rocky Colavito of the Tigers connected with one of Bob Purkey's pitches for a homer in the first inning and the Nationals tied it up in the sixth, filling the bases and then scoring the lone run on an infield hit by Bill White.... 1962, In the first game played in Washington's new park Maury Wills of the Dodgers put on a base-running exhibition by stealing second as a pinch runner for Stan Musial who had singled and again in the eighth, this time on his own, he thrilled the crowd by stealing third on a single to left when Colavito momentarily held the ball and then scoring on a short fly to right field. The Nationals triumphed 3-1 to win their fifth victory in seven games and to come within one game of tying the Americans. However the American League recovered to take the second game which was played in Wrigley Field, Chicago by a score of 9 to 4. The AL won this one by relying on their old weapon, the home run. Pete Runnels, Leon Wagner and Rocky Colavito slammed the round-trippers for the Americans. The game was also featured by the excellent pitching of the White Sox' Ray Herbert who entered the game in the third and faced only 10 batters until relieved by Hank Aguirre of the Tigers at the start of the sixth inning.

1st game, at Chicago (AL), July 6, 1933

					R.	H.	E.
National	000	002	000	---	2	8	0
American	012	001	00x	---	4	9	1

Pitchers--HALLAHAN, Warneke (3), Hubbell (7) vs. GOMEZ, Crowder (4), Grove (7). Homers--Ruth (AL), Frisch (NL). Attendance--49,200. Receipts--$56,378.50.

2nd game, at New York (NL), July 10, 1934

American	000	261	000	---	9	14	1
National	103	030	000	---	7	8	1

Pitchers--Gomez, Ruffing (4), HARDER (5) vs. Hubbell, Warneke (4), MUNGO (5), J. Dean (6), Frankhouse (9). Homers--Frisch (NL), Medwick (NL). Attendance--48,363. Receipts--$52,982.

3rd game, at Cleveland (AL), July 8, 1935

National	000	100	000	---	1	4	1
American	210	010	00x	---	4	8	0

Pitchers--WALKER, Schumacher (3), Derringer (7), J. Dean (8) vs. GOMEZ, Harder (7). Homer--Foxx (AL). Attendance- 69,812. Receipts--$82,179.12.

4th game, at Boston (NL), July 7, 1936

American	000	000	300	---	3	7	1
National	020	020	00x	---	4	9	0

Pitchers--GROVE, Rowe (4), Harder (7) vs. J. DEAN, Hubbell (4), C. Davis (7), Warneke (7). Homers--Gehrig (AL), Galan (NL). Attendance--25,534. Receipts--$24,588.-80.

5th game, at Washington (AL), July 7, 1937

National	000	111	000	---	3	13	0
American	002	312	00x	---	8	13	2

Pitchers--J. DEAN, Hubbell (4), Blanton (4), Grissom (5), Mungo (6), Walters (8) vs. GOMEZ, Bridges (4), Harder (7). Homer--Gehrig (AL). Attendance--31,391. Receipts--$28,475.18.

6th game, at Cincinnati (NL), July 6, 1938

American	000	000	001	---	1	7	4
National	100	100	20x	---	4	8	0

Pitchers--GOMEZ, Allen (4), Grove (7) vs. VANDER MEER, Lee (4), Brown (7). Homers--None. Attendance--27,607. Receipts--$38,469.05.

7th game, at New York (AL), July 11, 1939

National	001	000	000	---	1	7	1
American	000	210	00x	---	3	6	1

Pitchers--Derringer, LEE (4), Fette (7) vs. Ruffing, BRIDGES (4), Feller (6). Homer--J. DiMaggio (AL). Attendance--62,892. Receipts--$75,701.

8th game, at St. Louis (NL), July 9, 1940

American	000	000	000	---	0	3	1
National	300	000	01x	---	4	7	0

Pitchers--RUFFING, Newsom (4), Feller (7) vs. DERRINGER, Walters (3), Wyatt (5), French (7), Hubbell (9). Homer--West (NL). Attendance--32,373. Receipts--$36,-723.03.

9th game, at Detroit (AL), July 8, 1941

National	000	001	220	---	5	10	2
American	000	101	014	---	7	11	3

Pitchers--Wyatt, Derringer (3), Walters (5), PASSEAU (7) vs. Feller, Lee (4), Hudson (7), SMITH (8). Homers--Vaughan (NL) 2, Williams (AL). Attendance--54,675. Receipts--$63,267.08.

10th game, at New York (NL), July 6, 1942

American	300	000	000	---	3	7	0
National	000	000	010	---	1	6	1

Pitchers--CHANDLER, Benton (5), vs. M. COOPER, Vander Meer (4), Passeau (7), Walters (9). Homers--Boudreau (AL), York (AL), Owen (NL). Attendance--33,694. Receipts--$86,102.98.

11th game, at Philadelphia (AL), July 13, 1943

National	100	000	101	---	3	10	1
American	031	010	00x	---	5	8	2

Pitchers--M. COOPER, Vander Meer (3), Sewell (6), Javery (7) vs. LEONARD, Newhouser (4), Hughson (7). Homers--Doerr (AL), V. DiMaggio (NL). Attendance--31,938. Receipts--$65,674.

12th game, at Pittsburgh (NL), July 11, 1944

American	010	000	000	---	1	6	3
National	000	040	21x	---	7	12	1

Pitchers--Borowy, HUGHSON (4), Muncrief (5), Newhouser (7), Newsom (8) vs. Walters, RAFFENSBERGER (4), Sewell (6), Tobin (9). Homers--None. Attendance--29,589. Receipts--$81,275.

(NO GAME IN 1945)

13th game, at Boston (AL), July 9, 1946

National	000	000	000	---	0	3	0
American	200	130	24x	---	12	14	1

Pitchers--PASSEAU, Higbe (4), Blackwell (5), Sewell (8) vs. FELLER, Newhouser (4), Kramer (7). Homers- Williams (AL) 2, Keller (AL). Attendance--34,906. Receipts--$89,071.

14th game, at Chicago (NL), July 8, 1947

American	000	001	100	---	2	8	0
National	000	100	000	---	1	5	1

Pitchers--Newhouser, SHEA (4), Masterson (7), Page (8) vs. Blackwell, Brecheen (4), SAIN (7), Spahn (8). Homer Mize (NL). Attendance--41,123. Receipts--$105,314.90.

15th game, at St. Louis (AL), July 13, 1948

National	200	000	000	---	2	8	0
American	011	300	00x	---	5	6	0

Pitchers--Branca, SCHMITZ (4), Sain (4), Blackwell (6) vs. Masterson, RASCHI (4), Coleman (7). Homers--Musial (NL), Evers (AL). Attendance--34,009. Receipts--$93,447.07.

16th game, at Brooklyn (NL), July 12, 1949

American	400	202	300	---	11	13	1
National	212	002	000	---	7	12	5

Pitchers--Parnell, TRUCKS (2), Brissie (4), Raschi (7) vs. Spahn, NEWCOMBE (2), Munger (5), Bickford (6), Pollet (7), Blackwell (8), Roe (9). Homers- Musial (NL), Kiner (NL). Attendance--32,577. Receipts--$79,225.02.

17th game, at Chicago (AL), July 11, 1950

National	020	000	001 000 01	--	4	10	0
American	001	020	000 000 00	--	3	8	1

Pitchers--Roberts, Newcombe (4), Konstanty (6), Jansen (7), BLACKWELL (12) vs. Raschi, Lemon (4), Houtteman (7), Reynolds (10), GRAY (13), Feller (14). Homers--Kiner (NL), Schoendienst (NL). Attendance- 46,127. Receipts--$126,179.51.

18th game, at Detroit (AL), July 10, 1951

National	100	302	110	---	8	12	1
American	010	110	000	---	3	10	2

Pitchers--Roberts, MAGLIE (3), Newcombe (6), Blackwell (9) vs. Garver, LOPAT (4), Hutchinson (5), Parnell (8), Lemon (9). Homers--Musial (NL), Elliott (NL), Hodges (NL), Kiner (NL), Wertz (AL), Kell (AL). Attendance--52,075. Receipts--$124,294.07.

19th game, at Philadelphia (NL), July 8, 1952

American	000	20		---	2	5	0
National	100	20		---	3	3	0

Pitchers--Raschi, LEMON (3), Shantz (5) vs. Simmons, RUSH (4). Homers--Robinson (NL), Sauer (NL). Attendance --32,785. Receipts--$108,762.40.

20th game, at Cincinnati (NL), July 14, 1953

American	000	000	001	---	1	5	0
National	000	020	12x	---	5	10	0

Pitchers--Pierce, REYNOLDS (4), Garcia (6), Paige (8) vs. Roberts, SPAHN (4), Simmons (6), Dickson (8). Attendance--30,846. Receipts--$155,654.

21st game, at Cleveland (AL), July 13, 1954

National	000	520	020	---	9	14	0
American	004	121	03x	---	11	17	1

Roberts, Antonelli (4) Spahn (6), Grissom (6), CONLEY (8), Erskin (8) vs. Ford, Consuegra (4), Lemon (4), Porterfield (5), Keegan (8), STONE (8), Trucks (9). Homers--Rosen (AL) 2, Boone (AL), Doby (AL), Kluszewski (NL), Bell (NL). Attendance--68,751. Receipts--$292,678.

22nd game, at Milwaukee (NL), July 12, 1955

American	400	001	000	000	---	5	10	2
National	000	000	230	001	---	6	13	1

Pierce, Wynn (4), Ford (7), SULLIVAN (8) vs. Roberts, Haddix (4), Newcombe (7), Jones (8), Nuxhall (8), CONLEY (12). Homers--Mantle (AL), Musial (NL). Attendance--45,-314. Receipts--$179,545.50.

23rd game, at Washington (AL), July 10, 1956

National	001	211	200	---	7	11	0
American	000	003	000	---	3	11	0

FRIEND, Spahn (4), Antonelli (6) vs. PIERCE, Ford (4), Wilson (5), Brewer (6), Score (8), Wynn (9). Homers--Mays (NL), Musial (NL), Williams (AL), Mantle (AL). Attendance--28,843. Receipts--$105,928.50.

24th game, at St. Louis (NL), July 9, 1957

American	020	001	003	---	6	10	0
National	000	000	203	---	5	9	1

BUNNING, Loes (4), Wynn (7), Pierce (7), Moss (9), Grim (9) vs. SIMMONS, Burdette (2), Sanford (6), Jackson (7), Labine (9). Attendance--30,693. Receipts--$122,027.

25th game, at Baltimore (AL), July 8, 1958

National	210	000	000	---	3	4	2
American	110	011	00x	---	4	9	2

Spahn, FRIEND (4), Jackson (6), Farrell (7) vs. Turley, Narleski (2), WYNN (6), O'Dell (7). Attendance--48,829. Receipts--$202,492.

26th game, at Pittsburgh (NL), July 7, 1959 (1st game)

American	000	100	030	---	4	8	4
National	100	000	22X	---	5	9	1

Pitchers—Wynn, Duren (4), Bunning (7), FORD (8), Daley (8) vs Drysdale, Burdette (4), Face (7), ANTONELLI (8), Elston (9). Homers—Mathews (NL), Kaline (AL). Attendance—35,277. Receipts—$229,636.

27th game, at Los Angeles (NL), August 3, 1959 (2nd game)

American	012	000	110	---	5	6	0
National	100	010	100	---	3	6	3

Pitchers—WALKER, Wynn (4), Wilhelm (6), O'Dell (7), McLish (8) vs DRYSDALE, Conley (4), Jones (6), Face (8). Homers—Malzone (AL), Berra (AL), Robinson (NL), Gilliam (NL), Colavito (AL). Attendance—55,105. Receipts—$283,120.

28th game, at Kansas City (AL), July 11, 1960 (1st game)

National	311	000	000	---	5	12	4
American	000	001	020	---	3	6	1

Pitchers—FRIEND, McCormick (4), Face (6), Buhl (8), Law (9) vs MONBOUQUETTE, Estrada (3), Coates (4), Bell (6), Lary (8), Daley (9). Homers—Banks (NL), Crandall (NL), Kaline (AL) 2, Fox (AL). Attendance—30,619. Receipts—$151,238.38 (net).

29th game, at New York (AL), July 13, 1960 (2nd game)

National	021	000	102	---	6	10	0
American	000	000	000	---	0	8	0

Pitchers—LAW, Podres (3), S. Williams (5), Jackson (7), Henry (8), McDaniel (9) vs FORD, Wynn (4), Staley (6), Lary (8), Bell (9). Homers—Mathews (NL), Mays (NL), Musial (NL), Boyer (NL). Attendance—38,362. Receipts—$177,688.57 (net).

30th game, at San Francisco (NL), July 11, 1961 (1st game)

American	000	001	002	---	4	4	2
National	010	100	010	---	5	11	5

Pitchers—Ford, Lary (4), Donovan (4), Bunning (6), Fornieles (8), WILHELM (8) vs Spahn, Purkey (4), McCormick (6), Face (9), Koufax (9), MILLER (9). Homers—Killebrew (AL), Altman (NL). Attendance—44,115. Receipts—$259,230.81 (net).

31st game, at Boston (AL), July 31, 1961 (2nd game)

National	000	001	000	---	1	5	1
American	100	000	000	---	1	4	0

Pitchers—Bunning, Schwall (4), Pascual (7) vs Purkey, Mahaffey (3), Koufax (5), Miller (7). Homer—Colavito (AL). Attendance—31,851. Receipts—$172,298.19 (net).

32nd game, at Washington (AL), July 10, 1962 (1st game)

National	000	002	010	---	3	8	0
American	000	001	000	---	1	4	0

Pitchers—Bunning, PASCUAL (4), Donovan (7), Pappas (9) vs Drysdale, MARICHAL (4), Purkey (6), Shaw (8). Attendance—45,480. Receipts—$228,082.21.

33rd game, at Chicago (NL), July 30, 1962 (2nd game,

American	001	201	302	---	9	10	0
National	010	000	111	---	4	10	4

Pitchers—Stenhouse, HERBERT (3), Aguirre (6), Pappas (9) vs Podres, MAHAFFEY (3), Gibson (5), Farrell (7), Marichal (8). Homers—Runnels (AL), Wagner (AL), Colavito (AL), Roseboro (NL). Attendance—38,359. Receipts—$216,908.71.

IX UMPIRES

"Please Do Not Shoot the Umpire; he is Doing the Best he Can."

This was the inspiring prose which greeted the durable man in blue who umpired a game during the 1886 National League season in the Kansas City park. On the outfield barrier, for all to see, was this ode to the umpire which was not too far removed from the emotion of the day's fan and player.

Between baseball's earliest days and his present-day standing of absolute autocracy on the field of play, the umpire passed through one of the diamond's roughest and rowdiest eras. He could do no right in the eyes of the fan, the player, the owner, the press; he was wrong, blind, lame, incompetent and crooked, accusations which were hurled ceaselessly and shamefully. But in the long history of the sport it is interesting to note that the umpire—not the player—has been far removed from suspicion. Only one umpire has been expelled because of dishonesty: Richard Higham, in 1882, who committed the unpardonable sin of announcing to certain people the probable winners of games in which he was to officiate. But Higham's offense never may have occurred if the owners had the foresight to hire extra umpires and spread their work a bit more around the rest of the league.

Higham's high-handed tactics were suspected by William G. Thompson, president of the Detroit team, who thought his club was losing too many games in which Higham served as arbiter. Higham officiated 26 of the first 29 games played by Detroit, and private detectives learned the umpire's work was not always beyond reproach. They produced evidence in the form of a letter Higham allegedly had written in which he tipped off eventual winners of games in which he was to work, enough to expel baseball's only dishonest umpire.

In baseball's earliest days, before the start of the major leagues, the position of the umpire was dignified. He donned a Prince Albert coat, silk hat and cane. Stationed just outside the foul line between home and first, he was given a stool on which to rest one foot as he viewed the game. In those days of long-flowing whiskers, he gave his decisions deliberately.

Between the patriarchal overseer of the early 19th century and the nimble, forceful man-in-blue of the present, the umpiring profession has weathered many storms. "Kill the umpire! " once was more than a euphemism. Clarence (Brick) Owens got his nickname from the object thrown at him in a game. Minor league umpires have been tarred and feathered. Police protection used to be standard equipment for a long time even in the big leagues.

Founding fathers of professional baseball recognized the need for investing the umpire with real authority. For that reason they stated in the first set of pro rules, 1871, that there can be no appeal from a decision involving the umpire's judgment (fair or foul, safe or out, etc.). Protests can be based only on interpretation of the rules. This fundamental principle has not been changed since.

Hoping to insure the integrity of the umpire, league officials forbade any pay for working the game. The visiting club would submit three names as prospective umpires for the game, and the home team would select one. The system sagged so badly, the day's umpire often had to be picked from a volunteer in the stands.

Back in the pioneering National Association, a part-time prize fighter from Philadelphia, William B. McLean, quickly established himself as "King of Umpires." He ran the games so competently that clubs gladly paid his expenses for road trips, and he became the first umpire to officiate in every city.

McLean was responsible for another innovation. He commanded a fee of $5 a game. In the first two years of the National League, rules-makers tried to stick to the amateur tradition, but by 1878 it became obvious that capable officials could be obtained only by proper pay, and the McLean standard of $5 a game was written into the rules.

At first, the visiting club was required to pay the $5, while the home club paid all other expenses. Later, the home club became responsible for all umpiring costs.

In 1883, the American Association decided to pay the umpires out of the league treasury at the rate of $140 per month "plus traveling expenses and hotel bills, not to exceed $3 a day." Umpires by now were technically members of the league staff. They no longer could be removed in the middle of a game merely by agreement of the rival captains. Yet league headquarters still failed to back up the umpires in disputes with players. Fines didn't stick. Suspensions were easily rescinded.

Until the end of the 19th century, and well into the 20th, league games were handled by a single umpire. While the harassed official behind the plate ran part of the way down the baseline to judge a drive near the foul line in right field, baserunners would cut inside second base en route from first to third. In the boisterous 90's, fights often broke out because the third baseman would slyly grab the belt of the baserunner and restrain him while the lone umpire was busy watching the relay from the outfield.

In the early 1900's, a second umpire finally came into general use. It wasn't till 1910 that the rules spoke of an Umpire-in-Chief (plate umpire) and Field Umpire (for baseline decisions). Thirty years later, a third umpire became a regular sight. By now, it is taken for granted that there will be four umpires at all important games, with six being used at the World Series (one for each base, and one at each foul pole to decide between home runs and foul balls).

Leagues have always tried various stratagems to bolster the respect of umpires. The old AA ruled that no umpire while in uniform could enter a poolroom or saloon, under penalty of fine by the league president. They also halted the "undignified practice" of allowing the umpire to take testimony from spectators in case of doubt over whether a ball had left the field fair or foul, or whether a fair catch had been made in the outfield. The National League in the 1890's even wrote into the rules that the players must address him as "Mr. Umpire!"

Yet all these dodges to compel respect for the umpires faded when the belligerent players were allowed to intimidate the officials without reprisal from the league's top echelon. One of the main reasons the American League became soundly established at the start of this century was that its founder, Byron Bancroft (Ban) Johnson, removed rowdyism from the game by carefully selecting a staff of umpires and by completely backing every one of their field rulings, a wise move which put to an end the endless debates between the umpires and outraged players.

John McGraw, bred in the boisterous Old Oriole days, found himself practically manacled in the new AL, so he jumped into the NL.

For a few years, McGraw had a picnic with the arbiters. Then he crossed the path of a spunky little newcomer named Bill Klem. Ordered out of a game by Klem, the Little Napoleon raged, "I'll have your job for this!"

"If it's possible for you to take my job," answered Klem coldly, "then I don't want it."

Largely through the insistence of Klem, who was to earn an immortal niche as "The Old Arbitrator," the NL began raising its umpiring standards to meet the Americans. Through Klem's campaigning, World Series pay rose from $400 to $2,500. Umpires were provided with a separate clubhouse, so they no longer had to retreat to an old peanut shed or storage bin after a game, to use a sponge and fire bucket to swab the day's dust from their body.

Klem umpired in 18 World Series, a record. He brought dignity, respect and authority to the job. In 1949, the fans honored him with a special "Day" at the Polo Grounds. Sports writers awarded him a plaque for meritorious service to baseball over a long period of years, and in his brief but dramatic acceptance speech he announced his credo, "Baseball is more than a game to me—it's a religion!"

Klem started the practice of "getting on the ball" by crouching to judge each pitch from right over the catcher's shoulder. Cy Rigler was the one who started the sensible custom of raising the right arm to denote a strike. There are some 60,000 in the umpiring population of the United States, counting high school and sandlot games. The leagues have an elaborate scouting system to bring up the best. They look for a man with keen eyesight, knowledge of the rules, ability to get into the right position quickly, poise, decisiveness, impartiality (meaning an imperviousness to the hoots of a home crowd, which tries to sway decisions toward the home team), psychology of handling men and a flair for the game.

For his salary of about $10,000 to cover the six-month season, the big league umpire is a lonely man. He may not fraternize with the players on the field, nor can he travel in the same train or stay at the same hotel as the players. His future assignments are never made more than a week ahead, so his family life is practically nil during the season.

Umpires have a host of duties, besides the obvious ball-and-strike decisions (more than 200 of these a game for the plate umpire), safe-or-out and fair-or-foul. He administers rules as to equipment, conditions of the grounds, etc. He is the sole judge over whether to end a game because of climatic conditions or other circumstances.

Still, there are many decisions which an umpire is not allowed to make unless there is a direct protest. These are "appeal plays," and include declaring a runner out for failing to tag a bag. Klem once admitted that the deciding run of the fifth game of the 1911 World Series was scored by Larry Doyle, who slid half a foot wide of the plate to avoid a tag that never was made. Doyle brushed himself off, trotted to the clubhouse and Klem had no way of declaring him out, since the catcher also walked away.

Besides the aforementioned McLean, Rigler and Klem, there have been many famous umpires of long service, like Honest John Kelly, John Gaffney, Hank O'Day, Silk O'Loughlin, Tom Connolly, Bill Dinneen, Charles Moran, Billy Evans and many others. Bill McGowan set the Iron man mark by umpiring 2,541 consecutive AL games in 16½ seasons without missing an inning.

John K. Tener, who later became Governor of the state of Pennsylvania, umpired one season in the NL. On June 26, 1897 in Washington, Thomas J. Lynch umpired the first Giant game and John A. Heydler umpired the second. Lynch and Heydler later became presidents of the league.

ALL-TIME REGISTER

NATIONAL LEAGUE

Abbey, Charles S., 1897
Abbot, 1905
Adams, James, 1897
Allen, Hezekiah, 1876
Anderson, William, 1890
Andrews, George E., 1889, 1893, 1895, 1898-99
Arundel, John T., 1888
Ayers, 1876
Baker, Charles, 1884
Baker, Philip, 1889
Baldwin, Marcus E., 1892
Ballanfant, Edward L., 1936-57
Bannon, James H., 1894
Barker, Alfred L., 1876, 1880-81
Barlick, Albert J., 1940-43, 1946-55, 1958-1962
Barnie, William S., 1882, 1892
Barr, George M., 1931-49
Barton, 1876
Bates, 1877
Battin, Joseph V., 1882, 1889, 1891, 1895-96
Bausewine, George, 1908
Beard, Oliver P., 1894
Becannon, James M., 1885
Beck, Erwin T., 1902
Beckley, Jacob P., 1906
Beebe, Fred L., 1907
Behle, Frank, 1895-96, 1901
Berger, Frederick, 1886
Berger, John H., 1891
Betts, William G., 1893-96, 1898-99
Bigelow, 1877
Bittman, Henry, 1892-95, 1897
Blakiston, Robert J., 1884
Blodgett, C. W., 1876
Boggess, Lynton R., 1944-48, 1950-62
Boles, Charles, 1877
Bond, Thomas H., 1883, 1885
Bonner, Frank J., 1894
Boston, K. K., 1878
Boyle, Henry J., 1886
Boyle, John A., 1892, 1897
Bradley, George H., 1877, 1879-83
Brady, 1877
Brady, Jackson, 1887
Bransfield, William E., 1917
Bredburg, George W., 1877, 1879
Breitenstein, Theodore P., 1900
Brennan, John E., 1887, 1899
Brennan, William T., 1909, 1913, 1921
Briody, Charles F., 1882
Brockway, John, 1877, 1879
Brown, Samuel W., 1907
Brown, Thomas T., 1891, 1898-99, 1901-02
Brunton, Thomas H., 1879
Buckenberger, Alfred C., 1890
Budding, 1877
Buelow, Frederick W., 1901
Buffinton, Charles G., 1883, 1888-89, 1892
Bullymore, Charles L., 1882
Bunce, Joshua, 1877
Burke, 1892
Burkhart, Kenneth, 1957-62
Burlingame, Frank A., 1878
Burnham, George W., 1883, 1886-87, 1889, 1893, 1895
Burns, John S., 1884
Burns, Thomas E., 1892
Burns, Thomas P., 1895, 1899
Burtis, D. W., 1876-77
Bush, Garner C., 1911-12
Bushong, Albert J., 1880, 1890
Butler, Richard H., 1897
Byron, William J., 1913-19
Callahan, Edward J., 1881
Campbell, Al., 1886
Campbell, Daniel, 1893-97
Campbell, William M., 1939-40
Cantillon, Joseph D., 1902
Carey, S., 187
Carey, Thomas J., 1881-82
Carpenter, William B., 1897, 1904, 1906-07
Carrick, William M., 1900
Carroll, Frederick H., 1887
Carsey, Wilfred, 1894, 1896, 1901
Caruthers, Robert L., 1886, 1891, 1893
Casey, Daniel M., 1888
Caskin, Edward J., 1884
Cassidy, John P., 1882
Chamberlain, Elton P., 1894
Chance, Frank L., 1902
Chandler, Moses E., 1877
Chaplin, Harry, 1886
Chapman, John C., 1876, 1880, 1882-83, 1885
Chapman, John, 1880
Chill, Oliver P., 1916
Chipper, 1876
Clack, Robert H., 1876, 1897
Clark, Arthur F., 1890
Clarke, Robert M., 1930-31
Clarke, William J., 1893-94, 1896
Clarkson, Arthur H., 1892-96
Clarkson, John G., 1888, 1892-93
Cockill, George W., 1915
Cohen, 1893
Coleman, John F., 1884
Colgan, Harry W., 1899, 1901, 1903
Collins, Daniel T., 1876
Cone. J. F., 1876-77
Conlan, John B., 1941-62
Connell, Terence G., 1885, 1887
Connolly, John M., 1886-87, 1892-93
Connolly, Thomas H., 1898-1900
Conahan, 1896
Conway, John H., 1906
Coogan, Daniel G., 1895
Crandall, Robert, 1876-78
Crane, Edward N., 1892-93
Crane, Samuel N., 1886-87, 1890
Crawford, Henry, 1956-62
Cray, 1893
Crolius, Frederick J., 1901
Cronin, John J., 1902-03
Cross, John A., 1876, 1878-79
Cross, Lafayette N., 1892
Cunningham, Elmer E., 1896-97, 1900-01
Cuppy, George M., 1894
Curren, Peter, 1876
Curry, Wesley, 1885-86, 1889-90, 1898
Cusack, Stephen P., 1909
Cushman, Charles H., 1884-85, 1894, 1898
Cusick, Andrew, 1886-87
Daily, Cornelius F., 1886, 1891, 1894, 1896
Dailey, John J., 1882
Daly, Thomas P., 1901
Daniels, Charles F., 1876-80, 1887-88
Darling, Dell C., 1887
Dascoli, Frank, 1948-62
Davis, C. E., 1880
Day, 1879
Dealey, Patrick E., 1886
Deane, Henry C., 1876, 1878
Decker, Stewart M., 1883-85, 1888
Delmore, Victor, 1956-59
Devinney, Daniel, 1876-77
Dexter, Charles D., 1896-97
Dixon, Hal, 1953-60
Donahue, Francis R., 1897
Donahue, Timothy C., 1895-96
Donatelli, August J., 1950-62
Donlin, Michael J., 1900
Donnelly, Charles H., 1931-32
Donnelly, James B., 1896
Donohue, Michael R., 1930
Donovan, Timothy H., 1882
Donovan, William E., 1902
Dooin, Charles S., 1904
Doscher, John H., 1879-82, 1887
Douglass, William B., 1903
Dowse, Thomas J., 1890
Doyle, John J., 1911
Draper, John H., 1877
Ducharme, 1876-77
Duggleby, William J., 1905
Dunlap, Frederick C., 1879
Dunn, John, 1879
Dunn, Thomas P., 1939-46
Dunnigan, Joseph, 1881-82
Dwyer, John F., 1889, 1893-97, 1899, 1901
Dyler, John F., 1892, 1897
Eagan, John J., 1878, 1886
Earle, William M., 1892, 1894
Eason, Malcolm W., 1901-02, 1910-15
Ehret, Philip S., 1892, 1895-97
Ellick, Joseph J., 1886
Emslie, Robert D., 1891-1924
Engeln, William R., 1952-56
English, John W., 1876
Evans, Jacob, 1886
Farrell, Charles A., 1901-02
Feber, Fred W., 1879
Fenno, Norman, 1876
Ferguson, Robert V., 1879, 1884-85
Fessenden, Wallace C., 1889-90
Finch, R. B., 1880
Finneran, William E., 1911-12
Fisher, William C., 1876
Flaherty, Patrick J., 1904-1907
Flynn, John A., 1893
Force, David W., 1881
Forman, Allen, 1962
Foreman, Frank I., 1895
Foreman, John D., 1896
Foster, Clarence F., 1900
Fountain, Edward G., 1879
Fouser, William C., 1876
Frary, Robert, 1911
Freeman, John F., 1900
Fulmer, Charles J., 1881, 1886
Furlong, William E., 1877-80, 1882-84, 1888
Gaffney, John H., 1884-95
Galvin, James F., 1886-87, 1889, 1893, 1895
Ganzel, Charles W., 1901
Gardner, James A., 1899
Geer, William H., 1879
George, William M., 1889
German, Lester S., 1895
Getzein, Charles N., 1890
Gifford, James H., 1881
Gill, Thomas H., 1886
Gillean, Thomas, 1879-81
Gleason, John D., 1877
Gleason, William G., 1877
Gleason, William J., 1890, 1892
Glenn, John W., 1880
Goetz, Lawrence J., 1936-57
Goldsmith, Frederick E., 1886
Gore, Arthur J., 1947-56
Gorman, Thomas D., 1952-62
Grady, Michael W., 1895
Graves, Frank M., 1886, 1895
Griffith, Clark C., 1894
Grim, John H., 1892, 1895-96
Gross, Edward M., 1881
Gruber, Henry J., 1889
Guglielmo, Angelo, 1952
Guinney, Daniel, 1882-83
Gumbert, Addison C., 1892-1895
Gunning, Thomas F., 1884-85, 1887
Gunson, Joseph B., 1892
Guthrie, William J., 1913-1915
Hackett, Merton M., 1886
Haddock, George S., 1889
Haley, Ed, 1876
Hallman, William W., 1903
Hanlon, Edward H., 1892
Hardie, Louis W., 1887
Harrison, Peter A., 1916-20
Hart, Eugene F., 1920-29
Hart, William F., 1896-97, 1914-15
Hartley, John, 1894
Hastings, Winfield S., 1877
Hatfield, Gilbert, 1889
Hatfield, John V. B., 1876
Hawes, William A., 1881-82
Healy, John J., 1887
Hegeman, William H., 1881
Hemming, George E., 1895-96
Henderson, James H., 1895-96
Hengle, Edward S., 1887
Henline, Walter J., 1945-48
Hernon, Thomas H., 1894
Heuble, George A., 1876
Heydler, John A., 1895-98
Hickey, James L., 1882
Higham, Richard, 1881-82
Hiller, George J., 1881
Hines, Michael P., 1884
Hoagland, Willard A., 1894

Hodges, A. D., 1876-77, 1879
Hoffer, William L., 1896
Hogan, 1897
Hogriever, George C., 1893
Holland, John A., 1887
Holliday, James W., 1897, 1903
Hornung, Joseph M., 1892-93, 1896
Houtz, Charles, 1876, 1879
Howard, C. F., 1884
Howe, John, 1890
Hunt, John T., 1893, 1895, 1898-99
Hurst, Timothy C., 1891-98, 1900, 1903-04
Hyatt, Robert H., 1912
Irwin, Arthur A., 1881, 1902
Jacklitsch, Fred L., 1901
Jackowski, William, 1952-62
Jeffers, W. W., 1881
Jennings, Hugh A., 1893, 1900
Jevne, Frederick, 1892-95
Johnson, Harry S., 1914
Johnstone, James E., 1903-12
Jones, Henry M., 1890
Jorda, Louis D., 1927-31, 1940-52
Jose, 1889
Joyce, C. E., 1879
Julian, Joseph O., 1878
Kahle, 1905
Kane, Stephen J., 1906, 1909-10
Karger, Edwin, 1906
Kecher, W. H., 1910
Keefe, Timothy J., 1880, 1882-85, 1887 1892-96
Keenan, James W., 1881, 1890, 1893
Kelley, Joseph J., 1892, 1904
Kelley, W. W., 1877
Kellum, Winford A., 1905
Kelly, John O., 1882, 1884-85, 1888, 1897
Kelly, Michael J., 1893
Kelly, S., 1880
Kennedy, Charles, 1904
Kennedy, Michael J., 1884
Kenney John, 1876-77
Kerins, John A., 1888
Killen, Frank B., 1896-97
Kinslow, Thomas F., 1892
Kipp, Eden, 1881
Kitson, Frank R., 1902
Klem, William J., 1905-41
Kling, John G., 1901
Klusman, William F., 1892-93
Knell, Philip H., 1895
Knight, Alonzo P., 1876, 1888-89
Knowles, James, 1892
Krieg, William F., 1887
Lally, Daniel J., 1891-94, 1896
Landes, Stan, 1955-62
Lane, Frank, 1883
Laney, B., 1884
Lanigan, Charles, 1908
Latham, Walter A., 1899-1900, 1902
Laughlin, 1876
Lavers, George W., 1882
Lawler, Michael H., 1882
Leever, Samuel W., 1900, 1904
Libby, Stephen A., 1880
Lincoln, Frederick H., 1914, 1917
Lindeman, Vivian A., 1907
Long, William H., 1893, 1895, 1897
Lowell, William, 1882
Lundgren, Carl L., 1905-06
Lynch, J. T., 1880
Lynch, Thomas J., 1888-99, 1902
Macullar, John F., 1892
Maddox, Charles, 1882
Magee, Sherwood R., 1928
Magerkurth, George L., 1929-47
Mahoney, Michael J., 1892
Malone, Ferguson G., 1884, 1892
Maloney, William A., 1902
Manassau, Alfred S., 1899
Manning, James H., 1886, 1893
Mapledoram, Blake A., 1886
Martin, Alphonse C., 1876
Mason, Charles E., 1876
Mathews, Robert T., 1876, 1880, 1882
Mathewson, Christopher, 1901, 1907
Mayer, 1893
McAllister, Louis W., 1899
McCaffrey, Harry, 1885, 86
McCarthy, Thomas F. M., 1896
McCauley, Patrick M., 1896
McCauley, Allen B., 1890
McCormick, James, 1885
McCormick, William J., 1919-29
McCrum, 1892
McDermott, Michael J., 1890, 1897
McDonald, James F., 1895, 1897-99
McDowell, 1893
McElwee, Harvey, 1877
McFarland, Edward W., 1896
McFarland, Horace, 1896-97
McGann, Dennis L., 1903
McGarr, James B., 1895, 1899
McGee, 1876
McGinnis, 1910
McGinnity, Joseph J., 1900
McGinty, 1897
McGrew, Harry T., 1930-31, 1933-34
McGuire, James T., 1886-87, 1894, 1896-97, 1901
McGunnigle, Edward, 1888
McLaughlin, Edward J., 1929
McLaughlin, Michael, 1893
McLaughlin, Peter J., 1924-26
McLean, William B., 1876-80, 1882-84
McLeod, 1895
McMahon, John H., 1893
McMater, 1877
McMullen, John F., 1876
McQuaid, John H., 1889-95
Meagher, John, 1877
Mears, Charles W., 1894
Medart, William 1876-77
Meekin, Jouett, 1895-96
Megrue, Cliff, 1876
Mertes, Samuel B., 1903-05
Miller, George E., 1879
Miller, George F., 1893, 1896
Miller, Joseph H., 1884
Mills, Abraham G., 1877
Mitchell, Charles, 1892
Montague, 1877
Moran, 1894
Moran, August, 1903-04, 1910, 1918
Moran, Charles B., 1917-39
Moran, Patrick J., 1901
Morrill, John F., 1891, 1896
Morris, Edward, 1895, 1897
Morris, John S., 1876
Muir, Thomas, 1876
Mullane, Anthony J., 1893, 1897
Mullen, Peter C., 1893
Mullin, John, 1909
Mulvey, Joseph H., 1895
Murnane, Timothy H., 1886
Murphy, Henry, 1880
Murphy, Morgan E., 1893, 1896, 1898
Murphy, Martin W., 1886
Murphy, William H., 1895, 1897
Murray, Jeremiah J., 1893-95, 1900, 1905, 1910
Myers, George D., 1886
Myers, Henry C., 1890
Nash, William M., 1901
Needham, Thomas J., 1904, 1907
Newton, Eustace J., 1902
Nichols, Charles A., 1900-01
Nickerson, S. W., 1880
Nicol, Hugh N., 1894
Nolan, Edward S., 1881
Noonan, Peter J., 1906-07
O'Brien, John F., 1889
O'Brien, William, 1876
O'Connor, Arthur, 1914
O'Connor, John J., 1893-1901
O'Day, Henry F., 1888-89, 1893, 1895-1911, 1913, 1915-27
Odlin, Albert F., 1883
O'Hara, 1915
O'Leary, Daniel, 1879
O'Neill, Michael J., 1904
O'Rourke, James H., 1893-94
Orth, Albert L., 1901, 1912-17
Osborne, William, 1876
O'Sullivan, John J., 1922
Overall, Orval, 1905, 1910
Owens, Clarence B., 1908, 1912-13
Parker, George L., 1936-38
Pearce, Grayson S., 1886-87, 1892
Pearce, Richard J., 1878, 1882
Pears, Frank, 1897
Pelekoudas, Chris G., 1961-62
Peitz, Henry C., 1901, 1906
Pfeffer, Nathaniel F., 1897
Pfirman, Charles H., 1922-36
Phelan, 1896
Phelps, Edward J., 1912
Phillippe, Charles L., 1903
Pierce, 1893
Pike, Lipman E., 1890
Pinelli, Ralph A., 1935-56
Powell, Jack, 1923-24, 1933
Power, Charles B., 1893, 1895, 1902
Power, Thomas E., 1887-88, 1894-95
Powers, James T., 1895
Powers, Philip J., 1881, 1886-91
Pratt, Albert G., 1879-80, 1887
Pratt, Thomas J., 1886
Pryor, John, 1962
Quest, Joseph L., 1886-87
Quigley, Ernest C., 1913-37
Quinn, Joseph C., 1881-82
Quinn, Joseph J., 1889, 1894, 1896
Quinn, P. J., 1876
Quinn, William H., 1887
Reardon, John E., 1926-49
Redheffer, 1893, 1895
Reid, William A., 1882
Reilly, Charles T., 1892-95
Reilly, William, 1880
Reitz, Henry P., 1895
Remsen, John J., 1880
Rhines, William P., 1891, 1896
Rhodes, Eugene A., 1887
Richardson, Arthur H., 1887, 1892
Richmond, John L., 1883
Rigler, Charles, 1905-22, 1924-35
Riley, William J., 1880
Ritchie, F., 1876
Robb, Douglas W., 1948-52
Roberts, Lew, 1953-55
Robinson, Wilbert, 1898
Rocap, Adam, 1876
Roll, 1876
Rudderham, Francis F., 1907
Rudderham, John E., 1908
Ryan, James E., 1892
Ryan, Walter, 1946
Sanders, Alexander B., 1889
Schew, Augustus, 1880-81
Schmidt, Henry M., 1903
Schofield, J. W., 1880
Schriver, William F., 1901
Schurer, 1896
Scott, James, 1930-31
Sears, John W., 1934-45
Secory, Frank E., 1952-62
Sentelle, Leopold T., 1922-23
Serad, William T., 1884
Seward, Edward W., 1892-93
Seward, George E., 1876-79
Sheridan, John F., 1892-93, 1896-97
Simons, J., 1876
Skinner, S. A., 1886
Smith, 1876
Smith, Charles M., 1881-82
Smith, Edward E., 1890
Smith, George H., 1901
Smith, Vincent, 1957-62
Smith, William E., 1886
Smith, William W., 1898-99
Sneeden, 1895
Snyder, Charles N., 1892-95, 1898, 1901
Sommers, Joseph A., 1889, 1893
Stafford, John H., 1906
Stage, Charles W., 1893-95
Staley, Harry E., 1892, 1895
Stambaugh, Calvin G., 1876-79
Stark, Albert D., 1928-35, 1937-39, 1942
Stearns, Daniel E., 1880-81
Stein. Edward F., 1890. 1894, 1896
Steiner, Melvin J., 1961-62
Steinfeldt, Henry M., 1905
Sternburg, 1909
Stewart, William J., 1933-54
Stivetts, John C., 1894
Stockdale, M. J., 1915
Stocksdale, Otis H., 1895
Stricker, John A., 1892
Stricklett, Elmer E., 1907
Strief, George A., 1889-90
Sudol, Edward, 1957-62
Sugden, Joseph, 1887
Sullivan, David F., 1880-83, 1885, 1888
Sullivan, Dennis J., 1881
Sullivan, James E., 1896
Sullivan, Jeremiah, 1887
Sullivan, John R., 1882
Sullivan, Martin J., 1889.
Sullivan, Michael J., 1897
Summer, James G., 1876-77, 1879
Supple, 1906
Sutcliffe, Elmer E., 1889, 1892

Sutton, Ezra B., 1876
Swartwood, Cyrus E., 1894-1900
Sweasy, Charles J., 1879
Sweeney, James M., 1924-26
Tannehill, Jesse N., 1897, 1901-02
Tate, Edward F., 1888
Taylor, John B., 1899
Taylor, John W., 1901, 1905
Tener, John K., 1889
Terry, William J. 1892, 1895-96, 1900
Tilden, Otis, 1876, 1880
Tindall, 1890, 1896
Toole, Stephen J., 1888
Truby, Harry G., 1909
Tuthill, Benjamin, 1893, 1895
Twitchell, Lawrence G., 1894
Valentine, John G., 1887-88
Van Court, Eugene, 1884
Vaughn, Harry F., 1892, 1899
Venzon, Anthony, 1957-62
Vareo, Edward P., 1961-62
Viau, Leon, 1891
Vickery, Thomas G., 1890
Wade, Ben F., 1880
Walker, Thomas W., 1905
Walker, William E., 1876-77
Wall, Joseph F., 1901
Wallace, Roderick J., 1895
Walsh, Frank, 1877
Walsh, Michael F., 1876, 1879-82
Walters, 1892-93
Walton, G. W., 1876
Ward, John M., 1888
Warneke, Lonnie, 1949-55
Warner, Albert, 1898-99
Warner, John J., 1896-97, 1900, 1903
Warren, I. B., 1876
Waterman, Frederick A., 1880
Weaver, William B., 1893
Weeden, 1889-90
Weidman, George E., 1894, 1896
Weimer, Jacob W., 1905, 1907
Welch, Michael F., 1885-86, 1888, 1890
West, George, 1878
West, Milton D., 1890
Westervelt, Frederick E., 1922
Weyer, Lee H., 1961-62
Weyhing, August, 1894, 1899-1900
Wheeler, Robert, 1879
Whistler, Lewis, 1891
White, George F., 1876-78
White, Guy H., 1901-02
White, James L., 1880
White, William W., 1876
Whitney, James E., 1884, 1886
Wilbur, Charles E., 1879-80
Wilhelm, Irving K., 1904-05
Williams, Elisha A., 1876
Williams, James A., 1879
Willis, Victor G., 1903
Wilmot, Walter R., 1897
Wilson, Frank, 1923-28
Wilson, Frank A., 1896
Wilson, John A., 1887
Wilson, Parke A., 1894-96, 1899
Wilson, William C., 1890, 1892-93
Wise, Samuel W., 1889, 1893
Wolf, William V., 1895-97
Wood, George A., 1889, 1898
Wood, James B., 1876
Woulffe, James J., 1893
Wright, William H., 1876-77, 1885
Yeager, George E., 1901
York, Thomas J., 1886
Young, Denton T., 1896
Young, Irving M., 1905, 1907
Young, John W., 1879-81
Zacharias, Thomas, 1890
Zimmer, Charles L., 1889, 1904-05

AMERICAN LEAGUE

Adams, John H., 1903
Barry, Daniel, 1928
Basil, Stephen J., 1936-42
Berry, Charles F., 1942-62
Betts, William G., 1901
Boyer, James M., 1944-50
Campbell, William M., 1928-31
Cantillon, Joseph, 1901
Carrigan, Herve, 1961-62
Carpenter, William B., 1904
Caruthers, Robert L., 1902-03
Chill, Oliver P., 1914-16, 1919-22
Chylak, Nestor, 1954-62
Colliflower, James H., 1910
Connolly, Thomas H., 1901-31
Connor, Thomas, 1905-06
Cronin, John J., 1901
Dinneen, William H., 1909-37
Donnelly, Charles H., 1934-35
Drummond, Calvin T., 1960-62
Duffy, James F., 1951-55
Dwyer, John F., 1904
Egan, John J., 1903, 1907-14
Eldridge, Clarence E., 1914-15
Evans, William G., 1906-27
Ferguson, Charles A., 1913
Flaherty, John F., 1953-62
Friel, William E., 1920
Froese, Grover A., 1952-53
Geisel, Harry C., 1925-42
Grieve, William T. T., 1938-55
Guthrie, William J., 1922, 1928-32
Haller, Bill, 1962
Hart, Eugene F., 1912-13
Hart, William F., 1901
Haskell, John E., 1901
Hassett, James E., 1903
Hildebrand, George A., 1912-34
Holmes, Howard E., 1923-24
Honochick, George J., 1949-62
Hubbard, Robert C., 1936-51, 1954-62
Hurley, Edwin H., 1947-62
Hurst, Timothy C., 1905-09
Johnston, Charles E., 1936-37
Johnstone, James E., 1902
Jones, Nicholas I., 1944-9
Kelly, Thomas B., 1905
Kerin, John, 1908-10
Kerins, John A., 1903
King, Charles F., 1904
Kinnamon, William F., 1960-62
Linsalata, Joseph N., 1961-62
Kolls, Louis C., 1933-40
Mannassau, Alfred S., 1901
Marberry, Frederick, 1935
McCarthy, John, 1905
McCormick, William J., 1917
McGowan, William A., 1925-54
McGreevy, Edward, 1912-13
McKinley, William F., 1946-62
Moriarty, George J., 1917-26, 1929-40
Mullaney, Dominic J., 1915
Mullin, John, 1911-12
Nallin, Richard F., 1915-32
Napp, Lawrence A., 1951-62
O'Brien, Joseph, 1912, 1914
O'Loughlin, Frank H., 1902-18
Ormsby, Emmett T., 1923-41
Owens, Clarence B., 1916-37
Paparella, Joseph J., 1946-62
Parker, Harley P., 1911
Passarella, Arthur M., 1941-42, 1945-53
Pears, Frank, 1903
Perrine, Fred, 1909-12
Pipgras, George W., 1938-46
Quigley, Ernest C., 1906
Quinn, John A., 1935-42
Rice, John L., 1955-62
Robb, Douglas W., 1952-53
Rommel, Edwin A., 1938-59
Rowland, Clarence H., 1923-27
Rue, Joseph W., 1938-47
Runge, Edward P., 1954-62
Salerno, Al, 1962
Schwarts, Harry C., 1960-62
Sheridan, John F., 1901-14
Smith, William A., 1960-62
Soar, Albert H., 1950-62
Stafford, John H., 1907
Stevens, John W., 1948-62
Stewart, Ernest D., 1941-45
Stewart, Robert W., 1960-62
Summers, William R., 1933-59
Tabacchi, Frank, 1956-59
Umont, Frank, 1954-62
Van Graflan, Roy, 1927-33
Wallace, Roderick J., 1915-1916
Walsh, Edward A., 1922
Weafer, Harold L., 1943-47
Westervelt, Frederick E., 1911-12
Wilson, Frank, 1921-22

AMERICAN ASSOCIATION

Arnold, Frank W., 1889
Austin, Ed, 1890
Baldwin, Clarence G., 1887
Barnie, William S., 1882, 1884, 1887, 1889
Barnum, George W., 1890
Battin, Joseph V., 1882, 1886
Bass, John E., 1883
Bauer, Albert J., 1887, 1890
Becannon, James M., 1884
Becannon, William H., 1883
Bell, Frank G., 1889
Bittman, Henry, 1889
Blogg, Wesley C., 1886
Bloom, 1887*
Bond, Thomas H., 1884
Booth, Amos S., 1882
Bowes, Frank C., 1890
Boyle, John A., 1888
Brennan, James A., 1888
Brennan, John E., 1884
Briody, Charles F., 1888
Burkalow, Isaac, 1888
Burns, 1882
Burns, Thomas P., 1888
Bushong, Albert J., 1888-89
Butler, Charles, 1889
Butler, Ormond H., 1883, 1886
Campbell, Daniel, 1890
Carey, Thomas J., 1882
Carlin, William J., 1885-86, 1888-89
Carsey, Wilfred, 1891
Cassidy, John P., 1884
Chamberlain, Elton P., 1887, 1891
Clinton, J. L., 1886
Connell J., 1885
Connell, Terence G., 1884-86, 1889-90
Connelly, John M., 1885-1887
Connelly, William 1884
Cornell, 1884
Crandall, Robert, 1882
Creighton, 1889-90
Critchley, Morris A., 1884-85
Cross, Laaf yette N., 1889
Crowell, William T., 1888
Curry, Frank, 1886
Curry, Wesley, 1887, 1890
Cuthbert, Edgar E., 1887-88
Dailey, John J., 1883-84, 1889
Daniels, Charles F., 1883-85, 1889
Daniels, Lawrence, 1887
Darling, Dell C., 1891
Davis, James J., 1891
Devine, Walter J., 1890
DeVinney, Daniel, 1887
DeVinney, P. H., 1884
Devlin, Charles, 1888
Dolan, Thomas J., 1890
Donahue, James A., 1888
Doscher, John H., 1888, 1890
Dow, 1890
Dugan, 1887
Duke, Martin F., 1890
Dunlevy, Hugh, 1887
Dyler, John F., 1883-86
Easton, John E., 1891
Ehret, Philip S., 1890
Ellick, Joseph J., 1888-89
Emslie, Robert D., 1890
Ewing, William, 1882, 1889
Fell, 1885
Ferguson, Robert V., 1886-89, 1891
Fountain, Henry V., 1888
Fulmer, Charles J., 1888
Fulmer, Christopher, 1887
Gaffney, John H., 1888-89
Galvin, James F., 1885-86
Ganzel, Charles W., 1886
Geer, William H., 1887
Gill, Thomas H., 1886
Gleason, William G., 1891
Goldsby, Walton H., 1888
Goldsmith, Frederick E., 1888-89
Greenwood, William F., 1884
Griffith, Clark C., 1891
Griffith, E. A., 1884
Gunning, Thomas F., 1888-89
Healy, John J., 1890
Hecker, Guy J., 1888-89
Helburn, Hugo, 1887
Henderson, James H., 1889
Hengle, Edward S., 1889
Herr, Edward J., 1888
Hicks, Nathaniel W., 1885
Higgins, William H., 1890
Holbert, William H., 1888
Holland, John A., 1884
Holland, Willard A., 1889

Holliday, James W., 1888
Houtz, Charles, 1882
Hurley, Daniel, 1887
Irwin, John, 1885
Jennings, Alfred, 1882, 1884-85, 1887, 1889, 1891
Johnston, Richard F., 1884
Jones, Charles W., 1891
Julian, Joseph O., 1888
Keefe, Timothy J., 1884
Keenan, James W., 1887-88
Kelly, John O., 1882-88
Kerins, John A., 1889-90
Kilroy, Matthew A., 1887
Kirby, J. J., 1888
Kleinbacker, 1886
Knell, Philip H., 1891
Knight, Alonzo P., 1887
Latham, George W., 1884
Lawler, John F., 1884
Lilly, J., 1884
Little, 1884
Loughlin, 1885
Lynch, John H., 1884
Lyons, Toby A., 1891
Lyston, William E., 1890
Macullar, James F., 1891
Macullar, John F., 1886
Mack, Dennis J., 1886
Magner, John T., 1883-84, 1887
Malone, J. R., 1888
Marshall, 1887
Mathews, Robert T., 1888, 1891
Mattimore, Michael J., 1888
McCarthy, Thomas F. M., 1889
McCartney, Joseph, 1882
McCarty, John A., 1890
McCormick, 1888
McGee, Patrick, 1882, 1884
McGinnis, George M., 1888-89
McIntosh, 1882
McKelvy, Russell E., 1882
McLaughlin, Thomas, 1891
McLaughlin, William, 1882
McLean, William B., 1882, 1885, 1889-90
McMahon, John J., 1890
McNichol, Robert T., 1883
McQuade, James H., 1891
McQuade, John H., 1886-88
McSorley, John B., 1888
McSorley, Thomas S., 1884
Medart, William, 1887
Merrill, Edward S., 1884
Mitchell, 1887
Miller, Joseph H., 1884
Morgan, Henry W., 1884
Morton, Charles H., 1884, 1886
Mountain, Frank H., 1884
Mullen, Peter C., 1891
O'Brien, John K., 1890
O'Brien, William D., 1887-88
O'Connor, John J., 1889
O'Dea, Lawrence, 1890
Paasch, William, 1887-89
Parker, 1887
Pearce, Grayson S., 1882, 1884
Peoples, James E., 1888-90
Pike, Lipman, E., 1887, 1889
Pratt, Albert G., 1883, 1886
Quinn, A. J., 1886
Quinn, William H., 1884-85
Reeder, James E., 1884
Reising, Charles, 1882
Rice, 1885
Riley, William J., 1882, 1885
Robb, John, 1886
Ross, Robert T., 1882, 1884
Ruhl, Gus, 1882
Ryan, John, 1882
Sage, Henry, 1890
Schroder, 1890
Selman, Frank C., 1882
Serad, William T., 1888
Seward, George E., 1884
Sherman, 1890
Simmons, Joseph S., 1882
Skeenet, 1890
Skinner, 1884
Smith, Charles M., 1882, 1886
Smith, Frederick C., 1890
Smith, George, 1887
Sneed, John L., 1885
Snyder, Charles N., 1886, 1891
Sommer, Benjamin, 1883
Sommer, Joseph J., 1888
Sprague, Charles W., 1890
Stivetts, John C., 1891
Sullivan, David F., 1884
Sullivan, Theodore P., 1887
Sweeney, Charles J., 1887
Sylvester, Louis J., 1888
Talbot, 1887
Taylor, Walter, 1890
Terry, William J., 1884, 1888
Tinney, 1882
Toole, Stephen J., 1890
Townsend, George H., 1890
Traffley, William F., 1884
Tunnison, 1885-86
Valentine, John G., 1884-86
Vaughn, Harry F., 1891
Viau, Leon, 1888
Walsh, Michael F., 1882-83, 1885-88
West, 1885, 1887
Weyhing, August, 1891
Wheeler, Harry E., 1882
Wood, George A., 1886, 1891
Wright, 1884
Wright, Parry, 1884
York, Thomas J., 1886
Young, Benjamin F., 1887
Young, Joseph, 1890
Zimmer, Charles L., 1888

NATIONAL ASSOCIATION

Addy, Robert E., 1875
Allison, Arthur A., 1872, 1874
Allison, Douglas L., 1872-73, 1875
Allison, H., 1874
Alston, David, 1871-72, 1875
Annan, 1873
Arnold, Willis S., 1875
Barlow, Thomas H., 1875
Barnes, Roscoe C., 1874
Barrett, William, 1872, 1874
Barron, James, 1875
Barrows, Frederick, 1872
Batt, Thomas, 1871
Battin, Joseph V., 1874
Beals, Thomas J., 1874-75
Beardslee, J. J., 1871-73
Bechtel, George A., 1874
Beck, W. S., 1872
Bielaski, Oscar, 1874-75
Bigelow, W. J., 1875
Birdsall, David S., 1873-74
Blair, William J., 1873
Blodgett, C. W., 1875
Boake, J. L., 1871
Bordman, Frederick, 1875
Bomeisler, Theodore, 1871-75
Bonse, N., 1871
Boyd, William J., 1873, 1875
Bradley, George H., 1875
Brainard, Asa, 1872, 1875
Briggs, 1874
Brown, William, 1872, 1875
Bryant, 1875
Buck, 1871
Bunce, 1874
Burdock, John J., 1872-74
Bush, A. M., 1871
Carey, Thomas J., 1873,75
Cassidy, Joseph P., 1875
Cavanaugh, J. H., 1875
Chandler, Moses E., 1872, 1874
Chapman, John C., 1871-74
Clapp, John E., 1874-75
Clifton, 1872
Clinton, James L., 1873
Clinton, John L., 1875
Collins, Daniel T., 1875
Cone, J. F., 1873-75
Cope, Elias, 1871
Craver, William H., 1873
Cuthbert, Edgar E., 1875
Daniels, Charles F., 1874-75
Daubney, Thomas, 1871
David, L. N., 1874
Dawson, 1871
Dean, Harry J., 1871
Deane, Henry C., 1874
Dehlman, Harmon J., 1873-75
Demorest, 1872-73
Dobson, H. A., 1871
Dole, W. C., 1875
Dornlach, D.E., 1872
Douglass, Benjamin F., 1875
Draper, John H., 1871
Ellis, William R., 1871-72, 1875
English, John W., 1874-75
Erby, Frederick, 1872
Evans, George, 1872
Fellows, T. E., 1871
Fenoe, 1872
Ferguson, Robert V., 1871-75
Fisher, William C., 1871, 1875
Foley, Thomas J., 1874-75
Force, David W., 1873
Fulmer, Charles J., 1872-75
Garrigan, 1873
Geer, William H., 1874-75
Gerhardt, Joseph J., 1875
Ginn, 1875
Glenn, John W., 1874
Glover, Frank, 1873
Goodwin, J. C., 1871-72
Gould, Charles H., 1874-75
Graham, 1872
Halbach, A. C. N., 1873-74
Hall, George W., 1873-75
Hall, James, 1872
Hanford, Charles, 1874
Hastings, Winfield S., 1871-74
Hatfield John V. B., 1872-73
Hayhurst, Elias H., 1875
Haynie, James L., 1871
Hegeman, William H., 1871
Heim, J., 1871-72
Heubel, George A., 1875
Higham, Richard, 1873-75
Hodes, Charles, 1874
Hodges, A. D., 1874-75
Holly, Samuel J., 1871
Hooper, Michael H., 1872-74
Hosworth, 1872-74
Howard, 1872
Hynan, 1871
Jennings, Alfred, 1873
Kahn, S. L., 1875
Keerl, George W., 1872
Kent, John, 1875
Knight, G. H., 1875
Kohler, Henry, 1873
Lamb, Harry, 1875
Laughlin, Benjamin, 1873
Lennon, William F., 1871-72
Leonard, Andrew, 1872-73, 1875
Leonard, 1872
Leroy, Isaac, 1871
Locke, Marshall, 1873-74
Lowell, John A., 1872-73
Lush, M. R., 1871, 1873
MacDiarmed, Thomas, 1872
Mack, Dennis J., 1871-75
Malone, 1875
Marion, S. H., 1873
Martin, Alphonse C., 1871, 1873, 1875,
Martin, Lewis G., 1871, 1873-74
Mathews, Robert T., 1871, 1873-75
Mawny, J. H., 1871
Maxwell, Cortez, 1875
Mays, 1871
McCrea, 1872
McDonald, James F., 1872
McGeary, Michael H., 1872, 1875
McLean, Harry, 1871, 1873
McLean, William B., 1872-75
McMahon, W., 1871
McMullen, John F., 1874
McVey, Calvin A., 1875
Miller, Joseph W., 1872-73
Mills, Charles, 1871-72
Mincher, Edward J., 1872, 1875
Mincher, William E., 1875
Mitchell, C. L., 1874
Mitchell, F. B., 1875
Mosely, M., 1873
Murdock, 1872
Murnane, Timothy H., 1873-75
Nelson, J., 1872
Nichols, A. N., 1871
Norton, F., 1872
O'Brien, P., 1875
Pabor, Charles H., 1875
Parks, William R., 1875
Patterson, Daniel T., 1872, 1874
Pearce, Richard S., 1872
Pearson, S. W., 1872

Phelps, Cornelius C., 1874
Pike, J., 1875
Porter, 1874
Powers, W., 1872-73, 1875
Pratt, Thomas J., 1871-73
Quinn, Patrick, 1875
Radcliffe, John J., 1873
Rastall, J. N., 1872
Reach, Albert J., 1872-75
Reed, Hugh, 1871, 1873-74
Remsen, John J., 1873-74
Robinson, A. V., 1872
Robinson, Miley, 1873
Rogers, Morton, 1871-72
Ryan, John J., 1872, 1875
Sawyer, D., 1871
Schafer, Harry C., 1875
Schroeder, 1875
Schuester, John A., 1874-75
Sears, 1873
Selman, Frank C., 1873
Sensenderfer, John P. J., 1872-75
Simmons, Joseph S., 1871, 1874
Smith, Eb., 1872
Smith, George, 1872
Smith, Gustavus, 1872, 1875
Snyder, 1875
Stahl, G., 1875
Stanwood, 1872
Sutton, Ezra B., 1875
Swandell, John M., 1871-73
Sweasy, Charles J., 1871, 1873-74
Tate, William, 1874
Tighe, Edward, 1871
Treacy, Frederick, 1871, 1873, 1875
Tyler, C. T., 1871-74
Urell, E., 1873
Van Delft, 1875
Voltz, Edward, 1871-72
Walk, Frank, 1871
Walsh, Michael F., 1875
Wardell, 1874
Waterman, Frederick A., 1873
Weaver, C., 1873
Weigel, W. H., 1873-74
White, H. F., 1873
White, Warren W., 1874-75
Whiting, R., 1872
Wiggins, 1875
Wildey, John, 1871
Willard, Gardner, 1871
Wood, James B., 1871
Worth, Adam, 1875
Woulfe, 1871
Wright, George, 1871
Wright, William H., 1875
York, Thomas J., 1874
Young, Nicholas E., 1871-75

FEDERAL LEAGUE

Anderson, Oliver O., 1914
Brennan, William T., 1914-15
Brewer, 1915
Bush, Garnet C., 1914
Carpenter, 1914
Corcoran, Thomas W., 1914-15
Cross, Montford M., 1914
Cusack, Stephen P., 1914
Finneran, William E., 1915
Fyfe, Louis, 1915
Goeckel, E., 1914
Groom, Robert, 1914
Howell, Harry, 1915
Johnstone, James E., 1914-15
Kane, Stephen J., 1914
Langden, Joseph, 1915
Mannassau, Alfred S., 1914
Maxwell, J. A., 1914
McCormick, William J., 1914-15
Mullin, John, 1915
Murphy, J. A., 1914
O'Brien, Joseph, 1915
Quisser, 1914
Shannon, William P., 1914-15
Stocksdale, Otis H., 1915
Van Sickle, Charles F., 1914
Westervelt, Frederick E., 1915
Wilhelm, Irving K., 1915

PLAYERS' LEAGUE (1890)

Balkie
Barnes, Roscoe C.
Carney, John J.
Caskin, Edward J.
Comiskey, Charles A.
Daily, Cornelius F.
Ferguson, Robert V.
Gaffney, John H.
Gumbert, Addison C.
Gunning, Thomas F.
Haddock, George S.
Hallinan, W. W.
Holbert, William H.
Husted, William J.
Jones, Charles W.
Keefe, Timothy J.
Kelly, John O.,
Kilroy, Matthew A.
Knight, Alonzo P.
Leach, Henry
Madden, Michael J.
Matthews, John
Milligan, John
Murphy, Cornelius B.
O'Day, Henry F.
Pearce, Grayson S.
Sanders, Alexander B.
Sheridan, John F.
Snyder, Charles N.
Tener, John K.

UNION ASSOCIATION (1884)

Adler
Bradley, George W.
Burlingame, F. A.
Callahan, Edward J.
Carroll, Patrick
Crawford, Alexander
Cuthbert, Edgar E.
DeVinney, P. H.
Donovan
Dutton, Patrick J.
Furlong, William E.
Grady, John J.
Hengle, Edward S.
Hoberbeck
Holland, John A.
Hooper, Michael H.
Hoover
Hudson, Vincent D.
Jennings, Alfred
Jordan
Kelly, John O.
Lee, Thomas F.
Mapledoram, Blake A.
McCaffrey, Harry
McGunningle, William H.
McLaughlin, William
McManaway
McMinimum
Montgomery
O'Leary, Daniel
Powers, Charles B.
Seward, George E.
Stearns, Daniel E.
Sullivan, David F.
Timblin
Torry
Wheeler
Williams

X BASEBALL ADMINISTRATION

Baseball's first professional league, the National Association, folded because its forthright player-president, Bob Ferguson, had a blustering type of ballfield leadership that did not carry over into sorely needed executive diplomacy. NA directors ignored his roars for sorely needed reform. Suave, magnetic and dynamic William A. Hulbert proved perfect for establishing the National League on a permanent basis.

Col. A. G. Mills, an uncompromising administrator in the Hulbert mold, ruled the NL for two years before the iron-handed "Bismarck of Baseball" resigned when the league refused his demand to crack down on players who had jumped to the "outlaw" Union Association in 1884.

That brought kindly, honest and conciliatory Nicholas E. Young into power in 1885. Uncle Nick was so unaggressive that clubowners' cliques virtually ruled the sprawling 12-club NL in the Gay Nineties. Umpires were kicked and choked. The rowdy Baltimore Orioles were a law unto themselves. Young's timidity gave reign to excesses that eventually wrecked his administration and led to the establishment of the AL.

After two years of ruinous war between the leagues, genial and expansive Garry Herrmann, president of the Cincinnati Reds, engineered peace in January, 1903. For his valuable services, Herrmann was rewarded with the chairmanship of a new three-man National Commission which was to rule baseball for almost two full decades. The other Commission members were the league presidents, Ban Johnson and Harry Pulliam.

Baseball's triumvirate started disintegrating in the wake of the Browns vs. Pirates battle over title to George Sisler. When Herrmann cast the deciding vote with the AL club, Barney Dreyfuss of the Pirates howled at Herrmann's "treason" to his own league. He accused Herrmann of being under the influence of his old friend, AL president Johnson. Dreyfuss had pamphlets printed which intended to discredit Herrmann's decision. This insurrection died down, but the three-man Commission had lost face, and Dreyfuss at least succeeded in starting a snowballing drive to name a single Commissioner with no stake in baseball.

Johnson had trouble in his own league. The Yankees overruled him with a court injunction on the Carl Mays case, then drew support from the Red Sox and White Sox in a secession move aimed at switching to the NL. Meanwhile, NL president John A. Heydler felt the pressure of anti-Herrmann propaganda, and refused to vote to return the Reds' chief to the Commission in 1920. Since Johnson and Heydler couldn't agree on Herrmann's successor, baseball was without an actual chief in 1920, leaving the two presidents to settle their own league controversies.

On September 28, the Black Sox scandal exploded in a Chicago courtroom. Eight Chicago players were exposed as having agreed to lose the 1919 World Series to Cincinnati. The sports world was especially bitter that this crisis in baseball history should come at a time when there was no real governing head. In the nation's press, on the floor of Congress and from pulpits came cries to clean up the game for its very salvation.

COMMISSIONER'S OFFICE

Against this turbulent backdrop, Federal Judge K. M. Landis was ushered into baseball's throne room. The white-maned jurist had earned the gratitude of organized ball in 1915 by his deft handling of the dangerous lawsuit brought by the "outlaw" Federal League. He also had a reputation as a racket-buster, having fined Standard Oil Company $29,240,000 in a rebate case in 1907.

Though Landis was earning only $7,500 on the Federal bench, he didn't indicate immediate enthusiasm at baseball's offer of a seven-year contract at $50,000 per. He demanded and immediately was granted carte blanche in any matter he deemed "detrimental to baseball." Under this sweeping provision he wielded the big stick, often autocratically, yet with such crusading zeal that he restored the good name of the game.

The new Czar risked his crown that very first year when he fined Babe Ruth and suspended him for breaking the post-season barnstorming rule of 1921. Babe's immeasurable popularity caused the public to grumble over the drastic decree; but the complaints were tinged with a growing respect for this inflexible disciple of law and order.

In a quarter century as administrator, Landis became known as the "ballplayer's friend." He fought for extension of the annual draft to all minor leagues. He regarded the "farm system" as a similar stratagem to cover up capable players in the bushes, and in two earthquaking edicts the Great Emancipator freed 127 Cardinal farmhands in 1938 and 91 Tiger chattels in 1940. Other player petitions resulted in free agency for Tommy Henrich, Rick Ferrell, Phil Todt, Claude Jonnard and dozens of others.

Landis never compromised with even the slightest tint of gambling or dishonesty. He forced Giant owner Charles Stoneham and manager John McGraw to sell their interests in the Havana racetrack. He expelled Bill Cox, president of the Phillies, for betting on a game. Though the courts failed to convict the Black Sox, Landis blacklisted them from baseball for life: Joe Jackson, Ed Cicotte, Chick Gandil, Swede Risberg, Happy Felsch, Buck Weaver, Claude Williams and Fred McMullin. He also threw his dreaded black book in later years at players Benny Kauff, Cozy Dolan, Phil Douglas and Jim O'Connell. However, he exonerated Ty Cobb and Tris Speaker after Hubert (Dutch) Leonard had charged them in 1926 with collusion on a 1919 game.

Judge Landis died November 25, 1944. His assistant, Leslie O'Connor, took charge of affairs until U. S. Senator Albert Benjamin (Happy) Chandler was elected on April 24, 1945 for a seven-year term at $50,000 a year (later raised to $65,000). The former Class D ballplayer headed the game through its most prosperous years, but he met his share of administrative headaches.

Early in 1946, the free-spending Mexican League raided the majors. Chandler stemmed the tide by announcing a five-year ban against jumping players. Three years later, after the Jorge Pasquel-bankrolled league collapsed, Chandler declared general amnesty. However, Danny Gardella, former outfielder who had broken only the reserve clause of his Giant contract to take the "Mexican holiday" pressed a lawsuit against organized baseball's alleged monopoly. When this case received a favorable vote in the New York State Supreme Court, Chandler suddenly effected an out-of-court settlement with Gardella who, incidentally, was represented by Chandler's former classmate at Harvard Law School, Frederic A. Johnson.

In 1947, Chandler suspended Dodger manager Lippy Leo Durocher for a year, citing an accumulation of "incidents." Lippy took his medicine and returned the next year.

The Commissioner's vigilant administration of the rule against signing high school players brought him into head-on battle with Leslie O'Connor, former

Acting Commissioner, who was fined as White Sox general manager for signing a schoolboy. O'Connor claimed Chandler was overstepping his authority, and even threatened to go to court. Chandler held firm. Sox owners finally paid the fine and released O'Connor.

Seeking a renewal of his contract in December, 1950, Chandler received a majority vote, but not the required two-thirds. Clubowners then decided on a committee to select a new Commissioner "as soon as practicable." Chandler, whose contract ran to April, 1952, was voted out of office before his contract expired.

Ford C. Frick, who had advanced to the presidency of the National League after serving as a sportswriter on a New York newspaper, radio sportscaster and manager of the National League Service Bureau, became baseball's third commissioner on September 20, 1951. He signed a seven-year contract at a salary of $65,000 per year. In 1957, Frick signed his second seven-year contract.

Financially, the Commissioner's office is supported solely by the World Series. Fifteen percent of all net receipts of each game are set aside for the expenses (salaries, travel and overhead) involved in conducting the normal business of the office.

LEAGUE AGREEMENTS

Organized Baseball has five main documents: Major League Agreement, Major League Rules, Major-Minor League Agreements, Major-Minor League Rules and the National Association Rules.

Top man is the Commissioner. As specified in the Major League Agreement, and underwritten in the Major-Minor pact, his functions may be summarized as follows:

(a) To investigate any act detrimental to baseball.
(b) To decide on punitive action.
(c) To decide any interleague dispute brought to him by either league president.
(d) To determine any dispute involving a player.
(e) To formulate rules of procedure in cases under his control.

In case "detrimental conduct" originates outside of organized baseball, Article I, Section 4 says he "may pursue appropriate legal remedies, advocate remedial legislation and take such other steps as he may deem necessary and proper to the interests and morale of the players and the honor of the game."

Another important article in the Major League Agreement (to remain in force till January 1, 1970) stipulates that all contracts between clubs and their officers, players and other employes shall contain a clause binding the parties to submit to the discipline of the Commissioner.

Baseball's legislative arm is the joint meeting of major leagues. In interleague affairs, majority rules within each circuit, and then each league votes as a unit. In case of a tie, the Commissioner casts the deciding vote.

In the interim between league meetings, the majors are guided by an Executive Council. It consists of the Commissioner, both league presidents and one member elected by each of the leagues. However, in matters dealing with players' grievances, two active players are added to this Council, with majority to rule and all decisions binding and final.

Except in cases of critical clashes, the Major League Agreement is not as important as the Major League Rules. The latter is a lengthy covenant completely regulating league, club, player and umpire rights and responsibilities. The Commissioner is obliged to enforce these rules, and has no power to abrogate any of them on "detrimental to baseball" grounds. Any amendment passed by the majors, which affect the Major-Minor Agreement, must be submitted to a mail vote of all the minor leagues.

The Major-Minor League Agreement places the minors under jurisdiction of the Commissioner either in cases of "detrimental conduct" or in major-minor disputes. It also sets up a Major-Minor Executive Council for interim rule, and fixes the scale of payments in the annual player draft.

Major-Minor League Rules deal with protection of franchises, player limits, reserve lists, drafting, optional agreements, stock ownership, etc. As for the fifth charter of baseball's government, the National Association Agreement details a method of operation for the minors.

PLAYER-MANAGEMENT COMMITTEE

The aftermath of the Mexican League raids caused the owners some alarm. They reasoned that possibly the players felt insecure in their future and began to plan a series of new benefits. When the Pittsburgh players threatened their owner with unionization in order to bargain as a team for "better benefits," the owners went into action.

Each team was asked to select one player to represent it with the front office. Then each team voted on a player delegate to represent its league in the five-man Executive Council which votes on matters involving players' conditions. Thus was established a virtual "player-management committee" which led to the immediate adoption of a pension fund, insurance benefits, a minimum salary figure of $5,000, a maximum pay salary cut of 25 percent, and many additional gains. (The minimum salary figure has since been raised twice: to $6,000, and its current figure of $7,000.)

The Players' Pension Fund receives 60 percent of the TV-radio sponsorship of the All-Star and World Series games. The sponsor pays $3,250,000 annually for these events, with $3,000,000 as the fee set for the World Series. Sixty percent, or $1,800,000 of the overall sum, is placed in the Pension Fund. In addition, 60 per cent of the net gate receipts from the All-Star Game is allocated to the Fund.

The many economic benefits gained by the players came through the strength in their respective club player-representatives and by the efforts of J. Norman Lewis and James P. Durante, who served as the players' attorneys. They advised and counseled the players, helped frame their requests and drew up a list of other matters pertaining to the players' welfare and their financial security. However, just before the opening of the 1959 season, the players decided to dispense with the services of an attorney to represent them in negotiations with the owners.

The future of the retired ballplayer is indeed a healthy one and baseball's "retirement plan" is comparable to that of any major industry, and might possibly be a bit more liberal. As of the 1959 season, here is what today's player can foresee when he decides to retire from baseball:

5 years in the majors: receive $ 88 monthly at the age of 50.
10 years in the majors: receive $175 monthly at the age of 50.
15 years in the majors: receive $225 monthly at the age of 50.
20 years in the majors: receive $275 monthly at the age of 50.

The Pension Plan is figured on a graduated scale, and a retired player eligible for pension payments receives more if he doesn't apply for his monthly allotment until an age later than 50. For example, a retired player who doesn't request his monthly payments until he is 65, can receive approximately $550 per month if he has 20 years' service.

The clubs and players each contribute to the Players' Pension Fund, with the players assessed approximately a bit less than $300 a year.

OFFICIAL PLAYER'S CONTRACT

PARTIES. Between .... herein called the Club, and .... of ...., herein called the Player.

RECITAL. The Club is a member of the American League of Professional Baseball Clubs, a voluntary association of eight member clubs which has subscribed to the Major League Rules with the National League of Professional Baseball Clubs and its constituent clubs and to the Major-Minor League Rules with that League and the National Association of Baseball Leagues. The purpose of those rules is to insure the public wholesome and high-class professional baseball by defining the relations between the Club and Player, between club and club, between league and league, and by vesting in a designated Commissioner broad powers of control and discipline, and of decision in case of disputes.

AGREEMENT. In consideration of the facts above recited and of the promises of each to the other, the parties agree as follows:

EMPLOYMENT. 1. The Club hereby employs the Player to render, and the Player agrees to render, skilled services as a baseball player during the year ....196... including the Club's training season, the Club's exhibition games, the Club's playing season, and the World Series (or any other official series in which the Club may participate and in any receipts of which the player may be entitled to share).

PAYMENT. 2. For performance of the Player's services and promises hereunder the Club will pay the Player the sum of $................................ ...., as follows:

In semi-monthly installments after the commencement of the playing season covered by this contract, unless the Player is "abroad" with the Club for the purpose of playing games, in which event the amount then due shall be paid on the first week-day after the return "home" of the Club, the terms "home" and "abroad" meaning respectively at and away from the city in which the Club has its baseball field.

If a monthly rate of payment is stipulated above, it shall begin with the commencement of the Club's playing season (or such subsequent date as the Player's services may commence) and end with the termination of the Club's scheduled playing season, and shall be payable in semi-monthly installments as above provided.

If the player is in the service of the Club for part of the playing season only, he shall receive such proportion of the sum above mentioned, as the number of days of his actual employment in the Club's playing season bears to the number of days in said season.

Notwithstanding the rate of payment stipulated above, the minimum rate of payment to the Player for each day of service on a Major League Club shall be at the rate of $6,000 per year; except that such minimum rate of payment shall be at the rate of $7,000 per year retroactive to the beginning of the season if the Player is on a Major League Club's roster on June 15 and shall be at the rate of $7,000 per year if the Player physically joins a Major League Club between June 15 and August 31. If a player physically joins a Major League Club on or after September 1, the minimum rate of payment shall be at the rate of $6,000 per year for each day of service with such Major League Club.

LOYALTY. 3. (a) The Player agrees to perform his services hereunder diligently and faithfully, to keep himself in first class physical condition and to obey the Club's training rules, and pledges himself to the American public and to the Club to conform to high standards of personal conduct, fair play and good sportsmanship.

BASEBALL PROMOTION. (b) In addition to his services in connection with the actual playing of baseball, the Player agrees to cooperate with the Club and participate in any and all promotional activities of the Club and its League, which, in the opinion of the Club, will promote the welfare of the Club or professional baseball, and to observe and comply with all requirements of the Club respecting conduct and service of its team and its players, at all times whether on or off the field.

PICTURES AND PUBLIC APPEARANCES. (c) The Player agrees that his picture may be taken for still photographs, motion pictures or television at such times as the Club may designate and agrees that all rights in such pictures shall belong to the Club and may be used by the Club for publicity purposes in any manner it desires. The Player further agrees that during the playing season he will not make public appearances, participate in radio or television programs or permit his picture to be taken or write or sponsor newspaper or magazine articles or sponsor commercial products without the written consent of the Club, which shall not be withheld except in the reasonable interests of the Club or professional baseball.

PLAYER REPRESENTATIONS

ABILITY. 4. (a) The Player represents and agrees that he has exceptional and unique skill and ability as a baseball player; that his services to be rendered hereunder are of a special unusual and extraordinary character which gives them peculiar value which cannot be reasonably or adequately compensated for in damages at law, and that the Player's breach of this contract will cause the Club great and irreparable injury and damage. The Player agrees that, in addition to other remedies, the Club shall be entitled to injunctive and other equitable relief to prevent a breach of this contract by the Player, including, among others, the right to enjoin the Player from playing baseball for any other person or organization during the term of this contract.

CONDITION (b) The Player represents that he has no physical or mental defects, known to him, which would prevent or impair performance of his services.

INTEREST IN CLUB (c) The Player represents that he does not, directly or indirectly, own stock or have any financial interest in the ownership or earnings of any Major League club, except as hereinafter expressly set forth, and covenants that he will not hereafter, while connected with any Major League club, acquire or hold any such stock or interest except in accordance with Major League Rule 20 (e).

SERVICE 5. (a) The Player agrees that, while under contract, and prior to expiration of the Club's right to renew this contract, he will not play baseball otherwise than for the Club, except that the Player may participate in post-season games under the conditions prescribed in the Major League Rules. [Reference is made here to Major League Rule 18(b); see page 500.]

OTHER SPORTS (b) The Player and the Club recognize and agree that the Player's participation in other sports may impair or destroy his ability and skill as a baseball player. Accordingly the Player agrees that he will not engage in professional boxing or wrestling; and that, except with the written consent of the Club, he will not engage in any game or exhibition of football, basketball, hockey or other athletic sport.

ASSIGNMENT

6. (a) The Player agrees that this contract may be assigned by the Club (and reassigned by any assignee Club) to any other club in accordance with the Major League Rules and the Professional Baseball Rules.

NO SALARY REDUCTION (b) The amount stated in paragraph 2 hereof which is payable to the Player for the period stated in paragraph 1 hereof shall not be diminished by any such assignment, except for failure to report as provided in the next sub-paragraph (c).

REPORTING (c) The Player shall report to the assignee Club promptly (as provided in the Regulations) upon receipt of written notice from the Club of the assignment of this contract. If the Player fails so to report, he shall not be entitled to any payment for the period from the date he receives written notice of assignment until he reports to the assignee Club.

OBLIGATIONS OF ASSIGNOR AND ASSIGNEE CLUBS (d) Upon and after such assignment, all rights and obligations of the assignor Club hereunder shall become the rights and obligations of the assignee Club; provided, however, that

(1) The assignee Club shall be liable to the Player for payments accruing only from the date of assignment and shall not be liable (but the assignor shall remain liable) for payments accrued prior to that date.

(2) If at any time the assignee is a Major League Club, it shall be liable to pay the Player at the full rate stipulated in paragraph 2 hereof for the remainder of the period stated in paragraph 1 hereof and all prior assignors and assignees shall be relieved of liability for any payment for such period.

(3) Unless the assignor and assignee clubs agree otherwise, if the assignee Club is a National Association Club, the assignee Club shall be liable only to pay the Player at the rate usually paid by said assignee Club to other players of similar skill and ability in its classification and the assignor Club shall be liable to pay the difference for the remainder of the period stated in paragraph 1 hereof between an amount computed at the rate stipulated in paragraph 2 hereof and the amount so payable by the assignee Club.

MOVING EXPENSES (e) If this contract is assigned by a Major League Club to another Major League Club during the playing season, the assignor Club shall pay the Player, for all moving and other expenses resulting from such assignment, the sum of $300 if the contract is assigned between Clubs in the same zone; the sum of $600 if the contract is assigned between a Club in the Eastern Zone and a Club in the Central Zone; the sum of $900 if the contract is assigned between a Club in the Central Zone and a Club in the Western Zone; and the sum of $1,200 if the contract is assigned between a Club in the Eastern Zone and a Club in the Western Zone. The Eastern Zone shall include the Philadelphia and Pittsburgh Clubs in the National League and the Baltimore, Boston, New York and Washington Clubs in the American League; the Central Zone shall include the Chicago, Cincinnati, Milwaukee and St. Louis Clubs in the National League and the Chicago, Cleveland, Detroit and Kansas City Clubs in the American League; the Western Zone shall include the Los Angeles and San Francisco Clubs in the National League.

If this contract is assigned by a Major League Club to a National Association Club during the playing season, the assignor Club shall pay the Player his reasonable and actual moving expenses resulting from such assignment and shall reimburse the Player for up to one month's rental payments for living quarters in the city of the assignor Club for which he is legally obliged after the date of such assignment and for which he is not otherwise reimbursed.

"CLUB" (f) All references in other paragraphs of this contract to "the Club" shall be deemed to mean and include any assignee of this contract.

TERMINATION

BY PLAYER 7. (a) The Player may terminate this contract, upon written notice to the Club, if the Club shall default in the payments to the Player provided for in paragraph 2 hereof or shall fail to perform any other obligation agreed to be performed by the Club hereunder and if the Club shall fail to remedy such default within ten (10) days after the receipt by the Club of written notice of such default. The Player may also terminate this contract as provided in sub-paragraph (f) (4) of this paragraph 7.

BY CLUB (b) The Club may terminate this contract upon written notice to the Player (but only after requesting and obtaining waivers of this contract from all other Major League Clubs) if the Player shall at any time:

(1) fail, refuse or neglect to conform his personal conduct to the standards of good citizenship and good sportsmanship or to keep himself in first class physical condition or to obey the Club's training rules; or

(2) fail, in the opinion of the Club's management, to exhibit sufficient skill or competitive ability to qualify or continue as a member of the Club's team; or

(3) fail, refuse or neglect to render his services hereunder or in any other manner materially breach this contract.

(c) If this contract is terminated by the Club by reason of the Player's failure to render his services hereunder due to disability resulting directly from injury sustained in the course and within the scope of his employment hereunder and written notice of such injury is given by the Player as provided in the Regulations, the Player shall be entitled to receive his full salary for the season in which the injury was sustained, less all workmen's compensation payments paid or payable by reason of said injury.

(d) If this contract is terminated by the Club during the training season, payment by the Club of the Player's board, lodging and expense allowance during the training season to the date of termination and of the reasonable traveling expenses of the Player to his home city and the expert training and coaching provided by the Club to the Player during the training season shall be full payment to the Player.

(e) If this contract is terminated by the Club during the playing season, then, except in the case provided for in sub-paragraph (c) of this paragraph 7, the Player shall be entitled to receive as full payment hereunder such portion of the amount stipulated in paragraph 2 hereof as the number of days of his actual employment in the Club's playing season bears to the total number of days in said season, provided, however, that if this contract is terminated under sub-paragraph (b) (2) of this paragraph 7 for failure to exhibit sufficient skill or competitive ability, the Player shall be entitled to an additional amount equal to thirty (30) days payment at the rate stipulated in paragraph 2 hereof and the reasonable traveling expenses of the Player to his home.

PROCEDURE (f) If the Club proposes to terminate this contract in accordance with sub-paragraph (b) of this paragraph 7, the procedure shall be as follows:

(1) The Club shall request waivers from all other Major League clubs. Such waiver request must state that it is for the purpose of terminating this contract and it may not be withdrawn.

(2) Upon receipt of the waiver request, any other Major League club may claim assignment of this contract at a waiver price of $1.00, the priority of claims to be determined in accordance with the Major League Rules.

(3) If this contract is so claimed, the Club shall, promptly and before any assignment, notify the Player that it had requested waivers for the purpose of terminating this contract and that the contract had been claimed.

(4) Within 5 days after receipt of notice of such claim, the Player shall be entitled, by written notice to the Club, to terminate this contract on the date of his notice of termination. If the Player fails so to notify the Club, this contract shall be assigned to the claiming club.

(5) If the contract is not claimed, the Club shall promptly deliver written notice of termination to the Player at the expiration of the waiver period.

(g) Upon any termination of this contract by the Player, all obligations of both parties hereunder shall cease on the date of termination, except the obligation of the Club to pay the Player's compensation to said date.

REGULATIONS 8. The Player accepts as part of this contract the Regulations [reference is made here to the contract page on which the Regulations are printed; see page 499 of this book].

RULES 9. (a) The Club and the Player agree to accept, abide by and comply with all provisions of the Major League Rules and the Professional Baseball Rules which concern player conduct and player-club relationships and with all decisions of the Commissioner and the President of the Club's League, pursuant thereto.

DISPUTES (b) In case of dispute between the Player and the Club, the same shall be referred to the Commissioner as an arbitrator, and his decision shall be accepted by all parties as final; and the Club and the Player agree than any such dispute, or any claim or complaint by either party against the other, shall be presented to the Commissioner within one year from the date it arose.

PUBLICATION (c) The Club, the League President and the Commissioner, or any of them, may make public the findings, decision and record of any inquiry, investigation or hearing held or conducted, including in such record all evidence or information, given, received or obtained in connection therewith.

RENEWAL 10. (a) On or before January 15th (or if a Sunday, then the next preceding business day) of the year next following the last playing season covered by this contract, the Club may tender to the Player a contract for the term of that year by mailing the same to the Player at his address following his signature hereto, or if none be given, then at his last address of record with the Club. If prior to the March 1 next succeeding said January 15, the Player and the Club have not agreed upon the terms of such contract, then on or before 10 days after said March 1, the Club shall have the right by written notice to the Player at said address to renew this contract for the period of one year on the same terms, except that the amount payable to the Player shall be such as the Club shall fix in said notice; provided, however, that said amount, if fixed by a Major League Club, shall be an amount payable at a rate not less than 75% of the rate stipulated for the preceding year.

(b) The Club's right to renew this contract, as provided in sub-paragraph (a) of this paragraph 10, and the promise of the Player not to play otherwise than with the Club have been taken into consideration in determining the amount payable under paragraph 2 hereof.

11. This contract is subject to federal or state legislation, regulations, executive or other official orders or other governmental action, now or hereafter in effect respecting military, naval, air or other governmental service, which may directly or indirectly affect the Player, Club or the League and subject also to the right of the Commissioner to suspend the operation of this contract during any national emergency.

COMMISSIONER 12. The term "Commissioner" wherever used in this contract shall be deemed to mean the Commissioner designated under the Major League Agreement, or in the case of a vacancy in the office of Commissioner, the Executive Council or such other body or person or persons as shall be designated in the Major League Agreement to exercise the powers and duties of the Commissioner during such vacancy.

SUPPLEMENTAL AGREEMENTS The Club and the Player covenant that this contract fully sets forth all understandings and agreements between them, and agree that no other understandings or agreements, whether heretofore or hereafter made, shall be valid, recognizable, or of any effect whatsoever, unless expressly set forth in a new or supplemental contract executed by the Player and the Club (acting by its president, or such other officer as shall have been thereunto duly authorized by the president or Board of Directors, as evidenced by a certificate filed of record with the League President and Commissioner) and complying with the Major League Rules and the Professional Baseball Rules.

SPECIAL COVENANTS (Space is provided for the insertion here of special terms which may be appended to the contract, such as bonuses based on attendance, further Player restrictions or privileges, etc.)

APPROVAL This contract or any supplement hereto shall not be valid or effective unless and until approved by the League President.

Signed in duplicate this .... day of ...., A. D. 196 .....

....
(Player) (Club)

.... By ....
(Home address of Player) (Authorized Signature)

Social Security No. ....

Approved ...., 196...,

....

President, American League of Professional Baseball Clubs

REGULATIONS

1. The Club's playing season for each year covered by this contract and all renewals hereof shall be as fixed by the American League of Professional Baseball Clubs, or if this contract shall be assigned to a Club in another league, then by the league of which such assignee is a member.

2. The Player, when requested by the Club, must submit to a complete physical examination at the expense of the Club, and if necessary to treatment by a regular physician or dentist in good standing. Upon refusal of the Player to submit to a complete medical or dental examination the Club may consider such refusal a violation of this regulation and may take such action as it deems advisable under Regulation 5 of this contract. Disability directly resulting from injury sustained in the course and within the scope of his employment under this contract shall not impair the right of the Player to receive his full salary for the period of such disability or for the season in which the injury was sustained (whichever period is shorter), together with the reasonable medical and hospital expenses incurred by reason of the injury and during the term of this contract, less all workmen's compensation payments paid or payable by reason of said injury; but only upon the express prerequisite conditions that (a) written notice of such injury, including the time, place, cause and nature of the injury, is served upon and received by the Club within twenty days of the sustaining of said injury and (b) the Club shall have the right to designate the doctors and hospitals furnishing such medical and hospital services. Any other disability may be grounds for suspending or terminating this contract at the discretion of the Club.

3. The Club will furnish the Player with two complete uniforms, exclusive of shoes, the Player making a deposit of $30 therefor, which deposit will be returned to him at the end of the season or upon the termination of this contract, upon the surrender of the uniforms by him to the Club.

4. The Club will pay all proper and necessary traveling expenses of the Player while "abroad," or traveling with the Club in other cities, including board, lodging, Pullman accommodations, if available, and during the training season, an allowance of $25 per week, payable in advance, to cover other training trip expenses. The Club will also pay the reasonable traveling expenses of the Player to his home at the end of the season.

5. For violation by the Player of any regulation or other provision of this contract, the Club may impose a reasonable fine and deduct the amount thereof from the Player's salary or may suspend the Player without salary for a period not exceeding thirty days, or both, at the discretion of the Club. Written notice of the fine or suspension or both and of the reasons therefor shall in every case be given to the Player.

6. In order to enable the Player to fit himself for his duties under this contract, the Club may require the Player to report for practice at such places as the Club may designate and to participate in such exhibition contests as may be arranged by the Club for a period beginning not earlier than February 15 in 1947 and not earlier than March 1 in 1948 and subsequent years without any other compensation than that herein elsewhere provided, the Club, however, to pay the necessary traveling expenses, including Pullman accommodations, if available, and meals en route, of the Player from his home city to the training place of the Club, whether he be ordered to go there direct or by way of the home city of the Club. In the event of the failure of the Player to report for practice or to participate in the exhibition games, as provided for, he shall be required to get in playing condition to the satisfaction of the Club's team manager, and at the Player's own expense, before his salary shall commence.

7. In case of assignment of this contract the Player shall report promptly to the assignee club within 72 hours from the date he receives written notice from the Club of such assignment, if the Player is then not more than 1600 miles by most direct available railroad route from the assignee Club, plus an additional 24 hours for each additional 800 miles.

Post-Season Exhibition Games. Major League Rule 18 (b) provides:

Exhibition Games. (b) No Player shall participate in any exhibition game played during the period between the close of the Major League championship season and the following training season; except that a Player, with the written consent of the Commissioner, may participate in exhibition games which are played within thirty days after the close of the Major League championship season and which are approved by the Commissioner. Player conduct, on and off the field, in connection with such post-season exhibition games shall be subject to the discipline of the Commissioner. The Commissioner shall not approve more than three Players of any one Club on the same team. No Player shall participate in any exhibition game with or against any team which, during the current season or within one year, has had any ineligible player or which is or has been during the current season or within one year, managed and controlled by an ineligible player or by any person who has listed an ineligible player under an assumed name or who otherwise has violated, or attempted to violate, any exhibition game contract; or with or against any team which, during said season or within one year, has played against teams containing such ineligible players, or so managed or controlled. Any player violating this rule shall be fined not less than fifty dollars ($50) nor more than five hundred dollars ($500), except that in no event shall such fine be less than the consideration received by such player for participating in such game.

(Editor's note: The foregoing Official Contract is the standard form used in the American League. A similar document is used in the National League, since both major leagues observe the same basic guarantees and requirements. League presidents may impose additional restrictions, such as forbidding players to pose while wearing uniform in advertisements for beer or cigarettes.)

XI BASEBALL AUXILIARIES

It is true that the vast popularity of baseball is due to its national, year-round publicity in the form of box scores, daily reports, feature stories, notes, columns, etc., all dutifully reported in every newspaper in the land.

The morning-after straight result story of the game is eagerly absorbed by the fan for information and discussion with his neighbor and fellow-worker. The box score is as an important a way of life as the normal functions of the day. The afternoon paper carries the whys and hows of the previous day's game and the "confidential" information on how it was won or lost. This is called a "p.m." story and is usually composed from a so-called "angle" in which the writer is permitted more latitude of expression than his colleague on a morning paper. However, both types of stories have their vast audiences who, because of business and family duties, are forced to follow their favorites only through the words of an on-the-scene observer.

WRITERS

Baseball writing is probably as old as baseball playing. Ex-Senator William Cauldwell, editor of the *New York Mercury*, wrote baseball news in his paper as far back as 1853. Three years later, British-born Henry Chadwick became the first professional baseball writer. This is the same "Father Chadwick" who guided the development of official rules, edited annuals, crusaded for fundamental baseball reforms and served as the sport's "Chief Justice" for half a century.

Then came a string of other famous chroniclers of the sport: Charles Peverelly, who wrote the first history of the game; Mike Kelly, who introduced the shorthand system of scoring in 1861; the Rankin brothers of New York, W. M. Spink of St. Louis and many more. Among the earliest baseball scribes was Walt Whitman of the *Brooklyn Eagle*, whose stilted reporting ("Mr. Johnson struck the ball well in the seventh innings.") gave no portent of his classic poetry to come.

After the 1887 season, major league baseball writers banded into the first national organization, with George Munson of St. Louis as president. It was called the National Base Ball Reporters' Association and had a short but useful life. This group suggested a number of changes in the playing and scoring rules which were subsequently adopted. However, it broke up in 1890, when the Brotherhood war split baseball into two hostile camps.

The second attempt at a scribes' association grew out of the 1908 World Series, which climaxed endless hardships and indignities suffered by the working press. In Detroit, the press box could be reached only by climbing a rickety ladder. In Chicago, the press box was as wide open as a Barbary saloon, "crashed" by assorted actors, politicians, jockeys and pals of the club officials.

When Hugh Fullerton reached his press seat in the Cub ballpark, he found it already occupied by Louis Mann, the famous actor. Mann refused to vacate. So Fullerton plunked himself down in Mann's lap and covered the entire World Series game from that bizarre perch.

That did it. On October 10, 1908, the writers formed a temporary organization. A permanent union was formed two months later in New York, with 125 members, and Joe Jackson of Detroit as president. The first constitution of the Base Ball Writers' Association of America set up its objectives as (1) Better accommodations in press boxes, (2) More uniformity in scoring, and (3) Conferences with the majors' rules committee regarding playing rules.

The BBWAA has made great strides since that humble beginning. It now controls every major league press box, and even the clubowner is not allowed to enter his press box without permission of the scribes. It has been woven into the fabric of the big leagues to the extent of handling the official scoring for all games, picking the Most Valuable Players as well as Rookie for the Year, naming players to the Hall of Fame and serving on the joint major leagues' committee on playing rules.

RADIO and TELEVISION

Modern electronics have brought baseball its greatest popularity in history. Through the magic lantern of the television tube and the all-reaching sound of radio, a major league game can be seen and/or heard by just about everyone in the country. Whether this is good for the future profit growth of the game is something the clubowners must still decide.

The daily chatter of the radio play-by-play announcer and the casual flick of a TV dial can bring a major league contest into any room in an American home. The game is no longer isolated to its point of origin and the characteristics, performances and personal statistics of all the players are known to millions who have yet to see a "live" major league game.

Over the years, these lusty and lucrative wireless media have converted countless millions of new fans to baseball. . .brought over a hundred million dollars from sponsors into the coffers of the clubs . . .and, in a vital service that is too easily overlooked, brightened the lives of hospitalized veterans and other shut-ins.

It all started back in 1921, when Graham McNamee sat in front of a pie-sized microphone at the Polo Grounds and broadcast the eight games of the Yank-Giant World Series. Subsequent Series were aired, too, but it was not until 1934 that a sponsor moved in: Henry Ford signed a four-year contract at $100,000 per. Eventually the All-Star Game came into radio "gravy" too.

It was a big step from broadcasting special events to transmitting every game in the regular season. The first station to venture into daily baseball broadcasts directly from the ballpark was Chicago's WMAQ, with Hal Totten describing the games in 1924. This custom eventually blanketed practically every club in organized ball.

By 1959, more than a thousand radio stations were saturating the country with play-by-play, costing sponsors about $40,000,000. The Mutual Broadcasting System sent a "live" account of its cooperatively-sponsored Game of the Day through about 500 stations all over the nation. Television, too, with two major networks beaming big league baseball into non-major league areas, was on a coast-to-coast weekly schedule and creating vast problems for those minor league teams which played games in those cities where the fans could stay at home and watch a major league game via television.

A major headache arose when minor league clubs claimed that "invasion" of their territory by big league broadcasts was ruining their gate. The majors were eager to help, but feared placing any restraint on the all-engulfing networks lest organized baseball be hauled into court and sued on the touchy issue of "monopolistic practice in interstate commerce." As a compromise a 50-mile area of protection was set up to screen minor league games, but this couldn't be enforced, and the leagues had to set up special committees to handle radio and TV problems.

Television cameras were focussed on major league teams in action for the first time at Ebbets Field on August 26, 1939, at a Dodger-Red doubleheader. Though only a handful of TV sets existed in the entire metropolitan area at the time, National Broadcasting Company engineers moved their experimental equipment into Ebbets Field. Walter L. (Red) Barber, already famous as a radio broadcaster, gave this pioneering effort the full treatment by announcing the plays. Between games, Barber brought Bucky Walters and Dolph Camilli to the field cameras, for closeups that showed how Bucky gripped the ball for a curve and how Dolph kept his hand in the first baseman's mitt. The telecast went out over station W2XBS, atop the Empire State Building.

Bold and imaginative Larry MacPhail, Dodger president, encouraged the telecasters, and through 1940-41 on the average of one game a week was screened at Ebbets Field. The war put a quietus on TV activity, but when MacPhail headed the Yankees in 1946, he sold the first commercial rights. Metropolitan New York had fewer than 500 sets at the time, but Dumont paid $75,000 for season rights to Yankee games.

Video fees multiplied so rapidly that by 1950 Dumont was able to pay sportscaster Dizzy Dean $30,000, or more than he had ever gotten as a star pitcher with the Cards and Cubs. Since then the number one telecaster in areas like New York and Chicago has been handsomely rewarded by the sponsors and the ball clubs. In 1950 Commissioner A. B. Chandler closed a deal bringing baseball $6,000,000 for the TV rights alone to the World Series covering 1951-56. An even juicier deal for World Series TV-radio privileges was made with the start of the 1957 World Series. The sponsors (The Gillette Safety Razor Company) paid $3,000,000 annually for the exclusive TV-radio rights, or approximately $15,000,000 for the period from 1957 through 1962. This bonanza just about guaranteed the success of the costly ballplayers' pension fund.

Most of the outstanding sportscasters like Barber, Russ Hodges, Mel Allen,

Jim Britt, Bob Elson, etc., cut their eyeteeth in this profession. However, there are many former major league ballplayers who stepped right into sportscasting and made an instant hit: Dizzy Dean, Harry Heilmann, Jack Graney, Bump Hadley, Waite Hoyt, Gabby Street, Pie Traynor, Mel Ott, Bob Feller, Phil Rizzuto, Lou Boudreau, Frank McCormick, Joe Garagiola, Leo Durocher, George Kell, Rex Barney and Buddy Blattner.

With the increasing coverage of baseball by television and radio, many of the sportscasters became household names and their faces and voices became as familiar as those of the players. Some of the sportscasters doing play-by-play of major league baseball during the mid-1950's were Ernie Harwell, Herb Carneal, Curt Gowdy, Bob Murphy, Bill Crowley, Bob Elson, Don Wells, Jack Brickhouse, Vince Lloyd, Jack Quinlan, Jack Moran, George Bryson, Jimmy Dudley, Bob Neal, Ken Coleman, Bill McColgan, Van Patrick, Merle Harmon, Ed Edwards, Vince Scully, Jerry Doggett, Earl Gillespie; Blaine Walsh, Gene Kelly, Byron Saam, Claude Haring, Bob Prince, Jim Woods, Paul Long, Harry Caray, Jack Buck, Lon Simmons, Bob Wolff, Chuck Thompson, Bailey Goss and Lindsey Nelson.

STATISTICIANS

Baseball statisticians are a breed apart. Strange but admirable, they pursue Truth in the shape of cold, hard numbers. Never compromising, never relaxing, these busy beavers compile the totals and averages that form the only possible unbiased evaluation of a ballplayer.

Most amateur statisticians are like Thomas Gray's "Many a flower is born to blush unseen, and waste its sweetness on the desert air." Notable exception is John A. Heydler, a Washington linotype operator who kept exhaustive baseball records as a hobby. When Harry Pulliam became National League president in 1903 and found the league statistics in terrible shape, he hired Heydler as secretary and statistician. Honest John soon became the league's secretary-treasurer and eventually president.

Newspaper, wire service and radio demand nowadays for quick, accurate daily statistics during the season would put too great a strain on league offices, so the figure-tending is farmed out to pros: Elias Baseball Bureau (New York City) for the NL, Howe News Bureau (Chicago) for the AL. These two bureaus also act as official statisticians for most of the minor leagues and derive further income from club officials who want complete up-to-the-minute averages of the minor leagues—either to check on their farmhands' progress or to scout other prospects.

During the baseball season, the Howe and Elias offices employ a dozen or more figure filberts for such jobs as entering data in a master ledger from the official score sheets (which are large, detailed pages sent in by newspaperman designated by the league as official scorers); figuring out the five leading players in each department, for use in daily newspaper "boxes"; compiling full league averages for use in weekend editions; writing "leads," or short descriptive articles, to interpret and accompany the averages issued to papers and radio or TV stations; filing, mimeographing, checking, etc.

Someone once figured out that of the myriad statistics issued all season long, these bureaus err about once in every 3,500 figures. However, after some 7,057,600 "live" figures on file are quadruple-checked for official release each winter, they prove to be 99.9996 correct!

Irwin Howe founded his bureau in 1911, and Al Munro Elias started his a few years later. These baseball mills are now run respectively by John Phillips and Seymour Siwoff, who also edits the oldest and most famous annual of "best" records, *The Little Red Book,* which was first compiled by Charlie White and John B. Foster.

Both bureaus are antedated by the Heilbroner Baseball Bureau, founded in 1909 at Fort Wayne, Indiana, by ex-St. Louis Cardinal manager Louis Heilbroner. The HBB, a service bureau for all pro baseball, keeps personal cards and transaction records to cover every organized league. Ever since 1910, it has issued the annual Baseball Blue Book, the most complete and authentic directory of the game. Earle W. Moss is the Heilbroner chief.

The tremendous burden of daily, up-to-the game statistical information has placed greater emphasis on the figure filbert. Many clubs now carry full-time statisticians to record the inning-by-inning report of all games. Radio and TV announcers have added a season-long statistician to their staffs to prepare the latest in figures for their audiences.

CONCESSIONAIRES

"The hot dog is king," a Chicago Cub official once explained. "For every dollar we get in paid admissions, our total cost of operating the club $1.06. If we didn't have extra income from concessions in the ballpark, we'd have to lock our gates."

To save all the headaches that go with the catering business, practically all ball clubs lease the food-and-drink privileges at their park to established concessionaires like the Stevens family, Blake Harper, Jacobs Brothers, etc. The result is substantial revenue and no risk. Vending rights can prove quite lucrative, as when the all-time record was set at a Chicago White Sox doubleheader in 1950, averaging $1.05 spent per fan.

The royal family of sports caterers is the Stevens clan. Operating under the corporate title of Harry Mosley Stevens, Inc., the founder's four sons and several grandsons boomed the business beyond even the fabulous pace of old Harry M., who died a multi-millionaire 55 years after arriving here in 1879 from England, down to his last pound ($5). The Stevens concession empire embraces ballparks and racetracks stretching, as their letterhead proudly boasts, "From the Hudson to the Rio Grande."

"Columbus, 1492" may be the famous date for schoolboys, but "Columbus, 1887" is the memorable milestone in concession history. On a summer day in 1887, Harry M. Stevens went to a ballgame in Columbus, Ohio. He bought a scorecard, but couldn't decipher its garbled list of players. Soon after the last putout, he was in the club's front office, offering $700 for the privilege of printing and selling a decent scorecard in the park. Improving the design and selling space on his scorecard, Harry quickly recouped his initial investment and started operating in the black. To this day, the Stevens brothers still publish scorecards for the several ballparks in which they have catering rights.

Shortly after his scorecard success, Harry M. branched into the peanuts-and soda-pop line. He reached the big leagues for good in 1894, moving into the Polo Grounds. A few years later, at a cold and windy Giant game, he noticed his soft drinks sales lagging. So he rushed his vendors to buy up all the frankfurters and rolls in the neighborhood. He boiled the franks, split the rolls to form a natural bed for them and sold them to the chilled spectators, with the slogan that still rings up sales to this very day, "Get 'em while they're hot!"

Frankfurter sales proved popular from the first. Sports cartoonist Tad Dorgan liked to caricature the dachshund-shaped delicacy as animated dogs, but despite the whimsical "libel" on the beef ingredients, customers consumed the "hot dogs" in ever increasing numbers. Soon the item became world famous.

The Stevens business kept growing until now it employs almost 3,500 people on an average summer day. The Jacobs Brothers and other baseball concessionaires hire thousands of others.

The vendor in the ballpark is paid on salary plus commission. He (or she, since some concessionaires employ women to sell) usually has a minimum guarantee of $3 per day and averages from $16 to $20 daily, if the attendance is of normal size. A top vendor can make as much as $50 at a capacity crowd.

In the average big league ballpark, the total yearly consumption by fans include 700,000 bottles of pop, 800,000 hot dogs, 500,000 slabs of ice cream and 400,000 bags of peanuts.

FANS

Professional implies "for pay." Pay means money, money comes from the cash customer...and so, quite obviously, the most important factor in professional baseball is the fan. Everybody connected with sports recognizes this axiom. In fact, even the caustic newspaperman is treated graciously by the ball club, only because he represents a link with the thousands (or millions) of fans who read his story daily.

Rabid fans, who worship the baseball headliner, aren't adverse to making headlines themselves. There was the Dodger fan who shot a Giant rooter to death for making cynical cracks. En route to the electric chair, the murderer asked the chaplain, "Did the Bums beat the Giants today?" Then there was the Cleveland flagpole sitter who vowed not to leave his perch till the Indians returned to first place... the fan who climbed out of the Ebbets Field grandstand to assault umpire George Magerkurth... and the psychotic girl who shot Eddie Waitkus to prove her intense love for the Philly first baseman.

In the "old faithful" class, Arthur Felsch of Milwaukee rates notice because every year he parks outside the bleacher entrance about a week before the start of the World Series, and lives in a cardboard crate... just so he can have the honor of being the first one admitted to the park. However, the long-term rooters are usually more reserved and rarely make even a single line in the papers all their lives. In this latter category are such veterans as George Doerzbach, who saw 55 consecutive season opening games at Cleveland; Lou Schulte, who missed only seven Cincinnati home games in 24 years, and Hyman Pearlstone, who made at least one road trip a season with the defunct Philadelphia Athletics for 44 years.

Every ballpark abounds in favorite grandstand "characters." St. Louis had Mary Ott for many years, distracting enemy players with her penetrating whinny; Pittsburgh had a coal dealer who barked like a wounded seal; Cincinnati had Harry Thobe, retired bricklayer, who danced on the dugout roof while holding a red umbrella and wearing a red-banded straw hat. The "daffy Dodgers", as might be expected, always led the way in quaint customers: the late Shorty Laurice and his catch-as-catch-can Sym-phoney Band; Hilda Chester and her cowbell; Eddie Bettan with his tin whistle and explorer's helmet; Jack Pearce and his gas-filled balloons, etc.

The Hollywood influence has invaded baseball in recent years, and "fan clubs" seem to be the rage, numbering most of its membership among teen-age girls.

Brooklyn still recalls Abie the Iceman, who would hitch his ice wagon just outside Ebbets Field every afternoon and go in to jeer at the Dodgers. "Ya bums, ya!" he'd rasp. One day, manager Wilbert Robinson came up to Abie and said, "Wouldn't you like a season pass, so you can see the games free instead of having to pay every day? Here, take this. Just stop yelling at my boys. You make them nervous."

Abie accepted the pass joyfully. But a week later he knocked on the clubhouse door, came up to Uncle Robbie and said, "I can't stand it any more. Here's back your pass. I gotta yell—'cause they ARE bums!"

Patsy O'Toole, a Navin Field and then Briggs Stadium fixture, was Detroit's most prominent rooter. He would roar "you're a faker!" at opposing players and his bellow could be heard throughout the stands.

Cleveland once honored one of its patrons with a Special Fan's Night, showering the lucky fan with a number of gifts for his loyalty to the Indians. And the Chicago NL front office still continues a policy, started in 1951, of permitting one of its loyal followers from the rank of the every-day fan to throw out the first ball on Opening Day.

XII FEATURES

FAMOUS FAMILIES When a man wants his son to inherit his money, he writes a will. But all the penmanship and planning in the world cannot guarantee that a boy will inherit the skill, the strength or the spiritual drive of his father. Baseball immortals like Ty Cobb and Walter Johnson were frustrated when their sons showed no special aptitude or preference for the sport. Yet there are enough examples of father-and-son or brothers who made the majors to conclude that playing talent can run in a family.

Of all the great baseball clans, none could match the six Cleveland-born sons of Irish immigrants James Delahanty and Bridget Croke. Five of their boys made the majors. A sixth, Willie, starred in the minors and was drafted by the Dodgers --- but before he could report for National League duty, he was hit in the head by a pitched ball at Waterbury, Connecticut, and he had to give up the game soon afterward.

Big Ed Delahanty, eldest of the baseball tribe, is the only person ever to lead both the National and American Leagues in batting, with .408 for Philadelphia NL in 1899 and .376 for Washington AL in 1902. A prodigious slugger, he once hit four homers in one game and added a single for good measure. Jim Delahanty led the World Series hitters of 1909 with an average of .346. Brother Joe was the main prop for St. Louis NL at one time. Tom and Frank both played for Cleveland.

Another clan of shillelagh swingers de luxe was the O'Neill quartet of brothers, Mike, Steve, Jack and Jim. Brother trios include the families Boyer, Clarkson, Cross, DiMaggio, High Mansell, Sewell, Sowders and Wright.

Here is a comprehensive list of the major leagues' famous families:

FATHER AND SON

ARAGON—Angel, Angel Jr.
AVERILL—Howard E., Earl D.
BAGBY—James C., James C., Jr.
BARNHART—Clyde L., Victor D.
BERRY—Charles J., Charles F.
BERRY—Joseph H., Joseph H., Jr.
BRICKELL—Frederick B., Fritz D.
BRUCKER—Earle F., Earle F., Jr.
CAMILLI—Adolph L., Douglas J.
COLLINS—Edward T., Edward T., Jr.
COONEY—James J., James E. & John W.
CORRIDEN—John M., John M., Jr.
CROUCH—William H., William E.
DOSCHER—John H., John H., Jr.
ESCHEN—James G., Lawrence E.
GABRIELSON—Leonard H., Leonard G
GANZEL—Charles W., Foster P.
GILBERT—Lawrence W., Charles M. & Harold J.
GRAHAM—George F., John B.
GRIMES—Oscar R., Oscar R., Jr.
HOOD—Wallace J., Wallace J., Jr.
JOHNSON--Adam R., Adam R., Jr.
JOHNSON--Ernest R., Donald S.
KRAUSSE—Lewis B., Lewis B., Jr.
LEE—Thornton S., Donald E.
LERCHEN—Bertram R., George E.
LIEBHARDT--Glenn J., Glenn I.
LINDSTROM—Frederick C., Charles W.
LIVELY—Henry E., Everett A.
MACK—Cornelius, Earle T.
MAGGERT--Harl V., Harl W.
MALAY—Charles F., Joseph C.
MATTICK—Walter J., Robert J.
MEINKE—Frank L., Robert B.
MILLS—William G., Arthur G.
MOORE--Eugene, Eugene Jr.
MORTON—Guy, Guy Jr.
MUELLER—Walter J., Donald F.
NARLESKI—William E., Raymond E.
NICHOLS—Chester R., Chester R., Jr.
OKRIE—Frank A., Leonard J.
O'ROURKE—James H., James S.

O'ROURKE--Joseph P., Joseph L.
OSBORNE--Ernest P., Lawrence S.
PARTENHEIMER--Harold P., Stanwood W.
PILLETTE--Herman P., Duane X.
SAVIDGE--Ralph A., Donald S.
SCHULTZ--Joseph C., Joseph C., Jr.
SHEELY--Earl H., Hollis K.
SISLER--George H., David M. & Richard A.
SULLIVAN--William J., William J., Jr.
SUSCE--George C. M., George D.
TORRES--Ricardo J., Don G.
TRESH--Michael, Thomas Michael
TROSKY--Harold A., Harold A., Jr.
WAKEFIELD--Howard J., Richard C.
WALKER--Ewart G., Fred & Harry W.
WALSH--Edward A., Edward A., Jr.
WOOD--Joseph, Joseph F.
YOUNG--Delmar J., Delmar E.

BROTHERS

ACOSTA--Balmadero M., Jose
ADAMS--Richard L., Robert H.
ALLISON--Arthur A., Douglass L.
ALOU--Felipe R., Mateo R.
ARUNDEL--Harvey, John T.
ASPROMONTE--Kenneth J., Robert T.
BAILEY--James H., Lonas E.
BANNON--James H., Thomas E.
BARNES--Jesse L., Virgil J.
BAXES--Dimitrios S., Michael S.
BELL--Charles C., Frank G.
BERGEN--Martin, William A.
BIGBEE--Carson L., Lyle R.
BLANKENSHIP--Homer, Theodore
BLUEGE--Oswald L., Otto A.
BOLLING--Frank E., Milton J.
BOONE--Isaac M., James A.
BOYER--(3) Cletus L., Cloyd V. & Kenton L.
BOYLE--Edward J., John A.
BOYLE--James J., Ralph F.
BRASHEAR--Robert N., Roy P.
CAMNITZ--R. Harry, Samuel H.
CAMP--Llewellyn R., Winfield S.
CAMPBELL--Hugh, Michael
CANTWELL--Michael J., Thomas A.
CARLYLE--Hiram C., Roy E.
CASEY--Daniel M., Dennis P.
CHAPMAN--Calvin L., Edwin V.
CHIOZZA--Dino J., Louis P.
CHRISTOPHER--Loyd E., Russell O
CLAPP--Aaron B., John E.
CLARKE--Fred C., Joshua B.
CLARKE--Rufus R., Sumpter E.
CLARKSON--(3)Arthur H., John G. & Walter H.
CLEMONS--Robert E., Vernon J.
COFFMAN--George D., Samuel R.
COHEN--Andrew H., Sydney H.
CONNELL--Eugene J., Joseph B.
CONNOR--Joseph F., Roger
CONWAY--James P., Peter J.
CONWAY--Richard B., William
COONEY--James E., John W.
COOPER--Morton C., William W.
CORCORAN--Lawrence J., M.
COSCARART--Joseph M., Peter J.
COVELESKI--Harry F., Stanley
COVINGTON--Clarence C., William W.
CROSS--(3) Amos C., Frank A. & Lafayette N.
CUCCINELLO--Alfred E., Anthony F.
DAILY--Cornelius F., Edward M.
DALY--Joseph J., Thomas P.
DANNING--Harry, Ike
DARINGER--Clifford C., Rolla H.
DAUBERT--Harry J., Jacob E.
DAVENPORT--Arthur D., Claude E.
DEAN--Jay H., Paul D.
DEASLEY--James, Thomas H.
DELAHANTY--(5) Edward J., Frank G., James C., Joseph N., Thomas J.
DeMONTREVILLE--Eugene N., Leon

DICKEY—George W., William M.
DiMAGGIO—(3) Dominic P., Joseph P. & Vincent P.
DONAHUE—John A., Patrick W.
DONOVAN—Jeremiah F., Thomas J.
DONOVAN—Patrick J., William E.
DORGAN—Jeremiah F., Michael C.
DOYLE—Cornelius J., John J.
DRAKE—Samuel H., Solomon L.
DUGAN—Edward J., William E.
DURHAM—James G., Louis G.
EGGLER—David D., John
ENS—Anton, Jewel W.
ERAUTT—Edward L. S., Joseph M.
EVERS—John J., Joseph F.
EWING—John, William
FALK—Bibb A., Chester E.
FERRELL—Richard B., Wesley C.
FERRY—Alfred J., John F.
FINNEY—Harold W., Louis K.
FISHER—Chauncey B., Thomas C.
FISHER—Newton, Robert T.
FOGARTY—James G., Joseph J.
FOLEY—Thomas J., William B.
FORD—Eugene W., Russell W.
FOREMAN—Francis I., John D.
FREESE—Eugene L., George W.
FRIEL—Patrick H., William E.
FULLER—Henry W., William B.
GALVIN—James F., Louis
GANZEL—Charles W., John H.
GARBARK—Nathaniel M., Robert M.
GARDELLA—Alfred S., Daniel L.
GASTON—Alexander N., Nathaniel M.
GETTINGER—Charles H., Thomas L.
GILBERT—Charles M., Harold J.
GILBERT—Harry, John G.
GLEASON—Harry G., William J.
GLEASON—John D., William G.
GRABOWSKI—Albert F., Reginald J.
GRAVES—Joseph E., Samuel S.
GREGG—David C., Sylveanus A.
GRIMES—(Twins) Oscar R., Roy A.
GRISSOM—Leo T., Marvin E.
GROH—Henry K., Lewis C.
GUMBERT—Addison C., William S.
HACKETT—Mortimer M., Walter H.
HAFEY—Daniel A., Thomas F.
HALL—George W., James
HAMNER—Granville W., Wesley G.
HANDLEY—Eugene L., Lee E.
HARGARVE—Eugene F., William M.
HARRINGTON—Andrew F., Joseph C.
HATFIELD—Gilbert, John V.
HAYWORTH—Myron C., Raymond H.
HEMPHILL—Charles J., Frank V.
HENGLE—Edward S., Emory J.
HEVING—John A., Joseph W.
HIGH—(3) Andrew A., Charles E. & Hugh J.
HILL—Hugh E., William C.
HINCHMAN—Harry S., William W.
HITCHCOCK—James F., William C.
HOGAN—George E., William H.
HOVLIK—Edward C., Joseph
HOWARD—George E., Ivan C.
HUGHES—Edward H., Thomas J.
HUGHES—James J., Michael F.
HUNTER—(Twins) George H., William E.
IRWIN—Arthur A., John
JEFFCOAT—George E., Harold B.
JOHNSON—Chester L., Earl D.
JOHNSON—Robert L., Roy C.
JOHNSTON—James H., Wheeler R.
JONNARD—(Twins) Clarence J., Claude A.
JORGENS—Arndt L., Orville E.
KAPPEL—Henry, Joseph
KELL—Everett L., George C.
KELLER—Charles E., Howard K.
KELLNER—Alexander R., Walter J.
KELLY—George L., Reynolds C.
KILLEFER—Wade H., William L.
KILROY—Matthew A., Michael J.
KING—Marshall N., Stephen F.
KLING—John G., William
KNODE—Kenneth T., Robert T.
KNOTHE—George B., Wilfred E.
KOPF—William L., Walter H.
KRSNICH—Michael, Rocco P.
LARY—Alfred A., Frank S.
LELIVELT—John F., William J.
LILLARD—Robert E., William B.
LOBERT—Frank J., John B.
LOWDERMILK—Grover C., Louis B.
LUSH—Ernest B., William L.
MAHER—F., Thomas
MAISEL—Frederick C., George J.
MANCUSO—August R., Frank O.
MANSELL—(3) John, Michael R. & Thomas E.
MANUSH—Frank B., Henry E.
MARION—John W., Martin W.
MASKREY—Harry H., Samuel L.
MATHEWSON—Christopher, Henry
MATTOX, Cloy M., James P.
MAYER—James E., Samuel F.
McDANIEL—Lyndall D., Max V.
McFARLAN—Alexander S., Anderson D.
McFARLAND—Charles E., Lamont A.
McGEEHAN—Cornelius B., Daniel D.
McLAUGHLIN—Bernard, Francis M.
MEUSEL—Emil F., Robert W.
MEYER—Benjamin, Lee
MILAN—Horace R., Jesse C.
MILLER—Edmund J., Ralph H.
MILLER—Russell L., Walter J.
MOFFET—Joseph W., Samuel R.
MORIARTY—George J., William J.
MORRISON—John D., Philip M.

MORRISSEY—John H., Thomas J.
MUELLER—Clarence F., Walter J.
MURRAY—Edward F., William A.
MYERS—Lynn, William H.
O'BRIEN—(Twins) Edward J., John T
OGDEN—John M., Warren H.
OLIVO—Diomedes Antonio, Fred Emilio
O'NEILL—(4) James L., John J.,
Stephen F. Michael J.,
ONSLOW—Edward J., John J.
O'ROURKE—James H., John
ORTIZ—Oliverio N., Roberto G.
PARKER—Harley P., Jay
PARROTT—Thomas W., Walter E.
PATTERSON—Hamilton, William J. B.
PEITZ—Henry C., Joseph
PEPLOSKI—Henry S., Joseph A.
PFEFFER—Edward J., Francis X.
PIKE—J., Lipman E.
PIPGRAS—Edward J., George W.
RECCIUS—(3) J. William, (Twins)
Philip John,
RIDDLE—Elmer R., John L.
ROBINSON—Frederic H., Wilbert
ROETTGER—Oscar F., Walter H.
ROSENBERG—Harry, Louis C.
ROTH—Frank C., Robert F.
ROWE—David E., John C.
ROY—Charles R., Luther F.
RUSSELL—Allen E., Clarence D.
SADOWSKI—Edward Roman, Theodore
SAUER—Edward, Henry J.
SAY—James I., Lewis I.
SCANLAN—Frank A., William D.
SCHAFFER—George, Taylor
SCHANG—Robert M., Walter H.
SCHAREIN—Arthur O., George A.
SCHMIDT—Charles, Walter J.
SCHULTE—Herman J., Leonard W.
SEWELL—(3) James L., Joseph W.
& Thomas W.
SHANNON—(Twins) Joseph A. Maurice
SHANTZ—Robert C., Wilmer E.
SHERLOCK—John C., Vincent T.
SHERRY—Lawrence, Norman B.
SISLER—David M., Richard A.
SMITH—Charles E., Frederick V.
SNYDER—James, Joshua
SOWDERS—(3) John, Leonard,
& William J.
STAFFORD—James J., John J.
STAHL—Charles S., Garland
STANLEY—John L., Joseph B.
STOVALL—George T., Jesse C.
TANNEHILL—Jesse N., Lee F.
TEBEAU—George E., Oliver W.
THIELMAN—Henry J., John P.
THOMAS—Roy A., William M.
THOMPSON—Homer, Thomas C.
THRONEBERRY—Marvin E., Maynard F.
TOBIN—James A., John P.
TORRE—Frank J., Joseph P.
TRAFFLEY—John, William F.
TREACEY—Frederick, P.
TWOMBLY—Clarence E., George F.
TYLER—Frederick F., George A.
VAN CUYK—Christian G., John H.
WADE—Benjamin S., Jacob F.
WAGNER—Albert, John P.
WALKER—Ernest R., Ewart G.
WALKER—Fred, Harry W.
WALKER—Gerald H., Harvey W.
WALKER—Moses F., Welday W.
WANER—Lloyd J., Paul G.
WATT—Albert B., Frank M.
WEILAND—Edwin N., Robert G.
WESTLAKE—James P., Waldon T.
WEYHING—August, John
WHEAT—McKinley D., Zachary D.
WHITE—James L., William H.
WHITNEY—Arthur W., Frank T.
WILLIAMS—Arthur F., Walter M.
WILLIAMS—August R., Harry P.
WILTSE—George L., Lewis D.
WINGO—Absalom H., Ivy B.
WOOD—Fred S., Peter B.
WRIGHT—(3) George, Samuel,
& William H.
YOCHIM—Leonard J., Raymond A.

NIGHT BASEBALL

There's nothing new under the sun—nor under electric lights either. Though night baseball has been called the saviour of the modern game, it actually dates back to September, 1880. Two amateur teams tangled at Nantasket Beach, Massachusetts, and with the aid of arclights strung along the field they were able to complete nine full innings between 8 and 9:30 P.M.

The next night game of record was June 2, 1883, when the Quincys of Illinois beat a picked team of home players at Fort Wayne, Indiana, 19-11. Other 19th century games at night were strictly exhibitions, too. Baltimore played at Hartford, Connecticut, on July 23, 1890. Manager Ed Barrow arranged a game for his Paterson, New Jersey, team (boasting Honus Wagner at shortstop) on the night of July 4, 1896 at Wilmington, Delaware.

E. Lee Keyser boldly announced at the National Association meeting in the winter of 1929 that his Des Moines club would be the first in organized baseball to play a league game at night. However, Des Moines opened the season on the road, and Keyser, after having spent $19,000 to install lights, was robbed of the distinction when promoters at Independence, Kansas—a rival club in the Western Association—hastily posted some arclights and played against Muskogee on the night of April 28, 1930. Four days afterward, Des Moines staged its gala arclight affair.

Two seasons later, Larry MacPhail, as general manager of the Columbus Redbirds of the American Association, installed high-level lighting in his stadium. In 1935, as leader of Cincinnati, he introduced night ball to the majors, with President Roosevelt in the White House pressing a button that first turned on the Crosley Field lights. Later, as president of the Dodgers and Yanks, MacPhail put lights in Ebbets Field and Yankee Stadium. Now every team in the majors except Chicago's Wrigley Field NL has lights at home.

Originally, the big leagues limited each team to seven home night games a season. In 1942, ostensibly to cater to the defense worker, the limit was raised to 14, with Washington insisting on 21. Since the summer sun makes a blast furnace of the Kansas City, Los Angeles, Washington and St. Louis ballparks at mid-day, these cities now play practically all their mid-season games in the cooler evening air.

Introduced into organized ball strictly as a novelty, night baseball proved such an immediate success that it saved dozens of minor leagues in the depression years of the 1930's. It also wrought financial miracles for poorer major league clubs.

Modern engineering has made night baseball enjoyable for the players as well as fans. Boston's Fenway Park, for instance, is bathed in 10 times as much light as the average person gets while reading under his living room lamp. Scientific angling of the individual floodlights—and even specialized styles of mowing the grass—add up to optimum visibility. The owners don't stint, either, for Briggs Stadium's 1,386 floodlights are 1,500 watts each... enough power to light a city of 10,000 people!

SPRING TRAINING

With scattered exceptions, 19th century ballplayers trained at home. They would report to their home park a week or two before the season started, then shiver through a crude training period. In case of rain or snow, they would pitch, catch, bunt and run under the stands.

Today every team travels to a tropical clime for leisurely and luxurious spring training. Why? Certainly not in chase of the almighty dollar. The hard fact is that practically every club loses money in the venture... as much as $30,000 each spring. Yet they all indulge, for two compelling reasons:

(1) Conditioning. After five months of loafing, players would strain many more tendons and muscles if they had to work into regular season form in a chilly week or two.

(2) Publicity. When big league heroes cavort under the palms of Florida, and California, a full contingent of newspapermen, sportscasters and photographers are on hand to report daily progress to the baseball-hungry fans at home.

Whetting the customers' appetite by furnishing accounts of spring training, instead of letting the fans watch it first hand, is such valid psychology that even the minor league clubs of Southern cities train at distant bases. Clubowners have found it better salesmanship to bring in their club, fresh and unseen, for the opening of the championship season.

Once the teams got the spring wanderlust, even this country's boundaries couldn't contain them. The Yanks of 1911 were the first to leave the U.S. They trained on Bermuda's coral strand. The touring custom has become so prevalent in recent years that New York fans hardly batted an eye in 1947 when their three home teams trained and played spring exhibitions in such faraway places as Puerto Rico, Venezuela, Cuba, Panama and Hawaii.

As far back as 1884, the Boston Nationals played some spring games in New Orleans. However, the inaugural year of spring training is generally accepted as 1886, when Harry Wright brought his Phillies to Charleston, South Carolina, and Cap Anson took a dozen of his Chicago regulars for conditioning at Hot Springs, Arkansas.

These early "luxury" trips were hardly joyrides. Connie Mack tells of going South with the Washington club in '88: "It took us three nights and two days to reach Jacksonville, Florida. At night we'd travel Pullman, with two players sleeping in each berth, and by day we'd switch to coaches. The first hotel we tried wouldn't even register us. Manager Ted Sullivan scoured the town before he finally found us lodgings—though the hotel clerk made the strict stipulation that the ballplayers would not mingle with the other guests or eat in the same dining room."

By contrast, even the swankiest hotels nowadays vie for patronage by the ball clubs. Many a Chamber of Commerce lies awake nights thinking up ways to lure big league teams to their town as a training base, mindful of the priceless publicity and lucrative business that accrues.

NICKNAMES

Americans dote on nicknames. This habit is so ingrained, that in time a person's real name becomes obscured. Not many baseball fans, for instance, know the correct first names of Babe Ruth, Jake Flowers, Kiki Cuyler, Honus Wagner, Ping Bodie, Zack Taylor or Arky Vaughan. (Answers: George, D'Arcy, Hazen, John, Frank, James and Joseph).

A minor victim of this custom was Jeff Tesreau. While he was coaching Dartmouth's baseball team, townsfolk persuaded him to run for public office. He lost the race... only because local rules specified that a man's legal name must be written on the ballot in order for it to be valid. To the baseball public, which means most of America, the former Giant pitching hero was always "Jeff." Few ever knew him as Charles Monroe Tesreau!

Baseball players often resort to the direct approach, either by tagging someone for the color of his hair (Whitey Lockman, Red Ruffing, Blondy Ryan) or for some other obvious physical characteristic: Lefty Grove, Slim Sallee, Stubby Overmire, Fatty Fothergill, etc. On the other hand, they sometimes become whimsical, calling big fellows "Babe" (Phelps) or "Tiny" (Bonham).

No stick-in-the-muds, baseball folks keep 'em guessing by applying the same nickname for different reasons. Harold Reese is "Pee Wee" because he once was a champion at marbles (which are also known as "pee wees"); Peewee Wanninger, on the other hand simply was a little fellow. Spec Meadows, for his specs (spectacles); Spec Shea, because he's freckled... speckled.

Odell Hale was "Bad News" in tribute to his troubling enemy pitchers. However, Jim Galloway had the same nickname for another reason. The star infielder was a telegrapher before he came into pro ball. In order to break away from work for semipro games, he'd have a crony in another office fake a message to him that some relative was sick and had to see him. So many of these "bad news" wires came during the season that he soon acquired that nickname.

Among other appelations serving double duty are Birdie (Tebbetts, because he chirps like a bird; Cree, because he once played under the assumed name of Burdee). . . Zack (Taylor, because of a famous general by that name; Wheat, because his first name is Zachary). . . Spud (Chandler, to abbreviate his first name, Spurgeon; Davis, because he like "spuds," or potatoes) . . . Crab (Burkett, because of his crabby disposition; Evers, because of the sure way he clawed the ball). . . Cy (Young, shorted from "cyclone"; Williams, a rustic appelation for the hayseed-looking rookie).

Baseball dips heavily into the animal kingdom for nicknames indicating a resemblance: Ducky Medwick, Rabbit Maranville, Skeeter Newsome, Goose Goslin, Moose McCormick, Old Hoss Radbourn, Flea Clifton, Spider Jorgenson, Bullfrog Dietrich, Mule Haas, Ox Eckhardt, Hippo Vaughn, Monk Dubiel, Harry (The Cat) Brecheen, etc.

Loquaciousness is never overlooked. Hence Lippy Durocher, Gabby Hartnett, Dizzy Dean, Goofy Gomez, Buzzy Wares, Orator O'Rourke, Foghorn Kennedy.

Since comic strips have always been among the favorite reading matter of ballplayers, many nicknames are derived from that source, including Wimpy Quinn, Flash Gordon, Bing Miller, Skinny Shaner, Boob McNair, Li'l Abner Erickson, Nemo Liebold, Muggsy McGraw, Pinky Whitney, Dusty Rhodes, Buster Brown, Moon Mullen, Stinky Davis, Jeep Handley, Tarzan Parmelee, Popeye Mahaffey, Available Jones. Hack Wilson was tagged in honor of his physique, which resembled the great wrestler, Hackenschmidt; Firpo Marberry and Jeff Tesreau were nicknamed after the famous heavyweights, and Packy Rogers earned his tag for being as scrappy as Packy McFarland.

Since Mickey Cochrane was such a great catcher, subsequent receivers of any promise were called Mickey, too, even though their correct names happened to be Arnold Owen, Thompson Livingston and Newton Grasso. The ironic part of it all is that Mickey isn't even Cochrane's legitimate tag. His first name is Gordon, and he was called Mickey only because Bostonians thought he had a real Irish face, and "Mickey" is the catch-name for Irishmen, the way "Hans" is used for a German or "Ivan" for a Russian.

Some players are stuck with infant mispronounciations. When Harold Gilbert at the age of 2 said "Tookie" instead of rookie, the family never let him live it down. Players who had difficulty in saying "brother" as tots, wound up in the majors as Bubba Harris, Boo Ferriss and Bruz Hamner.

Predilections for certain foods got these fellows their nicknames: Nap Rucker, Pie Traynor, Salty Parker, Lemons Solters, Pretzels Pezzullo, Candy Cummings. Geographical handles include Dixie Walker, Tex Carleton, Bama Rowell and Arky Vaughan, the last two coming from Alabama and Arkansas.

Nationalities enter the picture, too, as in the cases of Greek George, Frenchy Bordagaray, Swede Hansen, Dutch Leonard, Jap Barbeau, Chink Mattick. Dapper dressers included Broadway Smith, Dude Esterbrook. Beau Bell and Count Mullane. Staid, sedate fellows earned appropriate soubriquets: Deacon Phillippe, Parson Nicholson and Preacher Roe.

Other interesting derivations: Casey Stengel, because he comes from Kansas City (KC); Grandma Murphy, for his rocking-chair motion when winding up; Satchel Paige, whose feet seemed as big as suitcases; Bruno Betzel, from the name of the dog that was his inseparable pal in boyhood; Beauty Bancroft, for yelling that word invariably when a teammate made a nice play; Wish Egan, shortened from his baptismal name of Aloysius; Suitcase Seeds, always seemed en route from one club to another; Pants Rowland, once tore his trousers sliding home; Cracker Schalk, whose rear view was square and small like a cracker when he squatted behind the plate.

LADIES' DAY

Ladies have been a welcome addition to the baseball scene, and club owners court their patronage intensely, after having unwittingly fallen into this gate-boosting bonanza through the much-maligned medium of radio and television.

Though perfected and best exploited only in recent years, Ladies' Day is no novelty. As far back as June 16, 1883, ladies were admitted free to the Polo Grounds to watch the Giants play Cleveland. Robert Lee Hedges of the Browns first established regular Ladies' Days in 1912, but they were admitted free only when accompanied by a man. Females congregated outside the gates and often latched themselves onto the first likely-looking escort.

Bob Quinn, director of the National Baseball Hall of Fame and Museum, was the first to initiate Ladies' Day as it is known today. While general manager of the St. Louis Browns in 1917, Quinn convinced owner Phil Ball that ladies should be admitted free on certain days with no strings attached. Ball, adamant at first, finally surrendered and established regular Ladies' Days. The custom became so popular that as many as 20,000 flocked to Sportsman's Park for a game. The Eastern cities were slow to adopt it, but finally joined the movement. Ladies' Days were soon adopted by every American League club, thanks to the insistence of Quinn, and the National League finally followed suit. In later years the teams were besieged by so many new fans, "converted" when they turned to baseball broadcasts as a relief from afternoon soap operas, that the moguls first admitted them only upon payment of 10-cent tax . . . then 25-cent tax . . . then 50-cent tax-plus-service-charge . . . then 75 cents. And still they come! Bargain-hunters though they are by nature, women are proving true fans by flocking to the ballparks even when Ladies' Day rates are not in effect.

FAMOUS FIRSTS

1845—First code of playing rules, by A. J. Cartwright.

1846—First match game, N.Y. Knickerbockers losing to New York Club, 23-1.

1849—First playing uniform, Knickerbockers' blue and white.

1853—First box score appeared in N.Y. *Clipper.*

1856—First regular baseball reporter, Henry Chadwick.

1857—First official rulebook published and edited by Chadwick...First baseball league: National Association of Baseball Players.

1858—First admission charged, 50 cents, All-Star N. Y. vs. Brooklyn, at Fashion Race Course, L. I.

1859—First college game, Amherst beat Williams.

1862—First enclosed ballpark, Union Grounds, Brooklyn.

1863—First calling of balls and strikes.

1864—First professional player, A. J. Reach, paid $1,000 for season by Philadelphia.

1865—First stolen base, Ed Cuthbert of Keystones.

1866—First slide to steal a base, Bob Addy of Rockford; Dicky Pearce of Atlantics first to lay down bunt.

1867—First prominent use of curve ball, W. A. Cummings.

1869—First salaried team, Cincinnati Red Stockings, who were also first team to wear short trousers.

1870—First demonstration at Brooklyn by Fred Goldsmith (Aug. 16) that a baseball really curves.

1871—First professional league, NA.

1873—First time two games played in one day. Resolutes at Boston, July 4.

1874—First foreign tour, Athletics and Boston to England.

1875—First mask, worn by Jim Tyng as invented by Harvard teammate Fred Thayer . . . . First glove, by Charles Waite.... First major league 1-0 game, Chicago beating St. Louis.

1876—First year of NL... First major team to play twice in one day, Cincinnati.

1877—First minor league organized, International Association.

1878—First turnstiles.

1879—First use of reserve clause in player contract.

1882—First salaried staff of umpires paid by league, AA, and adopted by NL the next year. . . First interleague playoff (World Series). . . First doubleheader Sept. 25 (Providence vs. Worcester) NL.

1884—First organization of a third "major league", UA.

1885—First use of chest protectors for catchers and umpires.

1886—First use of two umpires in one game, World Series. . . First Players' union recognized, "Brotherhood of Ball Players"...First spring training trip, Chicago NL at Hot Springs, Ark.

1887—First catcher to work continuously behind bat, Charles Zimmer.

1888—First round-the-world tour by baseball teams.

1892—First Sunday games permitted in NL.

1894—First player to hit four homers in one game, Bobby Lowe.

1901—First American League game, Chicago vs. Cleveland.

1902—First organization of minor leagues, National Association.

1903—First NL-AL World Series.

1907—First shin guards for catcher introduced by Roger Bresnahan.

1909—First unassisted triple play in majors, Neal Ball... First U.S. President at opening game, W. H. Taft.

1910—First use of cork center in baseball.

1913—First round-world tour by two major league teams, Giants and White Sox.

1919—First Sunday game allowed in New York.

1921—First baseball commissioner takes office, K. M. Landis. . First radio broadcast of World Series.

1926—First amplifiers used, Polo Grounds.

1933—First All-Star Game.

1935—First major league night game, at Cincinnati. . . First major league team to fly, Cincinnati.

1936—First players elected to Hall of Fame: Cobb, Ruth, Mathewson, Wagner and Johnson.

1939—First use of yellow baseball, Pittsburgh vs. Brooklyn. . . First telecast of game, in Brooklyn.

1941—First team to wear helmets at bat, Brooklyn.

1946—First Negro player in modern pro ball, Jackie Robinson at Montreal. . . First playoff in NL, St. Louis beating Brooklyn in two straight games.

1947—First Negro player in NL, Robinson; first in AL, Larry Doby.

ONE-DAY MAJOR LEAGUERS

Every young man who has ever played high school or college baseball harbors dreams of someday becoming a major leaguer. Such vision rarely becomes reality but Ty Cobb, unwittingly, made it so for eight awe-struck St. Joseph's (Philadelphia) College players on May 18, 1912.

The truculent Detroit Tigers came to Philadelphia on that date to play a scheduled game with the world champion Athletics, but Cobb was not allowed to play. A fracas in New York three days before when he climbed into the stands to chase down a heckler resulted in a suspension for the fiery Georgia Peach, league action by president Ban Johnson which the Tiger players considered unjust.

His teammates stood by Cobb. "If Ty doesn't play," they agreed, "neither do we. We'll strike." Reminded by manager Hugh Jennings that a forfeiture would result in a $5,000 fine, the players still remained adamant.

Athletics' manager Connie Mack, informed of the Tiger players' stand, approached Jennings and suggested he hire, for the one game, a group of collegians. Mack's idea made sense to Jennings who was worried lest he would be unable to place a team on the field. The Tiger pilot wasted no time. He had contracts drawn up and they were signed by Jack Coffey, Aloysius Travers, Pat Meany, Hap Ward, Billy Maharg, Jim McGarr, Dan McGarvey and Bill Leinhauser. The dream was realized for eight St. Joseph's collegians—they were to be Kings for a Day! Ed Irwin, a sandlotter, also was added to the day's Detroit roster.

The game itself was a travesty, but Detroit saved $5,000. Travers, later to be ordained a Catholic priest, pitched for the Tigers and established an all-time single game mark which still stands—most runs allowed in one game. The 20-year-old Travers was belted by 24-2, nine errors by his mates allowing 10 unearned runs.

Of the four hits collected by the Tigers two were obtained by the sandlotter, Irwin. He cracked two triples in three times at bat for a lifetime batting average of .667.

Of the nine one-day fill-ins only Maharg, later to become a professional boxer, was to play again. Four years later he appeared in the outfield of the Philadelphia Phillies, another one-day stand.

Perhaps the proudest of the collegians was Leinhauser, the wearer of Cobb's uniform. Eventually it was through Leinhauser, who was to become a Philadelphia police officer, that S. C. Thompson, co-author of THE OFFICIAL ENCYCLOPEDIA OF BASEBALL, was able to track down the full names and birth data on the one-shot big leaguers who saved the Detroit club $5,000.

NEGRO PLAYERS

Cap Anson, the giant of his day and one of the pillars of organized baseball, may have been one of the factors which mitigated against the Negro player in the early days of the majors. During the first 73 years of the majors only two Negro players managed to get into a big league box score before Jackie Robinson. Hank Thompson and Willard Brown donned major league uniforms in 1947 to become the first major leaguers of their race.

In 1884 the Walker brothers—Welday and Moses—played for Toledo of the American Association, a recognized major league at the time. Both quickly faded into oblivion although Moses was above average as a catcher.

Anson indicated his sentiments toward the Negro player when he brought his Chicago White Stockings to Newark, New Jersey in 1884 for an exhibition game with the local minor leaguers. George Stovey, artful Negro hurler, was scheduled to pitch against the big leaguers. When Anson discovered that his team would face the fast slants of a Negro, he refused to have his men play the Newark club unless Stovey was removed from the lineup. So the management kept Stovey out of the game.

Anson continued to crusade against the entrance of Negro players into the National League, because of their color not their ability.

Between the Walkers' brief tenure at Toledo, and Jackie Robinson's epochal entrance into Brooklyn in 1947, there were several Negro players in organized ball—all of them in the 19th century minor leagues. They included such standouts as shortstop Clarence Matthews, second baseman Frank Grant, first baseman Charles Kelly and second baseman J. W. (Bud) Fowler.

The first team of paid Negro players was a group of fellow waiters Frank Thompson recruited in 1885 at the Argyle Hotel, Babylon, Long Island. They played 10 games that summer against white teams on Long Island, then went on tour billed as the Cuban Giants. Thompson hoped to ease the social barriers by passing his team off as Cubans, and a few players furthered the illusion by chattering in a rapid Spanish-sounding gibberish on the field. Thompson added the nickname Giants because it was a popular team in the majors at that time. It remained a good tag, and later Negro teams were known as the Lincoln Giants, Chicago American Giants, Bacharach Giants, Brooklyn Royal Giants, etc.

None of these troupes could establish a stable league setup till 1920, when the Negro National League was formed in Kansas City. The next year a Negro Eastern League arose, and they started a regular World Series in 1924.

These leagues collapsed in the depression depths of 1932. Several years later, the Negro American and National Leagues opened shop, followed by a host of lesser leagues in the South. Player incomes were rounded out by winter ball in Mexico, Cuba and Venezuela, which had no color lines.

Between World Wars I and II, Negro baseball boasted such legendary heroes as shortstop John Henry Lloyd, catcher Josh Gibson, pitchers Cyclone Joe Williams and Cannonball Dick Redding, outfielder Oscar Charleston, etc. Only one of the fabled figures of this lost chapter in baseball history managed to benefit through modern emancipation: Leroy (Satchel) Paige, though well past 40 at the time, joined the Indians and helped pitch them to the pennant in 1948.

SPITBALL PITCHERS

The spitball pitcher—legally—is as extinct as the American buffalo. When Burleigh Grimes tossed his last dewy pitch in 1934, it marked the end of a hurling breed which was declared null and void as far back as 1920 when the game's administrators outlawed the pitch.

The 17 pitchers in the majors at the time the pitch was outlawed were permitted to continue their salivary trade, but no other hurler was allowed to introduce it if it wasn't already part of his mound repertoire.

There are still occasional squawks from the batters that they have been slipped a spitball every now and then, but the umpires are vigilant and have instructions to eject from the game any pitcher they detect resorting to the outlawed pitch.

Here is the list of spitball hurlers in action at the time the 1920 ban was imposed (showing first and last season of major league action):

NATIONAL	AMERICAN
Bill Doak (1912-29)	Yancey Ayers (1913-21)
Phil Douglas (1912-22)	Ray Caldwell (1910-21)
Dana Fillingim (1915-25)	Stan Coveleskie (1912-28)
Ray Fisher (1910-20)	Urban Faber (1914-33)
Marvin Goodwin (1916-25)	Hub Leonard (1913-25)
Burleigh Grimes (1916-34)	Jack Quinn (1909-33)
Clarence Mitchell (1911-32)	Allan Russell (1915-25)
Dick Rudolph (1910-27)	Urban Shocker (1916-28)
	Allen Sothoron (1914-26)

HANDICAPS

The bespectacled major league no longer is a novelty, and the nickname "specs," first applied to a player who wore glasses, has long since passed into limbo. However, baseball has known players who have played creditably despite the handicap of the loss of a leg, arm or eye.

A one-legged player was Bert Shepard, who lost his right limb as the result of an Army crash. Shepard had been a fair minor league prospect and was determined to make the majors, finally realizing his ambition in 1945 when he hurled for the Washington Senators.

Perhaps the most remarkable of all physically handicapped ball players was a pitcher, Hugh (One-Arm) Daly, who won 72 games in his career. Daly, who also played second base and shortstop, recorded a no-hit, no-run triumph and struck out 19 players in a game, still the all-time mark.

A handicap worked in favor of Mordecai Brown, the famous Chicago Cub pitcher of the early century, who didn't possess all the fingers on his pitching hand. The crippled digits on Brown's hand enabled him to grip the ball in such a manner that his curve was actually more effective.

Pete Gray, who had one arm, played the outfield for the 1945 St. Louis Browns and the loss of several toes didn't hamper pitcher Charley Ruffing and outfielder Hal Peck.

Harry Jasper lost the sight of an eye when hit by a batted ball, but he played several seasons of major league ball after the accident. Few knew Tom Sunkel's left eye was blinded by a cataract throughout his big league career. Still another one-eyed pitcher was Bill Irwin of the old Cincinnati club.

So much for one eyed players. How about the "four-eyes"....the eyeglass brigade? A bespectacled player used to be a rare spectacle indeed, with Will White of Cincinnati the lone lens wearer in the first 44 years of organized baseball. But recent generations produced dozens of examples to refute the saying, "Baseball doesn't make passes at players who wear glasses."

Trying to explain the eyeglass evolution, veteran Arlie Latham always insisted, "Back in the '80s, the diamond was laid out east to west, from batter to pitcher, so that the afternoon sun shone only in the batter's eyes. Nowadays the fields are turned around so that the sinking sun slants steadily into the fielders' faces. That's what ruins the players' eyes and that's why so many of them have to wear glasses."

A more likely explanation is that common sense has replaced common vanity. When people need glasses to correct their vision nowadays, they wear them.

FOREIGN TOURS

The Boston and Athletics teams, only ones to win pennants in the old National Association, made the first foreign baseball trip in 1874. They played in 14 baseball games and seven cricket matches in England and Ireland. Five years later Frank Bancroft took a barnstorming team to Havana, but it was a financial failure. The A's and Phillies had better results when they visited Cuba in 1886.

The first globe-circling ambassadors of the game were the 20 players headed by A. G. Spalding, who made a notable tour in 1888-89. The Chicago NL team played a picked club of league rivals, tagged the All-American nine, in such places as Auckland, New Zealand; Sydney and Melbourne, Australia; Ceylon; Egypt; Rome, Naples and Florence, Italy; Paris, several English cities and Dublin, Ireland. Though expenses ran to $50,000, the trip proved profitable.

The Reach All-America team toured Japan in 1908, and a year later the University of Wisconsin played a series of games there. But the first big league teams to show as units in that baseball-loving land were the Giants and White Sox, who toured the world in 1913-14 under the guidance of John McGraw and Charlie Comiskey. From here, the teams went on to play in Shanghai, Hong Kong, Manila, Australia, Ceylon, Egypt, Italy, France and Great Britain. . . 31 games in all, with Bill Klem as umpire.

McGraw and Comiskey planned a similar tour in 1924, but had to quit after playing in England, Ireland and France. The reason: poor attendances. However, baseball was at fever pitch in Japan, and a 1922 tour by major league barnstormers was quite successful. Herb Hunter, who organized the 1922 trip, rounded up another with the help of sportswriter Fred Lieb in 1931, using many World Series players. Four games in Tokyo drew 250,000! Soon after this, the Japanese developed professional teams for the first time.

Lefty O'Doul, one of the players on that 1931 junket to Japan, returned to that isle five times in later years, and became the second greatest sports idol over there. Lefty was overshadowed only by the immortal Babe Ruth, who headed Connie Mack's team of American Leaguers that whipped the best available Japanese competition in an 18-game series in 1934.

The New York Yankees visited Japan in 1955 and didn't lose a game in a tour which included stops at islands in the Pacific. It was the first time in more than 40 years that a major league team toured with almost the same playing roster that finished its regular season. The Dodgers and St. Louis Cardinals have also made post-season tours of the Orient.

BASEBALL BALLADS

Since every game is a new adventure, every season a new saga, baseball lends itself well to song and story. Even daily newspaper sportswriters sometimes attempt Homeric prose in praise of their latest hero. Sentiment runs so high, baseball odes don't have to be epics to capture popular appeal. Still, the game has inspired some gusty classics...like "Casey At The Bat," which, even if it doesn't rate as full-blown literature, must be accorded everlasting tribute for rescuing the horde of fading vaudevillians who recited "Casey" as a last prop against unemployment.

Back in 1869, when Cincinnati's Red Stockings were riding high through an unbeaten season, the players had their own theme song. It was written to the tune of "Bonnie Blue Flag." Just before each game, the mustachioed Reds would line up near home plate, hat in hand, to serenade the grandstand with:

We are a band of baseball players
From Cincinnati city.
We come to toss the ball around
And sing to you our ditty.

And if you listen to our song
We are about to sing,
We'll tell you all about baseball
And make the welkin ring.

Hurrah, hurrah,
For the noble game, hurrah.
Red Stockings all will toss the ball
And shout our loud hurrah.

Baseball polkas and poems turned up as frequently as pennant winners in those early years. Yet none of the 19th century compositions had the flair and flavor of that fictional opus written in 1888, and popularized by the masterful recitations of De Wolf Hopper, to wit:

CASEY AT THE BAT
By Ernest L. Thayer

The outlook wasn't brilliant for the Mudville nine that day;
The score stood four to two with but one inning more to play.
And then when Cooney died at first, and Barrows did the same,
A sickly silence fell upon the patrons of the game.

A straggling few got up to go in deep despair. The rest
Clung to that hope which springs eternal in the human breast.
They thought if only Casey could but get a whack at that—
We'd put up even money now with Casey at the bat.

But Flynn preceded Casey, as did also Jimmy Blake,
And the former was a lulu and the latter was a cake;
So upon the stricken multitude grim melancholy sat,
For there seemed but little chance of Casey's getting to the bat.

But Flynn let drive a single, to the wonderment of all,
And Blake, the much despised, tore the cover off the ball;
And when the dust had lifted and the men saw what had occurred,
There was Johnny safe at second and Flynn a-hugging third.

Then from 5,000 throats and more there rose a lusty yell;
It rambled through the valley, it rattled in the dell;
It knocked upon the mountain and recoiled upon the flat,
For Casey, mighty Casey, was advancing to the bat.

There was ease in Casey's manner as he stepped into his place;
There was pride in Casey's bearing and a smile on Casey's face.
And when, responding to the cheers, he lightly doffed his hat,
No stranger in the crowd could doubt 'twas Casey at the bat.

Ten thousand eyes were on him as he rubbed his hands with dirt;
Five thousand tongues applauded when he wiped them on his shirt.
Then while the writhing pitcher ground the ball into his hip,
Defiance gleamed in Casey's eye, a sneer curled Casey's lip.

And now the leather-covered sphere came hurtling through the air,
And Casey stood a-watching it in haughty grandeur there.
Close by the sturdy batsman the ball unheeded sped—
"That ain't my style," said Casey. "Strike one," the umpire said.

From the benches, black with people, there went up a muffled roar,
Like the beating of the storm waves on a stern and distant shore.
"Kill him! Kill the umpire!" shouted some one in the stand,
And it's likely they'd have killed him had not Casey raised his hand.

With a smile of Christian charity great Casey's visage shone;
He stilled the rising tumult, he bade the game go on;
He signaled to the pitcher, and once more the spheroid flew;
But Casey still ignored it, and the umpire said, "Strike two."

"Fraud!"cried the maddened thousands, and the echo answered "Fraud!"
But one scornful look from Casey and the audience was awed.
They saw his face grow stern and cold, they saw his muscles strain,
And they knew that Casey wouldn't let that ball go by again.

The sneer is gone from Casey's lip, his teeth are clenched in hate;
He pounds with cruel violence his bat upon the plate.
And now the pitcher holds the ball, and now he lets it go,
And now the air is shattered by the force of Casey's blow.

Oh! somewhere in this favored land the sun is shining bright;
The band is playing somewhere, and somewhere hearts are light.
And somewhere men are laughing, and somewhere children shout;
But there is no joy in Mudville—mighty Casey has struck out.

But the American public, notorious in its constant clamor for a "winner," wouldn't settle for a discredited Casey. In the very nature of baseball's campaign, "there is always another game tomorrow," so mighty Casey had to have his revenge. It remained for a proud young Southerner to redeem the fallen hero by composing this ode in 1906:

CASEY'S REVENGE
By James Wilson

There were saddened hearts in Mudville for a week or even more;
There were muttered oaths and curses—every fan in town was sore.
"Just think," said one, "how soft it looked with Casey at the bat,
And to think he'd go and spring a bush league trick like that."

All his past fame was forgotten—he was now a hopeless "shine"—
They called him "Strike-out Casey" from the Mayor down the line;
And as he came to bat each day his bosom heaved a sigh,
While a look of hopeless fury shone in Casey's eye.

He soon began to sulk and loaf—his batting eye went lame;
No home runs on the score card now were chalked against his name.
The fans without exception gave the manager no peace,
For one and all kept clamoring for Casey's quick release.

The lane is long, some one has said, that never turns again,
And Fate, though fickle, often gives another chance to men;
And Casey smiled—his rugged face no longer wore a frown—
The pitcher who had started all the trouble came to town.

All Mudville had assembled—ten thousand fans had come
To see the twirler who had put big Casey on the bum;
And when he stepped into the box the multitude went wild.
He doffed his cap in proud disdain—but Casey only smiled.

"Play ball!" the umpire's voice rang out—and then the game began;
But in that throng of thousands there was not a single fan
Who thought that Mudville had a chance, and with the setting sun
Their hopes sank low—the rival team was leading "four to one."

The last half of the ninth came round with no change in the score,
But when the first man up hit safe the crowd began to roar;
The din increased—the echo of ten thousand shouts was heard
When the pitcher hit the second and gave "four balls" to the third.

Three men on base—nobody out—three runs to tie the game!
A triple meant the highest niche in Mudville's hall of fame;
But here the rally ended and the gloom was deep as night,
When the fourth one "fouled to catcher" and the fifth "flew out to right."

A dismal, groaning chorus came—a scowl was on each face—
When Casey walked up, bat in hand, and slowly took his place.
His bloodshot eyes in fury gleamed—his teeth were clenched in hate;
He gave his cap a vicious hook and pounded on the plate.

The pitcher smiled and cut one loose—across the plate it sped—
Another hiss—another groan—"Strike one," the umpire said.
Zip! Like a shot the second curve broke just below his knee—
"Strike two!" the umpire roared aloud—but Casey made no plea.

No roasting for the umpire now—his was an easy lot;
But here the pitcher whirled again—was that a rifle shot?
A whack—a crack—and out through space the leather pellet flew:
A blot against the distant sky—a speck against the blue.

Above the fence in centre field in rapid whirling flight
The sphere sailed on—the blot grew dim and then was lost to sight;
Ten thousand hats were thrown in air—ten thousand threw a fit—
But no one ever found the ball that mighty Casey hit.

Oh! somewhere in this favored land dark clouds may hide the sun,
And somewhere bands no longer play and children have no fun;
And somewhere over blighted loves there hangs a heavy pall;
But Mudville hearts are happy now—for Casey hit the ball.

Around this same period, Jack Norworth and Albert Von Tilzer wrote a song that is destined to live as long as the game itself, "Take Me Out To The Ball Game." Norworth sang it in the Follies with his wife, the beauteous Nora Bayes. Almost overnight, it became the game's national anthem, and today it's as popular as ever.

Another lilting rhythm that became baseball legend was "Tinker to Evers to Chance," an eight-line lament penned by Franklin P. Adams of the old *New York Evening Mail.* Though this double play combination of the Cubs was not the greatest of all time, it was the most dreaded of its day. As F.P.A. versified:

These are the saddest of possible words:
"Tinker to Evers to Chance.'
Trio of bear Cubs and fleeter than birds,
"Tinker to Evers to Chance."
Ruthlessly pricking our gonfalon bubble,
Making a Giant hit into a double—
Words that are heavy with nothing but trouble:
"Tinker to Evers to Chance."

But baseball isn't all romance and poetry. The characters and situations rife in the sport are ripe material for literate wits; so it's no wonder that a sports-minded genius like Ring Lardner was able to weave such classic comedy as his "You Know Me Al" series. First a comic strip and later a series of short stories, this literary effort excels all the plays, books and movies written about the national pastime.

In recent years, baseball's best ballads have evolved from the writers' annual winter banquets held in the big cities. With tabs ranging up to $25 per plate, and guests numbering 1,500, they serve tender steaks...but not half so tender as the "hams", meaning the baseball writers disporting on the stage in hour-long topical revues. If the acting is sometimes punk, the lyrics never are. The scribes really outdo themselves with songs ranging from sentimental ballads to pungent parodies.

PLAYING EQUIPMENT

MANUFACTURE OF A BAT

Bats are made of ash, hackberry and hickory, but ash is preferred because of superior resiliency or "drive." The best white ash comes from Northeastern United States. Special bat timber experts determine which trees are suitable, and these are felled, cut into logs about 40 inches long and hauled to the timber mill. There they are sawed into either square or round billets before being sent to the bat factory.

Upon arrival at the yards of the factory, the billets are inspected, graded and then stacked loosely—so that air can circulate freely—for 10 to 18 months of seasoning. More than 3,000,000 billets are in the process of drying this way at any one time.

Billets which have split during seasoning are thrown out and the others hauled to the factory to go through a turning process that brings them into the approximate shape of a bat. They are then weighed and graded to see for which models they will best be suitable. The bat is then placed on a lathe alongside the original model and cut down to the same shape. The turner weighs and measures for fractional accuracy, then sands the embryo bat, which is finally stained and branded.

MANUFACTURE OF A BASEBALL

Harassed pitchers may swear there's a live jackrabbit inside the ball, but according to A.G. Spalding Bros. Inc.—which manufactures all the official American and National League baseballs in its plant at Chicopee, Massachusetts—actually the core consists of a cork composition containing a small percentage of rubber. This core is 13/16 of an inch in diameter.

Two black rubber shells, each approximately 5/32 of an inch thick, are wrapped around the core, with a thin cushion of red rubber between the edges of the hemispherical black rubber shells. Next comes a red rubber wrapping 3/32 of an inch thick. The entire "pill" is molded perfectly round to 4 1/8 inches circumference.

Wool is wound around the pill under precise humidity and tension control in three operations: first application, 121 yards of four-ply gray woolen yarn, brings size to 7 3/4 inches circumference; second winding, 45 yards of three-ply white woolen yarn, increases it to 8 3/16 inches circumference; third winding, 53 yards of three-ply gray woolen yarn, makes size of ball 8 3/4 inches circumference. Next comes 150 yards of fine cotton winding, coated with a layer of latex (rubber cement) to prevent unraveling. By now the overall circumference is 8 7/8 inches.

The covers, of selected horsehide leather between .050-.055 of an inch thick, are cut on a machine into the pattern of "a swollen figure 8," with 108 stitch-holes bordering each cover. Two such pieces are used to cover a baseball. After dampening the horsehide to make it pliable, the covers are hand-stitched with red cotton thread. Any pinching that occurs when the cover shrinks back tight is eliminated by rolling the balls. By now the circumference is the regulation 9-9 1/4 inches circumference and weighs between 5-5 1/4 ounces.

All the balls head for either of two stamping machines. One, for American League baseball, stamps the "Reach" trademark plus the AL president's autograph on the cover. The other, for official NL balls, registers the "Spalding" symbol as well as the league president's signature. Aside from the printing on the cover, the balls of both leagues are absolutely identical.

MANUFACTURE OF A GLOVE

Leather for baseball gloves comes from hides of native cows. Animals slaughtered in late May and early November (called Summer Hides) are preferred. The tanned leather is then taken to die-cutting machines.

Next step is stamping. This is done by applying heat and pressure while the glove palm is laid out flat. Fielders' gloves are then sewn inside out with finest quality cotton thread. More expensive gloves have an extra row of stitches around the thumb, sewed with wax linen thread. After sewing, gloves are turned and then stretched over a form heated to about 210 degrees Fahrenheit. They remain there long enough to set the shape, the operation ironing all the seams evenly and giving the glove a well tailored appearance.

Sewed linings are then inserted, followed by binding, wrist eyeletting and lacing. The gloves are then oiled, with warm oil rubbed in by hand. This waterproofs the leather and gives the glove a good feel and fine color.

The gloves are then "laid off" over another hot form. This consists of pulling the heel into position, ironing all wrinkles out of the lining, forming the pocket and putting a further set in the leather. One more inspection, and then they're ready for shipment.

CARE OF EQUIPMENT

Bats—Hit with the "label up," since batting against the grain invites breakage. Never hit the bat against sole of the shoe to dislodge mud or dirt, as chipping may result. Bats should not be left in dew-covered grass. In the offseason, rub the bat with linseed oil or tung oil, or with any good lubricant, like vaseline. Keep the bat in a dry place, but not near any excessive heat, lest it dry out. Many players advise bone-rubbing the bat as a further preservative.

Baseballs—Even a single broken stitch should be repaired immediately. Covers should be cleaned and kept dry.

Gloves—High temperatures and excessive moisture are the most common sources of trouble. In order to prevent green mold rot, keep the glove in a cool dry place. When wet, dry the glove immediately, but the action should not be forced. It should be dried at normal room temperature without use of artificial heat. If repeated wetting occurs, harshness in the leather may develop, but this can be counter-acted by applying neat's-foot oil or light paraffin (mineral) oil. Leather that has become soiled should be cleaned with saddle soap only. Use a moist cloth to work up a cream by rubbing over the soap. Rub the cloth over the leather until the lather works loose the dirt. Dirty lather should then be wiped off with a clean cloth, and the leather briskly rubbed with a clean cloth.

Shoes—Oil or other lubricant should be used often on uppers to maintain softness and strength. Since night games causes shoes to be soaked in dew, use treatment recommended in preceding paragraph for repeated wetting of gloves.

XIII MINOR LEAGUES

Baseball talent must originate from a starting point, and before the rapid advance of the electronic age a major leaguer who did not serve a gradual apprenticeship in the minors was a rarity.

The education was broad and more painstaking, the steps slower and progress was calculated in classification of lettered leagues, to wit: D, B, C, and on up the line. But the marvelous magic lantern which beamed big league games into minor league territories, and the speedy growth of radio and its far-reaching voice have helped to cut down on the number of leagues and accelerated the promotional scale of the ball player.

Before telecasts and broadcasts invaded minor league territory, the majors zealously guarded their lifeline of supply. Minor league franchises were stable; a fan could plan on seeing games in his home city year after year and he was reasonably certain his league would complete its appointed schedule of games. But times change, and so has the face of the minors.

Once on a firm, economic footing the minors now have a constant struggle to acquire enough franchises to fill out an even number of teams in order to shape a schedule. Cities drop by the wayside because of lagging attendances, and hasty efforts are made to keep a league in business by a constant shifting of franchises from one locale to another. New circuits run into financial straits almost immediately after a season opens, and reorganization is sometimes necessary before the halfway point if the league is to survive its campaign.

Not that the minors didn't face some of these hazards before television and the spread of radio and its "Game of the Day" broadcast, but it has become increasingly difficult for some of the lower classifications to carry on their business in the wake of diminishing gates, slim rosters and the televising of major league games into their cities.

HISTORY The minors are only six years younger than the advent of the first major circuit, the National Association. The International Association was founded following a conference in Pittsburgh on February 20, 1877, with James A. Williams of Columbus, Ohio, appointed the league's executive-secretary. W. A. (Candy) Cummings, of original curveball fame, was elected president of the league whose charter members included Rochester, New York; Allegheny of Pittsburgh; Buckeye of Columbus, Ohio; Manchester, New Hampshire; Live Oak of Lynn, Massachusetts; Maple Leaf of Guelph, Ontario, and Tecumseh of London, Ontario.

In this same year, 13 professional teams in the Midwest formed the League Alliance, playing whenever convenient or desirable. The Red Caps of St. Paul finished first, but the loosely knit league disbanded that fall. In 1877, too, a small circuit operated in New England. However, the International Association rates as the pioneer minor league because it was the only one of its time to be bound by strict rules and a regular schedule.

The first flag in the first bona fide minor league went to the alien entry of Tecumseh, a Canadian franchise using United States players. In the winning lineup were such former big leaguers as George H. Bradley, Herman Doscher, Fred Goldsmith and Phil Bowers.

In 1878, the International Association expanded to 11 teams. The leading sports newspaper of that time, the *New York Clipper*, offered a silk pennant to the top team and gold badges to the players with the best fielding average at each position.

The International dropped its Canadian entries to become the National Association for 1879, and lasted just two more seasons. Colorful ubiquitous Ted Sullivan enters the picture at this time, organizing the first Western League on January 2, 1879, at Rockford, Illinois. Of the four clubs in the loop—Davenport, Iowa; Omaha, Nebraska; Dubuque, Iowa, and Rockford—Sullivan's own team in Dubuque finished on top. The winners introduced such future big league heroes as Charlie Comiskey, Old Hoss Radbourn and Tom Loftus. This league lasted only two years.

Of half a dozen strong clubs forming the Eastern Championship Association in 1881, the Metropolitans of New York proved best. The Mets also won the League Alliance flag the next year. Baseball had two major leagues for the first time in 1882, and each used a strong new affiliate, the National League dealing with the Northwestern League and the American Association with the Inter-State Association. More leagues arose after the Tripartite Agreement of 1883 insured a modicum of protection from the marauding majors.

By 1884 there were eight minor leagues active. Most notable of these was the Eastern League, which has maintained a continuous history (despite various title changes) to become the International League of today—the oldest minor league of all. The metamorphosis can be traced as follows: 1884, Eastern League; 1885, New York State League; 1886-87, International League; 1888, International Association; 1889-90, International League; 1891, Eastern Association; 1892-1911, Eastern League; 1912-17, International League; 1918-19, New International League; 1920-to-date, International League.

Baseball flourished on the Pacific Coast in 1885, with the Haverly Club of San Francisco winning the pennant in the California League. That same year, Atlanta proved the class of the newly-organized Southern League (forerunner of the present Southern Association), which joined the National Agreement along with the New England, Canadian and New York leagues. The Texas League joined the official herd in 1888.

However, minor league ball remained a precarious venture. The majors no longer snatched their stars in midseason, but the lower clubs were liable to lose an entire roster at the end of each season. A basic reform was instituted at the instigation of *Sporting Life* editor Francis C. Richter in 1888—the National Agreement was amended to permit minor league clubs to reserve up to 14 players per club. The player-purchase system then came into vogue. Richter's Millenium Plan also included a player-draft, which went into effect in 1892.

MINORS' NATIONAL ASSOCIATION

Orphaned by the stormy war between the American and National Leagues, both of which scrapped the National Agreement in 1901, the minor leagues decided on the Ben Franklin credo, "We must all hang together or assuredly we shall hang separately."

The minors' own "Fourth of July" came on September 5, 1901, when representatives of seven leagues gathered in Chicago's Leland Hotel and proclaimed their Declaration of Independence. Patrick T. Powers of the Eastern League was elected president, and he suggested the formal name of National Association of Professional Base Ball Leagues. John H. Farrell of Auburn, New York, was elected executive secretary-treasurer, a powerful post he held for 32 years.

Armed with specific plans laid down at this parley, the leagues met the next month in New York. This was a virtual Constitutional Convention. They agreed on a new 10-year national pact, empowering a Board of Arbitration to administer the entire minor league structure. Salary limits, player reserves, drafting procedure and other rights and responsibilities were legislated. Charter member clubs were classified as follows:

Class A—Eastern League, Western League; Class B—Southern Association, Western Association, New York State League, New England League, Three-I (Indiana, Illinois, Iowa) League; Class C—Pacific Northwest League, Connecticut League.

Soon afterward, the budding body faced its first stern test. The Western League cried for protection against territorial invasion by the newly-reorganized American Association. AA president Thomas J. Hickey resigned as head of the National Association's Board of Arbitration, and the AA operated outside the Association in 1902.

At the fall meeting of 1902, the minor federation began to exert its power. It expelled Memphis for using a debarred player. It also banned any future pact with the majors which would destroy its new-found autonomy.

End of warfare between the AL and NL early in 1903 set the keynote for a peaceful conclave of minors that October. First, the delegates ratified the majors' newest National Agreement, which recognized the National Association as an integral part of organized baseball. Second, the AA-WL, squabble was settled as the Westerns, ruined by late-season floods and cold weather, folded in September and left the AA free to enter the minors' organization. Finally, the strong "outlaw" Pacific Coast League—having absorbed the California League—was admitted into the NA with special draft-proof privileges.

By now 19 leagues were in the fold. The National Association continued serene for a long time, reaching no great crisis till World War I. Only one league, the International, survived 1918. The next January, the troubled minors demanded an end to player options and draft by the majors. Instead, the majors terminated their mutual pact. Appointment of Judge K. M. Landis as high commissioner of baseball at the end of 1920 led to a new major-minor agreement, which has governed organized baseball with few alterations ever since.

The new National Agreement of 1921 restored the draft, but did not make it compulsory. The top minors remained draft-free until 1931, when the depression-ridden organization finally agreed to universal draft. As for National Association administration, the presidency shifted from Pat Powers to Michael H. Sexton in 1909, to Judge William G. Bramham in 1933 and to George M. Trautman in 1946. Secretary Farrell was shorn of power in 1933.

MINOR LEAGUE CLASSIFICATIONS

Baseball's far-flung minor league empire operates under a logical system. Clubs collect into leagues, within reasonable geographic limitations. Leagues are rated according to population, which is an index of potential support at the box office, and classification letters are then assigned. Here are the terms:

CLASS:	AAA	AA	A-1	A	B	C	D
Minimum League Population:	3,000,000	1,750,000	1,450,000	1,000,000	250,000	150,000	....
Payment for Player Drafted by Majors:	*$25,000	*$25,000	*$25,000	*$25,000	*$25,000	*$25,000	*$25,000
Monthly Payroll Limit:	....	....		$6,300	$4,800	$4,200	$3,400
Active Player Limit:	21	20	18	18	18	17	17
Reserve Player Limit:	38	37	32	32	27	24	21
Players Out on Option:	17	17	14	14	10	8	5
Waiver Claiming Price:	$5,000	$3,750	$1,750	$1,250	$500	$350	$100

**If player is first-year man, draft price by majors is $15,000.*

Besides the advantages of high classification apparent from this graduated scale, all drafting of players and umpires at the close of each season is done successively from the top class downward. Naturally, a club or league would like to qualify for as high a ranking as possible.

MAJOR FACTS IN THE MINORS

Historian Ben Morgan has compiled figures to show that every record ever made in the majors has been bettered in the minors—except Lou Gehrig's consecutive playing streak of 2,130 games... Largest paid attendance in minor league history is 57,713, August 7,1956, Columbus at Miami (Fla.), International League...Longest schedule was 225 games-per-club arranged by the Pacific Coast League in 1904. George Van Haltren went to bat 941 times that season...Every member of the 1937 Newark team of the International League rose to the majors, including two catchers, seven pitchers and the manager...Before he was able to earn a better living as a novelist, Zane Gray played the outfield for Newark of the Atlantic League in 1896...President Edward G. Barrow of the Atlantic League in 1898 brought the first woman into organized baseball, a pitcher named Lizzie Stroud (who played under the name of "Arlington")...When Corsicana of the Texas League beat Texarkana, 51-3, in July of 1902, Justin J. (Nig) Clarke made eight homers in eight at-bats and scored eight times... An average of less than one out of a hundred big leaguers completes his career without ever seeing minor league service ...International League president Frank J. Shaughnessy instituted the four-team post-season playoff system, now universal in the minors, in 1932... Joe Bauman, first baseman for Roswell (Longhorn League) set an all-time record for home runs in one season in 1954 when he hit 72...Joseph Wilhoit hit safely in 69 straight games for Wichita (Kan.) of the Western League in 1919...Bill Bell and Ron Necciai were the no-hit pitching phenomena of the 1952 Bristol (Tenn.) team in the Appalachian League, Bell pitched consecutive no-hitters, added a third later in the season; Necciai nailed 27 men on strike-outs in his no-hitter, and fanned 109 in 42 2/3 innings...Walter Carlisle, Vernon (Pacific Coast League), was the only outfielder in history to make an unassisted triple play, sixth inning, July 19, 1911, vs Los Angeles ...Only one pitcher ever led all the minors in one season in games won, strikeouts and ERA: Dizzy Dean, Houston (Texas League) 1931 ...Henry

Miller, Winnipeg (Northern League) hit a fungo 438 feet, two inches, in 1916 ... Evar Swanson, Columbus, Ohio (American Association), circled the bases in 13.3 seconds, in 1931 ... Al Rosen, Kansas City (American Association), hit five successive home runs July 26-27, 1948 ... Fastest game: Mobile at Atlanta (Southern Association), Sept. 19, 1910—32 minutes; fastest double-header: Los Angeles at Oakland (Pacific Coast League), July 30, 1905—1:38.

XIV OUTSIDE ORGANIZED BASEBALL

Hundreds of thousands of people play ball for money every year, yet they remain outside the province of organized baseball. Representing either small towns, industrial plants or private promoters, these part-time players bring their communities good baseball at low prices. Many of them eventually reach the big leagues.

Down in Carolina, textile mills have sponsored baseball teams for generations. They developed some of the most talented players in the majors, ranging through the years from Shoeless Joe Jackson to Marty Marion. Then there are colorful barnstorming teams, like the bewhiskered House of David nine from Benton Harbor, Michigan. Of the Independent promotors, none was as renowned as Max Rosner of the Bushwicks of New York, boasting such alumni as Lou Gehrig, Frank Frisch, Jimmy Ring, Hank Greenberg, Joe Judge, Tony Cuccinello, Waite Hoyt, etc.

SEMIPRO

Guiding spirit of semipro baseball's modern boom is Raymond Dumont, former newspaperman and sporting goods dealer in Wichita, Kansas. He inaugurated a state-wide tournament in 1931. Within four years it blossomed into a series involving hundreds of clubs, drawing 50,000 fans and paying $5,000 in prize money.

By 1935, Dumont's brainchild was ready for long pants. He staged a national tournament at Wichita, an invitation affair. It proved such a smashing success that the following January he organized the National Semipro Baseball Congress (which since has dropped the "Semipro" from its title). It proved to be a sound, enduring organization that is responsible for putting semipro ball into its healthiest condition in history.

The NBC charter qualifies any player not active in professional baseball. That opens the gate for hundreds of Service teams all over the country. Clubs are protected by issuance of a standard jump-proof player's contract. Umpires and scorers are chartered, too.

Thousands of teams in all states engage in district, state and regional tournaments to qualify two dozen teams for the national championships each August at Wichita. The championship team now receives a cash award of $10,000. The list of champions:

1935-Bismarck (N. D.) Corwin-Churchill
1936-Duncan (Okla.) Halliburtons
1937-Enid (Okla.) Eason Oilers
1938-Buford (Ga.) Bona Allens
1939-Duncan (Okla.) Halliburtons
1940-Enid (Okla.) Champlins
1941-Enid (Okla.) Champlins
1942-Wichita (Kan.) Boeing Bombers
1943-Camp Wheeler (Ga.) Spokes
1944-Sherman Field (Kan.) Flyers
1945-Enid (Okla.) Army Air Field
1946-St. Joseph (Mich.) Auscos
1947-Ft. Wayne (Ind.) G-E Club
1948-Ft. Wayne (Ind.) G-E Club
1949-Ft. Wayne (Ind.) G-E Club
1950-Ft. Wayne (Ind.) Capeharts
1951-Sinton (Tex.) Plymouth Oilers
1952-Ft. Myer (Va.) Military Dist. of Wash.
1953-Ft. Leonard Wood (Mo.) Hilltoppers
1954-Wichita (Kan.) Boeing Bombers
1955-Wichita (Kan.) Boeing Bombers

1956-Ft. Wayne (Ind.) Dairymen
1957-Sinton (Tex.) Plymouth Oilers
1958- Drain (Ore.) Black Sox
1959-Houston (Tex.) Feds
1960-Grand Rapids (Mich.) Sullivans
1961-Ponchatoula (La.) Athletica
1962-Wichita (Kans.) Rapid Transit Dreamliners

AMERICAN AMATEUR BASEBALL CONGRESS

The American Amateur Baseball Congress is the only coast-to-coast amateur baseball organization for teams above the age of American Legion Junior Baseball. Organized in 1935 with help from The Athletic Institute, it now operates in 39 states and one Canadian province with competition in its Major (unlimited age) division and Connie Mack (under 19 years of age) division. Final national competition to a championship in The Connie Mack division was made possible for the first time in 1959 by financial assistance from The Quaker Oats Company. In the past, competition in this age group has stopped at the regional level.

The list of Major Division National Champions:

1935-Bubba Hicks Tavern, Houston, Tex.
1936-Fraser's All-Stars, Lynn, Mass.
1937-J. J. Kohn Co., St. Paul, Minn.
1938-Progress Brewery, Oklahoma City, Okla.
1939-Linden (N. J.) A. C.
1940-Birmingham (Ala.) Paper Co.
1941-Fort Custer (Mich.) Reception Center, U. S. Army
1946-Clark Tructractors, Battle Creek, Mich.
1947-General Motors Coach Division, Pontiac, Mich.
1948-Stockham Valves and Fittings, Inc., Birmingham, Ala.
1949-Sutherland Paper Co., Kalamazoo, Mich.
1950-Park Grant Co., Watertown, S. D.
1951-Sutherland Paper Co., Kalamazoo, Mich.
1952-The Equitable Life Assurance Society, New York, N. Y.
1953-Hall Drug Co., Battle Creek, Mich.
1954-Mechanics Uniform Supply Co., Houston, Tex.
1955-Mechanics Uniform Supply Co., Houston, Tex.
1956-Stanley's Shoemen, Tacoma, Wash.
1957-Stockham Valves and Fittings, Inc., Birmingham, Ala.
1958-Glendale, O. (Cincinnati suburb)
1959-Advance Dry Wall, Dearborn, Mich.
1960-Cheney Studs, Seattle, Wash.
1961-Premier Gears, Portland, Ore.
1962-Archer Blowers, Portland, Ore.

The American Amateur Baseball Congress is a member of The National Committee for Amateur Baseball, a coordinating group for major amateur bodies operating on a national scale and including operating programs in at least two-thirds of the states of the United States.

COLLEGES

When Oliver Wendell Holmes (Harvard, Class of 1829) told a Boston reporter that baseball was one of his favorite sports in college, the noted author probably meant some version of New England "town ball," forerunner of our modern game. There is also a flaw to the first generally-accepted intercollegiate "baseball" game, July 1, 1859, when Amherst beat Williams, 66-32, for in that game the teams used 13 players on a side.

Intercollegiate championship baseball history really starts with the three great universities, Yale, Harvard and Princeton. Despite pioneering efforts by Amherst, Williams and New York schools like Columbia in the 1860's, the Big Three assumed command once they took up the sport. The first bona fide title went to Harvard, which beat each of its main rivals once in 1868. That season, an editorial appeared in the *Yale Courant* which read:

> "We are not an admirer of the National game. As to the amount of amusement to be obtained by this means, it is just about what might be extracted from a certain number of sand bags, basswood clubs, and common balls by educated, enlightened men under other circumstances. On the question of bodily damage we would suggest that the immense increase of accident insurance companies is probably due to no other cause, and if the mania does not presently cease the country will be without able-bodied men."

The Eli editor was wrong, of course. Able-bodied men survived in sufficient numbers. In fact, by the time the pros formed their first league, the 1871 National Association, college teams were good enough to be scheduled for numerous exhibition games. Harvard, Brown, Tufts, St. John's (Fordham) and others tangled with NA teams in '71. The practice continued for many decades. Collegians occasionally managed to beat the pros, too, as when the Harvard team of 1876 (with James Tyng wearing the first catcher's mask) beat the Boston Red Stockings of the National League, 7-6.

In the first dozen intercollegiate campaigns, 1868-79, Harvard won nine titles, Yale two and Princeton one. With the game developing on other campuses, an American College Base Ball Association was formed in 1880, including Princeton, Harvard, Brown, Dartmouth and Amherst. Yale stayed out at first, because of an argument on eligibility, but joined the next season, dethroned Princeton and remained on top for the next nine years—except for 1885, when Harvard went unbeaten.

The Big Three pulled out to form their own exclusive league again in 1887. However, even this elite clique was split by the general athletic rift between Harvard and Princeton in 1889, and the East didn't have a major college baseball group again till the Eastern Intercollegiate League (Ivy League) was formed 40 years later.

Western Conference baseball dates back to isolated games in the 1880's, with full Conference championship play beginning in 1895. Michigan and Chicago dominated the first few seasons. Illinois then reigned for many years, but only because Michigan stayed out of the conference from 1907-17, a period embracing the heyday of the Wolverines' immortal George Sisler.

Baseball was always popular in the Southern colleges. Down in the Southwest and out on the Pacific Coast the college game also tracks its origin to the 19th century. Still, it never could match the rapid strides of football; understandably so, since school is out during the best months for baseball play.

Up to the end of World War II, college baseball had sluggish going despite the efforts of great coaches like Jack Coombs (ex-Athletics), at Duke; Ray Fisher (Reds), Michigan; Jack Barry (A's), Holy Cross; Andy Coakley (A's), Columbia; Bib Falk (White Sox), Texas; Wally Roettger (Pirates), Illinois; Max Bishop (A's), Navy; Fred Lindstrom (Giants), Northwestern; Ethan Allen (Reds), Yale, and many others. In 1945 they banded into the American Association of College Baseball Coaches, and now, more than 200 strong, they are laying the groundwork for needed reform and progress.

In 1946, this coaches' group sponsored a Collegiate East-West All-Star Game at Fenway Park, Boston, using 40 players from 33 colleges. Out of this grew the annual "College World Series," staged by the National Collegiate Athletic Association on the same countrywide eight-district play used in 11 other NCAA sports. Results of this tournament:

YEAR	WINNER
1947	California

1948	USC	1959	Oklahoma State
1949	Texas	1960	Minnesota
1950	Texas	1961	USC
1951	Oklahoma	1962	Michigan
1952	Holy Cross		
1953	Michigan		
1954	Missouri		
1955	Wake Forest		
1956	Minnesota		
1957	California		
1958	Southern California		

AMERICAN LEGION BASEBALL

The simple inscription on a marble monument in the small community of Milbank, South Dakota, tells the story behind American Legion Baseball. It reads:

"In this city on July 17, 1925, by action of the South Dakota Department of The American Legion, the nation-wide organization of Legion Junior Baseball was first proposed as a program of service to the youth of America."

Actually, the program developed out of a survey made in 1925 by Major John L. Griffith, commissioner of the Western Conference. It showed boys drifting away from baseball, especially in small towns. He told the story to Frank G. McCormick, University of Minnesota athletic director, who also was state commander of the American Legion in South Dakota. McCormick proposed to the 1925 national convention that the group sponsor a junior baseball program, and the war veterans heartily approved.

Only fifteen states were represented in the first national tournament in 1926. Because of financial difficulties, the 1927 tourney was cancelled; but on a state level, the movement caught fire. Then, in 1928, Dan Sowers, director of the Legion's Americanism Commission, appeared before the executive council of organized baseball and asked for help. American League President E. S. Barnard and National League President John A. Heydler, together with Judge Landis, agreed to underwrite the national program up to $50,000 yearly.

That $50,000 yearly contribution from major league baseball has continued to underwrite American Legion Baseball. At present, the majors subsidize the program up to $60,000.

The yearly contribution from baseball has turned out to be a gilt-edged investment, for more than half the total number of big leaguers are graduates of American Legion Baseball.

By 1929, with the backing of the majors, every state in the union had teams in competition, and the championship game that year was carried over a national radio hook-up.

The year 1931 marked a milestone in the program, for it was in that season that Kirby Higbe, who was later to achieve fame as a major leaguer, made his debut. It was six years before Higbe made the big time, but he opened the doors for many more to follow, among them Phil Cavarretta, Howie Pollet, Bob Feller, Jim Hegan and others.

In 1938, the finals were broadcast over 3,000 radio stations, and major league umpires were used for the first time. The years 1940 and 1941 saw the program established as a national institution for American youth. During the war years, the program was restricted, but continued to prosper despite the many handicaps.

After the close of World War II, the program took on a new aspect and the number of participants increased tremendously. In fact, the number has increased virtually every year since the program's inception. In 1947, for example, there were 11,701 teams; in 1955, there were 18,123 teams. More than 19,000 teams and 250,000 youths competed in 1958.

No doubt a great many of these youths are already en route to the major leagues.

Since 1961 the National Executive Committee has dropped the word "Junior" and the program is now officially known as "American Legion Baseball." In 1961 the Executive Committee also dropped the age of eligibility so that eighteen-year-olds may now be eligible for American Legion Championship play.

Department (State) Champions have been pitted against each other in eight regional tournaments with all regional winners advancing to the national finals. This new schedule, adopted in 1960, has increased interest since it creates a much larger field and has made the program much more successful.

Former national commissioner Lou Brissie was replaced in May, 1961 by the present Director of the program George W. Rulow.

The past champions:

1926 - Cook Post No. 321 Yonkers, New York
1927 - No National Tournament
1928 - Oakland Post No. 5 Oakland, California
1929 - South Buffalo Post No. 721 Buffalo, New York
1930 - Baltimore & Ohio R.R. Post No. 81, Baltimore, Maryland
1931 - South Side Post No. 493 South Chicago, Illinois
1932 - Alvin Callender Post No. 132 New Orleans, Louisiana
1933 - National Post No. 467 Chicago, Illinois
1934 - Fort Cumberland Post No. 13 Cumberland, Maryland
1935 - Gaston Post No. 23 Gastonia, North Carolina
1936 - Spartanburg Post No. 28 Spartanburg, South Carolina
1937 - East Lynn Post No. 291 East Lynn, Massachusetts
1938 - San Diego Post No. 6 San Diego, California
1939 - Omaha Post No. 1 Omaha, Nebraska
1940 - Walter B. Hill Post No. 76 Albemarle, North Carolina
1941 - San Diego Post No. 6 San Diego, California
1942 - Sunrise Post No. 357 Los Angeles, California
1943 - Richfield Post No. 435 Minneapolis, Minnesota
1944 - Robert E. Bentley Post No. 50 Cincinnati, Ohio
1945 - Warren F. Hoyle Post No. 82 Shelby, North Carolina
1946 - Crescent City Post No. 125 New Orleans, Louisiana
1947 - Robert E. Bentley Post No. 50 Cincinnati, Ohio
1948 - Trenton Post No. 93 Trenton, New Jersey
1949 - Capt. Bill Erwin Post No. 337 Oakland, California
1950 - Capt. Bill Erwin Post No. 337 Oakland, California
1951 - Crenshaw Post No. 715 Los Angeles, California
1952 - Robert E. Bentley Post No. 50 Cincinnati, Ohio
1953 - Logan Wheeler Post No. 36 Yakima, Washington
1954 - Downtown Post No. 492 San Diego, California
1955 - U. S. Postal Employees Post No. 216 Cincinnati, Ohio
1956 - Fred W. Stockham Post No. 245, St. Louis, Missouri
1957 - Robert E. Bentley Post No. 50 Cincinnati, Ohio
1958 - Robert E. Bentley Post No. 50 Cincinnati, Ohio
1959-Thomas E. Edison Post No. 187 Detroit, Michigan
1960-Crescent City Post No. 125 New Orleans, Louisiana
1961-Frank Luke Jr.-John C. Greenway Phoenix, Arizona Post No. 1
1962-Anheuser-Busch, Inc. Post No. 299 St. Louis, Missouri

LITTLE LEAGUE BASEBALL

On the occasion of its 20th anniversary year in 1959, Little League Baseball occupied the unique position as the world's fastest growing youth movement. From all but obscure beginnings in the city of Williamsport, Pennsylvania, where a single league with three teams started the program on its way in 1939, Little League has mushroomed to more than 5,000 leagues in 22 countries.

Almost a million boys (better than one of every 12 boys in the age category) play Little League Baseball under the volunteer leadership, assistance and support of more than two million adults.

Through the early years of maturity, Little League operated on a modest scale in Pennsylvania, New Jersey and neighboring areas. From 15 leagues in 1947, the program expanded to 94 leagues in 1948 when the United States Rubber Company became the national sponsor of Little League. With the assistance and support of the Rubber Company the following ten years witnessed a phenomenal growth. While exercising no control in the administrative affairs of the program, the United States Rubber Company underwrote the annual World Series and supplied financial support to carry on the activities of the National Headquarters.

In 1957 a Little League Foundation was created to help make Little League self-supporting. Although withdrawing as sole sponsor, the Rubber Company became a member of the Foundation and continues its active interest in the program.

Little League Baseball is conventional baseball adapted to the mental and physical capacities of boys 12 years of age and under. It is regulation baseball with several exceptions, necessary in order that the strength of the young players will not be overtaxed. The exceptions to regular baseball are equipment, number of innings, size of field, distance of pitcher's mound to home plate and distance between bases.

Although Little League has grown and grown each year, it is significant that it has continued to be a local community project. Teams are formed in accordance with the prescribed rules, which help to eliminate boyish gangs and cliques. All the basic elements of Americanism are maintained through the close association the boys have on the baseball diamond. Little League makes no pretense of being a cure-all for juvenile delinquency, but surveys have indicated that in communities where the program is established, the boys behave and make their towns better places in which to live.

As soon as Little League baseball grew out of its Williamsport cradle, the non-profit corporation known as Little League Baseball, Inc., was formed, with a board of directors and with outstanding men of unquestionable integrity as officials. A full time staff, including President Peter J. McGovern operates the National Headquarters' office at 120 West Fourth Street, Williamsport.

As described by Dwight D. Eisenhower: "Under good leadership Little League Baseball develops teamwork and encourages sportsmanship in good natured acceptance of the results of the game as winners or losers. It develops fitness of mind and body in the finest tradition of American sport."

The past champions:

1947-Maynard, Williamsport, Pennsylvania
1948-Lock Haven, Pennsylvania
1949-Hammontown, New Jersey
1950-Houston, Texas
1951-Stamford, Connecticut
1952-Norwalk, Connecticut
1953-Birmingham, Alabama
1954-Schenectady, New York
1955-Morrisville, Pennsylvania
1956-Roswell, New Mexico
1957-Monterrey, Mexico
1958-Monterrey, Mexico
1959-Hamtramck, Michigan
1960-Levittown, Pennsylvania
1961-El Cajon-La Mesa, California
1962-San Jose, California

P-O-N-Y BASEBALL, INC.

Organized in Washington, Pennsylvania, in 1951, P-O-N-Y League Baseball was designed to provide the opportunity for graduates of Little League Baseball to continue their development. The purpose of the program: to provide wholesome, supervised recreation for boys, to teach them sportsmanship, teamwork, self-reliance, and other attributes needed by citizens of the future as they are reflected in the game of baseball.

The program is characterized by its cutdown diamond, halfway between the size of the Little League field and the regulation field, and its two year age span for players.

P-O-N-Y League, now operating in 40 states, Canada, Mexico, and in a number of other countries at U.S. military and government employee installations, has grown steadily as the following chart indicates:

YEAR	LEAGUES	TEAMS	PLAYERS
1952	106	511	8,176
1953	294	1,393	22,288
1954	461	2,208	35,328
1955	558	2,729	43,664
1956	610	3,190	51,040
1957	666	3,430	54,880
1958	786	3,978	63,236
1959	900	4,600	69,000
1960	1,062	5,557	83,355
1961	1,193	6,379	95,685
1962	1,270	6,806	102,090

P-O-N-Y League play is climaxed each season by a World Series held in Washington, Pennsylvania. The City of Houston League won the 1962 title to join champions which include: San Antonio, Texas, 1952; Fairmont, West Virginia, 1953; Monongahela, Pennsylvania, 1954; Washington, Pennsylvania, 1955; Joliet, Illinois, 1956, and Lufkin, Texas. 1957. Miami, Florida, 1958; Long Beach, California, 1959; Oak Park, Illinois, 1960; Hamtramck, Michigan, 1961.

In 1958, the P-O-N-Y Grads League was founded to extend the benefits of the P-O-N-Y program to boys 15 and 16 years old. P-O-N-Y Grads, played on a regulation diamond, was widely accepted, drawing 6,592 players on 412 teams in 90 leagues in its first year of operation. Miami, Florida, won the first P-O-N-Y Grads World Series held at Springfield, Illinois.

P-O-N-Y BASEBALL, Inc., the administrative headquarters for both P-O-N-Y League and P-O-N-Y Grads League, is located at 122-126 South Main Street, Washington, Pennsylvania. Joe E. Brown, world famed actor and comedian, is president, and Lew Hays serves as commissioner.

P-O-N-Y BASEBALL operates without the benefit of commercial sponsorship, and national headquarters is maintained almost exclusively by sanction fees paid by member leagues.

BABE RUTH LEAGUE

Babe Ruth League, Inc., a non-profit, tax exempt organization founded in 1952 to fill the baseball void for 13, 14 and 15 year-old boys, has mushroomed in a brief span of time to include more than 100,000 participants as the largest program in its age bracket.

The amazing annual growth of the program has seen Babe Ruth baseball spread to every state except South Dakota, to become established in seven Canadian provinces, and take a toehold in Europe where current leagues in France and Germany are expected to be only a forerunner of a busy European organization. Full sanction of the program by American military officials has given impetus to European growth.

Well established as an intermediary program between the Little League and the American Legion competitions, Babe Ruth baseball is played upon standard-sized diamonds and uses the rules of professional baseball except for a few basic additional requirements such as pitching limitations in consideration of the players' ages.

Each team roster contains at least five 13-year-old boys and no more than five 15-year-olds and the balance assures participation opportunities for each youngster. From 58 leagues and 274 teams in 1952, the program grew to 1,215 leagues and more than 6,800 teams in 1958.

Support of a wide cross-section of the public, including civic groups, parents' organizations, fraternal lodges, educational groups, veterans' bodies and youth clubs has been the backbone of the Babe Ruth organization.

The regular season is the main consideration of each league, with the average team playing more than 15 games. Additional training and education are provided through tournament competition, climaxing in the annual World Series.

Series winners include:

YEAR	WORLD CHAMPION
1952	Stamford, Connecticut
1953	Stamford, Connecticut
1954	Stamford, Connecticut
1955	Terre-Haute, Indiana
1956	Trenton, New Jersey
1957	Pensacola, Florida
1958	Charlotte, North Carolina
1959	Tulsa, Oklahoma
1960	Huntington, West Virginia
1961	San Carlos, California
1962	Trenton, New Jersey

Headquarters for Babe Ruth League, Inc., is 524½ Hamilton Avenue, Trenton, New Jersey.

XV PLAYING HINTS

HOW TO HIT BY TY COBB

The first item in scientific hitting is selection of bat. For a swing hitter (one who starts his bat far back and completes his swing with a full follow-through) I suggest a bat with the feel on the light side. For the one with a shorter, more compact swing, the bat should feel slightly heavy.

Next comes position. Never copy a batter with an exaggerated crouch. The best hitters stand up and have the look of a good hitter. In case your normal stance becomes uncomfortable while awaiting the delivery, breaking of the knees (a dip or slight squat) will relieve this. But of course you must always come back to the position first assumed.

The space between feet should be measured by how well balanced you feel. This will measure about 14 inches for players of average height. But don't think of this kind of thing in inches. Just stand so you feel balanced, and can step either into the pitch or away.

If you are able to put a little extra weight on the front foot and still feel balanced to step either way, so much the better. The ability to do this will assure proper stride and, when swinging, will bring the body and arms up to the ball more automatically. I emphasize the value of proper striding because over-striding is fatal. It causes uppercutting and fly balls, upsets coordination and costs freedom to step in or out.

A righthanded batter attempting to hit the ball to right, or opposite (from normal), field should use the closed stance. That means the left foot is about 4 inches closer to the plate than the right. Hitting to left field, his front foot is about 4 inches further away, or in open stance. The straightaway hitter lines up both feet with the line of the pitch.

I always had trouble hitting lefthanded pitching, especially curve ballers, until I went to the back line of the batter's box. That gave me the benefit of the extra inches from the pitcher, and the split-second extra time in which to judge the pitch.

Keep your arms, particularly the elbows, away from the body. This insures freedom of swing. I also recommend the elbow nearer the pitcher be raised and exaggerated. This, plus a slight bending of the body from the waist up, will give you better body balance, insures automatically hitting the ball out in front and brings your eyes in better focusing position.

Do all your "fixing" as to grip and stance before delivery, then forget about your swing. Watch the pitcher's every move and never let your eye leave the ball. Many batters are thrown out by a half-step, so once you've hit the ball, run with all the speed you have, no matter where the ball goes.

(*Condensed from "Famous Slugger Year Book," Copyright* 1950 *by Hillerich & Bradsby Co., Louisville, Ky.*)

HOW TO PITCH BY CARL HUBBELL

Pitching is the most important single factor in any game. . . as much as 70%, according to some deep thinkers. I would like to offer these "ten commandments" for pitching aspirants:

1: A limber arm. 2: A rugged physique, or, as an alternative, wiriness. 3: A repertoire, meaning a fast ball and at least one breaking ball, preferably a curve. 4: Control. 5: Competitive courage. 6: Endurance. 7: Intelligence. 8: The ability to size up a hitter. 9: Confidence. 10: Fielding skill.

Note that the list emphasizes developed skills over natural endowment. Development of these "extras" will give a pitcher the advantage over those relying entirely on physical assets.

Of course, the arm must be the primary consideration. Unless a boy can throw hard, or a "live" ball with reasonable speed, his pitching future can only be limited. Tricky deliveries may succeed on the sandlots, but as a pitcher moves into faster company, conditions eventually demand that he overpower a good hitter.

Pitching mechanics are important, too. A smooth, easy delivery, perfected by attention to detail, is an aid to control. Faulty form beats pitchers more often than opposing hitters, and often explains arm ailments.

The pitching delivery can be broken down and analyzed to reveal six distinct actions: Windup, Stretch, Leg Lift, Stride, Body Pivot and Follow Through.

The Windup promotes rhythm, so each pitcher can best judge his own style. It's usual to start with hands brought forward and then upward over the head. The Stretch brings the pitching arm behind the head. The Leg Lift gets drive into the motion, while the Stride is an important element for control. Most young pitchers tend to over-stride, thereby losing power and accuracy.

The weight shifts from rear to front foot in the Body Pivot. Follow Through enables the pitcher to get his body into the pitch and is also a control element. A pitcher constantly throwing the ball too high generally is failing to follow through properly.

To deliver a fast ball, the pitcher should grip it tightly, with index and middle fingers on top of the ball, and the thumb underneath. The fingers are usually placed across the seams, but if along them, then at the place where the seams are closest together. When pitched, the ball rolls from under the fingers. This reverse rotation gives the ball back-spin, causing it to "hop."

The grip for the curve is the same as for the fast ball. With the pitch, the ball rolls over the fingers as the wrist is snapped sharply to provide forward spin for the ball. The thumb does its work as it comes over with the wrist snap. The wrist snap should be sharp . . . the sharper the snap, the sharper the curve. All curves should be thrown low to a batter. The ball takes more spin that way, breaks away from the batter and is harder to hit.

The change of pace differs from the fast ball only in the manner in which it is held. Where the fast ball is gripped tightly, the change of pace is only lightly held by the fingers on top. Some pitchers lift these guiding fingers slightly as they let the ball go.

(*Condensed from "Playing the Giants Game," Copyright* 1949 *by National Exhibition Co., New York*)

HOW TO CATCH BY BILL DICKEY

Since a catcher's job requires endurance, he should be sturdy rather than fast afoot. Yet he has to be nimble to pounce on bunts and waste no time or steps chasing pop fouls. He must also have a good arm.

Brain-power must come with stamina in this job. The catcher mentally catalogues the batting strength and weakness of every player in the league. He needs fine judgment to mix up the pitches he calls for, in such a way as to pace the pitcher and baffle the hitter. He must decide when to call for a pitch-out, when to throw to a base, and also directs the throw of teammates who field bunts or slow rollers with men on base.

To give signals, the catcher squats on his haunches, feet comfortably apart about six inches, with the weight balanced on the ball of each foot. Signs come from the fingers of the right hand, which is held well up the thigh. The mitt helps shield the fingered signal from enemy coaches.

Just before the delivery, the catcher shifts into a quarter-crouch, with the left foot slightly forward and the legs slightly farther apart. The full face of his mitt is presented toward the pitcher, making a good target. By playing as close as possible to the batter, the catcher is less likely to miss foul tips, gets into best position to throw on steals, is best situated to catch low pitches in the strike zone and is poised to break for a bunt.

The right hand should be relaxed, while awaiting the pitch, with fingers loosely closed around the thumb. This avoids broken fingers on foul tips. As the ball thuds into the mitt, the mitt hand rolls over and traps the ball in the pocket, fingers automatically encircling the ball in correct throwing position.

If the pitch is above the belt, catch it with the fingers of the mitt pointed upward; if below, hold the fingers down. Don't just reach for a wide pitch—step in that direction, too. If the pitch is too low, drop your knees into the dirt to block it with a man on base.

Immediately after receiving the pitch, snap into a good throwing position by pivoting with the weight on the right foot, striding forward with the left, and throwing the ball overhand. . . especially for basestealers. The weight shifts from right foot to left as the throw is made, thus putting body and shoulders behind it. To nab a base-stealer, throw in a low trajectory. Bluff throws to keep runners close to the bag.

In fielding a bunt, use one hand only if the ball has stopped dead. If the bunt is rolling, place your mitt in front of it and scoop the ball into the mitt with your bare hand. Never take your eye off the ball, or try to throw it, before you actually have it.

Other tips: On pop fouls, flip off your mask immediately and toss it in opposite direction from ball. . . Tag with both hands when possible. . . With a man on first, hurry to cover third on a sacrifice bunt. . . Back up throws to first with none on. . . Practice exhaustively on catching high fouls, because the ball has terrific spin as it hits the mitt. . . Keep the mitt in a flat plane when catching pop-ups.

HOW TO PLAY FIRST BASE BY GEORGE SISLER

Everything else being equal, the tall left-hander has the edge as a first baseman. He can reach farther for high, wide or late throws, and he can throw more easily to the other bases. However, there have been smaller righthanded fielders who were good on defense.

When fielding a ball hit to him, the first baseman should, as the pitch is made, have his weight come over on the ball of each foot. Don't ever be back on your heels. If possible, advance toward the ball, judging the hop as it comes. A good fielder is one who can judge a bounce well. A long hop or short pickup is easiest to catch. The long pickup (sometimes called a short hop) is hardest, and should be avoided if possible. Catch the ball in front of you and "give" with the catch. Keep your eye on the grounder from the time it leaves the bat. Never be caught with your chin up in the air.

When not guarding the bag to keep the runner from taking too big a lead, the first baseman should play 20 to 25 feet back of the base and as far away from the foul line as the type of hitter would justify. On the hit to another infielder, go quickly to first base and find the bag with your left foot. Then turn to take the throw, shifting feet if necessary. I am against straddling the bag and kicking back to tag the base as the catch is made, because the first baseman would not have time for these actions if he were playing at his maximum depth to start with.

Here are some important tips on first base play:

(1) When the play is close and the ball is thrown into the runner, the left-handed first baseman must keep his left foot on the base, right foot forward, and make a one-handed, backhand catch of the ball.

(2) On close plays, stretch forward as far as possible to catch the ball as soon as possible. The last portion of the foot to touch the bag is the toe, and not the heel, because if you try to stretch with only the heel on the bag, it certainly will come off.

(3) Catch the ball with two hands if possible.

(4) Make long throws to third base overhanded.

(5) If the throw to you is bad, and you see you will not be able to stick on the bag while reaching the ball, then by all means leave the bag and make the catch. That will prevent the runner from taking an extra base.

(6) Shifting should be done with a little natural hop from side to side. Practice this a lot.

(7) Do not reach for a runner in tagging. Make him come to you. Be able to cover every portion of the bag with your tagging hand.

(8) If you are no longer needed at first base, move around and back up bases or go out for relays. Make yourself generally useful. Learn your role for cut-off plays.

(9) Catch all pop flies that are in your territory.

(10) When fielding a ball in such a way that the pitcher has to cover first, throw the ball to him underhanded and while moving toward him. Aim the toss chest-high and never conceal the ball from him.

HOW TO PLAY SECOND BASE BY ROGERS HORNSBY

The second baseman has many responsibilities that require not only skill but mental alertness. There are many things to do besides field ground balls and throw to first base . . . but as he has to field and throw many times in an average game, it is important that he reach the highest point of efficiency in these departments. That means hours and hours of practice.

Be set to make a quick start either to the left or right for a grounder. Be prepared to dash in for a slow, dribbling grounder or to turn around and run back for a short fly into the shallow outfield.

Do not overlook your training in mastering the art of catching a pop fly.

Proper position on the diamond is not fixed. Shift according to whether the batter is left or right handed, whether he is a notorious pull hitter or straight-away or slicer. Play the left handed pull hitter a bit deeper, say on the edge of the outfield grass, and closer to first than usual. If he is a very fast runner, however, you can't afford to play him quite that deep.

When expecting a sacrifice bunt, play closer to the batter and far enough toward first so you can cover that bag should the first baseman go in for a bunt. Be sure, however, not to leave your position too soon, or the batter may double-cross you by hitting through the vacant spot, or by dragging a bunt in that direction.

Also be alert in case the ball is bunted past the pitcher. In this case you have to field it and try for the putout at first.

When a double play is hoped for, then, regardless of whether a right or left-handed batter is at the plate, you must move toward second base so as to be in position to cover that bag in time for the double play. In order to pivot correctly, always try to touch the bag with your right foot, then step with the left foot in toward the pitcher's mound and make the throw to first.

In running to cover second, it is wise to straddle the bag, so that in case of a wide throw you can touch the bag with either foot for a forceout.

When runners on first and third try a double steal, the second baseman is important in breaking it up. In case of a pitchout, the second baseman runs to a spot 10 feet in front of the bag while the shortstop goes right to the bag. If the runner on third starts for home, the second baseman should cut off the throw from the catcher and return the ball to the plate. When the double steal is attempted without a pitchout, the bag is covered as in the usual manner with only a man on first, and the man who takes the throw at second base never waits for the tag but instead fires the ball right back to the catcher.

When a ball is hit to right or right center for extra bases, the second baseman should run out to take the relay throw. Make up your mind as you dash out whether the ball will be good for three bases or a homer, and you'll know where to relay the ball. If the ball should not be good for more than a double, then the second baseman should break for second to be in position for the throw. With the ball hit to left field, the shortstop takes the throw at second, with the second baseman backing him up in case of a wild throw.

(*Condensed from "How to Play," Copyright* 1951 *by The Sporting News, St. Louis*)

HOW TO PLAY SHORTSTOP BY HONUS WAGNER

A shortstop must have a good arm as the prime requisite. Next, he must be fast, able to shift his feet and ready to move in any direction. Keep trying. Don't be afraid of making an error. Seek the advice of older players, the coaches and manager. Above all, never lose sight of the ball.

Always keep in mind the number of outs, which bases are occupied and the score. Study each hitter. On a fast runner, you must handle the ball cleanly and hurry the throw. Shift for each batter, according to where he is most likely to hit.

Think out each play before it happens. If you boot the ball, think where you're going to throw it even before you pick it up, so no time is lost.

The hardest play for a shortstop to make is going to his right for a deep hit ball. Set yourself when you get your hands on the ball, and be in a position to throw to first. Another tough play is the slowly hit ball coming right at you, especially with a fast batter. Play this on your barehanded side so as to get the ball away quickly, picking the ball up and throwing it without hesitation in virtually a single motion.

In starting a double play, remember it is wiser to make sure of one out than lose two. Grab the ball and feed it to the second baseman letter-high. If the ball goes to your right, or deep, put something on the throw to second. If it's a grounder near second, flip it underhand to the second baseman.

When pivoting in a double play, be in motion when receiving the ball, step on second base with the right foot and remain on balance by stepping forward with the left before finally throwing to first.

With a runner on first, the shortstop covers second on a bunt. With runners on first and second, keep the runner as close to second as possible by feinting him back. To pick a runner off second, stand about five feet behind the line and slowly work your way up close behind him. Break for the bag when the runner is leaning toward the next base, so as to catch him off balance.

The shortstop takes most of the relays on long hits to the outfield; otherwise, he directs the player who does take the relay, as to where the throw should go.

With a runner on first and a hit to right field, the shortstop stands about 25 feet in front of third base, on the grass, awaiting and guiding the throw from the outfielder. If there is a chance for the third baseman to catch the runner coming from first, he yells to the shortstop, "Let it go!" The shortstop bluffs the catch, to discourage the batter from advancing during the ensuing play, but lets the ball go through to the third baseman.

Other tips: Shortstop gets pitching signs from catcher and relays them to outfielders by hand or voice signal. . .Whether short or second baseman covers base on attempted steal depends on batter and type of pitch. . .Tag a runner with almost the same motion you get the ball, then get rid of the ball as fast as you can. . . Size up a pop fly and yell for it as soon as you feel sure you can get it; otherwise yell for either the left or center fielder to take it.

(*Condensed from "How to Play Shortstop," by Honus Wagner, in April* 13, 1949 *issue of The Sporting News, St. Louis*)

HOW TO PLAY THIRD BASE BY PIE TRAYNOR

Like any other player on the field, the third baseman must always make up his mind—before each pitch—exactly what to do with the ball if it is hit to him. The number of men on base, the score, the inning, the number of outs, the speed afoot of batter and baserunners. . . all figure in the decision. But, like a woman's mind and the cost of living, that decision is subject to change without notice. A reckless baserunner may break, or a grounder may take a bad hop and the "correct" play becomes something entirely different from the preconceived strategy. Split-second thinking in such situations is not completely a matter of intuition. Experience counts!

Position play depends on the tactical situation of the game and the type of hitter. In general it is best to play behind the line. Move up against a lefthanded batter or notorious bunter. In any case, the third baseman must have a trained reflex to spring toward the plate the moment a bunt develops. When the batter snaps into the flatfooted, square-facing bunt posture, the third baseman should be charging in even before the pitch reaches the plate.

Hard-hit balls are the true test of a third baseman. If he can't field them, or at least block them, extra-base hits result. It takes more courage than skill to stop those smashes.

The swinging bunt, or topped dribbler by a batter taking full cut, is really tough. Since he can't get the jump on such a play, the third baseman reaches the ball late. To make up for lost time, the baseman must charge in, while keeping his eyes glued to the ball, scoop it up barehanded and make the throw to first with the same motion.

Many hard smashes reach the third baseman before the hitter has broken out of the batter's box. That leaves plenty of time for the throw. The baseman should straighten his body, take aim, cock his arm and coordinate his throw with the stride.

Many valuable putouts are made even when the third baseman can only knock down the ball. A quick recovery and immediate throw will turn the trick. The baseman should practice throwing from any position, since he must get rid of the ball as soon as possible, and he should cock his arm only for throws on which he has plenty of time.

Other hints for third basemen:

Straddle the bag to receive a throw. If the play is not close, leave the bag to take the throw.

Practice exhaustively on catching high pop fouls.

Range as far as possible on grounders to your left.

When fielding a grounder with less than two out and men on first and second, make the double play relay via second base. Never start the play be stepping on third, unless the act of fielding the ball brings you toward the bag.

Handle squeeze bunts with a barehanded scoop-up and underhand throw.

Never let the runner on third take a long lead. Feint him back.

If the pitcher fields a bunt with a man on base, direct his throw and hurry back to cover third base.

HOW TO PLAY THE OUTFIELD BY JOE DiMAGGIO

To be an outfielder in the majors today, a player must be a good, consistent hitter, exceptionally fast if he isn't a long-ball hitter, and a first-rate flychaser and thrower. A team is far better off with an outfielder who piles up errors trying for hard catches than with one who handles perfectly every ball hit to him but doesn't go after the tough ones.

Before every play, size up the possibilities. Know the hitter and where he is likely to hit certain types of pitches. Get the sign from the shortstop as to what type of pitch is coming, so you will know in which direction to break "with the crack of the bat." Curve balls are more likely to be pulled than fast balls. Pre-game practice will familiarize you with ground conditions (whether the bounce is likely to be hard or soft), wind, background, fences, etc. However, wind currents are tricky, so check occasionally with flags flying around the stands.

Make every catch in the best possible position from which to throw. I prefer to take fly balls with my hands above my head, left foot toward the plate, so as to save time making the throw. On ground balls, there is rarely any choice; when you catch up with it, the ball is usually hugging the ground. If it happens to be a bouncing ball, charge it in order to field it at the top of the hop, leaving you in good throwing position.

It is easier to catch a ball when standing still than on the dead run. Still, an outfielder who has a good jump on the ball may slow down in order to take the ball deliberately on the run to increase the force of his throw to beat a runner to the plate.

With a man on base, make up your mind in advance where you will throw, but be ready to react instantly to any change in circumstances. The safest rule to follow is: throw ahead of the runner. On throws to all bases, it is better to throw on one hop than on the fly. A bounding throw is more accurate and easier for a fielder to handle. Also, low throws set up cutoffs plays. Exception to the bounce-throw rule is when the ground is soft because of recent rain, and only when the outfielder is close enough to reach the base on the fly.

All outfielders should wear sunglasses. Never stare into the sun. Even with sunglasses, no outfielder can take a ball coming out of the sun. The sun-fielder should try to gauge the ball by getting a sidewise glimpse and shielding his eyes with his glove.

No outfielder is a real workman unless he can turn his back on the ball, run his legs off and take the catch over his shoulder. Practice this play till you are sure of it. Backpedalling outfielders get nowhere.

Other outfielding tips: Never gamble with a shoestring or diving catch unless a single would send in the tying or winning run. . .Use both hands for a catch, except where extra reach is necessary. . .Remember that balls hit wide of the centerfielder tend to swerve toward the nearer foul line. . .There are some advantages to playing shallow, but in these days of the lively ball it is dangerous

. . .Outfielders should back each other up and also back up the infield whenever possible. A ''bluff catch'' of a Texas Leaguer often keeps a runner from advancing an extra base.

(*Condensed from "Baseball for Everyone," Copyright* 1948 *by Whittlesey House, N.Y.*)

HOW TO UMPIRE BY BILLY EVANS

Umpiring is a mixture of good physique, good eyes, plenty of courage, pride in your work, a knowledge of the rules, getting the right angle, a respect for the ability of others—managers, players and umpires—plus plenty of common sense. There is no greater asset than common sense properly applied.

Anticipation is an umpire's greatest trouble-maker. It is invariably the source of calling plays too quickly. Instead of anticipating the play, let it happen, follow it intently to its completion before reaching a decision.

There is considerably more to umpiring than the mere calling of ball or strike—out or safe—fair or foul. True, they are six basic operations in the life of an umpire, but many other things are equally important.

Umpires are human—all opinions to the contrary—hence, they err. In all the 25 years that I umpired, I have never tried to prove infallibility. Rather, I have very forcefully stated that I called the play as I saw it, and that made the decision arrived at ''official.'' Even when positive I had not erred. I always regarded it as diplomacy to listen to the player's side of the argument. It is far easier to reason with the player who has let off steam rather than one who is burning up over an adverse decision and finds no one willing to listen. It is then that he goes berserk.

Never try to alibi your error. That makes two mistakes out of one. Umpires dislike ball players who alibi. In like manner, ball players have no particular use for the umpire who always has an alibi.

Don't work your thumb overtime, pointing the way to the clubhouse. Baseball is played on the field, not under the showers. Eject players from the game only as a last resort. Constantly work for some other solution. However, there are times when nothing but a nice cold shower will cool off a protesting player.

''Run your ball game, but don't overrun it.''

Umpiring is largely a matter of angles. There is a best angle or spot for every play. Be in the right spot and you reduce the chances to err to a minimum.

The right way on the bases is always to be on top of the play. If you are over the play and miss it, you are far more liable to get away with an incorrect ruling than if you rendered the same decision fifteen or twenty feet away from the play. Ball players like umpires who hustle.

In getting over a play, I think it helps the umpire's judgment if he comes to a stop as he focuses on the play rather than rendering the decision while on the run.

Never lose sight of the ball. If you know where the ball is at all times, it will keep you out of a lot of trouble. Nothing shows up an umpire more than not to see the hidden ball trick. It makes the umpire look far worse than the player who was trapped.

Keep your eye on the ball to the completion of every play. Never turn your head or run by a play after you have given a decision. A lot of things can happen to the ball while you are looking in some other direction after making final ruling.

(*Condensed from "Umpiring from the Inside," Copyright* 1947 *by Wm. G. Evans.*)

XVI OFFICIAL PLAYING RULES

EVOLUTION OF PLAYING RULES

1845 -- Alexander Cartwright formulated first formal code of playing rules, major differences from present being: game to end when one team makes 21 aces (runs), ball must be pitched underhand, only one base allowed when ball bounds out of field, ball caught on first bound is out.

1848 -- Runner out only at first if ball held on bag before reached by runner.

1854 -- New rule specified ball to weigh between 5½-6 ounces, and be between 2¾-3½ inches in diameter.

1857 -- Game based on nine innings, with five to be legal in event of interruption.

1858 -- Pitcher confined to area behind line 45 feet from home. Called strikes introduced.

1859 -- Bat limited in thickness to 2½ inches.

1860 -- Ball reduced in size and weight to present 9-9¼ inches, 5-5¼ ounces.

1863 -- Balls and strikes called.

1864 -- Fair ball caught on one bounce no longer out... Pitcher's box 6x6 feet...

1871 -- Batter allowed to call for high or low pitched ball (Abolished in 1887).

1872 -- Pitcher allowed to snap delivery, though still restricted to below-the-waist motion.

1876 -- Bat length limited to 42 inches... Pitcher's box reduced to 4x6 feet...

1877 -- Hitter exempted from time at bat if walked. Substitute player allowed to enter game only before fourth inning.

1879 -- Nine balls entitled batter to reach first base (Changed to eight in 1880, seven in 1881, six in 1884, seven in 1885, five in 1887, four in 1889 and ever since).

1880 -- Batter out if hit by batted ball.

1881 -- Pitching distance increased from 45 to 50 feet (Changed to present distance of 60 feet 6 inches in 1893)... Pitcher fined for hitting batter deliberately with ball (Eliminated in 1882).

1882 -- Three-foot baseline adopted... Umpires forbidden to reserve decisions on matter of judgment.

1883 -- Foul caught on one bounce no longer out... Pitching allowed from anywhere up to shoulder height.

1884 -- All restrictions on pitching style lifted... Pitcher allowed to take only one step before delivery.

1885 -- Portion of bat on one side allowed to be flat (Rescinded the next year).

1886 -- First and third bases placed within foul lines... Batter hit by pitched ball exempted from time at bat.

1887 -- Base on balls counted as base hit (Rescinded the next season)... Number of strikes raised to four (Returned to three the next year). Batter no longer allowed to call for high or low pitch.

1891 -- Substitute allowed at any time during game.

1894 -- Pitching box abolished for slab 12x4 inches... Foul bunt a strike... Sacrificing player exempted from time at bat.

1895 -- Foul tip ruled as strike... Pitcher's slab 24x6 inches... Infield pop fly rule adopted... Bat limited in length to 42 inches.

1899 -- Pitcher compelled to throw to base if he motions in that direction.

1900 -- Five-sided plate introduced.

1901 -- Fouls called strikes up to 2 in NL (by AL in 1903)

1901 -- Catcher required to remain right behind batter.

1904 -- Pitching mound limited to 15 inches above plate.

1908 -- Pitcher prohibited from soiling new ball... Sacrifice fly rule adopted (Abolished in 1931; restored 1939 for scoring fly, abolished 1940).

1920 -- Use of spitball and other external-application deliveries abolished, only exceptions being pitchers already using moist delivery in majors.

1925 -- Pitcher allowed to use resin bag.

1939 -- Pitcher permitted to place free foot either in front of or behind rubber... Outfield fly intentionally dropped ruled caught ball.

1940 -- Minimum home run distance increased from 235 to 250 feet.

1950 -- Rulebook entirely recodified, with several minor but no major changes (Typical: Home team must bat last).

1954 -- Outfield fly scoring a run ruled as sacrifice.

COMPLETE OFFICIAL RULES

DIVISIONS OF THE CODE

1.00—Objectives of the Game, the Playing Field, Equipment.
2.00—Definition of Terms.
3.00—Game Preliminaries.
4.00—Starting and Ending the Game.
5.00—Putting the Ball in Play, Dead Ball and Live Ball (in Play).
6.00—The Batter.
7.00—The Runner.
8.00—The Pitcher.
9.00—The Umpire.
10.00—The Official Scorer.

1.00—Objectives of the Game.

1.01 BASEBALL is a game between two teams of nine players each with adequate substitutes, under direction of a Manager, played in accordance with these rules, under jurisdiction of an umpire or umpires on an enclosed field.

1.02 THE OBJECT of each team is to win by scoring more runs than the opponent.

1.03 THE WINNER of the game shall be that team which shall have scored, in accordance with these rules, the greater number of runs at the conclusion of a regulation game.

1.04 THE PLAYING FIELD. The field shall be laid out according to the instructions below, supplemented by Diagrams No. 1 and No. 2 on adjoining pages.

The infield shall be a 90-foot square. The outfield shall be the area between two foul lines formed by extending two sides of the square, as in Diagram 1. The distance from home base to the nearest fence, stand or other obstruction on fair ground shall be 250 feet or more. A distance of 320 feet or more along the foul lines, and 400 feet or more to center field is preferable. The infield shall be graded so that the base lines and home plate are level, with a gradual slope from the base lines up to the pitcher's plate, which shall be 15 inches above the base line level. The infield and outfield, including the boundary lines, are fair ground and all other area is foul ground.

It is desirable that the line from home base through the pitcher's plate to second base shall run East-Northeast.

It is recommended that the distance from home plate to the backstop, and from the base lines to the nearest fence, stand or other obstruction on foul ground shall be 60 feet or more. See Diagram 1.

When location of home base is determined, with a steel tape measure 127 feet, 3⅜ inches in desired direction to establish second base. From home base, measure 90 feet towards first base; from second base, measure 90 feet towards first base; the intersection of these lines establishes first base. From home base, measure 90 feet towards third base; from second base, measure 90 feet toward third base; the intersection of these lines establishes third base. The distance between first base and third base is 127 feet, 3⅜ inches. All measurements from home base shall be taken from the point where the first and third base lines intersect.

The catcher's box, the batters' boxes, the coaches' boxes, the three-foot first base lines and the next batter's boxes shall be laid out as shown in Diagrams 1 and 2.

The foul lines and all other playing lines indicated in the diagrams by solid black lines shall be marked with wet lime, chalk or other white material.

The grass lines and dimensions shown on the diagrams are those customarily used in major league parks, but they are not mandatory and each club shall determine the size and shape of the grassed and bare areas of its playing field.

1.05 HOME BASE shall be a five-sided slab of whitened rubber. It shall be a 12-inch square with two of the corners filled in so that one edge is 17 inches long, two are 8½ inches and two are 12 inches. It shall be set in the ground with the point at the intersection of the lines extending from home base to first base and to third base; with the 17-inch edge facing the pitcher's plate, and the two 12-inch edges coinciding with the first and third base lines. The top edges of Home Base shall be beveled and the base shall be fixed in the ground level with the ground surface. (See drawing D in Diagram 2.)

1.06 FIRST, SECOND AND THIRD BASES shall be white canvas bags 15 inches square, not less than three nor more than five inches in thickness, filled with soft material, securely attached to the ground in positions shown in Diagram 2.

1.07 THE PITCHER'S PLATE shall be a rectangular slab of whitened rubber, 24 inches by 6 inches. It shall be set in the ground as shown in Diagrams 1 and 2, so that the distance between home base and the nearer edge of the pitcher's plate shall be 60 feet, 6 inches.

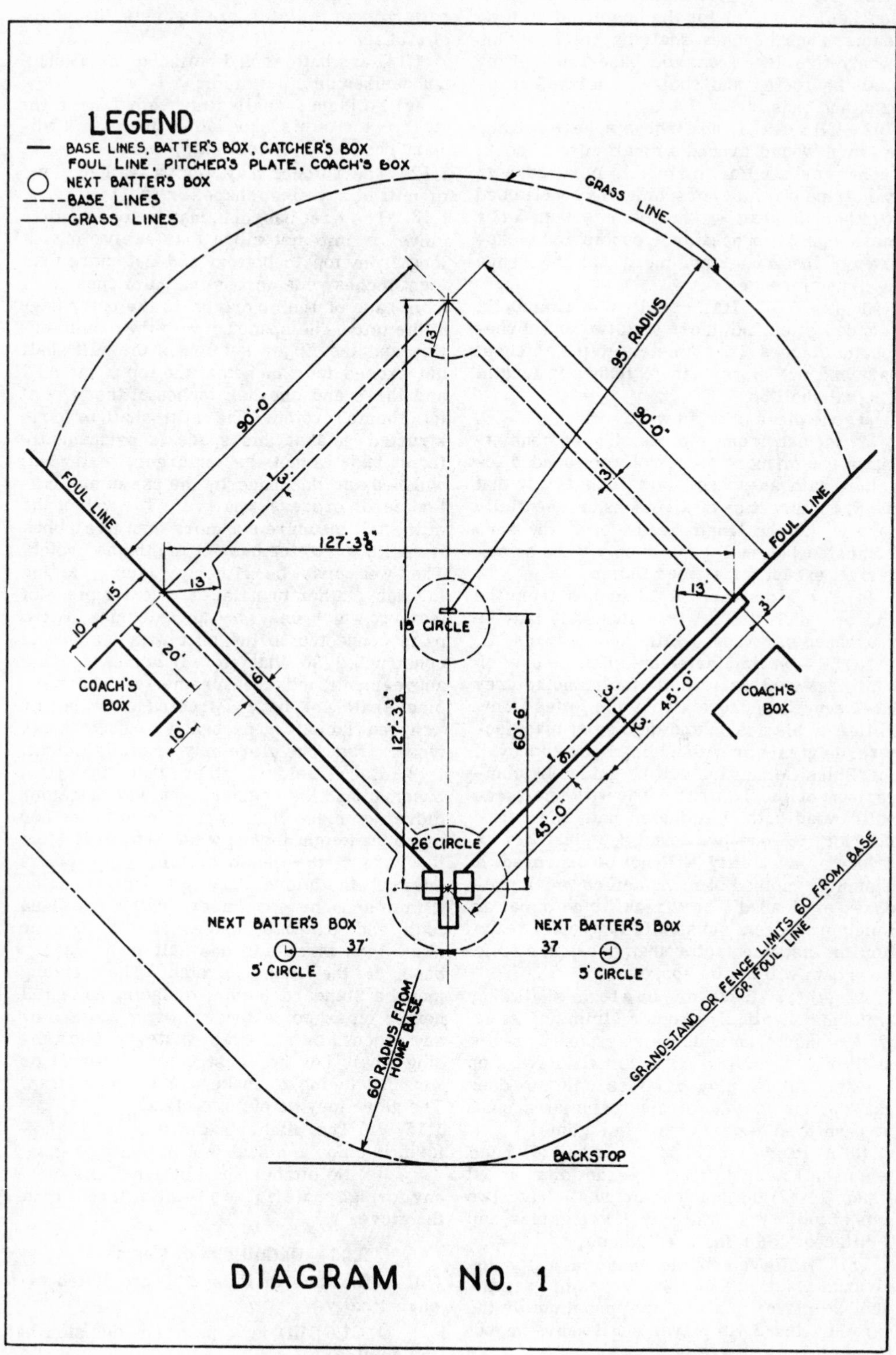
LEGEND
BASE LINES, BATTER'S BOX, CATCHER'S BOX
FOUL LINE, PITCHER'S PLATE, COACH'S BOX
NEXT BATTER'S BOX
BASE LINES
GRASS LINES
GRASS LINE
95' RADIUS
90'-0"
90'-0"
13'
FOUL LINE
FOUL LINE
127'-3 3/8"
13'
13'
15'
10'
20'
COACH'S BOX
COACH'S BOX
18' CIRCLE
127'-3 3/8"
60'-6"
45'-0"
45'-0"
26' CIRCLE
NEXT BATTER'S BOX
NEXT BATTER'S BOX
37'
37
5' CIRCLE
5' CIRCLE
60' RADIUS FROM HOME BASE
GRANDSTAND OR FENCE LIMITS 60 FROM BASE OR FOUL LINE
BACKSTOP

DIAGRAM NO. 1

1.08 The home club shall furnish players' benches, one each for the home and visiting teams. Such benches shall be not less than twenty-five feet from the base lines. They shall be roofed and shall be enclosed at the back and ends.

1.09 THE BALL shall be a sphere formed by yarn wound around a small core of cork, rubber or similar material, covered with two strips of white horsehide, tightly stitched together. It shall weigh not less than 5 nor more than 5¼ ounces avoirdupois and measure not less than 9 nor more than 9¼ inches in circumference.

1.10 (a) THE BAT shall be a smooth, rounded stick, not more than two and three-fourths inches in diameter at the thickest part and not more than 42 inches in length. The bat shall be

(1) one piece of solid wood, or

(2) formed from a block of wood consisting of two or more pieces of wood bonded together with an adhesive in such a way that the grain direction of all pieces is essentially parallel to the length of the bat. Any such laminated bat shall contain only wood or adhesive, except for a clear finish.

(b) For a distance of 18 inches from the end by which the bat is gripped, it may be roughened or wrapped with tape or twine.

NOTE—No laminated bat shall be used in a professional game until the manufacturer has secured approval from the Rules Committee of his design and method of manufacture. In giving or withholding such approval, the Rules Committee will be guided by comparison of the laminated bat with one-piece solid wood bats. Laminated bats which are inferior to one-piece solid wood bats in safety or durability will not be approved. A design or method of manufacture which produces a "loaded" or "freak" type of bat or which produces a substantially greater reaction or distance factor than one-piece solid wood bats will not be approved.

1.11 (a) (1) All players on a team shall wear uniforms identical in color, trim and style. (2) Any part of an undershirt exposed to view shall be of a uniform color for all players on a team. (3) No player whose uniform does not conform to that of his teammates shall be permitted to participate in a game.

(b) A league may provide that (1) each team shall wear a distinctive uniform at all times, or (2) that each team shall have two sets of uniforms, white for home games and a different color for road games.

(c) (1) Sleeve lengths may vary for individual players, but the sleeves of each individual player shall be of approximately the same length. (2) No player shall wear ragged, frayed or slit sleeves.

(d) No player shall attach to his uniform tape or other material of a different color from his uniform.

(e) No part of a uniform shall include a pattern that imitates or suggests the shape of a baseball.

(f) Glass buttons and polished metal shall not be used on a uniform.

(g) No player shall attach anything to the heel or toe of his shoe other than the ordinary shoe plate or toe plate.

1.12 The catcher may wear a leather glove or mitt of any size, shape, or weight.

1.13 The first baseman may wear a leather glove or mitt not more than twelve inches long from top to bottom and not more than eight inches wide across the palm, measured from base of thumb crotch to the outer edge of the mitt. The space between the thumb section and the finger section of the mitt shall not exceed four inches at the top of the mitt and three and one-half inches at the base of the thumb crotch. The mitt shall be constructed so that this space is permanently fixed and cannot be enlarged, extended, widened, or deepened by the use of any materials or process whatever. The web of the mitt shall measure not more than five inches from its top to the base of the thumb crotch. The web may be either a lacing, lacing through leather tunnels, or a center piece of leather which may be an extension of the palm connected to the mitt with lacing and constructed so that it will not exceed the above-mentioned measurements. The webbing shall not be constructed of wound or wrapped lacing or deepened to make a net type of trap. The glove may be of any weight.

1.14 Each fielder, other than the first baseman and the catcher, may wear a leather glove not more than twelve inches long nor more than eight inches wide, measured from the base of the thumb crotch to the outside edge of the glove. The space between the thumb and the forefinger shall not exceed four and one-half inches at the top nor more than three and one-half inches at the base of the thumb crotch. The webbing may be standard leather or lacing and shall not be enlarged, extended, or reinforced by any process or materials whatever. The webbing shall not be constructed of wound or wrapped lacing to make a net type of trap. The glove may be of any weight.

1.15 (a) The pitcher's glove shall be uniform in color and shall not be white or gray.

(b) No pitcher shall attach to his glove any foreign material of a color different from the glove.

2.00—Definitions of Terms

(All definitions in Rule 2.00 are listed alphabetically.)

ADJUDGED is a judgment decision by the umpire.

An APPEAL is the act of a fielder in claiming violation of the rules by the offensive team.

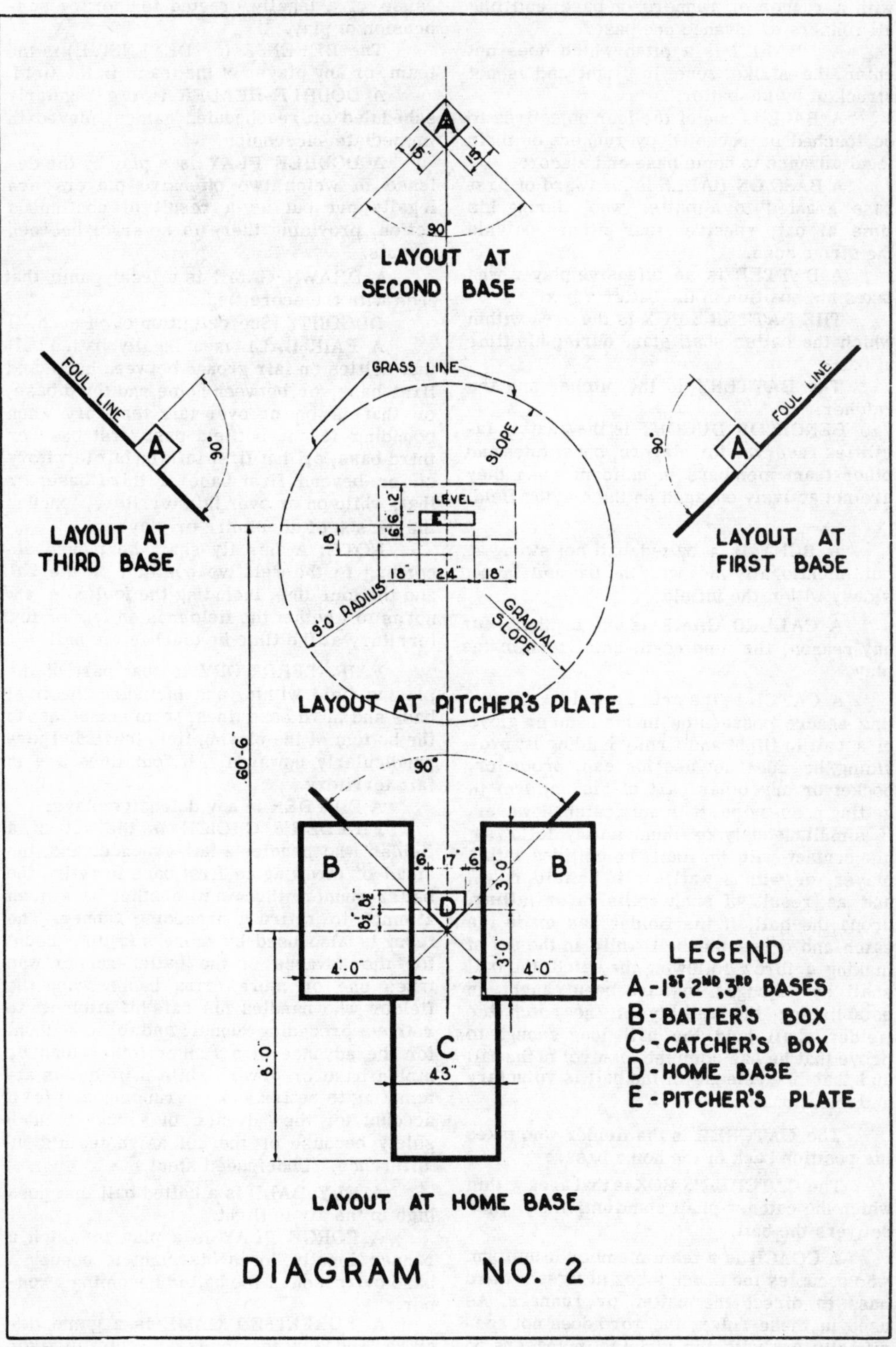
LAYOUT AT SECOND BASE
A
15'
15'
90°
FOUL LINE
A
90°
LAYOUT AT THIRD BASE
FOUL LINE
A
90°
LAYOUT AT FIRST BASE
GRASS LINE
SLOPE
LEVEL
6'
6'
12'
18'
E
18'
24"
18'
9'-0" RADIUS
GRADUAL SLOPE
LAYOUT AT PITCHER'S PLATE
60'-6"
90°
B
B
6"
17"
6"
3'-0"
D
3'-0"
4'-0"
4'-0"
C
43"
8'-0"
LAYOUT AT HOME BASE
LEGEND
A - 1ST, 2ND, 3RD BASES
B - BATTER'S BOX
C - CATCHER'S BOX
D - HOME BASE
E - PITCHER'S PLATE

DIAGRAM NO. 2

A BALK is an illegal act by the pitcher with a runner or runners on base, entitling all runners to advance one base.

A "BALL" is a pitch which does not enter the strike zone in flight and is not struck at by the batter.

A BASE is one of the four objectives to be touched or occupied by runners on their legal advance to home base and a score.

A BASE ON BALLS is an award of first base granted to a batter who, during his time at bat, receives four pitches outside the strike zone.

A BATTER is an offensive player who takes his position in the batter's box.

THE BATTER'S BOX is the area within which the batter shall stand during his time at bat.

The BATTERY is the pitcher and the catcher.

BENCH OR DUGOUT is the seating facilities reserved for players, substitutes and other team members in uniform when they are not actively engaged on the playing field.

A BUNT is a batted ball not swung at, but intentionally met with the bat and tapped slowly within the infield.

A CALLED GAME is one in which, for any reason, the umpire-in-chief terminates play.

A CATCH is the act of a fielder in getting secure possession in his hand or glove of a ball in flight and firmly holding it; providing he does not use his cap, protector, pocket or any other part of his uniform in getting possession. It is not a catch, however, if simultaneously or immediately following his contact with the ball, he collides with a player, or with a wall, or if he falls down, and as result of such collision or falling, drops the ball. If the fielder has made the catch and drops the ball while in the act of making a throw following the catch, the ball shall be adjudged to have been caught. In establishing the validity of the catch the fielder shall hold the ball long enough to prove that he has complete control of the ball and that his release of the ball is voluntary and intentional.

The CATCHER is the fielder who takes his position back of the home base.

The CATCHER'S BOX is that area within which the catcher shall stand until the pitcher delivers the ball.

A COACH is a team member in uniform who occupies the coach's box at first or third base to direct the batter or runners. As used in these rules, the word does not specifically apply to the assistant managers on professional teams called coaches, although these men frequently act as coaches, as defined in this rule.

A DEAD BALL is a ball out of play because of a legally created temporary suspension of play.

The DEFENSE (or DEFENSIVE) is the team, or any player of the team, in the field.

A DOUBLE-HEADER is two regularly scheduled or rescheduled games, played in immediate succession.

A DOUBLE PLAY is a play by the defense in which two offensive players are legally put out as a result of continuous action, providing there is no error between putouts.

A DRAWN GAME is a legal game that ends with the score tied.

DUGOUT. (See definition of "Bench.")

A FAIR BALL is a legally batted ball that settles on fair ground between home and first base, or between home and third base, or that is on or over fair territory when bounding to the outfield past first base or third base, or that first falls on fair territory on or beyond first base or third base; or that, while on or over fair territory, touches the person of an umpire or player.

NOTE: A fair fly shall be judged according to the relative position of the ball and the foul line, including the foul pole, and not as to whether the fielder is on fair or foul territory at the time he touches the ball.

FAIR TERRITORY is that part of the playing field within, and including the first base and third base lines, from home base to the bottom of the playing field fence and perpendicularly upwards. All foul lines are in fair territory.

A FIELDER is any defensive player.

FIELDER'S CHOICE is the act of a fielder who handles a fair grounder and, instead of throwing to first base to retire the batter-runner, throws to another base in an attempt to retire a preceding runner. The term is also used by scorers (a) to account for the advance of the batter-runner who takes one or more extra bases when the fielder who handles his safe hit attempts to retire a preceding runner; and (b) to account for the advance of a runner (other than by stolen base or error) while a fielder is attempting to retire another runner; and (c) to account for the advance of a runner made solely because of the defensive team's indifference. (Undefended steal.)

A FLY BALL is a batted ball that goes high in the air in flight.

A FORCE PLAY is a play in which a runner legally loses his right to occupy a base by reason of the batter becoming a runner.

A FORFEITED GAME is a game declared ended by the umpire-in-chief in favor of the offended team by the score of 9 to 0, for violation of the rules.

A FOUL BALL is a legally batted ball

that settles on foul territory between home and first base, or between home and third base, or that bounds past first or third base on or over foul territory, or that first falls on foul territory beyond first or third base, or that, while on or over foul territory, touches the person of an umpire or a player, or any object foreign to the natural ground.

NOTE: A foul fly shall be judged according to the relative position of the ball and the foul line, including the foul pole, and not as to whether the fielder is on foul or fair territory at the time he touches the ball.

FOUL TERRITORY is that part of the playing field outside the first and third base lines extended to the fence and perpendicularly upwards.

A FOUL TIP is a batted ball that goes sharp and direct from the bat to the catcher's hands and is legally caught. It is not a foul tip unless caught and any foul tip that is caught is a strike, and the ball is in play. It is not a catch if it is a rebound, unless the ball has first touched the catcher's glove or hand.

A GROUND BALL is a batted ball that rolls or bounces close to the ground.

The HOME TEAM is the team on whose grounds the game is played, or if the game is played on neutral ground, the home team shall be designated by mutual agreement.

ILLEGAL (or ILLEGALLY) is contrary to these rules.

An ILLEGAL PITCH is (1) delivered to the batter when the pitcher does not have his pivot foot in contact with the pitcher's plate; (2) a pitch delivered in violation of Rule 8.02 (a) (5), or (3) a quick return pitch. An illegal pitch when runners are on base is a balk.

An ILLEGALLY BATTED BALL is one hit by the batter with one or both feet outside the batter's box.

An INFIELDER is a fielder who occupies a position in the infield.

An INFIELD FLY is a fair fly ball (not including a line drive nor an attempted bunt) which can be caught by an infielder with ordinary effort, when first and second, or first, second and third bases are occupied, before two are out. The pitcher, catcher and any outfielder who stations himself in the infield on the play shall be considered infielders for the purpose of this rule.

When it seems apparent that a batted ball will be an Infield Fly, the umpire shall immediately declare "Infield Fly" for the benefit of the runners. If the ball is near the baselines, the umpire shall declare "Infield Fly, if Fair."

The ball is alive and runners may advance at the risk of the ball being caught, or retouch and advance after the ball is touched, the same as on any fly ball. If the hit becomes a foul ball, it is treated the same as any foul.

NOTE: If a declared Infield Fly is allowed to fall untouched to the ground, and bounces foul before passing first or third base, it is a foul ball. If a declared Infield Fly falls untouched to the ground outside the baseline, and bounces fair before passing first or third base, it is an Infield Fly.

IN FLIGHT describes a batted, thrown, or pitched ball which has not yet touched the ground or some object other than a fielder.

IN JEOPARDY is a term indicating that the ball is in play and an offensive player may be put out.

An INNING is that portion of a game within which the teams alternate on offense and defense and in which there are three putouts for each team.

INTERFERENCE.

(a) Offensive interference is an act by the team at bat which interferes with, obstructs, impedes, hinders or confuses any fielder attempting to make a play. If the umpire declares the batter or a runner out for interference, all other runners shall return to the last base that was, in the judgment of the umpire, legally touched at the time of the interference, unless otherwise provided by these rules.

(b) Defensive interference is an act by a fielder which hinders or prevents a batter from hitting a pitch.

(c) Umpire's interference occurs (1) When an umpire hinders, impedes or prevents a catcher's throw attempting to prevent a stolen base, or (2) When a fair ball touches an umpire before passing a fielder.

(d) Spectator interference occurs when a spectator reaches out of the stands, or goes on the playing field, and touches a live ball.

On any interference the ball is dead.

LEGAL (or LEGALLY) is in accordance with these rules.

A LIVE BALL is a ball which is in play.

OBSTRUCTION is the act of a fielder who, while not in possession of the ball and not in the act of fielding the ball, impedes the progress of any runner. Except for the runner actually obstructed, the ball remains in play and other runners may advance at their own risk.

OFFENSE is the team, or any player of he team, at bat.

OFFICIAL SCORER. See Rule 10.00.

An OUT is one of the three required retirements of an offensive team during its time at bat.

An OUTFIELDER is a fielder who occupies a position in the outfield, which is the area of the playing field most distant from home base.

OVERSLIDE (or OVERSLIDING) is the

act of an offensive player when his slide to a base, other than when advancing from home to first base, is with such momentum that he loses contact with the base, which act places him in jeopardy.

A PENALTY is the application of these rules following an illegal act.

The PERSON of a player or umpire is any part of his body, his clothing or his equipment.

A PITCH is a ball delivered to the batter by the pitcher.

A PITCHER is the fielder designated to deliver the pitch to the batter.

The pitcher's PIVOT FOOT is that foot which is in contact with the pitcher's plate as he delivers the pitch.

"PLAY" is the umpire's order to start the game or to resume action following any dead ball.

A QUICK RETURN pitch is one made with obvious intent to catch a batter off balance. It is an illegal pitch.

REGULATION GAME. See Rules 4.10 and 4.11.

A RETOUCH is the act of a runner in returning to a base as legally required.

A RUN (or SCORE) is the score made by an offensive player who advances from batter to runner and touches first, second, third and home bases in that order.

A RUN-DOWN is the act of the defense in an attempt to put out a runner between bases.

A RUNNER is an offensive player who is advancing toward, or touching, or returning to any base.

"SAFE" is a declaration by the umpire that a runner is entitled to the base for which he was trying.

SET POSITION is one of the two legal pitching positions.

SQUEEZE PLAY is a term to designate a play when a team, with a runner on third base, attempts to score that runner by means of a bunt.

A STRIKE is a legal pitch when so called by the umpire, which—

(a) Is struck at by the batter and is missed;

(b) Enters the strike zone in flight and is not struck at;

(c) Is fouled by the batter when he has less than two strikes;

(d) Is bunted foul;

(e) Touches the batter as he strikes at it;

(f) Touches the batter in flight in the strike zone; or

(g) Becomes a foul tip.

THE STRIKE ZONE is that space over home plate which is between the batter's arm-pits and the top of his knees when he assumes his natural stance.

A SUSPENDED GAME is a called game which is to be completed at a later date.

A TAG is the action of a fielder in touching a base with his body while holding the ball securely and firmly in his hand or glove; or touching a runner with the ball, or with his hand or glove holding the ball, while holding the ball securely and firmly in his hand or glove.

A THROW is the act of propelling the ball with the hand and arm to a given objective and is to be distinguished, always, from the pitch.

"TIME!" is the announcement by an umpire of a legal interruption of play, during which the ball is dead.

TOUCH. To touch a player or umpire is to touch any part of his body, clothing or his equipment.

A TRIPLE PLAY is a play by the defense in which three offensive players are legally put out as a result of continuous action, providing there is no error between putouts.

A WILD PITCH is one so high, so low, or so wide of the plate that it cannot be handled with ordinary effort by the catcher.

WIND-UP POSITION is one of the two legal pitching positions.

3.00—Game Preliminaries

3.01 Before the game begins the umpire shall—

(a) Require strict observance of all rules governing implements of play and equipment of players;

(b) Be sure all playing lines (heavy lines on Diagrams No. 1 and No. 2) are marked with lime, chalk or other white material easily distinguishable from the ground or grass;

(c) Receive from the home club a supply of regulation baseballs, the number and make to be certified to the home club by the league president. Each ball shall be enclosed in a sealed package bearing the signature of the league president, and the seal shall not be broken until just prior to game time when the umpire shall open each package to inspect the ball and remove its gloss. The umpire shall be the sole judge of the fitness of the balls to be used in the game;

(d) Be assured by the home club that at least one dozen regulation reserve balls are immediately available for use if required;

(e) Have in his possession at least two alternate balls and shall require replenishment of such supply of alternate balls as needed throughout the game. Such alternate balls shall be put in play when—

1. A ball has been batted out of the playing field or into the spectator area;

2. A ball has become discolored or unfit for further use;

3. The pitcher requests such alternate ball, which shall not be delivered to the pitcher until the previously used ball is dead.

3.02 No player shall intentionally discolor or damage the ball by rubbing it with soil, rosin, paraffin, licorice, sandpaper, emery-paper or other foreign substance.

PENALTY—The umpire shall demand the ball and remove the offender from the game. In case the umpire cannot locate the offender, and if the pitcher delivers such discolored or damaged ball to the batter, the pitcher shall be removed from the game at once and shall be suspended automatically for ten days.

3.03 A player, or players, may be substituted during a game at any time the ball is dead. A substitute player shall bat in the replaced player's position in the team's batting order. A player once removed from a game shall not re-enter that game. If a substitute enters the game in place of a Manager, the Manager may thereafter go to the coaching lines at his discretion. When two or more substitute players of the defensive team enter the game at the same time, the Manager, or his designated representative, shall, immediately before they take their position as fielders, designate to the umpire-in-chief such players' positions in the team's batting order and the umpire-in-chief shall so notify the official scorer. If this information is not immediately given to the umpire-in-chief, he shall have authority to designate the substitutes' places in the batting order.

3.04 A player whose name is on his team's batting order may not become a substitute runner for another member of his team.

3.05 (a) The pitcher named in the batting order handed the umpire-in-chief, as provided in Rules 4.01 (a) and 4.01 (b), shall pitch to the first batter or any substitute batter until such batter is put out or reaches first base, unless the pitcher sustains injury or illness which, in the judgment of the umpire-in-chief, incapacitates him from pitching.

(b) If the pitcher is replaced, the substitute pitcher shall pitch to the batter then at bat, or any substitute batter, until such batter is put out or reaches first base, or until the offensive team is put out, unless the substitute pitcher sustains injury or illness which, in the umpire-in-chief's judgment, incapacitates him for further play as a pitcher.

(c) If an improper substitution is made for the pitcher, the umpire shall direct the proper pitcher to return to the game until the provisions of this rule are fulfilled. If the improper pitcher is permitted to pitch, any play that results is legal. The improper pitcher becomes the proper pitcher as soon as he makes his first pitch to the batter, or as soon as any runner is put out.

3.06 The Manager of a team or his designated representative shall immediately notify the umpire-in-chief of any substitution and shall state to the umpire-in-chief the substitute's place in his batting order.

PENALTY—The league president shall assess a fine not to exceed $25.00 upon the Manager or his designated representative who fails to notify the umpire of a substitution.

3.07 The umpire-in-chief, after having been notified, shall immediately announce, or cause to be announced each substitution.

PENALTY—The league president shall assess a fine not to exceed $25.00 upon the umpire for each failure to announce a substitution.

3.08 (a) If no announcement of a substitution is made, the substitute shall be considered as having entered the game when—

(1) If a pitcher, he takes his place on the pitcher's plate;

(2) If a batter, he takes his place in the batter's box;

(3) If a fielder, he reaches the position usually occupied by the fielder he has replaced;

(4) If a runner, he takes the place of the runner he has replaced;

(b) Any play made by, or on, any of the above mentioned unannounced substitutes shall be legal.

3.09 Players in uniform shall not address nor mingle with spectators, not sit in the stands before, during, or after a game. No manager, captain, coach or player shall address any spectator before or during a game. Players of opposing teams shall not fraternize at any time while in uniform.

PENALTY—The league president shall impose fines, for violation of this rule, at his discretion.

3.10 (a) The Manager of the home team shall be the sole judge as to whether a game shall not be started because of unsuitable weather conditions or the unfit condition of the playing field, except for the second game of a double-header.

(b) EXCEPTION: Any league may permanently authorize its President to suspend the application of this rule as to that league during the closing weeks of its championship seasons in order to assure that the championship is decided each year on its merits. When the postponement of, and possible failure to play, a game in the final series of a championship season between any two teams might affect the final standing of any club in the league, the President, on appeal from any league member, may assume the authority granted the Home Team Manager by this rule.

(c) The umpire-in-chief of the first game shall be the sole judge as to whether the second game of a double-header shall not be started because of unsuitable weather conditions or the unfit condition of the playing field.

(d) The Umpire-in-Chief shall be the sole

judge as to whether and when play shall be suspended during a game because of unsuitable weather conditions or the unfit condition of the playing field; as to whether and when play shall be resumed after such suspension; and as to whether and when a game shall be terminated after such suspension.

3.11 Between games of a double-header, or whenever a GAME IS SUSPENDED because of the unfitness of the playing field, the umpire-in-chief shall have control of groundkeepers and assistants for the purpose of making the playing field fit for play.

PENALTY—For violation, the umpire-in-chief may forfeit the game to the visiting team.

3.12 When the umpire SUSPENDS PLAY he shall call "Time." At the umpire's call of "Play," the suspension is lifted and play resumes. Between the call of "Time" and the call of "Play" the ball is dead.

3.13 The Manager of the home team shall present to the Umpire-in-chief and the opposing Manager or Captain any ground rules he thinks necessary covering the overflow of spectators upon the playing field, batted or thrown balls into such overflow, or any other contingencies. If these rules are acceptable to the opposing Manager they shall be legal. If these rules are unacceptable to the opposing Manager, the Umpire-in-chief shall make and enforce any special ground rules he thinks are made necessary by ground conditions, which shall not conflict with the official playing rules.

3.14 Members of the offensive team shall carry all gloves and other equipment off the field and to the dugout while their team is at bat. No equipment shall be left lying on the field, either in fair or foul territory.

3.15 No person shall be allowed on the playing field during a game except players and coaches in uniform, managers, news photographers authorized by the home team, umpires, officers of the law in uniform and watchmen or other employees of the home club. In case of unintentional interference with play by any person herein authorized to be on the playing field, except umpires, the ball is alive and in play. If the interference is intentional, the ball shall be dead at the moment of the interference and the umpire shall impose such penalties as in his opinion will nullify the act of interference.

3.16 When there is spectator interference with any thrown ball, except a throw by the pitcher as provided in 7.05 (h), the ball shall be dead at the moment of interference and the umpire shall impose such penalties as in his opinion will nullify the act of interference.

3.17 Players and substitutes of both teams shall confine themselves to their team's benches unless actually participating in the play or preparing to enter the game, or coaching. No one except players, substitutes, Managers, coaches, trainers and bat boys shall occupy a bench or dugout during a game.

PENALTY—For violation the umpire may, after warning, remove the offender from the field. If the offender fails to obey the order in one minute he shall be liable to a fine by the league president.

3.18 The home team shall provide police protection sufficient to preserve order. If a person, or persons, enter the playing field during a game and interfere in any way with the play, the visiting team may refuse to play until the field is cleared.

PENALTY—If the field is not cleared in a reasonable length of time, which shall in no case be less than fifteen minutes after the visiting team's refusal to play, the umpire may forfeit the game to the visiting team.

4.00—Starting and Ending a Game.

4.01 Unless the home club shall have given previous notice that the game has been postponed or will be delayed in starting, the umpire, or umpires, shall enter the playing field five minutes before the hour set for the game to begin and proceed directly to home base where they shall be met by the managers of the opposing teams, or their representatives.

In sequence—

(a) First, the home manager shall give his batting order to the umpire-in-chief, in duplicate;

(b) Next, the visiting manager shall give his batting order to the umpire-in-chief, in duplicate.

(c) The umpire-in-chief shall make certain that the original and copies of the respective batting orders are identical, and then tender a copy of each batting order to the opposing manager. The copy retained by the umpire shall be the official batting order. The tender of the batting order by the umpire shall establish the batting orders. Thereafter, no substitutions shall be made by either manager, except as provided in these rules.

(d) As soon as the home team's batting order is handed to the umpire-in-chief the umpires are in charge of the playing field and from that moment they shall have sole authority to determine when a game shall be called, suspended or resumed on account of weather or the condition of the playing field.

4.02 The players of the home team shall take their defensive positions, the first batter of the visiting team shall take his position in the batter's box, the umpire shall call "Play" and the game shall start.

4.03 When the ball is put in play at the start of, or during a game, all fielders other than the catcher shall be on fair territory.

(a) The catcher shall station himself directly back of the plate. He may leave his position at any time to catch a pitch or make a play except that when the batter is being given an intentional base on balls, the catcher must stand with both feet within the lines of the catcher's box until the ball leaves the pitcher's hand.

PENALTY—Balk.

(b) The pitcher, while in the act of delivering the ball to the batter, shall take his legal position;

(c) Except the pitcher and the catcher, any fielder may station himself anywhere in fair territory.

(d) Except the batter, or a runner attempting to score, no offensive player shall cross the catcher's lines when the ball is in play.

4.04 The batting order shall be followed throughout the game unless a player is substituted for another. In that case the substitute shall take the place of the replaced player in the batting order.

4.05 (a) The offensive team shall station two coaches on the field during its term at bat, one near first base and one near third base. Failure to place two coaches on the field shall subject the manager to fine or suspension or both by the league president.

(b) Coaches shall be limited to two in number and shall (1) be in team uniform; (2) remain within the coach's box at all times; and (3) address players of their own team only.

PENALTY—The offending coach shall be removed from the game, and shall leave the playing field.

4.06 (a) No manager, player, substitute, coach, trainer or batboy shall at any time, whether from the bench, the coach's box or on the playing field, or elsewhere—

(1) Incite, or try to incite, by word or sign a demonstration by spectators;

(2) Use language which will in any manner refer to or reflect upon opposing players, an umpire, or any spectator;

(3) Call "Time," or employ any other word or phrase or commit any act while the ball is alive and in play for the obvious purpose of trying to make the pitcher commit a balk.

(b) No fielder shall take a position in the batter's line of vision, and with deliberate unsportsmanlike intent, act in a manner to distract the batter.

PENALTY—The offender shall be removed from the game and shall leave the playing field.

4.07 When a manager, player, trainer or coach is removed from the game he shall go to the club house. He shall remain in the club house or leave the grounds.

4.08 When the occupants of a player's bench show violent disapproval of an umpire's decision, the umpire shall first give warning that such disapproval shall cease. If such action continues—

PENALTY—The umpire shall order the offenders from the bench to the club house. If he is unable to detect the offender, or offenders, he may clear the bench of all substitute players. The manager or captain of the offending team shall have the privilege of recalling to the playing field only those players needed for substitution in the game.

4:09 HOW A TEAM SCORES.

(a) One run shall be scored each time a runner legally advances to and touches first, second, third and home base before three men are put out to end the inning.

EXCEPTION: A run is not scored if the runner advances to home base during a play in which the third out is made (1) by the batter-runner before he touches first base; (2) by any runner being forced out; or (3) by a preceding runner who is declared out because he failed to touch one of the bases.

(b) When the winning run is scored in the last half-inning of a regulation game, or in the last half of an extra inning, as the result of a base on balls, hit batsman or any other play with the bases full which forces the runner on third to advance, the umpire shall not declare the game ended until the runner forced to advance from third has touched home base and the batter-runner has touched first base.

PENALTY—If the runner on third refuses to advance to and touch home base in a reasonable time, the umpire shall disallow the run, call out the offending player and order the game resumed. If, with two out, the batter-runner refuses to advance to and touch first base, the umpire shall disallow the run, call out the offending player, and order the game resumed. If, with less than two out, the batter-runner refuses to advance to and touch first base, the run shall count, but the offending player shall be called out.

4.10 ENDING A GAME.

(a) A regulation game consists of nine innings, unless extended because of a tie score, or shortened (1) because the home team needs none of its half of the ninth or only a fraction of it; or (2) because the umpire calls the game.

NOTE: A league may adopt a rule providing that one game of a double-header shall be seven innings in length. In such games, any of these rules applying to the ninth inning shall apply to the seventh inning.

(b) The game ends when the visiting team completes its half of the ninth inning, if the visiting team has scored fewer runs than the home team has scored in eight innings.

(c) When it is necessary for the home team to use its half of the ninth inning (or its half of an extra inning after a tie) both the inning and the game end immediately when the winning run is scored before three men are out.

EXCEPTION: If the last batter in the final

half-inning of a game hits a home run over the fence or into a stand, all runners on base at the time, as well as the batter, are entitled to score by touching each base in order.

(d) If the score is tied when nine innings have been completed play shall continue until one team has scored more runs than the other in an equal number of completed innings, or until the game is ended as in subparagraph (c).

(e) If a game is called by the umpire, it is a regulation game (1) if five innings have been completed; (2) if the home team has scored more runs in four innings or before the completion of the fifth inning than the visiting team has scored in five completed innings, or (3) if more than five innings have been completed.

NOTE: If a game is called after five or more completed innings, the score shall be the score at the end of the last completed inning; except that if the home team has scored more total runs than the visiting team at the time the game is called, the score shall be the total number of runs scored by each team at that time.

(f) If a game is called before it becomes a regulation game as in sub-paragraph (e), the umpire shall declare "No Game."

4.11 A REGULATION DRAWN GAME shall be declared by the umpire-in-chief if he terminates play because of weather, darkness, or any other cause which makes further play impossible—

(a) If, after five or more completed innings, the score is tied;

(b) If, after five or more completed innings, the home team is at bat when play terminates and scores enough runs in an incompleted inning to make its total score equal the visiting team's total score;

(c) If the home team shall score, in its incomplete fifth inning, a run or runs to equal the visiting team's total score in its five complete half innings.

4.12 SUSPENDED GAMES.

(a) A league may establish the following rules providing for completion at a future date of games terminated before nine innings have been completed, for any of the following reasons:

(1) A curfew imposed by law;

(2) A time limit permissible under league rules;

(3) Light failure;

(4) Darkness in the second game of a Sunday double-header when because of any law, the lights may not be turned on.

(b) Such games shall be known as suspended games. No game shall be suspended after nine innings have been completed. No game called because of a curfew or time limit shall be a suspended game unless it has progressed far enough to have been a regulation game under the provisions of Rules 4.10 or 4.11. A game called under the provisions of 4.12 (a) (3) or (4) shall be a suspended game at any time after it starts.

NOTE: Weather and similar conditions shall take precedence in determining whether a called game shall be a suspended game. If a game is halted by weather, and subsequent light failure, or an intervening curfew or time limit prevent its resumption, it shall not be a suspended game. If a game is halted by light failure, and weather or field conditions prevent its resumption, it shall not be a suspended game.

(c) A suspended game shall be resumed and completed as follows:

(1) Immediately preceding the next scheduled single game between the two clubs on the same grounds; or

(2) Immediately preceding the next scheduled double-header between the two clubs on the same grounds, if no single game remains on the schedule; or

(3) If suspended on the last scheduled date between the two clubs in that city, transferred and played on the grounds of the opposing club, if possible,

(i) Immediately preceding the next scheduled single game, or

(ii) Immediately preceding the next scheduled double-header, if no single game remains on the schedule.

(4) If a suspended game has not been resumed and completed on the last date scheduled for the two clubs, it shall be a called game, and the final score shall be the score that would have prevailed had the game been called because of weather.

(d) A suspended game shall be resumed at the exact point of suspension of the original game. The completion of a suspended game is a continuation of the original game. The lineup and batting order of both teams shall be exactly the same as the lineup and batting order at the moment of suspension, subject to the rules governing substitution. Any player may be replaced by a player who had not been in the game prior to the suspension. No player removed before the suspension may be returned to the lineup.

A player who was not with the club when the game was suspended may be used as a substitute, even if he has taken the place of a player no longer with the club who would not have been eligible because he had been removed from the lineup before the game was suspended.

4.13 RULES GOVERNING DOUBLE-HEADERS.

(a) (1) Only two championship games shall be played on one date. Completion of a suspended game shall not violate this rule.

(2) If two games are scheduled to be played for one admission on one date, the first game shall be the regularly scheduled game for that day.

(b) After the start of the first game of a double-header, that game shall be completed before the second game of the double-header shall begin.

(c) The second game of a double-header shall begin twenty minutes after the first game is completed unless a longer interval (not to exceed thirty minutes) is declared by the umpire-in-chief and announced to the opposing managers at the end of the first game. EXCEPTION: If the league president has approved a request of the home club for a longer interval between games for some special event, the umpire-in-chief shall declare such longer interval and announce it to the opposing managers. The umpire-in-chief of the first game shall be the timekeeper controlling the interval between games.

(d) The umpire shall start the second game of a double-header, if at all possible, and play shall continue as long as ground conditions, local time restrictions or weather permit.

(e) When a regularly scheduled double-header is delayed in starting for any cause, any, game that is started is the first game of the double-header.

(f) When a rescheduled game is part of a double-header the rescheduled game shall be the second game, and the first game shall be the regularly scheduled game for that date.

4.14 The umpire-in-chief shall order the playing field lights turned on whenever in his opinion darkness makes further play in daylight hazardous.

4.15 The umpire may declare a game forfeited in favor of the opposing team when a team—

(a) Fails to appear upon the field, or being upon the field, refuses to start play within five minutes after the umpire has called "Play' at the appointed hour for beginning the game, unless such delayed appearance is, in the umpire's judgment, unavoidable;

(b) Employs tactics palpably designed to delay or shorten the game;

(c) Refuses to continue play during a game unless the game has been suspended or terminated by the umpire;

(d) Fails to resume play, after a suspension, within one minute after the umpire has called "Play";

(e) After warning by the umpire, wilfully and persistently violates any rules of the game;

(f) Fails to obey within a reasonable time the umpire's order for removal of a player from the game;

(g) Fails to appear for the second game of a double-header within twenty minutes after the close of the first game unless the umpire-in-chief of the first game shall have extended the time of the intermission.

PENALTY— The manager whose team has forfeited a game under any of the provisions of this rule shall be subject to fine and suspension by the league president. The manager is responsible for the actions of his players on the field.

4.16 A game shall be forfeited to the visiting team if, after it has been suspended, the orders of the umpire to ground keepers respecting preparation of the field for resumption of play are not complied with.

4.17 A game shall be forfeited to the opposing team when a team is unable or refuses to place nine players on the field.

4.18 If the umpire declares a game forfeited he shall transmit a written report to the league president within twenty-four hours thereafter, but failure of such transmittal shall not affect the forfeiture.

4.19 PROTESTING GAMES. Each league shall adopt rules governing procedure for protesting a game, when a manager claims that an umpire's decision is in violation of these rules. No protest shall be permitted on judgment decisions by the umpire.

5.00—Putting the Ball in Play. Live Ball.

5.01 At the time set for beginning the game the umpire shall call "Play."

5.02 After the umpire calls "Play" the ball is alive and in play and remains alive and in play until for legal cause, or at the umpire's call of "Time" suspending play, the ball becomes DEAD. While the ball is dead no player may be put out, no bases may be run and no runs may be scored, except that runners may advance one or more bases as the result of acts which occurred while the ball was alive (such as, but not limited to a balk, an overthrow, interference, or a home run or other fair hit out of the playing field).

5.03 The pitcher shall deliver the pitch to the batter who may elect to strike the ball, or who may not offer at it, as he chooses.

5.04 The offensive team's objective is to have its batter become a runner, and its runners advance.

5.05 The defensive team's objective is to prevent offensive players from becoming runners, or to prevent their advance around the bases.

5.06 When a batter becomes a runner and touches all bases legally he shall score one run for his team.

5.07 When three offensive players are legally put out, that team takes the field and the opposing team becomes the offensive team.

5.08 If a thrown ball accidentally touches a coach, or a pitched or thrown ball touches an umpire, the ball is alive and in play.

5.09 The ball becomes dead and runners advance one base, or return to their bases without liability to be put out, when—

(a) A pitched ball touches a batter or his clothing, while in his legal batting position; runners, if forced, advance;

(b) The plate umpire interferes with the catcher's attempt to throw; runners return;

(c) A balk is committed; runners advance;

(d) A ball is illegally batted; runners return;

(e) A foul is hit which is not caught; runners return;

(f) Offensive interference is called; runners return;

(g) A fair ball touches a runner or an umpire before it touches an infielder including the pitcher, or touches an umpire before it has passed an infielder other than the pitcher. If a fair ball goes through, or by, an infielder, and touches a runner immediately back of him, or touches a runner after being deflected by an infielder, the umpire shall not declare the runner out for being hit by a batted ball. In making such decision the umpire must be convinced that the ball passed through, or by, the infielder and that no other infielder had the chance to make a play on the ball; runners advance, if forced;

(h) A coach intentionally interferes with a thrown ball; runners return;

(i) The ball touches a spectator; runners advance;

(j) Any legal pitch hits a runner trying to score; runners advance one base.

5.10 The ball becomes dead when the umpire-in-chief suspends play by calling "time" when—

(a) In his judgment weather, darkness, or similar conditions, make further play immediately impossible. The umpire-in-chief shall have authority to call "Play" for resumption of the game whenever the weather and the condition of the playing field warrants it. After thirty minutes of such suspension the umpire shall have authority to terminate the game, but if there is any chance to resume play he may continue such suspension as long as his judgment warrants:

(b) An accident incapacitates a player or umpire. No umpire shall call "Time" because of an accident to player or umpire during a play until no further action is possible in that play. EXCEPTION: If an accident to a runner is such as to prevent him from proceeding to a base to which he is legally entitled, as on a home run hit out of the playing field, or an award of one or more bases, a substitute runner shall be permitted to complete the play;

(c) A manager requests "Time" for a substitution, or for conference with one of his players;

(d) The umpire wishes to examine the ball, or for any similar cause;

(e) A fielder, after catching a fly ball, falls into a bench, dugout or stand or falls across ropes into a crowd (when spectators are on the field), and runners may advance one base without liability to be put out. (NOTE: If player after making the catch steps into the dugout but does not fall, the ball is alive and in play and runners may advance at their own peril.)

5.11 After the ball is dead, after being hit out of the playing grounds or into the spectator area, or after a call of "time," or any other reason, play shall be resumed when the pitcher takes his place on the rubber with a new ball, or the same ball, in his possession and the umpire calls "play." The umpire shall call "play" as soon as the pitcher takes his place on the rubber with the ball in his possession.

6.00—The Batter.

6.01 (a) Each player of the offensive team shall bat in the order that his name appears in his team's batting order.

(b) The first batter in each inning after the first inning shall be the player whose name follows that of the last player who legally completed his time at bat in the preceding inning.

6.02 (a) The batter shall take his position in the batter's box promptly when it is his time at bat.

(b) The batter shall not leave his position in the batter's box after the pitcher comes to Set Position, or starts his windup.

PENALTY: If a pitcher pitches, the umpire shall call "Ball" or "Strike" as the case may be.

(c) If a batter refuses to take his position in the batter's box during his time at bat, the umpire shall order the pitcher to pitch, and shall call "Strike" on each such pitch. The batter may take his proper position after any such pitch, and the regular ball and strike count shall continue, but if he does not take his proper position before three strikes are called, he shall be declared out.

6.03 The batter's legal position shall be **with both feet within the batter's box.**

6.04 A batter has legally completed his time at bat when he is put out or becomes a runner.

6.05 A BATTER IS OUT WHEN—

(a) His fair or foul fly ball (other than a foul tip) is legally caught by a fielder.

(b) A third strike is legally caught by the catcher;

(c) A third strike is not caught by the catcher when first base is occupied before two are out;

(d) He bunts foul on the third strike;

(e) An Infield Fly is declared;

(f) He attempts to hit a third strike and the ball touches him;

(g) His fair ball touches him before touching a fielder;

(h) After hitting or bunting a fair ball, his bat hits the ball a second time in fair territory. The ball is dead and no runners may advance. If the batter-runner drops his bat and the ball rolls against the bat in fair territory and, in the umpire's judgment, there was no intention to interfere with the course of the ball, the ball is alive and in play;

(i) After hitting or bunting a foul ball, he intentionally deflects the course of the ball in any manner while running to first base. The ball is dead and no runners may advance;

(j) After a third strike, or after he hits a fair ball he or first base is tagged before he touches first base.

(k) In running the last half of the distance from home base to first base while the ball is being fielded to first base, he runs outside (to the right of) the three-foot line, or inside (to the left) of the foul line, and in the umpire's judgment in so doing interferes with the fielder taking the throw at first base; except that he may run outside (to the right of) the three-foot line or inside (to the left of) the foul line to avoid a fielder attempting to field a batted ball;

(l) A fielder intentionally drops a fair fly ball or line drive, with first, first and second, first and third, or first, second and third base occupied before two are out. Runners need not retouch, and may advance at their own peril;

(m) A preceding runner shall, in the umpire's judgment, intentionally interfere with the play of a fielder who is attempting to catch a thrown ball or to throw the ball in an attempt to complete any play;

(n) With two out, a runner on third base, and two strikes on the batter, the runner attempts to steal home base on a legal pitch and the ball touches the runner in the batter's strike zone. The umpire shall call "strike three," the batter is out and the run shall not count; with less than two out the umpire shall call "strike three," the ball is dead, and the run counts;

(o) Spectator interference clearly prevents a fielder from catching his fly ball.

6.06 A BATTER IS OUT FOR ILLEGAL ACTION WHEN—

(a) Either of his feet are outside the lines of the batter's box when he hits the ball;

(b) He steps from one batter's box to the other while the pitcher is in position ready to pitch;

(c) He interferes with the catcher's fielding or throwing by stepping out of the batter's box or making any other movement that hinders the catcher's play at home base. EXCEPTION: Batter is not out if any runner attempting to advance is put out, or if runner trying to score is called out for batter's interference.

6.07 BATTING OUT OF TURN

(a) A batter shall be called out, on appeal, when he fails to bat in his proper turn, and another batter completes a time at bat in his place.

(1) The proper batter may take his place in the batter's box at any time before the improper batter becomes a runner or is put out, and any balls and strikes shall be counted in the proper batter's time at bat.

(b) When an improper batter becomes a runner or is put out, and the defensive team appeals to the umpire before the first pitch to the next batter of either team, the umpire shall (1) declare the proper batter out; and (2) nullify any advance or score made because of a ball batted by the improper batter or because of the improper batter's advance to first base on a hit, an error, a base on balls, a hit batter, or otherwise.

NOTE: If a runner advances, while the improper batter is at bat, on a stolen base, balk, wild pitch or passed ball, such advance is legal.

(c) When an improper batter becomes a runner or is put out, and a pitch is made to the next batter of either team before an appeal is made, the improper batter thereby becomes the proper batter, and the results of his time at bat become legal.

(d) (1) When the proper batter is called out because he has failed to bat in turn, the next batter shall be the batter whose name follows that of the proper batter thus called out; (2) When an improper batter becomes a proper batter because no appeal is made before the next pitch, the next batter shall be the batter whose name follows that of such legalized improper batter. The instant an improper batter's actions are legalized, the batting order picks up with the name following that of the legalized improper batter.

APPROVED RULINGS

To illustrate various situations arising from batting out of turn, assume a first-inning batting order as follows: Abel - Baker - Charles - Daniel - Edward - Frank - George - Hooker - Irwin.

PLAY (1). Baker bats. With the count 2 balls and 1 strike, (a) the offensive team discovers the error or (b) the defensive team appeals. RULING: In either case, Abel replaces Baker, with the count on him 2 balls and 1 strike.

PLAY (2). Baker bats and doubles. The defensive team appeals (a) immediately or (b) after a pitch to Charles. RULING: (a) Abel is called out and Baker is the proper batter; (b) Baker stays on second and Charles is the proper batter.

PLAY (3). Abel walks. Baker walks. Charles forces Baker. Edward bats in Daniel's turn. While Edward is at bat, Abel scores and Charles goes to second on a wild pitch. Edward grounds out, sending Charles to third. The defensive team appeals (a) immediately or (b) after a pitch to Daniel. RULING: (a) Abel's run counts and Charles is entitled to second base since these advances were not made because of the improper batter batting the ball or advancing to first base. Charles must return to second base because his advance to third resulted from the improper batter batting a ball. Daniel is called out, and Edward is the proper batter; (b) Abel's run counts and Charles stays on third. The proper batter is Frank.

PLAY (4). With the bases full and two out, Hooker bats in Frank's turn, and triples, scoring three runs. The defensive team appeals (a) immediately, or (b) after a pitch to George. RULING: (a) Frank is called out and no runs score. George is the proper batter to lead off the second inning; (b) Hooker stays on third and three runs score. Irwin is the proper batter.

PLAY (5). After Play (4) (b) above, George continues at bat. (a) Hooker is picked off third base for the third out, or (b) George flies out, and no appeal is made. Who is the proper leadoff batter in the second inning? RULING. (a) Irwin. He became the proper batter as soon as the first pitch to George legalized Hooker's triple; (b) Hooker. When no appeal was made, the first pitch to the leadoff batter of the opposing team legalized George's time at bat.

PLAY (6). Daniel walks and Abel comes to bat. Daniel was an improper batter, and if an appeal is made before the first pitch to Abel, Abel is out, Daniel is removed from base, and Baker is the proper batter. There is no appeal, and a pitch is made to Abel. Daniel's walk is now legalized, and Edward thereby becomes the proper batter. Edward can replace Abel at any time before Abel is put out or becomes a runner. He does not do so, Abel flies out, and Baker comes to bat. Abel was an improper batter, and if an appeal is made before the first pitch to Baker, Edward is out, and the proper batter is Frank. There is no appeal, and a pitch is made to Baker. Abel's walk is now legalized, and the proper batter is Baker. Baker walks. Charles is the proper batter. Charles flies out. Now Daniel is the proper batter, but he is on second base. Who is the proper batter? RULING: The proper batter is Edward. Skip over the batter who is on base because of the opponents' indifference or lack of alertness when he batted out of turn.

6.08 THE BATTER BECOMES A RUNNER AND IS ENTITLED TO FIRST BASE WITHOUT LIABILITY TO BE PUT OUT (PROVIDED HE ADVANCES TO AND TOUCHES FIRST BASE) WHEN—

(a) "Four balls" have been called by the umpire;

(b) He is touched by a pitched ball which he is not attempting to hit unless

(1) The ball is in the strike zone when it touches the batter or,

(2) The batter makes no attempt to avoid being touched by the ball.

NOTE: If the ball is in the strike zone when it touches the batter, it shall be called a strike, whether or not the batter tries to avoid the ball. If the ball is outside the strike zone when it touches the batter, it shall be called a ball if he makes no attempt to avoid being touched.

(c) The catcher or any other fielder interferes with him, unless the batter reaches first base on a hit, an error, a base on balls, a hit batter or otherwise, and all other runners advance at least one base, in which case the play proceeds without reference to the interference;

APPROVED RULING: A runner who misses the first base to which he is advancing and who is called out on appeal shall be considered as having advanced one base for the purpose of this rule.

(d) A fair ball touches an umpire or a runner on fair ground before touching a fielder, provided that if a fair ball touches the umpire after having passed a fielder other than the pitcher, or having touched a fielder (including the pitcher), the ball shall be considered in play. Also, if a fair ball strikes the umpire on foul ground, the ball shall be in play.

6.09 THE BATTER BECOMES A RUNNER WHEN—

(a) He makes a fair hit;

(b) The third strike called by the umpire is not caught, providing (1) first base is unoccupied, or (2) first base is occupied with two out;

(c) Although interfered with by the catcher or any other fielder, he reaches first base on a hit, an error, a base on balls, a hit batter or otherwise, and all other runners advance at least one base;

(d) A fair ball, after having passed a fielder other than the pitcher, or after having been touched by a fielder, shall strike an umpire or runner on fair territory;

(e) A fair fly ball passes over a fence or into the stands at a distance from home base of 250 feet or more. Such hit entitles the batter to a home run when he shall have touched all bases legally. A fair fly ball that passes over a fence or into the stands at a point less than 250 feet from home base shall entitle the batter to advance to second base only;

(f) A fair ball, after striking the ground, bounds into the stands, or passes through, over or under a fence, or through or under a scoreboard, or through or under shrubbery, or vines on the fence, in which case the batter and the runners shall be entitled to advance two bases;

(g) Any fair ball which, either before or after striking the ground, passes through or under a fence, or through or under a scoreboard, or through any opening in the fence or scoreboard, or through or under shrubbery, or vines on the fence, or which sticks in a fence or scoreboard, in which case the batter and the runners shall be entitled to two bases;

(h) Any bounding fair ball is deflected by the fielder into the stands, or over or under a fence on fair or foul ground, in which case the batter and all runners shall be entitled to advance two bases;

(i) Any fair fly ball is deflected by the fielder into the stands, or over the fence into foul territory, in which case the batter shall be entitled to advance to second base; but if deflected into the stands or over the fence in fair territory, the batter shall be entitled to a home run. However, should such fair fly be deflected at a point less than 250 feet from home plate, the batter shall be entitled to two bases only.

7.00—The Runner.

7.01 A runner acquires the right to an unoccupied base when he touches it before he is out. He is then entitled to it until he is put out; or touches the next base; or is forced to vacate it for a succeeding runner.

7.02 In advancing, a runner shall touch first, second, third and home base in order. If forced to return, he shall retouch all bases in reverse order unless the ball is dead. In that case he may go directly to his original base. In running to first base he may overrun or overslide first base provided he return to the base at once.

PENALTY: If a runner fails to touch a base while advancing or reversing, he shall be declared out when a fielder tags him, the missed base or the base from which he started his advance. This is an appeal play.

7.03 Two runners may not occupy a base, but if, while the ball is alive, two runners are touching a base, the second runner shall be out when tagged. The preceding runner is entitled to the base.

7.04 EACH RUNNER, OTHER THAN THE BATTER, MAY WITHOUT LIABILITY OF BEING PUT OUT ADVANCE ONE BASE WHEN—

(a) There is a balk;

(b) The batter's advance without liability to be put out forces the runner to vacate his base; or when the batter hits a fair ball that touches another runner or the umpire before such ball has been touched by, or has passed a fielder, if the runner is forced to advance;

(c) He is obstructed by a fielder, including the catcher. The ball is in play with respect to all other runners;

(d) While he is attempting to steal a base. the batter is interfered with by any other fielder.

NOTE: When a runner is entitled to a base without liability to be put out, while the ball is in play, or under any rule in which the ball is in play after the runner reaches the base to which he is entitled, and the runner fails to touch the base to which he is entitled before attempting to advance to the next base, the runner shall forfeit his exemption from liability to be put out, and he may be put out by tagging the base or by tagging the runner before he returns to the missed base.

7.05 EACH RUNNER INCLUDING THE BATTER-RUNNER MAY, WITHOUT LIABILITY OF BEING PUT OUT, ADVANCE—

(a) To home base, scoring a run, if a fair ball goes over the field fence in flight and he touches all bases legally; or if a fair ball which, in the umpire's judgment, would have cleared the field fence in flight, is deflected by the act of a fielder in throwing his glove, cap, or any article of his apparel, the runner shall be awarded a home run;

(b) Three bases, if a fielder deliberately touches a fair ball with his cap, mask or any part of his uniform detached from its proper place on his person. The ball is in play and the batter may advance to home base at his peril;

(c) Three bases, if a fielder deliberately throws his glove at and touches a fair ball. The ball is in play and the batter may advance to home base at his peril;

(d) Two bases, if a fielder deliberately touches a thrown ball with his cap, mask or any part of his uniform detached from its proper place on his person. The ball is in play;

(e) Two bases, if a fielder deliberately throws his glove at and touches a thrown ball. The ball is in play;

(f) Two bases, if a fair ball touches a spectator, unless the spectator's interference clearly prevents a fielder from catching a fly ball; or if it bounces or is deflected into the stands outside the first or third base foul lines; or if it goes through or under a field fence, or through or under a scoreboard, or through or under shrubbery, or vines on the fence;

(g) Two bases when, with no spectators on the playing field, a thrown ball goes into the stands or into a player's bench (whether the ball rebounds into the field or not), or over or under or through a field fence, or on a slanting part of the screen above the break on the backstop, or remains in the meshes of a wire screen protecting the spectators. The ball is dead. When such thrown ball is the first throw by an infielder the umpire, in awarding such bases, shall be governed by the position of the runner, or runners, at the time the ball was pitched; but if a play intervenes between the first throw by an infielder and the throw into the stands, the umpire, in awarding such bases, shall be governed by the position of the runner or runners, at the time the throw was made into the stands.

When the throw is made by an outfielder or is the result of any following plays, or attempted plays, the award shall be governed by the position of the runner, or runners, when the last throw was made. (Note on "play intervenes"—Intervening play as used herein refers to a play or an attempt to make a play, by an infielder on a runner before the throw is made).

(h) One base, if a ball, pitched to the batter, or thrown by the pitcher from his position on the pitcher's plate to a base to catch a runner, goes into a stand, or player's bench, or over or through a field fence or backstop, or is touched by a spectator. The ball is dead.

NOTE: If such a wild pitch is ball four, the batter-runner is entitled to first base only.

7.06 (a) A batter who has become a runner is entitled to unimpeded progress as he advances around the bases. Whenever a fielder impedes the runner in any way, unless he is attempting to field a ball or has the ball in his possession, the umpire shall call "obstruction," the ball shall remain in play, and all runners shall be permitted to advance, without liability to be put out, to the bases which, in the judgment of the umpire, the runners would have reached had obstruction not been called.

(b) In a rundown play, if the runner is obstructed by any fielder who does not have the ball in his possession (unless the fielder is in the act of fielding the ball), the umpire shall call "Obstruction" and the runner shall be entitled to occupy the base he is attempting to reach when the obstruction occurs. If such base is held by a following runner, any following runner forced to vacate his base by the obstructed runner's return shall be permitted to return to his last-held base without liability to be put out.

7.07 If, with a runner on third base and trying to score by means of a squeeze play or a steal, the catcher or any other fielder steps on, or in front of home base without possession of the ball, or touches the batter or his bat, the pitcher shall be charged with a balk, the batter shall be awarded first base on the interference and the ball is dead.

7.08 ANY RUNNER IS OUT WHEN—

(a) He runs more than three feet away from a direct line between bases to avoid being tagged, unless his action is to avoid interference with a fielder fielding a batted ball;

(b) He intentionally interferes with a thrown ball; or hinders a fielder attempting to make a play on a batted ball;

(c) He is tagged, when the ball is alive, while off his base. The ball must be securely held by the fielder before and after the tag. If the impact of runner breaks a base loose from its position, no play can be made on that runner if he had reached that base safely;

(d) He fails to re-touch his base after a fair or foul ball is legally caught before he, or his base, is tagged by a fielder. He shall not be called out for failure to re-touch his base after the first following pitch. This is an appeal play;

• (e) He fails to reach the next base before a fielder tags him or the base, after he has been forced to advance by reason of the batter becoming a runner. However, if a following runner is put out on a force play, the force is removed and the runner must be tagged to be put out. The force is removed as soon as the runner touches the base to which he is forced to advance, and if he overslides or overruns the base, the runner must be tagged to be put out.

(f) He is hit by a fair ball in fair territory before it has touched or passed an infielder. The ball is dead and no runner may score, nor runners advance, except runners forced to advance.

EXCEPTION: If a runner is touching his base when touched by an Infield Fly, he is not out, although the batter is out.

NOTE: If a runner is touched by an Infield Fly when he is not touching his base, both runner and batter are out.

(g) He attempts to score on a play in which the batter interferes with the play at home base with less than two out. With two out, the interference puts the batter out and no score counts;

(h) He passes a preceding runner before such runner is out;

(i) After he has acquired legal possession of a base, he runs the bases in reverse order for the purpose of confusing the defense or making a travesty of the game. The umpire shall immediately call "Time" and declare the runner out;

(j) He fails to return at once to first base after overrunning or oversliding that base. If he attempts to run to second he is out when tagged. If, after overrunning or oversliding first base he starts toward the dugout, or toward his position, and fails to return to first base at once, he is out, on appeal, when he or the base is tagged.

(k) In running or sliding for home base, he fails to touch home base and makes no attempt to return to the base, when a fielder holds the ball in his hand, while touching home base, and appeals to the umpire for the decision.

7.09 It is interference by a batter or a runner when—

(a) After a third strike he hinders the catcher in his attempt to field the ball;

(b) After hitting or bunting a fair ball, his bat hits the ball a second time in fair territory. The ball is dead and no runners may advance. If the batter-runner drops his bat and the ball rolls against the bat in fair territory and, in the umpire's judgment, there was no intention to interfere with the course of the ball, the ball is alive and in play;

(c) He intentionally deflects the course of a foul ball in any manner;

(d) Before two are out and a runner on third base, the batter hinders a fielder in making a play at home base; the runner is out;

(e) Any member or members of the offensive team stand or gather around any base to which a runner is advancing, to confuse, hinder or add to the difficulty of the fielders. Such runner shall be declared out for the interference of his teammate or teammates;

(f) Any batter or runner who has just been retired hinders or impedes any following play being made on a runner. Such runner shall be declared out for the interference of his teammate;

(g) In the judgment of the umpire, the coach at third base, or first base, by touching or holding the runner, physically assists him in returning to, or leaving, third base or first base. The runner, however, shall not be declared out if no play is being made on him;

(h) With a runner on third base, the coach leaves his box and acts in any manner to draw a throw by a fielder;

(i) In running the last half of the distance from home base to first base while the ball is being fielded to first base, he runs outside (to the right of) the three-foot line, or inside (to the left of) the foul line and, in the umpire's judgment, interferes with the fielder taking the throw at first base, or attempting to field a batted ball;

(j) He fails to avoid a fielder who is attempting to field a batted ball, or intentionally interferes with a thrown ball; provided, that if two or more fielders attempt to field a batted ball and the runner comes in contact with one or more of them, the umpire shall determine which fielder is entitled to the benefit of this rule, and shall not declare the runner out for coming in contact with a fielder other than the one the umpire determines to be entitled to field such a ball;

(k) A fair ball touches him before touching a fielder. If a fair ball goes through, or by, an infielder, and touches a runner immediately back of him, or touches the runner after having been deflected by a fielder, the umpire shall not declare the runner out for being touched by a batted ball. In making such decision the umpire must be convinced that the ball passed through, or by the infielder, and that no other infielder had the chance to make a play on the ball. If, in the judgment of the umpire, the runner deliberately and intentionally kicks such a batted ball on which the infielder has missed a play, then the runner shall be called out for interference.

PENALTY FOR INTERFERENCE: The runner is out and the ball is dead.

7.10 Any runner shall be called out, on appeal, when—

(a) After a fly ball is caught, he fails to re-touch his base before he or his base is tagged;

(b) With the ball in play, while advancing or returning to a base, he fails to touch each base in order before he, or a missed base, is tagged;

(c) He overruns or overslides first base and fails to return to the base immediately, and he or the base is tagged;

(d) He fails to touch home base and makes no attempt to return to that base, and home base is tagged.

Any appeal under this rule must be made before the next legal pitch. If the violation occurs during a play which ends a half-inning, the appeal must be made before the defensive team leaves the field.

NOTE: Appeal plays may require an umpire to recognize any apparent "fourth out." If the third out is made during a play in which an appeal play is sustained on another runner, the appeal play decision takes precedence in determining the out. If there is more than one appeal during a play that ends a half-inning, the defense may elect to take the out that gives it the advantage. If the third out on appeal is a force play or failure of the batter-runner to touch first base, no runs can score on the play. Otherwise runs made before the appeal is sustained shall count. For the purposes of this rule, the defensive team has "left the field" when the pitcher and all in-fielders have left fair territory on their way to the bench or clubhouse.

7.11 The players or coaches of an offensive team shall vacate any space needed by a fielder who is attempting to field a batted or thrown ball.

PENALTY—Interference shall be called and the batter or runner on whom the play is being made shall be declared out.

7.12 Unless two are out, the status of a following runner is not affected by a preceding runner's failure to touch a base. If, upon appeal, the preceding runner is the third out, no runners following him shall score. If such third out is the result of a force play, neither preceding nor following runners shall score.

8.00—The Pitcher.

8.01 Legal pitching delivery. There are two legal pitching positions, the "Windup" position, and the "Set" position, and either position may be used at any time.

(a) The "Windup Position." The pitcher shall stand facing the batter, his pivot foot on, or in front of and touching the pitcher's plate, and the other foot free. From this position any natural movement associated with his delivery of the ball to the batter commits him to the pitch without interruption or alteration. He shall not raise either foot from the ground, except that in his actual delivery of the ball to the batter, he may take one step backward, and one step forward with his free foot.

(b) The "Set Position." Set position shall be indicated by the pitcher when he stands facing the batter with his entire pivot foot on, or in front of, and in contact with, and not off the end of the pitcher's plate, and his other foot in front of the pitcher's plate, holding the ball in both hands in front of his body and coming to a complete stop of at least one second. From such set position he may deliver the ball to the batter, throw to a base or step backward off the pitcher's plate with his pivot foot. Before assuming set position the pitcher may elect to make any natural preliminary motion such as that known as "the stretch." But if he so elects, he shall come to set position before delivering the ball to the batter. After assuming set position, any natural motion associated with his delivery of the ball to the batter commits him to the pitch without alteration or interruption.

(c) At any time during the pitcher's preliminary movements and until his natural pitching motion commits him to the pitch, he may throw to any base provided he steps directly toward such base before making the throw.

(d) If the pitcher makes an illegal pitch with the bases unoccupied, it shall be called a ball, unless the batter reaches first base on a hit, an error, a base on balls, a hit batter, or otherwise.

(e) If the pitcher removes his pivot foot from contact with the pitcher's plate by stepping backward with that foot, he thereby becomes an infielder and, if he makes a wild throw from that position, it shall be considered the same as a wild throw by any other infielder.

8.02 The pitcher shall not—

(a) (1) Apply a foreign substance of any kind to the ball; (2) expectorate either on the ball or his glove; (3) rub the ball on his glove, person or clothing; (4) deface the ball in any manner; (5) deliver what is called the "shine" ball, "spit" ball, "mud" ball or "emery" ball. The pitcher, of course, is allowed to rub the ball between his bare hands.

PENALTY—For violation of any part of this rule the umpire shall immediately disqualify the pitcher, and the league president shall suspend the pitcher for a period of ten days. If a pitch is delivered in violation of this rule, it shall be treated as an illegal pitch.

(b) Intentionally delay the game by throwing the ball to players other than the catcher, when the batter is in position, except in an attempt to retire a runner.

PENALTY—If, after warning by the umpire, such delaying action is repeated, the pitcher shall be removed from the game.

(c) Pitch at a batter's head, and if, in the umpire's opinion, such violation occurs, he shall call "Time" and warn the pitcher and the Manager of the defensive team that another such pitch will mean the immediate explusion of the pitcher from the game. If such pitch is repeated the umpire shall inflict the penalty.

PENALTY—The pitcher shall be removed from the game and from the grounds. The league president shall impose such fine and suspension as his judgment warrants.

8.03 When a pitcher takes his position at the beginning of each inning, or when he relieves another pitcher, he shall be permitted to pitch not to exceed eight prepatory pitches to his catcher during which play shall be suspended. Such preparatory pitches shall not consume more than one minute of time. If a sudden emergency causes a pitcher to be summoned into the game without any opportunity to warm up, the umpire-in-chief shall allow him as many pitches as the umpire deems necessary for him to be properly prepared to pitch.

8.04 When the bases are unoccupied, the pitcher shall deliver the ball to the batter within 20 seconds after taking his pitching position. Each time the pitcher delays the game by violating this rule, the umpire shall call "Ball."

NOTE—The intent of this rule is to avoid unnecessary delays. The umpire shall insist that the catcher return the ball promptly to the pitcher, and that the pitcher take his position on the rubber promptly. Obvious delay by the pitcher should instantly be penalized by the umpire.

8.05 If there is a runner, or runners, it is a balk when—

(a) The pitcher, while touching his plate, makes any motion naturally associated with his pitch and fails to make such delivery;

(b) The pitcher, while touching his plate, feints a throw to first base and fails to complete the throw;

(c) The pitcher, while touching his plate, fails to step directly toward a base before throwing to that base;

(d) The pitcher, while touching his plate, throws, or feints a throw to an unoccupied base, except for the purpose of making a play;

(e) The pitcher makes an illegal pitch;

(f) The pitcher delivers the ball to the batter while he is not facing the batter;

(g) The pitcher makes any motion naturally associated with his pitch while he is not touching the pitcher's plate;

(h) The pitcher unnecessarily delays the game;

(i) The pitcher, without having the ball,

stands on or astride the pitcher's plate or while off the plate, he feints a pitch;

(j) The pitcher, after coming to set position, removes one hand from the ball other than in an actual pitch, or in throwing to a base;

(k) The pitcher, while touching his plate, accidentally or intentionally drops the ball;

(l) The pitcher, while giving an intentional base on balls, pitches when the catcher is not in the catcher's box;

(m) The pitcher delivers the pitch from "set position" without coming to a stop of one full second.

PENALTY—The ball is dead, and each runner shall advance one base without liability to be put out unless the batter reaches first base on a hit, an error or otherwise, and all other runners advance at least one base, in which case the play proceeds without reference to the balk.

APPROVED RULING: A runner who misses the first base to which he is advancing and who is called out on appeal shall be considered as having advanced one base for the purpose of this rule.

9.00—The Umpire.

9.01 (a) The league president shall appoint one or more umpires to officiate at each league championship game. The umpires shall be responsible for the conduct of the game in accordance with these official rules and for maintaining discipline and order on the playing field during the game.

(b) Each umpire is the representative of the league and of professional baseball, and is authorized and required to enforce all of these rules. Each umpire has authority to order a player, coach, manager or club officer or employee to do or refrain from doing anything which affects the administering of these rules, and to enforce the prescribed penalties.

(c) Each umpire has authority to rule on any point not specifically covered in these rules.

(d) Each umpire has authority to disqualify any player, coach, manager or substitute for objecting to decisions or for unsportsmanlike conduct or language, and to remove such disqualified persons from the playing field. If an umpire disqualifies a player while a play is in progress, the disqualification shall not take effect until no further action is possible in that play.

(e) Each umpire has authority at his discretion to remove from the playing field (1) any person whose duties permit his presence on the field, such as ground crew members, ushers, photographers, newsmen, broadcasting crew members, etc., and (2) any spectator or other person not authorized to be on the playing field.

9.02 (a) Any umpire's decision which involves judgment, such as, but not limited to, whether a batted ball is fair or foul, whether a pitch is a strike or a ball, or whether a runner is safe or out, is final. No player, manager, coach or substitute shall object to any such judgment decisions.

(b) If there is reasonable doubt that any umpire's decision may be in conflict with the rules, the manager or captain only may appeal the decision and ask that a correct ruling be made. Such appeal shall be made only to the umpire who made the protested decision.

(c) If a decision is appealed, the umpire making the decision may ask another umpire for information before making a final decision. No umpire shall criticize, seek to reverse or interfere with another umpire's decision unless asked to do so by the umpire making it.

(d) No umpire may be replaced during a game unless he is injured or becomes ill.

9.03 (a) If there is only one umpire, he shall have complete jurisdiction in administering the rules. He may take any position on the playing field which will enable him to discharge his duties (usually behind the catcher, but sometimes behind the pitcher if there are runners.)

(b) If there are two or more umpires, one shall be designated umpire-in-chief and the others field umpires.

9.04 (a) The umpire-in-chief shall stand behind the catcher. (He is usually called the plate umpire.) His duties shall be to:

(1) Take full charge of, and be responsible for, the proper conduct of the game;

(2) Call and count balls and strikes;

(3) Call and declare fair balls and fouls except those called by field umpires;

(4) Make all decisions on the batter;

(5) Make all decisions except those commonly reserved for the field umpires;

(6) Decide when a game shall be forfeited;

(7) If a time limit has been set, announce the fact and the time set before the game starts;

(8) Inform the official scorer of the official batting order, and any changes in the lineups and batting order, on request;

(9) Announce any special ground rules, at his discretion.

(b) A field umpire may take any position on the playing field he thinks best suited to make impending decisions on the bases. His duties shall be to:

(1) Make all decisions on the bases except those specifically reserved to the umpire-in-chief;

(2) Take concurrent jurisdiction with the umpire-in-chief in calling "Time," balks, illegal pitches, or defacement or discoloration of the ball by any player;

(3) Aid the umpire-in-chief in every manner in enforcing the rules, and excepting the power to forfeit the game, shall have equal authority with the umpire-in-chief in administering and enforcing the rules and maintaining discipline.

(c) If different decisions should be made on one play by different umpires, the umpire-in-chief shall call all the umpires into consultation, with no manager or player present. After consultation, the umpire-in-chief (unless another umpire may have been designated by the league president) shall determine which decision shall prevail, based on which umpire was in best position and which decision was most likely correct. Play shall proceed as if only the final decision had been made.

9.05 (a) The umpire shall report to the league president within twelve hours after the end of a game all violations of rules and other incidents worthy of comment, including the disqualification of any trainer, manager, coach or player, and the reasons therefor.

(b) When any trainer, manager, coach or player is disqualified for a flagrant offense such as the use of obscene or indecent language, or an assault upon an umpire, trainer, manager, coach or player, the umpire shall forward full particulars to the league president within four hours after the end of the game.

(c) After receiving the umpire's report that a trainer, manager, coach or player has been disqualified, the league president shall impose such penalty as he deems justified, and shall notify the person penalized and the manager of the club of which the penalized person is a member. If the penalty includes a fine, the penalized person shall pay the amount of the fine to the league within five days after receiving notice of the fine. Failure to pay such fine within five days shall result in the offender being debarred from participation in any game and from sitting on the players' bench during any game, until the fine is paid.

THE RULES OF SCORING

Scoring Rules Committee

Cy Kritzer, *Buffalo Evening News*, Chairman
Warren W. Brown, *Chicago American*
James T. Gallagher

INDEX

10.00—The Official Scorer.

10.01 (a) The league president shall appoint an official scorer for each league championship game. The official scorer shall observe the game from a position in the press box. The scorer shall have sole authority to make all decisions involving judgment, such as whether a batter's advance to first base is the result of a hit or an error. He shall communicate such decisions to the press box and broadcasting booths by hand signals or over the press box loudspeaker system, and shall advise the public address announcer of such decisions if requested.

After each game, including drawn, forfeited and called games, the scorer shall prepare a report, on a form prescribed by the league president, listing the date of the game, where it was played, the names of the competing clubs and the umpires, the full score of the game, and all records of individual players compiled according to the system specified in these Official Scoring Rules. He shall forward this report to the league office within thirty-six hours after the game ends. He shall forward the report of any suspended game within thirty-six hours after the game has been completed, or after it becomes an official game because it cannot be completed, as provided by the Official Playing Rules.

(b) (1) To achieve uniformity in keeping the records of championship games, the scorer shall conform strictly to the Official Scoring Rules.

(2) If the teams change sides before three men are put out, the scorer shall immediately inform the umpire of the mistake.

(3) If the game is protested or suspended, the scorer shall make note of the exact situation at the time of the protest or suspension, including the score, the number of outs, the position of any runners, and the ball and strike count on the batter.

NOTE: It is important that a suspended game resume with exactly the same situation as existed at the time of suspension. If a protested game is ordered replayed from point of protest, it must be resumed with exactly the situation that existed just before the protested play.

(4) The scorer shall not make any decision conflicting with the Official Playing Rules, or with an umpire's decision.

(5) The scorer shall not call the attention of the umpire or of any member of either

team to the fact that a player is batting out of turn.

(c) The scorer is an official representative of the league, and is entitled to the respect and dignity of his office, and shall be accorded full protection by the league president. The scorer shall report to the president any indignity expressed by any manager, player, club employee or club officer in the course of, or as the result of, the discharge of his duties.

10.02 The official score report prescribed by the league president shall make provision for entering the information listed below, in a form convenient for the compilation of permanent statistical records:

(a) The following batting records for each player in the game:

(1) Number of times he batted, except that no time at bat shall be charged against a player when

(i) He hits a sacrifice bunt or sacrifice fly

(ii) He is awarded first base on four called balls

(iii) He is hit by a pitched ball

(iv) He is awarded first base because of interference or obstruction.

(2) Number of runs scored

(3) Number of safe hits

(4) Number of runs batted in

(5) Two-base hits

(6) Three-base hits

(7) Home runs

(8) Total bases on safe hits

(9) Stolen bases

(10) Sacrifice bunts

(11) Sacrifice flies

(12) Total number of bases on balls

(13) Separate listing of any intentional bases on balls

(14) Number of times hit by a pitched ball

(15) Number of times awarded first base for interference or obstruction

(16) Strikeouts

(b) The following fielding records for each player in the game:

(1) Number of putouts

(2) Number of assists

(3) Number of errors

(4) Number of double plays participated in

(5) Number of triple plays participated in

(c) The following records for each pitcher in the game:

(1) Number of innings pitched. NOTE—In computing innings pitched, divide each inning into three parts. If a starting pitcher is replaced with one out in the sixth inning, credit that pitcher with 5 1/3 innings. If a starting pitcher is replaced with none out in the sixth inning, credit that pitcher with 5 innings, and make the notation that he faced — batters in the sixth. If a relief pitcher retires two batters and is replaced, credit that pitcher with 2/3 innings pitched.

(2) Total number of batters faced

(3) Number of batters officially at bat against pitcher computed according to 10.02 (a) (1)

(4) Number of hits allowed

(5) Number of runs allowed

(6) Number of earned runs allowed

(7) Number of home runs allowed

(8) Number of sacrifice hits allowed

(9) Number of sacrifice flies allowed

(10) Total number of bases on balls allowed

(11) Separate listing of any intentional bases on balls allowed

(12) Number of batters hit by pitched balls

(13) Number of strikeouts

(14) Number of wild pitches

(15) Number of balks

(d) The following additional data:

(1) Name of the winning pitcher

(2) Name of the losing pitcher

(3) Names of the starting pitcher and the finishing pitcher for each team.

(e) Number of passed balls allowed by each catcher.

(f) Names of players participating in double plays and triple plays. EXAMPLE—Double Plays - Jones, Roberts and Smith (2). Triple Play - Jones and Smith.

(g) Number of runners left on base by each team. This total shall include all runners who get on base by any means and who do not score and are not put out. Include in this total a batter-runner whose batted ball results in another runner being retired for the third out.

(h) Names of batters who hit home runs with bases full.

(i) Names of batters who ground into force double plays.

(j) Names of runners caught stealing.

(k) Number of outs when winning run scored, if game is won in last half-inning.

(l) The score by innings for each team.

(m) Names of umpires, listed in this order (1) plate umpire, (2) first base umpire, (3) second base umpire, (4) third base umpire.

(n) Time required to play the game, with delays for weather or light failure deducted.

10.03 (a) In compiling the official score report, the official scorer shall list each player's name and his fielding position or positions in the order in which the player batted, or would have batted if the game ends before he gets to bat.

(b) Any player who enters the game as a substitute batter or substitute runner, whether or not he continues in the game thereafter, shall be identified in the batting order by a special symbol which shall refer to a separate record of substitute batters and runners. Lower case letters are recommended as symbols for substitute batters, and numerals as symbols for substitute runners. The record of substitute batters shall describe what the substitute batter accomplished. EXAMPLES— "a-Singled for ----- in third inning; b-Flied out for ----- in sixth inning; c-Forced -----for ------in seventh inning; d-Grounded out for --------in ninth inning; e-Ran for ------ in ninth inning."

The record of substitute batters and runners shall include the name of any such substitute whose name is announced, but who is removed for a second substitute before he actually gets into the game. Such substitution shall be recorded as "e-Announced as substitute for-----in seventh inning." Any such second substitute shall be recorded as batting or running for the first announced substitute.

HOW TO PROVE A BOX SCORE

(c) A box score is in balance (or proved) when the total of the team's times at bat, bases on balls received, hit batters, sacrifice bunts, sacrifice flies and batters awarded first base because of interference or obstruction, equals the total of that team's runs, players left on base and the opposing team's putouts.

WHEN PLAYER BATS OUT OF TURN

(d) When a player bats out of turn, and is put out, and the proper batter is called out before the ball is pitched to the next batter, charge the proper batter with a time at bat and score the putout and any assists the same as if the correct batting order had been followed. If an improper batter becomes a runner and the proper batter is called out for having missed his turn at bat, charge the proper batter with a time at bat, credit the putout to the catcher, and ignore everything entering into the improper batter's safe arrival on base. If more than one batter bats out of turn in succession, score all plays just as they occur, skipping the turn at bat of the player or players who first missed batting in the proper order.

DRAWN, FORFEITED AND CALLED GAMES

(e) (1) All individual and team records of any drawn or forfeited game which has reached or exceeded legal length when ended shall become a part of the official averages except that no pitcher shall be credited with a victory or charged with a defeat. (2) When a game is terminated before nine innings have been played, include only those individual and team records which have contributed to the official final score.

RUNS BATTED IN

10.04 (a) Credit the batter with a run batted in for every run which reaches home base because of the batter's safe hit, sacrifice bunt, sacrifice fly, caught foul fly, infield out or fielder's choice; or which is forced over the plate by reason of the batter becoming a runner with the bases full (on a base on balls, or an award of first base for being touched by a pitched ball, or for interference or obstruction).

(1) Credit a run batted in for the run scored by the batter who hits a home run. Credit a run batted in for each runner who is on base when the home run is hit and who scores ahead of the batter who hits the home run.

(2) Credit a run batted in for the run scored when, before two are out, an error is made on a play on which a runner from third base ordinarily would score.

(b) Do not credit a run batted in when the batter grounds into a force double play, or grounds into a double play in which the first out is made at first base and the second out is made by tagging a runner who was originally forced, attempting to advance one base, unless such runner is put out after reaching the base to which he was forced to advance.

(c) Scorer's judgment must determine whether a run batted in shall be credited for a run which scores when a fielder holds the ball, or throws to a wrong base. Ordinarily, if the runner keeps going, credit a run batted in; if the runner stops and takes off again when he notices the misplay, credit the run as scored on a fielder's choice.

BASE HITS

10.05 A base hit shall be scored in the following cases:

(a) When a batter reaches first base (or any succeeding base) safely on a fair ball which settles on the ground or strikes a fence before being touched by a fielder, or which clears a fence;

(b) When a batter reaches first base safely on a fair ball hit with such force, or so slowly, that any fielder attempting to make a play with it has no opportunity to do so;

NOTE: A hit shall be scored if the fielder attempting to handle the ball cannot make a play, even if such fielder deflects the ball from or cuts off another fielder who could have retired a runner.

(c) When a batter reaches first base safely on a fair ball which takes an unnatural bounce so that a fielder cannot handle it with ordinary effort, or which strikes the pitcher's plate or any base (including home plate) before being touched by a fielder and bounces so that a fielder cannot handle it with ordinary effort;

(d) When a batter reaches first base safely on a fair ball which has not been touched by a fielder and which is in fair territory when it reaches the outfield unless in the scorer's judgment it could have been handled with ordinary effort;

(e) When a fair ball which has not been touched by a fielder becomes "dead" by reason of touching the person or clothing of a runner or umpire. EXCEPTION: Do not score a hit when a runner is called out for having been struck by an Infield Fly;

(f) When the fielder unsuccessfully attempts to retire a preceding runner, and in the scorer's judgment the batter-runner would not have been retired at first base by perfect fielding.

NOTE: In applying the above rules, always give the batter the benefit of the doubt. A safe course to follow is to score a hit when exceptionally good fielding of a ball fails to result in a putout.

10.06 A base hit shall not be scored in the following cases:

(a) When a runner is forced out by a batted ball, or would have been forced out except for a fielding error;

(b) When the batter apparently hits safely and a runner who is forced to advance by reason of the batter becoming a runner fails to touch the first base to which he is advancing and is called out on appeal. Charge the batter with a time at bat but no hit;

(c) When the pitcher, the catcher or any infielder handles a batted ball and retires a preceding runner who is attempting to advance one base or to return to his original base, or would have retired such runner with ordinary effort except for a fielding error. Charge the batter with a time at bat but no hit.

(d) When a fielder fails in an attempt to retire a preceding runner, and in the scorer's judgment the batter-runner could have been retired at first base.

NOTE: This shall not apply if the fielder merely looks toward or feints toward another base before attempting to make the putout at first base.

(e) When a runner is called out for interference with a fielder attempting to field a batted ball, unless in the scorer's judgment the batter-runner would have been safe had the interference not occurred.

DETERMINING VALUE OF BASE HITS

10.07 Whether a safe hit shall be scored as a one-base hit, two-base hit, or three-base hit when no error or putout results shall be determined as follows:

(a) Subject to the provisions of 10.07 (b) and (c), it is a one-base hit if the batter stops at first base; it is a two-base hit if the batter stops at second base; it is a three-base hit if the batter stops at third base; it is a home run if the batter touches all bases and scores.

(b) When, with one or more runners on base, the batter advances more than one base on a safe hit and the defensive team makes an attempt to retire a preceding runner, the scorer shall determine whether the batter made a legitimate two-base hit or three-base hit, or whether he advanced beyond first base on the fielder's choice.

NOTE: Do not credit the batter with a three-base hit when a preceding runner is put out at the plate, or would have been out but for an error. Do not credit the batter with a two-base hit when a preceding runner trying to advance from first base is put out at third base, or would have been out but for an error. However, do not determine the value of base-hits by the number of bases advanced by a preceding runner. A batter may deserve a two-base hit even though a preceding runner advances one or no bases; he may deserve only a one-base hit even though he reaches second base and a preceding runner advances two bases. EXAMPLES: (1) Runner on first, batter hits to right fielder, who throws to third base in unsuccessful attempt to retire runner. Batter takes second base. Credit batter with one-base hit. (2) Runner on second. Batter hits fair fly ball. Runner holds up to determine if ball is caught, and advances only to third base, while batter takes second. Credit batter with two-base hit. (3) Runner on third. Batter hits high fair fly. Runner takes lead, then runs back to tag up, thinking ball will be caught. Ball falls safe, but runner cannot score, although batter has reached second. Credit batter with two-base hit.

(c) When the batter attempts to make a two-base hit or a three-base hit by sliding, he must hold the last base to which he advances. If he overslides and is tagged out before getting back to the base safely, he shall be credited with only as many bases as he attained safely. If he overslides second base and is tagged out, he shall be credited with a one-base hit; if he overslides third base and is tagged out he shall be credited with a two-base hit.

NOTE: If the batter over-runs second or third base and is tagged out trying to return, he shall be credited with the last base he touched. If he runs past second base after reaching that base on his feet, attempts to return and is tagged out, he shall be credited with a two-base hit. If he runs past third base after reaching that base on his feet, attempts to return and is tagged out, he shall be credited with a three-base hit.

(d) When the batter, after making a safe hit, is called out for having failed to touch a base, the last base he reached safely shall determine if he shall be credited with a one-base hit, a two-base hit or a three-base hit. If he is called out after missing home base, he shall be credited with a three-base hit. If he is called out for missing third base, he shall be credited with a two-base hit. If he is called out for missing second base, he shall be credited with a one-base hit. If he is called out for missing first base, he shall be charged with a time at bat, but no hit.

(e) When the batter is awarded two bases, three bases or a home run under the provisions of Playing Rules 7.05, he shall be credited with a two-base hit, a three-base hit or a home run, as the case may be.

GAME-ENDING HITS

(f) Subject to the provisions of 10.07 (g), when the batter ends a game with a safe hit which drives in as many runs as are necessary to put his team in the lead, he shall be credited with only as many bases on his hit as are advanced by the runner who scores the winning run, and then only if the batter runs out his hit for as many bases as are advanced by the runner who scores the winning run, touching each base in proper order.

NOTE: Apply this rule even when the batter is theoretically entitled to more bases because of being awarded an "automatic" extra-base hit under various provisions of Playing Rules 6.09 and 7.05.

(g) When the batter ends a game with a home run hit out of the playing field and touches all bases in proper order, his run and also the runs of all other runners who were on base when the home run was hit shall count in the final score even though this gives the winning team a margin in excess of one run.

SACRIFICES

10.08 (a) Score a sacrifice bunt when, before two are out, the batter advances one or more runners with a bunt and is retired at first base, or would have been retired except for a fielding error;

(b) Score a sacrifice bunt when, before two are out, the fielders handle a bunted ball without error in an unsuccessful attempt to retire a preceding runner advancing one base. EXCEPTION: When an attempt to turn a bunt into a putout of a preceding runner fails, and in the scorer's judgment perfect play would not have retired the batter at first base, the batter shall be credited with a one-base hit and not a sacrifice.

(c) Do not score a sacrifice bunt when any runner is retired attempting to advance one base on a bunt. Charge the batter with a time at bat.

(d) Score a sacrifice fly when, before two are out, the batter hits a fair fly ball which

(1) is caught, and a runner scores after the catch, or

(2) is dropped, and a runner scores, if, in the scorer's judgment, the runner could have scored after the catch had the fly been caught.

NOTE: Score a sacrifice fly in accordance with 10.08 (d) (2) even though another runner is forced out by reason of the batter becoming a runner.

PUTOUTS

10.09 A putout shall be recorded each time a fielder (1) catches a fly ball or a line drive, whether fair of foul; (2) catches a thrown ball which retires a batter or runner, or (3) tags a runner with the ball when the runner is off the base to which he legally is entitled.

(a) Automatic putouts shall be credited to the catcher as follows:

(1) When the batter is called out for an illegally batted ball;

(2) When the batter is called out for bunting foul for his third strike; (Note exception in 10.17 (a) (4).

(3) When the batter is called out for being touched by his own batted ball;

(4) When the batter is called out for interfering with the catcher;

(5) When the batter is called out for failing to bat in his proper turn; (See 10.03 (d).)

(b) Other automatic putouts shall be credited as follows (credit no assists on these plays except as specified):

(1) When the batter is called out on an Infield Fly which is not caught, credit the putout to the fielder who the scorer believes could have made the catch;

(2) When a runner is called out for being touched by a fair ball (including an Infield Fly) credit the putout to the fielder nearest the ball;

(3) When a runner is called out for running out of line to avoid being tagged, credit the putout to the fielder whom the runner avoided;

(4) When a runner is called out for passing another runner, credit the putout to the fielder nearest the point of passing;

(5) When a runner is called out for running the bases in reverse order, credit the putout to the fielder covering the base he left in starting his reverse run;

(6) When a runner is called out for having interfered with a fielder, credit the putout to the fielder with whom the runner interfered, unless the fielder was in the act of throwing the ball when the interference occurred, in which case credit the putout to the fielder for whom the throw was intended, and credit an assist to the fielder whose throw was interfered with;

(7) When the batter-runner is called out because of interference by a preceding runner, as provided in Playing Rule 6.05 (m), credit the putout to the first baseman. If the fielder interfered with was in the act of throwing the ball, credit him with an assist, but credit only one assist on any one play under the provisions of 10.09 (b).(6) and (7).

ASSISTS

10.10 An assist shall be credited to each player who throws or deflects a batted or thrown ball in such a way that a putout results, or would have resulted except for a subsequent error by any fielder. Only one assist and no more shall be credited to each player who throws or deflects the ball in a run-down play which results in a putout, or would have resulted in a putout, except for a subsequent error.

NOTE: Mere ineffective contact with the ball shall not be considered an assist. "Deflect" shall mean to slow down or change the direction of the ball and thereby effectively assist in retiring a batter or runner.

(a) Credit an assist to each player who throws or deflects the ball during a play which results in a runner being called out for interference, or for running out of line.

(b) Do not credit an assist to the pitcher on a strikeout, or when, as the result of a legal pitch caught by the catcher, a runner is retired, as when the catcher picks a runner off base, throws out a runner trying to steal, or tags a runner trying to steal home.

(c) Do not credit an assist to a fielder whose wild throw permits a runner to advance, even though the runner subsequently is retired as a result of continuous play.

A play which follows a misplay (whether or not it is an error) is a new play, and the player making any misplay shall not be credited with an assist unless he takes part in the new play.

DOUBLE PLAYS—TRIPLE PLAYS

10.11 Credit participation in the double play or triple play to each fielder who earns a putout or an assist when two or three players are put out between the time a pitch is delivered and the time the ball next becomes dead or is next in possession of the pitcher in pitching position, unless an error intervenes between putouts.

ERRORS

10.12 An error shall be charged for each misplay (fumble, muff or wild throw) which prolongs the time at bat of a batter or which prolongs the life of a runner, or which permits a runner to advance one or more bases. NOTE: Slow handling of the ball which does not involve mechanical misplay shall not be construed as an error.

(a) An error shall be charged against any fielder when he muffs a foul fly, to prolong the time at bat of a batter, whether the batter subsequently reaches first base or is put out.

(b) An error shall be charged against any fielder when he catches a thrown ball or a ground ball in time to put out the batter-runner and fails to tag first base or the batter-runner.

(c) An error shall be charged against any fielder when he catches a thrown ball or a ground ball in time to put out any runner on a force play and fails to tag the base or the runner.

(d) (1) An error shall be charged against any fielder whose wild throw permits a runner to reach a base safely, when in the scorer's judgment a good throw would have put out the runner. EXCEPTION: No error shall be charged under this section if the wild throw is made attempting to prevent a stolen base.

(2) An error shall be charged against any fielder whose wild throw in attempting to prevent a runner's advance permits that runner or any other runner to advance one or more bases beyond the base he would have reached had the throw not been wild.

(3) An error shall be charged against any fielder whose throw takes an unnatural bounce, or touches a base or the pitcher's plate, or touches a runner, a fielder or an umpire, thereby permitting any runner to advance. NOTE: Apply this rule even when it appears to be an injustice to a fielder whose throw was accurately directed. Every base advanced by a runner must be accounted for.

(4) Charge only one error on any wild throw, regardless of the number of bases advanced by one or more runners.

(e) An error shall be charged against any fielder whose failure to stop, or try to stop, an accurately thrown ball permits a runner to advance, providing there was occasion for the throw. If such throw be made to second base, the scorer shall determine whether it was the duty of the second baseman or the shortstop to stop the ball, and an error shall be charged to the negligent player.

NOTE: If in the scorer's judgment there was no occasion for the throw, an error shall be charged to the fielder who threw the ball.

(f) When an umpire awards the batter or any runner or runners one or more bases because of interference or obstruction, charge the fielder who committed the interference or obstruction with one error, no matter how many bases the batter, or runner or runners, may be advanced.

10.13 No error shall be charged in the following cases:

(a) No error shall be charged against the catcher when he makes a wild throw in attempting to prevent a stolen base, unless such wild throw permits the base-stealer to advance one or more extra bases, or in the scorer's judgment permits another runner to advance one or more bases.

(b) No error shall be charged against any fielder who makes a wild throw if in the scorer's judgment the runner would not have been put out with ordinary effort by a good throw, unless such wild throw permits any runner to advance beyond the base he would have reached had the throw not been wild.

(c) No error shall be charged against any fielder when he makes a wild throw in attempting to complete a double play or triple play, unless such wild throw enables any runner to advance beyond the base he would have reached had the throw not been wild.

NOTE: When a fielder muffs a thrown ball which, if held, would have completed a double play or triple play, charge an error to the fielder who drops the ball.

(d) No error shall be charged against any fielder when, after dropping a fly ball, a line drive or thrown ball, he recovers the ball in time to force out a runner at any base.

(e) No error shall be charged against any fielder who permits a foul fly to fall safe with a runner on third base before two are out, if in the scorer's judgment the fielder deliberately refuses the catch in order that the runner on third shall not score after the catch.

(f) Because the pitcher and catcher handle the ball much more than the other fielders, certain misplays on pitched balls are called "wild pitches" and "passed balls," and are defined elsewhere in this rule. No error shall be charged when a wild pitch or passed ball is scored.

(1) No error shall be charged when the batter is awarded first base on four called balls or because he was touched by a pitched ball, or when he reaches first base as the result of a wild pitch or passed ball.

(i) When the third strike is a wild pitch, permitting the batter to reach first base, score a strikeout and a wild pitch;

(ii) When the third strike is a passed ball, permitting the batter to reach first base, score a strikeout and a passed ball.

(2) No error shall be charged when a runner or runners advance as the result of a passed ball, a wild pitch or a balk.

(i) When the fourth called ball is a wild pitch or a passed ball, and as a result (a) the batter-runner advances to a base beyond first base; (b) any runner forced to advance by the base on balls, advances more than one base, or (c) any runner, not forced to advance, advances one or more bases, score the base on balls, and also the wild pitch or passed ball, as the case may be.

(ii) When the catcher recovers the ball after a wild pitch or passed ball on the third strike, and throws out the batter-runner at first base, or tags out the batter-runner, but another runner or runners advance, score the strikeout, the putout and assists, if any, and credit the advance of the other runner or runners as having been made on the play.

STOLEN BASES

10.14 A stolen base shall be credited to a runner whenever he advances one base unaided by a hit, a putout, an error, a force-out, a fielder's choice, a passed ball, a wild pitch or a balk, subject to the following:

(a) When a runner has started for a succeeding base before the pitcher delivers the ball and the pitch results in a wild pitch or a passed ball, credit the runner with a stolen base. EXCEPTION: If another runner also advances because of the pitch becoming a wild pitch or passed ball, the wild pitch or passed ball also shall be scored.

(b) When a runner is attempting to steal and any fielder makes a wild throw attempting to prevent the stolen base, credit a stolen base and no error, unless such wild throw permits the "stealing" runner to advance an extra base or bases, or permits any other runner to advance one or more bases, in which case credit the stolen base and charge one error to the player making the wild throw.

(c) When a runner, attempting to steal, evades being put out in a run-down play and advances to the next base without the aid of an error, credit the runner with a stolen base. If another runner also advances on the play, credit both runners with stolen bases. If a runner advances while another runner, attempting to steal, evades being put out in a run-down play and returns safely, without the aid of an error, to the base he originally occupied, credit a stolen base to the runner who advances.

(d) When a double or triple steal is attempted and one runner is thrown out before reaching and holding the base he is attempting to steal, no other runner shall be credited with a stolen base.

(e) When a runner is tagged out after oversliding a base, either while attempting to return to that base or to advance to the next base, he shall not be credited with a stolen base.

(f) When, in the scorer's judgment, a palpable muff of a thrown ball prevents a runner who is attempting to steal from being retired, it shall be scored as an error for the player muffing the throw, an assist for the player throwing the ball, and not a stolen base.

(g) No stolen base shall be scored when a runner advances solely because of the defensive team's indifference to his advance.

WILD PITCHES—PASSED BALLS

10. 15 (a) A wild pitch shall be scored when a legally delivered ball is so high, or so wide, or so low that the catcher does not stop and control the ball by ordinary effort, thereby permitting a runner or runners to advance.

(1) A wild pitch shall be scored when a legally delivered ball strikes the ground before reaching home plate and is not handled by the catcher, permitting a runner or runners to advance.

(b) A catcher shall be charged with a passed ball when he fails to hold or to control a legally pitched ball which should have been held or controlled with ordinary effort, thereby permitting a runner or runners to advance.

BASES ON BALLS

10.16 A base on balls shall be scored whenever a batter is awarded first base because of four balls having been pitched outside the the strike zone, but when the fourth such ball touches the batter it shall be scored as a "hit batter." (See 10.18 (h) for procedure when more than one pitcher is involved in giving a base on balls.)

(1) If a batter awarded a base on balls is called out for refusing to advance to first base, do not credit the base on balls. Charge a time at bat.

STRIKEOUTS

10.17 (a) A strikeout shall be scored whenever

(1) a batter is put out by a third strike caught by the catcher;

(2) A batter is put out by a third strike not caught when there is a runner on first before two are out;

(3) A batter becomes a runner because a third strike is not caught;

(4) A batter bunts foul on third strike. EXCEPTION: If such bunt on third strike results in a foul fly caught by any infielder, do not score a strikeout. Credit the fielder who catches such foul fly with a putout.

(b) When the batter leaves the game with two strikes against him, and the substitute batter completes a strikeout, charge the strikeout and the time at bat to the first batter. If the substitute batter completes the turn at bat in any other manner, score the action as having been that of the substitute batter.

EARNED RUNS

10.18 An earned run is a run for which the pitching is held accountable.

(a) An earned run shall be scored every time a runner reaches home base by the aid of safe hits, sacrifice bunts, a sacrifice fly, stolen bases, putouts, fielder's choices, bases on balls, hit batters, balks or wild pitches (including a wild pitch on third strike, which permits a batter to reach first base) before fielding chances have been offered to retire the offensive team.

(1) A wild pitch is solely the pitcher's fault, and contributes to an earned run just as a base on balls or a balk.

(b) No run shall be earned when scored by a runner who reaches first base (1) on a hit or otherwise after his time at bat is prolonged by a muffed foul fly; (2) because of interference or obstruction, or (3) because of any fielding error.

(c) No run shall be earned when scored by a runner whose life is prolonged by an error, if such runner would have been put out by errorless play.

(d) No run shall be earned when the runner's advance is aided by an error, a passed ball, or defensive interference or obstruction, if the scorer judges that the run would not have scored without the aid of such misplay.

(e) An error by a pitcher is treated exactly the same as an error by any other fielder in computing earned runs.

(f) Whenever a fielding error occurs, the pitching shall be given the benefit of the doubt in determining to which bases any runners would have advanced had the fielding of the defensive team been errorless.

(g) When pitchers are changed during an inning, the relief pitcher shall not be charged with any run (earned or unearned) scored by a runner who was on base at the time he entered the game, nor for runs scored by any runner who reaches base on a fielder's choice which retires a runner left on base by the preceding pitcher. NOTE: It is the intent of this rule to charge each pitcher with the number of runners he put on base, rather than with the individual runners. When a pitcher puts runners on base, and is relieved, he shall be charged with all runs subsequently scored up to and including the number of runners he left on base when he left the game, unless such runners are retired without action by the batter, i.e., caught stealing, picked off base, or called out for interference when a batter-runner does not reach first base on the play.

EXAMPLES: (1) P1 walks A and is relieved by P2. B grounds out, sending A to second. C flies out. D singles, scoring A. Charge run to P1. (2) P1 walks A and is relieved by P2. B forces A at second. C grounds out, sending B to second. D singles, scoring B. Charge run to P1. (3) P1 walks A and is relieved by P2. B singles, sending A to third. C grounds to short, and A is out at home, B going to second. D flies out. E singles, scoring B. Charge run to P1. (4) P1 walks A and is relieved by P2. B walks. C flies out. A is picked off second. D doubles, scoring B from first. Charge run to P2. (5) P1 walks A and is relieved by P2. P2 walks B and is relieved by P3. C forces A at third. D forces B at third. E hits home run, scoring three runs. Charge one run to P1; one run to P2, one run to P3. (6) P1 walks A, and is relieved by P2. P2 walks B. C singles, filling the bases. D forces A at home. E singles, scoring B and C. Charge one run to P1 and one run to P2.

(h) A relief pitcher shall not be held accountable when the first batter to whom he pitches reaches first base on four called balls if such batter has a decided advantage in the ball and strike count when pitchers are changed.

(1) If, when pitchers are changed, the count is

2 balls, no strike,
2 balls, 1 strike
3 balls, no strike,
3 balls, 1 strike,
3 balls, 2 strikes,

and the batter gets a base on balls, charge

that batter and the base on balls to the preceding pitcher, not to the relief pitcher.

(2) Any other action by such batter, such as reaching base on a hit, an error, a fielder's choice, a forceout, or being hit by a pitched ball, shall cause such batter to be charged to the relief pitcher. NOTE: The provisions of 10.18 (h)(2) shall not be construed as affecting or conflicting with the provisions of 10.18 (g).

(3) If, when pitchers are changed, the count is
2 balls, 2 strikes,
1 ball, 2 strikes,
1 ball, 1 strike,
1 ball, no strike,
no ball, 2 strikes,
no ball, 1 strike,
charge that batter and his action to the relief pitcher.

WINNING AND LOSING PITCHER

10.19 Determining the winning and losing pitcher of a game in which a team uses more than one pitcher often calls for careful consideration. Scorers shall be guided by these rules:

(a) Credit the starting pitcher with a game won only if he has pitched at least five complete innings and his team not only is in the lead when he is replaced but remains in the lead the remainder of the game.

(b) The "must pitch five complete innings" rule in respect to the starting pitcher shall be in effect for all games of six or more innings. In a five-inning game, credit the starting pitcher with a game won only if he has pitched at least four complete innings and his team not only is in the lead when he is replaced but remains in the lead the remainder of the game.

(c) When the starting pitcher cannot be credited with the victory because of the provisions of 10.19 (a) or (b) and more than one relief pitcher is used, the victory shall be awarded on the following basis:

(1) When, during the tenure of the starting pitcher, the winning team assumes the lead and maintains it to the finish of the game, credit the victory to the relief pitcher judged by the scorer to have been the most effective;

(2) Whenever the score is tied the game becomes a new contest insofar as the winning and losing pitchers are concerned;

(3) Once the opposing team assumes the lead all pitchers who have pitched up to that point are excluded from being credited with the victory except that if the pitcher against whose pitching the opposing team gained the lead continues to pitch until his team regains the lead, which it holds to the finish of the game, that pitcher would be the winning pitcher;

(4) Normally, the winning relief pitcher shall be the one who is the pitcher of record when his team assumes the lead and maintains it to the finish of the game.

EXCEPTION: Do not credit a victory to a relief pitcher who pitches briefly and ineffectively if a succeeding relief pitcher pitches effectively in helping to maintain his team in the lead. In such case, credit the succeeding relief pitcher with the victory.

(d) When a pitcher is removed for a substitute batter or substitute runner, all runs scored by his team during the inning in which he is removed shall be credited to his benefit in determining the pitcher of record when his team assumes the lead.

(e) Regardless of how many innings the first pitcher has pitched, he shall be charged with the loss of the game if he is replaced when his team is behind in the score, and his team thereafter fails either to tie the score or gain the lead.

(f) No pitcher shall be credited with pitching a shutout unless he pitches the complete game, or unless he enters the game with none out in the first inning, retires the side without a run scoring and pitches all the rest of the game. When two or more pitchers combine to pitch a shutout a notation to that effect should be included in the league's official pitching records.

(g) In some non-championship games (such as the Major League All-Star game) it is provided in advance that each pitcher shall work a stated number of innings, usually two or three. In such games, it is customary to credit the victory to the pitcher of record, whether starter or reliever, when the winning team takes a lead which it maintains to the end of the game, unless such pitcher is knocked out after the winning team has a commanding lead, and the scorer believes a subsequent pitcher is entitled to credit for the victory.

STATISTICS

10.20 The league president shall appoint an official statistician. The statistician shall maintain an accumulative record of all the batting, fielding, running and pitching records specified in 10.02 for every player who appears in a league championship game.

The statistician shall prepare a tabulated report at the end of the season, including all individual and team records for every championship game and shall submit this report to the league president. This report shall identify each player by his first name and surname, and shall indicate as to each batter whether he bats righthanded, lefthanded or both ways; as to each fielder and pitcher, whether he throws righthanded or lefthanded.

DETERMINING PERCENTAGE RECORDS

10.21 To compute

(a) Percentage of games won and lost, divide the number of games won by the total games won and lost;

(b) Batting average, divide the total number of safe hits (not the total bases on hits) by the total times at bat, as defined in 10.02 (a);

(c) Slugging percentage, divide the total bases of all safe hits by the total times at bat, as defined in 10.12 (a);

(d) Fielding average, divide the total putouts and assists by the total of putouts, assists and errors;

(e) Pitcher's earned-run average, multiply the total earned runs charged against his pitching by 9, and divide the result by the total number of innings he pitched.

10.22 To achieve uniformity in establishing the batting, pitching and fielding championships of professional leagues, such champions shall meet the following minimum performance standards:

(a) The individual batting champion shall be the player with the highest batting average, provided he is credited with as many or more total appearances at the plate in league championship games as the number of games scheduled for each club in his league that season, multiplied by 3.1. EXAMPLE: The major leagues schedule 154 games for each club. 154 times 3.1 equals 477. Some minor leagues schedule 140 games. 140 times 3.1 equals 434.

Total appearances at the plate shall include official times at bat, plus bases on balls, times hit by pitcher, sacrifice hits, sacrifice flies, and times awarded first base because of interference or obstruction.

(b) The individual pitching champion shall be the pitcher with the lowest earned-run average, providing that he has pitched at least as many innings as the number of games scheduled for each club in his league that season. EXAMPLE: 154 innings in a major league.

(c) The individual fielding champions shall be the fielders with the highest fielding average at each position, provided:

(1) A catcher must have participated as a catcher in at least one-half the number of games scheduled for each club in his league that season;

(2) An infielder or outfielder must have participated at his position in at least two-thirds of the number of games scheduled for each club in his league that season;

(3) A pitcher must have pitched at least as many innings as the number of games scheduled for each club in his league that season.

NOTES—CASE BOOK—COMMENT

The following notes, interpretations and approved rulings are a part of the Official Rules.

1.06 Clean, newly painted or whitewashed bases should be put in place after preliminary practice and just before the start of each game. If this be impossible, the base bags used in practice should be painted or whitewashed on the field before the game starts.

1.10 The bat must not be loaded with metal fillings. It is illegal.

(The following unnumbered official notes apply to paragraphs identified by definitions in Rule 2.00.)

BALL. If the pitch strikes the ground and bounces through the strike zone it is a "ball." If such a pitch hits the batter, he shall be awarded first base. If the batter swings at such a pitch after two strikes, the ball cannot be caught, for the purpose of Rules 6.05 (c) and 6.08 (b). If the batter hits such a pitch, the ensuing action shall be the same as if he hit the ball in flight.

FAIR BALL. If a fly ball lands in the infield between home and first base, or home and third base, and then bounces to foul territory without touching a player or umpire and before passing first or third base, it is a foul ball; or if the ball settles on foul territory or is touched by a player on foul territory, it is a foul ball. If any fielder fields such a foul ball in foul territory and throws the ball to first base, the batter is not out. If a fly ball lands on or beyond first or third base and then bounces to foul territory, it is a fair hit.

Clubs, increasingly, are erecting tall foul poles at the fence line with a wire netting extending along the side of the pole on fair territory above the fence to enable the umpires more accurately to judge fair and foul balls. The custom should become universal.

FORCE PLAY. Confusion regarding this play is removed by remembering that frequently the "force" situation is removed during the play. Example: Man on first, one out, ball hit sharply to first baseman who touches the bag and batter-runner is out. The force is removed at that moment and runner advancing to second must be tagged. If there had been a runner on third or second, and either of these runners scored before the tag-out at second, the run counts. Had the first baseman thrown to second and the ball then had been returned to first, the play at second was a force out, making two outs, and the return throw to first ahead of the runner would have made three outs. In that case, no run would score.

Example: NOT A FORCE OUT. One out. Runners on first and third. Batter flies out. Two out. Runner on third tags up and scores. Runner on first tries to retouch before throw from fielder reaches first baseman, but does not get back in time and is out. Three outs. If, in umpire's judgment, the runner from third touched home base before the ball was held at first base, the run counts.

FOUL BALL. Approved Ruling: The exact position of the ball determines whether it is foul or fair, not the position of the fielder's body when he touches the ball.

Approved Ruling: Without touching a fielder a batted ball hits pitcher's rubber and rebounds over catcher's head, or to foul territory between home and first, or between home and third base. This is a foul.

PITCH. Distinguish clearly the difference between a pitch and a thrown ball. A pitch is exclusively the delivery of the ball to the batter. All other deliveries of the ball by one player to another are thrown balls.

STRIKE ZONE. A batter has the right to expect that the area he is protecting shall be the same from day to day. Necessity for split-second decision by the batter makes it imperative that umpires practice diligently to attain a sameness in their estimation of the strike zone.

A crouch, assumed to confuse the pitcher, or to lower and narrow the natural-stance space for the reception of the pitch, shall be disregarded by the umpire. However, a batter's natural batting stance may be an exaggerated crouch.

3.01 (e) (3) After dead ball and when all play has ceased, the umpire shall deliver the alternate ball to the pitcher. Play shall not be resumed with an alternate ball after a fair batted ball or a ball thrown by a fielder goes out of the grounds or into a stand for spectators until the runners have reached the bases to which they are entitled.

3.04 This rule is intended to eliminate the practice of using so-called courtesy runners. No player in the game shall be permitted to act as a courtesy runner for a teammate. No player who has been in the game and has been taken out for a substitute shall return as a courtesy runner. Any player not in the lineup, if used as a runner, shall be considered as a substitute player.

3.06 Players for whom substitutions have been made may remain with their team on the bench or may "warm-up" pitchers. If a manager substitutes another player for himself, he may continue to direct his team from the bench or the coach's box. Major league umpires do not permit players for whom substitutions have been made, and who are permitted to remain on the bench, to address any remarks to any opposing player or manager, or to the umpires.

3.18 "Reasonable length of time" as used in this code always means that the umpire-in-chief shall be the sole judge of what is a reasonable length of time after the expiration of 15 minutes.

Forfeitures should always be the last resort of the umpire-in-chief after consultation with his colleagues. Every other resource should be exhausted before forfeiture. Patrons pay to see a game. They should not be disappointed.

4.07 When manager, player or other team member is removed from the game, he shall not sit in the stands adjacent to his team's bench.

4.09 Baseball is so genuinely a team game that an error of omission, as well as an error of commission, can, and frequently does, nullify the brilliant individual play of a teammate.

Approved Ruling: No run shall be scored on a play in which the third out is made on the batter before he reaches first base, safely.

Example: One out, Jones on second, Smith on first and the batter, Brown, hits safely. Jones easily crosses the plate. Smith, on the throw to the plate, is out. Two outs. But Brown missed first base (and, therefore, did not "reach first base safely"). The ball is thrown to first, an appeal is made and Brown is out. Three outs. But, since Jones crossed the plate "on a play in which the third out was made on the batter before he reached first base safely," Jones' score does not count.

Approved Ruling: Succeeding runners are not affected by an act of a preceding runner unless two are out.

Example: One out, Jones on second, Smith on first, and batter, Brown, hits home run inside the park. Jones fails to touch third on his way to the plate. Smith and Brown score. The defense holds the ball on third, appeals to umpire, and Jones is out. Smith's and Brown's runs count.

Approved Ruling: Two out, Jones on second, Smith on first and batter, Brown, hits home run inside the park. All three runs cross the plate. But Jones missed third base, and on appeal is declared out. Three outs. Smith's and Brown's runs are voided. No score on the play.

Approved Ruling: One out, Jones on third, Smith on second. Batter Brown flies out to center field. Two outs. Jones scores after catch and Smith scores on bad throw to plate. But Jones, on appeal, is adjudged to have left third before the catch and is out. Three outs. No runs.

Approved Ruling: Two out, bases full, batter hits home run over the fence. Batter, on appeal, is declared out for missing first base. Three outs. No run counts.

Here is a general statement that covers:

When a runner misses a base and a fielder holds the ball on a missed base, or on the base originally occupied by the runner, and appeals for the umpire's decision, the runner is out when the umpire sustains the appeal; all runners may score if possible, except that with two out the runner is out at the moment he misses the bag, if an appeal is made, as applied to succeeding runners.

Approved Ruling: One out, Jones on third, Smith on first, and Brown flies out to right field. Two outs. Jones tags up and after the catch, scores. Smith attempted to return to first but the right fielder's throw beat him to the base. Three outs. But, Jones had scored before the throw to catch Smith reached first base, hence Jones' run counts. It was not a force play.

5.06 A run legally scored cannot be nullified by subsequent action of the runner, such as but not limited to an effort to return to third base in the belief that he had left that base before a caught fly ball.

5.09 (g) If a batted ball hits an umpire working in the infield after it has bounded past, or over, the pitcher, it is a dead ball.

5.10 (a) The umpire-in-chief shall, at all times, try to complete a game. His authority to resume play following one or more suspensions of as much as thirty minutes each shall be absolute and he shall terminate a game only when there appears to be no possibility of completing it.

6.02 The batter leaves the batter's box at the risk of having a strike delivered and called, unless he requests the umpire to call "Time." The batter is not at liberty to step in and out of the batter's box at will.

6.05 (a) See Rule 2.00-CATCH. Catch is legal if ball is finally held by any fielder, even though juggled, or held by another fielder, before it touches the ground. Runners may leave their bases the instant the first fielder touches the ball. A fielder may reach over a fence, railing, rope or other line of demarcation to make a catch. He may jump on top of a railing, or canvas that may be on foul ground. No interference should be allowed when a fielder reaches over a fence, railing, rope or into a stand to catch a ball. He does so at his own risk.

6.05 (b) "Legally caught" means in the catcher's glove, before the ball touches the ground. It is not legal if the ball lodges in his clothing or paraphernalia; or if it strikes the umpire and is caught by the catcher on the rebound. If, on the third strike (not a foul tip) the ball passes the catcher and lodges in the umpire's mask or other paraphernalia the ball is dead, but the batter shall be entitled to first base and other runners shall advance one base.

6.05 (m) The objective of this rule is to penalize the offensive team for deliberate, unwarranted, unsportsmanlike action by the runner in leaving the baseline for the obvious purpose of crashing the pivot man on a double play, rather than trying to reach his base. Obviously this is an umpire's judgment play.

6.07 The umpire shall not direct the attention of any person to the presence in the batter's box of an improper batter. This rule is designed to require constant vigilance by the players and managers of both teams.

7.04 (c) The catcher, without the ball in his possession, has no right to block the pathway of the runner attempting to score. The base line belongs to the runner and the catcher should be there only when he is fielding a ball or when he already has the ball in his hand.

7.05 (b-c-d-e) The thrown glove or detached cap or mask, etc., must touch the ball. There is no penalty if the ball is not touched.

7.05 (c-e) This penalty shall not be invoked against a fielder whose glove is carried off his hand by the force of a batted or thrown ball, or when his glove flies off his hand as he makes an obvious effort to make a legitimate catch.

7.05 (g) In certain circumstances it is impossible to award a runner two bases. Example: Runner on first. Batter hits fly to short right. Runner holds up between first and second and batter comes around first and pulls up behind him. Ball falls safely. Outfielder, in throwing to first, throws ball into stand.

Approved Ruling: Since no runner, when the ball is dead, may advance beyond the base to which he is entitled, the runner originally on first goes to third base and the batter is held at second base.

7.06 (a) Running is as much a part of baseball as hitting, fielding and throwing. All runners must be protected in their right to go as far as the action of the play, their speed and their daring dictates. It is not only unsportsmanlike to deny them this right, but it is highly dangerous to the runners to be subjected to intentional obstruction.

7.08 (b) A runner who is adjudged to have hindered a fielder who is attempting to make a play on a batted ball is out whether it was intentional or not.

7.08 (d) Runners need not "tag up" on a foul tip. They may steal on a foul tip. If a so called foul tip is not caught, it becomes an ordinary foul. Runners then return to their bases.

7.08 (e) and (j) Oversliding or overrunning situations arise at bases other than first base. For instance, with one or none out and runners on first and second, or first, second and third, the ball is hit to an infielder who tries for the double play. The runner on first beats the throw to second base but overslides the base. The relay is made to first base and the batter-runner is out. The first baseman, seeing the runner at second base off the bag, makes the return throw to second and the runner is tagged off the base. Meanwhile runners have crossed the plate. The question is: Is this a force play? Was the force removed when the batter-runner was out at first base? Do the runs that crossed the plate during this play and before the third out was made when the runner was tagged at second, count? Answer: The runs score. It is not a force play. It is a tag play.

7.08 (f) If two runners are hit by the same fair ball, only the first one is out because the ball is instantly dead.

7.09 (e) and (j) If the batter or a runner continues to advance after he has been retired, he shall not by that act alone be considered as confusing, hindering or impeding the fielders.

7.10 (a) "Retouch," in this rule, means to tag up and start from a contact with the base after the ball is caught. A runner is not permitted to take a flying start from a position in back of his base.

8.01 (b) The pitcher in "set position" shall face the batter with the foot other than his pivot foot in front of a line which is an extension of the front edge of the pitcher's plate.

8.01 (c) The pitcher shall step "ahead of the throw." A snap throw followed by the step directly toward the base is a balk.

8.01 (e) The pitcher, while off the rubber, may throw to any base. If he makes a wild throw, such throw is the throw of an infielder and what follows is governed by the rules covering a ball thrown by a fielder.

8.02 (a) All umpires shall carry with them one official rosin bag. The umpire-in-chief is responsible for placing the rosin bag on the ground back of the pitcher's plate. If at any time the ball hits the rosin bag it is in play. In the case of rain or wet field, the umpire may instruct the pitcher to carry the rosin bag in his hip pocket. A pitcher may use the rosin bag for the purpose of applying rosin to his bare hand or hands. Neither the pitcher nor any other player shall dust the ball with the rosin bag; neither shall the pitcher, nor any other player, be permitted to apply rosin from the bag to his glove, or dust any part of his uniform with the rosin bag.

8.02 (b) Pitchers, particularly non-professionals, most frequently delay the game by taking their catcher's signs from positions off the pitcher's rubber. This is a bad habit and should be corrected by managers and coaches.

8.02 (c) To pitch at a batter's head is unsportsmanlike and highly dangerous. It should be—and is—condemned by everybody. Umpires should act without hesitation in enforcement of this rule.

GENERAL INSTRUCTIONS TO UMPIRES

9.00 Umpires, on the field, should not indulge in conversation with players. Keep out of the coaching box and do not talk to the coach on duty.

Keep your uniform in good condition. Be active and alert on the field.

Be courteous, always, to club officials; avoid visiting in club offices and thoughtless familiarity with attaches of contesting clubs. When you enter a ball park your sole duty is to umpire a ball game as the representative of baseball.

Do not allow criticism to keep you from studying out bad situations that may lead to protested games. Carry your Rule Book. It is better to consult the Rules and hold up the game ten minutes to decide a knotty problem than to have a game thrown out on protest and replayed.

Keep the game moving. A ball game is often helped by energetic and earnest work of the umpires.

You are the only official representative of baseball on the ball field. It is often a trying position which requires the exercise of much patience and good judgment, but do not forget that the first essential in working out a bad situation is to keep your own temper and self-control.

You no doubt are going to make mistakes, but never attempt to "even up" after having made one. Make all decisions as you see them and forget which is the home or visiting club.

Keep your eye everlastingly on the ball while it is in play. It is more vital to know just where a fly ball fell, or a thrown ball finished up, than whether or not a runner missed a base. Do not call the plays too quickly, or turn away too fast when a fielder is throwing to complete a double play. Watch out for dropped balls after you have called a man out.

Do not come running with your arm up or down, denoting "out" or "safe." Wait until the play is completed before making any arm motion.

Each umpire team should work out a simple set of signals, so the proper umpire can always right a manifestly wrong decision when convinced he has made an error. If sure you got the play correctly, do not be stampeded by players' appeals to "ask the other man." If not sure, ask one of your associates. Do not carry this to extremes, be alert and get your own plays. But remember! The first requisite is to get decisions correctly. If in doubt, don't hesitate to consult your associate. Umpire dignity is important but never as important as "being right."

A most important rule for umpires is always "BE IN POSITION TO SEE EVERY PLAY." Even though your decision may be 100% right, players still question it if they feel you were not in a spot to see the play clearly and definitely.

Finally, be courteous, impartial and firm, and so compel respect from all.

9.02 (a) There shall be no appeal from the decision of the umpire-in-chief on a half swing. His decision must and will be final, it being entirely a question of the umpire's judgment as to whether the batter struck at the pitch.

INDEX TO PLAYING RULES

(Note: Where Rule 2.00 is indexed, the definition of the indexed item includes important explanatory matter.)

Regulation Game—4.10, 4.11.
(7-inning Game 4.10 (a)—Note.)
Resuming Play after Dead Ball—5.11.
Restrictions on Players—
No Fraternizing 3.09; Barred from Stands 3.09; Confined to Bench 3.15.
Runner—
Entitled to Base 7.01, 7.03; Touch Requirements 7.02, 7.08 (d), 7.10; Runners Advance 7.04, 7.05, 7.06; Reverse Run Prohibited 7.08 (i); Runner Out 7.08, 7.09 (e-j), 7.10, 7.11.

Scoring Rules—Rule 10.00.
Scoring Runs—4.09, 6.05 (n), 7.07, 7.12.
Spectators—
Barred from Field 3.15; Touching Fair Ball 6.05 (o), 7.05 (f); Touching Pitched Ball 7.05 (h); Touching Thrown Ball 3.16.
Strike—2.00, 6.08 (b).
Substitutions—3.04, 3.05, 3.06, 3.07, 3.08, 4.04.
Suspended Games—4.12.

Time Limits—9.04 (a) (7).

Umpire—Rule 9.00.
Inspects Equipment and Playing Lines 3.01; Judge of Playing Conditions 3.12 (c-d), 5.10 (a); Controls Ground Crew 3.13; Controls Lights 4.14; Controls Newsmen and Photographers 9.01 (e); Time Limits 9.04 (a) (7); Umpire's Interference 5.09 (b), 5.09 (g), 6.08 (d); Touched by Pitch or Thrown Ball 5.08.
Unsportsmanlike Conduct—4.06 (b).

Wild Throws—5.08, 7.05 (g-h).

GLOSSARY OF SLANG TERMS

AFTERPIECE: Second game of a doubleheader.

ANNIE OAKLEY: Pass to game. Also, base on balls.

APPLE: Ball. Also called Pill, Horsehide, Onion, Sphere, etc.

AUTOMATIC STRIKE: Pitch following three-balls, no strikes count on batter.

BALTIMORE CHOP: Topped ball which bounces near plate and goes very high into the air.

BARNSTORM: Play post-season exhibition games.

BASES LOADED: Runners on first, second and third bases.

BEAN BALL: Pitch thrown at batter's head.

BENCH WARMER: Player who rarely gets into a game.

BLEEDER: Lucky hit via bad bounce or erratic roller. Also called Scratch hit.

BLOOPER: Weak fly which barely soars beyond the infielders. Also called Banjo Hit.

BLOW UP: Lose effectiveness suddenly.

BOOT: Miss a ground ball. Also called Bobble, Kick, etc.

BREAK ONE OFF: Throw a curve ball.

BULLPEN: Area where substitute pitchers warm up.

BUSHES: Minor leagues. Also called Sticks.

CHANGE UP: Slow pitch thrown with same motion as fast one. Also called Pulling the String, Let-Up, Change of Pace.

CHOKE: Grip a bat several inches from the bottom. Also means to fail in a critical situation.

CLEANUP: Fourth man in batting order.

CLUTCH HITTER: Player who hits safely when it counts most. Also called Money Player.

COUSIN: Pitcher easy for a certain batter to hit.

CRIPPLE: Pitch following three-balls, one-strike count on batter.

CYCLE: Single, double, triple, homer.

DISH: Home plate.

DRAG BUNT: Lightly pushed hit so

ball trickles to infielder too slowly for play on batter.

DUSTER: Pitch thrown close to batter's head.

FAN: Strike out. Also applied to rooter.

FIELDER'S CHOICE: Throwing to retire a baserunner not forced at the next base.

FLAG: Pennant, emblematic of league championship.

FOOT IN BUCKET: Stepping with forward foot away from line of pitch.

FOUR-FOR-O: Four trips to the plate with no hits. A batter "goes 4-for-0" or "gets 0-for-4."

FULL COUNT: Three balls, two strikes.

FUNGO: Player throws ball few feet in air and bats it himself.

GATE: Paid attendance.

GOAT: Player whose error or oversight proves costly.

GOPHER BALL: Pitch which is hit for a homer.

GRAND SLAM: Home run with bases loaded.

GRAPEFRUIT LEAGUE: Pre-season exhibition games.

HANDLE HIT: Ball hit with lower half of bat.

HILL: Pitcher's box. Also called Mound, Slab, Rubber, etc.

HIT-AND-RUN: Play in which runner breaks from first, causing either second baseman or shortstop to leave normal position to take throw at second base, followed by batter driving ball through "hole" vacated by fielder.

HIT THE DIRT: Slide. Also applied to batter falling hurriedly to ground to avoid pitch near his head.

HOMER: Home run. Also applied to umpire favoring home team.

HOOK: Curve ball. Also applied to right-handed hitter "pulling" or hitting the ball into left field, and vice versa.

HOOK SLIDE: Runner slides with body flung away from bag and with trailing foot "hooking" the bag, to offer minimum target for baseman's tag.

HOP: Sudden rise taken by fast pitch.

HOT CORNER: Third base.

IN THE HOLE: Disadvantage in ball-and-strikes count.

JOCKEY: Player who "rides" opposition team with taunts.

KEYSTONE: Second base.

KICK: Complain. Also applied to missing ball.

LEADOFF: First batter.

LEATHER MAN: Good fielder.

LEG HITTER: Player who gets most of his hits by beating out grounders.

LUMBER: Bat. Also called Willow, Stick, Hickory, etc.

MEAT HAND: Hand unprotected by glove.

MONKEY SUIT: Player's uniform.

MUFF: Get hands on a ball but fail to hold it.

NIGHTCAP: Second game of double-header. Also called Finale, Closer, etc.

NINE: Baseball team.

NUMBER 1: Fast ball.

NUMBER 2: Curve ball.

ON DECK: Player in circle near plate, waiting to follow current batter.

PASS: Base on balls. Also called Walk, Annie Oakley, Stroll, etc.

PAYOFF PITCH: Pitch following three-balls, two-strikes count on batter.

PEG: Hard throw. Also called Whip, Chuck, Fire, etc.

PERFECT GAME: Pitcher preventing any batter from reaching base safely.

PICKOFF: Catch runner off base by sudden throw from pitcher or catcher.

PICK-UP: Catch ball immediately after it hits ground.

PINCH HITTER: Player substituting for a batter due to hit.

PITCHOUT: Wide pitch to foil bunt or to enable catcher to throw out runner attempting to steal.

POP-UP: Short high fly which can easily be caught.

PORTSIDER: Lefthanded pitcher. Also called Southpaw.

PULL A ROCK: Make a stupid play.

RABBIT BALL: Lively-bouncing ball.

RAINCHECK: Ticket stub good for future admission if less than 4 1/2 innings have been played before game is called.

RECEIVER: Catcher.

RELIEF PITCHER: Substitute pitcher. Also called Fireman, Bullpenner, etc.

ROOKIE: First-year player.

ROLLER: Slow ground ball which trickles toward infielder.

RUN-AND-HIT: Play in which runner breaks with the pitch and batter is committed to hit at the ball.

SACK: Base. Also called Hassock, Cushion, Bag, etc.

SANDLOT: Informal field on vacant lot, meadow, yard, etc.

SCREWBALL: Zany. Also applied to pitch thrown with outward twist of hand.

SEMIPRO: One who receives money for playing but has regular job at same time outside of baseball.

SHUTOUT: No runs. Also called Whitewash, Blank, Kalsomine, etc.

SINKER: Pitch which suddenly dips downward.

SKIN INFIELD: Diamond devoid of grass.

SLICE: Hit to right field by right-handed batter, or left field by lefthander.

SOUTHPAW: A lefthanded thrower or batter.

SQUEEZE PLAY: Runner breaks from third with the pitch and batter bunts ball to enable runner to score.

STRAWBERRY: Bruise resulting from sliding.

SUN FIELD: Outfield position where fielder has to face directly into sun.

SWINGING BUNT: Topped ball which dribbles slowly.

TAKE A PITCH: Deliberately let a pitch pass without moving the bat.

TEE OFF: Hit the ball hard.

TEXAS LEAGUER: Hit over the infielder's head, but not carrying far enough to be caught by the outfielder.

TWIN BILL: Two games played in succession. Doubleheader.

WARM UP: Practice before getting into a game.

WOOD MAN: Good hitter.

HOW TO SCORE

Some people buy a scorecard only to fan themselves. Others use it as an identification chart, heeding the old hawkers' cry, "Ya can't tell the players without a scorecard!" But the customer who keeps score, hit-by-hit, out-by-out, undoubtedly derives greatest pleasure from the game.

With two out and bases loaded in the eighth, the score-keeping fan can tell at a glance whether the next batter has been easy for the pitcher all afternoon. He can also tell, on the next day or even the next year, just how that game progressed.

When it comes to keeping score, many fans prefer the simplest code: "1" for hit, "O" for out, "E" for error. At the other extreme is the super-statistical demon who makes a notation for every pitch (high or low, inside or outside, fast ball or curve), every shift in defensive position, every bounce of the ball. The happy medium is the system in vogue, with minor personal variations, among baseball writers and sportcasters: concise yet complete in listing essential details of play-by-play.

Experts all start with a system assigning a number to each position: 1 for pitcher, 2 for catcher, 3 for first base, 4 for second base, 5 for third base, 6 for shortstop, 7 for left field, 8 for center field, 9 for right field.

Next come the symbols to denote various plays. The popular code uses a single bar (-) for a single, double bar (=) for two base hit, three bars for triple and four bars for homer. When a player drives in any runs, the corresponding number of dots are placed after his scoring hit or grounder; thus (-7:) means the batter singled to left field and drove in two runs.

Other common abbreviations include W for walk, K for strikeout (with a backwards ꓘ when the batter swings at a third strike), E for error, O for out, s for stolen base or stealing, S for stretching, B for balk, b for bunt, WP for wild pitch, PB for passed ball, sac for sacrifice, F for foul out, L for line drive, PH for pinch hitter, PR for pinch runner. A double play is circled, so as to be spotted easily.

Modern scorecards have square boxes alongside the players' space for each inning. If a batter is retired, the play is simply written in the middle of the box: thus, 8 means a fly to the centerfielder; 63 means he grounded out, shortstop to first base.

TOWN: New York TEAM: Cardinals DATE: 10/5/43

PLAYERS	POS.	1	2	3	4	5	6	7	8	9	10
KLEIN	4	8		43		54			08 -8		
WALKER	8	9		9			ꓘ		9 54		
MUSIAL	9	8			43		43		02 -9		
W. COOPER	2		5 6-5		63		E6		54		
KUROWSKI	6		sac. 14		43		43			63	
SANDERS	3		ꓘ			7 E3 1 -4·		06 -9		6L	
LITWHILER	7		6 W			8		6		13	
MARION	6		=3·			43		(463)			
LANIER GARMS -8TH	1 PH			43		04 -8·			ꓘ		
BRECHEEN -9TH	1										
		>									
TOTALS		O	1 2 0 1	O	O	1 2 1 1	0 0 1 1	0 1 0 0	0 2 0 2	O	

When a batter reaches base, however, his progress on the basepaths is charted the same way as he actually runs, counter-clockwise, with the lower right hand corner representing first base and the succeeding corners of the square representing next bases. When "A" advances through the effort of teammate "B", the number of B's position is placed in the corner of A's box representing the base to which A advances.

At the bottom of each inning column is the "Totals" box. Runs, hits, errors and left on base are successively marked in the upper left, upper right, lower right corners... but if the total is "zero" for all of those, a large "O" is placed in the middle of the box.

These principles are best illustrated by referring to the accompanying scorecard of the opening game of the 1943 World Series, showing the Cardinals' page. In the second inning, for instance, W. Cooper led off with a single off the third baseman's glove, shown at lower right as (-5). He moved to second base on what No. 5, or the third baseman on his team, did. That's Kurowski, who sacrificed him along, pitcher to second baseman covering first (sac 14). Sanders fanned, swinging (backwards K). Litwhiler walked (W). Marion doubled past the first baseman, driving home W. Cooper, which is shown in Marion's upper right corner as (=3). However, Litwhiler, who reached third on Marion's drive (6, in Litwhiler's upper left corner), was out trying to stretch his advance into a score, right fielder to catcher (OS92). Totals for inning: one run, two hits, no errors, one left.

Other plays, as they come up, will lead you to adopt further symbols, like "T" for advanced on thrown ball, etc. Use as many letters as you wish, but never make the scoring chore more complicated than your potential use of the scorecard.

THE BOX SCORE

There is a summer epidemic, strictly Americana, which is manifest by millions of otherwise normal people staring transfixed at a newspaper item known as a baseball box score. They gaze with good reason, for these few inches of numbers and letters offer a marvelous capsule review of a particular game.

Though papers vary slightly in statistical style, the accompanying box score represents the most common and up-to-date form. The visiting team (Cincinnati) is carried on the left side, the home team (San Francisco) on the right. All the players used in any capacity whatever are listed under their team's name.

CINCINNATI (N.)	ab.	r.	h.	rbi.	SAN FRANCISCO (N.)	ab.	r.	h.	rbi.
Temple, 2b	2	1	2	1	O'Connell, 2b	0	0	0	0
Robinson, lf	4	0	0	0	Bressoud, 2b	2	2	0	0
Burgess, c	4	0	2	1	Spencer, ss	4	0	2	0
Bilko, 1b	4	0	2	0	Mays, cf	4	0	0	2
Miksis, 1b	0	0	0	0	Jablonski, 3b	4	0	1	0
Hoak, 3b	4	0	0	0	Davenport, 3b	0	0	0	0
Lynch, rf	3	0	0	0	Cepeda, 1b	4	3	3	0
Bell, cf	4	1	1	0	Sauer, lf	4	0	1	0
McMillan, ss	3	1	2	1	dLockman, lf	0	1	0	0
eFondy	1	0	0	0	Thomas, c	1	0	0	0
Nuxhall, p	1	0	0	0	aSchmidt, c	2	1	1	0
Acker, p	0	0	0	0	Taussig, rf	2	0	0	1
bThurman	0	0	0	0	cSpeake	1	0	0	0
Jeffcoat, p	0	0	0	0	King, rf	1	0	1	1
Lown, p	0	0	0	0	Gomez, p	2	0	0	0
					Worth'ton, p	1	0	1	2
Total	30	3	9	3	Total	32	7	10	6

aSingled for Thomas in 6th; bWalked for Acker in 7th; cFouled out for Taussig in 6th; dRan for Sauer in 8th; eFouled out for McMillan in 9th.

Cincinnati	1 0 0	0 2 0	0 0 0—3
San Francisco	0 0 1	1 1 1	0 3 x—7

E—Temple, Nuxhall, Burgess. A—Cincinnati 8, San Francisco 13. DP—Nuxhall, McMillan, Bilko; Bressoud, Spencer, Cepeda; Temple, Bilko; Sauer, Thomas. LOB—Cincinnati 5, San Francisco 8.

2B Hits—Burgess, Cepeda, Bell, McMillan, Bilko. Sacrifices—Nuxhall, Temple. SF—Mays, Temple, Worthington.

	IP.	H.	R.	ER.	BB.	SO.
Nuxhall (L, 2—3)	5⅓	6	4	3	3	0
Acker	⅔	1	0	0	0	0
Jeffcoat	†1	3	3	2	0	1
Lown	1	0	0	0	2	0
Gomez	*5	9	3	3	0	3
Worthington (W, 4—2)	4	0	0	0	2	1

*Pitched to two batters in 6th; †Pitched to four batters in 8th.

PB—Burgess. Umpires—Jackowski, Landis, Delmore, Barlick. Time—2:26. Attendance—20,297.

Any player used on defense has some letters placed after his name --- p for pitcher, c for catcher, 1b for first base, 2b for second base, 3b for third base, ss for shortstop, lf for left field, cf for center field, rf for right field. Any player used only as pinch hitter or pinch runner has a letter preceding his name, with the same letter carried under the team totals to indicate in what capacity and when the substitute was used.

Players' figures for the day are run alongside the corresponding name. As for the column heads (which sometimes are capitalized), "ab" is for "at bats," or the total number of times the player went to bat (excluding, of course, such occasions when the batter walked, sacrificed, was hit by pitcher or reached base by interference). The other symbols atop numerical columns are "r" for runs, "h" for hits and "rbi" for runs batted in.

Directly above the line score is inserted the names of all pinch-hitters and pinch-runners. The information contains the name of the player substituted for, the performance of the substitute and the inning he entered the game.

Next comes the line score, or inning-by-inning tally of the teams. The visiting team goes to bat first, and if the home team has enough runs not to have to play its ninth inning, an "x" goes into that spot instead.

The lower half of the box score lists errors (E), by players' names; assists (A), for each team; double plays (DP); number of men left on base (LOB) by each team, and the players who hit doubles, triples, homers, sacrifices and sacrifice flies.

The pitching summary is very complete and from the chart the fan can easily determine the effectiveness of each pitcher. Listed are innings pitched (IP); hits allowed (H); runs allowed (R); earned runs allowed (ER); bases on balls (BB) and strikeouts (SO).

The numbers after the names of the winning and losing pitchers signify their season won-lost record. "Time" means elapsed time of game. The umpires are listed in counterclockwise order, starting with the plate ump. "Attendance" usually means the total of paying customers.

JUDO

GREG ROZA

PowerKiDS press
New York

Published in 2020 by The Rosen Publishing Group, Inc.
29 East 21st Street, New York, NY 10010

First Edition

Editor: Greg Roza
Book Design: Reann Nye

Photo Credits: Series art Reinhold Leitner/Shutterstock.com; cover, p. 15 Everyonephoto Studio/Shutterstock.com; p. 5 Master1305/Shutterstock.com; p. 6 The Asahi Shimbun/Getty Images; p. 7 ullstein bild Dtl./ullstein bild/Getty Images; p. 9 David Finch/Getty Images Sport/Getty Images; p. 10 SAM PANTHAKY/AFP/Getty Images; p. 11 Africa Studio/Shutterstock.com; p. 12 © istockphoto.com/Kemter; p. 13 Nomad_Soul/Shutterstock.com; p. 14 CasarsaGuru/E+/Getty Images; p. 17 Jupiterimages/Goodshoot/Getty Images Plus/Getty Images; pp. 19, 22 Kaderov Andrii/Shutterstock.com; p. 21 Andia/Universal Images Group/Getty Images.

Library of Congress Cataloging-in-Publication Data

Names: Roza, Greg, author.
Title: Judo / Greg Roza.
Description: New York : PowerKids Press, [2020] | Series: Enter the dojo! Martial arts for kids | Includes index.
Identifiers: LCCN 2019013740| ISBN 9781725310100 (pbk.) | ISBN 9781725310124 (library bound) | ISBN 9781725310117 (6 pack)
Subjects: LCSH: Judo–Juvenile literature. | Martial arts–Juvenile literature.
Classification: LCC GV1114 .R7 2020 | DDC 796.815/2-dc23
LC record available at https://lccn.loc.gov/2019013740

Manufactured in the United States of America

The activities discussed and displayed in this book can cause serious injury when attempted by someone who is untrained in the martial arts. Never try to replicate the techniques in this book without the supervision of a trained martial arts instructor.

CPSIA Compliance Information: Batch #CWPK20. For Further Information contact Rosen Publishing, New York, New York at 1-800-237-9932.

CONTENTS

Get on the Mat

Judo is a martial art with a major difference from other martial arts. Judo doesn't include strikes or kicks. Instead, judo includes a large number of throws. Judo also includes joint locks, chokes, and pins.

Judoka—or people who practice judo—learn how to use someone's movements against them. They wait for the perfect opening and then move quickly to throw their **opponent** into the air and onto the mat. Once judoka hit the mat, they may use locks and chokes to force their opponent to submit, or give up. Judo is an exciting martial art to watch, and it's a lot of fun to practice.

Kiai!

Judo is a grappling martial art. That means it includes close fighting techniques, or methods, similar to wrestling.

Professional judo matches often look out of control! But judoka are highly trained and their moves are carefully planned.

Kano's Gentle Path

Jujitsu student Jigoro Kano introduced judo to the world in 1882. Jujitsu is an ancient **combat** style featuring painful joint locks and throws. Kano removed moves he felt were too dangerous. He focused more on throws than joint locks. He also borrowed concepts from other styles of martial arts.

JIGORO KANO

Kiai!

Starting around 1860, Japan went through many changes. The martial arts became less important as Japan changed from a warlike place to one with more structure and order. The many styles of jujitsu began to fade, but judo helped keep the ancient style alive.

Kano started training in jujitsu when he was a boy because he was small and frail. By 22, he was a jujitsu master and had created judo.

Kano called his new martial art "judo," which means "gentle path." He called his dojo "Kodokan," which means "a place to teach the path." Kano described judo as the "maximum efficient use of energy." Kano's new martial art stressed fitness, mental quickness, and healthy **competition**.

Olympic Judo

Kano continued to teach the benefits of judo to the world, and it quickly grew as a sport. Kano also came to be known as the father of Japanese physical education. In 1909, Kano became the first Asian member of the International Olympic Committee.

Kano passed away in 1938. In 1964, men's judo was added to the Olympic Games. Women's Olympic judo began in 1992. Olympic judo features the greatest judoka in the world. In 2012, American judoka Kayla Harrison made Olympic history by becoming the first American to win a gold medal in judo. She did it again in 2016.

Kiai!

Judo competitions such as the Olympics have special rules and ways of earning points. Competitors can earn a win with a stunning throw or a submission. They may earn points for lesser throws, locks, holds, and sweeps.

In this photo from 2016, Kayla Harrison (in white) uses a move called a reap to knock French judoka Audrey Tcheumeo off her feet. Harrison went on to win this match and become a two-time Olympic gold medal winner.

Throws

There are many judo throws. Throws require judoka to use opponents' **momentum** and weight against them. Most throws start by getting the opponent to move in a certain direction. Then the judoka takes advantage of that movement.

Kiai!

Tomoe nage, or the circular throw, is one of judo's most exciting moves. The judoka begins to crouch while placing a foot on the opponent's stomach. Then, as the opponent sinks to the ground, the judoka uses their foot and hands to toss the opponent over their head!

During a hip throw, lifting your leg will help flip your opponent faster. This is sometimes called a spring hip throw.

The ogoshi is a common hip throw. To perform it, the judoka quickly turns his body around so his back is against the opponent's body, and crouches down at the same time so he is lower than his opponent. Grabbing the opponent behind his back, the judoka straightens his knees and uses his hip to throw the opponent into the air.

Sweeps and Reaps

Throws aren't the only way to put your opponent on the mat. Judo includes sweeps and reaps. A sweep is a leg movement that trips an opponent. A reap is a move that involves both hands and feet.

OSOTO GARI

The students in this photo are practicing deashi harai, or the forward foot sweep.

One of the most common reaps is osoto gari, or large outer reap. This is accomplished by stepping forward and next to the opponent, and quickly swinging the leg closer to the opponent behind her. Next, the judoka swings that leg into the back of the opponent's legs while twisting her shoulders to get her off balance. This judo reap can often be seen during **MMA** matches.

Submission

After a successful throw, the match isn't over. Each judoka tries to make the other "tap out," or submit. This is done using joint locks and submission holds, such as chokes. These moves are common in jujitsu as well.

Kiai!

Chokes are moves that cut off a person's air supply. Chokes are a lot like joint locks—if an opponent gets you in a choke, tap out before you pass out!

It's important to know when to submit during a judo match. Once someone has an armbar on you, tap out! Your health is more important than a win.

One of the most common joint locks in judo is the armlock, or armbar. This involves securing the opponent's outstretched arm against your chest and lying back. This **hyperextends** the elbow joint. Someone in an armbar has little choice but to submit. Some judo masters can apply a "flying armbar." This means they jump onto an opponent's arm while they are standing up!

The Judo Dojo

Some dojos can only fit a few students at a time. Others have very large areas for classes and competitions. They may also have shops, changing rooms, and viewing areas. All dojos have mats to keep students safe.

Before even stepping on the mat for the first time, judo students need a uniform called a gi. Gis are usually all white but may feature patches and symbols. The gi is secured with a belt, or obi. The color of the belt shows what level the student has reached. Someone with a black belt has mastered all of the basic moves of a martial art.

Kiai!

Instructors who have a black belt in judo are referred to as "sensei," which is usually translated as "master" or "teacher." It's a sign of respect.

The judo gi is the only **equipment** you will need to buy. Gis aren't just for looks. Many judo and jujitsu moves require grabbing the opponent's sleeve, collar, or belt.

Starting Out

It takes time to learn judo. Beginner students, no matter their age, aren't allowed to learn throws until they learn how to fall properly. They learn the basic throws from their knees. This helps them avoid injuries, such as muscle strains and broken bones.

As judoka improve, they earn new belts and learn new skills. Eventually they start performing throws, sweeps, and reaps from their feet. They also learn submission moves and pins for when the match goes to the ground. Judo students are encouraged to join competitions as they improve. With time and **dedication**, almost anyone can become a talented judoka.

Kiai!

Like in other martial arts, judo students practice katas. Katas are traditional sets of movements that **simulate** a fight with one or more attackers. Judo katas stem from jujitsu and involve strikes and kicks.

Judo students work together to improve their skills. It's always proper to treat your fellow students with respect and to try to avoid injuring each other.

Moving Up

Just like school, judo dojos have a **curriculum**. Students must be able to perform certain judo moves before they can get a new belt. Students are also expected to perform other exercises, such as push-ups and sit-ups. Other requirements may include attendance, general respectfulness, and helping students with lower belts.

A judo test includes judo **sparring**, katas, and basic physical fitness exercises. Many instructors expect their students to know the proper Japanese words for judo moves. A test is usually very tiring! That's because students are being tested on their judo skills, but also their physical fitness and memory.

Kiai!

Black belts continue to learn, and they still need to pass tests. Any level over black belt is a "dan." The first dan is "shodan," which means "first step." Very few judo masters reach "judan," or "tenth step."

Belt colors depend on the country and the dojo. The colors may include white (for beginners), yellow, orange, green, blue, purple, brown, and black.

Be Excellent!

Throwing people around isn't the only skill you can learn in a judo dojo. Judo is physically demanding and can make you stronger when you stick with it. In time your **coordination**, **stamina**, and mental quickness will also improve. Many dojos focus on self-defense in addition to competition skills.

Learning a martial art requires respect for yourself, your fellow students, and your teachers. It requires a strong sense of self-control in order to succeed. It's also a lot of fun! Judo and the martial arts prepare you to be the best you can, in the dojo as well as out of it.

GLOSSARY

combat: Having to do with a fight between two or more people or groups.

competition: The act or process of trying to win a contest others are also trying to win.

coordination: The ability to move different parts of your body together well or easily.

curriculum: A detailed course of study.

dedication: Being able to stick with something and get good at it.

equipment: Tools or supplies needed for something.

hyperextend: To extend a body part so the angle between bones of a joint is greater than normal, causing pain or injury.

MMA: Mixed martial art, a modern sport that involves many styles of martial arts.

momentum: The strength or force that something has when it is moving.

opponent: Someone competing against another person.

simulate: To look or behave like something else.

spar: To practice a martial art with another person.

stamina: The ability to do something for a long period of time.

INDEX

Due to the changing nature of Internet links, PowerKids Press has developed an online list of websites related to the subject of this book. This site is updated regularly. Please use this link to access the list: www.powerkidslinks.com/ETD/Judo